PEARSON ALWAYS LEARNING

Intermediate & College Algebra

Custom Edition for Miami Dade College Wolfson
MAT 1033/MAC 1105

Taken from:
Beginning & Intermediate Algebra, Fifth Edition
by Elayn Martin-Gay

College Algebra: Enhanced with Graphing Utilities, Sixth Edition
by Michael Sullivan and Michael Sullivan, III

Cover image: Courtesy of Photodisc/Getty Images.

Taken from:

Beginning & Intermediate Algebra, Fifth Edition
by Elayn Martin-Gay

Boston, Massachusetts 02116

College Algebra: Enhanced with Graphing Utilities, Sixth Edition
by Michael Sullivan and Michael Sullivan, III

Upper Saddle River, New Jersey 07458

This special edition published in cooperation with Pearson Learning Solutions.

Pearson Learning Solutions, 501 Boylston Street, Suite 900, Boston, MA 02116
A Pearson Education Company
www.pearsoned.com

Printed in the United States of America

1 2 3 4 5 6 7 8 9 10 V011 17 16 15 14 13 12

000200010271724478

JHA

ISBN 10: 1-256-92532-2
ISBN 13: 978-1-256-92532-3

Contents

CHAPTER 3

FACTORING POLYNOMIALS 213

CHAPTER 4

RATIONAL EXPRESSIONS 279

CHAPTER 5

RATIONAL EXPONENTS, RADICALS, AND COMPLEX NUMBERS 368

APPENDICES

Chapter Test Prep Videos—provide step-by-step solutions to all exercises from the Chapter Test. These videos provide guidance and support for students when preparing for an exam. Optional English and Spanish subtitles are available. The Chapter Test Prep videos are available in MyMathLab® or on YouTube(go to http://www.youtube.com/SullivanCAEGU6e).

Chapters R-6 and Appendices A-C taken from *Beginning & Intermediate Algebra,* Fifth Edition, by Elayn Martin-Gay.

Chapters 7-13 taken from *College Algebra: Enhanced with Graphing Utilities,* Sixth Edition, by Michael Sullivan and Michael Sullivan, III.

Review of Real Numbers

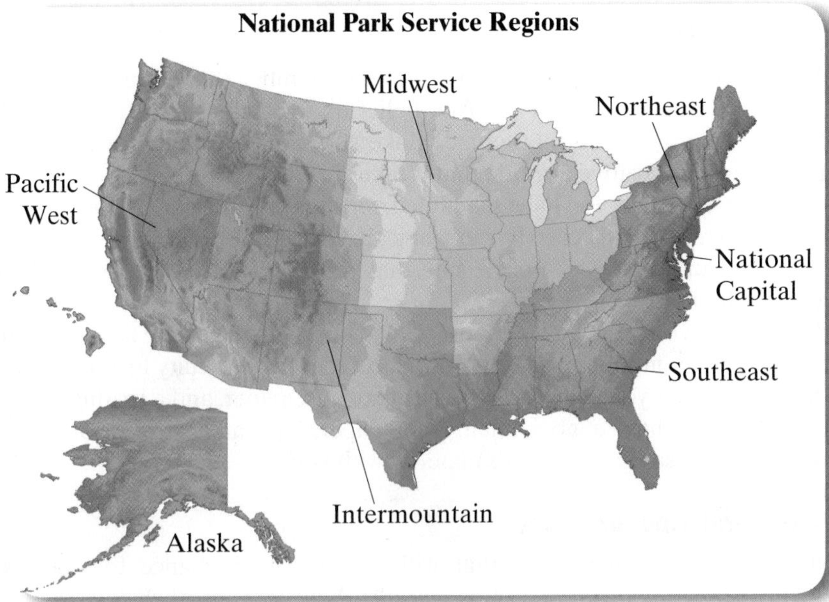

The National Park Service (NPS) is a federal agency that manages all national parks and many other historic monuments and properties. The NPS has 21,989 employees and had a total of 281 million recreational visitors in 2010 alone. The map above shows the different geographic regions of the NPS, and the bar graph below shows the number of recreational visits per year shown.

In Section R.2, Exercises 71 through 76, we shall study this bar graph further.

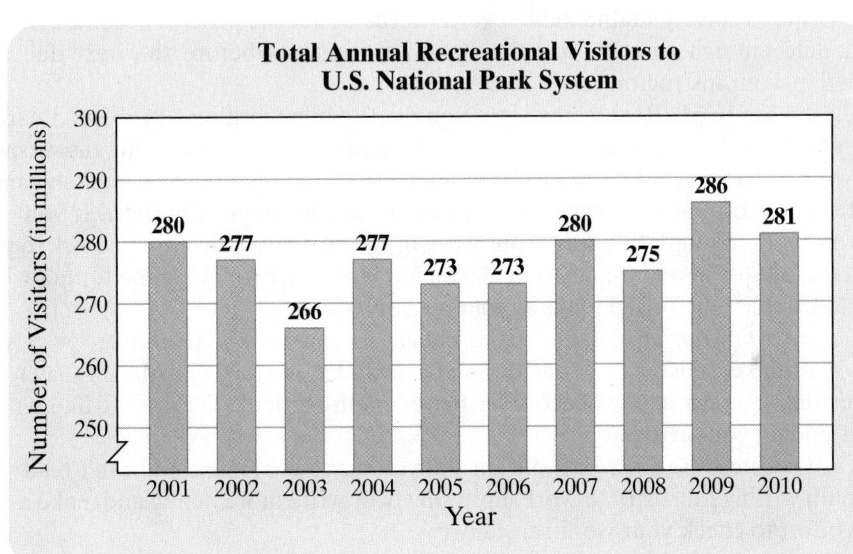

In this chapter, we review the basic symbols and words—the language—of arithmetic and introduce using variables in place of numbers. This is our starting place in the study of algebra.

R.1 Tips for Success in Mathematics 

OBJECTIVES

1. Get Ready for This Course.
2. Understand Some General Tips for Success.
3. Understand How to Use This Text.
4. Get Help as Soon as You Need It.
5. Learn How to Prepare for and Take an Exam.
6. Develop Good Time Management.

Before reading this section, remember that your instructor is your best source of information. Please see your instructor for any additional help or information.

OBJECTIVE

1 Getting Ready for This Course 

Now that you have decided to take this course, remember that a *positive attitude* will make all the difference in the world. Your belief that you can succeed is just as important as your commitment to this course. Make sure you are ready for this course by having the time and positive attitude that it takes to succeed.

Next, make sure that you have scheduled your math course at a time that will give you the best chance for success. For example, if you are also working, you may want to check with your employer to make sure that your work hours will not conflict with your course schedule.

On the day of your first class period, double-check your schedule and allow yourself extra time to arrive on time in case of traffic problems or difficulty locating your classroom. Make sure that you bring at least your textbook, paper, and a writing instrument. Are you required to have a lab manual, graph paper, calculator, or some other supplies besides this text? If so, also bring this material with you.

OBJECTIVE

2 General Tips for Success 

Following are some general tips that will increase your chance for success in a mathematics class. Many of these tips will also help you in other courses you may be taking.

Exchange names and phone numbers or email addresses with at least one other person in class. This contact person can be a great help if you miss an assignment or want to discuss math concepts or exercises that you find difficult.

Choose to attend all class periods. If possible, sit near the front of the classroom. This way, you will see and hear the presentation better. It may also be easier for you to participate in classroom activities.

> **Helpful Hint**
> **MyMathLab® and MathXL®** If you are doing your homework online, you can work and rework those exercises that you struggle with until you master them. Try working through all the assigned exercises twice before the due date.

Do your homework. You've probably heard the phrase "practice makes perfect" in relation to music and sports. It also applies to mathematics. You will find that the more time you spend solving mathematics exercises, the easier the process becomes. Be sure to schedule enough time to complete your assignments before the next due date assigned by your instructor.

> **Helpful Hint**
> **MyMathLab® and MathXL®** If you are completing your homework online, it's important to work each exercise on paper before submitting the answer. That way, you can check your work and follow your steps to find and correct any mistakes.

Check your work. Review the steps you made while working a problem. Learn to check your answers in the original problems. You may also compare your answers with the "Answers to Selected Exercises" section in the back of the book. If you have made a mistake, try to figure out what went wrong. Then correct your mistake. If you can't find what went wrong, don't erase your work or throw it away. Bring your work to your instructor, a tutor in a math lab, or a classmate. It is easier for someone to find where you had trouble if he or she looks at your original work.

Learn from your mistakes and be patient with yourself. Everyone, even your instructor, makes mistakes. (That definitely includes me—Elayn Martin-Gay.) Use your errors to learn and to become a better math student. The key is finding and understanding your errors.

Was your mistake a careless one, or did you make it because you can't read your own math writing? If so, try to work more slowly or write more neatly and make a conscious effort to check your work carefully.

Did you make a mistake because you don't understand a concept? Take the time to review the concept or ask questions to understand it better.

Did you skip too many steps? Skipping steps or trying to do too many steps mentally may lead to preventable mistakes.

Know how to get help if you need it. It's all right to ask for help. In fact, it's a good idea to ask for help whenever there is something that you don't understand. Make sure you know when your instructor has office hours and how to find his or her office. Find out whether math tutoring services are available on your campus. Check on the hours, location, and requirements of the tutoring service.

> **Helpful Hint**
> **MyMathLab®** and **MathXL®** When assignments are turned in online, keep a hard copy of your complete written work. You will need to refer to your written work to be able to ask questions and to study for tests later.

Organize your class materials, including homework assignments, graded quizzes and tests, and notes from your class or lab. All of these items will make valuable references throughout your course and when studying for upcoming tests and the final exam. Make sure that you can locate these materials when you need them.

Read your textbook before class. Reading a mathematics textbook is unlike reading a novel or a newspaper. Your pace will be much slower. It is helpful to have paper and a pencil with you when you read. Try to work out examples on your own as you encounter them in your text. You should also write down any questions that you want to ask in class. When you read a mathematics textbook, sometimes some of the information in a section will be unclear. But after you hear a lecture or watch a lecture video on that section, you will understand it much more easily than if you had not read your text beforehand.

Don't be afraid to ask questions. You are not the only person in class with questions. Other students are normally grateful that someone has spoken up.

> **Helpful Hint**
> **MyMathLab®** and **MathXL®** Be aware of assignments and due dates set by your instructor. Don't wait until the last minute to submit work online. Allow 6–8 hours before the deadline in case you have technology trouble.

Turn in assignments on time. This way, you can be sure that you will not lose points for being late. Show every step of a problem and be neat and organized. Also be sure that you understand which problems are assigned for homework. If allowed, you can always double-check the assignment with another student in your class.

OBJECTIVE

3 Using This Text 

Many helpful resources are available to you. It is important to become familiar with and use these resources. They should increase your chances for success in this course.

- *Practice Exercises.* Each example in every section has a parallel Practice exercise. As you read a section, try each Practice exercise after you've finished the corresponding example. This learn-by-doing approach will help you grasp ideas before you move on to other concepts. Answers are at the back of the text.
- *Chapter Test Prep Videos.* These videos provide solutions to all of the Chapter Test exercises worked out by the author. This supplement is very helpful before a test or exam.
- *Interactive DVD Lecture Series.* Exercises marked with a ▶ are fully worked out by the author on the DVDs. The lecture series provides approximately 20 minutes of instruction per section.

> **Helpful Hint**
> **MyMathLab®** In MyMathLab, you have access to the following video resources:
> - Lecture Videos for each section
> - Chapter Test Prep Videos
>
> Use these videos provided by the author to prepare for class, review, and study for tests.

- *Symbols at the Beginning of an Exercise Set.* If you need help with a particular section, the symbols listed at the beginning of each exercise set will remind you of the numerous supplements available.
- *Objectives.* The main section of exercises in each exercise set is referenced by an objective, such as 1 or 2, and by an example(s). There is also often a section of exercises entitled "Mixed Practice," which is referenced by two or more objectives or sections. These are mixed exercises written to prepare you for your next exam. Use all of this referencing if you have trouble completing an assignment from the exercise set.
- *Icons (Symbols).* Make sure that you understand the meaning of the icons that are beside many exercises. ▶ tells you that the corresponding exercise may be viewed on the video segment that corresponds to that section. ✎ tells you that this exercise is a writing exercise in which you should answer in complete sentences. △ tells you that the exercise involves geometry.
- *Integrated Reviews.* Found in the middle of each chapter, these reviews offer you a chance to practice—in one place—the many concepts that you have learned separately over several sections.
- *End-of-Chapter Opportunities.* There are many opportunities at the end of each chapter to help you understand the concepts of the chapter.

  Vocabulary Checks contain key vocabulary terms introduced in the chapter.

  Chapter Highlights contain chapter summaries and examples.

  Chapter Reviews contain review problems. The first part is organized section by section and the second part contains a set of mixed exercises.

Chapter Tests are sample tests to help you prepare for an exam. The Chapter Test Prep Videos, found in this text, contain all the Chapter Test exercises worked by the author.

Cumulative Reviews consist of material from the beginning of the book to the end of that particular chapter.

- *Student Resources in Your Textbook.* You will find a **Student Resources** section at the back of this textbook. It contains the following to help you study and prepare for tests:

  Study Skill Builders contain study skills advice. To increase your chance for success in the course, read these study tips and answer the questions.

  Bigger Picture—Study Guide Outline provides you with a study guide outline of the course, with examples.

  Practice Final provides you with a Practice Final Exam to help you prepare for a final. The video solutions to each question are provided in the Interactive DVD Lecture Series and within MyMathLab®.

- *Resources to Check Your Work.* The **Answers to Selected Exercises** section provides answers to all odd-numbered section exercises and all integrated review and chapter test exercises.

> **Helpful Hint**
> **MyMathLab®** and **MathXL®**
> - Use the **Help Me Solve This** button to get step-by-step help for the exercise you are working. You will need to work an additional exercise of the same type before you can get credit for having worked it correctly.
> - Use the **Video** button to view a video clip of the author working a similar exercise.

OBJECTIVE

4 Getting Help 

If you have trouble completing assignments or understanding the mathematics, get help as soon as you need it! This tip is presented as an objective on its own because it is so important. In mathematics, usually the material presented in one section builds on your understanding of the previous section. This means that if you don't understand the concepts covered during a class period, there is a good chance that you will not understand the concepts covered during the next class period. If this happens to you, get help as soon as you can.

Where can you get help? Many suggestions have been made in this section on where to get help, and now it is up to you to get it. Try your instructor, a tutoring center, or a math lab, or you may want to form a study group with fellow classmates. If you do decide to see your instructor or go to a tutoring center, make sure that you have a neat notebook and are ready with your questions.

OBJECTIVE

5 Preparing for and Taking an Exam 

Make sure that you allow yourself plenty of time to prepare for a test. If you think that you are a little "math anxious," it may be that you are not preparing for a test in a way that will ensure success. The way that you prepare for a test in mathematics is important. To prepare for a test:

> **Helpful Hint**
> **MyMathLab®** and **MathXL®**
> Review your written work for previous assignments. Then, go back and rework previous assignments. Open a previous assignment and click **Similar Exercise** to generate new exercises. Rework the exercises until you fully understand them and can work them without help features.

1. Review your previous homework assignments.
2. Review any notes from class and section-level quizzes you have taken. (If this is a final exam, also review chapter tests you have taken.)
3. Review concepts and definitions by reading the Chapter Highlights at the end of each chapter.
4. Practice working out exercises by completing the Chapter Review found at the end of each chapter. (If this is a final exam, go through a Cumulative Review. There is one at the end of each chapter except Chapter R. Choose the review found at the end of the latest chapter that you have covered in your course.) *Don't stop here!*
5. It is important to place yourself in conditions similar to test conditions to find out how you will perform. In other words, as soon as you feel that you know the material, get a few blank sheets of paper and take a sample test. A Chapter Test is available at the end of each chapter, or you can work selected problems from the Chapter

Review. Your instructor may also provide you with a review sheet. During this sample test, do not use your notes or your textbook. Then check your sample test. If you are not satisfied with the results, study the areas that you are weak in and try again.

6. On the day of the test, allow yourself plenty of time to arrive where you will be taking your exam.

When taking your test:

1. Read the directions on the test carefully.
2. Read each problem carefully as you take the test. Make sure that you answer the question asked.
3. Watch your time and pace yourself so that you can attempt each problem on your test.
4. If you have time, check your work and answers.
5. Do not turn your test in early. If you have extra time, spend it double-checking your work.

OBJECTIVE

6 Managing Your Time 

As a college student, you know the demands that classes, homework, work, and family place on your time. Some days, you probably wonder how you'll ever get everything done. One key to managing your time is developing a schedule. Here are some hints for making a schedule:

1. Make a list of all your weekly commitments for the term. Include classes, work, regular meetings, extracurricular activities, etc. You may also find it helpful to list such things as laundry, regular workouts, grocery shopping, etc.
2. Next, estimate the time needed for each item on the list. Also make a note of how often you will need to do each item. Don't forget to include time estimates for the reading, studying, and homework you do outside of your classes. You may want to ask your instructor for help estimating the time needed.
3. In the exercise set that follows, you are asked to block out a typical week on the schedule grid given. Start with items with fixed time slots like classes and work.
4. Next, include the items on your list with flexible time slots. Think carefully about how best to schedule items such as study time.
5. Don't fill up every time slot on the schedule. Remember that you need to allow time for eating, sleeping, and relaxing! You should also allow a little extra time in case some items take longer than planned.
6. If you find that your weekly schedule is too full for you to handle, you may need to make some changes in your workload, classload, or other areas of your life. You may want to talk to your advisor, manager or supervisor at work, or someone in your college's academic counseling center for help with such decisions.

R.1 Exercise Set

MyMathLab®

1. What is your instructor's name?
2. What are your instructor's office location and office hours?
3. What is the best way to contact your instructor?
4. Do you have the name and contact information of at least one other student in class?
5. Will your instructor allow you to use a calculator in this class?
6. Why is it important that you write step-by-step solutions to homework exercises and keep a hard copy of all work submitted?
7. Is a tutoring service available on campus? If so, what are its hours? What services are available?
8. Have you attempted this course before? If so, write down ways that you might improve your chances of success during this second attempt.
9. List some steps that you can take if you begin having trouble understanding the material or completing an assignment. If you are completing your homework in MyMathLab® and MathXL®, list the resources you can use for help.

10. How many hours of studying does your instructor advise for each hour of instruction?

11. What does the ╲ icon in this text mean?

12. What does the ▶ icon in this text mean?

13. What does the △ icon in this text mean?

14. What are Practice exercises?

15. When might be the best time to work a Practice exercise?

16. Where are the answers to Practice exercises?

17. What answers are contained in this text and where are they?

18. What and where are the study skills builders?

19. What and where are Integrated Reviews?

20. How many times is it suggested that you work through the homework exercises in MathXL® before the submission deadline?

21. How far in advance of the assigned due date is it suggested that homework be submitted online? Why?

22. Chapter Highlights are found at the end of each chapter. Find the Chapter R Highlights and explain how you might use it and how it might be helpful.

23. Chapter Reviews are found at the end of each chapter. Find the Chapter R Review and explain how you might use it and how it might be useful.

24. Chapter Tests are at the end of each chapter. Find the Chapter R Test and explain how you might use it and how it might be helpful when preparing for an exam on Chapter R. Include how the Chapter Test Prep Videos may help. If you are working in MyMathLab® and MathXL®, how can you use previous homework assignments to study?

25. Read or reread objective 6 and fill out the schedule grid below.

	Monday	*Tuesday*	*Wednesday*	*Thursday*	*Friday*	*Saturday*	*Sunday*
1:00 a.m.							
2:00 a.m.							
3:00 a.m.							
4:00 a.m.							
5:00 a.m.							
6:00 a.m.							
7:00 a.m.							
8:00 a.m.							
9:00 a.m.							
10:00 a.m.							
11:00 a.m.							
Noon							
1:00 p.m.							
2:00 p.m.							
3:00 p.m.							
4:00 p.m.							
5:00 p.m.							
6:00 p.m.							
7:00 p.m.							
8:00 p.m.							
9:00 p.m.							
10:00 p.m.							
11:00 p.m.							
Midnight							

R.2 Symbols and Sets of Numbers 

OBJECTIVES

1. Use a Number Line to Order Numbers.
2. Translate Sentences into Mathematical Statements.
3. Identify Natural Numbers, Whole Numbers, Integers, Rational Numbers, Irrational Numbers, and Real Numbers.
4. Find the Absolute Value of a Real Number.

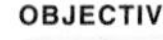

OBJECTIVE

1 Using a Number Line to Order Numbers 

We begin with a review of the set of natural numbers and the set of whole numbers and how we use symbols to compare these numbers. A **set** is a collection of objects, each of which is called a **member** or **element** of the set. A pair of brace symbols { } encloses the list of elements and is translated as "the set of" or "the set containing."

Natural Numbers

The set of **natural numbers** is $\{1, 2, 3, 4, 5, 6, \ldots\}$.

Whole Numbers

The set of **whole numbers** is $\{0, 1, 2, 3, 4, \ldots\}$.

The three dots (an ellipsis) means that the list continues in the same manner indefinitely.

These numbers can be pictured on a **number line.** We will use number lines often to help us visualize distance and relationships between numbers.

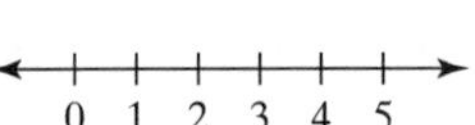

A number line

To draw a number line, first draw a line. Choose a point on the line and label it 0. To the right of 0, label any other point 1. Being careful to use the same distance as from 0 to 1, mark off equally spaced distances. Label these points 2, 3, 4, 5, and so on. Since the whole numbers continue indefinitely, it is not possible to show every whole number on this number line. The arrow at the right end of the line indicates that the pattern continues indefinitely.

Picturing whole numbers on a number line helps us see the order of the numbers. Symbols can be used to describe concisely in writing the order that we see.

The **equal symbol** $=$ means "is equal to."

The symbol $\neq$ means "is not equal to."

These symbols may be used to form a **mathematical statement.** The statement might be true or it might be false. The two statements below are both true.

$2 = 2$ states that "two is equal to two."

$2 \neq 6$ states that "two is not equal to six."

If two numbers are not equal, one number is larger than the other.
The symbol $>$ means "is greater than."
The symbol $<$ means "is less than." For example,

$3 < 5$ states that "three is less than five."

$2 > 0$ states that "two is greater than zero."

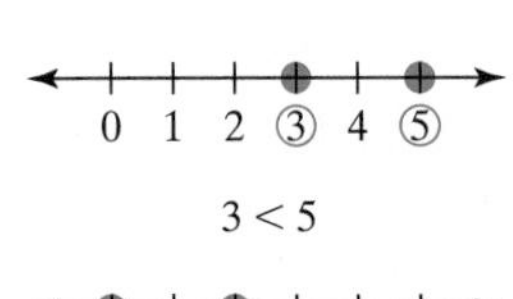

On a number line, we see that a number **to the right of** another number is **larger.** Similarly, a number **to the left of** another number is smaller. For example, 3 is to the left of 5 on a number line, which means that 3 is less than 5, or $3 < 5$. Similarly, 2 is to the right of 0 on a number line, which means 2 is greater than 0, or $2 > 0$. Since 0 is to the left of 2, we can also say that 0 is less than 2, or $0 < 2$.

The symbols $\neq$, $<$, and $>$ are called **inequality symbols.**

Helpful Hint

Notice that $2 > 0$ has exactly the same meaning as $0 < 2$. Switching the order of the numbers and reversing the direction of the inequality symbol does not change the meaning of the statement.

$3 < 5$ has the same meaning as $5 > 3$.

Also notice that, when the statement is true, the inequality arrow points to the smaller number.

EXAMPLE 1 Insert $<$, $>$, or $=$ in the space between each pair of numbers to make each statement true

a. 2 3 **b.** 7 4 **c.** 72 27

Solution

a. $2 < 3$ since 2 is to the left of 3 on the number line.

b. $7 > 4$ since 7 is to the right of 4 on the number line.

c. $72 > 27$ since 72 is to the right of 27 on the number line. □

PRACTICE 1 Insert $<$, $>$, or $=$ in the space between each pair of numbers to make each statement true.

a. 5 8 **b.** 6 4 **c.** 16 82

Two other symbols are used to compare numbers.
The symbol $\leq$ means "is less than or equal to."
The symbol $\geq$ means "is greater than or equal to." For example,

$7 \leq 10$ states that "seven is less than or equal to ten."

This statement is true since $7 < 10$ is true. If either $7 < 10$ or $7 = 10$ is true, then $7 \leq 10$ is true.

$3 \geq 3$ states that "three is greater than or equal to three."

This statement is true since $3 = 3$ is true. If either $3 > 3$ or $3 = 3$ is true, then $3 \geq 3$ is true.

The statement $6 \geq 10$ is false since neither $6 > 10$ nor $6 = 10$ is true. The symbols $\leq$ and $\geq$ are also called **inequality symbols.**

EXAMPLE 2 Tell whether each statement is true or false.

a. $8 \geq 8$ **b.** $8 \leq 8$ **c.** $23 \leq 0$ **d.** $23 \geq 0$

Solution

a. True. Since $8 = 8$ is true, then $8 \geq 8$ is true.

b. True. Since $8 = 8$ is true, then $8 \leq 8$ is true.

c. False. Since neither $23 < 0$ nor $23 = 0$ is true, then $23 \leq 0$ is false.

d. True. Since $23 > 0$ is true, then $23 \geq 0$ is true. □

PRACTICE 2 Tell whether each statement is true or false.

a. $9 \geq 3$ **b.** $3 \geq 8$ **c.** $25 \leq 25$ **d.** $4 \leq 14$

OBJECTIVE

2 Translating Sentences 

Now, let's use the symbols discussed to translate sentences into mathematical statements.

EXAMPLE 3 Translate each sentence into a mathematical statement.

a. Nine is less than or equal to eleven.

b. Eight is greater than one.

c. Three is not equal to four.

Solution

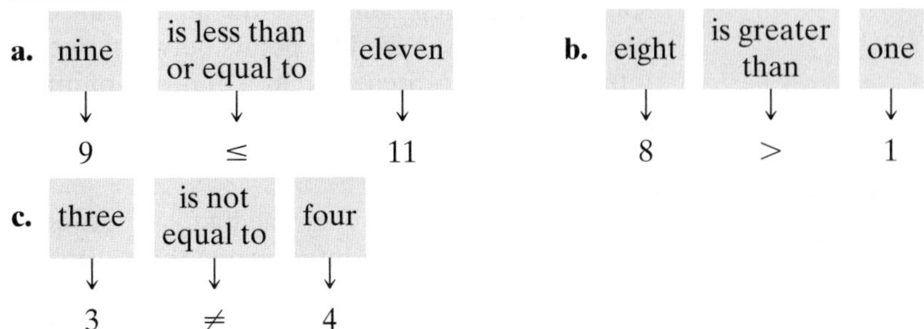

□

PRACTICE

3 Translate each sentence into a mathematical statement.

a. Three is less than eight.

b. Fifteen is greater than or equal to nine.

c. Six is not equal to seven.

OBJECTIVE

3 Identifying Common Sets of Numbers 

Whole numbers are not sufficient to describe many situations in the real world. For example, quantities less than zero must sometimes be represented, such as temperatures less than 0 degrees.

Numbers Less Than Zero on a Number Line

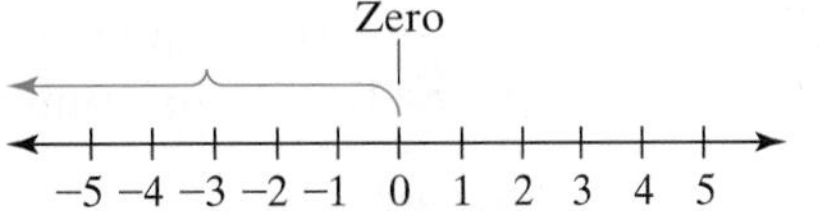

Numbers less than 0 are to the left of 0 and are labeled −1, −2, −3, and so on. A − sign, such as the one in −1, tells us that the number is to the left of 0 on a number line. In words, −1 is read "negative one." A + sign or no sign tells us that a number lies to the right of 0 on the number line. For example, 3 and +3 both mean positive three.

The numbers we have pictured are called the set of **integers.** Integers to the left of 0 are called **negative integers;** integers to the right of 0 are called **positive integers.** The integer **0 is neither positive nor negative.**

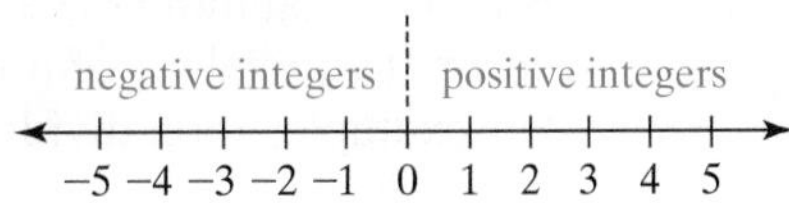

Integers

The set of **integers** is $\{\ldots, -3, -2, -1, 0, 1, 2, 3, \ldots\}$.

The ellipses (three dots) to the left and to the right indicate that the positive integers and the negative integers continue indefinitely.

EXAMPLE 4 Use an integer to express the number in the following. "Pole of Inaccessibility, Antarctica, is the coldest location in the world, with an average annual temperature of 72 degrees below zero." (*Source: The Guinness Book of Records*)

Solution The integer −72 represents 72 degrees below zero. □

PRACTICE

4 Use an integer to express the number in the following. The elevation of Laguna Salada in Mexico is 10 meters below sea level. (*Source: The World Almanac*)

A problem with integers in real-life settings arises when quantities are smaller than some integer but greater than the next smallest integer. On a number line, these quantities may be visualized by points between integers. Some of these quantities between integers can be represented as a quotient of integers. For example,

The point on a number line halfway between 0 and 1 can be represented by $\frac{1}{2}$, a quotient of integers.

The point on a number line halfway between 0 and −1 can be represented by $-\frac{1}{2}$. Other quotients of integers and their graphs are shown to the left.

These numbers, each of which can be represented as a quotient of integers, are examples of **rational numbers.** It's not possible to list the set of rational numbers using the notation that we have been using. For this reason, we will use a different notation.

Rational Numbers

$$\left\{ \frac{a}{b} \,\middle|\, a \text{ and } b \text{ are integers and } b \neq 0 \right\}$$

We read this set as "the set of all numbers $\frac{a}{b}$ such that a and b are integers and $\boldsymbol{b}$ **is not equal to 0.**" Notice that every integer is also a rational number since each integer can be expressed as a quotient of integers. For example, the integer 5 is also a rational number since $5 = \frac{5}{1}$.

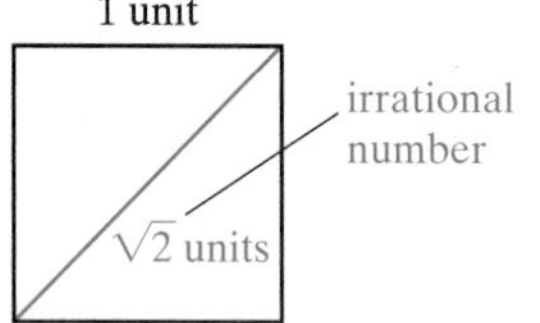

The number line also contains points that cannot be expressed as quotients of integers. These numbers are called **irrational numbers** because they cannot be represented by rational numbers. For example, $\sqrt{2}$ and π are irrational numbers.

Irrational Numbers

The set of **irrational numbers** is

{Nonrational numbers that correspond to points on the number line}.

That is, an irrational number is a number that cannot be expressed as a quotient of integers.

Both rational numbers and irrational numbers can be written as decimal numbers. The decimal equivalent of a rational number will either terminate or repeat in a pattern. For example, upon dividing we find that

Rational Numbers:

$$\frac{3}{4} = 0.75 \text{ (decimal number terminates or ends)}$$

$$\frac{2}{3} = 0.66666\ldots \text{ (decimal number repeats in a pattern)}$$

The decimal representation of an irrational number will neither terminate nor repeat. For example, the decimal representations of irrational numbers $\sqrt{2}$ and π are

Irrational Numbers:

$$\sqrt{2} = 1.414213562\ldots \text{ (decimal number does not terminate or repeat in a pattern)}$$

$$\pi = 3.141592653\ldots \text{ (decimal number does not terminate or repeat in a pattern)}$$

(For further review of decimals, see the Appendix.)

Combining the rational numbers with the irrational numbers gives the set of **real numbers.** One and only one point on a number line corresponds to each real number.

Real Numbers

The set of **real numbers** is

{All numbers that correspond to points on the number line}

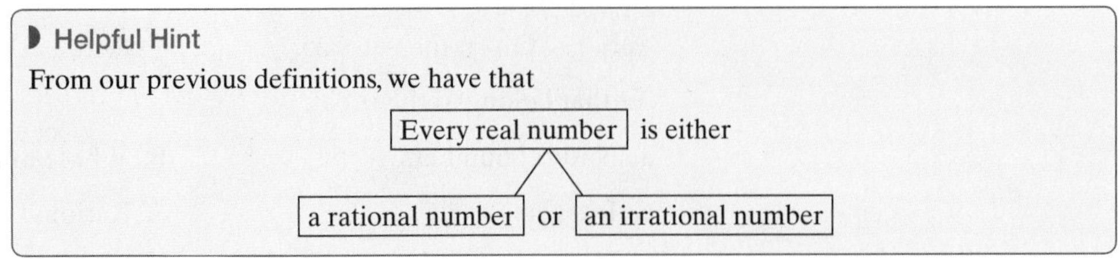

Helpful Hint

From our previous definitions, we have that

On the following number line, we see that real numbers can be positive, negative, or 0. Numbers to the left of 0 are called **negative numbers;** numbers to the right of 0 are called **positive numbers.** Positive and negative numbers are also called **signed numbers.**

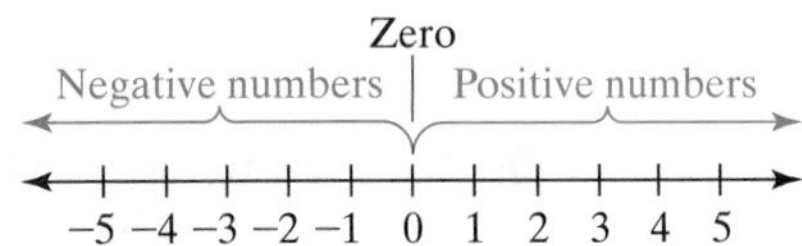

Several different sets of numbers have been discussed in this section. The following diagram shows the relationships among these sets of real numbers.

Common Sets of Numbers

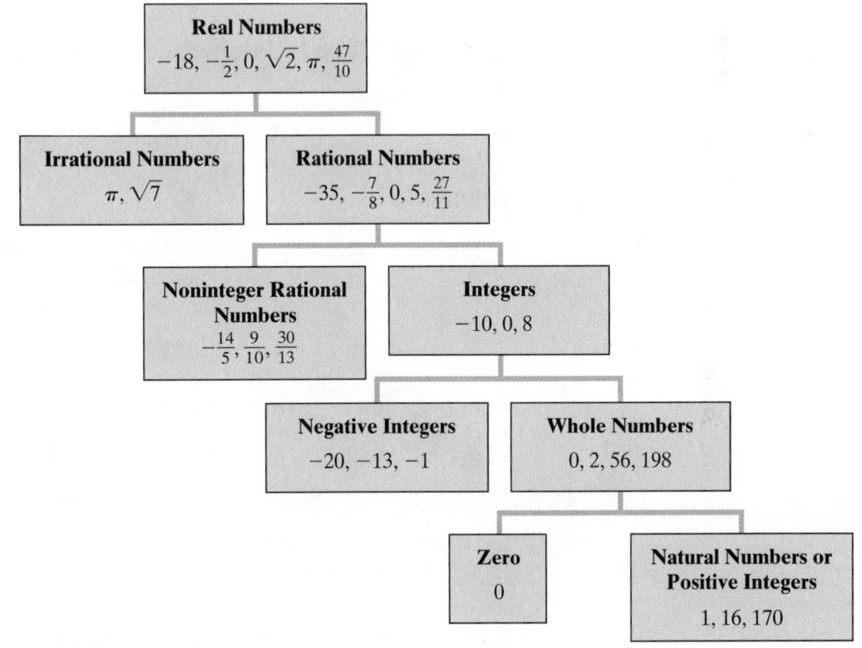

EXAMPLE 5 Given the set $\left\{-2, 0, \frac{1}{4}, -1.5, 112, -3, 11, \sqrt{2}\right\}$, list the numbers in this set that belong to the set of:

a. Natural numbers
b. Whole numbers
c. Integers
d. Rational numbers
e. Irrational numbers
f. Real numbers

Solution

a. The natural numbers are 11 and 112.

b. The whole numbers are 0, 11, and 112.

c. The integers are $-3, -2, 0, 11$, and 112.

d. Recall that integers are rational numbers also. The rational numbers are $-3, -2, -1.5, 0, \frac{1}{4}$, 11, and 112.

e. The irrational number is $\sqrt{2}$.

f. The real numbers are all numbers in the given set. □

PRACTICE
5 Given the set $\left\{25, \frac{7}{3}, -15, \frac{-3}{4}, \sqrt{5}, -3.7, 8.8, -99\right\}$, list the numbers in this set that belong to the set of:

a. Natural numbers
b. Whole numbers
c. Integers
d. Rational numbers
e. Irrational numbers
f. Real numbers

We now extend the meaning and use of inequality symbols such as $<$ and $>$ to all real numbers.

Order Property for Real Numbers

For any two real numbers a and b, a is less than b if a is to the left of b on a number line.

$a < b$ or also $b > a$

EXAMPLE 6 Insert $<, >$, or $=$ in the appropriate space to make each statement true.

a. $-1 \quad 0$
b. $7 \quad \frac{14}{2}$
c. $-5 \quad -6$

Solution

a. $-1 < 0$ since -1 is to the left of 0 on a number line.

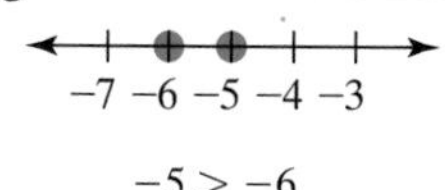

$-1 < 0$

b. $7 = \frac{14}{2}$ since $\frac{14}{2}$ simplifies to 7.

c. $-5 > -6$ since -5 is to the right of -6 on the number line.

$-5 > -6$

PRACTICE
6 Insert $<, >$, or $=$ in the appropriate space to make each statement true.

a. $0 \quad 3$
b. $15 \quad -5$
c. $3 \quad \frac{12}{4}$

OBJECTIVE
4 Finding the Absolute Value of a Real Number

A number line also helps us visualize the distance between numbers. The distance between a real number a and 0 is given a special name called the **absolute value** of a. "The absolute value of a" is written in symbols as $|a|$.

Absolute Value

The absolute value of a real number a, denoted by $|a|$, is the distance between a and 0 on a number line.

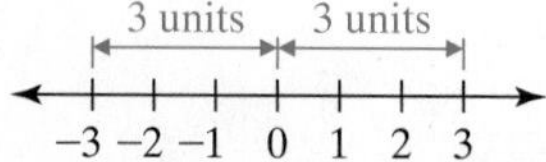

For example, $|3| = 3$ and $|-3| = 3$ since both 3 and -3 are a distance of 3 units from 0 on a number line.

Helpful Hint

Since $|a|$ is a distance, $|a|$ is always either positive or 0, never negative. That is, **for any real number a, $|a| \geq 0$.**

EXAMPLE 7 Find the absolute value of each number.

a. $|4|$ **b.** $|-5|$ **c.** $|0|$ **d.** $\left|-\frac{1}{2}\right|$ **e.** $|5.6|$

Solution

a. $|4| = 4$ since 4 is 4 units from 0 on a number line.

b. $|-5| = 5$ since -5 is 5 units from 0 on a number line.

c. $|0| = 0$ since 0 is 0 units from 0 on a number line.

d. $\left|-\frac{1}{2}\right| = \frac{1}{2}$ since $-\frac{1}{2}$ is $\frac{1}{2}$ unit from 0 on a number line.

e. $|5.6| = 5.6$ since 5.6 is 5.6 units from 0 on a number line. □

PRACTICE **7** Find the absolute value of each number.

a. $|-8|$ **b.** $|9|$ **c.** $|-2.5|$ **d.** $\left|\frac{5}{11}\right|$ **e.** $|\sqrt{3}|$

EXAMPLE 8 Insert $<$, $>$, or $=$ in the appropriate space to make each statement true.

a. $|0|$ 2 **b.** $|-5|$ 5 **c.** $|-3|$ $|-2|$ **d.** $|5|$ $|6|$ **e.** $|-7|$ $|6|$

Solution

a. $|0| < 2$ since $|0| = 0$ and $0 < 2$.

b. $|-5| = 5$ since $5 = 5$.

c. $|-3| > |-2|$ since $3 > 2$.

d. $|5| < |6|$ since $5 < 6$.

e. $|-7| > |6|$ since $7 > 6$. □

PRACTICE **8** Insert $<$, $>$, or $=$ in the appropriate space to make each statement true.

a. $|8|$ $|-8|$ **b.** $|-3|$ 0 **c.** $|-7|$ $|-11|$ **d.** $|3|$ $|2|$ **e.** $|0|$ $|-4|$

Vocabulary, Readiness & Video Check

Use the choices below to fill in each blank.

real	natural	whole	irrational
$\lvert b \rvert$	inequality	integers	rational

1. The ________ numbers are $\{0, 1, 2, 3, 4, \ldots\}$.
2. The ________ numbers are $\{1, 2, 3, 4, 5, \ldots\}$.
3. The symbols $\neq$, $\leq$, and $>$ are called ________ symbols.
4. The ________ are $\{\ldots, -3, -2, -1, 0, 1, 2, 3, \ldots\}$.
5. The ________ numbers are {all numbers that correspond to points on the number line}.
6. The ________ numbers are $\left\{\frac{a}{b} \middle| a \text{ and } b \text{ are integers}, b \neq 0\right\}$.
7. The ________ numbers are {nonrational numbers that correspond to points on the number line}.
8. The distance between a number b and 0 on a number line is ________.

Martin-Gay Interactive Videos

See Video R.2

Watch the section lecture video and answer the following questions.

OBJECTIVE 1

9. In Example 2, why is the symbol $<$ inserted between the two numbers?

OBJECTIVE 2

10. Write the sentence given in Example 4 and translate it to a mathematical statement, using symbols.

OBJECTIVE 3

11. Which sets of numbers does the number in Example 6 belong to? Why is this number not an irrational number?

OBJECTIVE 4

12. Complete this statement based on the lecture given before Example 8. The ______ of a real number a, denoted by $|a|$, is the distance between a and 0 on a number line.

R.2 Exercise Set

MyMathLab®

Insert $<, >,$ or $=$ in the appropriate space to make the statement true. See Example 1.

1. 7 3

2. 9 15

3. 6.26 6.26

4. 2.13 1.13

5. 0 7

6. 20 0

7. -2 2

8. -4 -6

9. The freezing point of water is 32° Fahrenheit. The boiling point of water is 212° Fahrenheit. Write an inequality statement using $<$ or $>$ comparing the numbers 32 and 212.

10. The freezing point of water is 0° Celsius. The boiling point of water is 100° Celsius. Write an inequality statement using $<$ or $>$ comparing the numbers 0 and 100.

△ **11.** An angle measuring 30° is shown and an angle measuring 45° is shown. Use the inequality symbol $\leq$ or $\geq$ to write a statement comparing the numbers 30 and 45.

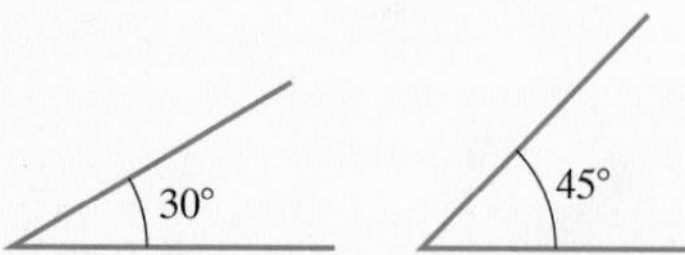

△ **12.** The sum of the measures of the angles of a triangle is 180°. The sum of the measures of the angles of a parallelogram is 360°. Use the inequality symbol $\leq$ or $\geq$ to write a statement comparing the numbers 360 and 180.

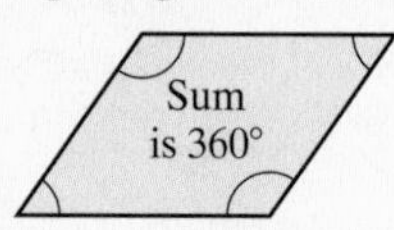

Are the following statements true or false? See Examples 2 and 6.

13. $11 \leq 11$

14. $4 \geq 7$

15. $10 > 11$

16. $17 > 16$

17. $3 + 8 \geq 3(8)$

18. $8 \cdot 8 \leq 8 \cdot 7$

19. $9 > 0$

20. $4 < 7$

21. $-6 > -2$

22. $0 < -15$

TRANSLATING

Write each sentence as a mathematical statement. See Example 3.

23. Eight is less than twelve.

24. Fifteen is greater than five.

25. Five is greater than or equal to four.

26. Negative ten is less than or equal to thirty-seven.

27. Fifteen is not equal to negative two.

28. Negative seven is not equal to seven.

Use integers to represent the values in each statement. See Example 4.

29. The highest elevation in California is Mt. Whitney, with an altitude of 14,494 feet. The lowest elevation in California is Death Valley, with an altitude of 282 feet below sea level. (*Source:* U.S. Geological Survey)

30. Driskill Mountain, in Louisiana, has an altitude of 535 feet. New Orleans, Louisiana, lies 8 feet below sea level. (*Source:* U.S. Geological Survey)

31. The number of graduate students at the University of Texas at Austin is 28,000 fewer than the number of undergraduate students. (*Source:* University of Texas at Austin)

32. The number of students admitted to the class of 2011 at UCLA was 38,792 fewer students than the number that had applied. (*Source:* UCLA)

33. Aaron Miller deposited \$350 in his savings account. He later withdrew \$126.

34. Aris Peña was deep-sea diving. During her dive, she ascended 30 feet and later descended 50 feet.

Tell which set or sets each number belongs to: natural numbers, whole numbers, integers, rational numbers, irrational numbers, and real numbers. See Example 5.

35. 0

36. $\frac{1}{4}$

37. -2

38. $-\frac{1}{2}$

39. 6

40. 5

41. $\frac{2}{3}$

42. $\sqrt{3}$

43. $-\sqrt{5}$

44. $-1\frac{5}{9}$

Tell whether each statement is true or false.

45. Every rational number is also an integer.
46. Every negative number is also a rational number.
47. Every natural number is positive.
48. Every rational number is also a real number.
49. 0 is a real number.
50. Every real number is also a rational number.
51. Every whole number is an integer.
52. $\frac{1}{2}$ is an integer.
53. A number can be both rational and irrational.
54. Every whole number is positive.

Insert <, >, or = in the appropriate space to make a true statement. See Examples 6 through 8.

55. $-10 \quad -100$

56. $-200 \quad -20$

57. $32 \quad 5.2$

58. $7.1 \quad -7$

59. $\frac{18}{3} \quad \frac{24}{3}$

60. $\frac{8}{2} \quad \frac{12}{3}$

61. $-51 \quad -50$

62. $|-20| \quad -200$

63. $|-5| \quad -4$

64. $0 \quad |0|$

65. $|-1| \quad |1|$

66. $\left|\frac{2}{5}\right| \quad \left|-\frac{2}{5}\right|$

67. $|-2| \quad |-3|$

68. $-500 \quad |-50|$

69. $|0| \quad |-8|$

70. $|-12| \quad \frac{24}{2}$

CONCEPT EXTENSIONS

The graph below is called a bar graph. This particular graph shows the annual numbers of recreational visitors to U.S. National Parks. Each bar represents a different year, and the height of the bar represents the number of visitors (in millions) in that year.

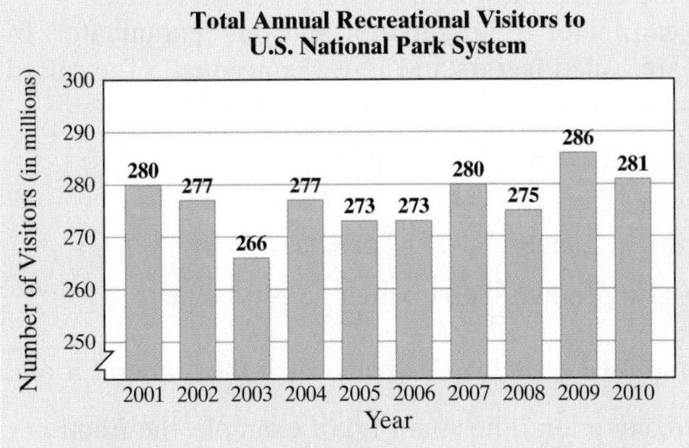

(*Note:* The ⚡ symbol means that some numbers are missing. Along the vertical data line, notice the numbers between 0 and 250 are missing or not shown.)

71. In which year(s) was the number of visitors the greatest?
72. What was the greatest number of visitors shown?
73. In what year(s) was the number of visitors greater than 280 million?
74. In what year(s) was the number of visitors less than 270 million?
75. Write an inequality statement comparing the number of annual visitors in 2001 and 2010.
76. Do you notice any trends shown by this bar graph?

The bar graph shows cranberry production from the top five cranberry-producing states.

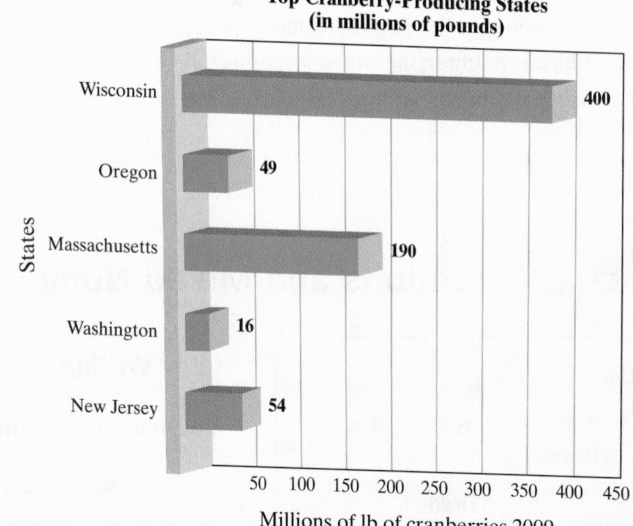

Data from National Agricultural Statistics Service

77. Write an inequality comparing the 2009 cranberry production in Oregon with the 2009 cranberry production in Washington.
78. Write an inequality comparing the 2009 cranberry production in Massachusetts with the 2009 cranberry production in Wisconsin.
79. Determine the difference between the 2009 cranberry production in Washington and the 2009 cranberry production in New Jersey.
80. According to the bar graph, which two states had almost equal 2009 cranberry crops?

The apparent magnitude of a star is the measure of its brightness as seen by someone on Earth. The smaller the apparent magnitude, the brighter the star. Use the apparent magnitudes in the table on page 16 to answer Exercises 81 through 86.

81. The apparent magnitude of the sun is -26.7. The apparent magnitude of the star Arcturus is -0.04. Write an inequality statement comparing the numbers -0.04 and -26.7.

Star	*Apparent Magnitude*	*Star*	*Apparent Magnitude*
Arcturus	−0.04	Spica	0.98
Sirius	−1.46	Rigel	0.12
Vega	0.03	Regulus	1.35
Antares	0.96	Canopus	−0.72
Sun	−26.7	Hadar	0.61

(Data from *Norton's Star Atlas and Reference Handbook*, 20th Edition, edited by Ian Ridpath. © 2004 Pearson Education, Inc.)

82. The apparent magnitude of Antares is 0.96. The apparent magnitude of Spica is 0.98. Write an inequality statement comparing the numbers 0.96 and 0.98.

83. Which is brighter, the sun or Arcturus?

84. Which is dimmer, Antares or Spica?

85. Which star listed is the brightest?

86. Which star listed is the dimmest?

Rewrite the following inequalities so that the inequality symbol points in the opposite direction and the resulting statement has the same meaning as the given one.

87. $25 \geq 20$

88. $-13 \leq 13$

89. $0 < 6$

90. $5 > 3$

91. $-10 > -12$

92. $-4 < -2$

93. In your own words, explain how to find the absolute value of a number.

94. Give an example of a real-life situation that can be described with integers but not with whole numbers.

R.3 Fractions and Mixed Numbers 

OBJECTIVES

1. Write Fractions in Simplest Form.
2. Multiply and Divide Fractions.
3. Add and Subtract Fractions.
4. Perform Operations on Mixed Numbers.

OBJECTIVE

1 Writing Fractions in Simplest Form 

A quotient of two numbers such as $\frac{2}{9}$ is called a **fraction.** The parts of a fraction are:

$$\text{Fraction bar} \rightarrow \frac{2}{9} \begin{array}{l} \leftarrow \text{Numerator} \\ \leftarrow \text{Denominator} \end{array}$$

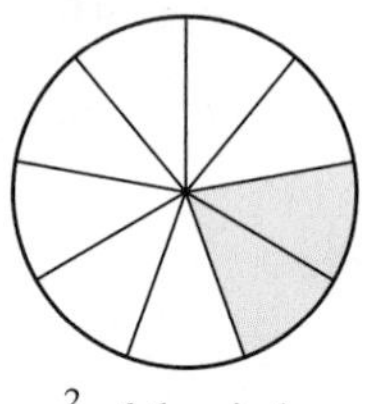

$\frac{2}{9}$ of the circle is shaded.

A fraction may be used to refer to part of a whole. For example, $\frac{2}{9}$ of the circle above is shaded. The denominator 9 tells us how many equal parts the whole circle is divided into, and the numerator 2 tells us how many equal parts are shaded.

To simplify fractions, we can factor the numerator and the denominator. In the statement $3 \cdot 5 = 15$, 3 and 5 are called **factors** and 15 is the **product.** (The raised dot symbol indicates multiplication.)

$$\underset{\text{factor}}{\underset{\uparrow}{3}} \cdot \underset{\text{factor}}{\underset{\uparrow}{5}} = \underset{\text{product}}{\underset{\uparrow}{15}}$$

To **factor** 15 means to write it as a product. The number 15 can be factored as $3 \cdot 5$ or as $1 \cdot 15$.

A fraction is said to be **simplified** or in **lowest terms** when the numerator and the denominator have no factors in common other than 1. For example, the fraction $\frac{5}{11}$ is in lowest terms since 5 and 11 have no common factors other than 1.

To help us simplify fractions, we write the numerator and the denominator as a product of **prime numbers.**

Prime Number and Composite Number

A **prime number** is a natural number, other than 1, whose only factors are 1 and itself. The first few prime numbers are

2, 3, 5, 7, 11, 13, 17, 19, 23, 29, and so on.

A natural number, other than 1, that is not a prime number is called a **composite number.**

Helpful Hint

The natural number 1 is neither prime nor composite.

Every composite number can be written as a product of prime numbers. We call this product of prime numbers the **prime factorization** of the composite number.

EXAMPLE 1 Write each of the following numbers as a product of primes.

a. 40 **b.** 63

Solution

a. First, write 40 as the product of any two whole numbers other than 1.

$$40 = 4 \cdot 10$$

Next, factor each of these numbers. Continue this process until all of the factors are prime numbers.

$$\begin{aligned} 40 &= 4 \cdot 10 \\ &\ \ \downarrow\searrow\ \ \downarrow\searrow \\ &= 2 \cdot 2 \cdot 2 \cdot 5 \end{aligned}$$

All the factors are now prime numbers. Then 40 written as a product of primes is

$$40 = 2 \cdot 2 \cdot 2 \cdot 5$$

b. $$\begin{aligned} 63 &= 9 \cdot 7 \\ &\ \ \downarrow\searrow\ \ \downarrow \\ &= 3 \cdot 3 \cdot 7 \end{aligned}$$ □

PRACTICE

1 Write each of the following numbers as a product of primes.

a. 36 **b.** 200

To use prime factors to write a fraction in lowest terms (or simplified form), apply the fundamental principle of fractions.

Fundamental Principle of Fractions

If $\frac{a}{b}$ is a fraction and c is a nonzero real number, then

$$\frac{a \cdot c}{b \cdot c} = \frac{a}{b}$$

To understand why this is true, we use the fact that since c is not zero, $\frac{c}{c} = 1$.

$$\frac{a \cdot c}{b \cdot c} = \frac{a}{b} \cdot \frac{c}{c} = \frac{a}{b} \cdot 1 = \frac{a}{b}$$

We will call this process dividing out the common factor of c.

EXAMPLE 2 Simplify each fraction (write it in lowest terms).

a. $\frac{42}{49}$ **b.** $\frac{11}{27}$ **c.** $\frac{88}{20}$

Solution

a. Write the numerator and the denominator as products of primes; then apply the fundamental principle to the common factor 7.

$$\frac{42}{49} = \frac{2 \cdot 3 \cdot 7}{7 \cdot 7} = \frac{2 \cdot 3}{7} \cdot \frac{7}{7} = \frac{2 \cdot 3}{7} = \frac{6}{7}$$

b. $\frac{11}{27} = \frac{11}{3 \cdot 3 \cdot 3}$

There are no common factors other than 1, so $\frac{11}{27}$ is already in simplest form.

c. $\frac{88}{20} = \frac{2 \cdot 2 \cdot 2 \cdot 11}{2 \cdot 2 \cdot 5} = \frac{2}{2} \cdot \frac{2}{2} \cdot \frac{2 \cdot 11}{5} = \frac{22}{5}$ □

PRACTICE 2 Write each fraction in lowest terms.

a. $\frac{63}{72}$ **b.** $\frac{64}{12}$ **c.** $\frac{7}{25}$

✓CONCEPT CHECK

Explain the error in the following steps.

a. $\frac{15}{55} = \frac{15}{55} = \frac{1}{5}$ b. $\frac{6}{7} = \frac{5+1}{5+2} = \frac{1}{2}$

OBJECTIVE

2 Multiplying and Dividing Fractions

To multiply two fractions, multiply numerator times numerator to obtain the numerator of the product; multiply denominator times denominator to obtain the denominator of the product.

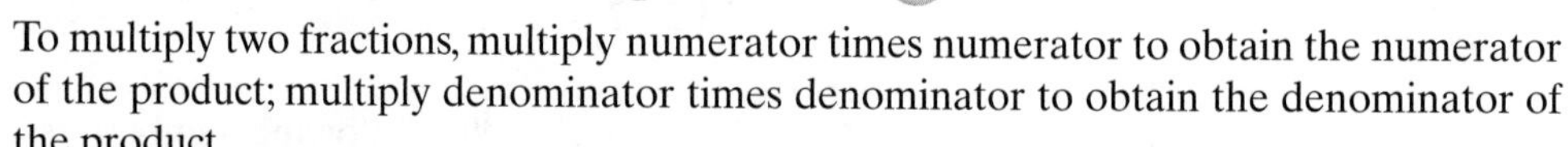

Multiplying Fractions

$$\frac{a}{b} \cdot \frac{c}{d} = \frac{a \cdot c}{b \cdot d} \quad \text{if } b \neq 0 \text{ and } d \neq 0$$

EXAMPLE 3 Multiply $\frac{2}{15}$ and $\frac{5}{13}$. Simplify the product if possible.

Solution

$$\frac{2}{15} \cdot \frac{5}{13} = \frac{2 \cdot 5}{15 \cdot 13}$$ Multiply numerators. Multiply denominators.

Next, simplify the product by dividing the numerator and the denominator by any common factors.

$$= \frac{2 \cdot \overset{1}{\cancel{5}}}{3 \cdot \underset{1}{\cancel{5}} \cdot 13}$$

$$= \frac{2}{39}$$ □

PRACTICE 3 Multiply $\frac{3}{8}$ and $\frac{7}{9}$. Simplify the product if possible.

Answers to Concept Check:
answers may vary

Before dividing fractions, we first define **reciprocals.** Two fractions are reciprocals of each other if their product is 1.

For example:

The reciprocal of $\frac{2}{3}$ is $\frac{3}{2}$ because $\frac{2}{3}\cdot\frac{3}{2} = \frac{6}{6} = 1$.

The reciprocal of 5 is $\frac{1}{5}$ because $5\cdot\frac{1}{5} = \frac{5}{1}\cdot\frac{1}{5} = \frac{5}{5} = 1$.

To divide fractions, multiply the first fraction by the reciprocal of the second fraction.

Dividing Fractions

$$\frac{a}{b} \div \frac{c}{d} = \frac{a}{b}\cdot\frac{d}{c}, \quad \text{if } b \neq 0,\ d \neq 0, \text{ and } c \neq 0$$

EXAMPLE 4 Divide. Simplify all quotients if possible.

a. $\frac{4}{5} \div \frac{5}{16}$ **b.** $\frac{7}{10} \div 14$ **c.** $\frac{3}{8} \div \frac{3}{10}$

Solution

a. $\frac{4}{5} \div \frac{5}{16} = \frac{4}{5}\cdot\frac{16}{5} = \frac{4\cdot 16}{5\cdot 5} = \frac{64}{25}$ — The numerator and denominator have no common factors.

b. $\frac{7}{10} \div 14 = \frac{7}{10} \div \frac{14}{1} = \frac{7}{10}\cdot\frac{1}{14} = \frac{\overset{1}{\cancel{7}}\cdot 1}{2\cdot 5\cdot 2\cdot \underset{1}{\cancel{7}}} = \frac{1}{20}$

c. $\frac{3}{8} \div \frac{3}{10} = \frac{3}{8}\cdot\frac{10}{3} = \frac{\overset{1}{\cancel{3}}\cdot \overset{1}{\cancel{2}}\cdot 5}{\underset{1}{\cancel{2}}\cdot 2\cdot 2\cdot \underset{1}{\cancel{3}}} = \frac{5}{4}$ □

PRACTICE 4 Divide. Simplify all quotients if possible.

a. $\frac{3}{4} \div \frac{4}{9}$ **b.** $\frac{5}{12} \div 15$ **c.** $\frac{7}{6} \div \frac{7}{15}$

OBJECTIVE 3 Adding and Subtracting Fractions

To add or subtract fractions with the same denominator, combine numerators and place the sum or difference over the common denominator.

Adding and Subtracting Fractions with the Same Denominator

$$\frac{a}{b} + \frac{c}{b} = \frac{a+c}{b}, \quad \text{if } b \neq 0$$

$$\frac{a}{b} - \frac{c}{b} = \frac{a-c}{b}, \quad \text{if } b \neq 0$$

EXAMPLE 5 Add or subtract as indicated. Simplify each result if possible.

a. $\frac{2}{7} + \frac{4}{7}$ **b.** $\frac{3}{10} + \frac{2}{10}$ **c.** $\frac{9}{7} - \frac{2}{7}$ **d.** $\frac{5}{3} - \frac{1}{3}$

Solution

a. $\frac{2}{7} + \frac{4}{7} = \frac{2+4}{7} = \frac{6}{7}$

b. $\frac{3}{10} + \frac{2}{10} = \frac{3+2}{10} = \frac{5}{10} = \frac{\overset{1}{\cancel{5}}}{2\cdot \underset{1}{\cancel{5}}} = \frac{1}{2}$

c. $\frac{9}{7} - \frac{2}{7} = \frac{9-2}{7} = \frac{7}{7} = 1$

d. $\frac{5}{3} - \frac{1}{3} = \frac{5-1}{3} = \frac{4}{3}$ □

PRACTICE 5 Add or subtract as indicated. Simplify each result if possible.

a. $\frac{8}{5} - \frac{3}{5}$ **b.** $\frac{8}{5} - \frac{2}{5}$ **c.** $\frac{3}{5} + \frac{1}{5}$ **d.** $\frac{5}{12} + \frac{1}{12}$

$\frac{3}{4} = \frac{12}{16}$

To add or subtract fractions without the same denominator, first write the fractions as equivalent fractions with a common denominator. **Equivalent fractions** are fractions that represent the same quantity. For example,

$$\frac{3}{4} \text{ and } \frac{12}{16} \text{ are equivalent fractions}$$

since they represent the same portion of a whole, as the diagram shows. Count the larger squares, and the shaded portion is $\frac{3}{4}$. Count the smaller squares, and the shaded portion is $\frac{12}{16}$. Thus, $\frac{3}{4} = \frac{12}{16}$.

We can write equivalent fractions by multiplying a given fraction by 1, as shown in the next example. Multiplying a fraction by 1 does not change the value of the fraction.

EXAMPLE 6 Write $\frac{2}{5}$ as an equivalent fraction with a denominator of 20.

Solution Since $5 \cdot 4 = 20$, multiply the fraction by $\frac{4}{4}$. Multiplying by $\frac{4}{4} = 1$ does not change the value of the fraction.

Multiply by $\frac{4}{4}$ or 1.

$$\frac{2}{5} = \frac{2}{5} \cdot \frac{4}{4} = \frac{2 \cdot 4}{5 \cdot 4} = \frac{8}{20}$$

Thus, $\frac{2}{5} = \frac{8}{20}$. □

PRACTICE 6 Write $\frac{2}{3}$ as an equivalent fraction with a denominator of 21.

To add or subtract with different denominators, we first write the fractions as **equivalent fractions** with the same denominator. We use the smallest or **least common denominator,** or **LCD.** (The LCD is the same as the least common multiple of the denominators.)

EXAMPLE 7 Add or subtract as indicated. Write each answer in simplest form.

a. $\frac{2}{5} + \frac{1}{4}$ **b.** $\frac{19}{6} - \frac{23}{12}$ **c.** $\frac{1}{2} + \frac{17}{22} - \frac{2}{11}$

Solution

a. Fractions must have a common denominator before they can be added or subtracted. Since 20 is the smallest number that both 5 and 4 divide into evenly, 20 is the **least common denominator** (LCD). Write both fractions as equivalent fractions with denominators of 20. Since

$$\frac{2}{5} \cdot \frac{4}{4} = \frac{2 \cdot 4}{5 \cdot 4} = \frac{8}{20} \quad \text{and} \quad \frac{1}{4} \cdot \frac{5}{5} = \frac{1 \cdot 5}{4 \cdot 5} = \frac{5}{20}$$

then

$$\frac{2}{5} + \frac{1}{4} = \frac{8}{20} + \frac{5}{20} = \frac{13}{20}$$

b. The LCD is 12. We write both fractions as equivalent fractions with denominators of 12.

$$\frac{19}{6} - \frac{23}{12} = \frac{38}{12} - \frac{23}{12}$$

$$= \frac{15}{12} = \frac{\overset{1}{\cancel{3}} \cdot 5}{2 \cdot 2 \cdot \underset{1}{\cancel{3}}} = \frac{5}{4}$$

c. The LCD for denominators 2, 22, and 11 is 22. First, write each fraction as an equivalent fraction with a denominator of 22. Then add or subtract from left to right.

$$\frac{1}{2} = \frac{1}{2} \cdot \frac{11}{11} = \frac{11}{22}, \quad \frac{17}{22} = \frac{17}{22}, \quad \text{and} \quad \frac{2}{11} = \frac{2}{11} \cdot \frac{2}{2} = \frac{4}{22}$$

Then

$$\frac{1}{2} + \frac{17}{22} - \frac{2}{11} = \frac{11}{22} + \frac{17}{22} - \frac{4}{22} = \frac{24}{22} = \frac{12}{11}$$

□

PRACTICE

7 Add or subtract as indicated. Write answers in simplest form.

a. $\frac{5}{11} + \frac{1}{7}$ **b.** $\frac{5}{21} - \frac{1}{6}$ **c.** $\frac{1}{3} + \frac{29}{30} - \frac{4}{5}$

OBJECTIVE

4 Performing Operations on Mixed Numbers

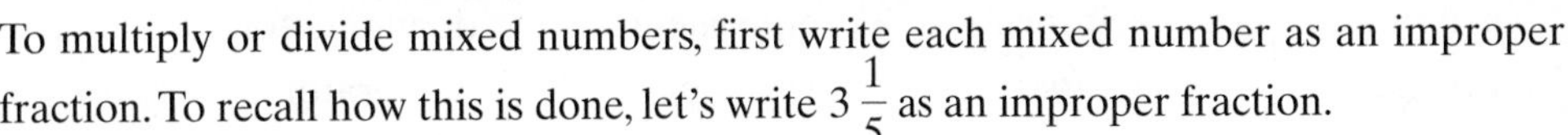

To multiply or divide mixed numbers, first write each mixed number as an improper fraction. To recall how this is done, let's write $3\frac{1}{5}$ as an improper fraction.

$$3\frac{1}{5} = 3 + \frac{1}{5} = \frac{15}{5} + \frac{1}{5} = \frac{16}{5}$$

Because of the steps above, notice that we can use a shortcut process for writing a mixed number as an improper fraction.

$$3\frac{1}{5} = \frac{5 \cdot 3 + 1}{5} = \frac{16}{5}$$

EXAMPLE 8 Divide: $2\frac{1}{8} \div 1\frac{2}{3}$

Solution First write each mixed number as an improper fraction.

$$2\frac{1}{8} = \frac{8 \cdot 2 + 1}{8} = \frac{17}{8}; \quad 1\frac{2}{3} = \frac{3 \cdot 1 + 2}{3} = \frac{5}{3}$$

Now divide as usual.

$$2\frac{1}{8} \div 1\frac{2}{3} = \frac{17}{8} \div \frac{5}{3} = \frac{17}{8} \cdot \frac{3}{5} = \frac{51}{40}$$

The fraction $\frac{51}{40}$ is improper. To write it as an equivalent mixed number, remember that the fraction bar means division and divide.

$$\begin{array}{r} 1\frac{11}{40} \\ 40\overline{)51} \\ \underline{-40} \\ 11 \end{array}$$

Thus, the quotient is $\frac{51}{40}$ or $1\frac{11}{40}$. □

PRACTICE

8 Multiply: $5\frac{1}{6} \cdot 4\frac{2}{5}$

As a general rule, if the original exercise contains mixed numbers, write the result as a mixed number if possible.

When adding or subtracting mixed numbers, you might want to use the following method.

EXAMPLE 9 Subtract: $50\frac{1}{6} - 38\frac{1}{3}$

Solution

$$\begin{array}{rcrcr} 50\frac{1}{6} & = & 50\frac{1}{6} & = & 49\frac{7}{6} \\ -38\frac{1}{3} & = & -38\frac{2}{6} & = & -38\frac{2}{6} \\ \hline & & & & 11\frac{5}{6} \end{array}$$

$50\frac{1}{6} = 49 + 1 + \frac{1}{6} = 49\frac{7}{6}$

□

PRACTICE 9 Subtract: $76\frac{1}{12} - 35\frac{1}{4}$

Vocabulary, Readiness & Video Check

Use the choices below to fill in each blank. Some choices may be used more than once.

simplified	reciprocals	equivalent	denominator
product	factors	fraction	numerator

1. A quotient of two numbers, such as $\frac{5}{8}$, is called a(n) ______________.
2. In the fraction $\frac{3}{11}$, the number 3 is called the ______________ and the number 11 is called the ______________.
3. To factor a number means to write it as a(n) ______________.
4. A fraction is said to be ______________ when the numerator and the denominator have no common factors other than 1.
5. In $7 \cdot 3 = 21$, the numbers 7 and 3 are called ______________ and the number 21 is called the ______________.
6. The fractions $\frac{2}{9}$ and $\frac{9}{2}$ are called ______________.
7. Fractions that represent the same quantity are called ______________ fractions.

Martin-Gay Interactive Videos

See Video R.3

Watch the section lecture video and answer the following questions.

OBJECTIVE 1

8. What is the common factor in the numerator and denominator of Example 1? What principle is used to simplify this fraction?

OBJECTIVE 2

9. During the solving of Example 3, what two things change in the first step?

OBJECTIVE 3

10. What is the first step needed in order to subtract the fractions in Example 6 and why?

OBJECTIVE 4

11. For Example 7, why is the sum not left as $4\frac{7}{6}$?

R.3 Exercise Set

MyMathLab®

Represent the shaded part of each geometric figure by a fraction.

1.

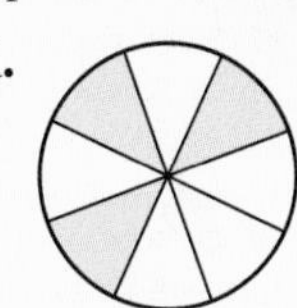

2.

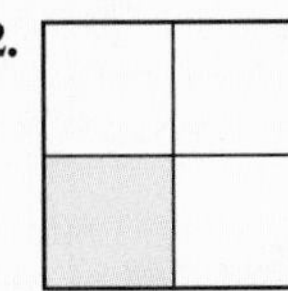

3.

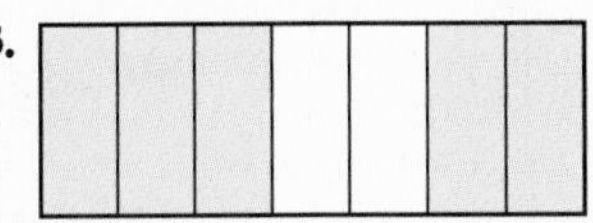

4.

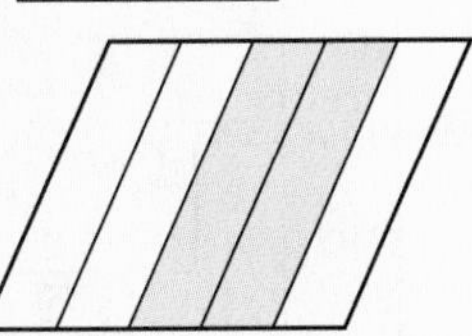

Write each number as a product of primes. See Example 1.

5. 33 **6.** 60 **7.** 98

8. 27 **9.** 20 **10.** 56

11. 75 **12.** 32 **13.** 45

14. 24

Write the fraction in lowest terms. See Example 2.

15. $\frac{2}{4}$ **16.** $\frac{3}{6}$ **17.** $\frac{10}{15}$

18. $\frac{15}{20}$ **19.** $\frac{3}{7}$ **20.** $\frac{5}{9}$

21. $\frac{18}{30}$ **22.** $\frac{42}{45}$ **23.** $\frac{120}{244}$

24. $\frac{360}{700}$

Multiply or divide as indicated. Simplify the answer if possible. See Examples 3 and 4.

25. $\frac{1}{2} \cdot \frac{3}{4}$ **26.** $\frac{7}{11} \cdot \frac{3}{5}$ **27.** $\frac{2}{3} \cdot \frac{3}{4}$

28. $\frac{7}{8} \cdot \frac{3}{21}$ **29.** $\frac{1}{2} \div \frac{7}{12}$ **30.** $\frac{7}{12} \div \frac{1}{2}$

31. $\frac{3}{4} \div \frac{1}{20}$ **32.** $\frac{3}{5} \div \frac{9}{10}$ **33.** $\frac{7}{10} \cdot \frac{5}{21}$

34. $\frac{3}{35} \cdot \frac{10}{63}$ **35.** $\frac{25}{9} \cdot \frac{1}{3}$ **36.** $\frac{1}{4} \cdot \frac{19}{6}$

The area of a plane figure is a measure of the amount of surface of the figure. Find the area of each figure below. (The area of a rectangle is the product of its length and width. The area of a triangle is $\frac{1}{2}$ the product of its base and height.)

△ **37.**

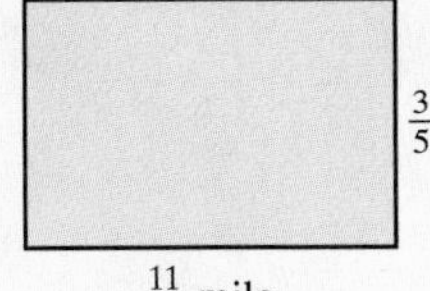

△ **38.**

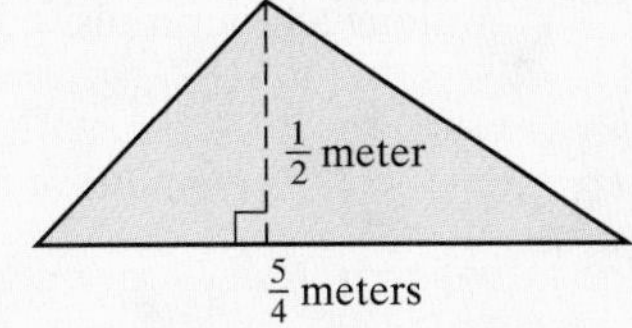

△ **39.**

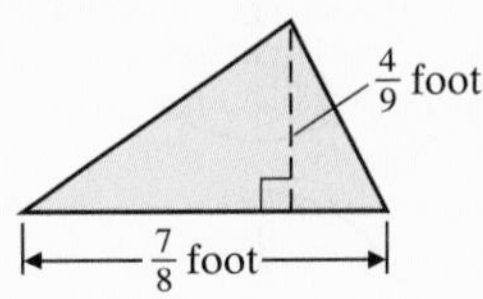

△ **40.**

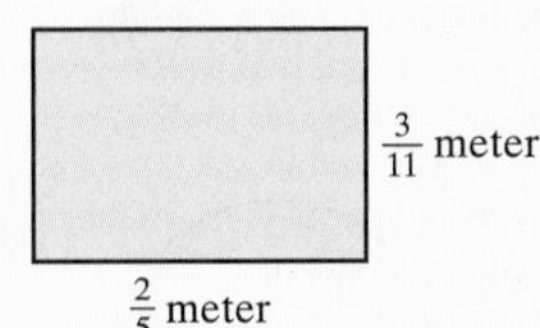

Add or subtract as indicated. Write the answer in lowest terms. See Example 5.

41. $\frac{4}{5} - \frac{1}{5}$ **42.** $\frac{6}{7} - \frac{1}{7}$

43. $\frac{4}{5} + \frac{1}{5}$ **44.** $\frac{6}{7} + \frac{1}{7}$

45. $\frac{17}{21} - \frac{10}{21}$ **46.** $\frac{18}{35} - \frac{11}{35}$

47. $\frac{23}{105} + \frac{4}{105}$ **48.** $\frac{13}{132} + \frac{35}{132}$

Write each fraction as an equivalent fraction with the given denominator. See Example 6.

49. $\frac{7}{10}$ with a denominator of 30

50. $\frac{2}{3}$ with a denominator of 9

51. $\frac{2}{9}$ with a denominator of 18

52. $\frac{8}{7}$ with a denominator of 56

53. $\frac{4}{5}$ with a denominator of 20

54. $\frac{4}{5}$ with a denominator of 25

Add or subtract as indicated. Write the answer in simplest form. See Example 7.

55. $\frac{2}{3} + \frac{3}{7}$ **56.** $\frac{3}{4} + \frac{1}{6}$

57. $\frac{4}{15} - \frac{1}{12}$ **58.** $\frac{11}{12} - \frac{1}{16}$

59. $\frac{5}{22} - \frac{5}{33}$ **60.** $\frac{7}{10} - \frac{8}{15}$

61. $\frac{12}{5} - 1$ **62.** $2 - \frac{3}{8}$

Each circle in Exercises 63–68 represents a whole, or 1. Use subtraction to determine the unknown part of the circle.

63.

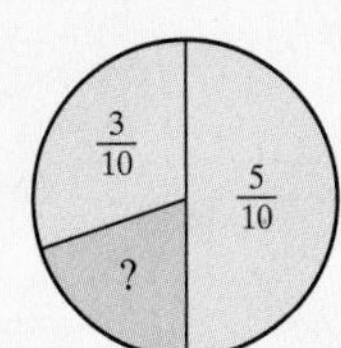

64.

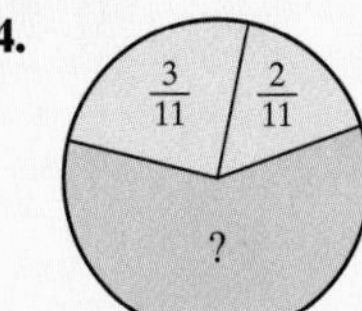

65.

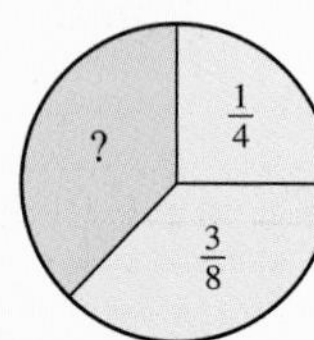

66.

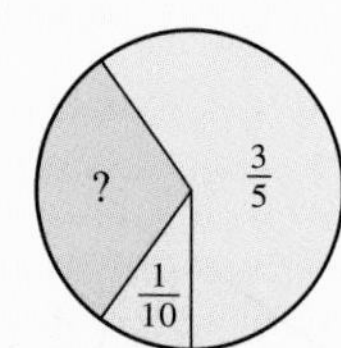

67.

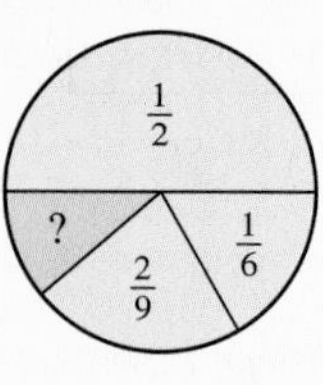

68.

$\frac{5}{12}$ $\frac{1}{3}$ $\frac{1}{6}$?

Perform the indicated operations. See Examples 8 and 9.

69. $5\frac{1}{9} \cdot 3\frac{2}{3}$

70. $2\frac{3}{4} \cdot 1\frac{7}{8}$

71. $8\frac{3}{5} \div 2\frac{9}{10}$

72. $1\frac{7}{8} \div 3\frac{8}{9}$

73. $17\frac{2}{5} + 30\frac{2}{3}$

74. $26\frac{11}{20} + 40\frac{7}{10}$

75. $8\frac{11}{12} - 1\frac{5}{6}$

76. $4\frac{7}{8} - 2\frac{3}{16}$

MIXED PRACTICE

Perform the following operations. Write answers in simplest form.

77. $\frac{10}{21} + \frac{5}{21}$

78. $\frac{11}{35} + \frac{3}{35}$

79. $\frac{10}{3} - \frac{5}{21}$

80. $\frac{11}{7} - \frac{3}{35}$

81. $\frac{2}{3} \cdot \frac{3}{5}$

82. $\frac{3}{4} \cdot \frac{7}{12}$

83. $\frac{2}{3} \div \frac{3}{5}$

84. $\frac{3}{4} \div \frac{7}{12}$

85. $5 + \frac{2}{3}$

86. $7 + \frac{1}{10}$

87. $7\frac{2}{5} \div \frac{1}{5}$

88. $9\frac{5}{6} \div \frac{1}{6}$

89. $\frac{1}{2} - \frac{14}{33}$

90. $\frac{7}{15} - \frac{7}{25}$

91. $\frac{23}{105} - \frac{2}{105}$

92. $\frac{57}{132} - \frac{13}{132}$

93. $1\frac{1}{2} + 3\frac{2}{3}$

94. $2\frac{3}{5} + 4\frac{7}{10}$

95. $\frac{2}{3} - \frac{5}{9} + \frac{5}{6}$

96. $\frac{8}{11} - \frac{1}{4} + \frac{1}{2}$

The perimeter of a plane figure is the total distance around the figure. Find the perimeter of each figure in Exercises 97 and 98.

△ **97.**

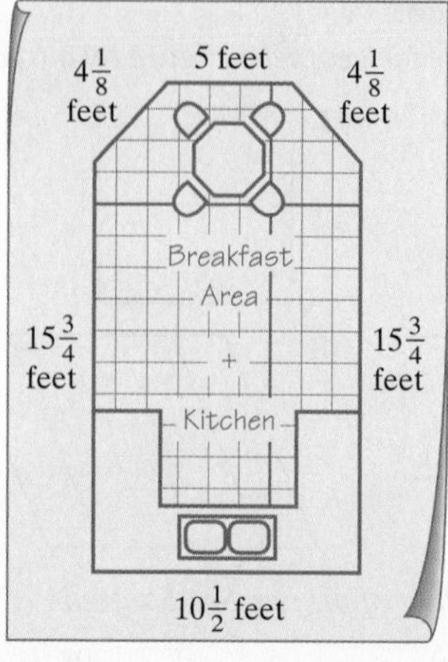

△ **98.**

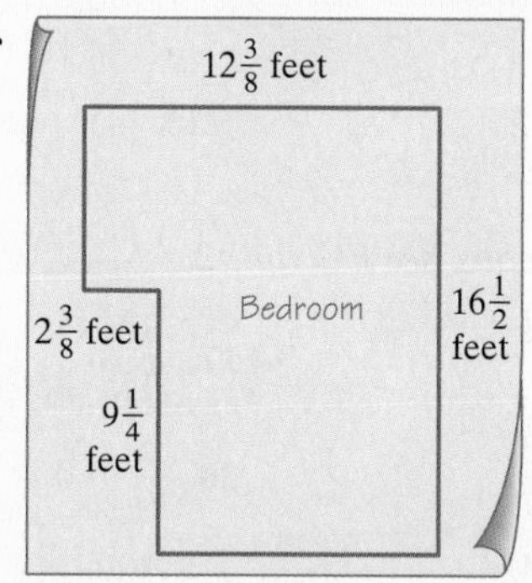

99. In your own words, explain how to add two fractions with different denominators.

100. In your own words, explain how to multiply two fractions.

The following trail chart is given to visitors at the Lakeview Forest Preserve.

Trail Name	*Distance (miles)*
Robin Path	$3\frac{1}{2}$
Red Falls	$5\frac{1}{2}$
Green Way	$2\frac{1}{8}$
Autumn Walk	$1\frac{3}{4}$

101. How much longer is Red Falls Trail than Green Way Trail?

102. Find the total distance traveled by someone who hiked along all four trails.

CONCEPT EXTENSIONS

The graph shown is called a circle graph or a pie chart. Use the graph to answer Exercises 103 through 106.

Fraction of U.S. Screens by Theater Type

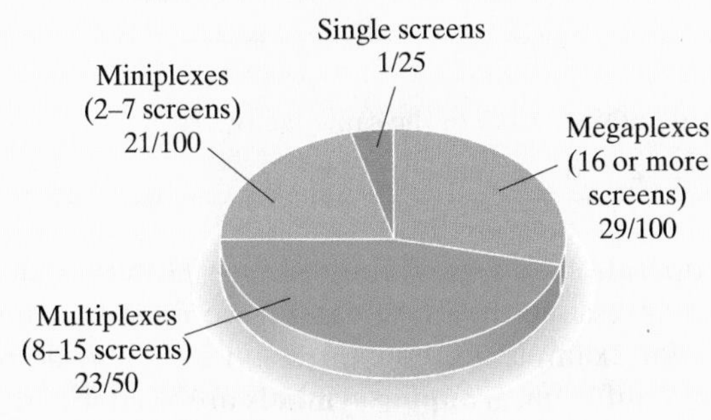

Data from Motion Picture Association of America

103. What fraction of U.S. movie screens are in miniplexes?

104. What fraction of U.S. movie screens are in single-screen theaters or multiplexes?

105. What theater type has the greatest fraction of screens?

106. What fraction of U.S. movie screens are in megaplexes or miniplexes?

For Exercises 107 through 110, determine whether the work is correct or incorrect. If incorrect, find the error and correct. See the Concept Check in this section.

107. $\frac{12}{24} = \frac{2+4+6}{2+4+6+12} = \frac{1}{12}$

108. $\frac{30}{60} = \frac{2\cdot 3\cdot 5}{2\cdot 2\cdot 3\cdot 5} = \frac{1}{2}$

109. $\frac{2}{7} + \frac{9}{7} = \frac{11}{14}$

110. $\frac{16}{28} = \frac{2\cdot 5 + 6\cdot 1}{2\cdot 5 + 6\cdot 3} = \frac{1}{3}$

R.4 Exponents, Order of Operations, Variable Expressions, and Equations

OBJECTIVES

1. Define and Use Exponents and the Order of Operations.
2. Evaluate Algebraic Expressions, Given Replacement Values for Variables.
3. Determine Whether a Number Is a Solution of a Given Equation.
4. Translate Phrases into Expressions and Sentences into Statements.

OBJECTIVE

1 Using Exponents and the Order of Operations

Frequently in algebra, products occur that contain repeated multiplication of the same factor. For example, the volume of a cube whose sides each measure 2 centimeters is $(2\cdot 2\cdot 2)$ cubic centimeters. We may use **exponential notation** to write such products in a more compact form. For example,

$$2\cdot 2\cdot 2 \quad \textit{may be written as} \quad 2^3.$$

The 2 in 2^3 is called the **base;** it is the repeated factor. The 3 in 2^3 is called the **exponent** and is the number of times the base is used as a factor. The expression 2^3 is called an **exponential expression.**

$$\underset{\text{base}}{2}^{\overset{\text{exponent}}{3}} = 2\cdot 2\cdot 2 = 8$$

2 is a factor 3 times

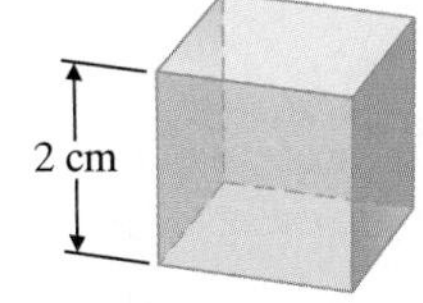

Volume is $(2\cdot 2\cdot 2)$ cubic centimeters.

EXAMPLE 1 Evaluate the following:

a. 3^2 [read as "3 squared" or as "3 to the second power"]

b. 5^3 [read as "5 cubed" or as "5 to the third power"]

c. 2^4 [read as "2 to the fourth power"]

d. 7^1 **e.** $\left(\frac{3}{7}\right)^2$

Solution

a. $3^2 = 3\cdot 3 = 9$

b. $5^3 = 5\cdot 5\cdot 5 = 125$

c. $2^4 = 2\cdot 2\cdot 2\cdot 2 = 16$

d. $7^1 = 7$

e. $\left(\frac{3}{7}\right)^2 = \left(\frac{3}{7}\right)\left(\frac{3}{7}\right) = \frac{9}{49}$ □

PRACTICE 1 Evaluate:

a. 1^3 **b.** 5^2 **c.** $\left(\frac{1}{10}\right)^2$ **d.** 9^1 **e.** $\left(\frac{2}{5}\right)^3$

> **Helpful Hint**
> $2^3 \neq 2 \cdot 3$ since 2^3 indicates repeated **multiplication** of the same factor.
> $$2^3 = 2 \cdot 2 \cdot 2 = 8, \text{ whereas } 2 \cdot 3 = 6.$$

Using symbols for mathematical operations is a great convenience. However, the more operation symbols present in an expression, the more careful we must be when performing the indicated operation. For example, in the expression $2 + 3 \cdot 7$, do we add first or multiply first? To eliminate confusion, **grouping symbols** are used. Examples of grouping symbols are parentheses ( ), brackets [ ], braces { }, and the fraction bar. If we wish $2 + 3 \cdot 7$ to be simplified by adding first, we enclose $2 + 3$ in parentheses.

$$(2 + 3) \cdot 7 = 5 \cdot 7 = 35$$

If we wish to multiply first, $3 \cdot 7$ may be enclosed in parentheses.

$$2 + (3 \cdot 7) = 2 + 21 = 23$$

To eliminate confusion when no grouping symbols are present, use the following agreed-upon order of operations.

Order of Operations

Simplify expressions using the order below. If grouping symbols such as parentheses are present, simplify expressions within those first, starting with the innermost set. If fraction bars are present, simplify the numerator and the denominator separately.

1. Evaluate exponential expressions.

2. Perform multiplications or divisions in order from left to right.

3. Perform additions or subtractions in order from left to right.

Now simplify $2 + 3 \cdot 7$. There are no grouping symbols and no exponents, so we multiply and then add.

$$\begin{aligned} 2 + 3 \cdot 7 &= 2 + 21 && \text{Multiply.} \\ &= 23 && \text{Add.} \end{aligned}$$

EXAMPLE 2 Simplify each expression.

a. $6 \div 3 + 5^2$ **b.** $20 \div 5 \cdot 4$ **c.** $\frac{2(12 + 3)}{|-15|}$ **d.** $3 \cdot 4^2$ **e.** $\frac{3}{2} \cdot \frac{1}{2} - \frac{1}{2}$

Solution

a. Evaluate 5^2 first.

$$6 \div 3 + 5^2 = 6 \div 3 + 25$$

Next divide, then add.

$$\begin{aligned} &= 2 + 25 && \text{Divide.} \\ &= 27 && \text{Add.} \end{aligned}$$

b. $\begin{aligned} 20 \div 5 \cdot 4 &= 4 \cdot 4 \\ &= 16 \end{aligned}$

> **Helpful Hint**
> Remember to multiply or divide in order from left to right.

c. First, simplify the numerator and the denominator separately.

$$\frac{2(12+3)}{|-15|} = \frac{2(15)}{15} \quad \text{Simplify numerator and denominator separately.}$$
$$= \frac{30}{15}$$
$$= 2 \quad \text{Simplify.}$$

d. In this example, only the 4 is squared. The factor of 3 is not part of the base because no grouping symbol includes it as part of the base.

$$3 \cdot 4^2 = 3 \cdot 16 \quad \text{Evaluate the exponential expression.}$$
$$= 48 \quad \text{Multiply.}$$

e. The order of operations applies to operations with fractions in exactly the same way as it applies to operations with whole numbers.

$$\frac{3}{2} \cdot \frac{1}{2} - \frac{1}{2} = \frac{3}{4} - \frac{1}{2} \quad \text{Multiply.}$$
$$= \frac{3}{4} - \frac{2}{4} \quad \text{The least common denominator is 4.}$$
$$= \frac{1}{4} \quad \text{Subtract.}$$

□

PRACTICE 2 Simplify each expression

a. $6 + 3 \cdot 9$ **b.** $4^3 \div 8 + 3$ **c.** $\left(\frac{2}{3}\right)^2 \cdot |-8|$

d. $\frac{9(14-6)}{|-2|}$ **e.** $\frac{7}{4} \cdot \frac{1}{4} - \frac{1}{4}$

Helpful Hint

Be careful when evaluating an exponential expression. In $3 \cdot 4^2$, the exponent 2 applies only to the base 4. In $(3 \cdot 4)^2$, we multiply first because of parentheses, so the exponent 2 applies to the product $3 \cdot 4$.

$$3 \cdot 4^2 = 3 \cdot 16 = 48 \qquad (3 \cdot 4)^2 = (12)^2 = 144$$

Expressions that include many grouping symbols can be confusing. When simplifying these expressions, keep in mind that grouping symbols separate the expression into distinct parts. Each is then simplified separately.

EXAMPLE 3 Simplify $\frac{3 + |4-3| + 2^2}{6-3}$.

Solution The fraction bar serves as a grouping symbol and separates the numerator and denominator. Simplify each separately. Also, the absolute value bars here serve as a grouping symbol. We begin in the numerator by simplifying within the absolute value bars.

$$\frac{3 + |4-3| + 2^2}{6-3} = \frac{3 + |1| + 2^2}{6-3} \quad \text{Simplify the expression inside the absolute value bars.}$$
$$= \frac{3 + 1 + 2^2}{3} \quad \text{Find the absolute value and simplify the denominator.}$$
$$= \frac{3+1+4}{3} \quad \text{Evaluate the exponential expression.}$$
$$= \frac{8}{3} \quad \text{Simplify the numerator.}$$

□

PRACTICE 3 Simplify $\frac{6^2 - 5}{3 + |6-5| \cdot 8}$.

EXAMPLE 4 Simplify $3[4 + 2(10 - 1)]$.

Solution Notice that both parentheses and brackets are used as grouping symbols. Start with the innermost set of grouping symbols.

> **Helpful Hint**
> Be sure to follow order of operations and resist the temptation to incorrectly add 4 and 2 first.

$$3[4 + 2(10 - 1)] = 3[4 + 2(9)] \quad \text{Simplify the expression in parentheses.}$$
$$= 3[4 + 18] \quad \text{Multiply.}$$
$$= 3[22] \quad \text{Add.}$$
$$= 66 \quad \text{Multiply.}$$

□

PRACTICE 4 Simplify $4[25 - 3(5 + 3)]$.

EXAMPLE 5 Simplify $\frac{8 + 2 \cdot 3}{2^2 - 1}$.

Solution

$$\frac{8 + 2 \cdot 3}{2^2 - 1} = \frac{8 + 6}{4 - 1} = \frac{14}{3}$$

□

PRACTICE 5 Simplify $\frac{36 \div 9 + 5}{5^2 - 3}$.

OBJECTIVE 2 Evaluating Algebraic Expressions

In algebra, we use symbols, usually letters such as x, y, or z, to represent unknown numbers. A symbol that is used to represent a number is called a **variable.** An **algebraic expression** is a collection of numbers, variables, operation symbols, and grouping symbols. For example,

$$2x, \quad -3, \quad 2x + 10, \quad 5(p^2 + 1), \quad \text{and} \quad \frac{3y^2 - 6y + 1}{5}$$

are algebraic expressions.

Expression	*Meaning*
$2x$	$2 \cdot x$
$5(p^2 + 1)$	$5 \cdot (p^2 + 1)$
$3y^2$	$3 \cdot y^2$
xy	$x \cdot y$

If we give a specific value to a variable, we can **evaluate an algebraic expression.** To evaluate an algebraic expression means to find its numerical value once we know the values of the variables.

Algebraic expressions are often used in problem solving. For example, the expression

$$16t^2$$

gives the distance in feet (neglecting air resistance) that an object will fall in t seconds.

EXAMPLE 6 Evaluate each expression if $x = 3$ and $y = 2$.

a. $2x - y$ **b.** $\frac{3x}{2y}$ **c.** $\frac{x}{y} + \frac{y}{2}$ **d.** $x^2 - y^2$

Solution

a. Replace x with 3 and y with 2.

$$\begin{aligned} 2x - y &= 2(3) - 2 && \text{Let } x = 3 \text{ and } y = 2. \\ &= 6 - 2 && \text{Multiply.} \\ &= 4 && \text{Subtract.} \end{aligned}$$

b. $\frac{3x}{2y} = \frac{3 \cdot 3}{2 \cdot 2} = \frac{9}{4}$ Let $x = 3$ and $y = 2$.

c. Replace x with 3 and y with 2. Then simplify.

$$\frac{x}{y} + \frac{y}{2} = \frac{3}{2} + \frac{2}{2} = \frac{5}{2}$$

d. Replace x with 3 and y with 2.

$$x^2 - y^2 = 3^2 - 2^2 = 9 - 4 = 5$$ □

PRACTICE **6** Evaluate each expression if $x = 2$ and $y = 5$.

a. $2x + y$ **b.** $\frac{4x}{3y}$ **c.** $\frac{3}{x} + \frac{x}{y}$ **d.** $x^3 + y^2$

OBJECTIVE

3 Determining Whether a Number Is a Solution of an Equation 

Many times, a problem-solving situation is modeled by an equation. An **equation** is a mathematical statement that two expressions have equal value. The equal symbol "=" is used to equate the two expressions. For example,

$$3 + 2 = 5, \quad 7x = 35, \quad \frac{2(x - 1)}{3} = 0, \text{ and } I = PRT \text{ are all equations.}$$

Helpful Hint
An equation contains the equal symbol "=". An algebraic expression does not.

✓CONCEPT CHECK
Which of the following are equations? Which are expressions?

a. $5x = 8$ **b.** $5x - 8$ **c.** $12y + 3x$ **d.** $12y = 3x$

When an equation contains a variable, deciding which values of the variable make an equation a true statement is called **solving** an equation for the variable. A **solution** of an equation is a value for the variable that makes the equation true. For example, 3 is a solution of the equation $x + 4 = 7$ because if x is replaced with 3, the statement is true.

$$\begin{aligned} x + 4 &= 7 \\ &\downarrow \\ 3 + 4 &= 7 && \text{Replace } x \text{ with 3.} \\ 7 &= 7 && \text{True} \end{aligned}$$

Similarly, 1 is not a solution of the equation $x + 4 = 7$ because $1 + 4 = 7$ is **not** a true statement.

Answers to Concept Check:
equations: a, d; expressions: b, c.

EXAMPLE 7 Decide whether 2 is a solution of $3x + 10 = 8x$.

Solution Replace x with 2 and see if a true statement results.

$$3x + 10 = 8x \quad \text{Original equation}$$
$$3(2) + 10 \stackrel{?}{=} 8(2) \quad \text{Replace } x \text{ with 2.}$$
$$6 + 10 \stackrel{?}{=} 16 \quad \text{Simplify each side.}$$
$$16 = 16 \quad \text{True}$$

Since we arrived at a true statement after replacing x with 2 and simplifying both sides of the equation, 2 is a solution of the equation. □

PRACTICE
7 Decide whether 4 is a solution of $9x - 6 = 7x$.

OBJECTIVE
4 Translating Phrases to Expressions and Sentences to Statements

Now that we know how to represent an unknown number by a variable, let's practice translating phrases into algebraic expressions and sentences into statements. Oftentimes, solving problems requires the ability to translate word phrases and sentences into symbols. Below is a list of some key words and phrases to help us translate.

Helpful Hint
Order matters when subtracting and dividing, so be especially careful with these translations.

Addition (+)	*Subtraction* (−)	*Multiplication* (·)	*Division* (÷)	*Equality* (=)
Sum	Difference of	Product	Quotient	Equals
Plus	Minus	Times	Divide	Gives
Added to	Subtracted from	Multiply	Into	Is/was/should be
More than	Less than	Twice	Ratio	Yields
Increased by	Decreased by	Of	Divided by	Amounts to
Total	Less			Represents/ Is the same as

EXAMPLE 8 Write an algebraic expression that represents each phrase. Let the variable x represent the unknown number.

a. The sum of a number and 3
b. The product of 3 and a number
c. Twice a number
d. 10 decreased by a number
e. 5 times a number, increased by 7

Solution

a. $x + 3$ since "sum" means to add
b. $3 \cdot x$ and $3x$ are both ways to denote the product of 3 and x
c. $2 \cdot x$ or $2x$
d. $10 - x$ because "decreased by" means to subtract
e. $\underbrace{5x}_{\text{5 times a number}} + 7$ □

PRACTICE
8 Write an algebraic expression that represents each phase. Let the variable x represent the unknown number.

a. Six times a number
b. A number decreased by 8
c. The product of a number and 9
d. Two times a number, plus 3
e. The sum of 7 and a number

> **Helpful Hint**
>
> Make sure you understand the difference when translating phrases containing "decreased by," "subtracted from," and "less than."
>
> | ***Phrase*** | ***Translation*** | |
> |---|---|---|
> | A number decreased by 10 | $x - 10$ | Notice the order. |
> | A number subtracted from 10 | $10 - x$ | |
> | 10 less than a number | $x - 10$ | |
> | A number less 10 | $x - 10$ | |

Now let's practice translating sentences into equations.

EXAMPLE 9 Write each sentence as an equation or inequality. Let x represent the unknown number.

a. The quotient of 15 and a number is 4.

b. Three subtracted from 12 is a number.

c. Four times a number, added to 17, is not equal to 21.

d. Triple a number is less than 48.

Solution

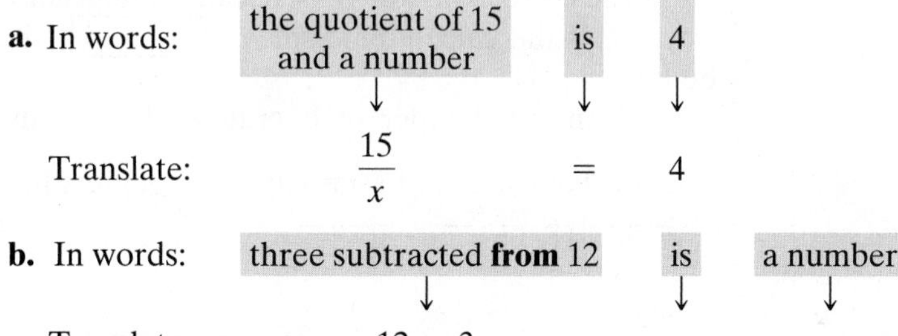

Care must be taken when the operation is subtraction. The expression $3 - 12$ would be incorrect. Notice that $3 - 12 \neq 12 - 3$.

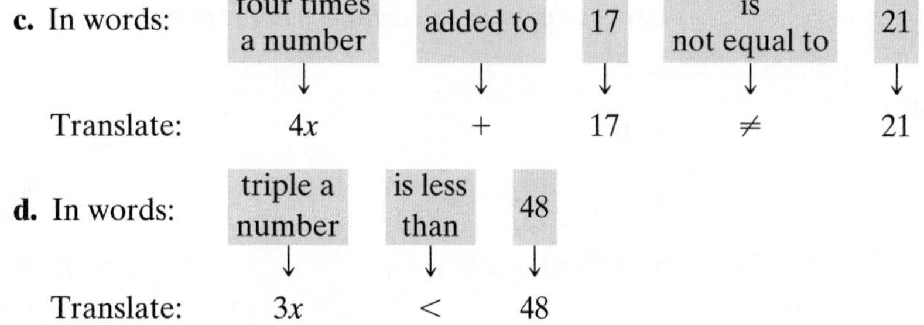

□

PRACTICE

9 Write each sentence as an equation or inequality. Let x represent the unknown number.

a. A number increased by 7 is equal to 13.

b. Two less than a number is 11.

c. Double a number, added to 9, is not equal to 25.

d. Five times 11 is greater than or equal to an unknown number.

Graphing Calculator Explorations

Exponents

To evaluate exponential expressions on a scientific calculator, find the key marked $\boxed{y^x}$ or $\boxed{\wedge}$. To evaluate, for example, 3^5, press the following keys: $\boxed{3}\ \boxed{y^x}\ \boxed{5}\ \boxed{=}$ or $\boxed{3}\ \boxed{\wedge}\ \boxed{5}\ \boxed{=}$.

↕ or

ENTER

The display should read $\boxed{243}$ or $\boxed{\begin{array}{l}3\wedge 5\\ \hfill 243\end{array}}$

Order of Operations

Some calculators follow the order of operations, and others do not. To see whether your calculator has the order of operations built in, use your calculator to find $2 + 3 \cdot 4$. To do this, press the following sequence of keys:

$\boxed{2}\ \boxed{+}\ \boxed{3}\ \boxed{\times}\ \boxed{4}\ \boxed{=}$.

↕ or

ENTER

The correct answer is 14 because the order of operations is to multiply before we add. If the calculator displays $\boxed{14}$, then it has the order of operations built in.

Even if the order of operations is built in, parentheses must sometimes be inserted. For example, to simplify $\frac{5}{12 - 7}$, press the keys

$\boxed{5}\ \boxed{\div}\ \boxed{(}\ \boxed{1}\ \boxed{2}\ \boxed{-}\ \boxed{7}\ \boxed{)}\ \boxed{=}$.

↕ or

ENTER

The display should read $\boxed{1}$ or $\boxed{\begin{array}{l}5/(12-7)\\ \hfill 1\end{array}}$

Use a calculator to evaluate each expression.

1. 5^4

2. 7^4

3. 9^5

4. 8^6

5. $2(20 - 5)$

6. $3(14 - 7) + 21$

7. $24(862 - 455) + 89$

8. $99 + (401 + 962)$

9. $\frac{4623 + 129}{36 - 34}$

10. $\frac{956 - 452}{89 - 86}$

Vocabulary, Readiness & Video Check

Use the choices below to fill in each blank.

equation	variable	base	grouping
expression	solution	solving	exponent

1. In the expression 5^2, the 5 is called the ___________ and the 2 is called the ___________.

2. The symbols ( ), [ ], and { } are examples of ___________ symbols.

3. A symbol that is used to represent a number is called a(n) __________.

4. A collection of numbers, variables, operation symbols, and grouping symbols is called a(n) __________.

5. A mathematical statement that two expressions are equal is called a(n) __________.

6. A value for the variable that makes an equation a true statement is called a(n) __________.

7. Deciding what values of a variable make an equation a true statement is called __________ the equation.

Martin-Gay Interactive Videos

See Video R.4

Watch the section lecture video and answer the following questions.

OBJECTIVE 1

8. In Example 3 and the lecture before, what is the main point made about the order of operations?

OBJECTIVE 2

9. What happens with the replacement value for z in Example 6 and why?

OBJECTIVE 3

10. Is the value 0 a solution of the equation given in Example 9? How is this determined?

OBJECTIVE 4

11. Earlier in this video the point was made that equations have =, while expressions do not. In the lecture before Example 10, translating from English to math is discussed and another difference between expressions and equations is explained. What is it?

R.4 Exercise Set

MyMathLab®

Evaluate. See Example 1.

1. 3^5
2. 2^5
3. 3^3
4. 4^4
5. 1^5
6. 1^8
7. 5^1
8. 8^1
9. 7^2
10. 9^2
11. $\left(\frac{2}{3}\right)^4$
12. $\left(\frac{6}{11}\right)^2$
13. $\left(\frac{1}{5}\right)^3$
14. $\left(\frac{1}{2}\right)^5$
15. $(1.2)^2$
16. $(1.5)^2$
17. $(0.04)^3$
18. $(0.03)^3$

MIXED PRACTICE

Simplify each expression. See Examples 2 through 5.

19. $5 + 6 \cdot 2$
20. $8 + 5 \cdot 3$
21. $4 \cdot 8 - 6 \cdot 2$
22. $12 \cdot 5 - 3 \cdot 6$
23. $2(8 - 3)$
24. $5(6 - 2)$
25. $2 + (5 - 2) + 4^2$
26. $6 - 2 \cdot 2 + 2^5$
27. $5 \cdot 3^2$
28. $2 \cdot 5^2$
29. $\frac{1}{4} \cdot \frac{2}{3} - \frac{1}{6}$
30. $\frac{3}{4} \cdot \frac{1}{2} + \frac{2}{3}$
31. $2[5 + 2(8 - 3)]$
32. $3[4 + 3(6 - 4)]$
33. $\frac{19 - 3 \cdot 5}{6 - 4}$
34. $\frac{4 \cdot 3 + 2}{4 + 3 \cdot 2}$
35. $\frac{|6 - 2| + 3}{8 + 2 \cdot 5}$
36. $\frac{15 - |3 - 1|}{12 - 3 \cdot 2}$
37. $\frac{3 + 3(5 + 3)}{3^2 + 1}$
38. $\frac{3 + 6(8 - 5)}{4^2 + 2}$
39. $\frac{6 + |8 - 2| + 3^2}{18 - 3}$
40. $\frac{16 + |13 - 5| + 4^2}{17 - 5}$
41. $2 + 3[10(4 \cdot 5 - 16) - 30]$
42. $3 + 4[8(5 \cdot 5 - 20) - 41]$
43. $\left(\frac{2}{3}\right)^3 + \frac{1}{9} + \frac{1}{3} \cdot \frac{4}{3}$
44. $\left(\frac{3}{8}\right)^2 + \frac{1}{4} + \frac{1}{8} \cdot \frac{3}{2}$

For Exercises 45 and 46, match each expression in the first column with its value in the second column.

45.	
a. $(6 + 2) \cdot (5 + 3)$	19
b. $(6 + 2) \cdot 5 + 3$	22
c. $6 + 2 \cdot 5 + 3$	64
d. $6 + 2 \cdot (5 + 3)$	43

46.	
a. $(1 + 4) \cdot 6 - 3$	15
b. $1 + 4 \cdot (6 - 3)$	13
c. $1 + 4 \cdot 6 - 3$	27
d. $(1 + 4) \cdot (6 - 3)$	22

Evaluate each expression when $x = 1$, $y = 3$, and $z = 5$. See Example 6.

47. $3y$

48. $4x$

49. $\frac{z}{5x}$

50. $\frac{y}{2z}$

51. $3x - 2$

52. $6y - 8$

53. $|2x + 3y|$

54. $|5z - 2y|$

55. $xy + z$

56. $yz - x$

57. $5y^2$

58. $2z^2$

Evaluate each expression if $x = 12$, $y = 8$, and $z = 4$. See Example 6.

59. $\frac{x}{z} + 3y$

60. $\frac{y}{z} + 8x$

61. $x^2 - 3y + x$

62. $y^2 - 3x + y$

63. $\frac{x^2 + z}{y^2 + 2z}$

64. $\frac{y^2 + x}{x^2 + 3y}$

Neglecting air resistance, the expression $16t^2$ gives the distance in feet an object will fall in t seconds.

65. Complete the chart below. To evaluate $16t^2$, remember to first find t^2, then multiply by 16.

Time t (in seconds)	*Distance $16t^2$ (in feet)*
1	
2	
3	
4	

66. Does an object fall the same distance *during* each second? Why or why not? (See Exercise 65.)

Decide whether the given number is a solution of the given equation. See Example 7.

67. Is 5 a solution of $3x + 30 = 9x$?

68. Is 6 a solution of $2x + 7 = 3x$?

69. Is 0 a solution of $2x + 6 = 5x - 1$?

70. Is 2 a solution of $4x + 2 = x + 8$?

71. Is 8 a solution of $2x - 5 = 5$?

72. Is 6 a solution of $3x - 10 = 8$?

73. Is 2 a solution of $x + 6 = x + 6$?

74. Is 10 a solution of $x + 6 = x + 6$?

75. Is 0 a solution of $x = 5x + 15$?

76. Is 1 a solution of $4 = 1 - x$?

TRANSLATING

Write each phrase as an algebraic expression. Let x represent the unknown number. See Example 8.

77. Fifteen more than a number

78. A number increased by 9

79. Five subtracted from a number

80. Five decreased by a number

81. The ratio of a number and 4

82. The quotient of a number and 9

83. Three times a number, increased by 22

84. Twice a number, decreased by 72

TRANSLATING

Write each sentence as an equation or inequality. Use x to represent any unknown number. See Example 9.

85. One increased by two equals the quotient of nine and three.

86. Four subtracted from eight is equal to two squared.

87. Three is not equal to four divided by two.

88. The difference of sixteen and four is greater than ten.

89. The sum of 5 and a number is 20.

90. Seven subtracted from a number is 0.

91. The product of 7.6 and a number is 17.

92. 9.1 times a number equals 4.

93. Thirteen minus three times a number is 13.

94. Eight added to twice a number is 42.

CONCEPT EXTENSIONS

Fill in each blank with one of the following:
add subtract multiply divide

95. To simplify the expression $1 + 3 \cdot 6$, first ________.

96. To simplify the expression $(1 + 3) \cdot 6$, first ________.

97. To simplify the expression $(20 - 4) \cdot 2$, first ________.

98. To simplify the expression $20 - 4 \div 2$, first ________.

99. Are parentheses necessary in the expression $2 + (3 \cdot 5)$? Explain your answer.

100. Are parentheses necessary in the expression $(2 + 3) \cdot 5$? Explain your answer.

Recall that perimeter measures the distance around a plane figure and area measures the amount of surface of a plane figure. The expression $2l + 2w$ gives the perimeter of the rectangle below (measured in units), and the expression lw gives its area (measured in square units). Complete the chart below for the given lengths and widths. Be sure to include units.

	Length: l	*Width: w*	*Perimeter of Rectangle: 2l + 2w*	*Area of Rectangle: lw*
101.	4 in.	3 in.		
102.	6 in.	1 in.		
103.	5.3 in.	1.7 in.		
104.	4.6 in.	2.4 in.		

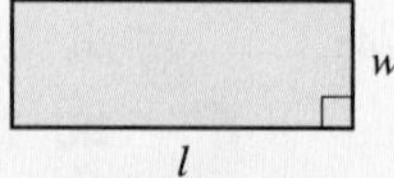

105. Study the perimeters and areas found in the chart on the previous page. Do you notice any trends?

106. In your own words, explain the difference between an expression and an equation.

107. Insert one set of parentheses so that the following expression simplifies to 32.

$$20 - 4 \cdot 4 \div 2$$

108. Insert one set of parentheses so that the following expression simplifies to 28.

$$2 \cdot 5 + 3^2$$

Determine whether each is an expression or an equation. See the Concept Check in this section.

109. a. $5x + 6$
b. $2a = 7$
c. $3a + 2 = 9$
d. $4x + 3y - 8z$
e. $5^2 - 2(6 - 2)$

110. a. $3x^2 - 26$
b. $3x^2 - 26 = 1$
c. $2x - 5 = 7x - 5$
d. $9y + x - 8$
e. $3^2 - 4(5 - 3)$

111. Why is 4^3 usually read as "four cubed"? (*Hint:* What is the volume of the **cube** below?)

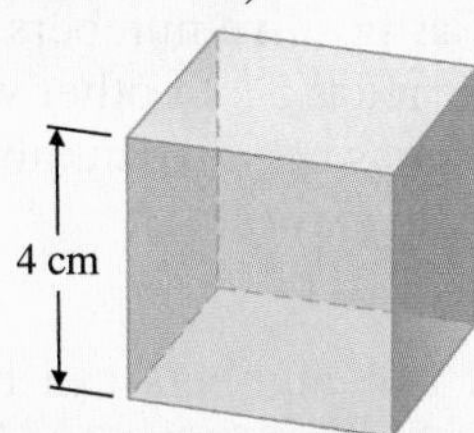

112. Why is 8^2 usually read as "eight squared"? (*Hint:* What is the area of the **square** below?)

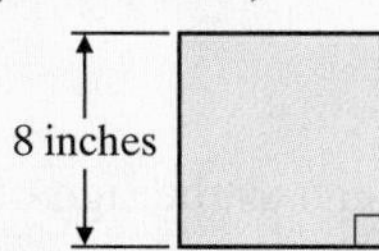

113. Write any expression, using 3 or more numbers, that simplifies to −11.

114. Write any expression, using 4 or more numbers, that simplifies to 7.

115. The area of a figure is the total enclosed surface of the figure. Area is measured in square units. The expression lw represents the area of a rectangle when l is its length and w is its width. Find the area of the following rectangular-shaped lot.

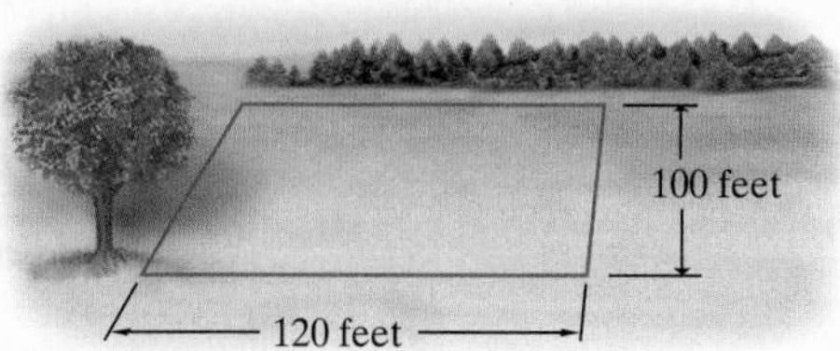

116. A trapezoid is a four-sided figure with exactly one pair of parallel sides. The expression $\frac{1}{2}h(B + b)$ represents its area, when B and b are the lengths of the two parallel sides and h is the height between these sides. Find the area if $B = 15$ inches, $b = 7$ inches, and $h = 5$ inches.

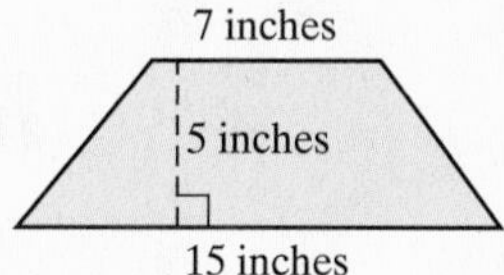

117. The expression $\frac{d}{t}$ represents the average speed in miles per hour if a distance of d miles is traveled in t hours. Find the speed to the nearest whole number if the distance between Dallas, Texas, and Kaw City, Oklahoma, is 432 miles, and it takes Peter Callac 8.5 hours to drive the distance.

118. The expression $\frac{I}{PT}$ represents the rate of interest being charged if a loan of P dollars for T years required I dollars in interest to be paid. Find the interest rate if a \$650 loan for 3 years to buy a used IBM personal computer requires \$126.75 in interest to be paid.

R.5 Adding Real Numbers 

OBJECTIVES

1. Add Real Numbers.
2. Solve Applications That Involve Addition of Real Numbers.
3. Find the Opposite of a Number.

OBJECTIVE

1 Adding Real Numbers 

Real numbers can be added, subtracted, multiplied, divided, and raised to powers, just as whole numbers can. We use a number line to help picture the addition of real numbers. We begin by adding numbers with the same sign.

EXAMPLE 1 Add: $3 + 2$

Solution Recall that 3 and 2 are called **addends.** We start at 0 on a number line and draw an arrow representing the addend 3. This arrow is three units long and points to the right since 3 is positive. From the tip of this arrow, we draw another arrow, representing the addend 2. The number below the tip of this arrow is the sum, 5.

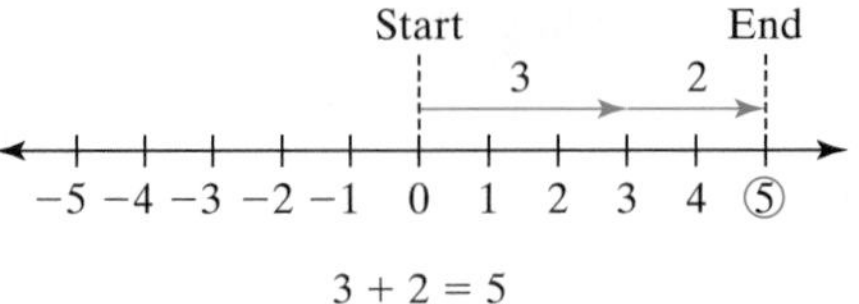

$$3 + 2 = 5$$

□

PRACTICE 1 Add using a number line: $2 + 4$.

EXAMPLE 2 Add: $-1 + (-2)$

Solution Here, -1 and -2 are addends. We start at 0 on a number line and draw an arrow representing -1. This arrow is one unit long and points to the left since -1 is negative. From the tip of this arrow, we draw another arrow, representing -2. The number below the tip of this arrow is the sum, -3.

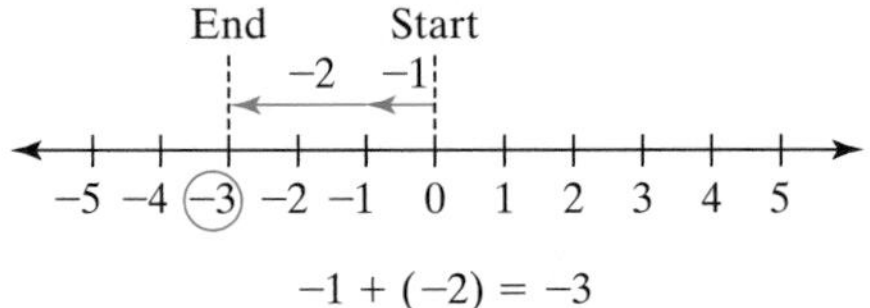

$$-1 + (-2) = -3$$

□

PRACTICE 2 Add using a number line: $-2 + (-3)$.

Thinking of signed numbers as money earned or lost might help make addition more meaningful. Earnings can be thought of as positive numbers. If \$1 is earned and later another \$3 is earned, the total amount earned is \$4. In other words, $1 + 3 = 4$.

On the other hand, losses can be thought of as negative numbers. If \$1 is lost and later another \$3 is lost, a total of \$4 is lost. In other words,

$$(-1) + (-3) = -4.$$

Using a number line each time we add two numbers can be time consuming. Instead, we can notice patterns in the previous examples and write rules for adding signed numbers. When adding two numbers with the same sign, notice that the sign of the sum is the same as the sign of the addends.

Adding Two Numbers with the Same Sign

Add their absolute values. Use their common sign as the sign of the sum.

EXAMPLE 3 Add.

a. $-3 + (-7)$ **b.** $-1 + (-20)$ **c.** $-2 + (-10)$

Solution Notice that each time, we are adding numbers with the same sign.

a. $-3 + (-7) = -10$ ← Add their absolute values: $3 + 7 = 10$.
↑ Use their common sign.

b. $-1 + (-20) = -21$ ← Add their absolute values: $1 + 20 = 21$.
↑ Common sign.

c. $-2 + (-10) = -12$ ← Add their absolute values.
↑ Common sign.

□

PRACTICE 3 Add. **a.** $-5 + (-8)$ **b.** $-31 + (-1)$

Adding numbers whose signs are not the same can also be pictured on a number line.

EXAMPLE 4 Add: $-4 + 6$

Solution

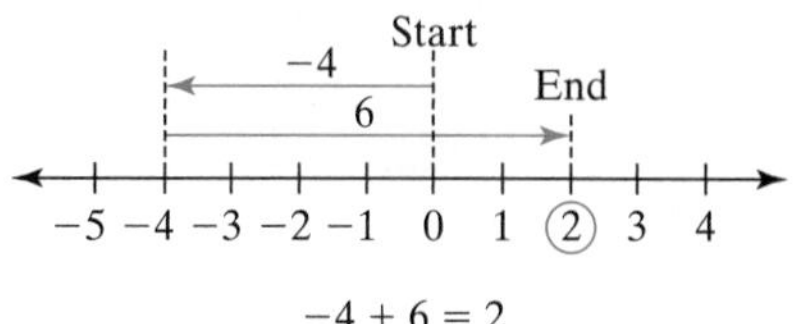

$$-4 + 6 = 2$$

□

PRACTICE 4 Add using a number line: $-3 + 8$.

Using temperature as an example, if the thermometer registers 4 degrees below 0 degrees and then rises 6 degrees, the new temperature is 2 degrees above 0 degrees. Thus, it is reasonable that $-4 + 6 = 2$.

Once again, we can observe a pattern: when adding two numbers with different signs, the sign of the sum is the same as the sign of the addend whose absolute value is larger.

Adding Two Numbers with Different Signs

Subtract the smaller absolute value from the larger absolute value. Use the sign of the number whose absolute value is larger as the sign of the sum.

EXAMPLE 5 Add.

a. $3 + (-7)$ **b.** $-2 + 10$ **c.** $0.2 + (-0.5)$

Solution Notice that each time, we are adding numbers with different signs.

a. $3 + (-7) = -4$ ← Subtract their absolute values: $7 - 3 = 4$.
The negative number, -7, has the larger absolute value so the sum is negative.

b. $-2 + 10 = 8$ ← Subtract their absolute values: $10 - 2 = 8$.
The positive number, 10, has the larger absolute value so the sum is positive.

c. $0.2 + (-0.5) = -0.3$ ← Subtract their absolute values: $0.5 - 0.2 = 0.3$.
The negative number, -0.5, has the larger absolute value so the sum is negative. □

PRACTICE 5 Add.

a. $15 + (-18)$ **b.** $-19 + 20$ **c.** $-0.6 + 0.4$

In general, we have the following:

Adding Real Numbers

To add two real numbers

1. with the *same sign,* add their absolute values. Use their common sign as the sign of the answer.
2. with *different signs,* subtract their absolute values. Give the answer the same sign as the number with the larger absolute value.

EXAMPLE 6 Add.

a. $-8 + (-11)$ **b.** $-5 + 35$ **c.** $0.6 + (-1.1)$

d. $-\frac{7}{10} + \left(-\frac{1}{10}\right)$ **e.** $11.4 + (-4.7)$ **f.** $-\frac{3}{8} + \frac{2}{5}$

Solution

a. $-8 + (-11) = -19$ Same sign. Add absolute values and use the common sign.

b. $-5 + 35 = 30$ Different signs. Subtract absolute values and use the sign of the number with the larger absolute value.

c. $0.6 + (-1.1) = -0.5$ Different signs.

d. $-\frac{7}{10} + \left(-\frac{1}{10}\right) = -\frac{8}{10} = -\frac{4}{5}$ Same sign.

e. $11.4 + (-4.7) = 6.7$

f. $-\frac{3}{8} + \frac{2}{5} = -\frac{15}{40} + \frac{16}{40} = \frac{1}{40}$ □

▶ **Helpful Hint**
Don't forget that a common denominator is needed when adding or subtracting fractions. The common denominator here is 40.

PRACTICE 6 Add.

a. $-\frac{3}{5} + \left(-\frac{2}{5}\right)$ **b.** $3 + (-9)$

c. $2.2 + (-1.7)$ **d.** $-\frac{2}{7} + \frac{3}{10}$

EXAMPLE 7 Add.

a. $3 + (-7) + (-8)$ **b.** $[7 + (-10)] + [-2 + |-4|]$

Solution

a. Perform the additions from left to right.

$$3 + (-7) + (-8) = -4 + (-8) \quad \text{Adding numbers with different signs.}$$
$$= -12 \quad \text{Adding numbers with like signs.}$$

b. Simplify inside brackets first.

$$[7 + (-10)] + [-2 + |-4|] = [-3] + [-2 + 4]$$
$$= [-3] + [2]$$
$$= -1 \quad \text{Add.}$$ □

▶ **Helpful Hint**
Don't forget that brackets are grouping symbols. We simplify within them first.

PRACTICE 7 Add.

a. $8 + (-5) + (-9)$ **b.** $[-8 + 5] + [-5 + |-2|]$

✓**CONCEPT CHECK**
What is wrong with the following calculation?
$5 + (-22) = 17$

Answer to Concept Check:
$5 + (-22) = -17$

OBJECTIVE 2 Solving Applications by Adding Real Numbers 

Positive and negative numbers are often used in everyday life. Stock market returns show gains and losses as positive and negative numbers. Temperatures in cold climates often dip into the negative range, commonly referred to as "below zero" temperatures. Bank statements report deposits and withdrawals as positive and negative numbers.

EXAMPLE 8 **Calculating Temperature**

In Philadelphia, Pennsylvania, the record extreme high temperature is 104°F. Decrease this temperature by 111 degrees, and the result is the record extreme low temperature. Find this temperature. (*Source:* National Climatic Data Center)

Solution:

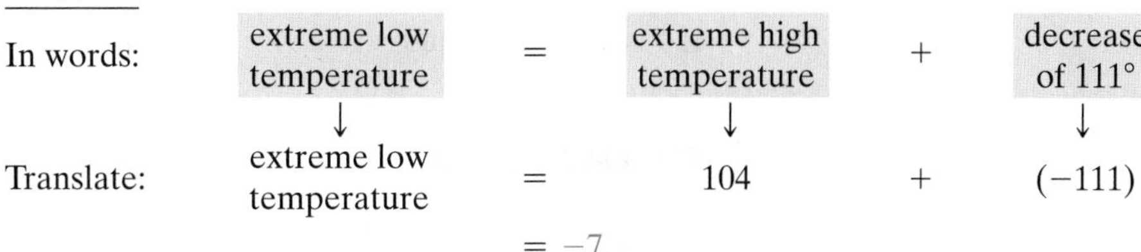

$= -7$

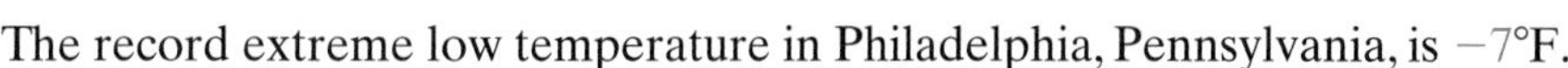

The record extreme low temperature in Philadelphia, Pennsylvania, is −7°F. □

PRACTICE

8 If the temperature was −7° Fahrenheit at 6 a.m., and it rose 4 degrees by 7 a.m. and then rose another 7 degrees in the hour from 7 a.m. to 8 a.m., what was the temperature at 8 a.m.?

OBJECTIVE

3 Finding the Opposite of a Number 

To help us subtract real numbers in the next section, we first review the concept of opposites. The graphs of 4 and −4 are shown on a number line below.

4 units 4 units

−5 −4 −3 −2 −1 0 1 2 3 4 5

Notice that 4 and −4 lie on opposite sides of 0, and each is 4 units away from 0.

This relationship between −4 and +4 is an important one. Such numbers are known as **opposites** or **additive inverses** of each other.

Opposites or Additive Inverses

Two numbers that are the same distance from 0 but lie on opposite sides of 0 are called **opposites** or **additive inverses** of each other.

EXAMPLE 9 Find the opposite or additive inverse of each number.

a. 5 **b.** −6 **c.** $\frac{1}{2}$ **d.** −4.5

Solution

a. The opposite of 5 is −5. Notice that 5 and −5 are on opposite sides of 0 when plotted on a number line and are equal distances away.

b. The opposite of −6 is 6.

c. The opposite of $\frac{1}{2}$ is $-\frac{1}{2}$.

d. The opposite of −4.5 is 4.5. □

PRACTICE

9 Find the opposite or additive inverse of each number.

a. $-\frac{5}{9}$ **b.** 8 **c.** 6.2 **d.** −3

We use the symbol "−" to represent the phrase "the opposite of" or "the additive inverse of." In general, if a is a number, we write the opposite or additive inverse of a as $-a$. We know that the opposite of -3 is 3. Notice that this translates as

the opposite of	−3	is	3
↓	↓	↓	↓
−	(−3)	=	3

This is true in general.

If a is a number, then $-(-a) = a$.

EXAMPLE 10 Simplify each expression.

a. $-(-10)$ **b.** $-\left(-\frac{1}{2}\right)$ **c.** $-(-2x)$ **d.** $-|-6|$

Solution

a. $-(-10) = 10$ **b.** $-\left(-\frac{1}{2}\right) = \frac{1}{2}$ **c.** $-(-2x) = 2x$

d. Since $|-6| = 6$, then $-|-6| = -6$. □

PRACTICE 10 Simplify each expression.

a. $-|-15|$ **b.** $-\left(-\frac{3}{5}\right)$ **c.** $-(-5y)$ **d.** $-(-8)$

Let's discover another characteristic about opposites. Notice that the sum of a number and its opposite is 0.

$$10 + (-10) = 0$$
$$-3 + 3 = 0$$
$$\frac{1}{2} + \left(-\frac{1}{2}\right) = 0$$

In general, we can write the following:

The sum of a number a and its opposite $-a$ is 0.

$$a + (-a) = 0$$

This is why opposites are also called additive inverses. Notice that this also means that the opposite of 0 is then 0 since $0 + 0 = 0$.

Vocabulary, Readiness & Video Check

Use the choices below to fill in each blank.

a positive number	n	opposites
a negative number	0	$-n$

1. Two numbers that are the same distance from 0 but lie on opposite sides of 0 are called ______________.
2. If n is a number, then $n + (-n) =$ ______________.
3. If n is a number, then $-(-n) =$ ______________.
4. The sum of two negative numbers is always ______________.

Martin-Gay Interactive Videos

See Video R.5

Watch the section lecture video and answer the following questions.

OBJECTIVE 1

5. Complete this statement based on the lecture given before Example 1. To add two numbers with the same sign, add their __________ and use their common sign as the sign of the sum.

OBJECTIVE 1

6. What is the sign of the sum in Example 6 and why?

OBJECTIVE 2

7. What is the real life application of negative numbers used in Example 9? The answer to Example 9 is –6. What does this number mean in the context of the problem?

OBJECTIVE 3

8. Example 12 illustrates the idea that if a is a real number, the opposite of $-a$ is a. Example 13 looks similar to Example 12, but it's actually quite different. Explain the difference.

R.5 Exercise Set

MyMathLab®

MIXED PRACTICE

Add. See Examples 1 through 7.

1. $6 + 3$
2. $9 + (-12)$
3. $-6 + (-8)$
4. $-6 + (-14)$
5. $8 + (-7)$
6. $6 + (-4)$
7. $-14 + 2$
8. $-10 + 5$
9. $-2 + (-3)$
10. $-7 + (-4)$
11. $-9 + (-3)$
12. $7 + (-5)$
13. $-7 + 3$
14. $-5 + 9$
15. $10 + (-3)$
16. $8 + (-6)$
17. $5 + (-7)$
18. $3 + (-6)$
19. $-16 + 16$
20. $23 + (-23)$
21. $27 + (-46)$
22. $53 + (-37)$
23. $-18 + 49$
24. $-26 + 14$
25. $-33 + (-14)$
26. $-18 + (-26)$
27. $6.3 + (-8.4)$
28. $9.2 + (-11.4)$
29. $|-8| + (-16)$
30. $|-6| + (-61)$
31. $117 + (-79)$
32. $144 + (-88)$
33. $-9.6 + (-3.5)$
34. $-6.7 + (-7.6)$
35. $-\frac{3}{8} + \frac{5}{8}$
36. $-\frac{5}{12} + \frac{7}{12}$
37. $-\frac{7}{16} + \frac{1}{4}$
38. $-\frac{5}{9} + \frac{1}{3}$
39. $-\frac{7}{10} + \left(-\frac{3}{5}\right)$
40. $-\frac{5}{6} + \left(-\frac{2}{3}\right)$
41. $-15 + 9 + (-2)$
42. $-9 + 15 + (-5)$
43. $-21 + (-16) + (-22)$
44. $-18 + (-6) + (-40)$
45. $-23 + 16 + (-2)$
46. $-14 + (-3) + 11$
47. $|5 + (-10)|$
48. $|7 + (-17)|$
49. $6 + (-4) + 9$
50. $8 + (-2) + 7$
51. $[-17 + (-4)] + [-12 + 15]$
52. $[-2 + (-7)] + [-11 + 22]$
53. $|9 + (-12)| + |-16|$
54. $|43 + (-73)| + |-20|$
55. $-1.3 + [0.5 + (-0.3) + 0.4]$
56. $-3.7 + [0.1 + (-0.6) + 8.1]$

Solve. See Example 8.

57. The low temperature in Anoka, Minnesota, was $-15°$ last night. During the day, it rose only $9°$. Find the high temperature for the day.
58. On January 2, 1943, the temperature was $-4°$ at 7:30 a.m. in Spearfish, South Dakota. Incredibly, it got $49°$ warmer in the next 2 minutes. To what temperature did it rise by 7:32?
59. The lowest point in Africa is -512 feet at Lake Assal in Djibouti. If you are standing at a point 658 feet above Lake Assal, what is your elevation? (*Source:* Microsoft Encarta)

60. The lowest elevation in Australia is -52 feet at Lake Eyre. If you are standing at a point 439 feet above Lake Eyre, what is your elevation? (*Source:* National Geographic Society)

A negative net income results when a company spends more money than it brings in.

61. Johnson Outdoors Inc. had the following quarterly net incomes during its 2009 fiscal year. (Data from Yahoo Finance)

Quarter of Fiscal 2009	*Net Income (in millions)*
First	2.5
Second	9
Third	−14.2
Fourth	−4.2

What was the total net income for fiscal year 2009?

62. LeapFrog Enterprises Inc. had the following quarterly net incomes during its 2009 fiscal year. (Data from Yahoo Finance)

Quarter of Fiscal 2009	*Net Income (in millions)*
First	−27.1
Second	−12.2
Third	7.2
Fourth	29.4

What was the total net income for fiscal year 2009?

In golf, scores that are under par for the entire round are shown as negative scores; positive scores are shown for scores that are over par, and 0 is par.

63. Sandra Gal was the winner of the 2011 LPGA Kia Classic in California. Her scores were −6, −5, −3, and −2. What was her overall score? (*Source:* Ladies Professional Golf Association)

64. During the 2011 PGA Waste Management Phoenix Open, Mark Wilson won with scores of −6, −7, −3, and −2. What was his overall score? (*Source:* Professional Golf Association)

Find each additive inverse or opposite. See Example 9.

65. 6 **66.** 4 **67.** −2

68. −8 **69.** 0 **70.** $-\frac{1}{4}$

71. $|-6|$ **72.** $|-11|$

Simplify each of the following. See Example 10.

73. $-|-2|$ **74.** $-(-3)$ **75.** $-|0|$

76. $\left|-\frac{2}{3}\right|$ **77.** $-\left|-\frac{2}{3}\right|$ **78.** $-(-7)$

Decide whether the given number is a solution of the given equation.

79. Is −4 a solution of $x + 9 = 5$?

80. Is 10 a solution of $7 = -x + 3$?

81. Is −1 a solution of $y + (-3) = -7$?

82. Is −6 a solution of $1 = y + 7$?

CONCEPT EXTENSIONS

The following bar graph shows each month's average daily low temperature in degrees Fahrenheit for Barrow, Alaska. Use this graph to answer Exercises 83 through 88.

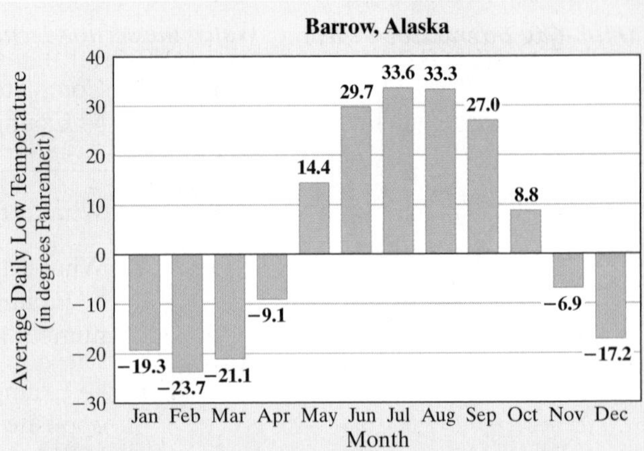

Data from National Climatic Data Center

83. For what month is the graphed temperature the highest?

84. For what month is the graphed temperature the lowest?

85. For what month is the graphed temperature positive *and* closest to 0°?

86. For what month is the graphed temperature negative *and* closest to 0°?

87. Find the average of the temperatures shown for the months of April, May, and October. (To find the average of three temperatures, find their sum and divide by 3.)

88. Find the average of the temperatures shown for the months of January, September, and October.

Each calculation below is incorrect. Find the error and correct it. See the Concept Check in this section.

89. $7 + (-10) \stackrel{?}{=} 17$ **90.** $-4 + 14 \stackrel{?}{=} -18$

91. $-10 + (-12) \stackrel{?}{=} -120$ **92.** $-15 + (-17) \stackrel{?}{=} 32$

If a is a positive number and b is a negative number, fill in the blanks with the words positive or negative.

93. $-a$ is ______. **94.** $-b$ is ______.

95. $a + a$ is ______. **96.** $b + b$ is ______.

For Exercises 97 through 100, determine whether each statement is true or false.

97. The sum of two negative numbers is always a negative number.

98. The sum of two positive numbers is always a positive number.

99. The sum of a positive number and a negative number is always a negative number.

100. The sum of zero and a negative number is always a negative number.

101. In your own words, explain how to find the opposite of a number.

102. In your own words, explain why 0 is the only number that is its own opposite.

103. Explain why adding a negative number to another negative number always gives a negative sum.

104. When a positive and a negative number are added, sometimes the sum is positive, sometimes it is zero, and sometimes it is negative. Explain why and when this happens.

R.6 Subtracting Real Numbers

OBJECTIVES

1. Subtract Real Numbers.
2. Add and Subtract Real Numbers.
3. Evaluate Algebraic Expressions Using Real Numbers.
4. Solve Applications That Involve Subtraction of Real Numbers.
5. Find Complementary and Supplementary Angles.

OBJECTIVE

1 Subtracting Real Numbers 

Now that addition of signed numbers has been discussed, we can explore subtraction. We know that $9 - 7 = 2$. Notice that $9 + (-7) = 2$ also. This means that

$$9 - 7 = 9 + (-7)$$

Notice that the difference of 9 and 7 is the same as the sum of 9 and the opposite of 7. In general, we have the following.

Subtracting Two Real Numbers

If a and b are real numbers, then $a - b = a + (-b)$.

In other words, to find the difference of two numbers, add the first number to the opposite of the second number.

EXAMPLE 1 Subtract.

a. $-13 - 4$ **b.** $5 - (-6)$ **c.** $3 - 6$ **d.** $-1 - (-7)$

Solution

add

a. $-13 - 4 = -13 + (-4)$ Add -13 to the opposite of $+4$, which is -4.

opposite

$= -17$

add

b. $5 - (-6) = 5 + (6)$ Add 5 to the opposite of -6, which is 6.

opposite

$= 11$

c. $3 - 6 = 3 + (-6)$ Add 3 to the opposite of 6, which is -6.

$= -3$

d. $-1 - (-7) = -1 + (7) = 6$ □

PRACTICE

1 Subtract.

a. $-7 - 6$ **b.** $-8 - (-1)$ **c.** $9 - (-3)$ **d.** $5 - 7$

Helpful Hint

Study the patterns indicated.

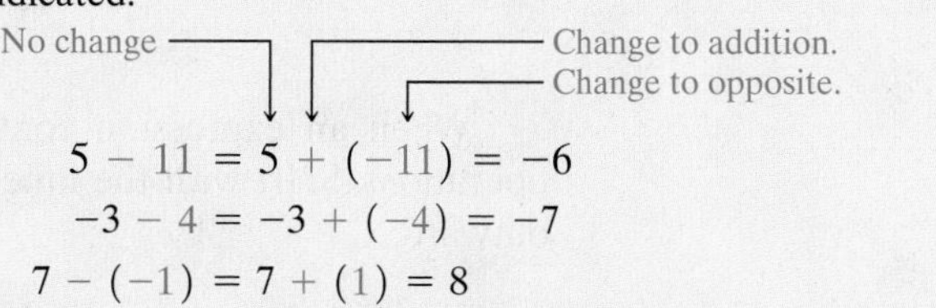

EXAMPLE 2 Subtract.

a. $5.3 - (-4.6)$ **b.** $-\frac{3}{10} - \frac{5}{10}$ **c.** $-\frac{2}{3} - \left(-\frac{4}{5}\right)$

Solution

a. $5.3 - (-4.6) = 5.3 + (4.6) = 9.9$

b. $-\frac{3}{10} - \frac{5}{10} = -\frac{3}{10} + \left(-\frac{5}{10}\right) = -\frac{8}{10} = -\frac{4}{5}$

c. $-\frac{2}{3} - \left(-\frac{4}{5}\right) = -\frac{2}{3} + \left(\frac{4}{5}\right) = -\frac{10}{15} + \frac{12}{15} = \frac{2}{15}$ The common denominator is 15. □

PRACTICE

2 Subtract.

a. $8.4 - (-2.5)$ **b.** $-\frac{5}{8} - \left(-\frac{1}{8}\right)$ **c.** $-\frac{3}{4} - \frac{1}{5}$

■

EXAMPLE 3 Subtract 8 from −4.

Solution Be careful when interpreting this: The order of numbers in subtraction is important. 8 is to be subtracted **from** −4.

$$-4 - 8 = -4 + (-8) = -12$$ □

PRACTICE

3 Subtract 5 from −2.

■

OBJECTIVE

2 Adding and Subtracting Real Numbers 

If an expression contains additions and subtractions, just write the subtractions as equivalent additions. Then simplify from left to right.

EXAMPLE 4 Simplify each expression.

a. $-14 - 8 + 10 - (-6)$ **b.** $1.6 - (-10.3) + (-5.6)$

Solution

a. $-14 - 8 + 10 - (-6) = -14 + (-8) + 10 + 6$
$= -6$

b. $1.6 - (-10.3) + (-5.6) = 1.6 + 10.3 + (-5.6)$
$= 6.3$ □

PRACTICE

4 Simplify each expression.

a. $-15 - 2 - (-4) + 7$ **b.** $3.5 + (-4.1) - (-6.7)$

■

When an expression contains parentheses and brackets, remember the order of operations. Start with the innermost set of parentheses or brackets and work your way outward.

EXAMPLE 5 Simplify each expression.

a. $-3 + [(-2 - 5) - 2]$ **b.** $2^3 - |10| + [-6 - (-5)]$

Solution

a. Start with the innermost sets of parentheses. Rewrite $-2 - 5$ as a sum.

$$
\begin{aligned}
-3 + [(-2 - 5) - 2] &= -3 + [(-2 + (-5)) - 2] \\
&= -3 + [(-7) - 2] && \text{Add: } -2 + (-5). \\
&= -3 + [-7 + (-2)] && \text{Write } -7 - 2 \text{ as a sum.} \\
&= -3 + [-9] && \text{Add.} \\
&= -12 && \text{Add.}
\end{aligned}
$$

b. Start simplifying the expression inside the brackets by writing $-6 - (-5)$ as a sum.

$$
\begin{aligned}
2^3 - |10| + [-6 - (-5)] &= 2^3 - |10| + [-6 + 5] \\
&= 2^3 - |10| + [-1] && \text{Add.} \\
&= 8 - 10 + (-1) && \text{Evaluate } 2^3 \text{ and } |10|. \\
&= 8 + (-10) + (-1) && \text{Write } 8 - 10 \text{ as a sum.} \\
&= -2 + (-1) && \text{Add.} \\
&= -3 && \text{Add.}
\end{aligned}
$$

□

PRACTICE

5 Simplify each expression.

a. $-4 + [(-8 - 3) - 5]$ **b.** $|-13| - 3^2 + [2 - (-7)]$

OBJECTIVE

3 Evaluating Algebraic Expressions 

Knowing how to evaluate expressions for given replacement values is helpful when checking solutions of equations and when solving problems whose unknowns satisfy given expressions. The next example illustrates this.

EXAMPLE 6 Find the value of each expression when $x = 2$ and $y = -5$.

a. $\dfrac{x - y}{12 + x}$ **b.** $x^2 - 3y$

Solution

a. Replace x with 2 and y with -5. Be sure to put parentheses around -5 to separate signs. Then simplify the resulting expression.

$$
\begin{aligned}
\frac{x - y}{12 + x} &= \frac{2 - (-5)}{12 + 2} \\
&= \frac{2 + 5}{14} \\
&= \frac{7}{14} = \frac{1}{2}
\end{aligned}
$$

b. Replace x with 2 and y with -5 and simplify.

$$
\begin{aligned}
x^2 - 3y &= 2^2 - 3(-5) \\
&= 4 - 3(-5) \\
&= 4 - (-15) \\
&= 4 + 15 \\
&= 19
\end{aligned}
$$

□

PRACTICE

6 Find the value of each expression when $x = -3$ and $y = 4$.

a. $\dfrac{7 - x}{2y + x}$ **b.** $y^2 + x$

Helpful Hint

For additional help when replacing variables with replacement values, first place parentheses around any variables.

For Example 6b on the previous page, we have

$$x^2 - 3y = \underbrace{(x)^2 - 3(y)}_{\text{Place parentheses around variables}} = \underbrace{(2)^2 - 3(-5)}_{\text{Replace variables with values}} = 4 - 3(-5) = 4 - (-15) = 4 + 15 = 19$$

OBJECTIVE

4 Solving Applications by Subtracting Real Numbers

One use of positive and negative numbers is in recording altitudes above and below sea level, as shown in the next example.

EXAMPLE 7 Finding a Change in Elevation

The highest point in the United States is the top of Mount McKinley, at a height of 20,320 feet above sea level. The lowest point is Death Valley, California, which is 282 feet below sea level. How much higher is Mount McKinley than Death Valley? (*Source:* U.S. Geological Survey)

Solution: To find "how much higher," we subtract. Don't forget that since Death Valley is 282 feet *below* sea level, we represent its height by −282. Draw a diagram to help visualize the problem.

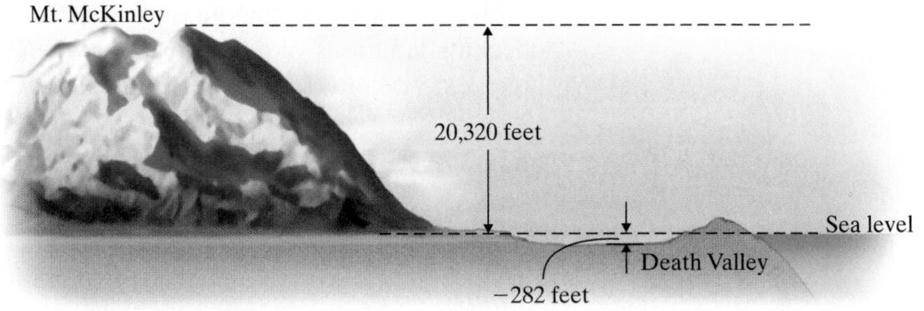

In words:	how much higher is Mt. McKinley	=	height of Mt. McKinley	minus	height of Death Valley
	↓	↓	↓	↓	↓
Translate:	how much higher is Mt. McKinley	=	20,320	−	(−282)

$$= 20{,}320 + 282$$
$$= 20{,}602$$

Thus, Mount McKinley is 20,602 feet higher than Death Valley. □

PRACTICE

7 On Tuesday morning, a bank account balance was \$282. On Thursday, the account balance had dropped to −\$75. Find the overall change in this account balance.

OBJECTIVE

5 Finding Complementary and Supplementary Angles

A knowledge of geometric concepts is needed by many professionals, such as doctors, carpenters, electronic technicians, gardeners, machinists, and pilots, just to name a few. With this in mind, we review the geometric concepts of **complementary** and **supplementary angles.**

Complementary and Supplementary Angles

Two angles are **complementary** if their sum is 90°.

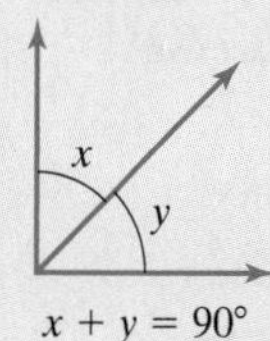

$x + y = 90°$

Two angles are **supplementary** if their sum is 180°.

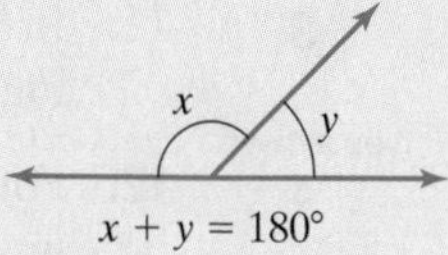

$x + y = 180°$

EXAMPLE 8 Find each unknown complementary or supplementary angle.

a.

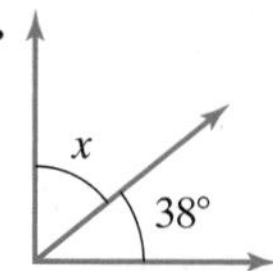

b.

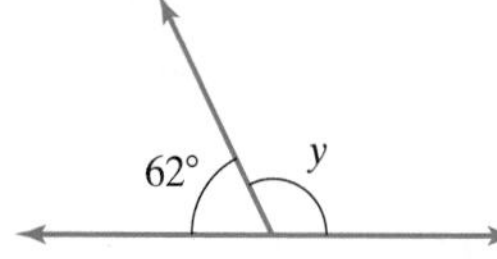

Solution

a. These angles are complementary, so their sum is 90°. This means that x is 90° − 38°.

$$x = 90° - 38° = 52°$$

b. These angles are supplementary, so their sum is 180°. This means that y is 180° − 62°.

$$y = 180° - 62° = 118°$$

PRACTICE

8 Find each unknown complementary or supplementary angle.

a.

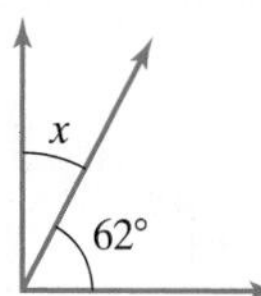

b.

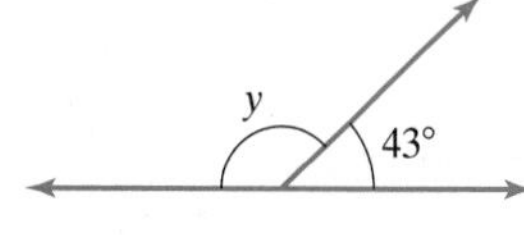

Vocabulary, Readiness & Video Check

Translate each phrase. Let x represent "a number." Use the choices below to fill in each blank.

$7 - x \qquad x - 7$

1. 7 minus a number ____________
2. 7 subtracted from a number ____________
3. A number decreased by 7 ____________
4. 7 less a number ____________
5. A number less than 7 ____________
6. A number subtracted from 7 ____________

Multiple choice: Select the correct lettered response following each exercise.

7. To evaluate $x - y$ for $x = -10$ and $y = -14$, we replace x with -10 and y with -14 and evaluate ______.

a. $10 - 14$ **b.** $-10 - 14$ **c.** $-14 - 10$ **d.** $-10 - (-14)$

8. The expression $-5 - 10$ equals ______.

a. $5 - 10$ **b.** $5 + 10$ **c.** $-5 + (-10)$ **d.** $10 - 5$

Martin-Gay Interactive Videos

See Video R.6

Watch the section lecture video and answer the following questions.

OBJECTIVE 1

9. Complete this statement based on the lecture given before Example 1. To subtract two real numbers, change the operation to ______ and take the ______ of the second number.

OBJECTIVE 2

10. When simplifying Example 5, what is the result of the first step and why is the expression rewritten in this way?

OBJECTIVE 3

11. In Example 7, why are you told to be especially careful when working with the replacement value in the numerator?

OBJECTIVE 4

12. For Example 8, why is the overall vertical change represented as a negative number?

OBJECTIVE 5

13. The definition of supplementary angles is given just before Example 9. Explain how this definition is used to solve Example 9.

R.6 Exercise Set

MyMathLab®

MIXED PRACTICE

Subtract. See Examples 1 and 2.

1. $-6 - 4$

2. $-12 - 8$

3. $4 - 9$

4. $8 - 11$

5. $16 - (-3)$

6. $12 - (-5)$

7. $\frac{1}{2} - \frac{1}{3}$

8. $\frac{3}{4} - \frac{7}{8}$

9. $-16 - (-18)$

10. $-20 - (-48)$

11. $-6 - 5$

12. $-8 - 4$

13. $7 - (-4)$

14. $3 - (-6)$

15. $-6 - (-11)$

16. $-4 - (-16)$

17. $16 - (-21)$

18. $15 - (-33)$

19. $9.7 - 16.1$

20. $8.3 - 11.2$

21. $-44 - 27$

22. $-36 - 51$

23. $-21 - (-21)$

24. $-17 - (-17)$

25. $-2.6 - (-6.7)$

26. $-6.1 - (-5.3)$

27. $-\frac{3}{11} - \left(-\frac{5}{11}\right)$

28. $-\frac{4}{7} - \left(-\frac{1}{7}\right)$

29. $-\frac{1}{6} - \frac{3}{4}$

30. $-\frac{1}{10} - \frac{7}{8}$

31. $8.3 - (-0.62)$

32. $4.3 - (-0.87)$

TRANSLATING

Translate each phrase to an expression and simplify. See Example 3.

33. Subtract -5 from 8.

34. Subtract 3 from -2.

35. Subtract -1 from -6.

36. Subtract 17 from 1.

37. Subtract 8 from 7.

38. Subtract 9 from -4.

39. Decrease -8 by 15.

40. Decrease 11 by -14.

Simplify each expression. (Remember the order of operations.) See Examples 4 and 5.

41. $-10 - (-8) + (-4) - 20$

42. $-16 - (-3) + (-11) - 14$

43. $5 - 9 + (-4) - 8 - 8$

44. $7 - 12 + (-5) - 2 + (-2)$

45. $-6 - (2 - 11)$

46. $-9 - (3 - 8)$

47. $3^3 - 8 \cdot 9$

48. $2^3 - 6 \cdot 3$

49. $2 - 3(8 - 6)$

50. $4 - 6(7 - 3)$

51. $(3 - 6) + 4^2$

52. $(2 - 3) + 5^2$

53. $-2 + [(8 - 11) - (-2 - 9)]$

54. $-5 + [(4 - 15) - (-6) - 8]$

55. $|-3| + 2^2 + [-4 - (-6)]$

56. $|-2| + 6^2 + (-3 - 8)$

Evaluate each expression when $x = -5$, $y = 4$, and $t = 10$. See Example 6.

57. $x - y$

58. $y - x$

59. $|x| + 2t - 8y$

60. $|x + t - 7y|$

61. $\dfrac{9 - x}{y + 6}$

62. $\dfrac{15 - x}{y + 2}$

63. $y^2 - x$

64. $t^2 - x$

65. $\dfrac{|x - (-10)|}{2t}$

66. $\dfrac{|5y - x|}{6t}$

Solve. See Example 7.

67. Within 24 hours in 1916, the temperature in Browning, Montana, fell from 44°F to −56°F. How large a drop in temperature was this?

68. Much of New Orleans is below sea level. If George descends 12 feet from an elevation of 5 feet above sea level, what is his new elevation?

69. The coldest temperature ever recorded on Earth was −129°F in Antarctica. The warmest temperature ever recorded was 136°F in the Sahara Desert. How many degrees warmer is 136°F than −129°F? (*Source: Questions Kids Ask,* Grolier Limited, 1991, and *The World Almanac*)

70. The coldest temperature ever recorded in the United States was −80°F in Alaska. The warmest temperature ever recorded was 134°F in California. How many degrees warmer is 134°F than −80°F? (*Source: The World Almanac*)

71. Mauna Kea in Hawaii has an elevation of 13,796 feet above sea level. The Mid-America Trench in the Pacific Ocean has an elevation of 21,857 feet below sea level. Find the difference in elevation between those two points. (*Source:* National Geographic Society and Defense Mapping Agency)

72. A woman received a statement of her charge account at Old Navy. She spent $93 on purchases last month. She returned an $18 top because she didn't like the color. She also returned a $26 nightshirt because it was damaged. What does she actually owe on her account?

73. A commercial jetliner hits an air pocket and drops 250 feet. After climbing 120 feet, it drops another 178 feet. What is its overall vertical change?

74. In some card games, it is possible to have a negative score. Lavonne Schultz currently has a score of 15 points. She then loses 24 points. What is her new score?

75. The highest point in Africa is Mt. Kilimanjaro, Tanzania, at an elevation of 19,340 feet. The lowest point is Lake Assal, Djibouti, at 512 feet below sea level. How much higher is Mt. Kilimanjaro than Lake Assal? (*Source:* National Geographic Society)

76. The airport in Bishop, California, is at an elevation of 4101 feet above sea level. The nearby Furnace Creek Airport in Death Valley, California, is at an elevation of 226 feet below sea level. How much higher in elevation is the Bishop Airport than the Furnace Creek Airport? (*Source:* National Climatic Data Center)

Find each unknown complementary or supplementary angle. See Example 8.

77.

y
50°

△ **78.**

x
50°

79.

60°
x

△ **80.**

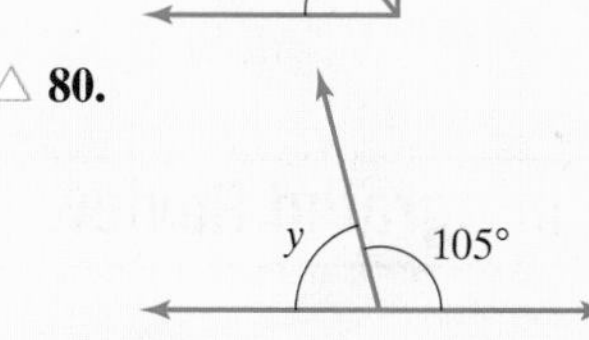

Decide whether the given number is a solution of the given equation.

81. Is −4 a solution of $x - 9 = 5$?

82. Is 3 a solution of $x - 10 = -7$?

83. Is −2 a solution of $-x + 6 = -x - 1$?

84. Is −10 a solution of $-x - 6 = -x - 1$?

85. Is 2 a solution of $-x - 13 = -15$?

86. Is 5 a solution of $4 = 1 - x$?

MIXED PRACTICE—TRANSLATING (*SECTIONS R.5, R.6*)

Translate each phrase to an algebraic expression. Use "x" to represent "a number."

87. The sum of −5 and a number.

88. The difference of −3 and a number.

89. Subtract a number from −20.

90. Add a number and −36.

CONCEPT EXTENSIONS

Recall the bar graph from Section R.5. It shows each month's average daily low temperature in degrees Fahrenheit for Barrow, Alaska. Use this graph to answer Exercises 91 through 94.

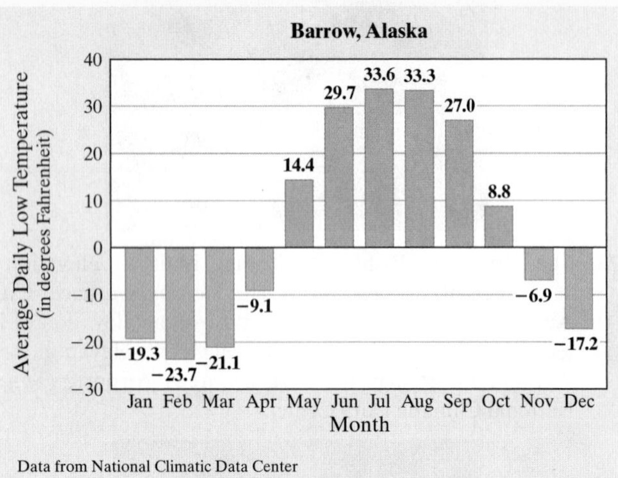

91. Record the monthly increases and decreases in the low temperature from the previous month.

Month	Monthly Increase or Decrease (from the previous month)
February	
March	
April	
May	
June	

92. Record the monthly increases and decreases in the low temperature from the previous month.

Month	Monthly Increase or Decrease (from the previous month)
July	
August	
September	
October	
November	
December	

93. Which month had the greatest increase in temperature?

94. Which month had the greatest decrease in temperature?

95. Find two numbers whose difference is −5.

96. Find two numbers whose difference is −9.

*Each calculation below is **incorrect.** Find the error and correct it.*

97. $9 - (-7) \stackrel{?}{=} 2$

98. $-4 - 8 \stackrel{?}{=} 4$

99. $10 - 30 \stackrel{?}{=} 20$

100. $-3 - (-10) \stackrel{?}{=} -13$

If p is a positive number and n is a negative number, determine whether each statement is true or false. Explain your answer.

101. $p - n$ is always a positive number.

102. $n - p$ is always a negative number.

103. $|n| - |p|$ is always a positive number.

104. $|n - p|$ is always a positive number.

Without calculating, determine whether each answer is positive or negative. Then use a calculator to find the exact difference.

105. 56,875 − 87,262

106. 4.362 − 7.0086

Integrated Review OPERATIONS ON REAL NUMBERS

Sections R.1–R.6

Answer the following with positive, negative, or 0.

1. The opposite of a positive number is a ______ number.
2. The sum of two negative numbers is a ______ number.
3. The absolute value of a negative number is a ______ number.
4. The absolute value of zero is ______.
5. The reciprocal of a positive number is a ______ number.
6. The sum of a number and its opposite is ______.
7. The absolute value of a positive number is a ______ number.
8. The opposite of a negative number is a ______ number.

Fill in the chart:

	Number	Opposite	Absolute Value
9.	$\frac{1}{7}$		
10.	$-\frac{12}{5}$		
11.		−3	
12.		$\frac{9}{11}$	

Perform each indicated operation and simplify.

13. $-19 + (-23)$

14. $7 - (-3)$

15. $-15 + 17$

16. $-8 - 10$

17. $18 + (-25)$

18. $-2 + (-37)$

19. $-14 - (-12)$

20. $5 - 14$

21. $4.5 - 7.9$

22. $-8.6 - 1.2$

23. $-\frac{3}{4} - \frac{1}{7}$

24. $\frac{2}{3} - \frac{7}{8}$

25. $-9 - (-7) + 4 - 6$

26. $11 - 20 + (-3) - 12$

27. $24 - 6(14 - 11)$

28. $30 - 5(10 - 8)$

29. $(7 - 17) + 4^2$

30. $9^2 + (10 - 30)$

31. $|-9| + 3^2 + (-4 - 20)$

32. $|-4 - 5| + 5^2 + (-50)$

33. $-7 + [(1 - 2) + (-2 - 9)]$

34. $-6 + [(-3 + 7) + (4 - 15)]$

35. Subtract 5 from 1.

36. Subtract -2 from -3.

37. Subtract $-\frac{2}{5}$ from $\frac{1}{4}$.

38. Subtract $\frac{1}{10}$ from $-\frac{5}{8}$.

39. $2(19 - 17)^3 - 3(-7 + 9)^2$

40. $3(10 - 9)^2 + 6(20 - 19)^3$

Evaluate each expression when $x = -2$, $y = -1$, and $z = 9$.

41. $x - y$

42. $x + y$

43. $y + z$

44. $z - y$

45. $\frac{|5z - x|}{y - x}$

46. $\frac{|-x - y + z|}{2z}$

R.7 Multiplying and Dividing Real Numbers

OBJECTIVES

1. Multiply Real Numbers.
2. Find the Reciprocal of a Real Number.
3. Divide Real Numbers.
4. Evaluate Expressions Using Real Numbers.
5. Solve Applications That Involve Multiplication or Division of Real Numbers.

OBJECTIVE

1 Multiplying Real Numbers

In this section, we discover patterns for multiplying and dividing real numbers. To discover sign rules for multiplication, recall that multiplication is repeated addition. Thus $3 \cdot 2$ means that 2 is an addend 3 times. That is,

$$2 + 2 + 2 = 3 \cdot 2$$

which equals 6. Similarly, $3 \cdot (-2)$ means -2 is an addend 3 times. That is,

$$(-2) + (-2) + (-2) = 3 \cdot (-2)$$

Since $(-2) + (-2) + (-2) = -6$, $3 \cdot (-2) = -6$. This suggests that the product of a positive number and a negative number is a negative number.

What about the product of two negative numbers? To find out, consider the following pattern.

Factor decreases by 1 each time

$$\left.\begin{aligned} -3 \cdot 2 &= -6 \\ -3 \cdot 1 &= -3 \\ -3 \cdot 0 &= 0 \end{aligned}\right\} \text{Product increases by 3 each time.}$$

This pattern continues as

Factor decreases by 1 each time

$$\left.\begin{aligned} -3 \cdot -1 &= 3 \\ -3 \cdot -2 &= 6 \end{aligned}\right\} \text{Product increases by 3 each time.}$$

This suggests that the product of two negative numbers is a positive number.

Multiplying Real Numbers

1. The product of two numbers with the *same* sign is a positive number.
2. The product of two numbers with *different* signs is a negative number.

EXAMPLE 1 Multiply.

a. $(-8)(4)$ **b.** $14(-1)$ **c.** $-9(-10)$

Solution

a. $-8(4) = -32$ **b.** $14(-1) = -14$ **c.** $-9(-10) = 90$ □

PRACTICE 1 Multiply.

a. $8(-5)$ **b.** $(-3)(-4)$ **c.** $(-6)(9)$

We know that every whole number multiplied by zero equals zero. This remains true for real numbers.

Zero as a Factor

If b is a real number, then $b \cdot 0 = 0$. Also, $0 \cdot b = 0$.

EXAMPLE 2 Perform the indicated operations.

a. $(7)(0)(-6)$ **b.** $(-2)(-3)(-4)$ **c.** $(-1)(5)(-9)$ **d.** $(-4)(-11) - (5)(-2)$

Solution

a. By the order of operations, we multiply from left to right. Notice that, because one of the factors is 0, the product is 0.

$$(7)(0)(-6) = 0(-6) = 0$$

b. Multiply two factors at a time, from left to right.

$$(-2)(-3)(-4) = (6)(-4) \quad \text{Multiply } (-2)(-3).$$
$$= -24$$

c. Multiply from left to right.

$$(-1)(5)(-9) = (-5)(-9) \quad \text{Multiply } (-1)(5).$$
$$= 45$$

d. Follow the rules for order of operations.

$$(-4)(-11) - (5)(-2) = 44 - (-10) \quad \text{Find each product.}$$
$$= 44 + 10 \quad \text{Add 44 to the opposite of } -10.$$
$$= 54 \quad \text{Add.}$$ □

PRACTICE 2 Perform the indicated operations.

a. $(-1)(-5)(-6)$ **b.** $(-3)(-2)(4)$

c. $(-4)(0)(5)$ **d.** $(-2)(-3) - (-4)(5)$

Helpful Hint

You may have noticed from the example that if we multiply:

- an *even* number of negative numbers, the product is *positive*.
- an *odd* number of negative numbers, the product is *negative*.

Answer to Concept Check
negative

✓CONCEPT CHECK

What is the sign of the product of five negative numbers? Explain.

Multiplying signed decimals or fractions is carried out exactly the same way as multiplying integers.

EXAMPLE 3 Multiply.

a. $(-1.2)(0.05)$ **b.** $\frac{2}{3}\cdot\left(-\frac{7}{10}\right)$ **c.** $\left(-\frac{4}{5}\right)(-20)$

Solution

a. The product of two numbers with different signs is negative.

$$\begin{aligned}(-1.2)(0.05) &= -[(1.2)(0.05)]\\ &= -0.06\end{aligned}$$

b. $\frac{2}{3}\cdot\left(-\frac{7}{10}\right) = -\frac{2\cdot 7}{3\cdot 10} = -\frac{2\cdot 7}{3\cdot 2\cdot 5} = -\frac{7}{15}$

c. $\left(-\frac{4}{5}\right)(-20) = \frac{4\cdot 20}{5\cdot 1} = \frac{4\cdot 4\cdot 5}{5\cdot 1} = \frac{16}{1}$ or 16 □

PRACTICE 3 Multiply.

a. $(0.23)(-0.2)$ **b.** $\left(-\frac{3}{5}\right)\cdot\left(\frac{4}{9}\right)$ **c.** $\left(-\frac{7}{12}\right)(-24)$

Now that we know how to multiply positive and negative numbers, let's see how we find the values of $(-4)^2$ and -4^2, for example. Although these two expressions look similar, the difference between the two is the parentheses. In $(-4)^2$, the parentheses tell us that the base, or repeated factor, is -4. In -4^2, only 4 is the base. Thus,

$(-4)^2 = (-4)(-4) = 16$ The base is -4.

$-4^2 = -(4\cdot 4) = -16$ The base is 4.

EXAMPLE 4 Evaluate.

a. $(-2)^3$ **b.** -2^3 **c.** $(-3)^2$ **d.** -3^2

Solution

a. $(-2)^3 = (-2)(-2)(-2) = -8$ The base is -2.

b. $-2^3 = -(2\cdot 2\cdot 2) = -8$ The base is 2.

c. $(-3)^2 = (-3)(-3) = 9$ The base is -3.

d. $-3^2 = -(3\cdot 3) = -9$ The base is 3. □

PRACTICE 4 Evaluate.

a. $(-6)^2$ **b.** -6^2 **c.** $(-4)^3$ **d.** -4^3

Helpful Hint

Be careful when identifying the base of an exponential expression.

$(-3)^2$	-3^2
Base is -3	Base is 3
$(-3)^2 = (-3)(-3) = 9$	$-3^2 = -(3\cdot 3) = -9$

OBJECTIVE

2 Finding Reciprocals 

Just as every difference of two numbers $a - b$ can be written as the sum $a + (-b)$, so too every quotient of two numbers can be written as a product. For example, the quotient $6 \div 3$ can be written as $6 \cdot \frac{1}{3}$. Recall that the pair of numbers 3 and $\frac{1}{3}$ has a special relationship. Their product is 1 and they are called reciprocals or **multiplicative inverses** of each other.

Reciprocals or Multiplicative Inverses

Two numbers whose product is 1 are called reciprocals or multiplicative inverses of each other.

Notice that **0 has no multiplicative inverse** since 0 multiplied by any number is never 1 but always 0.

EXAMPLE 5 Find the reciprocal of each number.

a. 22 **b.** $\frac{3}{16}$ **c.** -10 **d.** $-\frac{9}{13}$

Solution

a. The reciprocal of 22 is $\frac{1}{22}$ since $22 \cdot \frac{1}{22} = 1$.

b. The reciprocal of $\frac{3}{16}$ is $\frac{16}{3}$ since $\frac{3}{16} \cdot \frac{16}{3} = 1$.

c. The reciprocal of -10 is $-\frac{1}{10}$.

d. The reciprocal of $-\frac{9}{13}$ is $-\frac{13}{9}$. □

PRACTICE

5 Find the reciprocal of each number.

a. $\frac{8}{3}$ **b.** 15 **c.** $-\frac{2}{7}$ **d.** -5

OBJECTIVE

3 Dividing Real Numbers

We may now write a quotient as an equivalent product.

Quotient of Two Real Numbers

If a and b are real numbers and b is not 0, then

$$a \div b = \frac{a}{b} = a \cdot \frac{1}{b}$$

In other words, the quotient of two real numbers is the product of the first number and the multiplicative inverse or reciprocal of the second number.

EXAMPLE 6 Use the definition of the quotient of two numbers to divide.

a. $-18 \div 3$ **b.** $\frac{-14}{-2}$ **c.** $\frac{20}{-4}$

Solution

a. $-18 \div 3 = -18 \cdot \frac{1}{3} = -6$

b. $\frac{-14}{-2} = -14 \cdot -\frac{1}{2} = 7$

c. $\frac{20}{-4} = 20 \cdot -\frac{1}{4} = -5$ □

PRACTICE
6 Use the definition of the quotient of two numbers to divide.

a. $\frac{16}{-2}$ **b.** $24 \div (-6)$ **c.** $\frac{-35}{-7}$

Since the quotient $a \div b$ can be written as the product $a \cdot \frac{1}{b}$, it follows that sign patterns for dividing two real numbers are the same as sign patterns for multiplying two real numbers.

Multiplying and Dividing Real Numbers

1. The product or quotient of two numbers with the *same* sign is a positive number.
2. The product or quotient of two numbers with *different* signs is a negative number.

EXAMPLE 7 Divide.

a. $\frac{-24}{-4}$ **b.** $\frac{-36}{3}$ **c.** $\frac{2}{3} \div \left(-\frac{5}{4}\right)$ **d.** $-\frac{3}{2} \div 9$

Solution

a. $\frac{-24}{-4} = 6$ **b.** $\frac{-36}{3} = -12$ **c.** $\frac{2}{3} \div \left(-\frac{5}{4}\right) = \frac{2}{3} \cdot \left(-\frac{4}{5}\right) = -\frac{8}{15}$

d. $-\frac{3}{2} \div 9 = -\frac{3}{2} \cdot \frac{1}{9} = -\frac{3 \cdot 1}{2 \cdot 9} = -\frac{3 \cdot 1}{2 \cdot 3 \cdot 3} = -\frac{1}{6}$ □

PRACTICE
7 Divide.

a. $\frac{-18}{-6}$ **b.** $\frac{-48}{3}$ **c.** $\frac{3}{5} \div \left(-\frac{1}{2}\right)$ **d.** $-\frac{4}{9} \div 8$

✓CONCEPT CHECK

What is wrong with the following calculation?

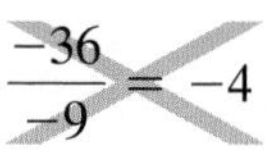

The definition of the quotient of two real numbers does not allow for division by 0 because 0 does not have a multiplicative inverse. There is no number we can multiply 0 by to get 1. How then do we interpret $\frac{3}{0}$? We say that division by 0 is not allowed or not defined and that $\frac{3}{0}$ does not represent a real number. The denominator of a fraction can never be 0.

Can the numerator of a fraction be 0? Can we divide 0 by a number? Yes. For example,

$$\frac{0}{3} = 0 \cdot \frac{1}{3} = 0$$

In general, the quotient of 0 and any nonzero number is 0.

Zero as a Divisor or Dividend

1. The quotient of any nonzero real number and 0 is undefined. In symbols, if $a \neq 0$, $\frac{a}{0}$ is **undefined.**
2. The quotient of 0 and any real number except 0 is 0. In symbols, if $a \neq 0$, $\frac{0}{a} = 0$.

Answer to Concept Check
$\frac{-36}{-9} = 4$

EXAMPLE 8 Perform the indicated operations.

a. $\frac{1}{0}$ **b.** $\frac{0}{-3}$ **c.** $\frac{0(-8)}{2}$

Solution

a. $\frac{1}{0}$ is undefined **b.** $\frac{0}{-3} = 0$ **c.** $\frac{0(-8)}{2} = \frac{0}{2} = 0$ □

PRACTICE 8 Perform the indicated operations.

a. $\frac{0}{-2}$ **b.** $\frac{-4}{0}$ **c.** $\frac{-5}{6(0)}$

Notice that $\frac{12}{-2} = -6$, $-\frac{12}{2} = -6$, and $\frac{-12}{2} = -6$. This means that

$$\frac{12}{-2} = -\frac{12}{2} = \frac{-12}{2}$$

In words, a single negative sign in a fraction can be written in the denominator, in the numerator, or in front of the fraction without changing the value of the fraction. Thus,

$$\frac{1}{-7} = \frac{-1}{7} = -\frac{1}{7}$$

In general, if a and b are real numbers, $b \neq 0$, then $\frac{a}{-b} = \frac{-a}{b} = -\frac{a}{b}$.

OBJECTIVE 4 Evaluating Expressions 

Examples combining basic arithmetic operations along with the principles of order of operations help us review these concepts.

EXAMPLE 9 Simplify each expression.

a. $\frac{(-12)(-3) + 3}{-7 - (-2)}$ **b.** $\frac{2(-3)^2 - 20}{-5 + 4}$

Solution

a. First, simplify the numerator and denominator separately, then divide.

$$\frac{(-12)(-3) + 3}{-7 - (-2)} = \frac{36 + 3}{-7 + 2}$$
$$= \frac{39}{-5} \text{ or } -\frac{39}{5}$$

b. Simplify the numerator and denominator separately, then divide.

$$\frac{2(-3)^2 - 20}{-5 + 4} = \frac{2 \cdot 9 - 20}{-5 + 4} = \frac{18 - 20}{-5 + 4} = \frac{-2}{-1} = 2$$ □

PRACTICE 9 Simplify each expression.

a. $\frac{(-8)(-11) - 4}{-9 - (-4)}$ **b.** $\frac{3(-2)^3 - 9}{-6 + 3}$

Using what we have learned about multiplying and dividing real numbers, we continue to practice evaluating algebraic expressions.

EXAMPLE 10 If $x = -2$ and $y = -4$, evaluate each expression.

a. $5x - y$ **b.** $x^4 - y^2$ **c.** $\frac{3x}{2y}$

Solution

a. Replace x with -2 and y with -4 and simplify.

$$5x - y = 5(-2) - (-4) = -10 - (-4) = -10 + 4 = -6$$

b. Replace x with -2 and y with -4.

$$x^4 - y^2 = (-2)^4 - (-4)^2 \quad \text{Substitute the given values for the variables.}$$
$$= 16 - (16) \quad \text{Evaluate exponential expressions.}$$
$$= 0 \quad \text{Subtract.}$$

c. Replace x with -2 and y with -4 and simplify.

$$\frac{3x}{2y} = \frac{3(-2)}{2(-4)} = \frac{-6}{-8} = \frac{3}{4}$$ □

PRACTICE 10 If $x = -5$ and $y = -2$, evaluate each expression.

a. $7y - x$ **b.** $x^2 - y^3$ **c.** $\frac{2x}{3y}$

OBJECTIVE 5 Solving Applications That Involve Multiplying or Dividing Numbers 

Many real-life problems involve multiplication and division of numbers.

EXAMPLE 11 Calculating a Total Golf Score

A professional golfer finished seven strokes under par (-7) for each of three days of a tournament. What was her total score for the tournament?

Solution Although the key word is "total," since this is repeated addition of the same number, we multiply.

In words:	golfer's total score	=	number of days	·	score each day
	↓	↓	↓	↓	↓
Translate:	golfer's total	=	3	·	(-7)
		= -21			

Thus, the golfer's total score was -21, or 21 strokes under par. □

PRACTICE 11 A card player had a score of -13 for each of four games. Find the total score.

Graphing Calculator Explorations 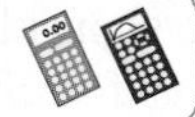

Entering Negative Numbers on a Scientific Calculator

To enter a negative number on a scientific calculator, find a key marked [+/−]. (On some calculators, this key is marked [CHS] for "change sign.") To enter -8, for example, press the keys [8] [+/−]. The display will read [−8].

(Continued on next page)

Entering Negative Numbers on a Graphing Calculator

To enter a negative number on a graphing calculator, find a key marked $\boxed{(-)}$. Do not confuse this key with the key $\boxed{-}$, which is used for subtraction. To enter -8, for example, press the keys $\boxed{(-)}$ $\boxed{8}$. The display will read $\boxed{-8}$.

Operations with Real Numbers

To evaluate $-2(7 - 9) - 20$ on a calculator, press the keys

$\boxed{2}\boxed{+/-}\boxed{\times}\boxed{(}\boxed{7}\boxed{-}\boxed{9}\boxed{)}\boxed{-}\boxed{2}\boxed{0}\boxed{=}$ or

$\boxed{(-)}\boxed{2}\boxed{(}\boxed{7}\boxed{-}\boxed{9}\boxed{)}\boxed{-}\boxed{2}\boxed{0}\boxed{\text{ENTER}}$

The display will read $\boxed{-16}$ or $\boxed{\begin{array}{r}-2(7-9)-20\\ -16\end{array}}$.

Use a calculator to simplify each expression.

1. $-38(26 - 27)$
2. $-59(-8) + 1726$
3. $134 + 25(68 - 91)$
4. $45(32) - 8(218)$
5. $\dfrac{-50(294)}{175 - 265}$
6. $\dfrac{-444 - 444.8}{-181 - 324}$
7. $9^5 - 4550$
8. $5^8 - 6259$
9. $(-125)^2$ (Be careful.)
10. -125^2 (Be careful.)

Vocabulary, Readiness & Video Check

Use the choices below to fill in each blank.

positive   0   negative   undefined

1. If n is a real number, then $n \cdot 0 =$ ________ and $0 \cdot n =$ ________.
2. If n is a real number, but not 0, then $\dfrac{0}{n} =$ ________ and we say $\dfrac{n}{0}$ is ________.
3. The product of two negative numbers is a ________ number.
4. The quotient of two negative numbers is a ________ number.
5. The quotient of a positive number and a negative number is a ________ number.
6. The product of a positive number and a negative number is a ________ number.
7. The reciprocal of a positive number is a ________ number.
8. The opposite of a positive number is a ________ number.

Martin-Gay Interactive Videos

See Video R.7

Watch the section lecture video and answer the following questions.

OBJECTIVE 1

9. Explain the significance of the use of parentheses when comparing Examples 6 and 7.

OBJECTIVE 2

10. In Example 9, why is the reciprocal equal to $\frac{3}{2}$ and not $-\frac{3}{2}$?

OBJECTIVE 3

11. Before Example 11, the sign rules for division of real numbers are discussed. Are the sign rules for division the same as for multiplication? Why or why not?

OBJECTIVE 4

12. In Example 17, the importance of placing the replacement values in parentheses when evaluating is emphasized. Why?

OBJECTIVE 5

13. In Example 18, explain why each loss of 4 yards is represented by -4 and not 4.

R.7 Exercise Set

MyMathLab®  

Multiply. See Examples 1 through 3.

1. $-6(4)$
2. $-8(5)$
3. $2(-1)$
4. $7(-4)$
5. $-5(-10)$
6. $-6(-11)$
7. $-3 \cdot 4$
8. $-2 \cdot 8$
9. $-7 \cdot 0$
10. $-6 \cdot 0$
11. $2(-9)$
12. $3(-5)$
13. $-\frac{1}{2}\left(-\frac{3}{5}\right)$
14. $-\frac{1}{8}\left(-\frac{1}{3}\right)$
15. $-\frac{3}{4}\left(-\frac{8}{9}\right)$
16. $-\frac{5}{6}\left(-\frac{3}{10}\right)$
17. $5(-1.4)$
18. $6(-2.5)$
19. $-0.2(-0.7)$
20. $-0.5(-0.3)$
21. $-10(80)$
22. $-20(60)$
23. $4(-7)$
24. $5(-9)$
25. $(-5)(-5)$
26. $(-7)(-7)$
27. $\frac{2}{3}\left(-\frac{4}{9}\right)$
28. $\frac{2}{7}\left(-\frac{2}{11}\right)$
29. $-11(11)$
30. $-12(12)$
31. $-\frac{20}{25}\left(\frac{5}{16}\right)$
32. $-\frac{25}{36}\left(\frac{6}{15}\right)$
33. $(-1)(2)(-3)(-5)$
34. $(-2)(-3)(-4)(-2)$

Perform the indicated operations. See Example 2.

35. $(-2)(5) - (-11)(3)$
36. $8(-3) - 4(-5)$
37. $(-6)(-1)(-2) - (-5)$
38. $20 - (-4)(3)(-2)$

Decide whether each statement is true or false.

39. The product of three negative integers is negative.
40. The product of three positive integers is positive.
41. The product of four negative integers is negative.
42. The product of four positive integers is positive.

Evaluate. See Example 4.

43. $(-2)^4$
44. -2^4
45. -1^5
46. $(-1)^5$
47. $(-5)^2$
48. -5^2
49. -7^2
50. $(-7)^2$

Find each reciprocal or multiplicative inverse. See Example 5.

51. 9
52. 100
53. $\frac{2}{3}$
54. $\frac{1}{7}$
55. -14
56. -8
57. $-\frac{3}{11}$
58. $-\frac{6}{13}$
59. 0.2
60. 1.5
61. $\frac{1}{-6.3}$
62. $\frac{1}{-8.9}$

Divide. See Examples 6 through 8.

63. $\frac{18}{-2}$
64. $\frac{20}{-10}$
65. $\frac{-16}{-4}$
66. $\frac{-18}{-6}$
67. $\frac{-48}{12}$
68. $\frac{-60}{5}$
69. $\frac{0}{-4}$
70. $\frac{0}{-9}$
71. $-\frac{15}{3}$
72. $-\frac{24}{8}$
73. $\frac{5}{0}$
74. $\frac{3}{0}$
75. $\frac{-12}{-4}$
76. $\frac{-45}{-9}$
77. $\frac{30}{-2}$
78. $\frac{14}{-2}$
79. $\frac{6}{7} \div \left(-\frac{1}{3}\right)$
80. $\frac{4}{5} \div \left(-\frac{1}{2}\right)$
81. $-\frac{5}{9} \div \left(-\frac{3}{4}\right)$
82. $-\frac{1}{10} \div \left(-\frac{8}{11}\right)$
83. $-\frac{4}{9} \div \frac{4}{9}$
84. $-\frac{5}{12} \div \frac{5}{12}$

MIXED PRACTICE

Simplify. See Examples 1 through 9.

85. $\frac{-9(-3)}{-6}$
86. $\frac{-6(-3)}{-4}$
87. $\frac{12}{9 - 12}$
88. $\frac{-15}{1 - 4}$
89. $\frac{-6^2 + 4}{-2}$
90. $\frac{3^2 + 4}{5}$
91. $\frac{8 + (-4)^2}{4 - 12}$
92. $\frac{6 + (-2)^2}{4 - 9}$
93. $\frac{22 + (3)(-2)}{-5 - 2}$
94. $\frac{-20 + (-4)(3)}{1 - 5}$
95. $\frac{-3 - 5^2}{2(-7)}$
96. $\frac{-2 - 4^2}{3(-6)}$
97. $\frac{6 - 2(-3)}{4 - 3(-2)}$
98. $\frac{8 - 3(-2)}{2 - 5(-4)}$
99. $\frac{-3 - 2(-9)}{-15 - 3(-4)}$
100. $\frac{-4 - 8(-2)}{-9 - 2(-3)}$
101. $\frac{|5 - 9| + |10 - 15|}{|2(-3)|}$
102. $\frac{|-3 + 6| + |-2 + 7|}{|-2 \cdot 2|}$

If $x = -5$ and $y = -3$, evaluate each expression. See Example 10.

103. $3x + 2y$
104. $4x + 5y$
105. $2x^2 - y^2$
106. $x^2 - 2y^2$
107. $x^3 + 3y$
108. $y^3 + 3x$
109. $\frac{2x - 5}{y - 2}$
110. $\frac{2y - 12}{x - 4}$
111. $\frac{-3 - y}{x - 4}$
112. $\frac{4 - 2x}{y + 3}$

TRANSLATING

Translate each phrase to an expression. Use x to represent "a number." See Example 11.

113. The product of -71 and a number

114. The quotient of -8 and a number

115. Subtract a number from -16.

116. The sum of a number and -12

117. -29 increased by a number

118. The difference of a number and -10

119. Divide a number by -33.

120. Multiply a number by -17.

Solve. See Example 11.

121. A football team lost four yards on each of three consecutive plays. Represent the total loss as a product of signed numbers and find the total loss.

122. Joe Norstrom lost $400 on each of seven consecutive days in the stock market. Represent his total loss as a product of signed numbers and find his total loss.

123. A deep-sea diver must move up or down in the water in short steps to keep from getting a physical condition called the "bends." Suppose a diver moves down from the surface in five steps of 20 feet each. Represent his total movement as a product of signed numbers and find the total depth.

124. A weather forecaster predicts that the temperature will drop five degrees each hour for the next six hours. Represent this drop as a product of signed numbers and find the total drop in temperature.

Decide whether the given number is a solution of the given equation.

125. Is 7 a solution of $-5x = -35$?

126. Is -4 a solution of $2x = x - 1$?

127. Is -20 a solution of $\frac{x}{10} = 2$?

128. Is -3 a solution of $\frac{45}{x} = -15$?

129. Is 5 a solution of $-3x - 5 = -20$?

130. Is -4 a solution of $2x + 4 = x + 8$?

CONCEPT EXTENSIONS

Study the bar graph below showing the average surface temperatures of planets. Use Exercises 131 and 132 to complete the planet temperatures on the graph. (Pluto is now classified as a dwarf planet.)

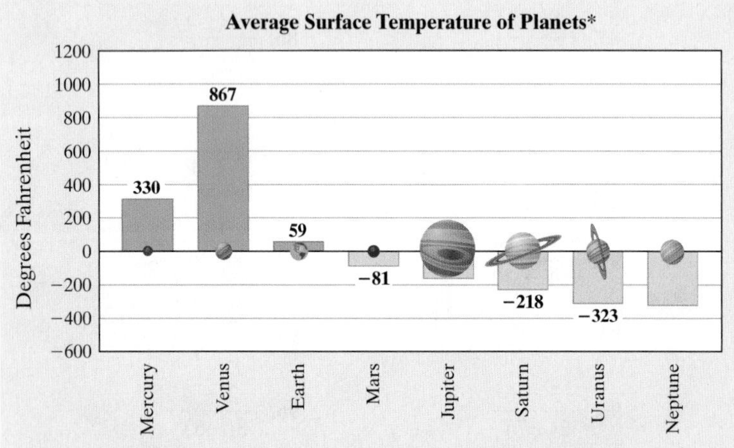

*For some planets, the temperature given is the temperature where the atmosphere pressure equals 1 Earth atmosphere; data from *The World Almanac*

131. The surface temperature of Jupiter is twice the temperature of Mars. Find this temperature.

132. The surface temperature of Neptune is equal to the temperature of Mercury divided by -1. Find this temperature.

133. Explain why the product of an even number of negative numbers is a positive number.

134. If a and b are any real numbers, is the statement $a \cdot b = b \cdot a$ always true? Why or why not?

135. Find any real numbers that are their own reciprocal.

136. Explain why 0 has no reciprocal.

If q is a negative number, r is a negative number, and t is a positive number, determine whether each expression simplifies to a positive or negative number. If it is not possible to determine, state so.

137. $\frac{q}{r \cdot t}$

138. $q^2 \cdot r \cdot t$

139. $q + t$

140. $t + r$

141. $t(q + r)$

142. $r(q - t)$

Write each of the following as an expression and evaluate.

143. The sum of -2 and the quotient of -15 and 3

144. The sum of 1 and the product of -8 and -5

145. Twice the sum of -5 and -3

146. 7 subtracted from the quotient of 0 and 5

R.8 Properties of Real Numbers

OBJECTIVES

1. Use the Commutative and Associative Properties.
2. Use the Distributive Property.
3. Use the Identity and Inverse Properties.

OBJECTIVE

1 Using the Commutative and Associative Properties

In this section, we give names to properties of real numbers with which we are already familiar. Throughout this section, the variables *a, b*, and *c* represent real numbers.

We know that order does not matter when adding numbers. For example, we know that $7 + 5$ is the same as $5 + 7$. This property is given a special name—the **commutative property of addition.** We also know that order does not matter when multiplying numbers. For example, we know that $-5(6) = 6(-5)$. This property means that multiplication is commutative also and is called the **commutative property of multiplication.**

Commutative Properties

Addition:	$a + b = b + a$
Multiplication:	$a \cdot b = b \cdot a$

These properties state that the *order* in which any two real numbers are added or multiplied does not change their sum or product. For example, if we let $a = 3$ and $b = 5$, then the commutative properties guarantee that

$$3 + 5 = 5 + 3 \quad \text{and} \quad 3 \cdot 5 = 5 \cdot 3$$

Helpful Hint

Is subtraction also commutative? Try an example. Does $3 - 2 = 2 - 3$? **No!** The left side of this statement equals 1; the right side equals -1. There is no commutative property of subtraction. Similarly, there is no commutative property for division. For example, $10 \div 2$ does not equal $2 \div 10$.

EXAMPLE 1 Use a commutative property to complete each statement.

a. $x + 5 =$ ________ **b.** $3 \cdot x =$ ________

Solution

a. $x + 5 = 5 + x$ By the commutative property of addition

b. $3 \cdot x = x \cdot 3$ By the commutative property of multiplication □

PRACTICE

1 Use a commutative property to complete each statement.

a. $x \cdot 8 =$ ___ **b.** $x + 17 =$ _____

✓CONCEPT CHECK

Which of the following pairs of actions are commutative?

a. "raking the leaves" and "bagging the leaves"
b. "putting on your left glove" and "putting on your right glove"
c. "putting on your coat" and "putting on your shirt"
d. "reading a novel" and "reading a newspaper"

Let's now discuss grouping numbers. We know that when we add three numbers, the way in which they are grouped or associated does not change their sum. For example, we know that $2 + (3 + 4) = 2 + 7 = 9$. This result is the same if we group the numbers differently. In other words, $(2 + 3) + 4 = 5 + 4 = 9$ also. Thus, $2 + (3 + 4) = (2 + 3) + 4$. This property is called the **associative property of addition.**

We also know that changing the grouping of numbers when multiplying does not change their product. For example, $2 \cdot (3 \cdot 4) = (2 \cdot 3) \cdot 4$ (check it). This is the **associative property of multiplication.**

Answers to Concept Check:
b, d

Associative Properties

Addition: $(a + b) + c = a + (b + c)$

Multiplication: $(a \cdot b) \cdot c = a \cdot (b \cdot c)$

These properties state that the way in which three numbers are *grouped* does not change their sum or their product.

EXAMPLE 2 Use an associative property to complete each statement.

a. $5 + (4 + 6) =$ _______ **b.** $(-1 \cdot 2) \cdot 5 =$ _______

Solution

a. $5 + (4 + 6) = (5 + 4) + 6$ By the associative property of addition

b. $(-1 \cdot 2) \cdot 5 = -1 \cdot (2 \cdot 5)$ By the associative property of multiplication □

PRACTICE

2 Use an associative property to complete each statement.

a. $(2 + 9) + 7 =$ _______ **b.** $-4 \cdot (2 \cdot 7) =$ _______

Helpful Hint

Remember the difference between the commutative properties and the associative properties. The commutative properties have to do with the *order* of numbers, and the associative properties have to do with the *grouping* of numbers.

Let's now illustrate how these properties can help us simplify expressions.

EXAMPLE 3 Simplify each expression.

a. $10 + (x + 12)$ **b.** $-3(7x)$

Solution

a. $10 + (x + 12) = 10 + (12 + x)$ By the commutative property of addition

$= (10 + 12) + x$ By the associative property of addition

$= 22 + x$ Add.

b. $-3(7x) = (-3 \cdot 7)x$ By the associative property of multiplication

$= -21x$ Multiply. □

PRACTICE

3 Simplify each expression.

a. $(5 + x) + 9$ **b.** $5(-6x)$

OBJECTIVE

2 Using the Distributive Property 

The **distributive property of multiplication over addition** is used repeatedly throughout algebra. It is useful because it allows us to write a product as a sum or a sum as a product.

We know that $7(2 + 4) = 7(6) = 42$. Compare that with $7(2) + 7(4) = 14 + 28 = 42$. Since both original expressions equal 42, they must equal each other, or

$$7(2 + 4) = 7(2) + 7(4)$$

This is an example of the distributive property. The product on the left side of the equal sign is equal to the sum on the right side. We can think of the 7 as being distributed to each number inside the parentheses.

Distributive Property of Multiplication Over Addition

$$a(b + c) = ab + ac$$

Since multiplication is commutative, this property can also be written as

$$(b + c)a = ba + ca$$

The distributive property can also be extended to more than two numbers inside the parentheses. For example,

$$\begin{aligned} 3(x + y + z) &= 3(x) + 3(y) + 3(z) \\ &= 3x + 3y + 3z \end{aligned}$$

Since we define subtraction in terms of addition, the distributive property is also true for subtraction. For example

$$\begin{aligned} 2(x - y) &= 2(x) - 2(y) \\ &= 2x - 2y \end{aligned}$$

EXAMPLE 4 Use the distributive property to write each expression without parentheses. Then simplify if possible.

a. $2(x + y)$ **b.** $-5(-3 + 2z)$ **c.** $5(x + 3y - z)$

d. $-1(2 - y)$ **e.** $-(3 + x - w)$ **f.** $\frac{1}{2}(6x + 14) + 10$

Solution

a. $$\begin{aligned} 2(x + y) &= 2 \cdot x + 2 \cdot y \\ &= 2x + 2y \end{aligned}$$

b. $$\begin{aligned} -5(-3 + 2z) &= -5(-3) + (-5)(2z) \\ &= 15 - 10z \end{aligned}$$

c. $$\begin{aligned} 5(x + 3y - z) &= 5(x) + 5(3y) - 5(z) \\ &= 5x + 15y - 5z \end{aligned}$$

d. $$\begin{aligned} -1(2 - y) &= (-1)(2) - (-1)(y) \\ &= -2 + y \end{aligned}$$

e. $$\begin{aligned} -(3 + x - w) &= -1(3 + x - w) \\ &= (-1)(3) + (-1)(x) - (-1)(w) \\ &= -3 - x + w \end{aligned}$$

> **Helpful Hint**
> Notice in part **(e)** that $-(3 + x - w)$ is first rewritten as $-1(3 + x - w)$.

f. $\frac{1}{2}(6x + 14) + 10 = \frac{1}{2}(6x) + \frac{1}{2}(14) + 10$ Apply the distributive property.

$= 3x + 7 + 10$ Multiply.

$= 3x + 17$ Add. □

PRACTICE

4 Use the distributive property to write each expression without parentheses. Then simplify if possible.

a. $5(x - y)$ **b.** $-6(4 + 2t)$

c. $2(3x - 4y - z)$ **d.** $(3 - y) \cdot (-1)$

e. $-(x - 7 + 2s)$ **f.** $\frac{1}{2}(2x + 4) + 9$

We can use the distributive property in reverse to write a sum as a product.

EXAMPLE 5 Use the distributive property to write each sum as a product.

a. $8 \cdot 2 + 8 \cdot x$ **b.** $7s + 7t$

Solution

a. $8 \cdot 2 + 8 \cdot x = 8(2 + x)$ **b.** $7s + 7t = 7(s + t)$

PRACTICE

5 Use the distributive property to write each sum as a product.

a. $5 \cdot w + 5 \cdot 3$ **b.** $9w + 9z$

OBJECTIVE

3 Using the Identity and Inverse Properties 

Next, we look at the **identity properties.**

The number 0 is called the identity for addition because when 0 is added to any real number, the result is the same real number. In other words, the *identity* of the real number is not changed.

The number 1 is called the identity for multiplication because when a real number is multiplied by 1, the result is the same real number. In other words, the *identity* of the real number is not changed.

Identities for Addition and Multiplication

0 is the identity element for addition.

$$a + 0 = a \quad \text{and} \quad 0 + a = a$$

1 is the identity element for multiplication.

$$a \cdot 1 = a \quad \text{and} \quad 1 \cdot a = a$$

Notice that 0 is the *only* number that can be added to any real number with the result that the sum is the same real number. Also, 1 is the *only* number that can be multiplied by any real number with the result that the product is the same real number.

Additive inverses or **opposites** were introduced in Section R.5. Two numbers are called additive inverses or opposites if their sum is 0. The additive inverse or opposite of 6 is -6 because $6 + (-6) = 0$. The additive inverse or opposite of -5 is 5 because $-5 + 5 = 0$.

Reciprocals or **multiplicative inverses** were introduced in Section R.3. Two nonzero numbers are called reciprocals or multiplicative inverses if their product is 1. The reciprocal or multiplicative inverse of $\frac{2}{3}$ is $\frac{3}{2}$ because $\frac{2}{3} \cdot \frac{3}{2} = 1$. Likewise, the reciprocal of -5 is $-\frac{1}{5}$ because $-5\left(-\frac{1}{5}\right) = 1$.

✓CONCEPT CHECK

Which of the following, $1, -\frac{10}{3}, \frac{3}{10}, 0, \frac{10}{3}, -\frac{3}{10}$, is the

a. opposite of $-\frac{3}{10}$?

b. reciprocal of $-\frac{3}{10}$?

Additive or Multiplicative Inverses

The numbers a and $-a$ are additive inverses or opposites of each other because their sum is 0; that is,

$$a + (-a) = 0$$

The numbers b and $\frac{1}{b}$ (for $b \neq 0$) are reciprocals or multiplicative inverses of each other because their product is 1; that is,

$$b \cdot \frac{1}{b} = 1$$

EXAMPLE 6 Name the property or properties illustrated by each true statement.

Solution

a. $3 \cdot y = y \cdot 3$	Commutative property of multiplication (order changed)
b. $(x + 7) + 9 = x + (7 + 9)$	Associative property of addition (grouping changed)
c. $(b + 0) + 3 = b + 3$	Identity element for addition
d. $0.2 \cdot (z \cdot 5) = 0.2 \cdot (5 \cdot z)$	Commutative property of multiplication (order changed)
e. $-2 \cdot \left(-\frac{1}{2}\right) = 1$	Multiplicative inverse property
f. $-2 + 2 = 0$	Additive inverse property
g. $-6 \cdot (y \cdot 2) = (-6 \cdot 2) \cdot y$	Commutative and associative properties of multiplication (order and grouping changed)

□

PRACTICE

6 Name the property or properties illustrated by each true statement.

a. $(7 \cdot 3x) \cdot 4 = (3x \cdot 7) \cdot 4$	Commutative property of multiplication
b. $6 + (3 + y) = (6 + 3) + y$	Associative property of addition
c. $8 + (t + 0) = 8 + t$	Identity element for addition
d. $-\frac{3}{4} \cdot \left(-\frac{4}{3}\right) = 1$	Multiplicative inverse property
e. $(2 + x) + 5 = 5 + (2 + x)$	Commutative property of addition
f. $3 + (-3) = 0$	Additive inverse property
g. $(-3b) \cdot 7 = (-3 \cdot 7) \cdot b$	Commutative and associative properties of multiplication

Answers to Concept Check:
a. $\frac{3}{10}$ **b.** $-\frac{10}{3}$

Vocabulary, Readiness & Video Check

Use the choices below to fill in each blank.

distributive property	associative property of multiplication	commutative property of addition
opposites or additive inverses	associative property of addition	
reciprocals or multiplicative inverses	commutative property of multiplication	

1. $x + 5 = 5 + x$ is a true statement by the ______________________.

2. $x \cdot 5 = 5 \cdot x$ is a true statement by the ______________________.

3. $3(y + 6) = 3 \cdot y + 3 \cdot 6$ is true by the ______________________.

4. $2 \cdot (x \cdot y) = (2 \cdot x) \cdot y$ is a true statement by the ______________________.

5. $x + (7 + y) = (x + 7) + y$ is a true statement by the ______________________.

6. The numbers $-\frac{2}{3}$ and $-\frac{3}{2}$ are called ______________________.

7. The numbers $-\frac{2}{3}$ and $\frac{2}{3}$ are called ______________________.

Martin-Gay Interactive Videos

See Video R.8

Watch the section lecture video and answer the following questions.

OBJECTIVE 1

8. The commutative properties are discussed in Examples 1 and 2 and the associative properties are discussed in Examples 3–7. What's the one word used again and again to describe the commutative property? The associative property?

OBJECTIVE 2

9. In Example 10, what point is made about the term 2?

OBJECTIVE 3

10. Complete these statements based on the lecture given before Example 12.

- The identify element for addition is _____ because if we add _____ to any real number, the result is that real number.
- The identify element for multiplication is _____ because any real number times _____ gives a result of that original real number.

R.8 Exercise Set

MyMathLab®

Use a commutative property to complete each statement. See Example 1.

1. $x + 16 =$ ______ **2.** $4 + y =$ ______

3. $-4 \cdot y =$ ______ **4.** $-2 \cdot x =$ ______

5. $xy =$ ______ **6.** $ab =$ ______

7. $2x + 13 =$ ______ **8.** $19 + 3y =$ ______

Use an associative property to complete each statement. See Example 2.

9. $(xy) \cdot z =$ ________ **10.** $3 \cdot (xy) =$ ________

11. $2 + (a + b) =$ ________ **12.** $(y + 4) + z =$ ________

13. $4 \cdot (ab) =$ ________ **14.** $(-3y) \cdot z =$ ________

15. $(a + b) + c =$ ________

16. $6 + (r + s) =$ ________

Use the commutative and associative properties to simplify each expression. See Example 3.

17. $8 + (9 + b)$ **18.** $(r + 3) + 11$

19. $4(6y)$ **20.** $2(42x)$

21. $\frac{1}{5}(5y)$ **22.** $\frac{1}{8}(8z)$

23. $(13 + a) + 13$ **24.** $7 + (x + 4)$

25. $-9(8x)$ **26.** $-3(12y)$

27. $\frac{3}{4}\left(\frac{4}{3}s\right)$ **28.** $\frac{2}{7}\left(\frac{7}{2}r\right)$

29. $\frac{2}{3} + \left(\frac{4}{3} + x\right)$ **30.** $\frac{7}{9} + \left(\frac{2}{9} + y\right)$

Use the distributive property to write each expression without parentheses. Then simplify the result. See Example 4.

31. $4(x + y)$
32. $7(a + b)$
33. $9(x - 6)$
34. $11(y - 4)$
35. $2(3x + 5)$
36. $5(7 + 8y)$
37. $7(4x - 3)$
38. $3(8x - 1)$
39. $3(6 + x)$
40. $2(x + 5)$
41. $-2(y - z)$
42. $-3(z - y)$
43. $-7(3y + 5)$
44. $-5(2r + 11)$
45. $5(x + 4m + 2)$
46. $8(3y + z - 6)$
47. $-4(1 - 2m + n)$
48. $-4(4 + 2p + 5q)$
49. $-(5x + 2)$
50. $-(9r + 5)$
51. $-(r - 3 - 7p)$
52. $-(q - 2 + 6r)$
53. $\frac{1}{2}(6x + 8)$
54. $\frac{1}{4}(4x - 2)$
55. $-\frac{1}{3}(3x - 9y)$
56. $-\frac{1}{5}(10a - 25b)$
57. $3(2r + 5) - 7$
58. $10(4s + 6) - 40$
59. $-9(4x + 8) + 2$
60. $-11(5x + 3) + 10$
61. $-4(4x + 5) - 5$
62. $-6(2x + 1) - 1$

Use the distributive property to write each sum as a product. See Example 5.

63. $4 \cdot 1 + 4 \cdot y$
64. $14 \cdot z + 14 \cdot 5$
65. $11x + 11y$
66. $9a + 9b$
67. $(-1) \cdot 5 + (-1) \cdot x$
68. $(-3)a + (-3)b$
69. $30a + 30b$
70. $25x + 25y$

Name the properties illustrated by each true statement. See Example 6.

71. $3 \cdot 5 = 5 \cdot 3$
72. $4(3 + 8) = 4 \cdot 3 + 4 \cdot 8$
73. $2 + (x + 5) = (2 + x) + 5$
74. $(x + 9) + 3 = (9 + x) + 3$
75. $9(3 + 7) = 9 \cdot 3 + 9 \cdot 7$
76. $1 \cdot 9 = 9$
77. $(4 \cdot y) \cdot 9 = 4 \cdot (y \cdot 9)$
78. $6 \cdot \frac{1}{6} = 1$
79. $0 + 6 = 6$
80. $(a + 9) + 6 = a + (9 + 6)$
81. $-4(y + 7) = -4 \cdot y + (-4) \cdot 7$
82. $(11 + r) + 8 = (r + 11) + 8$
83. $-4 \cdot (8 \cdot 3) = (8 \cdot -4) \cdot 3$
84. $r + 0 = r$

CONCEPT EXTENSIONS

Fill in the table with the opposite (additive inverse), and the reciprocal (multiplicative inverse). Assume that the value of each expression is not 0.

	Expression	*Opposite*	*Reciprocal*
85.	8		
86.	$-\frac{2}{3}$		
87.	x		
88.	$4y$		
89.			$\frac{1}{2x}$
90.		$7x$	

Decide whether each statement is true or false. See the second Concept Check in this section.

91. The opposite of $-\frac{a}{2}$ is $-\frac{2}{a}$.

92. The reciprocal of $-\frac{a}{2}$ is $\frac{a}{2}$.

Determine which pairs of actions are commutative. See the first Concept Check in this section.

93. "taking a test" and "studying for the test"
94. "putting on your shoes" and "putting on your socks"
95. "putting on your left shoe" and "putting on your right shoe"
96. "reading the sports section" and "reading the comics section"
97. "mowing the lawn" and "trimming the hedges"
98. "baking a cake" and "eating the cake"
99. "dialing a number" and "turning on the cell phone"
100. "feeding the dog" and "feeding the cat"

Name the property illustrated by each step.

101. a. $\triangle + (\square + \bigcirc) = (\square + \bigcirc) + \triangle$

b. $= (\bigcirc + \square) + \triangle$

c. $= \bigcirc + (\square + \triangle)$

102. a. $(x + y) + z = x + (y + z)$
b. $= (y + z) + x$
c. $= (z + y) + x$

103. Explain why 0 is called the identity element for addition.

104. Explain why 1 is called the identity element for multiplication.

105. Write an example that shows that division is not commutative.

106. Write an example that shows that subtraction is not commutative.

Chapter R Vocabulary Check

Fill in each blank with one of the words or phrases listed below.

set	inequality symbols	opposites	absolute value	numerator
denominator	grouping symbols	exponent	base	reciprocals
variable	equation	solution		

1. The symbols $\neq$, $<$, and $>$ are called ______________.
2. A mathematical statement that two expressions are equal is called a(n) ______________.
3. The ______________ of a number is the distance between that number and 0 on the number line.
4. A symbol used to represent a number is called a(n) ______________.
5. Two numbers that are the same distance from 0 but lie on opposite sides of 0 are called ______________.
6. The number in a fraction above the fraction bar is called the ______________.
7. A(n) ______________ of an equation is a value for the variable that makes the equation a true statement.
8. Two numbers whose product is 1 are called ______________.
9. In 2^3, the 2 is called the ______________ and the 3 is called the ______________.
10. The number in a fraction below the fraction bar is called the ______________.
11. Parentheses and brackets are examples of ______________.
12. A(n) ______________ is a collection of objects.

Chapter R Highlights

DEFINITIONS AND CONCEPTS	EXAMPLES
Section R.2 Symbols and Sets of Numbers	
A **set** is a collection of objects, called **elements,** enclosed in braces.	$\{a, c, e\}$
Natural Numbers: $\{1, 2, 3, 4, \dots\}$ **Whole Numbers:** $\{0, 1, 2, 3, 4, \dots\}$	Given the set $\left\{-3.4, \sqrt{3}, 0, \frac{2}{3}, 5, -4\right\}$, list the numbers that belong to the set of
Integers: $\{\dots, -3, -2, -1, 0, 1, 2, 3, \dots\}$	Natural numbers: 5 Whole numbers: 0, 5 Integers: $-4, 0, 5$
Rational Numbers: {real numbers that can be expressed as a quotient of integers}	Rational numbers: $-4, -3.4, 0, \frac{2}{3}, 5$
Irrational Numbers: {real numbers that cannot be expressed as a quotient of integers}	Irrational Numbers: $\sqrt{3}$
Real Numbers: {all numbers that correspond to a point on the number line}	Real numbers: $-4, -3.4, 0, \frac{2}{3}, \sqrt{3}, 5$

DEFINITIONS AND CONCEPTS	EXAMPLES
Section R.2 Symbols and Sets of Numbers (continued)	
A line used to picture numbers is called a **number line.**	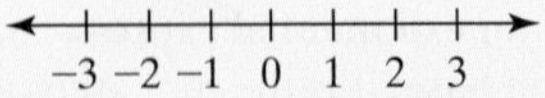
The **absolute value** of a real number a, denoted by $\lvert a \rvert$, is the distance between a and 0 on the number line.	$\lvert 5 \rvert = 5$ $\lvert 0 \rvert = 0$ $\lvert -2 \rvert = 2$
Symbols: $=$ is equal to	$-7 = -7$
$\neq$ is not equal to	$3 \neq -3$
$>$ is greater than	$4 > 1$
$<$ is less than	$1 < 4$
$\leq$ is less than or equal to	$6 \leq 6$
$\geq$ is greater than or equal to	$18 \geq -\frac{1}{3}$
Order Property for Real Numbers For any two real numbers a and b, a is less than b if a is to the left of b on a number line.	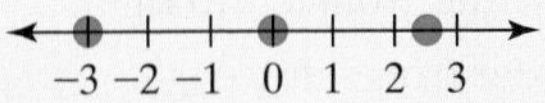 $-3 < 0$ $0 > -3$ $0 < 2.5$ $2.5 > 0$
Section R.3 Fractions and Mixed Numbers	
A quotient of two integers is called a **fraction.** The **numerator** of a fraction is the top number. The **denominator** of a fraction is the bottom number.	$\frac{13}{17}$ 13 ← numerator, 17 ← denominator
If $a \cdot b = c$, then a and b are **factors** and c is the **product.**	$7 \cdot 9 = 63$ (7 ↓ factor, 9 ↓ factor, 63 ↓ product)
A fraction is in **lowest terms** or **simplest form** when the numerator and the denominator have no factors in common other than 1.	$\frac{13}{17}$ is in simplest form.
To write a fraction in simplest form, factor the numerator and the denominator; then apply the fundamental principle.	Write in simplest form. $\frac{6}{14} = \frac{2 \cdot 3}{2 \cdot 7} = \frac{3}{7}$
Two fractions are **reciprocals** if their product is 1. The reciprocal of $\frac{a}{b}$ is $\frac{b}{a}$.	The reciprocal of $\frac{6}{25}$ is $\frac{25}{6}$.
To multiply fractions, numerator times numerator is the numerator of the product and denominator times denominator is the denominator of the product.	Perform the indicated operations. $\frac{2}{5} \cdot \frac{3}{7} = \frac{6}{35}$
To divide fractions, multiply the first fraction by the reciprocal of the second fraction.	$\frac{5}{9} \div \frac{2}{7} = \frac{5}{9} \cdot \frac{7}{2} = \frac{35}{18}$
To add fractions with the same denominator, add the numerators and place the sum over the common denominator.	$\frac{5}{11} + \frac{3}{11} = \frac{8}{11}$
To subtract fractions with the same denominator, subtract the numerators and place the difference over the common denominator.	$\frac{13}{15} - \frac{3}{15} = \frac{10}{15} = \frac{2}{3}$
Fractions that represent the same quantity are called **equivalent fractions.**	$\frac{1}{5} = \frac{1 \cdot 4}{5 \cdot 4} = \frac{4}{20}$ $\frac{1}{5}$ and $\frac{4}{20}$ are equivalent fractions.

DEFINITIONS AND CONCEPTS	EXAMPLES
Section R.4 Exponents, Order of Operations, Variable Expressions, and Equations	
The expression a^n is an **exponential expression.** The number a is called the **base;** it is the repeated factor. The number n is called the **exponent;** it is the number of times that the base is a factor.	$4^3 = 4 \cdot 4 \cdot 4 = 64$ $7^2 = 7 \cdot 7 = 49$
Order of Operations Simplify expressions in the following order. If grouping symbols are present, simplify expressions within those first, starting with the innermost set. Also, simplify the numerator and the denominator of a fraction separately. **1.** Simplify exponential expressions. **2.** Multiply or divide in order from left to right. **3.** Add or subtract in order from left to right.	$\frac{8^2 + 5(7 - 3)}{3 \cdot 7} = \frac{8^2 + 5(4)}{21}$ $= \frac{64 + 5(4)}{21}$ $= \frac{64 + 20}{21}$ $= \frac{84}{21}$ $= 4$
A symbol used to represent a number is called a **variable.**	Examples of variables are: q, x, z
An **algebraic expression** is a collection of numbers, variables, operation symbols, and grouping symbols.	Examples of algebraic expressions are: $5x, 2(y - 6), \frac{q^2 - 3q + 1}{6}$
To evaluate an algebraic expression containing a variable, substitute a given number for the variable and simplify.	Evaluate $x^2 - y^2$ if $x = 5$ and $y = 3$. $x^2 - y^2 = (5)^2 - 3^2$ $= 25 - 9$ $= 16$
A mathematical statement that two expressions are equal is called an **equation.**	Examples of equations are: $3x - 9 = 20$ $A = \pi r^2$
A **solution** of an equation is a value for the variable that makes the equation a true statement.	Determine whether 4 is a solution of $5x + 7 = 27$. $5x + 7 = 27$ $5(4) + 7 \stackrel{?}{=} 27$ $20 + 7 \stackrel{?}{=} 27$ $27 = 27$ True 4 is a solution.
Section R.5 Adding Real Numbers	
To Add Two Numbers with the Same Sign **1.** Add their absolute values. **2.** Use their common sign as the sign of the sum.	Add. $10 + 7 = 17$ $-3 + (-8) = -11$
To Add Two Numbers with Different Signs **1.** Subtract their absolute values. **2.** Use the sign of the number whose absolute value is larger as the sign of the sum.	$-25 + 5 = -20$ $14 + (-9) = 5$

DEFINITIONS AND CONCEPTS	EXAMPLES
Section R.5 Adding Real Numbers (continued)	
Two numbers that are the same distance from 0 but lie on opposite sides of 0 are called **opposites** or **additive inverses**. The opposite of a number a is denoted by $-a$.	The opposite of -7 is 7. The opposite of 123 is -123.
The sum of a number a and its opposite, $-a$, is 0. $a + (-a) = 0$ If a is a number, then $-(-a) = a$.	$-4 + 4 = 0$ $12 + (-12) = 0$ $-(-8) = 8$ $-(-14) = 14$
Section R.6 Subtracting Real Numbers	
To subtract two numbers a and b, add the first number a to the opposite of the second number b. $a - b = a + (-b)$	Subtract. $3 - (-44) = 3 + 44 = 47$ $-5 - 22 = -5 + (-22) = -27$ $-30 - (-30) = -30 + 30 = 0$
Section R.7 Multiplying and Dividing Real Numbers	
Quotient of two real numbers $\frac{a}{b} = a \cdot \frac{1}{b}$	Multiply or divide. $\frac{42}{2} = 42 \cdot \frac{1}{2} = 21$
Multiplying and Dividing Real Numbers The product or quotient of two numbers with the same sign is a positive number. The product or quotient of two numbers with different signs is a negative number.	$7 \cdot 8 = 56 \quad -7 \cdot (-8) = 56$ $-2 \cdot 4 = -8 \quad 2 \cdot (-4) = -8$ $\frac{90}{10} = 9 \quad \frac{-90}{-10} = 9$ $\frac{42}{-6} = -7 \quad \frac{-42}{6} = -7$
Products and Quotients Involving Zero The product of 0 and any number is 0. $b \cdot 0 = 0$ and $0 \cdot b = 0$	$-4 \cdot 0 = 0 \quad 0 \cdot \left(-\frac{3}{4}\right) = 0$
The quotient of a nonzero number and 0 is undefined. $\frac{b}{0}$ is undefined.	$\frac{-85}{0}$ is undefined.
The quotient of 0 and any nonzero number is 0. $\frac{0}{b} = 0$	$\frac{0}{18} = 0 \quad \frac{0}{-47} = 0$
Section R.8 Properties of Real Numbers	
Commutative Properties Addition: $a + b = b + a$ Multiplication: $a \cdot b = b \cdot a$	$3 + (-7) = -7 + 3$ $-8 \cdot 5 = 5 \cdot (-8)$
Associative Properties Addition: $(a + b) + c = a + (b + c)$ Multiplication: $(a \cdot b) \cdot c = a \cdot (b \cdot c)$	$(5 + 10) + 20 = 5 + (10 + 20)$ $(-3 \cdot 2) \cdot 11 = -3 \cdot (2 \cdot 11)$

(continued)

DEFINITIONS AND CONCEPTS	EXAMPLES
Section R.8 Properties of Real Numbers (continued)	
Two numbers whose product is 1 are called **multiplicative inverses** or **reciprocals.** The reciprocal of a nonzero number a is $\frac{1}{a}$ because $a \cdot \frac{1}{a} = 1$.	The reciprocal of 3 is $\frac{1}{3}$. The reciprocal of $-\frac{2}{5}$ is $-\frac{5}{2}$.
Distributive Property $a(b + c) = a \cdot b + a \cdot c$	$5(6 + 10) = 5 \cdot 6 + 5 \cdot 10$ $-2(3 + x) = -2 \cdot 3 + (-2)(x)$
Identities $a + 0 = a$ $\quad 0 + a = a$ $a \cdot 1 = a$ $\quad 1 \cdot a = a$	$5 + 0 = 5 \quad 0 + (-2) = -2$ $-14 \cdot 1 = -14 \quad 1 \cdot 27 = 27$
Inverses Additive or opposite: $a + (-a) = 0$ Multiplicative or reciprocal: $b \cdot \frac{1}{b} = 1$	$7 + (-7) = 0$ $3 \cdot \frac{1}{3} = 1$

Chapter R **Review**

(R.2) *Insert <, >, or = in the appropriate space to make the following statements true.*

1. 8 10

2. 7 2

3. $-4 \quad -5$

4. $\frac{12}{2} \quad -8$

5. $|-7| \quad |-8|$

6. $|-9| \quad -9$

7. $-|-1| \quad -1$

8. $|-14| \quad -(-14)$

9. 1.2 1.02

10. $-\frac{3}{2} \quad -\frac{3}{4}$

TRANSLATING

Translate each statement into symbols.

11. Four is greater than or equal to negative three.

12. Six is not equal to five.

13. 0.03 is less than 0.3.

14. New York City has 155 museums and 400 art galleries. Write an inequality comparing the numbers 155 and 400. (*Source:* Absolute Trivia.com)

Given the following sets of numbers, list the numbers in each set that also belong to the set of:

a. Natural numbers

b. Whole numbers

c. Integers

d. Rational numbers

e. Irrational numbers

f. Real numbers

15. $\left\{-6, 0, 1, 1\frac{1}{2}, 3, \pi, 9.62\right\}$

16. $\left\{-3, -1.6, 2, 5, \frac{11}{2}, 15.1, \sqrt{5}, 2\pi\right\}$

The following chart shows the gains and losses in dollars of Density Oil and Gas stock for a particular week.

Day	*Gain or Loss in Dollars*
Monday	+1
Tuesday	−2
Wednesday	+5
Thursday	+1
Friday	−4

17. Which day showed the greatest loss?

18. Which day showed the greatest gain?

(R.3) *Write the number as a product of prime factors.*

19. 36

20. 120

Perform the indicated operations. Write results in lowest terms.

21. $\frac{8}{15} \cdot \frac{27}{30}$

22. $\frac{7}{8} \div \frac{21}{32}$

23. $\frac{7}{15} + \frac{5}{6}$

24. $\frac{3}{4} - \frac{3}{20}$

25. $2\frac{3}{4} + 6\frac{5}{8}$

26. $7\frac{1}{6} - 2\frac{2}{3}$

27. $5 \div \frac{1}{3}$

28. $2 \cdot 8\frac{3}{4}$

Each circle represents a whole, or 1. Determine the unknown part of the circle.

29.

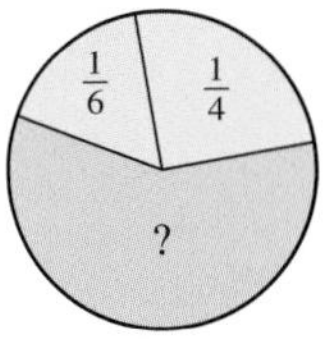

30.

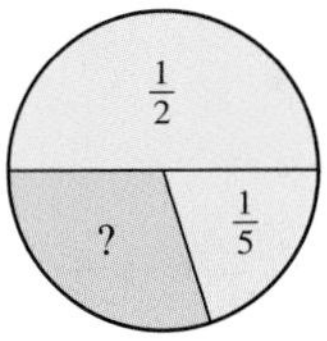

Find the area and the perimeter of each figure.

△ **31.**

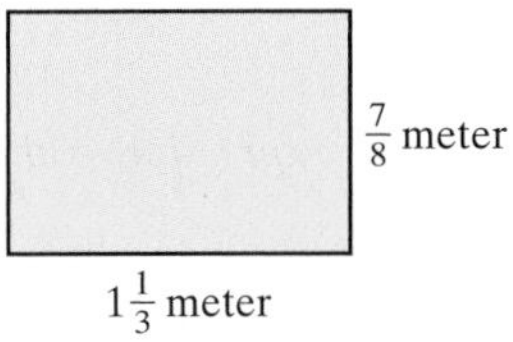

△ **32.**

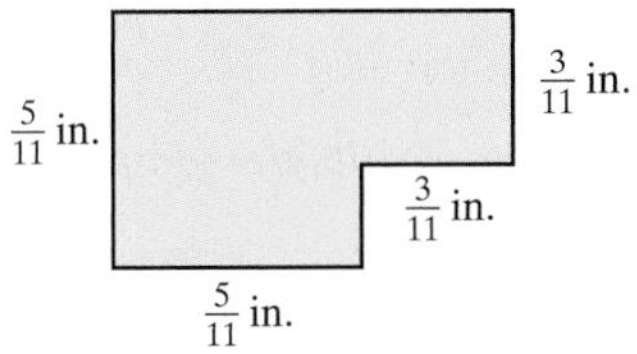

Octuplets were born in the U.S. in 2009. The following chart gives the octuplets' birthweights. The babies are listed in order of birth.

Baby	***Gender***	***Birthweight (pounds)***
Baby A	boy	$2\frac{1}{2}$
Baby B	girl	$2\frac{1}{8}$
Baby C	boy	$3\frac{1}{16}$
Baby D	girl	$2\frac{3}{16}$
Baby E	boy	$1\frac{3}{4}$
Baby F	boy	$2\frac{9}{16}$
Baby G	boy	$1\frac{13}{16}$
Baby H	boy	$2\frac{7}{16}$

33. What was the total weight of the boy octuplets?

34. What was the total weight of the girl octuplets?

35. Find the combined weight of all eight octuplets.

36. Which baby weighed the most?

37. Which baby weighed the least?

38. How much more did the heaviest baby weigh than the lightest baby?

(R.4) *Choose the correct answer for each statement.*

39. The expression $6 \cdot 3^2 + 2 \cdot 8$ simplifies to

a. -52 **b.** 448 **c.** 70 **d.** 64

40. The expression $68 - 5 \cdot 2^3$ simplifies to

a. -232 **b.** 28 **c.** 38 **d.** 504

Simplify each expression.

41. $\left(\frac{2}{7}\right)^2$

42. $\left(\frac{3}{4}\right)^3$

43. $3(1 + 2 \cdot 5) + 4$

44. $8 + 3(2 \cdot 6 - 1)$

45. $\dfrac{4 + |6 - 2| + 8^2}{4 + 6 \cdot 4}$

46. $5[3(2 + 5) - 5]$

TRANSLATING

Translate each word statement to symbols.

47. The difference of twenty and twelve is equal to the product of two and four.

48. The quotient of nine and two is greater than negative five.

Evaluate each expression if $x = 6$, $y = 2$, and $z = 8$.

49. $2x + 3y$

50. $x(y + 2z)$

51. $\dfrac{x}{y} + \dfrac{z}{2y}$

52. $x^2 - 3y^2$

△ **53.** The expression $180 - a - b$ represents the measure of the unknown angle of the given triangle. Replace a with 37 and b with 80 to find the measure of the unknown angle.

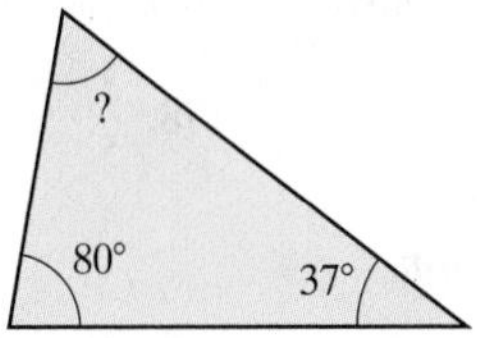

△ **54.** The expression $360 - a - b - c$ represents the measure of the unknown angle of the given quadrilateral. Replace a with 93, b with 80, and c with 82 to find the measure of the unknown angle.

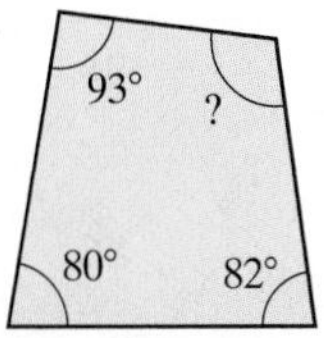

Decide whether the given number is a solution to the given equation.

55. Is $x = 3$ a solution of $7x - 3 = 18$?

56. Is $x = 1$ a solution of $3x^2 + 4 = x - 1$?

(R.5) *Find the additive inverse or the opposite.*

57. -9

58. $\dfrac{2}{3}$

59. $|-2|$

60. $-|-7|$

Find the following sums.

61. $-15 + 4$

62. $-6 + (-11)$

63. $\dfrac{1}{16} + \left(-\dfrac{1}{4}\right)$

64. $-8 + |-3|$

65. $-4.6 + (-9.3)$

66. $-2.8 + 6.7$

(R.6) *Perform the indicated operations.*

67. $6 - 20$

68. $-3.1 - 8.4$

69. $-6 - (-11)$

70. $4 - 15$

71. $-21 - 16 + 3(8 - 2)$

72. $\dfrac{11 - (-9) + 6(8 - 2)}{2 + 3 \cdot 4}$

Evaluate each expression for $x = 3$, $y = -6$, and $z = -9$. Then choose the correct evaluation.

73. $2x^2 - y + z$

a. 15 **b.** 3 **c.** 27 **d.** −3

74. $\dfrac{|y - 4x|}{2x}$

a. 3 **b.** 1 **c.** −1 **d.** −3

75. At the beginning of the week, the price of Density Oil and Gas stock from Exercises 17 and 18 is $50 per share. Find the price of a share of stock at the end of the week.

76. Find the price of a share of stock by the end of the day on Wednesday.

(R.7) *Find the multiplicative inverse or reciprocal.*

77. -6

78. $\dfrac{3}{5}$

Simplify each expression.

79. $6(-8)$

80. $(-2)(-14)$

81. $\dfrac{-18}{-6}$

82. $\dfrac{42}{-3}$

83. $\dfrac{4(-3) + (-8)}{2 + (-2)}$

84. $\dfrac{3(-2)^2 - 5}{-14}$

85. $\dfrac{-6}{0}$

86. $\dfrac{0}{-2}$

87. $-4^2 - (-3 + 5) \div (-1) \cdot 2$

88. $-5^2 - (2 - 20) \div (-3) \cdot 3$

If $x = -5$ and $y = -2$, evaluate each expression.

89. $x^2 - y^4$

90. $x^2 - y^3$

TRANSLATING

Translate each phrase to an expression. Use x to represent a number.

91. The product of –7 and a number

92. The quotient of a number and –13

93. Subtract a number from –20

94. The sum of –1 and a number

(R.8) *Name the property illustrated.*

95. $-6 + 5 = 5 + (-6)$

96. $6 \cdot 1 = 6$

97. $3(8 - 5) = 3 \cdot 8 - 3 \cdot (5)$

98. $4 + (-4) = 0$

99. $2 + (3 + 9) = (2 + 3) + 9$

100. $2 \cdot 8 = 8 \cdot 2$

101. $6(8 + 5) = 6 \cdot 8 + 6 \cdot 5$

102. $(3 \cdot 8) \cdot 4 = 3 \cdot (8 \cdot 4)$

103. $4 \cdot \dfrac{1}{4} = 1$

104. $8 + 0 = 8$

Use the distributive property to write each expression without parentheses.

105. $5(y - 2)$

106. $-3(z + y)$

107. $-(7 - x + 4z)$

108. $\dfrac{1}{2}(6z - 10)$

109. $-4(3x + 5) - 7$

110. $-8(2y + 9) - 1$

MIXED REVIEW

Insert $<$, $>$, or $=$ in the space between each pair of numbers.

111. $-|-11| \quad |11.4|$

112. $-1\frac{1}{2} \quad -2\frac{1}{2}$

Perform the indicated operations.

113. $-7.2 + (-8.1)$

114. $14 - 20$

115. $4(-20)$

116. $\dfrac{-20}{4}$

117. $-\dfrac{4}{5}\left(\dfrac{5}{16}\right)$

118. $-0.5(-0.3)$

119. $8 \div 2 \cdot 4$

120. $(-2)^4$

121. $\dfrac{-3 - 2(-9)}{-15 - 3(-4)}$

122. $5 + 2[(7 - 5)^2 + (1 - 3)]$

123. $-\dfrac{5}{8} \div \dfrac{3}{4}$

124. $\dfrac{-15 + (-4)^2 + |-9|}{10 - 2 \cdot 5}$

△ **125.** A trim carpenter needs a piece of quarter round molding $6\frac{1}{8}$ feet long for a bathroom. She finds a piece $7\frac{1}{2}$ feet long. How long a piece does she need to cut from the $7\frac{1}{2}$-foot-long molding in order to use it in the bathroom?

Chapter R Test

Translate the statement into symbols.

1. The absolute value of negative seven is greater than five.
2. The sum of nine and five is greater than or equal to four.

Simplify the expression.

3. $-13 + 8$
4. $-13 - (-2)$
5. $12 \div 4 \cdot 3 - 6 \cdot 2$
6. $(13)(-3)$
7. $(-6)(-2)$
8. $\dfrac{|-16|}{-8}$
9. $\dfrac{-8}{0}$
10. $\dfrac{|-6| + 2}{5 - 6}$
11. $\dfrac{1}{2} - \dfrac{5}{6}$
12. $5\frac{3}{4} - 1\frac{1}{8}$
13. $-0.6 + 1.875$
14. $3(-4)^2 - 80$
15. $6[5 + 2(3 - 8) - 3]$
16. $\dfrac{-12 + 3 \cdot 8}{4}$
17. $\dfrac{(-2)(0)(-3)}{-6}$

Insert $<, >,$ or $=$ in the appropriate space to make each of the following statements true.

18. $-3 \quad -7$
19. $4 \quad -8$
20. $2 \quad |-3|$
21. $|-2| \quad -1 - (-3)$
22. In the state of Massachusetts, there are 2221 licensed child care centers and 10,993 licensed home-based child care providers. Write an inequality statement comparing the numbers 2221 and 10,993. (*Source:* Children's Foundation)
23. Given $\left\{-5, -1, 0, \frac{1}{4}, 1, 7, 11.6, \sqrt{7}, 3\pi\right\}$, list the numbers in this set that also belong to the set of:
    - **a.** Natural numbers
    - **b.** Whole numbers
    - **c.** Integers
    - **d.** Rational numbers
    - **e.** Irrational numbers
    - **f.** Real numbers

If $x = 6$, $y = -2$, and $z = -3$, evaluate each expression.

24. $x^2 + y^2$
25. $x + yz$
26. $2 + 3x - y$
27. $\dfrac{y + z - 1}{x}$

Identify the property illustrated by each expression.

28. $8 + (9 + 3) = (8 + 9) + 3$
29. $6 \cdot 8 = 8 \cdot 6$
30. $-6(2 + 4) = -6 \cdot 2 + (-6) \cdot 4$
31. $\frac{1}{6}(6) = 1$
32. Find the opposite of -9.
33. Find the reciprocal of $-\frac{1}{3}$.

The New Orleans Saints were 22 yards from the goal when the following series of gains and losses occurred.

	Gains and Losses in Yards
First Down	5
Second Down	−10
Third Down	−2
Fourth Down	29

34. During which down did the greatest loss of yardage occur?
35. Was a touchdown scored?
36. The temperature at the Winter Olympics was a frigid 14 degrees below zero in the morning, but by noon it had risen 31 degrees. What was the temperature at noon?

37. A health insurance provider had net incomes of \$356 million, \$460 million, and −\$166 million in 3 consecutive years. What was the health insurance provider's total net income for these three years?
38. A stockbroker decided to sell 280 shares of stock, which decreased in value by \$1.50 per share yesterday. How much money did she lose?

CHAPTER 1 Graphing

We define and present techniques for solving and graphing linear equations and inequalities in two variables.

Tourism 2020 Vision is the World Tourism Organization's long-term forecast of world tourism through 2020. The broken-line graph below shows the forecasts. In Section 1.1, Exercises 1 through 6, we read a bar graph showing the top tourist destinations by country.

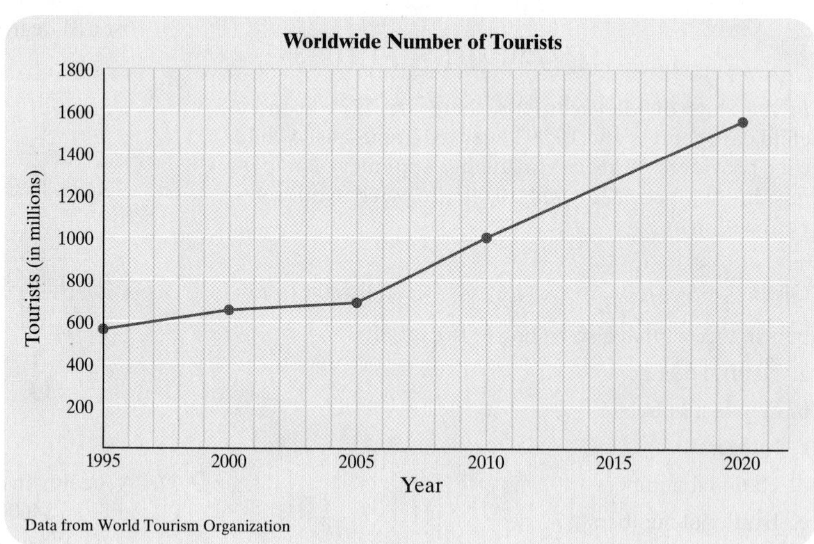

1.1 Reading Graphs and the Rectangular Coordinate System 

OBJECTIVES

1. Read Bar and Line Graphs.
2. Define the Rectangular Coordinate System and Plot Ordered Pairs of Numbers.
3. Graph Paired Data to Create a Scatter Diagram.
4. Determine Whether an Ordered Pair Is a Solution of an Equation in Two Variables.
5. Find the Missing Coordinate of an Ordered Pair Solution, Given One Coordinate of the Pair.

In today's world, where the exchange of information must be fast and entertaining, graphs are becoming increasingly popular. They provide a quick way of making comparisons, drawing conclusions, and approximating quantities.

OBJECTIVE

1 Reading Bar and Line Graphs 

A **bar graph** consists of a series of bars arranged vertically or horizontally. The bar graph in Example 1 shows a comparison of worldwide Internet users by region. The names of the regions are listed vertically and a bar is shown for each region. Corresponding to the length of the bar for each region is a number along a horizontal axis. These horizontal numbers are numbers of Internet users in millions.

EXAMPLE 1 The following bar graph shows the estimated number of Internet users worldwide by region as of a recent year.

a. Find the region that has the most Internet users and approximate the number of users.

b. How many more users are in the North America region than the Latin America/Caribbean region?

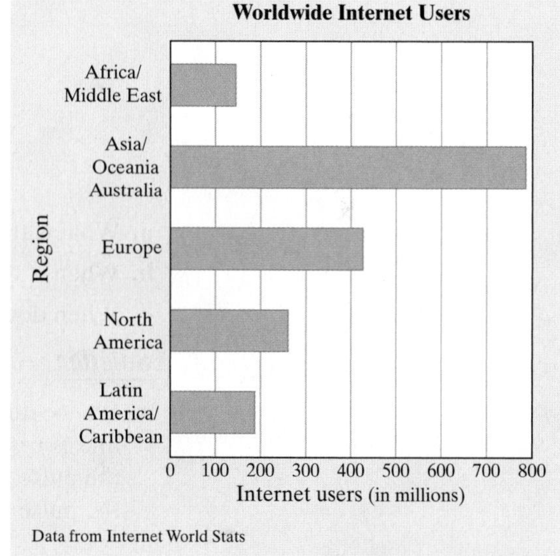

Solution

a. Since these bars are arranged horizontally, we look for the longest bar, which is the bar representing Asia/Oceania/Australia. To approximate the number associated with this region, we move from the right edge of this bar vertically downward to the Internet user axis. This region has approximately 785 million Internet users.

b. The North America region has approximately 260 million Internet users. The Latin America/Caribbean region has approximately 187 million Internet users. To find how many more users are in the North America region, we subtract $260 - 187 = 73$ million more Internet users. □

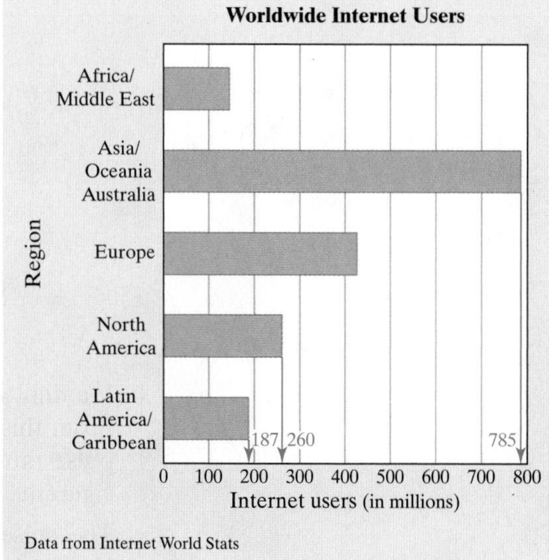

PRACTICE

1 Use the graph from Example 1 to answer the following.

a. Find the region with the fewest Internet users and approximate the number of users.

b. How many more users are in the Asia/Oceania/Australia region than in the Africa/Middle East region?

A **line graph** consists of a series of points connected by a line. The next graph is an example of a line graph. It is also sometimes called a **broken-line graph.**

EXAMPLE 2 The line graph shows the relationship between time spent smoking a cigarette and pulse rate. Time is recorded along the horizontal axis in minutes, with 0 minutes being the moment a smoker lights a cigarette. Pulse is recorded along the vertical axis in heartbeats per minute.

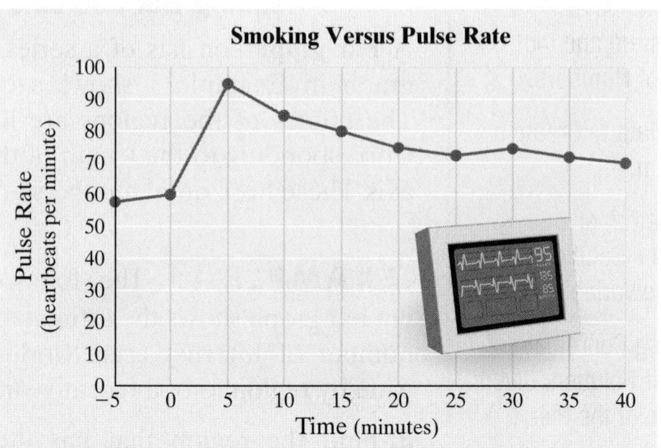

a. What is the pulse rate 15 minutes after a cigarette is lit?

b. When is the pulse rate the lowest?

c. When does the pulse rate show the greatest change?

Solution

a. We locate the number 15 along the time axis and move vertically upward until the line is reached. From this point on the line, we move horizontally to the left until the pulse rate axis is reached. Reading the number of beats per minute, we find that the pulse rate is 80 beats per minute 15 minutes after a cigarette is lit.

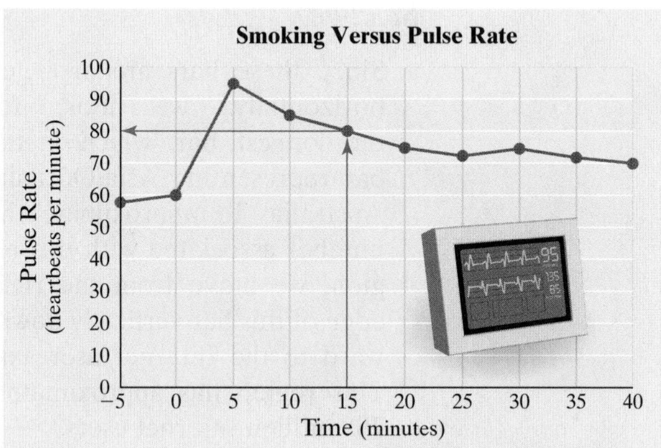

b. We find the lowest point of the line graph, which represents the lowest pulse rate. From this point, we move vertically downward to the time axis. We find that the pulse rate is the lowest at −5 minutes, which means 5 minutes *before* lighting a cigarette.

c. The pulse rate shows the greatest change during the 5 minutes between 0 and 5. Notice that the line graph is *steepest* between 0 and 5 minutes. □

PRACTICE 2 Use the graph from Example 2 to answer the following.

a. What is the pulse rate 40 minutes after lighting a cigarette?

b. What is the pulse rate when the cigarette is being lit?

c. When is the pulse rate the highest?

OBJECTIVE

2 Defining the Rectangular Coordinate System and Plotting Ordered Pairs of Numbers

Notice in the previous graph that two numbers are associated with each point of the graph. For example, we discussed earlier that 15 minutes after lighting a cigarette, the pulse rate is 80 beats per minute. If we agree to write the time first and the pulse rate second, we can say there is a point on the graph corresponding to the **ordered pair** of numbers $(15, 80)$. A few more ordered pairs are listed alongside their corresponding points.

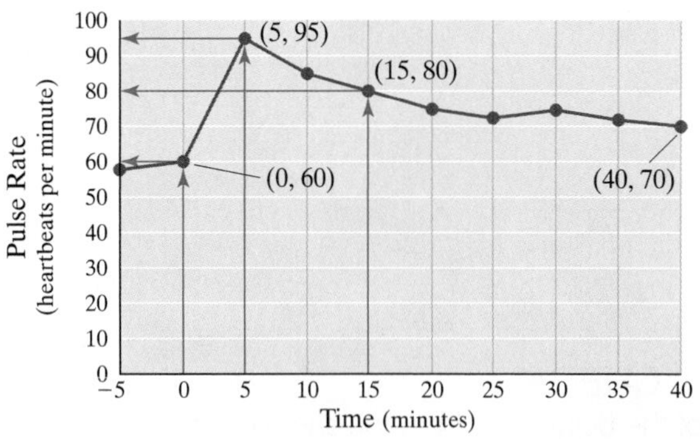

In general, we use this same ordered pair idea to describe the location of a point in a plane (such as a piece of paper). We start with a horizontal and a vertical axis. Each axis is a number line and, for the sake of consistency, we construct our axes to intersect at the 0 coordinate of both. This point of intersection is called the **origin.** Notice that these two number lines or axes divide the plane into four regions called **quadrants.** The quadrants are usually numbered with Roman numerals as shown. The axes are not considered to be in any quadrant.

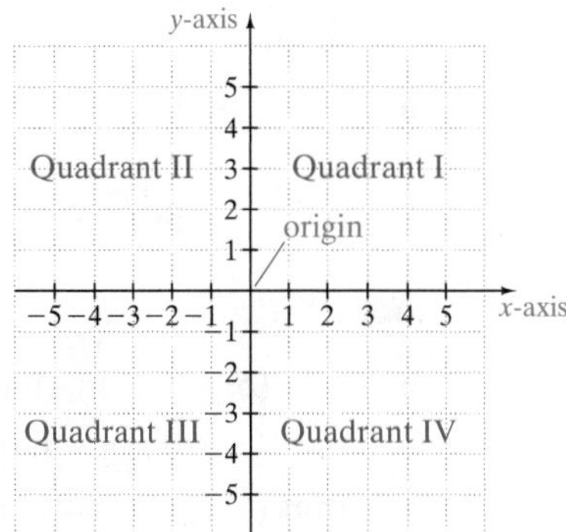

It is helpful to label axes, so we label the horizontal axis the ***x*-axis** and the vertical axis the ***y*-axis.** We call the system described above the **rectangular coordinate system.**

Just as with the pulse rate graph, we can then describe the locations of points by ordered pairs of numbers. We list the horizontal ***x*-axis** measurement first and the vertical ***y*-axis** measurement second.

To plot or graph the point corresponding to the ordered pair

$$(a, b)$$

we start at the origin. We then move a units left or right (right if a is positive, left if a is negative). From there, we move b units up or down (up if b is positive, down if b is negative). For example, to plot the point corresponding to the ordered pair (3, 2), we start at the origin, move 3 units right and from there move 2 units up. (See the figure to the left.) The x-value, 3, is called the ***x*-coordinate** and the y-value, 2, is called the ***y*-coordinate.** From now on, we will call the point with coordinates (3, 2) simply the point (3, 2). The point $(-2, 5)$ is graphed to the left also.

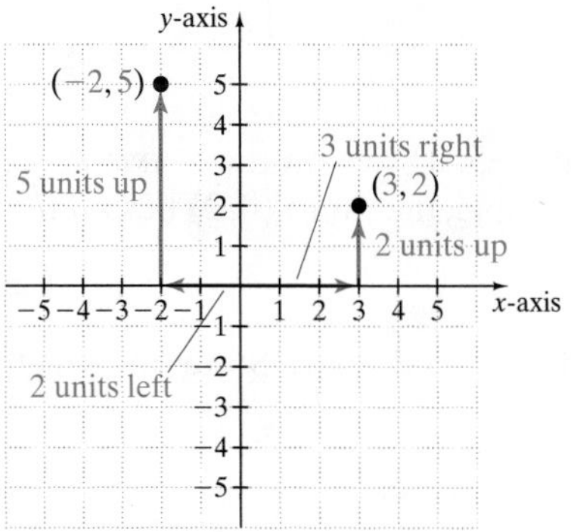

Does the order in which the coordinates are listed matter? Yes! Notice below that the point corresponding to the ordered pair (2, 3) is in a different location than the point corresponding to (3, 2). These two ordered pairs of numbers describe two different points of the plane.

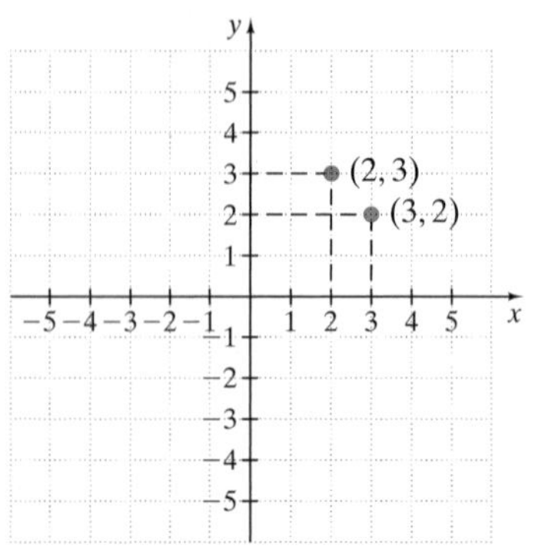

✓CONCEPT CHECK

Is the graph of the point $(-5, 1)$ in the same location as the graph of the point $(1, -5)$? Explain.

Helpful Hint

Don't forget that **each ordered pair corresponds to exactly one point in the plane and that each point in the plane corresponds to exactly one ordered pair.**

EXAMPLE 3 On a single coordinate system, plot each ordered pair. State in which quadrant, if any, each point lies.

a. $(5, 3)$ **b.** $(-5, 3)$ **c.** $(-2, -4)$ **d.** $(1, -2)$ **e.** $(0, 0)$

f. $(0, 2)$ **g.** $(-5, 0)$ **h.** $\left(0, -5\frac{1}{2}\right)$ **i.** $\left(4\frac{2}{3}, -3\right)$

Solution

a. Point $(5, 3)$ lies in quadrant I.

b. Point $(-5, 3)$ lies in quadrant II.

c. Point $(-2, -4)$ lies in quadrant III.

d. Point $(1, -2)$ lies in quadrant IV.

e.–h. Points $(0, 0)$, $(0, 2)$, $(-5, 0)$, and $\left(0, -5\frac{1}{2}\right)$ lie on axes, so they are not in any quadrant.

i. Point $\left(4\frac{2}{3}, -3\right)$ lies in quadrant IV.

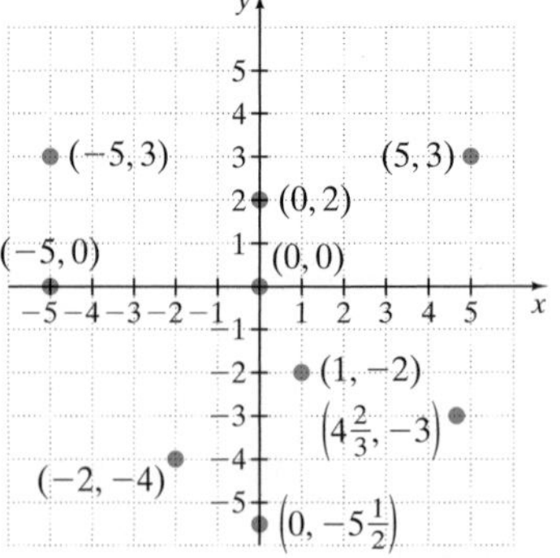

From Example 3, notice that the y-coordinate of any point on the x-axis is 0. For example, the point $(-5, 0)$ lies on the x-axis. Also, the x-coordinate of any point on the y-axis is 0. For example, the point $(0, 2)$ lies on the y-axis. □

PRACTICE

3 On a single coordinate system, plot each ordered pair. State in which quadrant, if any, each point lies.

a. $(4, -3)$ **b.** $(-3, 5)$ **c.** $(0, 4)$ **d.** $(-6, 1)$

e. $(-2, 0)$ **f.** $(5, 5)$ **g.** $\left(3\frac{1}{2}, 1\frac{1}{2}\right)$ **h.** $(-4, -5)$

Answer to Concept Check:
The graph of point $(-5, 1)$ lies in quadrant II and the graph of point $(1, -5)$ lies in quadrant IV. They are *not* in the same location.

✓CONCEPT CHECK

For each description of a point in the rectangular coordinate system, write an ordered pair that represents it.

a. Point A is located three units to the left of the y-axis and five units above the x-axis.

b. Point B is located six units below the origin.

OBJECTIVE

3 Graphing Paired Data 

Data that can be represented as an ordered pair is called **paired data.** Many types of data collected from the real world are paired data. For instance, the annual measurement of a child's height can be written as an ordered pair of the form (year, height in inches) and is paired data. The graph of paired data as points in the rectangular coordinate system is called a **scatter diagram.** Scatter diagrams can be used to look for patterns and trends in paired data.

EXAMPLE 4 The table gives the annual net sales (in billions of dollars) for Target stores for the years shown. (Data from www.retailsales.com)

Year	*Target Net Sales (in billions of dollars)*
2006	58
2007	61
2008	63
2009	63
2010	66

a. Write this paired data as a set of ordered pairs of the form (year, sales in billions of dollars).

b. Create a scatter diagram of the paired data.

c. What trend in the paired data does the scatter diagram show?

Solution

a. The ordered pairs are (2006, 58), (2007, 61), (2008, 63), (2009, 63), (2010, 66).

b. We begin by plotting the ordered pairs. Because the x-coordinate in each ordered pair is a year, we label the x-axis "Year" and mark the horizontal axis with the years given. Then we label the y-axis or vertical axis "Net Sales (in billions of dollars)." In this case we can mark the vertical axis in multiples of 2. Since no net sale is less than 58, we use the notation ⚡ to skip to 58, then proceed by multiples of 2.

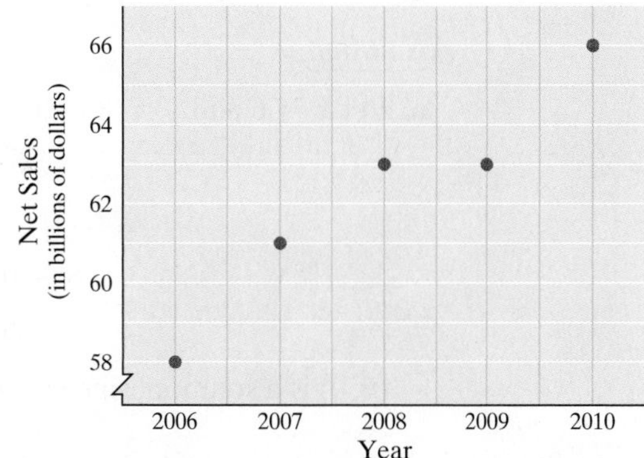

Answers to Concept Check:
a. $(-3, 5)$ **b.** $(0, -6)$

c. The scatter diagram shows that Target net sales were constant or steadily increased over the years 2006–2010. □

PRACTICE

4 The table gives the approximate annual number of wildfires (in thousands) that have occurred in the United States for the years shown. (Data from National Interagency Fire Center)

Year	*Wildfires (in thousands)*
2004	65
2005	67
2006	96
2007	86
2008	79
2009	79
2010	72

a. Write this paired data as a set of ordered pairs of the form (year, number of wildfires in thousands).

b. Create a scatter diagram of the paired data.

OBJECTIVE

4 Determining Whether an Ordered Pair Is a Solution 

Let's see how we can use ordered pairs to record solutions of equations containing two variables. An equation in one variable such as $x + 1 = 5$ has one solution, which is 4: The number 4 is the value of the variable x that makes the equation true.

An equation in two variables, such as $2x + y = 8$, has solutions consisting of two values, one for x and one for y. For example, $x = 3$ and $y = 2$ is a solution of $2x + y = 8$ because, if x is replaced with 3 and y with 2, we get a true statement.

$$2x + y = 8$$
$$2(3) + 2 = 8$$
$$8 = 8 \quad \text{True}$$

The solution $x = 3$ and $y = 2$ can be written as $(3, 2)$, an **ordered pair** of numbers. The first number, 3, is the x-value and the second number, 2, is the y-value.

In general, an ordered pair is a **solution** of an equation in two variables if replacing the variables by the values of the ordered pair results in a true statement.

EXAMPLE 5 Determine whether each ordered pair is a solution of the equation $x - 2y = 6$.

a. $(6, 0)$ **b.** $(0, 3)$ **c.** $\left(1, -\frac{5}{2}\right)$

Solution

a. Let $x = 6$ and $y = 0$ in the equation $x - 2y = 6$.

$$x - 2y = 6$$
$$6 - 2(0) = 6 \quad \text{Replace } x \text{ with 6 and } y \text{ with 0.}$$
$$6 - 0 = 6 \quad \text{Simplify.}$$
$$6 = 6 \quad \text{True}$$

$(6, 0)$ is a solution, since $6 = 6$ is a true statement.

b. Let $x = 0$ and $y = 3$.

$$\begin{aligned} x - 2y &= 6 \\ 0 - 2(3) &= 6 \quad \text{Replace } x \text{ with 0 and } y \text{ with 3.} \\ 0 - 6 &= 6 \\ -6 &= 6 \quad \text{False} \end{aligned}$$

(0, 3) is *not* a solution, since $-6 = 6$ is a false statement.

c. Let $x = 1$ and $y = -\frac{5}{2}$ in the equation.

$$\begin{aligned} x - 2y &= 6 \\ 1 - 2\left(-\frac{5}{2}\right) &= 6 \quad \text{Replace } x \text{ with 1 and } y \text{ with } -\frac{5}{2}. \\ 1 + 5 &= 6 \\ 6 &= 6 \quad \text{True} \end{aligned}$$

$\left(1, -\frac{5}{2}\right)$ is a solution, since $6 = 6$ is a true statement. □

PRACTICE

5 Determine whether each ordered pair is a solution of the equation $x + 3y = 6$.

a. (3, 1) **b.** (6, 0) **c.** $\left(-2, \frac{2}{3}\right)$

OBJECTIVE

5 Completing Ordered Pair Solutions

If one value of an ordered pair solution of an equation is known, the other value can be determined. To find the unknown value, replace one variable in the equation by its known value.

EXAMPLE 6 Complete the following ordered pair solutions for the equation $3x + y = 12$.

a. (0,) **b.** (, 6) **c.** (−1,)

Solution

a. In the ordered pair (0,), the x-value is 0. Let $x = 0$ in the equation and solve for y.

$$\begin{aligned} 3x + y &= 12 \\ 3(0) + y &= 12 \quad \text{Replace } x \text{ with 0.} \\ 0 + y &= 12 \\ y &= 12 \end{aligned}$$

The completed ordered pair is (0, 12).

b. In the ordered pair (, 6), the y-value is 6. Let $y = 6$ in the equation and solve for x.

$$\begin{aligned} 3x + y &= 12 \\ 3x + 6 &= 12 \quad \text{Replace } y \text{ with 6.} \\ 3x &= 6 \quad \text{Subtract 6 from both sides.} \\ x &= 2 \quad \text{Divide both sides by 3.} \end{aligned}$$

The ordered pair is (2, 6).

c. In the ordered pair $(-1,\ \ )$, the x-value is -1. Let $x = -1$ in the equation and solve for y.

$$3x + y = 12$$
$$3(-1) + y = 12 \quad \text{Replace } x \text{ with } -1.$$
$$-3 + y = 12$$
$$y = 15 \quad \text{Add 3 to both sides.}$$

The ordered pair is $(-1, 15)$. □

PRACTICE 6 Complete the following ordered pair solutions for the equation $2x - y = 8$.

a. $(0,\ \ )$ **b.** $(\ \ ,4)$ **c.** $(-3,\ \ )$

Solutions of equations in two variables can also be recorded in a **table of values,** as shown in the next example.

EXAMPLE 7 Complete the table for the equation $y = 3x$.

	x	y
a.	-1	
b.		0
c.		-9

Solution

a. Replace x with -1 in the equation and solve for y.

$$y = 3x$$
$$y = 3(-1) \quad \text{Let } x = -1.$$
$$y = -3$$

The ordered pair is $(-1, -3)$.

b. Replace y with 0 in the equation and solve for x.

$$y = 3x$$
$$0 = 3x \quad \text{Let } y = 0.$$
$$0 = x \quad \text{Divide both sides by 3.}$$

The ordered pair is $(0, 0)$.

c. Replace y with -9 in the equation and solve for x.

$$y = 3x$$
$$-9 = 3x \quad \text{Let } y = -9.$$
$$-3 = x \quad \text{Divide both sides by 3.}$$

The ordered pair is $(-3, -9)$. The completed table is shown to the left. □

x	y
-1	-3
0	0
-3	-9

PRACTICE 7 Complete the table for the equation $y = -4x$.

	x	y
a.	-2	
b.		-12
c.	0	

EXAMPLE 8 Complete the table for the equation

$$y = \frac{1}{2}x - 5.$$

	x	y
a.	−2	
b.	0	
c.		0

Solution

a. Let $x = -2$.

$$y = \frac{1}{2}x - 5$$
$$y = \frac{1}{2}(-2) - 5$$
$$y = -1 - 5$$
$$y = -6$$

b. Let $x = 0$.

$$y = \frac{1}{2}x - 5$$
$$y = \frac{1}{2}(0) - 5$$
$$y = 0 - 5$$
$$y = -5$$

c. Let $y = 0$.

$$y = \frac{1}{2}x - 5$$
$$0 = \frac{1}{2}x - 5 \quad \text{Now, solve for } x.$$
$$5 = \frac{1}{2}x \quad \text{Add 5.}$$
$$10 = x \quad \text{Multiply by 2.}$$

Ordered Pairs: $(-2, -6)$ $(0, -5)$ $(10, 0)$

The completed table is

x	y
−2	−6
0	−5
10	0

□

PRACTICE 8 Complete the table for the equation $y = \frac{1}{5}x - 2$.

	x	y
a.	−10	
b.	0	
c.		0

EXAMPLE 9 **Finding the Value of a Computer**

A computer was recently purchased for a small business for $2000. The business manager predicts that the computer will be used for 5 years and the value in dollars y of the computer in x years is $y = -300x + 2000$. Complete the table.

x	0	1	2	3	4	5
y						

Solution To find the value of y when x is 0, replace x with 0 in the equation. We use this same procedure to find y when x is 1 and when x is 2.

When x = 0,
$$y = -300x + 2000$$
$$y = -300 \cdot 0 + 2000$$
$$y = 0 + 2000$$
$$y = 2000$$

When x = 1,
$$y = -300x + 2000$$
$$y = -300 \cdot 1 + 2000$$
$$y = -300 + 2000$$
$$y = 1700$$

When x = 2,
$$y = -300x + 2000$$
$$y = -300 \cdot 2 + 2000$$
$$y = -600 + 2000$$
$$y = 1400$$

We have the ordered pairs (0, 2000), (1, 1700), and (2, 1400). This means that in 0 years, the value of the computer is $2000, in 1 year the value of the computer is $1700, and in

2 years the value is \$1400. To complete the table of values, we continue the procedure for $x = 3$, $x = 4$, and $x = 5$.

When $x = 3$,	**When $x = 4$,**	**When $x = 5$,**
$y = -300x + 2000$	$y = -300x + 2000$	$y = -300x + 2000$
$y = -300 \cdot 3 + 2000$	$y = -300 \cdot 4 + 2000$	$y = -300 \cdot 5 + 2000$
$y = -900 + 2000$	$y = -1200 + 2000$	$y = -1500 + 2000$
$y = 1100$	$y = 800$	$y = 500$

The completed table is

x	0	1	2	3	4	5
y	2000	1700	1400	1100	800	500

□

PRACTICE

9 A college student purchased a used car for \$12,000. The student predicted that she would need to use the car for four years and the value in dollars y of the car in x years is $y = -1800x + 12,000$. Complete this table.

x	0	1	2	3	4
y					

The ordered pair solutions recorded in the completed table for the example above are graphed below. Notice that the graph gives a visual picture of the decrease in value of the computer.

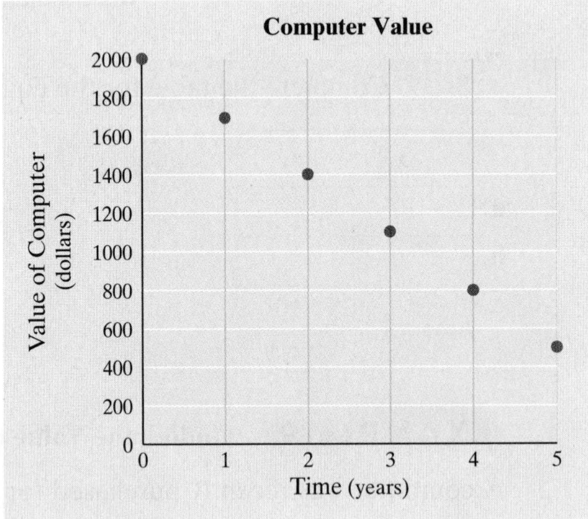

x	y
0	2000
1	1700
2	1400
3	1100
4	800
5	500

Vocabulary, Readiness & Video Check

Use the choices below to fill in each blank. The exercises below all have to do with the rectangular coordinate system.

origin	x-coordinate	x-axis	one	four
quadrants	y-coordinate	y-axis	solution	

1. The horizontal axis is called the __________ and the vertical axis is called the __________.
2. The intersection of the horizontal axis and the vertical axis is a point called the __________.
3. The axes divide the plane into regions called __________. There are __________ of these regions.
4. In the ordered pair of numbers $(-2, 5)$, the number -2 is called the __________ and the number 5 is called the __________.
5. Each ordered pair of numbers corresponds to __________ point in the plane.
6. An ordered pair is a(n) __________ of an equation in two variables if replacing the variables by the coordinates of the ordered pair results in a true statement.

Martin-Gay Interactive Videos *Watch the section lecture video and answer the following questions.*

See Video 1.1

OBJECTIVE 1
7. Examples 1–3 ask you to answer questions about a bar graph. What information is provided on the horizontal axis of this bar graph? On the vertical axis?

OBJECTIVE 2
8. Several points are plotted in Examples 4–11. Where do you always start when plotting a point? How does the 1st coordinate tell you to move? How does the 2nd coordinate tell you to move?

OBJECTIVE 3
9. In the lecture before Example 12, what connection is made between data and graphing?

OBJECTIVE 4
10. An ordered pair is a solution of an equation if, when the variables are replaced with their values, a true statement results. In Example 13, three ordered pairs are tested. What are the last two points to be tested? What lesson can be learned by the results of testing these two points and why?

OBJECTIVE 5
11. In Example 14, when one variable of a linear equation in two variables is replaced by a replacement value, what type of equation results?

1.1 Exercise Set

MyMathLab®

The following bar graph shows the top 10 tourist destinations and the number of tourists that visit each country per year. Use this graph to answer Exercises 1 through 6. See Example 1.

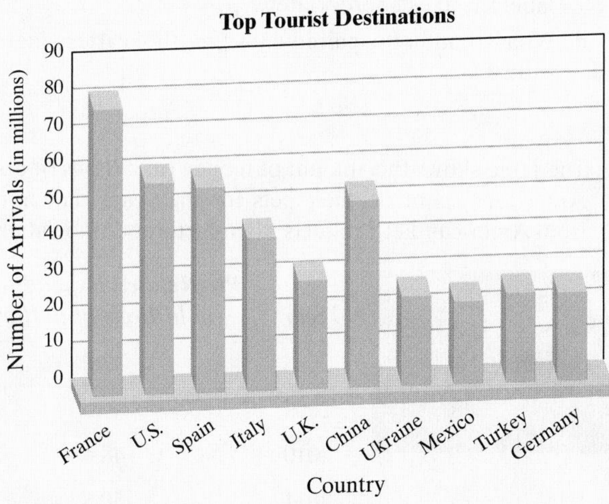

1. Which country shown is the most popular tourist destination?
2. Which country shown is the least popular tourist destination?
3. Which countries shown have more than 40 million tourists per year?
4. Which countries shown have fewer than 30 million tourists per year?
5. Estimate the number of tourists per year whose destination is Italy.
6. Estimate the number of tourists per year whose destination is the U.K.

The following line graph shows the paid attendance at each Super Bowl game from 2005 through 2011. Use this graph to answer Exercises 7 through 10. See Example 2.

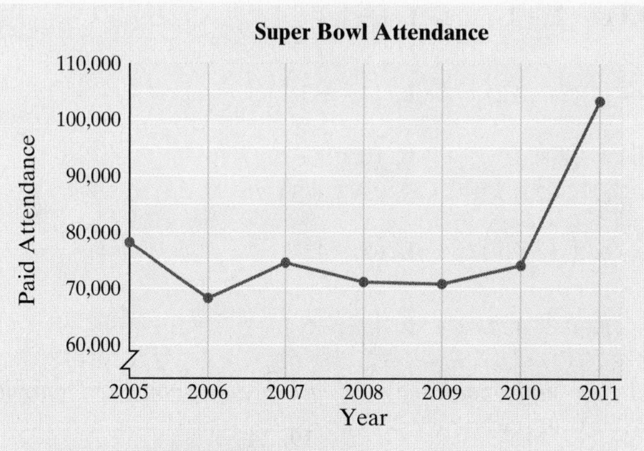

7. Estimate the Super Bowl attendance in 2009.
8. Estimate the Super Bowl attendance in 2010.
9. Find the year on the graph with the greatest Super Bowl attendance and approximate that attendance.
10. Find the year on the graph with the least Super Bowl attendance and approximate that attendance.

The line graph below shows the number of students per teacher in U.S. public elementary and secondary schools. Use this graph for Exercises 11 through 16. See Example 2.

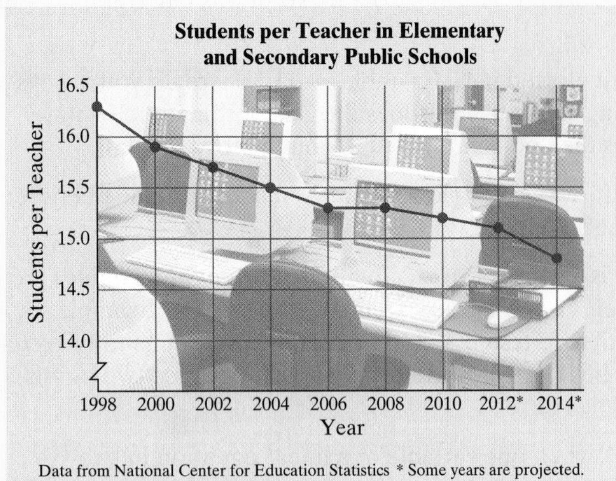

11. Approximate the number of students per teacher in 2000.

12. Approximate the number of students per teacher in 2012.

13. Between what years shown did the greatest decrease in number of students per teacher occur?

14. What was the first year shown that the number of students per teacher fell below 16?

15. What was the first year shown that the number of students per teacher fell below 15?

16. Discuss any trends shown by this line graph.

Plot each ordered pair. State in which quadrant or on which axis each point lies. See Example 3.

17. **a.** $(1, 5)$ **b.** $(-5, -2)$
c. $(-3, 0)$ **d.** $(0, -1)$
e. $(2, -4)$ **f.** $\left(-1, 4\frac{1}{2}\right)$
g. $(3.7, 2.2)$ **h.** $\left(\frac{1}{2}, -3\right)$

18. **a.** $(2, 4)$ **b.** $(0, 2)$
c. $(-2, 1)$ **d.** $(-3, -3)$
e. $\left(3\frac{3}{4}, 0\right)$ **f.** $(5, -4)$
g. $(-3.4, 4.8)$ **h.** $\left(\frac{1}{3}, -5\right)$

Find the x- and y-coordinates of each labeled point. See Example 3.

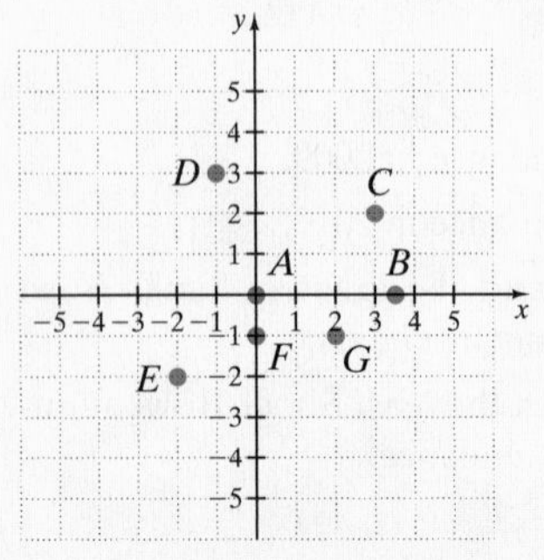

19. *A*

20. *B*

21. *C*

22. *D*

23. *E*

24. *F*

25. *G*

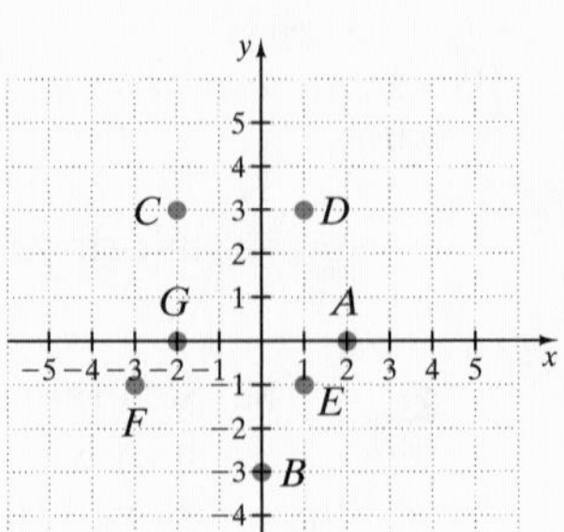

26. *A*

27. *B*

28. *C*

29. *D*

30. *E*

31. *F*

32. *G*

Solve. See Example 4.

33. The table shows the worldwide box office (in billions of dollars) for the movie industry during the years shown. (Data from Motion Picture Association of America)

Year	*Box Office (in billions of dollars)*
2006	25.5
2007	26.3
2008	27.7
2009	29.4
2010	31.8

a. Write this paired data as a set of ordered pairs of the form (year, box office).

b. In your own words, write the meaning of the ordered pair (2010, 31.8).

c. Create a scatter diagram of the paired data. Be sure to label the axes appropriately.

d. What trend in the paired data does the scatter diagram show?

34. The table shows the amount of money (in billions of dollars) Americans spent on their pets for the years shown. (Data from American Pet Products Manufacturers Association)

Year	*Pet-Related Expenditures (in billions of dollars)*
2008	43.2
2009	45.5
2010	48.4
2011	50.8

a. Write this paired data as a set of ordered pairs of the form (year, pet-related expenditures).

b. In your own words, write the meaning of the ordered pair (2011, 50.8).

c. Create a scatter diagram of the paired data. Be sure to label the axes appropriately.

d. What trend in the paired data does the scatter diagram show?

35. Minh, a psychology student, kept a record of how much time she spent studying for each of her 20-point psychology quizzes and her score on each quiz.

Hours Spent Studying	0.50	0.75	1.00	1.25	1.50	1.50	1.75	2.00
Quiz Score	10	12	15	16	18	19	19	20

a. Write the data as ordered pairs of the form (hours spent studying, quiz score).

b. In your own words, write the meaning of the ordered pair (1.25, 16).

c. Create a scatter diagram of the paired data. Be sure to label the axes appropriately.

d. What might Minh conclude from the scatter diagram?

36. A local lumberyard uses quantity pricing. The table shows the price per board for different amounts of lumber purchased.

Price per Board (in dollars)	***Number of Boards Purchased***
8.00	1
7.50	10
6.50	25
5.00	50
2.00	100

a. Write the data as ordered pairs of the form (price per board, number of boards purchased).

b. In your own words, write the meaning of the ordered pair (2.00, 100).

c. Create a scatter diagram of the paired data. Be sure to label the axes appropriately.

d. What trend in the paired data does the scatter diagram show?

37. The table shows the distance from the equator (in miles) and the average annual snowfall (in inches) for each of eight selected U.S. cities. (Data from National Climatic Data Center, Wake Forest University Albatross Project)

City	***Distance from Equator (in miles)***	***Average Annual Snowfall (in inches)***
1. Atlanta, GA	2313	2
2. Austin, TX	2085	1
3. Baltimore, MD	2711	21
4. Chicago, IL	2869	39
5. Detroit, MI	2920	42
6. Juneau, AK	4038	99
7. Miami, FL	1783	0
8. Winston-Salem, NC	2493	9

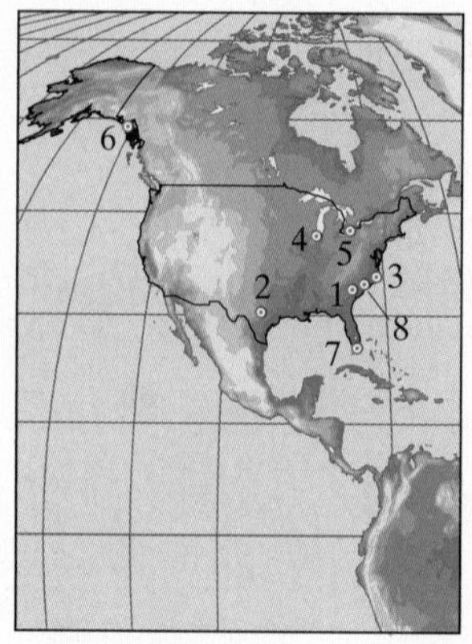

a. Write this paired data as a set of ordered pairs of the form (distance from equator, average annual snowfall).

b. Create a scatter diagram of the paired data. Be sure to label the axes appropriately.

c. What trend in the paired data does the scatter diagram show?

38. The table shows the average farm size (in acres) in the United States during the years shown. (Data from National Agricultural Statistics Service)

Year	***Average Farm Size (in acres)***
2001	438
2002	440
2003	441
2004	443
2005	445
2006	446

a. Write this paired data as a set of ordered pairs of the form (year, average farm size).

b. Create a scatter diagram of the paired data. Be sure to label the axes appropriately.

Determine whether each ordered pair is a solution of the given linear equation. See Example 5.

39. $2x + y = 7$; $(3, 1), (7, 0), (0, 7)$

40. $3x + y = 8$; $(2, 3), (0, 8), (8, 0)$

41. $x = -\frac{1}{3}y$; $(0, 0), (3, -9)$

42. $y = -\frac{1}{2}x$; $(0, 0), (4, 2)$

43. $x = 5$; $(4, 5), (5, 4), (5, 0)$

44. $y = -2$; $(-2, 2), (2, -2), (0, -2)$

Complete each ordered pair so that it is a solution of the given linear equation. See Examples 6 through 8.

45. $x - 4y = 4$; $(\quad, -2), (4, \quad)$

46. $x - 5y = -1$; $(\quad, -2), (4, \quad)$

47. $y = \frac{1}{4}x - 3$; $(-8, \quad), (\quad, 1)$

48. $y = \frac{1}{5}x - 2$; $(-10, \quad), (\quad, 1)$

Complete the table of ordered pairs for each linear equation. See Examples 6 through 8.

49. $y = -7x$

x	y
0	
−1	
	2

50. $y = -9x$

x	y
	0
−3	
	2

51. $y = -x + 2$

x	y
0	
	0
−3	

52. $x = -y + 4$

x	y
	0
0	
	−3

53. $y = \frac{1}{2}x$

x	y
0	
−6	
	1

54. $y = \frac{1}{3}x$

x	y
0	
−6	
	1

55. $x + 3y = 6$

x	y
0	
	0
	1

56. $2x + y = 4$

x	y
	4
2	
	2

57. $y = 2x - 12$

x	y
0	
	−2
3	

58. $y = 5x + 10$

x	y
	0
	5
0	

59. $2x + 7y = 5$

x	y
0	
	0
	1

60. $x - 6y = 3$

x	y
0	
1	
	−1

MIXED PRACTICE

Complete the table of ordered pairs for each equation. Then plot the ordered pair solutions. See Examples 1 through 7.

61. $x = -5y$

x	y
	0
	1
10	

62. $y = -3x$

x	y
0	
−2	
	9

63. $y = \frac{1}{3}x + 2$

x	y
0	
−3	
	0

64. $y = \frac{1}{2}x + 3$

x	y
0	
−4	
	0

Solve. See Example 9.

65. The cost in dollars y of producing x computer desks is given by $y = 80x + 5000$.

a. Complete the table.

x	100	200	300
y			

b. Find the number of computer desks that can be produced for $8600. (*Hint:* Find x when $y = 8600$.)

66. The hourly wage y of an employee at a certain production company is given by $y = 0.25x + 9$ where x is the number of units produced by the employee in an hour.

a. Complete the table.

x	0	1	5	10
y				

b. Find the number of units that an employee must produce each hour to earn an hourly wage of $12.25. (*Hint:* Find x when $y = 12.25$.)

67. The average annual cinema admission price y (in dollars) from 2001 through 2010 is given by $y = 0.24x + 5.28$. In this equation, x represents the number of years after 2000. (*Source:* Motion Picture Association of America)

a. Complete the table.

x	1	3	5
y			

b. Find the year in which the average cinema admission price was approximately $7.50. (*Hint:* Find x when $y = 7.50$ and round to the nearest whole number.)

c. Use the given equation to predict when the cinema admission price might be $9.00. (Use the hint for part b.)

d. In your own words, write the meaning of the ordered pair (5, 6.48).

68. The average amount of money y spent per person on recorded music from 2002 to 2009 is given by $y = -4.22x + 65.70$. In this equation, x represents the number of years after 2000. (*Source:* edgeqld.org)

a. Complete the table.

x	1	5	9
y			

b. Find the year in which the yearly average amount of money per person spent on recorded music was approximately \$30. (*Hint:* Find x when $y = 30$ and round to the nearest whole number.)

The graph below shows the number of U.S. Walmart stores for each year. Use this graph to answer Exercises 69 through 72.

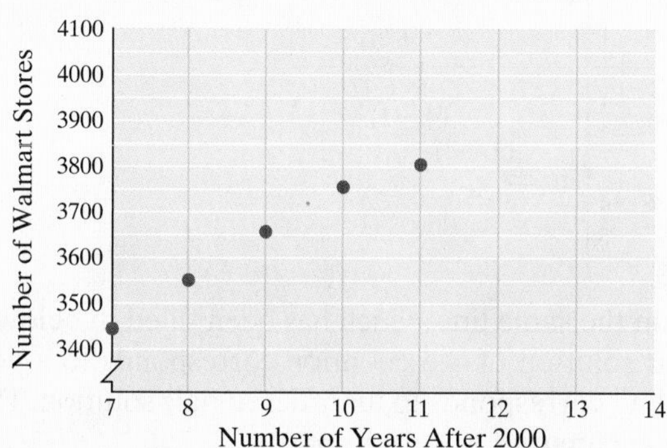

Data from Walmart

69. The ordered pair (10, 3755) is a point of the graph. Write a sentence describing the meaning of this ordered pair.

70. The ordered pair (11, 3804) is a point of the graph. Write a sentence describing the meaning of this ordered pair.

71. Estimate the increase in Walmart stores for years 8, 9, and 10.

72. Use a straightedge or ruler and this graph to predict the number of Walmart stores in the year 2014.

73. Describe what is similar about the coordinates of points whose graph lies on the x-axis.

74. Describe what is similar about the coordinates of points whose graph lies on the y-axis.

REVIEW AND PREVIEW

Solve each equation for y.

75. $x + y = 5$

76. $x - y = 3$

77. $2x + 4y = 5$

78. $5x + 2y = 7$

79. $10x = -5y$

80. $4y = -8x$

81. $x - 3y = 6$

82. $2x - 9y = -20$

CONCEPT EXTENSIONS

Answer each exercise with true or false.

83. Point $(-1, 5)$ lies in quadrant IV.

84. Point $(3, 0)$ lies on the y-axis.

85. For the point $\left(-\frac{1}{2}, 1.5\right)$, the first value, $-\frac{1}{2}$, is the x-coordinate and the second value, 1.5, is the y-coordinate.

86. The ordered pair $\left(2, \frac{2}{3}\right)$ is a solution of $2x - 3y = 6$.

For Exercises 87 through 91, fill in each blank with "0," "positive," or "negative." For Exercises 92 and 93, fill in each blank with "x" or "y."

	Point	Location
87.	(______, ______)	quadrant III
88.	(______, ______)	quadrant I
89.	(______, ______)	quadrant IV
90.	(______, ______)	quadrant II
91.	(______, ______)	origin
92.	(number, 0)	__-axis
93.	(0, number)	__-axis

94. Give an example of an ordered pair whose location is in (or on)

a. quadrant I

b. quadrant II

c. quadrant III

d. quadrant IV

e. x-axis

f. y-axis

Solve. See the first Concept Check in this section.

95. Is the graph of (3, 0) in the same location as the graph of (0, 3)? Explain why or why not.

96. Give the coordinates of a point such that if the coordinates are reversed, their location is the same.

97. In general, what points can have coordinates reversed and still have the same location?

98. In your own words, describe how to plot or graph an ordered pair of numbers.

Write an ordered pair for each point described. See the second Concept Check in this section.

99. Point C is four units to the right of the y-axis and seven units below the x-axis.

100. Point D is three units to the left of the origin.

Solve.

△ **101.** Find the perimeter of the rectangle whose vertices are the points with coordinates $(-1, 5)$, $(3, 5)$, $(3, -4)$, and $(-1, -4)$.

△ **102.** Find the area of the rectangle whose vertices are the points with coordinates $(5, 2)$, $(5, -6)$, $(0, -6)$, and $(0, 2)$.

103. Three vertices of a rectangle are $(-2, -3)$, $(-7, -3)$, and $(-7, 6)$.

a. Find the coordinates of the fourth vertex of the rectangle.

b. Find the perimeter of the rectangle.

c. Find the area of the rectangle.

104. Three vertices of a square are $(-4, -1)$, $(-4, 8)$, and $(5, 8)$.

a. Find the coordinates of the fourth vertex of the square.

b. Find the perimeter of the square.

c. Find the area of the square.

1.2 Graphing Linear Equations 

OBJECTIVES

1 Identify Linear Equations.

2 Graph a Linear Equation by Finding and Plotting Ordered Pair Solutions.

OBJECTIVE

1 Identifying Linear Equations 

In the previous section, we found that equations in two variables may have more than one solution. For example, both (6, 0) and (2, −2) are solutions of the equation $x - 2y = 6$. In fact, this equation has an infinite number of solutions. Other solutions include (0, −3), (4, −1), and (−2, −4). If we graph these solutions, notice that a pattern appears.

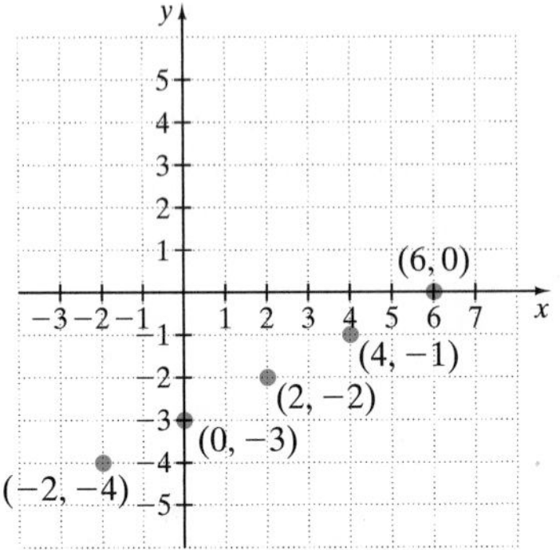

These solutions all appear to lie on the same line, which has been filled in below. It can be shown that every ordered pair solution of the equation corresponds to a point on this line, and every point on this line corresponds to an ordered pair solution. Thus, we say that this line is the **graph of the equation** $x - 2y = 6$.

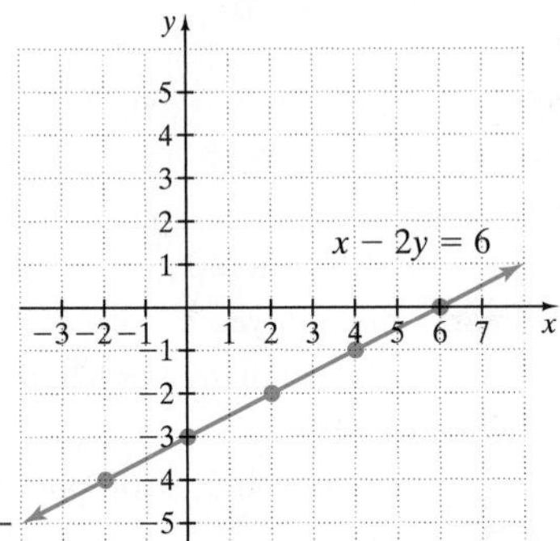

Helpful Hint

Notice that we can only show a part of a line on a graph. The arrowheads on each end of the line remind us that the line actually extends indefinitely in both directions.

The equation $x - 2y = 6$ is called a **linear equation in two variables** and **the graph of every linear equation in two variables is a line.**

Linear Equation in Two Variables

A linear equation in two variables is an equation that can be written in the form

$$Ax + By = C$$

where A, B, and C are real numbers and A and B are not both 0. **The graph of a linear equation in two variables is a straight line.**

The form $Ax + By = C$ is called **standard form.**

Helpful Hint

Notice in the form $Ax + By = C$, the understood exponent on both x and y is 1.

Examples of Linear Equations in Two Variables

$2x + y = 8$ (Standard Form) $\quad -2x = 7y \quad y = \frac{1}{3}x + 2 \quad y = 7$

Before we graph linear equations in two variables, let's practice identifying these equations.

EXAMPLE 1 Determine whether each equation is a linear equation in two variables.

a. $x - 1.5y = -1.6$ **b.** $y = -2x$ **c.** $x + y^2 = 9$ **d.** $x = 5$

Solution

a. This is a linear equation in two variables because it is written in the form $Ax + By = C$ with $A = 1$, $B = -1.5$, and $C = -1.6$.

b. This is a linear equation in two variables because it can be written in the form $Ax + By = C$.

$$y = -2x$$
$$2x + y = 0 \quad \text{Add } 2x \text{ to both sides.}$$

c. This is *not* a linear equation in two variables because y is squared.

d. This is a linear equation in two variables because it can be written in the form $Ax + By = C$.

$$x = 5$$
$$x + 0y = 5 \quad \text{Add } 0 \cdot y.$$

□

PRACTICE

1 Determine whether each equation is a linear equation in two variables.

a. $3x + 2.7y = -5.3$ **b.** $x^2 + y = 8$ **c.** $y = 12$ **d.** $5x = -3y$

OBJECTIVE

2 Graphing Linear Equations by Plotting Ordered Pair Solutions 

From geometry, we know that a straight line is determined by just two points. Graphing a linear equation in two variables, then, requires that we find just two of its infinitely many solutions. Once we do so, we plot the solution points and draw the line connecting the points. Usually, we find a third solution as well, as a check.

EXAMPLE 2 Graph the linear equation $2x + y = 5$.

Solution Find three ordered pair solutions of $2x + y = 5$. To do this, choose a value for one variable, x or y, and solve for the other variable. For example, let $x = 1$. Then $2x + y = 5$ becomes

$$2x + y = 5$$
$$2(1) + y = 5 \quad \text{Replace } x \text{ with 1.}$$
$$2 + y = 5 \quad \text{Multiply.}$$
$$y = 3 \quad \text{Subtract 2 from both sides.}$$

Since $y = 3$ when $x = 1$, the ordered pair $(1, 3)$ is a solution of $2x + y = 5$. Next, let $x = 0$.

$$2x + y = 5$$
$$2(0) + y = 5 \quad \text{Replace } x \text{ with 0.}$$
$$0 + y = 5$$
$$y = 5$$

The ordered pair $(0, 5)$ is a second solution.

The two solutions found so far allow us to draw the straight line that is the graph of all solutions of $2x + y = 5$. However, we find a third ordered pair as a check. Let $y = -1$.

$$
\begin{aligned}
2x + y &= 5 \\
2x + (-1) &= 5 \quad \text{Replace } y \text{ with } -1. \\
2x - 1 &= 5 \\
2x &= 6 \quad \text{Add 1 to both sides.} \\
x &= 3 \quad \text{Divide both sides by 2.}
\end{aligned}
$$

The third solution is $(3, -1)$. These three ordered pair solutions are listed in table form as shown. The graph of $2x + y = 5$ is the line through the three points.

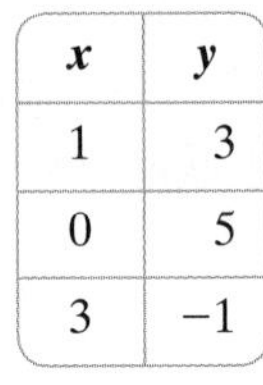

x	y
1	3
0	5
3	−1

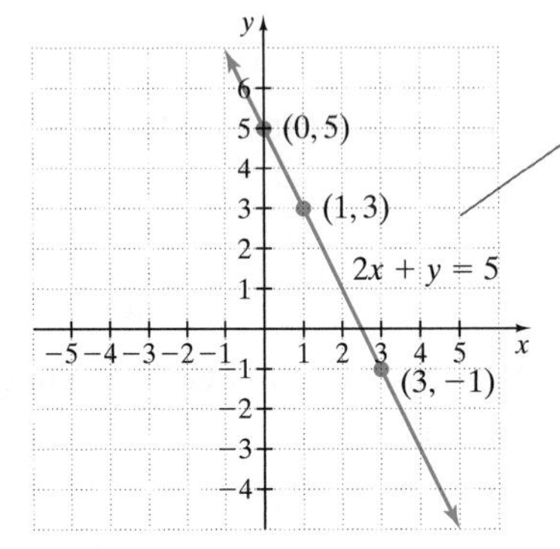

Helpful Hint

All three points should fall on the same straight line. If not, check your ordered pair solutions for a mistake.

PRACTICE **2** Graph the linear equation $x + 3y = 9$.

EXAMPLE 3 Graph the linear equation $-5x + 3y = 15$.

Solution Find three ordered pair solutions of $-5x + 3y = 15$.

Let $x = 0$.

$$
\begin{aligned}
-5x + 3y &= 15 \\
-5 \cdot 0 + 3y &= 15 \\
0 + 3y &= 15 \\
3y &= 15 \\
y &= 5
\end{aligned}
$$

Let $y = 0$.

$$
\begin{aligned}
-5x + 3y &= 15 \\
-5x + 3 \cdot 0 &= 15 \\
-5x + 0 &= 15 \\
-5x &= 15 \\
x &= -3
\end{aligned}
$$

Let $x = -2$.

$$
\begin{aligned}
-5x + 3y &= 15 \\
-5(-2) + 3y &= 15 \\
10 + 3y &= 15 \\
3y &= 5 \\
y &= \frac{5}{3}
\end{aligned}
$$

The ordered pairs are $(0, 5)$, $(-3, 0)$, and $\left(-2, \frac{5}{3}\right)$. The graph of $-5x + 3y = 15$ is the line through the three points.

x	y
0	5
−3	0
−2	$\frac{5}{3} = 1\frac{2}{3}$

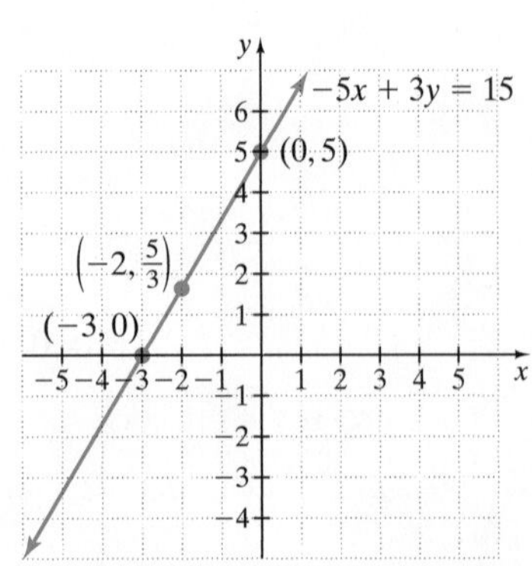

PRACTICE **3** Graph the linear equation $3x - 4y = 12$.

EXAMPLE 4 Graph the linear equation $y = 3x$.

Solution To graph this linear equation, we find three ordered pair solutions. Since this equation is solved for y, choose three x values.

If $x = 2$, $y = 3 \cdot 2 = 6$.
If $x = 0$, $y = 3 \cdot 0 = 0$.
If $x = -1$, $y = 3 \cdot -1 = -3$.

x	y
2	6
0	0
−1	−3

Next, graph the ordered pair solutions listed in the table above and draw a line through the plotted points as shown below. The line is the graph of $y = 3x$. Every point on the graph represents an ordered pair solution of the equation and every ordered pair solution is a point on this line.

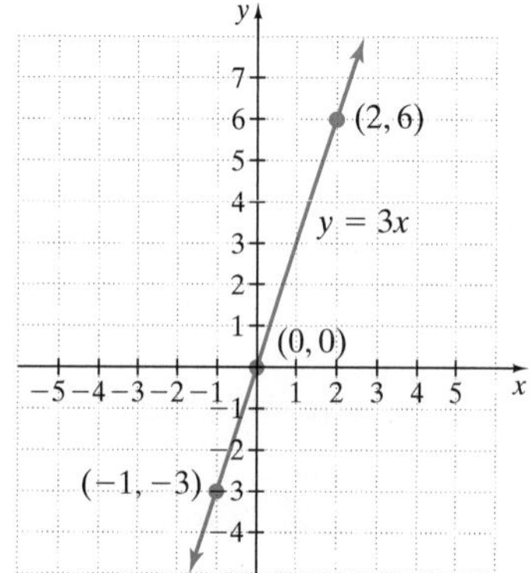

□

PRACTICE
4 Graph the linear equation $y = -2x$.

> **Helpful Hint**
> When graphing a linear equation in two variables, if it is
> - solved for y, it may be easier to find ordered pair solutions by choosing x-values. If it is
> - solved for x, it may be easier to find ordered pair solutions by choosing y-values.

EXAMPLE 5 Graph the linear equation $y = -\frac{1}{3}x + 2$.

Solution Find three ordered pair solutions, graph the solutions, and draw a line through the plotted solutions. To avoid fractions, choose x values that are multiples of 3 to substitute in the equation. When a multiple of 3 is multiplied by $-\frac{1}{3}$, the result is an integer. See the calculations shown above the table.

If $x = 6$, then $y = -\frac{1}{3} \cdot 6 + 2 = -2 + 2 = 0$

If $x = 0$, then $y = -\frac{1}{3} \cdot 0 + 2 = 0 + 2 = 2$

If $x = -3$, then $y = -\frac{1}{3} \cdot -3 + 2 = 1 + 2 = 3$

x	y
6	0
0	2
−3	3

□

PRACTICE
5 Graph the linear equation $y = \frac{1}{2}x + 3$.

Let's compare the graphs in Examples 4 and 5. The graph of $y = 3x$ tilts upward (as we follow the line from left to right) and the graph of $y = -\frac{1}{3}x + 2$ tilts downward (as we follow the line from left to right). We will learn more about the tilt, or slope, of a line in Section 1.4.

EXAMPLE 6 Graph the linear equation $y = -2$.

Solution: The equation $y = -2$ can be written in standard form as $0x + y = -2$. No matter what value we replace x with, y is always -2.

x	y
0	−2
3	−2
−2	−2

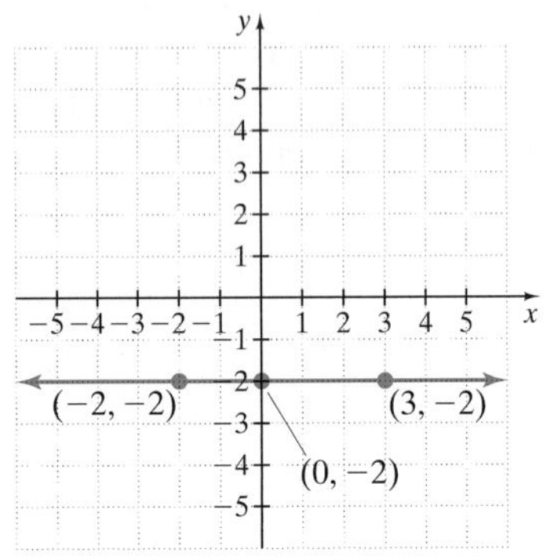

Notice that the graph of $y = -2$ is a horizontal line. □

PRACTICE 6 Graph the linear equation $x = -2$.

EXAMPLE 7 Graph the linear equation $y = 3x + 6$ and compare this graph with the graph of $y = 3x$ in Example 4.

Solution Find ordered pair solutions, graph the solutions, and draw a line through the plotted solutions. We choose x values and substitute in the equation $y = 3x + 6$.

If $x = -3$, then $y = 3(-3) + 6 = -3$.
If $x = 0$, then $y = 3(0) + 6 = 6$.
If $x = 1$, then $y = 3(1) + 6 = 9$.

x	y
−3	−3
0	6
1	9

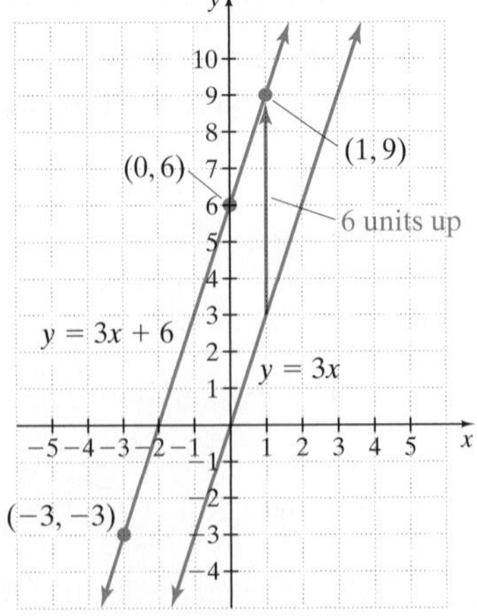

The most startling similarity is that both graphs appear to have the same upward tilt as we move from left to right. Also, the graph of $y = 3x$ crosses the y-axis at the origin, while the graph of $y = 3x + 6$ crosses the y-axis at 6. In fact, the graph of $y = 3x + 6$ is the same as the graph of $y = 3x$ moved vertically upward 6 units. □

PRACTICE

7 Graph the linear equation $y = -2x + 3$ and compare this graph with the graph of $y = -2x$ in Practice 4.

Notice that the graph of $y = 3x + 6$ crosses the y-axis at 6. This happens because when $x = 0$, $y = 3x + 6$ becomes $y = 3 \cdot 0 + 6 = 6$. The graph contains the point $(0, 6)$, which is on the y-axis.

In general, if a linear equation in two variables is solved for y, we say that it is written in the form $y = mx + b$. The graph of this equation contains the point $(0, b)$ because when $x = 0$, $y = mx + b$ is $y = m \cdot 0 + b = b$.

The graph of $y = mx + b$ crosses the y-axis at $(0, b)$.

We will review this again in Section 1.5.

Linear equations are often used to model real data as seen in the next example.

EXAMPLE 8 **Estimating the Number of Registered Nurses**

The occupation expected to have the most employment growth in the next few years is registered nurse. The number of people y (in thousands) employed as registered nurses in the United States can be estimated by the linear equation $y = 58.1x + 2619$, where x is the number of years after the year 2008. (Data from U.S. Bureau of Labor Statistics)

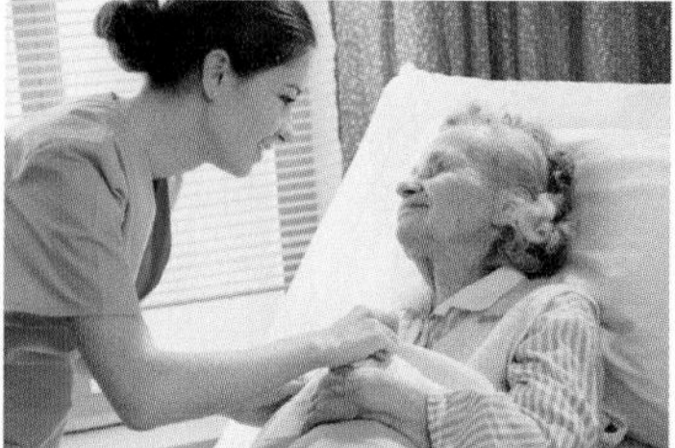

a. Graph the equation.

b. Use the graph to predict the number of registered nurses in the year 2018.

Solution:

a. To graph $y = 58.1x + 2619$, choose x-values and substitute in the equation.

If $x = 0$, then $y = 58.1(0) + 2619 = 2619$.
If $x = 2$, then $y = 58.1(2) + 2619 = 2735.2$.
If $x = 5$, then $y = 58.1(5) + 2619 = 2909.5$.

x	y
0	2619
2	2735.2
5	2909.5

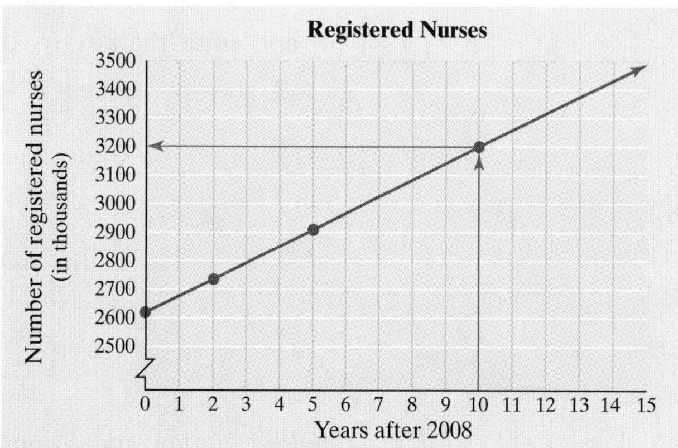

b. To use the graph to *predict* the number of registered nurses in the year 2018, we need to find the y-coordinate that corresponds to $x = 10$. (10 years after 2008 is the year 2018.) To do so, find 10 on the x-axis. Move vertically upward to the graphed line and then horizontally to the left. We approximate the number on the y-axis to be 3200. Thus, in the year 2018, we predict that there will be 3200 thousand registered nurses. (The actual value, using 10 for x, is 3200.) □

PRACTICE

8 One of the occupations expected to have a large growth in employment in the next few years is computer software application engineers. The number of people y (in thousands) employed as computer software application engineers in the United States can be estimated by the linear equation $y = 17.5x + 515$, where x is the number of years after 2008. (*Source:* Based on data from the Bureau of Labor Statistics)

a. Graph the equation.

b. Use the graph to predict the number of computer software application engineers in the year 2020.

Helpful Hint

Make sure you understand that models are mathematical approximations of the data for the known years. (For example, see the model in Example 8.) Any number of unknown factors can affect future years, so be cautious when using models to predict.

Graphing Calculator Explorations

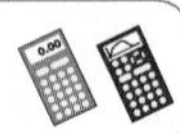

In this section, we begin an optional study of graphing calculators and graphing software packages for computers. These graphers use the same point plotting technique that was introduced in this section. The advantage of this graphing technology is, of course, that graphing calculators and computers can find and plot ordered pair solutions much faster than we can. Note, however, that the features described in these boxes may not be available on all graphing calculators.

The rectangular screen where a portion of the rectangular coordinate system is displayed is called a **window.** We call it a **standard window** for graphing when both the x- and y-axes show coordinates between -10 and 10. This information is often displayed in the window menu on a graphing calculator as

Xmin = −10
Xmax = 10
Xscl = 1 The scale on the x-axis is one unit per tick mark.
Ymin = −10
Ymax = 10
Yscl = 1 The scale on the y-axis is one unit per tick mark.

To use a graphing calculator to graph the equation $y = 2x + 3$, press the [Y=] key and enter the keystrokes [2] [x] [+] [3]. The top row should now read $Y_1 = 2x + 3$. Next press the [GRAPH] key, and the display should look like this:

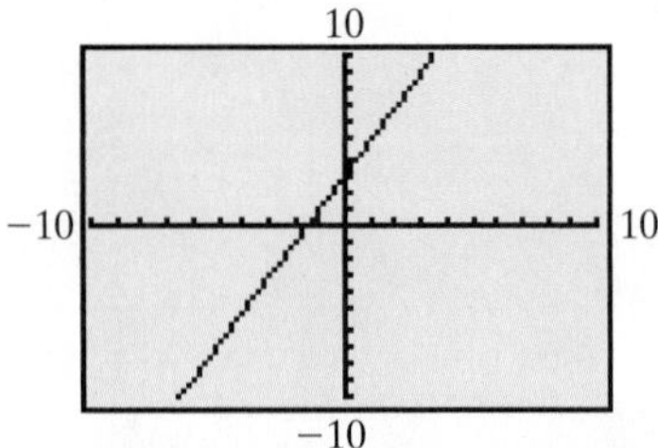

Use a standard window and graph the following linear equations. (Unless otherwise stated, use a standard window when graphing.) See graphing answer section.

1. $y = -3x + 7$

2. $y = -x + 5$

3. $y = 2.5x - 7.9$

4. $y = -1.3x + 5.2$

5. $y = -\frac{3}{10}x + \frac{32}{5}$

6. $y = \frac{2}{9}x - \frac{22}{3}$

Vocabulary, Readiness & Video Check

Martin-Gay Interactive Videos

See Video 1.2

Watch the section lecture video and answer the following questions.

OBJECTIVE 1

1. Exponents aren't mentioned in the definition of a linear equation in two variables. However, in determining whether Example 3 is a linear equation in two variables, the exponents or powers on the variables are discussed. Explain.

OBJECTIVE 2

2. In the lecture before Example 5, it's mentioned that you need only two points to determine a line. Why then are three ordered pair solutions found in Examples 5–7?

OBJECTIVE 2

3. What does a graphed line represent as discussed at the end of Examples 5 and 7?

1.2 Exercise Set

MyMathLab®

Determine whether each equation is a linear equation in two variables. See Example 1.

1. $-x = 3y + 10$
2. $y = x - 15$
3. $x = y$
4. $x = y^3$
5. $x^2 + 2y = 0$
6. $0.01x - 0.2y = 8.8$
7. $y = -1$
8. $x = 25$

For each equation, find three ordered pair solutions by completing the table. Then use the ordered pairs to graph the equation. See Examples 2 through 7.

9. $x - y = 6$

x	y
	0
4	
	−1

10. $x - y = 4$

x	y
0	
	2
−1	

11. $y = -4x$

x	y
1	
0	
−1	

12. $y = -5x$

x	y
1	
0	
−1	

13. $y = \frac{1}{3}x$

x	y
0	
6	
−3	

14. $y = \frac{1}{2}x$

x	y
0	
−4	
2	

15. $y = -4x + 3$

x	y
0	
1	
2	

16. $y = -5x + 2$

x	y
0	
1	
2	

MIXED PRACTICE

Graph each linear equation. See Examples 2 through 7.

17. $x + y = 1$
18. $x + y = 7$
19. $x - y = -2$
20. $-x + y = 6$
21. $x - 2y = 6$
22. $-x + 5y = 5$
23. $y = 6x + 3$
24. $y = -2x + 7$
25. $x = -4$
26. $y = 5$
27. $y = 3$
28. $x = -1$
29. $y = x$
30. $y = -x$
31. $x = -3y$
32. $x = -5y$
33. $x + 3y = 9$
34. $2x + y = 2$
35. $y = \frac{1}{2}x + 2$
36. $y = \frac{1}{4}x + 3$
37. $3x - 2y = 12$
38. $2x - 7y = 14$
39. $y = -3.5x + 4$
40. $y = -1.5x - 3$

Graph each pair of linear equations on the same set of axes. Discuss how the graphs are similar and how they are different. See Example 7.

41. $y = 5x; y = 5x + 4$
42. $y = 2x; y = 2x + 5$
43. $y = -2x; y = -2x - 3$
44. $y = x; y = x - 7$
45. $y = \frac{1}{2}x; y = \frac{1}{2}x + 2$
46. $y = -\frac{1}{4}x; y = -\frac{1}{4}x + 3$

The graph of $y = 5x$ is given below as well as Figures a–d. For Exercises 47 through 50, match each equation with its graph. Hint: Recall that if an equation is written in the form $y = mx + b$, its graph crosses the y-axis at $(0, b)$.

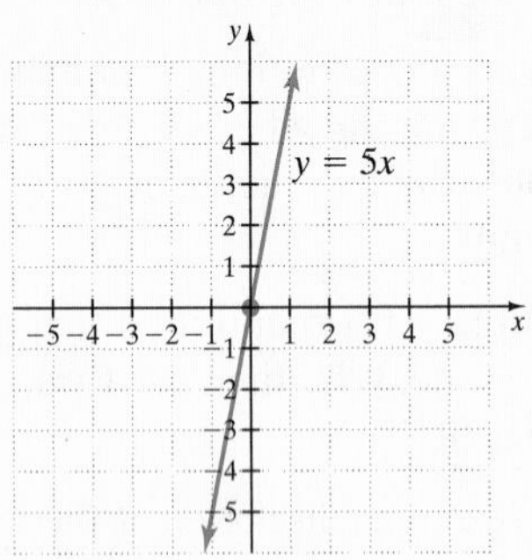

47. $y = 5x + 5$

48. $y = 5x - 4$

49. $y = 5x - 1$

50. $y = 5x + 2$

a.

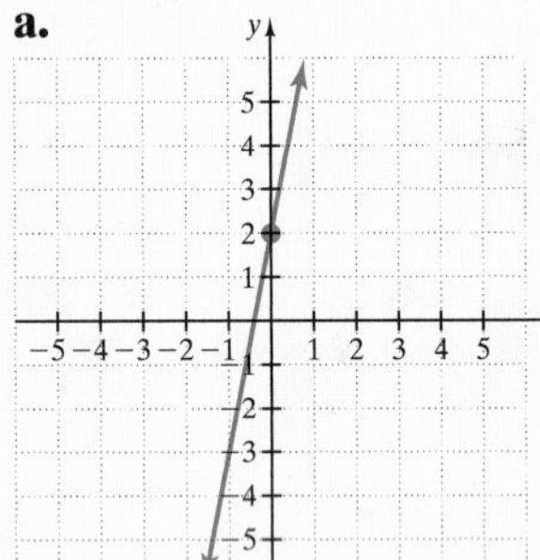

b.

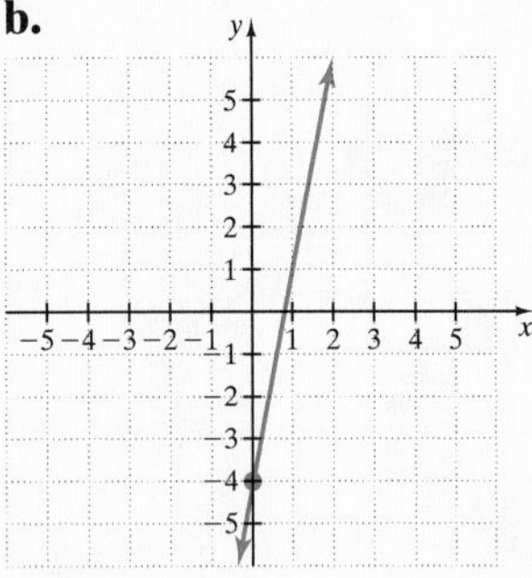

c.

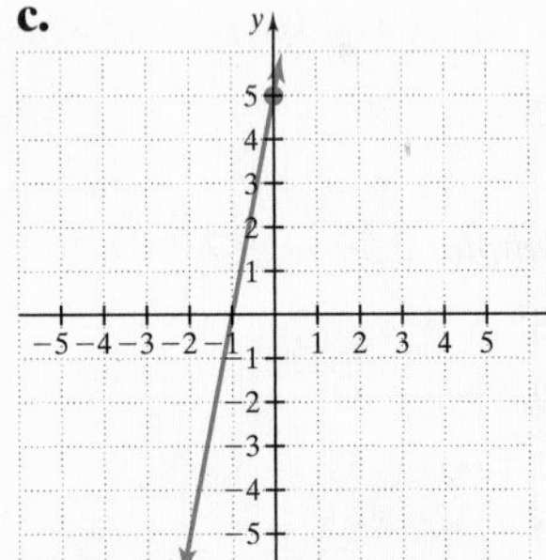

d.

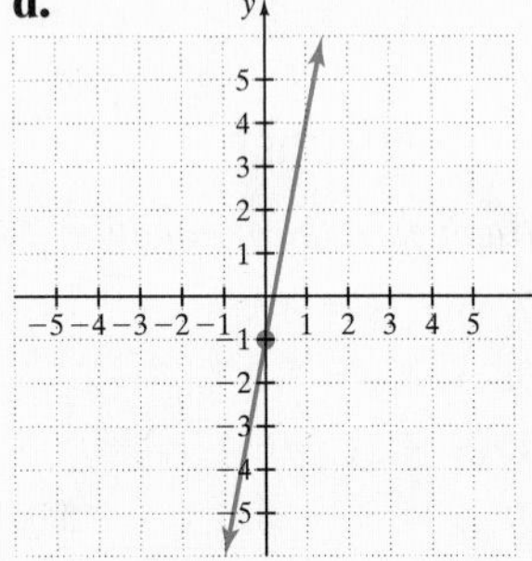

Solve. See Example 8.

51. Jogging is one of the few sports that has been consistently increasing over the past few years. The number of people jogging (in millions) from the years 2000 to 2009 is given by the equation $y = x + 23$, where x is the number of years after 2000. (*Source:* Based on data from the National Sporting Goods Association)

a. Use this equation or a graph of it to complete the ordered pair (8,).

b. Write a sentence explaining the meaning of the answer to part (a).

c. If this trend continues, how many joggers will there be in 2017?

52. The revenue y (in billions of dollars) for Home Depot stores during the years 2006 through 2010 is given by the equation $y = -3x + 79$, where x is the number of years after 2006. (*Source:* Based on data from Home Depot stores)

a. Use this equation or a graph of it to complete the ordered pair (4,).

b. Write a sentence explaining the meaning of the answer to part (a).

c. If this trend continues, predict the revenue for Home Depot stores for the year 2015.

53. One American rite of passage is a driver's license. The number of people y (in millions) who have a driver's license can be estimated by the linear equation $y = 2.2x + 190$, where x is the number of years after 2000. (Data from Federal Highway Administration)

a. Use this equation to complete the ordered pair (8,).

b. Write a sentence explaining the meaning of the ordered pair in part (a).

c. If this trend continues, predict the number of people with driver's licenses in 2016.

54. The percent of U.S. households y with at least one computer can be approximated by the linear equation $y = 4.3x + 51$, where x is the number of years since 2000. (Data from *Statistical Abstract of the United States*)

a. Use the equation to complete the ordered pair (9,).

b. Write a sentence explaining the meaning of the ordered pair found in part (a).

c. If this trend continues, predict the percent of U.S. households that have at least one computer in 2012.

d. Explain any issues with your answer to part (c).

REVIEW AND PREVIEW

△ **55.** The coordinates of three vertices of a rectangle are $(-2, 5)$, $(4, 5)$, and $(-2, -1)$. Find the coordinates of the fourth vertex. See Section 1.1.

△ **56.** The coordinates of two vertices of a square are $(-3, -1)$ and $(2, -1)$. Find the coordinates of two pairs of points possible for the third and fourth vertices. See Section 1.1.

Complete each table. See Section 1.1.

57. $x - y = -3$

x	y
0	
	0

58. $y - x = 5$

x	y
0	
	0

59. $y = 2x$

x	y
0	
	0

60. $x = -3y$

x	y
0	
	0

CONCEPT EXTENSIONS

Write each statement as an equation in two variables. Then graph the equation.

61. The y-value is 5 more than the x-value.

62. The y-value is twice the x-value.

63. Two times the x-value, added to three times the y-value, is 6.

64. Five times the x-value, added to twice the y-value, is -10.

△ **65.** The perimeter of the trapezoid below is 22 centimeters. Write a linear equation in two variables for the perimeter. Find y if x is 3 cm.

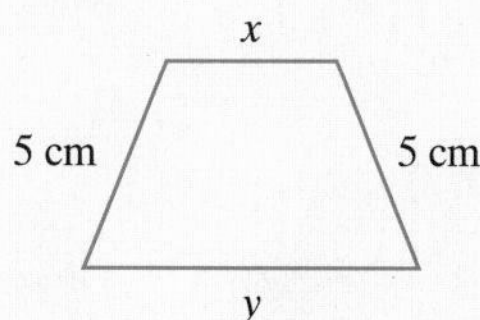

△ **66.** The perimeter of the rectangle below is 50 miles. Write a linear equation in two variables for this perimeter. Use this equation to find x when y is 20.

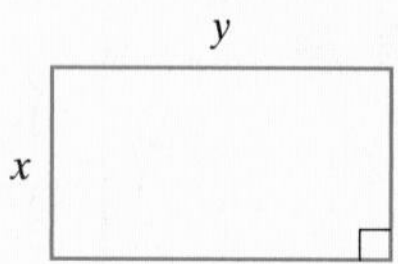

67. Explain how to find ordered pair solutions of linear equations in two variables.

68. If (a, b) is an ordered pair solution of $x + y = 5$, is (b, a) also a solution? Explain why or why not.

69. Graph the nonlinear equation $y = x^2$ by completing the table shown. Plot the ordered pairs and connect them with a smooth curve.

x	y
0	
1	
−1	
2	
−2	

70. Graph the nonlinear equation $y = |x|$ by completing the table shown. Plot the ordered pairs and connect them. This curve is "V" shaped.

$y = |x|$

x	y
0	
1	
−1	
2	
−2	

1.3 Intercepts 

OBJECTIVES

1 Identify Intercepts of a Graph.

2 Graph a Linear Equation by Finding and Plotting Intercepts.

3 Identify and Graph Vertical and Horizontal Lines.

OBJECTIVE

1 Identifying Intercepts 

In this section, we graph linear equations in two variables by identifying intercepts. For example, the graph of $y = 4x - 8$ is shown on the right. Notice that this graph crosses the y-axis at the point $(0, -8)$. This point is called the ***y*-intercept.** Likewise, the graph crosses the x-axis at (2, 0), and this point is called the ***x*-intercept.**

The intercepts are $(2, 0)$ and $(0, -8)$.

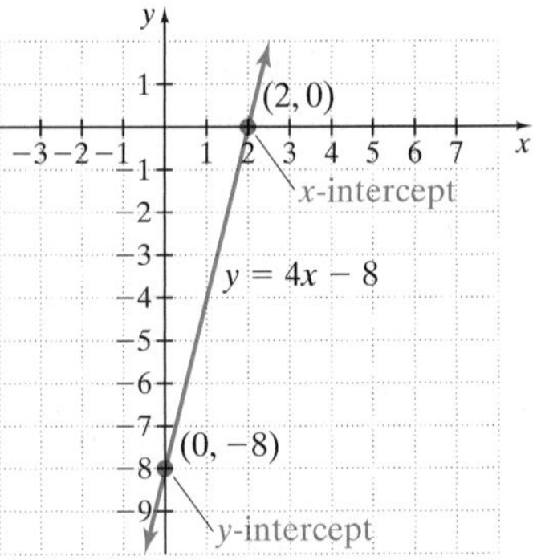

Helpful Hint

If a graph crosses the x-axis at $(-3, 0)$ and the y-axis at $(0, 7)$, then

$(-3, 0)$ x-intercept $(0, 7)$ y-intercept

Notice that for the y-intercept, the x-value is 0 and for the x-intercept, the y-value is 0.
Note: Sometimes in mathematics, you may see just the number 7 stated as the y-intercept, and -3 stated as the x-intercept.

EXAMPLES Identify the x- and y-intercepts.

1.

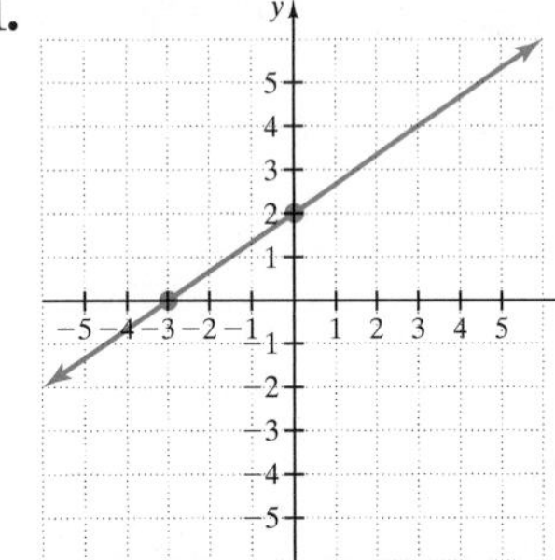

Solution

x-intercept: $(-3, 0)$
y-intercept: $(0, 2)$

2.

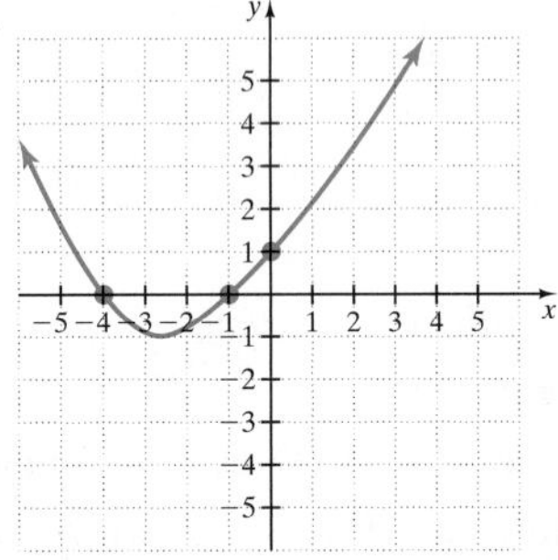

Solution

x-intercepts: $(-4, 0)$, $(-1, 0)$
y-intercept: $(0, 1)$

Helpful Hint

Notice that any time (0, 0) is a point of a graph, then it is an x-intercept and a y-intercept. Why? It is the only point that lies on both axes.

3.

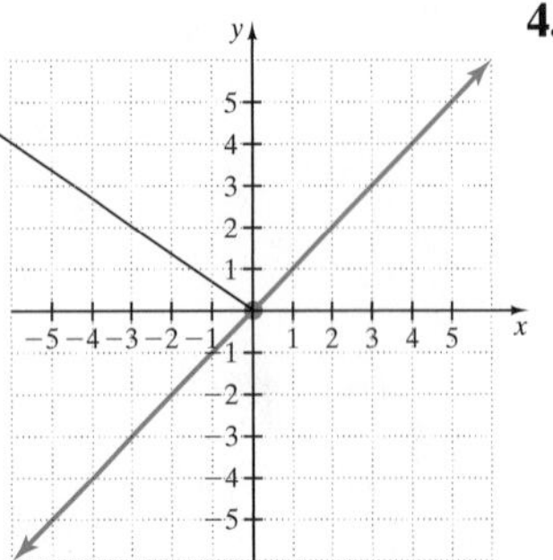

Solution

x-intercept: $(0, 0)$
y-intercept: $(0, 0)$

4.

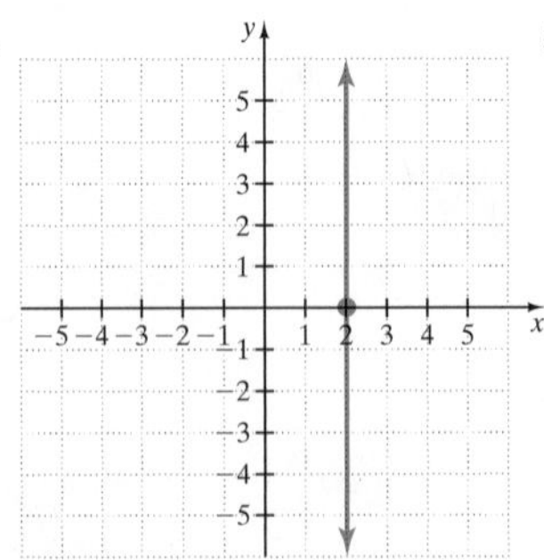

Solution

x-intercept: $(2, 0)$
y-intercept: none

5.

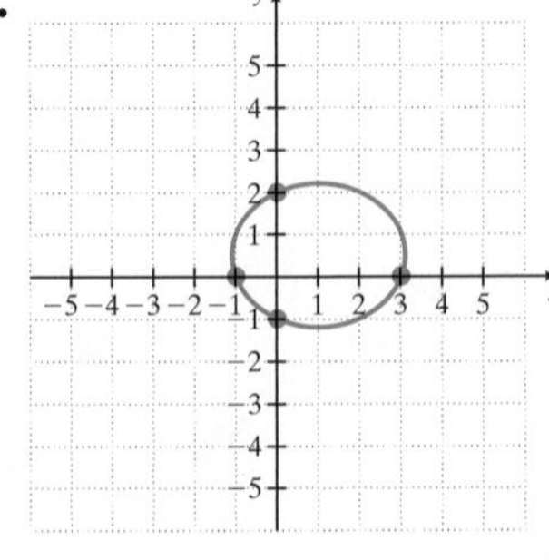

Solution

x-intercepts: $(-1, 0)$, $(3, 0)$
y-intercepts: $(0, 2)$, $(0, -1)$ □

PRACTICE
1–5 Identify the x- and y-intercepts.

1.

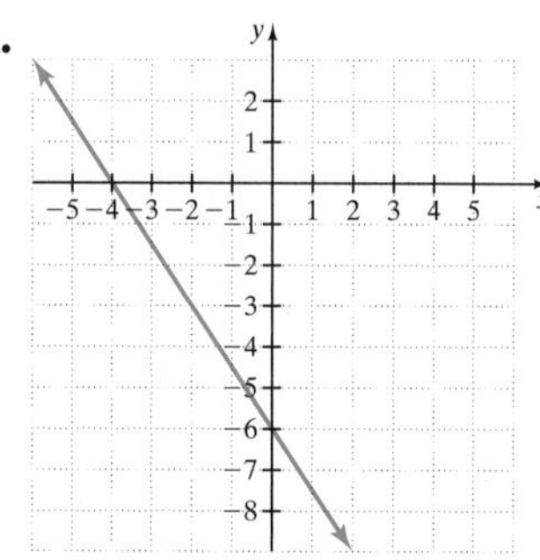

2.

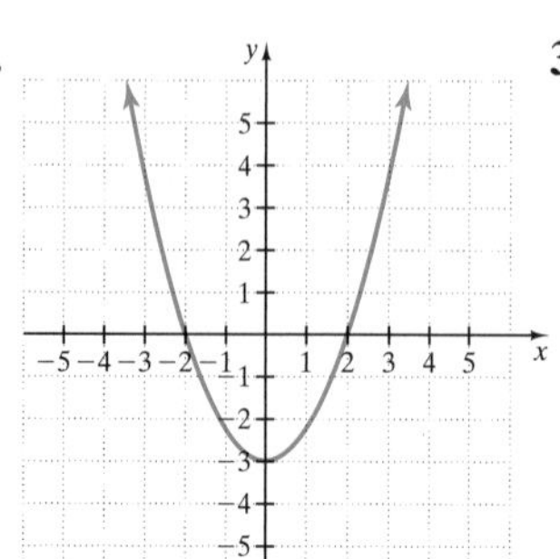

3.

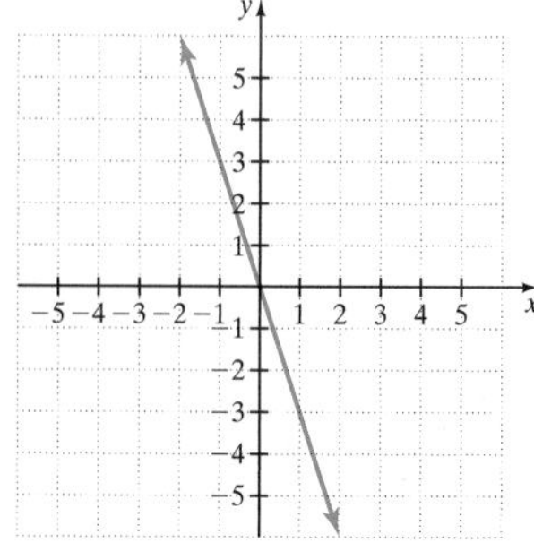

4.

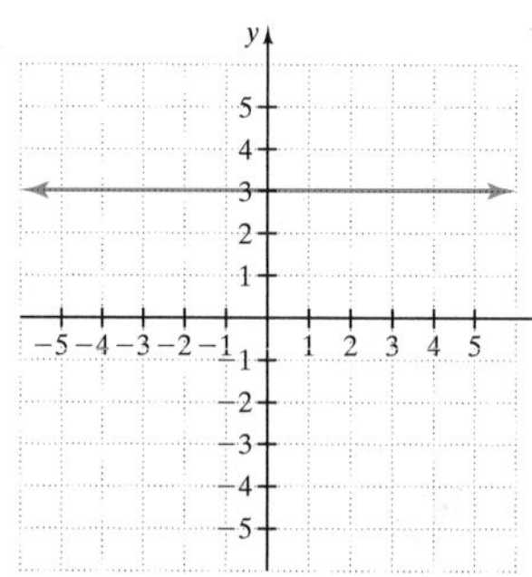

5.

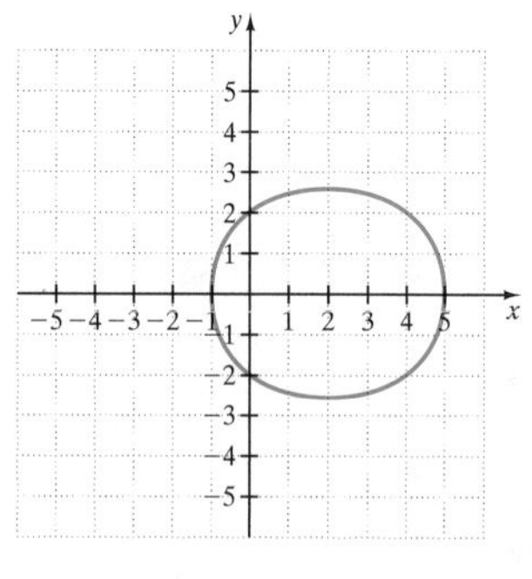

OBJECTIVE
2 Using Intercepts to Graph a Linear Equation 

Given the equation of a line, intercepts are usually easy to find since one coordinate is 0.

One way to find the y-intercept of a line, given its equation, is to let $x = 0$, since a point on the y-axis has an x-coordinate of 0. To find the x-intercept of a line, let $y = 0$, since a point on the x-axis has a y-coordinate of 0.

Finding x- and y-intercepts

To find the x-intercept, let $y = 0$ and solve for x.
To find the y-intercept, let $x = 0$ and solve for y.

EXAMPLE 6 Graph $x - 3y = 6$ by finding and plotting intercepts.

Solution Let $y = 0$ to find the x-intercept and let $x = 0$ to find the y-intercept.

$$\begin{aligned} \text{Let } y &= 0 \\ x - 3y &= 6 \\ x - 3(0) &= 6 \\ x - 0 &= 6 \\ x &= 6 \end{aligned} \qquad\qquad \begin{aligned} \text{Let } x &= 0 \\ x - 3y &= 6 \\ 0 - 3y &= 6 \\ -3y &= 6 \\ y &= -2 \end{aligned}$$

The x-intercept is $(6, 0)$ and the y-intercept is $(0, -2)$. We find a third ordered pair solution to check our work. If we let $y = -1$, then $x = 3$. Plot the points $(6, 0)$, $(0, -2)$, and $(3, -1)$. The graph of $x - 3y = 6$ is the line drawn through these points, as shown on page 104.

x	y
6	0
0	−2
3	−1

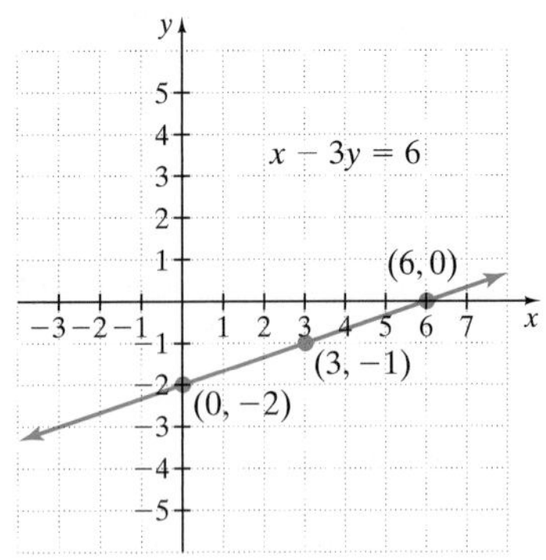

PRACTICE 6 Graph $x + 2y = -4$ by finding and plotting intercepts.

EXAMPLE 7 Graph $x = -2y$ by plotting intercepts.

Solution Let $y = 0$ to find the x-intercept and $x = 0$ to find the y-intercept.

Let $y = 0$	Let $x = 0$
$x = -2y$	$x = -2y$
$x = -2(0)$	$0 = -2y$
$x = 0$	$0 = y$

Both the x-intercept and y-intercept are $(0, 0)$. In other words, when $x = 0$, then $y = 0$, which gives the ordered pair $(0, 0)$. Also, when $y = 0$, then $x = 0$, which gives the same ordered pair $(0, 0)$. This happens when the graph passes through the origin. Since two points are needed to determine a line, we must find at least one more ordered pair that satisfies $x = -2y$. We will let $y = -1$ to find a second ordered pair solution and let $y = 1$ as a checkpoint.

Let $y = -1$	Let $y = 1$
$x = -2(-1)$	$x = -2(1)$
$x = 2$	$x = -2$

The ordered pairs are $(0, 0)$, $(2, -1)$, and $(-2, 1)$. Plot these points to graph $x = -2y$.

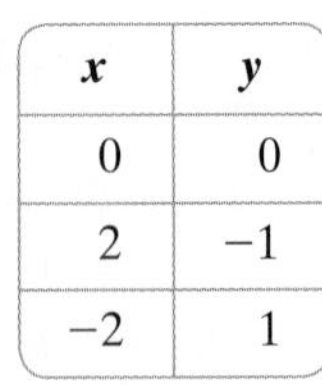

x	y
0	0
2	−1
−2	1

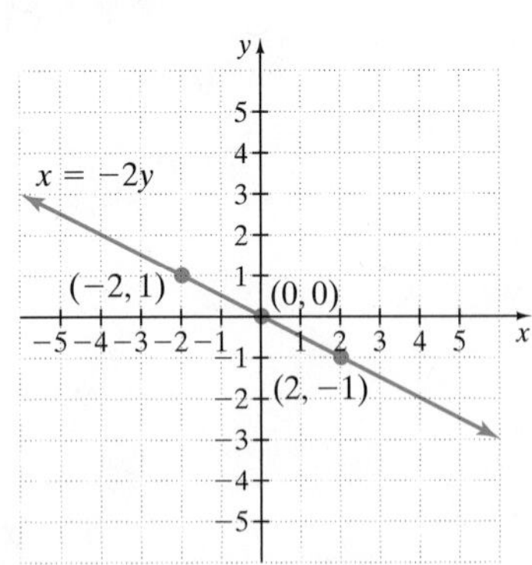

PRACTICE 7 Graph $x = 3y$ by plotting intercepts.

EXAMPLE 8 Graph $4x = 3y - 9$.

Solution Find the x- and y-intercepts, and then choose $x = 2$ to find a checkpoint.

Let $y = 0$	Let $x = 0$	Let $x = 2$
$4x = 3(0) - 9$	$4 \cdot 0 = 3y - 9$	$4(2) = 3y - 9$
$4x = -9$	$9 = 3y$	$8 = 3y - 9$
Solve for x.	Solve for y.	Solve for y.
$x = -\frac{9}{4}$ or $-2\frac{1}{4}$	$3 = y$	$17 = 3y$
		$\frac{17}{3} = y$ or $y = 5\frac{2}{3}$

The ordered pairs are $\left(-2\frac{1}{4}, 0\right)$, $(0, 3)$, and $\left(2, 5\frac{2}{3}\right)$. The equation $4x = 3y - 9$ is graphed as follows.

x	y
$-2\frac{1}{4}$	0
0	3
2	$5\frac{2}{3}$

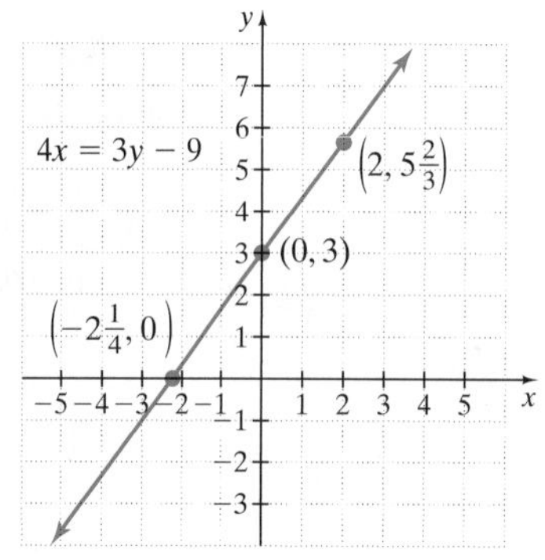

□

PRACTICE 8 Graph $3x = 2y + 4$.

OBJECTIVE

3 Graphing Vertical and Horizontal Lines

The equation $x = c$, where c is a real number constant, is a linear equation in two variables because it can be written in the form $x + 0y = c$. The graph of this equation is a vertical line as shown in the next example.

EXAMPLE 9 Graph $x = 2$.

Solution The equation $x = 2$ can be written as $x + 0y = 2$. For any y-value chosen, notice that x is 2. No other value for x satisfies $x + 0y = 2$. Any ordered pair whose x-coordinate is 2 is a solution of $x + 0y = 2$. We will use the ordered pair solutions $(2, 3)$, $(2, 0)$, and $(2, -3)$ to graph $x = 2$.

x	y
2	3
2	0
2	−3

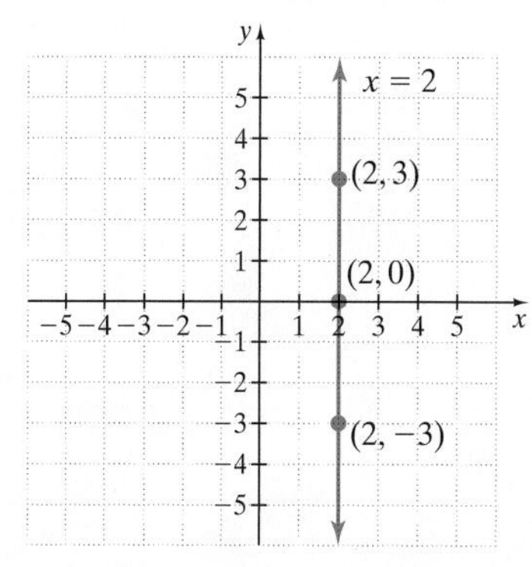

The graph is a vertical line with x-intercept $(2, 0)$. Note that this graph has no y-intercept because x is never 0. □

PRACTICE
9 Graph $x = -2$.

Vertical Lines

The graph of $x = c$, where c is a real number, is a vertical line with x-intercept $(c, 0)$.

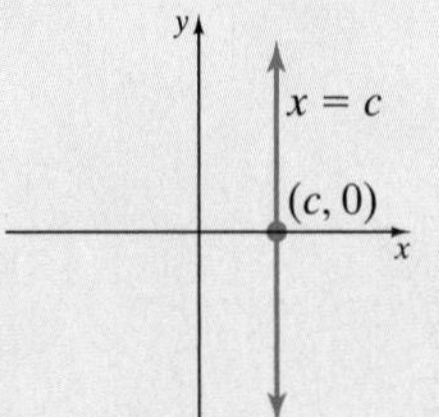

EXAMPLE 10 Graph $y = -3$.

Solution The equation $y = -3$ can be written as $0x + y = -3$. For any x-value chosen, y is -3. If we choose 4, 1, and -2 as x-values, the ordered pair solutions are $(4, -3)$, $(1, -3)$, and $(-2, -3)$. Use these ordered pairs to graph $y = -3$. The graph is a horizontal line with y-intercept $(0, -3)$ and no x-intercept.

x	y
4	-3
1	-3
-2	-3

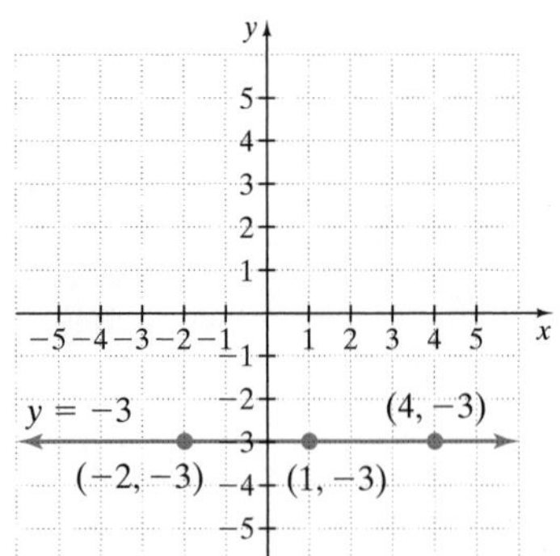

□

PRACTICE
10 Graph $y = 2$.

Horizontal Lines

The graph of $y = c$, where c is a real number, is a horizontal line with y-intercept $(0, c)$.

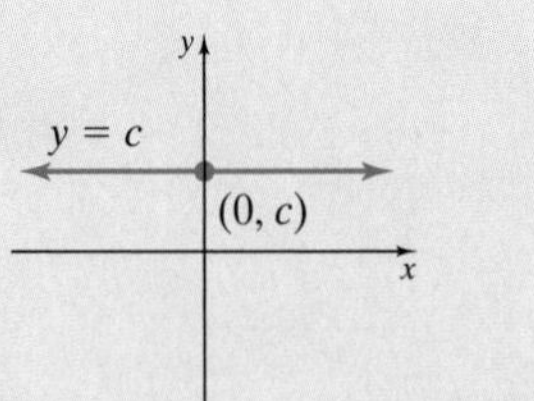

Graphing Calculator Explorations 

You may have noticed that to use the $\boxed{Y=}$ key on a grapher to graph an equation, the equation must be solved for y. For example, to graph $2x + 3y = 7$, we solve this equation for y.

$$
\begin{aligned}
2x + 3y &= 7 \\
3y &= -2x + 7 && \text{Subtract } 2x \text{ from both sides.} \\
\frac{3y}{3} &= -\frac{2x}{3} + \frac{7}{3} && \text{Divide both sides by 3.} \\
y &= -\frac{2}{3}x + \frac{7}{3} && \text{Simplify.}
\end{aligned}
$$

$2x + 3y = 7$ or $y = -\frac{2}{3}x + \frac{7}{3}$

10

−10 10

−10

To graph $2x + 3y = 7$ or $y = -\frac{2}{3}x + \frac{7}{3}$, press the $\boxed{Y=}$ key and enter

$$Y_1 = -\frac{2}{3}x + \frac{7}{3}$$

Graph each linear equation.

1. $x = 3.78y$ **2.** $-2.61y = x$ **3.** $3x + 7y = 21$

4. $-4x + 6y = 21$ **5.** $-2.2x + 6.8y = 15.5$ **6.** $5.9x - 0.8y = -10.4$

Vocabulary, Readiness & Video Check

Use the choices below to fill in each blank. Some choices may be used more than once. Exercises 1 and 2 come from Section 1.2.

x	vertical	x-intercept	linear
y	horizontal	y-intercept	standard

1. An equation that can be written in the form $Ax + By = C$ is called a(n) ________ equation in two variables.
2. The form $Ax + By = C$ is called ________ form.
3. The graph of the equation $y = -1$ is a ________ line.
4. The graph of the equation $x = 5$ is a ________ line.
5. A point where a graph crosses the y-axis is called a(n) ________.
6. A point where a graph crosses the x-axis is called a(n) ________.
7. Given an equation of a line, to find the x-intercept (if there is one), let ________ = 0 and solve for ________.
8. Given an equation of a line, to find the y-intercept (if there is one), let ________ = 0 and solve for ________.

Martin-Gay Interactive Videos

See Video 1.3

Watch the section lecture video and answer the following questions.

OBJECTIVE 1

9. At the end of Example 2, patterns are discussed. What reason is given for why x-intercepts have y-values of 0? For why y-intercepts have x-values of 0?

OBJECTIVE 2

10. In Example 3, the goal is to use the x- and y-intercepts to graph a line. Yet once the two intercepts are found, a third point is also found before the line is graphed. Why do think this practice of finding a third point is continued?

OBJECTIVE 3

11. From Examples 5 and 6, what can you say about the coefficient of x when the equation of a horizontal line is written as $Ax + By = C$? What about the coefficient of y when the equation of a vertical line is written as $Ax + By = C$?

1.3 Exercise Set

MyMathLab®

Identify the intercepts. See Examples 1 through 5.

1.

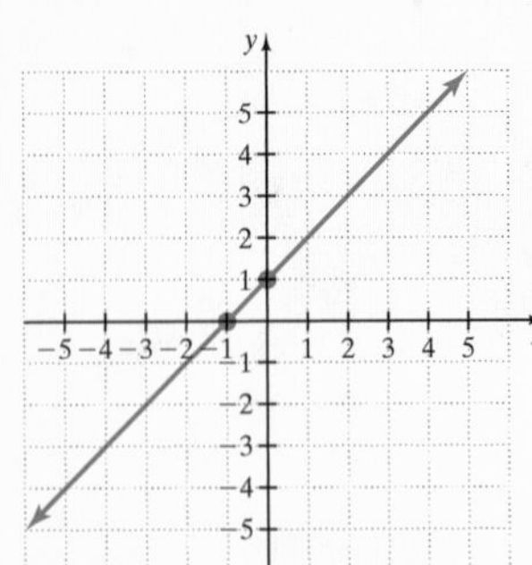

2.

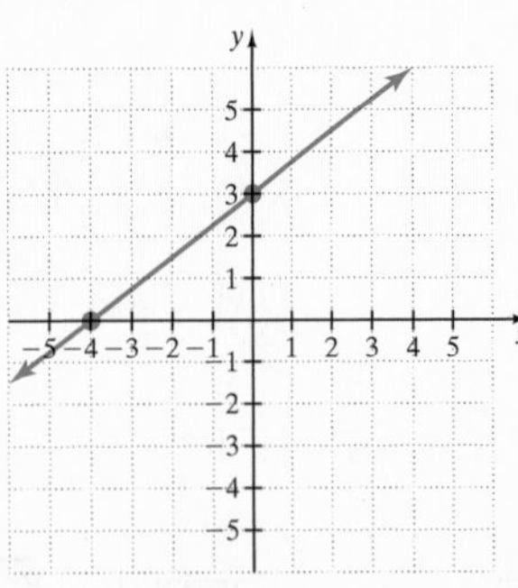

3.

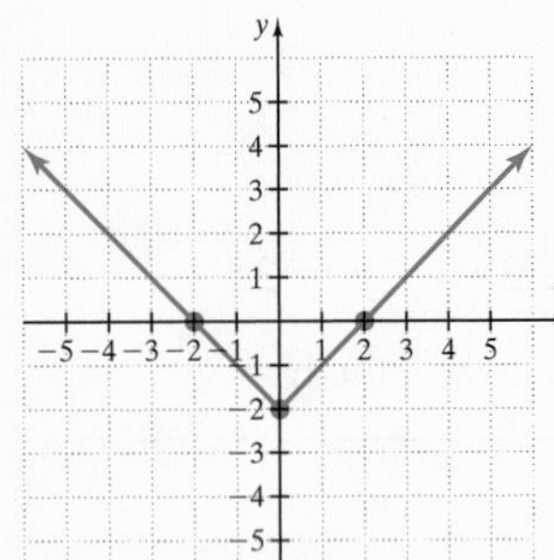

4.

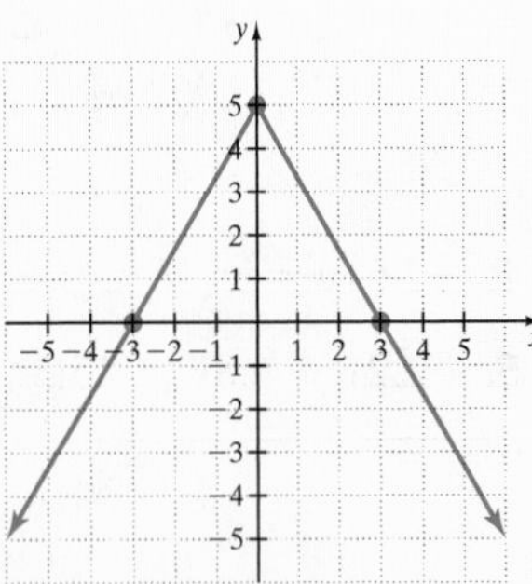

5.

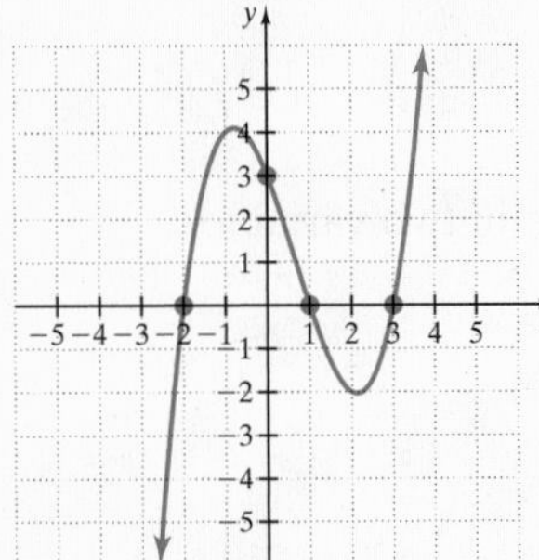

6.

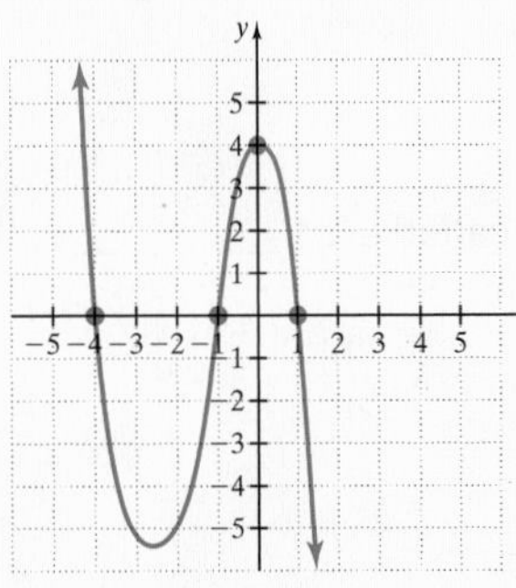

7.

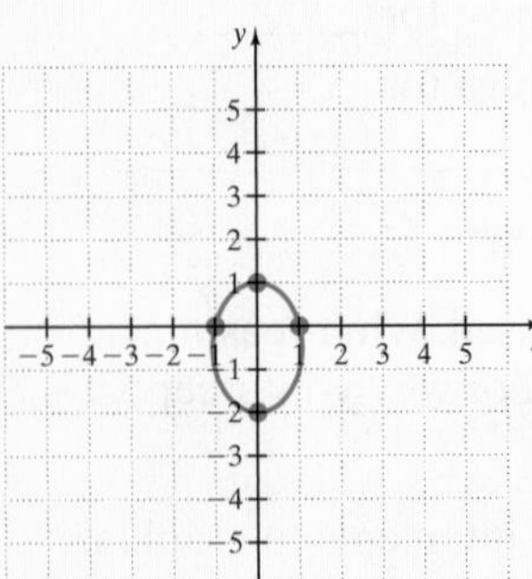

8.

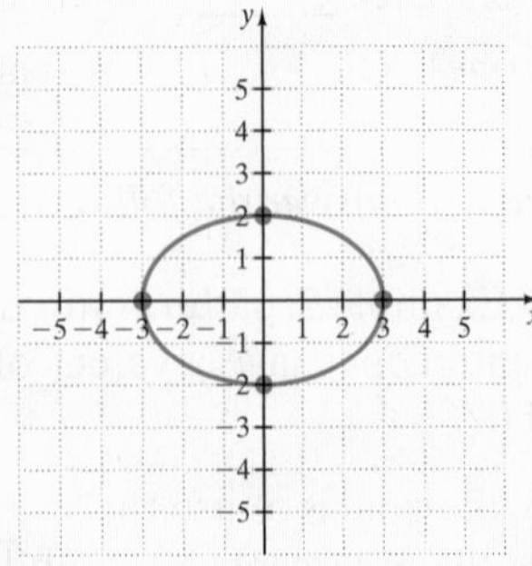

Solve. See Examples 1 through 5.

9. What is the greatest number of intercepts for a line?
10. What is the least number of intercepts for a line?
11. What is the least number of intercepts for a circle?
12. What is the greatest number of intercepts for a circle?

Graph each linear equation by finding and plotting its intercepts. See Examples 6 through 8.

13. $x - y = 3$
14. $x - y = -4$
15. $x = 5y$
16. $x = 2y$
17. $-x + 2y = 6$
18. $x - 2y = -8$
19. $2x - 4y = 8$
20. $2x + 3y = 6$
21. $y = 2x$
22. $y = -2x$
23. $y = 3x + 6$
24. $y = 2x + 10$

Graph each linear equation. See Examples 9 and 10.

25. $x = -1$
26. $y = 5$
27. $y = 0$
28. $x = 0$
29. $y + 7 = 0$
30. $x - 2 = 0$
31. $x + 3 = 0$
32. $y - 6 = 0$

MIXED PRACTICE

Graph each linear equation. See Examples 6 through 10.

33. $x = y$
34. $x = -y$
35. $x + 8y = 8$
36. $x + 3y = 9$
37. $5 = 6x - y$
38. $4 = x - 3y$
39. $-x + 10y = 11$
40. $-x + 9y = 10$
41. $x = -4\frac{1}{2}$
42. $x = -1\frac{3}{4}$
43. $y = 3\frac{1}{4}$
44. $y = 2\frac{1}{2}$
45. $y = -\frac{2}{3}x + 1$
46. $y = -\frac{3}{5}x + 3$
47. $4x - 6y + 2 = 0$
48. $9x - 6y + 3 = 0$

For Exercises 49 through 54, match each equation with its graph. See Graphs A.–F. below and on the next page.

49. $y = 3$
50. $y = 2x + 2$
51. $x = -1$
52. $x = 3$
53. $y = 2x + 3$
54. $y = -2x$

A.

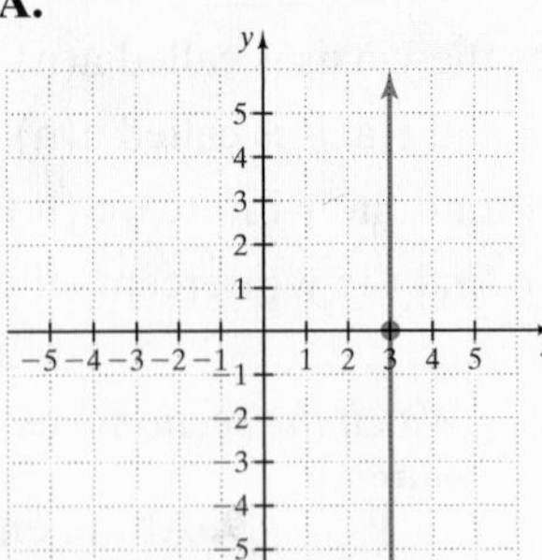

B.

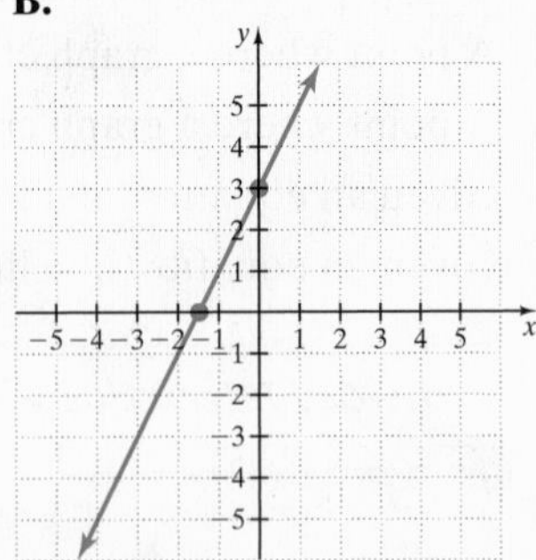

C.

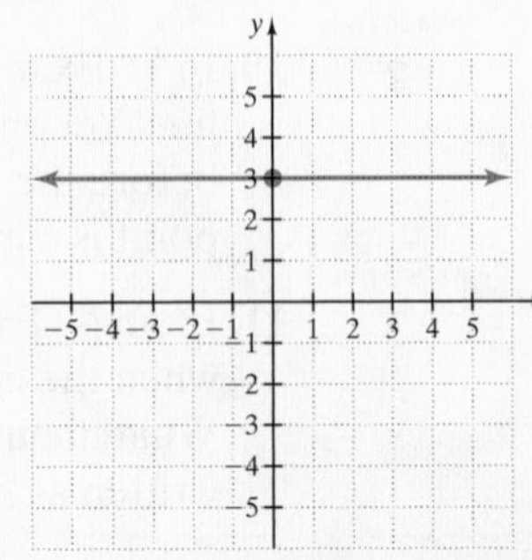

D.

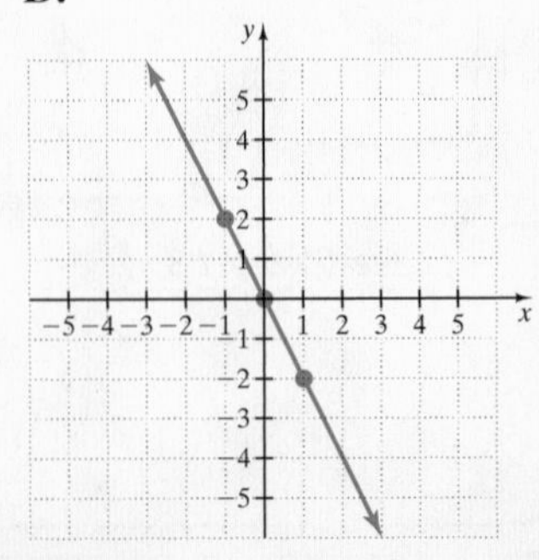

E.

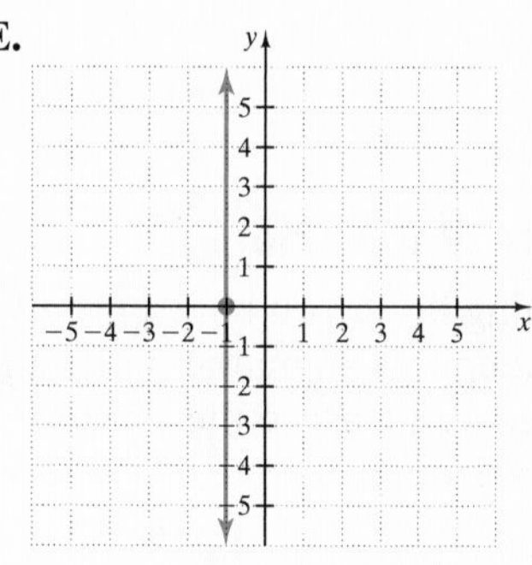

F.

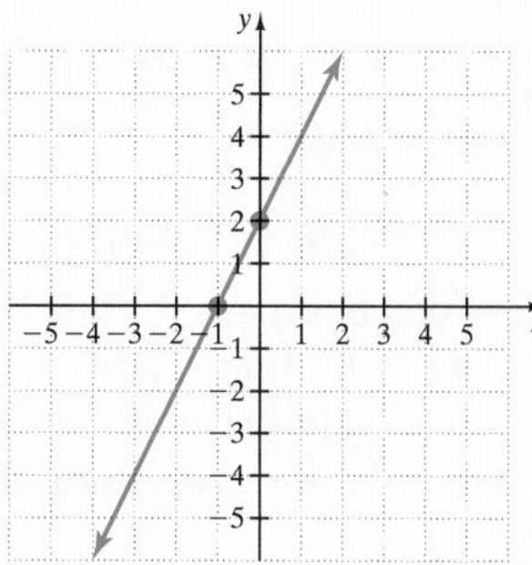

REVIEW AND PREVIEW

Simplify. See Sections R.4 through R.7.

55. $\dfrac{-6-3}{2-8}$

56. $\dfrac{4-5}{-1-0}$

57. $\dfrac{-8-(-2)}{-3-(-2)}$

58. $\dfrac{12-3}{10-9}$

59. $\dfrac{0-6}{5-0}$

60. $\dfrac{2-2}{3-5}$

CONCEPT EXTENSIONS

Answer the following true or false.

61. All lines have an x-intercept *and* a y-intercept.

62. The graph of $y = 4x$ contains the point $(0, 0)$.

63. The graph of $x + y = 5$ has an x-intercept of $(5, 0)$ and a y-intercept of $(0, 5)$.

64. The graph of $y = 5x$ contains the point $(5, 1)$.

The production supervisor at Alexandra's Office Products finds that it takes 3 hours to manufacture a particular office chair and 6 hours to manufacture an office desk. A total of 1200 hours is available to produce office chairs and desks of this style. The linear equation that models this situation is $3x + 6y = 1200$, where x represents the number of chairs produced and y the number of desks manufactured. Use this information for Exercises 65 through 68.

65. Complete the ordered pair solution (0,) of this equation. Describe the manufacturing situation that corresponds to this solution.

66. Complete the ordered pair solution (, 0) of this equation. Describe the manufacturing situation that corresponds to this solution.

67. If 50 desks are manufactured, find the greatest number of chairs that can be made.

68. If 50 chairs are manufactured, find the greatest number of desks that can be made.

69. Since 2002, admissions at movie theaters in the U.S. and Canada have mostly been in a decline. The number of people y (in billions) who go to movie theaters each year can be estimated by the equation $y = -0.025x + 1.55$, where x represents the number of years since 2002. (*Source:* Based on data from Motion Picture Association of America)

a. Find the x-intercept of this equation.

b. What does this x-intercept mean?

c. Use part (b) to comment on your opinion of the limitations of using equations to model real data.

70. The price of admission to a movie theater has been steadily increasing. The price of regular admission y (in dollars) to a movie theater may be represented by the equation $y = 0.24x + 5.28$, where x is the number of years after 2000. (*Source:* Based on data from Motion Picture Association of America)

a. Find the x-intercept of this equation.

b. What does this x-intercept mean?

c. Use part (b) to comment on your opinion of the limitations of using equations to model real data.

Two lines in the same plane that do not intersect are called **parallel lines.**

△ **71.** Draw a line parallel to the line $x = 5$ that intersects the x-axis at $(1, 0)$. What is the equation of this line?

△ **72.** Draw a line parallel to the line $y = -1$ that intersects the y-axis at $(0, -4)$. What is the equation of this line?

73. Discuss whether a vertical line ever has a y-intercept.

74. Explain why it is a good idea to use three points to graph a linear equation.

75. Discuss whether a horizontal line ever has an x-intercept.

76. Explain how to find intercepts.

1.4 Slope and Rate of Change 

OBJECTIVES

1. Find the Slope of a Line Given Two Points of the Line.
2. Find the Slope of a Line Given Its Equation.
3. Find the Slopes of Horizontal and Vertical Lines.
4. Compare the Slopes of Parallel and Perpendicular Lines.
5. Interpret Slope as a Rate of Change.

OBJECTIVE

1 Finding the Slope of a Line Given Two Points of the Line 

Thus far, much of this chapter has been devoted to graphing lines. You have probably noticed by now that a key feature of a line is its slant or steepness. In mathematics, the slant or steepness of a line is formally known as its **slope.** We measure the slope of a line by the ratio of vertical change to the corresponding horizontal change as we move along the line.

On the line below, for example, suppose that we begin at the point $(1, 2)$ and move to the point $(4, 6)$. The vertical change is the change in y-coordinates: $6 - 2$ or 4 units. The corresponding horizontal change is the change in x-coordinates: $4 - 1 = 3$ units. The ratio of these changes is

$$\text{slope} = \frac{\text{change in } y \text{ (vertical change)}}{\text{change in } x \text{ (horizontal change)}} = \frac{4}{3}$$

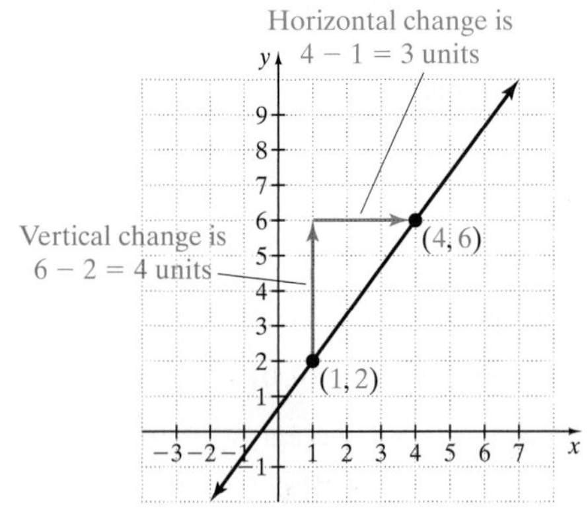

The slope of this line, then, is $\frac{4}{3}$. This means that for every 4 units of change in y-coordinates, there is a corresponding change of 3 units in x-coordinates.

Helpful Hint

It makes no difference what two points of a line are chosen to find its slope. The slope of a line is the same everywhere on the line.

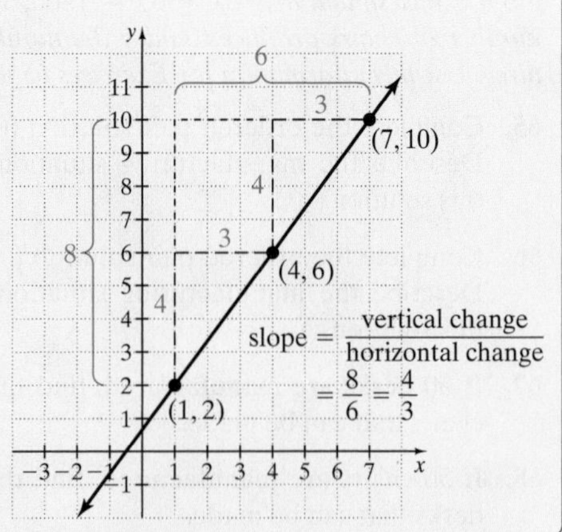

To find the slope of a line, then, choose two points of the line. Label the two x-coordinates of two points x_1 and x_2 (read "x sub one" and "x sub two"), and label the corresponding y-coordinates y_1 and y_2.

The vertical change or **rise** between these points is the difference in the y-coordinates: $y_2 - y_1$. The horizontal change or **run** between the points is the difference of the x-coordinates: $x_2 - x_1$. The slope of the line is the ratio of $y_2 - y_1$ to $x_2 - x_1$, and we traditionally use the letter m to denote slope: $m = \frac{y_2 - y_1}{x_2 - x_1}$.

Slope of a Line

The slope m of the line containing the points (x_1, y_1) and (x_2, y_2) is given by

$$m = \frac{\text{rise}}{\text{run}} = \frac{\text{change in } y}{\text{change in } x} = \frac{y_2 - y_1}{x_2 - x_1}, \quad \text{as long as } x_2 \neq x_1$$

EXAMPLE 1 Find the slope of the line through $(-1, 5)$ and $(2, -3)$. Graph the line.

Solution If we let (x_1, y_1) be $(-1, 5)$, then $x_1 = -1$ and $y_1 = 5$. Also, let (x_2, y_2) be $(2, -3)$ so that $x_2 = 2$ and $y_2 = -3$. Then, by the definition of slope,

$$m = \frac{y_2 - y_1}{x_2 - x_1} = \frac{-3 - 5}{2 - (-1)} = \frac{-8}{3} = -\frac{8}{3}$$

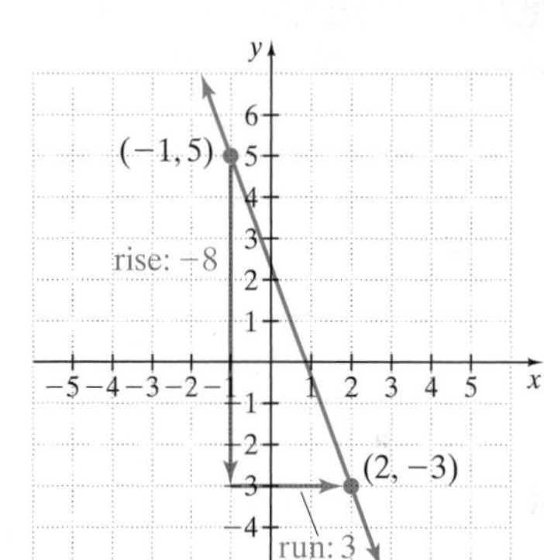

The slope of the line is $-\frac{8}{3}$. □

PRACTICE

1 Find the slope of the line through $(-4, 11)$ and $(2, 5)$.

Helpful Hint

When finding slope, it makes no difference which point is identified as (x_1, y_1) and which is identified as (x_2, y_2). Just remember that whatever y-value is first in the numerator, its corresponding x-value must be first in the denominator. Another way to calculate the slope in Example 1 is:

$$m = \frac{y_2 - y_1}{x_2 - x_1} = \frac{5 - (-3)}{-1 - 2} = \frac{8}{-3} \text{ or } -\frac{8}{3} \quad \leftarrow \text{Same slope as found in Example 1}$$

✓CONCEPT CHECK

The points $(-2, -5)$, $(0, -2)$, $(4, 4)$, and $(10, 13)$ all lie on the same line. Work with a partner and verify that the slope is the same no matter which points are used to find slope.

Answer to Concept Check:

$m = \frac{3}{2}$

EXAMPLE 2 Find the slope of the line through $(-1, -2)$ and $(2, 4)$. Graph the line.

Solution Let (x_1, y_1) be $(2, 4)$ and (x_2, y_2) be $(-1, -2)$.

$$m = \frac{y_2 - y_1}{x_2 - x_1}$$

$$= \frac{-2 - 4}{-1 - 2} \quad \begin{array}{l} y\text{-value} \\ \text{corresponding } x\text{-value} \end{array}$$

$$= \frac{-6}{-3} = 2$$

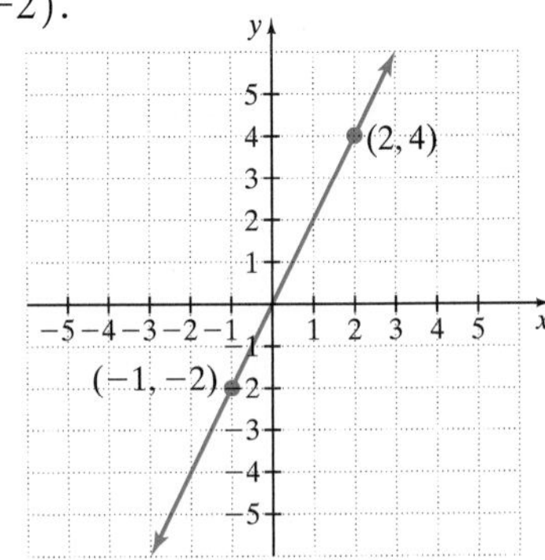

Helpful Hint

The slope for Example 2 is the same if we let (x_1, y_1) be $(-1, -2)$ and (x_2, y_2) be $(2, 4)$.

$$m = \frac{4 - (-2)}{2 - (-1)} = \frac{6}{3} = 2$$

(y-value in the numerator; corresponding x-value in the denominator)

PRACTICE 2 Find the slope of the line through $(-3, -1)$ and $(3, 1)$.

✓CONCEPT CHECK

What is wrong with the following slope calculation for the points $(3, 5)$ and $(-2, 6)$?

$$m = \frac{5 - 6}{-2 - 3} = \frac{-1}{-5} = \frac{1}{5}$$

(crossed out)

Notice that the slope of the line in Example 1 is negative, whereas the slope of the line in Example 2 is positive. Let your eye follow the line with negative slope from left to right and notice that the line "goes down." Following the line with positive slope from left to right, notice that the line "goes up." This is true in general.

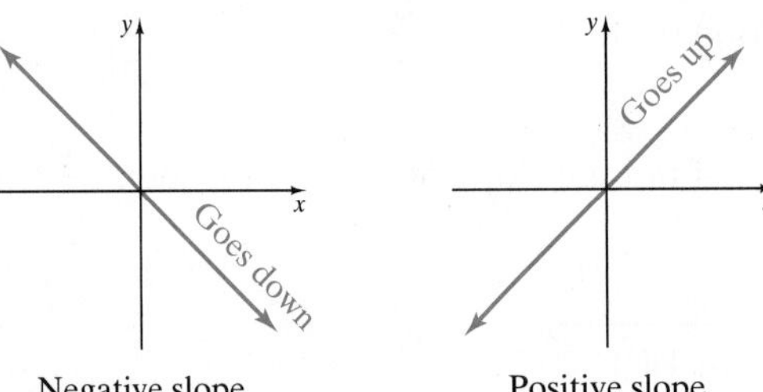

Negative slope　　Positive slope

Helpful Hint

To decide whether a line "goes up" or "goes down," always follow the line from left to right.

OBJECTIVE 2

Finding the Slope of a Line Given Its Equation 

As we have seen, the slope of a line is defined by two points on the line. Thus, if we know the equation of a line, we can find its slope by finding two of its points. For example, let's find the slope of the line

$$y = 3x + 2$$

To find two points, we can choose two values for x and substitute to find corresponding y-values. If $x = 0$, for example, $y = 3 \cdot 0 + 2$ or $y = 2$. If $x = 1$, $y = 3 \cdot 1 + 2$ or $y = 5$. This gives the ordered pairs $(0, 2)$ and $(1, 5)$. Using the definition for slope, we have

$$m = \frac{5 - 2}{1 - 0} = \frac{3}{1} = 3 \quad \text{The slope is 3.}$$

Notice that the slope, 3, is the same as the coefficient of x in the equation $y = 3x + 2$.

Also, recall from Section 1.2 that the graph of an equation of the form $y = mx + b$ has y-intercept $(0, b)$.

Answer to Concept Check:
The order in which the x- and y-values are used must be the same.

$$m = \frac{5 - 6}{3 - (-2)} = \frac{-1}{5} = -\frac{1}{5}$$

This means that the y-intercept of the graph of $y = 3x + 2$ is $(0, 2)$. This is true in general and the form $y = mx + b$ is appropriately called the **slope-intercept form.**

$$y = \underset{\text{slope}}{\underset{\uparrow}{m}}x + \underset{\substack{y\text{-intercept} \\ (0,\, b)}}{\underset{\uparrow}{b}}$$

Slope-Intercept Form

When a linear equation in two variables is written in slope-intercept form,

$$y = mx + b$$

m is the slope of the line and $(0, b)$ is the y-intercept of the line.

EXAMPLE 3 Find the slope and y-intercept of the line whose equation is $y = \frac{3}{4}x + 6$

Solution The equation is in slope-intercept form, $y = mx + b$.

$$y = \frac{3}{4}x + 6$$

The coefficient of x, $\frac{3}{4}$, is the slope and the constant term, 6, is the y-value of the y-intercept, $(0, 6)$. □

PRACTICE

3 Find the slope and y-intercept of the line whose equation is $y = \frac{2}{3}x - 2$.

EXAMPLE 4 Find the slope and the y-intercept of the line whose equation is $-y = 5x - 2$.

Solution: Remember, the equation must be solved for y (not $-y$) in order for it to be written in slope-intercept form.

To solve for y, let's divide both sides of the equation by -1.

$$-y = 5x - 2$$

$$\frac{-y}{-1} = \frac{5x}{-1} - \frac{2}{-1} \quad \text{Divide both sides by } -1.$$

$$y = -5x + 2 \quad \text{Simplify.}$$

The coefficient of x, -5, is the slope and the constant term, 2, is the y-value of the y-intercept, $(0, 2)$. □

PRACTICE

4 Find the slope and y-intercept of the line whose equation is $-y = -6x + 5$.

EXAMPLE 5 Find the slope and the y-intercept of the line whose equation is $3x - 4y = 4$.

Solution Write the equation in slope-intercept form by solving for y.

$$3x - 4y = 4$$

$$-4y = -3x + 4 \quad \text{Subtract } 3x \text{ from both sides.}$$

$$\frac{-4y}{-4} = \frac{-3x}{-4} + \frac{4}{-4} \quad \text{Divide both sides by } -4.$$

$$y = \frac{3}{4}x - 1 \quad \text{Simplify.}$$

The coefficient of x, $\frac{3}{4}$, is the slope, and the y-intercept is $(0, -1)$. □

PRACTICE
5 Find the slope and the y-intercept of the line whose equation is $5x + 2y = 8$.

OBJECTIVE
3 Finding Slopes of Horizontal and Vertical Lines 

Recall that if a line tilts upward from left to right, its slope is positive. If a line tilts downward from left to right, its slope is negative. Let's now find the slopes of two special lines, horizontal and vertical lines.

EXAMPLE 6 Find the slope of the line $y = -1$.

Solution Recall that $y = -1$ is a horizontal line with y-intercept $(0, -1)$. To find the slope, find two ordered pair solutions of $y = -1$. Solutions of $y = -1$ must have a y-value of -1. Let's use points $(2, -1)$ and $(-3, -1)$, which are on the line.

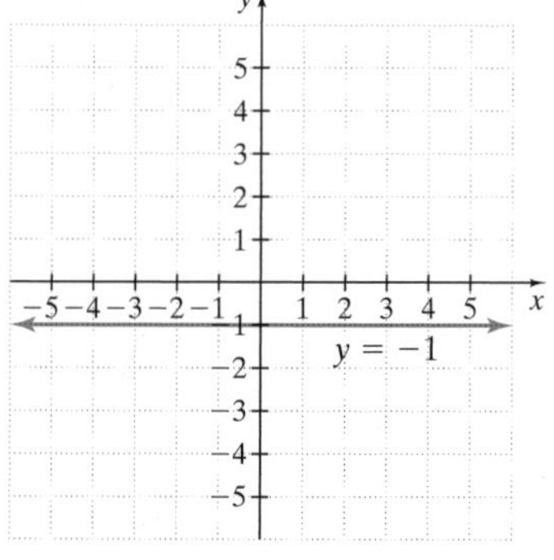

$$m = \frac{y_2 - y_1}{x_2 - x_1} = \frac{-1 - (-1)}{-3 - 2} = \frac{0}{-5} = 0$$

The slope of the line $y = -1$ is 0 and its graph is shown. □

PRACTICE
6 Find the slope of the line $y = 3$.

Any two points of a horizontal line will have the same y-values. This means that the y-values will always have a difference of 0 for all horizontal lines. Thus, **all horizontal lines have a slope 0.**

EXAMPLE 7 Find the slope of the line $x = 5$.

Solution Recall that the graph of $x = 5$ is a vertical line with x-intercept $(5, 0)$.

To find the slope, find two ordered pair solutions of $x = 5$. Solutions of $x = 5$ must have an x-value of 5. Let's use points $(5, 0)$ and $(5, 4)$, which are on the line.

$$m = \frac{y_2 - y_1}{x_2 - x_1} = \frac{4 - 0}{5 - 5} = \frac{4}{0}$$

Since $\frac{4}{0}$ is undefined, we say the slope of the vertical line $x = 5$ is undefined, and its graph is shown.

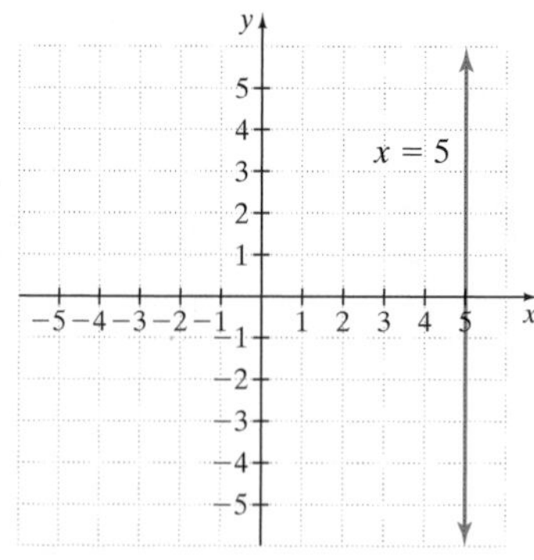

□

PRACTICE
7 Find the slope of the line $x = -4$.

Any two points of a vertical line will have the same x-values. This means that the x-values will always have a difference of 0 for all vertical lines. Thus **all vertical lines have undefined slope.**

> **Helpful Hint**
> Slope of 0 and undefined slope are not the same. Vertical lines have undefined slope or no slope, while horizontal lines have a slope of 0.

Here is a general review of slope.

Summary of Slope

Slope m of the line through (x_1, y_1) and (x_2, y_2) is given by the equation $m = \dfrac{y_2 - y_1}{x_2 - x_1}$.

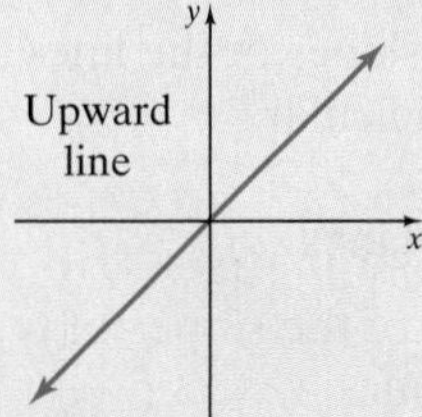

Positive slope: $m > 0$

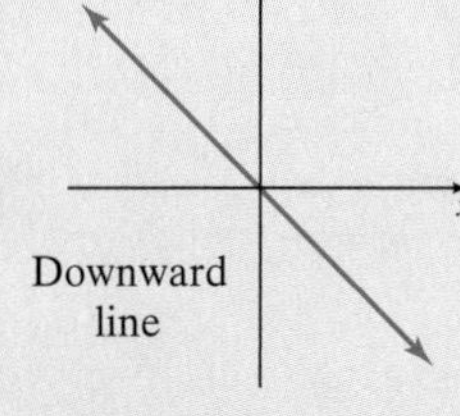

Negative slope: $m < 0$

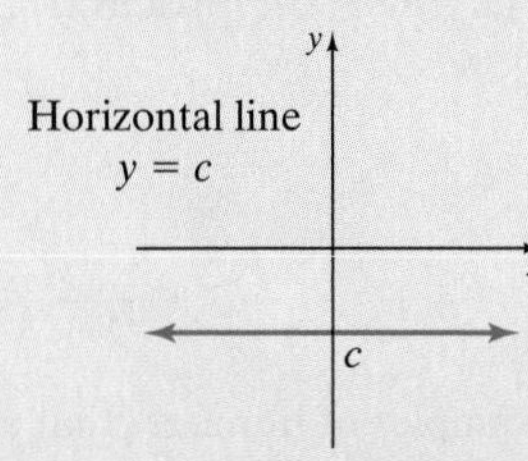

Zero slope: $m = 0$

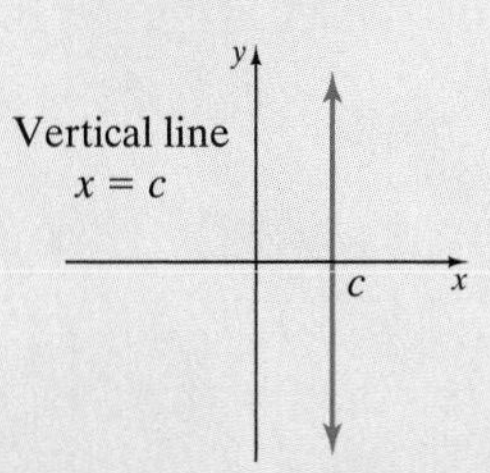

Undefined slope or no slope

OBJECTIVE

4 Slopes of Parallel and Perpendicular Lines 

Two lines in the same plane are **parallel** if they do not intersect. Slopes of lines can help us determine whether lines are parallel. Parallel lines have the same steepness, so it follows that they have the same slope.

For example, the graphs of

$$y = -2x + 4$$

and

$$y = -2x - 3$$

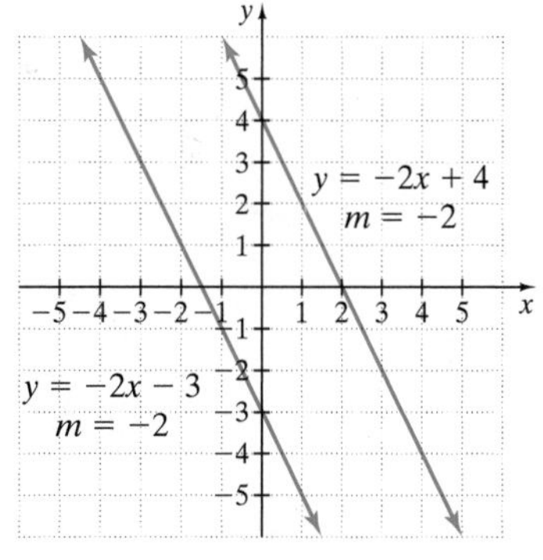

are shown. These lines have the same slope, -2. They also have different y-intercepts, so the lines are distinct and parallel. (If the y-intercepts were the same also, the lines would be the same.)

Parallel Lines

Nonvertical parallel lines have the same slope and different y-intercepts.

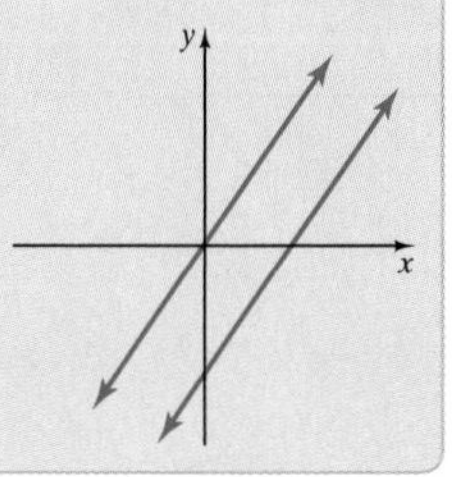

Two lines are **perpendicular** if they lie in the same plane and meet at a 90° (right) angle. How do the slopes of perpendicular lines compare? The product of the slopes of two perpendicular lines is -1.

For example, the graphs of

$$y = 4x + 1$$

and

$$y = -\frac{1}{4}x - 3$$

are shown. The slopes of the lines are 4 and $-\frac{1}{4}$. Their product is $4\left(-\frac{1}{4}\right) = -1$, so the lines are perpendicular.

Perpendicular Lines

If the product of the slopes of two lines is -1, then the lines are perpendicular.

(Two nonvertical lines are perpendicular if the slope of one is the negative reciprocal of the slope of the other.)

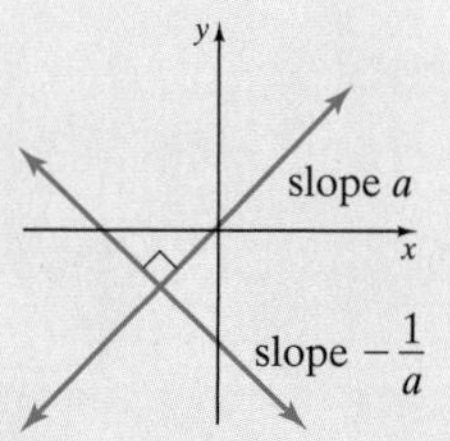

Helpful Hint

Here are examples of numbers that are negative (opposite) reciprocals.

Number	*Negative Reciprocal*	*Their Product Is* -1.
$\frac{2}{3}$	$-\frac{3}{2}$	$\frac{2}{3} \cdot -\frac{3}{2} = -\frac{6}{6} = -1$
-5 or $-\frac{5}{1}$	$\frac{1}{5}$	$-5 \cdot \frac{1}{5} = -\frac{5}{5} = -1$

Helpful Hint

Here are a few important facts about vertical and horizontal lines.

- Two distinct vertical lines are parallel.
- Two distinct horizontal lines are parallel.
- A horizontal line and a vertical line are always perpendicular.

EXAMPLE 8 Determine whether each pair of lines is parallel, perpendicular, or neither.

a. $y = -\frac{1}{5}x + 1$
$2x + 10y = 3$

b. $x + y = 3$
$-x + y = 4$

c. $3x + y = 5$
$2x + 3y = 6$

Solution

a. The slope of the line $y = -\frac{1}{5}x + 1$ is $-\frac{1}{5}$. We find the slope of the second line by solving its equation for y.

$$2x + 10y = 3$$

$$10y = -2x + 3 \quad \text{Subtract } 2x \text{ from both sides.}$$

$$y = \frac{-2}{10}x + \frac{3}{10} \quad \text{Divide both sides by 10.}$$

$$y = -\frac{1}{5}x + \frac{3}{10} \quad \text{Simplify.}$$

The slope of this line is $-\frac{1}{5}$ also. Since the lines have the same slope and different y-intercepts, they are parallel, as shown in the figure on the next page.

b. To find each slope, we solve each equation for y.

$$x + y = 3 \qquad\qquad -x + y = 4$$
$$y = -x + 3 \qquad\qquad y = x + 4$$

The slope is -1.   The slope is 1.

The slopes are not the same, so the lines are not parallel. Next we check the product of the slopes: $(-1)(1) = -1$. Since the product is -1, the lines are perpendicular, as shown in the figure.

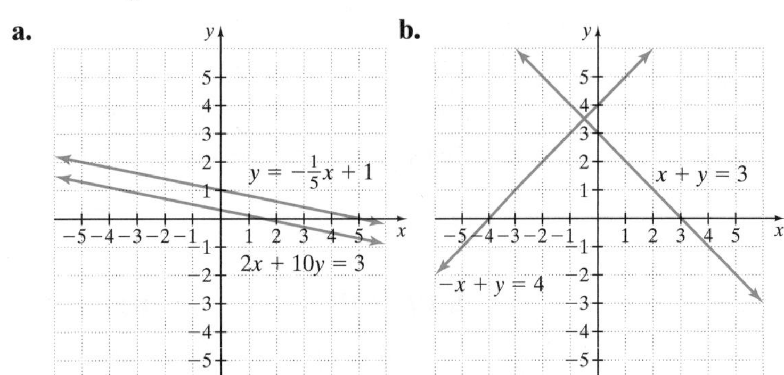

c. We solve each equation for y to find each slope. The slopes are -3 and $-\frac{2}{3}$. The slopes are not the same and their product is not -1. Thus, the lines are neither parallel nor perpendicular. □

PRACTICE

8 Determine whether each pair of lines is parallel, perpendicular, or neither.

a. $y = -5x + 1$
$x - 5y = 10$

b. $x + y = 11$
$2x + y = 11$

c. $2x + 3y = 21$
$6y = -4x - 2$

✓CONCEPT CHECK

Consider the line $-6x + 2y = 1$.

a. Write the equations of two lines parallel to this line.

b. Write the equations of two lines perpendicular to this line.

OBJECTIVE

5 Slope as a Rate of Change 

Slope can also be interpreted as a rate of change. In other words, slope tells us how fast y is changing with respect to x. To see this, let's look at a few of the many real-world applications of slope. For example, the pitch of a roof, used by builders and architects, is its slope. The pitch of the roof on the left is $\frac{7}{10}\left(\frac{\text{rise}}{\text{run}}\right)$. This means that the roof rises vertically 7 feet for every horizontal 10 feet. The rate of change for the roof is 7 vertical feet (y) per 10 horizontal feet (x).

The grade of a road is its slope written as a percent. A 7% grade, as shown below, means that the road rises (or falls) 7 feet for every horizontal 100 feet. $\left(\text{Recall that } 7\% = \frac{7}{100}.\right)$ Here, the slope of $\frac{7}{100}$ gives us the rate of change. The road rises (in our diagram) 7 vertical feet (y) for every 100 horizontal feet (x).

Answers to Concept Check:
a. any two lines with $m = 3$ and y-intercept not $\left(0, \frac{1}{2}\right)$
b. any two lines with $m = -\frac{1}{3}$

EXAMPLE 9 **Finding the Grade of a Road**

At one part of the road to the summit of Pikes Peak, the road rises at a rate of 15 vertical feet for a horizontal distance of 250 feet. Find the grade of the road.

Solution Recall that the grade of a road is its slope written as a percent.

$$\text{grade} = \frac{\text{rise}}{\text{run}} = \frac{15}{250} = 0.06 = 6\%$$

15 feet

250 feet

The grade is 6%. □

PRACTICE

9 One part of the Mt. Washington (New Hampshire) cog railway rises about 1794 feet over a horizontal distance of 7176 feet. Find the grade of this part of the railway.

EXAMPLE 10 **Finding the Slope of a Line**

The following graph shows annual food and drink sales y (in billions of dollars) for year x. Find the slope of the line and attach the proper units for the rate of change. Then write a sentence explaining the meaning of the slope for this application.

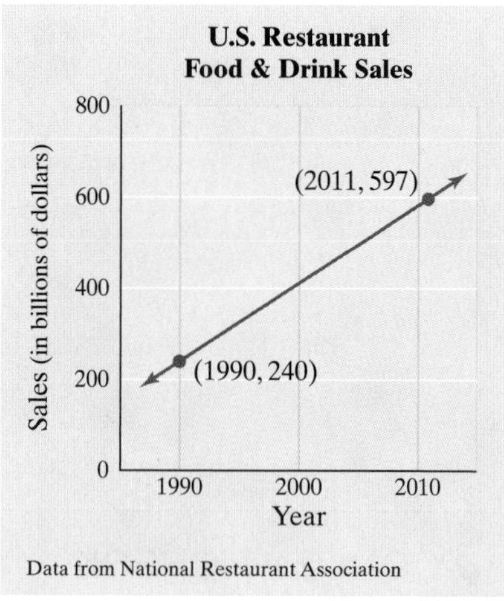

Data from National Restaurant Association

Solution Use (1990, 240) and (2011, 597) to calculate slope.

$$m = \frac{597 - 240}{2011 - 1990} = \frac{357}{21} = \frac{17 \text{ billion dollars}}{1 \text{ year}}$$

This means that the rate of change of restaurant food and drink sales increases by 17 billion dollars every 1 year, or $17 billion per year. □

PRACTICE

10 The following graph shows the cost y (in dollars) of having laundry done at the Wash-n-Fold, where x is the number of pounds of laundry. Find the slope of the line, and attach the proper units for the rate of change.

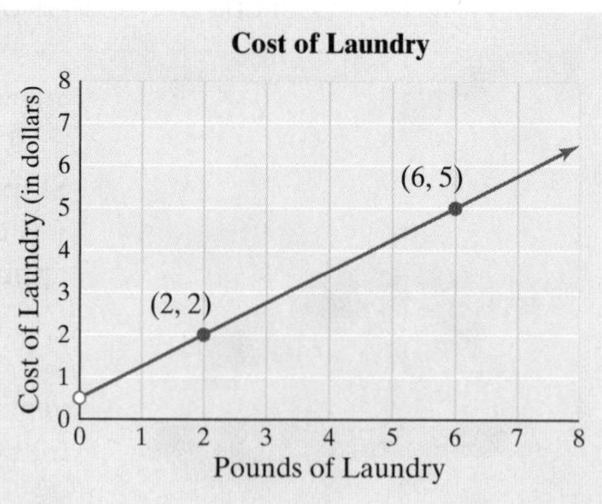

Graphing Calculator Explorations

It is possible to use a grapher to sketch the graph of more than one equation on the same set of axes. This feature can be used to confirm our findings from Section 1.2 when we learned that the graph of an equation written in the form $y = mx + b$ has a y-intercept of b. For example, graph the equations $y = \frac{2}{5}x$, $y = \frac{2}{5}x + 7$, and

$y = \frac{2}{5}x - 4$ on the same set of axes. To do so, press the $\boxed{Y=}$ key and enter the equations on the first three lines.

$$Y_1 = \left(\frac{2}{5}\right)x$$

$$Y_2 = \left(\frac{2}{5}\right)x + 7$$

$$Y_3 = \left(\frac{2}{5}\right)x - 4$$

The screen should look like:

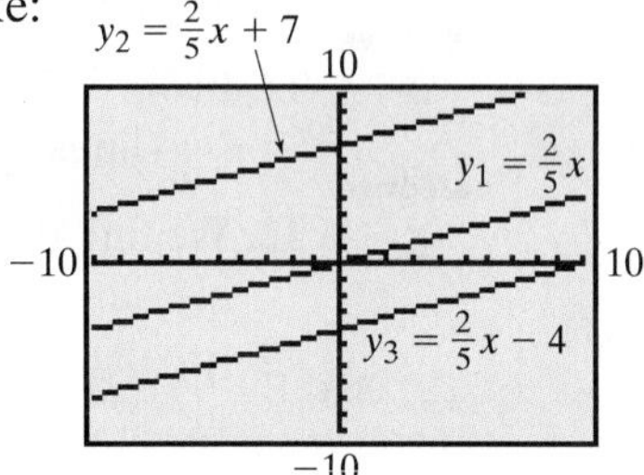

Notice that all three graphs appear to have the same positive slope. The graph of $y = \frac{2}{5}x + 7$ is the graph of $y = \frac{2}{5}x$ moved 7 units upward with a y-intercept of 7. Also, the graph of $y = \frac{2}{5}x - 4$ is the graph of $y = \frac{2}{5}x$ moved 4 units downward with a y-intercept of −4.

Graph the equations on the same set of axes. Describe the similarities and differences in their graphs.

1. $y = 3.8x, y = 3.8x - 3, y = 3.8x + 9$

2. $y = -4.9x, y = -4.9x + 1, y = -4.9x + 8$

3. $y = \frac{1}{4}x; y = \frac{1}{4}x + 5, y = \frac{1}{4}x - 8$

4. $y = -\frac{3}{4}x, y = -\frac{3}{4}x - 5, y = -\frac{3}{4}x + 6$

Vocabulary, Readiness & Video Check

Use the choices below to fill in each blank. Not all choices will be used.

m	x	0	positive	undefined
b	y	slope	negative	

1. The measure of the steepness or tilt of a line is called ________.

2. If an equation is written in the form $y = mx + b$, the value of the letter ________ is the value of the slope of the graph.

3. The slope of a horizontal line is ________.

4. The slope of a vertical line is ________.

5. If the graph of a line moves upward from left to right, the line has ________ slope.

6. If the graph of a line moves downward from left to right, the line has ________ slope.

7. Given two points of a line, slope $= \frac{\text{change in\_\_}}{\text{change in\_\_}}$.

Martin-Gay Interactive Videos

See Video 1.4

Watch the section lecture video and answer the following questions.

OBJECTIVE 1

8. What important point is made during Example 1 having to do with the order of the points in the slope formula?

OBJECTIVE 2

9. From Example 5, how do you write an equation in "slope-intercept form"? Once the equation is in slope-intercept form, how do you identify the slope?

OBJECTIVE 3

10. In the lecture after Example 8, different slopes are summarized. What is the difference between zero slope and undefined slope? What does "no slope" mean?

OBJECTIVE 4

11. From Example 10, what form of the equations is best to determine if two lines are parallel or perpendicular? Why?

OBJECTIVE 5

12. Writing the slope as a rate of change in Example 11 gave real-life meaning to the slope. What step in the general strategy for problem solving does this correspond to?

1.4 Exercise Set

MyMathLab®

Find the slope of the line that passes through the given points. See Examples 1 and 2.

1. $(-1, 5)$ and $(6, -2)$
2. $(3, 1)$ and $(2, 6)$
3. $(-4, 3)$ and $(-4, 5)$
4. $(6, -6)$ and $(6, 2)$
5. $(-2, 8)$ and $(1, 6)$
6. $(4, -3)$ and $(2, 2)$
7. $(5, 1)$ and $(-2, 1)$
8. $(0, 13)$ and $(-4, 13)$

Find the slope of each line if it exists. See Examples 1 and 2.

9.

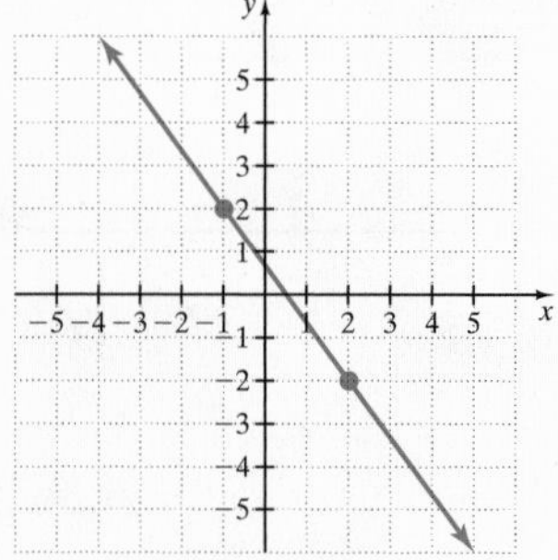

10.

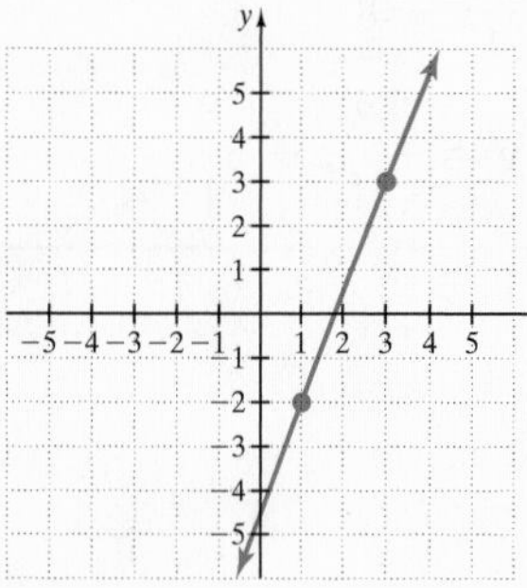

11.

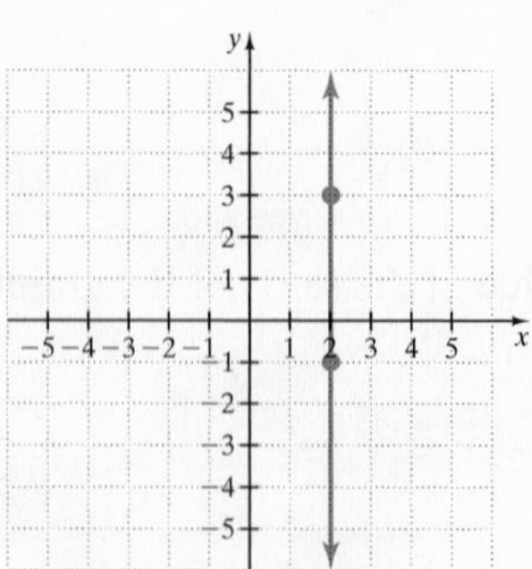

12.

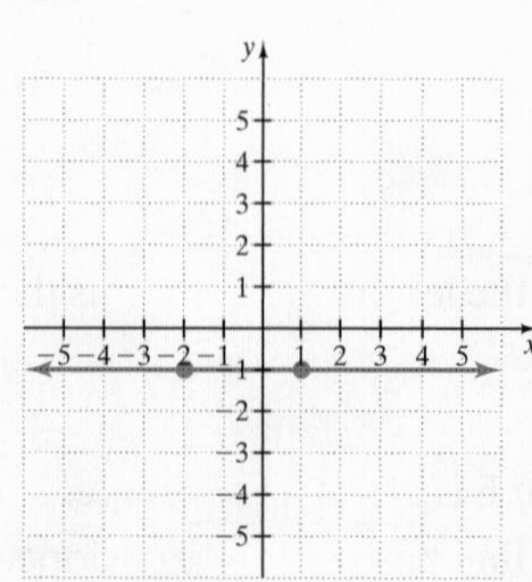

13.

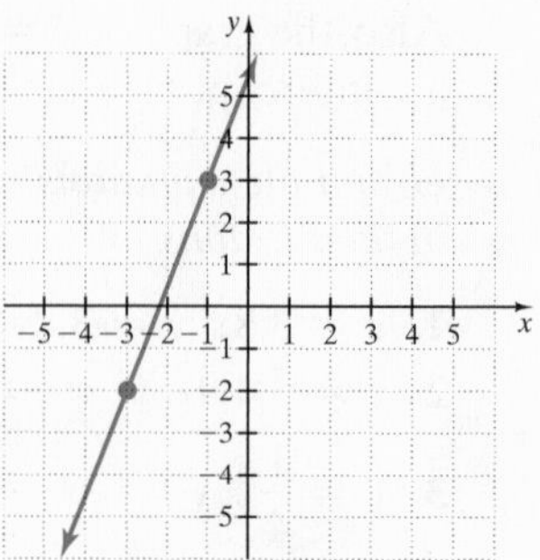

14.

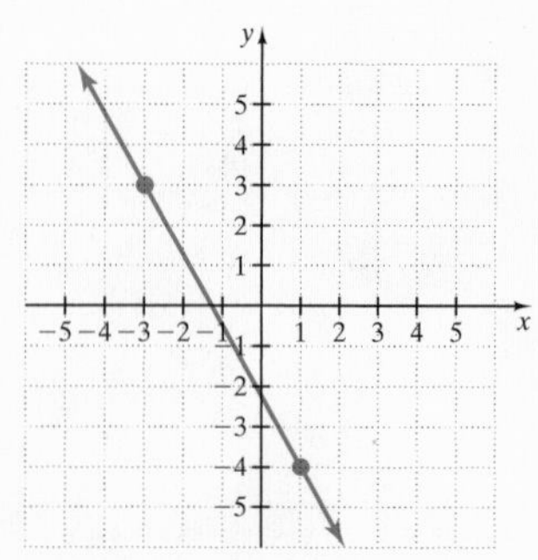

State whether the slope of the line is positive, negative, 0, or is undefined. See the top box on p. 115.

15.

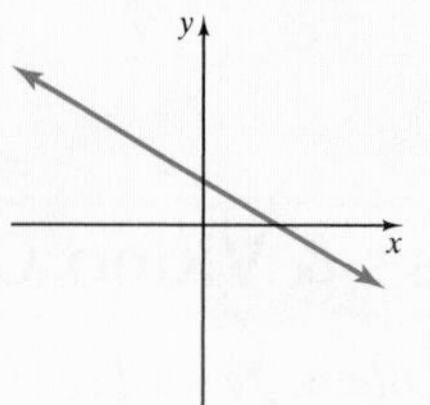

16.

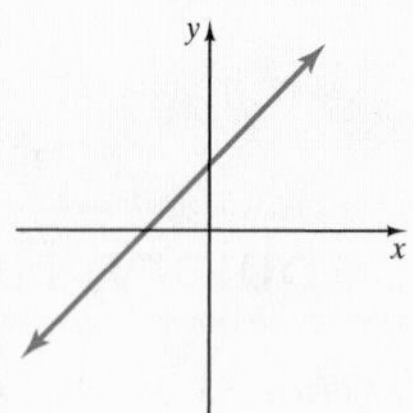

17.

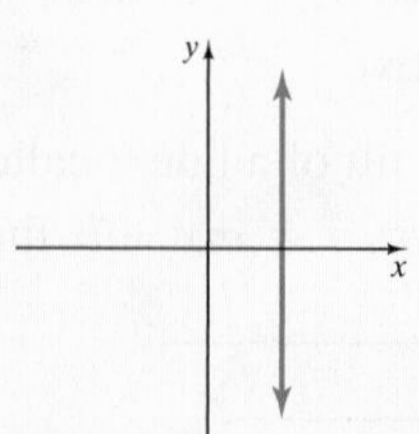

18.

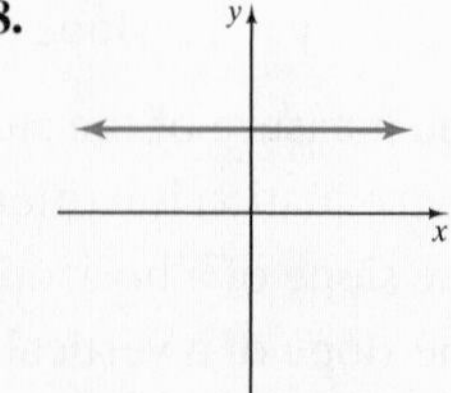

Decide whether a line with the given slope is upward, downward, horizontal, or vertical. See the top box on p. 115.

19. $m = \frac{7}{6}$ __________

20. $m = -3$ __________

21. $m = 0$ __________

22. m is undefined. __________

For each graph, determine which line has the greater slope. See the top box on p. 115.

23.

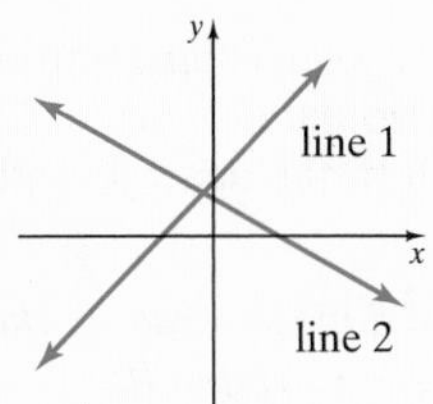

24.

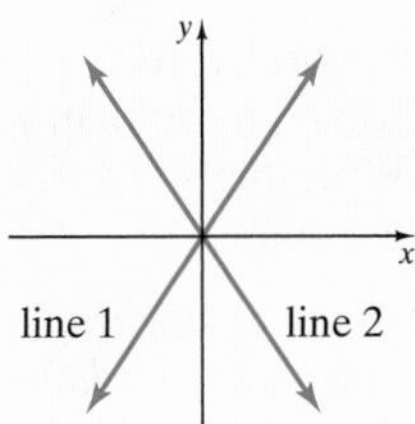

25.

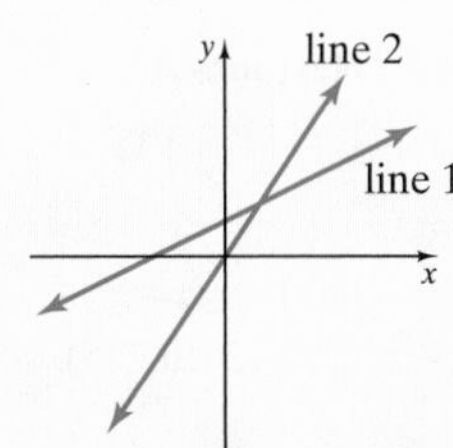

26.

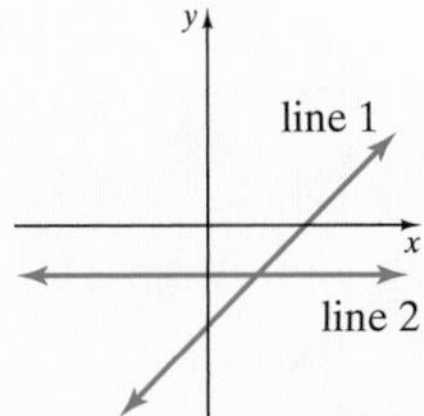

In Exercises 27 through 32, match each line with its slope. See Examples 1 and 2 and the top box on p. 115.

A. $m = 0$ **B.** undefined slope **C.** $m = 3$

D. $m = 1$ **E.** $m = -\frac{1}{2}$ **F.** $m = -\frac{3}{4}$

27.

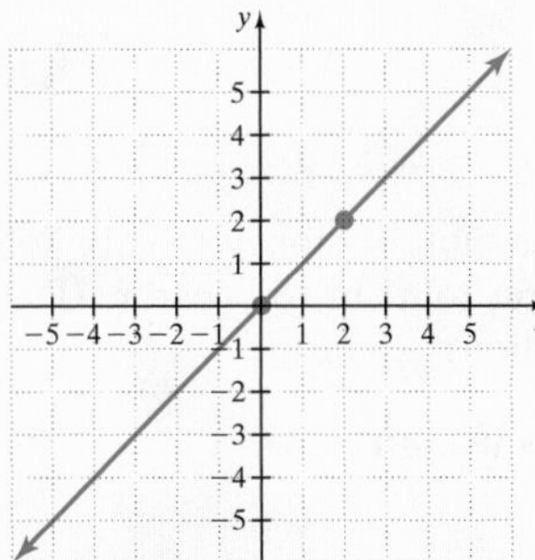

28.

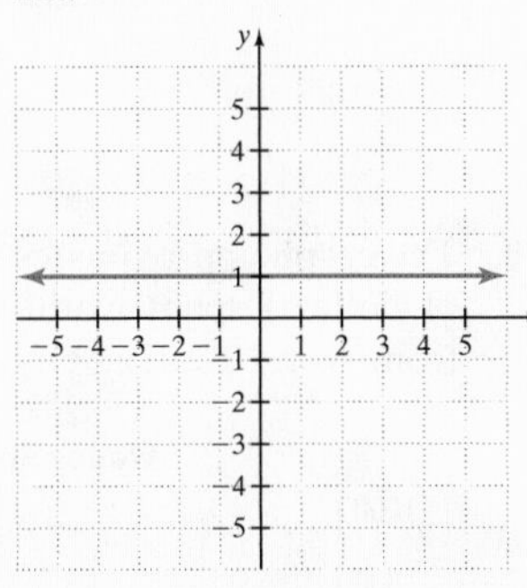

29.

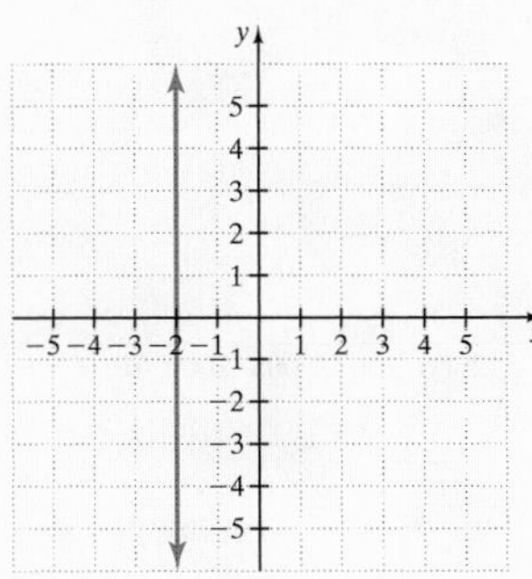

30.

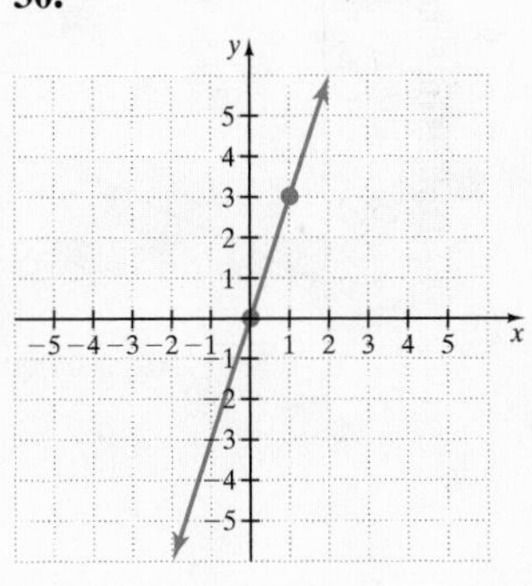

31.

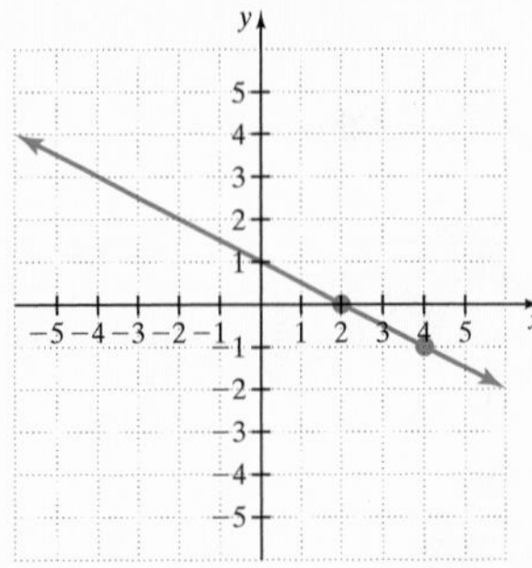

32.

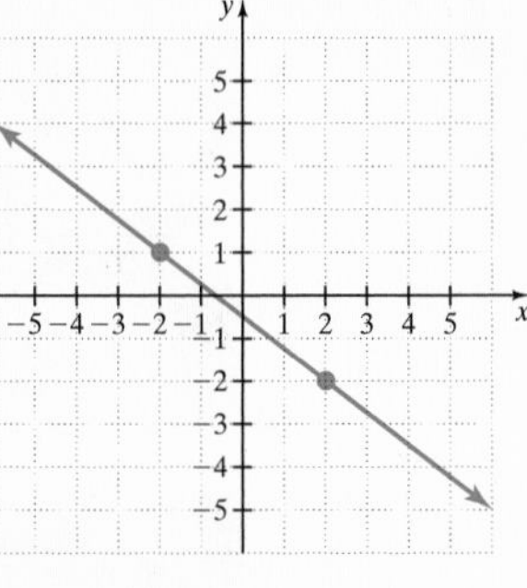

Find the slope of each line. See Examples 6 and 7.

33. $x = 6$

34. $y = 4$

35. $y = -4$

36. $x = 2$

37. $x = -3$

38. $y = -11$

39. $y = 0$

40. $x = 0$

MIXED PRACTICE

Find the slope of each line. See Examples 3 through 7.

41. $y = 5x - 2$

42. $y = -2x + 6$

43. $y = -0.3x + 2.5$

44. $y = -7.6x - 0.1$

45. $2x + y = 7$

46. $-5x + y = 10$

47. $2x - 3y = 10$

48. $3x - 5y = 1$

49. $x = 1$

50. $y = -2$

51. $x = 2y$

52. $x = -4y$

53. $y = -3$

54. $x = 5$

55. $-3x - 4y = 6$

56. $-4x - 7y = 9$

57. $20x - 5y = 1.2$

58. $24x - 3y = 5.7$

△ *Find the slope of the line that is* ***(a)*** *parallel and* ***(b)*** *perpendicular to the line through each pair of points. See Example 8.*

59. $(-3, -3)$ and $(0, 0)$

60. $(6, -2)$ and $(1, 4)$

61. $(-8, -4)$ and $(3, 5)$

62. $(6, -1)$ and $(-4, -10)$

△ *Determine whether each pair of lines is parallel, perpendicular, or neither. See Example 8.*

63. $y = \frac{2}{9}x + 3$
$y = -\frac{2}{9}x$

64. $y = \frac{1}{5}x + 20$
$y = -\frac{1}{5}x$

65. $x - 3y = -6$
$y = 3x - 9$

66. $y = 4x - 2$
$4x + y = 5$

67. $6x = 5y + 1$
$-12x + 10y = 1$

68. $-x + 2y = -2$
$2x = 4y + 3$

69. $6 + 4x = 3y$
$3x + 4y = 8$

70. $10 + 3x = 5y$
$5x + 3y = 1$

The pitch of a roof is its slope. Find the pitch of each roof shown. See Example 9.

71.

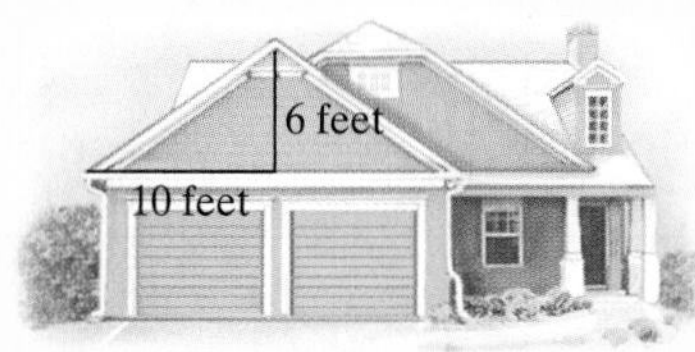

72.

The grade of a road is its slope written as a percent. Find the grade of each road shown. See Example 9.

73.

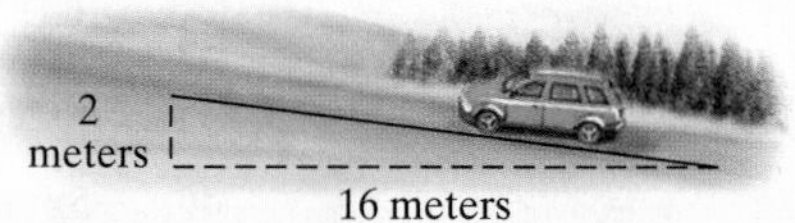

74.

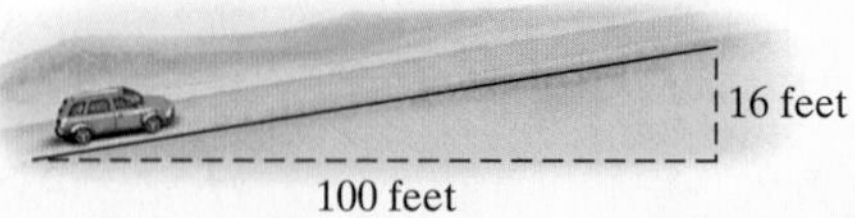

75. One of Japan's superconducting "bullet" trains is researched and tested at the Yamanashi Maglev Test Line near Otsuki City. The steepest section of the track has a rise of 2580 meters for a horizontal distance of 6450 meters. What is the grade of this section of track? (*Source:* Japan Railways Central Co.)

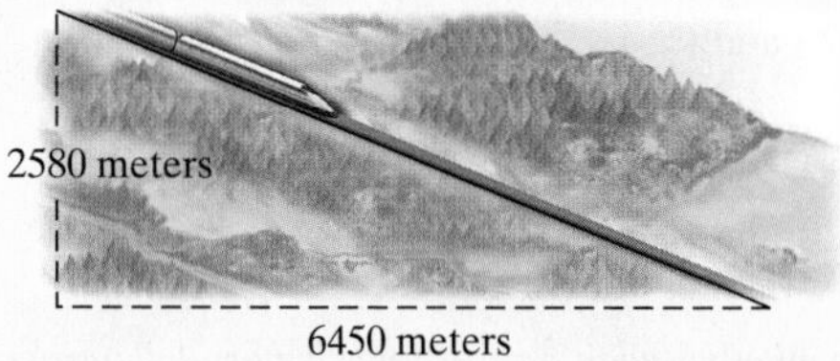

76. Professional plumbers suggest that a sewer pipe should rise 0.25 inch for every horizontal foot. Find the recommended slope for a sewer pipe. Round to the nearest hundredth.

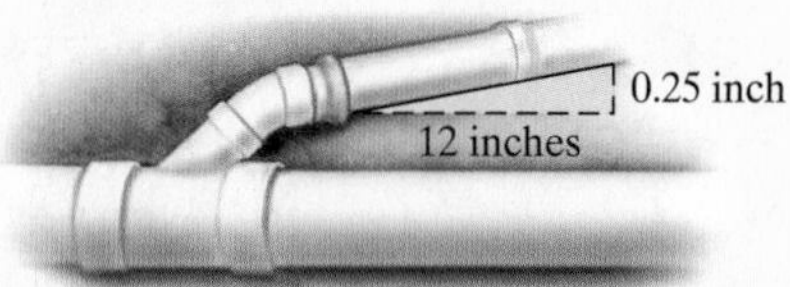

77. There has been controversy over the past few years about the world's steepest street. The *Guinness Book of Records* actually listed Baldwin Street, in Dunedin, New Zealand, as the world's steepest street, but Canton Avenue in the Pittsburgh neighborhood of Beechview may be steeper. Calculate each grade to the nearest percent.

		Grade (%)
Canton Avenue	for every 30 meters of horizontal distance, the vertical change is 11 meters	
Baldwin Street	for every 2.86 meters of horizontal distance, the vertical change is 1 meter	

78. According to federal regulations, a wheelchair ramp should rise no more than 1 foot for a horizontal distance of 12 feet. Write the slope as a grade. Round to the nearest tenth of a percent.

Find the slope of each line and write the slope as a rate of change. Don't forget to attach the proper units. See Example 10.

79. This graph approximates the number of U.S. households that have televisions y (in millions) for year x.

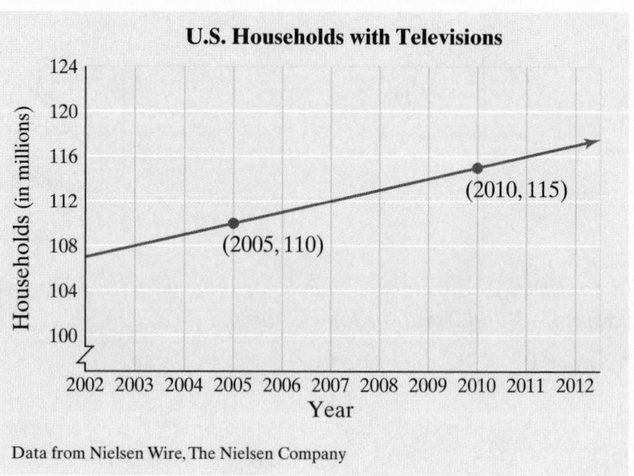

80. The graph approximates the amount of money y (in billions of dollars) spent worldwide on tourism for year x. (Data from World Tourism Organization)

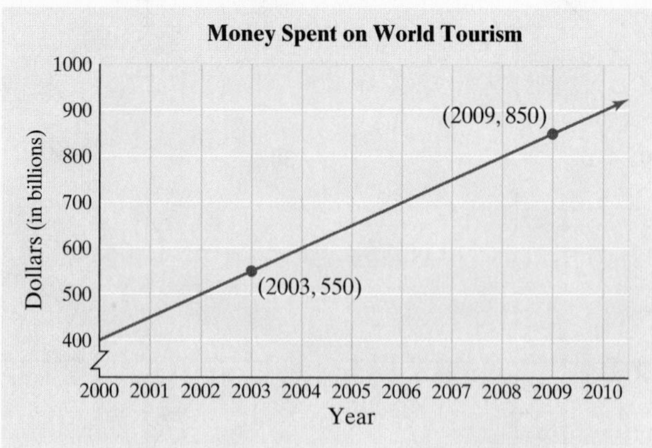

For Exercises 81 and 82, write the slope as a decimal.

81. The graph below shows the total cost y (in dollars) of owning and operating a compact car where x is the number of miles driven.

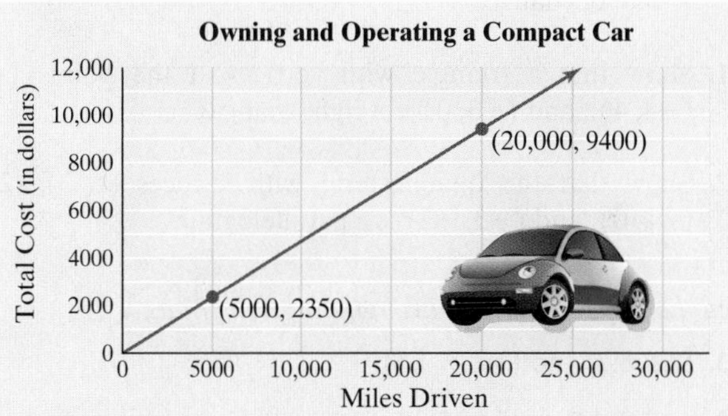

82. Americans are keeping their cars longer. The graph below shows the median age y (in years) of automobiles in the United States for the years shown. (Data from Bureau of Transportation Statistics)

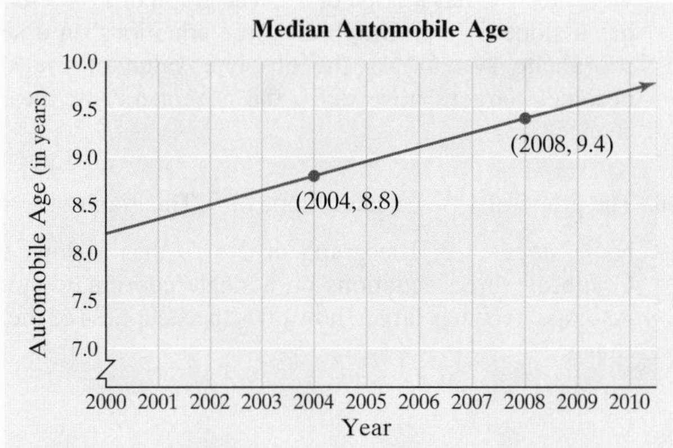

REVIEW AND PREVIEW

Solve each equation for y.

83. $y - (-6) = 2(x - 4)$

84. $y - 7 = -9(x - 6)$

85. $y - 1 = -6(x - (-2))$

86. $y - (-3) = 4(x - (-5))$

CONCEPT EXTENSIONS

Solve. See a Concept Check in this section.

87. Verify that the points $(2, 1)$, $(0, 0)$, $(-2, -1)$ and $(-4, -2)$ are all on the same line by computing the slope between each pair of points. (See the first Concept Check.)

88. Given the points $(2, 3)$ and $(-5, 1)$, can the slope of the line through these points be calculated by $\frac{1 - 3}{2 - (-5)}$? Why or why not? (See the second Concept Check.)

89. Write the equations of three lines parallel to $10x - 5y = -7$. (See the third Concept Check.)

90. Write the equations of two lines perpendicular to $10x - 5y = -7$. (See the third Concept Check.)

The following line graph shows the average fuel economy (in miles per gallon) of passenger automobiles produced during each of the model years shown. Use this graph to answer Exercises 91 through 96.

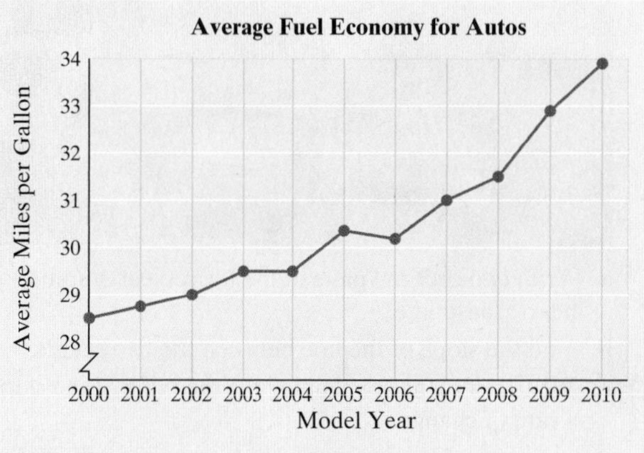

91. Between what two years shown was there a decrease in average fuel economy for automobiles?

92. What was the average fuel economy (in miles per gallon) for automobiles produced during 2008?

93. During which of the model years shown was average fuel economy the lowest?
What was the average fuel economy for that year?

94. During which of the model years shown was average fuel economy the highest?
What was the average fuel economy for that year?

95. Of the following line segments, which has the greatest slope: from 2002 to 2003, from 2006 to 2007, or from 2008 to 2009?

96. Which line segment has a slope of 0?

Solve.

97. Find x so that the pitch of the roof is $\frac{1}{3}$.

98. Find x so that the pitch of the roof is $\frac{2}{5}$.

99. Approximately 2207 heart transplants were performed in the United States in 2007. In 2010, the number of heart transplants in the United States rose to 2333. (*Source:* Organ Procurement and Transplantation Network)

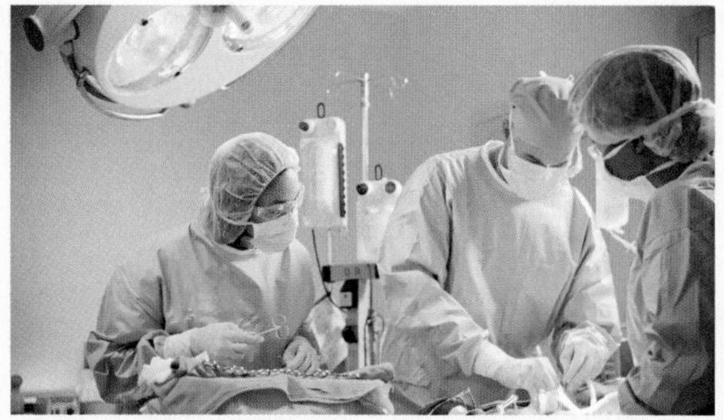

a. Write two ordered pairs of the form (year, number of heart transplants).

b. Find the slope of the line between the two points.

c. Write a sentence explaining the meaning of the slope as a rate of change.

100. The average price of an acre of U.S. farmland was $1210 in 2002. In 2008, the price of an acre rose to $2350. (*Source:* National Agricultural Statistics Services)

a. Write two ordered pairs of the form (year, price of an acre).

b. Find the slope of the line through the two points.

c. Write a sentence explaining the meaning of the slope as a rate of change.

101. Show that a triangle with vertices at the points $(1, 1)$, $(-4, 4)$, and $(-3, 0)$ is a right triangle.

102. Show that the quadrilateral with vertices $(1, 3)$, $(2, 1)$, $(-4, 0)$, and $(-3, -2)$ is a parallelogram.

Find the slope of the line through the given points.

103. $(2.1, 6.7)$ and $(-8.3, 9.3)$

104. $(-3.8, 1.2)$ and $(-2.2, 4.5)$

105. $(2.3, 0.2)$ and $(7.9, 5.1)$

106. $(14.3, -10.1)$ and $(9.8, -2.9)$

107. The graph of $y = -\frac{1}{3}x + 2$ has a slope of $-\frac{1}{3}$. The graph of $y = -2x + 2$ has a slope of -2. The graph of $y = -4x + 2$ has a slope of -4. Graph all three equations on a single coordinate system. As the absolute value of the slope becomes larger, how does the steepness of the line change?

108. The graph of $y = \frac{1}{2}x$ has a slope of $\frac{1}{2}$. The graph of $y = 3x$ has a slope of 3. The graph of $y = 5x$ has a slope of 5. Graph all three equations on a single coordinate system. As slope becomes larger, how does the steepness of the line change?

Integrated Review SUMMARY ON SLOPE & GRAPHING LINEAR EQUATIONS

Sections 1.1–1.4

Find the slope of each line.

1.

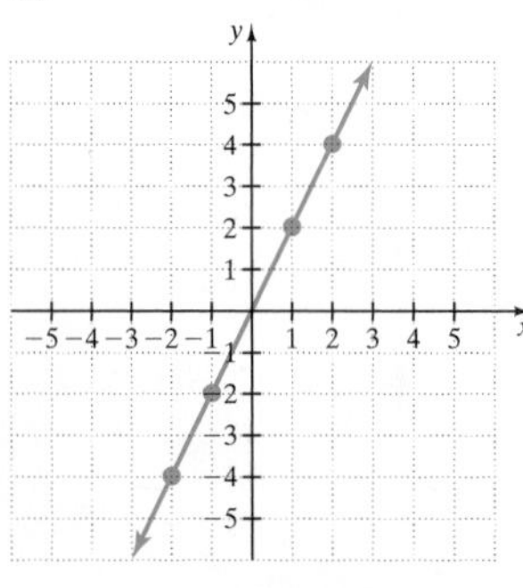

2.

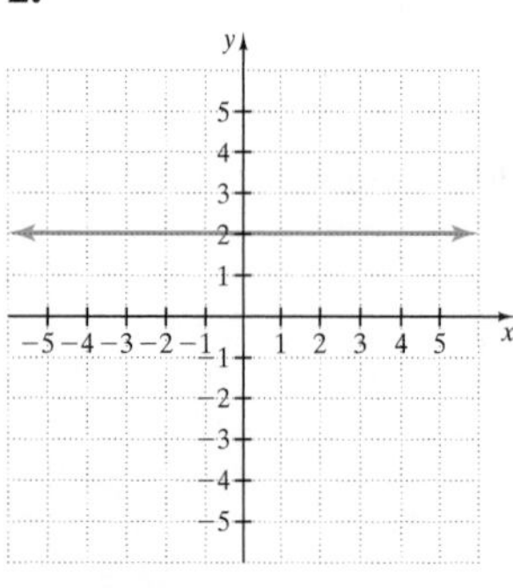

3.

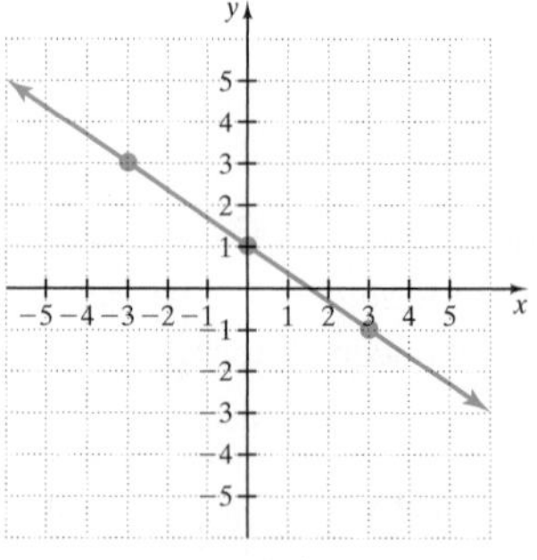

4.

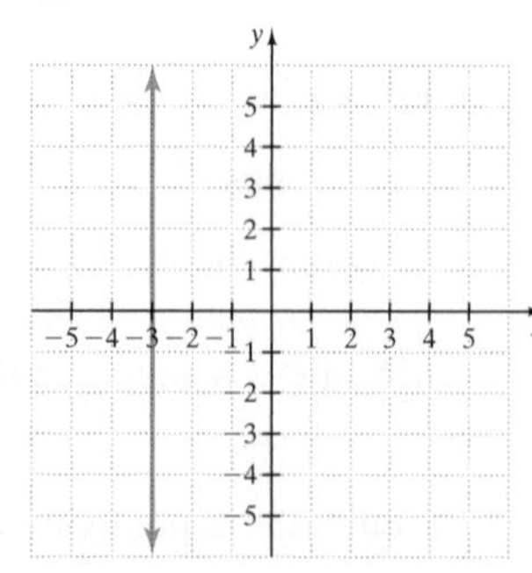

Graph each linear equation.

5. $y = -2x$

6. $x + y = 3$

7. $x = -1$

8. $y = 4$

9. $x - 2y = 6$

10. $y = 3x + 2$

11. $5x + 3y = 15$

12. $2x - 4y = 8$

Determine whether the lines through the points are parallel, perpendicular, or neither.

13. $y = -\frac{1}{5}x + \frac{1}{3}$
$3x = -15y$

14. $x - y = \frac{1}{2}$
$3x - y = \frac{1}{2}$

15. In the years 2000 through 2009 the number of bridges on public roads (in thousands) in the United States can be modeled by the linear equation $y = 1.7x + 587$ where x is years after 2000 and y is number of bridges (in thousands). (*Source:* U.S. Dept. of Transportation)

a. Find the y-intercept of this line.

b. Write a sentence explaining the meaning of this intercept.

c. Find the slope of this line.

d. Write a sentence explaining the meaning of the slope as a rate of change.

16. Online advertising is a means of promoting products and services using the Internet. The revenue (in billions of dollars) for online advertising for the years 2003 through 2010 is given by $y = 3.3x - 3.1$, where x is the number of years after 2000.

a. Use this equation to complete the ordered pair (9,   ).

b. Write a sentence explaining the meaning of the answer to part (a).

1.5 Equations of Lines

OBJECTIVES

1 Use the Slope-Intercept Form to Graph a Linear Equation.

2 Use the Slope-Intercept Form to Write an Equation of a Line.

3 Use the Point-Slope Form to Find an Equation of a Line Given Its Slope and a Point of the Line.

4 Use the Point-Slope Form to Find an Equation of a Line Given Two Points of the Line.

5 Find Equations of Vertical and Horizontal Lines.

6 Use the Point-Slope Form to Solve Problems.

Recall that the form $y = mx + b$ is appropriately called the *slope-intercept form* of a linear equation. (m ↑ slope; b ↑ y-intercept is $(0, b)$)

Slope-Intercept Form

When a linear equation in two variables is written in **slope-intercept form,**

$$y = mx + b$$

(m ↑ slope; b ↑ $(0, b)$, y-intercept)

then m is the slope of the line and $(0, b)$ is the y-intercept of the line.

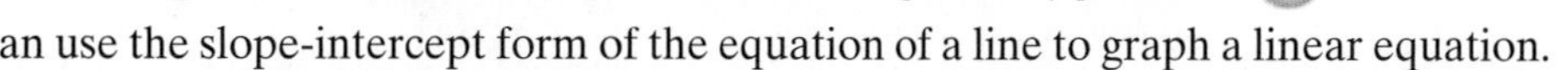

OBJECTIVE

1 Using the Slope-Intercept Form to Graph an Equation

We can use the slope-intercept form of the equation of a line to graph a linear equation.

EXAMPLE 1 Use the slope-intercept form to graph the equation

$$y = \frac{3}{5}x - 2$$

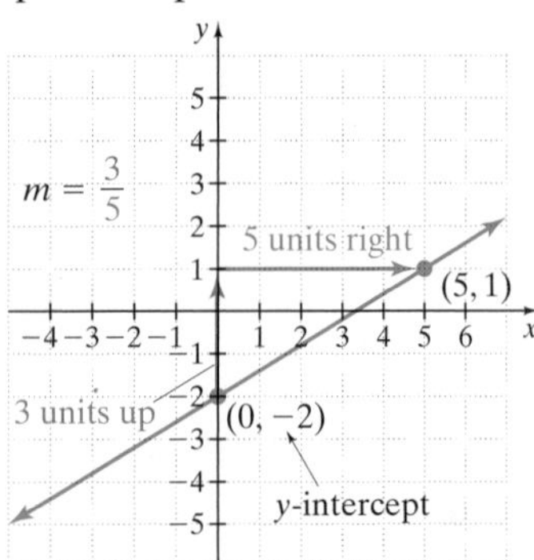

Solution Since the equation $y = \frac{3}{5}x - 2$ is written in slope-intercept form $y = mx + b$, the slope of its graph is $\frac{3}{5}$ and the y-intercept is $(0, -2)$. To graph this equation, we begin by plotting the point $(0, -2)$. From this point, we can find another point of the graph by using the slope $\frac{3}{5}$ and recalling that slope is $\frac{\text{rise}}{\text{run}}$. We start at the y-intercept and move 3 units up since the numerator of the slope is 3; then we move 5 units to the right since the denominator of the slope is 5. We stop at the point (5, 1). The line through $(0, -2)$ and (5, 1) is the graph of $y = \frac{3}{5}x - 2$. □

PRACTICE 1 Graph $y = \frac{2}{3}x - 5$.

EXAMPLE 2 Use the slope-intercept form to graph the equation $4x + y = 1$.

Solution First we write the given equation in slope-intercept form.

$$4x + y = 1$$
$$y = -4x + 1$$

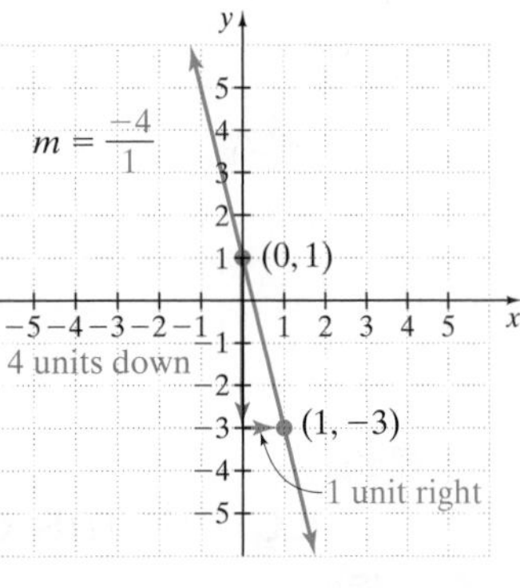

The graph of this equation will have slope -4 and y-intercept (0, 1). To graph this line, we first plot the point (0, 1). To find another point of the graph, we use the slope -4, which can be written as $\frac{-4}{1}$ $\left(\frac{4}{-1}\text{ could also be used}\right)$. We start at the point (0, 1) and move 4 units down (since the numerator of the slope is -4) and then 1 unit to the right (since the denominator of the slope is 1).

We arrive at the point $(1, -3)$. The line through (0, 1) and $(1, -3)$ is the graph of $4x + y = 1$. □

> **Helpful Hint**
> In Example 2, if we interpret the slope of -4 as $\frac{4}{-1}$, we arrive at $(-1, 5)$ for a second point. Notice that this point is also on the line.

PRACTICE 2 Use the slope-intercept form to graph the equation $3x - y = 2$.

OBJECTIVE 2 Using the Slope-Intercept Form to Write an Equation 

The slope-intercept form can also be used to write the equation of a line when we know its slope and y-intercept.

EXAMPLE 3 Find an equation of the line with y-intercept $(0, -3)$ and slope of $\frac{1}{4}$.

Solution We are given the slope and the y-intercept. We let $m = \frac{1}{4}$ and $b = -3$ and write the equation in slope-intercept form, $y = mx + b$.

$$y = mx + b$$
$$y = \frac{1}{4}x + (-3) \quad \text{Let } m = \frac{1}{4} \text{ and } b = -3.$$
$$y = \frac{1}{4}x - 3 \quad \text{Simplify.}$$

□

PRACTICE

3 Find an equation of the line with y-intercept $(0, 7)$ and slope of $\frac{1}{2}$.

OBJECTIVE

3 Writing an Equation Given Slope and a Point 

Thus far, we have seen that we can write an equation of a line if we know its slope and y-intercept. We can also write an equation of a line if we know its slope and any point on the line. To see how we do this, let m represent slope and (x_1, y_1) represent the point on the line. Then if (x, y) is any other point of the line, we have that

$$\frac{y - y_1}{x - x_1} = m$$

$$y - y_1 = m(x - x_1) \quad \text{Multiply both sides by } (x - x_1).$$

(m is the slope.)

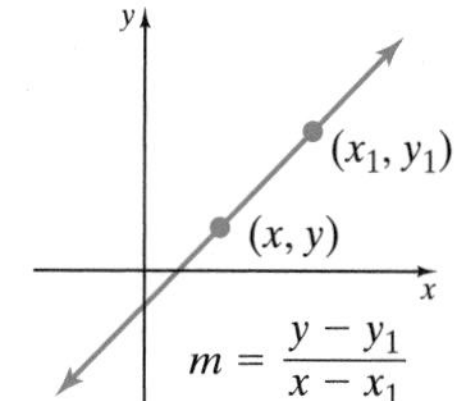

This is the *point-slope form* of the equation of a line.

Point-Slope Form of the Equation of a Line

The **point-slope form** of the equation of a line is

$$y - y_1 = m(x - x_1)$$

(m: slope; (x_1, y_1): point on the line)

where m is the slope of the line and (x_1, y_1) is a point on the line.

EXAMPLE 4 Find an equation of the line with slope -2 that passes through $(-1, 5)$. Write the equation in slope-intercept form, $y = mx + b$, and in standard form, $Ax + By = C$.

Solution Since the slope and a point on the line are given, we use point-slope form $y - y_1 = m(x - x_1)$ to write the equation. Let $m = -2$ and $(-1, 5) = (x_1, y_1)$.

$$y - y_1 = m(x - x_1)$$

$$y - 5 = -2[x - (-1)] \quad \text{Let } m = -2 \text{ and } (x_1, y_1) = (-1, 5).$$

$$y - 5 = -2(x + 1) \quad \text{Simplify.}$$

$$y - 5 = -2x - 2 \quad \text{Use the distributive property.}$$

To write the equation in slope-intercept form, $y = mx + b$, we simply solve the equation for y. To do this, we add 5 to both sides.

$$y - 5 = -2x - 2$$

$$y = -2x + 3 \quad \text{Slope-intercept form.}$$

$$2x + y = 3 \quad \text{Add } 2x \text{ to both sides and we have standard form.}$$

□

PRACTICE

4 Find an equation of the line passing through (2, 3) with slope 4. Write the equation in standard form: $Ax + By = C$.

OBJECTIVE

4 Writing an Equation Given Two Points 

We can also find an equation of a line when we are given any two points of the line.

EXAMPLE 5 Find an equation of the line through $(2, 5)$ and $(-3, 4)$. Write the equation in standard form.

Solution First, use the two given points to find the slope of the line.

$$m = \frac{4 - 5}{-3 - 2} = \frac{-1}{-5} = \frac{1}{5}$$

Next we use the slope $\frac{1}{5}$ and either one of the given points to write the equation in point-slope form. We use $(2, 5)$. Let $x_1 = 2$, $y_1 = 5$, and $m = \frac{1}{5}$.

$$y - y_1 = m(x - x_1) \quad \text{Use point-slope form.}$$

$$y - 5 = \frac{1}{5}(x - 2) \quad \text{Let } x_1 = 2,\ y_1 = 5, \text{ and } m = \frac{1}{5}.$$

$$5(y - 5) = 5 \cdot \frac{1}{5}(x - 2) \quad \text{Multiply both sides by 5 to clear fractions.}$$

$$5y - 25 = x - 2 \quad \text{Use the distributive property and simplify.}$$

$$-x + 5y - 25 = -2 \quad \text{Subtract } x \text{ from both sides.}$$

$$-x + 5y = 23 \quad \text{Add 25 to both sides.}$$

□

PRACTICE 5 Find an equation of the line through $(-1, 6)$ and $(3, 1)$. Write the equation in standard form.

> **Helpful Hint**
> Multiply both sides of the equation $-x + 5y = 23$ by -1, and it becomes $x - 5y = -23$. Both $-x + 5y = 23$ and $x - 5y = -23$ are in standard form, and they are equations of the same line.

OBJECTIVE 5

Finding Equations of Vertical and Horizontal Lines

Recall from Section 1.3 that:

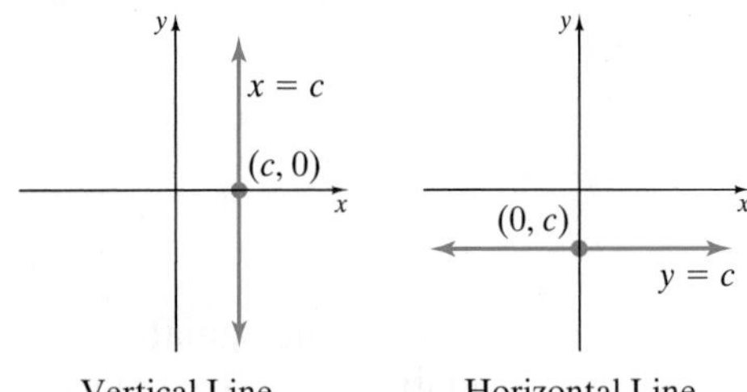

EXAMPLE 6 Find an equation of the vertical line through $(-1, 5)$.

Solution The equation of a vertical line can be written in the form $x = c$, so an equation for a vertical line passing through $(-1, 5)$ is $x = -1$.

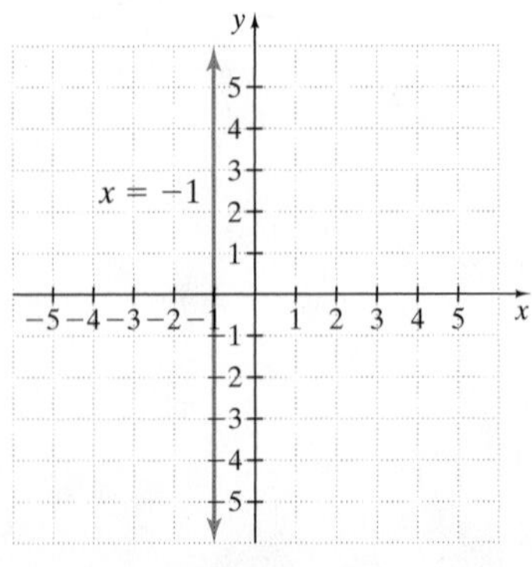

□

PRACTICE 6 Find an equation of the vertical line through $(3, -2)$.

EXAMPLE 7 Find an equation of the line parallel to the line $y = 5$ and passing through $(-2, -3)$.

Solution Since the graph of $y = 5$ is a horizontal line, any line parallel to it is also horizontal. The equation of a horizontal line can be written in the form $y = c$. An equation for the horizontal line passing through

$$(-2, -3) \text{ is } y = -3.$$

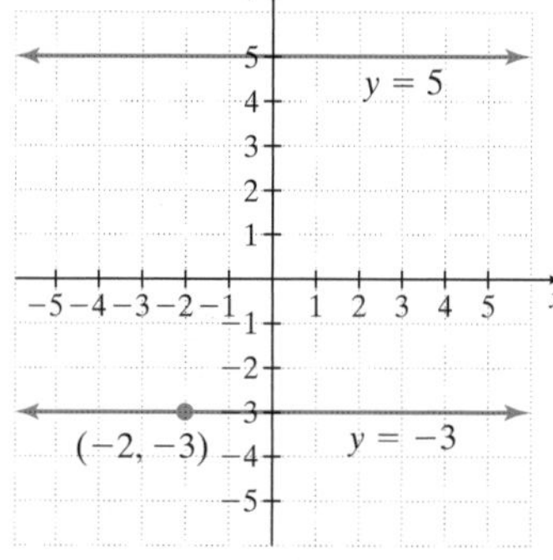

□

PRACTICE 7 Find an equation of the line parallel to the line $y = -2$ and passing through $(4, 3)$.

OBJECTIVE

6 Using the Point-Slope Form to Solve Problems

Problems occurring in many fields can be modeled by linear equations in two variables. The next example is from the field of marketing and shows how consumer demand of a product depends on the price of the product.

EXAMPLE 8 **Predicting the Sales of T-Shirts**

A web-based T-shirt company has learned that by pricing a clearance-sale T-shirt at \$6, sales will reach 2000 T-shirts per day. Raising the price to \$8 will cause the sales to fall to 1500 T-shirts per day.

a. Assume that the relationship between sales price and number of T-shirts sold is linear and write an equation describing this relationship. Write the equation in slope-intercept form.

b. Predict the daily sales of T-shirts if the price is \$7.50.

Solution

a. First, use the given information and write two ordered pairs. Ordered pairs will be in the form (sales price, number sold) so that our ordered pairs are (6, 2000) and (8, 1500). Use the point-slope form to write an equation. To do so, we find the slope of the line that contains these points.

$$m = \frac{2000 - 1500}{6 - 8} = \frac{500}{-2} = -250$$

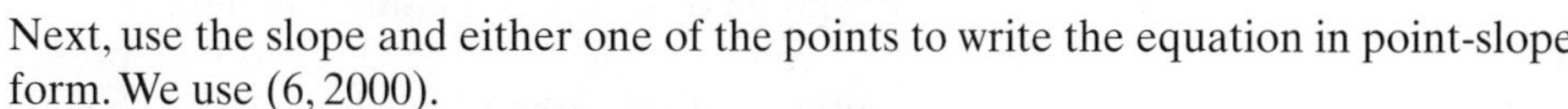

Next, use the slope and either one of the points to write the equation in point-slope form. We use (6, 2000).

$$y - y_1 = m(x - x_1) \quad \text{Use point-slope form.}$$
$$y - 2000 = -250(x - 6) \quad \text{Let } x_1 = 6, y_1 = 2000, \text{ and } m = -250.$$
$$y - 2000 = -250x + 1500 \quad \text{Use the distributive property.}$$
$$y = -250x + 3500 \quad \text{Write in slope-intercept form.}$$

b. To predict the sales if the price is \$7.50, we find y when $x = 7.50$.

$$y = -250x + 3500$$
$$y = -250(7.50) + 3500 \quad \text{Let } x = 7.50.$$
$$y = -1875 + 3500$$
$$y = 1625$$

If the price is \$7.50, sales will reach 1625 T-shirts per day. □

PRACTICE

8 The new *Camelot* condos were selling at a rate of 30 per month when they were priced at \$150,000 each. Lowering the price to \$120,000 caused the sales to rise to 50 condos per month.

a. Assume that the relationship between number of condos sold and price is linear, and write an equation describing this relationship. Write the equation in slope-intercept form.

b. How should the condos be priced if the developer wishes to sell 60 condos per month?

The preceding example may also be solved by using ordered pairs of the form (number sold, sales price).

Forms of Linear Equations

$Ax + By = C$	**Standard form** of a linear equation. A and B are not both 0.
$y = mx + b$	**Slope-intercept form** of a linear equation. The slope is m and the y-intercept is $(0, b)$.
$y - y_1 = m(x - x_1)$	**Point-slope form** of a linear equation. The slope is m and (x_1, y_1) is a point on the line.
$y = c$	**Horizontal line** The slope is 0 and the y-intercept is $(0, c)$.
$x = c$	**Vertical line** The slope is undefined and the x-intercept is $(c, 0)$.

Parallel and Perpendicular Lines

Nonvertical parallel lines have the same slope.

The product of the slopes of two nonvertical perpendicular lines is -1.

Graphing Calculator Explorations 

A grapher is a very useful tool for discovering patterns. To discover the change in the graph of a linear equation caused by a change in slope, try the following. Use a standard window and graph a linear equation in the form $y = mx + b$. Recall that the graph of such an equation will have slope m and y-intercept b.

First, graph $y = x + 3$. To do so, press the [Y =] key and enter $Y_1 = x + 3$. Notice that this graph has slope 1 and that the y-intercept is 3. Next, on the same set of axes, graph $y = 2x + 3$ and $y = 3x + 3$ by pressing [Y =] and entering $Y_2 = 2x + 3$ and $Y_3 = 3x + 3$.

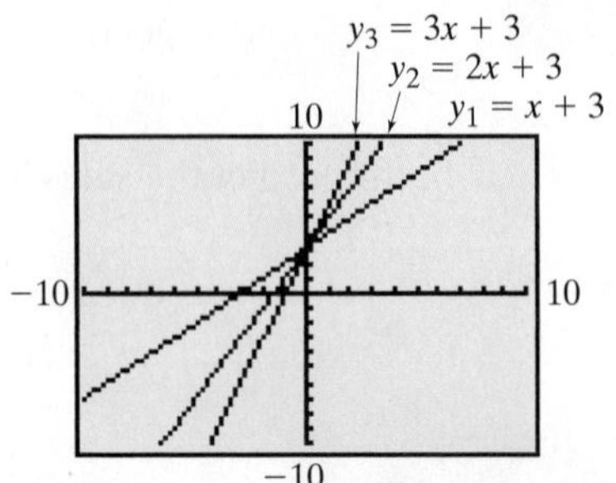

Notice the difference in the graph of each equation as the slope changes from 1 to 2 to 3. How would the graph of $y = 5x + 3$ appear? To see the change in the graph caused by a change in negative slope, try graphing $y = -x + 3$, $y = -2x + 3$, and $y = -3x + 3$ on the same set of axes.

Use a grapher to graph the following equations. For each exercise, graph the first equation and use its graph to predict the appearance of the other equations. Then graph the other equations on the same set of axes and check your prediction.

1. $y = x; y = 6x, y = -6x$

2. $y = -x; y = -5x, y = -10x$

3. $y = \frac{1}{2}x + 2; y = \frac{3}{4}x + 2, y = x + 2$

4. $y = x + 1; y = \frac{5}{4}x + 1, y = \frac{5}{2}x + 1$

5. $y = -7x + 5; y = 7x + 5$

6. $y = 3x - 1; y = -3x - 1$

Vocabulary, Readiness & Video Check

Use the choices below to fill in each blank. Some choices may be used more than once and some not at all.

b	(y_1, x_1)	point-slope	vertical	standard
m	(x_1, y_1)	slope-intercept	horizontal	

1. The form $y = mx + b$ is called __________ form. When a linear equation in two variables is written in this form, __________ is the slope of its graph and (0, __________) is its y-intercept.

2. The form $y - y_1 = m(x - x_1)$ is called __________ form. When a linear equation in two variables is written in this form, __________ is the slope of its graph and __________ is a point on the graph.

Martin-Gay Interactive Videos

See Video 1.5

Watch the section lecture video and answer the following questions.

OBJECTIVE 1

3. We can use the slope-intercept form to graph a line. Complete these statements based on Example 1. Start by graphing the __________.
Find another point by applying the slope to this point—rewrite the slope as a __________ if necessary.

OBJECTIVE 2

4. In Example 3, what is the y-intercept?

OBJECTIVE 3

5. In Example 4 we use the point-slope form to find the equation of a line given the slope and a point. How do we then write this equation in standard form?

OBJECTIVE 4

6. The lecture before Example 5 discusses how to find the equation of a line given two points. Is there any circumstance when you might want to use the slope-intercept form to find the equation of a line given two points? If so, when?

OBJECTIVE 5

7. Solve Examples 6 and 7 again, this time using the point $(-2, -3)$ in each exercise.

OBJECTIVE 6

8. From Example 8, we are told to use ordered pairs of the form (time, speed). Explain why it is important to keep track of how you define your ordered pairs and/or define your variables.

1.5 Exercise Set

MyMathLab®

Use the slope-intercept form to graph each equation. See Examples 1 and 2.

1. $y = 2x + 1$
2. $y = -4x - 1$
3. $y = \frac{2}{3}x + 5$
4. $y = \frac{1}{4}x - 3$
5. $y = -5x$
6. $y = -6x$
7. $4x + y = 6$
8. $-3x + y = 2$
9. $4x - 7y = -14$
10. $3x - 4y = 4$
11. $x = \frac{5}{4}y$
12. $x = \frac{3}{2}y$

Write an equation of the line with each given slope, m, and y-intercept, (0, b). See Example 3.

13. $m = 5, b = 3$
14. $m = -3, b = -3$
15. $m = -4, b = -\frac{1}{6}$
16. $m = 2, b = \frac{3}{4}$
17. $m = \frac{2}{3}, b = 0$
18. $m = -\frac{4}{5}, b = 0$
19. $m = 0, b = -8$
20. $m = 0, b = -2$
21. $m = -\frac{1}{5}, b = \frac{1}{9}$
22. $m = \frac{1}{2}, b = -\frac{1}{3}$

Find an equation of each line with the given slope that passes through the given point. Write the equation in the form $Ax + By = C$. See Example 4.

23. $m = 6;\ (2, 2)$
24. $m = 4;\ (1, 3)$
25. $m = -8;\ (-1, -5)$
26. $m = -2;\ (-11, -12)$
27. $m = \frac{3}{2};\ (5, -6)$
28. $m = \frac{2}{3};\ (-8, 9)$
29. $m = -\frac{1}{2};\ (-3, 0)$
30. $m = -\frac{1}{5};\ (4, 0)$

Find an equation of the line passing through each pair of points. Write the equation in the form $Ax + By = C$. See Example 5.

31. $(3, 2)$ and $(5, 6)$
32. $(6, 2)$ and $(8, 8)$
33. $(-1, 3)$ and $(-2, -5)$
34. $(-4, 0)$ and $(6, -1)$
35. $(2, 3)$ and $(-1, -1)$
36. $(7, 10)$ and $(-1, -1)$
37. $(0, 0)$ and $\left(-\frac{1}{8}, \frac{1}{13}\right)$
38. $(0, 0)$ and $\left(-\frac{1}{2}, \frac{1}{3}\right)$

Find an equation of each line. See Example 6.

39. Vertical line through $(0, 2)$
40. Horizontal line through $(1, 4)$
41. Horizontal line through $(-1, 3)$
42. Vertical line through $(-1, 3)$
43. Vertical line through $\left(-\frac{7}{3}, -\frac{2}{5}\right)$
44. Horizontal line through $\left(\frac{2}{7}, 0\right)$

Find an equation of each line. See Example 7.

45. △ Parallel to $y = 5$, through $(1, 2)$
46. △ Perpendicular to $y = 5$, through $(1, 2)$
47. △ Perpendicular to $x = -3$, through $(-2, 5)$
48. △ Parallel to $y = -4$, through $(0, -3)$
49. △ Parallel to $x = 0$, through $(6, -8)$
50. △ Perpendicular to $x = 7$, through $(-5, 0)$

MIXED PRACTICE

See Examples 1 through 7. Find an equation of each line described. Write each equation in slope-intercept form (solved for y), when possible.

51. With slope $-\frac{1}{2}$, through $\left(0, \frac{5}{3}\right)$
52. With slope $\frac{5}{7}$, through $(0, -3)$
53. Through $(10, 7)$ and $(7, 10)$
54. Through $(5, -6)$ and $(-6, 5)$
55. With undefined slope, through $\left(-\frac{3}{4}, 1\right)$
56. With slope 0, through $(6.7, 12.1)$
57. Slope 1, through $(-7, 9)$
58. Slope 5, through $(6, -8)$
59. Slope -5, y-intercept $(0, 7)$
60. Slope -2; y-intercept $(0, -4)$
61. Through $(6, 7)$, parallel to the x-axis
62. Through $(1, -5)$, parallel to the y-axis
63. Through $(2, 3)$ and $(0, 0)$
64. Through $(4, 7)$ and $(0, 0)$
65. Through $(-2, -3)$, perpendicular to the y-axis
66. Through $(0, 12)$, perpendicular to the x-axis
67. Slope $-\frac{4}{7}$, through $(-1, -2)$
68. Slope $-\frac{3}{5}$, through $(4, 4)$

Solve. Assume each exercise describes a linear relationship. Write the equations in slope-intercept form. See Example 8.

69. A rock is dropped from the top of a 400-foot cliff. After 1 second, the rock is traveling 32 feet per second. After 3 seconds, the rock is traveling 96 feet per second.

a. Assume that the relationship between time and speed is linear and write an equation describing this relationship. Use ordered pairs of the form (time, speed).

b. Use this equation to determine the speed of the rock 4 seconds after it was dropped.

70. A Hawaiian fruit company is studying the sales of a pineapple sauce to see if this product is to be continued. At the end of its first year, profits on this product amounted to $30,000. At the end of the fourth year, profits were $66,000.

a. Assume that the relationship between years on the market and profit is linear and write an equation describing this relationship. Use ordered pairs of the form (years on the market, profit).

b. Use this equation to predict the profit at the end of 7 years.

71. Sales of hybrid (gas-electric) vehicles have been decreasing for the past few years. In 2007, 356 thousand new gasoline-electric hybrid vehicles were sold in the United States. In 2009, only were 290 thousand were sold. (*Source:* U.S. Energy Information Administration)

a. Write an equation describing the relationship between time and number of registered gasoline-electric hybrid vehicles sold. Use ordered pairs of the form (years past 2007, number of hybrids sold).

b. Use this equation to predict the number of gasoline-electric hybrids sold in the year 2015.

72. In 2011, there were 960 thousand eating establishments in the United States. In 2006, there were 935 thousand eating establishments. (*Source:* National Restaurant Association)

a. Write an equation describing the relationship between time and number of eating establishments. Use ordered pairs of the form (years past 2006, number of eating establishments in thousands).

b. Use this equation to predict the number of eating establishments in 2018.

73. In 2006, the U.S. population per square mile of land area was 85. In 2011, the person per square mile population was 88.

a. Write an equation describing the relationship between year and persons per square mile. Use ordered pairs of the form (years past 2006, persons per square mile).

b. Use this equation to predict the person per square mile population in 2020.

74. In 2005, there were a total of 150 thousand apparel and accessory stores. In 2009, there were a total of 157 thousand apparel and accessory stores. (*Source:* U.S. Bureau of the Census. *County Business Patterns*)

a. Write an equation describing this relationship. Use ordered pairs of the form (years past 2005, numbers of stores in thousands).

b. Use this equation to predict the number of apparel and accessory stores in 2015.

75. It has been said that newspapers are disappearing, replaced by various electronic media. In 2001, newspaper circulation (number of copies it distributed in a day) was about 60 million. In 2009, this circulation dropped to 46 million. (*Source:* Newspaper Asso. of America)

a. Write an equation describing the relationship between time and circulation. Use ordered pairs of the form (years past 2001, number of newspapers circulated).

b. Use this equation to predict the newspaper circulation in 2017.

76. A certain chain of book stores is slowly closing down stores. Suppose that in 2006 there were 3991 stores and in 2010 there were 3200 stores.

a. Write an equation describing the relationship between time and number of store locations. Use ordered pairs of the form (years past 2006, number of stores).

b. Use this equation to predict the number of stores in 2018.

77. The Pool Fun Company has learned that, by pricing a newly released Fun Noodle at $3, sales will reach 10,000 Fun Noodles per day during the summer. Raising the price to $5 will cause sales to fall to 8000 Fun Noodles per day.

a. Assume that the relationship between price and number of Fun Noodles sold is linear and write an equation describing this relationship. Use ordered pairs of the form (price, number sold).

b. Predict the daily sales of Fun Noodles if the price is $3.50.

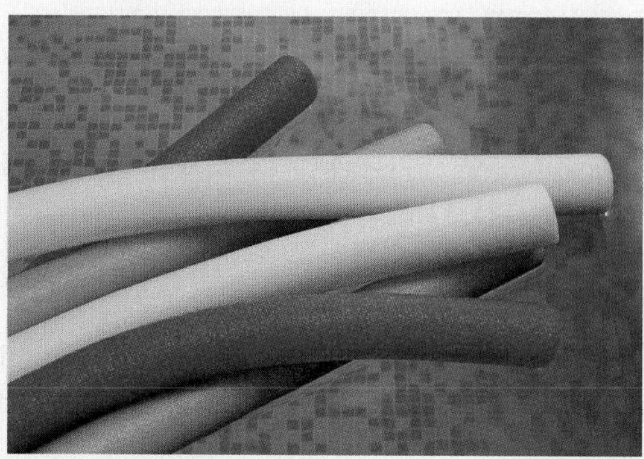

78. The value of a building bought in 2000 may be depreciated (or decreased) as time passes for income tax purposes. Seven years after the building was bought, this value was $225,000 and 12 years after it was bought, this value was $195,000.

a. If the relationship between number of years past 2000 and the depreciated value of the building is linear, write an equation describing this relationship. Use ordered pairs of the form (years past 2000, value of building).

b. Use this equation to estimate the depreciated value of the building in 2018.

REVIEW AND PREVIEW

Find the value of $x^2 - 3x + 1$ for each given value of x. See Section R.7.

79. 2 **80.** 5 **81.** −1 **82.** −3

For each graph, determine whether any x-values correspond to two or more y-values. See Section 1.1.

83.

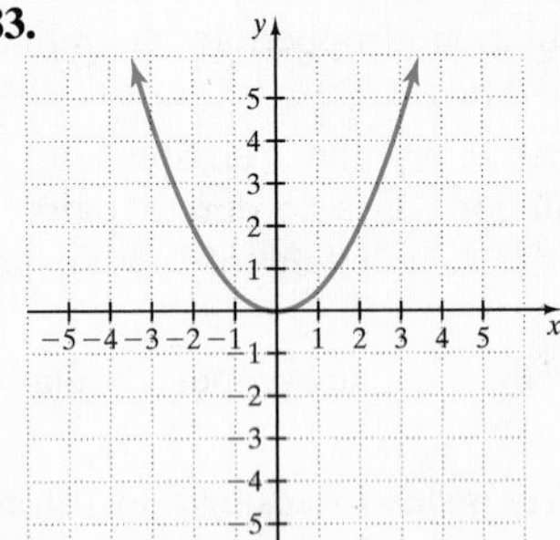

84.

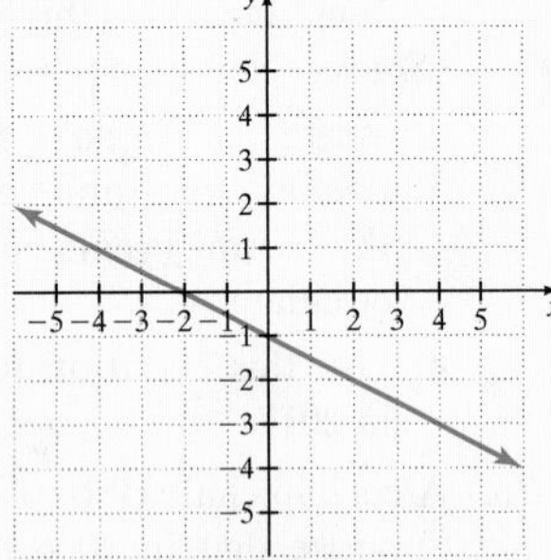

85.

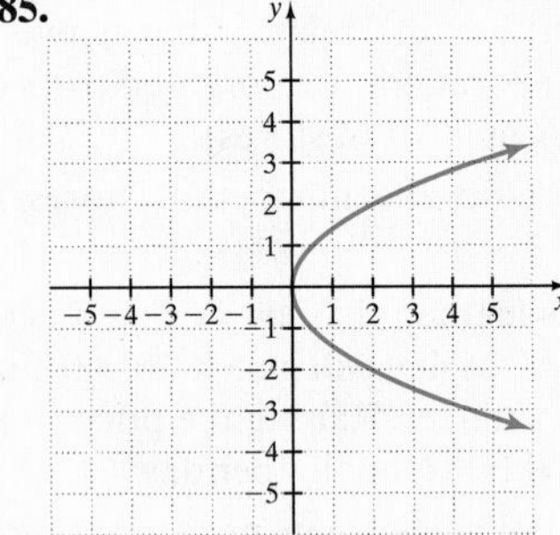

86.

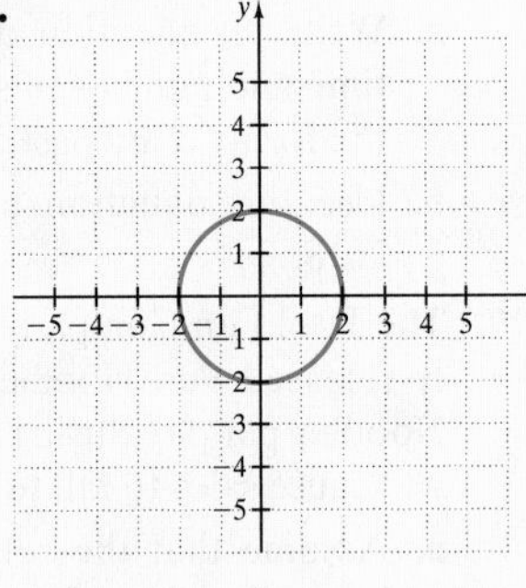

CONCEPT EXTENSIONS

For Exercises 87 through 90, identify the form that the linear equation in two variables is written in. For Exercises 91 and 92, identify the appearance of the graph of the equation.

87. $y - 7 = 4(x + 3)$; ____________ form

88. $5x - 9y = 11$; ____________ form

89. $y = \frac{3}{4}x - \frac{1}{3}$; ____________ form

90. $y + 2 = \frac{-1}{3}(x - 2)$; ____________ form

91. $y = \frac{1}{2}$; ____________ line **92.** $x = -17$; ____________ line

93. Given the equation of a nonvertical line, explain how to find the slope without finding two points on the line.

94. Given two points on a nonvertical line, explain how to use the point-slope form to find the equation of the line.

95. Write an equation in standard form of the line that contains the point $(-1, 2)$ and is

a. parallel to the line $y = 3x - 1$.

b. perpendicular to the line $y = 3x - 1$.

96. Write an equation in standard form of the line that contains the point $(4, 0)$ and is

a. parallel to the line $y = -2x + 3$.

b. perpendicular to the line $y = -2x + 3$.

97. Write an equation in standard form of the line that contains the point $(3, -5)$ and is

a. parallel to the line $3x + 2y = 7$.

b. perpendicular to the line $3x + 2y = 7$.

98. Write an equation in standard form of the line that contains the point $(-2, 4)$ and is

a. parallel to the line $x + 3y = 6$.

b. perpendicular to the line $x + 3y = 6$.

Chapter 1 Vocabulary Check

Fill in each blank with one of the words listed below.

relation	function	domain	range	standard	slope-intercept
y-axis	*x*-axis	solution	linear	slope	point-slope
x-intercept	*y*-intercept	*y*	*x*		

1. An ordered pair is a(n) ____________ of an equation in two variables if replacing the variables by the coordinates of the ordered pair results in a true statement.
2. The vertical number line in the rectangular coordinate system is called the ____________.
3. A(n) ____________ equation can be written in the form $Ax + By = C$.

4. A(n) ______________ is a point of the graph where the graph crosses the x-axis.
5. The form $Ax + By = C$ is called ______________ form.
6. A(n) ______________ is a point of the graph where the graph crosses the y-axis.
7. The equation $y = 7x - 5$ is written in ______________ form.
8. The equation $y + 1 = 7(x - 2)$ is written in ______________ form.
9. To find an x-intercept of a graph, let ______________ = 0.
10. The horizontal number line in the rectangular coordinate system is called the ______________.
11. To find a y-intercept of a graph, let ______________ = 0.
12. The ______________ of a line measures the steepness or tilt of a line.
13. A set of ordered pairs that assigns to each x-value exactly one y-value is called a(n) ______________.
14. The set of all x-coordinates of a relation is called the ______________ of the relation.
15. The set of all y-coordinates of a relation is called the ______________ of the relation.
16. A set of ordered pairs is called a(n) ______________.

Chapter 1 Highlights

DEFINITIONS AND CONCEPTS	EXAMPLES

Section 1.1 Reading Graphs and the Rectangular Coordinate System

The **rectangular coordinate system** consists of a plane and a vertical and a horizontal number line intersecting at their 0 coordinates. The vertical number line is called the **y-axis** and the horizontal number line is called the **x-axis.** The point of intersection of the axes is called the **origin.**

To **plot** or **graph** an ordered pair means to find its corresponding point on a rectangular coordinate system.

To plot or graph an ordered pair such as $(3, -2)$, start at the origin. Move 3 units to the right and, from there, 2 units down.

To plot or graph $(-3, 4)$ start at the origin. Move 3 units to the left and, from there, 4 units up.

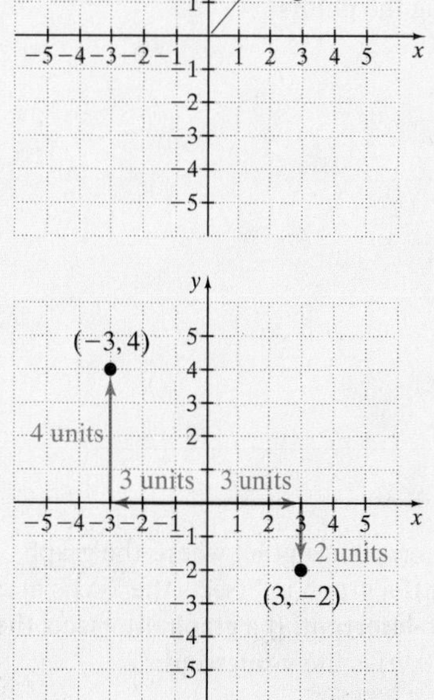

(*continued*)

DEFINITIONS AND CONCEPTS	EXAMPLES
Section 1.1 Reading Graphs and the Rectangular Coordinate System (continued)	
An ordered pair is a **solution** of an equation in two variables if replacing the variables by the coordinates of the ordered pair results in a true statement.	Determine whether $(-1, 5)$ is a solution of $2x + 3y = 13$. $2x + 3y = 13$ $2(-1) + 3 \cdot 5 = 13$ Let $x = -1, y = 5$ $-2 + 15 = 13$ $13 = 13$ True
If one coordinate of an ordered pair solution is known, the other value can be determined by substitution.	Complete the ordered pair solution (0,) for the equation $x - 6y = 12$. $x - 6y = 12$ $0 - 6y = 12$ Let $x = 0$. $\frac{-6y}{-6} = \frac{12}{-6}$ Divide by -6. $y = -2$ The ordered pair solution is $(0, -2)$.
Section 1.2 Graphing Linear Equations	
A **linear equation in two variables** is an equation that can be written in the form $Ax + By = C$ where A and B are not both 0. The form $Ax + By = C$ is called **standard form.**	***Linear Equations*** $3x + 2y = -6$ $x = -5$ $y = 3$ $y = -x + 10$ $x + y = 10$ is in standard form.
To graph a linear equation in two variables, find three ordered pair solutions. Plot the solution points and draw the line connecting the points.	Graph $x - 2y = 5$. 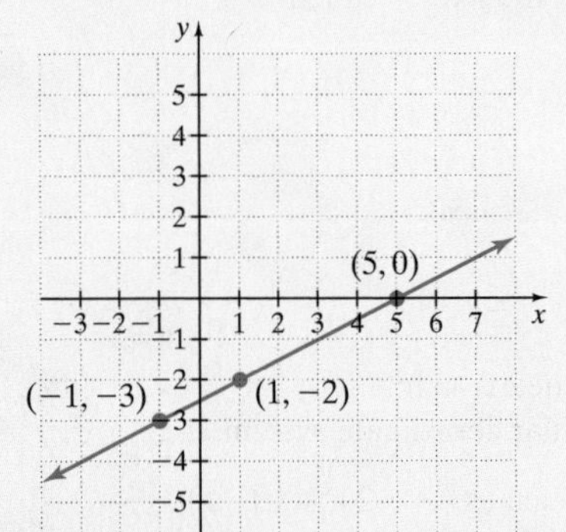
Section 1.3 Intercepts	
An **intercept** of a graph is a point where the graph intersects an axis. If a graph intersects the x-axis at a, then $(a, 0)$ is the ***x*-intercept.** If a graph intersects the y-axis at b, then $(0, b)$ is the ***y*-intercept.**	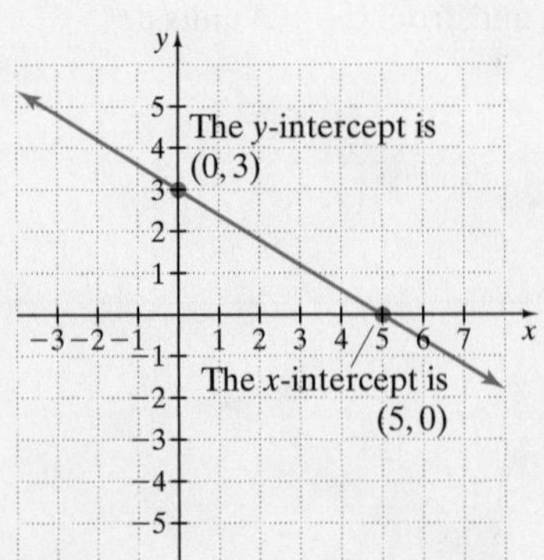

x	y
5	0
1	−2
−1	−3

DEFINITIONS AND CONCEPTS	EXAMPLES
Section 1.3 Intercepts (continued)	

To find the *x*-intercept, let $y = 0$ and solve for x.

To find the *y*-intercept, let $x = 0$ and solve for y.

Graph $2x - 5y = -10$ by finding intercepts.

If $y = 0$, then

$$2x - 5 \cdot 0 = -10$$
$$2x = -10$$
$$\frac{2x}{2} = \frac{-10}{2}$$
$$x = -5$$

If $x = 0$, then

$$2 \cdot 0 - 5y = -10$$
$$-5y = -10$$
$$\frac{-5y}{-5} = \frac{-10}{-5}$$
$$y = 2$$

The x-intercept is $(-5, 0)$. The y-intercept is $(0, 2)$.

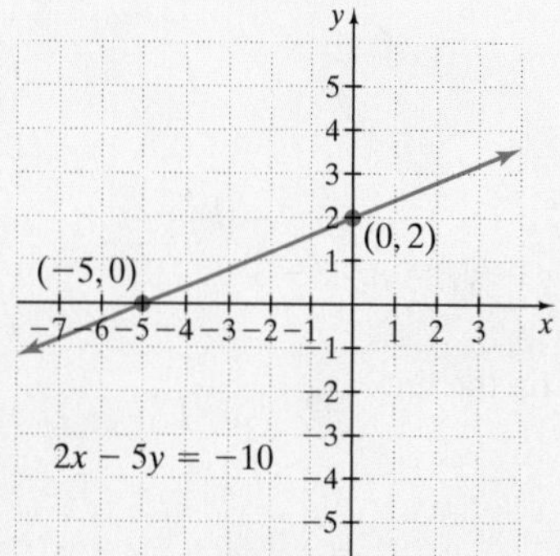

The graph of $x = c$ is a vertical line with x-intercept $(c, 0)$.

The graph of $y = c$ is a horizontal line with y-intercept $(0, c)$.

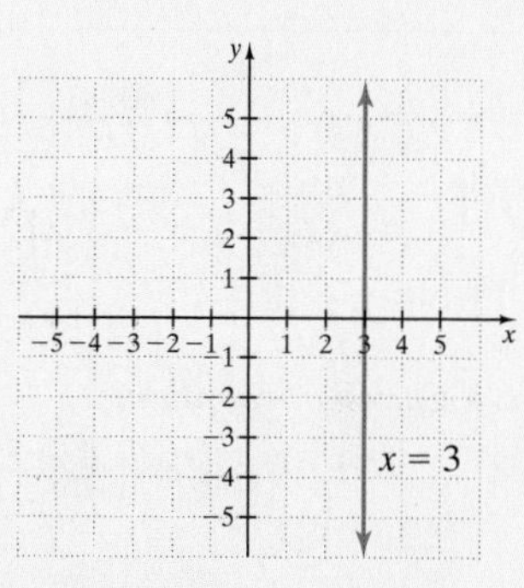

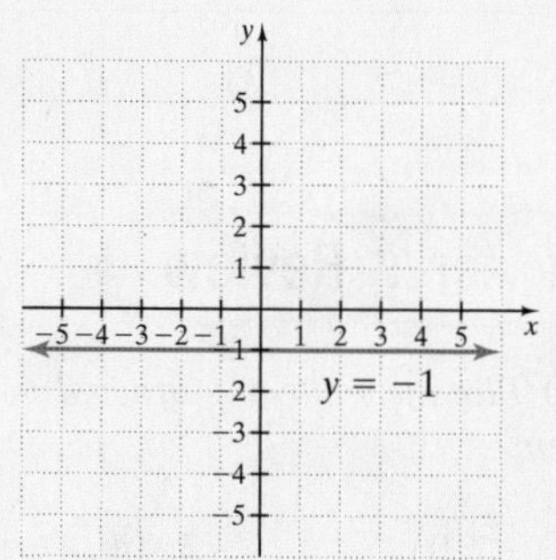

Section 1.4 Slope and Rate of Change

The **slope *m*** of the line through points (x_1, y_1) and (x_2, y_2) is given by

$$m = \frac{y_2 - y_1}{x_2 - x_1} \quad \text{as long as } x_2 \neq x_1$$

The slope of the line through points $(-1, 6)$ and $(-5, 8)$ is

$$m = \frac{y_2 - y_1}{x_2 - x_1} = \frac{8 - 6}{-5 - (-1)} = \frac{2}{-4} = -\frac{1}{2}$$

A horizontal line has slope 0.
The slope of a vertical line is undefined.

The slope of the line $y = -5$ is 0.
The line $x = 3$ has undefined slope.

Nonvertical parallel lines have the same slope.

Two nonvertical lines are perpendicular if the slope of one is the negative reciprocal of the slope of the other.

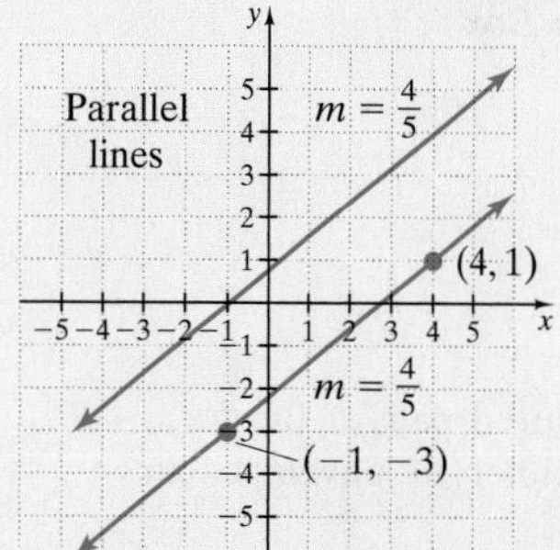

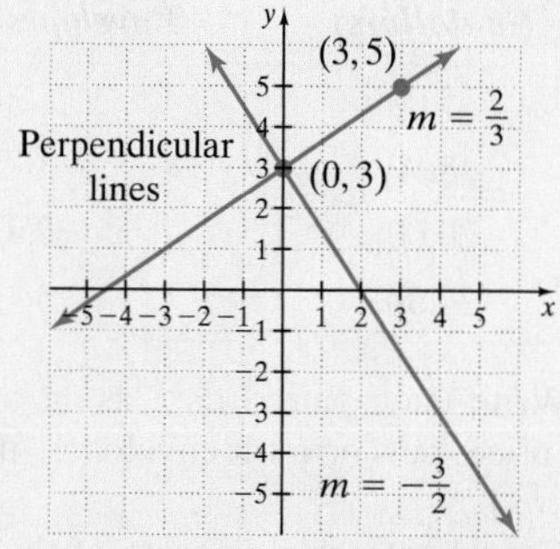

DEFINITIONS AND CONCEPTS	EXAMPLES
Section 1.5 Equations of Lines	
Slope-Intercept Form $y = mx + b$ m is the slope of the line. $(0, b)$ is the y-intercept.	Find the slope and the y-intercept of the line whose equation is $2x + 3y = 6$. Solve for y: $2x + 3y = 6$ $3y = -2x + 6$ Subtract $2x$. $y = -\frac{2}{3}x + 2$ Divide by 3. The slope of the line is $-\frac{2}{3}$ and the y-intercept is $(0, 2)$. Find an equation of the line with slope 3 and y-intercept $(0, -1)$. The equation is $y = 3x - 1$.
Point-Slope Form $y - y_1 = m(x - x_1)$ m is the slope. (x_1, y_1) is a point on the line.	Find an equation of the line with slope $\frac{3}{4}$ that contains the point $(-1, 5)$. $y - 5 = \frac{3}{4}[x - (-1)]$ $4(y - 5) = 3(x + 1)$ Multiply by 4. $4y - 20 = 3x + 3$ Distribute. $-3x + 4y = 23$ Subtract $3x$ and add 20.

Chapter 1 Review

(1.1) Plot the following ordered pairs on a Cartesian coordinate system.

1. $(-7, 0)$ **2.** $\left(0, 4\frac{4}{5}\right)$

3. $(-2, -5)$ **4.** $(1, -3)$

5. $(0.7, 0.7)$ **6.** $(-6, 4)$

7. A local office supply store uses quantity pricing. The table shows the price per box of #10 security envelopes for different numbers of envelopes in a box purchased.

Price per Box of Envelopes (in dollars)	*Number of Envelopes in Box*
5.00	50
8.50	100
20.00	250
27.00	500

a. Write each paired data as an ordered pair of the form (price per box of envelopes, number of envelopes in box).

b. Create a scatter diagram of the paired data. Be sure to label the axes appropriately.

8. The table shows the annual overnight stays in national parks. (Data from National Park Service)

Year	*Overnight Stays in National Parks (in millions)*
2005	13.8
2006	13.6
2007	14.1
2008	13.9
2009	14.6
2010	14.6

a. Write each paired data as an ordered pair of the form (year, number of overnight stays).

b. Create a scatter diagram of the paired data. Be sure to label the axes properly.

Determine whether each ordered pair is a solution of the given equation.

9. $7x - 8y = 56$; $(0, 56)$, $(8, 0)$

10. $-2x + 5y = 10$; $(-5, 0)$, $(1, 1)$

11. $x = 13$; $(13, 5)$, $(13, 13)$

12. $y = 2$; $(7, 2)$, $(2, 7)$

Complete the ordered pairs so that each is a solution of the given equation.

13. $-2 + y = 6x$; $(7, \quad)$

14. $y = 3x + 5$; $\left(\quad , -8 \right)$

Complete the table of values for each given equation; then plot the ordered pairs. Use a single coordinate system for each exercise.

15. $9 = -3x + 4y$

x	y
	0
	3
9	

16. $x = 2y$

x	y
	0
	5
	−5

The cost in dollars of producing x compact disc holders is given by $y = 5x + 2000$. Use this equation for Exercises 17 and 18.

17. Complete the following table.

x	y
1	
100	
1000	

18. Find the number of compact disc holders that can be produced for $6430.

(1.2) *Graph each linear equation.*

19. $x - y = 1$

20. $x + y = 6$

21. $x - 3y = 12$

22. $5x - y = -8$

23. $x = 3y$

24. $y = -2x$

25. $2x - 3y = 6$

26. $4x - 3y = 12$

(1.3) *Identify the intercepts.*

27.

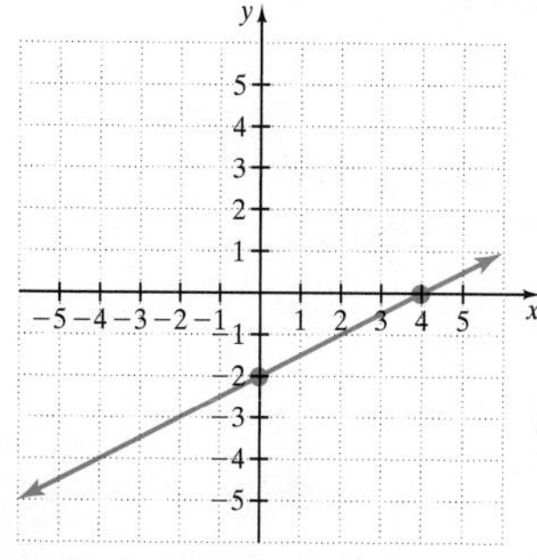

28.

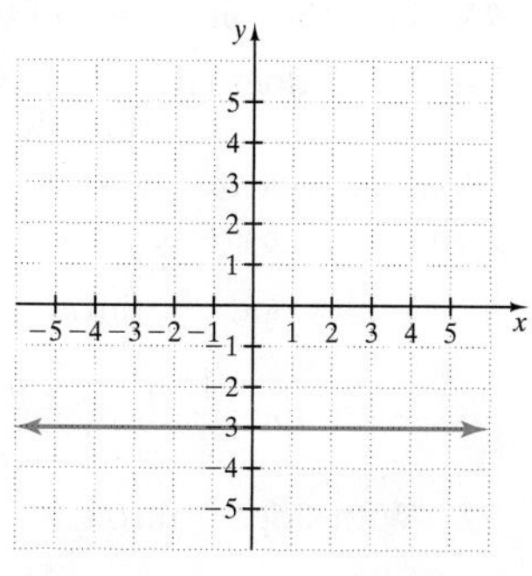

29.

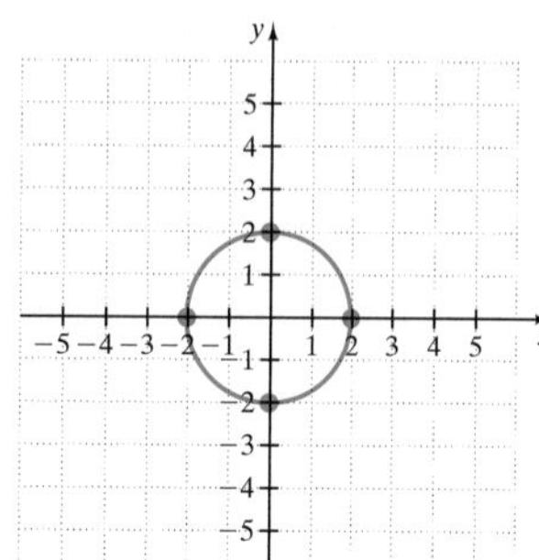

30.

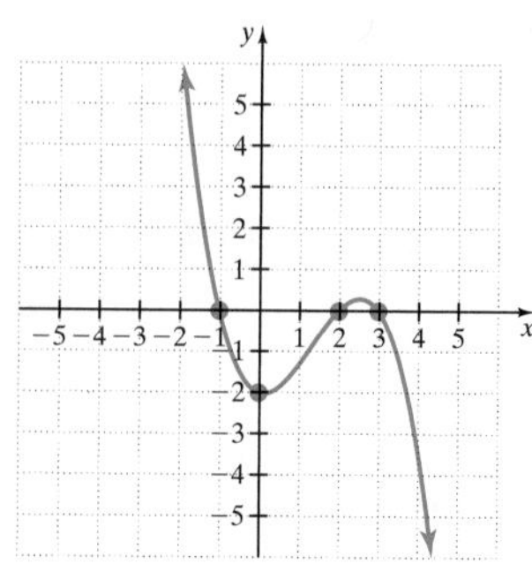

Graph each linear equation by finding its intercepts.

31. $x - 3y = 12$

32. $-4x + y = 8$

33. $y = -3$

34. $x = 5$

35. $y = -3x$

36. $x = 5y$

37. $x - 2 = 0$

38. $y + 6 = 0$

(1.4) *Find the slope of each line.*

39.

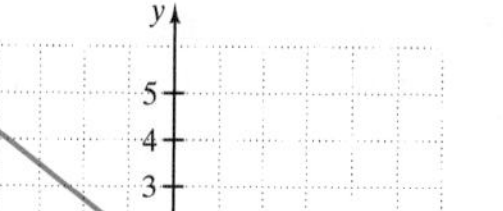

40.

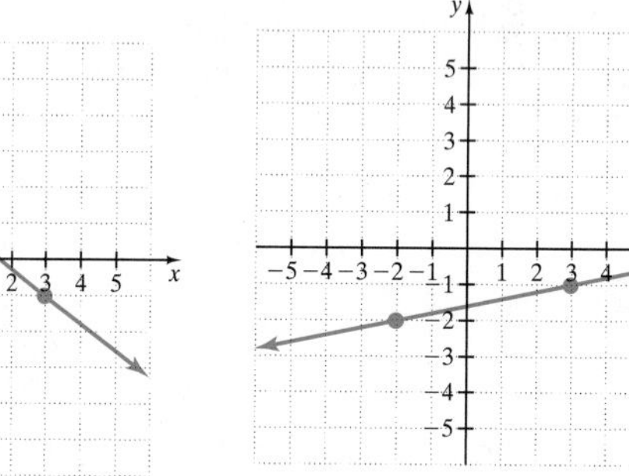

In Exercises 41 through 44, match each line with its slope.

a.

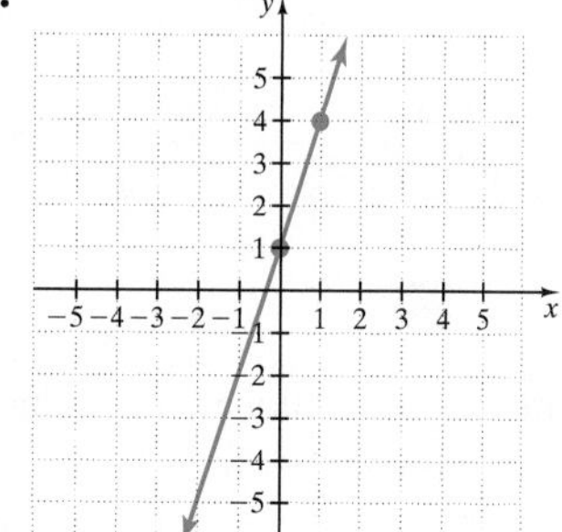

b.

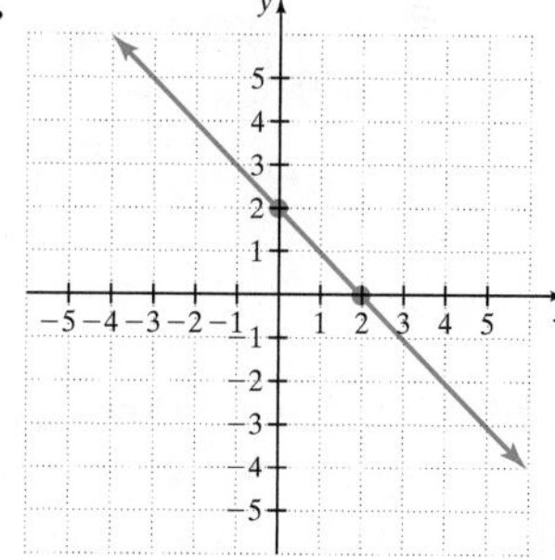

c.

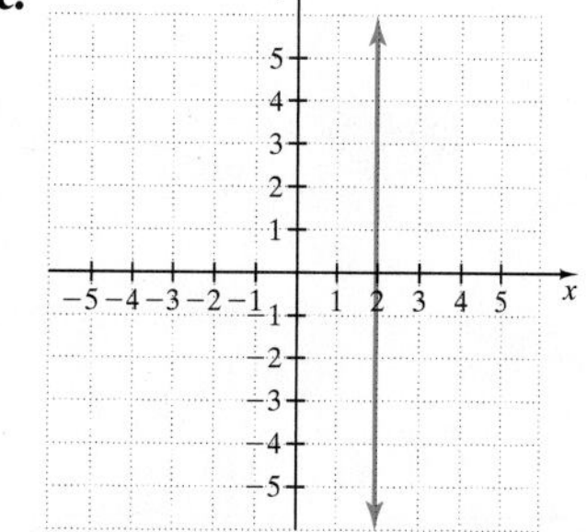

d.

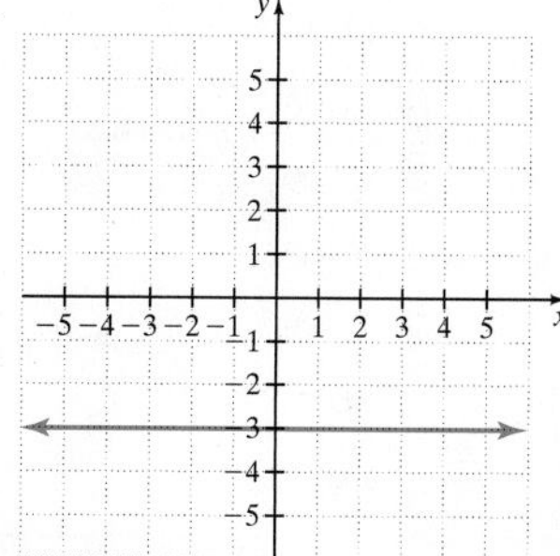

41. $m = 0$

42. $m = -1$

43. undefined slope

44. $m = 3$

Find the slope of the line that goes through the given points.

45. $(2, 5)$ and $(6, 8)$

46. $(4, 7)$ and $(1, 2)$

47. $(1, 3)$ and $(-2, -9)$

48. $(-4, 1)$ and $(3, -6)$

Find the slope of each line.

49. $y = 3x + 7$

50. $x - 2y = 4$

51. $y = -2$

52. $x = 0$

Determine whether each pair of lines is parallel, perpendicular, or neither.

53. $x - y = -6$
$x + y = 3$

54. $3x + y = 7$
$-3x - y = 10$

55. $y = 4x + \frac{1}{2}$
$4x + 2y = 1$

56. $x = 4$
$y = -2$

Find the slope of each line and write the slope as a rate of change. Don't forget to attach the proper units.

57. The graph below approximates the number of U.S. college students (in thousands) earning an associate's degree for each year x.

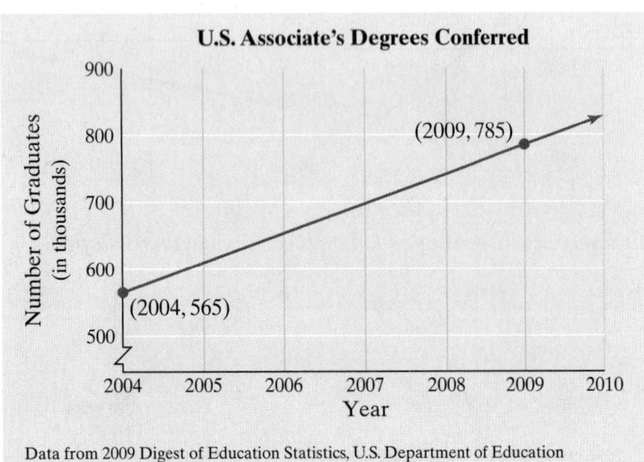

58. The graph below approximates the number of kidney transplants y in the United States for year x.

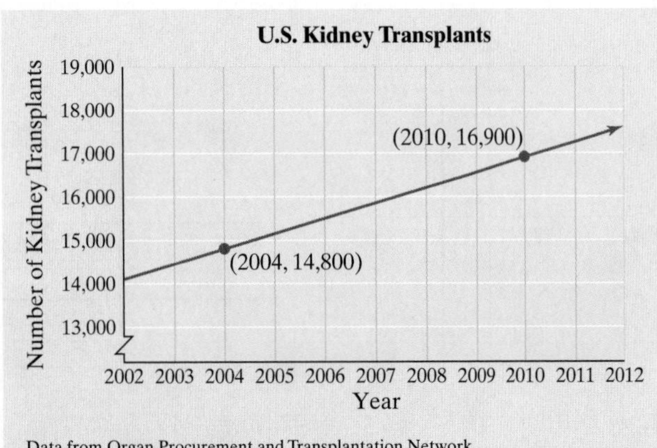

***(1.5)** Determine the slope and the y-intercept of the graph of each equation.*

59. $3x + y = 7$

60. $x - 6y = -1$

61. $y = 2$

62. $x = -5$

Use the slope-intercept form to graph each equation.

63. $y = 3x - 1$

64. $y = -3x$

65. $5x - 3y = 15$

66. $-x + 2y = 8$

Write an equation of each line in slope-intercept form.

67. slope -5; y-intercept $\left(0, \frac{1}{2}\right)$

68. slope $\frac{2}{3}$; y-intercept $(0, 6)$

Match each equation with its graph.

69. $y = -4x$

70. $y = 2x$

71. $y = 2x - 1$

72. $y = -2x + 1$

a.

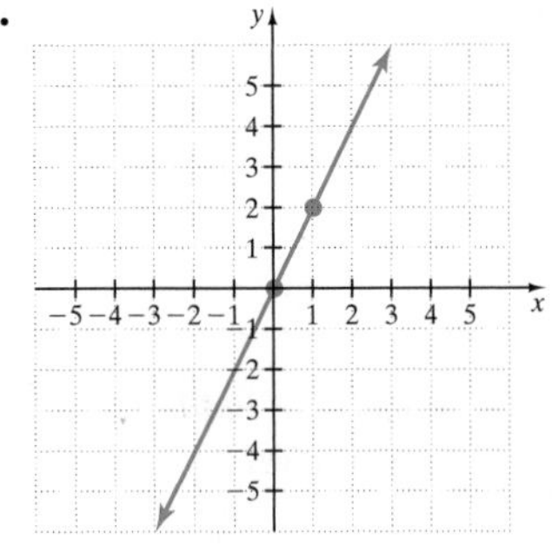

b.

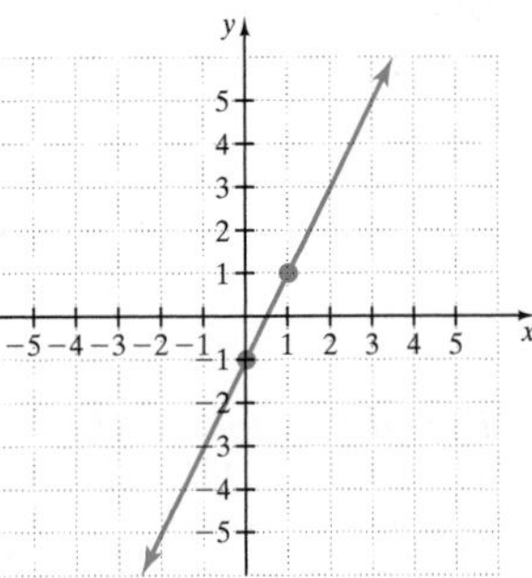

c.

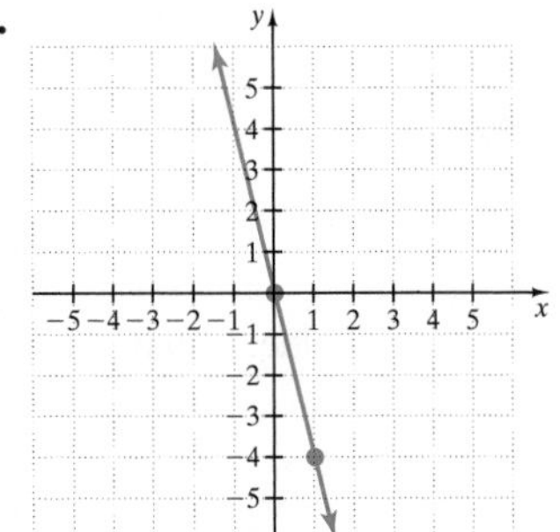

d.

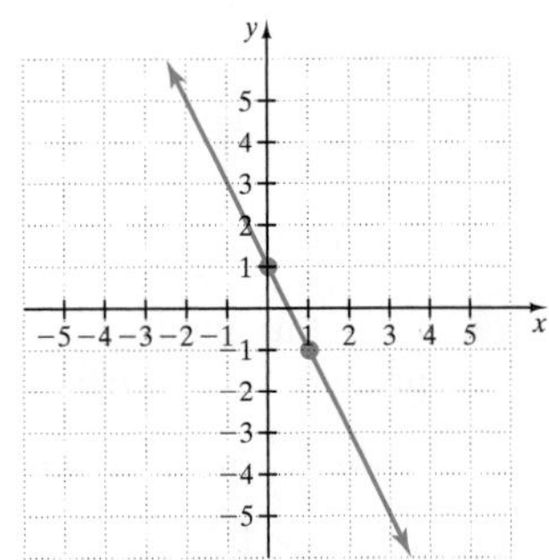

College is getting more expensive every year. The average cost for tuition and fees at a public two-year college y from 1995 through 2011 can be approximated by the linear equation $y = 56x + 1859$, where x is the number of years after 1995. Use this information for Exercises 73 and 74. (Source: The College Board: Trends in College Pricing 2010)

73. Find the y-intercept of this equation.

74. What does the y-intercept mean?

Write an equation of each line. Write each equation in standard form, $Ax + By = C$, or $x = c$ or $y = c$ form.

75. With slope -3, through $(0, -5)$

76. With slope $\frac{1}{2}$, through $\left(0, -\frac{7}{2}\right)$

77. With slope 0, through $(-2, -3)$

78. With 0 slope, through the origin

79. With slope −6, through $(2, -1)$

80. With slope 12, through $\left(\frac{1}{2}, 5\right)$

81. Through $(0, 6)$ and $(6, 0)$

82. Through $(0, -4)$ and $(-8, 0)$

83. Vertical line, through $(5, 7)$

84. Horizontal line, through $(-6, 8)$

85. Through $(6, 0)$, perpendicular to $y = 8$

86. Through $(10, 12)$, perpendicular to $x = -2$

Chapter 1 Test

MyMathLab®

You Tube

Graph the following.

1. $y = \frac{1}{2}x$

2. $2x + y = 8$

3. $5x - 7y = 10$

4. $y = -1$

5. $x - 3 = 0$

For Exercises 6 through 10, find the slopes of the lines.

6.

7.

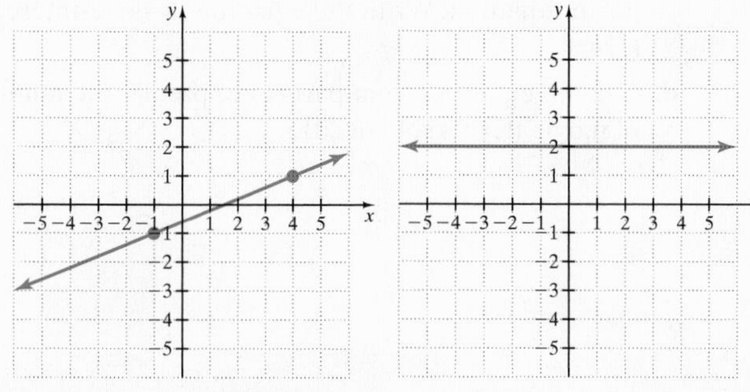

8. Through $(6, -5)$ and $(-1, 2)$

9. $-3x + y = 5$

10. $x = 6$

11. Determine the slope and the y-intercept of the graph of $7x - 3y = 2$.

12. Determine whether the graphs of $y = 2x - 6$ and $-4x = 2y$ are parallel lines, perpendicular lines, or neither.

Find equations of the following lines. Write the equation in standard form.

13. With slope of $-\frac{1}{4}$, through $(2, 2)$

14. Through the origin and $(6, -7)$

15. Through $(2, -5)$ and $(1, 3)$

16. Through $(-5, -1)$ and parallel to $x = 7$

17. With slope $\frac{1}{8}$ and y-intercept $(0, 12)$

Determine whether each graph is the graph of a function.

18.

19.

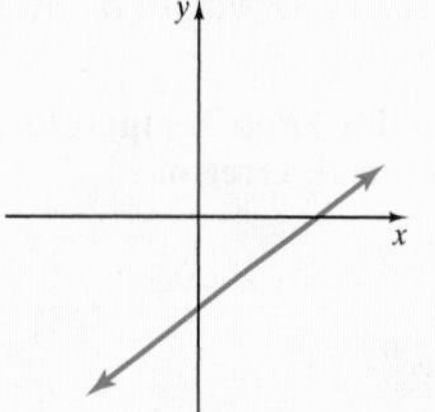

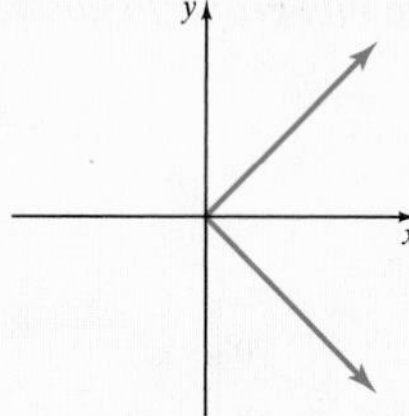

Given the following functions, find the indicated function values.

20. $h(x) = x^3 - x$

a. $h(-1)$ **b.** $h(0)$ **c.** $h(4)$

21. Find the domain of $y = \frac{1}{x + 1}$.

For Exercises 22 and 23,

a. *Identify the x- and y-intercepts.*

b. *Find the domain and the range of each function graphed.*

22.

23.

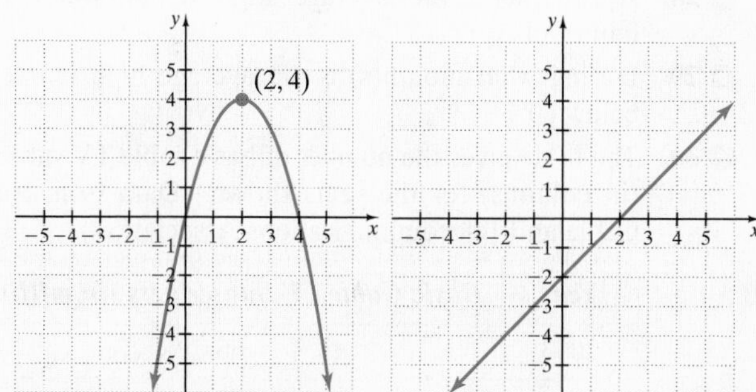

24. If $f(7) = 20$, write the corresponding ordered pair.

Use the bar graph below to answer Exercises 25 and 26.

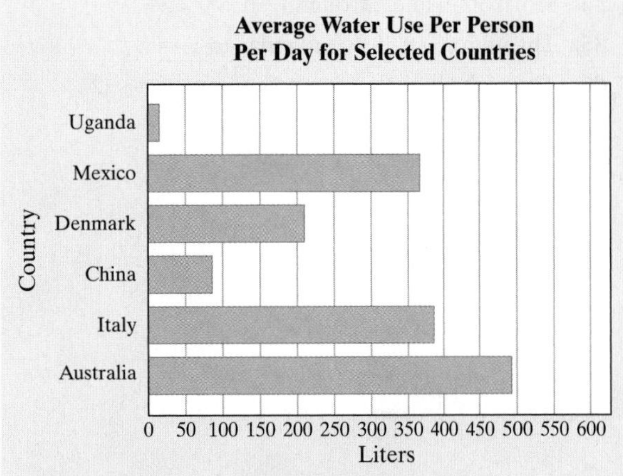

25. Estimate the average water use per person per day in Denmark.

26. Estimate the average water use per person per day in Australia.

Use this graph to answer Exercises 27 through 29.

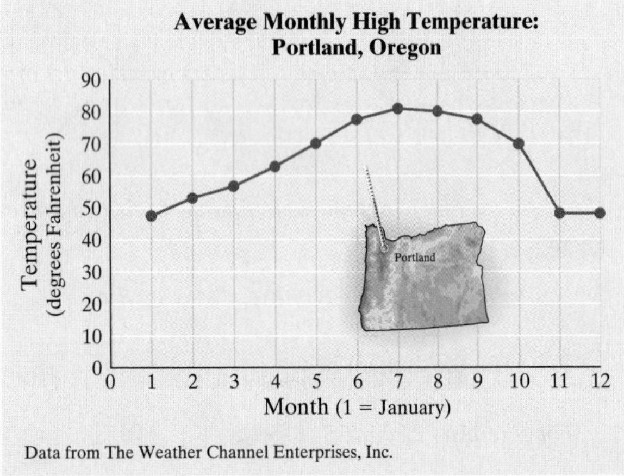

27. During what month is the average high temperature the greatest?

28. Approximate the average high temperature for the month of April.

29. During what month(s) is the average high temperature below 60°F?

30. The table gives the number of basic cable TV subscribers (in millions) for the years shown. (Data from National Cable and Telecommunications Association)

Year	*Basic Cable TV Subscribers (in millions)*
2003	66.0
2004	65.4
2005	65.4
2006	65.6
2007	64.9
2008	63.7
2009	62.1

a. Write this data as a set of ordered pairs of the form (year, number of basic cable TV subscribers in millions).

b. Create a scatter diagram of the data. Be sure to label the axes properly.

31. This graph approximates the number of movie ticket sales y (in millions) for the year x.

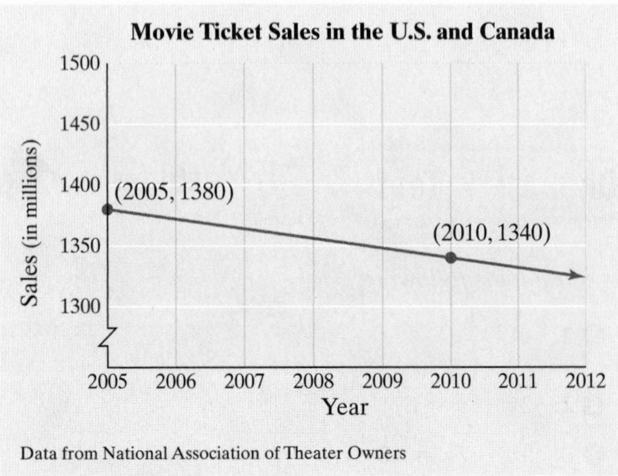

a. Find the slope of the line and write the slope as a rate of change. Don't forget to attach the proper units.

b. Write two ordered pairs of the form (years past 2005, number of tickets sold in millions).

c. Use the two ordered pairs from part (b) to write a linear equation. Write the equation in slope-intercept form.

d. Use the equation from part (c) to predict the number of movie tickets sold in 2015.

Chapter 1 Cumulative Review

1. Insert $<$, $>$, or $=$ in the space between each pair of numbers to make each statement true.

a. 2 3 **b.** 7 4 **c.** 72 27

2. Write the fraction $\frac{56}{64}$ in lowest terms.

3. Multiply $\frac{2}{15}$ and $\frac{5}{13}$. Simplify the product if possible.

4. Add: $\frac{10}{3} + \frac{5}{21}$

5. Simplify $\frac{3 + |4 - 3| + 2^2}{6 - 3}$.

6. Simplify $16 - 3 \cdot 3 + 2^4$.

7. Add.

a. $-8 + (-11)$ **b.** $-5 + 35$

c. $0.6 + (-1.1)$ **d.** $-\frac{7}{10} + \left(-\frac{1}{10}\right)$

e. $11.4 + (-4.7)$ **f.** $-\frac{3}{8} + \frac{2}{5}$

8. Simplify $|9 + (-20)| + |-10|$.

9. Simplify each expression.

a. $-14 - 8 + 10 - (-6)$

b. $1.6 - (-10.3) + (-5.6)$

10. Simplify $-9 - (3 - 8)$.

11. If $x = -2$ and $y = -4$, evaluate each expression.

a. $5x - y$ **b.** $x^4 - y^2$

c. $\frac{3x}{2y}$

12. Is -20 a solution of $\frac{x}{-10} = 2$?

13. Simplify each expression.

a. $10 + (x + 12)$

b. $-3(7x)$

14. Simplify $(12 + x) - (4x - 7)$.

15. Identify the numerical coefficient in each term.

a. $-3y$ **b.** $22z^4$

c. y **d.** $-x$

e. $\frac{x}{7}$

16. Multiply $-5(x - 7)$.

17. Solve $x - 7 = 10$ for x.

18. Solve $5(3 + z) - (8z + 9) = -4$.

19. Solve $\frac{5}{2}x = 15$.

20. Solve $\frac{x}{4} - 1 = -7$.

21. If x is the first of three consecutive integers, express the sum of the three integers in terms of x. Simplify if possible.

22. Solve $\frac{x}{3} - 2 = \frac{x}{3}$.

23. Solve $\frac{2(a + 3)}{3} = 6a + 2$.

24. Solve $x + 2y = 6$ for y.

25. The 112th Congress began on January 3, 2011, and had a total of 435 Democratic and Republican representatives. There were 49 fewer Democratic representatives than Republican. Find the number of representatives from each party. (*Source*: Wikipedia .com).

26. Solve $5(x + 4) \geq 4(2x + 3)$. Write the solution set in interval notation.

27. Charles Pecot can afford enough fencing to enclose a rectangular garden with a perimeter of 140 feet. If the width of his garden must be 30 feet, find the length.

28. Solve $-3 < 4x - 1 \leq 2$. Write the solution set in interval notation.

29. Solve $y = mx + b$ for x.

30. Complete the table for $y = -5x$.

x	y
0	
−1	
	−10

31. A chemist working on his doctoral degree at Massachusetts Institute of Technology needs 12 liters of a 50% acid solution for a lab experiment. The stockroom has only 40% and 70% solutions. How much of each solution should be mixed together to form 12 liters of a 50% solution?

32. Graph: $y = -3x + 5$

33. Graph $x \geq -1$. Then write the solutions in interval notation.

34. Find the x- and y-intercepts of $2x + 4y = -8$.

35. Solve $-1 \le 2x - 3 < 5$. Graph the solution set and write it in interval notation.

36. Graph $x = 2$ on a rectangular coordinate system.

37. Determine whether each ordered pair is a solution of the equation $x - 2y = 6$.

a. $(6, 0)$ **b.** $(0, 3)$

c. $\left(1, -\frac{5}{2}\right)$

38. Find the slope of the line through $(0, 5)$ and $(-5, 4)$.

39. Determine whether each equation is a linear equation in two variables.

a. $x - 1.5y = -1.6$ **b.** $y = -2x$

c. $x + y^2 = 9$ **d.** $x = 5$

40. Find the slope of the line $x = -10$.

41. Find the slope of the line $y = -1$.

42. Find the slope and y-intercept of the line whose equation is $2x - 5y = 10$.

43. Find an equation of the line with y-intercept $(0, -3)$ and slope of $\frac{1}{4}$.

44. Write an equation of the line through $(2, 3)$ and $(0, 0)$. Write the equation in standard form.

CHAPTER 2

Solving Systems of Linear Equations

According to the Bureau of Labor Statistics, workers age 55 years and over are projected to have the greatest increase in the labor force during the years 2008 to 2018. These workers are anticipated to increase from 18.1% to 23.9% of the labor force during this period. Workers age 25 to 34 years are projected to increase also, but not at the same rate. In Section 2.3, Exercise 73, we will predict when these two age groups will have the same percent of the labor force.

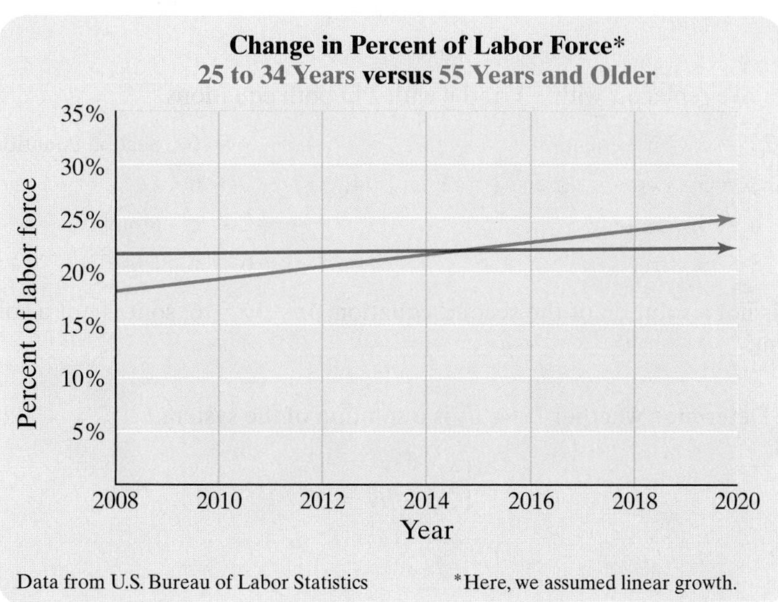

Data from U.S. Bureau of Labor Statistics *Here, we assumed linear growth.

In Chapter 1, we graphed equations containing two variables. Equations like these are often needed to represent relationships between two different values. There are also many real-life opportunities to compare and contrast two such equations, called a system of equations. This chapter presents linear systems and ways we solve these systems and apply them to real-life situations.

2.1 Solving Systems of Linear Equations by Graphing 

OBJECTIVES

1. Determine if an Ordered Pair Is a Solution of a System of Equations in Two Variables.
2. Solve a System of Linear Equations by Graphing.
3. Without Graphing, Determine the Number of Solutions of a System.

A **system of linear equations** consists of two or more linear equations. In this section, we focus on solving systems of linear equations containing two equations in two variables. Examples of such linear systems are

$$\begin{cases} 3x - 3y = 0 \\ x = 2y \end{cases} \quad \begin{cases} x - y = 0 \\ 2x + y = 10 \end{cases} \quad \begin{cases} y = 7x - 1 \\ y = 4 \end{cases}$$

OBJECTIVE

1 Deciding Whether an Ordered Pair Is a Solution 

A **solution** of a system of two equations in two variables is an ordered pair of numbers that is a solution of both equations in the system.

EXAMPLE 1 Determine whether (12, 6) is a solution of the system

$$\begin{cases} 2x - 3y = 6 \\ x = 2y \end{cases}$$

Solution To determine whether (12, 6) is a solution of the system, we replace x with 12 and y with 6 in both equations.

$2x - 3y = 6$	First equation	$x = 2y$	Second equation
$2(12) - 3(6) \stackrel{?}{=} 6$	Let $x = 12$ and $y = 6$.	$12 \stackrel{?}{=} 2(6)$	Let $x = 12$ and $y = 6$.
$24 - 18 \stackrel{?}{=} 6$	Simplify.	$12 = 12$	True
$6 = 6$	True		

Since (12, 6) is a solution of both equations, it is a solution of the system. □

PRACTICE

1 Determine whether (4, 12) is a solution of the system.

$$\begin{cases} 4x - y = 2 \\ y = 3x \end{cases}$$

EXAMPLE 2 Determine whether $(-1, 2)$ is a solution of the system

$$\begin{cases} x + 2y = 3 \\ 4x - y = 6 \end{cases}$$

Solution We replace x with -1 and y with 2 in both equations.

$x + 2y = 3$	First equation	$4x - y = 6$	Second equation
$-1 + 2(2) \stackrel{?}{=} 3$	Let $x = -1$ and $y = 2$.	$4(-1) - 2 \stackrel{?}{=} 6$	Let $x = -1$ and $y = 2$.
$-1 + 4 \stackrel{?}{=} 3$	Simplify.	$-4 - 2 \stackrel{?}{=} 6$	Simplify.
$3 = 3$	True	$-6 = 6$	False

$(-1, 2)$ is not a solution of the second equation, $4x - y = 6$, so it is not a solution of the system. □

PRACTICE

2 Determine whether $(-4, 1)$ is a solution of the system.

$$\begin{cases} x - 3y = -7 \\ 2x + 9y = 1 \end{cases}$$

OBJECTIVE

2 Solving Systems of Equations by Graphing

Since a solution of a system of two equations in two variables is a solution common to both equations, it is also a point common to the graphs of both equations. Let's practice finding solutions of both equations in a system—that is, solutions of a system—by graphing and identifying points of intersection.

EXAMPLE 3 Solve the system of equations by graphing.

$$\begin{cases} -x + 3y = 10 \\ x + y = 2 \end{cases}$$

Solution On a single set of axes, graph each linear equation.

$-x + 3y = 10$

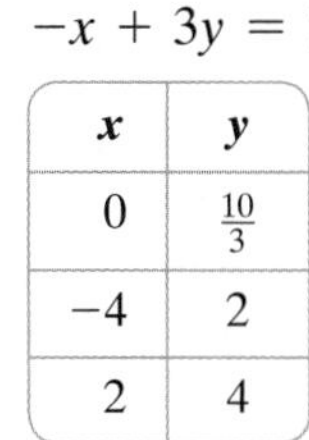

x	y
0	$\frac{10}{3}$
−4	2
2	4

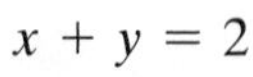

$x + y = 2$

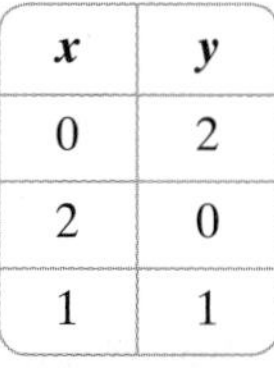

x	y
0	2
2	0
1	1

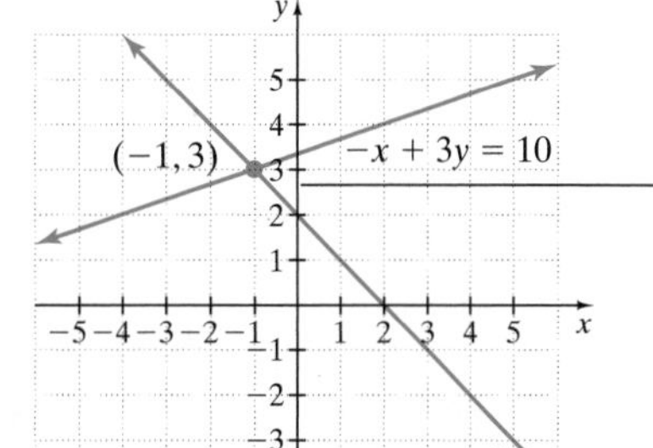

Helpful Hint
The point of intersection gives the solution of the system.

The two lines appear to intersect at the point $(-1, 3)$. To check, we replace x with -1 and y with 3 in both equations.

$-x + 3y = 10$	First equation	$x + y = 2$	Second equation
$-(-1) + 3(3) \stackrel{?}{=} 10$	Let $x = -1$ and $y = 3$.	$-1 + 3 \stackrel{?}{=} 2$	Let $x = -1$ and $y = 3$.
$1 + 9 \stackrel{?}{=} 10$	Simplify.	$2 = 2$	True
$10 = 10$	True		

$(-1, 3)$ checks, so it is the solution of the system and the solution set is $\{(-1, 3)\}$. (Note: For single ordered-pair solutions, we shall list the ordered pair only.) □

PRACTICE

3 Solve the system of equations by graphing:

$$\begin{cases} x - y = 3 \\ x + 2y = 18 \end{cases}$$

Helpful Hint

Neatly drawn graphs can help when you are estimating the solution of a system of linear equations by graphing.

In the example above, notice that the two lines intersected in a point. This means that the system has 1 solution.

EXAMPLE 4 Solve the system of equations by graphing.

$$\begin{cases} 2x + 3y = -2 \\ x = 2 \end{cases}$$

Solution We graph each linear equation on a single set of axes.

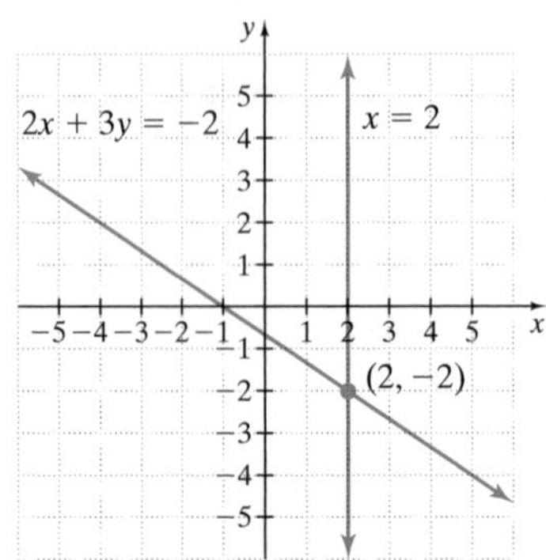

The two lines appear to intersect at the point $(2, -2)$. To determine whether $(2, -2)$ is the solution, we replace x with 2 and y with -2 in both equations.

$2x + 3y = -2$	First equation	$x = 2$	Second equation
$2(2) + 3(-2) \stackrel{?}{=} -2$	Let $x = 2$ and $y = -2$.	$2 \stackrel{?}{=} 2$	Let $x = 2$.
$4 + (-6) \stackrel{?}{=} -2$	Simplify.	$2 = 2$	True
$-2 = -2$	True		

Since a true statement results in both equations, $(2, -2)$ is the solution of the system. □

PRACTICE 4 Solve the system of equations by graphing.

$$\begin{cases} -4x + 3y = -3 \\ y = -5 \end{cases}$$

A system of equations that has at least one solution as in Examples 3 and 4 is said to be a **consistent system.** A system that has no solution is said to be an **inconsistent system.**

EXAMPLE 5 Solve the following system of equations by graphing.

$$\begin{cases} 2x + y = 7 \\ 2y = -4x \end{cases}$$

Solution Graph the two lines in the system.

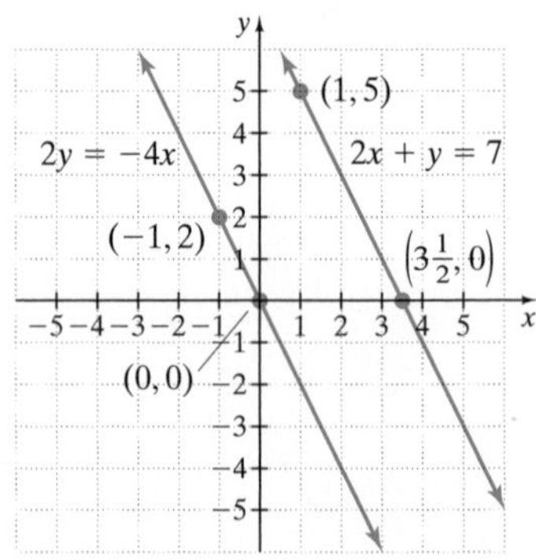

The lines **appear** to be parallel. To confirm this, write both equations in slope-intercept form by solving each equation for y.

$2x + y = 7$	First equation	$2y = -4x$	Second equation
$\mathbf{y = -2x + 7}$	Subtract $2x$ from both sides.	$\frac{2y}{2} = \frac{-4x}{2}$	Divide both sides by 2.
		$\mathbf{y = -2x}$	

Recall that when an equation is written in slope-intercept form, the coefficient of x is the slope. Since both equations have the same slope, -2, but different y-intercepts, the lines are parallel and have no points in common. Thus, there is no solution of the system and the system is inconsistent. To indicate this, we can say the system has no solution or the solution set is $\{\ \}$ or $\varnothing$. □

PRACTICE 5 Solve the system of equations by graphing.

$$\begin{cases} 3y = 9x \\ 6x - 2y = 12 \end{cases}$$

In Examples 3, 4, and 5, the graphs of the two linear equations of each system are different. When this happens, we call these equations **independent equations.** If the graphs of the two equations in a system are identical, we call the equations **dependent equations.**

EXAMPLE 6 Solve the system of equations by graphing.

$$\begin{cases} x - y = 3 \\ -x + y = -3 \end{cases}$$

Solution Graph each line.

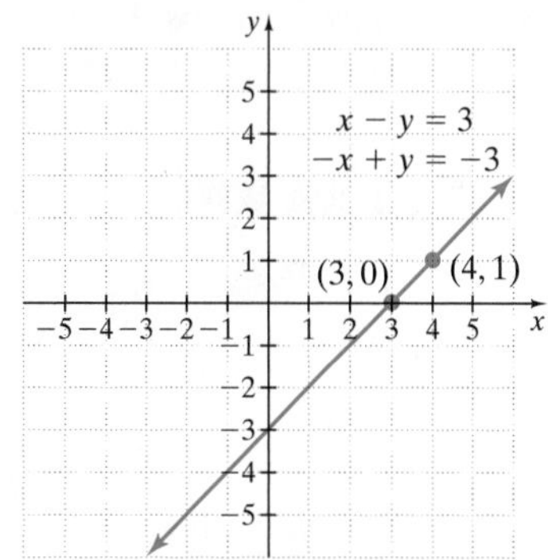

These graphs **appear** to be identical. To confirm this, write each equation in slope-intercept form.

$x - y = 3$	First equation	$-x + y = -3$	Second equation
$-y = -x + 3$	Subtract x from both sides.	$\mathbf{y = x - 3}$	Add x to both sides.
$\dfrac{-y}{-1} = \dfrac{-x}{-1} + \dfrac{3}{-1}$	Divide both sides by -1.		
$\mathbf{y = x - 3}$			

The equations are identical and so must be their graphs. The lines have an infinite number of points in common. Thus, there is an infinite number of solutions of the system and this is a consistent system. The equations are dependent equations. Here, we can say that there are an infinite number of solutions or the solution set is $\{(x, y) \mid x - y = 3\}$ or equivalently $\{(x, y) \mid -x + y = -3\}$ since the equations describe identical ordered pairs. The second set is read "the set of all ordered pairs (x, y) such that $-x + y = -3$. □

PRACTICE 6 Solve the system of equations by graphing.

$$\begin{cases} x - y = 4 \\ -2x + 2y = -8 \end{cases}$$

As we have seen, three different situations can occur when graphing the two lines associated with the two equations in a linear system:

One point of intersection: one solution | Parallel lines: no solution | Same line: infinite number of solutions

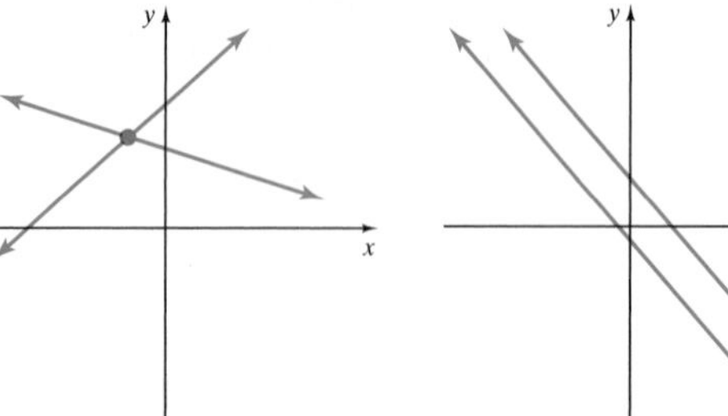

Consistent system
(at least one solution)
Independent equations
(graphs of equations differ)

Inconsistent system
(no solution)
Independent equations
(graphs of equations differ)

Consistent system
(at least one solution)
Dependent equations
(graphs of equations identical)

OBJECTIVE

3 Finding the Number of Solutions of a System without Graphing 

You may have suspected by now that graphing alone is not an accurate way to solve a system of linear equations. For example, a solution of $\left(\frac{1}{2}, \frac{2}{9}\right)$ is unlikely to be read correctly from a graph. The next two sections present two accurate methods of solving these systems. In the meantime, we can decide how many solutions a system has by writing each equation in the slope-intercept form.

EXAMPLE 7 Without graphing, determine the number of solutions of the system.

$$\begin{cases} \frac{1}{2}x - y = 2 \\ x = 2y + 5 \end{cases}$$

Solution First write each equation in slope-intercept form.

$\frac{1}{2}x - y = 2$ First equation

$\frac{1}{2}x = y + 2$ Add y to both sides.

$\frac{1}{2}x - 2 = y$ Subtract 2 from both sides.

$x = 2y + 5$ Second equation

$x - 5 = 2y$ Subtract 5 from both sides.

$\frac{x}{2} - \frac{5}{2} = \frac{2y}{2}$ Divide both sides by 2.

$\frac{1}{2}x - \frac{5}{2} = y$ Simplify.

The slope of each line is $\frac{1}{2}$, but they have different y-intercepts. This tells us that the lines representing these equations are parallel. Since the lines are parallel, the system has no solution and is inconsistent. □

PRACTICE

7 Without graphing, determine the number of solutions of the system.

$$\begin{cases} 5x + 4y = 6 \\ x - y = 3 \end{cases}$$

EXAMPLE 8 Without graphing, determine the number of solutions of the system.

$$\begin{cases} 3x - y = 4 \\ x + 2y = 8 \end{cases}$$

Solution Once again, the slope-intercept form helps determine how many solutions this system has.

$3x - y = 4$	First equation	$x + 2y = 8$	Second equation
$3x = y + 4$	Add y to both sides.	$x = -2y + 8$	Subtract $2y$ from both sides.
$3x - 4 = y$	Subtract 4 from both sides.	$x - 8 = -2y$	Subtract 8 from both sides.
		$\frac{x}{-2} - \frac{8}{-2} = \frac{-2y}{-2}$	Divide both sides by -2.
		$-\frac{1}{2}x + 4 = y$	Simplify.

The slope of the second line is $-\frac{1}{2}$, whereas the slope of the first line is 3. Since the slopes are not equal, the two lines are neither parallel nor identical and must intersect. Therefore, this system has one solution and is consistent. □

PRACTICE
8 Without graphing, determine the number of solutions of the system.

$$\begin{cases} -\frac{2}{3}x + y = 6 \\ 3y = 2x + 5 \end{cases}$$

Graphing Calculator Explorations

A graphing calculator may be used to approximate solutions of systems of equations. For example, to approximate the solution of the system

$$\begin{cases} y = -3.14x - 1.35 \\ y = 4.88x + 5.25, \end{cases}$$

first graph each equation on the same set of axes. Then use the intersect feature of your calculator to approximate the point of intersection.

The approximate point of intersection is $(-0.82, 1.23)$.

Solve each system of equations. Approximate the solutions to two decimal places.

1. $\begin{cases} y = -2.68x + 1.21 \\ y = 5.22x - 1.68 \end{cases}$

2. $\begin{cases} y = 4.25x + 3.89 \\ y = -1.88x + 3.21 \end{cases}$

3. $\begin{cases} 4.3x - 2.9y = 5.6 \\ 8.1x + 7.6y = -14.1 \end{cases}$

4. $\begin{cases} -3.6x - 8.6y = 10 \\ -4.5x + 9.6y = -7.7 \end{cases}$

Vocabulary, Readiness & Video Check

Fill in each blank with one of the words or phrases listed below.

system of linear equations	solution	consistent
dependent	inconsistent	independent

1. In a system of linear equations in two variables, if the graphs of the equations are the same, the equations are ____________________ equations.

2. Two or more linear equations are called a(n) ____________________.

3. A system of equations that has at least one solution is called a(n) ____________________ system.

4. A(n) ____________________ of a system of two equations in two variables is an ordered pair of numbers that is a solution of both equations in the system.

5. A system of equations that has no solution is called a(n) ____________________ system.

6. In a system of linear equations in two variables, if the graphs of the equations are different, the equations are ____________________ equations.

Watch the section lecture video and answer the following questions.

OBJECTIVE 1

7. In Example 1, the first ordered pair is a solution of the first equation of the system. Why is this not enough to determine whether the first ordered pair is a solution of the system?

OBJECTIVE 2

8. From Examples 2 and 3, why is finding the solution of a system of equations from a graph considered "guessing" and this proposed solution checked algebraically?

OBJECTIVE 3

9. From Examples 5–7, explain how the slope-intercept form tells us how many solutions a system of equations has.

2.1 Exercise Set

MyMathLab®

Each rectangular coordinate system shows the graph of the equations in a system of equations. Use each graph to determine the number of solutions for each associated system. If the system has only one solution, give its coordinates.

1.

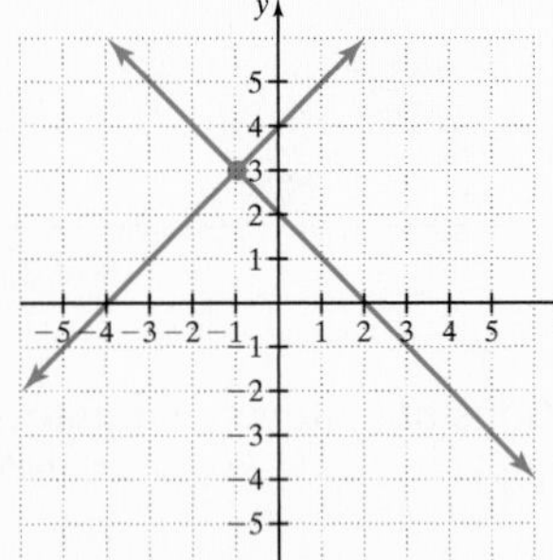

2.

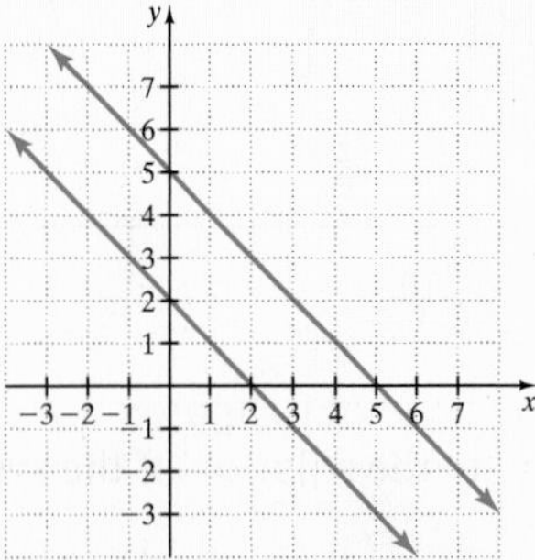

3.

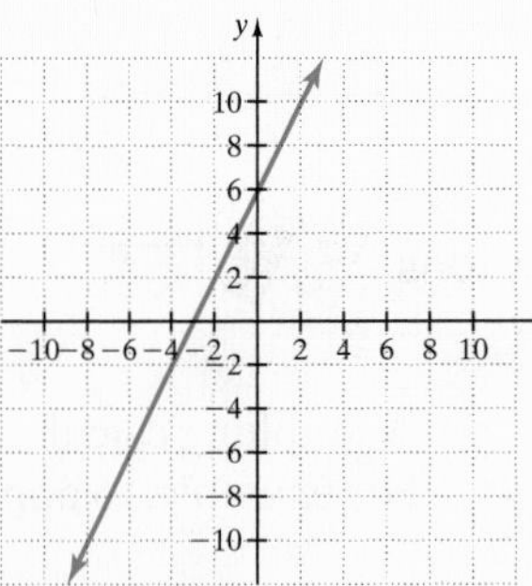

4.

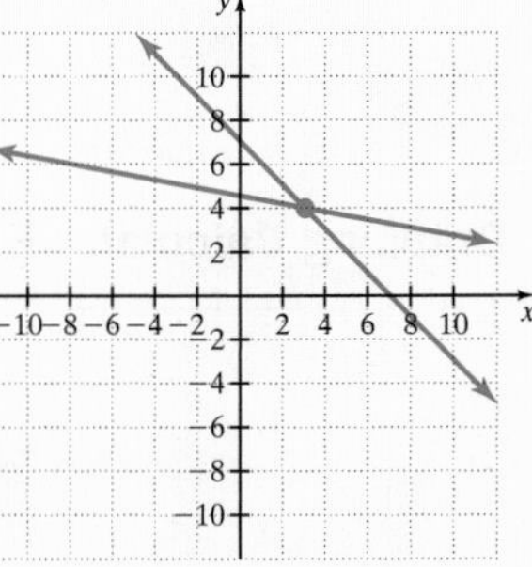

Determine whether each ordered pair is a solution of the system of linear equations. See Examples 1 and 2.

5. $\begin{cases} x + y = 8 \\ 3x + 2y = 21 \end{cases}$
   a. $(2, 4)$
   b. $(5, 3)$

6. $\begin{cases} 2x + y = 5 \\ x + 3y = 5 \end{cases}$
   a. $(5, 0)$
   b. $(2, 1)$

7. $\begin{cases} 3x - y = 5 \\ x + 2y = 11 \end{cases}$
   a. $(3, 4)$
   b. $(0, -5)$

8. $\begin{cases} 2x - 3y = 8 \\ x - 2y = 6 \end{cases}$
   a. $(-2, -4)$
   b. $(7, 2)$

9. $\begin{cases} 2y = 4x + 6 \\ 2x - y = -3 \end{cases}$
   a. $(-3, -3)$
   b. $(0, 3)$

10. $\begin{cases} x + 5y = -4 \\ -2x = 10y + 8 \end{cases}$
   a. $(-4, 0)$
   b. $(6, -2)$

11. $\begin{cases} -2 = x - 7y \\ 6x - y = 13 \end{cases}$
   a. $(-2, 0)$
   b. $\left(\frac{1}{2}, \frac{5}{14}\right)$

12. $\begin{cases} 4x = 1 - y \\ x - 3y = -8 \end{cases}$
   a. $(0, 1)$
   b. $\left(\frac{1}{6}, \frac{1}{3}\right)$

MIXED PRACTICE

Solve each system of linear equations by graphing. See Examples 3 through 6.

13. $\begin{cases} x + y = 4 \\ x - y = 2 \end{cases}$

14. $\begin{cases} x + y = 3 \\ x - y = 5 \end{cases}$

15. $\begin{cases} x + y = 6 \\ -x + y = -6 \end{cases}$

16. $\begin{cases} x + y = 1 \\ -x + y = -3 \end{cases}$

17. $\begin{cases} y = 2x \\ 3x - y = -2 \end{cases}$

18. $\begin{cases} y = -3x \\ 2x - y = -5 \end{cases}$

19. $\begin{cases} y = x + 1 \\ y = 2x - 1 \end{cases}$

20. $\begin{cases} y = 3x - 4 \\ y = x + 2 \end{cases}$

21. $\begin{cases} 2x + y = 0 \\ 3x + y = 1 \end{cases}$

22. $\begin{cases} 2x + y = 1 \\ 3x + y = 0 \end{cases}$

23. $\begin{cases} y = -x - 1 \\ y = 2x + 5 \end{cases}$

24. $\begin{cases} y = x - 1 \\ y = -3x - 5 \end{cases}$

25. $\begin{cases} x + y = 5 \\ x + y = 6 \end{cases}$

26. $\begin{cases} x - y = 4 \\ x - y = 1 \end{cases}$

27. $\begin{cases} 2x - y = 6 \\ y = 2 \end{cases}$

28. $\begin{cases} x + y = 5 \\ x = 4 \end{cases}$

29. $\begin{cases} x - 2y = 2 \\ 3x + 2y = -2 \end{cases}$

30. $\begin{cases} x + 3y = 7 \\ 2x - 3y = -4 \end{cases}$

31. $\begin{cases} 2x + y = 4 \\ 6x = -3y + 6 \end{cases}$

32. $\begin{cases} y + 2x = 3 \\ 4x = 2 - 2y \end{cases}$

33. $\begin{cases} y - 3x = -2 \\ 6x - 2y = 4 \end{cases}$

34. $\begin{cases} x - 2y = -6 \\ -2x + 4y = 12 \end{cases}$

35. $\begin{cases} x = 3 \\ y = -1 \end{cases}$

36. $\begin{cases} x = -5 \\ y = 3 \end{cases}$

37. $\begin{cases} y = x - 2 \\ y = 2x + 3 \end{cases}$

38. $\begin{cases} y = x + 5 \\ y = -2x - 4 \end{cases}$

39. $\begin{cases} 2x - 3y = -2 \\ -3x + 5y = 5 \end{cases}$

40. $\begin{cases} 4x - y = 7 \\ 2x - 3y = -9 \end{cases}$

41. $\begin{cases} 6x - y = 4 \\ \frac{1}{2}y = -2 + 3x \end{cases}$

42. $\begin{cases} 3x - y = 6 \\ \frac{1}{3}y = -2 + x \end{cases}$

Without graphing, decide.

a. Are the graphs of the equations identical lines, parallel lines, or lines intersecting at a single point?
b. How many solutions does the system have? See Examples 7 and 8.

43. $\begin{cases} 4x + y = 24 \\ x + 2y = 2 \end{cases}$

44. $\begin{cases} 3x + y = 1 \\ 3x + 2y = 6 \end{cases}$

45. $\begin{cases} 2x + y = 0 \\ 2y = 6 - 4x \end{cases}$

46. $\begin{cases} 3x + y = 0 \\ 2y = -6x \end{cases}$

47. $\begin{cases} 6x - y = 4 \\ \frac{1}{2}y = -2 + 3x \end{cases}$

48. $\begin{cases} 3x - y = 2 \\ \frac{1}{3}y = -2 + 3x \end{cases}$

49. $\begin{cases} x = 5 \\ y = -2 \end{cases}$

50. $\begin{cases} y = 3 \\ x = -4 \end{cases}$

51. $\begin{cases} 3y - 2x = 3 \\ x + 2y = 9 \end{cases}$

52. $\begin{cases} 2y = x + 2 \\ y + 2x = 3 \end{cases}$

53. $\begin{cases} 6y + 4x = 6 \\ 3y - 3 = -2x \end{cases}$

54. $\begin{cases} 8y + 6x = 4 \\ 4y - 2 = 3x \end{cases}$

55. $\begin{cases} x + y = 4 \\ x + y = 3 \end{cases}$

56. $\begin{cases} 2x + y = 0 \\ y = -2x + 1 \end{cases}$

REVIEW AND PREVIEW

Solve each equation.

57. $5(x - 3) + 3x = 1$
58. $-2x + 3(x + 6) = 17$
59. $4\left(\frac{y + 1}{2}\right) + 3y = 0$
60. $-y + 12\left(\frac{y - 1}{4}\right) = 3$
61. $8a - 2(3a - 1) = 6$
62. $3z - (4z - 2) = 9$

CONCEPT EXTENSIONS

63. Draw a graph of two linear equations whose associated system has the solution $(-1, 4)$.
64. Draw a graph of two linear equations whose associated system has the solution $(3, -2)$.
65. Draw a graph of two linear equations whose associated system has no solution.
66. Draw a graph of two linear equations whose associated system has an infinite number of solutions.
67. The ordered pair $(-2, 3)$ is a solution of all three independent equations:

$$x + y = 1$$
$$2x - y = -7$$
$$x + 3y = 7$$

Describe the graph of all three equations on the same axes.

68. Explain how to use a graph to determine the number of solutions of a system.

The double-line graph below shows the number of pounds of fishery products from U.S. domestic catch and from imports. Use this graph to answer Exercises 69 and 70.

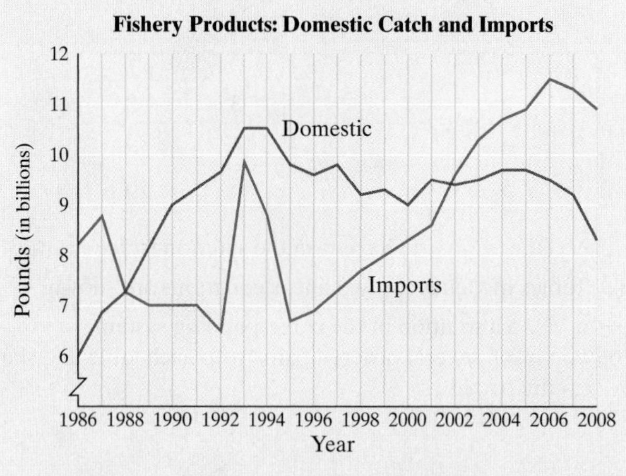

69. Between what pairs of years did the number of pounds of imported fishery products equal the number of pounds of domestic catch?
70. For what year(s) was the number of pounds of imported fishery products less than the number of pounds of domestic catch?

The double-line graph below shows the average attendance per game for the years shown for the Minnesota Twins and the Texas Rangers baseball teams. Use this for Exercises 71 and 72.

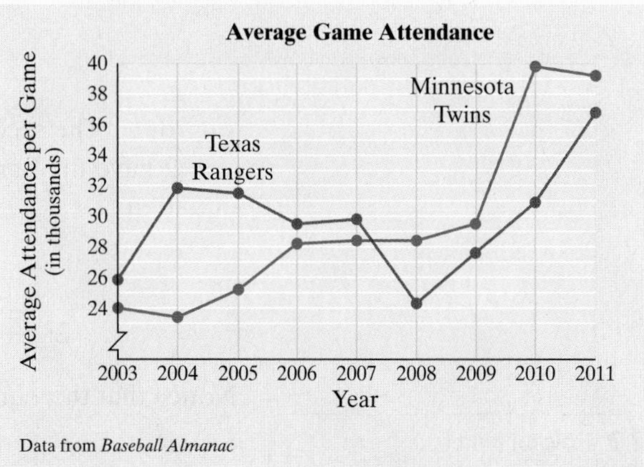

71. In what year(s) was the average attendance per game for the Texas Rangers greater than the average attendance per game for the Minnesota Twins?
72. In what year was the average attendance per game for the Texas Rangers closest to the average attendance per game for the Minnesota Twins, 2006 or 2009?
73. Construct a system of two linear equations that has $(1, 3)$ as a solution.
74. Construct a system of two linear equations that has $(0, 7)$ as a solution.

75. Below are tables of values for two linear equations.
a. Find a solution of the corresponding system.
b. Graph several ordered pairs from each table and sketch the two lines.

x	y
1	3
2	5
3	7
4	9
5	11

x	y
1	6
2	7
3	8
4	9
5	10

c. Does your graph confirm the solution from part (a)?

76. Tables of values for two linear equations are shown.
a. Find a solution of the corresponding system.
b. Graph several ordered pairs from each table and sketch the two lines.

x	y
−3	5
−1	1
0	−1
1	−3
2	−5

x	y
−3	7
−1	1
0	−2
1	−5
2	−8

c. Does your graph confirm the solution from part (a)?

77. Explain how writing each equation in a linear system in slope-intercept form helps determine the number of solutions of a system.

78. Is it possible for a system of two linear equations in two variables to be inconsistent but with dependent equations? Why or why not?

2.2 Solving Systems of Linear Equations by Substitution 

OBJECTIVE

1 Use the Substitution Method to Solve a System of Linear Equations.

OBJECTIVE

1 Using the Substitution Method 

As we stated in the preceding section, graphing alone is not an accurate way to solve a system of linear equations. In this section, we discuss a second, more accurate method for solving systems of equations. This method is called the **substitution method** and is introduced in the next example.

EXAMPLE 1 Solve the system:

$$\begin{cases} 2x + y = 10 & \text{First equation} \\ x = y + 2 & \text{Second equation} \end{cases}$$

Solution The second equation in this system is $x = y + 2$. This tells us that x and $y + 2$ have the same value. This means that we may substitute $y + 2$ for x in the first equation.

$$2x + y = 10 \quad \text{First equation}$$
$$2(y + 2) + y = 10 \quad \text{Substitute } y + 2 \text{ for } x \text{ since } x = y + 2.$$

Notice that this equation now has one variable, y. Let's now solve this equation for y.

Helpful Hint
Don't forget the distributive property.

$$\begin{aligned} 2(y + 2) + y &= 10 \\ 2y + 4 + y &= 10 && \text{Use the distributive property.} \\ 3y + 4 &= 10 && \text{Combine like terms.} \\ 3y &= 6 && \text{Subtract 4 from both sides.} \\ y &= 2 && \text{Divide both sides by 3.} \end{aligned}$$

Now we know that the y-value of the ordered pair solution of the system is 2. To find the corresponding x-value, we replace y with 2 in the equation $x = y + 2$ and solve for x.

$$\begin{aligned} x &= y + 2 \\ x &= 2 + 2 && \text{Let } y = 2. \\ x &= 4 \end{aligned}$$

The solution of the system is the ordered pair (4, 2). Since an ordered pair solution must satisfy both linear equations in the system, we could have chosen the equation $2x + y = 10$ to find the corresponding x-value. The resulting x-value is the same.

Check: We check to see that (4, 2) satisfies both equations of the original system.

First Equation		***Second Equation***	
$2x + y = 10$		$x = y + 2$	
$2(4) + 2 \stackrel{?}{=} 10$		$4 \stackrel{?}{=} 2 + 2$	Let $x = 4$ and $y = 2$.
$10 = 10$	True	$4 = 4$	True

The solution of the system is (4, 2).

A graph of the two equations shows the two lines intersecting at the point (4, 2).

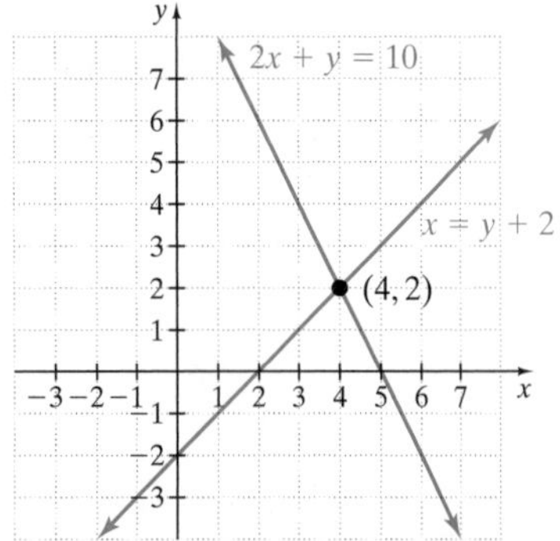

□

PRACTICE 1 Solve the system:

$$\begin{cases} 2x - y = 9 \\ x = y + 1 \end{cases}$$

■

EXAMPLE 2 Solve the system:

$$\begin{cases} 5x - y = -2 \\ y = 3x \end{cases}$$

Solution The second equation is solved for y in terms of x. We substitute $3x$ for y in the first equation.

$$5x - y = -2 \quad \text{First equation}$$

$$5x - (3x) = -2 \quad \text{Substitute } 3x \text{ for } y.$$

Now we solve for x.

$$5x - 3x = -2$$

$$2x = -2 \quad \text{Combine like terms.}$$

$$x = -1 \quad \text{Divide both sides by 2.}$$

The x-value of the ordered pair solution is -1. To find the corresponding y-value, we replace x with -1 in the second equation, $y = 3x$.

$$y = 3x \quad \text{Second equation}$$

$$y = 3(-1) \quad \text{Let } x = -1.$$

$$y = -3$$

Check to see that the solution of the system is $(-1, -3)$. □

(Continued on next page)

PRACTICE 2 Solve the system:

$$\begin{cases} 7x - y = -15 \\ y = 2x \end{cases}$$

To solve a system of equations by substitution, we first need an equation solved for one of its variables, as in Examples 1 and 2. If neither equation in a system is solved for x or y, this will be our first step.

EXAMPLE 3 Solve the system:

$$\begin{cases} x + 2y = 7 \\ 2x + 2y = 13 \end{cases}$$

Solution We choose one of the equations and solve for x or y. We will solve the first equation for x by subtracting $2y$ from both sides.

$x + 2y = 7$ First equation

$x = 7 - 2y$ Subtract $2y$ from both sides.

Since $x = 7 - 2y$, we now substitute $7 - 2y$ for x in the second equation and solve for y.

$2x + 2y = 13$ Second equation

$2(7 - 2y) + 2y = 13$ Let $x = 7 - 2y$.

$14 - 4y + 2y = 13$ Use the distributive property.

$14 - 2y = 13$ Simplify.

$-2y = -1$ Subtract 14 from both sides.

$y = \frac{1}{2}$ Divide both sides by -2.

> **Helpful Hint**
> Don't forget to insert parentheses when substituting $7 - 2y$ for x.

To find x, we let $y = \frac{1}{2}$ in the equation $x = 7 - 2y$.

$x = 7 - 2y$

$x = 7 - 2\left(\frac{1}{2}\right)$ Let $y = \frac{1}{2}$.

$x = 7 - 1$

$x = 6$

> **Helpful Hint**
> To find x, any equation in two variables equivalent to the original equations of the system may be used. We used this equation since it is solved for x.

The solution is $\left(6, \frac{1}{2}\right)$. Check the solution in both equations of the original system. □

PRACTICE 3 Solve the system:

$$\begin{cases} x + 3y = 6 \\ 2x + 3y = 10 \end{cases}$$

The following steps may be used to solve a system of equations by the substitution method.

Solving a System of Two Linear Equations by the Substitution Method

Step 1. Solve one of the equations for one of its variables.

Step 2. Substitute the expression for the variable found in Step 1 into the other equation.

Step 3. Solve the equation from Step 2 to find the value of one variable.

Step 4. Substitute the value found in Step 3 in any equation containing both variables to find the value of the other variable.

Step 5. Check the proposed solution in the original system.

✓CONCEPT CHECK

As you solve the system $\begin{cases} 2x + y = -5 \\ x - y = 5 \end{cases}$ you find that $y = -5$. Is this the solution of the system?

EXAMPLE 4 Solve the system:

$$\begin{cases} 7x - 3y = -14 \\ -3x + y = 6 \end{cases}$$

Solution To avoid introducing fractions, we will solve the second equation for y.

$$-3x + y = 6 \quad \text{Second equation}$$
$$y = 3x + 6$$

Next, substitute $3x + 6$ for y in the first equation.

$$\begin{aligned} 7x - 3y &= -14 && \text{First equation} \\ 7x - 3(3x + 6) &= -14 && \text{Let } y = 3x + 6. \\ 7x - 9x - 18 &= -14 && \text{Use the distributive property.} \\ -2x - 18 &= -14 && \text{Simplify.} \\ -2x &= 4 && \text{Add 18 to both sides.} \\ x &= -2 && \text{Divide both sides by } -2. \end{aligned}$$

To find the corresponding y-value, substitute -2 for x in the equation $y = 3x + 6$. Then $y = 3(-2) + 6$ or $y = 0$. The solution of the system is $(-2, 0)$. Check this solution in both equations of the system. □

PRACTICE
4 Solve the system:

$$\begin{cases} 5x + 3y = -9 \\ -2x + y = 8 \end{cases}$$

Helpful Hint
When solving a system of equations by the substitution method, begin by solving an equation for one of its variables. If possible, solve for a variable that has a coefficient of 1 or -1. This way, we avoid working with time-consuming fractions.

✓CONCEPT CHECK

To avoid fractions, which of the equations below would you use to solve for x?

a. $3x - 4y = 15$ **b.** $14 - 3y = 8x$ **c.** $7y + x = 12$

Answers to Concept Check:
1. No, the solution will be an ordered pair.
2. c

EXAMPLE 5 Solve the system:

$$\begin{cases} \frac{1}{2}x - y = 3 \\ x = 6 + 2y \end{cases}$$

(Continued on next page)

Solution The second equation is already solved for x in terms of y. Thus we substitute $6 + 2y$ for x in the first equation and solve for y.

$$\frac{1}{2}x - y = 3 \quad \text{First equation}$$

$$\frac{1}{2}\overbrace{(6 + 2y)} - y = 3 \quad \text{Let } x = 6 + 2y.$$

$$3 + y - y = 3 \quad \text{Use the distributive property.}$$

$$3 = 3 \quad \text{Simplify.}$$

Arriving at a true statement such as $3 = 3$ indicates that the two linear equations in the original system are equivalent. This means that their graphs are identical and there is an infinite number of solutions of the system. Any solution of one equation is also a solution of the other. For the solution, we can write "infinite number of solutions" or, in set notation, $\left\{(x, y) \middle| \frac{1}{2}x - y = 3\right\}$ or $\{(x, y) | x = 6 + 2y\}$.

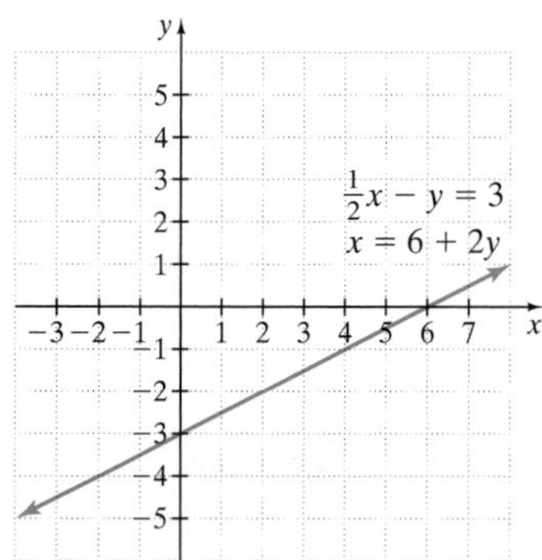

□

PRACTICE 5 Solve the system:

$$\begin{cases} \frac{1}{4}x - y = 2 \\ x = 4y + 8 \end{cases}$$

EXAMPLE 6 Use substitution to solve the system.

$$\begin{cases} 6x + 12y = 5 \\ -4x - 8y = 0 \end{cases}$$

Solution Choose the second equation and solve for y.

$$-4x - 8y = 0 \quad \text{Second equation}$$

$$-8y = 4x \quad \text{Add } 4x \text{ to both sides.}$$

$$\frac{-8y}{-8} = \frac{4x}{-8} \quad \text{Divide both sides by } -8.$$

$$y = -\frac{1}{2}x \quad \text{Simplify.}$$

Now replace y with $-\frac{1}{2}x$ in the first equation.

$$6x + 12y = 5 \quad \text{First equation}$$

$$6x + 12\left(-\frac{1}{2}x\right) = 5 \quad \text{Let } y = -\frac{1}{2}x.$$

$$6x + (-6x) = 5 \quad \text{Simplify.}$$

$$0 = 5 \quad \text{Combine like terms.}$$

The false statement $0 = 5$ indicates that this system has no solution and is inconsistent. The graph of the linear equations in the system is a pair of parallel lines. For the solution, we can write "no solution" or, in set notation, write $\{\ \}$ or $\varnothing$.

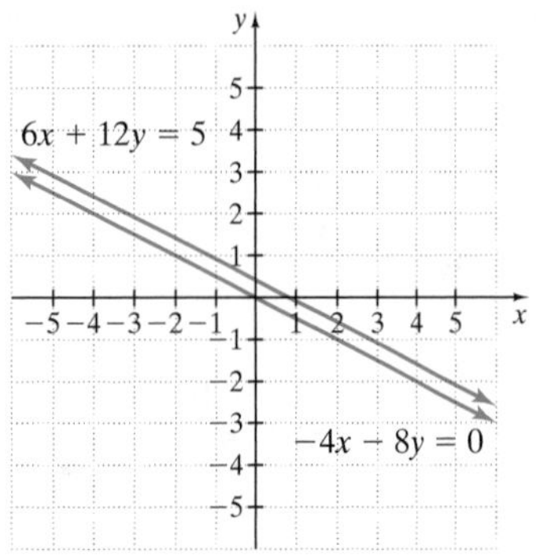

Answers to Concept Check:
a. parallel lines
b. intersect at one point
c. identical graphs

PRACTICE 6 Use substitution to solve the system.

$$\begin{cases} 4x - 3y = 12 \\ -8x + 6y = -30 \end{cases}$$

✓CONCEPT CHECK

Describe how the graphs of the equations in a system appear if the system has

a. no solution
b. one solution
c. an infinite number of solutions

Vocabulary, Readiness & Video Check

Give the solution of each system. If the system has no solution or an infinite number of solutions, say so. If the system has one solution, find it.

1. $\begin{cases} y = 4x \\ -3x + y = 1 \end{cases}$
When solving, you obtain $x = 1$

2. $\begin{cases} 4x - y = 17 \\ -8x + 2y = 0 \end{cases}$
When solving, you obtain $0 = 34$

3. $\begin{cases} 4x - y = 17 \\ -8x + 2y = -34 \end{cases}$
When solving, you obtain $0 = 0$

4. $\begin{cases} 5x + 2y = 25 \\ x = y + 5 \end{cases}$
When solving, you obtain $y = 0$

5. $\begin{cases} x + y = 0 \\ 7x - 7y = 0 \end{cases}$
When solving, you obtain $x = 0$

6. $\begin{cases} y = -2x + 5 \\ 4x + 2y = 10 \end{cases}$
When solving, you obtain $0 = 0$

Martin-Gay Interactive Videos

See Video 2.2

Watch the section lecture video and answer the following question.

OBJECTIVE 1

7. The systems in Examples 2–4 all need one of their equations solved for a variable as a first step. What important part of the substitution method is emphasized in each example?

2.2 Exercise Set

MyMathLab®  

Solve each system of equations by the substitution method. See Examples 1 and 2.

1. $\begin{cases} x + y = 3 \\ x = 2y \end{cases}$

2. $\begin{cases} x + y = 20 \\ x = 3y \end{cases}$

3. $\begin{cases} x + y = 6 \\ y = -3x \end{cases}$

4. $\begin{cases} x + y = 6 \\ y = -4x \end{cases}$

5. $\begin{cases} y = 3x + 1 \\ 4y - 8x = 12 \end{cases}$

6. $\begin{cases} y = 2x + 3 \\ 5y - 7x = 18 \end{cases}$

7. $\begin{cases} y = 2x + 9 \\ y = 7x + 10 \end{cases}$

8. $\begin{cases} y = 5x - 3 \\ y = 8x + 4 \end{cases}$

MIXED PRACTICE

Solve each system of equations by the substitution method. See Examples 1 through 6.

9. $\begin{cases} 3x - 4y = 10 \\ y = x - 3 \end{cases}$

10. $\begin{cases} 4x - 3y = 10 \\ y = x - 5 \end{cases}$

11. $\begin{cases} x + 2y = 6 \\ 2x + 3y = 8 \end{cases}$

12. $\begin{cases} x + 3y = -5 \\ 2x + 2y = 6 \end{cases}$

13. $\begin{cases} 3x + 2y = 16 \\ x = 3y - 2 \end{cases}$

14. $\begin{cases} 2x + 3y = 18 \\ x = 2y - 5 \end{cases}$

15. $\begin{cases} 2x - 5y = 1 \\ 3x + y = -7 \end{cases}$

16. $\begin{cases} 3y - x = 6 \\ 4x + 12y = 0 \end{cases}$

17. $\begin{cases} 4x + 2y = 5 \\ -2x = y + 4 \end{cases}$

18. $\begin{cases} 2y = x + 2 \\ 6x - 12y = 0 \end{cases}$

19. $\begin{cases} 4x + y = 11 \\ 2x + 5y = 1 \end{cases}$

20. $\begin{cases} 3x + y = -14 \\ 4x + 3y = -22 \end{cases}$

21. $\begin{cases} x + 2y + 5 = -4 + 5y - x \\ 2x + x = y + 4 \end{cases}$
(*Hint:* First simplify each equation.)

22. $\begin{cases} 5x + 4y - 2 = -6 + 7y - 3x \\ 3x + 4x = y + 3 \end{cases}$
(*Hint:* See Exercise 21.)

23. $\begin{cases} 6x - 3y = 5 \\ x + 2y = 0 \end{cases}$

24. $\begin{cases} 10x - 5y = -21 \\ x + 3y = 0 \end{cases}$

25. $\begin{cases} 3x - y = 1 \\ 2x - 3y = 10 \end{cases}$

26. $\begin{cases} 2x - y = -7 \\ 4x - 3y = -11 \end{cases}$

27. $\begin{cases} -x + 2y = 10 \\ -2x + 3y = 18 \end{cases}$

28. $\begin{cases} -x + 3y = 18 \\ -3x + 2y = 19 \end{cases}$

29. $\begin{cases} 5x + 10y = 20 \\ 2x + 6y = 10 \end{cases}$

30. $\begin{cases} 6x + 3y = 12 \\ 9x + 6y = 15 \end{cases}$

31. $\begin{cases} 3x + 6y = 9 \\ 4x + 8y = 16 \end{cases}$

32. $\begin{cases} 2x + 4y = 6 \\ 5x + 10y = 16 \end{cases}$

33. $\begin{cases} \frac{1}{3}x - y = 2 \\ x - 3y = 6 \end{cases}$

34. $\begin{cases} \frac{1}{4}x - 2y = 1 \\ x - 8y = 4 \end{cases}$

35. $\begin{cases} x = \frac{3}{4}y - 1 \\ 8x - 5y = -6 \end{cases}$

36. $\begin{cases} x = \frac{5}{6}y - 2 \\ 12x - 5y = -9 \end{cases}$

Solve each system by the substitution method. First, simplify each equation by combining like terms.

37. $\begin{cases} -5y + 6y = 3x + 2(x - 5) - 3x + 5 \\ 4(x + y) - x + y = -12 \end{cases}$

38. $\begin{cases} 5x + 2y - 4x - 2y = 2(2y + 6) - 7 \\ 3(2x - y) - 4x = 1 + 9 \end{cases}$

REVIEW AND PREVIEW

Write equivalent equations by multiplying both sides of the given equation by the given nonzero number.

39. $3x + 2y = 6$ by -2
40. $-x + y = 10$ by 5
41. $-4x + y = 3$ by 3
42. $5a - 7b = -4$ by -4

Add the expressions by combining any like terms.

43. $\begin{array}{r} 3n + 6m \\ \underline{2n - 6m} \end{array}$

44. $\begin{array}{r} -2x + 5y \\ \underline{2x + 11y} \end{array}$

45. $\begin{array}{r} -5a - 7b \\ \underline{5a - 8b} \end{array}$

46. $\begin{array}{r} 9q + p \\ \underline{-9q - p} \end{array}$

CONCEPT EXTENSIONS

47. Explain how to identify a system with no solution when using the substitution method.

48. Occasionally, when using the substitution method, we obtain the equation $0 = 0$. Explain how this result indicates that the graphs of the equations in the system are identical.

Solve. See a Concept Check in this section.

49. As you solve the system $\begin{cases} 3x - y = -6 \\ -3x + 2y = 7 \end{cases}$, you find that $y = 1$. Is this the solution to the system?

50. As you solve the system $\begin{cases} x = 5y \\ y = 2x \end{cases}$, you find that $x = 0$ and $y = 0$. What is the solution to this system?

51. To avoid fractions, which of the equations below would you use if solving for y? Explain why.

    a. $\frac{1}{2}x - 4y = \frac{3}{4}$
    b. $8x - 5y = 13$
    c. $7x - y = 19$

52. Give the number of solutions for a system if the graphs of the equations in the system are

    a. lines intersecting in one point
    b. parallel lines
    c. same line

53. The number of men and women receiving bachelor's degrees each year has been steadily increasing. For the years 1970 through the projection of 2014, the number of men receiving degrees (in thousands) is given by the equation $y = 3.9x + 443$, and for women, the equation is $y = 14.2x + 314$ where x is the number of years after 1970. (*Source:* National Center for Education Statistics)

a. Use the substitution method to solve this system of equations. (Round your final results to the nearest whole numbers.)

b. Explain the meaning of your answer to part (a).

c. Sketch a graph of the system of equations. Write a sentence describing the trends for men and women receiving bachelor's degrees.

54. The number of Adult Contemporary Music radio stations in the United States from 2000 to 2009 is given by the equation $y = -11x + 734$, where x is the number of years after 2000. The number of Spanish radio stations is given by $y = 31x + 542$ for the same time period. (*Source:* M Street Corporation)

a. Use the substitution method to solve this system of equations. (Round your numbers to the nearest tenth.)

b. Explain the meaning of your answer to part (a).

c. Sketch a graph of the system of equations. Write a sentence describing the trends in the popularity of these two types of music formats.

Solve each system by substitution. When necessary, round answers to the nearest hundredth.

55. $\begin{cases} y = 5.1x + 14.56 \\ y = -2x - 3.9 \end{cases}$

56. $\begin{cases} y = 3.1x - 16.35 \\ y = -9.7x + 28.45 \end{cases}$

57. $\begin{cases} 3x + 2y = 14.05 \\ 5x + y = 18.5 \end{cases}$

58. $\begin{cases} x + y = -15.2 \\ -2x + 5y = -19.3 \end{cases}$

2.3 Solving Systems of Linear Equations by Addition 

OBJECTIVE

1 Use the Addition Method to Solve a System of Linear Equations.

OBJECTIVE

1 Using the Addition Method 

We have seen that substitution is an accurate way to solve a linear system. Another method for solving a system of equations accurately is the **addition** or **elimination method.** The addition method is based on the addition property of equality: adding equal quantities to both sides of an equation does not change the solution of the equation. In symbols,

$$\text{if } A = B \text{ and } C = D, \text{ then } A + C = B + D.$$

EXAMPLE 1 Solve the system:

$$\begin{cases} x + y = 7 \\ x - y = 5 \end{cases}$$

Solution Since the left side of each equation is equal to the right side, we add equal quantities by adding the left sides of the equations together and the right sides of the equations together. This adding eliminates the variable y and gives us an equation in one variable, x. We can then solve for x.

Helpful Hint

Notice in Example 1 that our goal when solving a system of equations by the addition method is to eliminate a variable when adding the equations.

$$\begin{aligned} x + y &= 7 && \text{First equation} \\ x - y &= 5 && \text{Second equation} \\ 2x \quad &= 12 && \text{Add the equations.} \\ x &= 6 && \text{Divide both sides by 2.} \end{aligned}$$

The x-value of the solution is 6. To find the corresponding y-value, let $x = 6$ in either equation of the system. We will use the first equation.

$$\begin{aligned} x + y &= 7 && \text{First equation} \\ 6 + y &= 7 && \text{Let } x = 6. \\ y &= 7 - 6 && \text{Solve for } y. \\ y &= 1 && \text{Simplify.} \end{aligned}$$

(Continued on next page)

Check: The solution is $(6, 1)$. Check this in both equations.

First Equation		*Second Equation*	
$x + y = 7$		$x - y = 5$	
$6 + 1 \stackrel{?}{=} 7$		$6 - 1 \stackrel{?}{=} 5$	Let $x = 6$ and $y = 1$.
$7 = 7$	True	$5 = 5$	True

Thus, the solution of the system is (6, 1) and the graphs of the two equations intersect at the point (6, 1) as shown next.

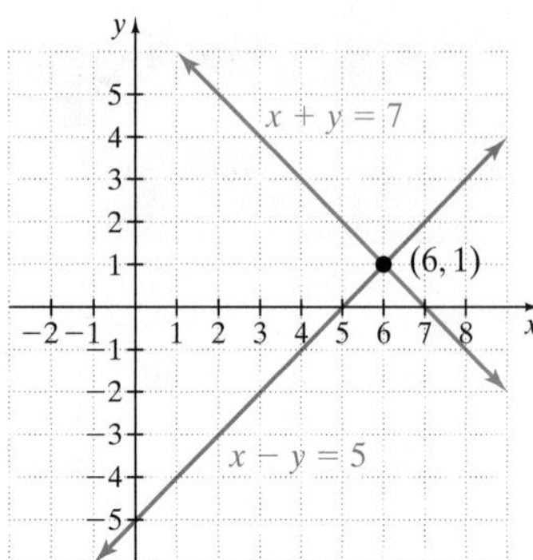

□

PRACTICE 1 Solve the system: $\begin{cases} x - y = 2 \\ x + y = 8 \end{cases}$

EXAMPLE 2 Solve the system: $\begin{cases} -2x + y = 2 \\ -x + 3y = -4 \end{cases}$

Solution If we simply add the two equations, the result is still an equation in two variables. However, remember from Example 1 that our goal is to eliminate one of the variables. Notice what happens if we multiply *both sides* of the first equation by -3, which we are allowed to do by the multiplication property of equality. The system

$$\begin{cases} -3(-2x + y) = -3(2) \\ -x + 3y = -4 \end{cases} \quad \text{simplifies to} \quad \begin{cases} 6x - 3y = -6 \\ -x + 3y = -4 \end{cases}$$

Now add the resulting equations and the y-variable is eliminated.

$$\begin{aligned} 6x - 3y &= -6 \\ -x + 3y &= -4 \\ \hline 5x \quad\quad &= -10 \quad \text{Add.} \\ x &= -2 \quad \text{Divide both sides by 5.} \end{aligned}$$

To find the corresponding y-value, let $x = -2$ in any of the preceding equations containing both variables. We use the first equation of the original system.

$$\begin{aligned} -2x + y &= 2 \quad \text{First equation} \\ -2(-2) + y &= 2 \quad \text{Let } x = -2. \\ 4 + y &= 2 \\ y &= -2 \quad \text{Subtract 4 from both sides.} \end{aligned}$$

The solution is $(-2, -2)$. Check this ordered pair in both equations of the original system. □

PRACTICE 2 Solve the system: $\begin{cases} x - 2y = 11 \\ 3x - y = 13 \end{cases}$

> **Helpful Hint**
> When finding the second value of an ordered pair solution, any equation equivalent to one of the original equations in the system may be used.

In Example 2, the decision to multiply the first equation by -3 was no accident. **To eliminate a variable** when adding two equations, **the coefficient of the variable in one equation must be the opposite of its coefficient in the other equation.**

> **Helpful Hint**
> Be sure to multiply *both sides* of an equation by a chosen number when solving by the addition method. A common mistake is to multiply only the side containing the variables.

EXAMPLE 3 Solve the system: $\begin{cases} 2x - y = 7 \\ 8x - 4y = 1 \end{cases}$

Solution Multiply both sides of the first equation by -4 and the resulting coefficient of x is -8, the opposite of 8, the coefficient of x in the second equation. The system becomes

> **Helpful Hint**
> Don't forget to multiply **both** sides by -4.

$$\begin{cases} -4(2x - y) = -4(7) \\ 8x - 4y = 1 \end{cases} \quad \text{simplifies to} \quad \begin{cases} -8x + 4y = -28 \\ 8x - 4y = 1 \end{cases}$$

Now add the resulting equations.

$$\begin{aligned} -8x + 4y &= -28 \\ 8x - 4y &= 1 \quad \text{Add the equations.} \\ \hline 0 &= -27 \quad \text{False} \end{aligned}$$

When we add the equations, both variables are eliminated and we have $0 = -27$, a false statement. This means that the system has no solution. The graphs of these equations are parallel lines. For the solution, we can write "no solution" or, in set notation, { } or ∅. □

PRACTICE 3 Solve the system: $\begin{cases} x - 3y = 5 \\ 2x - 6y = -3 \end{cases}$

EXAMPLE 4 Solve the system: $\begin{cases} 3x - 2y = 2 \\ -9x + 6y = -6 \end{cases}$

Solution First we multiply both sides of the first equation by 3, then we add the resulting equations.

$$\begin{cases} 3(3x - 2y) = 3(2) \\ -9x + 6y = -6 \end{cases} \quad \text{simplifies to} \quad \begin{cases} 9x - 6y = 6 \\ -9x + 6y = -6 \quad \text{Add the equations.} \end{cases}$$
$$0 = 0 \quad \text{True}$$

Both variables are eliminated and we have $0 = 0$, a true statement. Whenever you eliminate a variable and get the equation $0 = 0$, the system has an infinite number of solutions. The graphs of these equations are identical. The solution is "infinite number of solutions" or, in set notation, $\{(x, y) \mid 3x - 2y = 2\}$ or $\{(x, y) \mid -9x + 6y = -6\}$ □

PRACTICE 4 Solve the system: $\begin{cases} 4x - 3y = 5 \\ -8x + 6y = -10 \end{cases}$

Answer to Concept Check: b

> **✓CONCEPT CHECK**
> Suppose you are solving the system
> $$\begin{cases} 3x + 8y = -5 \\ 2x - 4y = 3 \end{cases}$$
> You decide to use the addition method and begin by multiplying both sides of the first equation by -2. In which of the following was the multiplication performed correctly? Explain.
>
> **a.** $-6x - 16y = -5$ **b.** $-6x - 16y = 10$

EXAMPLE 5 Solve the system: $\begin{cases} 3x + 4y = 13 \\ 5x - 9y = 6 \end{cases}$

Solution We can eliminate the variable y by multiplying the first equation by 9 and the second equation by 4.

$$\begin{cases} 9(3x + 4y) = 9(13) \\ 4(5x - 9y) = 4(6) \end{cases} \quad \text{simplifies to} \quad \begin{cases} 27x + 36y = 117 \\ 20x - 36y = 24 \end{cases}$$

$$47x \qquad = 141 \quad \text{Add the equations.}$$

$$x = 3 \quad \text{Divide both sides by 47.}$$

To find the corresponding y-value, we let $x = 3$ in any equation in this example containing two variables. Doing so in any of these equations will give $y = 1$. The solution to this system is (3, 1). Check to see that (3, 1) satisfies each equation in the original system. □

PRACTICE 5 Solve the system: $\begin{cases} 4x + 3y = 14 \\ 3x - 2y = 2 \end{cases}$

If we had decided to eliminate x instead of y in Example 5, the first equation could have been multiplied by 5 and the second by -3. Try solving the original system this way to check that the solution is (3, 1).

The following steps summarize how to solve a system of linear equations by the addition method.

Solving a System of Two Linear Equations by the Addition Method

Step 1. Rewrite each equation in standard form $Ax + By = C$.

Step 2. If necessary, multiply one or both equations by a nonzero number so that the coefficients of a chosen variable in the system are opposites.

Step 3. Add the equations.

Step 4. Find the value of one variable by solving the resulting equation from Step 3.

Step 5. Find the value of the second variable by substituting the value found in Step 4 into either of the original equations.

Step 6. Check the proposed solution in the original system.

✓CONCEPT CHECK

Suppose you are solving the system

$$\begin{cases} -4x + 7y = 6 \\ x + 2y = 5 \end{cases}$$

by the addition method.

a. What step(s) should you take if you wish to eliminate x when adding the equations?

b. What step(s) should you take if you wish to eliminate y when adding the equations?

EXAMPLE 6 Solve the system: $\begin{cases} -x - \dfrac{y}{2} = \dfrac{5}{2} \\ \dfrac{x}{6} - \dfrac{y}{2} = 0 \end{cases}$

Solution: We begin by clearing each equation of fractions. To do so, we multiply both sides of the first equation by the LCD, 2, and both sides of the second equation by the LCD, 6. Then the system

Answers to Concept Check:

a. multiply the second equation by 4

b. possible answer: multiply the first equation by -2 and the second equation by 7

$$\begin{cases} 2\left(-x - \dfrac{y}{2}\right) = 2\left(\dfrac{5}{2}\right) \\ 6\left(\dfrac{x}{6} - \dfrac{y}{2}\right) = 6(0) \end{cases} \quad \text{simplifies to} \quad \begin{cases} -2x - y = 5 \\ x - 3y = 0 \end{cases}$$

We can now eliminate the variable x by multiplying the second equation by 2.

$$\begin{cases} -2x - y = 5 \\ 2(x - 3y) = 2(0) \end{cases} \quad \text{simplifies to} \quad \begin{cases} -2x - y = 5 \\ 2x - 6y = 0 \end{cases}$$

$$-7y = 5 \quad \text{Add the equations.}$$

$$y = -\frac{5}{7} \quad \text{Solve for } y.$$

To find x, we could replace y with $-\frac{5}{7}$ in one of the equations with two variables.

Instead, let's go back to the simplified system and multiply by appropriate factors to eliminate the variable y and solve for x. To do this, we multiply the first equation by -3. Then the system

$$\begin{cases} -3(-2x - y) = -3(5) \\ x - 3y = 0 \end{cases} \quad \text{simplifies to} \quad \begin{cases} 6x + 3y = -15 \\ x - 3y = 0 \end{cases}$$

$$7x = -15 \quad \text{Add the equations.}$$

$$x = -\frac{15}{7} \quad \text{Solve for } x.$$

Check the ordered pair $\left(-\frac{15}{7}, -\frac{5}{7}\right)$ in both equations of the original system. The solution is $\left(-\frac{15}{7}, -\frac{5}{7}\right)$. □

PRACTICE

6 Solve the system: $\begin{cases} -2x + \dfrac{3y}{2} = 5 \\ -\dfrac{x}{2} - \dfrac{y}{4} = \dfrac{1}{2} \end{cases}$

Vocabulary, Readiness & Video Check

Given the system $\begin{cases} 3x - 2y = -9 \\ x + 5y = 14 \end{cases}$ *read each row (Step 1, Step 2, and Result). Then answer whether the result is true or false.*

	Step 1	*Step 2*	*Result*	*True or False?*
1.	Multiply 2nd equation through by -3.	Add the resulting equation to the 1st equation.	The y's are eliminated.	
2.	Multiply 2nd equation through by -3.	Add the resulting equation to the 1st equation.	The x's are eliminated.	
3.	Multiply 1st equation by 5 and 2nd equation by 2.	Add the two new equations.	The y's are eliminated.	
4.	Multiply 1st equation by 5 and 2nd equation by -2.	Add the two new equations.	The y's are eliminated.	

Martin-Gay Interactive Videos

See Video 2.3

Watch the section lecture video and answer the following question.

OBJECTIVE 1

5. For the addition/elimination methods, sometimes you need to multiply an equation through by a nonzero number so that the coefficients of a variable are opposites, as is shown in Example 2. What property allows us to do this? What important reminder is made at this step?

2.3 Exercise Set

MyMathLab®

Solve each system of equations by the addition method. See Example 1.

1. $\begin{cases} 3x + y = 5 \\ 6x - y = 4 \end{cases}$

2. $\begin{cases} 4x + y = 13 \\ 2x - y = 5 \end{cases}$

3. $\begin{cases} x - 2y = 8 \\ -x + 5y = -17 \end{cases}$

4. $\begin{cases} x - 2y = -11 \\ -x + 5y = 23 \end{cases}$

Solve each system of equations by the addition method. If a system contains fractions or decimals, you may want to clear each equation of fractions or decimals first. See Examples 2 through 6.

5. $\begin{cases} 3x + y = -11 \\ 6x - 2y = -2 \end{cases}$

6. $\begin{cases} 4x + y = -13 \\ 6x - 3y = -15 \end{cases}$

7. $\begin{cases} 3x + 2y = 11 \\ 5x - 2y = 29 \end{cases}$

8. $\begin{cases} 4x + 2y = 2 \\ 3x - 2y = 12 \end{cases}$

9. $\begin{cases} x + 5y = 18 \\ 3x + 2y = -11 \end{cases}$

10. $\begin{cases} x + 4y = 14 \\ 5x + 3y = 2 \end{cases}$

11. $\begin{cases} x + y = 6 \\ x - y = 6 \end{cases}$

12. $\begin{cases} x - y = 1 \\ -x + 2y = 0 \end{cases}$

13. $\begin{cases} 2x + 3y = 0 \\ 4x + 6y = 3 \end{cases}$

14. $\begin{cases} 3x + y = 4 \\ 9x + 3y = 6 \end{cases}$

15. $\begin{cases} -x + 5y = -1 \\ 3x - 15y = 3 \end{cases}$

16. $\begin{cases} 2x + y = 6 \\ 4x + 2y = 12 \end{cases}$

17. $\begin{cases} 3x - 2y = 7 \\ 5x + 4y = 8 \end{cases}$

18. $\begin{cases} 6x - 5y = 25 \\ 4x + 15y = 13 \end{cases}$

19. $\begin{cases} 8x = -11y - 16 \\ 2x + 3y = -4 \end{cases}$

20. $\begin{cases} 10x + 3y = -12 \\ 5x = -4y - 16 \end{cases}$

21. $\begin{cases} 4x - 3y = 7 \\ 7x + 5y = 2 \end{cases}$

22. $\begin{cases} -2x + 3y = 10 \\ 3x + 4y = 2 \end{cases}$

23. $\begin{cases} 4x - 6y = 8 \\ 6x - 9y = 16 \end{cases}$

24. $\begin{cases} 9x - 3y = 12 \\ 12x - 4y = 18 \end{cases}$

25. $\begin{cases} 2x - 5y = 4 \\ 3x - 2y = 4 \end{cases}$

26. $\begin{cases} 6x - 5y = 7 \\ 4x - 6y = 7 \end{cases}$

27. $\begin{cases} \frac{x}{3} + \frac{y}{6} = 1 \\ \frac{x}{2} - \frac{y}{4} = 0 \end{cases}$

28. $\begin{cases} \frac{x}{2} + \frac{y}{8} = 3 \\ x - \frac{y}{4} = 0 \end{cases}$

29. $\begin{cases} \frac{10}{3}x + 4y = -4 \\ 5x + 6y = -6 \end{cases}$

30. $\begin{cases} \frac{3}{2}x + 4y = 1 \\ 9x + 24y = 6 \end{cases}$

31. $\begin{cases} x - \frac{y}{3} = -1 \\ -\frac{x}{2} + \frac{y}{8} = \frac{1}{4} \end{cases}$

32. $\begin{cases} 2x - \frac{3y}{4} = -3 \\ x + \frac{y}{9} = \frac{13}{3} \end{cases}$

33. $\begin{cases} -4(x + 2) = 3y \\ 2x - 2y = 3 \end{cases}$

34. $\begin{cases} -9(x + 3) = 8y \\ 3x - 3y = 8 \end{cases}$

35. $\begin{cases} \frac{x}{3} - y = 2 \\ -\frac{x}{2} + \frac{3y}{2} = -3 \end{cases}$

36. $\begin{cases} \frac{x}{2} + \frac{y}{4} = 1 \\ -\frac{x}{4} - \frac{y}{8} = 1 \end{cases}$

37. $\begin{cases} \frac{3}{5}x - y = -\frac{4}{5} \\ 3x + \frac{y}{2} = -\frac{9}{5} \end{cases}$

38. $\begin{cases} 3x + \frac{7}{2}y = \frac{3}{4} \\ -\frac{x}{2} + \frac{5}{3}y = -\frac{5}{4} \end{cases}$

39. $\begin{cases} 3.5x + 2.5y = 17 \\ -1.5x - 7.5y = -33 \end{cases}$

40. $\begin{cases} -2.5x - 6.5y = 47 \\ 0.5x - 4.5y = 37 \end{cases}$

41. $\begin{cases} 0.02x + 0.04y = 0.09 \\ -0.1x + 0.3y = 0.8 \end{cases}$

42. $\begin{cases} 0.04x - 0.05y = 0.105 \\ 0.2x - 0.6y = 1.05 \end{cases}$

MIXED PRACTICE

Solve each system by either the addition method or the substitution method.

43. $\begin{cases} 2x - 3y = -11 \\ y = 4x - 3 \end{cases}$

44. $\begin{cases} 4x - 5y = 6 \\ y = 3x - 10 \end{cases}$

45. $\begin{cases} x + 2y = 1 \\ 3x + 4y = -1 \end{cases}$

46. $\begin{cases} x + 3y = 5 \\ 5x + 6y = -2 \end{cases}$

47. $\begin{cases} 2y = x + 6 \\ 3x - 2y = -6 \end{cases}$

48. $\begin{cases} 3y = x + 14 \\ 2x - 3y = -16 \end{cases}$

49. $\begin{cases} y = 2x - 3 \\ y = 5x - 18 \end{cases}$

50. $\begin{cases} y = 6x - 5 \\ y = 4x - 11 \end{cases}$

51. $\begin{cases} x + \frac{1}{6}y = \frac{1}{2} \\ 3x + 2y = 3 \end{cases}$

52. $\begin{cases} x + \frac{1}{3}y = \frac{5}{12} \\ 8x + 3y = 4 \end{cases}$

53. $\begin{cases} \frac{x+2}{2} = \frac{y+11}{3} \\ \frac{x}{2} = \frac{2y+16}{6} \end{cases}$

54. $\begin{cases} \frac{2x+5}{2} = \frac{4y+14}{4} \\ \frac{x}{3} = \frac{2y+2}{6} \end{cases}$

55. $\begin{cases} 2x + 3y = 14 \\ 3x - 4y = -69.1 \end{cases}$

56. $\begin{cases} 5x - 2y = -19.8 \\ -3x + 5y = -3.7 \end{cases}$

REVIEW AND PREVIEW

Translating *Rewrite the following sentences using mathematical symbols. Do not solve the equations.*

57. Twice a number, added to 6, is 3 less than the number.

58. The sum of three consecutive integers is 66.

59. Three times a number, subtracted from 20, is 2.

60. Twice the sum of 8 and a number is the difference of the number and 20.

61. The product of 4 and the sum of a number and 6 is twice the number.

62. If the quotient of twice a number and 7 is subtracted from the reciprocal of the number, the result is 2.

CONCEPT EXTENSIONS

Solve. See a Concept Check in this section.

63. To solve this system by the addition method and eliminate the variable y,

$$\begin{cases} 4x + 2y = -7 \\ 3x - y = -12 \end{cases}$$

by what value would you multiply the second equation? What do you get when you complete the multiplication?

64. Given the system of linear equations $\begin{cases} 3x - y = -8 \\ 5x + 3y = 2 \end{cases}$, use the addition method and

a. Solve the system by eliminating x.

b. Solve the system by eliminating y.

65. Suppose you are solving the system $\begin{cases} 3x + 8y = -5 \\ 2x - 4y = 3. \end{cases}$

You decide to use the addition method by multiplying both sides of the second equation by 2. In which of the following was the multiplication performed correctly? Explain.

a. $4x - 8y = 3$

b. $4x - 8y = 6$

66. Suppose you are solving the system $\begin{cases} -2x - y = 0 \\ -2x + 3y = 6. \end{cases}$

You decide to use the addition method by multiplying both sides of the first equation by 3, then adding the resulting equation to the second equation. Which of the following is the correct sum? Explain.

a. $-8x = 6$

b. $-8x = 9$

67. When solving a system of equations by the addition method, how do we know when the system has no solution?

68. Explain why the addition method might be preferred over the substitution method for solving the system $\begin{cases} 2x - 3y = 5 \\ 5x + 2y = 6. \end{cases}$

69. Use the system of linear equations below to answer the questions.

$$\begin{cases} x + y = 5 \\ 3x + 3y = b \end{cases}$$

a. Find the value of b so that the system has an infinite number of solutions.

b. Find a value of b so that there are no solutions to the system.

70. Use the system of linear equations below to answer the questions.

$$\begin{cases} x + y = 4 \\ 2x + by = 8 \end{cases}$$

a. Find the value of b so that the system has an infinite number of solutions.

b. Find a value of b so that the system has a single solution.

Solve each system by the addition method.

71. $\begin{cases} 1.2x + 3.4y = 27.6 \\ 7.2x - 1.7y = -46.56 \end{cases}$

72. $\begin{cases} 5.1x - 2.4y = 3.15 \\ -15.3x + 1.2y = 27.75 \end{cases}$

73. Two age groups predicted to increase in percent of the workforce are those age 25–34 and those age 55 and older. The percent of workers age 25–34 predicted for 2008 through 2018 can be approximated by $0.05x - y = -21.6$. The percent of workers age 55 and older for the same years can be approximated by $0.58x - y = -18.1$. For both equations, x is the number of years since 2008 and y is the percent of the workforce. (*Source:* Bureau of Labor Statistics)

a. Use the addition method to solve the system:

$$\begin{cases} 0.05x - y = -21.6 \\ 0.58x - y = -18.1 \end{cases}$$

(Round answer to the nearest whole.)

b. Use your result from part (a) and estimate the year in which both percents will be the same.

c. Use your results from part (a) and part (b) to estimate the percent of workers age 25–34 and those age 55 and older.

74. Two occupations predicted to greatly increase in the number of jobs are pharmacy technicians and network system analysts. The number of pharmacy technician jobs predicted for 2006 through 2016 can be approximated by $9.1x - y = -295$. The number of network system analyst jobs predicted for 2006 through 2016 can be approximated by $14x - y = -262$. For both equations, x is the number of years since 2006, and y is the number of jobs in the thousands. (*Source:* Bureau of Labor Statistics)

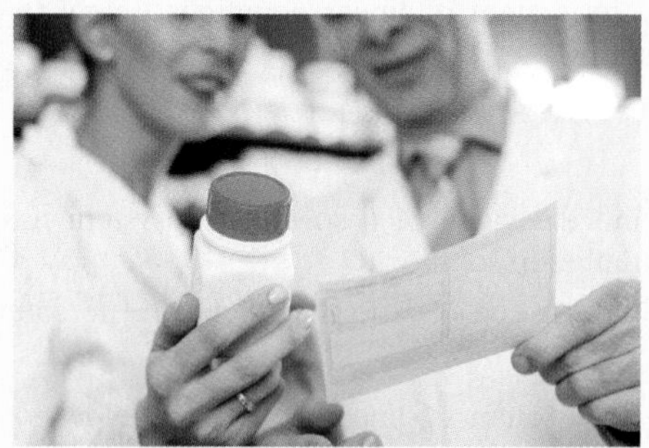

a. Use the addition method to solve this system of equations.

$$\begin{cases} 9.1x - y = -295 \\ 14x - y = -262 \end{cases}$$

(Eliminate y first and solve for x. Round this result to the nearest whole.)

b. Interpret your solution from part (a).

c. Using the year in your answer to part (b), estimate the number of pharmacy technician jobs and network system analyst jobs in that year.

Integrated Review SOLVING SYSTEMS OF EQUATIONS

Sections 2.1–2.3

Solve each system by either the addition method or the substitution method.

1. $\begin{cases} 2x - 3y = -11 \\ y = 4x - 3 \end{cases}$

2. $\begin{cases} 4x - 5y = 6 \\ y = 3x - 10 \end{cases}$

3. $\begin{cases} x + y = 3 \\ x - y = 7 \end{cases}$

4. $\begin{cases} x - y = 20 \\ x + y = -8 \end{cases}$

5. $\begin{cases} x + 2y = 1 \\ 3x + 4y = -1 \end{cases}$

6. $\begin{cases} x + 3y = 5 \\ 5x + 6y = -2 \end{cases}$

7. $\begin{cases} y = x + 3 \\ 3x - 2y = -6 \end{cases}$

8. $\begin{cases} y = -2x \\ 2x - 3y = -16 \end{cases}$

9. $\begin{cases} y = 2x - 3 \\ y = 5x - 18 \end{cases}$

10. $\begin{cases} y = 6x - 5 \\ y = 4x - 11 \end{cases}$

11. $\begin{cases} x + \frac{1}{6}y = \frac{1}{2} \\ 3x + 2y = 3 \end{cases}$

12. $\begin{cases} x + \frac{1}{3}y = \frac{5}{12} \\ 8x + 3y = 4 \end{cases}$

13. $\begin{cases} x - 5y = 1 \\ -2x + 10y = 3 \end{cases}$

14. $\begin{cases} -x + 2y = 3 \\ 3x - 6y = -9 \end{cases}$

15. $\begin{cases} 0.2x - 0.3y = -0.95 \\ 0.4x + 0.1y = 0.55 \end{cases}$

16. $\begin{cases} 0.08x - 0.04y = -0.11 \\ 0.02x - 0.06y = -0.09 \end{cases}$

17. $\begin{cases} x = 3y - 7 \\ 2x - 6y = -14 \end{cases}$

18. $\begin{cases} y = \frac{x}{2} - 3 \\ 2x - 4y = 0 \end{cases}$

19. $\begin{cases} 2x + 5y = -1 \\ 3x - 4y = 33 \end{cases}$

20. $\begin{cases} 7x - 3y = 2 \\ 6x + 5y = -21 \end{cases}$

21. Which method, substitution or addition, would you prefer to use to solve the system below? Explain your reasoning.

$$\begin{cases} 3x + 2y = -2 \\ y = -2x \end{cases}$$

22. Which method, substitution or addition, would you prefer to use to solve the system below? Explain your reasoning.

$$\begin{cases} 3x - 2y = -3 \\ 6x + 2y = 12 \end{cases}$$

2.4 Solving Systems of Linear Equations in Three Variables 

OBJECTIVE

1 Solve a System of Three Linear Equations in Three Variables.

In this section, the algebraic methods of solving systems of two linear equations in two variables are extended to systems of three linear equations in three variables. We call the equation $3x - y + z = -15$, for example, a **linear equation in three variables** since there are three variables and each variable is raised only to the power 1. A solution of this equation is an **ordered triple (x, y, z)** that makes the equation a true statement. For example, the ordered triple $(2, 0, -21)$ is a solution of $3x - y + z = -15$ since replacing x with 2, y with 0, and z with -21 yields the true statement $3(2) - 0 + (-21) = -15$. The graph of this equation is a plane in three-dimensional space, just as the graph of a linear equation in two variables is a line in two-dimensional space.

Although we will not discuss the techniques for graphing equations in three variables, visualizing the possible patterns of intersecting planes gives us insight into the possible patterns of solutions of a system of three three-variable linear equations. There are four possible patterns.

1. Three planes have a single point in common. This point represents the single solution of the system. This system is **consistent.**

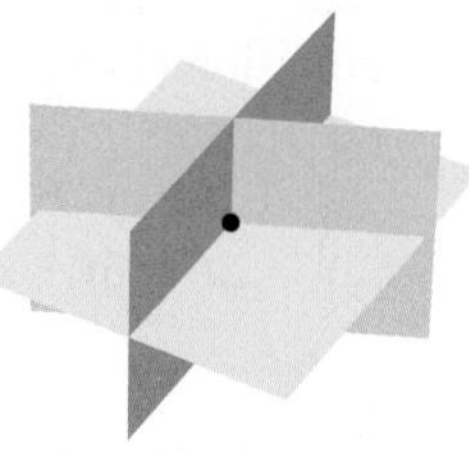

2. Three planes intersect at no point common to all three. This system has no solution. A few ways that this can occur are shown. This system is **inconsistent.**

3. Three planes intersect at all the points of a single line. The system has infinitely many solutions. This system is **consistent.**

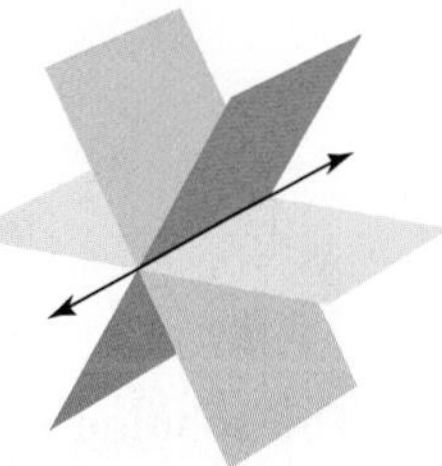

4. Three planes coincide at all points on the plane. The system is consistent, and the equations are **dependent.**

OBJECTIVE

1 Solving a System of Three Linear Equations in Three Variables 

Just as with systems of two equations in two variables, we can use the elimination or substitution method to solve a system of three equations in three variables. To use the elimination method, we eliminate a variable and obtain a system of two equations in two variables. Then we use the methods we learned in the previous two sections to solve the system of two equations.

EXAMPLE 1 Solve the system.

$$\begin{cases} 3x - y + z = -15 & \text{Equation (1)} \\ x + 2y - z = 1 & \text{Equation (2)} \\ 2x + 3y - 2z = 0 & \text{Equation (3)} \end{cases}$$

Solution Add equations (1) and (2) to eliminate z.

$$\begin{array}{r} 3x - y + z = -15 \\ \underline{x + 2y - z = 1} \\ 4x + y \quad = -14 \end{array} \quad \text{Equation (4)}$$

> **Helpful Hint**
> Don't forget to add two other equations besides equations (1) and (2) *and* to **eliminate the same variable.**

Next, add two *other* equations and *eliminate z again*. To do so, multiply both sides of equation (1) by 2 and add this resulting equation to equation (3). Then

$$\begin{cases} 2(3x - y + z) = 2(-15) \\ 2x + 3y - 2z = 0 \end{cases} \text{simplifies to} \begin{cases} 6x - 2y + 2z = -30 \\ \underline{2x + 3y - 2z = 0} \end{cases}$$
$$8x + y \quad = -30 \quad \text{Equation (5)}$$

Now solve equations (4) and (5) for x and y. To solve by elimination, multiply both sides of equation (4) by -1 and add this resulting equation to equation (5). Then

$$\begin{cases} -1(4x + y) = -1(-14) \\ 8x + y = -30 \end{cases} \text{simplifies to} \begin{cases} -4x - y = 14 \\ \underline{8x + y = -30} \end{cases}$$
$$4x \quad = -16 \quad \text{Add the equations.}$$
$$x = -4 \quad \text{Solve for } x.$$

Replace x with -4 in equation (4) or (5).

$$\begin{aligned} 4x + y &= -14 && \text{Equation (4)} \\ 4(-4) + y &= -14 && \text{Let } x = -4. \\ y &= 2 && \text{Solve for } y. \end{aligned}$$

Finally, replace x with -4 and y with 2 in equation (1), (2), or (3).

$$\begin{aligned} x + 2y - z &= 1 && \text{Equation (2)} \\ -4 + 2(2) - z &= 1 && \text{Let } x = -4 \text{ and } y = 2. \\ -4 + 4 - z &= 1 \\ -z &= 1 \\ z &= -1 \end{aligned}$$

The solution is $(-4, 2, -1)$. To check, let $x = -4$, $y = 2$, and $z = -1$ in all three original equations of the system.

Equation (1)	***Equation (2)***	***Equation (3)***
$3x - y + z = -15$	$x + 2y - z = 1$	$2x + 3y - 2z = 0$
$3(-4) - 2 + (-1) \stackrel{?}{=} -15$	$-4 + 2(2) - (-1) \stackrel{?}{=} 1$	$2(-4) + 3(2) - 2(-1) \stackrel{?}{=} 0$
$-12 - 2 - 1 \stackrel{?}{=} -15$	$-4 + 4 + 1 \stackrel{?}{=} 1$	$-8 + 6 + 2 \stackrel{?}{=} 0$
$-15 = -15$ True	$1 = 1$ True	$0 = 0$ True

All three statements are true, so the solution is $(-4, 2, -1)$. □

PRACTICE 1 Solve the system. $\begin{cases} 3x + 2y - z = 0 \\ x - y + 5z = 2 \\ 2x + 3y + 3z = 7 \end{cases}$

EXAMPLE 2 Solve the system.

$$\begin{cases} 2x - 4y + 8z = 2 & (1) \\ -x - 3y + z = 11 & (2) \\ x - 2y + 4z = 0 & (3) \end{cases}$$

Solution Add equations (2) and (3) to eliminate x, and the new equation is

$$-5y + 5z = 11 \quad (4)$$

To eliminate x again, multiply both sides of equation (2) by 2 and add the resulting equation to equation (1). Then

$$\begin{cases} 2x - 4y + 8z = 2 \\ 2(-x - 3y + z) = 2(11) \end{cases} \text{ simplifies to } \begin{cases} 2x - 4y + 8z = 2 \\ -2x - 6y + 2z = 22 \end{cases}$$
$$-10y + 10z = 24 \quad (5)$$

Next, solve for y and z using equations (4) and (5). Multiply both sides of equation (4) by -2 and add the resulting equation to equation (5).

$$\begin{cases} -2(-5y + 5z) = -2(11) \\ -10y + 10z = 24 \end{cases} \text{ simplifies to } \begin{cases} 10y - 10z = -22 \\ -10y + 10z = 24 \end{cases}$$
$$0 = 2 \quad \text{False}$$

Since the statement is false, this system is inconsistent and has no solution. The solution set is the empty set $\{ \}$ or $\varnothing$. □

PRACTICE 2 Solve the system. $\begin{cases} 6x - 3y + 12z = 4 \\ -6x + 4y - 2z = 7 \\ -2x + y - 4z = 3 \end{cases}$

The elimination method is summarized next.

Solving a System of Three Linear Equations by the Elimination Method

Step 1. Write each equation in standard form $Ax + By + Cz = D$.

Step 2. Choose a pair of equations and use the equations to eliminate a variable.

Step 3. Choose any **other** pair of equations and eliminate the **same variable** as in Step 2.

Step 4. Two equations in two variables should be obtained from Step 2 and Step 3. Use methods from Section 2.2 or 2.3 to solve this system for both variables.

Step 5. To solve for the third variable, substitute the values of the variables found in Step 4 into any of the original equations containing the third variable.

Step 6. Check the ordered triple solution in *all three* original equations.

Helpful Hint
Make sure you read closely and follow Step 3.

✓CONCEPT CHECK

In the system

$$\begin{cases} x + y + z = 6 & \text{Equation (1)} \\ 2x - y + z = 3 & \text{Equation (2)} \\ x + 2y + 3z = 14 & \text{Equation (3)} \end{cases}$$

equations (1) and (2) are used to eliminate y. Which action could be used to finish solving best? Why?

a. Use (1) and (2) to eliminate z. **b.** Use (2) and (3) to eliminate y.
c. Use (1) and (3) to eliminate x.

EXAMPLE 3 Solve the system.

$$\begin{cases} 2x + 4y = 1 & (1) \\ 4x - 4z = -1 & (2) \\ y - 4z = -3 & (3) \end{cases}$$

Solution Notice that equation (2) has no term containing the variable y. Let us eliminate y using equations (1) and (3). Multiply both sides of equation (3) by -4 and add the resulting equation to equation (1). Then

$$\begin{cases} 2x + 4y = 1 \\ -4(y - 4z) = -4(-3) \end{cases} \quad \text{simplifies to} \quad \begin{cases} 2x + 4y = 1 \\ - 4y + 16z = 12 \end{cases}$$

$$2x + 16z = 13 \quad (4)$$

Next, solve for z using equations (4) and (2). Multiply both sides of equation (4) by -2 and add the resulting equation to equation (2).

$$\begin{cases} -2(2x + 16z) = -2(13) \\ 4x - 4z = -1 \end{cases} \quad \text{simplifies to} \quad \begin{cases} -4x - 32z = -26 \\ 4x - 4z = -1 \end{cases}$$

$$-36z = -27$$

$$z = \frac{3}{4}$$

Replace z with $\frac{3}{4}$ in equation (3) and solve for y.

$$y - 4\left(\frac{3}{4}\right) = -3 \quad \text{Let } z = \frac{3}{4} \text{ in equation (3).}$$

$$y - 3 = -3$$

$$y = 0$$

Replace y with 0 in equation (1) and solve for x.

$$2x + 4(0) = 1$$

$$2x = 1$$

$$x = \frac{1}{2}$$

The solution is $\left(\frac{1}{2}, 0, \frac{3}{4}\right)$. Check to see that this solution satisfies all three equations of the system. □

PRACTICE 3 Solve the system. $\begin{cases} 3x + 4y = 0 \\ 9x - 4z = 6 \\ -2y + 7z = 1 \end{cases}$

Answer to Concept Check: b

EXAMPLE 4 Solve the system.

$$\begin{cases} x - 5y - 2z = 6 & (1) \\ -2x + 10y + 4z = -12 & (2) \\ \frac{1}{2}x - \frac{5}{2}y - z = 3 & (3) \end{cases}$$

Solution Multiply both sides of equation (3) by 2 to eliminate fractions and multiply both sides of equation (2) by $-\frac{1}{2}$ so that the coefficient of x is 1. The resulting system is then

$$\begin{cases} x - 5y - 2z = 6 & (1) \\ x - 5y - 2z = 6 & \text{Multiply (2) by } -\frac{1}{2}. \\ x - 5y - 2z = 6 & \text{Multiply (3) by 2.} \end{cases}$$

All three equations are identical, and therefore equations (1), (2), and (3) are all equivalent. There are infinitely many solutions of this system. The equations are dependent. The solution set can be written as $\{(x, y, z) \mid x - 5y - 2z = 6\}$. □

PRACTICE **4** Solve the system. $\begin{cases} 2x + y - 3z = 6 \\ x + \frac{1}{2}y - \frac{3}{2}z = 3 \\ -4x - 2y + 6z = -12 \end{cases}$

As mentioned earlier, we can also use the substitution method to solve a system of linear equations in three variables.

EXAMPLE 5 Solve the system:

$$\begin{cases} x - 4y - 5z = 35 & (1) \\ x - 3y = 0 & (2) \\ -y + z = -55 & (3) \end{cases}$$

Solution Notice in equations (2) and (3) that a variable is missing. Also notice that both equations contain the variable y. Let's use the substitution method by solving equation (2) for x and equation (3) for z and substituting the results in equation (1).

$$\begin{aligned} x - 3y &= 0 && (2) \\ x &= 3y && \text{Solve equation (2) for } x. \\ -y + z &= -55 && (3) \\ z &= y - 55 && \text{Solve equation (3) for } z. \end{aligned}$$

Now substitute $3y$ for x and $y - 55$ for z in equation (1).

> **Helpful Hint**
> Do not forget to distribute.

$$\begin{aligned} x - 4y - 5z &= 35 && (1) \\ 3y - 4y - 5(y - 55) &= 35 && \text{Let } x = 3y \text{ and } z = y - 55. \\ 3y - 4y - 5y + 275 &= 35 && \text{Use the distributive law and multiply.} \\ -6y + 275 &= 35 && \text{Combine like terms.} \\ -6y &= -240 && \text{Subtract 275 from both sides.} \\ y &= 40 && \text{Solve.} \end{aligned}$$

(Continued on next page)

To find x, recall that $x = 3y$ and substitute 40 for y. Then $x = 3y$ becomes $x = 3 \cdot 40 = 120$. To find z, recall that $z = y - 55$ and substitute 40 for y, also. Then $z = y - 55$ becomes $z = 40 - 55 = -15$. The solution is $(120, 40, -15)$. □

PRACTICE 5 Solve the system. $\begin{cases} x + 2y + 4z = 16 \\ x \qquad + 2z = -4 \\ \qquad y - 3z = 30 \end{cases}$

Vocabulary, Readiness & Video Check

Solve.

1. Choose the equation(s) that has $(-1, 3, 1)$ as a solution.
   a. $x + y + z = 3$ **b.** $-x + y + z = 5$ **c.** $-x + y + 2z = 0$ **d.** $x + 2y - 3z = 2$
2. Choose the equation(s) that has $(2, 1, -4)$ as a solution.
   a. $x + y + z = -1$ **b.** $x - y - z = -3$ **c.** $2x - y + z = -1$ **d.** $-x - 3y - z = -1$
3. Use the result of Exercise 1 to determine whether $(-1, 3, 1)$ is a solution of the system below. Explain your answer.
   $\begin{cases} x + y + z = 3 \\ -x + y + z = 5 \\ x + 2y - 3z = 2 \end{cases}$
4. Use the result of Exercise 2 to determine whether $(2, 1, -4)$ is a solution of the system below. Explain your answer.
   $\begin{cases} x + y + z = -1 \\ x - y - z = -3 \\ 2x - y + z = -1 \end{cases}$

Martin-Gay Interactive Videos

See Video 2.4

Watch the section lecture video and answer the following question.

OBJECTIVE 1

5. From Example 1 and the lecture before, why does Step 3 stress that the same variable be eliminated from two other equations?

2.4 Exercise Set

MyMathLab®

Solve each system. See Examples 1 through 5.

1. $\begin{cases} x - y + z = -4 \\ 3x + 2y - z = 5 \\ -2x + 3y - z = 15 \end{cases}$

2. $\begin{cases} x + y - z = -1 \\ -4x - y + 2z = -7 \\ 2x - 2y - 5z = 7 \end{cases}$

5. $\begin{cases} 2x + 2y + z = 1 \\ -x + y + 2z = 3 \\ x + 2y + 4z = 0 \end{cases}$

6. $\begin{cases} 2x - 3y + z = 5 \\ x + y + z = 0 \\ 4x + 2y + 4z = 4 \end{cases}$

3. $\begin{cases} x + y = 3 \\ 2y = 10 \\ 3x + 2y - 3z = 1 \end{cases}$

4. $\begin{cases} 5x = 5 \\ 2x + y = 4 \\ 3x + y - 4z = -15 \end{cases}$

7. $\begin{cases} x - 2y + z = -5 \\ -3x + 6y - 3z = 15 \\ 2x - 4y + 2z = -10 \end{cases}$

8. $\begin{cases} 3x + y - 2z = 2 \\ -6x - 2y + 4z = -4 \\ 9x + 3y - 6z = 6 \end{cases}$

9. $\begin{cases} 4x - y + 2z = 5 \\ 2y + z = 4 \\ 4x + y + 3z = 10 \end{cases}$

10. $\begin{cases} 5y - 7z = 14 \\ 2x + y + 4z = 10 \\ 2x + 6y - 3z = 30 \end{cases}$

11. $\begin{cases} x + 5z = 0 \\ 5x + y = 0 \\ y - 3z = 0 \end{cases}$

12. $\begin{cases} x - 5y = 0 \\ x - z = 0 \\ -x + 5z = 0 \end{cases}$

13. $\begin{cases} 6x - 5z = 17 \\ 5x - y + 3z = -1 \\ 2x + y = -41 \end{cases}$

14. $\begin{cases} x + 2y = 6 \\ 7x + 3y + z = -33 \\ x - z = 16 \end{cases}$

15. $\begin{cases} x + y + z = 8 \\ 2x - y - z = 10 \\ x - 2y - 3z = 22 \end{cases}$

16. $\begin{cases} 5x + y + 3z = 1 \\ x - y + 3z = -7 \\ -x + y = 1 \end{cases}$

17. $\begin{cases} x + 2y - z = 5 \\ 6x + y + z = 7 \\ 2x + 4y - 2z = 5 \end{cases}$

18. $\begin{cases} 4x - y + 3z = 10 \\ x + y - z = 5 \\ 8x - 2y + 6z = 10 \end{cases}$

19. $\begin{cases} 2x - 3y + z = 2 \\ x - 5y + 5z = 3 \\ 3x + y - 3z = 5 \end{cases}$

20. $\begin{cases} 4x + y - z = 8 \\ x - y + 2z = 3 \\ 3x - y + z = 6 \end{cases}$

21. $\begin{cases} -2x - 4y + 6z = -8 \\ x + 2y - 3z = 4 \\ 4x + 8y - 12z = 16 \end{cases}$

22. $\begin{cases} -6x + 12y + 3z = -6 \\ 2x - 4y - z = 2 \\ -x + 2y + \frac{z}{2} = -1 \end{cases}$

23. $\begin{cases} 2x + 2y - 3z = 1 \\ y + 2z = -14 \\ 3x - 2y = -1 \end{cases}$

24. $\begin{cases} 7x + 4y = 10 \\ x - 4y + 2z = 6 \\ y - 2z = -1 \end{cases}$

25. $\begin{cases} x + 2y - z = 5 \\ -3x - 2y - 3z = 11 \\ 4x + 4y + 5z = -18 \end{cases}$

26. $\begin{cases} 3x - 3y + z = -1 \\ 3x - y - z = 3 \\ -6x + 4y + 3z = -8 \end{cases}$

27. $\begin{cases} \frac{3}{4}x - \frac{1}{3}y + \frac{1}{2}z = 9 \\ \frac{1}{6}x + \frac{1}{3}y - \frac{1}{2}z = 2 \\ \frac{1}{2}x - y + \frac{1}{2}z = 2 \end{cases}$

28. $\begin{cases} \frac{1}{3}x - \frac{1}{4}y + z = -9 \\ \frac{1}{2}x - \frac{1}{3}y - \frac{1}{4}z = -6 \\ x - \frac{1}{2}y - z = -8 \end{cases}$

REVIEW AND PREVIEW

Translating *Solve.*

29. The sum of two numbers is 45 and one number is twice the other. Find the numbers.

30. The difference of two numbers is 5. Twice the smaller number added to five times the larger number is 53. Find the numbers.

Solve.

31. $2(x - 1) - 3x = x - 12$

32. $7(2x - 1) + 4 = 11(3x - 2)$

33. $-y - 5(y + 5) = 3y - 10$

34. $z - 3(z + 7) = 6(2z + 1)$

CONCEPT EXTENSIONS

35. Write a single linear equation in three variables that has $(-1, 2, -4)$ as a solution. (There are many possibilities.) Explain the process you used to write an equation.

36. Write a system of three linear equations in three variables that has $(2, 1, 5)$ as a solution. (There are many possibilities.) Explain the process you used to write an equation.

37. Write a system of linear equations in three variables that has the solution $(-1, 2, -4)$. Explain the process you used to write your system.

38. When solving a system of three equation in three unknowns, explain how to determine that a system has no solution.

39. The fraction $\frac{1}{24}$ can be written as the following sum:

$$\frac{1}{24} = \frac{x}{8} + \frac{y}{4} + \frac{z}{3}$$

where the numbers x, y, and z are solutions of

$$\begin{cases} x + y + z = 1 \\ 2x - y + z = 0 \\ -x + 2y + 2z = -1 \end{cases}$$

Solve the system and see that the sum of the fractions is $\frac{1}{24}$.

40. The fraction $\frac{1}{18}$ can be written as the following sum:

$$\frac{1}{18} = \frac{x}{2} + \frac{y}{3} + \frac{z}{9}$$

where the numbers x, y, and z are solutions of

$$\begin{cases} x + 3y + z = -3 \\ -x + y + 2z = -14 \\ 3x + 2y - z = 12 \end{cases}$$

Solve the system and see that the sum of the fractions is $\frac{1}{18}$.

Solving systems involving more than three variables can be accomplished with methods similar to those encountered in this section. Apply what you already know to solve each system of equations in four variables.

41. $\begin{cases} x + y \qquad\quad - w = 0 \\ \qquad y + 2z + w = 3 \\ x \qquad - z \qquad = 1 \\ 2x - y \qquad - w = -1 \end{cases}$

42. $\begin{cases} 5x + 4y \qquad\quad = 29 \\ \qquad y + z - w = -2 \\ 5x \qquad + z \qquad = 23 \\ \qquad y - z + w = 4 \end{cases}$

43. $\begin{cases} x + y + z + w = 5 \\ 2x + y + z + w = 6 \\ x + y + z \qquad = 2 \\ x + y \qquad\qquad = 0 \end{cases}$

44. $\begin{cases} 2x \qquad - z \qquad = -1 \\ \qquad y + z + w = 9 \\ \qquad y \qquad - 2w = -6 \\ x + y \qquad\qquad = 3 \end{cases}$

45. Write a system of three linear equations in three variables that are dependent equations.

46. What is the solution to the system in Exercise 45?

2.5 Systems of Linear Equations and Problem Solving

OBJECTIVES

1. Solve Problems That Can Be Modeled by a System of Two Linear Equations.
2. Solve Problems with Cost and Revenue Functions.
3. Solve Problems That Can Be Modeled by a System of Three Linear Equations.

OBJECTIVE

1 Solving Problems Modeled by Systems of Two Equations 

Thus far, we have solved problems by writing one-variable equations and solving for the variable. Some of these problems can be solved, perhaps more easily, by writing a system of equations, as illustrated in this section.

EXAMPLE 1 **Predicting Equal Consumption of Red Meat and Poultry**

America's consumption of red meat has decreased most years since 2000, while consumption of poultry has increased. The function $y = -0.56x + 113.6$ approximates the annual pounds of red meat consumed per capita, where x is the number of years since 2000. The function $y = 0.76x + 68.57$ approximates the annual pounds of poultry consumed per capita, where x is also the number of years since 2000. If this trend continues, determine the year when the annual consumption of red meat and poultry will be equal. (*Source:* USDA: Economic Research Service)

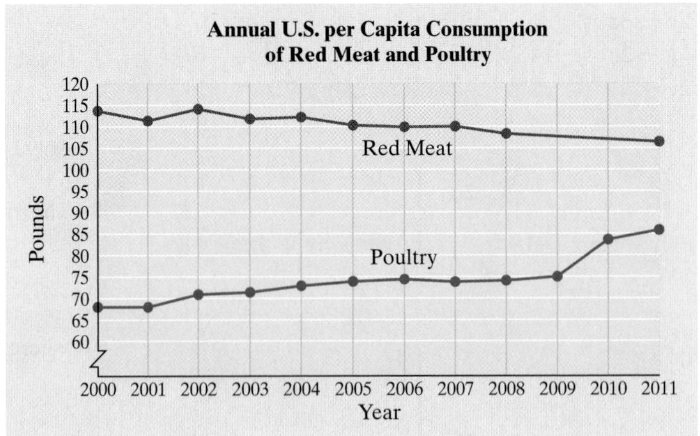

Solution:

1. UNDERSTAND. Read and reread the problem and guess a year. Let's guess the year 2020. This year is 20 years since 2000, so $x = 20$. Now let $x = 20$ in each given function.

$$\text{Red meat: } y = -0.56x + 113.6 = -0.56(20) + 113.6 = 102.4 \text{ pounds}$$
$$\text{Poultry: } y = 0.76x + 68.57 = 0.76(20) + 68.57 = 83.77 \text{ pounds}$$

Since the projected pounds in 2020 for red meat and poultry are not the same, we guessed incorrectly, but we do have a better understanding of the problem. We know that the year will be later than 2020.

2. TRANSLATE. We are already given the system of equations.

3. SOLVE. We want to know the year x in which pounds y are the same, so we solve the system:

$$\begin{cases} y = -0.56x + 113.6 \\ y = 0.76x + 68.57 \end{cases}$$

Since both equations are solved for y, one way to solve is to use the substitution method.

$$y = 0.76x + 68.57 \qquad \text{Second equation}$$

$$-0.56x + 113.6 = 0.76x + 68.57 \qquad \text{Let } y = -0.56x + 113.6$$

$$-1.32x = -45.03$$

$$x = \frac{-45.03}{-1.32} \approx 34.11$$

4. INTERPRET. Since we are only asked to find the year, we need only solve for x.

Check: To check, see whether $x \approx 34.11$ gives approximately the same number of pounds of red meat and poultry.

$$\text{Red meat: } y = -0.56x + 113.6 = -0.56(34.11) + 113.6 \approx 94.4984 \text{ pounds}$$

$$\text{Poultry: } y = 0.76x + 68.57 = 0.76(34.11) + 68.57 \approx 94.4936 \text{ pounds}$$

Since we rounded the number of years, the numbers of pounds do differ slightly. They differ only by 0.0048, so we can assume we solved correctly.

State: The consumption of red meat and poultry will be the same about 34.11 years after 2000, or 2034.11. Thus, in the year 2034, we predict the consumption will be the same. □

PRACTICE

1 Read Example 1. If we use the years 2005, 2006, 2007, and 2008 only to write functions approximating the consumption of red meat and poultry, we have the following:

$$\text{Red Meat: } y = -0.54x + 110.6$$

$$\text{Poultry: } y = -0.36x + 74.1$$

where x is the number of years since 2005 and y is pounds per year consumed.

a. Assuming this trend continues, predict the year when consumption of red meat and poultry will be the same. Round to the nearest year.

b. Does your answer differ from the answer to Example 1? Why or why not?

For Example 1, the equations in the system were given to us. Let's now practice writing our own system of equations that we will use to solve an application.

Many of the applications solved earlier using one-variable equations can also be solved using two equations in **two** variables. We use the same problem-solving steps that have been used throughout this text. The only difference is that two variables are assigned to represent the two unknown quantities and that the stated problem is translated into **two** equations.

Problem-Solving Steps

Step 1. UNDERSTAND the problem. During this step, become comfortable with the problem. Some ways of doing this are to

Read and reread the problem.

Choose two variables to represent the two unknowns.

Construct a drawing if possible.

Propose a solution and check. Pay careful attention to how you check your proposed solution. This will help when writing equations to model the problem.

Step 2. TRANSLATE the problem into two equations.

Step 3. SOLVE the system of equations.

Step 4. INTERPRET the results: **Check** the proposed solution in the stated problem and **state** your conclusion.

EXAMPLE 2 **Finding Unknown Numbers**

Find two numbers whose sum is 37 and whose difference is 21.

Solution

1. UNDERSTAND. Read and reread the problem. Suppose that one number is 20. If their sum is 37, the other number is 17 because $20 + 17 = 37$. Is their difference 21? No; $20 - 17 = 3$. Our proposed solution is incorrect, but we now have a better understanding of the problem.

Since we are looking for two numbers, we let

x = first number

y = second number

2. TRANSLATE. Since we have assigned two variables to this problem, we translate our problem into two equations.

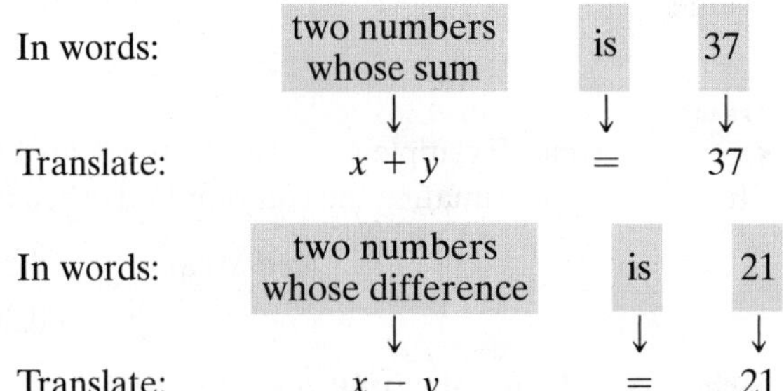

3. SOLVE. Now we solve the system

$$\begin{cases} x + y = 37 \\ x - y = 21 \end{cases}$$

Notice that the coefficients of the variable y are opposites. Let's then solve by the addition method and begin by adding the equations.

$$\begin{aligned} x + y &= 37 \\ x - y &= 21 \\ \hline 2x \quad &= 58 \end{aligned} \qquad \text{Add the equations.}$$

$$x = \frac{58}{2} = 29 \qquad \text{Divide both sides by 2.}$$

Now we let $x = 29$ in the first equation to find y.

$$x + y = 37 \quad \text{First equation}$$
$$29 + y = 37$$
$$y = 8 \quad \text{Subtract 29 from both sides.}$$

4. INTERPRET. The solution of the system is $(29, 8)$.

Check: Notice that the sum of 29 and 8 is $29 + 8 = 37$, the required sum. Their difference is $29 - 8 = 21$, the required difference.

State: The numbers are 29 and 8. □

PRACTICE

2 Find two numbers whose sum is 30 and whose difference is 6.

EXAMPLE 3 Finding Unknown Numbers

A first number is 4 less than a second number. Four times the first number is 6 more than twice the second. Find the numbers.

Solution

1. UNDERSTAND. Read and reread the problem and guess a solution. If a first number is 10 and this is 4 less than a second number, the second number is 14. Four times the first number is $4(10)$, or 40. This is not equal to 6 more than twice the second number, which is $2(14) + 6$ or 34. Although we guessed incorrectly, we now have a better understanding of the problem.

Since we are looking for two numbers, we will let

$x =$ first number

$y =$ second number

2. TRANSLATE. Since we have assigned two variables to this problem, we will translate the given facts into two equations. For the first statement we have

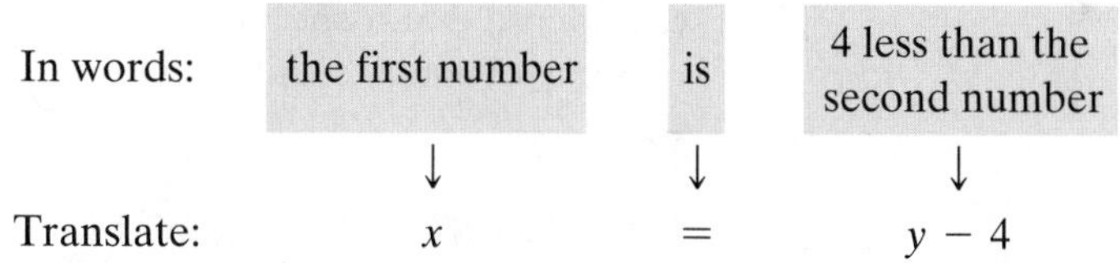

In words:	the first number	is	4 less than the second number
	↓	↓	↓
Translate:	x	$=$	$y - 4$

Next we translate the second statement into an equation.

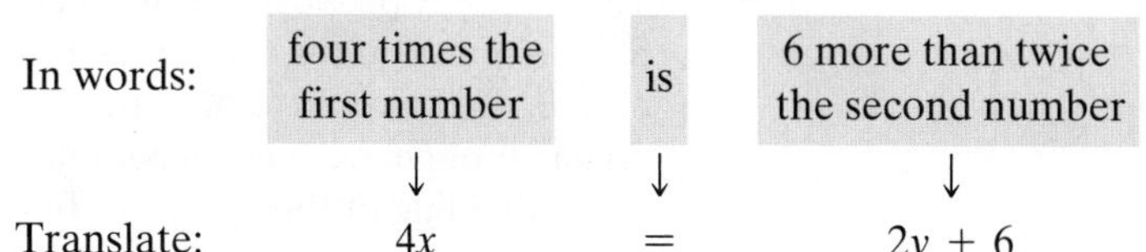

In words:	four times the first number	is	6 more than twice the second number
	↓	↓	↓
Translate:	$4x$	$=$	$2y + 6$

3. SOLVE. Here we solve the system

$$\begin{cases} x = y - 4 \\ 4x = 2y + 6 \end{cases}$$

Since the first equation expresses x in terms of y, we will use substitution. We substitute $y - 4$ for x in the second equation and solve for y.

$$4x = 2y + 6 \quad \text{Second equation}$$
$$4(y - 4) = 2y + 6$$
$$4y - 16 = 2y + 6 \quad \text{Let } x = y - 4.$$
$$2y = 22$$
$$y = 11$$

(Continued on next page)

Now we replace y with 11 in the equation $x = y - 4$ and solve for x. Then $x = y - 4$ becomes $x = 11 - 4 = 7$. The ordered pair solution of the system is $(7, 11)$.

4. INTERPRET. Since the solution of the system is $(7, 11)$, then the first number we are looking for is 7 and the second number is 11.

Check: Notice that 7 *is* 4 less than 11, and 4 times 7 *is* 6 more than twice 11. The proposed numbers, 7 and 11, are correct.

State: The numbers are 7 and 11. □

PRACTICE

3 A first number is 5 more than a second number. Twice the first number is 2 less than 3 times the second number. Find the numbers.

EXAMPLE 4 Solving a Problem about Prices

The Cirque du Soleil show Varekai is performing locally. Matinee admission for 4 adults and 2 children is \$374, while admission for 2 adults and 3 children is \$285.

a. What is the price of an adult's ticket?

b. What is the price of a child's ticket?

c. Suppose that a special rate of \$1000 is offered for groups of 20 persons. Should a group of 4 adults and 16 children use the group rate? Why or why not?

Solution

1. UNDERSTAND. Read and reread the problem and guess a solution. Let's suppose that the price of an adult's ticket is \$50 and the price of a child's ticket is \$40. To check our proposed solution, let's see if admission for 4 adults and 2 children is \$374. Admission for 4 adults is 4(\$50) or \$200 and admission for 2 children is 2(\$40) or \$80. This gives a total admission of \$200 + \$80 = \$280, not the required \$374. Again, though, we have accomplished the purpose of this process: We have a better understanding of the problem. To continue, we let

   A = the price of an adult's ticket and
   C = the price of a child's ticket

2. TRANSLATE. We translate the problem into two equations using both variables.

In words:	admission for 4 adults	and	admission for 2 children	is	\$374
	↓	↓	↓	↓	↓
Translate:	$4A$	$+$	$2C$	$=$	374
In words:	admission for 2 adults	and	admission for 3 children	is	\$285
	↓	↓	↓	↓	↓
Translate:	$2A$	$+$	$3C$	$=$	285

3. SOLVE. We solve the system.

$$\begin{cases} 4A + 2C = 374 \\ 2A + 3C = 285 \end{cases}$$

Since both equations are written in standard form, we solve by the addition method. First we multiply the second equation by -2 so that when we add the equations, we eliminate the variable A. Then the system

$$\begin{cases} 4A + 2C = 374 \\ -2(2A + 3C) = -2(285) \end{cases} \quad \text{simplifies to} \quad \begin{cases} 4A + 2C = 374 \\ -4A - 6C = -570 \end{cases}$$

Add the equations.

$$-4C = -196$$

$$C = 49 \text{ or } \$49\text{, the children's ticket price.}$$

To find A, we replace C with 49 in the first equation.

$$4A + 2C = 374 \quad \text{First equation}$$
$$4A + 2(49) = 374 \quad \text{Let } C = 49$$
$$4A + 98 = 374$$
$$4A = 276$$
$$A = 69 \text{ or } \$69\text{, the adult's ticket price}$$

4. INTERPRET.

Check: Notice that 4 adults and 2 children will pay

$4(\$69) + 2(\$49) = \$276 + \$98 = \$374$, the required amount. Also, the price for 2 adults and 3 children is $2(\$69) + 3(\$49) = \$138 + \$147 = \$285$, the required amount.

State: Answer the three original questions.

a. Since $A = 69$, the price of an adult's ticket is \$69.

b. Since $C = 49$, the price of a child's ticket is \$49.

c. The regular admission price for 4 adults and 16 children is

$$4(\$69) + 16(\$49) = \$276 + \$784$$
$$= \$1060$$

This is \$60 more than the special group rate of \$1000, so they should request the group rate. □

PRACTICE

4 It is considered a premium game when the Red Sox or the Yankees come to Texas to play the Rangers. Admission for one of these games for three adults and three children under 14 is \$75, while admission for two adults and four children is \$62. (*Source:* MLB.com, Texas Rangers)

a. What is the price of an adult admission at Ameriquest Park?

b. What is the price of a child's admission?

c. Suppose that a special rate of \$200 is offered for groups of 20 persons. Should a group of 5 adults and 15 children use the group rate? Why or why not?

EXAMPLE 5 **Finding the Rate of Speed**

Two cars leave Indianapolis, one traveling east and the other west. After 3 hours, they are 297 miles apart. If one car is traveling 5 mph faster than the other, what is the speed of each?

Solution

1. UNDERSTAND. Read and reread the problem. Let's guess a solution and use the formula $d = rt$ (distance = rate · time) to check. Suppose that one car is traveling at a rate of 55 miles per hour. This means that the other car is traveling at a rate of 50 miles per hour since we are told that one car is traveling 5 mph faster than the other. To find the distance apart after 3 hours, we will first find the distance traveled by each car. One car's distance is rate · time $= 55(3) = 165$ miles. The other car's distance is rate · time $= 50(3) = 150$ miles. Since one car is traveling east and the other west, their distance apart is the sum of their distances, or 165 miles + 150 miles = 315 miles. Although this distance apart is not the required distance of 297 miles, we now have a better understanding of the problem.

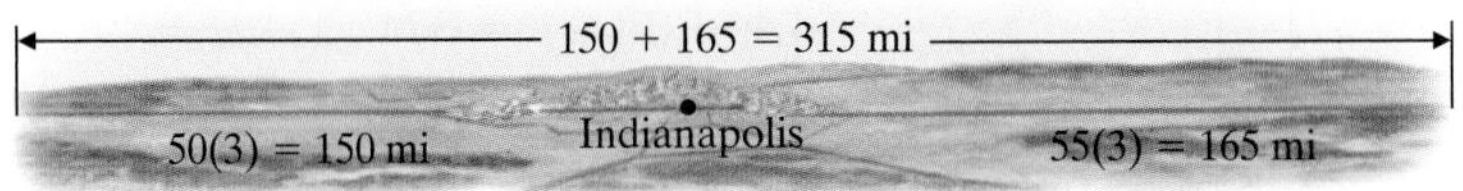

Let's model the problem with a system of equations. We will let

$x =$ speed of one car

$y =$ speed of the other car

We summarize the information on the following chart. Both cars have traveled 3 hours. Since distance = rate · time, their distances are $3x$ and $3y$ miles, respectively.

	Rate •	***Time*** =	***Distance***
One Car	x	3	$3x$
Other Car	y	3	$3y$

2. TRANSLATE. We can now translate the stated conditions into two equations.

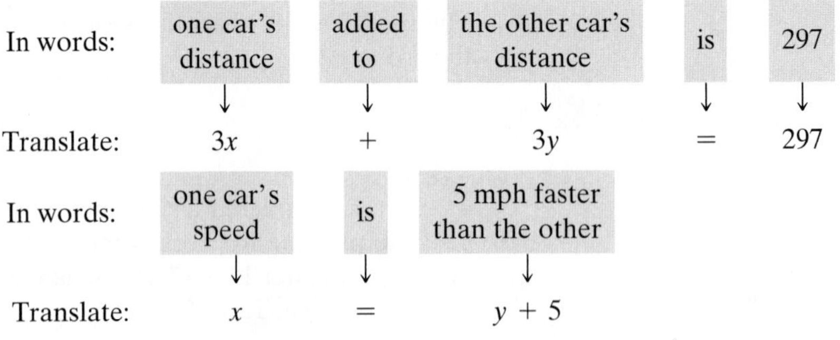

3. SOLVE. Here we solve the system

$$\begin{cases} 3x + 3y = 297 \\ x = y + 5 \end{cases}$$

Again, the substitution method is appropriate. We replace x with $y + 5$ in the first equation and solve for y.

$$
\begin{aligned}
3x + 3y &= 297 && \text{First equation} \\
3(y + 5) + 3y &= 297 && \text{Let } x = y + 5. \\
3y + 15 + 3y &= 297 \\
6y &= 282 \\
y &= 47
\end{aligned}
$$

To find x, we replace y with 47 in the equation $x = y + 5$. Then $x = 47 + 5 = 52$. The ordered pair solution of the system is $(52, 47)$.

4. INTERPRET. The solution $(52, 47)$ means that the cars are traveling at 52 mph and 47 mph, respectively.

Check: Notice that one car is traveling 5 mph faster than the other. Also, if one car travels 52 mph for 3 hours, the distance is $3(52) = 156$ miles. The other car traveling for 3 hours at 47 mph travels a distance of $3(47) = 141$ miles. The sum of the distances $156 + 141$ is 297 miles, the required distance.

> **Helpful Hint**
> Don't forget to attach units if appropriate.

State: The cars are traveling at 52 mph and 47 mph. □

PRACTICE

5 In 2007, the French train TGV V150 became the fastest conventional rail train in the world. It broke the 1990 record of the next fastest conventional rail train, the French TGV Atlantique. Assume the V150 and the Atlantique left the same station in Paris, with one heading west and one heading east. After 2 hours, they were 2150 kilometers apart. If the V150 is 75 kph faster than the Atlantique, what is the speed of each?

EXAMPLE 6 Mixing Solutions

Lynn Pike, a pharmacist, needs 70 liters of a 50% alcohol solution. She has available a 30% alcohol solution and an 80% alcohol solution. How many liters of each solution should she mix to obtain 70 liters of a 50% alcohol solution?

Solution

1. UNDERSTAND. Read and reread the problem. Next, guess the solution. Suppose that we need 20 liters of the 30% solution. Then we need $70 - 20 = 50$ liters of the 80% solution. To see if this gives us 70 liters of a 50% alcohol solution, let's find the amount of pure alcohol in each solution.

number of liters	×	alcohol strength	=	amount of pure alcohol
↓		↓		↓
20 liters	×	0.30	=	6 liters
50 liters	×	0.80	=	40 liters
70 liters	×	0.50	=	35 liters

Since 6 liters + 40 liters = 46 liters and not 35 liters, our guess is incorrect, but we have gained some insight as to how to model and check this problem.

We will let

$$
\begin{aligned}
x &= \text{amount of 30\% solution, in liters} \\
y &= \text{amount of 80\% solution, in liters}
\end{aligned}
$$

(Continued on next page)

and use a table to organize the given data.

	Number of Liters	*Alcohol Strength*	*Amount of Pure Alcohol*
30% Solution	x	30%	$0.30x$
80% Solution	y	80%	$0.80y$
50% Solution Needed	70	50%	$(0.50)(70)$

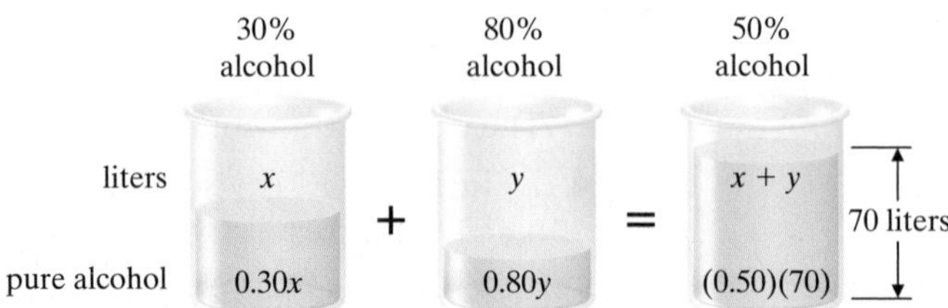

2. TRANSLATE. We translate the stated conditions into two equations.

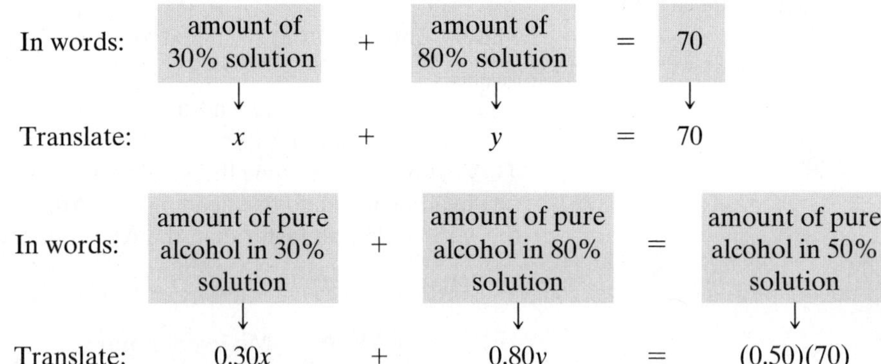

In words: amount of 30% solution + amount of 80% solution = 70

Translate: $x + y = 70$

In words: amount of pure alcohol in 30% solution + amount of pure alcohol in 80% solution = amount of pure alcohol in 50% solution

Translate: $0.30x + 0.80y = (0.50)(70)$

3. SOLVE. Here we solve the system

$$\begin{cases} x + y = 70 \\ 0.30x + 0.80y = (0.50)(70) \end{cases}$$

To solve this system, we use the elimination method. We multiply both sides of the first equation by -3 and both sides of the second equation by 10. Then

$$\begin{cases} -3(x + y) = -3(70) \\ 10(0.30x + 0.80y) = 10(0.50)(70) \end{cases} \quad \text{simplifies to} \quad \begin{cases} -3x - 3y = -210 \\ 3x + 8y = 350 \end{cases}$$

$$5y = 140$$
$$y = 28$$

Now we replace y with 28 in the equation $x + y = 70$ and find that $x + 28 = 70$, or $x = 42$.

The ordered pair solution of the system is $(42, 28)$.

4. INTERPRET.

Check: Check the solution in the same way that we checked our guess.

State: The pharmacist needs to mix 42 liters of 30% solution and 28 liters of 80% solution to obtain 70 liters of 50% solution. □

PRACTICE 6 Keith Robinson is a chemistry teacher who needs 1 liter of a solution of 5% hydrochloric acid to carry out an experiment. If he only has a stock solution of 99% hydrochloric acid, how much water (0% acid) and how much stock solution (99%) of HCL must he mix to get 1 liter of 5% solution? Round answers to the nearest hundredth of a liter.

✓CONCEPT CHECK

Suppose you mix an amount of 25% acid solution with an amount of 60% acid solution. You then calculate the acid strength of the resulting acid mixture. For which of the following results should you suspect an error in your calculation? Why?

a. 14% **b.** 32% **c.** 55%

OBJECTIVE

2 Solving Problems with Cost and Revenue Functions 

Recall that businesses are often computing cost and revenue functions or equations to predict sales, to determine whether prices need to be adjusted, and to see whether the company is making or losing money. Recall also that the value at which revenue equals cost is called the break-even point. When revenue is less than cost, the company is losing money; when revenue is greater than cost, the company is making money.

EXAMPLE 7 **Finding a Break-Even Point**

A manufacturing company recently purchased \$3000 worth of new equipment to offer new personalized stationery to its customers. The cost of producing a package of personalized stationery is \$3.00, and it is sold for \$5.50. Find the number of packages that must be sold for the company to break even.

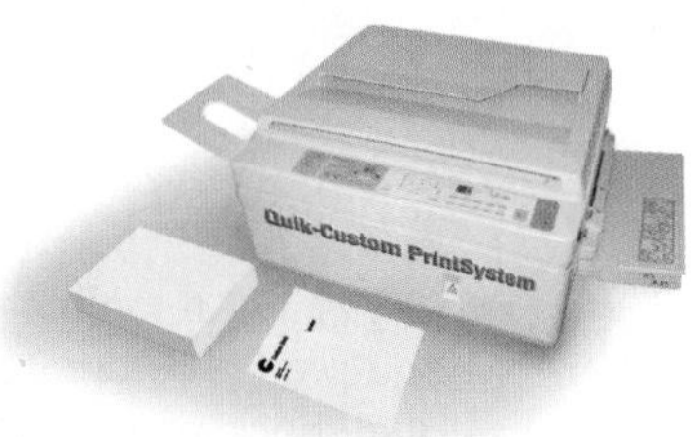

Solution

1. UNDERSTAND. Read and reread the problem. Notice that the cost to the company will include a one-time cost of \$3000 for the equipment and then \$3.00 per package produced. The revenue will be \$5.50 per package sold.

   To model this problem, we will let

   x = number of packages of personalized stationery
   $C(x)$ = total cost of producing x packages of stationery
   $R(x)$ = total revenue from selling x packages of stationery

2. TRANSLATE. The revenue equation is

In words:	revenue for selling x packages of stationery	=	price per package	·	number of packages
	↓		↓		↓
Translate:	$R(x)$	=	5.5	·	x

The cost equation is

In words:	cost for producing x packages of stationery	=	cost per package	·	number of packages	+	cost for equipment
	↓		↓		↓		↓
Translate:	$C(x)$	=	3	·	x	+	3000

Since the break-even point is when $R(x) = C(x)$, we solve the equation

$$5.5x = 3x + 3000$$

(Continued on next page)

Answer to Concept Check:
a; answers may vary

3. SOLVE.

$$5.5x = 3x + 3000$$
$$2.5x = 3000 \quad \text{Subtract } 3x \text{ from both sides.}$$
$$x = 1200 \quad \text{Divide both sides by 2.5.}$$

4. INTERPRET.

Check: To see whether the break-even point occurs when 1200 packages are produced and sold, see if revenue equals cost when $x = 1200$. When $x = 1200$, $R(x) = 5.5x = 5.5(1200) = 6600$ and $C(x) = 3x + 3000 = 3(1200) + 3000 = 6600$. Since $R(1200) = C(1200) = 6600$, the break-even point is 1200.

State: The company must sell 1200 packages of stationery to break even. The graph of this system is shown.

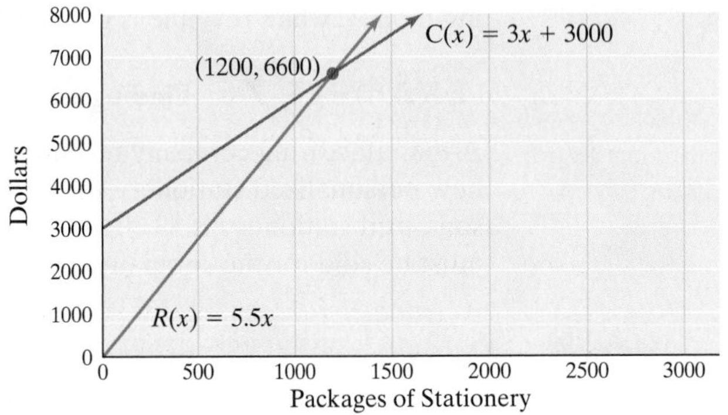

□

PRACTICE

7 An online-only electronics firm recently purchased \$3000 worth of new equipment to create shock-proof packaging for its products. The cost of producing one shock-proof package is \$2.50, and the firm charges the customer \$4.50 for the packaging. Find the number of packages that must be sold for the company to break even.

OBJECTIVE

3 Solving Problems Modeled by Systems of Three Equations 

To introduce problem solving by writing a system of three linear equations in three variables, we solve a problem about triangles.

EXAMPLE 8 Finding Angle Measures

The measure of the largest angle of a triangle is 80° more than the measure of the smallest angle, and the measure of the remaining angle is 10° more than the measure of the smallest angle. Find the measure of each angle.

Solution

1. UNDERSTAND. Read and reread the problem. Recall that the sum of the measures of the angles of a triangle is 180°. Then guess a solution. If the smallest angle measures 20°, the measure of the largest angle is 80° more, or $20° + 80° = 100°$. The measure of the remaining angle is 10° more than the measure of the smallest angle, or $20° + 10° = 30°$. The sum of these three angles is $20° + 100° + 30° = 150°$, not the required 180°. We now know that the measure of the smallest angle is greater than 20°.

To model this problem, we will let

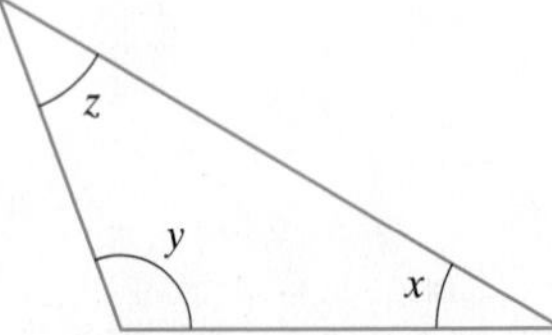

x = degree measure of the smallest angle
y = degree measure of the largest angle
z = degree measure of the remaining angle

2. TRANSLATE. We translate the given information into three equations.

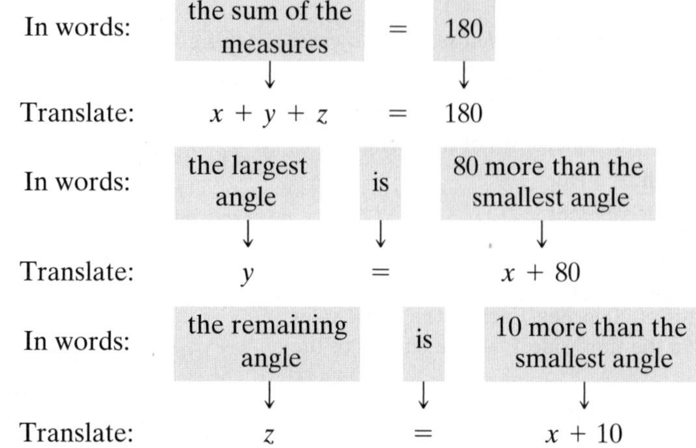

3. SOLVE. We solve the system

$$\begin{cases} x + y + z = 180 \\ y = x + 80 \\ z = x + 10 \end{cases}$$

Since y and z are both expressed in terms of x, we will solve using the substitution method. We substitute $y = x + 80$ and $z = x + 10$ in the first equation. Then

$$x + y + z = 180$$

$$x + (x + 80) + (x + 10) = 180 \quad \text{First equation}$$

$$3x + 90 = 180 \quad \text{Let } y = x + 80 \text{ and } z = x + 10.$$

$$3x = 90$$

$$x = 30$$

Then $y = x + 80 = 30 + 80 = 110$, and $z = x + 10 = 30 + 10 = 40$. The ordered triple solution is (30, 110, 40).

4. INTERPRET.

Check: Notice that $30° + 40° + 110° = 180°$. Also, the measure of the largest angle, 110°, is 80° more than the measure of the smallest angle, 30°. The measure of the remaining angle, 40°, is 10° more than the measure of the smallest angle, 30°. □

PRACTICE

8 The measure of the largest angle of a triangle is 40° more than the measure of the smallest angle, and the measure of the remaining angle is 20° more than the measure of the smallest angle. Find the measure of each angle.

Vocabulary, Readiness & Video Check

Martin-Gay Interactive Videos

See Video 2.5

Watch the section lecture video and answer the following questions.

OBJECTIVE 1

1. In Example 1 and the lecture before, the problem-solving steps for solving applications are mentioned. What is the difference here from when we've used these steps in the past?

OBJECTIVE 2

2. Based on Example 6, explain the meaning of a break-even point. How do you find the break-even point algebraically?

OBJECTIVE 3

3. In Example 7, why is the ordered triple not the final stated solution to the application?

2.5 Exercise Set

MyMathLab®  

Without actually solving each problem, choose each correct solution by deciding which choice satisfies the given conditions.

△ **1.** The length of a rectangle is 3 feet longer than the width. The perimeter is 30 feet. Find the dimensions of the rectangle.

a. length = 8 feet; width = 5 feet
b. length = 8 feet; width = 7 feet
c. length = 9 feet; width = 6 feet

△ **2.** An isosceles triangle, a triangle with two sides of equal length, has a perimeter of 20 inches. Each of the equal sides is one inch longer than the third side. Find the lengths of the three sides.

a. 6 inches, 6 inches, and 7 inches
b. 7 inches, 7 inches, and 6 inches
c. 6 inches, 7 inches, and 8 inches

3. Two computer disks and three notebooks cost \$17. However, five computer disks and four notebooks cost \$32. Find the price of each.

a. notebook = \$4; computer disk = \$3
b. notebook = \$3; computer disk = \$4
c. notebook = \$5; computer disk = \$2

4. Two music CDs and four music cassette tapes cost a total of \$40. However, three music CDs and five cassette tapes cost \$55. Find the price of each.

a. CD = \$12; cassette = \$4
b. CD = \$15; cassette = \$2
c. CD = \$10; cassette = \$5

5. Kesha has a total of 100 coins, all of which are either dimes or quarters. The total value of the coins is \$13.00. Find the number of each type of coin.

a. 80 dimes; 20 quarters
b. 20 dimes; 44 quarters
c. 60 dimes; 40 quarters

6. Samuel has 28 gallons of saline solution available in two large containers at his pharmacy. One container holds three times as much as the other container. Find the capacity of each container.

a. 15 gallons; 5 gallons
b. 20 gallons; 8 gallons
c. 21 gallons; 7 gallons

TRANSLATING

Write a system of equations in x and y describing each situation. Do not solve the system. See Example 2.

7. A smaller number and a larger number add up to 15 and have a difference of 7. (Let x be the larger number.)

8. The total of two numbers is 16. The first number plus 2 more than 3 times the second equals 18. (Let x be the first number.)

9. Keiko has a total of \$6500, which she has invested in two accounts. The larger account is \$800 greater than the smaller account. (Let x be the amount of money in the larger account.)

10. Dominique has four times as much money in his savings account as in his checking account. The total amount is \$2300. (Let x be the amount of money in his checking account.)

MIXED PRACTICE

Solve. See Examples 1 through 6. For Exercises 13 and 14, the solutions have been started for you.

11. Two numbers total 83 and have a difference of 17. Find the two numbers.

12. The sum of two numbers is 76 and their difference is 52. Find the two numbers.

13. One number is two more than a second number. Twice the first is 4 less than 3 times the second. Find the numbers.

Start the solution:

1. UNDERSTAND the problem. Since we are looking for two numbers, let

x = one number
y = second number

2. TRANSLATE. Since we have assigned two variables, we will translate the facts into two equations. (Fill in the blanks.)

First equation:

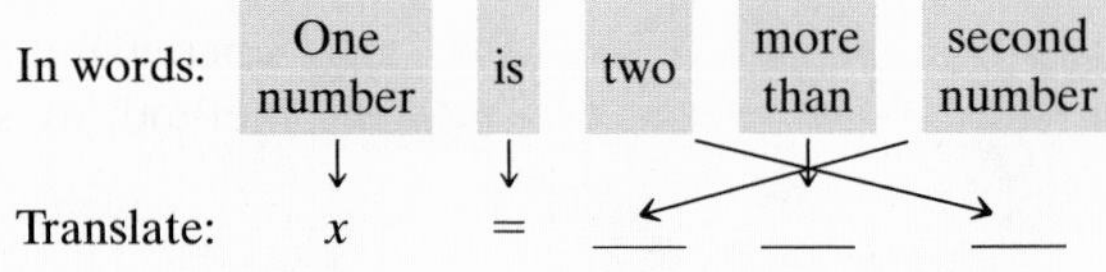

Second equation:

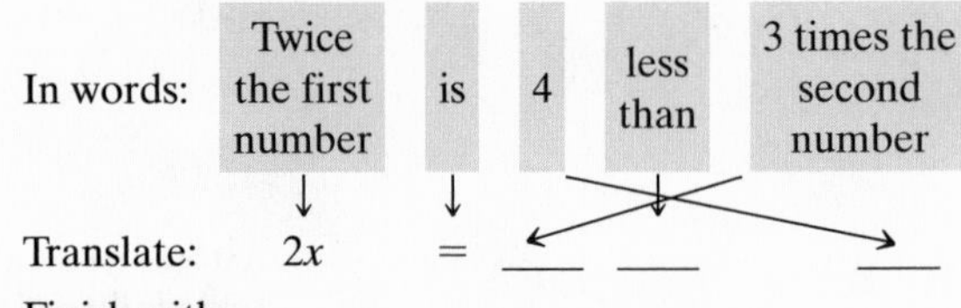

Finish with:

3. SOLVE the system and
4. INTERPRET the results.

14. Three times one number minus a second is 8, and the sum of the numbers is 12. Find the numbers.

Start the solution:

1. UNDERSTAND the problem. Since we are looking for two numbers, let

x = one number
y = second number

2. TRANSLATE. Since we have assigned two variables, we will translate the facts into two equations. (Fill in the blanks.)

First equation:

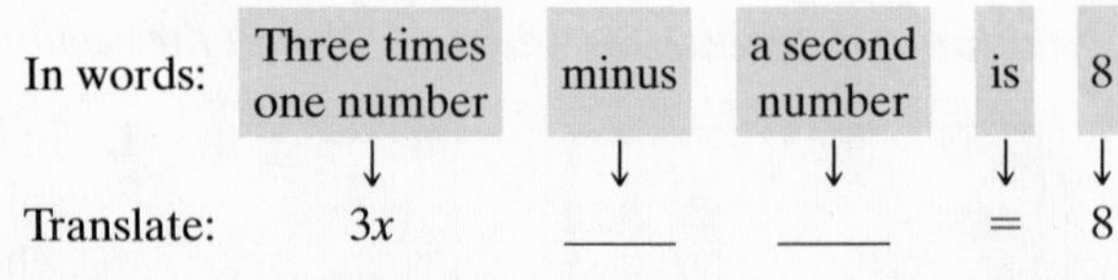

Second equation:

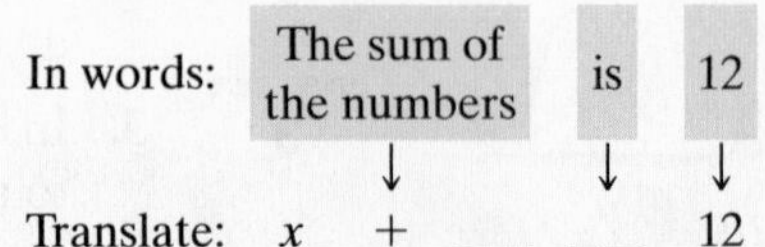

Finish with:

3. SOLVE the system and
4. INTERPRET the results.

15. A first number plus twice a second number is 8. Twice the first number, plus the second, totals 25. Find the numbers.

16. One number is 4 more than twice the second number. Their total is 25. Find the numbers.

17. Miguel Cabrera of the Detroit Tigers led Major League Baseball in runs batted in for the 2010 regular season. Alex Rodriguez of the New York Yankees, who came in second to Cabrera, had 1 fewer run batted in for the 2010 regular season. Together, these two players brought home 251 runs during the 2010 regular season. How many runs batted in did each player account for? (*Source:* Major League Baseball)

18. The highest scorer during the WNBA 2010 regular season was Cappie Pondexter of the New York Liberty. Over the season, Pondexter scored 13 more points than the second-highest scorer, Angel McCoughtry of the Atlanta Dream. Together, Pondexter and McCoughtry scored 1445 points during the 2010 regular season. How many points did each player score over the course of the season? (*Source:* Women's National Basketball Association)

19. Ann Marie Jones has been pricing Amtrak train fares for a group trip to New York. Three adults and four children must pay \$159. Two adults and three children must pay \$112. Find the price of an adult's ticket and find the price of a child's ticket.

20. Last month, Jerry Papa purchased two DVDs and five CDs at Wall-to-Wall Sound for \$65. This month, he bought four DVDs and three CDs for \$81. Find the price of each DVD and find the price of each CD.

21. Johnston and Betsy Waring have a jar containing 80 coins, all of which are either quarters or nickels. The total value of the coins is \$14.60. How many of each type of coin do they have?

22. Sarah and Keith Robinson purchased 40 stamps, a mixture of 44¢ and 20¢ stamps. Find the number of each type of stamp if they spent \$16.40.

23. Norman and Suzanne Scarpulla own 35 shares of McDonald's stock and 69 shares of The Ohio Art Company stock (makers of Etch A Sketch and other toys). On a particular day in 2011, their stock portfolio consisting of these two stocks was worth \$2814. The McDonald's stock was \$70 more per share than The Ohio Art Company stock. What was the price of each stock on that day? (*Source:* Yahoo finance)

24. Saralee Rose has investments in Google and Nintendo stock. During a particular day in 2011, Google stock was at \$540 per share, and Nintendo stock was at \$30 per share. Saralee's portfolio made up of these two stocks was worth \$20,610 at that time. If Saralee owns 16 more shares of Google stock than she owns of Nintendo stock, how many shares of each type of stock does she own?

25. Twice last month, Judy Carter rented a car from Enterprise in Fresno, California, and traveled around the Southwest on business. Enterprise rents this car for a daily fee plus an additional charge per mile driven. Judy recalls that her first trip lasted 4 days, she drove 450 miles, and the rental cost her \$240.50. On her second business trip, she drove the same model of car a distance of 200 miles in 3 days and paid \$146.00 for the rental. Find the daily fee and the mileage charge.

26. Joan Gundersen rented the same car model twice from Hertz, which rents this car model for a daily fee plus an additional charge per mile driven. Joan recalls that the car rented for 5 days and driven for 300 miles cost her \$178, while the same model car rented for 4 days and driven for 500 miles cost \$197. Find the daily fee and find the mileage charge.

27. Pratap Puri rowed 18 miles down the Delaware River in 2 hours, but the return trip took him $4\frac{1}{2}$ hours. Find the rate Pratap can row in still water and find the rate of the current.

Let x = rate Pratap can row in still water and
y = rate of the current

	d	$=$ r	$\cdot$ t
Downstream		$x + y$	
Upstream		$x - y$	

28. The Jonathan Schultz family took a canoe 10 miles down the Allegheny River in $1\frac{1}{4}$ hours. After lunch, it took them 4 hours to return. Find the rate of the current.

Let x = rate the family can row in still water and
y = rate of the current

	d	$=$ r	$\cdot$ t
Downstream		$x + y$	
Upstream		$x - y$	

29. Dave and Sandy Hartranft are frequent flyers with Delta Airlines. They often fly from Philadelphia to Chicago, a distance of 780 miles. On one particular trip, they fly into the wind, and the flight takes 2 hours. The return trip, with the wind behind them, only takes $1\frac{1}{2}$ hours. If the wind speed is the same on each trip, find the speed of the wind and find the speed of the plane in still air.

30. With a strong wind behind it, a United Airlines jet flies 2400 miles from Los Angeles to Orlando in $4\frac{3}{4}$ hours. The return trip takes 6 hours because the plane flies into the wind. If the wind speed is the same on each trip, find the speed of the plane in still air and find the wind speed to the nearest tenth of a mile per hour.

31. Kevin Briley began a 114-mile bicycle trip to build up stamina for a triathlete competition. Unfortunately, his bicycle chain broke, so he finished the trip walking. The whole trip took 6 hours. If Kevin walks at a rate of 4 miles per hour and rides at 24 miles per hour, find the amount of time he spent on the bicycle.

32. In Canada, eastbound and westbound trains travel along the same track, with sidings to pull onto to avoid accidents. Two trains are now 150 miles apart, with the westbound train traveling twice as fast as the eastbound train. A warning must be issued to pull one train onto a siding or else the trains will crash in $1\frac{1}{4}$ hours. Find the speed of the eastbound train and the speed of the westbound train.

33. Doreen Schmidt is a chemist with Gemco Pharmaceutical. She needs to prepare 12 liters of a 9% hydrochloric acid solution. Find the amount of a 4% solution and the amount of a 12% solution she should mix to get this solution.

Concentration Rate	*Liters of Solution*	*Liters of Pure Acid*
0.04	x	$0.04x$
0.12	y	?
0.09	12	?

34. Elise Everly is preparing 15 liters of a 25% saline solution. Elise has two other saline solutions, with strengths of 40% and 10%. Find the amount of 40% solution and the amount of 10% solution she should mix to get 15 liters of a 25% solution.

Concentration Rate	*Liters of Solution*	*Liters of Pure Salt*
0.40	x	$0.40x$
0.10	y	?
0.25	15	?

35. Wayne Osby blends coffee for a local coffee café. He needs to prepare 200 pounds of blended coffee beans selling for \$3.95 per pound. He intends to do this by blending together a high-quality bean costing \$4.95 per pound and a cheaper bean costing \$2.65 per pound. To the nearest pound, find how much high-quality coffee bean and how much cheaper coffee bean he should blend.

36. Macadamia nuts cost an astounding \$16.50 per pound, but research by an independent firm says that mixed nuts sell better if macadamias are included. The standard mix costs \$9.25 per pound. Find how many pounds of macadamias and how many pounds of the standard mix should be combined to produce 40 pounds that will cost \$10 per pound. Find the amounts to the nearest tenth of a pound.

△ **37.** Recall that two angles are complementary if the sum of their measures is 90°. Find the measures of two complementary angles if one angle is twice the other.

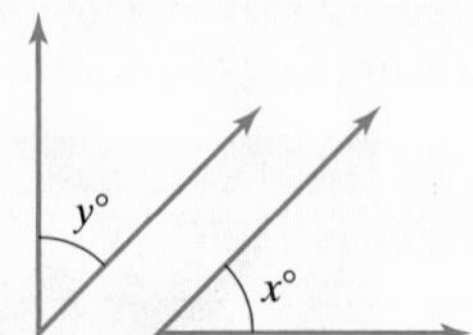

△ **38.** Recall that two angles are supplementary if the sum of their measures is 180°. Find the measures of two supplementary angles if one angle is 20° more than four times the other.

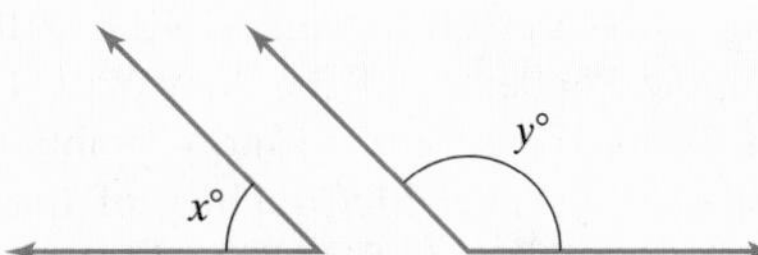

△ **39.** Find the measures of two complementary angles if one angle is 10° more than three times the other.

△ **40.** Find the measures of two supplementary angles if one angle is 18° more than twice the other.

41. Kathi and Robert Hawn had a pottery stand at the annual Skippack Craft Fair. They sold some of their pottery at the original price of \$9.50 each but later decreased the price of each by \$2. If they sold all 90 pieces and took in \$721, find how many they sold at the original price and how many they sold at the reduced price.

42. A charity fund-raiser consisted of a spaghetti supper where a total of 387 people were fed. They charged \$6.80 for adults and half price for children. If they took in \$2444.60, find how many adults and how many children attended the supper.

43. The Santa Fe National Historic Trail is approximately 1200 miles between Old Franklin, Missouri, and Santa Fe, New Mexico. Suppose that a group of hikers start from each town and walk the trail toward each other. They meet after a total hiking time of 240 hours. If one group travels $\frac{1}{2}$ mile per hour slower than the other group, find the rate of each group. (*Source:* National Park Service)

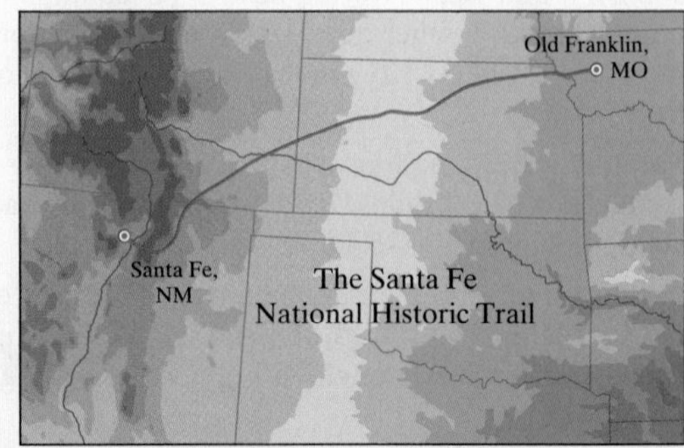

44. California 1 South is a historic highway that stretches 123 miles along the coast from Monterey to Morro Bay. Suppose that two antique cars start driving this highway, one from each town. They meet after 3 hours. Find the rate of each car if one car travels 1 mile per hour faster than the other car. (*Source:* National Geographic)

45. A 30% solution of fertilizer is to be mixed with a 60% solution of fertilizer to get 150 gallons of a 50% solution. How many gallons of the 30% solution and 60% solution should be mixed?

46. A 10% acid solution is to be mixed with a 50% acid solution to get 120 ounces of a 20% acid solution. How many ounces of the 10% solution and 50% solution should be mixed?

47. Traffic signs are regulated by the *Manual on Uniform Traffic Control Devices* (MUTCD). According to this manual, if the sign below is placed on a freeway, its perimeter must be 144 inches. Also, its length is 12 inches longer than its width. Find the dimensions of this sign.

48. According to the MUTCD (see Exercise 47), this sign must have a perimeter of 60 inches. Also, its length must be 6 inches longer than its width. Find the dimensions of this sign.

49. In the United States, the percent of adult blogging has changed within the various age ranges. From 2007 to 2009, the function $y = -4.5x + 24$ can be used to estimate the percent of adults under 30 who blogged, and the function $y = 2x + 7$ can be used to estimate the percent of adults over 30 who blogged. For both functions, x is the number of years after 2007. (*Source:* Pew Internet & American Life Project)

a. If this trend continued, estimate the year in which the percent of adults under 30 and the percent of adults over 30 who blogged was the same.

b. Use these equations to predict the percent of adults under 30 who blog and the percent of adults over 30 who blog for the current year.

50. The rate of fatalities per 100 million vehicle-miles has been decreasing for both automobiles and light trucks (pickups, sport-utility vehicles, and minivans). For the years 2001 through 2009, the function $y = -0.06x + 1.7$ can be used to estimate the rate of fatalities per 100 million vehicle-miles for automobiles during this period, and the function $y = -0.08x + 2.1$ can be used to estimate the rate of fatalities per 100 million vehicle-miles for light trucks during this period. For both functions, x is the number of years since 2000. (*Source:* Bureau of Statistics, U.S. Department of Transportation)

a. If this trend continues, predict the year in which the fatality rate for automobiles equals the fatality rate for light trucks.

b. Use these equations to predict the fatality rate per million vehicle-miles for automobiles and light trucks for the current year.

51. The annual U.S. per capita consumption of cheddar cheese has remained about the same since the millennium, while the consumption of mozzarella cheese has increased. For the years 2000–2010, the function $y = 0.06x + 9.7$ approximates the annual U.S. per capita consumption of cheddar cheese in pounds, and the function $y = 0.21x + 9.3$ approximates the annual U.S. per capita consumption of mozzarella cheese in pounds. For both functions, x is the number of years after 2000.

a. Explain how the given function verifies that the consumption of cheddar cheese has remained the same, while the given function verifies that the consumption of mozzarella cheese has increased.

b. Based on this information, determine the year in which the pounds of cheddar cheese consumed equaled the pounds of mozzarella cheese consumed. (*Source:* Based on data from the U.S. Department of Agriculture)

52. Two of the major job categories defined by the U.S. Department of Labor are manufacturing jobs and jobs in the service sector. Jobs in the manufacturing sector have decreased nearly every year since the 1960s. During the same time period, service sector jobs have been steadily increasing. For the years from 1988 through 2009, the function $y = -0.225x + 16.1$ approximates the percent of jobs in the U.S. economy that are manufacturing jobs, while the function $y = 0.45x + 21.7$ approximates the percent of jobs that are service sector jobs. (*Source:* Based on data from the U.S. Department of Labor)

a. Explain how the decrease in manufacturing jobs can be verified by the given function, and the increase of service sector jobs can be verified by the given function.

b. Based on this information, determine the year when the percent of manufacturing jobs and the percent of service sector jobs were the same.

△ **53.** In the figure, line l and line m are parallel lines cut by transversal t. Find the values of x and y.

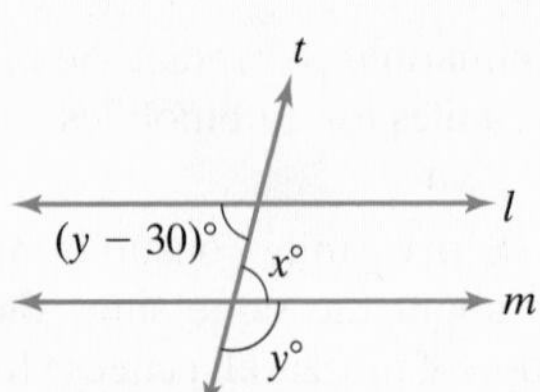

△ **54.** Find the values of x and y in the following isosceles triangle.

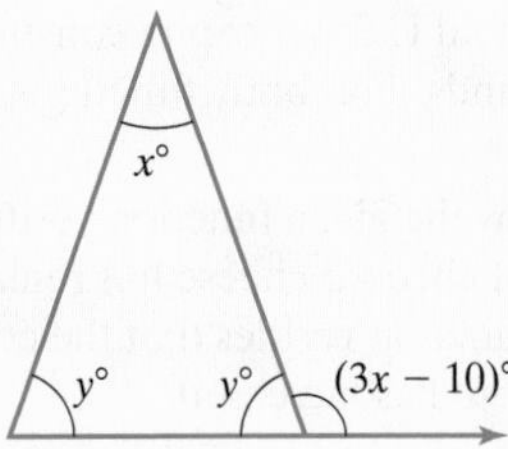

Given the cost function $C(x)$ and the revenue function $R(x)$, find the number of units x that must be sold to break even. See Example 7.

55. $C(x) = 30x + 10{,}000$ $R(x) = 46x$

56. $C(x) = 12x + 15{,}000$ $R(x) = 32x$

57. $C(x) = 1.2x + 1500$ $R(x) = 1.7x$

58. $C(x) = 0.8x + 900$ $R(x) = 2x$

59. $C(x) = 75x + 160{,}000$ $R(x) = 200x$

60. $C(x) = 105x + 70{,}000$ $R(x) = 245x$

61. The planning department of Abstract Office Supplies has been asked to determine whether the company should introduce a new computer desk next year. The department estimates that \$6000 of new manufacturing equipment will need to be purchased and that the cost of constructing each desk will be \$200. The department also estimates that the revenue from each desk will be \$450.

a. Determine the revenue function $R(x)$ from the sale of x desks.

b. Determine the cost function $C(x)$ for manufacturing x desks.

c. Find the break-even point.

62. Baskets, Inc., is planning to introduce a new woven basket. The company estimates that \$500 worth of new equipment will be needed to manufacture this new type of basket and that it will cost \$15 per basket to manufacture. The company also estimates that the revenue from each basket will be \$31.

a. Determine the revenue function $R(x)$ from the sale of x baskets.

b. Determine the cost function $C(x)$ for manufacturing x baskets.

c. Find the break-even point. Round up to the nearest whole basket.

Solve. See Example 8.

63. Rabbits in a lab are to be kept on a strict daily diet that includes 30 grams of protein, 16 grams of fat, and 24 grams of carbohydrates. The scientist has only three food mixes available with the following grams of nutrients per unit.

	Protein	*Fat*	*Carbohydrate*
Mix A	4	6	3
Mix B	6	1	2
Mix C	4	1	12

Find how many units of each mix are needed daily to meet each rabbit's dietary need.

64. Gerry Gundersen mixes different solutions with concentrations of 25%, 40%, and 50% to get 200 liters of a 32% solution. If he uses twice as much of the 25% solution as of the 40% solution, find how many liters of each kind he uses.

65. The perimeter of a quadrilateral (four-sided polygon) is 29 inches. The longest side is twice as long as the shortest side. The other two sides are equally long and are 2 inches longer than the shortest side. Find the lengths of all four sides.

66. The measure of the largest angle of a triangle is 90° more than the measure of the smallest angle, and the measure of the remaining angle is 30° more than the measure of the smallest angle. Find the measure of each angle.

67. The sum of three numbers is 40. The first number is five more than the second number. It is also twice the third. Find the numbers.

68. The sum of the digits of a three-digit number is 15. The tens-place digit is twice the hundreds-place digit, and the ones-place digit is 1 less than the hundreds-place digit. Find the three-digit number.

69. During the 2010–2011 regular NBA season, the top-scoring player was Kevin Durant of the Oklahoma City Thunder. Durant scored a total of 2161 points during the regular season. The number of free throws (each worth one point) he made was 14 more than four times the number of three-point field goals he made. The number of two-point field goals that Durant made was 28 less than the number of free throws he made. How many free throws, two-point field goals, and three-point field goals did Kevin Durant make during the 2010–2011 NBA season? (*Source*: National Basketball Association)

70. For 2010, the WNBA's top scorer was Diana Taurasi of the Phoenix Mercury. She scored a total of 745 points during the regular season. The number of two-point field goals Taurasi made was 36 fewer than two times the number of three-point field goals she made. The number of free throws (each worth one point) she made was 61 more than the number of two-point field goals she made. Find how many free throws, two-point field goals, and three-point field goals Diana Taurasi made during the 2010 regular season. (*Source*: Women's National Basketball Association)

71. Find the values of x, y, and z in the following triangle.

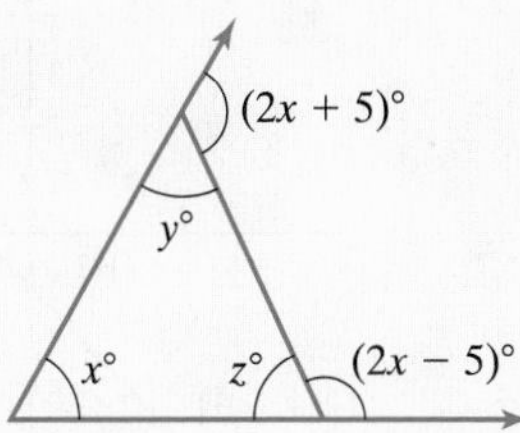

72. The sum of the measures of the angles of a quadrilateral is 360°. Find the values of x, y, and z in the following quadrilateral.

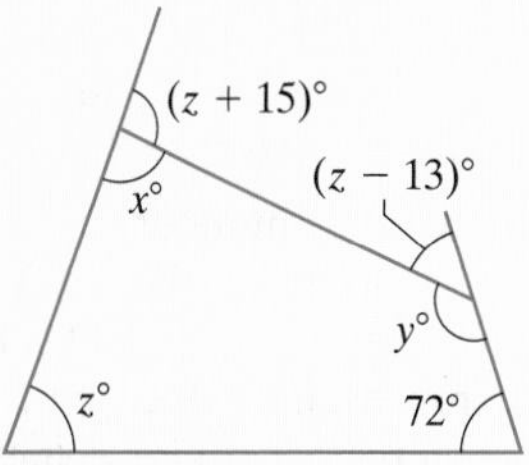

REVIEW AND PREVIEW

Solve each linear inequality. Write your solution in interval notation.

73. $-3x < -9$

74. $2x - 7 \le 5x + 11$

75. $4(2x - 1) \ge 0$

76. $\frac{2}{3}x < \frac{1}{3}$

CONCEPT EXTENSIONS

Solve. See the Concept Check in this section.

77. Suppose you mix an amount of candy costing \$0.49 a pound with candy costing \$0.65 a pound. Which of the following costs per pound could result?

a. \$0.58 **b.** \$0.72 **c.** \$0.29

78. Suppose you mix a 50% acid solution with pure acid (100%). Which of the following acid strengths are possible for the resulting acid mixture?

a. 25% **b.** 150% **c.** 62% **d.** 90%

79. Dale and Sharon Mahnke have decided to fence off a garden plot behind their house, using their house as the "fence" along one side of the garden. The length (which runs parallel to the house) is 3 feet less than twice the width. Find the dimensions if 33 feet of fencing is used along the three sides requiring it.

80. Judy McElroy plans to erect 152 feet of fencing around her rectangular horse pasture. A river bank serves as one side length of the rectangle. If each width is 4 feet longer than half the length, find the dimensions.

81. Find the values of $a, b,$ and c such that the equation $y = ax^2 + bx + c$ has ordered pair solutions $(1, 6), (-1, -2),$ and $(0, -1)$. To do so, substitute each ordered pair solution into the equation. Each time, the result is an equation in three unknowns: a, b, and c. Then solve the resulting system of three linear equations in three unknowns, a, b, and c.

82. Find the values of a, b, and c such that the equation $y = ax^2 + bx + c$ has ordered pair solutions $(1, 2)$, $(2, 3)$, and $(-1, 6)$. (*Hint:* See Exercise 81.)

83. Data (x, y) for the total number (in thousands) of college-bound students who took the ACT assessment in the year x are approximately $(3, 927)$, $(11, 1179)$, and $(19, 1495)$, where $x = 3$ represents 1993 and $x = 11$ represents 2001. Find the values a, b, and c such that the equation $y = ax^2 + bx + c$ models these data. According to your model, how many students will take the ACT in 2015? (*Source:* ACT, Inc.)

84. Monthly normal rainfall data (x, y) for Portland, Oregon, are $(4, 2.47)$, $(7, 0.58)$, $(8, 1.07)$, where x represents time in months (with $x = 1$ representing January) and y represents rainfall in inches. Find the values of a, b, and c rounded to 2 decimal places such that the equation $y = ax^2 + bx + c$ models this data. According to your model, how much rain should Portland expect during September? (*Source:* National Climatic Data Center)

The function $f(x) = -8.6x + 275$ represents the U.S. average number of monthly calls (sent or received) per wireless subscriber and the function $f(x) = 204.9x - 1217$ represents the average number of text messages (sent or received) per wireless subscriber. For both functions, x is the number of years since 2000, and these functions are good for the years 2006–2010.

85. Solve the system formed by these functions. Round each coordinate to the nearest whole number.

86. Use your answer to Exercise 85 to predict the year in which the monthly calls and text messages are/were the same.

2.6 Graphing Linear Inequalities in Two Variables and Systems of Linear Inequalities

OBJECTIVE

1 Graph a Linear Inequality in Two Variables.

2 Solve a System of Linear Inequalities.

In this section, we first learn to graph a single linear inequality in two variables. Then we solve systems of linear inequalities.

Recall that a linear equation in two variables is an equation that can be written in the form $Ax + By = C$ where $A, B,$ and C are real numbers and A and B are not both 0. The definition of a linear inequality is the same except that the equal sign is replaced with an inequality sign.

A **linear inequality in two variables** is an inequality that can be written in one of the forms:

$$Ax + By < C \qquad Ax + By \le C$$
$$Ax + By > C \qquad Ax + By \ge C$$

where A, B, and C are real numbers and A and B are not both 0. Just as for linear equations in x and y, an ordered pair is a **solution** of an inequality in x and y if replacing the variables by coordinates of the ordered pair results in a true statement.

OBJECTIVE

1 Graphing Linear Inequalities in Two Variables

The linear equation $x - y = 1$ is graphed next. Recall that all points on the line correspond to ordered pairs that satisfy the equation $x - y = 1$.

Notice the line defined by $x - y = 1$ divides the rectangular coordinate system plane into 2 sides. All points on one side of the line satisfy the inequality $x - y < 1$ and all points on the other side satisfy the inequality $x - y > 1$. The graph below shows a few examples of this.

Check	$x - y < 1$
$(1, 3)$	$1 - 3 < 1$ True
$(-2, 1)$	$-2 - 1 < 1$ True
$(-4, -4)$	$-4 - (-4) < 1$ True

Check	$x - y > 1$
$(4, 1)$	$4 - 1 > 1$ True
$(2, -2)$	$2 - (-2) > 1$ True
$(0, -4)$	$0 - (-4) > 1$ True

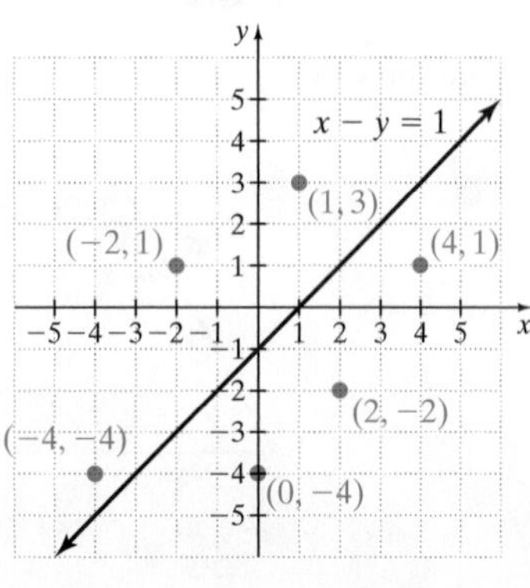

The graph of $x - y < 1$ is the region shaded blue, and the graph of $x - y > 1$ is the region shaded red below.

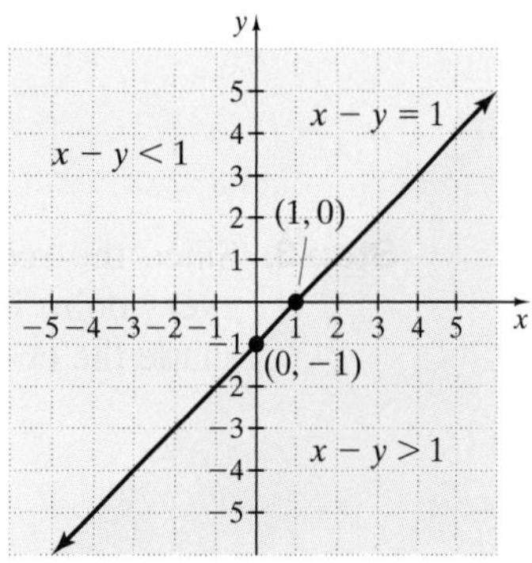

The region to the left of the line and the region to the right of the line are called **half-planes.** Every line divides the plane (similar to a sheet of paper extending indefinitely in all directions) into two half-planes; the line is called the **boundary.**

Recall that the inequality $x - y \le 1$ means

$$x - y = 1 \quad \text{or} \quad x - y < 1$$

Thus, the graph of $x - y \le 1$ is the half-plane $x - y < 1$ along with the boundary line $x - y = 1$.

Graphing a Linear Inequality in Two Variables

Step 1. Graph the boundary line found by replacing the inequality sign with an equal sign. If the inequality sign is $>$ or $<$, graph a dashed boundary line (indicating that the points on the line are not solutions of the inequality). If the inequality sign is $\ge$ or $\le$, graph a solid boundary line (indicating that the points on the line are solutions of the inequality).

Step 2. Choose a point, *not* on the boundary line, as a test point. Substitute the coordinates of this test point into the *original* inequality.

Step 3. If a true statement is obtained in Step 2, shade the half-plane that contains the test point. If a false statement is obtained, shade the half-plane that does not contain the test point.

EXAMPLE 1 Graph: $x + y < 7$

Solution

Step 1. First we graph the boundary line by graphing the equation $x + y = 7$. We graph this boundary as a dashed line because the inequality sign is $<$, and thus the points on the line are not solutions of the inequality $x + y < 7$.

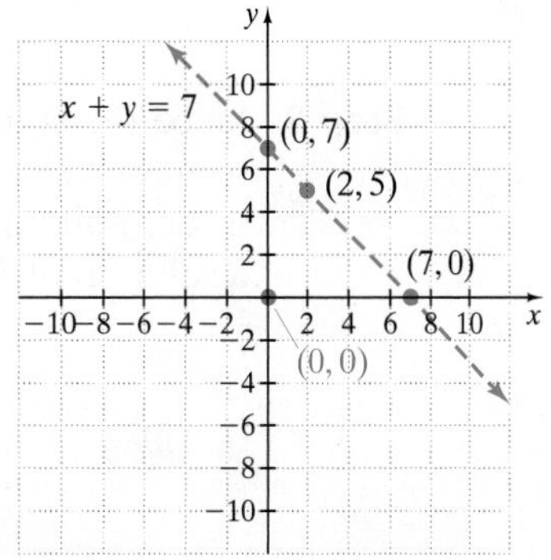

Step 2. Next, we choose a test point, being careful not to choose a point on the boundary line. We choose (0, 0). Substitute the coordinates of (0, 0) into $x + y < 7$.

$$x + y < 7 \quad \text{Original inequality}$$
$$0 + 0 \overset{?}{<} 7 \quad \text{Replace } x \text{ with 0 and } y \text{ with 0.}$$
$$0 < 7 \quad \text{True}$$

Step 3. Since the result is a true statement, (0, 0) is a solution of $x + y < 7$, and every point in the same half-plane as (0, 0) is also a solution. To indicate this, shade the entire half-plane containing (0, 0), as shown.

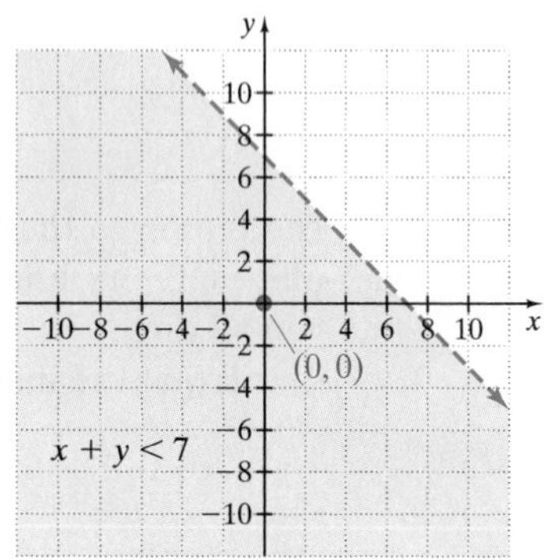

□

PRACTICE
1 Graph: $x + y > 5$

■

✓CONCEPT CHECK

Determine whether (0, 0) is included in the graph of

a. $y \geq 2x + 3$ b. $x < 7$ c. $2x - 3y < 6$

EXAMPLE 2 Graph: $2x - y \geq 3$

Solution

Step 1. We graph the boundary line by graphing $2x - y = 3$. We draw this line as a solid line because the inequality sign is $\geq$, and thus the points on the line are solutions of $2x - y \geq 3$.

Step 2. Once again, (0, 0) is a convenient test point since it is not on the boundary line. We substitute 0 for x and 0 for y into the original inequality.

$$2x - y \geq 3$$
$$2(0) - 0 \geq 3 \quad \text{Let } x = 0 \text{ and } y = 0.$$
$$0 \geq 3 \quad \text{False}$$

Step 3. Since the statement is false, no point in the half-plane containing (0, 0) is a solution. Therefore, we shade the half-plane that does not contain (0, 0). Every point in the shaded half-plane and every point on the boundary line is a solution of $2x - y \geq 3$.

Answers to Concept Check:
a. no **b.** yes **c.** yes

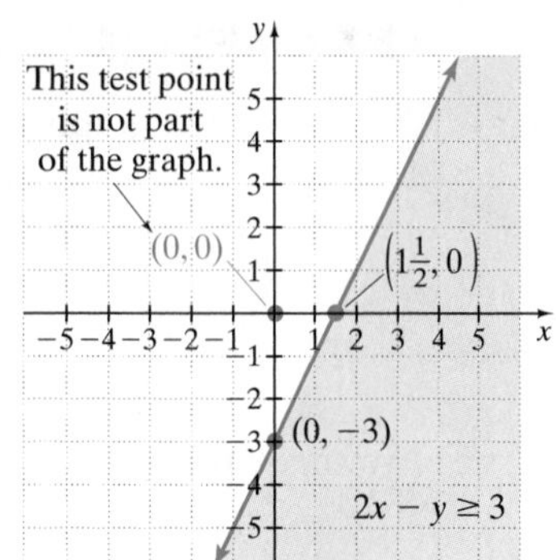

□

PRACTICE 2 Graph: $3x - y \geq 4$

> **Helpful Hint**
> When graphing an inequality, make sure the test point is substituted into the **original inequality.** For Example 2, we substituted the test point (0, 0) into the **original inequality** $2x - y \geq 3$, *not* $2x - y = 3$.

EXAMPLE 3 Graph: $x > 2y$

Solution

Step 1. We find the boundary line by graphing $x = 2y$. The boundary line is a dashed line since the inequality symbol is $>$.

Step 2. We cannot use (0, 0) as a test point because it is a point on the boundary line. We choose instead (0, 2).

$$x > 2y$$
$$0 > 2(2) \quad \text{Let } x = 0 \text{ and } y = 2.$$
$$0 > 4 \quad \text{False}$$

Step 3. Since the statement is false, we shade the half-plane that does not contain the test point (0, 2), as shown.

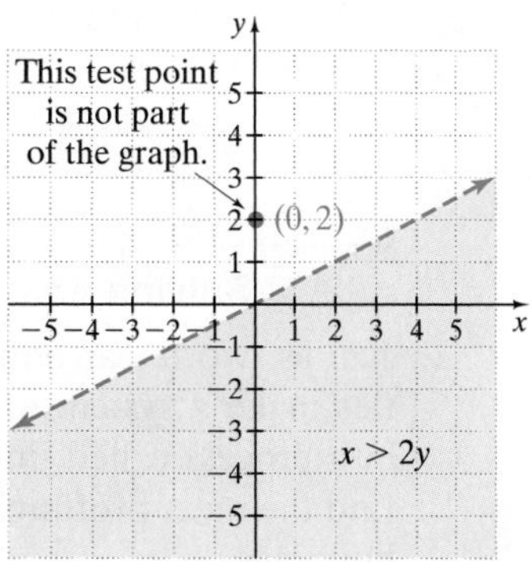

□

PRACTICE 3 Graph: $x > 3y$

EXAMPLE 4 Graph: $5x + 4y \le 20$

Solution We graph the solid boundary line $5x + 4y = 20$ and choose (0, 0) as the test point.

$$5x + 4y \le 20$$
$$5(0) + 4(0) \stackrel{?}{\le} 20 \quad \text{Let } x = 0 \text{ and } y = 0.$$
$$0 \le 20 \quad \text{True}$$

We shade the half-plane that contains (0, 0), as shown.

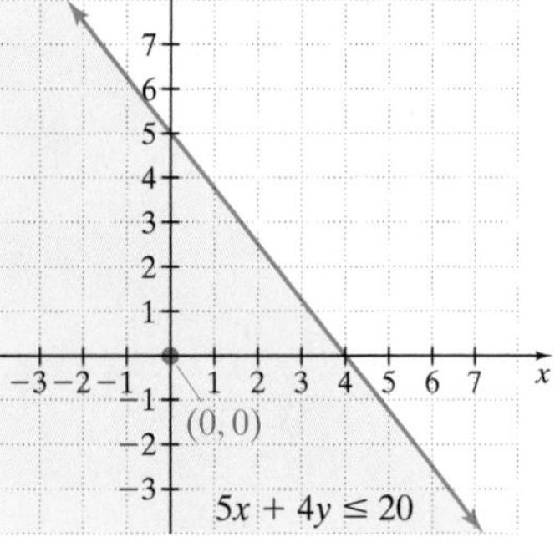

PRACTICE
4 Graph: $3x + 4y \ge 12$

EXAMPLE 5 Graph: $y > 3$

Solution We graph the dashed boundary line $y = 3$ and choose (0, 0) as the test point. (Recall that the graph of $y = 3$ is a horizontal line with y-intercept 3.)

$$y > 3$$
$$0 \stackrel{?}{>} 3 \quad \text{Let } y = 0.$$
$$0 > 3 \quad \text{False}$$

We shade the half-plane that does not contain (0, 0), as shown.

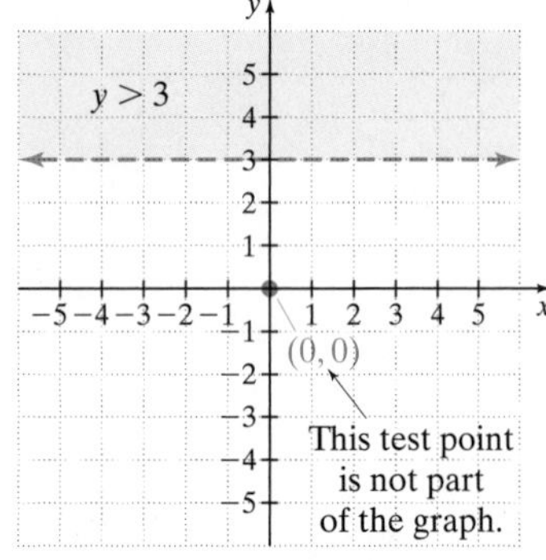

PRACTICE
5 Graph: $x > 3$

OBJECTIVE
2 Solving Systems of Linear Inequalities 

Just as two linear equations make a system of linear equations, two linear inequalities make a **system of linear inequalities.** Systems of inequalities are very important in a process called linear programming. Many businesses use linear programming to find the most profitable way to use limited resources such as employees, machines, or buildings.

A **solution of a system of linear inequalities** is an ordered pair that satisfies each inequality in the system. The set of all such ordered pairs is the solution set of the system. Graphing this set gives us a picture of the solution set. We can graph a system of inequalities by graphing each inequality in the system and identifying the region of overlap.

EXAMPLE 6 Graph the solution of the system: $\begin{cases} 3x \geq y \\ x + 2y \leq 8 \end{cases}$

Solution We begin by graphing each inequality on the same set of axes. The graph of the solution region of the system is the region contained in the graphs of both inequalities. It is their intersection.

First, graph $3x \geq y$. The boundary line is the graph of $3x = y$. Sketch a solid boundary line since the inequality $3x \geq y$ means $3x > y$ or $3x = y$. The test point $(1, 0)$ satisfies the inequality, so shade the half-plane that includes $(1, 0)$.

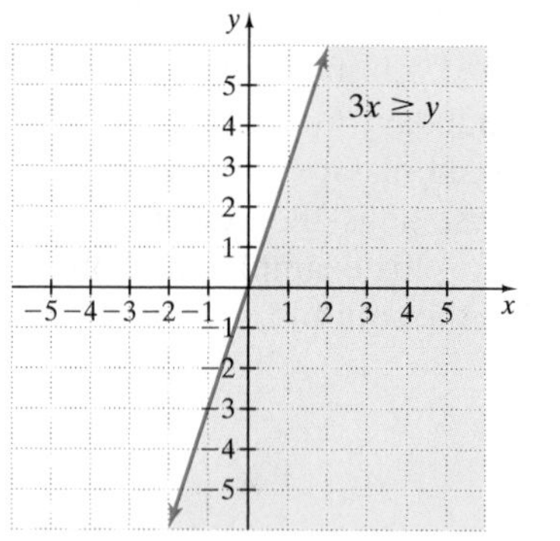

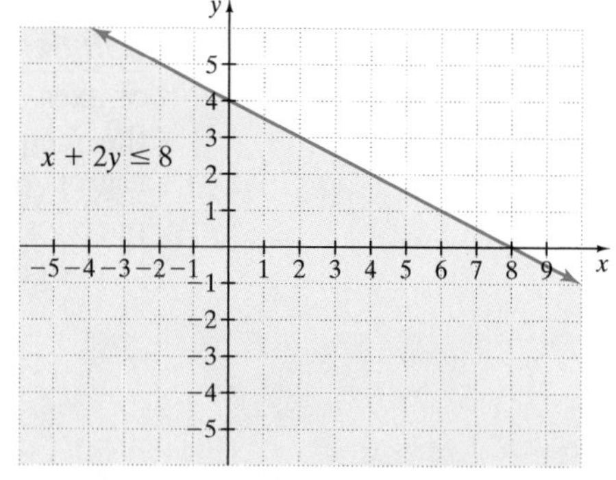

Next, sketch a solid boundary line $x + 2y = 8$ on the same set of axes. The test point $(0, 0)$ satisfies the inequality $x + 2y \leq 8$, so shade the half-plane that includes $(0, 0)$. (For clarity, the graph of $x + 2y \leq 8$ is shown on a separate set of axes.)

An ordered pair solution of the system must satisfy both inequalities. These solutions are points that lie in both shaded regions. The solution region of the system is the purple shaded region as seen below. This solution region includes parts of both boundary lines.

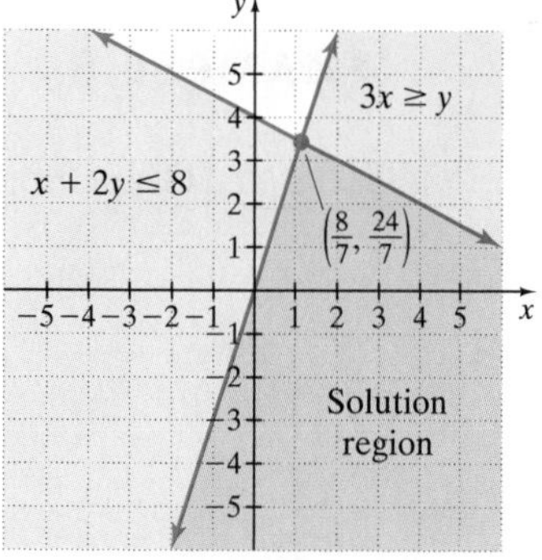

□

PRACTICE 6 Graph the solution of the system: $\begin{cases} 4x \leq y \\ x + 3y \geq 9 \end{cases}$

In linear programming, it is sometimes necessary to find the coordinates of the **corner point:** the point at which the two boundary lines intersect. To find the point of intersection, solve the related linear system

$$\begin{cases} 3x = y \\ x + 2y = 8 \end{cases}$$

by the substitution method or the addition method. The lines intersect at $\left(\frac{8}{7}, \frac{24}{7}\right)$, the corner point of the graph.

Graphing the Solution Region of a System of Linear Inequalities

Step 1. Graph each inequality in the system on the same set of axes.

Step 2. The solutions (or solution region) of the system are the points common to the graphs of all the inequalities in the system.

EXAMPLE 7 Graph the solution of the system: $\begin{cases} x - y < 2 \\ x + 2y > -1 \end{cases}$

Solution Graph both inequalities on the same set of axes. Both boundary lines are dashed lines since the inequality symbols are $<$ and $>$. The solution region of the system is the region shown by the purple shading. In this example, the boundary lines are not a part of the solution.

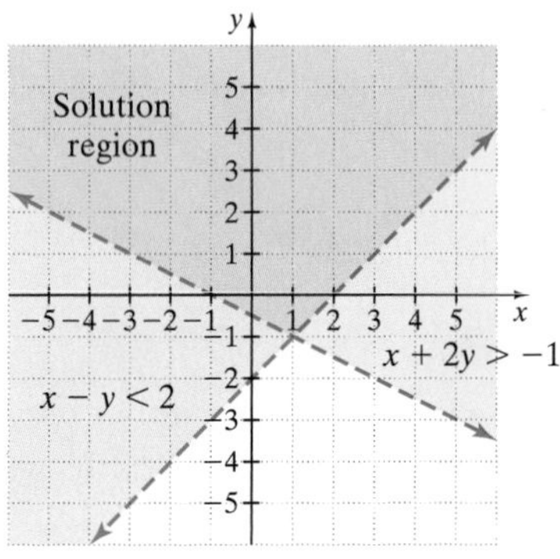

□

PRACTICE 7 Graph the solution of the system: $\begin{cases} x - y > 4 \\ x + 3y < -4 \end{cases}$

EXAMPLE 8 Graph the solution of the system: $\begin{cases} -3x + 4y < 12 \\ x \geq 2 \end{cases}$

Solution Graph both inequalities on the same set of axes.

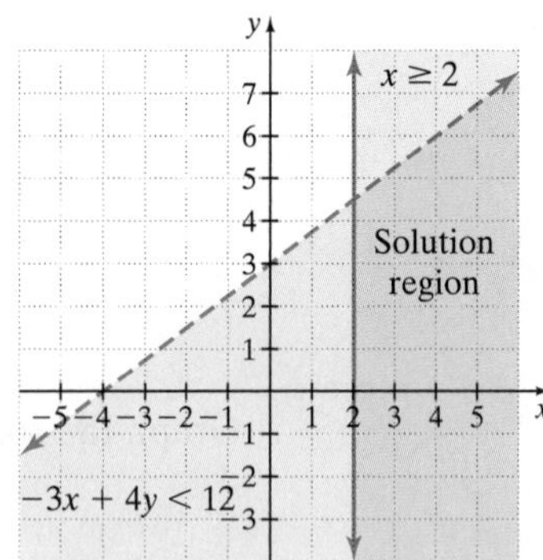

The solution region of the system is the purple shaded region, including a portion of the line $x = 2$. □

PRACTICE 8 Graph the solution of the system: $\begin{cases} y \leq 6 \\ -2x + 5y > 10 \end{cases}$

Vocabulary, Readiness & Video Check

Use the choices below to fill in each blank. Some choices may be used more than once and some not at all.

true	$x < 3$	$y < 3$	half-planes	yes
false	$x \leq 3$	$y \leq 3$	linear inequality in two variables	no

1. The statement $5x - 6y < 7$ is an example of a(n) ______________________.
2. A boundary line divides a plane into two regions called ______________________.
3. True or false: The graph of $5x - 6y < 7$ includes its corresponding boundary line. ______________________
4. True or false: When graphing a linear inequality, to determine which side of the boundary line to shade, choose a point *not* on the boundary line. ______________________
5. True or false: The boundary line for the inequality $5x - 6y < 7$ is the graph of $5x - 6y = 7$.
____
6. The graph of ______________________ is

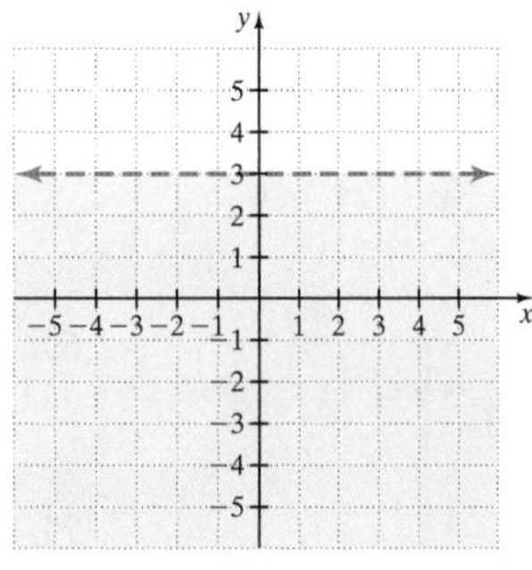

State whether the graph of each inequality includes its corresponding boundary line. Answer yes or no.

7. $y \geq x + 4$
8. $x - y > -7$
9. $y \geq x$
10. $x > 0$

Martin-Gay Interactive Videos

See Video 2.6

Watch the section lecture video and answer the following questions.

OBJECTIVE 1

11. From Example 1, how do you find the equation of the boundary line? How do you determine if the points on the boundary line are solutions of the inequality?

OBJECTIVE 2

12. In Example 2, did the graph of the first inequality of the system limit where we could choose the test point for the second inequality? Why or why not?

2.6 Exercise Set

MyMathLab®

Determine whether the ordered pairs given are solutions of the linear inequality in two variables.

1. $x - y > 3$; $(2, -1), (5, 1)$
2. $y - x < -2$; $(2, 1), (5, -1)$
3. $3x - 5y \leq -4$; $(-1, -1), (4, 0)$
4. $2x + y \geq 10$; $(-1, -4), (5, 0)$
5. $x < -y$; $(0, 2), (-5, 1)$
6. $y > 3x$; $(0, 0), (-1, -4)$

MIXED PRACTICE

Graph each inequality. See Examples 1 through 5.

7. $x + y \leq 1$
8. $x + y \geq -2$
9. $2x + y > -4$
10. $x + 3y \leq 3$
11. $x + 6y \leq -6$
12. $7x + y > -14$
13. $2x + 5y > -10$
14. $5x + 2y \leq 10$
15. $x + 2y \leq 3$
16. $2x + 3y > -5$

17. $2x + 7y > 5$
18. $3x + 5y \le -2$
19. $x - 2y \ge 3$
20. $4x + y \le 2$
21. $5x + y < 3$
22. $x + 2y > -7$
23. $4x + y < 8$
24. $9x + 2y \ge -9$
25. $y \ge 2x$
26. $x < 5y$
27. $x \ge 0$
28. $y \le 0$
29. $y \le -3$
30. $x > -\frac{2}{3}$
31. $2x - 7y > 0$
32. $5x + 2y \le 0$
33. $3x - 7y \ge 0$
34. $-2x - 9y > 0$
35. $x > y$
36. $x \le -y$
37. $x - y \le 6$
38. $x - y > 10$
39. $-\frac{1}{4}y + \frac{1}{3}x > 1$
40. $\frac{1}{2}x - \frac{1}{3}y \le -1$
41. $-x < 0.4y$
42. $0.3x \ge 0.1y$

In Exercises 43 through 48, match each inequality with its graph.

a. $x > 2$
b. $y < 2$
c. $y < 2x$
d. $y \le -3x$
e. $2x + 3y < 6$
f. $3x + 2y > 6$

43.

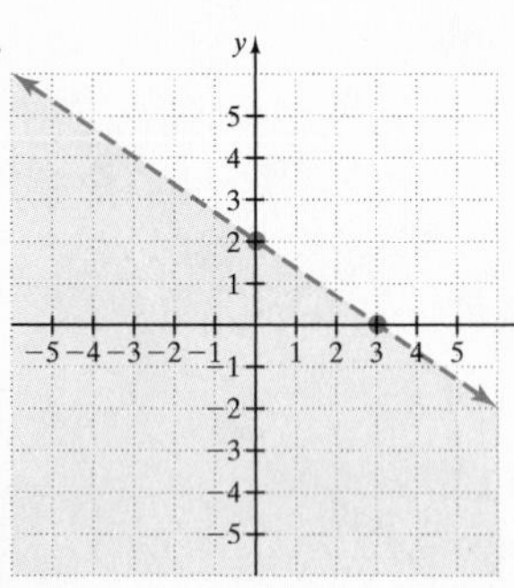

44.

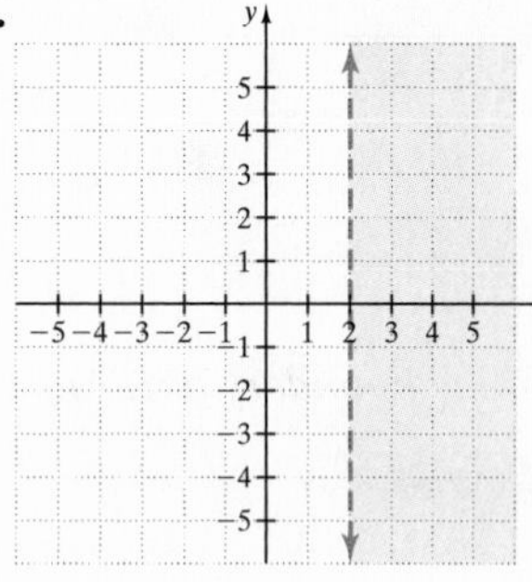

45.

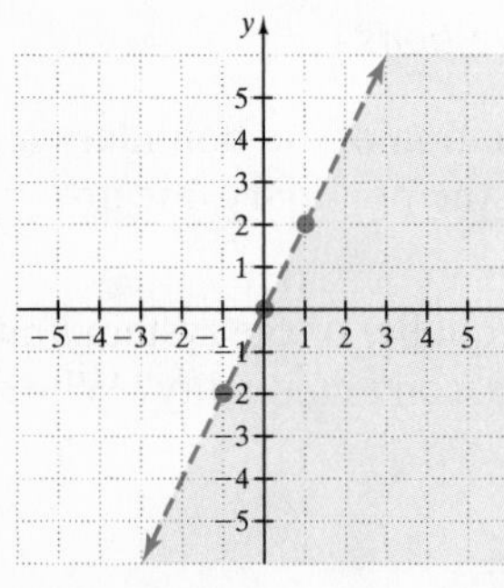

46.

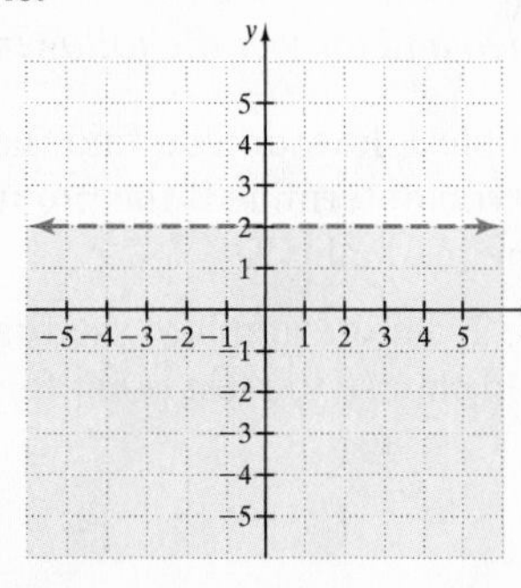

47.

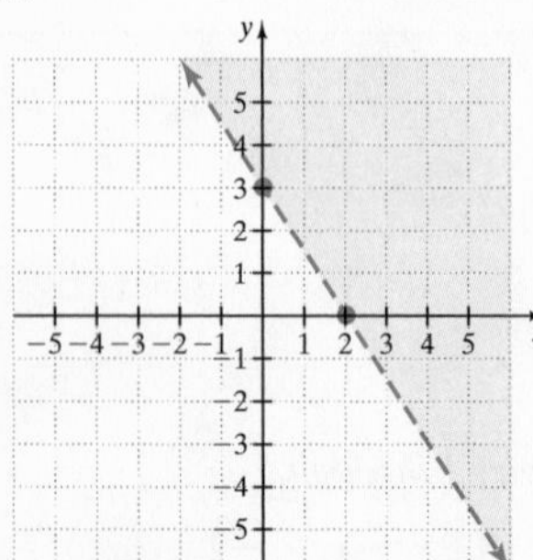

48.

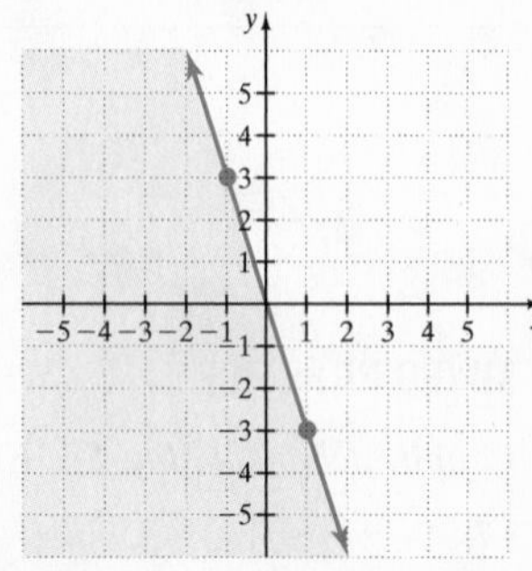

Graph the solution of each system of linear inequalities. See Examples 6 through 8.

49. $\begin{cases} y \ge x + 1 \\ y \ge 3 - x \end{cases}$

50. $\begin{cases} y \ge x - 3 \\ y \ge -1 - x \end{cases}$

51. $\begin{cases} y < 3x - 4 \\ y \le x + 2 \end{cases}$

52. $\begin{cases} y \le 2x + 1 \\ y > x + 2 \end{cases}$

53. $\begin{cases} y \le -2x - 2 \\ y \ge x + 4 \end{cases}$

54. $\begin{cases} y \le 2x + 4 \\ y \ge -x - 5 \end{cases}$

55. $\begin{cases} y \ge -x + 2 \\ y \le 2x + 5 \end{cases}$

56. $\begin{cases} y \ge x - 5 \\ y \le -3x + 3 \end{cases}$

57. $\begin{cases} x \ge 3y \\ x + 3y \le 6 \end{cases}$

58. $\begin{cases} -2x < y \\ x + 2y < 3 \end{cases}$

59. $\begin{cases} y + 2x \ge 0 \\ 5x - 3y \le 12 \end{cases}$

60. $\begin{cases} y + 2x \le 0 \\ 5x + 3y \ge -2 \end{cases}$

61. $\begin{cases} 3x - 4y \ge -6 \\ 2x + y \le 7 \end{cases}$

62. $\begin{cases} 4x - y \ge -2 \\ 2x + 3y \le -8 \end{cases}$

63. $\begin{cases} x \le 2 \\ y \ge -3 \end{cases}$

64. $\begin{cases} x \ge -3 \\ y \ge -2 \end{cases}$

65. $\begin{cases} y \ge 1 \\ x < -3 \end{cases}$

66. $\begin{cases} y > 2 \\ x \ge -1 \end{cases}$

67. $\begin{cases} 2x + 3y < -8 \\ x \ge -4 \end{cases}$

68. $\begin{cases} 3x + 2y \le 6 \\ x < 2 \end{cases}$

69. $\begin{cases} 2x - 5y \le 9 \\ y \le -3 \end{cases}$

70. $\begin{cases} 2x + 5y \le -10 \\ y \ge 1 \end{cases}$

71. $\begin{cases} y \ge \frac{1}{2}x + 2 \\ y \le \frac{1}{2}x - 3 \end{cases}$

72. $\begin{cases} y \ge -\frac{3}{2}x + 3 \\ y < -\frac{3}{2}x + 6 \end{cases}$

REVIEW AND PREVIEW

Evaluate each expression for the given replacement value.

73. x^2 if x is -5
74. x^3 if x is -5
75. $2x^3$ if x is -1
76. $3x^2$ if x is -1

CONCEPT EXTENSIONS

Determine whether (1, 1) is included in each graph. See the Concept Check in this section.

77. $3x + 4y < 8$
78. $y > 5x$
79. $y \ge -\frac{1}{2}x$
80. $x > 3$

81. Write an inequality whose solutions are all pairs of numbers x and y whose sum is at least 13. Graph the inequality.

82. Write an inequality whose solutions are all the pairs of numbers x and y whose sum is at most -4. Graph the inequality.

83. Explain why a point on the boundary line should not be chosen as the test point.

84. Describe the graph of a linear inequality.

85. The price for a taxi cab in a small city is \$2.50 per mile, x, while traveling, and \$0.25 every minute, y, while waiting. If you have \$20 to spend on a cab ride, the inequality

$$2.5x + 0.25y \le 20$$

represents your situation. Graph this inequality in the first quadrant only.

86. A word processor charges \$22 per hour, x, for typing a first draft, and \$15 per hour, y, for making changes and typing a second draft. If you need a document typed and have \$100, the inequality

$$22x + 15y \leq 100$$

represents your situation. Graph the inequality in the first quadrant only.

87. In Exercises 85 and 86, why were you instructed to graph each inequality in the first quadrant only?

88. Scott Sambracci and Sara Thygeson are planning their wedding. They have calculated that they want the cost of their wedding ceremony, x, plus the cost of their reception, y, to be no more than \$5000.

a. Write an inequality describing this relationship.

b. Graph this inequality.

c. Why should we be interested in only quadrant I of this graph?

89. It's the end of the budgeting period for Dennis Fernandes, and he has \$500 left in his budget for car rental expenses. He plans to spend this budget on a sales trip throughout southern Texas. He will rent a car that costs \$30 per day and \$0.15 per mile, and he can spend no more than \$500.

a. Write an inequality describing this situation. Let x = number of days and let y = number of miles.

b. Graph this inequality.

c. Why should we be interested in only quadrant I of this graph?

90. Explain how to decide which region to shade to show the solution region of the following system.

$$\begin{cases} x \geq 3 \\ y \geq -2 \end{cases}$$

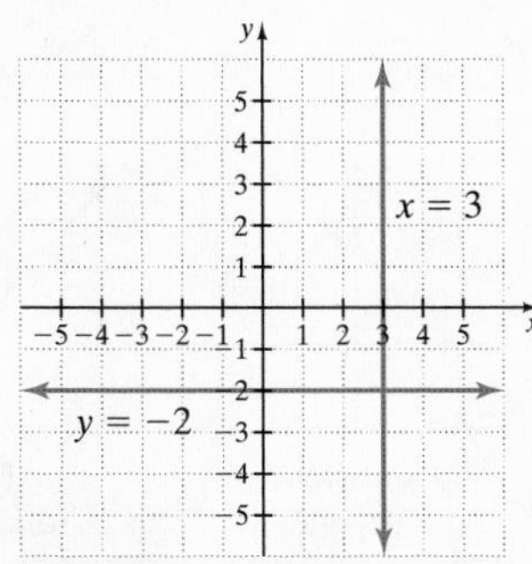

For each system of inequalities, choose the corresponding graph.

91. $\begin{cases} y < 5 \\ x > 3 \end{cases}$ **92.** $\begin{cases} y > 5 \\ x < 3 \end{cases}$ **93.** $\begin{cases} y \leq 5 \\ x < 3 \end{cases}$

94. $\begin{cases} y > 5 \\ x \geq 3 \end{cases}$

A.

B.

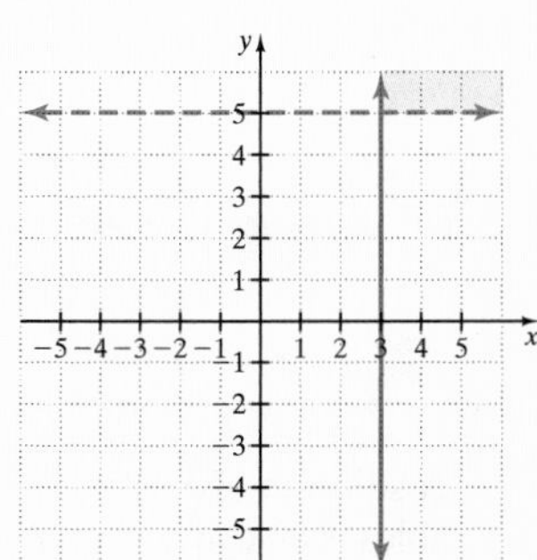

C.

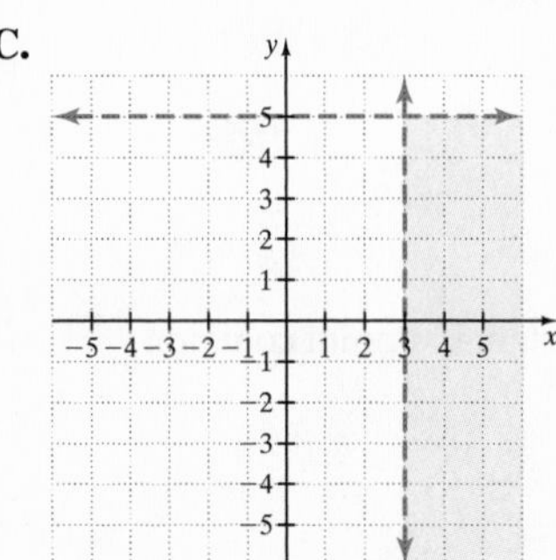

D.

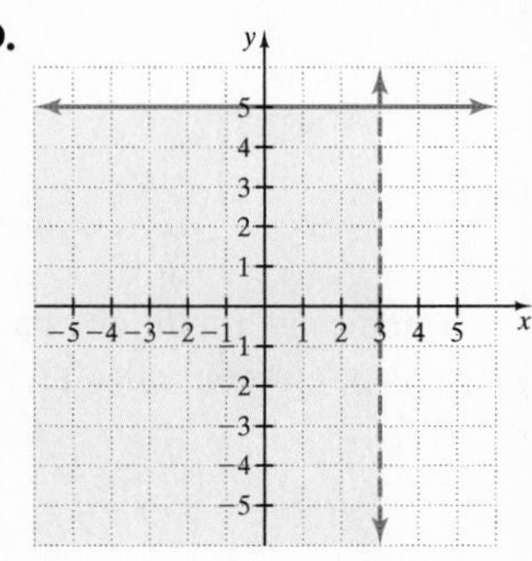

95. Graph the solution of $\begin{cases} 2x - y \leq 6 \\ x \geq 3 \\ y > 2 \end{cases}$

96. Graph the solution of $\begin{cases} x + y < 5 \\ y < 2x \\ x \geq 0 \\ y \geq 0 \end{cases}$

97. Describe the location of the solution region of the system

$$\begin{cases} x > 0 \\ y > 0. \end{cases}$$

Chapter 2 Vocabulary Check

Fill in each blank with one of the words or phrases listed below.

system of linear equations	solution	consistent	independent
dependent	inconsistent	substitution	addition

1. In a system of linear equations in two variables, if the graphs of the equations are the same, the equations are ____________________ equations.
2. Two or more linear equations are called a(n) ____________________.
3. A system of equations that has at least one solution is called a(n) ____________________ system.
4. A(n) ____________________ of a system of two equations in two variables is an ordered pair of numbers that is a solution of both equations in the system.

5. Two algebraic methods for solving systems of equations are ____________ and ____________.
6. A system of equations that has no solution is called a(n) ____________ system.
7. In a system of linear equations in two variables, if the graphs of the equations are different, the equations are ____________ equations.

Chapter 2 Highlights

DEFINITIONS AND CONCEPTS	EXAMPLES
Section 2.1 Solving Systems of Linear Equations by Graphing	
A **solution** of a system of two equations in two variables is an ordered pair of numbers that is a solution of both equations in the system.	Determine whether $(-1, 3)$ is a solution of the system: $\begin{cases} 2x - y = -5 \\ x = 3y - 10 \end{cases}$ Replace x with -1 and y with 3 in both equations. $2x - y = -5$; $2(-1) - 3 \stackrel{?}{=} -5$; $-5 = -5$ True. $x = 3y - 10$; $-1 \stackrel{?}{=} 3 \cdot 3 - 10$; $-1 = -1$ True. $(-1, 3)$ is a solution of the system.
Graphically, a solution of a system is a point common to the graphs of both equations.	Solve by graphing. $\begin{cases} 3x - 2y = -3 \\ x + y = 4 \end{cases}$ 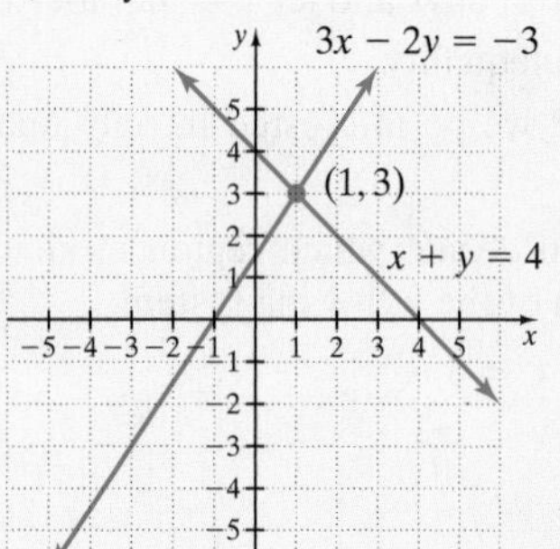
A system of equations with at least one solution is a **consistent system.** A system that has no solution is an **inconsistent system.** If the graphs of two linear equations are identical, the equations are **dependent.** If their graphs are different, the equations are **independent.**	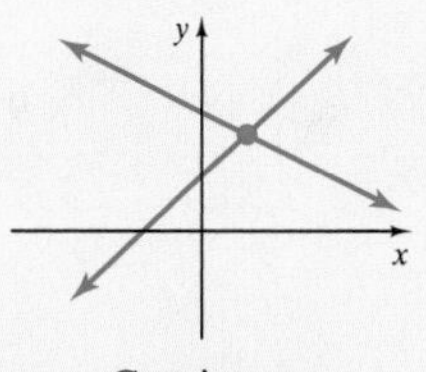 Consistent and independent 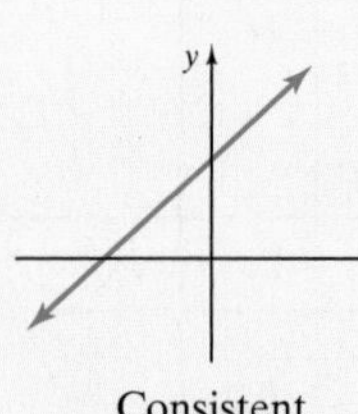 Consistent and dependent 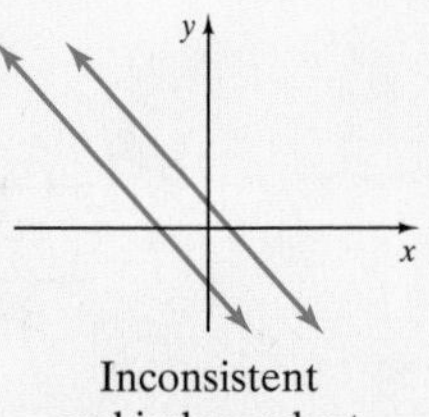 Inconsistent and independent
Section 2.2 Solving Systems of Linear Equations by Substitution	
To solve a system of linear equations by the substitution method: **Step 1.** Solve one equation for a variable. **Step 2.** Substitute the expression for the variable into the other equation. **Step 3.** Solve the equation from Step 2 to find the value of one variable. **Step 4.** Substitute the value from Step 3 in either original equation to find the value of the other variable. **Step 5.** Check the solution in both equations.	Solve by substitution. $\begin{cases} 3x + 2y = 1 \\ x = y - 3 \end{cases}$ Substitute $y - 3$ for x in the first equation. $3x + 2y = 1$; $3(y - 3) + 2y = 1$; $3y - 9 + 2y = 1$; $5y = 10$; $y = 2$ Divide by 5. To find x, substitute 2 for y in $x = y - 3$ so that $x = 2 - 3$ or -1. The solution $(-1, 2)$ checks.

DEFINITIONS AND CONCEPTS	EXAMPLES
Section 2.3 Solving Systems of Linear Equations by Addition	
To solve a system of linear equations by the addition method: **Step 1.** Rewrite each equation in standard form $Ax + By = C$. **Step 2.** Multiply one or both equations by a nonzero number so that the coefficients of a variable are opposites. **Step 3.** Add the equations. **Step 4.** Find the value of one variable by solving the resulting equation. **Step 5.** Substitute the value from Step 4 into either original equation to find the value of the other variable. **Step 6.** Check the solution in both equations.	Solve by addition. $\begin{cases} x - 2y = 8 \\ 3x + y = -4 \end{cases}$ Multiply both sides of the first equation by -3. $\begin{cases} -3x + 6y = -24 \\ 3x + y = -4 \end{cases}$ $7y = -28$ Add. $y = -4$ Divide by 7. To find x, let $y = -4$ in an original equation. $x - 2(-4) = 8$ First equation $x + 8 = 8$ $x = 0$ The solution $(0, -4)$ checks.
If solving a system of linear equations by substitution or addition yields a true statement such as $-2 = -2$, then the graphs of the equations in the system are identical and there is an infinite number of solutions of the system.	Solve: $\begin{cases} 2x - 6y = -2 \\ x = 3y - 1 \end{cases}$ Substitute $3y - 1$ for x in the first equation. $2(3y - 1) - 6y = -2$ $6y - 2 - 6y = -2$ $-2 = -2$ True The system has an infinite number of solutions. In set notation, we write $\{(x, y) \mid 2x - 6y = -2\}$ or $\{(x, y) \mid x = 3y - 1\}$.
Section 2.4 Solving Systems of Linear Equations in Three Variables	
A **solution** of an equation in three variables x, y, and z is an **ordered triple** (x, y, z) that makes the equation a true statement.	Verify that $(-2, 1, 3)$ is a solution of $2x + 3y - 2z = -7$. Replace x with -2, y with 1, and z with 3. $2(-2) + 3(1) - 2(3) \stackrel{?}{=} -7$ $-4 + 3 - 6 \stackrel{?}{=} -7$ $-7 = -7$ True $(-2, 1, 3)$ is a solution.
Solving a System of Three Linear Equations by the Elimination Method **Step 1.** Write each equation in standard form, $Ax + By + Cz = D$. **Step 2.** Choose a pair of equations and use them to eliminate a variable. **Step 3.** Choose any other pair of equations and eliminate the same variable. **Step 4.** Solve the system of two equations in two variables from Steps 2 and 3. **Step 5.** Solve for the third variable by substituting the values of the variables from Step 4 into any of the original equations. **Step 6.** Check the solution in all three original equations.	Solve: $\begin{cases} 2x + y - z = 0 & (1) \\ x - y - 2z = -6 & (2) \\ -3x - 2y + 3z = -22 & (3) \end{cases}$ **1.** Each equation is written in standard form. **2.** $2x + y - z = 0$ (1) $x - y - 2z = -6$ (2) $3x - 3z = -6$ (4) Add. **3.** Eliminate y from equations (1) and (3) also. $4x + 2y - 2z = 0$ Multiply equation (1) by 2 $-3x - 2y + 3z = -22$ (3) $x + z = -22$ (5) Add.

(continued)

DEFINITIONS AND CONCEPTS	EXAMPLES
	Section 2.4 Solving Systems of Linear Equations in Three Variables (continued)

4. Solve.

$$\begin{cases} 3x - 3z = -6 & (4) \\ x + z = -22 & (5) \end{cases}$$

$$\begin{aligned} x - z &= -2 \\ \underline{x + z} &\underline{= -22} \quad \text{Divide equation (4) by 3} \\ 2x &= -24 \quad \text{Add.} \\ x &= -12 \end{aligned}$$

To find z, use equation (5).

$$\begin{aligned} x + z &= -22 \\ -12 + z &= -22 \\ z &= -10 \end{aligned}$$

5. To find y, use equation (1).

$$\begin{aligned} 2x + y - z &= 0 \\ 2(-12) + y - (-10) &= 0 \\ -24 + y + 10 &= 0 \\ y &= 14 \end{aligned}$$

6. The solution $(-12, 14, -10)$ checks.

Section 2.5 Systems of Linear Equations and Problem Solving

Problem-solving steps

1. UNDERSTAND. Read and reread the problem.

Two angles are supplementary if their sum is 180°.

The larger of two supplementary angles is three times the smaller, decreased by twelve. Find the measure of each angle. Let

x = measure of smaller angle

y = measure of larger angle

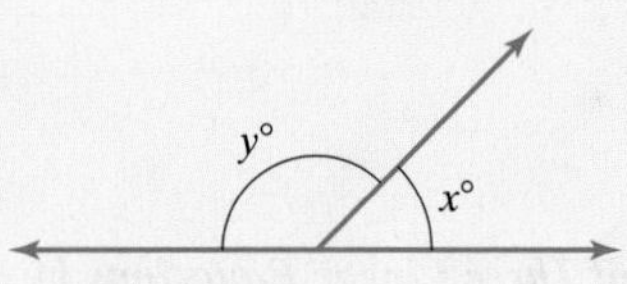

2. TRANSLATE.

In words:

the sum of supplementary angles	is	180°
↓	↓	↓
Translate: $x + y$	$=$	180

In words:

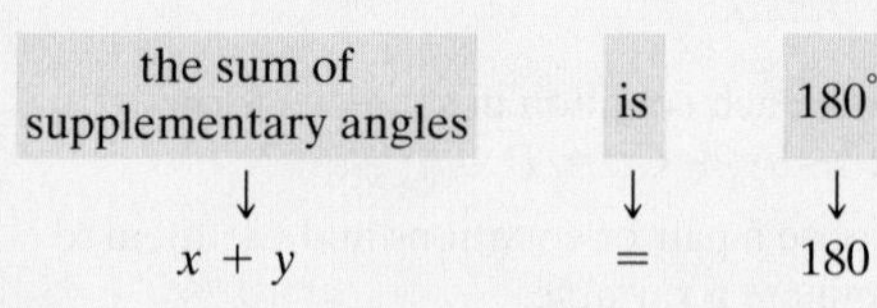

larger angle	is	3 times smaller	decreased by	12
↓	↓	↓	↓	↓
Translate: y	$=$	$3x$	$-$	12

3. SOLVE.

Solve the system:

$$\begin{cases} x + y = 180 \\ y = 3x - 12 \end{cases}$$

(continued)

DEFINITIONS AND CONCEPTS	EXAMPLES
Section 2.5 Systems of Linear Equations and Problem Solving (continued)	
	Use the substitution method and replace y with $3x - 12$ in the first equation. $$\begin{aligned} x + y &= 180 \\ x + (3x - 12) &= 180 \\ 4x &= 192 \\ x &= 48 \end{aligned}$$ Since $y = 3x - 12$, then $y = 3 \cdot 48 - 12$ or 132.
4. INTERPRET.	The solution checks. The smaller angle measures 48° and the larger angle measures 132°.
Section 2.6 Graphing Linear Inequalities in Two Variables and Systems of Linear Inequalities	
A **linear inequality in two variables** is an inequality that can be written in one of the forms: $$\begin{array}{ll} Ax + By < C & Ax + By \le C \\ Ax + By > C & Ax + By \ge C \end{array}$$	***Linear Inequalities*** $$\begin{array}{ll} 2x - 5y < 6 & x \ge -5 \\ y > -8x & y \le 2 \end{array}$$
To graph a linear inequality **1.** Graph the boundary line by graphing the related equation. Draw the line solid if the inequality symbol is $\le$ or $\ge$. Draw the line dashed if the inequality symbol is $<$ or $>$. **2.** Choose a test point not on the line. Substitute its coordinates into the original inequality. **3.** If the resulting inequality is true, shade the half-plane that contains the test point. If the inequality is not true, shade the half-plane that does not contain the test point.	Graph $2x - y \le 4$. **1.** Graph $2x - y = 4$. Draw a solid line because the inequality symbol is $\le$. **2.** Check the test point (0, 0) in the inequality $2x - y \le 4$. $2 \cdot 0 - 0 \le 4$ Let $x = 0$ and $y = 0$. $0 \le 4$ True **3.** The inequality is true so we shade the half-plane containing (0, 0). 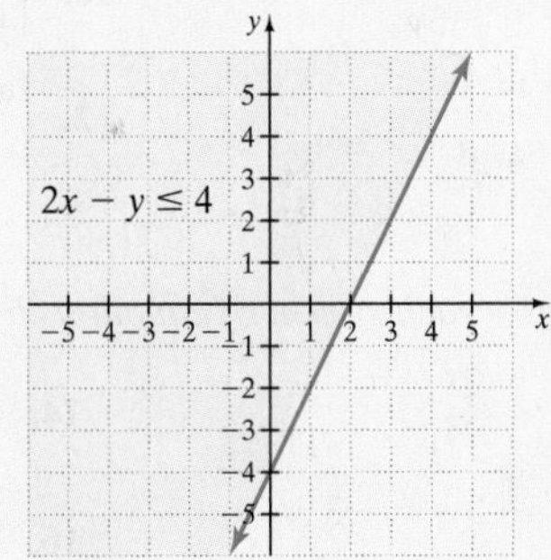
A system of linear inequalities consists of two or more linear inequalities. To graph a system of inequalities, graph each inequality in the system. The overlapping region is the solution of the system.	System of Linear Inequalities $$\begin{cases} x - y \ge 3 \\ y \le -2x \end{cases}$$ 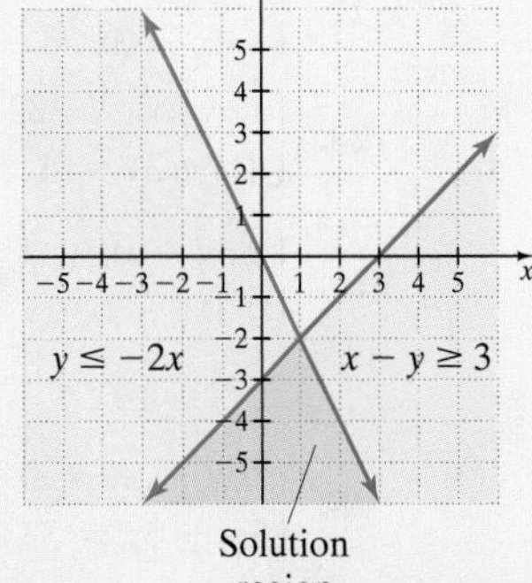

Chapter 2 Review

(2.1) *Determine whether any of the following ordered pairs satisfy the system of linear equations.*

1. $\begin{cases} 2x - 3y = 12 \\ 3x + 4y = 1 \end{cases}$

a. $(12, 4)$ **b.** $(3, -2)$ **c.** $(-3, 6)$

2. $\begin{cases} 4x + y = 0 \\ -8x - 5y = 9 \end{cases}$

a. $\left(\frac{3}{4}, -3\right)$ **b.** $(-2, 8)$ **c.** $\left(\frac{1}{2}, -2\right)$

3. $\begin{cases} 5x - 6y = 18 \\ 2y - x = -4 \end{cases}$

a. $(-6, -8)$ **b.** $\left(3, \frac{5}{2}\right)$ **c.** $\left(3, -\frac{1}{2}\right)$

4. $\begin{cases} 2x + 3y = 1 \\ 3y - x = 4 \end{cases}$

a. $(2, 2)$ **b.** $(-1, 1)$ **c.** $(2, -1)$

Solve each system of equations by graphing.

5. $\begin{cases} x + y = 5 \\ x - y = 1 \end{cases}$

6. $\begin{cases} x + y = 3 \\ x - y = -1 \end{cases}$

7. $\begin{cases} x = 5 \\ y = -1 \end{cases}$

8. $\begin{cases} x = -3 \\ y = 2 \end{cases}$

9. $\begin{cases} 2x + y = 5 \\ x = -3y \end{cases}$

10. $\begin{cases} 3x + y = -2 \\ y = -5x \end{cases}$

11. $\begin{cases} y = 3x \\ -6x + 2y = 6 \end{cases}$

12. $\begin{cases} x - 2y = 2 \\ -2x + 4y = -4 \end{cases}$

(2.2) *Solve each system of equations by the substitution method.*

13. $\begin{cases} y = 2x + 6 \\ 3x - 2y = -11 \end{cases}$

14. $\begin{cases} y = 3x - 7 \\ 2x - 3y = 7 \end{cases}$

15. $\begin{cases} x + 3y = -3 \\ 2x + y = 4 \end{cases}$

16. $\begin{cases} 3x + y = 11 \\ x + 2y = 12 \end{cases}$

17. $\begin{cases} 4y = 2x + 6 \\ x - 2y = -3 \end{cases}$

18. $\begin{cases} 9x = 6y + 3 \\ 6x - 4y = 2 \end{cases}$

19. $\begin{cases} x + y = 6 \\ y = -x - 4 \end{cases}$

20. $\begin{cases} -3x + y = 6 \\ y = 3x + 2 \end{cases}$

(2.3) *Solve each system of equations by the addition method.*

21. $\begin{cases} 2x + 3y = -6 \\ x - 3y = -12 \end{cases}$

22. $\begin{cases} 4x + y = 15 \\ -4x + 3y = -19 \end{cases}$

23. $\begin{cases} 2x - 3y = -15 \\ x + 4y = 31 \end{cases}$

24. $\begin{cases} x - 5y = -22 \\ 4x + 3y = 4 \end{cases}$

25. $\begin{cases} 2x - 6y = -1 \\ -x + 3y = \frac{1}{2} \end{cases}$

26. $\begin{cases} 0.6x - 0.3y = -1.5 \\ 0.04x - 0.02y = -0.1 \end{cases}$

27. $\begin{cases} \frac{3}{4}x + \frac{2}{3}y = 2 \\ x + \frac{y}{3} = 6 \end{cases}$

28. $\begin{cases} 10x + 2y = 0 \\ 3x + 5y = 33 \end{cases}$

(2.4) *Solve each system of equations in three variables.*

29. $\begin{cases} x + z = 4 \\ 2x - y = 4 \\ x + y - z = 0 \end{cases}$

30. $\begin{cases} 2x + 5y = 4 \\ x - 5y + z = -1 \\ 4x - z = 11 \end{cases}$

31. $\begin{cases} 4y + 2z = 5 \\ 2x + 8y = 5 \\ 6x + 4z = 1 \end{cases}$

32. $\begin{cases} 5x + 7y = 9 \\ 14y - z = 28 \\ 4x + 2z = -4 \end{cases}$

33. $\begin{cases} 3x - 2y + 2z = 5 \\ -x + 6y + z = 4 \\ 3x + 14y + 7z = 20 \end{cases}$

34. $\begin{cases} x + 2y + 3z = 11 \\ y + 2z = 3 \\ 2x + 2z = 10 \end{cases}$

35. $\begin{cases} 7x - 3y + 2z = 0 \\ 4x - 4y - z = 2 \\ 5x + 2y + 3z = 1 \end{cases}$

36. $\begin{cases} x - 3y - 5z = -5 \\ 4x - 2y + 3z = 13 \\ 5x + 3y + 4z = 22 \end{cases}$

(2.5) *Solve each problem by writing and solving a system of linear equations.*

37. The sum of two numbers is 16. Three times the larger number decreased by the smaller number is 72. Find the two numbers.

38. The Forrest Theater can seat a total of 360 people. They take in \$15,150 when every seat is sold. If orchestra section tickets cost \$45 and balcony tickets cost \$35, find the number of seats in the orchestra section and the number of seats in the balcony.

39. A riverboat can head 340 miles upriver in 19 hours, but the return trip takes only 14 hours. Find the current of the river and find the speed of the riverboat in still water to the nearest tenth of a mile.

	d	= *r*	· *t*
Upriver	340	$x - y$	19
Downriver	340	$x + y$	14

40. Find the amount of a 6% acid solution and the amount of a 14% acid solution Pat Mayfield should combine to prepare 50 cc (cubic centimeters) of a 12% solution.

41. A deli charges \$3.80 for a breakfast of three eggs and four strips of bacon. The charge is \$2.75 for two eggs and three strips of bacon. Find the cost of each egg and the cost of each strip of bacon.

42. An exercise enthusiast alternates between jogging and walking. He traveled 15 miles during the past 3 hours. He jogs at a rate of 7.5 miles per hour and walks at a rate of 4 miles per hour. Find how much time, to the nearest hundredth of an hour, he actually spent jogging and how much time he spent walking.

43. Chris Kringler has \$2.77 in her coin jar—all in pennies, nickels, and dimes. If she has 53 coins in all and four more nickels than dimes, find how many of each type of coin she has.

44. An employee at See's Candy Store needs a special mixture of candy. She has creme-filled chocolates that sell for \$3.00 per pound, chocolate-covered nuts that sell for \$2.70 per pound, and chocolate-covered raisins that sell for \$2.25 per pound. She wants to have twice as many raisins as nuts in the mixture. Find how many pounds of each she should use to make 45 pounds worth \$2.80 per pound.

45. The perimeter of an isosceles (two sides equal) triangle is 73 centimeters. If the unequal side is 7 centimeters longer than the two equal sides, find the lengths of the three sides.

46. The sum of three numbers is 295. One number is five more than a second and twice the third. Find the numbers.

(2.6) *Graph the following inequalities.*

47. $3x - 4y \leq 0$

48. $3x - 4y \geq 0$

49. $x + 6y < 6$

50. $y \leq -4$

51. $y \geq -7$

52. $x \geq -y$

Graph the solution region of the following systems of linear inequalities.

53. $\begin{cases} y \geq 2x - 3 \\ y \leq -2x + 1 \end{cases}$

54. $\begin{cases} y \leq -3x - 3 \\ y \leq 2x + 7 \end{cases}$

55. $\begin{cases} x + 2y > 0 \\ x - y \leq 6 \end{cases}$

56. $\begin{cases} 4x - y \leq 0 \\ 3x - 2y \geq -5 \end{cases}$

57. $\begin{cases} 3x - 2y \leq 4 \\ 2x + y \geq 5 \end{cases}$

58. $\begin{cases} -2x + 3y > -7 \\ x \geq -2 \end{cases}$

MIXED REVIEW

Solve each system of equations by graphing.

59. $\begin{cases} x - 2y = 1 \\ 2x + 3y = -12 \end{cases}$

60. $\begin{cases} 3x - y = -4 \\ 6x - 2y = -8 \end{cases}$

Solve each system of equations.

61. $\begin{cases} x + 4y = 11 \\ 5x - 9y = -3 \end{cases}$

62. $\begin{cases} x + 9y = 16 \\ 3x - 8y = 13 \end{cases}$

63. $\begin{cases} y = -2x \\ 4x + 7y = -15 \end{cases}$

64. $\begin{cases} 3y = 2x + 15 \\ -2x + 3y = 21 \end{cases}$

65. $\begin{cases} 3x - y = 4 \\ 4y = 12x - 16 \end{cases}$

66. $\begin{cases} x + y = 19 \\ x - y = -3 \end{cases}$

67. $\begin{cases} x - 3y = -11 \\ 4x + 5y = -10 \end{cases}$

68. $\begin{cases} -x - 15y = 44 \\ 2x + 3y = 20 \end{cases}$

69. $\begin{cases} x - 3y + 2z = 0 \\ 9y - z = 22 \\ 5x + 3z = 10 \end{cases}$

70. $\begin{cases} x - 4y = 4 \\ \frac{1}{8}x - \frac{1}{2}y = 3 \end{cases}$

Solve each problem by writing and solving a system of linear equations.

71. The sum of two numbers is 12. Three times the smaller number increased by the larger number is 20. Find the numbers.

72. The difference of two numbers is −18. Twice the smaller decreased by the larger is −23. Find the two numbers.

73. Emma Hodges has a jar containing 65 coins, all of which are either nickels or dimes. The total value of the coins is \$5.30. How many of each type does she have?

74. Sarah and Owen Hebert purchased 26 stamps, a mixture of 17¢ and 20¢ stamps. Find the number of each type of stamp if they spent \$4.93.

75. The perimeter of a triangle is 126 units. The length of one side is twice the length of the shortest side. The length of the third side is fourteen more than the length of the shortest side. Find the length of the sides of the triangles.

Chapter 2 Test

MyMathLab®   YouTube

Answer each question true or false.

1. A system of two linear equations in two variables can have exactly two solutions.

2. Although (1, 4) is not a solution of $x + 2y = 6$, it can still be a solution of the system $\begin{cases} x + 2y = 6 \\ x + y = 5 \end{cases}$.

3. If the two equations in a system of linear equations are added and the result is $3 = 0$, the system has no solution.

4. If the two equations in a system of linear equations are added and the result is $3x = 0$, the system has no solution.

Is the ordered pair a solution of the given linear system?

5. $\begin{cases} 2x - 3y = 5 \\ 6x + y = 1 \end{cases}$; $(1, -1)$

6. $\begin{cases} 4x - 3y = 24 \\ 4x + 5y = -8 \end{cases}$; $(3, -4)$

7. Use graphing to find the solutions of the system $\begin{cases} y - x = 6 \\ y + 2x = -6 \end{cases}$

8. Use the substitution method to solve the system $\begin{cases} 3x - 2y = -14 \\ x + 3y = -1 \end{cases}$

9. Use the substitution method to solve the system $\begin{cases} \frac{1}{2}x + 2y = -\frac{15}{4} \\ 4x = -y \end{cases}$

10. Use the addition method to solve the system $\begin{cases} 3x + 5y = 2 \\ 2x - 3y = 14 \end{cases}$

11. Use the addition method to solve the system $\begin{cases} 4x - 6y = 7 \\ -2x + 3y = 0 \end{cases}$

Solve each system using the substitution method or the addition method.

12. $\begin{cases} 3x + y = 7 \\ 4x + 3y = 1 \end{cases}$

13. $\begin{cases} 3(2x + y) = 4x + 20 \\ x - 2y = 3 \end{cases}$

14. $\begin{cases} \frac{x - 3}{2} = \frac{2 - y}{4} \\ \frac{7 - 2x}{3} = \frac{y}{2} \end{cases}$

Solve each problem by writing and using a system of linear equations.

15. Two numbers have a sum of 124 and a difference of 32. Find the numbers.

16. Find the amount of a 12% saline solution a lab assistant should add to 80 cc (cubic centimeters) of a 22% saline solution to have a 16% solution.

17. Texas and Missouri are the states with the most farms. Texas has 140 thousand more farms than Missouri and the total number of farms for these two states is 356 thousand. Find the number of farms for each state.

18. Two hikers start at opposite ends of the St. Tammany Trail and walk toward each other. The trail is 36 miles long and they meet in 4 hours. If one hiker is twice as fast as the other, find both hiking speeds.

19. $\begin{cases} 2x - 3y = 4 \\ 3y + 2z = 2 \\ x - z = -5 \end{cases}$

20. $\begin{cases} 3x - 2y - z = -1 \\ 2x - 2y = 4 \\ 2x - 2z = -12 \end{cases}$

21. The measure of the largest angle of a triangle is three less than 5 times the measure of the smallest angle. The measure of the remaining angle is 1 less than twice the measure of the smallest angle. Find the measure of each angle.

Chapter 2 Cumulative Review

1. Insert $<, >,$ or $=$ in the appropriate space between the paired numbers to make each statement true.

   a. $-1 \quad 0$ b. $7 \quad \frac{14}{2}$ c. $-5 \quad -6$

2. Evaluate.

   a. 5^2 b. 2^5

3. Name the property or properties illustrated by each true statement.

   a. $3 \cdot y = y \cdot 3$
   b. $(x + 7) + 9 = x + (7 + 9)$
   c. $(b + 0) + 3 = b + 3$
   d. $0.2 \cdot (z \cdot 5) = 0.2 \cdot (5 \cdot z)$
   e. $-2 \cdot \left(-\frac{1}{2}\right) = 1$
   f. $-2 + 2 = 0$
   g. $-6 \cdot (y \cdot 2) = (-6 \cdot 2) \cdot y$

4. Evaluate $y^2 - 3x$ for $x = 8$ and $y = 5$.

5. Write the phrase as an algebraic expression, then simplify if possible: Subtract $4x - 2$ from $2x - 3$.

6. Simplify: $7 - 12 + (-5) - 2 + (-2)$

7. Solve: $7 = -5(2a - 1) - (-11a + 6)$.

8. Evaluate $2y^2 - x^2$ for $x = -7$ and $y = -3$.

9. Solve: $\frac{5}{2}x = 15$

10. Simplify: $0.4y - 6.7 + y - 0.3 - 2.6y$

11. Solve: $\frac{x}{2} - 1 = \frac{2}{3}x - 3$

12. Solve: $7(x - 2) - 6(x + 1) = 20$

13. Twice the sum of a number and 4 is the same as four times the number, decreased by 12. Find the number.

14. Solve: $5(y - 5) = 5y + 10$

15. Solve $y = mx + b$ for x.

16. Five times the sum of a number and -1 is the same as 6 times the number. Find the number.

17. Solve $-2x \leq -4$. Write the solution set in interval notation.

18. Solve $P = a + b + c$ for b.

19. Graph $x = -2y$ by plotting intercepts.

20. Solve $3x + 7 \geq x - 9$. Write the solution set in interval notation.

21. Find the slope of the line through $(-1, 5)$ and $(2, -3)$.

22. Complete the table of values for $x - 3y = 3$

x	y
	-1
3	
	2

23. Find the slope and y-intercept of the line whose equation is $y = \frac{3}{4}x + 6$.

24. Find the slope of a line parallel to the line passing through $(-1, 3)$ and $(2, -8)$.

25. Find the slope and the y-intercept of the line whose equation is $3x - 4y = 4$.

26. Find the slope and y-intercept of the line whose equation is $y = 7x$.

27. Find an equation of the line passing through $(-1, 5)$ with slope -2. Write the equation in slope-intercept form, $y = mx + b$, and in standard form, $Ax + By = C$.

28. Determine whether the lines are parallel, perpendicular, or neither.

$$y = 4x - 5$$
$$-4x + y = 7$$

29. Find an equation of the vertical line through $(-1, 5)$.

30. Write an equation of the line with slope -5, through $(-2, 3)$.

31. Find the domain and the range of the relation $\{(0, 2), (3, 3), (-1, 0), (3, -2)\}$.

32. If $f(x) = 5x^2 - 6$, find $f(0)$ and $f(-2)$.

33. Determine whether each relation is also a function.

   a. $\{(-1, 1), (2, 3), (7, 3), (8, 6)\}$
   b. $\{(0, -2), (1, 5), (0, 3), (7, 7)\}$

34. Determine whether each graph is also the graph of a function.

a. **b.** **c.**

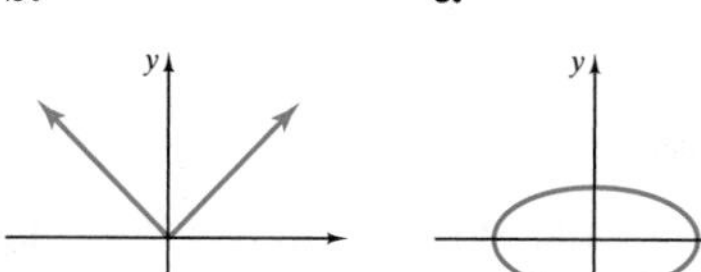

35. Determine the number of solutions of the system.

$$\begin{cases} 3x - y = 4 \\ x + 2y = 8 \end{cases}$$

36. Determine whether each ordered pair is a solution of the given system.

$$\begin{cases} 2x - y = 6 \\ 3x + 2y = -5 \end{cases}$$

a. $(1, -4)$ **b.** $(0, 6)$ **c.** $(3, 0)$

Solve each system.

37. $\begin{cases} x + 2y = 7 \\ 2x + 2y = 13 \end{cases}$

38. $\begin{cases} 3x - 4y = 10 \\ y = 2x \end{cases}$

39. $\begin{cases} x + y = 7 \\ x - y = 5 \end{cases}$

40. $\begin{cases} x = 5y - 3 \\ x = 8y + 4 \end{cases}$

41. Solve the system.

$$\begin{cases} 3x - y + z = -15 \\ x + 2y - z = 1 \\ 2x + 3y - 2z = 0 \end{cases}$$

42. Solve the system.

$$\begin{cases} x - 2y + z = 0 \\ 3x - y - 2z = -15 \\ 2x - 3y + 3z = 7 \end{cases}$$

43. A first number is 4 less than a second number. Four times the first number is 6 more than twice the second. Find the numbers.

44. Find two numbers whose sum is 37 and whose difference is 21.

CHAPTER 3

Factoring Polynomials

This chapter deals with an operation that is the reverse process of multiplying, called *factoring*. Factoring is an important algebraic skill because this process allows us to write a sum as a product.

At the end of this chapter, we use factoring to help us solve equations other than linear equations, and in Chapter 4, we use factoring to simplify and perform arithmetic operations on rational expressions.

As shown on the circle graph below, games and music are the leading moneymakers in the digital market. Record companies' revenue from digital music channels grew 6% in a recent year to total $4.6 billion in the United States alone. From 2004 to 2010, the digital music market increased 1000%.

In Section 3.1, Exercise 109, we explore digital music downloads further.

Global Digital Revenues

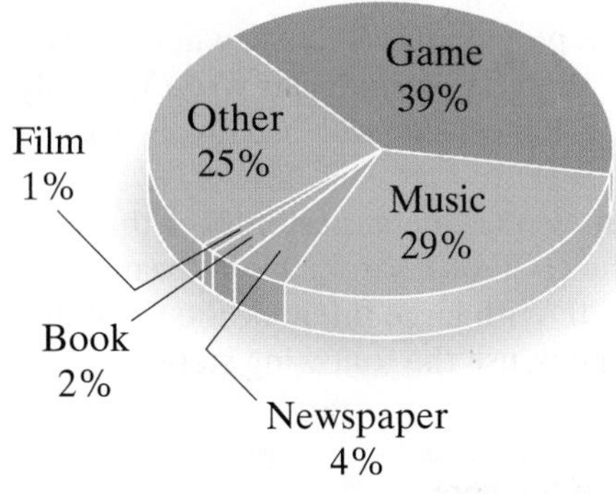

Data from NPD Group; Pollstar; Recording Industry Association of America (RIAA); U.S. Department of Labor; and Tera Consultants

3.1 The Greatest Common Factor and Factoring by Grouping 

OBJECTIVES

1. Find the Greatest Common Factor of a List of Integers.
2. Find the Greatest Common Factor of a List of Terms.
3. Factor Out the Greatest Common Factor from a Polynomial.
4. Factor a Polynomial by Grouping.

In the product $2 \cdot 3 = 6$, the numbers 2 and 3 are called **factors** of 6 and $2 \cdot 3$ is a **factored form** of 6. This is true of polynomials also. Since $(x + 2)(x + 3) = x^2 + 5x + 6$, $(x + 2)$ and $(x + 3)$ are factors of $x^2 + 5x + 6$, and $(x + 2)(x + 3)$ is a factored form of the polynomial.

$$\underbrace{2 \cdot 3}_{\text{a factored form of 6}} = 6 \qquad \text{(2: factor, 3: factor, 6: product)}$$

$$\underbrace{x^2 \cdot x^3}_{\text{a factored form of } x^5} = x^5 \qquad (x^2\text{: factor, } x^3\text{: factor, } x^5\text{: product})$$

$$\underbrace{(x + 2)(x + 3)}_{\text{a factored form of } x^2 + 5x + 6} = x^2 + 5x + 6 \qquad ((x+2)\text{: factor, } (x+3)\text{: factor, } x^2+5x+6\text{: product})$$

The process of writing a polynomial as a product is called **factoring** the polynomial.

Do you see that factoring is the reverse process of multiplying?

$$x^2 + 5x + 6 = (x + 2)(x + 3)$$

(factoring: left to right; multiplying: right to left)

✓CONCEPT CHECK

Multiply: $2(x - 4)$

What do you think the result of factoring $2x - 8$ would be? Why?

OBJECTIVE

1 Finding the Greatest Common Factor of a List of Integers 

The first step in factoring a polynomial is to see whether the terms of the polynomial have a common factor. If there is one, we can write the polynomial as a product by **factoring out** the common factor. We will usually factor out the **greatest common factor (GCF).**

The GCF of a list of integers is the largest integer that is a factor of all the integers in the list. For example, the GCF of 12 and 20 is 4 because 4 is the largest integer that is a factor of both 12 and 20. With large integers, the GCF may not be found easily by inspection. When this happens, use the following steps.

Finding the GCF of a List of Integers

Step 1. Write each number as a product of prime numbers.

Step 2. Identify the common prime factors.

Step 3. The product of all common prime factors found in Step 2 is the greatest common factor. If there are no common prime factors, the greatest common factor is 1.

Recall from Section R.3 that a prime number is a whole number other than 1 whose only factors are 1 and itself.

Answers to Concept Check:
$2x - 8$; The result would be $2(x - 4)$ because factoring is the reverse process of multiplying.

EXAMPLE 1 Find the GCF of each list of numbers.

a. 28 and 40 **b.** 55 and 21 **c.** 15, 18, and 66

Solution

a. Write each number as a product of primes.

$$28 = 2 \cdot 2 \cdot 7 = 2^2 \cdot 7$$
$$40 = 2 \cdot 2 \cdot 2 \cdot 5 = 2^3 \cdot 5$$

There are two common factors, each of which is 2, so the GCF is

$$\text{GCF} = 2 \cdot 2 = 4$$

b. $55 = 5 \cdot 11$

$21 = 3 \cdot 7$

There are no common prime factors; thus, the GCF is 1.

c. $15 = 3 \cdot 5$

$18 = 2 \cdot 3 \cdot 3 = 2 \cdot 3^2$

$66 = 2 \cdot 3 \cdot 11$

The only prime factor common to all three numbers is 3, so the GCF is

$$\text{GCF} = 3$$

□

PRACTICE

1 Find the GCF of each list of numbers.

a. 36 and 42 **b.** 35 and 44 **c.** 12, 16, and 40

OBJECTIVE

2 Finding the Greatest Common Factor of a List of Terms

The greatest common factor of a list of variables raised to powers is found in a similar way. For example, the GCF of x^2, x^3, and x^5 is x^2 because each term contains a factor of x^2 and no higher power of x is a factor of each term.

$$x^2 = x \cdot x$$
$$x^3 = x \cdot x \cdot x$$
$$x^5 = x \cdot x \cdot x \cdot x \cdot x$$

There are two common factors, each of which is x, so the GCF $= x \cdot x$ or x^2.

From this example, we see that **the GCF of a list of common variables raised to powers is the variable raised to the smallest exponent in the list.**

EXAMPLE 2 Find the GCF of each list of terms.

a. x^3, x^7, and x^5 **b.** y, y^4, and y^7

Solution

a. The GCF is x^3, since 3 is the smallest exponent to which x is raised.

b. The GCF is y^1 or y, since 1 is the smallest exponent on y. □

PRACTICE

2 Find the GCF of each list of terms.

a. y^7, y^4, and y^6 **b.** x, x^4, and x^2

In general, the **greatest common factor (GCF) of a list of terms** is the product of the GCF of the numerical coefficients and the GCF of the variable factors.

$$20x^2y^2 = 2 \cdot 2 \cdot 5 \cdot x \cdot x \cdot y \cdot y$$
$$6xy^3 = 2 \cdot 3 \cdot x \cdot y \cdot y \cdot y$$
$$\text{GCF} = 2 \cdot x \cdot y \cdot y = 2xy^2$$

> **Helpful Hint**
>
> Remember that the GCF of a list of terms contains the smallest exponent on each common variable.
>
> The GCF of x^5y^6, x^2y^7, and x^3y^4 is x^2y^4. (Smallest exponent on x; Smallest exponent on y)

EXAMPLE 3 Find the GCF of each list of terms.

a. $6x^2$, $10x^3$, and $-8x$ **b.** $-18y^2$, $-63y^3$, and $27y^4$ **c.** a^3b^2, a^5b, and a^6b^2

Solution

a.
$$6x^2 = 2 \cdot 3 \cdot x^2$$
$$10x^3 = 2 \cdot 5 \cdot x^3$$
$$-8x = -1 \cdot 2 \cdot 2 \cdot 2 \cdot x^1$$
→ The GCF of x^2, x^3, and x^1 is x^1 or x.

$$\text{GCF} = 2 \cdot x^1 \quad \text{or} \quad 2x$$

b.
$$-18y^2 = -1 \cdot 2 \cdot 3 \cdot 3 \cdot y^2$$
$$-63y^3 = -1 \cdot 3 \cdot 3 \cdot 7 \cdot y^3$$
$$27y^4 = 3 \cdot 3 \cdot 3 \cdot y^4$$
→ The GCF of y^2, y^3, and y^4 is y^2.

$$\text{GCF} = 3 \cdot 3 \cdot y^2 \quad \text{or} \quad 9y^2$$

c. The GCF of a^3, a^5, and a^6 is a^3.

The GCF of b^2, b, and b^2 is b.

Thus, the GCF of a^3b^2, a^5b, and a^6b^2 is a^3b. □

PRACTICE

3 Find the GCF of each list of terms.

a. $5y^4$, $15y^2$, and $-20y^3$ **b.** $4x^2$, x^3, and $3x^8$ **c.** a^4b^2, a^3b^5, and a^2b^3

OBJECTIVE

3 Factoring Out the Greatest Common Factor

The first step in factoring a polynomial is to find the GCF of its terms. Once we do so, we can write the polynomial as a product by **factoring out** the GCF.

The polynomial $8x + 14$, for example, contains two terms: $8x$ and 14. The GCF of these terms is 2. We factor out 2 from each term by writing each term as a product of 2 and the term's remaining factors.

$$8x + 14 = 2 \cdot 4x + 2 \cdot 7$$

Using the distributive property, we can write

$$8x + 14 = 2 \cdot 4x + 2 \cdot 7$$
$$= 2(4x + 7)$$

Thus, a factored form of $8x + 14$ is $2(4x + 7)$. We can check by multiplying:

$$2(4x + 7) = 2 \cdot 4x + 2 \cdot 7 = 8x + 14.$$

> **Helpful Hint**
>
> A factored form of $8x + 14$ is *not*
>
> $$2 \cdot 4x + 2 \cdot 7$$
>
> Although the *terms* have been factored (written as a product), the *polynomial* $8x + 14$ has not been factored (written as a product).
>
> A factored form of $8x + 14$ is the *product* $2(4x + 7)$.

✓CONCEPT CHECK
Which of the following is/are factored form(s) of $7t + 21$?
a. 7 **b.** $7 \cdot t + 7 \cdot 3$ **c.** $7(t + 3)$ **d.** $7(t + 21)$

EXAMPLE 4 Factor each polynomial by factoring out the GCF.

a. $6t + 18$ **b.** $y^5 - y^7$

Solution

a. The GCF of terms $6t$ and 18 is 6.

$$6t + 18 = 6 \cdot t + 6 \cdot 3$$
$$= 6(t + 3) \quad \text{Apply the distributive property.}$$

Our work can be checked by multiplying 6 and $(t + 3)$.

$$6(t + 3) = 6 \cdot t + 6 \cdot 3 = 6t + 18, \text{ the original polynomial.}$$

b. The GCF of y^5 and y^7 is y^5. Thus,

$$y^5 - y^7 = y^5(1) - y^5(y^2)$$
$$= y^5(1 - y^2)$$

Helpful Hint
Don't forget the 1.

□

PRACTICE 4 Factor each polynomial by factoring out the GCF.

a. $4t + 12$ **b.** $y^8 + y^4$

EXAMPLE 5 Factor: $-9a^5 + 18a^2 - 3a$

Solution

$$-9a^5 + 18a^2 - 3a = (3a)(-3a^4) + (3a)(6a) + (3a)(-1)$$
$$= 3a(-3a^4 + 6a - 1)$$

Helpful Hint
Don't forget the -1.

□

PRACTICE 5 Factor $-8b^6 + 16b^4 - 8b^2$.

In Example 5, we could have chosen to factor out a $-3a$ instead of $3a$. If we factor out a $-3a$, we have

$$-9a^5 + 18a^2 - 3a = (-3a)(3a^4) + (-3a)(-6a) + (-3a)(1)$$
$$= -3a(3a^4 - 6a + 1)$$

Helpful Hint
Notice the changes in signs when factoring out $-3a$.

EXAMPLES Factor.

6. $6a^4 - 12a = 6a(a^3 - 2)$

7. $\frac{3}{7}x^4 + \frac{1}{7}x^3 - \frac{5}{7}x^2 = \frac{1}{7}x^2(3x^2 + x - 5)$

8. $15p^2q^4 + 20p^3q^5 + 5p^3q^3 = 5p^2q^3(3q + 4pq^2 + p)$ □

PRACTICES 6–8 Factor.

6. $5x^4 - 20x$ **7.** $\frac{5}{9}z^5 + \frac{1}{9}z^4 - \frac{2}{9}z^3$ **8.** $8a^2b^4 - 20a^3b^3 + 12ab^3$

Answer to Concept Check: c

EXAMPLE 9 Factor: $5(x + 3) + y(x + 3)$

Solution The binomial $(x + 3)$ is the greatest common factor. Use the distributive property to factor out $(x + 3)$.

$$5(x + 3) + y(x + 3) = (x + 3)(5 + y)$$

□

PRACTICE 9 Factor $8(y - 2) + x(y - 2)$.

EXAMPLE 10 Factor: $3m^2n(a + b) - (a + b)$

Solution The greatest common factor is $(a + b)$.

$$3m^2n(a + b) - 1(a + b) = (a + b)(3m^2n - 1)$$

□

PRACTICE 10 Factor $7xy^3(p + q) - (p + q)$

OBJECTIVE 4

Factoring by Grouping

Once the GCF is factored out, we can often continue to factor the polynomial, using a variety of techniques. We discuss here a technique for factoring polynomials called **factoring by grouping.**

EXAMPLE 11 Factor $xy + 2x + 3y + 6$ by grouping. Check by multiplying.

Solution The GCF of the first two terms is x, and the GCF of the last two terms is 3.

$$xy + 2x + 3y + 6 = (xy + 2x) + (3y + 6) \quad \text{Group terms.}$$
$$= x(y + 2) + 3(y + 2) \quad \text{Factor out GCF from each grouping.}$$

> **Helpful Hint**
> Notice that this form, $x(y + 2) + 3(y + 2)$, is *not* a factored form of the original polynomial. It is a sum, not a product.

Next we factor out the common binomial factor, $(y + 2)$.

$$x(y + 2) + 3(y + 2) = (y + 2)(x + 3)$$

Now the result is a factored form because it is a product. We were able to write the polynomial as a product because of the common binomial factor, $(y + 2)$, that appeared. If this does not happen, try rearranging the terms of the original polynomial.

Check: Multiply $(y + 2)$ by $(x + 3)$.

$$(y + 2)(x + 3) = xy + 2x + 3y + 6,$$

the original polynomial.

Thus, the factored form of $xy + 2x + 3y + 6$ is the product $(y + 2)(x + 3)$. □

PRACTICE 11 Factor $xy + 3y + 4x + 12$ by grouping. Check by multiplying.

You may want to try these steps when factoring by grouping.

To Factor a Four-Term Polynomial by Grouping

Step 1. Group the terms in two groups of two terms so that each group has a common factor.

Step 2. Factor out the GCF from each group.

Step 3. If there is now a common binomial factor in the groups, factor it out.

Step 4. If not, rearrange the terms and try these steps again.

EXAMPLES Factor by grouping.

12. $15x^3 - 10x^2 + 6x - 4$

$= (15x^3 - 10x^2) + (6x - 4)$ Group the terms.

$= 5x^2(3x - 2) + 2(3x - 2)$ Factor each group.

$= (3x - 2)(5x^2 + 2)$ Factor out the common factor, $(3x - 2)$.

13. $3x^2 + 4xy - 3x - 4y$

$= (3x^2 + 4xy) + (-3x - 4y)$

$= x(3x + 4y) - 1(3x + 4y)$ Factor each group. A -1 is factored from the second pair of terms so that there is a common factor, $(3x + 4y)$.

$= (3x + 4y)(x - 1)$ Factor out the common factor, $(3x + 4y)$.

14. $2a^2 + 5ab + 2a + 5b$

$= (2a^2 + 5ab) + (2a + 5b)$ Factor each group. An understood 1 is written before $(2a+5b)$ to help remember that $(2a+5b)$ is $1(2a+5b)$.

$= a(2a + 5b) + 1(2a + 5b)$

$= (2a + 5b)(a + 1)$ Factor out the common factor, $(2a + 5b)$. □

Helpful Hint
Notice the factor of 1 is written when $(2a + 5b)$ is factored out.

PRACTICES
12–14

12. Factor $40x^3 - 24x^2 + 15x - 9$ by grouping.
13. Factor $2xy + 3y^2 - 2x - 3y$ by grouping.
14. Factor $7a^3 + 5a^2 + 7a + 5$ by grouping.

EXAMPLES Factor by grouping.

15. $3xy + 2 - 3x - 2y$

Notice that the first two terms have no common factor other than 1. However, if we rearrange these terms, a grouping emerges that does lead to a common factor.

$3xy + 2 - 3x - 2y$

$= (3xy - 3x) + (-2y + 2)$

$= 3x(y - 1) - 2(y - 1)$ Factor -2 from the second group so that there is a common factor, $(y - 1)$.

$= (y - 1)(3x - 2)$ Factor out the common factor, $(y - 1)$.

16. $5x - 10 + x^3 - x^2 = 5(x - 2) + x^2(x - 1)$

There is no common binomial factor that can now be factored out. No matter how we rearrange the terms, no grouping will lead to a common factor. Thus, this polynomial is not factorable by grouping. □

PRACTICES
15–16

15. Factor $4xy + 15 - 12x - 5y$ by grouping.
16. Factor $9y - 18 + y^3 - 4y^2$ by grouping.

Helpful Hint
One more reminder: When **factoring** a polynomial, make sure the polynomial is written as a **product.** For example, it is true that

$$3x^2 + 4xy - 3x - 4y = \underbrace{x(3x + 4y) - 1(3x + 4y)}_{\text{but is not a factored form}},$$

since it is a **sum (difference),** not a **product.** A factored form of $3x^2 + 4xy - 3x - 4y$ is the product $(3x + 4y)(x - 1)$.

Factoring out a greatest common factor first makes factoring by any method easier, as we see in the next example.

EXAMPLE 17 Factor: $4ax - 4ab - 2bx + 2b^2$

Solution First, factor out the common factor 2 from all four terms.

$4ax - 4ab - 2bx + 2b^2$

$= 2(2ax - 2ab - bx + b^2)$ Factor out 2 from all four terms.

$= 2[2a(x - b) - b(x - b)]$ Factor each pair of terms. A "$-b$" is factored from the second pair so that there is a common factor, $x - b$.

$= 2(x - b)(2a - b)$ Factor out the common binomial. □

Helpful Hint

Throughout this chapter, we will be factoring polynomials. Even when the instructions do not so state, it is always a good idea to check your answers by multiplying.

PRACTICE 17 Factor $3xy - 3ay - 6ax + 6a^2$.

Vocabulary, Readiness & Video Check

Use the choices below to fill in each blank. Some choices may be used more than once and some may not be used at all.

greatest common factor   factors   factoring   true   false   least   greatest

1. Since $5 \cdot 4 = 20$, the numbers 5 and 4 are called ______________ of 20.
2. The ______________ of a list of integers is the largest integer that is a factor of all the integers in the list.
3. The greatest common factor of a list of common variables raised to powers is the variable raised to the ______________ exponent in the list.
4. The process of writing a polynomial as a product is called ______________.
5. True or false: A factored form of $7x + 21 + xy + 3y$ is $7(x + 3) + y(x + 3)$. ______________
6. True or false: A factored form of $3x^3 + 6x + x^2 + 2$ is $3x(x^2 + 2)$. ______________

Martin-Gay Interactive Videos

See Video 3.1

Watch the section lecture video and answer the following questions.

OBJECTIVE 1
7. Based on Example 1, give a general definition for the greatest common factor (GCF) of a list of numbers.

OBJECTIVE 2
8. In Example 3, why are the numbers factored out, but not the variables?

OBJECTIVE 3
9. From Example 5, how can the number of terms in the other factor, once you factor out the GCF, help you determine if your factorization is correct?

OBJECTIVE 4
10. In Examples 7 and 8, what are you reminded to always do first when factoring a polynomial? Also, explain how a polynomial looks if it suggests it might be factored by grouping.

3.1 Exercise Set

MyMathLab®

Find the GCF for each list. See Examples 1 through 3.

1. 32, 36
2. 36, 90
3. 18, 42, 84
4. 30, 75, 135
5. 24, 14, 21
6. 15, 25, 27
7. y^2, y^4, y^7
8. x^3, x^2, x^5
9. z^7, z^9, z^{11}
10. y^8, y^{10}, y^{12}
11. $x^{10}y^2, xy^2, x^3y^3$
12. p^7q, p^8q^2, p^9q^3
13. $14x, 21$
14. $20y, 15$
15. $12y^4, 20y^3$
16. $32x^5, 18x^2$
17. $-10x^2, 15x^3$
18. $-21x^3, 14x$
19. $12x^3, -6x^4, 3x^5$
20. $15y^2, 5y^7, -20y^3$

21. $-18x^2y, 9x^3y^3, 36x^3y$

22. $7x^3y^3, -21x^2y^2, 14xy^4$

23. $20a^6b^2c^8, 50a^7b$

24. $40x^7y^2z, 64x^9y$

Factor out the GCF from each polynomial. See Examples 4 through 10.

25. $3a + 6$

26. $18a + 12$

27. $30x - 15$

28. $42x - 7$

29. $x^3 + 5x^2$

30. $y^5 + 6y^4$

31. $6y^4 + 2y^3$

32. $5x^2 + 10x^6$

33. $4x - 8y + 4$

34. $7x + 21y - 7$

35. $6x^3 - 9x^2 + 12x$

36. $12x^3 + 16x^2 - 8x$

37. $a^7b^6 - a^3b^2 + a^2b^5 - a^2b^2$

38. $x^9y^6 + x^3y^5 - x^4y^3 + x^3y^3$

39. $8x^5 + 16x^4 - 20x^3 + 12$

40. $9y^6 - 27y^4 + 18y^2 + 6$

41. $\frac{1}{3}x^4 + \frac{2}{3}x^3 - \frac{4}{3}x^5 + \frac{1}{3}x$

42. $\frac{2}{5}y^7 - \frac{4}{5}y^5 + \frac{3}{5}y^2 - \frac{2}{5}y$

43. $y(x^2 + 2) + 3(x^2 + 2)$

44. $x(y^2 + 1) - 3(y^2 + 1)$

45. $z(y + 4) - 3(y + 4)$

46. $8(x + 2) - y(x + 2)$

47. $r(z^2 - 6) + (z^2 - 6)$

48. $q(b^3 - 5) + (b^3 - 5)$

Factor a negative number or a GCF with a negative coefficient from each polynomial. See Example 5.

49. $-2x - 14$

50. $-7y - 21$

51. $-2x^5 + x^7$

52. $-5y^3 + y^6$

53. $-6a^4 + 9a^3 - 3a^2$

54. $-5m^6 + 10m^5 - 5m^3$

Factor each four-term polynomial by grouping. If this is not possible, write "not factorable by grouping." See Examples 11 through 17.

55. $x^3 + 2x^2 + 5x + 10$

56. $x^3 + 4x^2 + 3x + 12$

57. $5x + 15 + xy + 3y$

58. $xy + y + 2x + 2$

59. $6x^3 - 4x^2 + 15x - 10$

60. $16x^3 - 28x^2 + 12x - 21$

61. $5m^3 + 6mn + 5m^2 + 6n$

62. $8w^2 + 7wv + 8w + 7v$

63. $2y - 8 + xy - 4x$

64. $6x - 42 + xy - 7y$

65. $2x^3 - x^2 + 8x - 4$

66. $2x^3 - x^2 - 10x + 5$

67. $3x - 3 + x^3 - 4x^2$

68. $7x - 21 + x^3 - 2x^2$

69. $4x^2 - 8xy - 3x + 6y$

70. $5xy - 15x - 6y + 18$

71. $5q^2 - 4pq - 5q + 4p$

72. $6m^2 - 5mn - 6m + 5n$

73. $2x^4 + 5x^3 + 2x^2 + 5x$

74. $4y^4 + y^2 + 20y^3 + 5y$

75. $12x^2y - 42x^2 - 4y + 14$

76. $90 + 15y^2 - 18x - 3xy^2$

MIXED PRACTICE

Factor. See Examples 4 through 17.

77. $32xy - 18x^2$

78. $10xy - 15x^2$

79. $y(x + 2) - 3(x + 2)$

80. $z(y - 4) + 3(y - 4)$

81. $14x^3y + 7x^2y - 7xy$

82. $5x^3y - 15x^2y + 10xy$

83. $28x^3 - 7x^2 + 12x - 3$

84. $15x^3 + 5x^2 - 6x - 2$

85. $-40x^8y^6 - 16x^9y^5$

86. $-21x^3y - 49x^2y^2$

87. $6a^2 + 9ab^2 + 6ab + 9b^3$

88. $16x^2 + 4xy^2 + 8xy + 2y^3$

REVIEW AND PREVIEW

Multiply.

89. $(x + 2)(x + 5)$

90. $(y + 3)(y + 6)$

91. $(b + 1)(b - 4)$

92. $(x - 5)(x + 10)$

Fill in the chart by finding two numbers that have the given product and sum. The first column is filled in for you.

		93.	94.	95.	96.	97.	98.
Two Numbers	4, 7						
Their Product	28	12	20	8	16	−10	−24
Their Sum	11	8	9	−9	−10	3	−5

CONCEPT EXTENSIONS

See the Concept Checks in this section.

99. Which of the following is/are factored form(s) of $8a - 24$?

 a. $8 \cdot a - 24$ b. $8(a - 3)$
 c. $4(2a - 12)$ d. $8 \cdot a - 2 \cdot 12$

100. Which of the following is/are factored form(s) of $-2x + 14$?

 a. $-2(x + 7)$ b. $-2 \cdot x + 14$
 c. $-2(x - 14)$ d. $-2(x - 7)$

Determine whether the following expressions are factored.

101. $(a + 6)(a + 2)$

102. $(x + 5)(x + y)$

103. $5(2y + z) - b(2y + z)$

104. $3x(a + 2b) + 2(a + 2b)$

105. Construct a binomial whose greatest common factor is $5a^3$. (*Hint:* Multiply $5a^3$ by a binomial whose terms contain no common factor other than 1. $5a^3(\square + \square)$.)

106. Construct a trinomial whose greatest common factor is $2x^2$. See the hint for Exercise 105.

107. Explain how you can tell whether a polynomial is written in factored form.

108. Construct a four-term polynomial that can be factored by grouping.

109. The number (in millions) of single digital downloads annually in the United States each year during 2004–2010 can be modeled by the polynomial $-20x^2 + 300x + 120$, where x is the number of years since 2004. (*Source:* Recording Industry Association of America)

a. Find the number of single digital downloads in 2010. To do so, let $x = 6$ and evaluate $-20x^2 + 300x + 120$.

b. Use this expression to predict the number of single digital downloads in 2014.

c. Factor the polynomial $-20x^2 + 300x + 120$ by factoring -20 from each term.

110. The number (in thousands) of students who graduated from U.S. public high schools each year during 2000–2009 can be modeled by $0.8x^2 + 44x + 2552$, where x is the number of years since 2000. (*Source:* Digest of Education Statistics)

a. Find the number of students who graduated from U.S. high schools in 2005. To do so, let $x = 5$ and evaluate $0.8x^2 + 44x + 2552$.

b. Use this expression to predict the number of students who will graduate from U.S. high schools in 2015.

c. Factor the polynomial $0.8x^2 + 44x + 2552$ by factoring out 0.8 from each term.

Write an expression for the area of each shaded region. Then write the expression as a factored polynomial.

△ **111.**

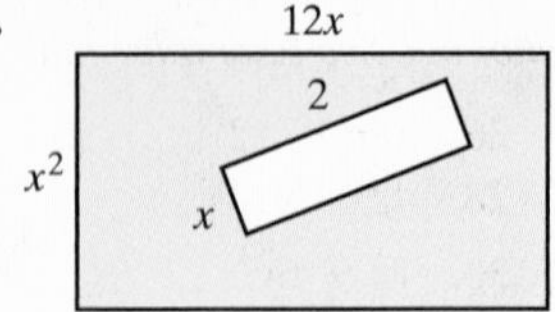

△ **112.**

*Write an expression for the length of each rectangle. (**Hint:** Factor the area binomial and recall that Area = width · length.)*

△ **113.**

Area is $(4n^4 - 24n)$ square units

?

$4n$ units

△ **114.**

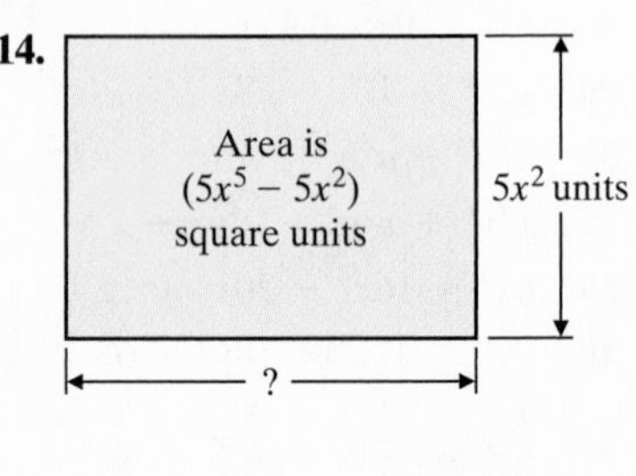

Factor each polynomial by grouping.

115. $x^{2n} + 2x^n + 3x^n + 6$
(**Hint:** Don't forget that $x^{2n} = x^n \cdot x^n$.)

116. $x^{2n} + 6x^n + 10x^n + 60$

117. $3x^{2n} + 21x^n - 5x^n - 35$

118. $12x^{2n} - 10x^n - 30x^n + 25$

3.2 Factoring Trinomials of the Form $x^2 + bx + c$

OBJECTIVES

1 Factor Trinomials of the Form $x^2 + bx + c$.

2 Factor Out the Greatest Common Factor and Then Factor a Trinomial of the Form $x^2 + bx + c$.

OBJECTIVE

1 Factoring Trinomials of the Form $x^2 + bx + c$

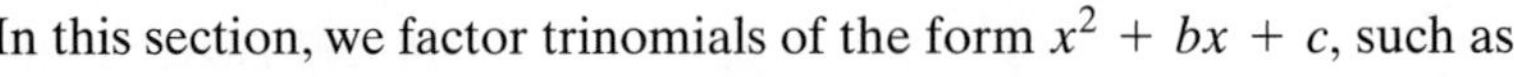

In this section, we factor trinomials of the form $x^2 + bx + c$, such as

$$x^2 + 4x + 3, \quad x^2 - 8x + 15, \quad x^2 + 4x - 12, \quad r^2 - r - 42$$

Notice that for these trinomials, the coefficient of the squared variable is 1.

Recall that factoring means to write as a product and that factoring and multiplying are reverse processes. Using the FOIL method of multiplying binomials, we have that

$$\begin{aligned}(x + 3)(x + 1) &= \overset{F}{x^2} + \overset{O}{1x} + \overset{I}{3x} + \overset{L}{3} \\ &= x^2 + 4x + 3\end{aligned}$$

Thus, a factored form of $x^2 + 4x + 3$ is $(x + 3)(x + 1)$.

Notice that the product of the first terms of the binomials is $x \cdot x = x^2$, the first term of the trinomial. Also, the product of the last two terms of the binomials is $3 \cdot 1 = 3$, the third term of the trinomial. The sum of these same terms is $3 + 1 = 4$, the coefficient of the middle term, x, of the trinomial.

The product of these numbers is 3.

$$x^2 + 4x + 3 = (x + 3)(x + 1)$$

The sum of these numbers is 4.

Many trinomials, such as the one above, factor into two binomials. To factor $x^2 + 7x + 10$, let's assume that it factors into two binomials and begin by writing two pairs of parentheses. The first term of the trinomial is x^2, so we use x and x as the first terms of the binomial factors.

$$x^2 + 7x + 10 = (x + \square)(x + \square)$$

To determine the last term of each binomial factor, we look for two integers whose product is 10 and whose sum is 7. Since our numbers must have a positive product and a positive sum, we list pairs of positive integer factors of 10 only.

Positive Factors of 10	***Sum of Factors***
1, 10	$1 + 10 = 11$
2, 5	$2 + 5 = 7$

The correct pair of numbers is 2 and 5 because their product is 10 and their sum is 7. Now we can fill in the last terms of the binomial factors.

$$x^2 + 7x + 10 = (x + 2)(x + 5)$$

Check: To see if we have factored correctly, multiply.

$$\begin{aligned}(x + 2)(x + 5) &= x^2 + 5x + 2x + 10 \\ &= x^2 + 7x + 10 \quad \text{Combine like terms.}\end{aligned}$$

Helpful Hint

Since multiplication is commutative, the factored form of $x^2 + 7x + 10$ can be written as either $(x + 2)(x + 5)$ or $(x + 5)(x + 2)$.

Factoring a Trinomial of the Form $x^2 + bx + c$

The factored form of $x^2 + bx + c$ is

The product of these numbers is c.

$$x^2 + bx + c = (x + \square)(x + \square)$$

The sum of these numbers is b.

EXAMPLE 1 Factor: $x^2 + 7x + 12$

Solution We begin by writing the first terms of the binomial factors.

$$(x + \square)(x + \square)$$

Next we look for two numbers whose product is 12 and whose sum is 7. Since our numbers must have a positive product and a positive sum, we look at pairs of positive factors of 12 only.

(Continued on next page)

Positive Factors of 12	*Sum of Factors*
1, 12	13
2, 6	8
3, 4	7

Correct sum, so the numbers are 3 and 4.

Thus, $x^2 + 7x + 12 = (x + 3)(x + 4)$

Check: $(x + 3)(x + 4) = x^2 + 4x + 3x + 12 = x^2 + 7x + 12$. □

PRACTICE
1 Factor $x^2 + 5x + 6$.

EXAMPLE 2 Factor: $x^2 - 12x + 35$

Solution Again, we begin by writing the first terms of the binomials.

$$(x + \square)(x + \square)$$

Now we look for two numbers whose product is 35 and whose sum is -12. Since our numbers must have a positive product and a negative sum, we look at pairs of negative factors of 35 only.

Negative Factors of 35	*Sum of Factors*
−1, −35	−36
−5, −7	−12

Correct sum, so the numbers are −5 and −7.

Thus, $x^2 - 12x + 35 = (x - 5)(x - 7)$

Check: To check, multiply $(x - 5)(x - 7)$. □

PRACTICE
2 Factor $x^2 - 17x + 70$.

EXAMPLE 3 Factor: $x^2 + 4x - 12$

Solution $x^2 + 4x - 12 = (x + \square)(x + \square)$

We look for two numbers whose product is -12 and whose sum is 4. Since our numbers must have a negative product, we look at pairs of factors with opposite signs.

Factors of −12	*Sum of Factors*
−1, 12	11
1, −12	−11
−2, 6	4
2, −6	−4
−3, 4	1
3, −4	−1

Correct sum, so the numbers are −2 and 6.

Thus, $x^2 + 4x - 12 = (x - 2)(x + 6)$ □

PRACTICE
3 Factor $x^2 + 5x - 14$.

EXAMPLE 4 Factor: $r^2 - r - 42$

Solution Because the variable in this trinomial is r, the first term of each binomial factor is r.

$$r^2 - r - 42 = (r + \square)(r + \square)$$

Now we look for two numbers whose product is -42 and whose sum is -1, the numerical coefficient of r. The numbers are 6 and -7. Therefore,

$$r^2 - r - 42 = (r + 6)(r - 7)$$ □

PRACTICE **4** Factor $p^2 - 2p - 63$.

EXAMPLE 5 Factor: $a^2 + 2a + 10$

Solution Look for two numbers whose product is 10 and whose sum is 2. Neither 1 and 10 nor 2 and 5 give the required sum, 2. We conclude that $a^2 + 2a + 10$ is not factorable with integers. A polynomial such as $a^2 + 2a + 10$ is called a **prime polynomial.** □

PRACTICE **5** Factor $b^2 + 5b + 1$.

EXAMPLE 6 Factor: $x^2 + 7xy + 6y^2$

Solution

$$x^2 + 7xy + 6y^2 = (x + \square)(x + \square)$$

Recall that the middle term $7xy$ is the same as $7yx$. Thus, we can see that $7y$ is the "coefficient" of x. We then look for two terms whose product is $6y^2$ and whose sum is $7y$. The terms are $6y$ and $1y$ or $6y$ and y because $6y \cdot y = 6y^2$ and $6y + y = 7y$. Therefore,

$$x^2 + 7xy + 6y^2 = (x + 6y)(x + y)$$ □

PRACTICE **6** Factor $x^2 + 7xy + 12y^2$.

EXAMPLE 7 Factor: $x^4 + 5x^2 + 6$

Solution As usual, we begin by writing the first terms of the binomials. Since the greatest power of x in this polynomial is x^4, we write

$$(x^2 + \square)(x^2 + \square) \quad \text{since } x^2 \cdot x^2 = x^4$$

Now we look for two factors of 6 whose sum is 5. The numbers are 2 and 3. Thus,

$$x^4 + 5x^2 + 6 = (x^2 + 2)(x^2 + 3)$$ □

PRACTICE **7** Factor $x^4 + 13x^2 + 12$.

If the terms of a polynomial are not written in descending powers of the variable, you may want to do so before factoring.

EXAMPLE 8 Factor: $40 - 13t + t^2$

Solution First, we rearrange terms so that the trinomial is written in descending powers of t.

$$40 - 13t + t^2 = t^2 - 13t + 40$$

(Continued on next page)

Next, try to factor.

$$t^2 - 13t + 40 = (t + \square)(t + \square)$$

Now we look for two factors of 40 whose sum is -13. The numbers are -8 and -5. Thus,

$$t^2 - 13t + 40 = (t - 8)(t - 5)$$

□

PRACTICE 8 Factor $48 - 14x + x^2$.

The following sign patterns may be useful when factoring trinomials.

> **Helpful Hint**
>
> A positive constant in a trinomial tells us to look for two numbers with the same sign. The sign of the coefficient of the middle term tells us whether the signs are both positive or both negative.
>
> both positive ↓, same sign ↙
>
> $$x^2 + 10x + 16 = (x + 2)(x + 8)$$
>
> both negative ↓, same sign ↙
>
> $$x^2 - 10x + 16 = (x - 2)(x - 8)$$
>
> A negative constant in a trinomial tells us to look for two numbers with opposite signs.
>
> opposite signs ↓
>
> $$x^2 + 6x - 16 = (x + 8)(x - 2)$$
>
> opposite signs ↓
>
> $$x^2 - 6x - 16 = (x - 8)(x + 2)$$

OBJECTIVE 2

Factoring Out the Greatest Common Factor

Remember that the first step in factoring any polynomial is to factor out the greatest common factor (if there is one other than 1 or -1).

EXAMPLE 9 Factor: $3m^2 - 24m - 60$

Solution First we factor out the greatest common factor, 3, from each term.

$$3m^2 - 24m - 60 = 3(m^2 - 8m - 20)$$

Now we factor $m^2 - 8m - 20$ by looking for two factors of -20 whose sum is -8. The factors are -10 and 2. Therefore, the complete factored form is

$$3m^2 - 24m - 60 = 3(m + 2)(m - 10)$$

□

> **Helpful Hint**
>
> Remember to write the common factor 3 as part of the factored form.

PRACTICE 9 Factor $4x^2 - 24x + 36$.

EXAMPLE 10 Factor: $2x^4 - 26x^3 + 84x^2$

Solution

$$2x^4 - 26x^3 + 84x^2 = 2x^2(x^2 - 13x + 42) \quad \text{Factor out common factor, } 2x^2.$$
$$= 2x^2(x - 6)(x - 7) \quad \text{Factor } x^2 - 13x + 42.$$

□

PRACTICE 10 Factor $3y^4 - 18y^3 - 21y^2$.

Vocabulary, Readiness & Video Check

Fill in each blank with "true" or "false."

1. To factor $x^2 + 7x + 6$, we look for two numbers whose product is 6 and whose sum is 7. ______

2. We can write the factorization $(y + 2)(y + 4)$ also as $(y + 4)(y + 2)$. ______

3. The factorization $(4x - 12)(x - 5)$ is completely factored. ______

4. The factorization $(x + 2y)(x + y)$ may also be written as $(x + 2y)^2$. ______

Complete each factored form.

5. $x^2 + 9x + 20 = (x + 4)(x \quad)$

6. $x^2 + 12x + 35 = (x + 5)(x \quad)$

7. $x^2 - 7x + 12 = (x - 4)(x \quad)$

8. $x^2 - 13x + 22 = (x - 2)(x \quad)$

9. $x^2 + 4x + 4 = (x + 2)(x \quad)$

10. $x^2 + 10x + 24 = (x + 6)(x \quad)$

Martin-Gay Interactive Videos

See Video 3.2

Watch the section lecture video and answer the following questions.

OBJECTIVE 1

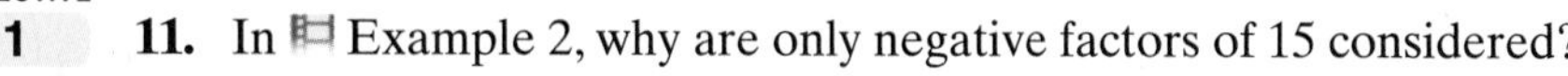

11. In Example 2, why are only negative factors of 15 considered?

OBJECTIVE 2

12. In Example 5, we know we need a positive and a negative factor of -10. How do we determine which factor is negative?

3.2 Exercise Set

MyMathLab®

Factor each trinomial completely. If a polynomial can't be factored, write "prime." See Examples 1 through 8.

1. $x^2 + 7x + 6$

2. $x^2 + 6x + 8$

3. $y^2 - 10y + 9$

4. $y^2 - 12y + 11$

5. $x^2 - 6x + 9$

6. $x^2 - 10x + 25$

7. $x^2 - 3x - 18$

8. $x^2 - x - 30$

9. $x^2 + 3x - 70$

10. $x^2 + 4x - 32$

11. $x^2 + 5x + 2$

12. $x^2 - 7x + 5$

13. $x^2 + 8xy + 15y^2$

14. $x^2 + 6xy + 8y^2$

15. $a^4 - 2a^2 - 15$

16. $y^4 - 3y^2 - 70$

17. $13 + 14m + m^2$

18. $17 + 18n + n^2$

19. $10t - 24 + t^2$

20. $6q - 27 + q^2$

21. $a^2 - 10ab + 16b^2$

22. $a^2 - 9ab + 18b^2$

MIXED PRACTICE

Factor each trinomial completely. Some of these trinomials contain a greatest common factor (other than 1). Don't forget to factor out the GCF first. See Examples 1 through 10.

23. $2z^2 + 20z + 32$

24. $3x^2 + 30x + 63$

25. $2x^3 - 18x^2 + 40x$

26. $3x^3 - 12x^2 - 36x$

27. $x^2 - 3xy - 4y^2$

28. $x^2 - 4xy - 77y^2$

29. $x^2 + 15x + 36$

30. $x^2 + 19x + 60$

31. $x^2 - x - 2$

32. $x^2 - 5x - 14$

33. $r^2 - 16r + 48$

34. $r^2 - 10r + 21$

35. $x^2 + xy - 2y^2$

36. $x^2 - xy - 6y^2$
37. $3x^2 + 9x - 30$
38. $4x^2 - 4x - 48$
39. $3x^2 - 60x + 108$
40. $2x^2 - 24x + 70$
41. $x^2 - 18x - 144$
42. $x^2 + x - 42$
43. $r^2 - 3r + 6$
44. $x^2 + 4x - 10$
45. $x^2 - 8x + 15$
46. $x^2 - 9x + 14$
47. $6x^3 + 54x^2 + 120x$
48. $3x^3 + 3x^2 - 126x$
49. $4x^2y + 4xy - 12y$
50. $3x^2y - 9xy + 45y$
51. $x^2 - 4x - 21$
52. $x^2 - 4x - 32$
53. $x^2 + 7xy + 10y^2$
54. $x^2 - 2xy - 15y^2$
55. $64 + 24t + 2t^2$
56. $50 + 20t + 2t^2$
57. $x^3 - 2x^2 - 24x$
58. $x^3 - 3x^2 - 28x$
59. $2t^5 - 14t^4 + 24t^3$
60. $3x^6 + 30x^5 + 72x^4$
61. $5x^3y - 25x^2y^2 - 120xy^3$
62. $7a^3b - 35a^2b^2 + 42ab^3$
63. $162 - 45m + 3m^2$
64. $48 - 20n + 2n^2$
65. $-x^2 + 12x - 11$ (Factor out -1 first.)
66. $-x^2 + 8x - 7$ (Factor out -1 first.)
67. $\frac{1}{2}y^2 - \frac{9}{2}y - 11$ (Factor out $\frac{1}{2}$ first.)
68. $\frac{1}{3}y^2 - \frac{5}{3}y - 8$ (Factor out $\frac{1}{3}$ first.)
69. $x^3y^2 + x^2y - 20x$
70. $a^2b^3 + ab^2 - 30b$

REVIEW AND PREVIEW

Multiply.

71. $(2x + 1)(x + 5)$
72. $(3x + 2)(x + 4)$
73. $(5y - 4)(3y - 1)$
74. $(4z - 7)(7z - 1)$
75. $(a + 3b)(9a - 4b)$
76. $(y - 5x)(6y + 5x)$

CONCEPT EXTENSIONS

77. Write a polynomial that factors as $(x - 3)(x + 8)$.
78. To factor $x^2 + 13x + 42$, think of two numbers whose ______ is 42 and whose ______ is 13.

Complete each sentence in your own words.

79. If $x^2 + bx + c$ is factorable and c is negative, then the signs of the last-term factors of the binomials are opposite because…
80. If $x^2 + bx + c$ is factorable and c is positive, then the signs of the last-term factors of the binomials are the same because…

Remember that perimeter means distance around. Write the perimeter of each rectangle as a simplified polynomial. Then factor the polynomial.

81. Rectangle with sides $4x + 33$ and $x^2 + 10x$

82. Rectangle with sides $12x^2$ and $2x^3 + 16x$

83. An object is thrown upward from the top of an 80-foot building with an initial velocity of 64 feet per second. Neglecting air resistance, the height of the object after t seconds is given by $-16t^2 + 64t + 80$. Factor this polynomial.

84. An object is thrown upward from the top of a 112-foot building with an initial velocity of 96 feet per second. Neglecting air resistance, the height of the object after t seconds is given by $-16t^2 + 96t + 112$. Factor this polynomial.

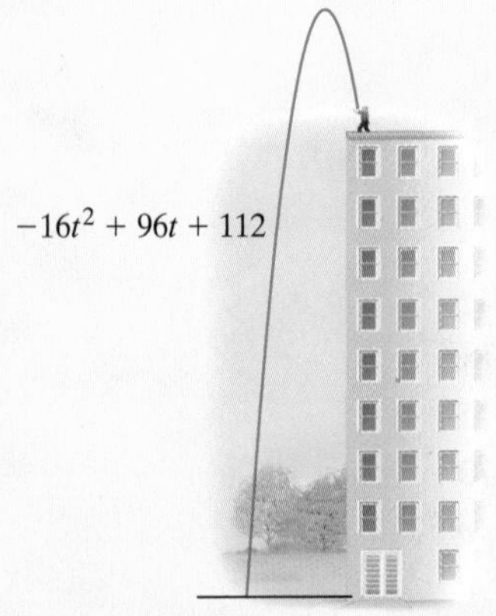

Factor each trinomial completely.

85. $x^2 + \frac{1}{2}x + \frac{1}{16}$

86. $x^2 + x + \frac{1}{4}$

87. $z^2(x + 1) - 3z(x + 1) - 70(x + 1)$

88. $y^2(x + 1) - 2y(x + 1) - 15(x + 1)$

Factor each trinomial. (**Hint:** *Notice that* $x^{2n} + 4x^n + 3$ *factors as* $(x^n + 1)(x^n + 3)$. **Remember:** $x^n \cdot x^n = x^{n+n}$ *or* x^{2n}.)

89. $x^{2n} + 8x^n - 20$

90. $x^{2n} + 5x^n + 6$

Find a positive value of c so that each trinomial is factorable.

91. $x^2 + 6x + c$

92. $t^2 + 8t + c$

93. $y^2 - 4y + c$

94. $n^2 - 16n + c$

Find a positive value of b so that each trinomial is factorable.

95. $x^2 + bx + 15$

96. $y^2 + by + 20$

97. $m^2 + bm - 27$

98. $x^2 + bx - 14$

3.3 Factoring Trinomials of the Form $ax^2 + bx + c$ and Perfect Square Trinomials

OBJECTIVES

1. Factor Trinomials of the Form $ax^2 + bx + c$, Where $a \neq 1$.
2. Factor Out a GCF Before Factoring a Trinomial of the Form $ax^2 + bx + c$.
3. Factor Perfect Square Trinomials.

OBJECTIVE

1 Factoring Trinomials of the Form $ax^2 + bx + c$ 

In this section, we factor trinomials of the form $ax^2 + bx + c$, such as

$$3x^2 + 11x + 6, \qquad 8x^2 - 22x + 5, \qquad \text{and} \qquad 2x^2 + 13x - 7$$

Notice that the coefficient of the squared variable in these trinomials is a number other than 1. We will factor these trinomials using a trial-and-check method based on our work in the last section.

To begin, let's review the relationship between the numerical coefficients of the trinomial and the numerical coefficients of its factored form. For example, since $(2x + 1)(x + 6) = 2x^2 + 13x + 6$,

$$\text{a factored form of } 2x^2 + 13x + 6 \text{ is } (2x + 1)(x + 6)$$

Notice that $2x$ and x are factors of $2x^2$, the first term of the trinomial. Also, 6 and 1 are factors of 6, the last term of the trinomial, as shown:

$$2x^2 + 13x + 6 = (2x + 1)(x + 6)$$

$2x \cdot x$

$1 \cdot 6$

Also notice that $13x$, the middle term, is the sum of the following products:

$$2x^2 + 13x + 6 = (2x + 1)(x + 6)$$

$1x$

$+12x$

$13x$ Middle term

Let's use this pattern to factor $5x^2 + 7x + 2$. First, we find factors of $5x^2$. Since all numerical coefficients in this trinomial are positive, we will use factors with positive numerical coefficients only. Thus, the factors of $5x^2$ are $5x$ and x. Let's try these factors as first terms of the binomials. Thus far, we have

$$5x^2 + 7x + 2 = (5x + \square)(x + \square)$$

Next, we need to find positive factors of 2. Positive factors of 2 are 1 and 2. Now we try possible combinations of these factors as second terms of the binomials until we obtain a middle term of $7x$.

$$(5x+1)(x+2) = 5x^2 + 11x + 2$$

$1x + 10x = 11x$ → Incorrect middle term

Let's try switching factors 2 and 1.

$$(5x+2)(x+1) = 5x^2 + 7x + 2$$

$2x + 5x = 7x$ → Correct middle term

Thus the factored form of $5x^2 + 7x + 2$ is $(5x+2)(x+1)$. To check, we multiply $(5x+2)$ and $(x+1)$. The product is $5x^2 + 7x + 2$.

EXAMPLE 1 Factor: $3x^2 + 11x + 6$

Solution Since all numerical coefficients are positive, we use factors with positive numerical coefficients. We first find factors of $3x^2$.

$$\text{Factors of } 3x^2\text{:} \quad 3x^2 = 3x \cdot x$$

If factorable, the trinomial will be of the form

$$3x^2 + 11x + 6 = (3x + \square)(x + \square)$$

Next we factor 6.

$$\text{Factors of 6:} \quad 6 = 1 \cdot 6, \quad 6 = 2 \cdot 3$$

Now we try combinations of factors of 6 until a middle term of $11x$ is obtained. Let's try 1 and 6 first.

$$(3x+1)(x+6) = 3x^2 + 19x + 6$$

$1x + 18x = 19x$ → **Incorrect** middle term

Now let's next try 6 and 1.

$$(3x+6)(x+1)$$

Before multiplying, notice that the terms of the factor $3x + 6$ have a common factor of 3. The terms of the original trinomial $3x^2 + 11x + 6$ have no common factor other than 1, so the terms of its factors will also contain no common factor other than 1. This means that $(3x+6)(x+1)$ is not a factored form.

Next let's try 2 and 3 as last terms.

$$(3x+2)(x+3) = 3x^2 + 11x + 6$$

$2x + 9x = 11x$ → **Correct** middle term

Thus a factored form of $3x^2 + 11x + 6$ is $(3x+2)(x+3)$. □

PRACTICE 1 Factor: $2x^2 + 11x + 15$.

Helpful Hint

If the terms of a trinomial have no common factor (other than 1), then the terms of neither of its binomial factors will contain a common factor (other than 1).

✓ CONCEPT CHECK

Do the terms of $3x^2 + 29x + 18$ have a common factor? Without multiplying, decide which of the following factored forms could not be a factored form of $3x^2 + 29x + 18$.

a. $(3x + 18)(x + 1)$ **b.** $(3x + 2)(x + 9)$ **c.** $(3x + 6)(x + 3)$ **d.** $(3x + 9)(x + 2)$

EXAMPLE 2 Factor: $8x^2 - 22x + 5$

Solution Factors of $8x^2$: $8x^2 = 8x \cdot x$, $8x^2 = 4x \cdot 2x$

We'll try $8x$ and x.

$$8x^2 - 22x + 5 = (8x + \square)(x + \square)$$

Since the middle term, $-22x$, has a negative numerical coefficient, we factor 5 into negative factors.

Factors of 5: $5 = -1 \cdot -5$

Let's try -1 and -5.

$$(8x - 1)(x - 5) = 8x^2 - 41x + 5$$

$$\begin{array}{r} -1x \\ +(-40x) \\ \hline -41x \end{array} \longrightarrow \text{Incorrect middle term}$$

Now let's try -5 and -1.

$$(8x - 5)(x - 1) = 8x^2 - 13x + 5$$

$$\begin{array}{r} -5x \\ +(-8x) \\ \hline -13x \end{array} \longrightarrow \text{Incorrect middle term}$$

Don't give up yet! We can still try other factors of $8x^2$. Let's try $4x$ and $2x$ with -1 and -5.

$$(4x - 1)(2x - 5) = 8x^2 - 22x + 5$$

$$\begin{array}{r} -2x \\ +(-20x) \\ \hline -22x \end{array} \longrightarrow \text{Correct middle term}$$

A factored form of $8x^2 - 22x + 5$ is $(4x - 1)(2x - 5)$. □

PRACTICE 2 Factor: $15x^2 - 22x + 8$.

EXAMPLE 3 Factor: $2x^2 + 13x - 7$

Solution Factors of $2x^2$: $2x^2 = 2x \cdot x$

Factors of -7: $-7 = -1 \cdot 7$, $-7 = 1 \cdot -7$

(Continued on next page)

Answers to Concept Check:
no; a, c, d

We try possible combinations of these factors:

$$(2x + 1)(x - 7) = 2x^2 - 13x - 7 \quad \text{Incorrect middle term}$$
$$(2x - 1)(x + 7) = 2x^2 + 13x - 7 \quad \text{Correct middle term}$$

A factored form of $2x^2 + 13x - 7$ is $(2x - 1)(x + 7)$. □

PRACTICE 3 Factor: $4x^2 + 11x - 3$.

EXAMPLE 4 Factor: $10x^2 - 13xy - 3y^2$

Solution Factors of $10x^2$: $10x^2 = 10x \cdot x$, $10x^2 = 2x \cdot 5x$

Factors of $-3y^2$: $-3y^2 = -3y \cdot y$, $-3y^2 = 3y \cdot -y$

We try some combinations of these factors:

Correct ↓ (first term), Correct ↓ (last term)

$$(10x - 3y)(x + y) = 10x^2 + 7xy - 3y^2$$
$$(x + 3y)(10x - y) = 10x^2 + 29xy - 3y^2$$
$$(5x + 3y)(2x - y) = 10x^2 + xy - 3y^2$$
$$(2x - 3y)(5x + y) = 10x^2 - 13xy - 3y^2 \quad \text{Correct middle term}$$

A factored form of $10x^2 - 13xy - 3y^2$ is $(2x - 3y)(5x + y)$. □

PRACTICE 4 Factor: $21x^2 + 11xy - 2y^2$.

EXAMPLE 5 Factor: $3x^4 - 5x^2 - 8$

Solution Factors of $3x^4$: $3x^4 = 3x^2 \cdot x^2$

Factors of -8: $-8 = -2 \cdot 4, 2 \cdot -4, -1 \cdot 8, 1 \cdot -8$

Try combinations of these factors:

Correct ↓ (first term), Correct ↓ (last term)

$$(3x^2 - 2)(x^2 + 4) = 3x^4 + 10x^2 - 8$$
$$(3x^2 + 4)(x^2 - 2) = 3x^4 - 2x^2 - 8$$
$$(3x^2 + 8)(x^2 - 1) = 3x^4 + 5x^2 - 8 \quad \text{Incorrect sign on middle term, so switch signs in binomial factors.}$$
$$(3x^2 - 8)(x^2 + 1) = 3x^4 - 5x^2 - 8 \quad \text{Correct middle term.}$$

A factored form of $3x^4 - 5x^2 - 8$ is $(3x^2 - 8)(x^2 + 1)$. □

PRACTICE 5 Factor: $2x^4 - 5x^2 - 7$.

Helpful Hint

Study the last two lines of Example 5. If a factoring attempt gives you a middle term whose numerical coefficient is the opposite of the desired numerical coefficient, try switching the signs of the last terms in the binomials.

Switched signs

$$(3x^2 + 8)(x^2 - 1) = 3x^4 + 5x^2 - 8 \quad \text{Middle term: } +5x^2$$
$$(3x^2 - 8)(x^2 + 1) = 3x^4 - 5x^2 - 8 \quad \text{Middle term: } -5x^2$$

OBJECTIVE

2 Factoring Out the Greatest Common Factor 

Don't forget that the first step in factoring any polynomial is to look for a common factor to factor out.

EXAMPLE 6 Factor: $24x^4 + 40x^3 + 6x^2$

Solution Notice that all three terms have a common factor of $2x^2$. Thus we factor out $2x^2$ first.

$$24x^4 + 40x^3 + 6x^2 = 2x^2(12x^2 + 20x + 3)$$

Next we factor $12x^2 + 20x + 3$.

Factors of $12x^2$: $12x^2 = 4x \cdot 3x$, $12x^2 = 12x \cdot x$, $12x^2 = 6x \cdot 2x$

Since all terms in the trinomial have positive numerical coefficients, we factor 3 using positive factors only.

Factors of 3: $3 = 1 \cdot 3$

We try some combinations of the factors.

$$2x^2(4x + 3)(3x + 1) = 2x^2(12x^2 + 13x + 3)$$
$$2x^2(12x + 1)(x + 3) = 2x^2(12x^2 + 37x + 3)$$
$$2x^2(2x + 3)(6x + 1) = 2x^2(12x^2 + 20x + 3) \quad \text{Correct middle term}$$

A factored form of $24x^4 + 40x^3 + 6x^2$ is $2x^2(2x + 3)(6x + 1)$. □

> **Helpful Hint**
> Don't forget to include the common factor in the factored form.

PRACTICE
6 Factor: $3x^3 + 17x^2 + 10x$

When the term containing the squared variable has a negative coefficient, you may want to first factor out a common factor of -1.

EXAMPLE 7 Factor: $-6x^2 - 13x + 5$

Solution We begin by factoring out a common factor of -1.

$$-6x^2 - 13x + 5 = -1(6x^2 + 13x - 5) \quad \text{Factor out } -1.$$
$$= -1(3x - 1)(2x + 5) \quad \text{Factor } 6x^2 + 13x - 5.$$
□

PRACTICE
7 Factor: $-8x^2 + 2x + 3$

OBJECTIVE

3 Factoring Perfect Square Trinomials

A trinomial that is the square of a binomial is called a **perfect square trinomial.** For example,

$$(x + 3)^2 = (x + 3)(x + 3)$$
$$= x^2 + 6x + 9$$

Thus $x^2 + 6x + 9$ is a perfect square trinomial.

We discovered special product formulas for squaring binomials.

$$(a + b)^2 = a^2 + 2ab + b^2 \quad \text{and} \quad (a - b)^2 = a^2 - 2ab + b^2$$

Because multiplication and factoring are reverse processes, we can now use these special products to help us factor perfect square trinomials. If we reverse these equations, we have the following.

Factoring Perfect Square Trinomials

$$a^2 + 2ab + b^2 = (a + b)^2$$
$$a^2 - 2ab + b^2 = (a - b)^2$$

Helpful Hint

Notice that for both given forms of a perfect square trinomial, the last term is positive. This is because the last term is a square.

To use these equations to help us factor, we must first be able to recognize a perfect square trinomial. A trinomial is a perfect square when

1. two terms, a^2 and b^2, are squares and
2. the remaining term is $2 \cdot a \cdot b$ or $-2 \cdot a \cdot b$. That is, this term is twice the product of a and b, or its opposite.

When a trinomial fits this description, its factored form is $(a + b)^2$ or $(a - b)^2$.

EXAMPLE 8 Factor: $x^2 + 12x + 36$

Solution First, is this a perfect square trinomial?

$$x^2 + 12x + 36$$

1. $x^2 = (x)^2$ and $36 = 6^2$.
2. Is the middle term $2 \cdot x \cdot 6$? Yes, $2 \cdot x \cdot 6 = 12x$, the middle term.

Thus, $x^2 + 12x + 36$ factors as $(x + 6)^2$. □

PRACTICE 8 Factor $x^2 + 14x + 49$.

EXAMPLE 9 Factor: $25x^2 + 25xy + 4y^2$

Solution Is this a perfect square trinomial?

$$25x^2 + 25xy + 4y^2$$

1. $25x^2 = (5x)^2$ and $4y^2 = (2y)^2$.
2. Is the middle term $2 \cdot 5x \cdot 2y$? **No,** $2 \cdot 5x \cdot 2y = 20xy$, **not** the middle term $25xy$.

Therefore, $25x^2 + 25xy + 4y^2$ is not a perfect square trinomial. It is factorable, though. Using earlier techniques, we find that $25x^2 + 25xy + 4y^2$ factors as $(5x + 4y)(5x + y)$. □

Helpful Hint

A perfect square trinomial can also be factored by other methods.

PRACTICE 9 Factor $4x^2 + 20xy + 9y^2$.

EXAMPLE 10 Factor: $4m^4 - 4m^2 + 1$

Solution Is this a perfect square trinomial?

$$4m^4 - 4m^2 + 1$$

1. $4m^4 = (2m^2)^2$ and $1 = 1^2$.
2. Is the middle term $2 \cdot 2m^2 \cdot 1$ or $-2 \cdot 2m^2 \cdot 1$? Yes, $-2 \cdot 2m^2 \cdot 1 = -4m^2$, the middle term.

Thus, $4m^4 - 4m^2 + 1$ factors as $(2m^2 - 1)^2$. □

PRACTICE 10 Factor $36n^4 - 12n^2 + 1$.

EXAMPLE 11 Factor: $162x^3 - 144x^2 + 32x$

Solution Don't forget to look first for a common factor. There is a greatest common factor of $2x$ in this trinomial.

$$\begin{aligned} 162x^3 - 144x^2 + 32x &= 2x(81x^2 - 72x + 16) \\ &= 2x[(9x)^2 - 2 \cdot 9x \cdot 4 + 4^2] \\ &= 2x(9x - 4)^2 \end{aligned}$$

□

PRACTICE 11 Factor $12x^3 - 84x^2 + 147x$.

Vocabulary, Readiness & Video Check

Use the choices below to fill in each blank. Some choices will be used more than once and some not used at all.

$5y^2$	$(x + 5y)^2$	perfect square trinomial
$(5y)^2$	$(x - 5y)^2$	perfect square binomial

1. A ________________ is a trinomial that is the square of a binomial.

2. The term $25y^2$ written as a square is ________________.

3. The expression $x^2 + 10xy + 25y^2$ is called a ________________.

4. The factorization $(x + 5y)(x + 5y)$ may also be written as ________________.

Complete each factorization.

5. $2x^2 + 5x + 3$ factors as $(2x + 3)(\ ?\ )$.
a. $(x + 3)$ **b.** $(2x + 1)$ **c.** $(3x + 4)$ **d.** $(x + 1)$

6. $7x^2 + 9x + 2$ factors as $(7x + 2)(\ ?\ )$.
a. $(3x + 1)$ **b.** $(x + 1)$ **c.** $(x + 2)$ **d.** $(7x + 1)$

Martin-Gay Interactive Videos

See Video 3.3

Watch the section lecture video and answer the following questions.

OBJECTIVE 1

7. From Example 1, explain in general terms how you would go about factoring a trinomial with a first-term coefficient $\neq 1$.

OBJECTIVE 2

8. From Examples 3 and 5, how can factoring the GCF from a trinomial help you save time when trying to factor the remaining trinomial?

OBJECTIVE 3

9. Describe in words the special patterns that the trinomials in Examples 7 and 8 have that identify them as perfect square trinomials.

3.3 Exercise Set

MyMathLab®

Complete each factored form. See Examples 1 through 5, and 8 through 10.

1. $5x^2 + 22x + 8 = (5x + 2)(\quad)$

2. $2y^2 + 27y + 25 = (2y + 25)(\quad)$

3. $50x^2 + 15x - 2 = (5x + 2)(\quad)$

4. $6y^2 + 11y - 10 = (2y + 5)(\quad)$

5. $25x^2 - 20x + 4 = (5x - 2)(\quad)$

6. $4y^2 - 20y + 25 = (2y - 5)(\quad)$

Factor completely. See Examples 1 through 5.

7. $2x^2 + 13x + 15$

8. $3x^2 + 8x + 4$

9. $8y^2 - 17y + 9$

10. $21x^2 - 31x + 10$

11. $2x^2 - 9x - 5$

12. $36r^2 - 5r - 24$

13. $20r^2 + 27r - 8$

14. $3x^2 + 20x - 63$
15. $10x^2 + 31x + 3$
16. $12x^2 + 17x + 5$
17. $2m^2 + 17m + 10$
18. $3n^2 + 20n + 5$
19. $6x^2 - 13xy + 5y^2$
20. $8x^2 - 14xy + 3y^2$
21. $15m^2 - 16m - 15$
22. $25n^2 - 5n - 6$

Factor completely. See Examples 1 through 7.

23. $12x^3 + 11x^2 + 2x$
24. $8a^3 + 14a^2 + 3a$
25. $21b^2 - 48b - 45$
26. $12x^2 - 14x - 10$
27. $7z + 12z^2 - 12$
28. $16t + 15t^2 - 15$
29. $6x^2y^2 - 2xy^2 - 60y^2$
30. $8x^2y + 34xy - 84y$
31. $4x^2 - 8x - 21$
32. $6x^2 - 11x - 10$
33. $-x^2 + 2x + 24$
34. $-x^2 + 4x + 21$
35. $4x^3 - 9x^2 - 9x$
36. $6x^3 - 31x^2 + 5x$
37. $24x^2 - 58x + 9$
38. $36x^2 + 55x - 14$

Factor each perfect square trinomial completely. See Examples 8 through 11.

39. $x^2 + 22x + 121$
40. $x^2 + 18x + 81$
41. $x^2 - 16x + 64$
42. $x^2 - 12x + 36$
43. $16a^2 - 24a + 9$
44. $25x^2 - 20x + 4$
45. $x^4 + 4x^2 + 4$
46. $m^4 + 10m^2 + 25$
47. $2n^2 - 28n + 98$
48. $3y^2 - 6y + 3$
49. $16y^2 + 40y + 25$
50. $9y^2 + 48y + 64$

MIXED PRACTICE

Factor each trinomial completely. See Examples 1 through 11 and Section 3.2.

51. $2x^2 - 7x - 99$
52. $2x^2 + 7x - 72$
53. $24x^2 + 41x + 12$
54. $24x^2 - 49x + 15$
55. $3a^2 + 10ab + 3b^2$
56. $2a^2 + 11ab + 5b^2$
57. $-9x + 20 + x^2$
58. $-7x + 12 + x^2$
59. $p^2 + 12pq + 36q^2$
60. $m^2 + 20mn + 100n^2$
61. $x^2y^2 - 10xy + 25$
62. $x^2y^2 - 14xy + 49$
63. $40a^2b + 9ab - 9b$
64. $24y^2x + 7yx - 5x$
65. $30x^3 + 38x^2 + 12x$
66. $6x^3 - 28x^2 + 16x$
67. $6y^3 - 8y^2 - 30y$
68. $12x^3 - 34x^2 + 24x$
69. $10x^4 + 25x^3y - 15x^2y^2$
70. $42x^4 - 99x^3y - 15x^2y^2$
71. $-14x^2 + 39x - 10$
72. $-15x^2 + 26x - 8$
73. $16p^4 - 40p^3 + 25p^2$
74. $9q^4 - 42q^3 + 49q^2$
75. $x + 3x^2 - 2$
76. $y + 8y^2 - 9$
77. $8x^2 + 6xy - 27y^2$
78. $54a^2 + 39ab - 8b^2$
79. $1 + 6x^2 + x^4$
80. $1 + 16x^2 + x^4$
81. $9x^2 - 24xy + 16y^2$
82. $25x^2 - 60xy + 36y^2$
83. $18x^2 - 9x - 14$
84. $42a^2 - 43a + 6$
85. $-27t + 7t^2 - 4$
86. $-3t + 4t^2 - 7$
87. $49p^2 - 7p - 2$
88. $3r^2 + 10r - 8$
89. $m^3 + 18m^2 + 81m$
90. $y^3 + 12y^2 + 36y$
91. $5x^2y^2 + 20xy + 1$
92. $3a^2b^2 + 12ab + 1$
93. $6a^5 + 37a^3b^2 + 6ab^4$
94. $5m^5 + 26m^3h^2 + 5mh^4$

REVIEW AND PREVIEW

Multiply the following.

95. $(x - 2)(x + 2)$
96. $(y^2 + 3)(y^2 - 3)$
97. $(a + 3)(a^2 - 3a + 9)$
98. $(z - 2)(z^2 + 2z + 4)$

The following graph shows the percent of text message users in each age group. See Section 1.1.

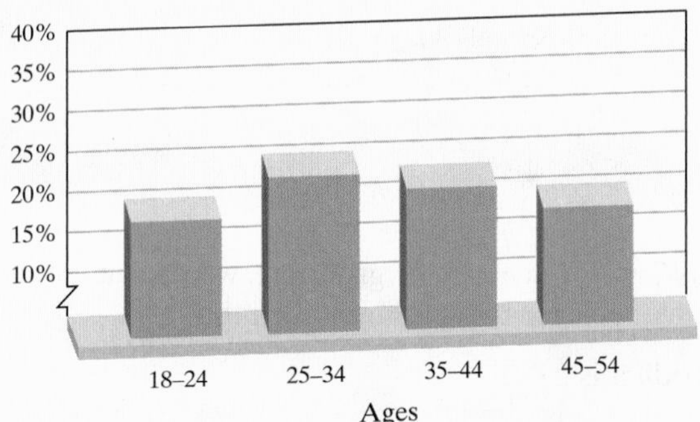

Data from CellSigns, Inc.

99. What range of ages shown has the highest percent of text message users?

100. What range of ages shown has the lowest percent of text message users?

101. Describe any trend you see.

102. Why don't the percents shown in the graph add to 100%?

CONCEPT EXTENSIONS

See the Concept Check in this section.

103. Do the terms of $4x^2 + 19x + 12$ have a common factor (other than 1)?

104. Without multiplying, decide which of the following factored forms is not a factored form of $4x^2 + 19x + 12$.

a. $(2x + 4)(2x + 3)$ **b.** $(4x + 4)(x + 3)$

c. $(4x + 3)(x + 4)$ **d.** $(2x + 2)(2x + 6)$

105. Describe a perfect square trinomial.

106. Write the perfect square trinomial that factors as $(x + 3y)^2$.

Write the perimeter of each figure as a simplified polynomial. Then factor the polynomial.

107.

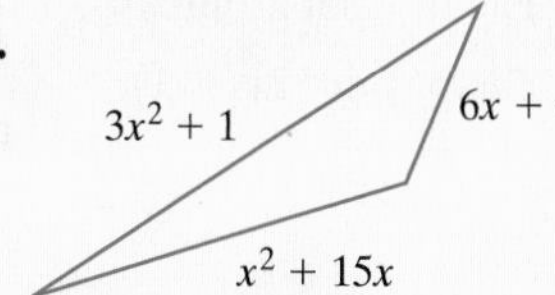

108.

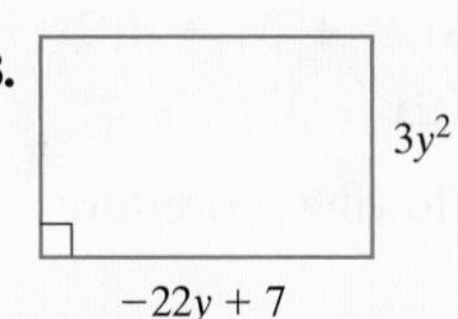

Factor each trinomial completely.

109. $4x^2 + 2x + \frac{1}{4}$

110. $27x^2 + 2x - \frac{1}{9}$

111. $4x^2(y - 1)^2 + 10x(y - 1)^2 + 25(y - 1)^2$

112. $3x^2(a + 3)^3 - 10x(a + 3)^3 + 25(a + 3)^3$

113. Fill in the blank so that $x^2 +$ ______ $x + 16$ is a perfect square trinomial.

114. Fill in the blank so that $9x^2 +$ ______ $x + 25$ is a perfect square trinomial.

The area of the largest square in the figure is $(a + b)^2$. Use this figure to answer Exercises 115 and 116.

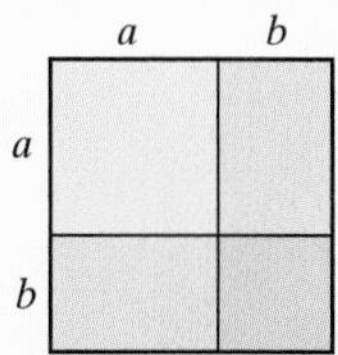

△ **115.** Write the area of the largest square as the sum of the areas of the smaller squares and rectangles.

△ **116.** What factoring formula from this section is visually represented by this square?

Find a positive value of b so that each trinomial is factorable.

117. $3x^2 + bx - 5$

118. $2y^2 + by + 3$

Find a positive value of c so that each trinomial is factorable.

119. $5x^2 + 7x + c$

120. $11y^2 - 40y + c$

Factor completely. Don't forget to first factor out the greatest common factor.

121. $-12x^3y^2 + 3x^2y^2 + 15xy^2$

122. $-12r^3x^2 + 38r^2x^2 + 14rx^2$

123. $4x^2(y - 1)^2 + 20x(y - 1)^2 + 25(y - 1)^2$

124. $3x^2(a + 3)^3 - 28x(a + 3)^3 + 25(a + 3)^3$

Factor.

125. $3x^{2n} + 17x^n + 10$

126. $2x^{2n} + 5x^n - 12$

127. In your own words, describe the steps you will use to factor a trinomial.

3.4 Factoring Trinomials of the Form $ax^2 + bx + c$ by Grouping

OBJECTIVE

1 Use the Grouping Method to Factor Trinomials of the Form $ax^2 + bx + c$.

OBJECTIVE

1 Using the Grouping Method

There is an alternative method that can be used to factor trinomials of the form $ax^2 + bx + c, a \neq 1$. This method is called the **grouping method** because it uses factoring by grouping as we learned in Section 3.1.

To see how this method works, recall from Section 3.2 that to factor a trinomial such as $x^2 + 11x + 30$, we find two numbers such that

$$\underset{\text{Sum is } 11.}{x^2 + \overset{\text{Product is } 30}{11x + 30}}$$

To factor a trinomial such as $2x^2 + 11x + 12$ by grouping, we use an extension of the method in Section 3.2. Here we look for two numbers such that

Product is $2 \cdot 12 = 24$

$$2x^2 + 11x + 12$$

Sum is 11.

This time, we use the two numbers to write

$$\begin{aligned} &2x^2 + 11x + 12 \text{ as} \\ &= 2x^2 + \square x + \square x + 12 \end{aligned}$$

Then we factor by grouping. Since we want a positive product, 24, and a positive sum, 11, we consider pairs of positive factors of 24 only.

Factors of 24	*Sum of Factors*	
1, 24	25	
2, 12	14	
3, 8	11	Correct sum

The factors are 3 and 8. Now we use these factors to write the middle term $11x$ as $3x + 8x$ (or $8x + 3x$). We replace $11x$ with $3x + 8x$ in the original trinomial and then we can factor by grouping.

$$\begin{aligned} 2x^2 + 11x + 12 &= 2x^2 + 3x + 8x + 12 \\ &= (2x^2 + 3x) + (8x + 12) && \text{Group the terms.} \\ &= x(2x + 3) + 4(2x + 3) && \text{Factor each group.} \\ &= (2x + 3)(x + 4) && \text{Factor out } (2x + 3). \end{aligned}$$

In general, we have the following procedure.

To Factor Trinomials by Grouping

Step 1. Factor out a greatest common factor if there is one other than 1.

Step 2. For the resulting trinomial $ax^2 + bx + c$, find two numbers whose product is $a \cdot c$ and whose sum is b.

Step 3. Write the middle term, bx, using the factors found in Step 2.

Step 4. Factor by grouping.

EXAMPLE 1 Factor $3x^2 + 31x + 10$ by grouping.

Solution

Step 1. The terms of this trinomial contain no greatest common factor other than 1 (or −1).

Step 2. In $3x^2 + 31x + 10$, $a = 3$, $b = 31$, and $c = 10$.

Let's find two numbers whose product is $a \cdot c$ or $3(10) = 30$ and whose sum is b or 31. The numbers are 1 and 30.

Factors of 30	*Sum of Factors*	
5, 6	11	
3, 10	13	
2, 15	17	
1, 30	31	Correct sum

Step 3. Write $31x$ as $1x + 30x$ so that $3x^2 + 31x + 10 = 3x^2 + 1x + 30x + 10$.

Step 4. Factor by grouping.

$$3x^2 + 1x + 30x + 10 = x(3x + 1) + 10(3x + 1)$$
$$= (3x + 1)(x + 10)$$

□

PRACTICE 1 Factor $5x^2 + 61x + 12$ by grouping.

EXAMPLE 2 Factor $8x^2 - 14x + 5$ by grouping.

Solution

Step 1. The terms of this trinomial contain no greatest common factor other than 1.

Step 2. This trinomial is of the form $ax^2 + bx + c$ with $a = 8, b = -14$, and $c = 5$. Find two numbers whose product is $a \cdot c$ or $8 \cdot 5 = 40$, and whose sum is b or -14.

The numbers are -4 and -10.

Factors of 40	*Sum of Factors*	
−40, −1	−41	
−20, −2	−22	
−10, −4	−14	Correct sum

Step 3. Write $-14x$ as $-4x - 10x$ so that

$$8x^2 - 14x + 5 = 8x^2 - 4x - 10x + 5$$

Step 4. Factor by grouping.

$$8x^2 - 4x - 10x + 5 = 4x(2x - 1) - 5(2x - 1)$$
$$= (2x - 1)(4x - 5)$$

□

PRACTICE 2 Factor $12x^2 - 19x + 5$ by grouping.

EXAMPLE 3 Factor $6x^2 - 2x - 20$ by grouping.

Solution

Step 1. First factor out the greatest common factor, 2.

$$6x^2 - 2x - 20 = 2(3x^2 - x - 10)$$

Step 2. Next, notice that $a = 3, b = -1$, and $c = -10$ in the resulting trinomial. Find two numbers whose product is $a \cdot c$ or $3(-10) = -30$ and whose sum is b, -1. The numbers are -6 and 5.

Step 3. $3x^2 - x - 10 = 3x^2 - 6x + 5x - 10$

(Continued on next page)

Step 4. $3x^2 - 6x + 5x - 10 = 3x(x - 2) + 5(x - 2)$
$= (x - 2)(3x + 5)$

The factored form of $6x^2 - 2x - 20 = 2(x - 2)(3x + 5)$.

Don't forget to include the common factor of 2. □

PRACTICE 3 Factor $30x^2 - 14x - 4$ by grouping.

EXAMPLE 4 Factor $18y^4 + 21y^3 - 60y^2$ by grouping.

Solution

Step 1. First factor out the greatest common factor, $3y^2$.

$$18y^4 + 21y^3 - 60y^2 = 3y^2(6y^2 + 7y - 20)$$

Step 2. Notice that $a = 6, b = 7$, and $c = -20$ in the resulting trinomial. Find two numbers whose product is $a \cdot c$ or $6(-20) = -120$ and whose sum is 7. It may help to factor -120 as a product of primes and -1.

$$-120 = 2 \cdot 2 \cdot 2 \cdot 3 \cdot 5 \cdot (-1)$$

Then choose pairings of factors until you have a pairing whose sum is 7.

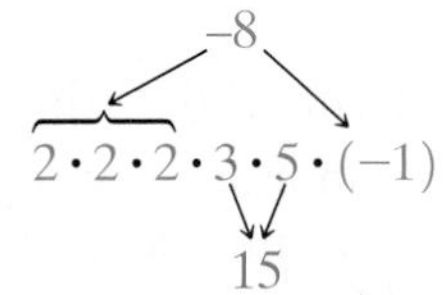

The numbers are -8 and 15.

Step 3. $6y^2 + 7y - 20 = 6y^2 - 8y + 15y - 20$

Step 4. $6y^2 - 8y + 15y - 20 = 2y(3y - 4) + 5(3y - 4)$
$= (3y - 4)(2y + 5)$

The factored form of $18y^4 + 21y^3 - 60y^2$ is $3y^2(3y - 4)(2y + 5)$.

Don't forget to include the common factor of $3y^2$. □

PRACTICE 4 Factor $40m^4 + 5m^3 - 35m^2$ by grouping.

EXAMPLE 5 Factor $4x^2 + 20x + 25$ by grouping.

Solution

Step 1. The terms of this trinomial contain no greatest common factor other than 1 (or -1).

Step 2. In $4x^2 + 20x + 25, a = 4, b = 20$, and $c = 25$. Find two numbers whose product is $a \cdot c$ or $4 \cdot 25 = 100$ and whose sum is 20. The numbers are 10 and 10.

Step 3. Write $20x$ as $10x + 10x$ so that

$$4x^2 + 20x + 25 = 4x^2 + 10x + 10x + 25$$

Step 4. Factor by grouping.

$$4x^2 + 10x + 10x + 25 = 2x(2x + 5) + 5(2x + 5)$$
$$= (2x + 5)(2x + 5)$$

The factored form of $4x^2 + 20x + 25$ is $(2x + 5)(2x + 5)$ or $(2x + 5)^2$. □

PRACTICE 5 Factor $16x^2 + 24x + 9$ by grouping.

A trinomial that is the square of a binomial, such as the trinomial in Example 5, is called a **perfect square trinomial.** There are special product formulas we can use to help us recognize and factor these trinomials. To study these formulas further, see Section 3.3, Objective 3. **Remember:** A perfect square trinomial, such as the one in Example 5, may be factored by special product formulas or by other methods of factoring trinomials, such as by grouping.

Vocabulary, Readiness & Video Check

For each trinomial $ax^2 + bx + c$, choose two numbers whose product is $a \cdot c$ and whose sum is b.

1. $x^2 + 6x + 8$

a. 4, 2 **b.** 7, 1 **c.** 6, 2 **d.** 6, 8

2. $x^2 + 11x + 24$

a. 6, 4 **b.** 24, 1 **c.** 8, 3 **d.** 2, 12

3. $2x^2 + 13x + 6$

a. 2, 6 **b.** 12, 1 **c.** 13, 1 **d.** 3, 4

4. $4x^2 + 8x + 3$

a. 4, 3 **b.** 4, 4 **c.** 12, 1 **d.** 2, 6

Martin-Gay Interactive Videos

See Video 3.4

Watch the section lecture video and answer the following question.

OBJECTIVE 1

5. In the lecture following Example 1, why does writing a term as the sum or difference of two terms suggest we'd then try to factor by grouping?

3.4 Exercise Set

MyMathLab®

Factor each polynomial by grouping. Notice that Step 3 has already been done in these exercises. See Examples 1 through 5.

1. $x^2 + 3x + 2x + 6$

2. $x^2 + 5x + 3x + 15$

3. $y^2 + 8y - 2y - 16$

4. $z^2 + 10z - 7z - 70$

5. $8x^2 - 5x - 24x + 15$

6. $4x^2 - 9x - 32x + 72$

7. $5x^4 - 3x^2 + 25x^2 - 15$

8. $2y^4 - 10y^2 + 7y^2 - 35$

MIXED PRACTICE

Factor each trinomial by grouping. Exercises 9–12 are broken into parts to help you get started. See Examples 1 through 5.

9. $6x^2 + 11x + 3$

a. Find two numbers whose product is $6 \cdot 3 = 18$ and whose sum is 11.

b. Write $11x$ using the factors from part (a).

c. Factor by grouping.

10. $8x^2 + 14x + 3$

a. Find two numbers whose product is $8 \cdot 3 = 24$ and whose sum is 14.

b. Write $14x$ using the factors from part (a).

c. Factor by grouping.

11. $15x^2 - 23x + 4$

a. Find two numbers whose product is $15 \cdot 4 = 60$ and whose sum is -23.

b. Write $-23x$ using the factors from part (a).

c. Factor by grouping.

12. $6x^2 - 13x + 5$

a. Find two numbers whose product is $6 \cdot 5 = 30$ and whose sum is -13.

b. Write $-13x$ using the factors from part (a).

c. Factor by grouping.

13. $21y^2 + 17y + 2$

14. $15x^2 + 11x + 2$

15. $7x^2 - 4x - 11$
16. $8x^2 - x - 9$
17. $10x^2 - 9x + 2$
18. $30x^2 - 23x + 3$
19. $2x^2 - 7x + 5$
20. $2x^2 - 7x + 3$
21. $12x + 4x^2 + 9$
22. $20x + 25x^2 + 4$
23. $4x^2 - 8x - 21$
24. $6x^2 - 11x - 10$
25. $10x^2 - 23x + 12$
26. $21x^2 - 13x + 2$
27. $2x^3 + 13x^2 + 15x$
28. $3x^3 + 8x^2 + 4x$
29. $16y^2 - 34y + 18$
30. $4y^2 - 2y - 12$
31. $-13x + 6 + 6x^2$
32. $-25x + 12 + 12x^2$
33. $54a^2 - 9a - 30$
34. $30a^2 + 38a - 20$
35. $20a^3 + 37a^2 + 8a$
36. $10a^3 + 17a^2 + 3a$
37. $12x^3 - 27x^2 - 27x$
38. $30x^3 - 155x^2 + 25x$
39. $3x^2y + 4xy^2 + y^3$
40. $6r^2t + 7rt^2 + t^3$
41. $20z^2 + 7z + 1$
42. $36z^2 + 6z + 1$
43. $5x^2 + 50xy + 125y^2$
44. $3x^2 + 42xy + 147y^2$
45. $24a^2 - 6ab - 30b^2$
46. $30a^2 + 5ab - 25b^2$
47. $15p^4 + 31p^3q + 2p^2q^2$
48. $20s^4 + 61s^3t + 3s^2t^2$
49. $162a^4 - 72a^2 + 8$
50. $32n^4 - 112n^2 + 98$
51. $35 + 12x + x^2$
52. $33 + 14x + x^2$
53. $6 - 11x + 5x^2$
54. $5 - 12x + 7x^2$

REVIEW AND PREVIEW

Multiply.

55. $(x - 2)(x + 2)$
56. $(y - 5)(y + 5)$
57. $(y + 4)(y + 4)$
58. $(x + 7)(x + 7)$
59. $(9z + 5)(9z - 5)$
60. $(8y + 9)(8y - 9)$
61. $(x - 3)(x^2 + 3x + 9)$
62. $(2z - 1)(4z^2 + 2z + 1)$

CONCEPT EXTENSIONS

Write the perimeter of each figure as a simplified polynomial. Then factor the polynomial.

63.

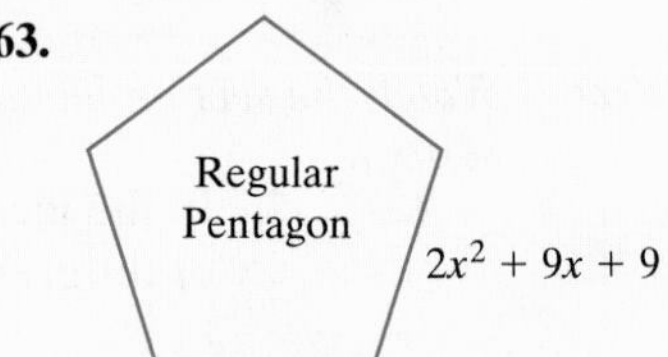

64.

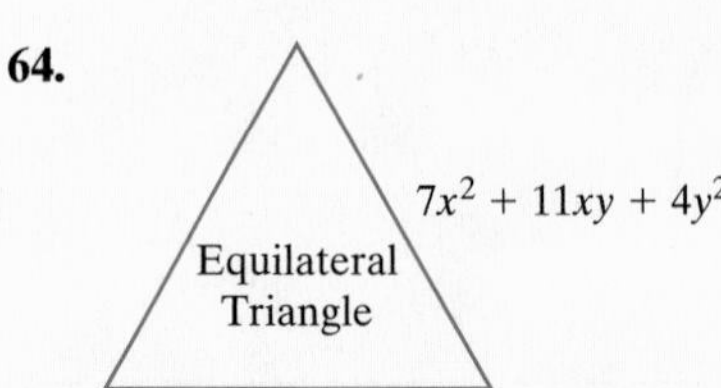

Factor each polynomial by grouping.

65. $x^{2n} + 2x^n + 3x^n + 6$
(***Hint:*** Don't forget that $x^{2n} = x^n \cdot x^n$.)
66. $x^{2n} + 6x^n + 10x^n + 60$
67. $3x^{2n} + 16x^n - 35$
68. $12x^{2n} - 40x^n + 25$
69. In your own words, explain how to factor a trinomial by grouping.

3.5 Factoring Binomials

OBJECTIVES

1 Factor the Difference of Two Squares.

2 Factor the Sum or Difference of Two Cubes.

OBJECTIVE

1 Factoring the Difference of Two Squares

The product of the sum and difference of two terms, a and b:

$$(a + b)(a - b) = a^2 - b^2$$

For example, the product of $x + 3$ and $x - 3$ is

$$(x + 3)(x - 3) = x^2 - 9$$

The binomial $x^2 - 9$ is called a **difference of squares**. In this section, we reverse the pattern for the product of a sum and difference to factor the binomial difference of squares.

Factoring the Difference of Two Squares

$$a^2 - b^2 = (a + b)(a - b)$$

Helpful Hint

Since multiplication is commutative, remember that the order of factors does not matter. In other words,

$$a^2 - b^2 = (a + b)(a - b) \text{ or } (a - b)(a + b)$$

EXAMPLE 1 Factor: $x^2 - 25$

Solution $x^2 - 25$ is the difference of two squares since $x^2 - 25 = x^2 - 5^2$. Therefore,

$$x^2 - 25 = x^2 - 5^2 = (x + 5)(x - 5)$$

Multiply to check. □

PRACTICE
1 Factor $x^2 - 81$.

EXAMPLE 2 Factor each difference of squares.

a. $4x^2 - 1$ **b.** $25a^2 - 9b^2$ **c.** $y^2 - \frac{4}{9}$

Solution

a. $4x^2 - 1 = (2x)^2 - 1^2 = (2x + 1)(2x - 1)$

b. $25a^2 - 9b^2 = (5a)^2 - (3b)^2 = (5a + 3b)(5a - 3b)$

c. $y^2 - \frac{4}{9} = y^2 - \left(\frac{2}{3}\right)^2 = \left(y + \frac{2}{3}\right)\left(y - \frac{2}{3}\right)$ □

PRACTICE
2 Factor each difference of squares.

a. $9x^2 - 1$ **b.** $36a^2 - 49b^2$ **c.** $p^2 - \frac{25}{36}$

EXAMPLE 3 Factor: $x^4 - y^6$

Solution This is a difference of squares since $x^4 = (x^2)^2$ and $y^6 = (y^3)^2$. Thus,

$$x^4 - y^6 = (x^2)^2 - (y^3)^2 = (x^2 + y^3)(x^2 - y^3)$$ □

PRACTICE
3 Factor $p^4 - q^{10}$.

EXAMPLE 4 Factor each binomial.

a. $y^4 - 16$ **b.** $x^2 + 4$

Solution

a. $y^4 - 16 = (y^2)^2 - 4^2$

$= (y^2 + 4)\underbrace{(y^2 - 4)}$ Factor the difference of two squares. This binomial can be factored further since it is the difference of two squares.

$= (y^2 + 4)(y + 2)(y - 2)$ Factor the difference of two squares.

(Continued on next page)

b. $x^2 + 4$

Note that the binomial $x^2 + 4$ is the *sum* of two squares since we can write $x^2 + 4$ as $x^2 + 2^2$. We might try to factor using $(x + 2)(x + 2)$ or $(x - 2)(x - 2)$. But when we multiply to check, we find that neither factoring is correct.

$$(x + 2)(x + 2) = x^2 + 4x + 4$$
$$(x - 2)(x - 2) = x^2 - 4x + 4$$

In both cases, the product is a trinomial, not the required binomial. In fact, $x^2 + 4$ is a prime polynomial. □

PRACTICE 4 Factor each binomial.

a. $z^4 - 81$ **b.** $m^2 + 49$

> **Helpful Hint**
> When factoring, don't forget:
> - See whether the terms have a greatest common factor (GCF) (other than 1) that can be factored out.
> - Other than a GCF, the **sum** of two squares cannot be factored using real numbers.
> - Factor completely. Always check to see whether any factors can be factored further.

EXAMPLES Factor each binomial.

5. $4x^3 - 49x = x(4x^2 - 49)$ Factor out the common factor, x.
$= x[(2x)^2 - 7^2]$
$= x(2x + 7)(2x - 7)$ Factor the difference of two squares.

6. $162x^4 - 2 = 2(81x^4 - 1)$ Factor out the common factor, 2.
$= 2(9x^2 + 1)(9x^2 - 1)$ Factor the difference of two squares.
$= 2(9x^2 + 1)(3x + 1)(3x - 1)$ Factor the difference of two squares. □

PRACTICES 5–6 Factor each binomial.

5. $36y^3 - 25y$ **6.** $80y^4 - 5$

EXAMPLE 7 Factor: $-49x^2 + 16$

Solution Factor as is, or, if you like, rearrange terms.

Factor as is: $-49x^2 + 16 = -1(49x^2 - 16)$ Factor out -1.
$= -1(7x + 4)(7x - 4)$ Factor the difference of two squares.

Rewrite binomial: $-49x^2 + 16 = 16 - 49x^2 = 4^2 - (7x)^2$
$= (4 + 7x)(4 - 7x)$

> **Helpful Hint**
> When rearranging terms, keep in mind that the sign of a term is in front of the term.

Both factorizations are correct and are equal. To see this, factor -1 from $(4 - 7x)$ in the second factorization. □

PRACTICE 7 Factor $-9x^2 + 100$.

OBJECTIVE

2 Factoring the Sum or Difference of Two Cubes 

Although the sum of two squares usually does not factor, the sum or difference of two cubes can be factored and reveals factoring patterns. The pattern for the sum of cubes is illustrated by multiplying the binomial $x + y$ and the trinomial $x^2 - xy + y^2$.

$$\begin{array}{rrrr} & x^2 & - xy & + y^2 \\ & & x & + y \\ \hline & x^2y & -xy^2 & + y^3 \\ x^3 & - x^2y & + xy^2 & \\ \hline x^3 & & & + y^3 \end{array}$$

Thus, $(x + y)(x^2 - xy + y^2) = x^3 + y^3$ Sum of cubes

The pattern for the difference of two cubes is illustrated by multiplying the binomial $x - y$ by the trinomial $x^2 + xy + y^2$. The result is

$$(x - y)(x^2 + xy + y^2) = x^3 - y^3 \qquad \text{Difference of cubes}$$

Factoring the Sum or Difference of Two Cubes

$$a^3 + b^3 = (a + b)(a^2 - ab + b^2)$$
$$a^3 - b^3 = (a - b)(a^2 + ab + b^2)$$

Recall that "factor" means "to write as a product." Above are patterns for writing sums and differences as products.

EXAMPLE 8 Factor: $x^3 + 8$

Solution First, write the binomial in the form $a^3 + b^3$.

$$x^3 + 8 = x^3 + 2^3 \qquad \text{Write in the form } a^3 + b^3.$$

If we replace a with x and b with 2 in the formula above, we have

$$\begin{aligned} x^3 + 2^3 &= (x + 2)[x^2 - (x)(2) + 2^2] \\ &= (x + 2)(x^2 - 2x + 4) \end{aligned}$$

□

PRACTICE

8 Factor $x^3 + 64$.

Helpful Hint

When factoring sums or differences of cubes, notice the sign patterns.

same sign

$$x^3 + y^3 = (x + y)(x^2 - xy + y^2)$$

opposite signs always positive

same sign

$$x^3 - y^3 = (x - y)(x^2 + xy + y^2)$$

opposite signs always positive

EXAMPLE 9 Factor: $y^3 - 27$

Solution

$$\begin{aligned} y^3 - 27 &= y^3 - 3^3 && \text{Write in the form } a^3 - b^3. \\ &= (y - 3)[y^2 + (y)(3) + 3^2] \\ &= (y - 3)(y^2 + 3y + 9) \end{aligned}$$

□

PRACTICE

9 Factor $x^3 - 125$.

EXAMPLE 10 Factor: $64x^3 + 1$

Solution

$$\begin{aligned} 64x^3 + 1 &= (4x)^3 + 1^3 \\ &= (4x + 1)[(4x)^2 - (4x)(1) + 1^2] \\ &= (4x + 1)(16x^2 - 4x + 1) \end{aligned}$$

□

PRACTICE

10 Factor $27y^3 + 1$.

EXAMPLE 11 Factor: $54a^3 - 16b^3$

Solution Remember to factor out common factors first before using other factoring methods.

$$\begin{aligned} 54a^3 - 16b^3 &= 2(27a^3 - 8b^3) && \text{Factor out the GCF 2.} \\ &= 2[(3a)^3 - (2b)^3] && \text{Difference of two cubes} \\ &= 2(3a - 2b)[(3a)^2 + (3a)(2b) + (2b)^2] \\ &= 2(3a - 2b)(9a^2 + 6ab + 4b^2) \end{aligned}$$

□

PRACTICE

11 Factor $32x^3 - 500y^3$.

Graphing Calculator Explorations

Graphing

A graphing calculator is a convenient tool for evaluating an expression at a given replacement value. For example, let's evaluate $x^2 - 6x$ when $x = 2$. To do so, store the value 2 in the variable x and then enter and evaluate the algebraic expression.

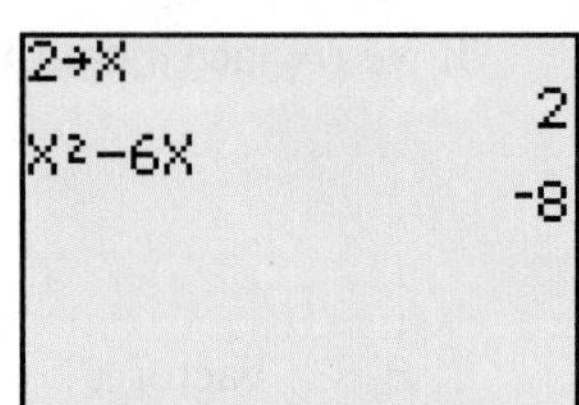

The value of $x^2 - 6x$ when $x = 2$ is -8. You may want to use this method for evaluating expressions as you explore the following.

We can use a graphing calculator to explore factoring patterns numerically. Use your calculator to evaluate $x^2 - 2x + 1$, $x^2 - 2x - 1$, and $(x - 1)^2$ for each value of x given in the table. What do you observe?

	$x^2 - 2x + 1$	$x^2 - 2x - 1$	$(x - 1)^2$
$x = 5$			
$x = -3$			
$x = 2.7$			
$x = -12.1$			
$x = 0$			

Notice in each case that $x^2 - 2x - 1 \neq (x - 1)^2$. Because for each x in the table the value of $x^2 - 2x + 1$ and the value of $(x - 1)^2$ are the same, we might guess that $x^2 - 2x + 1 = (x - 1)^2$. We can verify our guess algebraically with multiplication:

$$(x - 1)(x - 1) = x^2 - x - x + 1 = x^2 - 2x + 1$$

Vocabulary, Readiness & Video Check

Use the choices below to fill in each blank. Some choices may be used more than once and some choices may not be used at all.

true	difference of two squares	sum of two cubes
false	difference of two cubes	

1. The expression $x^3 - 27$ is called a ________________.
2. The expression $x^2 - 49$ is called a ________________.
3. The expression $z^3 + 1$ is called a ________________.
4. True or false: The binomial $y^2 + 9$ factors as $(y + 3)^2$. ________________

Write each term as a square.

5. $49x^2$
6. $25y^4$

Write each term as a cube.

7. $8y^3$
8. x^6

Martin-Gay Interactive Videos

See Video 3.5

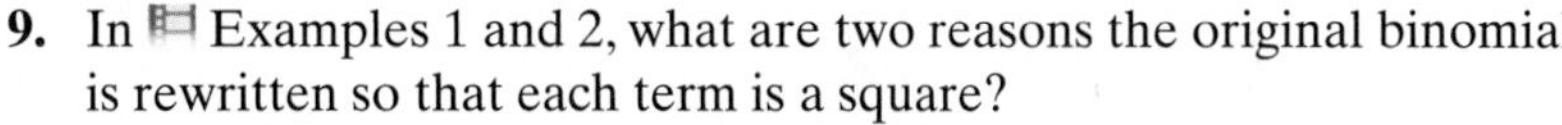

Watch the section lecture video and answer the following questions.

OBJECTIVE 1 — 9. In 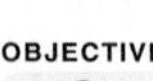 Examples 1 and 2, what are two reasons the original binomial is rewritten so that each term is a square?

OBJECTIVE 1 — 10. From Example 3, what is a prime polynomial?

OBJECTIVE 2 — 11. In Examples 6–8, what tips are given to remember how to factor the sum or difference of two cubes rather than memorizing the formulas?

3.5 Exercise Set

MyMathLab®

Factor each binomial completely. See Examples 1 through 7.

1. $x^2 - 4$
2. $x^2 - 36$
3. $81p^2 - 1$
4. $49m^2 - 1$
5. $25y^2 - 9$
6. $49a^2 - 16$
7. $121m^2 - 100n^2$
8. $169a^2 - 49b^2$
9. $x^2y^2 - 1$
10. $a^2b^2 - 16$
11. $x^2 - \frac{1}{4}$
12. $y^2 - \frac{1}{16}$
13. $-4r^2 + 1$
14. $-9t^2 + 1$
15. $16r^2 + 1$
16. $49y^2 + 1$
17. $-36 + x^2$
18. $-1 + y^2$
19. $m^4 - 1$
20. $n^4 - 16$
21. $m^4 - n^{18}$
22. $n^4 - r^6$

Factor the sum or difference of two cubes. See Examples 8 through 11.

23. $x^3 + 125$
24. $p^3 + 1$
25. $8a^3 - 1$
26. $27y^3 - 1$
27. $m^3 + 27n^3$
28. $y^3 + 64z^3$
29. $5k^3 + 40$
30. $6r^3 + 162$
31. $x^3y^3 - 64$
32. $a^3b^3 - 8$
33. $250r^3 - 128t^3$
34. $24x^3 - 81y^3$

MIXED PRACTICE

Factor each binomial completely. See Examples 1 through 11.

35. $r^2 - 64$
36. $q^2 - 121$
37. $x^2 - 169y^2$
38. $x^2 - 225y^2$
39. $27 - t^3$
40. $125 - r^3$
41. $18r^2 - 8$
42. $32t^2 - 50$
43. $9xy^2 - 4x$
44. $36x^2y - 25y$
45. $8m^3 + 64$
46. $2x^3 + 54$
47. $xy^3 - 9xyz^2$
48. $x^3y - 4xy^3$
49. $36x^2 - 64y^2$
50. $225a^2 - 81b^2$
51. $144 - 81x^2$
52. $12x^2 - 27$
53. $x^3y^3 - z^6$
54. $a^3b^3 - c^9$
55. $49 - \frac{9}{25}m^2$
56. $100 - \frac{4}{81}n^2$
57. $t^3 + 343$
58. $s^3 + 216$
59. $n^3 + 49n$
60. $y^3 + 64y$
61. $x^6 - 81x^2$
62. $n^9 - n^5$
63. $64p^3q - 81pq^3$
64. $100x^3y - 49xy^3$
65. $27x^2y^3 + xy^2$
66. $8x^3y^3 + x^3y$
67. $125a^4 - 64ab^3$
68. $64m^4 - 27mn^3$
69. $16x^4 - 64x^2$
70. $25y^4 - 100y^2$

REVIEW AND PREVIEW

Solve each equation.

71. $x - 6 = 0$
72. $y + 5 = 0$
73. $2m + 4 = 0$
74. $3x - 9 = 0$
75. $5z - 1 = 0$
76. $4a + 2 = 0$

CONCEPT EXTENSIONS

Factor each expression completely.

77. $(x + 2)^2 - y^2$
78. $(y - 6)^2 - z^2$
79. $a^2(b - 4) - 16(b - 4)$
80. $m^2(n + 8) - 9(n + 8)$
81. $(x^2 + 6x + 9) - 4y^2$ (***Hint:*** Factor the trinomial in parentheses first.)
82. $(x^2 + 2x + 1) - 36y^2$
83. $x^{2n} - 100$
84. $x^{2n} - 81$
85. What binomial multiplied by $(x - 6)$ gives the difference of two squares?
86. What binomial multiplied by $(5 + y)$ gives the difference of two squares?
87. In your own words, explain how to tell whether a binomial is a difference of squares. Then explain how to factor a difference of squares.
88. In your own words, explain how to tell whether a binomial is a sum of cubes. Then explain how to factor a sum of cubes.
89. The Toroweap Overlook, on the North Rim of the Grand Canyon, lies 3000 vertical feet above the Colorado River. The view is spectacular, and the sheer drop is dramatic. A film crew creating a documentary about the Grand Canyon has suspended a camera platform 296 feet below the Overlook. A camera filter comes loose and falls to the river below. The height of the filter above the river after t seconds is given by the expression $2704 - 16t^2$.
    a. Find the height of the filter above the river after 3 seconds.
    b. Find the height of the filter above the river after 7 seconds.
    c. To the nearest whole second, estimate when the filter lands in the river.
    d. Factor $2704 - 16t^2$.

90. An object is dropped from the top of Pittsburgh's USX Tower, which is 841 feet tall. (*Source: World Almanac* research) The height of the object after t seconds is given by the expression $841 - 16t^2$.
    a. Find the height of the object after 2 seconds.
    b. Find the height of the object after 5 seconds.
    c. To the nearest whole second, estimate when the object hits the ground.
    d. Factor $841 - 16t^2$.

91. At this writing, the world's second tallest building is the Taipei 101 in Taipei, Taiwan, at a height of 1671 feet. (*Source:* Council on Tall Buildings and Urban Habitat) Suppose a worker is suspended 71 feet below the top of the pinnacle atop the building, at a height of 1600 feet above the ground. If the worker accidentally drops a bolt, the height of the bolt after t seconds is given by the expression $1600 - 16t^2$.

a. Find the height of the bolt after 3 seconds.

b. Find the height of the bolt after 7 seconds.

c. To the nearest whole second, estimate when the bolt hits the ground.

d. Factor $1600 - 16t^2$.

92. A performer with the Moscow Circus is planning a stunt involving a free fall from the top of the Moscow State University building, which is 784 feet tall. (*Source:* Council on Tall Buildings and Urban Habitat) Neglecting air resistance, the performer's height above gigantic cushions positioned at ground level after t seconds is given by the expression $784 - 16t^2$.

a. Find the performer's height after 2 seconds.

b. Find the performer's height after 5 seconds.

c. To the nearest whole second, estimate when the performer reaches the cushions positioned at ground level.

d. Factor $784 - 16t^2$.

Integrated Review CHOOSING A FACTORING STRATEGY

Sections 3.1–3.5

The following steps may be helpful when factoring polynomials.

Factoring a Polynomial

Step 1. Are there any common factors? If so, factor out the GCF.

Step 2. How many terms are in the polynomial?

a. If there are **two** terms, decide if one of the following can be applied.

i. Difference of two squares: $a^2 - b^2 = (a + b)(a - b)$.

ii. Difference of two cubes: $a^3 - b^3 = (a - b)(a^2 + ab + b^2)$.

iii. Sum of two cubes: $a^3 + b^3 = (a + b)(a^2 - ab + b^2)$.

b. If there are **three** terms, try one of the following.

i. Perfect square trinomial: $a^2 + 2ab + b^2 = (a + b)^2$
$a^2 - 2ab + b^2 = (a - b)^2$.

ii. If not a perfect square trinomial, factor using the methods presented in Sections 3.2 through 3.4.

c. If there are **four** or more terms, try factoring by grouping.

Step 3. See if any factors in the factored polynomial can be factored further.

Step 4. Check by multiplying.

Study the next five examples to help you use the steps above.

EXAMPLE 1 Factor $10t^2 - 17t + 3$.

Solution

Step 1. The terms of this polynomial have no common factor (other than 1).

Step 2. There are three terms, so this polynomial is a trinomial. This trinomial is not a perfect square trinomial, so factor using methods from earlier sections.

$$\text{Factors of } 10t^2\text{: } \quad 10t^2 = 2t \cdot 5t, \qquad 10t^2 = t \cdot 10t$$

(Continued on next page)

Since the middle term, $-17t$, has a negative numerical coefficient, find negative factors of 3.

Factors of 3: $3 = -1 \cdot -3$

Try different combinations of these factors. The correct combination is

$$(2t - 3)(5t - 1) = 10t^2 - 17t + 3$$

$-15t$
$-2t$
$-17t$ Correct middle term

Step 3. No factor can be factored further, so we have factored completely.

Step 4. To check, multiply $2t - 3$ and $5t - 1$.

$$(2t - 3)(5t - 1) = 10t^2 - 2t - 15t + 3 = 10t^2 - 17t + 3$$

The factored form of $10t^2 - 17t + 3$ is $(2t - 3)(5t - 1)$. □

PRACTICE 1 Factor $6x^2 - 11x + 3$.

EXAMPLE 2 Factor $2x^3 + 3x^2 - 2x - 3$.

Solution

Step 1. There are no factors common to all terms.

Step 2. Try factoring by grouping since this polynomial has four terms.

$2x^3 + 3x^2 - 2x - 3 = x^2(2x + 3) - 1(2x + 3)$ Factor out the greatest common factor for each pair of terms.

$= (2x + 3)(x^2 - 1)$ Factor out $2x + 3$.

Step 3. The binomial $x^2 - 1$ can be factored further. It is the difference of two squares.

$= (2x + 3)(x + 1)(x - 1)$ Factor $x^2 - 1$ as a difference of squares.

Step 4. Check by finding the product of the three binomials. The polynomial factored completely is $(2x + 3)(x + 1)(x - 1)$. □

PRACTICE 2 Factor $3x^3 + x^2 - 12x - 4$.

EXAMPLE 3 Factor $12m^2 - 3n^2$.

Solution

Step 1. The terms of this binomial contain a greatest common factor of 3.

$12m^2 - 3n^2 = 3(4m^2 - n^2)$ Factor out the greatest common factor.

Step 2. The binomial $4m^2 - n^2$ is a difference of squares.

$= 3(2m + n)(2m - n)$ Factor the difference of squares.

Step 3. No factor can be factored further.

Step 4. We check by multiplying.

$$3(2m + n)(2m - n) = 3(4m^2 - n^2) = 12m^2 - 3n^2$$

The factored form of $12m^2 - 3n^2$ is $3(2m + n)(2m - n)$. □

PRACTICE 3 Factor $27x^2 - 3y^2$.

EXAMPLE 4 Factor $x^3 + 27y^3$.

Solution

Step 1. The terms of this binomial contain no common factor (other than 1).

Step 2. This binomial is the sum of two cubes.

$$\begin{aligned} x^3 + 27y^3 &= (x)^3 + (3y)^3 \\ &= (x + 3y)[x^2 - x(3y) + (3y)^2] \\ &= (x + 3y)(x^2 - 3xy + 9y^2) \end{aligned}$$

Step 3. No factor can be factored further.

Step 4. We check by multiplying.

$$\begin{aligned} (x + 3y)(x^2 - 3xy + 9y^2) &= x(x^2 - 3xy + 9y^2) + 3y(x^2 - 3xy + 9y^2) \\ &= x^3 - 3x^2y + 9xy^2 + 3x^2y - 9xy^2 + 27y^3 \\ &= x^3 + 27y^3 \end{aligned}$$

Thus, $x^3 + 27y^3$ factored completely is $(x + 3y)(x^2 - 3xy + 9y^2)$. □

PRACTICE **4** Factor $8a^3 + b^3$.

EXAMPLE 5 Factor $30a^2b^3 + 55a^2b^2 - 35a^2b$.

Solution

Step 1. $30a^2b^3 + 55a^2b^2 - 35a^2b = 5a^2b(6b^2 + 11b - 7)$ Factor out the GCF.

Step 2. $= 5a^2b(2b - 1)(3b + 7)$ Factor the resulting trinomial.

Step 3. No factor can be factored further.

Step 4. Check by multiplying.

The trinomial factored completely is $5a^2b(2b - 1)(3b + 7)$. □

PRACTICE **5** Factor $60x^3y^2 - 66x^2y^2 - 36xy^2$.

Factor the following completely.

1. $x^2 + 2xy + y^2$
2. $x^2 - 2xy + y^2$
3. $a^2 + 11a - 12$
4. $a^2 - 11a + 10$
5. $a^2 - a - 6$
6. $a^2 - 2a + 1$
7. $x^2 + 2x + 1$
8. $x^2 + x - 2$
9. $x^2 + 4x + 3$
10. $x^2 + x - 6$
11. $x^2 + 7x + 12$
12. $x^2 + x - 12$
13. $x^2 + 3x - 4$
14. $x^2 - 7x + 10$
15. $x^2 + 2x - 15$
16. $x^2 + 11x + 30$
17. $x^2 - x - 30$
18. $x^2 + 11x + 24$
19. $2x^2 - 98$
20. $3x^2 - 75$
21. $x^2 + 3x + xy + 3y$
22. $3y - 21 + xy - 7x$
23. $x^2 + 6x - 16$
24. $x^2 - 3x - 28$
25. $4x^3 + 20x^2 - 56x$
26. $6x^3 - 6x^2 - 120x$
27. $12x^2 + 34x + 24$
28. $8a^2 + 6ab - 5b^2$
29. $4a^2 - b^2$
30. $28 - 13x - 6x^2$
31. $20 - 3x - 2x^2$
32. $x^2 - 2x + 4$
33. $a^2 + a - 3$
34. $6y^2 + y - 15$
35. $4x^2 - x - 5$
36. $x^2y - y^3$
37. $4t^2 + 36$
38. $x^2 + x + xy + y$
39. $ax + 2x + a + 2$
40. $18x^3 - 63x^2 + 9x$
41. $12a^3 - 24a^2 + 4a$
42. $x^2 + 14x - 32$
43. $x^2 - 14x - 48$
44. $16a^2 - 56ab + 49b^2$
45. $25p^2 - 70pq + 49q^2$
46. $7x^2 + 24xy + 9y^2$
47. $125 - 8y^3$
48. $64x^3 + 27$

49. $-x^2 - x + 30$
50. $-x^2 + 6x - 8$
51. $14 + 5x - x^2$
52. $3 - 2x - x^2$
53. $3x^4y + 6x^3y - 72x^2y$
54. $2x^3y + 8x^2y^2 - 10xy^3$
55. $5x^3y^2 - 40x^2y^3 + 35xy^4$
56. $4x^4y - 8x^3y - 60x^2y$
57. $12x^3y + 243xy$
58. $6x^3y^2 + 8xy^2$
59. $4 - x^2$
60. $9 - y^2$
61. $3rs - s + 12r - 4$
62. $x^3 - 2x^2 + 3x - 6$
63. $4x^2 - 8xy - 3x + 6y$
64. $4x^2 - 2xy - 7yz + 14xz$
65. $6x^2 + 18xy + 12y^2$
66. $12x^2 + 46xy - 8y^2$
67. $xy^2 - 4x + 3y^2 - 12$
68. $x^2y^2 - 9x^2 + 3y^2 - 27$
69. $5(x + y) + x(x + y)$
70. $7(x - y) + y(x - y)$
71. $14t^2 - 9t + 1$
72. $3t^2 - 5t + 1$
73. $3x^2 + 2x - 5$
74. $7x^2 + 19x - 6$
75. $x^2 + 9xy - 36y^2$
76. $3x^2 + 10xy - 8y^2$
77. $1 - 8ab - 20a^2b^2$
78. $1 - 7ab - 60a^2b^2$
79. $9 - 10x^2 + x^4$
80. $36 - 13x^2 + x^4$
81. $x^4 - 14x^2 - 32$
82. $x^4 - 22x^2 - 75$
83. $x^2 - 23x + 120$
84. $y^2 + 22y + 96$
85. $6x^3 - 28x^2 + 16x$
86. $6y^3 - 8y^2 - 30y$
87. $27x^3 - 125y^3$
88. $216y^3 - z^3$
89. $x^3y^3 + 8z^3$
90. $27a^3b^3 + 8$
91. $2xy - 72x^3y$
92. $2x^3 - 18x$
93. $x^3 + 6x^2 - 4x - 24$
94. $x^3 - 2x^2 - 36x + 72$
95. $6a^3 + 10a^2$
96. $4n^2 - 6n$
97. $a^2(a + 2) + 2(a + 2)$
98. $a - b + x(a - b)$
99. $x^3 - 28 + 7x^2 - 4x$
100. $a^3 - 45 - 9a + 5a^2$

CONCEPT EXTENSIONS

Factor.

101. $(x - y)^2 - z^2$
102. $(x + 2y)^2 - 9$
103. $81 - (5x + 1)^2$
104. $b^2 - (4a + c)^2$
105. Explain why it makes good sense to factor out the GCF first, before using other methods of factoring.
106. The sum of two squares usually does not factor. Is the sum of two squares $9x^2 + 81y^2$ factorable?
107. Which of the following are equivalent to $(x + 10)(x - 7)$?
   a. $(x - 7)(x + 10)$
   b. $-1(x + 10)(x - 7)$
   c. $-1(x + 10)(7 - x)$
   d. $-1(-x - 10)(7 - x)$
108. Which of the following are equivalent to $(x - 2)(x - 5)$?
   a. $-1(x + 2)(x + 5)$
   b. $(x - 5)(x - 2)$
   c. $(5 - x)(2 - x)$
   d. $-1(x + 2)(x - 5)$

3.6 Solving Quadratic Equations by Factoring

OBJECTIVES

1 Solve Quadratic Equations by Factoring.
2 Solve Equations with Degree Greater than 2 by Factoring.
3 Find the x-Intercepts of the Graph of a Quadratic Equation in Two Variables.

In this section, we introduce a new type of equation—the **quadratic equation.**

Quadratic Equation

A quadratic equation is one that can be written in the form

$$ax^2 + bx + c = 0$$

where a, b, and c are real numbers and $a \neq 0$.

Some examples of quadratic equations are shown below.

$$x^2 - 9x - 22 = 0 \qquad 4x^2 - 28 = -49 \qquad x(2x - 7) = 4$$

The form $ax^2 + bx + c = 0$ is called the **standard form** of a quadratic equation. The quadratic equation $x^2 - 9x - 22 = 0$ is the only equation above that is in standard form.

Quadratic equations model many real-life situations. For example, let's suppose we want to know how long before a person diving from a 144-foot cliff reaches the ocean. The answer to this question is found by solving the quadratic equation $-16t^2 + 144 = 0$. (See Example 1 in Section 3.7.)

OBJECTIVE

1 Solving Quadratic Equations by Factoring 

Some quadratic equations can be solved by making use of factoring and the **zero factor property.**

Zero Factor Theorem

If a and b are real numbers and if $ab = 0$, then $a = 0$ or $b = 0$.

This theorem states that if the product of two numbers is 0, then at least one of the numbers must be 0.

EXAMPLE 1 Solve: $(x - 3)(x + 1) = 0$

Solution If this equation is to be a true statement, then either the factor $x - 3$ must be 0 or the factor $x + 1$ must be 0. In other words, either

$$x - 3 = 0 \quad \text{or} \quad x + 1 = 0$$

If we solve these two linear equations, we have

$$x = 3 \quad \text{or} \quad x = -1$$

Thus, 3 and -1 are both solutions of the equation $(x - 3)(x + 1) = 0$. To check, we replace x with 3 in the original equation. Then we replace x with -1 in the original equation.

Check: Let $x = 3$.

$(x - 3)(x + 1) = 0$

$(3 - 3)(3 + 1) \stackrel{?}{=} 0$ Replace x with 3.

$0(4) = 0$ True

Let $x = -1$.

$(x - 3)(x + 1) = 0$

$(-1 - 3)(-1 + 1) \stackrel{?}{=} 0$ Replace x with -1.

$(-4)(0) = 0$ True

The solutions are 3 and -1, or we say that the solution set is $\{-1, 3\}$. □

PRACTICE

1 Solve: $(x + 4)(x - 5) = 0$.

Helpful Hint

The zero factor property says that *if a product is 0, then a factor is 0.*

If $a \cdot b = 0$, then $a = 0$ or $b = 0$.
If $x(x + 5) = 0$, then $x = 0$ or $x + 5 = 0$.
If $(x + 7)(2x - 3) = 0$, then $x + 7 = 0$ or $2x - 3 = 0$.

Use this property only when the product is 0.

For example, if $a \cdot b = 8$, we do not know the value of a or b. The values may be $a = 2, b = 4$ or $a = 8, b = 1$, or any other two numbers whose product is 8.

EXAMPLE 2 Solve: $(x - 5)(2x + 7) = 0$

Solution: The product is 0. By the zero factor property, this is true only when a factor is 0. To solve, we set each factor equal to 0 and solve the resulting linear equations.

$$(x - 5)(2x + 7) = 0$$

$$x - 5 = 0 \quad \text{or} \quad 2x + 7 = 0$$

$$x = 5 \qquad\qquad 2x = -7$$

$$x = -\frac{7}{2}$$

(Continued on next page)

Check: Let $x = 5$.

$$(x - 5)(2x + 7) = 0$$
$$(5 - 5)(2 \cdot 5 + 7) \stackrel{?}{=} 0 \quad \text{Replace } x \text{ with 5.}$$
$$0 \cdot 17 \stackrel{?}{=} 0$$
$$0 = 0 \quad \text{True}$$

Let $x = -\frac{7}{2}$.

$$(x - 5)(2x + 7) = 0$$
$$\left(-\frac{7}{2} - 5\right)\left(2\left(-\frac{7}{2}\right) + 7\right) \stackrel{?}{=} 0 \quad \text{Replace } x \text{ with } -\frac{7}{2}.$$
$$\left(-\frac{17}{2}\right)(-7 + 7) \stackrel{?}{=} 0$$
$$\left(-\frac{17}{2}\right) \cdot 0 \stackrel{?}{=} 0$$
$$0 = 0 \quad \text{True}$$

The solutions are 5 and $-\frac{7}{2}$. □

PRACTICE 2 Solve: $(x - 12)(4x + 3) = 0$

EXAMPLE 3 Solve: $x(5x - 2) = 0$

Solution

$$x(5x - 2) = 0$$
$$x = 0 \quad \text{or} \quad 5x - 2 = 0 \quad \text{Use the zero factor property.}$$
$$5x = 2$$
$$x = \frac{2}{5}$$

Check: Let $x = 0$.

$$x(5x - 2) = 0$$
$$0(5 \cdot 0 - 2) \stackrel{?}{=} 0 \quad \text{Replace } x \text{ with 0.}$$
$$0(-2) \stackrel{?}{=} 0$$
$$0 = 0 \quad \text{True}$$

Let $x = \frac{2}{5}$.

$$x(5x - 2) = 0$$
$$\frac{2}{5}\left(5 \cdot \frac{2}{5} - 2\right) \stackrel{?}{=} 0 \quad \text{Replace } x \text{ with } \frac{2}{5}.$$
$$\frac{2}{5}(2 - 2) \stackrel{?}{=} 0$$
$$\frac{2}{5}(0) \stackrel{?}{=} 0$$
$$0 = 0 \quad \text{True}$$

The solutions are 0 and $\frac{2}{5}$. □

PRACTICE 3 Solve: $x(7x - 6) = 0$.

EXAMPLE 4 Solve: $x^2 - 9x - 22 = 0$

Solution One side of the equation is 0. However, to use the zero factor property, one side of the equation must be 0 *and* the other side must be written as a product (must be factored). Thus, we must first factor this polynomial.

$$x^2 - 9x - 22 = 0$$
$$(x - 11)(x + 2) = 0 \quad \text{Factor.}$$

Now we can apply the zero factor property.

$$x - 11 = 0 \quad \text{or} \quad x + 2 = 0$$
$$x = 11 \qquad\qquad x = -2$$

Check: Let $x = 11$. Let $x = -2$.

$$\begin{aligned} x^2 - 9x - 22 &= 0 \\ 11^2 - 9\cdot 11 - 22 &\stackrel{?}{=} 0 \\ 121 - 99 - 22 &\stackrel{?}{=} 0 \\ 22 - 22 &\stackrel{?}{=} 0 \\ 0 &= 0 \quad \text{True} \end{aligned}$$

$$\begin{aligned} x^2 - 9x - 22 &= 0 \\ (-2)^2 - 9(-2) - 22 &\stackrel{?}{=} 0 \\ 4 + 18 - 22 &\stackrel{?}{=} 0 \\ 22 - 22 &\stackrel{?}{=} 0 \\ 0 &= 0 \quad \text{True} \end{aligned}$$

The solutions are 11 and -2. □

PRACTICE
4 Solve: $x^2 - 8x - 48 = 0$.

EXAMPLE 5 Solve: $4x^2 - 28x = -49$

Solution First we rewrite the equation in standard form so that one side is 0. Then we factor the polynomial.

$$\begin{aligned} 4x^2 - 28x &= -49 \\ 4x^2 - 28x + 49 &= 0 \quad \text{Write in standard form by adding 49 to both sides.} \\ (2x - 7)(2x - 7) &= 0 \quad \text{Factor.} \end{aligned}$$

Next we use the zero factor property and set each factor equal to 0. Since the factors are the same, the related equations will give the same solution.

$$2x - 7 = 0 \quad \text{or} \quad 2x - 7 = 0 \qquad \text{Set each factor equal to 0.}$$
$$2x = 7 \qquad\qquad 2x = 7 \qquad \text{Solve.}$$
$$x = \frac{7}{2} \qquad\qquad x = \frac{7}{2}$$

Check: Although $\frac{7}{2}$ occurs twice, there is a single solution. Check this solution in the original equation. The solution is $\frac{7}{2}$. □

PRACTICE
5 Solve: $9x^2 - 24x = -16$.

The following steps may be used to solve a quadratic equation by factoring.

To Solve Quadratic Equations by Factoring

Step 1. Write the equation in standard form so that one side of the equation is 0.
Step 2. Factor the quadratic expression completely.
Step 3. Set each factor containing a variable equal to 0.
Step 4. Solve the resulting equations.
Step 5. Check each solution in the original equation.

Since it is not always possible to factor a quadratic polynomial, not all quadratic equations can be solved by factoring. Other methods of solving quadratic equations are presented in Chapter 6.

EXAMPLE 6 Solve: $x(2x - 7) = 4$

Solution First we write the equation in standard form; then we factor.

$$x(2x - 7) = 4$$
$$2x^2 - 7x = 4 \quad \text{Multiply.}$$
$$2x^2 - 7x - 4 = 0 \quad \text{Write in standard form.}$$
$$(2x + 1)(x - 4) = 0 \quad \text{Factor.}$$
$$2x + 1 = 0 \text{ or } x - 4 = 0 \quad \text{Set each factor equal to zero.}$$
$$2x = -1 \qquad x = 4 \quad \text{Solve.}$$
$$x = -\frac{1}{2}$$

Check the solutions in the original equation. The solutions are $-\frac{1}{2}$ and 4. □

Helpful Hint
To solve the equation $x(2x - 7) = 4$, do **not** set each factor equal to 4. Remember that to apply the zero factor property, one side of the equation must be 0 and the other side of the equation must be in factored form.

PRACTICE
6 Solve: $x(3x + 7) = 6$.

✓CONCEPT CHECK
Explain the error and solve the equation correctly.

$$(x - 3)(x + 1) = 5$$
$$x - 3 = 5 \text{ or } x + 1 = 5$$
$$x = 8 \text{ or } x = 4$$

EXAMPLE 7 Solve: $-2x^2 - 4x + 30 = 0$.

Solution The equation is in standard form, so we begin by factoring out a common factor of -2.

$$-2x^2 - 4x + 30 = 0$$
$$-2(x^2 + 2x - 15) = 0 \quad \text{Factor out } -2.$$
$$-2(x + 5)(x - 3) = 0 \quad \text{Factor the quadratic.}$$

Next, set each factor **containing a variable** equal to 0.

$$x + 5 = 0 \text{ or } x - 3 = 0 \quad \text{Set each factor containing a variable equal to 0.}$$
$$x = -5 \text{ or } x = 3 \quad \text{Solve.}$$

Note: The factor -2 is a constant term containing no variables and can never equal 0. The solutions are -5 and 3. □

PRACTICE
7 Solve: $-3x^2 - 6x + 72 = 0$.

Answer to Concept Check:
To use the zero factor property, one side of the equation must be 0, not 5. Correctly, $(x - 3)(x + 1) = 5$, $x^2 - 2x - 3 = 5$, $x^2 - 2x - 8 = 0$, $(x - 4)(x + 2) = 0$, $x - 4 = 0$ or $x + 2 = 0$, $x = 4$ or $x = -2$.

OBJECTIVE
2 Solving Equations with Degree Greater than Two by Factoring 

Some equations involving polynomials of degree higher than 2 may also be solved by factoring and then applying the zero factor theorem.

EXAMPLE 8 Solve: $3x^3 - 12x = 0$.

Solution Factor the left side of the equation. Begin by factoring out the common factor of $3x$.

$$3x^3 - 12x = 0$$

$$3x(x^2 - 4) = 0 \quad \text{Factor out the GCF } 3x.$$

$$3x(x + 2)(x - 2) = 0 \quad \text{Factor } x^2 - 4\text{, a difference of squares.}$$

$$3x = 0 \quad \text{or} \quad x + 2 = 0 \quad \text{or} \quad x - 2 = 0 \quad \text{Set each factor equal to 0.}$$

$$x = 0 \quad \text{or} \quad x = -2 \quad \text{or} \quad x = 2 \quad \text{Solve.}$$

Thus, the equation $3x^3 - 12x = 0$ has three solutions: 0, -2, and 2. To check, replace x with each solution in the original equation.

***Let x* = 0.**	***Let x* = −2.**	***Let x* = 2.**
$3(0)^3 - 12(0) \stackrel{?}{=} 0$	$3(-2)^3 - 12(-2) \stackrel{?}{=} 0$	$3(2)^3 - 12(2) \stackrel{?}{=} 0$
$0 = 0$	$3(-8) + 24 \stackrel{?}{=} 0$	$3(8) - 24 \stackrel{?}{=} 0$
	$0 = 0$	$0 = 0$

Substituting 0, -2, or 2 into the original equation results each time in a true equation. The solutions are 0, -2, and 2. □

PRACTICE

8 Solve: $7x^3 - 63x = 0$.

EXAMPLE 9 Solve: $(5x - 1)(2x^2 + 15x + 18) = 0$.

Solution

$$(5x - 1)(2x^2 + 15x + 18) = 0$$

$$(5x - 1)(2x + 3)(x + 6) = 0 \quad \text{Factor the trinomial.}$$

$$5x - 1 = 0 \quad \text{or} \quad 2x + 3 = 0 \quad \text{or} \quad x + 6 = 0 \quad \text{Set each factor equal to 0.}$$

$$5x = 1 \quad \text{or} \quad 2x = -3 \quad \text{or} \quad x = -6 \quad \text{Solve.}$$

$$x = \frac{1}{5} \quad \text{or} \quad x = -\frac{3}{2}$$

The solutions are $\frac{1}{5}$, $-\frac{3}{2}$, and -6. Check by replacing x with each solution in the original equation. The solutions are -6, $-\frac{3}{2}$, and $\frac{1}{5}$. □

PRACTICE

9 Solve: $(3x - 2)(2x^2 - 13x + 15) = 0$.

EXAMPLE 10 Solve: $2x^3 - 4x^2 - 30x = 0$.

Solution Begin by factoring out the GCF $2x$.

$$2x^3 - 4x^2 - 30x = 0$$

$$2x(x^2 - 2x - 15) = 0 \quad \text{Factor out the GCF } 2x.$$

$$2x(x - 5)(x + 3) = 0 \quad \text{Factor the quadratic.}$$

$$2x = 0 \quad \text{or} \quad x - 5 = 0 \quad \text{or} \quad x + 3 = 0 \quad \text{Set each factor containing a variable equal to 0.}$$

$$x = 0 \quad \text{or} \quad x = 5 \quad \text{or} \quad x = -3 \quad \text{Solve.}$$

Check by replacing x with each solution in the cubic equation. The solutions are -3, 0, and 5. □

PRACTICE

10 Solve: $5x^3 + 5x^2 - 30x = 0$.

OBJECTIVE

3 Finding x-Intercepts of the Graph of a Quadratic Equation 

In Chapter 1, we graphed linear equations in two variables, such as $y = 5x - 6$. Recall that to find the x-intercept of the graph of a linear equation, let $y = 0$ and solve for x. This is also how to find the x-intercepts of the graph of a **quadratic equation in two variables,** such as $y = x^2 - 5x + 4$.

EXAMPLE 11 Find the x-intercepts of the graph of $y = x^2 - 5x + 4$.

Solution Let $y = 0$ and solve for x.

$$y = x^2 - 5x + 4$$
$$0 = x^2 - 5x + 4 \quad \text{Let } y = 0.$$
$$0 = (x - 1)(x - 4) \quad \text{Factor.}$$
$$x - 1 = 0 \quad \text{or} \quad x - 4 = 0 \quad \text{Set each factor equal to 0.}$$
$$x = 1 \quad \text{or} \quad x = 4 \quad \text{Solve.}$$

The x-intercepts of the graph of $y = x^2 - 5x + 4$ are $(1, 0)$ and $(4, 0)$.

The graph of $y = x^2 - 5x + 4$ is shown in the margin. □

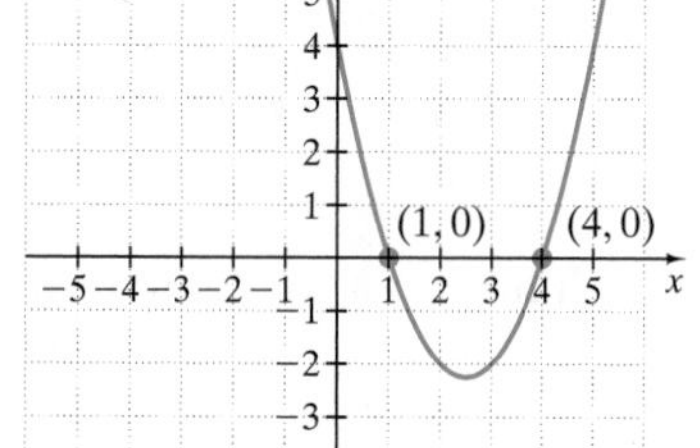

PRACTICE

11 Find the x-intercepts of the graph of $y = x^2 - 6x + 8$.

In general, a quadratic equation in two variables is one that can be written in the form $y = ax^2 + bx + c$ where $a \neq 0$. The graph of such an equation is called a **parabola** and will open up or down depending on the sign of a.

Notice that the x-intercepts of the graph of $y = ax^2 + bx + c$ are the real number solutions of $0 = ax^2 + bx + c$. Also, the real number solutions of $0 = ax^2 + bx + c$ are the x-intercepts of the graph of $y = ax^2 + bx + c$. We study more about graphs of quadratic equations in two variables in Chapter 6.

Graph of $y = ax^2 + bx + c$
x-intercepts are solutions of $0 = ax^2 + bx + c$

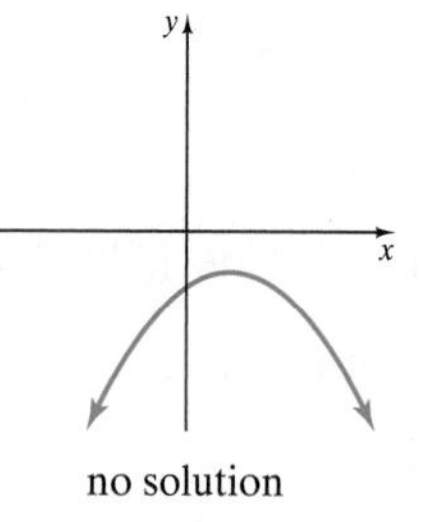
no solution

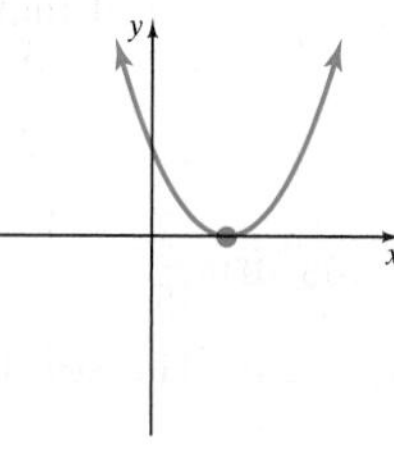
1 solution

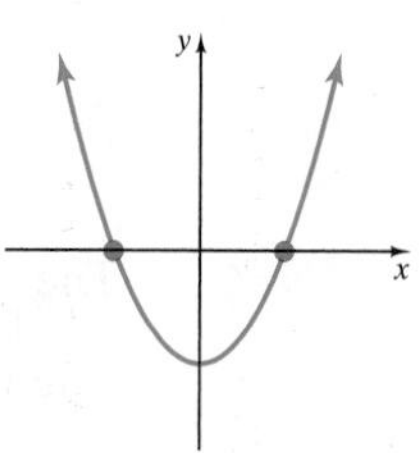
2 solutions

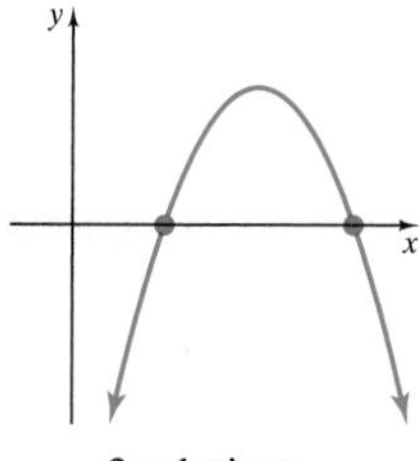
2 solutions

Graphing Calculator Explorations 

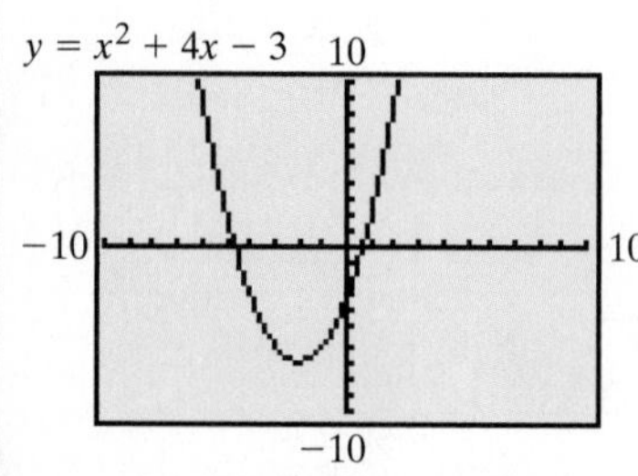

A grapher may be used to find solutions of a quadratic equation whether the related quadratic polynomial is factorable or not. For example, let's use a grapher to approximate the solutions of $0 = x^2 + 4x - 3$. To do so, graph $y_1 = x^2 + 4x - 3$. Recall that the x-intercepts of this graph are the solutions of $0 = x^2 + 4x - 3$.

Notice that the graph appears to have an x-intercept between -5 and -4 and one between 0 and 1. Many graphers contain a TRACE feature. This feature activates a graph cursor that can be used to *trace* along a graph while the corresponding x- and y-coordinates are shown on the screen. Use the TRACE feature to confirm that x-intercepts lie between -5 and -4 and between 0 and 1. To approximate the x-intercepts to the nearest tenth, use a ROOT or a ZOOM feature on your grapher or redefine the viewing window. (A ROOT feature calculates the x-intercept. A ZOOM feature magnifies the viewing window around a specific location such as the graph cursor.) If we redefine the window to [0, 1] on the x-axis and [−1, 1] on the y-axis, the graph to the left is generated.

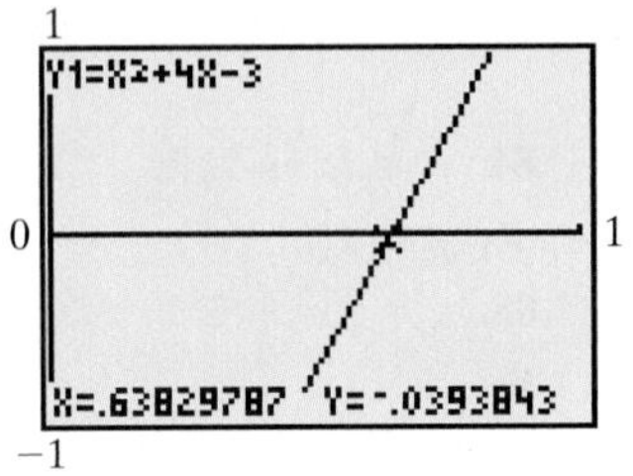

By using the TRACE feature, we can conclude that one x-intercept is approximately 0.6 to the nearest tenth. By repeating these steps for the other x-intercept, we find that it is approximately −4.6.

Use a grapher to approximate the real number solutions to the nearest tenth. If an equation has no real number solution, state so.

1. $3x^2 - 4x - 6 = 0$ **2.** $x^2 - x - 9 = 0$

3. $2x^2 + x + 2 = 0$ **4.** $-4x^2 - 5x - 4 = 0$

5. $-x^2 + x + 5 = 0$ **6.** $10x^2 + 6x - 3 = 0$

Vocabulary, Readiness & Video Check

Use the choices below to fill in each blank. Not all choices will be used.

−3, 5	$a = 0$ or $b = 0$	0	linear
3, −5	quadratic	1	

1. An equation that can be written in the form $ax^2 + bx + c = 0$, with $a \neq 0$, is called a _________ equation.

2. If the product of two numbers is 0, then at least one of the numbers must be _________.

3. The solutions to $(x - 3)(x + 5) = 0$ are _________.

4. If $a \cdot b = 0$, then _______________.

Martin-Gay Interactive Videos

See Video 3.6 

Watch the section lecture video and answer the following questions.

OBJECTIVE 1

5. As shown in Examples 1–3, what two things have to be true in order to use the zero factor theorem?

OBJECTIVE 2

6. Example 4 implies that the zero factor theorem can be used with any number of factors on one side of the equation so long as the other side of the equation is zero. Why do you think this is true?

OBJECTIVE 3

7. From Example 5, how does finding the x-intercepts of the graph of a quadratic equation in two variables lead to solving a quadratic equation?

3.6 Exercise Set

MyMathLab®

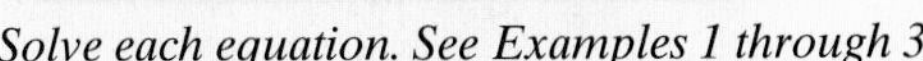

Solve each equation. See Examples 1 through 3.

1. $(x - 6)(x - 7) = 0$

2. $(x - 10)(x - 5) = 0$

3. $(x - 2)(x + 1) = 0$

4. $(x + 4)(x - 10) = 0$

5. $(x + 9)(x + 17) = 0$

6. $(x + 11)(x + 1) = 0$

7. $x(x + 6) = 0$

8. $x(x - 7) = 0$

9. $3x(x - 8) = 0$

10. $2x(x + 12) = 0$

11. $(2x + 3)(4x - 5) = 0$

12. $(3x - 2)(5x + 1) = 0$

13. $(2x - 7)(7x + 2) = 0$

14. $(9x + 1)(4x - 3) = 0$

15. $\left(x - \frac{1}{2}\right)\left(x + \frac{1}{3}\right) = 0$

16. $\left(x + \frac{2}{9}\right)\left(x - \frac{1}{4}\right) = 0$

17. $(x + 0.2)(x + 1.5) = 0$

18. $(x + 1.7)(x + 2.3) = 0$

Solve. See Examples 4 through 7.

19. $x^2 - 13x + 36 = 0$

20. $x^2 + 2x - 63 = 0$

21. $x^2 + 2x - 8 = 0$

22. $x^2 - 5x + 6 = 0$

23. $x^2 - 7x = 0$

24. $x^2 - 3x = 0$

25. $x^2 - 4x = 32$

26. $x^2 - 5x = 24$

27. $x^2 = 16$

28. $x^2 = 9$

29. $(x + 4)(x - 9) = 4x$

30. $(x + 3)(x + 8) = x$

31. $x(3x - 1) = 14$

32. $x(4x - 11) = 3$

33. $-3x^2 + 75 = 0$

34. $-2y^2 + 72 = 0$

35. $24x^2 + 44x = 8$

36. $6x^2 + 57x = 30$

Solve each equation. See Examples 8 through 10.

37. $x^3 - 12x^2 + 32x = 0$
38. $x^3 - 14x^2 + 49x = 0$
39. $(4x - 3)(16x^2 - 24x + 9) = 0$
40. $(2x + 5)(4x^2 + 20x + 25) = 0$
41. $4x^3 - x = 0$
42. $4y^3 - 36y = 0$
43. $32x^3 - 4x^2 - 6x = 0$
44. $15x^3 + 24x^2 - 63x = 0$

MIXED PRACTICE

Solve each equation. See Examples 1 through 10. (A few exercises are linear equations.)

45. $(x + 3)(x - 2) = 0$
46. $(x - 6)(x + 7) = 0$
47. $x^2 + 20x = 0$
48. $x^2 + 15x = 0$
49. $4(x - 7) = 6$
50. $5(3 - 4x) = 9$
51. $4y^2 - 1 = 0$
52. $4y^2 - 81 = 0$
53. $(2x + 3)(2x^2 - 5x - 3) = 0$
54. $(2x - 9)(x^2 + 5x - 36) = 0$
55. $x^2 - 15 = -2x$
56. $x^2 - 26 = -11x$
57. $30x^2 - 11x - 30 = 0$
58. $12x^2 + 7x - 12 = 0$
59. $5x^2 - 6x - 8 = 0$
60. $9x^2 + 7x = 2$
61. $6y^2 - 22y - 40 = 0$
62. $3x^2 - 6x - 9 = 0$
63. $(y - 2)(y + 3) = 6$
64. $(y - 5)(y - 2) = 28$
65. $3x^3 + 19x^2 - 72x = 0$
66. $36x^3 + x^2 - 21x = 0$
67. $x^2 + 14x + 49 = 0$
68. $x^2 + 22x + 121 = 0$
69. $12y = 8y^2$
70. $9y = 6y^2$
71. $7x^3 - 7x = 0$
72. $3x^3 - 27x = 0$
73. $3x^2 + 8x - 11 = 13 - 6x$
74. $2x^2 + 12x - 1 = 4 + 3x$
75. $3x^2 - 20x = -4x^2 - 7x - 6$
76. $4x^2 - 20x = -5x^2 - 6x - 5$

Find the x-intercepts of the graph of each equation. See Example 11.

77. $y = (3x + 4)(x - 1)$
78. $y = (5x - 3)(x - 4)$
79. $y = x^2 - 3x - 10$
80. $y = x^2 + 7x + 6$
81. $y = 2x^2 + 11x - 6$
82. $y = 4x^2 + 11x + 6$

For Exercises 83 through 88, match each equation with its graph. See Example 11.

83. $y = (x + 2)(x - 1)$
84. $y = (x - 5)(x + 2)$
85. $y = x(x + 3)$
86. $y = x(x - 4)$
87. $y = 2x^2 - 8$
88. $y = 2x^2 - 2$

a.

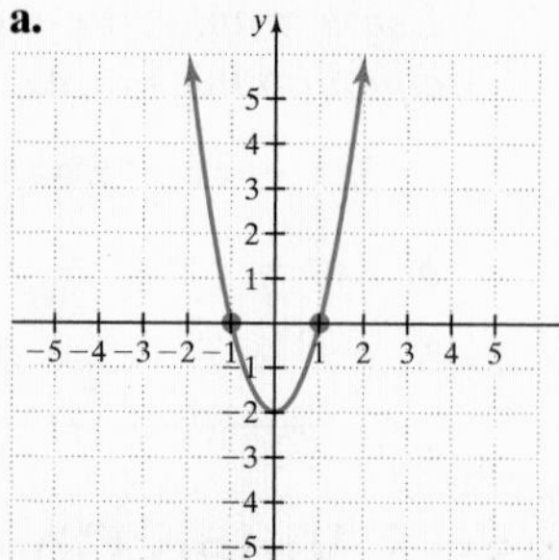

b.

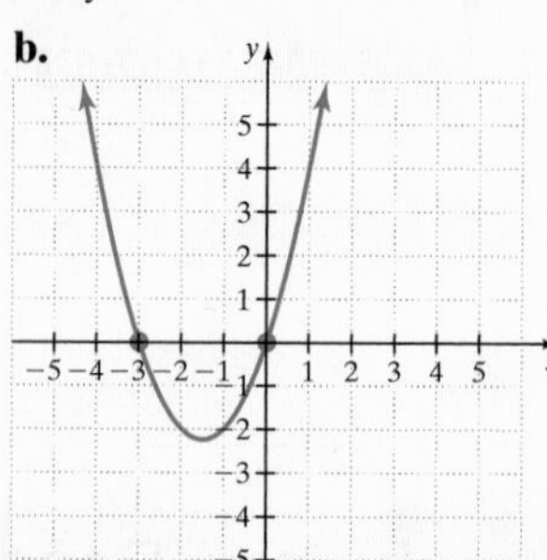

c.

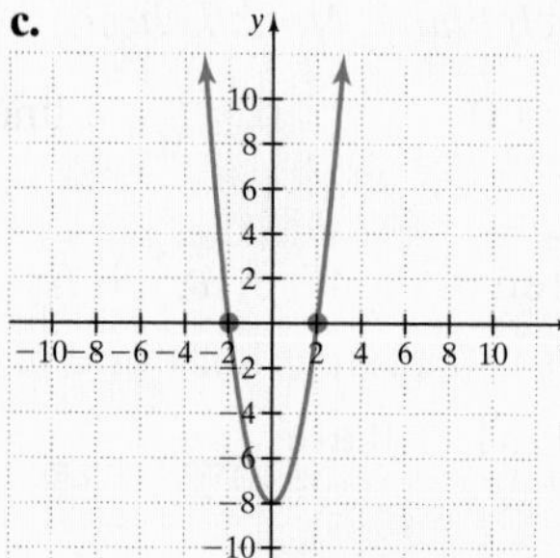

d.

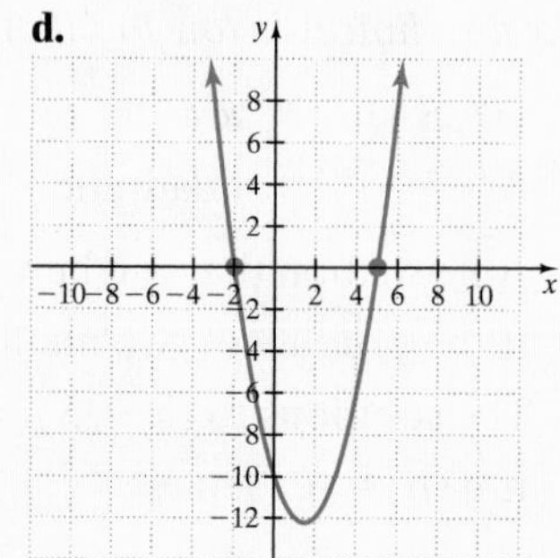

e.

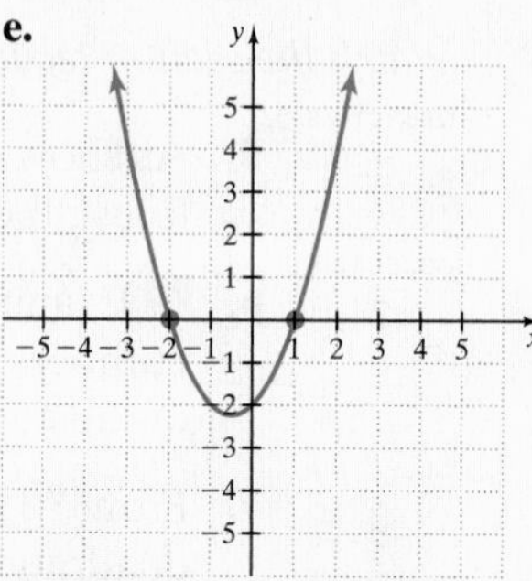

f.

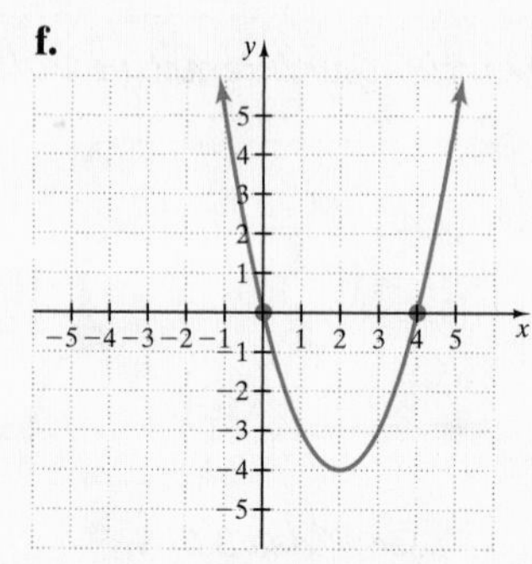

REVIEW AND PREVIEW

Perform the following operations. Write all results in lowest terms. See Section R.3.

89. $\frac{3}{5} + \frac{4}{9}$
90. $\frac{2}{3} + \frac{3}{7}$
91. $\frac{7}{10} - \frac{5}{12}$
92. $\frac{5}{9} - \frac{5}{12}$
93. $\frac{7}{8} \div \frac{7}{15}$
94. $\frac{5}{12} - \frac{3}{10}$
95. $\frac{4}{5} \cdot \frac{7}{8}$
96. $\frac{3}{7} \cdot \frac{12}{17}$

CONCEPT EXTENSIONS

For Exercises 97 and 98, see the Concept Check in this section.

97. Explain the error and solve correctly:

$$x(x - 2) = 8$$
$$x = 8 \quad \text{or} \quad x - 2 = 8$$
$$x = 10$$

98. Explain the error and solve correctly:

$$(x - 4)(x + 2) = 0$$
$$x = -4 \quad \text{or} \quad x = 2$$

99. Write a quadratic equation that has two solutions, 6 and -1. Leave the polynomial in the equation in factored form.

100. Write a quadratic equation that has two solutions, 0 and -2. Leave the polynomial in the equation in factored form.

101. Write a quadratic equation in standard form that has two solutions, 5 and 7.

102. Write an equation that has three solutions, 0, 1, and 2.

103. A compass is accidentally thrown upward and out of an air balloon at a height of 300 feet. The height, y, of the compass at time x in seconds is given by the equation

$$y = -16x^2 + 20x + 300$$

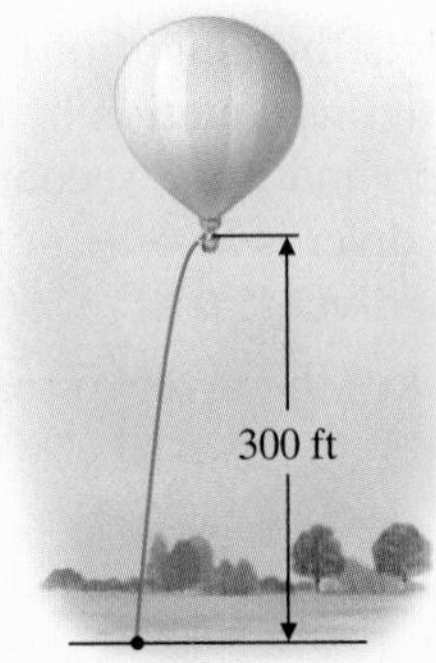

a. Find the height of the compass at the given times by filling in the table below.

time, x	0	1	2	3	4	5	6
height, y							

b. Use the table to determine when the compass strikes the ground.

c. Use the table to approximate the maximum height of the compass.

d. Plot the points (x, y) on a rectangular coordinate system and connect them with a smooth curve. Explain your results.

104. A rocket is fired upward from the ground with an initial velocity of 100 feet per second. The height, y, of the rocket at any time x is given by the equation

$$y = -16x^2 + 100x$$

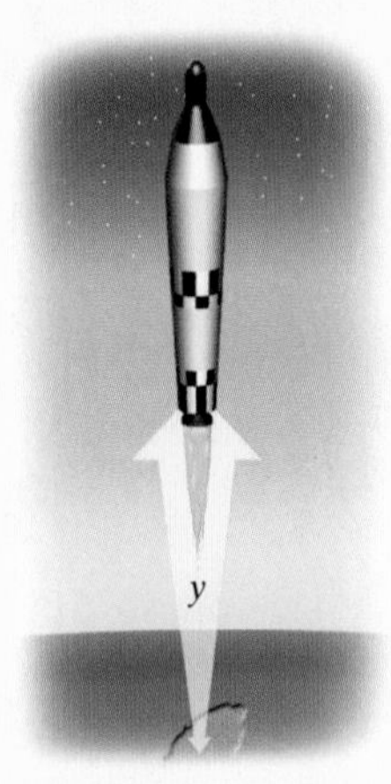

a. Find the height of the rocket at the given times by filling in the table below.

time, x	0	1	2	3	4	5	6	7
height, y								

b. Use the table to approximate when the rocket strikes the ground to the nearest second.

c. Use the table to approximate the maximum height of the rocket.

d. Plot the points (x, y) on a rectangular coordinate system and connect them with a smooth curve. Explain your results.

Solve each equation. First, multiply the binomial.

To solve $(x - 6)(2x - 3) = (x + 2)(x + 9)$, see below.

$$(x - 6)(2x - 3) = (x + 2)(x + 9)$$
$$2x^2 - 15x + 18 = x^2 + 11x + 18$$
$$x^2 - 26x = 0$$
$$x(x - 26) = 0$$
$$x = 0 \quad \text{or} \quad x - 26 = 0$$
$$x = 26$$

105. $(x - 3)(3x + 4) = (x + 2)(x - 6)$

106. $(2x - 3)(x + 6) = (x - 9)(x + 2)$

107. $(2x - 3)(x + 8) = (x - 6)(x + 4)$

108. $(x + 6)(x - 6) = (2x - 9)(x + 4)$

3.7 Quadratic Equations and Problem Solving

OBJECTIVE

1 Solve Problems That Can Be Modeled by Quadratic Equations.

OBJECTIVE

1 Solving Problems Modeled by Quadratic Equations

Some problems may be modeled by quadratic equations. When solving these problems, keep in mind that a solution of an equation that models a problem may not be a solution to the problem. For example, a person's age or the length of a rectangle is always a positive number. Discard solutions that do not make sense as solutions of the problem.

EXAMPLE 1 **Finding Free-Fall Time**

Since the 1940s, one of the top tourist attractions in Acapulco, Mexico, is watching the cliff divers off the La Quebrada. The divers' platform is about 144 feet above the sea. These divers must time their descent just right, since they land in the crashing Pacific, in an inlet that is at most $9\frac{1}{2}$ feet deep. Neglecting air resistance, the height h in feet of a cliff diver above the ocean after t seconds is given by the quadratic equation $h = -16t^2 + 144$.

Find out how long it takes the diver to reach the ocean.

Solution

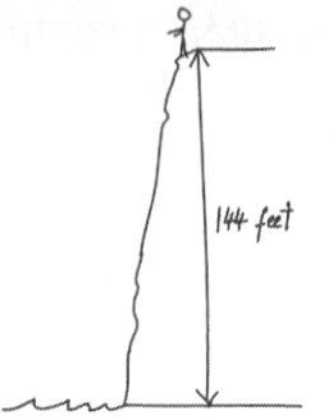

1. UNDERSTAND. Read and reread the problem. Then draw a picture of the problem.

   The equation $h = -16t^2 + 144$ models the height of the falling diver at time t. Familiarize yourself with this equation by finding the height of the diver at time $t = 1$ second and $t = 2$ seconds.

   When $t = 1$ second, the height of the diver is $h = -16(1)^2 + 144 = 128$ feet.
   When $t = 2$ seconds, the height of the diver is $h = -16(2)^2 + 144 = 80$ feet.

2. TRANSLATE. To find out how long it takes the diver to reach the ocean, we want to know the value of t for which $h = 0$.

3. SOLVE.

$$0 = -16t^2 + 144$$
$$0 = -16(t^2 - 9) \quad \text{Factor out } -16.$$
$$0 = -16(t - 3)(t + 3) \quad \text{Factor completely.}$$
$$t - 3 = 0 \quad \text{or} \quad t + 3 = 0 \quad \text{Set each factor containing a variable equal to 0.}$$
$$t = 3 \quad \text{or} \quad t = -3 \quad \text{Solve.}$$

4. INTERPRET. Since the time t cannot be negative, the proposed solution is 3 seconds.

Check: Verify that the height of the diver when t is 3 seconds is 0.

When $t = 3$ seconds, $h = -16(3)^2 + 144 = -144 + 144 = 0$.

State: It takes the diver 3 seconds to reach the ocean. □

PRACTICE

1 Cliff divers also frequent the falls at Waimea Falls Park in Oahu, Hawaii. One of the popular diving spots is 64 feet high. Neglecting air resistance, the height of a diver above the pool after t seconds is $h = -16t^2 + 64$. Find how long it takes a diver to reach the pool.

EXAMPLE 2 **Finding an Unknown Number**

The square of a number plus three times the number is 70. Find the number.

Solution

1. UNDERSTAND. Read and reread the problem. Suppose that the number is 5. The square of 5 is 5^2 or 25. Three times 5 is 15. Then $25 + 15 = 40$, not 70, so the number is not 5. Remember, the purpose of proposing a number, such as 5, is to understand the problem better. Now that we do, we will let $x =$ the number.

2. TRANSLATE.

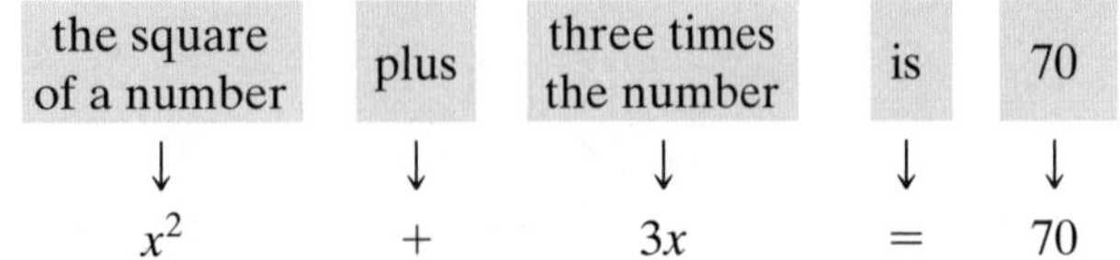

the square of a number	plus	three times the number	is	70
↓	↓	↓	↓	↓
x^2	$+$	$3x$	$=$	70

3. SOLVE.

$$x^2 + 3x = 70$$

$$x^2 + 3x - 70 = 0 \quad \text{Subtract 70 from both sides.}$$

$$(x + 10)(x - 7) = 0 \quad \text{Factor.}$$

$$x + 10 = 0 \quad \text{or} \quad x - 7 = 0 \quad \text{Set each factor equal to 0.}$$

$$x = -10 \qquad x = 7 \quad \text{Solve.}$$

4. INTERPRET.

Check: The square of -10 is $(-10)^2$, or 100. Three times -10 is $3(-10)$ or -30. Then $100 + (-30) = 70$, the correct sum, so -10 checks.

The square of 7 is 7^2 or 49. Three times 7 is 3(7), or 21. Then $49 + 21 = 70$, the correct sum, so 7 checks.

State: There are two numbers. They are -10 and 7. □

PRACTICE

2 The square of a number minus eight times the number is equal to forty-eight. Find the number.

EXAMPLE 3 Finding the Dimensions of a Sail

The height of a triangular sail is 2 meters less than twice the length of the base. If the sail has an area of 30 square meters, find the length of its base and the height.

Solution

1. UNDERSTAND. Read and reread the problem. Since we are finding the length of the base and the height, we let

$$x = \text{the length of the base}$$

and since the height is 2 meters less than twice the base,

$$2x - 2 = \text{the height}$$

An illustration is shown to the right.

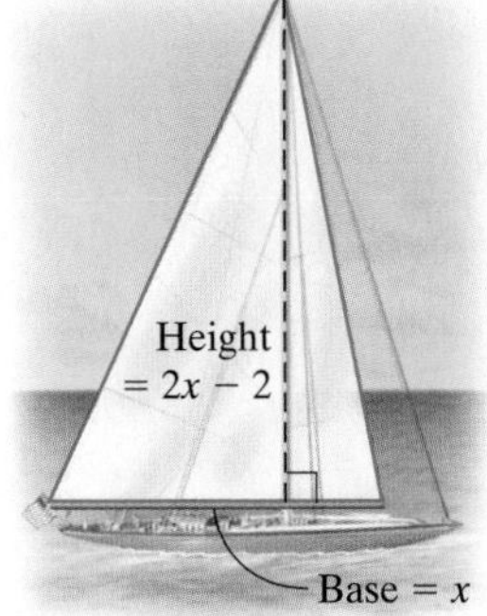

2. TRANSLATE. We are given that the area of the triangle is 30 square meters, so we use the formula for area of a triangle.

area of triangle	=	$\frac{1}{2}$	·	base	·	height
↓		↓		↓		↓
30	=	$\frac{1}{2}$	·	x	·	$(2x - 2)$

(Continued on next page)

3. SOLVE. Now we solve the quadratic equation.

$$30 = \frac{1}{2}x(2x - 2)$$

$$30 = x^2 - x \qquad \text{Multiply.}$$

$$x^2 - x - 30 = 0 \qquad \text{Write in standard form.}$$

$$(x - 6)(x + 5) = 0 \qquad \text{Factor.}$$

$$x - 6 = 0 \quad \text{or} \quad x + 5 = 0 \qquad \text{Set each factor equal to 0.}$$

$$x = 6 \qquad\qquad x = -5$$

4. INTERPRET. Since x represents the length of the base, we discard the solution -5. The base of a triangle cannot be negative. The base is then 6 meters and the height is $2(6) - 2 = 10$ meters.

Check: To check this problem, we recall that $\frac{1}{2}\text{base} \cdot \text{height} = \text{area}$, or

$$\frac{1}{2}(6)(10) = 30 \qquad \text{The required area}$$

State: The base of the triangular sail is 6 meters and the height is 10 meters. □

PRACTICE

3 An engineering team from Georgia Tech earned second place in a flight competition, with their triangular shaped paper hang glider. The base of their prize-winning entry was 1 foot less than three times the height. If the area of the triangular glider wing was 210 square feet, find the dimensions of the wing. (*Source: The Technique* [Georgia Tech's newspaper], April 18, 2003)

Study the following diagrams for a review of consecutive integers.

Examples

If x is the first integer, then consecutive integers are $x, x + 1, x + 2, \ldots$

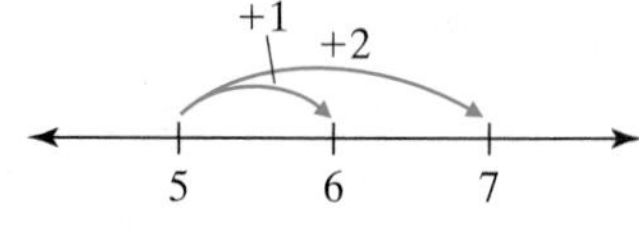

If x is the first even integer, then consecutive even integers are $x, x + 2, x + 4, \ldots$

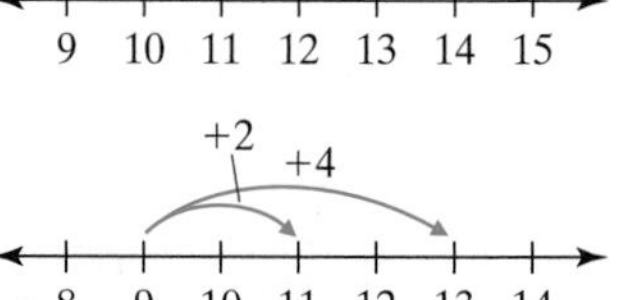

If x is the first odd integer, then consecutive odd integers are $x, x + 2, x + 4, \ldots$

+2 +4

8 9 10 11 12 13 14

EXAMPLE 4 Finding Consecutive Even Integers

Find two consecutive even integers whose product is 34 more than their sum.

Solution

1. UNDERSTAND. Read and reread the problem. Let's just choose two consecutive even integers to help us better understand the problem. Let's choose 10 and 12. Their product is $10(12) = 120$ and their sum is $10 + 12 = 22$. The product is $120 - 22$, or 98 greater than the sum. Thus our guess is incorrect, but we have a better understanding of this example.

Let's let x and $x + 2$ be the consecutive even integers.

2. TRANSLATE.

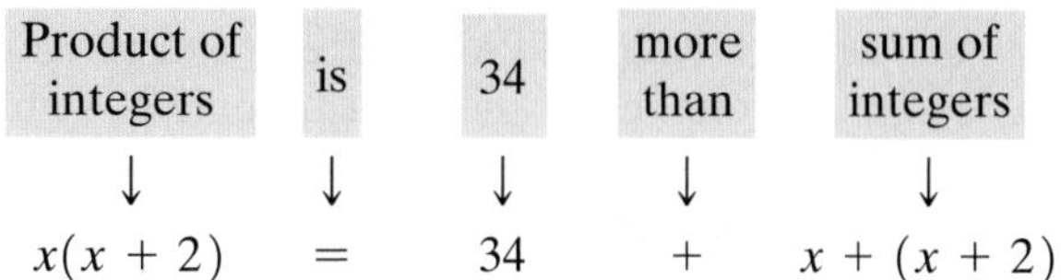

3. SOLVE. Now we solve the equation.

$$x(x + 2) = 34 + x + (x + 2)$$

$$x^2 + 2x = 34 + x + x + 2 \quad \text{Multiply.}$$

$$x^2 + 2x = 2x + 36 \quad \text{Combine like terms.}$$

$$x^2 - 36 = 0 \quad \text{Write in standard form.}$$

$$(x + 6)(x - 6) = 0 \quad \text{Factor.}$$

$$x + 6 = 0 \quad \text{or} \quad x - 6 = 0 \quad \text{Set each factor equal to 0.}$$

$$x = -6 \qquad x = 6 \quad \text{Solve.}$$

4. INTERPRET. If $x = -6$, then $x + 2 = -6 + 2$, or -4.
If $x = 6$, then $x + 2 = 6 + 2$, or 8.

Check: $-6, -4$

$$-6(-4) \stackrel{?}{=} 34 + (-6) + (-4)$$
$$24 \stackrel{?}{=} 34 + (-10)$$
$$24 = 24 \quad \text{True}$$

$6, 8$

$$6(8) \stackrel{?}{=} 34 + 6 + 8$$
$$48 \stackrel{?}{=} 34 + 14$$
$$48 = 48 \quad \text{True}$$

State: The two consecutive even integers are -6 and -4 or 6 and 8. □

PRACTICE

4 Find two consecutive integers whose product is 41 more than their sum.

The next example uses the **Pythagorean theorem** and consecutive integers. Before we review this theorem, recall that a **right triangle** is a triangle that contains a 90° or right angle. The **hypotenuse** of a right triangle is the side opposite the right angle and is the longest side of the triangle. The **legs** of a right triangle are the other sides of the triangle.

Helpful Hint

If you use this formula, don't forget that c represents the length of the hypotenuse.

Pythagorean Theorem

In a right triangle, the sum of the squares of the lengths of the two legs is equal to the square of the length of the hypotenuse.

$$(\text{leg})^2 + (\text{leg})^2 = (\text{hypotenuse})^2 \quad \text{or} \quad a^2 + b^2 = c^2$$

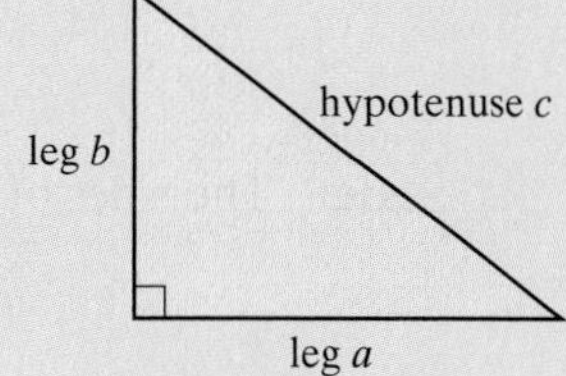

EXAMPLE 5 **Finding the Dimensions of a Triangle**

Find the lengths of the sides of a right triangle if the lengths can be expressed as three consecutive even integers.

(Continued on next page)

Solution

1. UNDERSTAND. Read and reread the problem. Let's suppose that the length of one leg of the right triangle is 4 units. Then the other leg is the next even integer, or 6 units, and the hypotenuse of the triangle is the next even integer, or 8 units. Remember that the hypotenuse is the longest side. Let's see if a triangle with sides of these lengths forms a right triangle. To do this, we check to see whether the Pythagorean theorem holds true.

$$4^2 + 6^2 \stackrel{?}{=} 8^2$$
$$16 + 36 \stackrel{?}{=} 64$$
$$52 = 64 \quad \text{False}$$

4 units, 8 units, 6 units

Our proposed numbers do not check, but we now have a better understanding of the problem.

We let x, $x + 2$, and $x + 4$ be three consecutive even integers. Since these integers represent lengths of the sides of a right triangle, we have the following.

$$x = \text{one leg}$$
$$x + 2 = \text{other leg}$$
$$x + 4 = \text{hypotenuse (longest side)}$$

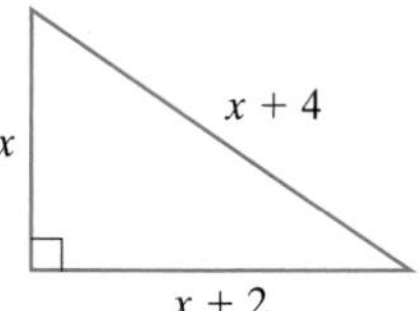

2. TRANSLATE. By the Pythagorean theorem, we have that

$$(\text{leg})^2 + (\text{leg})^2 = (\text{hypotenuse})^2$$
$$(x)^2 + (x + 2)^2 = (x + 4)^2$$

3. SOLVE. Now we solve the equation.

$$x^2 + (x + 2)^2 = (x + 4)^2$$
$$x^2 + x^2 + 4x + 4 = x^2 + 8x + 16 \quad \text{Multiply.}$$
$$2x^2 + 4x + 4 = x^2 + 8x + 16 \quad \text{Combine like terms.}$$
$$x^2 - 4x - 12 = 0 \quad \text{Write in standard form.}$$
$$(x - 6)(x + 2) = 0 \quad \text{Factor.}$$
$$x - 6 = 0 \quad \text{or} \quad x + 2 = 0 \quad \text{Set each factor equal to 0.}$$
$$x = 6 \qquad\qquad x = -2$$

4. INTERPRET. We discard $x = -2$ since length cannot be negative. If $x = 6$, then $x + 2 = 8$ and $x + 4 = 10$.

Check: Verify that

$$(\text{leg})^2 + (\text{leg})^2 = (\text{hypotenuse})^2$$
$$6^2 + 8^2 \stackrel{?}{=} 10^2$$
$$36 + 64 \stackrel{?}{=} 100$$
$$100 = 100 \quad \text{True}$$

State: The sides of the right triangle have lengths 6 units, 8 units, and 10 units.

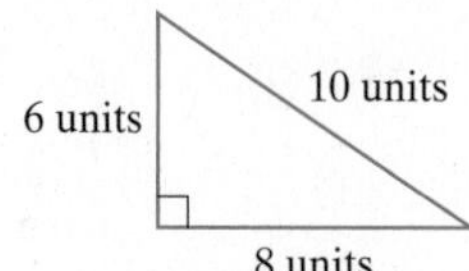

□

PRACTICE 5 Find the dimensions of a right triangle where the second leg is 1 unit less than double the first leg, and the hypotenuse is 1 unit more than double the length of the first leg.

Vocabulary, Readiness & Video Check

Martin-Gay Interactive Videos

See Video 3.7

Watch the section lecture video and answer the following question.

OBJECTIVE 1

1. In each of Examples 1–3, why aren't both solutions of the translated equation accepted as solutions to the application?

3.7 Exercise Set

MyMathLab®

MIXED PRACTICE

See Examples 1 through 5 for all exercises.

TRANSLATING

For Exercises 1 through 6, represent each given condition using a single variable, x.

△ **1.** The length and width of a rectangle whose length is 4 centimeters more than its width

△ **2.** The length and width of a rectangle whose length is twice its width

3. Two consecutive odd integers

4. Two consecutive even integers

△ **5.** The base and height of a triangle whose height is one more than four times its base

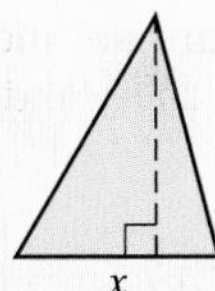

△ **6.** The base and height of a trapezoid whose base is three less than five times its height

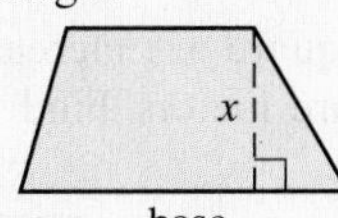

Use the information given to find the dimensions of each figure.

△ **7.** The *area* of the square is 121 square units. Find the length of its sides.

x

△ **8.** The *area* of the rectangle is 84 square inches. Find its length and width.

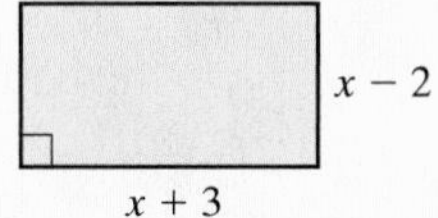

△ **9.** The *perimeter* of the quadrilateral is 120 centimeters. Find the lengths of the sides.

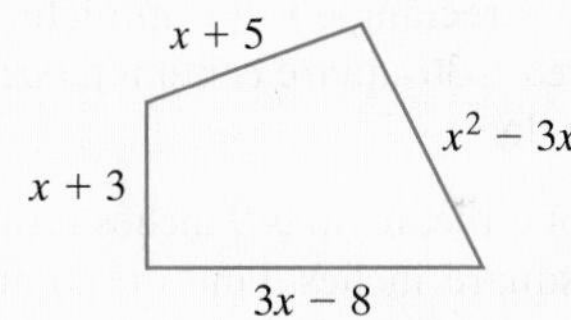

△ **10.** The *perimeter* of the triangle is 85 feet. Find the lengths of its sides.

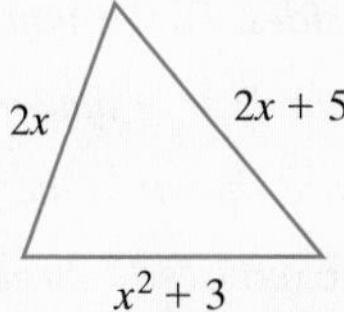

△ **11.** The *area* of the parallelogram is 96 square miles. Find its base and height.

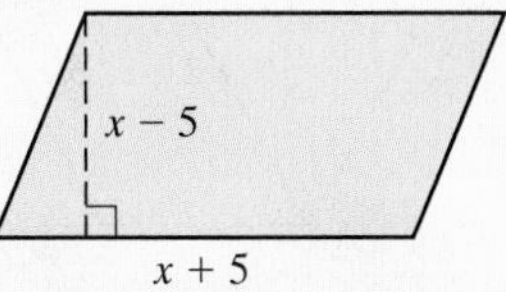

△ **12.** The *area* of the circle is 25π square kilometers. Find its radius.

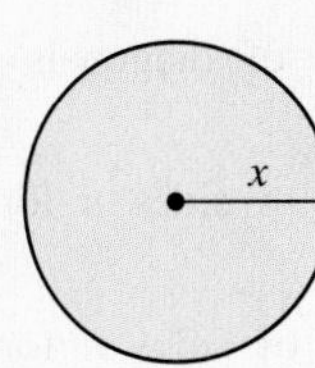

Solve.

13. An object is thrown upward from the top of an 80-foot building with an initial velocity of 64 feet per second. The height h of the object after t seconds is given by the quadratic equation $h = -16t^2 + 64t + 80$. When will the object hit the ground?

14. A hang glider pilot accidentally drops her compass from the top of a 400-foot cliff. The height h of the compass after t seconds is given by the quadratic equation $h = -16t^2 + 400$. When will the compass hit the ground?

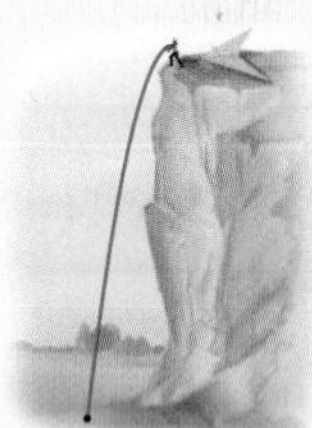

△ 15. The width of a rectangle is 7 centimeters less than twice its length. Its area is 30 square centimeters. Find the dimensions of the rectangle.

△ 16. The length of a rectangle is 9 inches more than its width. Its area is 112 square inches. Find the dimensions of the rectangle.

The equation $D = \frac{1}{2}n(n - 3)$ *gives the number of diagonals D for a polygon with n sides. For example, a polygon with 6 sides has* $D = \frac{1}{2} \cdot 6(6 - 3)$ *or* $D = 9$ *diagonals. (See if you can count all 9 diagonals. Some are shown in the figure.) Use this equation,* $D = \frac{1}{2}n(n - 3)$, *for Exercises 17 through 20.*

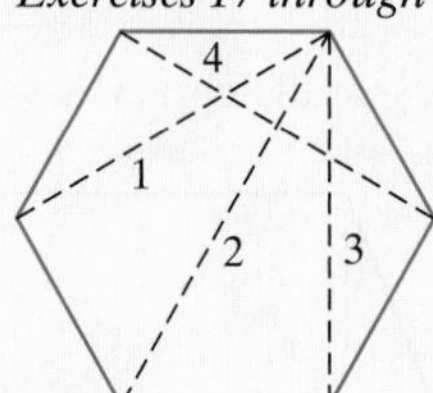

△ 17. Find the number of diagonals for a polygon that has 12 sides.

△ 18. Find the number of diagonals for a polygon that has 15 sides.

△ 19. Find the number of sides n for a polygon that has 35 diagonals.

△ 20. Find the number of sides n for a polygon that has 14 diagonals.

Solve.

21. The sum of a number and its square is 132. Find the number(s).

22. The sum of a number and its square is 182. Find the number(s).

23. The product of two consecutive room numbers is 210. Find the room numbers.

24. The product of two consecutive page numbers is 260. Find the page numbers.

25. A ladder is leaning against a building so that the distance from the ground to the top of the ladder is one foot less than the length of the ladder. Find the length of the ladder if the distance from the bottom of the ladder to the building is 5 feet.

26. Use the given figure to find the length of the guy wire.

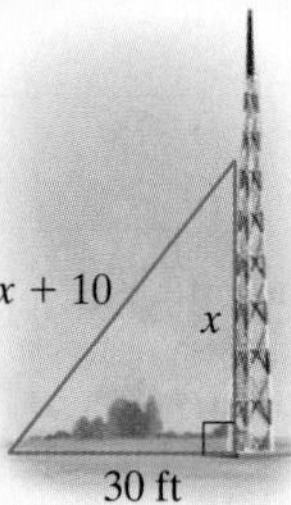

△ 27. If the sides of a square are increased by 3 inches, the area becomes 64 square inches. Find the length of the sides of the original square.

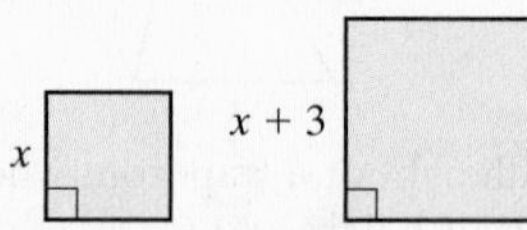

△ 28. If the sides of a square are increased by 5 meters, the area becomes 100 square meters. Find the length of the sides of the original square.

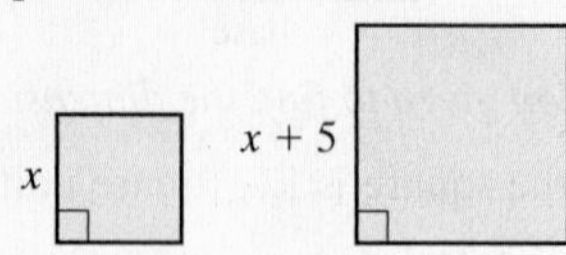

△ **29.** One leg of a right triangle is 4 millimeters longer than the smaller leg and the hypotenuse is 8 millimeters longer than the smaller leg. Find the lengths of the sides of the triangle.

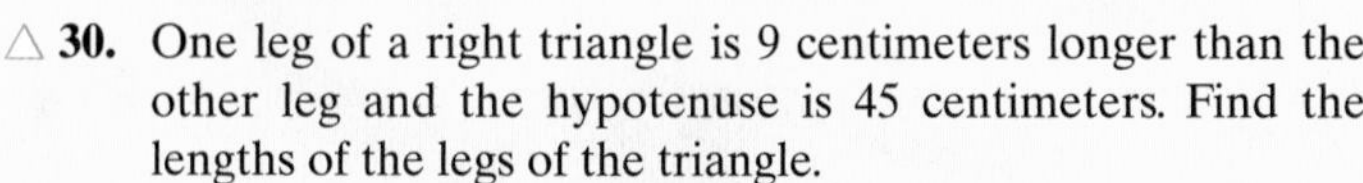

△ **30.** One leg of a right triangle is 9 centimeters longer than the other leg and the hypotenuse is 45 centimeters. Find the lengths of the legs of the triangle.

△ **31.** The length of the base of a triangle is twice its height. If the area of the triangle is 100 square kilometers, find the height.

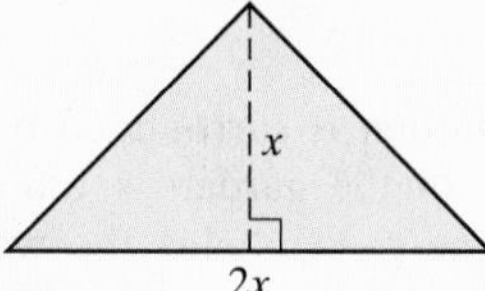

△ **32.** The height of a triangle is 2 millimeters less than the base. If the area is 60 square millimeters, find the base.

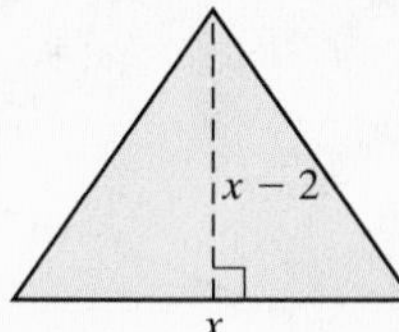

△ **33.** Find the length of the shorter leg of a right triangle if the longer leg is 12 feet more than the shorter leg and the hypotenuse is 12 feet less than twice the shorter leg.

△ **34.** Find the length of the shorter leg of a right triangle if the longer leg is 10 miles more than the shorter leg and the hypotenuse is 10 miles less than twice the shorter leg.

35. An object is dropped from 39 feet below the tip of the pinnacle atop one of the 1483-foot-tall Petronas Twin Towers in Kuala Lumpur, Malaysia. (*Source:* Council on Tall Buildings and Urban Habitat) The height h of the object after t seconds is given by the equation $h = -16t^2 + 1444$. Find how many seconds pass before the object reaches the ground.

36. An object is dropped from the top of 311 South Wacker Drive, a 961-foot-tall office building in Chicago. (*Source:* Council on Tall Buildings and Urban Habitat) The height h of the object after t seconds is given by the equation $h = -16t^2 + 961$. Find how many seconds pass before the object reaches the ground.

37. At the end of 2 years, P dollars invested at an interest rate r compounded annually increases to an amount, A dollars, given by

$$A = P(1 + r)^2$$

Find the interest rate if \$100 increased to \$144 in 2 years. Write your answer as a percent.

38. At the end of 2 years, P dollars invested at an interest rate r compounded annually increases to an amount, A dollars, given by

$$A = P(1 + r)^2$$

Find the interest rate if \$2000 increased to \$2420 in 2 years. Write your answer as a percent.

△ **39.** Find the dimensions of a rectangle whose width is 7 miles less than its length and whose area is 120 square miles.

△ **40.** Find the dimensions of a rectangle whose width is 2 inches less than half its length and whose area is 160 square inches.

41. If the cost, C, for manufacturing x units of a certain product is given by $C = x^2 - 15x + 50$, find the number of units manufactured at a cost of \$9500.

42. If a switchboard handles n telephones, the number C of telephone connections it can make simultaneously is given by the equation $C = \frac{n(n-1)}{2}$. Find how many telephones are handled by a switchboard making 120 telephone connections simultaneously.

REVIEW AND PREVIEW

The following double-line graph shows a comparison of the number of annual visitors (in millions) to Glacier National Park and Gettysburg National Military Park for the years shown. Use this graph to answer Exercises 43 through 50. See Section 1.1.

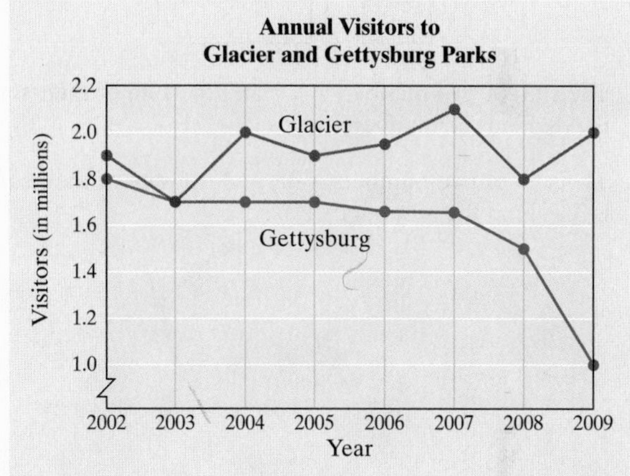

43. Approximate the number of visitors to Glacier National Park in 2009.

44. Approximate the number of visitors to Gettysburg National Military Park in 2009.

45. Approximate the number of visitors to Glacier National Park in 2005.

46. Approximate the number of visitors to Gettysburg National Military Park in 2005.

47. Determine the year that the colored lines in this graph intersect.

48. For what years on the graph is the number of visitors to Glacier Park greater than the number of visitors to Gettysburg Park?

49. In your own words, explain the meaning of the point of intersection in the graph.

50. Describe the trends shown in this graph and speculate as to why these trends have occurred.

Write each fraction in simplest form. See Section R.3.

51. $\frac{20}{35}$ **52.** $\frac{24}{32}$ **53.** $\frac{27}{18}$

54. $\frac{15}{27}$ **55.** $\frac{14}{42}$ **56.** $\frac{45}{50}$

CONCEPT EXTENSIONS

△ **57.** Two boats travel at right angles to each other after leaving the same dock at the same time. One hour later, the boats are 17 miles apart. If one boat travels 7 miles per hour faster than the other boat, find the rate of each boat.

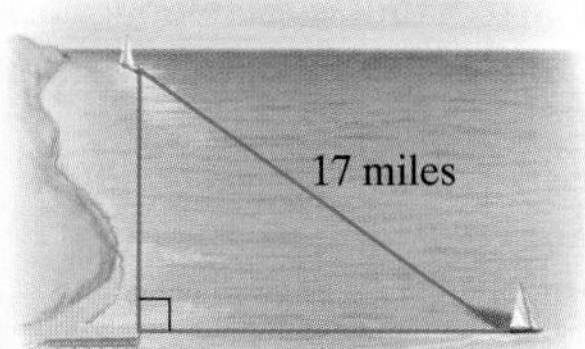

△ **58.** The side of a square equals the width of a rectangle. The length of the rectangle is 6 meters longer than its width. The sum of the areas of the square and the rectangle is 176 square meters. Find the side of the square.

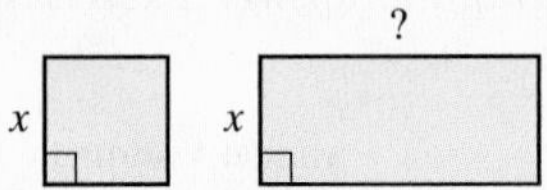

59. The sum of two numbers is 20, and the sum of their squares is 218. Find the numbers.

60. The sum of two numbers is 25, and the sum of their squares is 325. Find the numbers.

△ **61.** A rectangular pool is surrounded by a walk 4 meters wide. The pool is 6 meters longer than its width. If the total area of the pool and walk is 576 square meters more than the area of the pool, find the dimensions of the pool.

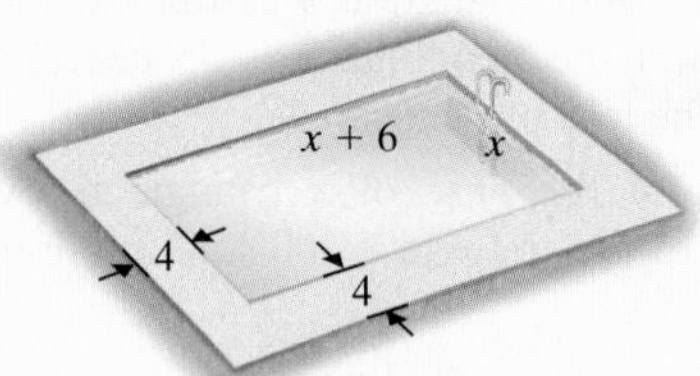

△ **62.** A rectangular garden is surrounded by a walk of uniform width. The area of the garden is 180 square yards. If the dimensions of the garden plus the walk are 16 yards by 24 yards, find the width of the walk.

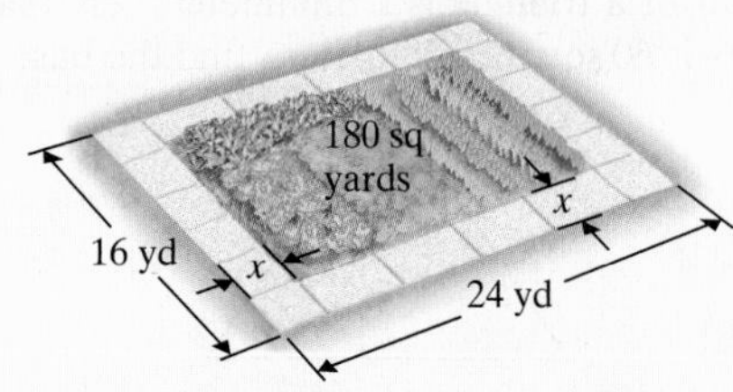

63. Write down two numbers whose sum is 10. Square each number and find the sum of the squares. Use this work to write a word problem like Exercise 59. Then give the word problem to a classmate to solve.

64. Write down two numbers whose sum is 12. Square each number and find the sum of the squares. Use this work to write a word problem like Exercise 60. Then give the word problem to a classmate to solve.

Chapter 3 Vocabulary Check

Fill in each blank with one of the words or phrases listed below. Not all choices will be used and some choices may be used more than once.

factoring	quadratic equation	perfect square trinomial	0
greatest common factor	hypotenuse	sum of two cubes	1
difference of two cubes	difference of two squares	triangle	leg

1. An equation that can be written in the form $ax^2 + bx + c = 0$ (with a not 0) is called a ____________.

2. ____________ is the process of writing an expression as a product.

3. The ____________ of a list of terms is the product of all common factors.

4. A trinomial that is the square of some binomial is called a ____________.

5. The expression $a^2 - b^2$ is called a ____________.

6. The expression $a^3 - b^3$ is called a ____________.

7. The expression $a^3 + b^3$ is called a ____________.

8. By the zero factor property, if the product of two numbers is 0, then at least one of the numbers must be ____________.

9. In a right triangle, the side opposite the right angle is called the ____________.

10. In a right triangle, each side adjacent to the right angle is called a ____________.

11. The Pythagorean theorem states that $(\text{leg})^2 + (\text{leg})^2 = (\underline{\qquad\qquad})^2$.

Chapter 3 Highlights

DEFINITIONS AND CONCEPTS	EXAMPLES
Section 3.1 The Greatest Common Factor and Factoring by Grouping	
Factoring is the process of writing an expression as a product.	Factor: $6 = 2 \cdot 3$ $x^2 + 5x + 6 = (x + 2)(x + 3)$
To Find the GCF of a List of Integers **Step 1.** Write each number as a product of primes. **Step 2.** Identify the common prime factors. **Step 3.** The product of all common factors is the greatest common factor. If there are no common prime factors, the GCF is 1.	Find the GCF of 12, 36, and 48. $12 = 2 \cdot 2 \cdot 3$ $36 = 2 \cdot 2 \cdot 3 \cdot 3$ $48 = 2 \cdot 2 \cdot 2 \cdot 2 \cdot 3$ $\text{GCF} = 2 \cdot 2 \cdot 3 = 12$
The GCF of a list of common variables raised to powers is the variable raised to the smallest exponent in the list.	The GCF of z^5, z^3, and z^{10} is z^3.
The GCF of a list of terms is the product of all common factors.	Find the GCF of $8x^2y$, $10x^3y^2$, and $26x^2y^3$. The GCF of 8, 10, and 26 is 2. The GCF of x^2, x^3, and x^2 is x^2. The GCF of y, y^2, and y^3 is y. The GCF of the terms is $2x^2y$.
To Factor by Grouping **Step 1.** Arrange the terms so that the first two terms have a common factor and the last two have a common factor. **Step 2.** For each pair of terms, factor out the pair's GCF. **Step 3.** If there is now a common binomial factor, factor it out. **Step 4.** If there is no common binomial factor, begin again, rearranging the terms differently. If no rearrangement leads to a common binomial factor, the polynomial cannot be factored.	Factor $10ax + 15a - 6xy - 9y$. **Step 1.** $10ax + 15a - 6xy - 9y$ **Step 2.** $5a(2x + 3) - 3y(2x + 3)$ **Step 3.** $(2x + 3)(5a - 3y)$
Section 3.2 Factoring Trinomials of the Form $x^2 + bx + c$	
The product of these numbers is c. $x^2 + bx + c = (x + \square)(x + \square)$ The sum of these numbers is b.	Factor: $x^2 + 7x + 12$ $3 + 4 = 7$ $\quad 3 \cdot 4 = 12$ $x^2 + 7x + 12 = (x + 3)(x + 4)$

DEFINITIONS AND CONCEPTS	EXAMPLES
Section 3.3 Factoring Trinomials of the Form $ax^2 + bx + c$ and Perfect Square Trinomials	
To factor $ax^2 + bx + c$, try various combinations of factors of ax^2 and c until a middle term of bx is obtained when checking.	Factor: $3x^2 + 14x - 5$ Factors of $3x^2$: $3x, x$ Factors of -5: $-1, 5$ and $1, -5$. $(3x - 1)(x + 5)$ $-1x$ $+15x$ **Correct** middle term $14x$
A **perfect square trinomial** is a trinomial that is the square of some binomial.	Perfect square trinomial = square of binomial $x^2 + 4x + 4 = (x + 2)^2$ $25x^2 - 10x + 1 = (5x - 1)^2$
Factoring Perfect Square Trinomials: $a^2 + 2ab + b^2 = (a + b)^2$ $a^2 - 2ab + b^2 = (a - b)^2$	Factor: $x^2 + 6x + 9 = x^2 + 2 \cdot x \cdot 3 + 3^2 = (x + 3)^2$ $4x^2 - 12x + 9 = (2x)^2 - 2 \cdot 2x \cdot 3 + 3^2 = (2x - 3)^2$
Section 3.4 Factoring Trinomials of the Form $ax^2 + bx + c$ by Grouping	
To Factor $ax^2 + bx + c$ by Grouping	Factor: $3x^2 + 14x - 5$
Step 1. Find two numbers whose product is $a \cdot c$ and whose sum is b.	**Step 1.** Find two numbers whose product is $3 \cdot (-5)$ or -15 and whose sum is 14. They are 15 and -1.
Step 2. Rewrite bx, using the factors found in Step 1.	**Step 2.** $3x^2 + 14x - 5$ $= 3x^2 + 15x - 1x - 5$
Step 3. Factor by grouping.	**Step 3.** $= 3x(x + 5) - 1(x + 5)$ $= (x + 5)(3x - 1)$
Section 3.5 Factoring Binomials	
Difference of Squares $a^2 - b^2 = (a + b)(a - b)$	Factor: $x^2 - 9 = x^2 - 3^2 = (x + 3)(x - 3)$
Sum or Difference of Cubes $a^3 + b^3 = (a + b)(a^2 - ab + b^2)$ $a^3 - b^3 = (a - b)(a^2 + ab + b^2)$	$y^3 + 8 = y^3 + 2^3 = (y + 2)(y^2 - 2y + 4)$ $125z^3 - 1 = (5z)^3 - 1^3 = (5z - 1)(25z^2 + 5z + 1)$
Integrated Review—Choosing a Factoring Strategy	
To Factor a Polynomial,	Factor: $2x^4 - 6x^2 - 8$
Step 1. Factor out the GCF.	**Step 1.** $2x^4 - 6x^2 - 8 = 2(x^4 - 3x^2 - 4)$
Step 2. **a.** If two terms, **i.** $a^2 - b^2 = (a + b)(a - b)$ **ii.** $a^3 - b^3 = (a - b)(a^2 + ab + b^2)$ **iii.** $a^3 + b^3 = (a + b)(a^2 - ab + b^2)$	
b. If three terms, **i.** $a^2 + 2ab + b^2 = (a + b)^2$ **ii.** Methods in Sections 3.2 and 3.3	**Step 2.** **b.ii.** $= 2(x^2 + 1)(x^2 - 4)$
c. If four or more terms, try factoring by grouping.	*(continued)*

DEFINITIONS AND CONCEPTS	EXAMPLES
Integrated Review—Choosing a Factoring Strategy (continued)	
Step 3. See if any factors can be factored further.	**Step 3.** $= 2(x^2 + 1)(x + 2)(x - 2)$
Step 4. Check by multiplying.	**Step 4.** Check by multiplying. $2(x^2 + 1)(x + 2)(x - 2) = 2(x^2 + 1)(x^2 - 4)$ $= 2(x^4 - 3x^2 - 4)$ $= 2x^4 - 6x^2 - 8$
Section 3.6 Solving Quadratic Equations by Factoring	
A **quadratic equation** is an equation that can be written in the form $ax^2 + bx + c = 0$ with a not 0. The form $ax^2 + bx + c = 0$ is called the **standard form** of a quadratic equation.	***Quadratic Equation*** / ***Standard Form*** $x^2 = 16$ / $x^2 - 16 = 0$ $y = -2y^2 + 5$ / $2y^2 + y - 5 = 0$
Zero Factor Theorem	
If a and b are real numbers and if $ab = 0$, then $a = 0$ or $b = 0$.	If $(x + 3)(x - 1) = 0$, then $x + 3 = 0$ or $x - 1 = 0$
To solve quadratic equations by factoring,	Solve: $3x^2 = 13x - 4$
Step 1. Write the equation in standard form: $ax^2 + bx + c = 0$.	**Step 1.** $3x^2 - 13x + 4 = 0$
Step 2. Factor the quadratic.	**Step 2.** $(3x - 1)(x - 4) = 0$
Step 3. Set each factor containing a variable equal to 0.	**Step 3.** $3x - 1 = 0$ or $x - 4 = 0$
Step 4. Solve the equations.	**Step 4.** $3x = 1$ or $x = 4$ $x = \frac{1}{3}$
Step 5. Check in the original equation.	**Step 5.** Check both $\frac{1}{3}$ and 4 in the original equation.
Section 3.7 Quadratic Equations and Problem Solving	
Problem-Solving Steps	A garden is in the shape of a rectangle whose length is two feet more than its width. If the area of the garden is 35 square feet, find its dimensions.
1. UNDERSTAND the problem.	**1.** Read and reread the problem. Guess a solution and check your guess. Let x be the width of the rectangular garden. Then $x + 2$ is the length. 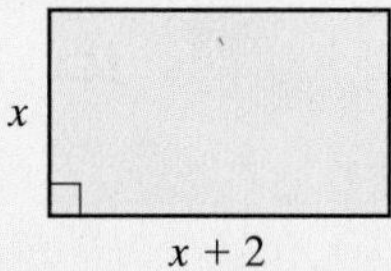
2. TRANSLATE.	**2.** In words: length · width = area ↓ ↓ ↓ Translate: $(x + 2) \cdot x = 35$
	(continued)

DEFINITIONS AND CONCEPTS	EXAMPLES
Section 3.7 Quadratic Equations and Problem Solving (continued)	
3. SOLVE.	**3.** $(x + 2)x = 35$ $x^2 + 2x - 35 = 0$ $(x - 5)(x + 7) = 0$ $x - 5 = 0$ or $x + 7 = 0$ $x = 5$ or $x = -7$
4. INTERPRET.	**4.** Discard the solution of -7 since x represents width. **Check:** If x is 5 feet then $x + 2 = 5 + 2 = 7$ feet. The area of a rectangle whose width is 5 feet and whose length is 7 feet is (5 feet)(7 feet) or 35 square feet. **State:** The garden is 5 feet by 7 feet.

Chapter 3 Review

(3.1) *Complete the factoring.*

1. $6x^2 - 15x = 3x(\quad)$

2. $2x^3y + 6x^2y^2 + 8xy^3 = 2xy(\quad)$

Factor the GCF from each polynomial.

3. $20x^2 + 12x$

4. $6x^2y^2 - 3xy^3$

5. $3x(2x + 3) - 5(2x + 3)$

6. $5x(x + 1) - (x + 1)$

Factor each polynomial by grouping.

7. $3x^2 - 3x + 2x - 2$

8. $3a^2 + 9ab + 3b^2 + ab$

9. $10a^2 + 5ab + 7b^2 + 14ab$

10. $6x^2 + 10x - 3x - 5$

(3.2) *Factor each trinomial.*

11. $x^2 + 6x + 8$

12. $x^2 - 11x + 24$

13. $x^2 + x + 2$

14. $x^2 - x + 2$

15. $x^2 + 4xy - 12y^2$

16. $x^2 + 8xy + 15y^2$

17. $72 - 18x - 2x^2$

18. $32 + 12x - 4x^2$

19. $10a^3 - 110a^2 + 100a$

20. $5y^3 - 50y^2 + 120y$

21. To factor $x^2 + 2x - 48$, think of two numbers whose product is ____ and whose sum is ____.

22. What is the first step in factoring $3x^2 + 15x + 30$?

(3.3) or (3.4) *Factor each trinomial.*

23. $2x^2 + 13x + 6$

24. $4x^2 + 4x - 3$

25. $6x^2 + 5xy - 4y^2$

26. $18x^2 - 9xy - 20y^2$

27. $10y^3 + 25y^2 - 60y$

28. $60y^3 - 39y^2 + 6y$

29. $18x^2 - 60x + 50$

30. $4x^2 - 28xy + 49y^2$

(3.5) *Factor each binomial.*

31. $4x^2 - 9$

32. $9t^2 - 25s^2$

33. $16x^2 + y^2$

34. $x^3 - 8y^3$

35. $8x^3 + 27$

36. $2x^3 + 8x$

37. $54 - 2x^3y^3$

38. $9x^2 - 4y^2$

39. $16x^4 - 1$

40. $x^4 + 16$

(3.6) *Solve the following equations.*

41. $(x + 6)(x - 2) = 0$

42. $3x(x + 1)(7x - 2) = 0$

43. $4(5x + 1)(x + 3) = 0$

44. $x^2 + 8x + 7 = 0$

45. $x^2 - 2x - 24 = 0$

46. $x^2 + 10x = -25$
47. $x(x - 10) = -16$
48. $(3x - 1)(9x^2 - 6x + 1) = 0$
49. $56x^2 - 5x - 6 = 0$
50. $20x^2 - 7x - 6 = 0$
51. $5(3x + 2) = 4$
52. $6x^2 - 3x + 8 = 0$
53. $12 - 5t = -3$
54. $5x^3 + 20x^2 + 20x = 0$
55. $4t^3 - 5t^2 - 21t = 0$
56. Write a quadratic equation that has the two solutions 4 and 5.

(3.7) Use the given information to choose the correct dimensions.

△ 57. The perimeter of a rectangle is 24 inches. The length is twice the width. Find the dimensions of the rectangle.

- a. 5 inches by 7 inches
- b. 5 inches by 10 inches
- c. 4 inches by 8 inches
- d. 2 inches by 10 inches

△ 58. The area of a rectangle is 80 square meters. The length is one more than three times the width. Find the dimensions of the rectangle.

- a. 8 meters by 10 meters
- b. 4 meters by 13 meters
- c. 4 meters by 20 meters
- d. 5 meters by 16 meters

Use the given information to find the dimensions of each figure.

△ 59. The *area* of the square is 81 square units. Find the length of a side.

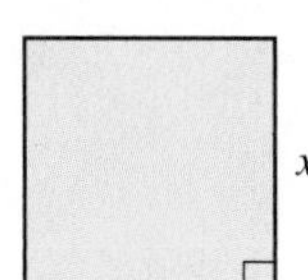

△ 60. The *perimeter* of the quadrilateral is 47 units. Find the lengths of the sides.

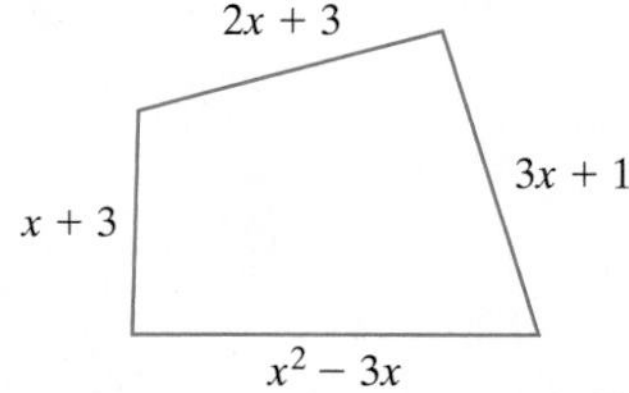

△ 61. A flag for a local organization is in the shape of a rectangle whose length is 15 inches less than twice its width. If the area of the flag is 500 square inches, find its dimensions.

△ 62. The base of a triangular sail is four times its height. If the area of the triangle is 162 square yards, find the base.

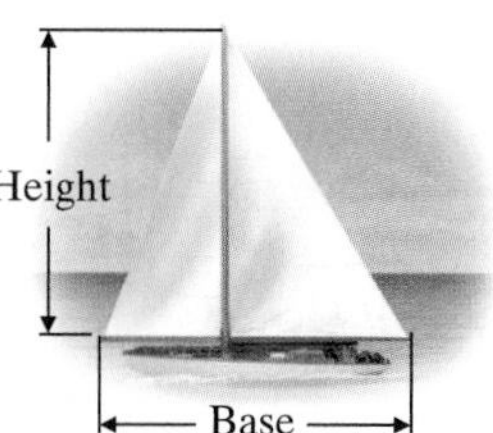

63. Find two consecutive positive integers whose product is 380.

64. Find two consecutive positive even integers whose product is 440.

65. A rocket is fired from the ground with an initial velocity of 440 feet per second. Its height h after t seconds is given by the equation

$$h = -16t^2 + 440t$$

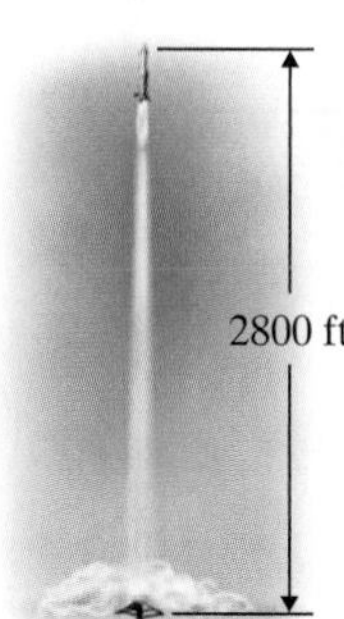

a. Find how many seconds pass before the rocket reaches a height of 2800 feet. Explain why two answers are obtained.

b. Find how many seconds pass before the rocket reaches the ground again.

△ 66. An architect's squaring instrument is in the shape of a right triangle. Find the length of the longer leg of the right triangle if the hypotenuse is 8 centimeters longer than the longer leg and the shorter leg is 8 centimeters shorter than the longer leg.

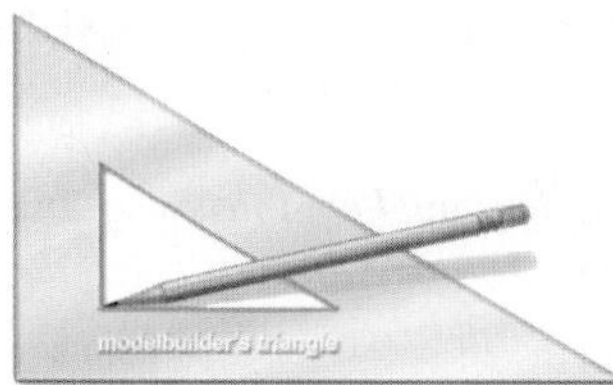

MIXED REVIEW

Factor completely.

67. $7x - 63$
68. $11x(4x - 3) - 6(4x - 3)$
69. $m^2 - \frac{4}{25}$
70. $3x^3 - 4x^2 + 6x - 8$
71. $xy + 2x - y - 2$
72. $2x^2 + 2x - 24$
73. $3x^3 - 30x^2 + 27x$
74. $4x^2 - 81$

75. $2x^2 - 18$

76. $16x^2 - 24x + 9$

77. $5x^2 + 20x + 20$

78. $2x^2 + 5x - 12$

79. $4x^2y - 6xy^2$

80. $125x^3 + 27$

81. $24x^2 - 3x - 18$

82. $(x + 7)^2 - y^2$

83. $x^2(x + 3) - 4(x + 3)$

84. $54a^3b - 2b$

Write the perimeter of each figure as a simplified polynomial. Then factor each polynomial.

△ **85.**

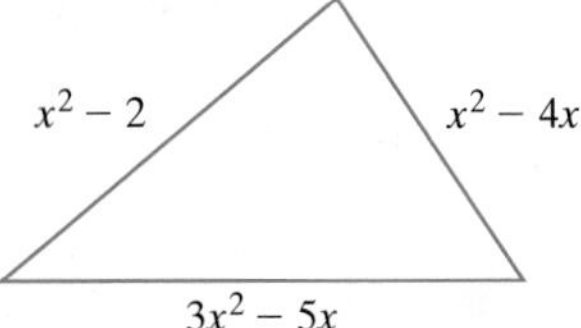

△ **86.**

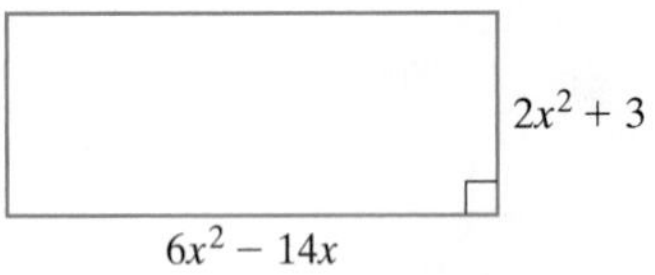

Solve.

87. $2x^2 - x - 28 = 0$

88. $x^2 - 2x = 15$

89. $2x(x + 7)(x + 4) = 0$

90. $x(x - 5) = -6$

91. $x^2 = 16x$

Solve.

△ **92.** The perimeter of the following triangle is 48 inches. Find the lengths of its sides.

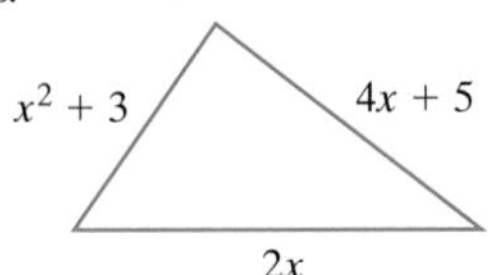

93. The width of a rectangle is 4 inches less than its length. Its area is 12 square inches. Find the dimensions of the rectangle.

94. A 6-foot-tall person drops an object from the top of the Westin Peachtree Plaza in Atlanta, Georgia. The Westin building is 723 feet tall. (*Source: World Almanac* research) The height h of the object after t seconds is given by the equation $h = -16t^2 + 729$. Find how many seconds pass before the object reaches the ground.

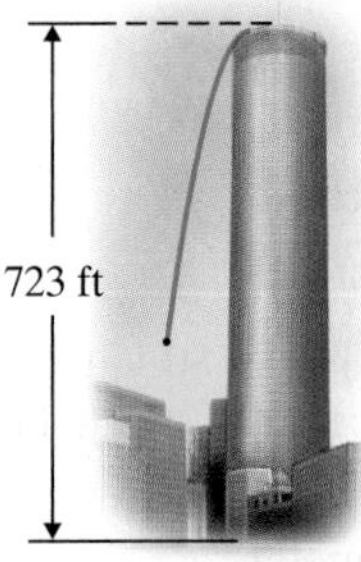

Write an expression for the area of the shaded region. Then write the expression as a factored polynomial.

△ **95.**

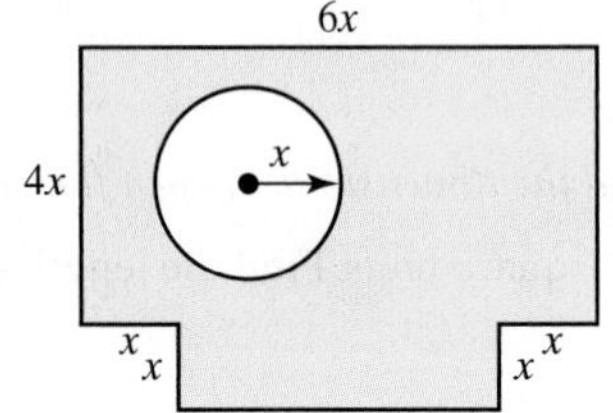

Chapter 3 Test

MyMathLab®

YouTube

Factor each polynomial completely. If a polynomial cannot be factored, write "prime."

1. $x^2 + 11x + 28$

2. $49 - m^2$

3. $y^2 + 22y + 121$

4. $4(a + 3) - y(a + 3)$

5. $x^2 + 4$

6. $y^2 - 8y - 48$

7. $x^2 + x - 10$

8. $9x^3 + 39x^2 + 12x$

9. $3a^2 + 3ab - 7a - 7b$

10. $3x^2 - 5x + 2$

11. $x^2 + 14xy + 24y^2$

12. $180 - 5x^2$

13. $6t^2 - t - 5$

14. $xy^2 - 7y^2 - 4x + 28$

15. $x - x^5$

16. $-xy^3 - x^3y$

17. $64x^3 - 1$

18. $8y^3 - 64$

Solve each equation.

19. $(x - 3)(x + 9) = 0$

20. $x^2 + 5x = 14$

21. $x(x + 6) = 7$

22. $3x(2x - 3)(3x + 4) = 0$

23. $5t^3 - 45t = 0$

24. $t^2 - 2t - 15 = 0$

25. $6x^2 = 15x$

Solve each problem.

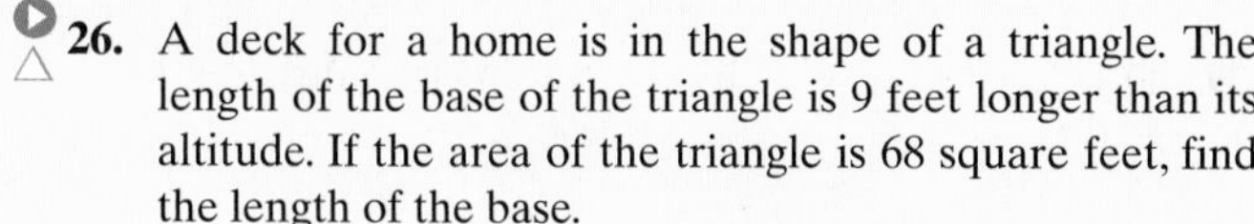

26. A deck for a home is in the shape of a triangle. The length of the base of the triangle is 9 feet longer than its altitude. If the area of the triangle is 68 square feet, find the length of the base.

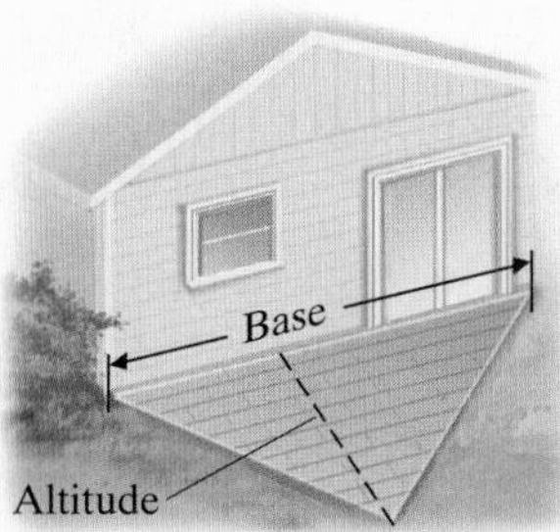

27. The sum of two numbers is 17 and the sum of their squares is 145. Find the numbers.

28. An object is dropped from the top of the Woolworth Building on Broadway in New York City. The height h of the object after t seconds is given by the equation

$$h = -16t^2 + 784$$

Find how many seconds pass before the object reaches the ground.

29. Find the lengths of the sides of a right triangle if the hypotenuse is 10 centimeters longer than the shorter leg and 5 centimeters longer than the longer leg.

Chapter 3 Cumulative Review

1. Translate each sentence into a mathematical statement.
  a. Nine is less than or equal to eleven.
  b. Eight is greater than one.
  c. Three is not equal to four.

2. Insert $<$ or $>$ in the space to make each statement true.
  a. $|-5| \quad |-3|$
  b. $|0| \quad |-2|$

3. Simplify each fraction (write it in lowest terms).
  a. $\frac{42}{49}$ **b.** $\frac{11}{27}$ **c.** $\frac{88}{20}$

4. Evaluate $\frac{x}{y} + 5x$ if $x = 20$ and $y = 10$.

5. Simplify: $\frac{8 + 2 \cdot 3}{2^2 - 1}$

6. Evaluate $\frac{x}{y} + 5x$ if $x = -20$ and $y = 10$.

7. Add.
  a. $3 + (-7) + (-8)$
  b. $[7 + (-10)] + [-2 + |-4|]$

8. Evaluate $\frac{x}{y} + 5x$ if $x = -20$ and $y = -10$.

9. Multiply.
  a. $(-8)(4)$
  b. $14(-1)$
  c. $(-9)(-10)$

10. Simplify: $5 - 2(3x - 7)$

11. Simplify each expression by combining like terms.
  a. $7x - 3x$ **b.** $10y^2 + y^2$
  c. $8x^2 + 2x - 3x$ **d.** $9n^2 - 5n^2 + n^2$

12. Solve: $0.8y + 0.2(y - 1) = 1.8$

Solve.

13. $\frac{y}{7} = 20$

14. $\frac{x}{-7} = -4$

15. $-3x = 33$

16. $-\frac{2}{3}x = -22$

17. $8(2 - t) = -5t$

18. $-z = \frac{7z + 3}{5}$

19. Balsa wood sticks are commonly used to build models (for example, bridge models). A 48-inch balsa wood stick is to be cut into two pieces so that the longer piece is 3 times the shorter. Find the length of each piece.

20. Solve $3x + 9 \le 5(x - 1)$. Write the solution set using interval notation.

21. Graph the linear equation $y = -\frac{1}{3}x + 2$.

22. Is the ordered pair $(-1, 2)$ a solution of $-7x - 8y = -9$?

23. Find the slope and the y-intercept of the line whose equation is $3x - 4y = 4$.

24. Find the slope of the line through $(5, -6)$ and $(5, 2)$.

25. Evaluate each expression for the given value of x.
  a. $2x^3$; x is 5 **b.** $\frac{9}{x^2}$; x is -3

26. Find the slope and y-intercept of the line whose equation is $7x - 3y = 2$.

27. Find the degree of each term.
  a. $3x^2$ **b.** -2^3x^5 **c.** y
  d. $12x^2yz^3$ **e.** 5

28. Find an equation of the vertical line through $(0, 7)$.

29. Subtract: $(2x^3 + 8x^2 - 6x) - (2x^3 - x^2 + 1)$

30. Find an equation of the line with slope 4 and y-intercept $\left(0, \frac{1}{2}\right)$. Write the equation in standard form.

31. Multiply $(3x + 2)(2x - 5)$.

32. Write an equation of the line through $(-4, 0)$ and $(6, -1)$. Write the equation in standard form.

33. Multiply $(3y + 1)^2$.

34. Solve the system: $\begin{cases} -x + 3y = 18 \\ -3x + 2y = 19 \end{cases}$

35. Simplify by writing each expression with positive exponents only.

a. 3^{-2} **b.** $2x^{-3}$

c. $2^{-1} + 4^{-1}$ **d.** $(-2)^{-4}$

e. y^{-4}

36. Simplify: $\dfrac{(5a^7)^2}{a^5}$

37. Write each number in scientific notation.

a. 367,000,000

b. 0.000003

c. 20,520,000,000

d. 0.00085

38. Multiply $(3x - 7y)^2$.

39. Divide $x^2 + 7x + 12$ by $x + 3$ using long division.

40. Simplify: $\dfrac{(xy)^{-3}}{(x^5y^6)^3}$

41. Find the GCF of each list of terms.

a. x^3, x^7, and x^5 **b.** y, y^4, and y^7

Factor.

42. $z^3 + 7z + z^2 + 7$

43. $x^2 + 7x + 12$

44. $2x^3 + 2x^2 - 84x$

45. $8x^2 - 22x + 5$

46. $-4x^2 - 23x + 6$

47. $25a^2 - 9b^2$

48. $9xy^2 - 16x$

49. Solve: $(x - 3)(x + 1) = 0$

50. Solve $x^2 - 13x = -36$.

CHAPTER 4 Rational Expressions

Many sport statistics are calculated using formulas containing rational expressions. Below are a few examples:

Sport	*Formula*	*Explanation*
Baseball	$S = \dfrac{h + d + 2t + 3r}{b}$	A baseball player's slugging percentage S, where h = number of hits, d = number of doubles, t = number of triples, r = number of home runs, and b = number of at bats
NCAA Football	$R_{\text{NCAA}} = \dfrac{100C + 330T - 200I + 8.4Y}{A}$	A quarterback's rating in NCAA football R, where C = the number of completed passes, A = the number of attempted passes, T = the number of touchdown passes, Y = the number of yards in the completed passes, and I = the number of interceptions
NFL Football	$R_{\text{NFL}} = \dfrac{a + b + c + d}{6} \times 100$	A quarterback's rating in NFL football R, where $a, b, c,$ and d are each formulas containing rational expressions.

(*Source:* Wikipedia.org.)

In Section 4.1, Exercises 65 and 66, you will have the opportunity to calculate some sport statistics.

In this chapter, we expand our knowledge of algebraic expressions to include algebraic fractions, called *rational expressions.* We explore the operations of addition, subtraction, multiplication, and division using principles similar to the principles for numerical fractions.

4.1 Rational Functions and Simplifying Rational Expressions 

OBJECTIVES

1 Find the Domain of a Rational Function.

2 Simplify or Write Rational Expressions in Lowest Terms.

3 Write Equivalent Rational Expressions of the Form $-\frac{a}{b} = \frac{-a}{b} = \frac{a}{-b}$.

4 Use Rational Functions in Applications.

As we reviewed in Chapter R, a rational number is a number that can be written as a quotient of integers. A **rational expression** is also a quotient; it is a quotient of polynomials.

Rational Expression

A rational expression is an expression that can be written in the form

$$\frac{P}{Q},$$

where P and Q are polynomials and $Q \neq 0$.

Rational Expressions

$$-\frac{2}{7} \qquad \frac{3y^3}{8} \qquad \frac{-4p}{p^3 + 2p + 1} \qquad \frac{5x^2 - 3x + 2}{3x + 7}$$

The first rational expression (or fraction) above is $-\frac{2}{7}$. For a negative fraction such as $-\frac{2}{7}$, recall from Section R.7 that

$$-\frac{2}{7} = \frac{2}{-7} = \frac{-2}{7}$$

In general, for any fraction,

$$\frac{-a}{b} = \frac{a}{-b} = -\frac{a}{b}, \qquad b \neq 0$$

This is also true for rational expressions. For example,

$$\underbrace{\frac{-(x + 2)}{x}} = \frac{x + 2}{-x} = -\frac{x + 2}{x}$$

Notice the parentheses.

Rational expressions are sometimes used to describe functions. For example, we call the function $f(x) = \frac{x^2 + 2}{x - 3}$ a **rational function** since $\frac{x^2 + 2}{x - 3}$ is a rational expression.

OBJECTIVE

1 Finding the Domain of a Rational Function 

As with fractions, a rational expression is **undefined** if the denominator is 0. If a variable in a rational expression is replaced with a number that makes the denominator 0, we say that the rational expression is **undefined** for this value of the variable. For example, the rational expression $\frac{x^2 + 2}{x - 3}$ is undefined when x is 3, because replacing x with 3 results in a denominator of 0. For this reason, we must exclude 3 from the domain of the function $f(x) = \frac{x^2 + 2}{x - 3}$.

The domain of f is then

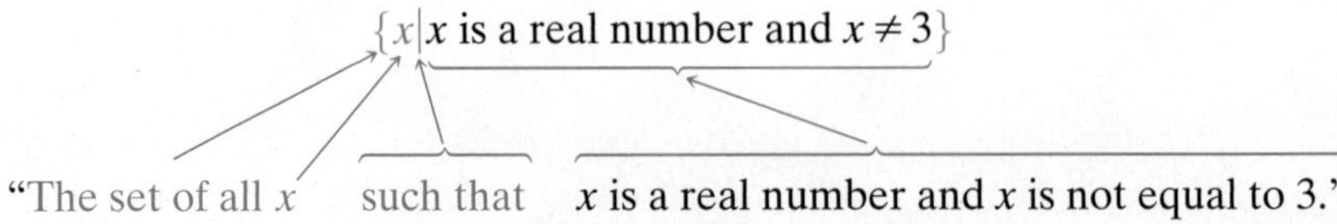

In this section, we will use this set builder notation to write domains.
Unless told otherwise, we assume that the domain of a function described by an equation is the set of all real numbers for which the equation is defined.

EXAMPLE 1 Find the domain of each rational function.

a. $f(x) = \dfrac{8x^3 + 7x^2 + 20}{2}$ **b.** $g(x) = \dfrac{5x^2 - 3}{x - 1}$ **c.** $f(x) = \dfrac{7x - 2}{x^2 - 2x - 15}$

Solution The domain of each function will contain all real numbers except those values that make the denominator 0.

a. No matter what the value of x, the denominator of $f(x) = \dfrac{8x^3 + 7x^2 + 20}{2}$ is never 0, so the domain of f is $\{x|x \text{ is a real number}\}$.

b. To find the values of x that make the denominator of $g(x)$ equal to 0, we solve the equation "denominator = 0":

$$x - 1 = 0, \quad \text{or} \quad x = 1$$

The domain must exclude 1 since the rational expression is undefined when x is 1. The domain of g is $\{x|x \text{ is a real number and } x \neq 1\}$.

c. We find the domain by setting the denominator equal to 0.

$$x^2 - 2x - 15 = 0 \quad \text{Set the denominator equal to 0 and solve.}$$
$$(x - 5)(x + 3) = 0$$
$$x - 5 = 0 \quad \text{or} \quad x + 3 = 0$$
$$x = 5 \quad \text{or} \quad x = -3$$

If x is replaced with 5 or with -3, the rational expression is undefined.
The domain of f is $\{x|x \text{ is a real number and } x \neq 5, x \neq -3\}$. □

PRACTICE
1 Find the domain of each rational function.

a. $f(x) = \dfrac{4x^5 - 3x^2 + 2}{-6}$ **b.** $g(x) = \dfrac{6x^2 + 1}{x + 3}$ **c.** $h(x) = \dfrac{8x - 3}{x^2 - 5x + 6}$

✓CONCEPT CHECK

For which of these values (if any) is the rational expression $\dfrac{x - 3}{x^2 + 2}$ undefined?

a. 2 b. 3 c. -2 d. 0 e. None of these

OBJECTIVE
2 Simplifying Rational Expressions

Recall that a fraction is in lowest terms or simplest form if the numerator and denominator have no common factors other than 1 (or -1). For example, $\dfrac{3}{13}$ is in lowest terms since 3 and 13 have no common factors other than 1 (or -1).

To **simplify** a rational expression, or to write it in lowest terms, we use a method similar to simplifying a fraction.

Recall that to simplify a fraction, we essentially "remove factors of 1." Our ability to do this comes from these facts:

- If $c \neq 0$, then $\dfrac{c}{c} = 1$. For example, $\dfrac{7}{7} = 1$ and $\dfrac{-8.65}{-8.65} = 1$.
- $n \cdot 1 = n$. For example, $-5 \cdot 1 = -5$, $126.8 \cdot 1 = 126.8$, and $\dfrac{a}{b} \cdot 1 = \dfrac{a}{b}, b \neq 0$.

Answer to Concept Check: e

In other words, we have the following:

$$\frac{a \cdot c}{b \cdot c} = \underbrace{\frac{a}{b} \cdot \frac{c}{c}}_{} = \frac{a}{b}$$

Since $\frac{a}{b} \cdot 1 = \frac{a}{b}$

Let's practice simplifying a fraction by simplifying $\frac{15}{65}$.

$$\frac{15}{65} = \frac{3 \cdot 5}{13 \cdot 5} = \frac{3}{13} \cdot \frac{5}{5} = \frac{3}{13} \cdot 1 = \frac{3}{13}$$

Let's use the same technique and simplify the rational expression $\frac{x^2 - 9}{x^2 + x - 6}$.

$$\frac{x^2 - 9}{x^2 + x - 6} = \frac{(x - 3)(x + 3)}{(x - 2)(x + 3)}$$ Factor the numerator and the denominator.

$$= \frac{(x - 3)\,(x + 3)}{(x - 2)\,(x + 3)}$$ Look for common factors.

$$= \frac{x - 3}{x - 2} \cdot \frac{x + 3}{x + 3}$$

$$= \frac{x - 3}{x - 2} \cdot 1$$ Write $\frac{x + 3}{x + 3}$ as 1.

$$= \frac{x - 3}{x - 2}$$ Multiply to remove a factor of 1.

This "removing a factor of 1" is stated in the principle below:

Fundamental Principle of Rational Expressions

For any rational expression $\frac{P}{Q}$ and any polynomial R, where $R \neq 0$,

$$\frac{PR}{QR} = \frac{P}{Q} \cdot \frac{R}{R} = \frac{P}{Q} \cdot 1 = \frac{P}{Q}$$

or, simply,

$$\frac{PR}{QR} = \frac{P}{Q}$$

In general, the following steps may be used to simplify rational expressions or to write a rational expression in lowest terms.

Simplifying or Writing a Rational Expression in Lowest Terms

Step 1. Completely factor the numerator and denominator of the rational expression.

Step 2. Divide out factors common to the numerator and denominator. (This is the same as "removing a factor of 1.")

For now, we assume that variables in a rational expression do not represent values that make the denominator 0.

EXAMPLE 2 Simplify each rational expression.

a. $\frac{2x^2}{10x^3 - 2x^2}$ **b.** $\frac{9x^2 + 13x + 4}{8x^2 + x - 7}$

Solution

a. $\frac{2x^2}{10x^3 - 2x^2} = \frac{2x^2 \cdot 1}{2x^2(5x - 1)} = 1 \cdot \frac{1}{5x - 1} = \frac{1}{5x - 1}$

b. $\frac{9x^2 + 13x + 4}{8x^2 + x - 7} = \frac{(9x + 4)(x + 1)}{(8x - 7)(x + 1)}$ Factor the numerator and denominator.

$= \frac{9x + 4}{8x - 7} \cdot 1$ Since $\frac{x + 1}{x + 1} = 1$

$= \frac{9x + 4}{8x - 7}$ Simplest form □

PRACTICE

2 Simplify each rational expression.

a. $\frac{5z^4}{10z^5 - 5z^4}$ **b.** $\frac{5x^2 + 13x + 6}{6x^2 + 7x - 10}$

Just as for numerical fractions, we can use a shortcut notation. Remember that as long as exact factors in both the numerator and denominator are divided out, we are "removing a factor of 1." We will use the following notation to show this:

$\frac{x^2 - 9}{x^2 + x - 6} = \frac{(x - 3)(x + 3)}{(x - 2)(x + 3)}$ A factor of 1 is identified by the shading.

$= \frac{x - 3}{x - 2}$ Remove a factor of 1.

Thus, the rational expression $\frac{x^2 - 9}{x^2 + x - 6}$ has the same value as the rational expression $\frac{x - 3}{x - 2}$ for all values of x except 2 and -3. (Remember that when x is 2, the denominator of both rational expressions is 0 and when x is -3, the original rational expression has a denominator of 0.)

As we simplify rational expressions, we will assume that the simplified rational expression is equal to the original rational expression for all real numbers except those for which the original denominator is 0.

EXAMPLE 3 Simplify each rational expression.

a. $\frac{2 + x}{x + 2}$ **b.** $\frac{2 - x}{x - 2}$

Solution

a. $\frac{2 + x}{x + 2} = \frac{x + 2}{x + 2} = 1$ By the commutative property of addition, $2 + x = x + 2$.

b. $\frac{2 - x}{x - 2}$

The terms in the numerator of $\frac{2 - x}{x - 2}$ differ by sign from the terms of the denominator, so the polynomials are opposites of each other and the expression simplifies to -1. To see this, we factor out -1 from the numerator or the denominator. If -1 is factored from the numerator, then

$$\frac{2 - x}{x - 2} = \frac{-1(-2 + x)}{x - 2} = \frac{-1(x - 2)}{x - 2} = \frac{-1}{1} = -1$$

(Continued on next page)

Helpful Hint

When the numerator and the denominator of a rational expression are opposites of each other, the expression simplifies to -1.

If -1 is factored from the denominator, the result is the same.

$$\frac{2-x}{x-2} = \frac{2-x}{-1(-x+2)} = \frac{2-x}{-1\,(2-x)} = \frac{1}{-1} = -1$$

□

PRACTICE 3 Simplify each rational expression.

a. $\frac{x+3}{3+x}$ b. $\frac{3-x}{x-3}$

EXAMPLE 4 Simplify $\frac{18-2x^2}{x^2-2x-3}$.

Solution

$$\frac{18-2x^2}{x^2-2x-3} = \frac{2(9-x^2)}{(x+1)(x-3)}$$ Factor.

$$= \frac{2(3+x)(3-x)}{(x+1)(x-3)}$$ Factor completely.

$$= \frac{2(3+x)\cdot -1\,(x-3)}{(x+1)\,(x-3)}$$ Notice the opposites $3-x$ and $x-3$. Write $3-x$ as $-1(x-3)$ and simplify.

$$= -\frac{2(3+x)}{x+1}$$

□

PRACTICE 4 Simplify $\frac{20-5x^2}{x^2+x-6}$.

Helpful Hint

When simplifying a rational expression, we look for **common *factors,* not common *terms.***

$$\frac{x\cdot(x+2)}{x\cdot x} = \frac{x+2}{x}$$

Common factors. These can be divided out.

$$\frac{x+2}{x}$$

Common terms. There is no factor of 1 that can be generated.

✓CONCEPT CHECK

Recall that we can only remove *factors* of 1. Which of the following are *not* true? Explain why.

a. $\frac{3-1}{3+5}$ simplifies to $-\frac{1}{5}$.

b. $\frac{2x+10}{2}$ simplifies to $x+5$.

c. $\frac{37}{72}$ simplifies to $\frac{3}{2}$.

d. $\frac{2x+3}{2}$ simplifies to $x+3$.

EXAMPLE 5 Simplify each rational expression.

a. $\frac{x^3+8}{2+x}$ b. $\frac{2y^2+2}{y^3-5y^2+y-5}$

Solution

a. $$\frac{x^3+8}{2+x} = \frac{(x+2)\,(x^2-2x+4)}{x+2}$$ Factor the sum of the two cubes.

$$= x^2-2x+4$$ Divide out common factors.

Answers to Concept Check: a, c, d

b. $\dfrac{2y^2 + 2}{y^3 - 5y^2 + y - 5} = \dfrac{2(y^2 + 1)}{(y^3 - 5y^2) + (y - 5)}$ Factor the numerator; group the denominator.

$= \dfrac{2(y^2 + 1)}{y^2(y - 5) + 1(y - 5)}$ Factor the denominator by grouping.

$= \dfrac{2(y^2 + 1)}{(y - 5)(y^2 + 1)}$

$= \dfrac{2}{y - 5}$ Divide out common factors. □

PRACTICE

5 Simplify each rational expression.

a. $\dfrac{x^3 + 64}{4 + x}$ **b.** $\dfrac{5z^2 + 10}{z^3 - 3z^2 + 2z - 6}$

✓CONCEPT CHECK

Does $\dfrac{n}{n + 2}$ simplify to $\dfrac{1}{2}$? Why or why not?

OBJECTIVE

3 Writing Equivalent Forms of Rational Expressions

From Example 3, we have

$$\frac{2 + x}{x + 2} = \frac{x + 2}{x + 2} = 1 \quad \text{and} \quad \frac{2 - x}{x - 2} = \frac{2 - x}{-1(2 - x)} = \frac{1}{-1} = -1.$$

When performing operations on rational expressions, equivalent forms of answers often result. For this reason, it is very important to be able to recognize equivalent answers.

EXAMPLE 6 List some equivalent forms of $-\dfrac{5x - 1}{x + 9}$.

Solution To do so, recall that $-\dfrac{a}{b} = \dfrac{-a}{b} = \dfrac{a}{-b}$. Thus

$$-\frac{5x - 1}{x + 9} = \frac{-(5x - 1)}{x + 9} = \frac{-5x + 1}{x + 9} \quad \text{or} \quad \frac{1 - 5x}{x + 9}$$

Also,

$$-\frac{5x - 1}{x + 9} = \frac{5x - 1}{-(x + 9)} = \frac{5x - 1}{-x - 9} \quad \text{or} \quad \frac{5x - 1}{-9 - x}$$

Thus $-\dfrac{5x - 1}{x + 9} = \dfrac{-(5x - 1)}{x + 9} = \dfrac{-5x + 1}{x + 9} = \dfrac{5x - 1}{-(x + 9)} = \dfrac{5x - 1}{-x - 9}$ □

▶ **Helpful Hint**

Remember, a negative sign in front of a fraction or rational expression may be moved to the numerator or the denominator, but *not* both.

PRACTICE

6 List some equivalent forms of $-\dfrac{x + 3}{6x - 11}$.

Keep in mind that many rational expressions may look different, but in fact be equivalent.

Answers to Concept Check:
no; answers may vary.

OBJECTIVE

4 Using Rational Functions in Applications 

Rational functions occur often in real-life situations.

EXAMPLE 7 **Cost for Pressing Compact Discs**

For the ICL Production Company, the rational function $C(x) = \dfrac{2.6x + 10{,}000}{x}$ describes the company's cost per disc of pressing x compact discs. Find the cost per disc for pressing:

a. 100 compact discs **b.** 1000 compact discs

Solution

a. $C(100) = \dfrac{2.6(100) + 10{,}000}{100} = \dfrac{10{,}260}{100} = 102.6$

The cost per disc for pressing 100 compact discs is \$102.60.

b. $C(1000) = \dfrac{2.6(1000) + 10{,}000}{1000} = \dfrac{12{,}600}{1000} = 12.6$

The cost per disc for pressing 1000 compact discs is \$12.60. Notice that as more compact discs are produced, the cost per disc decreases. □

PRACTICE

7 A company's cost per tee shirt for silk screening x tee shirts is given by the rational function $C(x) = \dfrac{3.2x + 400}{x}$. Find the cost per tee shirt for printing:

a. 100 tee shirts **b.** 1000 tee shirts

Graphing Calculator Explorations 

(Note: The information below about *connected* mode and *dot* mode may not apply to your graphing calculator.)

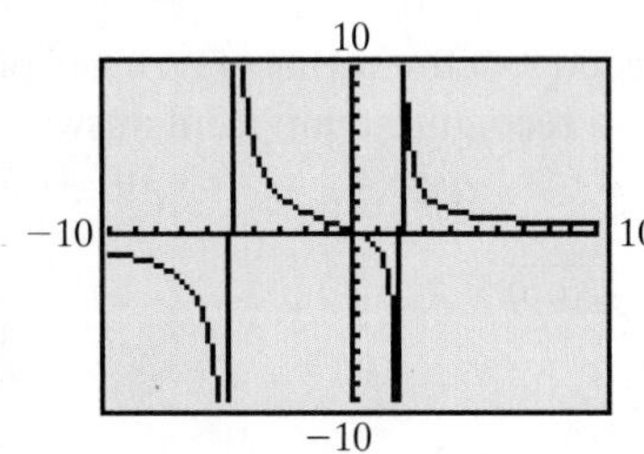

Recall that since the rational expression $\dfrac{7x - 2}{(x - 2)(x + 5)}$ is not defined when $x = 2$ or when $x = -5$, we say that the domain of the rational function $f(x) = \dfrac{7x - 2}{(x - 2)(x + 5)}$ is all real numbers except 2 and −5. This domain can be written as $\{x|x \text{ is a real number and } x \neq 2, x \neq -5\}$. This means that the graph of $f(x)$ should not cross the vertical lines $x = 2$ and $x = -5$. The graph of $f(x)$ in *connected* mode is to the left. In connected mode the graphing calculator tries to connect all dots of the graph so that the result is a smooth curve. This is what has happened in the graph. Notice that the graph appears to contain vertical lines at $x = 2$ and at $x = -5$. We know that this cannot happen because the function is not defined at $x = 2$ and at $x = -5$. We also know that this cannot happen because the graph of this function would not pass the vertical line test.

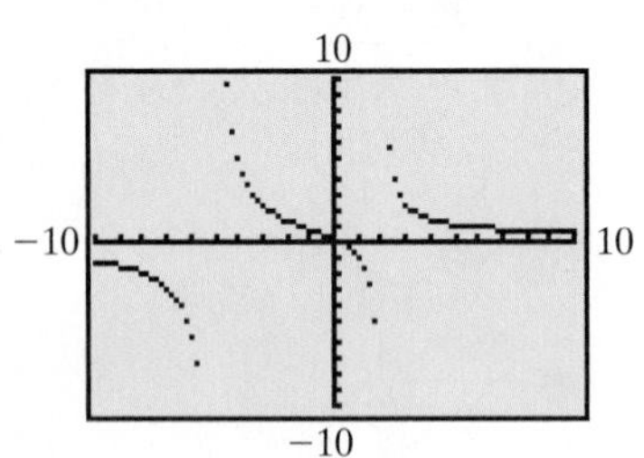

The graph of $f(x)$ in *dot* mode is to the left. In dot mode the graphing calculator will not connect dots with a smooth curve. Notice that the vertical lines have disappeared, and we have a better picture of the graph. The graph, however, actually appears more like the hand-drawn graph below. By using a Table feature, a Calculate Value feature, or by tracing, we can see that the function is not defined at $x = 2$ and at $x = -5$.

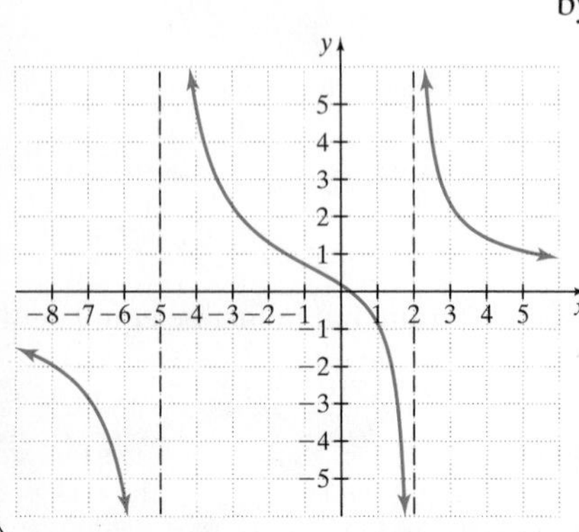

Find the domain of each rational function. Then graph each rational function and use the graph to confirm the domain.

1. $f(x) = \dfrac{x + 1}{x^2 - 4}$

2. $g(x) = \dfrac{5x}{x^2 - 9}$

3. $h(x) = \dfrac{x^2}{2x^2 + 7x - 4}$

4. $f(x) = \dfrac{3x + 2}{4x^2 - 19x - 5}$

Vocabulary, Readiness & Video Check

Use the choices below to fill in each blank. Some choices may not be used.

1	true	rational	simplified	$\frac{-a}{-b}$	$\frac{-a}{b}$	$\frac{a}{-b}$
−1	false	domain	0			

1. A ______________ expression is an expression that can be written as the quotient $\frac{P}{Q}$ of two polynomials P and Q as long as $Q \neq 0$.

2. A rational expression is undefined if the denominator is ______________.

3. The ______________ of the rational function $f(x) = \frac{2}{x}$ is $\{x \mid x \text{ is a real number and } x \neq 0\}$.

4. A rational expression is ______________ if the numerator and denominator have no common factors other than 1 or −1.

5. The expression $\frac{x^2 + 2}{2 + x^2}$ simplifies to ______________.

6. The expression $\frac{y - z}{z - y}$ simplifies to ______________.

7. For a rational expression, $-\frac{a}{b} = \underline{\quad\quad} = \underline{\quad\quad}$.

8. True or false: $\frac{a - 6}{a + 2} = \frac{-(a - 6)}{-(a + 2)} = \frac{-a + 6}{-a - 2}$. ______________

Martin-Gay Interactive Videos

See Video 4.1

Watch the section lecture video and answer the following questions.

OBJECTIVE 1

9. Why can't the denominators of rational expressions be zero? How can we find the domain of a rational function?

OBJECTIVE 2

10. In Example 6, why isn't a factor of x divided out of the expression at the end?

OBJECTIVE 3

11. From Example 8, if we move a negative sign from in front of a rational expression to either the numerator or denominator, when do we insert parentheses and why?

OBJECTIVE 4

12. From Example 9, why do we subtract parts a. and b. to find the answer to part c.?

4.1 Exercise Set

MyMathLab®

Find the domain of each rational expression. See Example 1.

1. $f(x) = \frac{5x - 7}{4}$

2. $g(x) = \frac{4 - 3x}{2}$

3. $s(t) = \frac{t^2 + 1}{2t}$

4. $v(t) = -\frac{5t + t^2}{3t}$

5. $f(x) = \frac{3x}{7 - x}$

6. $f(x) = \frac{-4x}{-2 + x}$

7. $f(x) = \frac{x}{3x - 1}$

8. $g(x) = \frac{-2}{2x + 5}$

9. $R(x) = \frac{3 + 2x}{x^3 + x^2 - 2x}$

10. $h(x) = \frac{5 - 3x}{2x^2 - 14x + 20}$

11. $C(x) = \frac{x + 3}{x^2 - 4}$

12. $R(x) = \frac{5}{x^2 - 7x}$

Study Example 6. Then list four equivalent forms for each rational expression.

13. $-\frac{x-10}{x+8}$

14. $-\frac{x+11}{x-4}$

15. $-\frac{5y-3}{y-12}$

16. $-\frac{8y-1}{y-15}$

MIXED PRACTICE

Simplify each expression. See Examples 2 through 5.

17. $\frac{x+7}{7+x}$

18. $\frac{y+9}{9+y}$

19. $\frac{x-7}{7-x}$

20. $\frac{y-9}{9-y}$

21. $\frac{2}{8x+16}$

22. $\frac{3}{9x+6}$

23. $\frac{-5a-5b}{a+b}$

24. $\frac{-4x-4y}{x+y}$

25. $\frac{7x+35}{x^2+5x}$

26. $\frac{9x+99}{x^2+11x}$

27. $\frac{x+5}{x^2-4x-45}$

28. $\frac{x-3}{x^2-6x+9}$

29. $\frac{5x^2+11x+2}{x+2}$

30. $\frac{12x^2+4x-1}{2x+1}$

31. $\frac{x^3+7x^2}{x^2+5x-14}$

32. $\frac{x^4-10x^3}{x^2-17x+70}$

33. $\frac{2x^2-8}{4x-8}$

34. $\frac{5x^2-500}{35x+350}$

35. $\frac{4-x^2}{x-2}$

36. $\frac{49-y^2}{y-7}$

37. $\frac{11x^2-22x^3}{6x-12x^2}$

38. $\frac{24y^2-8y^3}{15y-5y^2}$

39. $\frac{x^2+xy+2x+2y}{x+2}$

40. $\frac{ab+ac+b^2+bc}{b+c}$

41. $\frac{x^3+8}{x+2}$

42. $\frac{x^3+64}{x+4}$

43. $\frac{x^3-1}{1-x}$

44. $\frac{3-x}{x^3-27}$

45. $\frac{2xy+5x-2y-5}{3xy+4x-3y-4}$

46. $\frac{2xy+2x-3y-3}{2xy+4x-3y-6}$

47. $\frac{3x^2-5x-2}{6x^3+2x^2+3x+1}$

48. $\frac{2x^2-x-3}{2x^3-3x^2+2x-3}$

49. $\frac{9x^2-15x+25}{27x^3+125}$

50. $\frac{8x^3-27}{4x^2+6x+9}$

MIXED PRACTICE

Simplify each expression. Then determine whether the given answer is correct. See Examples 3 through 6.

51. $\frac{9-x^2}{x-3}$; Answer: $-3-x$

52. $\frac{100-x^2}{x-10}$; Answer: $-10-x$

53. $\frac{7-34x-5x^2}{25x^2-1}$; Answer: $\frac{x+7}{-5x-1}$

54. $\frac{2-15x-8x^2}{64x^2-1}$; Answer: $\frac{x+2}{-8x-1}$

Find each function value. See Example 7.

55. If $f(x)=\frac{x+8}{2x-1}$, find $f(2)$, $f(0)$, and $f(-1)$.

56. If $f(x)=\frac{x-2}{-5+x}$, find $f(-5)$, $f(0)$, and $f(10)$.

57. If $g(x)=\frac{x^2+8}{x^3-25x}$, find $g(3)$, $g(-2)$, and $g(1)$.

58. If $s(t)=\frac{t^3+1}{t^2+1}$, find $s(-1)$, $s(1)$, and $s(2)$.

Solve. See Example 7.

59. The total revenue from the sale of a popular book is approximated by the rational function $R(x)=\frac{1000x^2}{x^2+4}$, where x is the number of years since publication and $R(x)$ is the total revenue in millions of dollars.

a. Find the total revenue at the end of the first year.

b. Find the total revenue at the end of the second year.

c. Find the revenue during the second year only.

d. Find the domain of function R.

60. The function $f(x)=\frac{100{,}000x}{100-x}$ models the cost in dollars for removing x percent of the pollutants from a bayou in which a nearby company dumped creosol.

a. Find the cost of removing 20% of the pollutants from the bayou. [*Hint:* Find $f(20)$.]

b. Find the cost of removing 60% of the pollutants and then 80% of the pollutants.

c. Find $f(90)$, then $f(95)$, and then $f(99)$. What happens to the cost as x approaches 100%?

d. Find the domain of function f.

61. The dose of medicine prescribed for a child depends on the child's age A in years and the adult dose D for the medication. Young's Rule is a formula used by pediatricians that gives a child's dose C as

$$C = \frac{DA}{A + 12}$$

Suppose that an 8-year-old child needs medication, and the normal adult dose is 1000 mg. What size dose should the child receive?

62. Calculating body-mass index is a way to gauge whether a person should lose weight. Doctors recommend that body-mass index values fall between 18.5 and 25. The formula for body-mass index B is

$$B = \frac{703w}{h^2}$$

where w is weight in pounds and h is height in inches. Should a 148-pound person who is 5 feet 6 inches tall lose weight?

63. Anthropologists and forensic scientists use a measure called the cephalic index to help classify skulls. The cephalic index of a skull with width W and length L from front to back is given by the formula

$$C = \frac{100W}{L}$$

A long skull has an index value less than 75, a medium skull has an index value between 75 and 85, and a broad skull has an index value over 85. Find the cephalic index of a skull that is 5 inches wide and 6.4 inches long. Classify the skull.

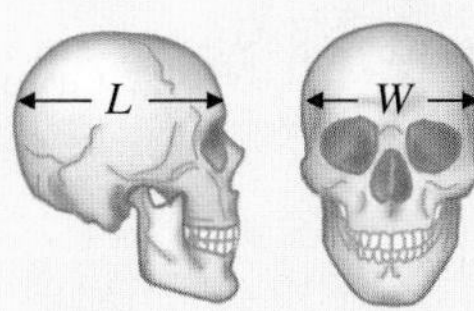

64. A company's gross profit margin P can be computed with the formula $P = \frac{R - C}{R}$, where $R =$ the company's revenue and $C =$ cost of goods sold. During a recent fiscal year, computer company Apple had revenues of \$32.5 billion and cost of goods sold \$21.3 billion. (*Source:* Apple, Inc.) What was Apple's gross profit margin in this year? Express the answer as a percent, rounded to the nearest tenth of a percent.

65. A baseball player's slugging percentage S can be calculated with the following formula:

$$S = \frac{h + d + 2t + 3r}{b}, \text{ where } h = \text{number of hits,}$$

$d =$ number of doubles, $t =$ number of triples, $r =$ number of home runs, and $b =$ number of at bats. In 2010, Albert Pujols of the St. Louis Cardinals led Major League Baseball in slugging percent. During the 2010 season, Pujols had 587 at bats, 183 hits, 39 doubles, 1 triple, and 42 home runs. (*Source:* Major League Baseball) Calculate Pujols' 2010 slugging percent. Round to the nearest tenth of a percent.

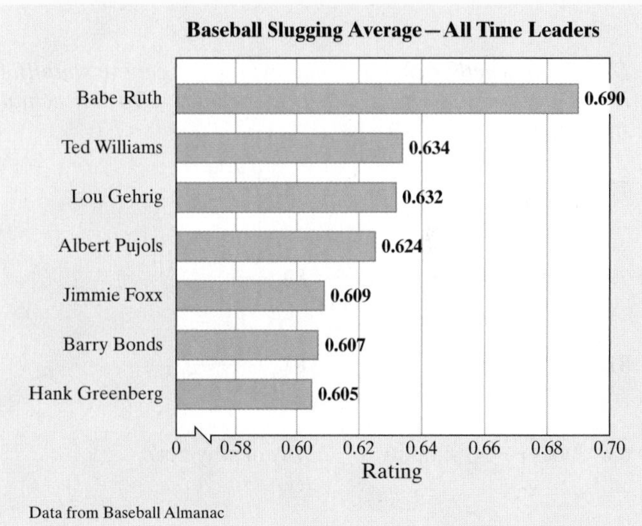

66. To calculate a quarterback's rating in NCAA football, you may use the formula $\frac{100C + 330T - 200I + 8.4Y}{A}$, where $C =$ the number of completed passes, $A =$ the number of attempted passes, $T =$ the number of touchdown passes, $Y =$ the number of yards in the completed passes, and $I =$ the number of interceptions. Cam Newton of Auburn University was selected as the 2010 winner of the Heisman Memorial Trophy as the Most Outstanding Football Player. Newton, a junior quarterback, ended the season with 280 attempts, 185 completions, 2854 yards, 30 touchdowns, and only 7 interceptions. Calculate Newton's quarterback rating for the 2010 season. (*Source:* NCAA) Round the answer to the nearest tenth.

REVIEW AND PREVIEW

Perform each indicated operation. See Section R.3.

67. $\frac{1}{3} \cdot \frac{9}{11}$

68. $\frac{5}{27} \cdot \frac{2}{5}$

69. $\frac{1}{3} \div \frac{1}{4}$

70. $\frac{7}{8} \div \frac{1}{2}$

71. $\frac{13}{20} \div \frac{2}{9}$

72. $\frac{8}{15} \div \frac{5}{8}$

CONCEPT EXTENSIONS

Which of the following are incorrect and why? See the second Concept Check in this section.

73. $\frac{5a - 15}{5}$ simplifies to $a - 3$?

74. $\frac{7m - 9}{7}$ simplifies to $m - 9$?

75. $\frac{1 + 2}{1 + 3}$ simplifies to $\frac{2}{3}$?

76. $\frac{46}{54}$ simplifies to $\frac{6}{5}$?

Determine whether each rational expression can be simplified. If yes, does it simplify to 1, –1, or neither? (Do not actually simplify.)

77. $\frac{x}{x + 7}$

78. $\frac{x + 9}{x - 9}$

79. $\frac{3 + x}{x + 3}$

80. $\frac{8 + x}{x + 8}$

81. $\frac{5 - x}{x - 5}$

82. $\frac{x - 7}{-x + 7}$

83. Does $\frac{x}{x + 5}$ simplify to $\frac{1}{5}$? Why or why not?

84. Does $\frac{x + 7}{x}$ simplify to 7? Why or why not?

85. In your own words explain how to simplify a rational expression.

86. In your own words, explain how to find the domain of a rational function.

87. Graph a portion of the function $f(x) = \frac{20x}{100 - x}$. To do so, complete the given table, plot the points, and then connect the plotted points with a smooth curve. (Note: The domain of this function is all real numbers except 100. We are graphing just a portion of this function.)

x	0	10	30	50	70	90	95	99
y or $f(x)$								

88. The domain of the function $f(x) = \frac{1}{x}$ is all real numbers except 0. This means that the graph of this function will be in two pieces: one piece corresponding to x values less than 0 and one piece corresponding to x values greater than 0. Graph the function by completing the following tables, separately plotting the points, and connecting each set of plotted points with a smooth curve.

x	$\frac{1}{4}$	$\frac{1}{2}$	1	2	4
y or $f(x)$					

x	–4	–2	–1	$-\frac{1}{2}$	$-\frac{1}{4}$
y or $f(x)$					

How does the graph of $y = \frac{x^2 - 9}{x - 3}$ compare to the graph of $y = x + 3$? Recall that $\frac{x^2 - 9}{x - 3} = \frac{(x + 3)(x - 3)}{x - 3} = x + 3$ as long as x is not 3. This means that the graph of $y = \frac{x^2 - 9}{x - 3}$ is the same as the graph of $y = x + 3$ with $x \neq 3$. To graph $y = \frac{x^2 - 9}{x - 3}$, then, graph the linear equation $y = x + 3$ and place an open dot on the graph at 3. This open dot or interruption of the line at 3 means $x \neq 3$.

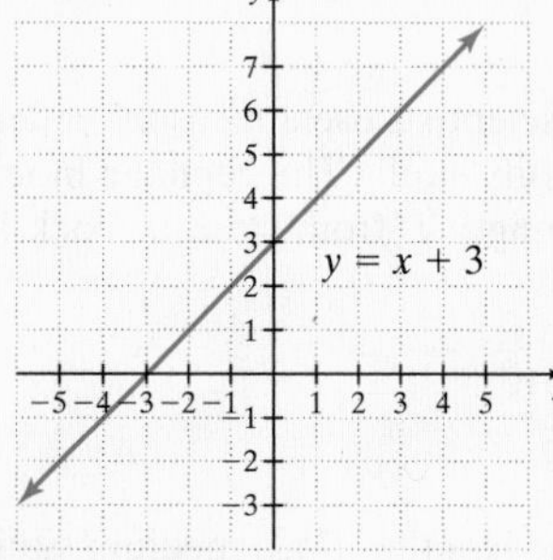

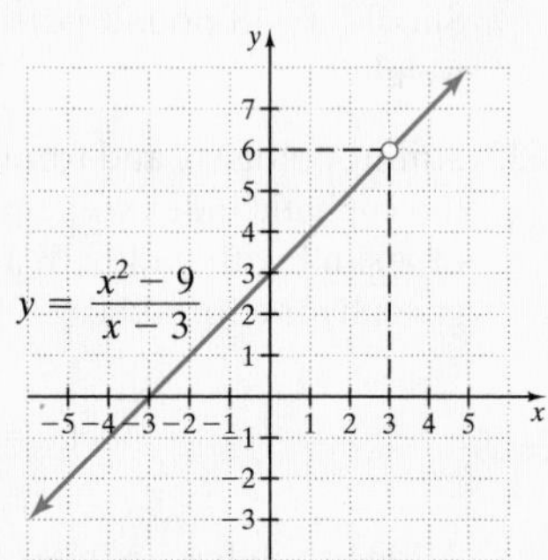

89. Graph $y = \frac{x^2 - 16}{x - 4}$.

90. Graph $y = \frac{x^2 - 25}{x + 5}$.

91. Graph $y = \frac{x^2 - 6x + 8}{x - 2}$.

92. Graph $y = \frac{x^2 + x - 12}{x + 4}$.

4.2 Multiplying and Dividing Rational Expressions 

OBJECTIVES

1. Multiply Rational Expressions.
2. Divide Rational Expressions.
3. Multiply or Divide Rational Expressions.
4. Convert Between Units of Measure.

OBJECTIVE

1 Multiplying Rational Expressions 

Just as simplifying rational expressions is similar to simplifying number fractions, multiplying and dividing rational expressions is similar to multiplying and dividing number fractions.

Fractions	***Rational Expressions***
Multiply: $\frac{3}{5} \cdot \frac{10}{11}$	Multiply: $\frac{x-3}{x+5} \cdot \frac{2x+10}{x^2-9}$

Multiply numerators and multiply denominators.

$\frac{3}{5} \cdot \frac{10}{11} = \frac{3 \cdot 10}{5 \cdot 11}$	$\frac{x-3}{x+5} \cdot \frac{2x+10}{x^2-9} = \frac{(x-3) \cdot (2x+10)}{(x+5) \cdot (x^2-9)}$

Simplify by factoring numerators and denominators.

$= \frac{3 \cdot 2 \cdot 5}{5 \cdot 11}$	$= \frac{(x-3) \cdot 2(x+5)}{(x+5)(x+3)(x-3)}$

Apply the fundamental principle.

$= \frac{3 \cdot 2}{11}$ or $\frac{6}{11}$	$= \frac{2}{x+3}$

Multiplying Rational Expressions

If $\frac{P}{Q}$ and $\frac{R}{S}$ are rational expressions, then

$$\frac{P}{Q} \cdot \frac{R}{S} = \frac{PR}{QS}$$

To multiply rational expressions, multiply the numerators and multiply the denominators.

Note: Recall that for Sections 4.1, 4.2, 4.4 and 4.5 we assume variables in rational expressions have only those replacement values for which the expressions are defined.

EXAMPLE 1 Multiply.

a. $\frac{25x}{2} \cdot \frac{1}{y^3}$ **b.** $\frac{-7x^2}{5y} \cdot \frac{3y^5}{14x^2}$

Solution To multiply rational expressions, multiply the numerators and multiply the denominators of both expressions. Then simplify if possible.

a. $\frac{25x}{2} \cdot \frac{1}{y^3} = \frac{25x \cdot 1}{2 \cdot y^3} = \frac{25x}{2y^3}$

The expression $\frac{25x}{2y^3}$ is in simplest form.

b. $\frac{-7x^2}{5y} \cdot \frac{3y^5}{14x^2} = \frac{-7x^2 \cdot 3y^5}{5y \cdot 14x^2}$ Multiply.

The expression $\frac{-7x^2 \cdot 3y^5}{5y \cdot 14x^2}$ is not in simplest form, so we factor the numerator and the denominator and divide out common factors.

$$= \frac{-1 \cdot 7 \cdot 3 \cdot x^2 \cdot y \cdot y^4}{5 \cdot 2 \cdot 7 \cdot x^2 \cdot y}$$

$$= -\frac{3y^4}{10}$$

□

(Continued on next page)

PRACTICE

1 Multiply.

a. $\frac{4a}{5} \cdot \frac{3}{b^2}$ **b.** $\frac{-3p^4}{q^2} \cdot \frac{2q^3}{9p^4}$

When multiplying rational expressions, it is usually best to factor each numerator and denominator. This will help us when we divide out common factors to write the product in lowest terms.

EXAMPLE 2 Multiply: $\frac{x^2 + x}{3x} \cdot \frac{6}{5x + 5}$

Solution

$$\frac{x^2 + x}{3x} \cdot \frac{6}{5x + 5} = \frac{x(x + 1)}{3x} \cdot \frac{2 \cdot 3}{5(x + 1)}$$ Factor numerators and denominators.

$$= \frac{x(x + 1) \cdot 2 \cdot 3}{3x \cdot 5(x + 1)}$$ Multiply.

$$= \frac{2}{5}$$ Simplify by dividing out common factors. □

PRACTICE

2 Multiply: $\frac{x^2 - x}{5x} \cdot \frac{15}{x^2 - 1}$

The following steps may be used to multiply rational expressions.

Multiplying Rational Expressions

Step 1. Completely factor numerators and denominators.

Step 2. Multiply numerators and multiply denominators.

Step 3. Simplify or write the product in lowest terms by dividing out common factors.

✓CONCEPT CHECK

Which of the following is a true statement?

a. $\frac{1}{3} \cdot \frac{1}{2} = \frac{1}{5}$ b. $\frac{2}{x} \cdot \frac{5}{x} = \frac{10}{x}$ c. $\frac{3}{x} \cdot \frac{1}{2} = \frac{3}{2x}$ d. $\frac{x}{7} \cdot \frac{x + 5}{4} = \frac{2x + 5}{28}$

EXAMPLE 3 Multiply: $\frac{3x + 3}{5x - 5x^2} \cdot \frac{2x^2 + x - 3}{4x^2 - 9}$

Solution

$$\frac{3x + 3}{5x - 5x^2} \cdot \frac{2x^2 + x - 3}{4x^2 - 9} = \frac{3(x + 1)}{5x(1 - x)} \cdot \frac{(2x + 3)(x - 1)}{(2x - 3)(2x + 3)}$$ Factor.

$$= \frac{3(x + 1)(2x + 3)(x - 1)}{5x(1 - x)(2x - 3)(2x + 3)}$$ Multiply.

$$= \frac{3(x + 1)(x - 1)}{5x(1 - x)(2x - 3)}$$ Divide out common factors.

Answer to Concept Check: c

Next, recall that $x - 1$ and $1 - x$ are opposites so that $x - 1 = -1(1 - x)$.

$$= \frac{3(x+1)(-1)(1-x)}{5x(1-x)(2x-3)}$$ Write $x - 1$ as $-1(1 - x)$.

$$= \frac{-3(x+1)}{5x(2x-3)} \quad \text{or} \quad -\frac{3(x+1)}{5x(2x-3)}$$ Divide out common factors. □

PRACTICE
3 Multiply: $\frac{6-3x}{6x+6x^2} \cdot \frac{3x^2-2x-5}{x^2-4}$.

OBJECTIVE
2 Dividing Rational Expressions 

We can divide by a rational expression in the same way we divide by a fraction. To divide by a fraction, multiply by its reciprocal.

Helpful Hint

Don't forget how to find reciprocals. The reciprocal of $\frac{a}{b}$ is $\frac{b}{a}$, $a \neq 0, b \neq 0$.

For example, to divide $\frac{3}{2}$ by $\frac{7}{8}$, multiply $\frac{3}{2}$ by $\frac{8}{7}$.

$$\frac{3}{2} \div \frac{7}{8} = \frac{3}{2} \cdot \frac{8}{7} = \frac{3 \cdot 4 \cdot 2}{2 \cdot 7} = \frac{12}{7}$$

Dividing Rational Expressions

If $\frac{P}{Q}$ and $\frac{R}{S}$ are rational expressions and $\frac{R}{S}$ is not 0, then

$$\frac{P}{Q} \div \frac{R}{S} = \frac{P}{Q} \cdot \frac{S}{R} = \frac{PS}{QR}$$

To divide two rational expressions, multiply the first rational expression by the reciprocal of the second rational expression.

EXAMPLE 4 Divide: $\frac{3x^3y^7}{40} \div \frac{4x^3}{y^2}$

Solution

$$\frac{3x^3y^7}{40} \div \frac{4x^3}{y^2} = \frac{3x^3y^7}{40} \cdot \frac{y^2}{4x^3}$$ Multiply by the reciprocal of $\frac{4x^3}{y^2}$.

$$= \frac{3x^3y^9}{160x^3}$$

$$= \frac{3y^9}{160}$$ Simplify. □

PRACTICE
4 Divide: $\frac{5a^3b^2}{24} \div \frac{10a^5}{6}$

EXAMPLE 5 Divide: $\frac{(x+2)^2}{10} \div \frac{2x+4}{5}$

Solution:

$$\frac{(x+2)^2}{10} \div \frac{2x+4}{5} = \frac{(x+2)^2}{10} \cdot \frac{5}{2x+4}$$ Multiply by the reciprocal of $\frac{2x+4}{5}$.

$$= \frac{(x+2)(x+2) \cdot 5}{5 \cdot 2 \cdot 2 \cdot (x+2)}$$ Factor and multiply.

$$= \frac{x+2}{4}$$ Simplify. □

> **Helpful Hint**
> Remember, **to Divide by a Rational Expression**, multiply by its reciprocal.

PRACTICE 5 Divide $\frac{(x-5)^2}{3}$ by $\frac{4x-20}{9}$.

The following may be used to divide by a rational expression.

Dividing by a Rational Expression
Multiply by its reciprocal.

EXAMPLE 6 Divide: $\frac{6x+2}{x^2-1} \div \frac{3x^2+x}{x-1}$

Solution

$$\frac{6x+2}{x^2-1} \div \frac{3x^2+x}{x-1} = \frac{6x+2}{x^2-1} \cdot \frac{x-1}{3x^2+x}$$ Multiply by the reciprocal.

$$= \frac{2(3x+1)(x-1)}{(x+1)(x-1) \cdot x(3x+1)}$$ Factor and multiply.

$$= \frac{2}{x(x+1)}$$ Simplify. □

PRACTICE 6 Divide $\frac{10x-2}{x^2-9} \div \frac{5x^2-x}{x+3}$.

EXAMPLE 7 Divide: $\frac{2x^2-11x+5}{5x-25} \div \frac{4x-2}{10}$

Solution

$$\frac{2x^2-11x+5}{5x-25} \div \frac{4x-2}{10} = \frac{2x^2-11x+5}{5x-25} \cdot \frac{10}{4x-2}$$ Multiply by the reciprocal.

$$= \frac{(2x-1)(x-5) \cdot 2 \cdot 5}{5(x-5) \cdot 2(2x-1)}$$ Factor and multiply.

$$= \frac{1}{1} \text{ or } 1$$ Simplify. □

PRACTICE 7 Divide $\frac{3x^2-11x-4}{2x-8} \div \frac{9x+3}{6}$.

OBJECTIVE

3 Multiplying or Dividing Rational Expressions 

Let's make sure that we understand the difference between multiplying and dividing rational expressions.

Rational Expressions	
Multiplication	Multiply the numerators and multiply the denominators.
Division	Multiply by the reciprocal of the divisor.

EXAMPLE 8 Multiply or divide as indicated.

a. $\frac{x-4}{5} \cdot \frac{x}{x-4}$ **b.** $\frac{x-4}{5} \div \frac{x}{x-4}$ **c.** $\frac{x^2-4}{2x+6} \cdot \frac{x^2+4x+3}{2-x}$

Solution

a. $\frac{x-4}{5} \cdot \frac{x}{x-4} = \frac{(x-4) \cdot x}{5 \cdot (x-4)} = \frac{x}{5}$

b. $\frac{x-4}{5} \div \frac{x}{x-4} = \frac{x-4}{5} \cdot \frac{x-4}{x} = \frac{(x-4)^2}{5x}$

c. $\frac{x^2-4}{2x+6} \cdot \frac{x^2+4x+3}{2-x} = \frac{(x-2)(x+2) \cdot (x+1)(x+3)}{2(x+3) \cdot (2-x)}$ Factor and multiply.

$= \frac{(x-2)(x+2) \cdot (x+1)(x+3)}{2(x+3) \cdot (2-x)}$

$= \frac{-1(x+2)(x+1)}{2}$ Divide out common factors. Recall that $\frac{x-2}{2-x} = -1$

$= -\frac{(x+2)(x+1)}{2}$ □

PRACTICE

8 Multiply or divide as indicated.

a. $\frac{y+9}{8x} \cdot \frac{y+9}{2x}$ **b.** $\frac{y+9}{8x} \div \frac{y+9}{2}$ **c.** $\frac{35x-7x^2}{x^2-25} \cdot \frac{x^2+3x-10}{x^2+4x}$

OBJECTIVE

4 Converting Between Units of Measure 

How many square inches are in 1 square foot?

How many cubic feet are in a cubic yard?

If you have trouble answering these questions, this section will be helpful to you.

Now that we know how to multiply fractions and rational expressions, we can use this knowledge to help us convert between units of measure. To do so, we will use **unit fractions.** A unit fraction is a fraction that equals 1. For example, since 12 in. = 1 ft, we have the unit fractions

$$\frac{12 \text{ in.}}{1 \text{ ft}} = 1 \quad \text{and} \quad \frac{1 \text{ ft}}{12 \text{ in.}} = 1$$

EXAMPLE 9 18 square feet = ____ square yards

Solution: Let's multiply 18 square feet by a unit fraction that has square feet in the denominator and square yards in the numerator. From the diagram, you can see that

1 square yard = 9 square feet

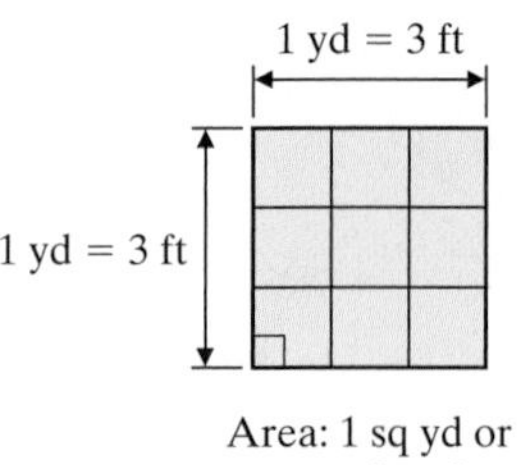

Area: 1 sq yd or 9 sq ft

Thus,

$$18 \text{ sq ft} = \frac{18 \text{ sq ft}}{1} \cdot 1 = \frac{\overset{2}{\cancel{18}} \cancel{\text{sq ft}}}{1} \cdot \frac{1 \text{ sq yd}}{\underset{1}{\cancel{9}} \cancel{\text{sq ft}}}$$

$$= \frac{2 \cdot 1}{1 \cdot 1} \text{ sq yd} = 2 \text{ sq yd}$$

Thus, 18 sq ft = 2 sq yd.

Draw a diagram of 18 sq ft to help you see that this is reasonable. □

PRACTICE
9 288 square inches = ____ square feet

EXAMPLE 10 5.2 square yards = ____ square feet

Solution:

$$5.2 \text{ sq yd} = \frac{5.2 \text{ sq yd}}{1} \cdot 1 = \frac{5.2 \cancel{\text{sq yd}}}{1} \cdot \frac{9 \text{ sq ft}}{1 \cancel{\text{sq yd}}}$$ ← Units converting to / ← Units given

$$= \frac{5.2 \cdot 9}{1 \cdot 1} \text{ sq ft}$$

$$= 46.8 \text{ sq ft}$$

Thus, 5.2 sq yd = 46.8 sq ft.

Draw a diagram to see that this is reasonable. □

PRACTICE
10 3.5 square feet = ____ square inches

EXAMPLE 11 **Converting from Cubic Feet to Cubic Yards**

The largest building in the world by volume is The Boeing Company's Everett, Washington, factory complex, where Boeing's wide-body jetliners, the 747, 767, and 777, are built. The volume of this factory complex is 472,370,319 cubic feet. Find the volume of this Boeing facility in cubic yards. (*Source:* The Boeing Company)

Solution: There are 27 cubic feet in 1 cubic yard. (See the diagram.)

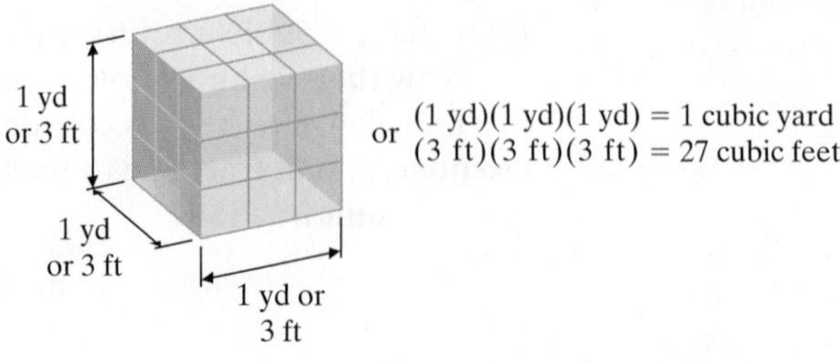

$$472{,}370{,}319 \text{ cu ft} = 472{,}370{,}319 \cancel{\text{cu ft}} \cdot \frac{1 \text{ cu yd}}{27 \cancel{\text{cu ft}}}$$

$$= \frac{472{,}370{,}319}{27} \text{ cu yd}$$

$$= 17{,}495{,}197 \text{ cu yd}$$ □

PRACTICE 11 The largest casino in the world is the Venetian, in Macau, on the southern tip of China. The gaming area for this casino is approximately 61,000 *square yards*. Find the size of the gaming area in *square feet*. (*Source: USA Today*)

> **Helpful Hint**
>
> When converting among units of measurement, if possible write the unit fraction so that **the numerator contains the units you are converting to** and **the denominator contains the original units.**
>
> $$48 \text{ in.} = \frac{48 \cancel{\text{in.}}}{1} \cdot \overbrace{\frac{1 \text{ ft}}{12 \cancel{\text{in.}}}}^{\text{Unit fraction}} \begin{matrix} \leftarrow \text{Units converting to} \\ \leftarrow \text{Original units} \end{matrix}$$
>
> $$= \frac{48}{12} \text{ ft} = 4 \text{ ft}$$

EXAMPLE 12 At the 2008 Summer Olympics, Jamaican athlete Usain Bolt won the gold medal in the men's 100-meter track event. He ran the distance at an average speed of 33.9 feet per second. Convert this speed to miles per hour. (*Source:* Beijing 2008 Olympics Committee)

Solution: Recall that 1 mile = 5280 feet and 1 hour = 3600 seconds $(60 \cdot 60)$.

$$33.9 \text{ feet/second} = \frac{33.9 \text{ feet}}{1 \text{ second}} \cdot \underbrace{\frac{3600 \text{ seconds}}{1 \text{ hour}} \cdot \frac{1 \text{ mile}}{5280 \text{ feet}}}_{\text{Unit fractions}}$$

$$= \frac{33.9 \cdot 3600}{5280} \text{ miles/hour}$$

$$\approx 23.1 \text{ miles/hour (rounded to the nearest tenth)}$$ □

PRACTICE 12 The cheetah is the fastest land animal, being clocked at about 102.7 feet per second. Convert this to miles per hour. Round to the nearest tenth. (*Source: World Almanac and Book of Facts*)

Vocabulary, Readiness & Video Check

Use one of the choices below to fill in the blank.

opposites   reciprocals

1. The expressions $\frac{x}{2y}$ and $\frac{2y}{x}$ are called ________.

Multiply or divide as indicated.

2. $\frac{a}{b} \cdot \frac{c}{d} =$ ________

3. $\frac{a}{b} \div \frac{c}{d} =$ ________

4. $\frac{x}{7} \cdot \frac{x}{6} =$ ________

5. $\frac{x}{7} \div \frac{x}{6} =$ ________

Martin-Gay Interactive Videos

See Video 4.2

Watch the section lecture video and answer the following questions.

OBJECTIVE 1

6. Would you say a person needs to be quite comfortable with factoring polynomials in order to be successful with multiplying rational expressions? Explain, referencing Example 2 in your answer.

OBJECTIVE 2

7. Based on the lecture before Example 3, complete the following statements. Dividing rational expressions is exactly like dividing _____. Therefore, to divide by a rational expression, multiply by its _____.

OBJECTIVE 3

8. In Examples 4 and 5, determining the operation is the first step in deciding how to simplify. Why do you think this is so?

OBJECTIVE 4

9. When converting between units of measurement, a unit fraction may be used. What units are used in the numerator and what units are used in the denominator of your unit fraction?

4.2 Exercise Set

MyMathLab®

Find each product and simplify if possible. See Examples 1 through 3.

1. $\frac{3x}{y^2}\cdot\frac{7y}{4x}$

2. $\frac{9x^2}{y}\cdot\frac{4y}{3x^3}$

3. $\frac{8x}{2}\cdot\frac{x^5}{4x^2}$

4. $\frac{6x^2}{10x^3}\cdot\frac{5x}{12}$

5. $-\frac{5a^2b}{30a^2b^2}\cdot b^3$

6. $-\frac{9x^3y^2}{18xy^5}\cdot y^3$

7. $\frac{x}{2x-14}\cdot\frac{x^2-7x}{5}$

8. $\frac{4x-24}{20x}\cdot\frac{5}{x-6}$

9. $\frac{6x+6}{5}\cdot\frac{10}{36x+36}$

10. $\frac{x^2+x}{8}\cdot\frac{16}{x+1}$

11. $\frac{(m+n)^2}{m-n}\cdot\frac{m}{m^2+mn}$

12. $\frac{(m-n)^2}{m+n}\cdot\frac{m}{m^2-mn}$

13. $\frac{x^2-25}{x^2-3x-10}\cdot\frac{x+2}{x}$

14. $\frac{a^2-4a+4}{a^2-4}\cdot\frac{a+3}{a-2}$

15. $\frac{x^2+6x+8}{x^2+x-20}\cdot\frac{x^2+2x-15}{x^2+8x+16}$

16. $\frac{x^2+9x+20}{x^2-15x+44}\cdot\frac{x^2-11x+28}{x^2+12x+35}$

Find each quotient and simplify. See Examples 4 through 7.

17. $\frac{5x^7}{2x^5}\div\frac{15x}{4x^3}$

18. $\frac{9y^4}{6y}\div\frac{y^2}{3}$

19. $\frac{8x^2}{y^3}\div\frac{4x^2y^3}{6}$

20. $\frac{7a^2b}{3ab^2}\div\frac{21a^2b^2}{14ab}$

21. $\frac{(x-6)(x+4)}{4x}\div\frac{2x-12}{8x^2}$

22. $\frac{(x+3)^2}{5}\div\frac{5x+15}{25}$

23. $\frac{3x^2}{x^2-1}\div\frac{x^5}{(x+1)^2}$

24. $\frac{9x^5}{a^2-b^2}\div\frac{27x^2}{3b-3a}$

25. $\frac{m^2-n^2}{m+n}\div\frac{m}{m^2+nm}$

26. $\frac{(m-n)^2}{m+n}\div\frac{m^2-mn}{m}$

27. $\frac{x+2}{7-x}\div\frac{x^2-5x+6}{x^2-9x+14}$

28. $\frac{x-3}{2-x}\div\frac{x^2+3x-18}{x^2+2x-8}$

29. $\frac{x^2+7x+10}{x-1}\div\frac{x^2+2x-15}{x-1}$

30. $\frac{x+1}{(x+1)(2x+3)}\div\frac{20x+100}{2x+3}$

MIXED PRACTICE

Multiply or divide as indicated. See Examples 1 through 8.

31. $\frac{5x-10}{12}\div\frac{4x-8}{8}$

32. $\frac{6x+6}{5}\div\frac{9x+9}{10}$

33. $\frac{x^2+5x}{8}\cdot\frac{9}{3x+15}$

34. $\frac{3x^2 + 12x}{6} \cdot \frac{9}{2x + 8}$

35. $\frac{7}{6p^2 + q} \div \frac{14}{18p^2 + 3q}$

36. $\frac{3x + 6}{20} \div \frac{4x + 8}{8}$

37. $\frac{3x + 4y}{x^2 + 4xy + 4y^2} \cdot \frac{x + 2y}{2}$

38. $\frac{x^2 - y^2}{3x^2 + 3xy} \cdot \frac{3x^2 + 6x}{3x^2 - 2xy - y^2}$

39. $\frac{(x + 2)^2}{x - 2} \div \frac{x^2 - 4}{2x - 4}$

40. $\frac{x + 3}{x^2 - 9} \div \frac{5x + 15}{(x - 3)^2}$

41. $\frac{x^2 - 4}{24x} \div \frac{2 - x}{6xy}$

42. $\frac{3y}{3 - x} \div \frac{12xy}{x^2 - 9}$

43. $\frac{a^2 + 7a + 12}{a^2 + 5a + 6} \cdot \frac{a^2 + 8a + 15}{a^2 + 5a + 4}$

44. $\frac{b^2 + 2b - 3}{b^2 + b - 2} \cdot \frac{b^2 - 4}{b^2 + 6b + 8}$

45. $\frac{5x - 20}{3x^2 + x} \cdot \frac{3x^2 + 13x + 4}{x^2 - 16}$

46. $\frac{9x + 18}{4x^2 - 3x} \cdot \frac{4x^2 - 11x + 6}{x^2 - 4}$

47. $\frac{8n^2 - 18}{2n^2 - 5n + 3} \div \frac{6n^2 + 7n - 3}{n^2 - 9n + 8}$

48. $\frac{36n^2 - 64}{3n^2 + 10n + 8} \div \frac{3n^2 - 13n + 12}{n^2 - 5n - 14}$

49. Find the quotient of $\frac{x^2 - 9}{2x}$ and $\frac{x + 3}{8x^4}$.

50. Find the quotient of $\frac{4x^2 + 4x + 1}{4x + 2}$ and $\frac{4x + 2}{16}$.

Multiply or divide as indicated. Some of these expressions contain 4-term polynomials and sums and differences of cubes. See Examples 1 through 8.

51. $\frac{a^2 + ac + ba + bc}{a - b} \div \frac{a + c}{a + b}$

52. $\frac{x^2 + 2x - xy - 2y}{x^2 - y^2} \div \frac{2x + 4}{x + y}$

53. $\frac{3x^2 + 8x + 5}{x^2 + 8x + 7} \cdot \frac{x + 7}{x^2 + 4}$

54. $\frac{16x^2 + 2x}{16x^2 + 10x + 1} \cdot \frac{1}{4x^2 + 2x}$

55. $\frac{x^3 + 8}{x^2 - 2x + 4} \cdot \frac{4}{x^2 - 4}$

56. $\frac{9y}{3y - 3} \cdot \frac{y^3 - 1}{y^3 + y^2 + y}$

57. $\frac{a^2 - ab}{6a^2 + 6ab} \div \frac{a^3 - b^3}{a^2 - b^2}$

58. $\frac{x^3 + 27y^3}{6x} \div \frac{x^2 - 9y^2}{x^2 - 3xy}$

Convert as indicated. See Examples 9 through 12.

59. 10 square feet = ________ square inches.

60. 1008 square inches = ________ square feet.

61. 45 square feet = ________ square yards.

62. 2 square yards = ________ square inches.

63. 3 cubic yards = ________ cubic feet.

64. 2 cubic yards = ________ cubic inches.

65. 50 miles per hour = ________ feet per second (round to the nearest whole).

66. 10 feet per second = ________ miles per hour (round to the nearest tenth).

67. 6.3 square yards = ________ square feet.

68. 3.6 square yards = ________ square feet.

69. In January 2010, the Burj Khalifa Tower officially became the tallest building in the world. This tower has a curtain wall (the exterior skin of the building) that is approximately 133,500 square yards. Convert this to square feet. (*Source:* Burj Khalifa)

70. The Pentagon, headquarters for the Department of Defense, contains 3,705,793 square feet of office and storage space. Convert this to square yards. Round to the nearest square yard. (*Source:* U.S. Department of Defense)

71. On October 9, 2007, Russ Wicks set a new stock car world speed record of 359.2 feet/second on the Bonneville Salt Flats in Utah. Convert this speed to miles/hour. Round to the nearest tenth. (*Source:* RussWicks.com)

72. On October 4, 2004, the rocket plane *SpaceShipOne* shot to an altitude of more than 100 km for the second time inside a week to claim the $10 million Ansari X-Prize. At one point in its flight, *SpaceShipOne* was traveling past Mach 1, about 930 miles per hour. Find this speed in feet per second. (*Source:* Space.com)

REVIEW AND PREVIEW

Perform each indicated operation. See Section R.3.

73. $\frac{1}{5} + \frac{4}{5}$

74. $\frac{3}{15} + \frac{6}{15}$

75. $\frac{9}{9} - \frac{19}{9}$

76. $\frac{4}{3} - \frac{8}{3}$

77. $\frac{6}{5} + \left(\frac{1}{5} - \frac{8}{5}\right)$

78. $-\frac{3}{2} + \left(\frac{1}{2} - \frac{3}{2}\right)$

Graph each linear equation. See Section 1.2.

79. $x - 2y = 6$

80. $5x - y = 10$

CONCEPT EXTENSIONS

Identify each statement as true or false. If false, correct the multiplication. See the Concept Check in this section.

81. $\frac{4}{a}\cdot\frac{1}{b}=\frac{4}{ab}$

82. $\frac{2}{3}\cdot\frac{2}{4}=\frac{2}{7}$

83. $\frac{x}{5}\cdot\frac{x+3}{4}=\frac{2x+3}{20}$

84. $\frac{7}{a}\cdot\frac{3}{a}=\frac{21}{a}$

△ **85.** Find the area of the rectangle.

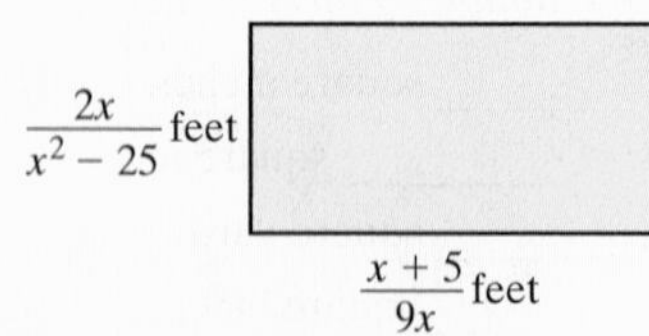

△ **86.** Find the area of the square.

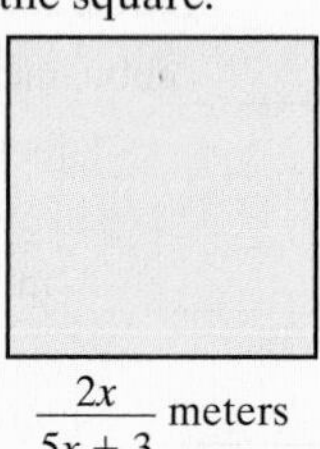

Multiply or divide as indicated.

87. $\left(\frac{x^2-y^2}{x^2+y^2}\div\frac{x^2-y^2}{3x}\right)\cdot\frac{x^2+y^2}{6}$

88. $\left(\frac{x^2-9}{x^2-1}\cdot\frac{x^2+2x+1}{2x^2+9x+9}\right)\div\frac{2x+3}{1-x}$

89. $\left(\frac{2a+b}{b^2}\cdot\frac{3a^2-2ab}{ab+2b^2}\right)\div\frac{a^2-3ab+2b^2}{5ab-10b^2}$

90. $\left(\frac{x^2y^2-xy}{4x-4y}\div\frac{3y-3x}{8x-8y}\right)\cdot\frac{y-x}{8}$

91. In your own words, explain how you multiply rational expressions.

92. Explain how dividing rational expressions is similar to dividing rational numbers.

4.3 Dividing Polynomials

OBJECTIVES

1. Divide a Polynomial by a Monomial.
2. Use Long Division to Divide a Polynomial by Another Polynomial.

OBJECTIVE

1 Dividing by a Monomial

Now that we know how to add, subtract, and multiply polynomials, we practice dividing polynomials.

To divide a polynomial by a monomial, recall addition of fractions. Fractions that have a common denominator are added by adding the numerators:

$$\frac{a}{c}+\frac{b}{c}=\frac{a+b}{c}$$

If we read this equation from right to left and let *a*, *b*, and *c* be monomials, $c \neq 0$, we have the following:

Dividing a Polynomial by a Monomial

Divide each term of the polynomial by the monomial.

$$\frac{a+b}{c}=\frac{a}{c}+\frac{b}{c},\quad c\neq 0$$

Throughout this section, we assume that denominators are not 0.

EXAMPLE 1 Divide $6m^2+2m$ by $2m$.

Solution We begin by writing the quotient in fraction form. Then we divide each term of the polynomial $6m^2+2m$ by the monomial $2m$.

$$\frac{6m^2+2m}{2m}=\frac{6m^2}{2m}+\frac{2m}{2m}$$

$$=3m+1 \qquad \text{Simplify.}$$

Check: We know that if $\frac{6m^2 + 2m}{2m} = 3m + 1$, then $2m \cdot (3m + 1)$ must equal $6m^2 + 2m$. Thus, to check, we multiply.

$$2m(3m + 1) = 2m(3m) + 2m(1) = 6m^2 + 2m$$

The quotient $3m + 1$ checks. □

PRACTICE

1 Divide $8t^3 + 4t^2$ by $4t^2$

EXAMPLE 2 Divide $\frac{9x^5 - 12x^2 + 3x}{3x^2}$.

Solution

$$\frac{9x^5 - 12x^2 + 3x}{3x^2} = \frac{9x^5}{3x^2} - \frac{12x^2}{3x^2} + \frac{3x}{3x^2} \quad \text{Divide each term by } 3x^2.$$

$$= 3x^3 - 4 + \frac{1}{x} \quad \text{Simplify.}$$

Notice that the quotient is not a polynomial because of the term $\frac{1}{x}$. This expression is called a rational expression. Although the quotient of two polynomials is not always a polynomial, we may still check by multiplying.

Check: $3x^2\left(3x^3 - 4 + \frac{1}{x}\right) = 3x^2(3x^3) - 3x^2(4) + 3x^2\left(\frac{1}{x}\right)$

$= 9x^5 - 12x^2 + 3x$ □

PRACTICE

2 Divide $\frac{16x^6 + 20x^3 - 12x}{4x^2}$.

EXAMPLE 3 Divide $\frac{8x^2y^2 - 16xy + 2x}{4xy}$.

Solution

$$\frac{8x^2y^2 - 16xy + 2x}{4xy} = \frac{8x^2y^2}{4xy} - \frac{16xy}{4xy} + \frac{2x}{4xy} \quad \text{Divide each term by } 4xy.$$

$$= 2xy - 4 + \frac{1}{2y} \quad \text{Simplify.}$$

Check: $4xy\left(2xy - 4 + \frac{1}{2y}\right) = 4xy(2xy) - 4xy(4) + 4xy\left(\frac{1}{2y}\right)$

$= 8x^2y^2 - 16xy + 2x$ □

PRACTICE

3 Divide $\frac{15x^4y^4 - 10xy + y}{5xy}$.

✓CONCEPT CHECK

In which of the following is $\frac{x + 5}{5}$ simplified correctly?

a. $\frac{x}{5} + 1$ **b.** x **c.** $x + 1$

Answer to Concept Check: a

OBJECTIVE

2 Using Long Division to Divide by a Polynomial

To divide a polynomial by a polynomial other than a monomial, we use a process known as long division. Polynomial long division is similar to number long division, so we review long division by dividing 13 into 3660.

Helpful Hint
Recall that 3660 is called the dividend.

```
    281
13)3660
   26↓    2·13 = 26
   106    Subtract and bring down the next digit in the dividend.
   104↓   8·13 = 104
    20    Subtract and bring down the next digit in the dividend.
    13    1·13 = 13
     7    Subtract. There are no more digits to bring down, so the remainder is 7.
```

The quotient is 281 R 7, which can be written as $281\frac{7}{13}$. (7 ← remainder, 13 ← divisor)

Recall that division can be checked by multiplication. To check a division problem such as this one, we see that

$$13 \cdot 281 + 7 = 3660$$

Now we demonstrate long division of polynomials.

EXAMPLE 4 Divide $x^2 + 7x + 12$ by $x + 3$ using long division.

Solution

To subtract, change the signs of these terms and add.

$$\begin{array}{r} x \\ x + 3\overline{)x^2 + 7x + 12} \\ \underline{-x^2 \mp 3x } \\ 4x + 12 \end{array}$$

How many times does x divide x^2? $\frac{x^2}{x} = x$.
Multiply: $x(x + 3)$.
Subtract and bring down the next term.

Now we repeat this process.

$$\begin{array}{r} x + 4 \\ x + 3\overline{)x^2 + 7x + 12} \\ \underline{-x^2 \mp 3x } \\ 4x + 12 \\ \underline{-4x \mp 12} \\ 0 \end{array}$$

How many times does x divide $4x$? $\frac{4x}{x} = 4$.

To subtract, change the signs of these terms and add.

Multiply: $4(x + 3)$.
Subtract. The remainder is 0.

The quotient is $x + 4$.

Check: We check by multiplying.

divisor	·	quotient	+	remainder	=	dividend
↓		↓		↓		↓
$(x + 3)$	·	$(x + 4)$	+	0	=	$x^2 + 7x + 12$

The quotient checks. □

PRACTICE
4 Divide $x^2 + 5x + 6$ by $x + 2$ using long division.

EXAMPLE 5 Divide $6x^2 + 10x - 5$ by $3x - 1$ using long division.

Solution

$$\begin{array}{r} 2x + 4 \\ 3x - 1\overline{)6x^2 + 10x - 5} \\ \underline{-6x^2 \pm 2x } \\ 12x - 5 \\ \underline{-12x \pm 4} \\ -1 \end{array}$$

$\frac{6x^2}{3x} = 2x$, so $2x$ is a term of the quotient.
Multiply $2x(3x - 1)$.
Subtract and bring down the next term.
$\frac{12x}{3x} = 4$, multiply $4(3x - 1)$
Subtract. The remainder is -1.

Thus $(6x^2 + 10x - 5)$ divided by $(3x - 1)$ is $(2x + 4)$ with a remainder of -1. This can be written as

$$\frac{6x^2 + 10x - 5}{3x - 1} = 2x + 4 + \frac{-1}{3x - 1} \begin{array}{l} \leftarrow \text{remainder} \\ \leftarrow \text{divisor} \end{array}$$

Check: To check, we multiply $(3x - 1)(2x + 4)$. Then we add the remainder, -1, to this product.

$$\begin{aligned}(3x - 1)(2x + 4) + (-1) &= (6x^2 + 12x - 2x - 4) - 1 \\ &= 6x^2 + 10x - 5\end{aligned}$$

The quotient checks. □

PRACTICE 5 Divide $4x^2 + 8x - 7$ by $2x + 1$ using long division.

In Example 5, the degree of the divisor, $3x - 1$, is 1 and the degree of the remainder, -1, is 0. The division process is continued until the degree of the remainder polynomial is less than the degree of the divisor polynomial.

Writing the dividend and divisor in a form with descending order of powers and with no missing terms is helpful when dividing polynomials.

EXAMPLE 6 Divide $\frac{4x^2 + 7 + 8x^3}{2x + 3}$.

Solution Before we begin the division process, we rewrite

$$4x^2 + 7 + 8x^3 \quad \text{as} \quad 8x^3 + 4x^2 + 0x + 7$$

Notice that we have written the polynomial in descending order and have represented the missing x term by $0x$.

$$\begin{array}{r|l} & 4x^2 - 4x + 6 \\ \hline 2x + 3 & 8x^3 + 4x^2 + 0x + 7 \\ & \underline{\overset{-}{8x^3} \overset{-}{+} 12x^2} \\ & \quad -8x^2 + 0x \\ & \quad \underline{\overset{+}{-8x^2} \overset{+}{-} 12x} \\ & \qquad 12x + 7 \\ & \qquad \underline{\overset{-}{12x} \overset{-}{+} 18} \\ & \qquad\quad -11 \end{array} \quad \text{Remainder}$$

Thus, $\frac{4x^2 + 7 + 8x^3}{2x + 3} = 4x^2 - 4x + 6 + \frac{-11}{2x + 3}$. □

PRACTICE 6 Divide $\frac{11x - 3 + 9x^3}{3x + 2}$.

EXAMPLE 7 Divide $\frac{2x^4 - x^3 + 3x^2 + x - 1}{x^2 + 1}$.

Solution Before dividing, rewrite the divisor polynomial

$$x^2 + 1 \quad \text{as} \quad x^2 + 0x + 1$$

The $0x$ term represents the missing x^1 term in the divisor.

$$
\begin{array}{r}
2x^2 - x + 1 \\
x^2 + 0x + 1 \overline{\smash{)}\,2x^4 - x^3 + 3x^2 + x - 1} \\
\underline{2x^4 + 0x^3 + 2x^2 } \\
-x^3 + x^2 + x \\
\underline{-x^3 - 0x^2 - x } \\
x^2 + 2x - 1 \\
\underline{x^2 + 0x + 1} \\
2x - 2 \quad \text{Remainder}
\end{array}
$$

Thus, $\dfrac{2x^4 - x^3 + 3x^2 + x - 1}{x^2 + 1} = 2x^2 - x + 1 + \dfrac{2x - 2}{x^2 + 1}$. □

PRACTICE 7 Divide $\dfrac{3x^4 - 2x^3 - 3x^2 + x + 4}{x^2 + 2}$.

EXAMPLE 8 Divide $x^3 - 8$ by $x - 2$.

Solution: Notice that the polynomial $x^3 - 8$ is missing an x^2-term and an x-term. We'll represent these terms by inserting $0x^2$ and $0x$.

$$
\begin{array}{r}
x^2 + 2x + 4 \\
x - 2 \overline{\smash{)}\,x^3 + 0x^2 + 0x - 8} \\
\underline{x^3 - 2x^2 } \\
2x^2 + 0x \\
\underline{2x^2 - 4x } \\
4x - 8 \\
\underline{4x - 8} \\
0
\end{array}
$$

Thus, $\dfrac{x^3 - 8}{x - 2} = x^2 + 2x + 4$.

Check: To check, see that $(x^2 + 2x + 4)(x - 2) = x^3 - 8$. □

PRACTICE 8 Divide $x^3 + 27$ by $x + 3$.

Vocabulary, Readiness & Video Check

Use the choices below to fill in each blank. Choices may be used more than once.

dividend divisor quotient

1. In $6\overline{)18}^{\,3}$, the 18 is the ________, the 3 is the ________ and the 6 is the ________.

2. In $x + 1\overline{)x^2 + 3x + 2}$ with quotient $x + 2$, the $x + 1$ is the ________, the $x^2 + 3x + 2$ is the ________ and the $x + 2$ is the ________.

Simplify each expression mentally.

3. $\dfrac{a^6}{a^4}$ **4.** $\dfrac{p^8}{p^3}$ **5.** $\dfrac{y^2}{y}$ **6.** $\dfrac{a^3}{a}$

Martin-Gay Interactive Videos

Watch the section lecture video and answer the following questions.

OBJECTIVE 1

7. The lecture before  Example 1 begins with adding two fractions with the same denominator. From there, the lecture continues to a method for dividing a polynomial by a monomial. What role does the monomial play in the fraction example?

OBJECTIVE 2

8. In  Example 5, you're told that although you don't have to fill in missing powers in the divisor and the dividend, it really is a good idea to do so. Why?

See Video 4.3

4.3 Exercise Set

MyMathLab®

Perform each division. See Examples 1 through 3.

1. $\dfrac{12x^4 + 3x^2}{x}$

2. $\dfrac{15x^2 - 9x^5}{x}$

3. $\dfrac{20x^3 - 30x^2 + 5x + 5}{5}$

4. $\dfrac{8x^3 - 4x^2 + 6x + 2}{2}$

5. $\dfrac{15p^3 + 18p^2}{3p}$

6. $\dfrac{14m^2 - 27m^3}{7m}$

7. $\dfrac{-9x^4 + 18x^5}{6x^5}$

8. $\dfrac{6x^5 + 3x^4}{3x^4}$

9. $\dfrac{-9x^5 + 3x^4 - 12}{3x^3}$

10. $\dfrac{6a^2 - 4a + 12}{-2a^2}$

11. $\dfrac{4x^4 - 6x^3 + 7}{-4x^4}$

12. $\dfrac{-12a^3 + 36a - 15}{3a}$

Find each quotient using long division. See Examples 4 and 5.

13. $\dfrac{x^2 + 4x + 3}{x + 3}$

14. $\dfrac{x^2 + 7x + 10}{x + 5}$

15. $\dfrac{2x^2 + 13x + 15}{x + 5}$

16. $\dfrac{3x^2 + 8x + 4}{x + 2}$

17. $\dfrac{2x^2 - 7x + 3}{x - 4}$

18. $\dfrac{3x^2 - x - 4}{x - 1}$

19. $\dfrac{9a^3 - 3a^2 - 3a + 4}{3a + 2}$

20. $\dfrac{4x^3 + 12x^2 + x - 14}{2x + 3}$

21. $\dfrac{8x^2 + 10x + 1}{2x + 1}$

22. $\dfrac{3x^2 + 17x + 7}{3x + 2}$

23. $\dfrac{2x^3 + 2x^2 - 17x + 8}{x - 2}$

24. $\dfrac{4x^3 + 11x^2 - 8x - 10}{x + 3}$

Find each quotient using long division. Don't forget to write the polynomials in descending order and fill in any missing terms. See Examples 6 through 8.

25. $\dfrac{x^2 - 36}{x - 6}$

26. $\dfrac{a^2 - 49}{a - 7}$

27. $\dfrac{x^3 - 27}{x - 3}$

28. $\dfrac{x^3 + 64}{x + 4}$

29. $\dfrac{1 - 3x^2}{x + 2}$

30. $\dfrac{7 - 5x^2}{x + 3}$

31. $\dfrac{-4b + 4b^2 - 5}{2b - 1}$

32. $\dfrac{-3y + 2y^2 - 15}{2y + 5}$

MIXED PRACTICE

Divide. If the divisor contains 2 or more terms, use long division. See Examples 1 through 8.

33. $\dfrac{a^2b^2 - ab^3}{ab}$

34. $\frac{m^3n^2 - mn^4}{mn}$

35. $\frac{8x^2 + 6x - 27}{2x - 3}$

36. $\frac{18w^2 + 18w - 8}{3w + 4}$

37. $\frac{2x^2y + 8x^2y^2 - xy^2}{2xy}$

38. $\frac{11x^3y^3 - 33xy + x^2y^2}{11xy}$

39. $\frac{2b^3 + 9b^2 + 6b - 4}{b + 4}$

40. $\frac{2x^3 + 3x^2 - 3x + 4}{x + 2}$

41. $\frac{5x^2 + 28x - 10}{x + 6}$

42. $\frac{2x^2 + x - 15}{x + 3}$

43. $\frac{10x^3 - 24x^2 - 10x}{10x}$

44. $\frac{2x^3 + 12x^2 + 16}{4x^2}$

45. $\frac{6x^2 + 17x - 4}{x + 3}$

46. $\frac{2x^2 - 9x + 15}{x - 6}$

47. $\frac{30x^2 - 17x + 2}{5x - 2}$

48. $\frac{4x^2 - 13x - 12}{4x + 3}$

49. $\frac{3x^4 - 9x^3 + 12}{-3x}$

50. $\frac{8y^6 - 3y^2 - 4y}{4y}$

51. $\frac{x^3 + 6x^2 + 18x + 27}{x + 3}$

52. $\frac{x^3 - 8x^2 + 32x - 64}{x - 4}$

53. $\frac{y^3 + 3y^2 + 4}{y - 2}$

54. $\frac{3x^3 + 11x + 12}{x + 4}$

55. $\frac{5 - 6x^2}{x - 2}$

56. $\frac{3 - 7x^2}{x - 3}$

Divide.

57. $\frac{x^5 + x^2}{x^2 + x}$

58. $\frac{x^6 - x^4}{x^3 + 1}$

REVIEW AND PREVIEW

Multiply each expression.

59. $2a(a^2 + 1)$

60. $-4a(3a^2 - 4)$

61. $2x(x^2 + 7x - 5)$

62. $4y(y^2 - 8y - 4)$

63. $-3xy(xy^2 + 7x^2y + 8)$

64. $-9xy(4xyz + 7xy^2z + 2)$

65. $9ab(ab^2c + 4bc - 8)$

66. $-7sr(6s^2r + 9sr^2 + 9rs + 8)$

CONCEPT EXTENSIONS

67. The perimeter of a square is $(12x^3 + 4x - 16)$ feet. Find the length of its side.

Perimeter is $(12x^3 + 4x - 16)$ feet

△ 68. The volume of the swimming pool shown is $(36x^5 - 12x^3 + 6x^2)$ cubic feet. If its height is $2x$ feet and its width is $3x$ feet, find its length.

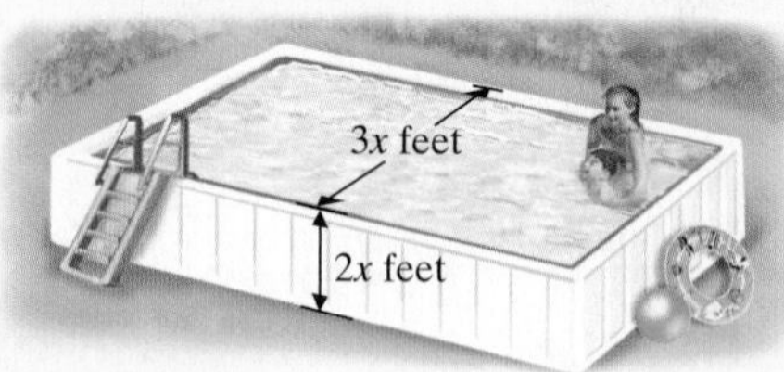

69. In which of the following is $\frac{a + 7}{7}$ simplified correctly? See the Concept Check in this section.

a. $a + 1$ **b.** a **c.** $\frac{a}{7} + 1$

70. In which of the following is $\frac{5x + 15}{5}$ simplified correctly? See the Concept Check in this section.

a. $x + 15$ **b.** $x + 3$ **c.** $x + 1$

71. Explain how to check a polynomial long division result when the remainder is 0.

72. Explain how to check a polynomial long division result when the remainder is not 0.

△ **73.** The area of the following parallelogram is $(10x^2 + 31x + 15)$ square meters. If its base is $(5x + 3)$ meters, find its height.

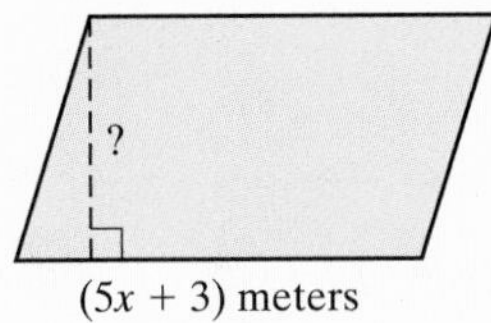

△ **74.** The area of the top of the Ping-Pong table is $(49x^2 + 70x - 200)$ square inches. If its length is $(7x + 20)$ inches, find its width.

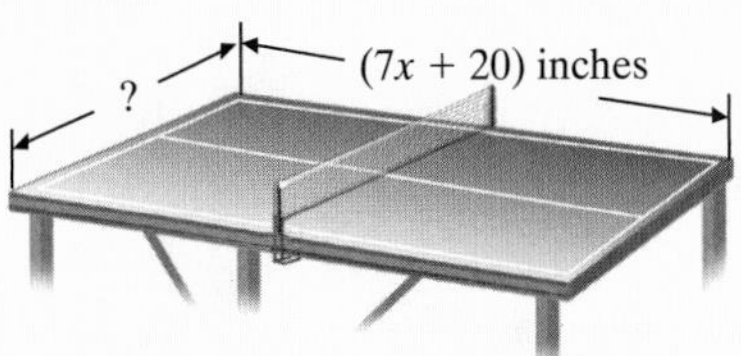

75. $(18x^{10a} - 12x^{8a} + 14x^{5a} - 2x^{3a}) \div 2x^{3a}$

76. $(25y^{11b} + 5y^{6b} - 20y^{3b} + 100y^{b}) \div 5y^{b}$

4.4 Adding and Subtracting Rational Expressions with Common Denominators and Least Common Denominator

OBJECTIVES

1 Add and Subtract Rational Expressions with the Same Denominator.

2 Find the Least Common Denominator of a List of Rational Expressions.

3 Write a Rational Expression as an Equivalent Expression Whose Denominator Is Given.

OBJECTIVE 1

Adding and Subtracting Rational Expressions with the Same Denominator

Like multiplication and division, addition and subtraction of rational expressions is similar to addition and subtraction of rational numbers. In this section, we add and subtract rational expressions with a common (or the same) denominator.

Add: $\frac{6}{5} + \frac{2}{5}$

Add: $\frac{9}{x + 2} + \frac{3}{x + 2}$

Add the numerators and place the sum over the common denominator.

$$\frac{6}{5} + \frac{2}{5} = \frac{6 + 2}{5}$$

$$= \frac{8}{5} \quad \text{Simplify.}$$

$$\frac{9}{x + 2} + \frac{3}{x + 2} = \frac{9 + 3}{x + 2}$$

$$= \frac{12}{x + 2} \quad \text{Simplify.}$$

Adding and Subtracting Rational Expressions with Common Denominators

If $\frac{P}{R}$ and $\frac{Q}{R}$ are rational expressions, then

$$\frac{P}{R} + \frac{Q}{R} = \frac{P + Q}{R} \quad \text{and} \quad \frac{P}{R} - \frac{Q}{R} = \frac{P - Q}{R}$$

To add or subtract rational expressions, add or subtract the numerators and place the sum or difference over the common denominator.

EXAMPLE 1 Add: $\frac{5m}{2n} + \frac{m}{2n}$

Solution

$$\frac{5m}{2n} + \frac{m}{2n} = \frac{5m + m}{2n} \quad \text{Add the numerators.}$$

$$= \frac{6m}{2n} \quad \text{Simplify the numerator by combining like terms.}$$

$$= \frac{3m}{n} \quad \text{Simplify by applying the fundamental principle.}$$

□

PRACTICE 1 Add: $\frac{7a}{4b} + \frac{a}{4b}$

EXAMPLE 2 Subtract: $\frac{2y}{2y - 7} - \frac{7}{2y - 7}$

Solution

$$\frac{2y}{2y - 7} - \frac{7}{2y - 7} = \frac{2y - 7}{2y - 7} \quad \text{Subtract the numerators.}$$

$$= \frac{1}{1} \text{ or } 1 \quad \text{Simplify.}$$

□

PRACTICE 2 Subtract: $\frac{3x}{3x - 2} - \frac{2}{3x - 2}$

EXAMPLE 3 Subtract: $\frac{3x^2 + 2x}{x - 1} - \frac{10x - 5}{x - 1}$

Solution

$$\frac{3x^2 + 2x}{x - 1} - \frac{10x - 5}{x - 1} = \frac{(3x^2 + 2x) - (10x - 5)}{x - 1} \quad \text{Subtract the numerators. Notice the parentheses.}$$

$$= \frac{3x^2 + 2x - 10x + 5}{x - 1} \quad \text{Use the distributive property.}$$

$$= \frac{3x^2 - 8x + 5}{x - 1} \quad \text{Combine like terms.}$$

$$= \frac{(x - 1)(3x - 5)}{x - 1} \quad \text{Factor.}$$

$$= 3x - 5 \quad \text{Simplify.}$$

□

Helpful Hint

Parentheses are inserted so that the entire numerator, $10x - 5$, is subtracted.

PRACTICE 3 Subtract: $\frac{4x^2 + 15x}{x + 3} - \frac{8x + 15}{x + 3}$

Helpful Hint

Notice how the numerator $10x - 5$ has been subtracted in Example 3.

This – sign applies to the entire numerator of $10x - 5$.

So parentheses are inserted here to indicate this.

$$\frac{3x^2 + 2x}{x - 1} - \frac{10x - 5}{x - 1} = \frac{3x^2 + 2x - (10x - 5)}{x - 1}$$

OBJECTIVE

2 Finding the Least Common Denominator 

To add and subtract fractions with **unlike** denominators, first find a least common denominator (LCD) and then write all fractions as equivalent fractions with the LCD.

For example, suppose we add $\frac{8}{3}$ and $\frac{2}{5}$. The LCD of denominators 3 and 5 is 15, since 15 is the least common multiple (LCM) of 3 and 5. That is, 15 is the smallest number that both 3 and 5 divide into evenly.

Next, rewrite each fraction so that its denominator is 15.

$$\frac{8}{3} + \frac{2}{5} = \frac{8(5)}{3(5)} + \frac{2(3)}{5(3)} = \frac{40}{15} + \frac{6}{15} = \frac{40 + 6}{15} = \frac{46}{15}$$

↑ ↑

We are multiplying by 1.

To add or subtract rational expressions with unlike denominators, we also first find an LCD and then write all rational expressions as equivalent expressions with the LCD. The **least common denominator (LCD) of a list of rational expressions** is a polynomial of least degree whose factors include all the factors of the denominators in the list.

Finding the Least Common Denominator (LCD)

Step 1. Factor each denominator completely.

Step 2. The least common denominator (LCD) is the product of all unique factors found in Step 1, each raised to a power equal to the greatest number of times that the factor appears in any one factored denominator.

EXAMPLE 4 Find the LCD for each pair.

a. $\frac{1}{8}, \frac{3}{22}$ **b.** $\frac{7}{5x}, \frac{6}{15x^2}$

Solution

a. Start by finding the prime factorization of each denominator.

$$8 = 2 \cdot 2 \cdot 2 = 2^3 \quad \text{and}$$
$$22 = 2 \cdot 11$$

Next, write the product of all the unique factors, each raised to a power equal to the greatest number of times that the factor appears in any denominator.

The greatest number of times that the factor 2 appears is 3.

The greatest number of times that the factor 11 appears is 1.

$$\text{LCD} = 2^3 \cdot 11^1 = 8 \cdot 11 = 88$$

b. Factor each denominator.

$$5x = 5 \cdot x \quad \text{and}$$
$$15x^2 = 3 \cdot 5 \cdot x^2$$

The greatest number of times that the factor 5 appears is 1.

The greatest number of times that the factor 3 appears is 1.

The greatest number of times that the factor x appears is 2.

$$\text{LCD} = 3^1 \cdot 5^1 \cdot x^2 = 15x^2$$

□

PRACTICE

4 Find the LCD for each pair.

a. $\frac{3}{14}, \frac{5}{21}$ **b.** $\frac{4}{9y}, \frac{11}{15y^3}$

EXAMPLE 5 Find the LCD of

a. $\frac{7x}{x+2}$ and $\frac{5x^2}{x-2}$ **b.** $\frac{3}{x}$ and $\frac{6}{x+4}$

Solution

a. The denominators $x + 2$ and $x - 2$ are completely factored already. The factor $x + 2$ appears once and the factor $x - 2$ appears once.

$$\text{LCD} = (x+2)(x-2)$$

b. The denominators x and $x + 4$ cannot be factored further. The factor x appears once and the factor $x + 4$ appears once.

$$\text{LCD} = x(x+4)$$

□

PRACTICE 5 Find the LCD of

a. $\frac{16}{y-5}$ and $\frac{3y^3}{y-4}$ **b.** $\frac{8}{a}$ and $\frac{5}{a+2}$

EXAMPLE 6 Find the LCD of $\frac{6m^2}{3m+15}$ and $\frac{2}{(m+5)^2}$.

Solution We factor each denominator.

$$3m + 15 = 3(m+5)$$

$$(m+5)^2 = (m+5)^2 \quad \text{This denominator is already factored.}$$

The greatest number of times that the factor 3 appears is 1.

The greatest number of times that the factor $m + 5$ appears *in any one denominator* is 2.

$$\text{LCD} = 3(m+5)^2$$

□

PRACTICE 6 Find the LCD of $\frac{2x^3}{(2x-1)^2}$ and $\frac{5x}{6x-3}$.

✓CONCEPT CHECK

Choose the correct LCD of $\frac{x}{(x+1)^2}$ and $\frac{5}{x+1}$.

a. $x + 1$ **b.** $(x+1)^2$ **c.** $(x+1)^3$ **d.** $5x(x+1)^2$

EXAMPLE 7 Find the LCD of $\frac{t-10}{t^2-t-6}$ and $\frac{t+5}{t^2+3t+2}$.

Solution Start by factoring each denominator.

$$t^2 - t - 6 = (t-3)(t+2)$$

$$t^2 + 3t + 2 = (t+1)(t+2)$$

$$\text{LCD} = (t-3)(t+2)(t+1)$$

□

PRACTICE 7 Find the LCD of $\frac{x-5}{x^2+5x+4}$ and $\frac{x+8}{x^2-16}$.

Answer to Concept Check: b

EXAMPLE 8 Find the LCD of $\frac{2}{x-2}$ and $\frac{10}{2-x}$.

Solution The denominators $x - 2$ and $2 - x$ are opposites. That is, $2 - x = -1(x - 2)$. Use $x - 2$ or $2 - x$ as the LCD.

$$\text{LCD} = x - 2 \qquad \text{or} \qquad \text{LCD} = 2 - x$$

□

PRACTICE 8 Find the LCD of $\frac{5}{3-x}$ and $\frac{4}{x-3}$.

OBJECTIVE 3 **Writing Equivalent Rational Expressions**

Next we practice writing a rational expression as an equivalent rational expression with a given denominator. To do this, we multiply by a form of 1. Recall that multiplying an expression by 1 produces an equivalent expression. In other words,

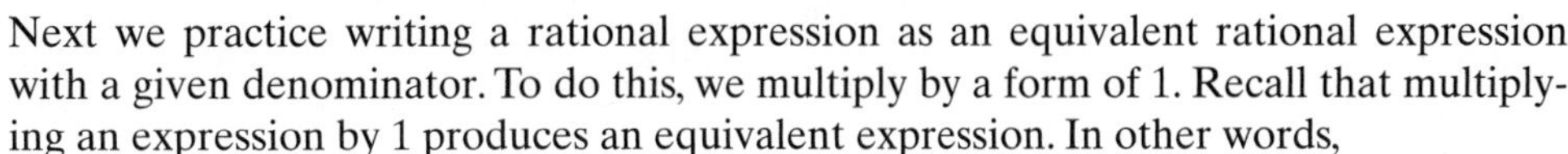

$$\frac{P}{Q} = \frac{P}{Q}\cdot 1 = \frac{P}{Q}\cdot\frac{R}{R} = \frac{PR}{QR}.$$

EXAMPLE 9 Write each rational expression as an equivalent rational expression with the given denominator.

a. $\frac{4b}{9a} = \frac{}{27a^2b}$ **b.** $\frac{7x}{2x+5} = \frac{}{6x+15}$

Solution

a. We can ask ourselves: "What do we multiply $9a$ by to get $27a^2b$?" The answer is $3ab$, since $9a(3ab) = 27a^2b$. So we multiply by 1 in the form of $\frac{3ab}{3ab}$.

$$\frac{4b}{9a} = \frac{4b}{9a}\cdot 1$$
$$= \frac{4b}{9a}\cdot\frac{3ab}{3ab}$$
$$= \frac{4b(3ab)}{9a(3ab)} = \frac{12ab^2}{27a^2b}$$

b. First, factor the denominator on the right.

$$\frac{7x}{2x+5} = \frac{}{3(2x+5)}$$

To obtain the denominator on the right from the denominator on the left, we multiply by 1 in the form of $\frac{3}{3}$.

$$\frac{7x}{2x+5} = \frac{7x}{2x+5}\cdot\frac{3}{3} = \frac{7x\cdot 3}{(2x+5)\cdot 3} = \frac{21x}{3(2x+5)} \text{ or } \frac{21x}{6x+15}$$

□

PRACTICE 9 Write each rational expression as an equivalent fraction with the given denominator.

a. $\frac{3x}{5y} = \frac{}{35xy^2}$ **b.** $\frac{9x}{4x+7} = \frac{}{8x+14}$

EXAMPLE 10 Write the rational expression as an equivalent rational expression with the given denominator.

$$\frac{5}{x^2 - 4} = \frac{}{(x - 2)(x + 2)(x - 4)}$$

Solution First, factor the denominator $x^2 - 4$ as $(x - 2)(x + 2)$.

If we multiply the original denominator $(x - 2)(x + 2)$ by $x - 4$, the result is the new denominator $(x - 2)(x + 2)(x - 4)$. Thus, we multiply by 1 in the form of $\frac{x - 4}{x - 4}$.

$$\frac{5}{\underbrace{x^2 - 4}} = \frac{5}{\underbrace{(x - 2)(x + 2)}_{\text{Factored denominator}}} = \frac{5}{(x - 2)(x + 2)} \cdot \frac{x - 4}{x - 4}$$

$$= \frac{5(x - 4)}{(x - 2)(x + 2)(x - 4)}$$

$$= \frac{5x - 20}{(x - 2)(x + 2)(x - 4)}$$

□

PRACTICE

10 Write the rational expression as an equivalent rational expression with the given denominator.

$$\frac{3}{x^2 - 2x - 15} = \frac{}{(x - 2)(x + 3)(x - 5)}$$

Vocabulary, Readiness & Video Check

Use the choices below to fill in each blank. Not all choices will be used.

$\frac{9}{22}$ $\frac{5}{22}$ $\frac{9}{11}$ $\frac{5}{11}$ $\frac{ac}{b}$ $\frac{a - c}{b}$ $\frac{a + c}{b}$ $\frac{5 - 6 + x}{x}$ $\frac{5 - (6 + x)}{x}$

1. $\frac{7}{11} + \frac{2}{11} =$ ________

2. $\frac{7}{11} - \frac{2}{11} =$ ________

3. $\frac{a}{b} + \frac{c}{b} =$ ________

4. $\frac{a}{b} - \frac{c}{b} =$ ________

5. $\frac{5}{x} - \frac{6 + x}{x} =$ ________

Martin-Gay Interactive Videos

See Video 4.4

Watch the section lecture video and answer the following questions.

OBJECTIVE 1

6. In Example 3, why is it important to place parentheses around the second numerator when writing as one expression?

OBJECTIVE 2

7. In Example 4 and 5, we factor the denominators completely. How does this help determine the LCD?

OBJECTIVE 3

8. Based on Example 6, complete the following statements. To write an equivalent rational expression, you multiply the ________ of a rational expression by the same expression as the denominator. This means you're multiplying the original rational expression by a factor of ________ and therefore not changing the ________ of the original expression.

4.4 Exercise Set

MyMathLab®  

Add or subtract as indicated. Simplify the result if possible. See Examples 1 through 3.

1. $\frac{a+1}{13}+\frac{8}{13}$
2. $\frac{x+1}{7}+\frac{6}{7}$
3. $\frac{4m}{3n}+\frac{5m}{3n}$
4. $\frac{3p}{2q}+\frac{11p}{2q}$
5. $\frac{4m}{m-6}-\frac{24}{m-6}$
6. $\frac{8y}{y-2}-\frac{16}{y-2}$
7. $\frac{9}{3+y}+\frac{y+1}{3+y}$
8. $\frac{9}{y+9}+\frac{y-5}{y+9}$
9. $\frac{5x^2+4x}{x-1}-\frac{6x+3}{x-1}$
10. $\frac{x^2+9x}{x+7}-\frac{4x+14}{x+7}$
11. $\frac{4a}{a^2+2a-15}-\frac{12}{a^2+2a-15}$
12. $\frac{3y}{y^2+3y-10}-\frac{6}{y^2+3y-10}$
13. $\frac{2x+3}{x^2-x-30}-\frac{x-2}{x^2-x-30}$
14. $\frac{3x-1}{x^2+5x-6}-\frac{2x-7}{x^2+5x-6}$
15. $\frac{2x+1}{x-3}+\frac{3x+6}{x-3}$
16. $\frac{4p-3}{2p+7}+\frac{3p+8}{2p+7}$
17. $\frac{2x^2}{x-5}-\frac{25+x^2}{x-5}$
18. $\frac{6x^2}{2x-5}-\frac{25+2x^2}{2x-5}$
19. $\frac{5x+4}{x-1}-\frac{2x+7}{x-1}$
20. $\frac{7x+1}{x-4}-\frac{2x+21}{x-4}$

Find the LCD for each list of rational expressions. See Examples 4 through 8.

21. $\frac{19}{2x}, \frac{5}{4x^3}$
22. $\frac{17x}{4y^5}, \frac{2}{8y}$
23. $\frac{9}{8x}, \frac{3}{2x+4}$
24. $\frac{1}{6y}, \frac{3x}{4y+12}$
25. $\frac{2}{x+3}, \frac{5}{x-2}$
26. $\frac{-6}{x-1}, \frac{4}{x+5}$
27. $\frac{x}{x+6}, \frac{10}{3x+18}$
28. $\frac{12}{x+5}, \frac{x}{4x+20}$
29. $\frac{8x^2}{(x-6)^2}, \frac{13x}{5x-30}$
30. $\frac{9x^2}{7x-14}, \frac{6x}{(x-2)^2}$
31. $\frac{1}{3x+3}, \frac{8}{2x^2+4x+2}$
32. $\frac{19x+5}{4x-12}, \frac{3}{2x^2-12x+18}$
33. $\frac{5}{x-8}, \frac{3}{8-x}$
34. $\frac{2x+5}{3x-7}, \frac{5}{7-3x}$
35. $\frac{5x+1}{x^2+3x-4}, \frac{3x}{x^2+2x-3}$
36. $\frac{4}{x^2+4x+3}, \frac{4x-2}{x^2+10x+21}$
37. $\frac{2x}{3x^2+4x+1}, \frac{7}{2x^2-x-1}$
38. $\frac{3x}{4x^2+5x+1}, \frac{5}{3x^2-2x-1}$
39. $\frac{1}{x^2-16}, \frac{x+6}{2x^3-8x^2}$
40. $\frac{5}{x^2-25}, \frac{x+9}{3x^3-15x^2}$

Rewrite each rational expression as an equivalent rational expression with the given denominator. See Examples 9 and 10.

41. $\frac{3}{2x}=\frac{}{4x^2}$
42. $\frac{3}{9y^5}=\frac{}{72y^9}$
43. $\frac{6}{3a}=\frac{}{12ab^2}$
44. $\frac{5}{4y^2x}=\frac{}{32y^3x^2}$
45. $\frac{9}{2x+6}=\frac{}{2y(x+3)}$
46. $\frac{4x+1}{3x+6}=\frac{}{3y(x+2)}$
47. $\frac{9a+2}{5a+10}=\frac{}{5b(a+2)}$
48. $\frac{5+y}{2x^2+10}=\frac{}{4(x^2+5)}$
49. $\frac{x}{x^3+6x^2+8x}=\frac{}{x(x+4)(x+2)(x+1)}$
50. $\frac{5x}{x^3+2x^2-3x}=\frac{}{x(x-1)(x-5)(x+3)}$
51. $\frac{9y-1}{15x^2-30}=\frac{}{30x^2-60}$
52. $\frac{6m-5}{3x^2-9}=\frac{}{12x^2-36}$

MIXED PRACTICE

Perform the indicated operations.

53. $\frac{5x}{7}+\frac{9x}{7}$
54. $\frac{5x}{7}\cdot\frac{9x}{7}$
55. $\frac{x+3}{4}\div\frac{2x-1}{4}$
56. $\frac{x+3}{4}-\frac{2x-1}{4}$
57. $\frac{x^2}{x-6}-\frac{5x+6}{x-6}$
58. $\frac{x^2+5x}{x^2-25}\cdot\frac{3x-15}{x^2}$

59. $\frac{-2x}{x^3 - 8x} + \frac{3x}{x^3 - 8x}$

60. $\frac{-2x}{x^3 - 8x} \div \frac{3x}{x^3 - 8x}$

61. $\frac{12x - 6}{x^2 + 3x} \cdot \frac{4x^2 + 13x + 3}{4x^2 - 1}$

62. $\frac{x^3 + 7x^2}{3x^3 - x^2} \div \frac{5x^2 + 36x + 7}{9x^2 - 1}$

REVIEW AND PREVIEW

Perform each indicated operation. See Section R.3.

63. $\frac{2}{3} + \frac{5}{7}$

64. $\frac{9}{10} - \frac{3}{5}$

65. $\frac{1}{6} - \frac{3}{4}$

66. $\frac{11}{15} + \frac{5}{9}$

67. $\frac{1}{12} + \frac{3}{20}$

68. $\frac{7}{30} + \frac{3}{18}$

CONCEPT EXTENSIONS

For Exercises 69 and 70, see the Concept Check in this section.

69. Choose the correct LCD of $\frac{11a^3}{4a - 20}$ and $\frac{15a^3}{(a - 5)^2}$.

a. $4a(a - 5)(a + 5)$ **b.** $a - 5$ **c.** $(a - 5)^2$

d. $4(a - 5)^2$ **e.** $(4a - 20)(a - 5)^2$

70. Choose the correct LCD of $\frac{5}{14x^2}$ and $\frac{y}{6x^3}$.

a. $84x^5$ **b.** $84x^3$

c. $42x^3$ **d.** $42x^5$

For Exercises 71 and 72, an algebra student approaches you with each incorrect solution. Find the error and correct the work shown below.

71. $\frac{2x - 6}{x - 5} - \frac{x + 4}{x - 5} = \frac{2x - 6 - x + 4}{x - 5} = \frac{x - 2}{x - 5}$

72. $\frac{x}{x + 3} + \frac{2}{x + 3} = \frac{x + 2}{x + 3} = \frac{2}{3}$

Multiple choice. Select the correct result.

73. $\frac{3}{x} + \frac{y}{x} =$

a. $\frac{3 + y}{x^2}$ **b.** $\frac{3 + y}{2x}$ **c.** $\frac{3 + y}{x}$

74. $\frac{3}{x} - \frac{y}{x} =$

a. $\frac{3 - y}{x^2}$ **b.** $\frac{3 - y}{2x}$ **c.** $\frac{3 - y}{x}$

75. $\frac{3}{x} \cdot \frac{y}{x} =$

a. $\frac{3y}{x}$ **b.** $\frac{3y}{x^2}$ **c.** $3y$

76. $\frac{3}{x} \div \frac{y}{x} =$

a. $\frac{3}{y}$ **b.** $\frac{y}{3}$ **c.** $\frac{3}{x^2y}$

Write each rational expression as an equivalent expression with a denominator of $x - 2$.

77. $\frac{5}{2 - x}$

78. $\frac{8y}{2 - x}$

79. $-\frac{7 + x}{2 - x}$

80. $\frac{x - 3}{-(x - 2)}$

△ 81. A square has a side of length $\frac{5}{x - 2}$ meters. Express its perimeter as a rational expression.

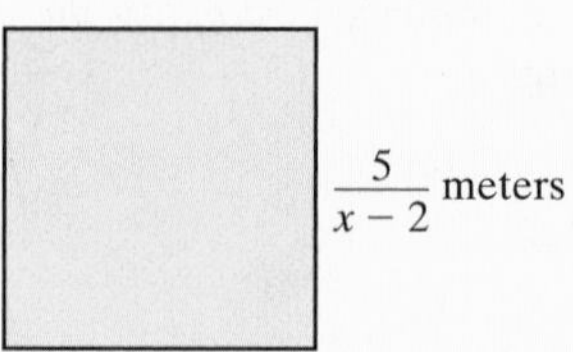

△ 82. A trapezoid has sides of the indicated lengths. Find its perimeter.

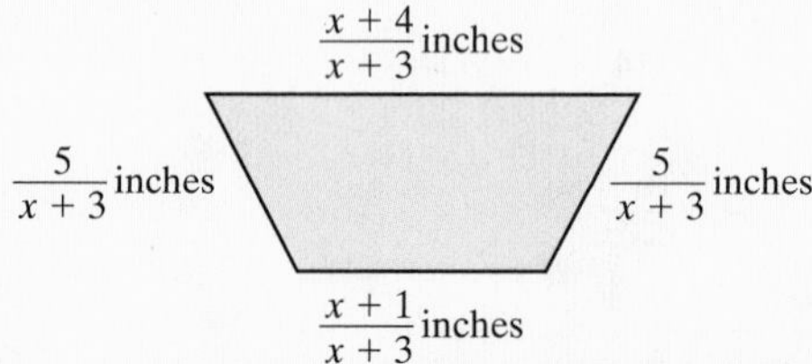

83. Write two rational expressions with the same denominator whose sum is $\frac{5}{3x - 1}$.

84. Write two rational expressions with the same denominator whose difference is $\frac{x - 7}{x^2 + 1}$.

85. The planet Mercury revolves around the sun in 88 Earth days. It takes Jupiter 4332 Earth days to make one revolution around the sun. (*Source:* National Space Science Data Center) If the two planets are aligned as shown in the figure, how long will it take for them to align again?

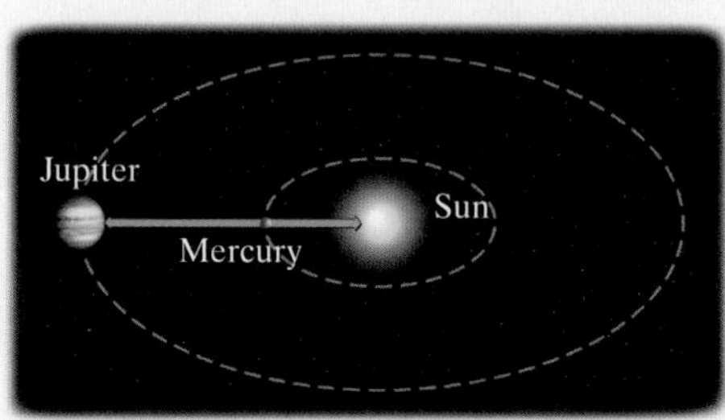

86. You are throwing a barbecue and you want to make sure that you purchase the same number of hot dogs as hot dog buns. Hot dogs come 8 to a package and hot dog buns come 12 to a package. What is the least number of each type of package you should buy?

87. Write some instructions to help a friend who is having difficulty finding the LCD of two rational expressions.

88. Explain why the LCD of the rational expressions $\frac{7}{x + 1}$ and $\frac{9x}{(x + 1)^2}$ is $(x + 1)^2$ and not $(x + 1)^3$.

89. In your own words, describe how to add or subtract two rational expressions with the same denominators.

90. Explain the similarities between subtracting $\frac{3}{8}$ from $\frac{7}{8}$ and subtracting $\frac{6}{x + 3}$ from $\frac{9}{x + 3}$.

4.5 Adding and Subtracting Rational Expressions with Unlike Denominators

OBJECTIVE

1 Add and Subtract Rational Expressions with Unlike Denominators.

OBJECTIVE

1 Adding and Subtracting Rational Expressions with Unlike Denominators

Let's add $\frac{3}{8}$ and $\frac{1}{6}$. From the previous section, the LCD of 8 and 6 is 24. Now let's write equivalent fractions with denominator 24 by multiplying by different forms of 1.

$$\frac{3}{8} = \frac{3}{8} \cdot 1 = \frac{3}{8} \cdot \frac{3}{3} = \frac{3 \cdot 3}{8 \cdot 3} = \frac{9}{24}$$

$$\frac{1}{6} = \frac{1}{6} \cdot 1 = \frac{1}{6} \cdot \frac{4}{4} = \frac{1 \cdot 4}{6 \cdot 4} = \frac{4}{24}$$

Now that the denominators are the same, we may add.

$$\frac{3}{8} + \frac{1}{6} = \frac{9}{24} + \frac{4}{24} = \frac{9+4}{24} = \frac{13}{24}$$

We add or subtract rational expressions the same way. You may want to use the steps below.

Adding or Subtracting Rational Expressions with Unlike Denominators

Step 1. Find the LCD of the rational expressions.

Step 2. Rewrite each rational expression as an equivalent expression whose denominator is the LCD found in Step 1.

Step 3. Add or subtract numerators and write the sum or difference over the common denominator.

Step 4. Simplify or write the rational expression in simplest form.

EXAMPLE 1 Perform each indicated operation.

a. $\frac{a}{4} - \frac{2a}{8}$ **b.** $\frac{3}{10x^2} + \frac{7}{25x}$

Solution

a. First, we must find the LCD. Since $4 = 2^2$ and $8 = 2^3$, the LCD $= 2^3 = 8$. Next we write each fraction as an equivalent fraction with the denominator 8, then we subtract.

$$\frac{a}{4} - \frac{2a}{8} = \frac{a(2)}{4(2)} - \frac{2a}{8} = \frac{2a}{8} - \frac{2a}{8} = \frac{2a - 2a}{8} = \frac{0}{8} = 0$$

Multiplying the numerator and denominator by 2 is the same as multiplying by $\frac{2}{2}$ or 1.

b. Since $10x^2 = 2 \cdot 5 \cdot x \cdot x$ and $25x = 5 \cdot 5 \cdot x$, the LCD $= 2 \cdot 5^2 \cdot x^2 = 50x^2$. We write each fraction as an equivalent fraction with a denominator of $50x^2$.

$$\frac{3}{10x^2} + \frac{7}{25x} = \frac{3(5)}{10x^2(5)} + \frac{7(2x)}{25x(2x)}$$

$$= \frac{15}{50x^2} + \frac{14x}{50x^2}$$

$$= \frac{15 + 14x}{50x^2}$$ Add numerators. Write the sum over the common denominator.

□

PRACTICE 1 Perform each indicated operation.

a. $\frac{2x}{5} - \frac{6x}{15}$ **b.** $\frac{7}{8a} + \frac{5}{12a^2}$

EXAMPLE 2 Subtract: $\frac{6x}{x^2 - 4} - \frac{3}{x + 2}$

Solution Since $x^2 - 4 = (x + 2)(x - 2)$, the LCD $= (x - 2)(x + 2)$. We write equivalent expressions with the LCD as denominators.

$$\frac{6x}{x^2 - 4} - \frac{3}{x + 2} = \frac{6x}{(x - 2)(x + 2)} - \frac{3(x - 2)}{(x + 2)(x - 2)}$$

$$= \frac{6x - 3(x - 2)}{(x + 2)(x - 2)}$$ Subtract numerators. Write the difference over the common denominator.

$$= \frac{6x - 3x + 6}{(x + 2)(x - 2)}$$ Apply the distributive property in the numerator.

$$= \frac{3x + 6}{(x + 2)(x - 2)}$$ Combine like terms in the numerator.

Next we factor the numerator to see if this rational expression can be simplified.

$$= \frac{3(x + 2)}{(x + 2)(x - 2)}$$ Factor.

$$= \frac{3}{x - 2}$$ Divide out common factors to simplify. □

PRACTICE 2 Subtract: $\frac{12x}{x^2 - 25} - \frac{6}{x + 5}$

EXAMPLE 3 Add: $\frac{2}{3t} + \frac{5}{t + 1}$

Solution The LCD is $3t(t + 1)$. We write each rational expression as an equivalent rational expression with a denominator of $3t(t + 1)$.

$$\frac{2}{3t} + \frac{5}{t + 1} = \frac{2(t + 1)}{3t(t + 1)} + \frac{5(3t)}{(t + 1)(3t)}$$

$$= \frac{2(t + 1) + 5(3t)}{3t(t + 1)}$$ Add numerators. Write the sum over the common denominator.

$$= \frac{2t + 2 + 15t}{3t(t + 1)}$$ Apply the distributive property in the numerator.

$$= \frac{17t + 2}{3t(t + 1)}$$ Combine like terms in the numerator. □

PRACTICE 3 Add: $\frac{3}{5y} + \frac{2}{y + 1}$

EXAMPLE 4 Subtract: $\frac{7}{x - 3} - \frac{9}{3 - x}$

Solution To find a common denominator, we notice that $x - 3$ and $3 - x$ are opposites. That is, $3 - x = -(x - 3)$. We write the denominator $3 - x$ as $-(x - 3)$ and simplify.

$$\frac{7}{x-3} - \frac{9}{3-x} = \frac{7}{x-3} - \frac{9}{-(x-3)}$$

$$= \frac{7}{x-3} - \frac{-9}{x-3}$$ Apply $\frac{a}{-b} = \frac{-a}{b}$.

$$= \frac{7-(-9)}{x-3}$$ Subtract numerators. Write the difference over the common denominator.

$$= \frac{16}{x-3}$$ □

PRACTICE 4 Subtract: $\frac{6}{x-5} - \frac{7}{5-x}$

EXAMPLE 5 Add: $1 + \frac{m}{m+1}$

Solution Recall that 1 is the same as $\frac{1}{1}$. The LCD of $\frac{1}{1}$ and $\frac{m}{m+1}$ is $m + 1$.

$$1 + \frac{m}{m+1} = \frac{1}{1} + \frac{m}{m+1}$$ Write 1 as $\frac{1}{1}$.

$$= \frac{1(m+1)}{1(m+1)} + \frac{m}{m+1}$$ Multiply both the numerator and the denominator of $\frac{1}{1}$ by $m + 1$.

$$= \frac{m+1+m}{m+1}$$ Add numerators. Write the sum over the common denominator.

$$= \frac{2m+1}{m+1}$$ Combine like terms in the numerator. □

PRACTICE 5 Add: $2 + \frac{b}{b+3}$

EXAMPLE 6 Subtract: $\frac{3}{2x^2+x} - \frac{2x}{6x+3}$

Solution First, we factor the denominators.

$$\frac{3}{2x^2+x} - \frac{2x}{6x+3} = \frac{3}{x(2x+1)} - \frac{2x}{3(2x+1)}$$

The LCD is $3x(2x + 1)$. We write equivalent expressions with denominators of $3x(2x + 1)$.

$$= \frac{3(3)}{x(2x+1)(3)} - \frac{2x(x)}{3(2x+1)(x)}$$

$$= \frac{9-2x^2}{3x(2x+1)}$$ Subtract numerators. Write the difference over the common denominator. □

PRACTICE 6 Subtract: $\frac{5}{2x^2+3x} - \frac{3x}{4x+6}$

EXAMPLE 7 Add: $\frac{2x}{x^2 + 2x + 1} + \frac{x}{x^2 - 1}$

Solution First we factor the denominators.

$$\frac{2x}{x^2 + 2x + 1} + \frac{x}{x^2 - 1} = \frac{2x}{(x + 1)(x + 1)} + \frac{x}{(x + 1)(x - 1)}$$

Now we write the rational expressions as equivalent expressions with denominators of $(x + 1)(x + 1)(x - 1)$, the LCD.

$$= \frac{2x(x - 1)}{(x + 1)(x + 1)(x - 1)} + \frac{x(x + 1)}{(x + 1)(x - 1)(x + 1)}$$

$$= \frac{2x(x - 1) + x(x + 1)}{(x + 1)^2(x - 1)}$$ Add numerators. Write the sum over the common denominator.

$$= \frac{2x^2 - 2x + x^2 + x}{(x + 1)^2(x - 1)}$$ Apply the distributive property in the numerator.

$$= \frac{3x^2 - x}{(x + 1)^2(x - 1)} \quad \text{or} \quad \frac{x(3x - 1)}{(x + 1)^2(x - 1)}$$ □

PRACTICE 7 Add: $\frac{2x}{x^2 + 7x + 12} + \frac{3x}{x^2 - 9}$

The numerator was factored as a last step to see if the rational expression could be simplified further. Since there are no factors common to the numerator and the denominator, we can't simplify further.

Vocabulary, Readiness & Video Check

Match each exercise with the first step needed to perform the operation. Do not actually perform the operation.

1. $\frac{3}{4} - \frac{y}{4}$ **2.** $\frac{2}{a} \cdot \frac{3}{(a + 6)}$ **3.** $\frac{x + 1}{x} \div \frac{x - 1}{x}$ **4.** $\frac{9}{x - 2} - \frac{x}{x + 2}$

a. Multiply the first rational expression by the reciprocal of the second rational expression.
b. Find the LCD. Write each expression as an equivalent expression with the LCD as denominator.
c. Multiply numerators and multiply denominators.
d. Subtract numerators. Place the difference over a common denominator.

Martin-Gay Interactive Videos

See Video 4.5

Watch the section lecture video and answer the following question.

OBJECTIVE 1 **5.** What special case is shown in Example 2 and what's the purpose of presenting it?

4.5 Exercise Set

MyMathLab®

MIXED PRACTICE

Perform each indicated operation. Simplify if possible. See Examples 1 through 7.

1. $\frac{4}{2x} + \frac{9}{3x}$
2. $\frac{15}{7a} + \frac{8}{6a}$
3. $\frac{15a}{b} - \frac{6b}{5}$
4. $\frac{4c}{d} - \frac{8d}{5}$
5. $\frac{3}{x} + \frac{5}{2x^2}$
6. $\frac{14}{3x^2} + \frac{6}{x}$
7. $\frac{6}{x+1} + \frac{10}{2x+2}$
8. $\frac{8}{x+4} - \frac{3}{3x+12}$
9. $\frac{3}{x+2} - \frac{2x}{x^2-4}$
10. $\frac{5}{x-4} + \frac{4x}{x^2-16}$
11. $\frac{3}{4x} + \frac{8}{x-2}$
12. $\frac{5}{y^2} - \frac{y}{2y+1}$
13. $\frac{6}{x-3} + \frac{8}{3-x}$
14. $\frac{15}{y-4} + \frac{20}{4-y}$
15. $\frac{9}{x-3} + \frac{9}{3-x}$
16. $\frac{5}{a-7} + \frac{5}{7-a}$
17. $\frac{-8}{x^2-1} - \frac{7}{1-x^2}$
18. $\frac{-9}{25x^2-1} + \frac{7}{1-25x^2}$
19. $\frac{5}{x} + 2$
20. $\frac{7}{x^2} - 5x$
21. $\frac{5}{x-2} + 6$
22. $\frac{6y}{y+5} + 1$
23. $\frac{y+2}{y+3} - 2$
24. $\frac{7}{2x-3} - 3$
25. $\frac{-x+2}{x} - \frac{x-6}{4x}$
26. $\frac{-y+1}{y} - \frac{2y-5}{3y}$
27. $\frac{5x}{x+2} - \frac{3x-4}{x+2}$
28. $\frac{7x}{x-3} - \frac{4x+9}{x-3}$
29. $\frac{3x^4}{7} - \frac{4x^2}{21}$
30. $\frac{5x}{6} + \frac{11x^2}{2}$
31. $\frac{1}{x+3} - \frac{1}{(x+3)^2}$
32. $\frac{5x}{(x-2)^2} - \frac{3}{x-2}$
33. $\frac{4}{5b} + \frac{1}{b-1}$
34. $\frac{1}{y+5} + \frac{2}{3y}$
35. $\frac{2}{m} + 1$
36. $\frac{6}{x} - 1$
37. $\frac{2x}{x-7} - \frac{x}{x-2}$
38. $\frac{9x}{x-10} - \frac{x}{x-3}$
39. $\frac{6}{1-2x} - \frac{4}{2x-1}$
40. $\frac{10}{3n-4} - \frac{5}{4-3n}$
41. $\frac{7}{(x+1)(x-1)} + \frac{8}{(x+1)^2}$
42. $\frac{5}{(x+1)(x+5)} - \frac{2}{(x+5)^2}$
43. $\frac{x}{x^2-1} - \frac{2}{x^2-2x+1}$
44. $\frac{x}{x^2-4} - \frac{5}{x^2-4x+4}$
45. $\frac{3a}{2a+6} - \frac{a-1}{a+3}$
46. $\frac{1}{x+y} - \frac{y}{x^2-y^2}$
47. $\frac{y-1}{2y+3} + \frac{3}{(2y+3)^2}$
48. $\frac{x-6}{5x+1} + \frac{6}{(5x+1)^2}$
49. $\frac{5}{2-x} + \frac{x}{2x-4}$
50. $\frac{-1}{a-2} + \frac{4}{4-2a}$
51. $\frac{15}{x^2+6x+9} + \frac{2}{x+3}$

52. $\frac{2}{x^2 + 4x + 4} + \frac{1}{x + 2}$

53. $\frac{13}{x^2 - 5x + 6} - \frac{5}{x - 3}$

54. $\frac{-7}{y^2 - 3y + 2} - \frac{2}{y - 1}$

55. $\frac{70}{m^2 - 100} + \frac{7}{2(m + 10)}$

56. $\frac{27}{y^2 - 81} + \frac{3}{2(y + 9)}$

57. $\frac{x + 8}{x^2 - 5x - 6} + \frac{x + 1}{x^2 - 4x - 5}$

58. $\frac{x + 4}{x^2 + 12x + 20} + \frac{x + 1}{x^2 + 8x - 20}$

59. $\frac{5}{4n^2 - 12n + 8} - \frac{3}{3n^2 - 6n}$

60. $\frac{6}{5y^2 - 25y + 30} - \frac{2}{4y^2 - 8y}$

MIXED PRACTICE

Perform the indicated operations. Addition, subtraction, multiplication, and division of rational expressions are included here.

61. $\frac{15x}{x + 8} \cdot \frac{2x + 16}{3x}$

62. $\frac{9z + 5}{15} \cdot \frac{5z}{81z^2 - 25}$

63. $\frac{8x + 7}{3x + 5} - \frac{2x - 3}{3x + 5}$

64. $\frac{2z^2}{4z - 1} - \frac{z - 2z^2}{4z - 1}$

65. $\frac{5a + 10}{18} \div \frac{a^2 - 4}{10a}$

66. $\frac{9}{x^2 - 1} \div \frac{12}{3x + 3}$

67. $\frac{5}{x^2 - 3x + 2} + \frac{1}{x - 2}$

68. $\frac{4}{2x^2 + 5x - 3} + \frac{2}{x + 3}$

REVIEW AND PREVIEW

Solve the following linear and quadratic equations.

69. $3x + 5 = 7$

70. $5x - 1 = 8$

71. $2x^2 - x - 1 = 0$

72. $4x^2 - 9 = 0$

73. $4(x + 6) + 3 = -3$

74. $2(3x + 1) + 15 = -7$

CONCEPT EXTENSIONS

Perform each indicated operation.

75. $\frac{3}{x} - \frac{2x}{x^2 - 1} + \frac{5}{x + 1}$

76. $\frac{5}{x - 2} + \frac{7x}{x^2 - 4} - \frac{11}{x}$

77. $\frac{5}{x^2 - 4} + \frac{2}{x^2 - 4x + 4} - \frac{3}{x^2 - x - 6}$

78. $\frac{8}{x^2 + 6x + 5} - \frac{3x}{x^2 + 4x - 5} + \frac{2}{x^2 - 1}$

79. $\frac{9}{x^2 + 9x + 14} - \frac{3x}{x^2 + 10x + 21} + \frac{x + 4}{x^2 + 5x + 6}$

80. $\frac{x + 10}{x^2 - 3x - 4} - \frac{8}{x^2 + 6x + 5} - \frac{9}{x^2 + x - 20}$

81. A board of length $\frac{3}{x + 4}$ inches was cut into two pieces. If one piece is $\frac{1}{x - 4}$ inches, express the length of the other piece as a rational expression.

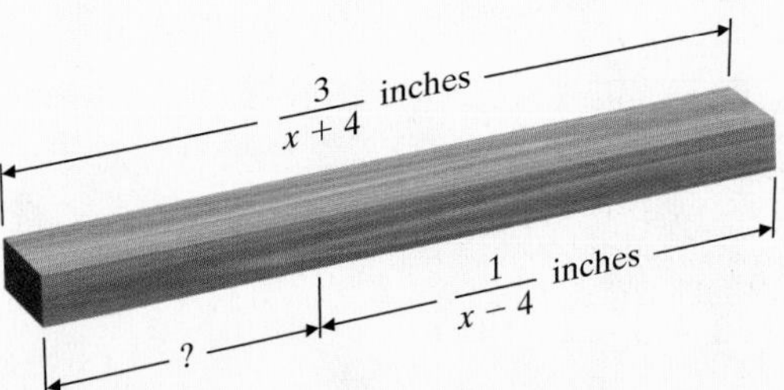

△ 82. The length of a rectangle is $\frac{3}{y - 5}$ feet, while its width is $\frac{2}{y}$ feet. Find its perimeter and then find its area.

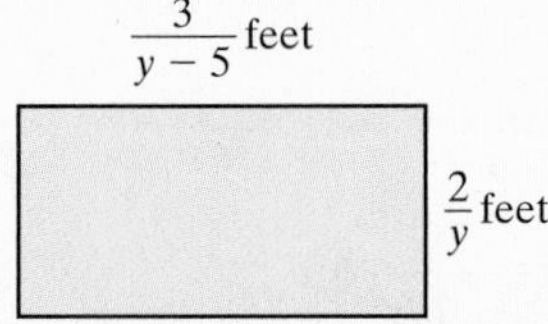

83. In ice hockey, penalty killing percentage is a statistic calculated as $1 - \frac{G}{P}$, where G = opponent's power play goals and P = opponent's power play opportunities. Simplify this expression.

84. The dose of medicine prescribed for a child depends on the child's age A in years and the adult dose D for the medication. Two expressions that give a child's dose are Young's Rule, $\frac{DA}{A + 12}$, and Cowling's Rule, $\frac{D(A + 1)}{24}$. Find an expression for the difference in the doses given by these expressions.

85. Explain when the LCD of the rational expressions in a sum is the product of the denominators.

86. Explain when the LCD is the same as one of the denominators of a rational expression to be added or subtracted.

△ **87.** Two angles are said to be complementary if the sum of their measures is 90°. If one angle measures $\frac{40}{x}$ degrees, find the measure of its complement.

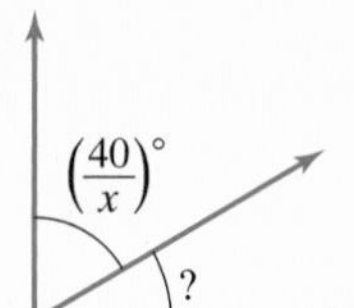

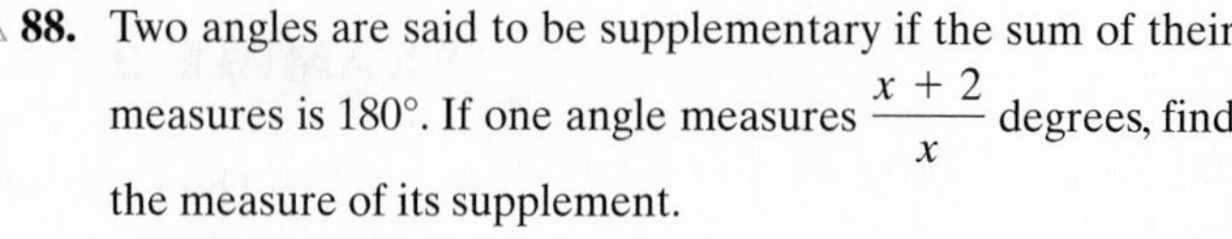
△ **88.** Two angles are said to be supplementary if the sum of their measures is 180°. If one angle measures $\frac{x+2}{x}$ degrees, find the measure of its supplement.

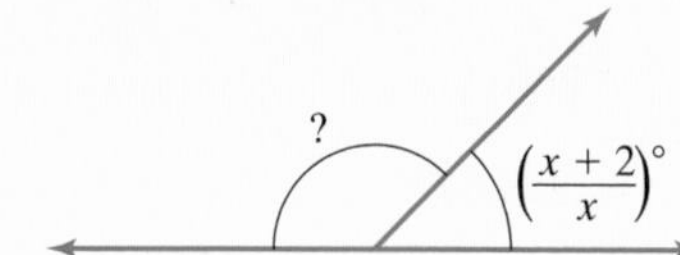

89. In your own words, explain how to add two rational expressions with different denominators.

90. In your own words, explain how to subtract two rational expressions with different denominators.

4.6 Solving Equations Containing Rational Expressions 

OBJECTIVES

1 Solve Equations Containing Rational Expressions.

2 Solve Equations Containing Rational Expressions for a Specified Variable.

OBJECTIVE

1 Solving Equations Containing Rational Expressions 

We solved equations containing fractions. In this section, we continue the work by solving equations containing rational expressions.

Examples of Equations Containing Rational Expressions

$$\frac{x}{2}+\frac{8}{3}=\frac{1}{6} \quad \text{and} \quad \frac{4x}{x^2+x-30}+\frac{2}{x-5}=\frac{1}{x+6}$$

To solve equations such as these, use the multiplication property of equality to clear the equation of fractions by multiplying both sides of the equation by the LCD.

EXAMPLE 1 Solve: $\frac{x}{2}+\frac{8}{3}=\frac{1}{6}$

Solution The LCD of denominators 2, 3, and 6 is 6, so we multiply both sides of the equation by 6.

$$6\left(\frac{x}{2}+\frac{8}{3}\right)=6\left(\frac{1}{6}\right)$$

$$6\left(\frac{x}{2}\right)+6\left(\frac{8}{3}\right)=6\left(\frac{1}{6}\right) \quad \text{Use the distributive property.}$$

$$3\cdot x+16=1 \quad \text{Multiply and simplify.}$$

$$3x=-15 \quad \text{Subtract 16 from both sides.}$$

$$x=-5 \quad \text{Divide both sides by 3.}$$

Helpful Hint
Make sure that *each* term is multiplied by the LCD, 6.

Check: To check, we replace x with -5 in the original equation.

$$\frac{x}{2}+\frac{8}{3}=\frac{1}{6}$$

$$\frac{-5}{2}+\frac{8}{3}\stackrel{?}{=}\frac{1}{6} \quad \text{Replace } x \text{ with } -5$$

$$\frac{1}{6}=\frac{1}{6} \quad \text{True}$$

This number checks, so the solution is -5. □

PRACTICE
1 Solve: $\frac{x}{3}+\frac{4}{5}=\frac{2}{15}$

EXAMPLE 2 Solve: $\frac{t-4}{2} - \frac{t-3}{9} = \frac{5}{18}$

Solution The LCD of denominators 2, 9, and 18 is 18, so we multiply both sides of the equation by 18.

$$18\left(\frac{t-4}{2} - \frac{t-3}{9}\right) = 18\left(\frac{5}{18}\right)$$

$$18\left(\frac{t-4}{2}\right) - 18\left(\frac{t-3}{9}\right) = 18\left(\frac{5}{18}\right) \quad \text{Use the distributive property.}$$

Helpful Hint
Multiply *each* term by 18.

$$9(t-4) - 2(t-3) = 5 \quad \text{Simplify.}$$
$$9t - 36 - 2t + 6 = 5 \quad \text{Use the distributive property.}$$
$$7t - 30 = 5 \quad \text{Combine like terms.}$$
$$7t = 35$$
$$t = 5 \quad \text{Solve for } t.$$

Check:

$$\frac{t-4}{2} - \frac{t-3}{9} = \frac{5}{18}$$
$$\frac{5-4}{2} - \frac{5-3}{9} \stackrel{?}{=} \frac{5}{18} \quad \text{Replace } t \text{ with 5.}$$
$$\frac{1}{2} - \frac{2}{9} \stackrel{?}{=} \frac{5}{18} \quad \text{Simplify.}$$
$$\frac{5}{18} = \frac{5}{18} \quad \text{True}$$

The solution is 5. □

PRACTICE 2 Solve: $\frac{x+4}{4} - \frac{x-3}{3} = \frac{11}{12}$

Recall from Section 4.1 that a rational expression is defined for all real numbers except those that make the denominator of the expression 0. This means that if an equation contains *rational expressions with variables in the denominator*, we must be certain that the proposed solution does not make the denominator 0. If replacing the variable with the proposed solution makes the denominator 0, the rational expression is undefined and this proposed solution must be rejected.

EXAMPLE 3 Solve: $3 - \frac{6}{x} = x + 8$

Solution In this equation, 0 cannot be a solution because if x is 0, the rational expression $\frac{6}{x}$ is undefined. The LCD is x, so we multiply both sides of the equation by x.

$$x\left(3 - \frac{6}{x}\right) = x(x + 8)$$

$$x(3) - x\left(\frac{6}{x}\right) = x \cdot x + x \cdot 8 \quad \text{Use the distributive property.}$$

Helpful Hint
Multiply *each* term by x.

$$3x - 6 = x^2 + 8x \quad \text{Simplify.}$$

Now we write the quadratic equation in standard form and solve for x.

$$0 = x^2 + 5x + 6$$
$$0 = (x + 3)(x + 2) \quad \text{Factor.}$$
$$x + 3 = 0 \quad \text{or} \quad x + 2 = 0 \quad \text{Set each factor equal to 0 and solve.}$$
$$x = -3 \qquad\qquad x = -2$$

Notice that neither −3 nor −2 makes the denominator in the original equation equal to 0.

Check: To check these solutions, we replace x in the original equation by −3, and then by −2.

If $x = -3$:

$$3 - \frac{6}{x} = x + 8$$
$$3 - \frac{6}{-3} \stackrel{?}{=} -3 + 8$$
$$3 - (-2) \stackrel{?}{=} 5$$
$$5 = 5 \quad \text{True}$$

If $x = -2$:

$$3 - \frac{6}{x} = x + 8$$
$$3 - \frac{6}{-2} \stackrel{?}{=} -2 + 8$$
$$3 - (-3) \stackrel{?}{=} 6$$
$$6 = 6 \quad \text{True}$$

□

Both −3 and −2 are solutions.

PRACTICE 3 Solve: $8 + \frac{7}{x} = x + 2$

The following steps may be used to solve an equation containing rational expressions.

Solving an Equation Containing Rational Expressions

Step 1. Multiply both sides of the equation by the LCD of all rational expressions in the equation.

Step 2. Remove any grouping symbols and solve the resulting equation.

Step 3. Check the solution in the original equation.

EXAMPLE 4 Solve: $\frac{4x}{x^2 + x - 30} + \frac{2}{x - 5} = \frac{1}{x + 6}$

Solution The denominator $x^2 + x - 30$ factors as $(x + 6)(x - 5)$. The LCD is then $(x + 6)(x - 5)$, so we multiply both sides of the equation by this LCD.

$$(x + 6)(x - 5)\left(\frac{4x}{x^2 + x - 30} + \frac{2}{x - 5}\right) = (x + 6)(x - 5)\left(\frac{1}{x + 6}\right) \quad \text{Multiply by the LCD.}$$

$$(x + 6)(x - 5) \cdot \frac{4x}{x^2 + x - 30} + (x + 6)(x - 5) \cdot \frac{2}{x - 5} \quad \text{Apply the distributive property.}$$
$$= (x + 6)(x - 5) \cdot \frac{1}{x + 6}$$

$$4x + 2(x + 6) = x - 5 \quad \text{Simplify.}$$
$$4x + 2x + 12 = x - 5 \quad \text{Apply the distributive property.}$$
$$6x + 12 = x - 5 \quad \text{Combine like terms.}$$
$$5x = -17$$
$$x = -\frac{17}{5} \quad \text{Divide both sides by 5.}$$

Check: Check by replacing x with $-\frac{17}{5}$ in the original equation. The solution is $-\frac{17}{5}$.

□

PRACTICE 4 Solve: $\frac{6x}{x^2 - 5x - 14} - \frac{3}{x + 2} = \frac{1}{x - 7}$

EXAMPLE 5 Solve: $\frac{2x}{x-4} = \frac{8}{x-4} + 1$

Solution Multiply both sides by the LCD, $x - 4$.

$$(x-4)\left(\frac{2x}{x-4}\right) = (x-4)\left(\frac{8}{x-4} + 1\right)$$ Multiply by the LCD. Notice that 4 cannot be a solution.

$$(x-4)\cdot\frac{2x}{x-4} = (x-4)\cdot\frac{8}{x-4} + (x-4)\cdot 1$$ Use the distributive property.

$$2x = 8 + (x-4)$$ Simplify.

$$2x = 4 + x$$

$$x = 4$$

Notice that 4 makes the denominators 0 in the original equation. Therefore, 4 is *not* a solution.

This equation has *no solution*. □

PRACTICE 5 Solve: $\frac{7}{x-2} = \frac{3}{x-2} + 4$

> **Helpful Hint**
> As we can see from Example 5, it is important to check the proposed solution(s) in the *original* equation.

✓**CONCEPT CHECK**

When can we clear fractions by multiplying through by the LCD?

a. When adding or subtracting rational expressions

b. When solving an equation containing rational expressions

c. Both of these

d. Neither of these

EXAMPLE 6 Solve: $x + \frac{14}{x-2} = \frac{7x}{x-2} + 1$

Solution Notice the denominators in this equation. We can see that 2 can't be a solution. The LCD is $x - 2$, so we multiply both sides of the equation by $x - 2$.

$$(x-2)\left(x + \frac{14}{x-2}\right) = (x-2)\left(\frac{7x}{x-2} + 1\right)$$

$$(x-2)(x) + (x-2)\left(\frac{14}{x-2}\right) = (x-2)\left(\frac{7x}{x-2}\right) + (x-2)(1)$$

$$x^2 - 2x + 14 = 7x + x - 2$$ Simplify.

$$x^2 - 2x + 14 = 8x - 2$$ Combine like terms.

$$x^2 - 10x + 16 = 0$$ Write the quadratic equation in standard form.

$$(x-8)(x-2) = 0$$ Factor.

$$x - 8 = 0 \quad \text{or} \quad x - 2 = 0$$ Set each factor equal to 0.

$$x = 8 \qquad\qquad x = 2$$ Solve.

Answer to Concept Check: b

(Continued on next page)

As we have already noted, 2 can't be a solution of the original equation. So we need only replace x with 8 in the original equation. We find that 8 is a solution; the only solution is 8. □

PRACTICE 6 Solve: $x + \frac{x}{x-5} = \frac{5}{x-5} - 7$

OBJECTIVE 2

Solving Equations for a Specified Variable

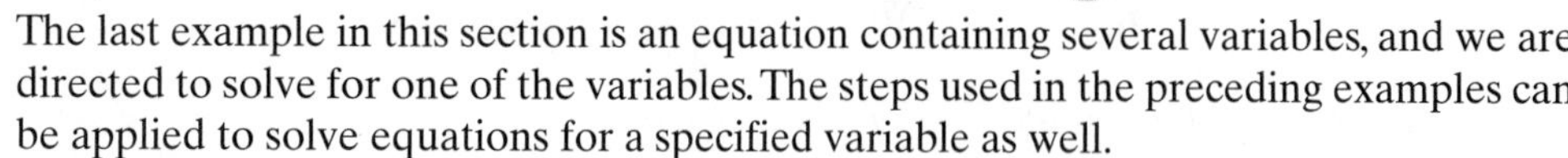

The last example in this section is an equation containing several variables, and we are directed to solve for one of the variables. The steps used in the preceding examples can be applied to solve equations for a specified variable as well.

EXAMPLE 7 Solve $\frac{1}{a} + \frac{1}{b} = \frac{1}{x}$ for x.

Solution (This type of equation often models a work problem, as we shall see in Section 4.8.) The LCD is abx, so we multiply both sides by abx.

$$abx\left(\frac{1}{a} + \frac{1}{b}\right) = abx\left(\frac{1}{x}\right)$$

$$abx\left(\frac{1}{a}\right) + abx\left(\frac{1}{b}\right) = abx \cdot \frac{1}{x}$$

$$bx + ax = ab \quad \text{Simplify.}$$

$$x(b + a) = ab \quad \text{Factor out } x \text{ from each term on the left side.}$$

$$\frac{x(b + a)}{b + a} = \frac{ab}{b + a} \quad \text{Divide both sides by } b + a.$$

$$x = \frac{ab}{b + a} \quad \text{Simplify.}$$

This equation is now solved for x. □

PRACTICE 7 Solve: $\frac{1}{a} + \frac{1}{b} = \frac{1}{x}$ for b

Graphing Calculator Explorations

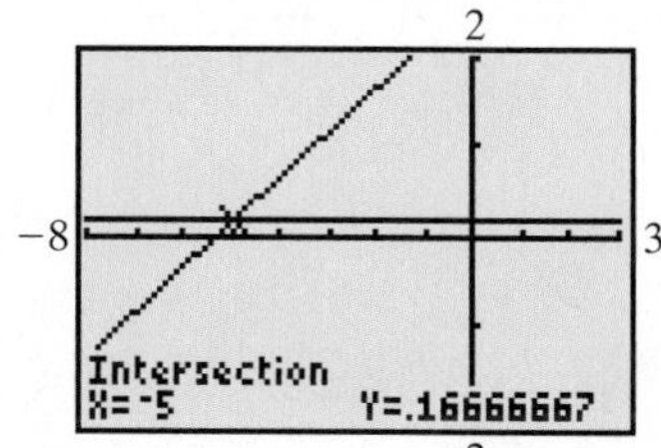

A graphing calculator may be used to check solutions of equations containing rational expressions. For example, to check the solution of Example 1, $\frac{x}{2} + \frac{8}{3} = \frac{1}{6}$, graph $y_1 = \frac{x}{2} + \frac{8}{3}$ and $y_2 = \frac{1}{6}$.

Use TRACE and ZOOM, or use INTERSECT, to find the point of intersection. The point of intersection has an x-value of -5, so the solution of the equation is -5.

Use a graphing calculator to check the examples of this section.

1. Example 2

2. Example 3

3. Example 5

4. Example 6

Vocabulary, Readiness & Video Check

Multiple choice. Choose the correct response.

1. Multiply both sides of the equation $\frac{3x}{2} + 5 = \frac{1}{4}$ by 4. The result is:

a. $3x + 5 = 1$ **b.** $6x + 5 = 1$ **c.** $6x + 20 = 1$ **d.** $6x + 9 = 1$

2. Multiply both sides of the equation $\frac{1}{x} - \frac{3}{5x} = 2$ by $5x$. The result is:

a. $1 - 3 = 10x$ **b.** $5 - 3 = 10x$ **c.** $1 - 3 = 7x$ **d.** $5 - 3 = 7x$

Choose the correct LCD for the fractions in each equation.

3. Equation: $\frac{9}{x} + \frac{3}{4} = \frac{1}{12}$; LCD:_____

a. $4x$ **b.** $12x$ **c.** $48x$ **d.** x

4. Equation: $\frac{8}{3x} - \frac{1}{x} = \frac{7}{9}$; LCD:_____

a. x **b.** $3x$ **c.** $27x$ **d.** $9x$

5. Equation: $\frac{9}{x-1} = \frac{7}{(x-1)^2}$; LCD:_____

a. $(x - 1)^2$ **b.** $x - 1$ **c.** $(x - 1)^3$ **d.** 63

6. Equation: $\frac{1}{x-2} - \frac{3}{x^2-4} = 8$; LCD:_____

a. $(x - 2)$ **b.** $x + 2$ **c.** $x^2 - 4$ **d.** $(x - 2)(x^2 - 4)$

Martin-Gay Interactive Videos

See Video 4.6

Watch the section lecture video and answer the following questions.

OBJECTIVE 1 — **7.** After multiplying through by the LCD and then simplifying, why is it important to take a moment and determine whether you have a linear or a quadratic equation before you finish solving the problem?

OBJECTIVE 1 — **8.** From Examples 2–5, what extra step is needed when checking solutions to an equation containing rational expressions?

OBJECTIVE 2 — **9.** The steps for solving Example 6 for a specified variable are the same as what other steps? How do you treat this specified variable?

4.6 Exercise Set

MyMathLab®

Solve each equation and check each solution. See Examples 1 through 3.

1. $\frac{x}{5} + 3 = 9$

2. $\frac{x}{5} - 2 = 9$

3. $\frac{x}{2} + \frac{5x}{4} = \frac{x}{12}$

4. $\frac{x}{6} + \frac{4x}{3} = \frac{x}{18}$

5. $2 - \frac{8}{x} = 6$

6. $5 + \frac{4}{x} = 1$

7. $2 + \frac{10}{x} = x + 5$

8. $6 + \frac{5}{y} = y - \frac{2}{y}$

9. $\frac{a}{5} = \frac{a-3}{2}$

10. $\frac{b}{5} = \frac{b+2}{6}$

11. $\frac{x-3}{5} + \frac{x-2}{2} = \frac{1}{2}$

12. $\frac{a+5}{4} + \frac{a+5}{2} = \frac{a}{8}$

Solve each equation and check each proposed solution. See Examples 4 through 6.

13. $\frac{3}{2a-5} = -1$

14. $\frac{6}{4-3x} = -3$

15. $\frac{4y}{y-4} + 5 = \frac{5y}{y-4}$

16. $\frac{2a}{a+2} - 5 = \frac{7a}{a+2}$

17. $2 + \frac{3}{a-3} = \frac{a}{a-3}$

18. $\frac{2y}{y-2} - \frac{4}{y-2} = 4$

19. $\frac{1}{x+3} + \frac{6}{x^2-9} = 1$

20. $\frac{1}{x+2} + \frac{4}{x^2-4} = 1$

21. $\frac{2y}{y+4} + \frac{4}{y+4} = 3$

22. $\frac{5y}{y+1} - \frac{3}{y+1} = 4$

23. $\frac{2x}{x+2} - 2 = \frac{x-8}{x-2}$

24. $\frac{4y}{y-3} - 3 = \frac{3y-1}{y+3}$

MIXED PRACTICE

Solve each equation. See Examples 1 through 6.

25. $\frac{2}{y} + \frac{1}{2} = \frac{5}{2y}$

26. $\frac{6}{3y} + \frac{3}{y} = 1$

27. $\frac{a}{a-6} = \frac{-2}{a-1}$

28. $\frac{5}{x-6} = \frac{x}{x-2}$

29. $\frac{11}{2x} + \frac{2}{3} = \frac{7}{2x}$

30. $\frac{5}{3} - \frac{3}{2x} = \frac{3}{2}$

31. $\frac{2}{x-2} + 1 = \frac{x}{x+2}$

32. $1 + \frac{3}{x+1} = \frac{x}{x-1}$

33. $\frac{x+1}{3} - \frac{x-1}{6} = \frac{1}{6}$

34. $\frac{3x}{5} - \frac{x-6}{3} = -\frac{2}{5}$

35. $\frac{t}{t-4} = \frac{t+4}{6}$

36. $\frac{15}{x+4} = \frac{x-4}{x}$

37. $\frac{y}{2y+2} + \frac{2y-16}{4y+4} = \frac{2y-3}{y+1}$

38. $\frac{1}{x+2} = \frac{4}{x^2-4} - \frac{1}{x-2}$

39. $\frac{4r-4}{r^2+5r-14} + \frac{2}{r+7} = \frac{1}{r-2}$

40. $\frac{3}{x+3} = \frac{12x+19}{x^2+7x+12} - \frac{5}{x+4}$

41. $\frac{x+1}{x+3} = \frac{x^2-11x}{x^2+x-6} - \frac{x-3}{x-2}$

42. $\frac{2t+3}{t-1} - \frac{2}{t+3} = \frac{5-6t}{t^2+2t-3}$

Solve each equation for the indicated variable. See Example 7.

43. $R = \frac{E}{I}$ for I (Electronics: resistance of a circuit)

44. $T = \frac{V}{Q}$ for Q (Water purification: settling time)

45. $T = \frac{2U}{B+E}$ for B (Merchandising: stock turnover rate)

46. $i = \frac{A}{t+B}$ for t (Hydrology: rainfall intensity)

47. $B = \frac{705w}{h^2}$ for w (Health: body-mass index)

△ 48. $\frac{A}{W} = L$ for W (Geometry: area of a rectangle)

49. $N = R + \frac{V}{G}$ for G (Urban forestry: tree plantings per year)

50. $C = \frac{D(A+1)}{24}$ for A (Medicine: Cowling's Rule for child's dose)

△ 51. $\frac{C}{\pi r} = 2$ for r (Geometry: circumference of a circle)

52. $W = \frac{CE^2}{2}$ for C (Electronics: energy stored in a capacitor)

53. $\frac{1}{y} + \frac{1}{3} = \frac{1}{x}$ for x

54. $\frac{1}{5} + \frac{2}{y} = \frac{1}{x}$ for x

REVIEW AND PREVIEW

TRANSLATING

Write each phrase as an expression.

55. The reciprocal of x

56. The reciprocal of $x + 1$

57. The reciprocal of x, added to the reciprocal of 2

58. The reciprocal of x, subtracted from the reciprocal of 5

Answer each question.

59. If a tank is filled in 3 hours, what fractional part of the tank is filled in 1 hour?

60. If a strip of beach is cleaned in 4 hours, what fractional part of the beach is cleaned in 1 hour?

Identify the x- and y-intercepts. See Section 1.3.

61.

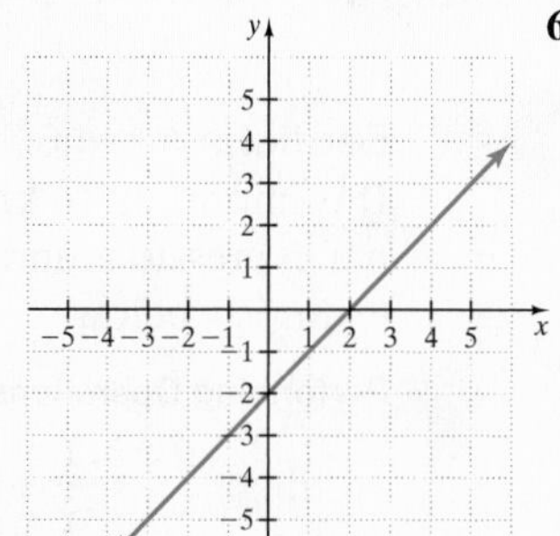

62.

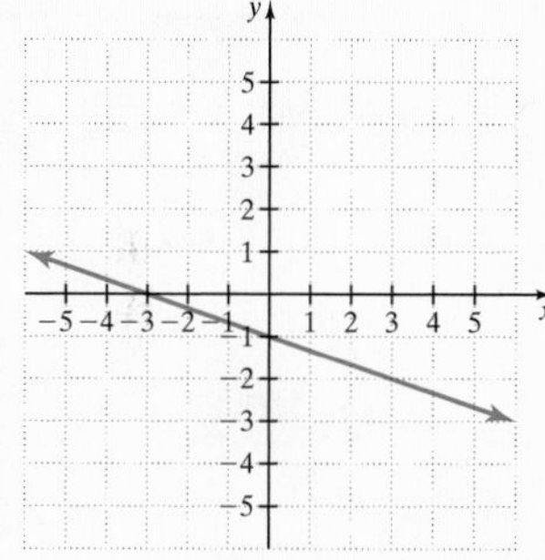

63.

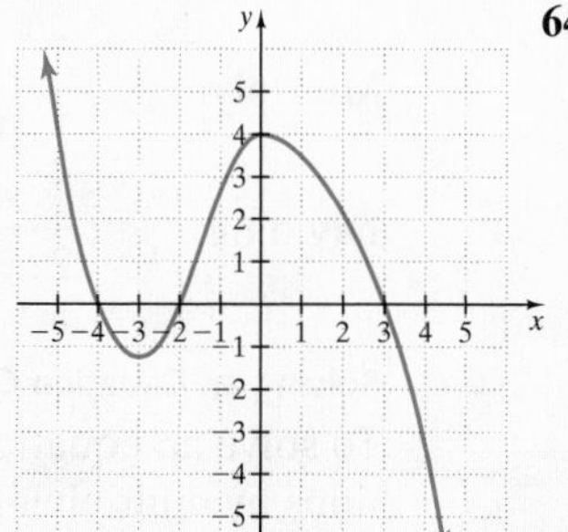

64.

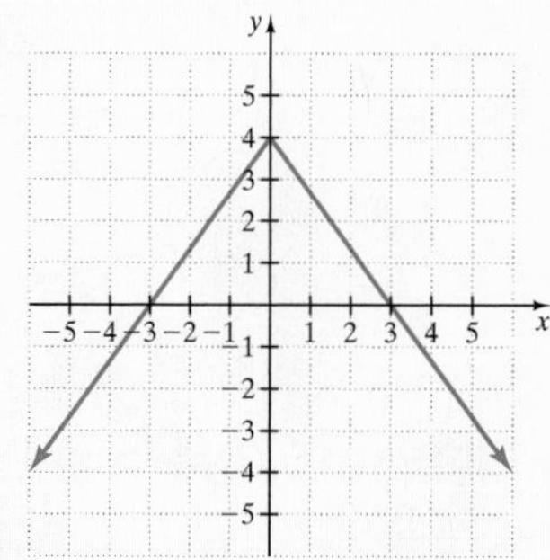

CONCEPT EXTENSIONS

65. Explain the difference between solving an equation such as $\frac{x}{2} + \frac{3}{4} = \frac{x}{4}$ for x and performing an operation such as adding $\frac{x}{2} + \frac{3}{4}$.

66. When solving an equation such as $\frac{y}{4} = \frac{y}{2} - \frac{1}{4}$, we may multiply all terms by 4. When subtracting two rational expressions such as $\frac{y}{2} - \frac{1}{4}$, we may not. Explain why.

Determine whether each of the following is an equation or an expression. If it is an equation, then solve it for its variable. If it is an expression, perform the indicated operation.

△ 67. $\frac{1}{x} + \frac{5}{9}$

68. $\frac{1}{x} + \frac{5}{9} = \frac{2}{3}$

69. $\frac{5}{x-1} - \frac{2}{x} = \frac{5}{x(x-1)}$

70. $\frac{5}{x-1} - \frac{2}{x}$

Recall that two angles are supplementary if the sum of their measures is 180°. Find the measures of the following supplementary angles.

△ 71. △ 72.

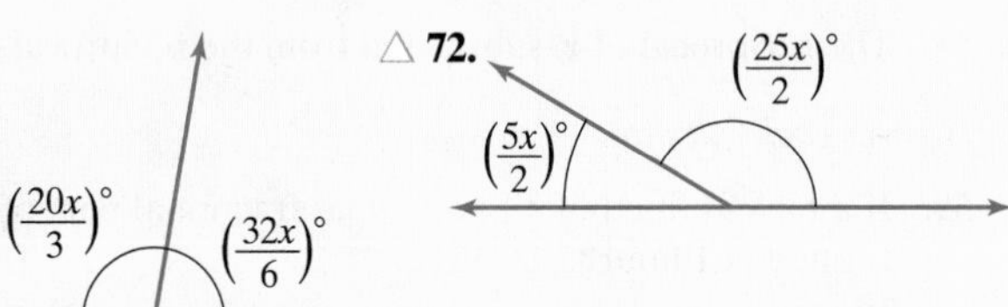

Recall that two angles are complementary if the sum of their measures is 90°. Find the measures of the following complementary angles.

△ 73. △ 74.

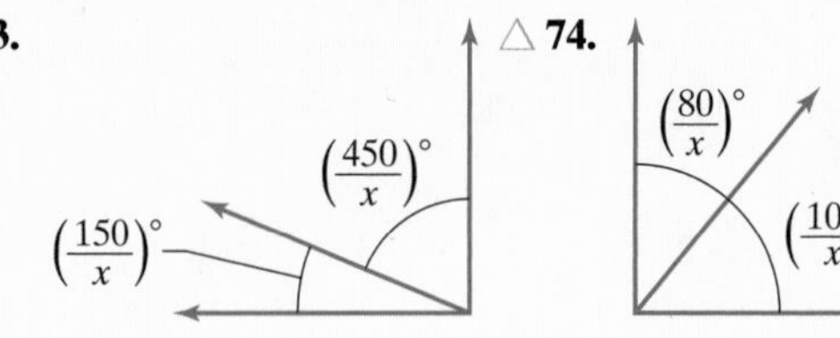

Solve each equation.

75. $\frac{5}{a^2 + 4a + 3} + \frac{2}{a^2 + a - 6} - \frac{3}{a^2 - a - 2} = 0$

76. $\frac{-2}{a^2 + 2a - 8} + \frac{1}{a^2 + 9a + 20} = \frac{-4}{a^2 + 3a - 10}$

Integrated Review SUMMARY ON RATIONAL EXPRESSIONS

Sections 4.1–4.6

It is important to know the difference between performing operations with rational expressions and solving an equation containing rational expressions. Study the examples below.

Performing Operations with Rational Expressions

Adding: $\frac{1}{x} + \frac{1}{x+5} = \frac{1 \cdot (x+5)}{x(x+5)} + \frac{1 \cdot x}{x(x+5)} = \frac{x+5+x}{x(x+5)} = \frac{2x+5}{x(x+5)}$

Subtracting: $\frac{3}{x} - \frac{5}{x^2y} = \frac{3 \cdot xy}{x \cdot xy} - \frac{5}{x^2y} = \frac{3xy-5}{x^2y}$

Multiplying: $\frac{2}{x} \cdot \frac{5}{x-1} = \frac{2 \cdot 5}{x(x-1)} = \frac{10}{x(x-1)}$

Dividing: $\frac{4}{2x+1} \div \frac{x-3}{x} = \frac{4}{2x+1} \cdot \frac{x}{x-3} = \frac{4x}{(2x+1)(x-3)}$

Solving an Equation Containing Rational Expressions

To solve an equation containing rational expressions, we clear the equation of fractions by multiplying both sides by the LCD.

$$\frac{3}{x} - \frac{5}{x-1} = \frac{1}{x(x-1)}$$ Note that x can't be 0 or 1.

$$x(x-1)\left(\frac{3}{x}\right) - x(x-1)\left(\frac{5}{x-1}\right) = x(x-1) \cdot \frac{1}{x(x-1)}$$ Multiply both sides by the LCD.

$$3(x-1) - 5x = 1$$ Simplify.

$$3x - 3 - 5x = 1$$ Use the distributive property.

$$-2x - 3 = 1$$ Combine like terms.

$$-2x = 4$$ Add 3 to both sides.

$$x = -2$$ Divide both sides by -2.

Determine whether each of the following is an equation or an expression. If it is an equation, solve it for its variable. If it is an expression, perform the indicated operation.

1. $\frac{1}{x} + \frac{2}{3}$
2. $\frac{3}{a} + \frac{5}{6}$
3. $\frac{1}{x} + \frac{2}{3} = \frac{3}{x}$
4. $\frac{3}{a} + \frac{5}{6} = 1$
5. $\frac{2}{x - 1} - \frac{1}{x}$
6. $\frac{4}{x - 3} - \frac{1}{x}$
7. $\frac{2}{x + 1} - \frac{1}{x} = 1$
8. $\frac{4}{x - 3} - \frac{1}{x} = \frac{6}{x(x - 3)}$
9. $\frac{15x}{x + 8} \cdot \frac{2x + 16}{3x}$
10. $\frac{9z + 5}{15} \cdot \frac{5z}{81z^2 - 25}$
11. $\frac{2x + 1}{x - 3} + \frac{3x + 6}{x - 3}$
12. $\frac{4p - 3}{2p + 7} + \frac{3p + 8}{2p + 7}$
13. $\frac{x + 5}{7} = \frac{8}{2}$
14. $\frac{1}{2} = \frac{x - 1}{8}$
15. $\frac{5a + 10}{18} \div \frac{a^2 - 4}{10a}$
16. $\frac{9}{x^2 - 1} + \frac{12}{3x + 3}$
17. $\frac{x + 2}{3x - 1} + \frac{5}{(3x - 1)^2}$
18. $\frac{4}{(2x - 5)^2} + \frac{x + 1}{2x - 5}$
19. $\frac{x - 7}{x} - \frac{x + 2}{5x}$
20. $\frac{10x - 9}{x} - \frac{x - 4}{3x}$
21. $\frac{3}{x + 3} = \frac{5}{x^2 - 9} - \frac{2}{x - 3}$
22. $\frac{9}{x^2 - 4} + \frac{2}{x + 2} = \frac{-1}{x - 2}$
23. Explain the difference between solving an equation such as $\frac{x}{5} + \frac{3}{10} = \frac{x}{10}$, for x and performing an operation such as adding $\frac{x}{5} + \frac{3}{10}$.
24. When solving an equation such as $\frac{y}{10} = \frac{y}{5} - \frac{1}{10}$, we may multiply all terms by 4. When subtracting two rational expressions such as $\frac{y}{5} - \frac{1}{10}$, we may not. Explain why.

4.7 Simplifying Complex Fractions 

OBJECTIVES

1. Simplify Complex Fractions by Simplifying the Numerator and Denominator and Then Dividing.
2. Simplify Complex Fractions by Multiplying by a Common Denominator.
3. Simplify Expressions with Negative Exponents.

A rational expression whose numerator, denominator, or both contain one or more rational expressions is called a **complex rational expression** or a **complex fraction.**

Complex Fractions

$$\frac{\frac{1}{a}}{\frac{b}{2}} \qquad \frac{\frac{x}{2y^2}}{\frac{6x - 2}{9y}} \qquad \frac{x + \frac{1}{y}}{y + 1}$$

The parts of a complex fraction are

$$\frac{\left.\frac{x}{y + 2}\right\}}{\left.7 + \frac{1}{y}\right\}}$$

← Numerator of complex fraction
← Main fraction bar
← Denominator of complex fraction

Our goal in this section is to simplify complex fractions. A complex fraction is simplified when it is in the form $\frac{P}{Q}$, where P and Q are polynomials that have no common factors. Two methods of simplifying complex fractions are introduced. The first method evolves from the definition of a fraction as a quotient.

OBJECTIVE

1 Simplifying Complex Fractions: Method 1 

Simplifying a Complex Fraction: Method I

Step 1. Simplify the numerator and the denominator of the complex fraction so that each is a single fraction.

Step 2. Perform the indicated division by multiplying the numerator of the complex fraction by the reciprocal of the denominator of the complex fraction.

Step 3. Simplify if possible.

EXAMPLE 1 Simplify each complex fraction.

a. $\dfrac{\frac{2x}{27y^2}}{\frac{6x^2}{9}}$ **b.** $\dfrac{\frac{5x}{x+2}}{\frac{10}{x-2}}$ **c.** $\dfrac{\frac{x}{y^2}+\frac{1}{y}}{\frac{y}{x^2}+\frac{1}{x}}$

Solution

a. The numerator of the complex fraction is already a single fraction, and so is the denominator. Perform the indicated division by multiplying the numerator, $\frac{2x}{27y^2}$, by the reciprocal of the denominator, $\frac{6x^2}{9}$. Then simplify.

$$\frac{\frac{2x}{27y^2}}{\frac{6x^2}{9}} = \frac{2x}{27y^2} \div \frac{6x^2}{9}$$

$$= \frac{2x}{27y^2}\cdot\frac{9}{6x^2} \quad \text{Multiply by the reciprocal of } \frac{6x^2}{9}.$$

$$= \frac{2x\cdot 9}{27y^2\cdot 6x^2}$$

$$= \frac{1}{9xy^2}$$

> **Helpful Hint**
> Both the numerator and denominator are single fractions, so we perform the indicated division.

b. $$\frac{\frac{5x}{x+2}}{\frac{10}{x-2}} = \frac{5x}{x+2} \div \frac{10}{x-2} = \frac{5x}{x+2}\cdot\frac{x-2}{10} \quad \text{Multiply by the reciprocal of } \frac{10}{x-2}.$$

$$= \frac{5x(x-2)}{2\cdot 5(x+2)}$$

$$= \frac{x(x-2)}{2(x+2)} \quad \text{Simplify.}$$

c. First simplify the numerator and the denominator of the complex fraction separately so that each is a single fraction. Then perform the indicated division.

$$\frac{\frac{x}{y^2}+\frac{1}{y}}{\frac{y}{x^2}+\frac{1}{x}} = \frac{\frac{x}{y^2}+\frac{1\cdot y}{y\cdot y}}{\frac{y}{x^2}+\frac{1\cdot x}{x\cdot x}} \quad \begin{array}{l}\text{Simplify the numerator. The LCD is } y^2.\\ \text{Simplify the denominator. The LCD is } x^2.\end{array}$$

$$= \frac{\frac{x+y}{y^2}}{\frac{y+x}{x^2}} \quad \text{Add.}$$

$$= \frac{x+y}{y^2}\cdot\frac{x^2}{y+x} \quad \text{Multiply by the reciprocal of } \frac{y+x}{x^2}.$$

$$= \frac{x^2(x+y)}{y^2(y+x)}$$

$$= \frac{x^2}{y^2} \quad \text{Simplify.}$$

□

PRACTICE 1 Simplify each complex fraction.

a. $\dfrac{\frac{5k}{36m}}{\frac{15k}{9}}$ b. $\dfrac{\frac{8x}{x-4}}{\frac{3}{x+4}}$ c. $\dfrac{\frac{5}{a}+\frac{b}{a^2}}{\frac{5a}{b^2}+\frac{1}{b}}$

✓CONCEPT CHECK

Which of the following are equivalent to $\dfrac{\frac{5}{y}}{\frac{2}{z}}$?

a. $\frac{5}{y} \div \frac{2}{z}$ b. $\frac{5}{y} \cdot \frac{z}{2}$ c. $\frac{5}{y} \div \frac{z}{2}$

OBJECTIVE

2 Simplifying Complex Fractions: Method 2 

Next we look at another method of simplifying complex fractions. With this method, we multiply the numerator and the denominator of the complex fraction by the LCD of all fractions in the complex fraction.

Simplifying a Complex Fraction: Method 2

Step 1. Multiply the numerator and the denominator of the complex fraction by the LCD of the fractions in both the numerator and the denominator.

Step 2. Simplify.

EXAMPLE 2 Simplify each complex fraction.

a. $\dfrac{\frac{5x}{x+2}}{\frac{10}{x-2}}$ b. $\dfrac{\frac{x}{y^2}+\frac{1}{y}}{\frac{y}{x^2}+\frac{1}{x}}$

Solution

a. Notice we are reworking Example 1b using method 2. The least common denominator of $\frac{5x}{x+2}$ and $\frac{10}{x-2}$ is $(x + 2)(x - 2)$. Multiply both the numerator, $\frac{5x}{x+2}$, and the denominator, $\frac{10}{x-2}$, by the LCD.

$$\frac{\frac{5x}{x+2}}{\frac{10}{x-2}} = \frac{\left(\frac{5x}{x+2}\right)\cdot(x+2)(x-2)}{\left(\frac{10}{x-2}\right)\cdot(x+2)(x-2)}$$ Multiply numerator and denominator by the LCD.

$$= \frac{5x\cdot(x-2)}{2\cdot 5\cdot(x+2)}$$ Simplify.

$$= \frac{x(x-2)}{2(x+2)}$$ Simplify.

(Continued on next page)

Answer to Concept Check:
a and b

b. Here, we are reworking Example 1c using method 2. The least common denominator of $\frac{x}{y^2}, \frac{1}{y}, \frac{y}{x^2}$, and $\frac{1}{x}$ is x^2y^2.

$$\frac{\frac{x}{y^2}+\frac{1}{y}}{\frac{y}{x^2}+\frac{1}{x}} = \frac{\left(\frac{x}{y^2}+\frac{1}{y}\right)\cdot x^2y^2}{\left(\frac{y}{x^2}+\frac{1}{x}\right)\cdot x^2y^2}$$ Multiply the numerator and denominator by the LCD.

$$= \frac{\frac{x}{y^2}\cdot x^2y^2 + \frac{1}{y}\cdot x^2y^2}{\frac{y}{x^2}\cdot x^2y^2 + \frac{1}{x}\cdot x^2y^2}$$ Use the distributive property.

$$= \frac{x^3 + x^2y}{y^3 + xy^2}$$ Simplify.

$$= \frac{x^2(x+y)}{y^2(y+x)}$$ Factor.

$$= \frac{x^2}{y^2}$$ Simplify. □

PRACTICE

2 Use method 2 to simplify:

a. $\dfrac{\frac{8x}{x-4}}{\frac{3}{x+4}}$ **b.** $\dfrac{\frac{b}{a^2}+\frac{1}{a}}{\frac{a}{b^2}+\frac{1}{b}}$

OBJECTIVE

3 Simplifying Expressions with Negative Exponents 

If an expression contains negative exponents, write the expression as an equivalent expression with positive exponents.

EXAMPLE 3 Simplify.

$$\frac{x^{-1} + 2xy^{-1}}{x^{-2} - x^{-2}y^{-1}}$$

Solution This fraction does not appear to be a complex fraction. If we write it by using only positive exponents, however, we see that it is a complex fraction.

$$\frac{x^{-1} + 2xy^{-1}}{x^{-2} - x^{-2}y^{-1}} = \frac{\frac{1}{x}+\frac{2x}{y}}{\frac{1}{x^2}-\frac{1}{x^2y}}$$

The LCD of $\frac{1}{x}, \frac{2x}{y}, \frac{1}{x^2}$, and $\frac{1}{x^2y}$ is x^2y. Multiply both the numerator and denominator by x^2y.

$$= \frac{\left(\frac{1}{x}+\frac{2x}{y}\right)\cdot x^2y}{\left(\frac{1}{x^2}-\frac{1}{x^2y}\right)\cdot x^2y}$$

$$= \frac{\frac{1}{x}\cdot x^2y + \frac{2x}{y}\cdot x^2y}{\frac{1}{x^2}\cdot x^2y - \frac{1}{x^2y}\cdot x^2y}$$ Apply the distributive property.

$$= \frac{xy + 2x^3}{y-1} \text{ or } \frac{x(y+2x^2)}{y-1}$$ Simplify. □

PRACTICE 3 Simplify: $\dfrac{3x^{-1} + x^{-2}y^{-1}}{y^{-2} + xy^{-1}}$

EXAMPLE 4 Simplify: $\dfrac{(2x)^{-1} + 1}{2x^{-1} - 1}$

Solution

$$\frac{(2x)^{-1} + 1}{2x^{-1} - 1} = \frac{\frac{1}{2x} + 1}{\frac{2}{x} - 1}$$ Write using positive exponents.

$$= \frac{\left(\frac{1}{2x} + 1\right) \cdot 2x}{\left(\frac{2}{x} - 1\right) \cdot 2x}$$ The LDC of $\frac{1}{2x}$ and $\frac{2}{x}$ is $2x$.

$$= \frac{\frac{1}{2x} \cdot 2x + 1 \cdot 2x}{\frac{2}{x} \cdot 2x - 1 \cdot 2x}$$ Use distributive property.

$$= \frac{1 + 2x}{4 - 2x} \text{ or } \frac{1 + 2x}{2(2 - x)}$$ Simplify. □

> **Helpful Hint**
> Don't forget that $(2x)^{-1} = \frac{1}{2x}$, but $2x^{-1} = 2 \cdot \frac{1}{x} = \frac{2}{x}$.

PRACTICE 4 Simplify: $\dfrac{(3x)^{-1} - 2}{5x^{-1} + 2}$

Vocabulary, Readiness & Video Check

Complete the steps by writing the simplified complex fraction.

1. $\dfrac{\frac{7}{x}}{\frac{1}{x} + \frac{z}{x}} = \dfrac{x\left(\frac{7}{x}\right)}{x\left(\frac{1}{x}\right) + x\left(\frac{z}{x}\right)} =$ ______

2. $\dfrac{\frac{x}{4}}{\frac{x^2}{2} + \frac{1}{4}} = \dfrac{4\left(\frac{x}{4}\right)}{4\left(\frac{x^2}{2}\right) + 4\left(\frac{1}{4}\right)} =$ ______

Write with positive exponents.

3. $x^{-2} =$ ______

4. $y^{-3} =$ ______

5. $2x^{-1} =$ ______

6. $(2x)^{-1} =$ ______

7. $(9y)^{-1} =$ ______

8. $9y^{-2} =$ ______

Martin-Gay Interactive Videos

See Video 4.7

Watch the section lecture video and answer the following questions.

OBJECTIVE 1
9. From Example 2, before you can rewrite the complex fraction as division, describe how it must appear.

OBJECTIVE 2
10. How does finding an LCD in method 2, as in Example 3, differ from finding an LCD in method 1? In your answer, mention the purpose of the LCD in each method.

OBJECTIVE 3
11. Based on Example 4, what connection is there between negative exponents and complex fractions?

4.7 Exercise Set

MyMathLab®

Simplify each complex fraction. See Examples 1 and 2.

1. $\dfrac{\frac{10}{3x}}{\frac{5}{6x}}$

2. $\dfrac{\frac{15}{2x}}{\frac{5}{6x}}$

3. $\dfrac{1+\frac{2}{5}}{2+\frac{3}{5}}$

4. $\dfrac{2+\frac{1}{7}}{3-\frac{4}{7}}$

5. $\dfrac{\frac{4}{x-1}}{\frac{x}{x-1}}$

6. $\dfrac{\frac{x}{x+2}}{\frac{2}{x+2}}$

7. $\dfrac{1-\frac{2}{x}}{x+\frac{4}{9x}}$

8. $\dfrac{5-\frac{3}{x}}{x+\frac{2}{3x}}$

9. $\dfrac{\frac{4x^2-y^2}{xy}}{\frac{2}{y}-\frac{1}{x}}$

10. $\dfrac{\frac{x^2-9y^2}{xy}}{\frac{1}{y}-\frac{3}{x}}$

11. $\dfrac{\frac{x+1}{3}}{\frac{2x-1}{6}}$

12. $\dfrac{\frac{x+3}{12}}{\frac{4x-5}{15}}$

13. $\dfrac{\frac{2}{x}+\frac{3}{x^2}}{\frac{4}{x^2}-\frac{9}{x}}$

14. $\dfrac{\frac{2}{x^2}+\frac{1}{x}}{\frac{4}{x^2}-\frac{1}{x}}$

15. $\dfrac{\frac{1}{x}+\frac{2}{x^2}}{x+\frac{8}{x^2}}$

16. $\dfrac{\frac{1}{y}+\frac{3}{y^2}}{y+\frac{27}{y^2}}$

17. $\dfrac{\frac{4}{5-x}+\frac{5}{x-5}}{\frac{2}{x}+\frac{3}{x-5}}$

18. $\dfrac{\frac{3}{x-4}-\frac{2}{4-x}}{\frac{2}{x-4}-\frac{2}{x}}$

19. $\dfrac{\frac{x+2}{x}-\frac{2}{x-1}}{\frac{x+1}{x}+\frac{x+1}{x-1}}$

20. $\dfrac{\frac{5}{a+2}-\frac{1}{a-2}}{\frac{3}{2+a}+\frac{6}{2-a}}$

21. $\dfrac{\frac{2}{x}+3}{\frac{4}{x^2}-9}$

22. $\dfrac{2+\frac{1}{x}}{4x-\frac{1}{x}}$

23. $\dfrac{1-\frac{x}{y}}{\frac{x^2}{y^2}-1}$

24. $\dfrac{1-\frac{2}{x}}{x-\frac{4}{x}}$

25. $\dfrac{\frac{-2x}{x-y}}{\frac{y}{x^2}}$

26. $\dfrac{\frac{7y}{x^2+xy}}{\frac{y^2}{x^2}}$

27. $\dfrac{\frac{2}{x}+\frac{1}{x^2}}{\frac{y}{x^2}}$

28. $\dfrac{\frac{5}{x^2}-\frac{2}{x}}{\frac{1}{x}+2}$

29. $\dfrac{\frac{x}{9}-\frac{1}{x}}{1+\frac{3}{x}}$

30. $\dfrac{\frac{x}{4}-\frac{4}{x}}{1-\frac{4}{x}}$

31. $\dfrac{\frac{x-1}{x^2-4}}{1+\frac{1}{x-2}}$

32. $\dfrac{\frac{x+3}{x^2-9}}{1+\frac{1}{x-3}}$

33. $\dfrac{\frac{2}{x+5}+\frac{4}{x+3}}{\frac{3x+13}{x^2+8x+15}}$

34. $\dfrac{\frac{2}{x+2}+\frac{6}{x+7}}{\frac{4x+13}{x^2+9x+14}}$

Simplify. See Examples 3 and 4.

35. $\dfrac{x^{-1}}{x^{-2}+y^{-2}}$

36. $\dfrac{a^{-3}+b^{-1}}{a^{-2}}$

37. $\dfrac{2a^{-1}+3b^{-2}}{a^{-1}-b^{-1}}$

38. $\dfrac{x^{-1}+y^{-1}}{3x^{-2}+5y^{-2}}$

39. $\dfrac{1}{x-x^{-1}}$

40. $\dfrac{x^{-2}}{x+3x^{-1}}$

41. $\dfrac{a^{-1}+1}{a^{-1}-1}$

42. $\dfrac{a^{-1}-4}{4+a^{-1}}$

43. $\dfrac{3x^{-1}+(2y)^{-1}}{x^{-2}}$

44. $\dfrac{5x^{-2}-3y^{-1}}{x^{-1}+y^{-1}}$

45. $\dfrac{2a^{-1}+(2a)^{-1}}{a^{-1}+2a^{-2}}$

46. $\dfrac{a^{-1}+2a^{-2}}{2a^{-1}+(2a)^{-1}}$

47. $\dfrac{5x^{-1}+2y^{-1}}{x^{-2}y^{-2}}$

48. $\dfrac{x^{-2}y^{-2}}{5x^{-1}+2y^{-1}}$

49. $\dfrac{5x^{-1}-2y^{-1}}{25x^{-2}-4y^{-2}}$

50. $\dfrac{3x^{-1}+3y^{-1}}{4x^{-2}-9y^{-2}}$

REVIEW AND PREVIEW

Simplify.

51. $\dfrac{3x^3y^2}{12x}$

52. $\dfrac{-36xb^3}{9xb^2}$

53. $\dfrac{144x^5y^5}{-16x^2y}$

54. $\dfrac{48x^3y^2}{-4xy}$

Solve the following.

55. If $P(x) = -x^2$, find $P(-3)$.

56. If $f(x) = x^2 - 6$, find $f(-1)$.

CONCEPT EXTENSIONS

Solve. See the Concept Check in this section.

57. Which of the following are equivalent to $\dfrac{\frac{x+1}{9}}{\frac{y-2}{5}}$?

a. $\dfrac{x+1}{9} \div \dfrac{y-2}{5}$ **b.** $\dfrac{x+1}{9} \cdot \dfrac{y-2}{5}$ **c.** $\dfrac{x+1}{9} \cdot \dfrac{5}{y-2}$

58. Which of the following are equivalent to $\dfrac{\frac{a}{7}}{\frac{b}{13}}$?

a. $\dfrac{a}{7} \cdot \dfrac{b}{13}$ **b.** $\dfrac{a}{7} \div \dfrac{b}{13}$ **c.** $\dfrac{a}{7} \div \dfrac{13}{b}$ **d.** $\dfrac{a}{7} \cdot \dfrac{13}{b}$

59. When the source of a sound is traveling toward a listener, the pitch that the listener hears due to the Doppler effect is given by the complex rational compression $\dfrac{a}{1 - \dfrac{s}{770}}$, where a is the actual pitch of the sound and s is the speed of the sound source. Simplify this expression.

60. In baseball, the earned run average (ERA) statistic gives the average number of earned runs scored on a pitcher per game. It is computed with the following expression: $\dfrac{E}{\dfrac{I}{9}}$, where E is the number of earned runs scored on a pitcher and I is the total number of innings pitched by the pitcher. Simplify this expression.

61. Which of the following are equivalent to $\dfrac{\dfrac{1}{x}}{\dfrac{3}{y}}$?

a. $\dfrac{1}{x} \div \dfrac{3}{y}$ **b.** $\dfrac{1}{x} \cdot \dfrac{y}{3}$ **c.** $\dfrac{1}{x} \div \dfrac{y}{3}$

62. Which of the following are equivalent to $\dfrac{5}{\dfrac{2}{a}}$?

a. $\dfrac{5}{1} \div \dfrac{2}{a}$ **b.** $\dfrac{1}{5} \div \dfrac{2}{a}$ **c.** $\dfrac{5}{1} \cdot \dfrac{2}{a}$

63. In your own words, explain one method for simplifying a complex fraction.

64. Explain your favorite method for simplifying a complex fraction and why.

Simplify.

65. $\dfrac{1}{1 + (1 + x)^{-1}}$

66. $\dfrac{(x + 2)^{-1} + (x - 2)^{-1}}{(x^2 - 4)^{-1}}$

67. $\dfrac{x}{1 - \dfrac{1}{1 + \dfrac{1}{x}}}$

68. $\dfrac{x}{1 - \dfrac{1}{1 - \dfrac{1}{x}}}$

69. $\dfrac{\dfrac{2}{y^2} - \dfrac{5}{xy} - \dfrac{3}{x^2}}{\dfrac{2}{y^2} + \dfrac{7}{xy} + \dfrac{3}{x^2}}$

70. $\dfrac{\dfrac{2}{x^2} - \dfrac{1}{xy} - \dfrac{1}{y^2}}{\dfrac{1}{x^2} - \dfrac{3}{xy} + \dfrac{2}{y^2}}$

71. $\dfrac{3(a + 1)^{-1} + 4a^{-2}}{(a^3 + a^2)^{-1}}$

72. $\dfrac{9x^{-1} - 5(x - y)^{-1}}{4(x - y)^{-1}}$

In the study of calculus, the difference quotient $\dfrac{f(a + h) - f(a)}{h}$ *is often found and simplified. Find and simplify this quotient for each function f(x) by following steps* **a** *through* **d.**

a. *Find* $(a + h)$. **b.** *Find* $f(a)$.

c. *Use steps* **a** *and* **b** *to find* $\dfrac{f(a + h) - f(a)}{h}$

d. *Simplify the result of step* **c.**

73. $f(x) = \dfrac{1}{x}$

74. $f(x) = \dfrac{5}{x}$

75. $\dfrac{3}{x + 1}$

76. $\dfrac{2}{x^2}$

4.8 Proportion and Problem Solving with Rational Equations

OBJECTIVES

1. Solve Proportions.
2. Use Proportions to Solve Problems.
3. Solve Problems About Numbers.
4. Solve Problems About Work.
5. Solve Problems About Distance.

OBJECTIVE

1 Solving Proportions

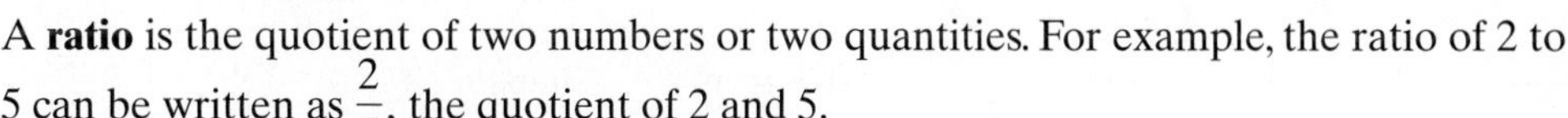

A **ratio** is the quotient of two numbers or two quantities. For example, the ratio of 2 to 5 can be written as $\dfrac{2}{5}$, the quotient of 2 and 5.

If two ratios are equal, we say the ratios are **in proportion** to each other. A **proportion** is a mathematical statement that two ratios are equal.

For example, the equation $\dfrac{1}{2} = \dfrac{4}{8}$ is a proportion, as is $\dfrac{x}{5} = \dfrac{8}{10}$, because both sides of the equations are ratios. When we want to emphasize the equation as a proportion, we

read the proportion $\dfrac{1}{2} = \dfrac{4}{8}$ **as "one is to two as four is to eight"**

In a proportion, cross products are equal. To understand cross products, let's start with the proportion

$$\frac{a}{b} = \frac{c}{d}$$

and multiply both sides by the LCD, bd.

$$bd\left(\frac{a}{b}\right) = bd\left(\frac{c}{d}\right) \quad \text{Multiply both sides by the LCD, } bd.$$

$$\underbrace{ad}_{\text{Cross product}} = \underbrace{bc}_{\text{Cross product}} \quad \text{Simplify.}$$

Notice why ad and bc are called cross products.

ad $\frac{a}{b} = \frac{c}{d}$ bc

Cross Products

If $\frac{a}{b} = \frac{c}{d}$, then $ad = bc$.

For example, if

$$\frac{1}{2} = \frac{4}{8}, \text{ then } 1 \cdot 8 = 2 \cdot 4 \text{ or}$$
$$8 = 8$$

Notice that a proportion contains four numbers (or expressions). If any three numbers are known, we can solve and find the fourth number.

EXAMPLE 1 Solve for x: $\frac{45}{x} = \frac{5}{7}$

Solution This is an equation with rational expressions, and also a proportion. Below are two ways to solve.

Since this is a rational equation, we can use the methods of the previous section.

$$\frac{45}{x} = \frac{5}{7}$$

$7x \cdot \frac{45}{x} = 7x \cdot \frac{5}{7}$ Multiply both sides by the LCD $7x$.

$7 \cdot 45 = x \cdot 5$ Divide out common factors.

$315 = 5x$ Multiply.

$\frac{315}{5} = \frac{5x}{5}$ Divide both sides by 5.

$63 = x$ Simplify.

Since this is also a proportion, we may set cross products equal.

$$\frac{45}{x} = \frac{5}{7}$$

$45 \cdot 7 = x \cdot 5$ Set cross products equal.

$315 = 5x$ Multiply.

$\frac{315}{5} = \frac{5x}{5}$ Divide both sides by 5.

$63 = x$ Simplify.

Check: Both methods give us a solution of 63. To check, substitute 63 for x in the original proportion. The solution is 63. □

PRACTICE 1 Solve for x: $\frac{36}{x} = \frac{4}{11}$

In this section, if the rational equation is a proportion, we will use cross products to solve.

EXAMPLE 2 Solve for x: $\frac{x-5}{3} = \frac{x+2}{5}$

Solution

$$\frac{x-5}{3} = \frac{x+2}{5}$$

$$
\begin{aligned}
5(x-5) &= 3(x+2) && \text{Set cross products equal.}\\
5x - 25 &= 3x + 6 && \text{Multiply.}\\
5x &= 3x + 31 && \text{Add 25 to both sides.}\\
2x &= 31 && \text{Subtract } 3x \text{ from both sides.}\\
\frac{2x}{2} &= \frac{31}{2} && \text{Divide both sides by 2.}\\
x &= \frac{31}{2}
\end{aligned}
$$

Check: Verify that $\frac{31}{2}$ is the solution. □

PRACTICE 2 Solve for x: $\frac{3x+2}{9} = \frac{x-1}{2}$

OBJECTIVE 2 Using Proportions to Solve Problems 

Proportions can be used to model and solve many real-life problems. When using proportions in this way, it is important to judge whether the solution is reasonable. Doing so helps us decide if the proportion has been formed correctly..

EXAMPLE 3 **Calculating the Cost of Recordable Compact Discs**

Three boxes of CD-Rs (recordable compact discs) cost \$37.47. How much should 5 boxes cost?

Solution

1. UNDERSTAND. Read and reread the problem. We know that the cost of 5 boxes is more than the cost of 3 boxes, or \$37.47, and less than the cost of 6 boxes, which is double the cost of 3 boxes, or 2(\$37.47) = \$74.94. Let's suppose that 5 boxes cost \$60.00. To check, we see if 3 boxes is to 5 boxes as the *price* of 3 boxes is to the *price* of 5 boxes. In other words, we see if

$$\frac{3 \text{ boxes}}{5 \text{ boxes}} = \frac{\text{price of 3 boxes}}{\text{price of 5 boxes}}$$

or

$$\frac{3}{5} = \frac{37.47}{60.00}$$

$$3(60.00) = 5(37.47) \quad \text{Set cross products equal.}$$

or

$$180.00 = 187.35 \quad \text{Not a true statement.}$$

(Continued on next page)

Thus, \$60 is not correct, but we now have a better understanding of the problem.

Let x = price of 5 boxes of CD-Rs.

2. TRANSLATE.

$$\frac{3\text{ boxes}}{5\text{ boxes}} = \frac{\text{price of 3 boxes}}{\text{price of 5 boxes}}$$

$$\frac{3}{5} = \frac{37.47}{x}$$

3. SOLVE.

$$\frac{3}{5} = \frac{37.47}{x}$$

$$3x = 5(37.47) \quad \text{Set cross products equal.}$$

$$3x = 187.35$$

$$x = 62.45 \quad \text{Divide both sides by 3.}$$

4. INTERPRET.

Check: Verify that 3 boxes is to 5 boxes as \$37.47 is to \$62.45. Also, notice that our solution is a reasonable one as discussed in Step 1.

State: Five boxes of CD-Rs cost \$62.45. □

PRACTICE

3 Four 2-liter bottles of Diet Pepsi cost \$5.16. How much will seven 2-liter bottles cost?

Helpful Hint

The proportion $\frac{5\text{ boxes}}{3\text{ boxes}} = \frac{\text{price of 5 boxes}}{\text{price of 3 boxes}}$ could also have been used to solve Example 3. Notice that the cross products are the same.

Similar triangles have the same shape but not necessarily the same size. In similar triangles, the measures of corresponding angles are equal, and corresponding sides are in proportion.

If triangle ABC and triangle XYZ shown are similar, then we know that the measure of angle A = the measure of angle X, the measure of angle B = the measure of angle Y, and the measure of angle C = the measure of angle Z. We also know that corresponding sides are in proportion: $\frac{a}{x} = \frac{b}{y} = \frac{c}{z}$.

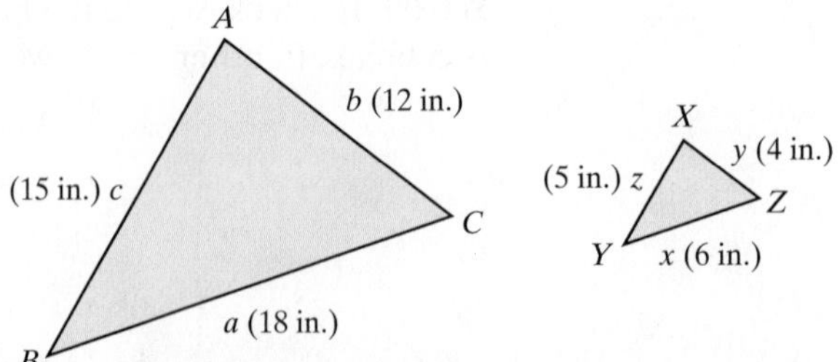

In this section, we will position similar triangles so that they have the same orientation.

To show that corresponding sides are in proportion for the triangles above, we write the ratios of the corresponding sides.

$$\frac{a}{x} = \frac{18}{6} = 3 \quad \frac{b}{y} = \frac{12}{4} = 3 \quad \frac{c}{z} = \frac{15}{5} = 3$$

EXAMPLE 4 **Finding the Length of a Side of a Triangle**

If the following two triangles are similar, find the missing length x.

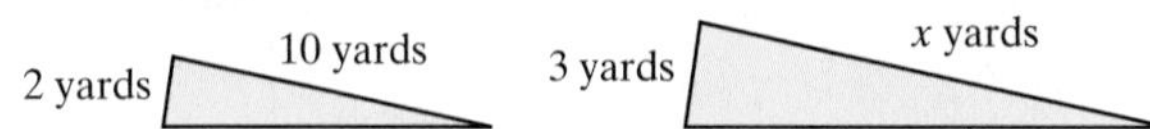

Solution

1. UNDERSTAND. Read the problem and study the figure.
2. TRANSLATE. Since the triangles are similar, their corresponding sides are in proportion and we have

$$\frac{2}{3} = \frac{10}{x}$$

3. SOLVE. To solve, we multiply both sides by the LCD, $3x$, or cross multiply.

$$2x = 30$$
$$x = 15 \quad \text{Divide both sides by 2.}$$

4. INTERPRET.

Check: To check, replace x with 15 in the original proportion and see that a true statement results.

State: The missing length is 15 yards. □

PRACTICE
4 If the following two triangles are similar, find x.

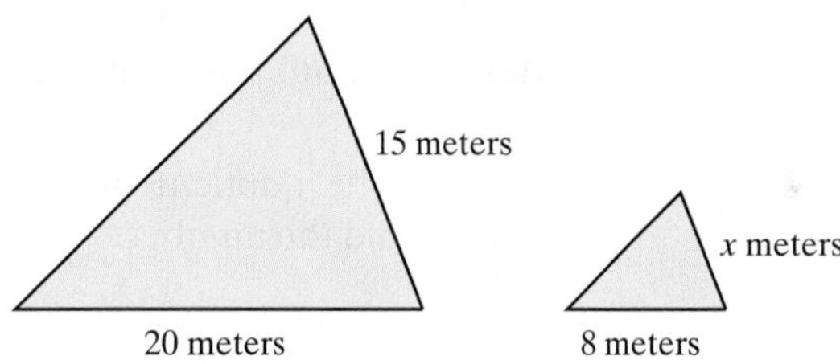

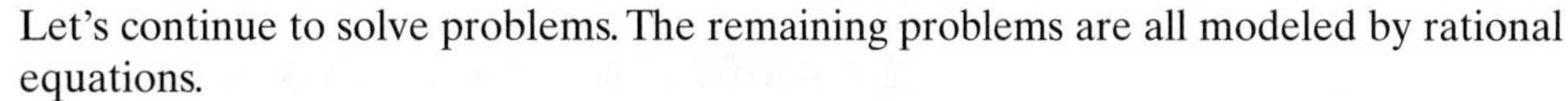

OBJECTIVE
3 **Solving Problems About Numbers**

Let's continue to solve problems. The remaining problems are all modeled by rational equations.

EXAMPLE 5 **Finding an Unknown Number**

The quotient of a number and 6, minus $\frac{5}{3}$, is the quotient of the number and 2. Find the number.

Solution

1. UNDERSTAND. Read and reread the problem. Suppose that the unknown number is 2, then we see if the quotient of 2 and 6, or $\frac{2}{6}$, minus $\frac{5}{3}$ is equal to the quotient of 2 and 2, or $\frac{2}{2}$.

$$\frac{2}{6} - \frac{5}{3} = \frac{1}{3} - \frac{5}{3} = -\frac{4}{3}, \text{ not } \frac{2}{2}$$

Don't forget that the purpose of a proposed solution is to better understand the problem.

Let x = the unknown number.

2. TRANSLATE.

In words:	the quotient of x and 6	minus	$\frac{5}{3}$	is	the quotient of x and 2
	↓	↓	↓	↓	↓
Translate:	$\frac{x}{6}$	$-$	$\frac{5}{3}$	$=$	$\frac{x}{2}$

3. SOLVE. Here, we solve the equation $\frac{x}{6} - \frac{5}{3} = \frac{x}{2}$. We begin by multiplying both sides of the equation by the LCD, 6.

$$6\left(\frac{x}{6} - \frac{5}{3}\right) = 6\left(\frac{x}{2}\right)$$

$$6\left(\frac{x}{6}\right) - 6\left(\frac{5}{3}\right) = 6\left(\frac{x}{2}\right) \quad \text{Apply the distributive property.}$$

$$x - 10 = 3x \quad \text{Simplify.}$$

$$-10 = 2x \quad \text{Subtract } x \text{ from both sides.}$$

$$\frac{-10}{2} = \frac{2x}{2} \quad \text{Divide both sides by 2.}$$

$$-5 = x \quad \text{Simplify.}$$

4. INTERPRET.

Check: To check, we verify that "the quotient of -5 and 6 minus $\frac{5}{3}$ is the quotient of -5 and 2," or $-\frac{5}{6} - \frac{5}{3} = -\frac{5}{2}$.

State: The unknown number is -5. □

PRACTICE

5 The quotient of a number and 5, minus $\frac{3}{2}$, is the quotient of the number and 10. Find the number.

OBJECTIVE

4 Solving Problems About Work 

The next example is often called a work problem. Work problems usually involve people or machines doing a certain task.

EXAMPLE 6 **Finding Work Rates**

Sam Waterton and Frank Schaffer work in a plant that manufactures automobiles. Sam can complete a quality control tour of the plant in 3 hours, while his assistant, Frank, needs 7 hours to complete the same job. The regional manager is coming to inspect the plant facilities, so both Sam and Frank are directed to complete a quality control tour together. How long will this take?

Solution

1. UNDERSTAND. Read and reread the problem. The key idea here is the relationship between the **time** (hours) it takes to complete the job and the **part of the job** completed in 1 unit of time (hour). For example, if the **time** it takes Sam to complete the job is 3 hours, the **part of the job** he can complete in 1 hour is $\frac{1}{3}$. Similarly, Frank can complete $\frac{1}{7}$ of the job in 1 hour.

Let $x =$ the **time** in hours it takes Sam and Frank to complete the job together. Then $\frac{1}{x} =$ the **part of the job** they complete in 1 hour.

	Hours to Complete Total Job	*Part of Job Completed in 1 Hour*
Sam	3	$\frac{1}{3}$
Frank	7	$\frac{1}{7}$
Together	x	$\frac{1}{x}$

2. TRANSLATE.

In words:	part of job Sam completes in 1 hour	added to	part of job Frank completes in 1 hour	is equal to	part of job they complete together in 1 hour
	↓	↓	↓	↓	↓
Translate:	$\frac{1}{3}$	$+$	$\frac{1}{7}$	$=$	$\frac{1}{x}$

3. SOLVE. Here, we solve the equation $\frac{1}{3} + \frac{1}{7} = \frac{1}{x}$. We begin by multiplying both sides of the equation by the LCD, $21x$.

$$21x\left(\frac{1}{3}\right) + 21x\left(\frac{1}{7}\right) = 21x\left(\frac{1}{x}\right)$$

$$7x + 3x = 21 \quad \text{Simplify.}$$

$$10x = 21$$

$$x = \frac{21}{10} \quad \text{or} \quad 2\frac{1}{10} \text{ hours}$$

4. INTERPRET.

Check: Our proposed solution is $2\frac{1}{10}$ hours. This proposed solution is reasonable since $2\frac{1}{10}$ hours is more than half of Sam's time and less than half of Frank's time.

Check this solution in the originally *stated* problem.

State: Sam and Frank can complete the quality control tour in $2\frac{1}{10}$ hours. □

PRACTICE

6 Cindy Liu and Mary Beckwith own a landscaping company. Cindy can complete a certain garden planting in 3 hours, while Mary takes 4 hours to complete the same job. If both of them work together, how long will it take to plant the garden?

✓CONCEPT CHECK

Solve $E = mc^2$

a. for m. b. for c^2.

Answers to Concept Check:

a. $m = \frac{E}{c^2}$ **b.** $c^2 = \frac{E}{m}$

OBJECTIVE

5 Solving Problems About Distance 

Next we look at a problem solved by the distance formula,

$$d = r \cdot t$$

EXAMPLE 7 **Finding Speeds of Vehicles**

A car travels 180 miles in the same time that a truck travels 120 miles. If the car's speed is 20 miles per hour faster than the truck's, find the car's speed and the truck's speed.

Solution

1. UNDERSTAND. Read and reread the problem. Suppose that the truck's speed is 45 miles per hour. Then the car's speed is 20 miles per hour more, or 65 miles per hour.

We are given that the car travels 180 miles in the same time that the truck travels 120 miles. To find the time it takes the car to travel 180 miles, remember that since $d = rt$, we know that $\frac{d}{r} = t$.

Car's Time	***Truck's Time***
$t = \frac{d}{r} = \frac{180}{65} = 2\frac{50}{65} = 2\frac{10}{13}$ hours	$t = \frac{d}{r} = \frac{120}{45} = 2\frac{30}{45} = 2\frac{2}{3}$ hours

Since the times are not the same, our proposed solution is not correct. But we have a better understanding of the problem.

Let $x =$ the speed of the truck.

Since the car's speed is 20 miles per hour faster than the truck's, then

$$x + 20 = \text{the speed of the car}$$

Use the formula $d = r \cdot t$ or **d**istance = **r**ate · **t**ime. Prepare a chart to organize the information in the problem.

> **Helpful Hint**
> If $d = r \cdot t$,
> then $t = \frac{d}{r}$
> or $time = \frac{distance}{rate}$.

	Distance = ***Rate*** · ***Time***		
Truck	120	x	$\frac{120}{x}$ ← distance / ← rate
Car	180	$x + 20$	$\frac{180}{x + 20}$ ← distance / ← rate

2. TRANSLATE. Since the car and the truck travel the same amount of time, we have that

In words: car's time = truck's time

Translate: $\frac{180}{x + 20} = \frac{120}{x}$

3. SOLVE. We begin by multiplying both sides of the equation by the LCD, $x(x + 20)$, or cross multiplying.

$$\frac{180}{x + 20} = \frac{120}{x}$$

$$180x = 120(x + 20)$$

$$180x = 120x + 2400 \quad \text{Use the distributive property.}$$

$$60x = 2400 \quad \text{Subtract } 120x \text{ from both sides.}$$

$$x = 40 \quad \text{Divide both sides by 60.}$$

4. INTERPRET. The speed of the truck is 40 miles per hour. The speed of the car must then be $x + 20$ or 60 miles per hour.

Check: Find the time it takes the car to travel 180 miles and the time it takes the truck to travel 120 miles.

Car's Time	***Truck's Time***
$t = \frac{d}{r} = \frac{180}{60} = 3$ hours	$t = \frac{d}{r} = \frac{120}{40} = 3$ hours

Since both travel the same amount of time, the proposed solution is correct.

State: The car's speed is 60 miles per hour and the truck's speed is 40 miles per hour. □

PRACTICE

7 A bus travels 180 miles in the same time that a car travels 240 miles. If the car's speed is 15 mph faster than the speed of the bus, find the speed of the car and the speed of the bus.

Vocabulary, Readiness & Video Check

Without solving algebraically, select the best choice for each exercise.

1. One person can complete a job in 7 hours. A second person can complete the same job in 5 hours. How long will it take them to complete the job if they work together?

a. more than 7 hours
b. between 5 and 7 hours
c. less than 5 hours

2. One inlet pipe can fill a pond in 30 hours. A second inlet pipe can fill the same pond in 25 hours. How long before the pond is filled if both inlet pipes are on?

a. less than 25 hours
b. between 25 and 30 hours
c. more than 30 hours

TRANSLATING

Given the variable in the first column, use the phrase in the second column to translate to an expression and then continue to the phrase in the third column to translate to another expression.

3.	A number: x	The reciprocal of the number:	The reciprocal of the number, decreased by 3:
4.	A number: y	The reciprocal of the number:	The reciprocal of the number, increased by 2:
5.	A number: z	The sum of the number and 5:	The reciprocal of the sum of the number and 5:
6.	A number: x	The difference of the number and 1:	The reciprocal of the difference of the number and 1:
7.	A number: y	Twice the number:	Eleven divided by twice the number:
8.	A number: z	Triple the number:	Negative ten divided by triple the number:

Martin-Gay Interactive Videos

See Video 4.8

Watch the section lecture video and answer the following questions.

OBJECTIVE 1

9. Based on Examples 1 and 2, can proportions only be solved by using cross products? Explain.

OBJECTIVE 2

10. In Example 3 we are told there are many ways to set up a correct proportion. Why does this fact make it even more important to check that your solution is reasonable?

OBJECTIVE 3

11. What words or phrases in Example 5 told you to translate to an equation containing rational expressions?

OBJECTIVE 4

12. From Example 6, how can you determine a somewhat reasonable answer to a work problem before you even begin to solve it?

OBJECTIVE 5

13. The following problem is worded like Example 7 in the video, but using different quantities.

A car travels 325 miles in the same time that a motorcycle travels 290 miles. If the car's speed is 7 miles per hour more than the motorcycle's, find the speed of the car and the speed of the motorcycle. Fill in the table and set up an equation based on this problem (do not solve). Use Example 7 in the video as a model for your work.

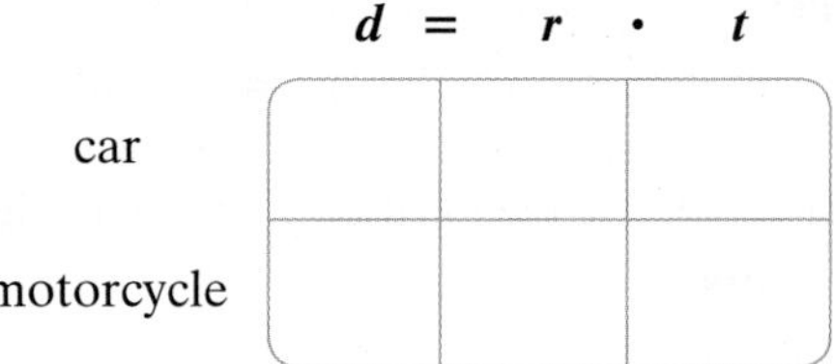

	d	$=$ r	$\cdot$ t
car			
motorcycle			

4.8 Exercise Set

MyMathLab®

Solve each proportion. See Examples 1 and 2.

1. $\frac{2}{3} = \frac{x}{6}$

2. $\frac{x}{2} = \frac{16}{6}$

3. $\frac{x}{10} = \frac{5}{9}$

4. $\frac{9}{4x} = \frac{6}{2}$

5. $\frac{x + 1}{2x + 3} = \frac{2}{3}$

6. $\frac{x + 1}{x + 2} = \frac{5}{3}$

7. $\frac{9}{5} = \frac{12}{3x + 2}$

8. $\frac{6}{11} = \frac{27}{3x - 2}$

Solve. See Example 3.

9. The ratio of the weight of an object on Earth to the weight of the same object on Pluto is 100 to 3. If an elephant weighs 4100 pounds on Earth, find the elephant's weight on Pluto.

10. If a 170-pound person weighs approximately 65 pounds on Mars, about how much does a 9000-pound satellite weigh? Round your answer to the nearest pound.

11. There are 110 calories per 28.8 grams of Frosted Flakes cereal. Find how many calories are in 43.2 grams of this cereal.

12. On an architect's blueprint, 1 inch corresponds to 4 feet. Find the length of a wall represented by a line that is $3\frac{7}{8}$ inches long on the blueprint.

Find the unknown length x or y in the following pairs of similar triangles. See Example 4.

△ 13.

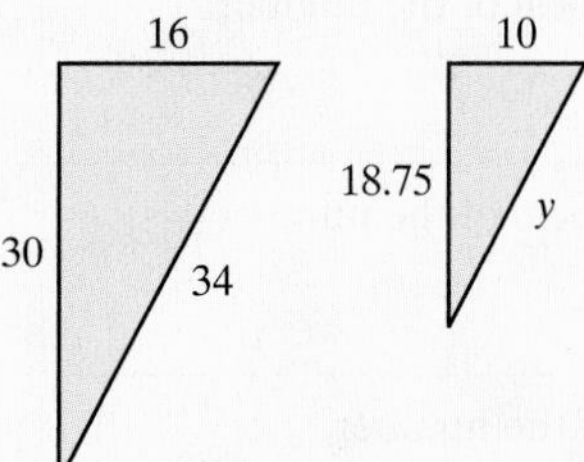

△ 14.

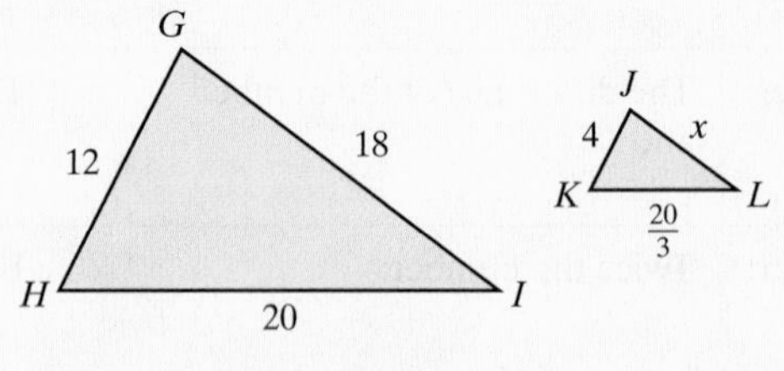

△ 15.

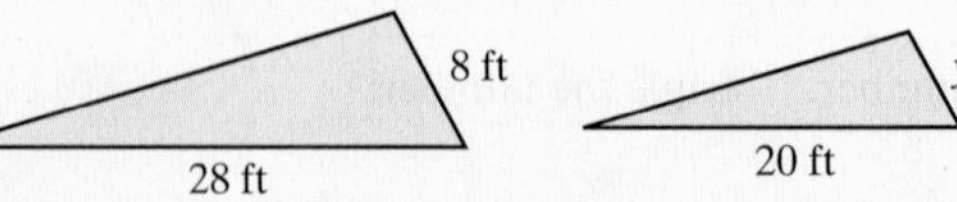

△ 16.

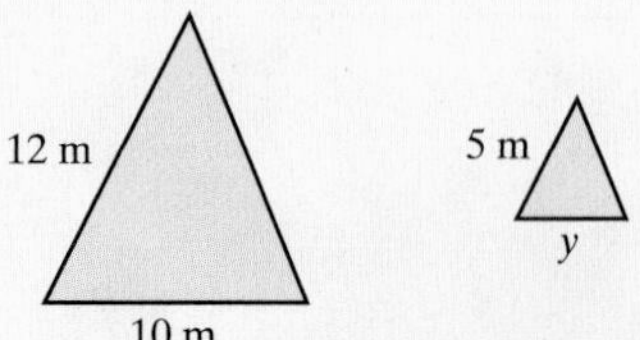

Solve the following. See Example 5.

17. Three times the reciprocal of a number equals 9 times the reciprocal of 6. Find the number.

18. Twelve divided by the sum of x and 2 equals the quotient of 4 and the difference of x and 2. Find x.

19. If twice a number added to 3 is divided by the number plus 1, the result is three halves. Find the number.

20. A number added to the product of 6 and the reciprocal of the number equals -5. Find the number.

See Example 6.

21. Smith Engineering found that an experienced surveyor surveys a roadbed in 4 hours. An apprentice surveyor needs 5 hours to survey the same stretch of road. If the two work together, find how long it takes them to complete the job.

22. An experienced bricklayer constructs a small wall in 3 hours. The apprentice completes the job in 6 hours. Find how long it takes if they work together.

23. In 2 minutes, a conveyor belt moves 300 pounds of recyclable aluminum from the delivery truck to a storage area. A smaller belt moves the same quantity of cans the same distance in 6 minutes. If both belts are used, find how long it takes to move the cans to the storage area.

24. Find how long it takes the conveyor belts described in Exercise 23 to move 1200 pounds of cans. (*Hint:* Think of 1200 pounds as four 300-pound jobs.)

See Example 7.

25. A jogger begins her workout by jogging to the park, a distance of 12 miles. She then jogs home at the same speed but along a different route. This return trip is 18 miles and her time is one hour longer. Find her jogging speed. Complete the accompanying chart and use it to find her jogging speed.

	Distance	=	*Rate*	·	*Time*
Trip to Park	12				
Return Trip	18				

26. A boat can travel 9 miles upstream in the same amount of time it takes to travel 11 miles downstream. If the current of the river is 3 miles per hour, complete the chart below and use it to find the speed of the boat in still water.

	Distance	=	*Rate*	·	*Time*
Upstream	9		$r - 3$		
Downstream	11		$r + 3$		

27. A cyclist rode the first 20-mile portion of his workout at a constant speed. For the 16-mile cooldown portion of his workout, he reduced his speed by 2 miles per hour. Each portion of the workout took the same time. Find the cyclist's speed during the first portion and find his speed during the cooldown portion.

28. A semi-truck travels 300 miles through the flatland in the same amount of time that it travels 180 miles through mountains. The rate of the truck is 20 miles per hour slower in the mountains than in the flatland. Find both the flatland rate and mountain rate.

MIXED PRACTICE

*Solve the following. See Examples 1 through 7. (*Note: *Some exercises can be modeled by equations without rational expressions.)*

29. A human factors expert recommends that there be at least 9 square feet of floor space in a college classroom for every student in the class. Find the minimum floor space that 40 students need.

30. Due to space problems at a local university, a 20-foot by 12-foot conference room is converted into a classroom. Find the maximum number of students the room can accommodate. (See Exercise 29.)

31. One-fourth equals the quotient of a number and 8. Find the number.

32. Four times a number added to 5 is divided by 6. The result is $\frac{7}{2}$. Find the number.

33. Marcus and Tony work for Lombardo's Pipe and Concrete. Mr. Lombardo is preparing an estimate for a customer. He knows that Marcus lays a slab of concrete in 6 hours. Tony lays the same size slab in 4 hours. If both work on the job and the cost of labor is \$45.00 per hour, decide what the labor estimate should be.

34. Mr. Dodson can paint his house by himself in 4 days. His son needs an additional day to complete the job if he works by himself. If they work together, find how long it takes to paint the house.

35. A pilot can travel 400 miles with the wind in the same amount of time as 336 miles against the wind. Find the speed of the wind if the pilot's speed in still air is 230 miles per hour.

36. A fisherman on Pearl River rows 9 miles downstream in the same amount of time he rows 3 miles upstream. If the current is 6 miles per hour, find how long it takes him to cover the 12 miles.

37. Find the unknown length y.

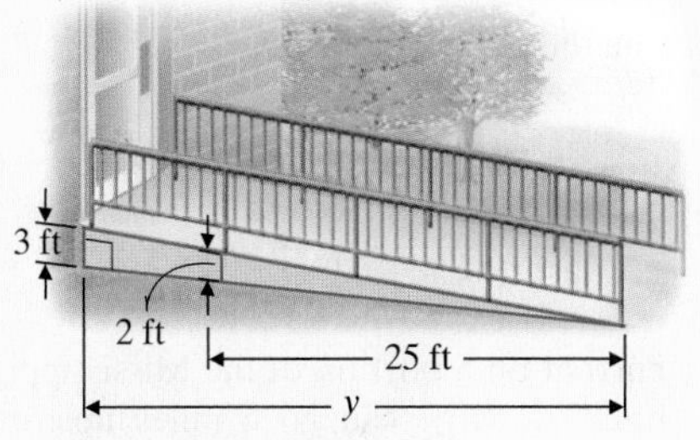

38. Find the unknown length y.

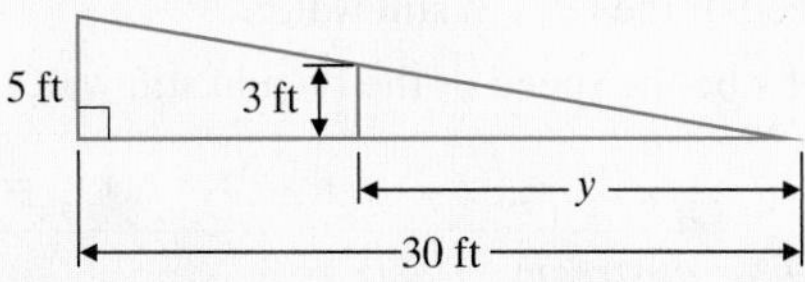

39. Suppose two trains leave Holbrook, Arizona, at the same time, traveling in opposite directions. One train travels 10 mph faster than the other. In 3.5 hours, the trains are 322 miles apart. Find the speed of each train.

40. Suppose two cars leave Brinkley, Arkansas, at the same time, traveling in opposite directions. One car travels 8 mph faster than the other car. In 2.5 hours, the cars are 280 miles apart. Find the speed of each car.

41. Two divided by the difference of a number and 3, minus 4 divided by the number plus 3, equals 8 times the reciprocal of the difference of the number squared and 9. What is the number?

42. If 15 times the reciprocal of a number is added to the ratio of 9 times the number minus 7 and the number plus 2, the result is 9. What is the number?

43. A pilot flies 630 miles with a tailwind of 35 miles per hour. Against the wind, he flies only 455 miles in the same amount of time. Find the rate of the plane in still air.

44. A marketing manager travels 1080 miles in a corporate jet and then an additional 240 miles by car. If the car ride takes one hour longer than the jet ride takes, and if the rate of the jet is 6 times the rate of the car, find the time the manager travels by jet and find the time the manager travels by car.

45. To mix weed killer with water correctly, it is necessary to mix 8 teaspoons of weed killer with 2 gallons of water. Find how many gallons of water are needed to mix with the entire box if it contains 36 teaspoons of weed killer.

46. The directions for a certain bug spray concentrate is to mix 3 ounces of concentrate with 2 gallons of water. How many ounces of concentrate are needed to mix with 5 gallons of water?

47. A boater travels 16 miles per hour on the water on a still day. During one particular windy day, he finds that he travels 48 miles with the wind behind him in the same amount of time that he travels 16 miles into the wind. Find the rate of the wind.

Let x be the rate of the wind.

	r ×	t =	d
with wind	$16 + x$		48
into wind	$16 - x$		16

48. The current on a portion of the Mississippi River is 3 miles per hour. A barge can go 6 miles upstream in the same amount of time it takes to go 10 miles downstream. Find the speed of the boat in still water.

Let x be the speed of the boat in still water.

	r ×	t =	d
upstream	$x - 3$		6
downstream	$x + 3$		10

49. Two hikers are 11 miles apart and walking toward each other. They meet in 2 hours. Find the rate of each hiker if one hiker walks 1.1 mph faster than the other.

50. On a 255-mile trip, Gary Alessandrini traveled at an average speed of 70 mph, got a speeding ticket, and then traveled at 60 mph for the remainder of the trip. If the entire trip took 4.5 hours and the speeding ticket stop took 30 minutes, how long did Gary speed before getting stopped?

51. One custodian cleans a suite of offices in 3 hours. When a second worker is asked to join the regular custodian, the job takes only $1\frac{1}{2}$ hours. How long does it take the second worker to do the same job alone?

52. One person proofreads a copy for a small newspaper in 4 hours. If a second proofreader is also employed, the job can be done in $2\frac{1}{2}$ hours. How long does it take for the second proofreader to do the same job alone?

△ **53.** An architect is completing the plans for a triangular deck. Use the diagram below to find the missing dimension.

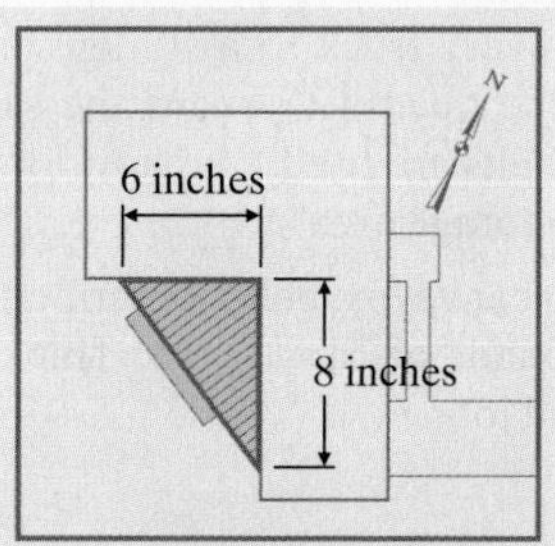

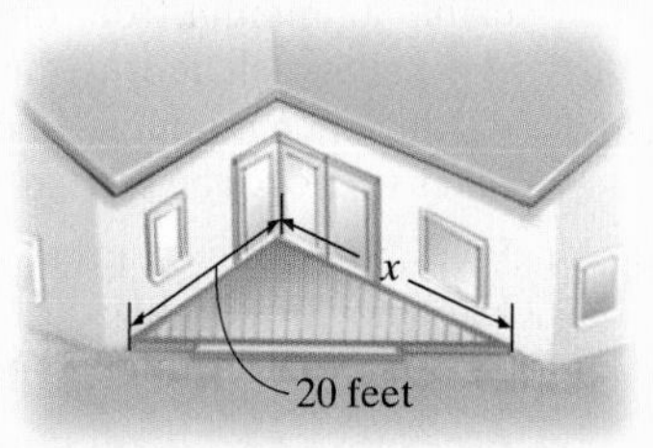

△ **54.** A student wishes to make a small model of a triangular mainsail to study the effects of wind on the sail. The smaller model will be the same shape as a regular-size sailboat's mainsail. Use the following diagram to find the missing dimensions.

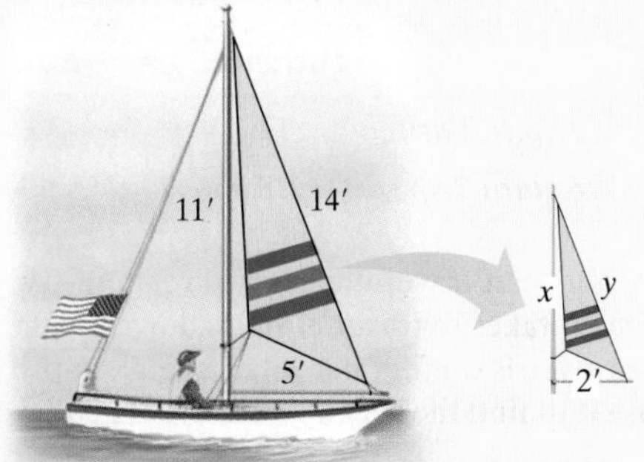

55. The manufacturers of cans of salted mixed nuts state that the ratio of peanuts to other nuts is 3 to 2. If 324 peanuts are in a can, find how many other nuts should also be in the can.

56. There are 1280 calories in a 14-ounce portion of Eagle Brand Milk. Find how many calories are in 2 ounces of Eagle Brand Milk.

57. A jet plane traveling at 500 mph overtakes a propeller plane traveling at 200 mph that had a 2-hour head start. How far from the starting point are the planes?

58. How long will it take a bus traveling at 60 miles per hour to overtake a car traveling at 40 mph if the car had a 1.5-hour head start?

59. One pipe fills a storage pool in 20 hours. A second pipe fills the same pool in 15 hours. When a third pipe is added and all three are used to fill the pool, it takes only 6 hours. Find how long it takes the third pipe to do the job.

60. One pump fills a tank in 9 hours. A second pump fills the same tank in 6 hours. When a third pump is added and all three are used to fill the tank, it takes only 3 hours. Find how long it takes the third pump to fill the tank.

61. A car travels 280 miles in the same time that a motorcycle travels 240 miles. If the car's speed is 10 miles per hour more than the motorcycle's, find the speed of the car and the speed of the motorcycle.

62. A bus traveled on a level road for 3 hours at an average speed 20 miles per hour faster than it traveled on a winding road. The time spent on the winding road was 4 hours. Find the average speed on the level road if the entire trip was 305 miles.

63. In 6 hours, an experienced cook prepares enough pies to supply a local restaurant's daily order. Another cook prepares the same number of pies in 7 hours. Together with a third cook, they prepare the pies in 2 hours. Find how long it takes the third cook to prepare the pies alone.

64. Mrs. Smith balances the company books in 8 hours. It takes her assistant 12 hours to do the same job. If they work together, find how long it takes them to balance the books.

65. The quotient of a number and 3, minus 1, equals $\frac{5}{3}$. Find the number.

66. The quotient of a number and 5, minus 1, equals $\frac{7}{5}$. Find the number.

67. Currently, the Toyota Corolla is the best-selling car in the world. Suppose that during a test drive of two Corollas, one car travels 224 miles in the same time that the second car travels 175 miles. If the speed of the first car is 14 miles per hour faster than the speed of the second car, find the speed of both cars. (*Source: Top Ten of Everything*)

68. The second best-selling car is the Volkswagen Golf. A driver of this car took a day trip around the California coastline driving at two speeds. He drove 70 miles at a slower speed and 300 miles at a speed 40 miles per hour faster. If the time spent driving the faster speed was twice that spent at the slower speed, find the two speeds during the trip. (*Source: Top Ten of Everything*)

69. A pilot can fly an MD-11 2160 miles with the wind in the same time she can fly 1920 miles against the wind. If the speed of the wind is 30 mph, find the speed of the plane in still air. (*Source*: Air Transport Association of America)

70. A pilot can fly a DC-10 1365 miles against the wind in the same time he can fly 1575 miles with the wind. If the speed of the plane in still air is 490 miles per hour, find the speed of the wind. (*Source*: Air Transport Association of America)

Given that the following pairs of triangles are similar, find each missing length.

△ 71.

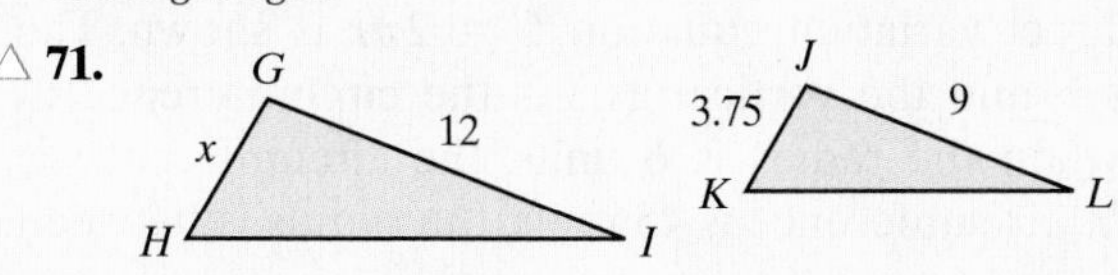

△ 72.

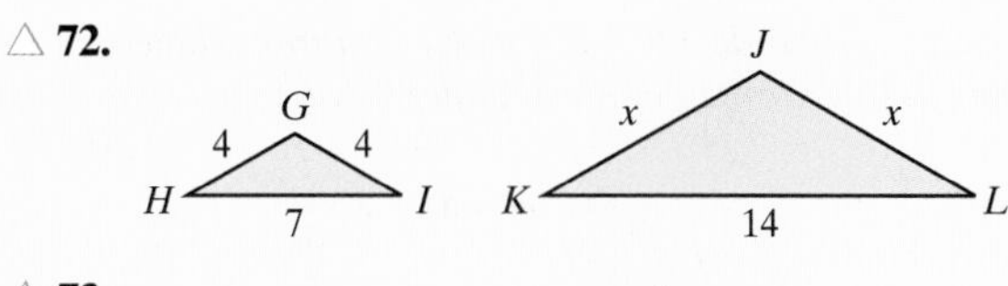

△ 73.

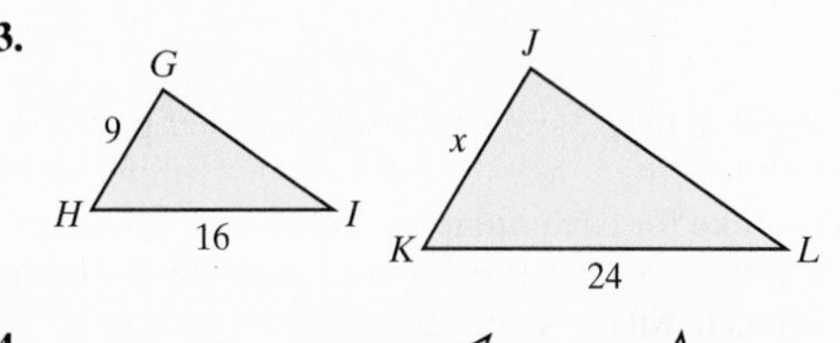

△ 74.

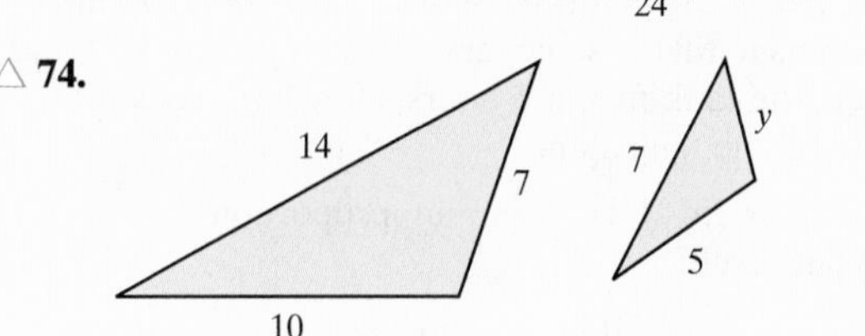

REVIEW AND PREVIEW

Find the slope of the line through each pair of points. Use the slope to determine whether the line is vertical, horizontal, or moves upward or downward from left to right. See Section 1.4.

75. $(-2, 5), (4, -3)$
76. $(0, 4), (2, 10)$
77. $(-3, -6), (1, 5)$
78. $(-2, 7), (3, -2)$
79. $(3, 7), (3, -2)$
80. $(0, -4), (2, -4)$

CONCEPT EXTENSIONS

The following bar graph shows the capacity of the United States to generate electricity from the wind in the years shown. Use this graph for Exercises 81 and 82.

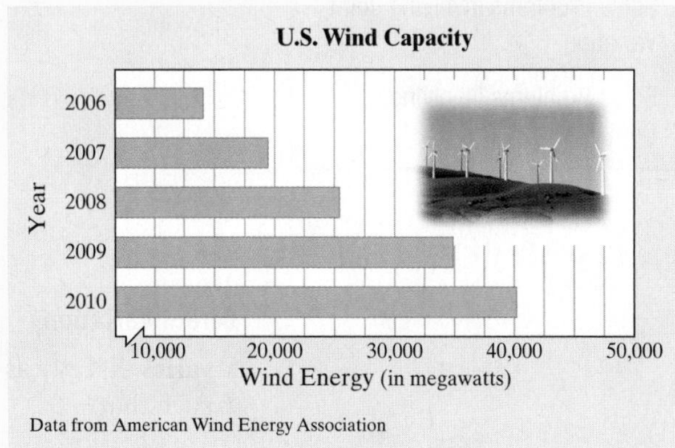

81. Find the approximate megawatt capacity in 2010.
82. Find the approximate megawatt capacity in 2009.

In general, 1000 megawatts will serve the average electricity needs of 560,000 people. Use this fact and the preceding graph to answer Exercises 83 and 84.

83. In 2010, the number of megawatts that were generated from wind served the electricity needs of how many people? (Round to the nearest ten-thousand.)

84. How many megawatts of electricity are needed to serve the city or town in which you live?

For Exercises 85 and 86 decide whether we can immediately use cross products to solve for x. Do not actually solve.

85. $\frac{2-x}{5} = \frac{1+x}{3}$

86. $\frac{2}{5} - x = \frac{1+x}{3}$

Solve.

87. One pump fills a tank 3 times as fast as another pump. If the pumps work together, they fill the tank in 21 minutes. How long does it take for each pump to fill the tank?

88. It takes 9 hours for pump A to fill a tank alone. Pump B takes 15 hours to fill the same tank alone. If pumps A, B, and C are used, the tank fills in 5 hours. How long does it take pump C to fill the tank alone?

89. For what value of x is $\frac{x}{x-1}$ in proportion to $\frac{x+1}{x}$? Explain your result.

90. If x is 10, is $\frac{2}{x}$ in proportion to $\frac{x}{50}$? Explain why or why not.

91. Person A can complete a job in 5 hours, and person B can complete the same job in 3 hours. Without solving algebraically, discuss reasonable and unreasonable answers for how long it would take them to complete the job together.

92. A hyena spots a giraffe 0.5 mile away and begins running toward it. The giraffe starts running away from the hyena just as the hyena begins running toward it. A hyena can run at a speed of 40 mph and a giraffe can run at 32 mph. How long will it take for the hyena to overtake the giraffe? (*Source: World Almanac and Book of Facts*)

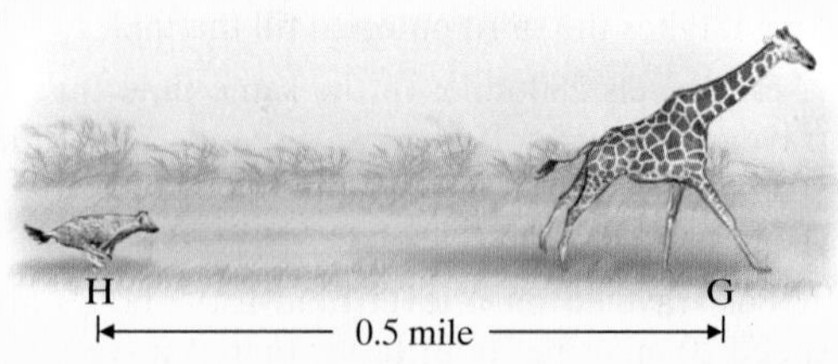

Solve. See the Concept Check in this section.

Solve $D = RT$

93. for R

94. for T

4.9 Variation and Problem Solving 

OBJECTIVES

1. Solve Problems Involving Direct Variation.
2. Solve Problems Involving Inverse Variation.
3. Solve Problems Involving Joint Variation.
4. Solve Problems Involving Combined Variation.

OBJECTIVE

1 Solving Problems Involving Direct Variation 

A very familiar example of direct variation is the relationship of the circumference C of a circle to its radius r. The formula $C = 2\pi r$ expresses that the circumference is always 2π times the radius. In other words, C is always a constant multiple (2π) of r. Because it is, we say that **C varies directly as r**, that **C varies directly with r**, or that **C is directly proportional to r.**

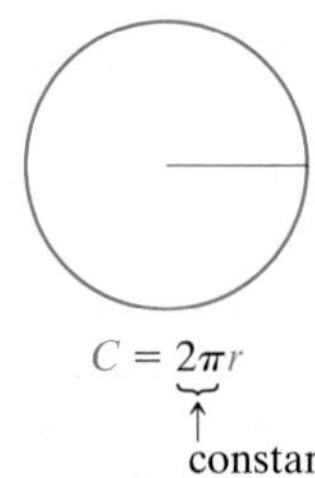

$C = 2\pi r$

↑ constant

Direct Variation

y varies directly as x, or y is directly proportional to x, if there is a nonzero constant k such that

$$y = kx$$

The number k is called the **constant of variation** or the **constant of proportionality.**

In the above definition, the relationship described between x and y is a linear one. In other words, the graph of $y = kx$ is a line. The slope of the line is k, and the line passes through the origin.

For example, the graph of the direct variation equation $C = 2\pi r$ is shown. The horizontal axis represents the radius r, and the vertical axis is the circumference C. From the graph, we can read that when the radius is 6 units, the circumference is approximately 38 units. Also, when the circumference is 45 units, the radius is between 7 and 8 units. Notice that as the radius increases, the circumference increases.

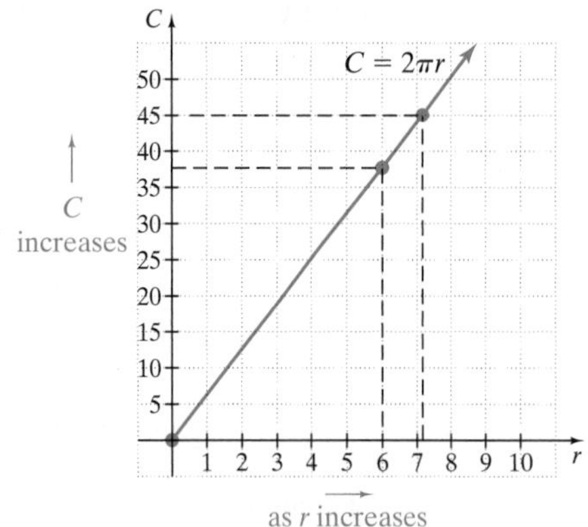

EXAMPLE 1 Suppose that y varies directly as x. If y is 5 when x is 30, find the constant of variation and the direct variation equation.

Solution Since y varies directly as x, we write $y = kx$. If $y = 5$ when $x = 30$, we have that

$$y = kx$$

$$5 = k(30) \quad \text{Replace } y \text{ with 5 and } x \text{ with 30.}$$

$$\frac{1}{6} = k \quad \text{Solve for } k.$$

The constant of variation is $\frac{1}{6}$.

After finding the constant of variation k, the direct variation equation can be written as $y = \frac{1}{6}x$. □

PRACTICE

1 Suppose that y varies directly as x. If y is 20 when x is 15, find the constant of variation and the direct variation equation.

EXAMPLE 2 **Using Direct Variation and Hooke's Law**

Hooke's law states that the distance a spring stretches is directly proportional to the weight attached to the spring. If a 40-pound weight attached to the spring stretches the spring 5 inches, find the distance that a 65-pound weight attached to the spring stretches the spring.

Solution

1. UNDERSTAND. Read and reread the problem. Notice that we are given that the distance a spring stretches is **directly proportional** to the weight attached. We let

$d =$ the distance stretched

$w =$ the weight attached

The constant of variation is represented by k.

d

65 lb

2. TRANSLATE. Because d is directly proportional to w, we write

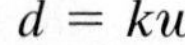

$$d = kw$$

3. SOLVE. When a weight of 40 pounds is attached, the spring stretches 5 inches. That is, when $w = 40$, $d = 5$.

$$d = kw$$
$$5 = k(40) \quad \text{Replace } d \text{ with 5 and } w \text{ with 40.}$$
$$\frac{1}{8} = k \quad \text{Solve for } k.$$

Now when we replace k with $\frac{1}{8}$ in the equation $d = kw$, we have

$$d = \frac{1}{8}w$$

To find the stretch when a weight of 65 pounds is attached, we replace w with 65 to find d.

$$d = \frac{1}{8}(65)$$
$$= \frac{65}{8} = 8\frac{1}{8} \quad \text{or} \quad 8.125$$

4. INTERPRET.

Check: Check the proposed solution of 8.125 inches in the original problem.

State: The spring stetches 8.125 inches when a 65-pound weight is attached. □

PRACTICE

2 Use Hooke's law as stated in Example 2. If a 36-pound weight attached to a spring stretches the spring 9 inches, find the distance that a 75-pound weight attached to the spring stretches the spring.

OBJECTIVE

2 Solving Problems Involving Inverse Variation 

When y is proportional to the **reciprocal** of another variable x, we say that ***y* varies inversely as *x*,** or that ***y* is inversely proportional to *x*.** An example of the inverse variation relationship is the relationship between the pressure that a gas exerts and the volume of its container. As the volume of a container decreases, the pressure of the gas it contains increases.

Inverse Variation

***y* varies inversely as *x*, or *y* is inversely proportional to *x*,** if there is a nonzero constant k such that

$$y = \frac{k}{x}$$

The number k is called the **constant of variation** or the **constant of proportionality.**

Notice that $y = \frac{k}{x}$ is a rational equation. Its graph for $k > 0$ and $x > 0$ is shown. From the graph, we can see that as x increases, y decreases.

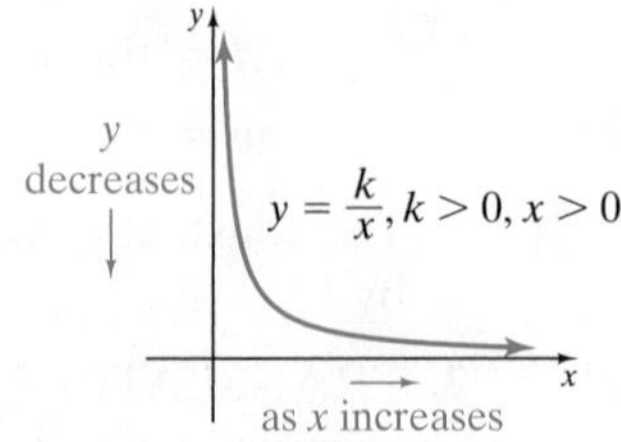

EXAMPLE 3 Suppose that u varies inversely as w. If u is 3 when w is 5, find the constant of variation and the inverse variation equation.

Solution Since u varies inversely as w, we have $u = \frac{k}{w}$. We let $u = 3$ and $w = 5$, and we solve for k.

$$u = \frac{k}{w}$$

$$3 = \frac{k}{5} \quad \text{Let } u = 3 \text{ and } w = 5.$$

$$15 = k \quad \text{Multiply both sides by 5.}$$

The constant of variation k is 15. This gives the inverse variation equation

$$u = \frac{15}{w}$$ □

PRACTICE

3 Suppose that b varies inversely as a. If b is 5 when a is 9, find the constant of variation and the inverse variation equation.

EXAMPLE 4 Using Inverse Variation and Boyle's Law

Boyle's law says that if the temperature stays the same, the pressure P of a gas is inversely proportional to the volume V. If a cylinder in a steam engine has a pressure of 960 kilopascals when the volume is 1.4 cubic meters, find the pressure when the volume increases to 2.5 cubic meters.

Solution

1. UNDERSTAND. Read and reread the problem. Notice that we are given that the pressure of a gas is *inversely proportional* to the volume. We will let $P =$ the pressure and $V =$ the volume. The constant of variation is represented by k.
2. TRANSLATE. Because P is inversely proportional to V, we write

$$P = \frac{k}{V}$$

When $P = 960$ kilopascals, the volume $V = 1.4$ cubic meters. We use this information to find k.

$$960 = \frac{k}{1.4} \quad \text{Let } P = 960 \text{ and } V = 1.4.$$

$$1344 = k \quad \text{Multiply both sides by 1.4.}$$

Thus, the value of k is 1344. Replacing k with 1344 in the variation equation, we have

$$P = \frac{1344}{V}$$

Next we find P when V is 2.5 cubic meters.

3. SOLVE.

$$P = \frac{1344}{2.5} \quad \text{Let } V = 2.5.$$

$$= 537.6$$

4. INTERPRET.

Check: Check the proposed solution in the original problem.

State: When the volume is 2.5 cubic meters, the pressure is 537.6 kilopascals. □

PRACTICE

4 Use Boyle's law as stated in Example 4. If $P = 350$ kilopascals when $V = 2.8$ cubic meters, find the pressure when the volume decreases to 1.5 cubic meters.

OBJECTIVE

3 Solving Problems Involving Joint Variation 

Sometimes the ratio of a variable to the product of many other variables is constant. For example, the ratio of distance traveled to the product of speed and time traveled is always 1.

$$\frac{d}{rt} = 1 \quad \text{or} \quad d = rt$$

Such a relationship is called **joint variation.**

Joint Variation

If the ratio of a variable y to the product of two or more variables is constant, then **y varies jointly as,** or **is jointly proportional to,** the other variables. If

$$y = kxz$$

then the number k is the **constant of variation** or the **constant of proportionality.**

✓CONCEPT CHECK

Which type of variation is represented by the equation $xy = 8$? Explain.

a. Direct variation b. Inverse variation c. Joint variation

EXAMPLE 5 **Expressing Surface Area**

The lateral surface area of a cylinder varies jointly as its radius and height. Express this surface area S in terms of radius r and height h.

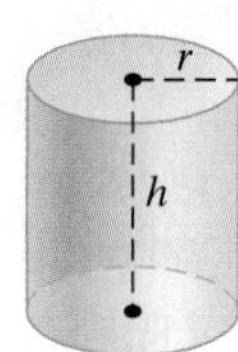

Solution Because the surface area varies jointly as the radius r and the height h, we equate S to a constant multiple of r and h.

$$S = krh$$

In the equation $S = krh$, it can be determined that the constant k is 2π, and we then have the formula $S = 2\pi rh$. (The lateral surface area formula does not include the areas of the two circular bases.) □

PRACTICE

5 The area of a regular polygon varies jointly as its apothem and its perimeter. Express the area in terms of the apothem a and the perimeter p.

OBJECTIVE

4 Solving Problems Involving Combined Variation 

There are many examples of variation in which y may vary directly or inversely as a *power* of x. Also there are combinations of direct, inverse, and joint variation. We will call these variations **combined variation.**

EXAMPLE 6 Suppose that y varies directly as the square of x. If y is 24 when x is 2, find the constant of variation and the variation equation.

Solution Since y varies directly as the square of x, we have

$$y = kx^2$$

Answer to Concept Check:
b; answers may vary

Now let $y = 24$ and $x = 2$ and solve for k.

$$y = kx^2$$
$$24 = k \cdot 2^2$$
$$24 = 4k$$
$$6 = k$$

The constant of variation is 6, so the variation equation is

$$y = 6x^2$$

□

PRACTICE

6 Suppose that y varies inversely as the cube of x. If y is $\frac{1}{2}$ when x is 2, find the constant of variation and the variation equation.

EXAMPLE 7 Finding Column Weight

The maximum weight that a circular column can support is directly proportional to the fourth power of its diameter and is inversely proportional to the square of its height. A 2-meter-diameter column that is 8 meters in height can support 1 ton. Find the weight that a 1-meter-diameter column that is 4 meters in height can support.

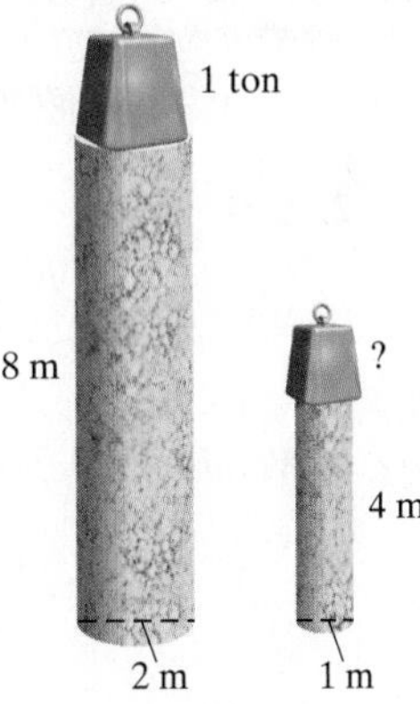

Solution

1. UNDERSTAND. Read and reread the problem. Let w = weight, d = diameter, h = height, and k = the constant of variation.

2. TRANSLATE. Since w is directly proportional to d^4 and inversely proportional to h^2, we have

$$w = \frac{kd^4}{h^2}$$

3. SOLVE. To find k, we are given that a 2-meter-diameter column that is 8 meters in height can support 1 ton. That is, $w = 1$ when $d = 2$ and $h = 8$, or

$$1 = \frac{k \cdot 2^4}{8^2} \quad \text{Let } w = 1, d = 2, \text{ and } h = 8.$$

$$1 = \frac{k \cdot 16}{64}$$

$$4 = k \quad \text{Solve for } k.$$

Now replace k with 4 in the equation $w = \frac{kd^4}{h^2}$ and we have

$$w = \frac{4d^4}{h^2}$$

To find weight w for a 1-meter-diameter column that is 4 meters in height, let $d = 1$ and $h = 4$.

$$w = \frac{4 \cdot 1^4}{4^2}$$

$$w = \frac{4}{16} = \frac{1}{4}$$

4. INTERPRET.

Check: Check the proposed solution in the original problem.

State: The 1-meter-diameter column that is 4 meters in height can support $\frac{1}{4}$ ton of weight. □

PRACTICE

7 Suppose that y varies directly as z and inversely as the cube of x. If y is 15 when $z = 5$ and $x = 3$, find the constant of variation and the variation equation.

Vocabulary, Readiness & Video Check

State whether each equation represents direct, inverse, or joint variation.

1. $y = 5x$ **2.** $y = \frac{700}{x}$ **3.** $y = 5xz$ **4.** $y = \frac{1}{2}abc$

5. $y = \frac{9.1}{x}$ **6.** $y = 2.3x$ **7.** $y = \frac{2}{3}x$ **8.** $y = 3.1st$

Martin-Gay Interactive Videos

See Video 4.9 

Watch the section lecture video and answer the following questions.

OBJECTIVE 1

9. Based on the lecture before Example 1, what kind of equation is a direct variation equation? What does k, the constant of variation, represent in this equation?

OBJECTIVE 2

10. In Example 3, why is it not necessary to replace the given values of x and y in the inverse variation equation in order to find k?

OBJECTIVE 3

11. Based on Example 5 and the lecture before, what is the variation equation for "y varies jointly as the square of a and the fifth power of b"?

OBJECTIVE 4

12. From Example 6, what kind of variation does a combined variation application involve?

4.9 Exercise Set

MyMathLab®  

If y varies directly as x, find the constant of variation and the direct variation equation for each situation. See Example 1.

1. $y = 4$ when $x = 20$

2. $y = 9$ when $x = 54$

3. $y = 6$ when $x = 4$

4. $y = 12$ when $x = 8$

5. $y = 7$ when $x = \frac{1}{2}$

6. $y = 11$ when $x = \frac{1}{3}$

7. $y = 0.2$ when $x = 0.8$

8. $y = 0.4$ when $x = 2.5$

Solve. See Example 2.

△ **9.** The weight of a synthetic ball varies directly with the cube of its radius. A ball with a radius of 2 inches weighs 1.20 pounds. Find the weight of a ball of the same material with a 3-inch radius.

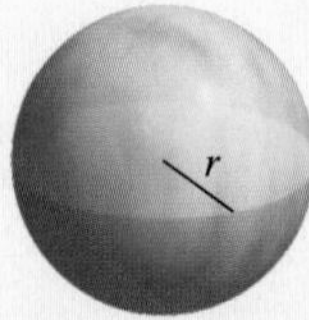

10. At sea, the distance to the horizon is directly proportional to the square root of the elevation of the observer. If a person

who is 36 feet above the water can see 7.4 miles, find how far a person 64 feet above the water can see. Round to the nearest tenth of a mile.

11. The amount P of pollution varies directly with the population N of people. Kansas City has a population of 460,000 and produces about 270,000 tons of pollutants. Find how many tons of pollution we should expect St. Louis to produce if we know that its population is 319,000. Round to the nearest whole ton. (*Source:* Wikipedia)

12. Charles's law states that if the pressure P stays the same, the volume V of a gas is directly proportional to its temperature T. If a balloon is filled with 20 cubic meters of a gas at a temperature of 300 K, find the new volume if the temperature rises to 360 K while the pressure stays the same.

If y varies inversely as x, find the constant of variation and the inverse variation equation for each situation. See Example 3.

13. $y = 6$ when $x = 5$

14. $y = 20$ when $x = 9$

15. $y = 100$ when $x = 7$

16. $y = 63$ when $x = 3$

17. $y = \frac{1}{8}$ when $x = 16$

18. $y = \frac{1}{10}$ when $x = 40$

19. $y = 0.2$ when $x = 0.7$

20. $y = 0.6$ when $x = 0.3$

Solve. See Example 4.

21. Pairs of markings a set distance apart are made on highways so that police can detect drivers exceeding the speed limit. Over a fixed distance, the speed R varies inversely with the time T. In one particular pair of markings, R is 45 mph when T is 6 seconds. Find the speed of a car that travels the given distance in 5 seconds.

22. The weight of an object on or above the surface of Earth varies inversely as the square of the distance between the object and Earth's center. If a person weighs 160 pounds on Earth's surface, find the individual's weight if he moves 200 miles above Earth. Round to the nearest whole pound. (Assume that Earth's radius is 4000 miles.)

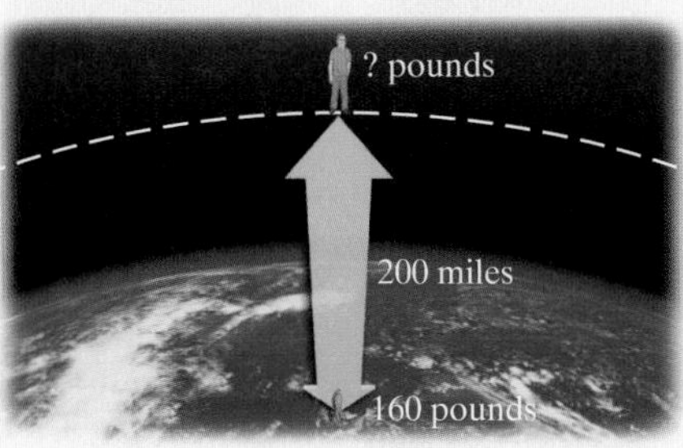

23. If the voltage V in an electric circuit is held constant, the current I is inversely proportional to the resistance R. If the current is 40 amperes when the resistance is 270 ohms, find the current when the resistance is 150 ohms.

24. Because it is more efficient to produce larger numbers of items, the cost of producing a certain computer DVD is inversely proportional to the number produced. If 4000 can be produced at a cost of \$1.20 each, find the cost per DVD when 6000 are produced.

25. The intensity I of light varies inversely as the square of the distance d from the light source. If the distance from the light source is doubled (see the figure), determine what happens to the intensity of light at the new location.

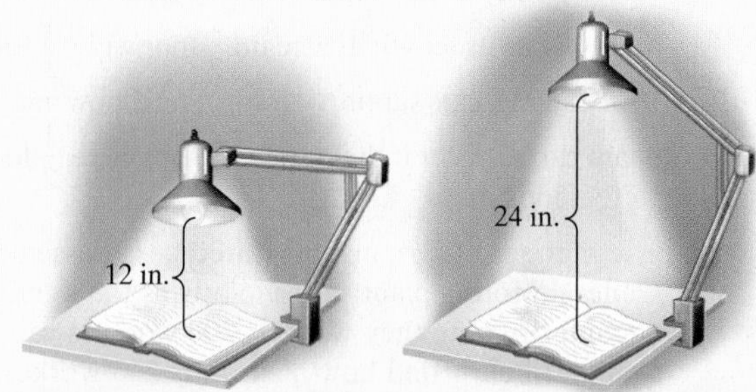

26. The maximum weight that a circular column can hold is inversely proportional to the square of its height. If an 8-foot column can hold 2 tons, find how much weight a 10-foot column can hold.

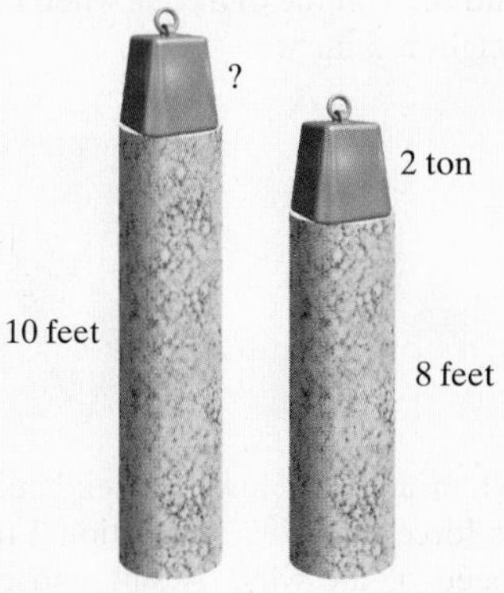

MIXED PRACTICE

Write each statement as an equation. Use k as the constant of variation. See Example 5.

27. x varies jointly as y and z.

28. P varies jointly as R and the square of S.

29. r varies jointly as s and the cube of t.

30. a varies jointly as b and c.

For each statement, find the constant of variation and the variation equation. See Examples 5 and 6.

31. y varies directly as the cube of x; $y = 9$ when $x = 3$

32. y varies directly as the cube of x; $y = 32$ when $x = 4$

33. y varies directly as the square root of x; $y = 0.4$ when $x = 4$

34. y varies directly as the square root of x; $y = 2.1$ when $x = 9$

35. y varies inversely as the square of x; $y = 0.052$ when $x = 5$

36. y varies inversely as the square of x; $y = 0.011$ when $x = 10$

37. y varies jointly as x and the cube of z; $y = 120$ when $x = 5$ and $z = 2$

38. y varies jointly as x and the square of z; $y = 360$ when $x = 4$ and $z = 3$

Solve. See Example 7.

△ **39.** The maximum weight that a rectangular beam can support varies jointly as its width and the square of its height and inversely as its length. If a beam $\frac{1}{2}$ foot wide, $\frac{1}{3}$ foot high, and 10 feet long can support 12 tons, find how much a similar beam can support if the beam is $\frac{2}{3}$ foot wide, $\frac{1}{2}$ foot high, and 16 feet long.

40. The number of cars manufactured on an assembly line at a General Motors plant varies jointly as the number of workers and the time they work. If 200 workers can produce 60 cars in 2 hours, find how many cars 240 workers should be able to make in 3 hours.

△ **41.** The volume of a cone varies jointly as its height and the square of its radius. If the volume of a cone is 32π cubic inches when the radius is 4 inches and the height is 6 inches, find the volume of a cone when the radius is 3 inches and the height is 5 inches.

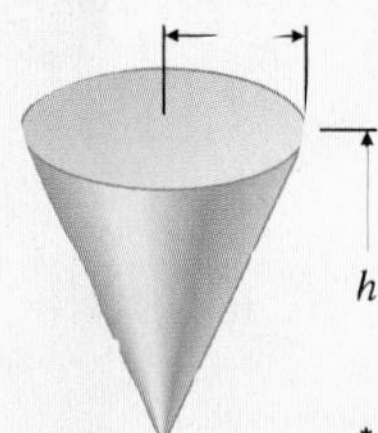

△ **42.** When a wind blows perpendicularly against a flat surface, its force is jointly proportional to the surface area and the speed of the wind. A sail whose surface area is 12 square feet experiences a 20-pound force when the wind speed is 10 miles per hour. Find the force on an 8-square-foot sail if the wind speed is 12 miles per hour.

43. The intensity of light (in foot-candles) varies inversely as the square of x, the distance in feet from the light source. The intensity of light 2 feet from the source is 80 foot-candles. How far away is the source if the intensity of light is 5 foot-candles?

44. The horsepower that can be safely transmitted to a shaft varies jointly as the shaft's angular speed of rotation (in revolutions per minute) and the cube of its diameter. A 2-inch shaft making 120 revolutions per minute safely transmits 40 horsepower. Find how much horsepower can be safely transmitted by a 3-inch shaft making 80 revolutions per minute.

MIXED PRACTICE

Write an equation to describe each variation. Use k for the constant of proportionality. See Examples 1 through 7.

45. y varies directly as x

46. p varies directly as q

47. a varies inversely as b

48. y varies inversely as x

49. y varies jointly as x and z

50. y varies jointly as q, r, and t

51. y varies inversely as x^3

52. y varies inversely as a^4

53. y varies directly as x and inversely as p^2

54. y varies directly as a^5 and inversely as b

REVIEW AND PREVIEW

Find the exact circumference and area of each circle. See the inside cover for a list of geometric formulas.

△ **55.** 4 in.

△ **56.** 6 cm

△ **57.** 9 cm

△ **58.** 7 m

Simplify. See Sections R.2, R.4, and R.5.

59. $|-1.2|$

60. $-|7|$

61. $-\left|-\frac{1}{2}\right|$

62. $|0|$

63. $\left(\frac{2}{3}\right)^3$

64. $-\left|\frac{1}{5}\right|$

65. $|-3|$

66. $\left(\frac{5}{11}\right)^2$

CONCEPT EXTENSIONS

Solve. See the Concept Check in this section. Choose the type of variation that each equation represents. **a.** *Direct variation* **b.** *Inverse variation* **c.** *Joint variation*

67. $y = \frac{2}{3}x$

68. $y = \frac{0.6}{x}$

69. $y = 9ab$

70. $xy = \frac{2}{11}$

71. The horsepower to drive a boat varies directly as the cube of the speed of the boat. If the speed of the boat is to double, determine the corresponding increase in horsepower required.

72. The volume of a cylinder varies jointly as the height and the square of the radius. If the height is halved and the radius is doubled, determine what happens to the volume.

73. Suppose that y varies directly as x. If x is doubled, what is the effect on y?

74. Suppose that y varies directly as x^2. If x is doubled, what is the effect on y?

Complete the following table for the inverse variation $y = \frac{k}{x}$ *over each given value of k. Plot the points on a rectangular coordinate system.*

x	$\frac{1}{4}$	$\frac{1}{2}$	1	2	4
$y = \frac{k}{x}$					

75. $k = 3$ **76.** $k = 1$ **77.** $k = \frac{1}{2}$ **78.** $k = 5$

Chapter 4 Vocabulary Check

Fill in each blank with one of the words or phrases listed below. Not all choices will be used.

least common denominator	simplifying	reciprocals	numerator	$\frac{-a}{b}$ $\frac{a}{-b}$
cross products	ratio	proportion		
rational expression	domain	complex fraction	denominator	$\frac{-a}{-b}$

1. A(n) ________________ is an expression that can be written in the form $\frac{P}{Q}$, where P and Q are polynomials and Q is not 0.

2. In a(n) ________________, the numerator or denominator or both may contain fractions.

3. For a rational expression, $-\frac{a}{b} =$ ________________ $=$ ________________.

4. A rational expression is undefined when the ________________ is 0.

5. The process of writing a rational expression in lowest terms is called ________________.

6. The expressions $\frac{2x}{7}$ and $\frac{7}{2x}$ are called ________________.

7. The ________________ of a list of rational expressions is a polynomial of least degree whose factors include all factors of the denominators in the list.

8. A(n) ________________ is the quotient of two numbers.

9. $\frac{x}{2} = \frac{7}{16}$ is an example of a(n) ________________.

10. If $\frac{a}{b} = \frac{c}{d}$, then ad and bc are called ________________.

11. The ________________ of the rational function $f(x) = \frac{1}{x-3}$ is $\{x \mid x \text{ is a real number}, x \neq 3\}$.

Chapter 4 Highlights

DEFINITIONS AND CONCEPTS	EXAMPLES
Section 4.1 Rational Functions and Simplifying Rational Expressions	
A **rational expression** is an expression that can be written in the form $\frac{P}{Q}$, where P and Q are polynomials and Q does not equal 0.	$\frac{7y^3}{4}, \frac{x^2+6x+1}{x-3}, \frac{-5}{s^3+8}$
To find values for which a rational expression is undefined, find values for which the denominator is 0.	Find any values for which the expression $\frac{5y}{y^2-4y+3}$ is undefined. $y^2-4y+3=0$ Set the denominator equal to 0. $(y-3)(y-1)=0$ Factor. $y-3=0$ or $y-1=0$ Set each factor equal to 0. $y=3$ $\quad y=1$ Solve. The expression is undefined when y is 3 and when y is 1.
To Simplify a Rational Expression **Step 1.** Factor the numerator and denominator. **Step 2.** Divide out factors common to the numerator and denominator. (This is the same as removing a factor of 1.)	Simplify: $\frac{4x+20}{x^2-25}$ $\frac{4x+20}{x^2-25}=\frac{4(x+5)}{(x+5)(x-5)}=\frac{4}{x-5}$
A **rational function** is a function described by a rational expression.	$f(x)=\frac{2x-6}{7}, \quad h(t)=\frac{t^2-3t+5}{t-1}$
Section 4.2 Multiplying and Dividing Rational Expressions	
To multiply rational expressions, **Step 1.** Factor numerators and denominators. **Step 2.** Multiply numerators and multiply denominators. **Step 3.** Write the product in simplest form. $\frac{P}{Q}\cdot\frac{R}{S}=\frac{PR}{QS}$	Multiply: $\frac{4x+4}{2x-3}\cdot\frac{2x^2+x-6}{x^2-1}$ $\frac{4x+4}{2x-3}\cdot\frac{2x^2+x-6}{x^2-1}=\frac{4(x+1)}{2x-3}\cdot\frac{(2x-3)(x+2)}{(x+1)(x-1)}$ $=\frac{4(x+1)(2x-3)(x+2)}{(2x-3)(x+1)(x-1)}$ $=\frac{4(x+2)}{x-1}$
To divide by a rational expression, multiply by the reciprocal. $\frac{P}{Q}\div\frac{R}{S}=\frac{P}{Q}\cdot\frac{S}{R}=\frac{PS}{QR}$	Divide: $\frac{15x+5}{3x^2-14x-5}\div\frac{15}{3x-12}$ $\frac{15x+5}{3x^2-14x-5}\div\frac{15}{3x-12}=\frac{5(3x+1)}{(3x+1)(x-5)}\cdot\frac{3(x-4)}{3\cdot 5}$ $=\frac{x-4}{x-5}$
Section 4.3 Dividing Polynomials	
To divide a polynomial by a monomial: $\frac{a+b}{c}=\frac{a}{c}+\frac{b}{c}$	Divide: $\frac{15x^5-10x^3+5x^2-2x}{5x^2}=\frac{15x^5}{5x^2}-\frac{10x^3}{5x^2}+\frac{5x^2}{5x^2}-\frac{2x}{5x^2}$ $=3x^3-2x+1-\frac{2}{5x}$
To divide a polynomial by a polynomial other than a monomial, use long division.	$5x-1+\frac{-4}{2x+3}$ $2x+3\overline{)10x^2+13x-7}$ $\underline{10x^2 \mp 15x}$ (signs changed: $-10x^2-15x$) $-2x-7$ $\underline{\mp 2x \mp 3}$ (signs changed: $+2x+3$) -4

DEFINITIONS AND CONCEPTS	EXAMPLES
Section 4.4 Adding and Subtracting Rational Expressions with Common Denominators and Least Common Denominator	
To add or subtract rational expressions with the same denominator, add or subtract numerators and place the sum or difference over a common denominator. $$\frac{P}{R}+\frac{Q}{R}=\frac{P+Q}{R}$$ $$\frac{P}{R}-\frac{Q}{R}=\frac{P-Q}{R}$$	Perform indicated operations. $$\frac{5}{x+1}+\frac{x}{x+1}=\frac{5+x}{x+1}$$ $$\frac{2y+7}{y^2-9}-\frac{y+4}{y^2-9}=\frac{(2y+7)-(y+4)}{y^2-9}=\frac{2y+7-y-4}{y^2-9}=\frac{y+3}{(y+3)(y-3)}=\frac{1}{y-3}$$
To find the least common denominator (LCD), **Step 1.** Factor the denominators. **Step 2.** The LCD is the product of all unique factors, each raised to a power equal to the greatest number of times that it appears in any one factored denominator.	Find the LCD for $$\frac{7x}{x^2+10x+25} \text{ and } \frac{11}{3x^2+15x}$$ $$x^2+10x+25=(x+5)(x+5)$$ $$3x^2+15x=3x(x+5)$$ LCD is $3x(x+5)(x+5)$ or $3x(x+5)^2$
Section 4.5 Adding and Subtracting Rational Expressions with Unlike Denominators	
To add or subtract rational expressions with unlike denominators, **Step 1.** Find the LCD. **Step 2.** Rewrite each rational expression as an equivalent expression whose denominator is the LCD. **Step 3.** Add or subtract numerators and place the sum or difference over the common denominator. **Step 4.** Write the result in simplest form.	Perform the indicated operation. $$\frac{9x+3}{x^2-9}-\frac{5}{x-3}=\frac{9x+3}{(x+3)(x-3)}-\frac{5}{x-3}$$ LCD is $(x+3)(x-3)$. $$=\frac{9x+3}{(x+3)(x-3)}-\frac{5(x+3)}{(x-3)(x+3)}=\frac{9x+3-5(x+3)}{(x+3)(x-3)}=\frac{9x+3-5x-15}{(x+3)(x-3)}=\frac{4x-12}{(x+3)(x-3)}=\frac{4(x-3)}{(x+3)(x-3)}=\frac{4}{x+3}$$
Section 4.6 Solving Equations Containing Rational Expressions	
To solve an equation containing rational expressions, **Step 1.** Multiply both sides of the equation by the LCD of all rational expressions in the equation.	Solve: $\frac{5x}{x+2}+3=\frac{4x-6}{x+2}$

(continued)

DEFINITIONS AND CONCEPTS	EXAMPLES
Section 4.6 Solving Equations Containing Rational Expressions (continued)	
Step 2. Remove any grouping symbols and solve the resulting equation. **Step 3.** Check the solution in the original equation.	$(x+2)\left(\frac{5x}{x+2}+3\right)=(x+2)\left(\frac{4x-6}{x+2}\right)$ $(x+2)\left(\frac{5x}{x+2}\right)+(x+2)(3)=(x+2)\left(\frac{4x-6}{x+2}\right)$ $5x+3x+6=4x-6$ $4x=-12$ $x=-3$ The solution checks and the solution is -3.
Section 4.7 Simplifying Complex Fractions	
Method 1: Simplify the numerator and the denominator so that each is a single fraction. Then perform the indicated division and simplify if possible.	Simplify $\frac{\frac{x+2}{x}}{x-\frac{4}{x}}$. Method 1: $\frac{\frac{x+2}{x}}{\frac{x\cdot x}{1\cdot x}-\frac{4}{x}}=\frac{\frac{x+2}{x}}{\frac{x^2-4}{x}}$ $=\frac{x+2}{x}\cdot\frac{x}{(x+2)(x-2)}=\frac{1}{x-2}$
Method 2: Multiply the numerator and the denominator of the complex fraction by the LCD of the fractions in both the numerator and the denominator. Then simplify if possible.	Method 2: $\frac{\left(\frac{x+2}{x}\right)\cdot x}{\left(x-\frac{4}{x}\right)\cdot x}=\frac{x+2}{x\cdot x-\frac{4}{x}\cdot x}$ $=\frac{x+2}{x^2-4}=\frac{x+2}{(x+2)(x-2)}=\frac{1}{x-2}$
Section 4.8 Proportion and Problem Solving with Rational Equations	
A **ratio** is the quotient of two numbers or two quantities. A **proportion** is a mathematical statement that two ratios are equal.	***Proportions*** $\frac{2}{3}=\frac{8}{12}$ $\frac{x}{7}=\frac{15}{35}$
Cross products: If $\frac{a}{b}=\frac{c}{d}$, then $ad=bc$.	***Cross Products*** $2\cdot 12$ or 24 $\quad \frac{2}{3}=\frac{8}{12}$ $\quad 3\cdot 8$ or 24
	Solve: $\frac{3}{4}=\frac{x}{x-1}$ $\frac{3}{4}=\frac{x}{x-1}$ $3(x-1)=4x$ Set cross products equal. $3x-3=4x$ $-3=x$

DEFINITIONS AND CONCEPTS	EXAMPLES

Section 4.8 Proportion and Problem Solving with Rational Equations

Problem-Solving Steps

1. UNDERSTAND. Read and reread the problem.

A small plane and a car leave Kansas City, Missouri, and head for Minneapolis, Minnesota, a distance of 450 miles. The speed of the plane is 3 times the speed of the car, and the plane arrives 6 hours ahead of the car. Find the speed of the car.

Let $x =$ the speed of the car.

Then $3x =$ the speed of the plane.

	Distance =	***Rate · Time***	
Car	450	x	$\frac{450}{x}$ $\left(\frac{\text{distance}}{\text{rate}}\right)$
Plane	450	$3x$	$\frac{450}{3x}$ $\left(\frac{\text{distance}}{\text{rate}}\right)$

2. TRANSLATE.

In words: plane's time + 6 hours = car's time

Translate: $\frac{450}{3x}$ + 6 + $\frac{450}{x}$

3. SOLVE.

$$\frac{450}{3x} + 6 = \frac{450}{x}$$

$$3x\left(\frac{450}{3x}\right) + 3x(6) = 3x\left(\frac{450}{x}\right)$$

$$450 + 18x = 1350$$

$$18x = 900$$

$$x = 50$$

4. INTERPRET.

Check this solution in the originally stated problem. **State** the conclusion: The speed of the car is 50 miles per hour.

Section 4.9 Variation and Problem Solving

y **varies directly as** x, or y is **directly proportional to** x, if there is a nonzero constant k such that

$$y = kx$$

The circumference of a circle C varies directly as its radius r.

$$C = \underbrace{2\pi}_{k} r$$

y **varies inversely as** x, or y is **inversely proportional to** x, if there is a nonzero constant k such that

$$y = \frac{k}{x}$$

Pressure P varies inversely with volume V.

$$P = \frac{k}{V}$$

y **varies jointly as** x and z or y is **jointly proportional to** x and z if there is a nonzero constant k such that

$$y = kxz$$

The lateral surface area S of a cylinder varies jointly as its radius r and height h.

$$S = \underbrace{2\pi}_{k} rh$$

Chapter 4 Review

(4.1) Find the domain for each rational function.

1. $f(x) = \dfrac{3 - 5x}{7}$
2. $g(x) = \dfrac{2x + 4}{11}$
3. $f(x) = \dfrac{-3x^2}{x - 5}$
4. $h(x) = \dfrac{4x}{3x - 12}$
5. $f(x) = \dfrac{x^3 + 2}{x^2 + 8x}$
6. $G(x) = \dfrac{20}{3x^2 - 48}$

Simplify each rational expression.

7. $\dfrac{x + 12}{12 - x}$
8. $\dfrac{2x}{2x^2 - 2x}$
9. $\dfrac{x + 7}{x^2 - 49}$
10. $\dfrac{2x^2 + 4x - 30}{x^2 + x - 20}$

Simplify each expression. This section contains four-term polynomials and sums and differences of two cubes.

11. $\dfrac{x^2 + xa + xb + ab}{x^2 - xc + bx - bc}$
12. $\dfrac{x^2 + 5x - 2x - 10}{x^2 - 3x - 2x + 6}$
13. $\dfrac{4 - x}{x^3 - 64}$
14. $\dfrac{x^2 - 4}{x^3 + 8}$

The average cost (per bookcase) of manufacturing x bookcases is given by the rational function

$$C(x) = \frac{35x + 4200}{x}$$

15. Find the average cost per bookcase of manufacturing 50 bookcases.
16. Find the average cost per bookcase of manufacturing 100 bookcases.

(4.2) Perform each indicated operation and simplify.

17. $\dfrac{15x^3y^2}{z} \cdot \dfrac{z}{5xy^3}$
18. $\dfrac{-y^3}{8} \cdot \dfrac{9x^2}{y^3}$
19. $\dfrac{x^2 - 9}{x^2 - 4} \cdot \dfrac{x - 2}{x + 3}$
20. $\dfrac{2x + 5}{x - 6} \cdot \dfrac{2x}{-x + 6}$
21. $\dfrac{x^2 - 5x - 24}{x^2 - x - 12} \div \dfrac{x^2 - 10x + 16}{x^2 + x - 6}$
22. $\dfrac{4x + 4y}{xy^2} \div \dfrac{3x + 3y}{x^2y}$
23. $\dfrac{x^2 + x - 42}{x - 3} \cdot \dfrac{(x - 3)^2}{x + 7}$
24. $\dfrac{2a + 2b}{3} \cdot \dfrac{a - b}{a^2 - b^2}$
25. $\dfrac{2x^2 - 9x + 9}{8x - 12} \div \dfrac{x^2 - 3x}{2x}$
26. $\dfrac{x^2 - y^2}{x^2 + xy} \div \dfrac{3x^2 - 2xy - y^2}{3x^2 + 6x}$
27. $\dfrac{x - y}{4} \div \dfrac{y^2 - 2y - xy + 2x}{16x + 24}$
28. $\dfrac{5 + x}{7} \div \dfrac{xy + 5y - 3x - 15}{7y - 35}$

(4.3) Divide.

29. $\dfrac{x^2 + 21x + 49}{7x^2}$
30. $\dfrac{5a^3b - 15ab^2 + 20ab}{-5ab}$
31. $(a^2 - a + 4) \div (a - 2)$
32. $(4x^2 + 20x + 7) \div (x + 5)$
33. $\dfrac{a^3 + a^2 + 2a + 6}{a - 2}$
34. $\dfrac{9b^3 - 18b^2 + 8b - 1}{3b - 2}$
35. $\dfrac{4x^4 - 4x^3 + x^2 + 4x - 3}{2x - 1}$
36. $\dfrac{-10x^2 - x^3 - 21x + 18}{x - 6}$
37. The area of the rectangle below is $(15x^3 - 3x^2 + 60)$ square feet. If its length is $3x^2$ feet, find its width.

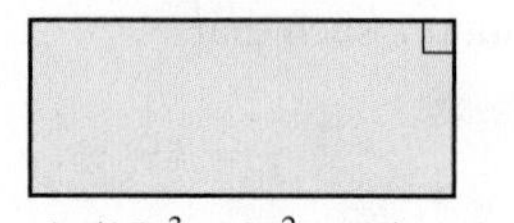

Area is $(15x^3 - 3x^2 + 60)$ sq feet

38. The perimeter of the equilateral triangle below is $(21a^3b^6 + 3a - 3)$ units. Find the length of a side.

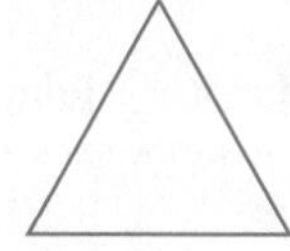

Perimeter is $(21a^3b^6 + 3a - 3)$ units

(4.4) Perform each indicated operation and simplify.

39. $\frac{x}{x^2+9x+14}+\frac{7}{x^2+9x+14}$

40. $\frac{x}{x^2+2x-15}+\frac{5}{x^2+2x-15}$

41. $\frac{4x-5}{3x^2}-\frac{2x+5}{3x^2}$

42. $\frac{9x+7}{6x^2}-\frac{3x+4}{6x^2}$

Find the LCD of each pair of rational expressions.

43. $\frac{x+4}{2x}, \frac{3}{7x}$

44. $\frac{x-2}{x^2-5x-24}, \frac{3}{x^2+11x+24}$

Rewrite each rational expression as an equivalent expression whose denominator is the given polynomial.

45. $\frac{5}{7x}=\frac{}{14x^3y}$

46. $\frac{9}{4y}=\frac{}{16y^3x}$

47. $\frac{x+2}{x^2+11x+18}=\frac{}{(x+2)(x-5)(x+9)}$

48. $\frac{3x-5}{x^2+4x+4}=\frac{}{(x+2)^2(x+3)}$

(4.5) Perform each indicated operation and simplify.

49. $\frac{4}{5x^2}-\frac{6}{y}$

50. $\frac{2}{x-3}-\frac{4}{x-1}$

51. $\frac{4}{x+3}-2$

52. $\frac{3}{x^2+2x-8}+\frac{2}{x^2-3x+2}$

53. $\frac{2x-5}{6x+9}-\frac{4}{2x^2+3x}$

54. $\frac{x-1}{x^2-2x+1}-\frac{x+1}{x-1}$

Find the perimeter and the area of each figure.

△ 55.

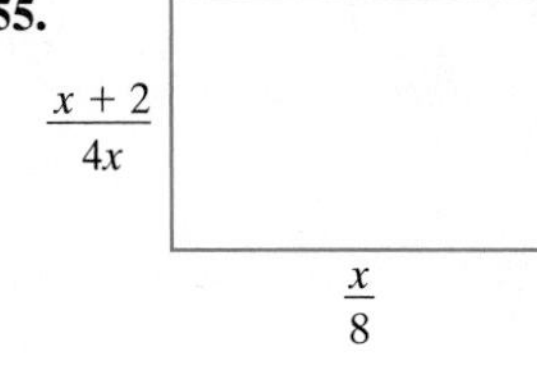

56.

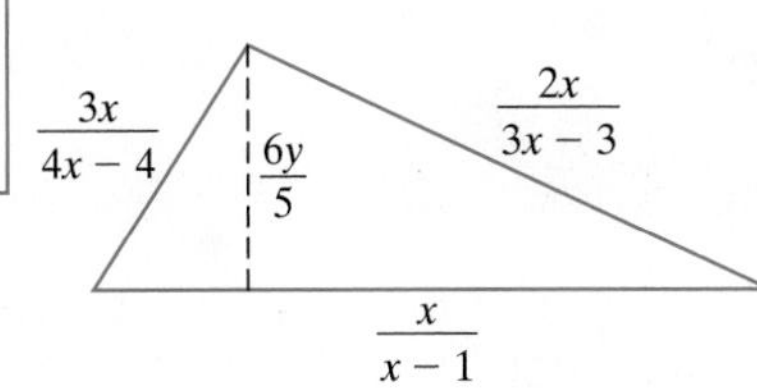

(4.6) Solve each equation.

57. $\frac{n}{10}=9-\frac{n}{5}$

58. $\frac{2}{x+1}-\frac{1}{x-2}=-\frac{1}{2}$

59. $\frac{y}{2y+2}+\frac{2y-16}{4y+4}=\frac{y-3}{y+1}$

60. $\frac{2}{x-3}-\frac{4}{x+3}=\frac{8}{x^2-9}$

61. $\frac{x-3}{x+1}-\frac{x-6}{x+5}=0$

62. $x+5=\frac{6}{x}$

Solve the equation for the indicated variable.

63. $\frac{4A}{5b}=x^2$, for b

64. $\frac{x}{7}+\frac{y}{8}=10$, for y

(4.7) Simplify each complex fraction.

65. $\frac{\frac{5x}{27}}{-\frac{10xy}{21}}$

66. $\frac{\frac{3}{5}+\frac{2}{7}}{\frac{1}{5}+\frac{5}{6}}$

67. $\frac{3-\frac{1}{y}}{2-\frac{1}{y}}$

68. $\frac{\frac{6}{x+2}+4}{\frac{8}{x+2}-4}$

69. $\frac{\frac{x-3}{x+3}+\frac{x+3}{x-3}}{\frac{x-3}{x+3}-\frac{x+3}{x-3}}$

70. $\frac{\frac{3}{x-1}-\frac{2}{1-x}}{\frac{2}{x-1}-\frac{2}{x}}$

71. $\frac{x+y^{-1}}{\frac{x}{y}}$

72. $\frac{x-xy^{-1}}{\frac{1+x}{y}}$

(4.8) Solve each proportion.

73. $\frac{x}{2}=\frac{12}{4}$

74. $\frac{20}{1}=\frac{x}{25}$

75. $\frac{2}{x-1}=\frac{3}{x+3}$

76. $\frac{4}{y-3}=\frac{2}{y-3}$

Solve.

77. A machine can process 300 parts in 20 minutes. Find how many parts can be processed in 45 minutes.

78. As his consulting fee, Mr. Visconti charges $90.00 per day. Find how much he charges for 3 hours of consulting. Assume an 8-hour work day.

79. Five times the reciprocal of a number equals the sum of $\frac{3}{2}$ the reciprocal of the number and $\frac{7}{6}$. What is the number?

80. The reciprocal of a number equals the reciprocal of the difference of 4 and the number. Find the number.

81. A car travels 90 miles in the same time that a car traveling 10 miles per hour slower travels 60 miles. Find the speed of each car.

82. The current in a bayou near Lafayette, Louisiana, is 4 miles per hour. A paddle boat travels 48 miles upstream in the same amount of time it takes to travel 72 miles downstream. Find the speed of the boat in still water.

83. When Mark and Maria manicure Mr. Stergeon's lawn, it takes them 5 hours. If Mark works alone, it takes 7 hours. Find how long it takes Maria alone.

84. It takes pipe A 20 days to fill a fish pond. Pipe B takes 15 days. Find how long it takes both pipes together to fill the pond.

Given that the pairs of triangles are similar, find each missing length x.

85.

86.

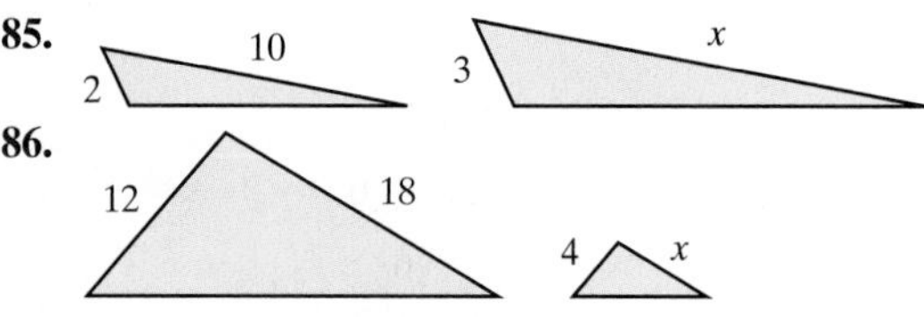

(4.9) Solve each variation problem.

87. A is directly proportional to B. If $A = 6$ when $B = 14$, find A when $B = 21$.

88. C is inversely proportional to D. If $C = 12$ when $D = 8$, find C when $D = 24$.

89. According to Boyle's law, the pressure exerted by a gas is inversely proportional to the volume, as long as the temperature stays the same. If a gas exerts a pressure of 1250 pounds per square inch when the volume is 2 cubic feet, find the volume when the pressure is 800 pounds per square inch.

90. The surface area of a sphere varies directly as the square of its radius. If the surface area is 36π square inches when the radius is 3 inches, find the surface area when the radius is 4 inches.

MIXED REVIEW

Simplify each rational expression.

91. $\dfrac{4x + 12}{8x^2 + 24x}$

92. $\dfrac{x^3 - 6x^2 + 9x}{x^2 + 4x - 21}$

Perform the indicated operations and simplify.

93. $\dfrac{x^2 + 9x + 20}{x^2 - 25} \cdot \dfrac{x^2 - 9x + 20}{x^2 + 8x + 16}$

94. $\dfrac{x^2 - x - 72}{x^2 - x - 30} \div \dfrac{x^2 + 6x - 27}{x^2 - 9x + 18}$

95. $\dfrac{x}{x^2 - 36} + \dfrac{6}{x^2 - 36}$

96. $\dfrac{5x - 1}{4x} - \dfrac{3x - 2}{4x}$

97. $\dfrac{4}{3x^2 + 8x - 3} + \dfrac{2}{3x^2 - 7x + 2}$

98. $\dfrac{3x}{x^2 + 9x + 14} - \dfrac{6x}{x^2 + 4x - 21}$

Solve.

99. $\dfrac{4}{a - 1} + 2 = \dfrac{3}{a - 1}$

100. $\dfrac{x}{x + 3} + 4 = \dfrac{x}{x + 3}$

Solve.

101. The quotient of twice a number and three, minus one-sixth, is the quotient of the number and two. Find the number.

102. Mr. Crocker can paint his house by himself in three days. His son will need an additional day to complete the job if he works alone. If they work together, find how long it takes to paint the house.

Given that the following pairs of triangles are similar, find each missing length.

103.

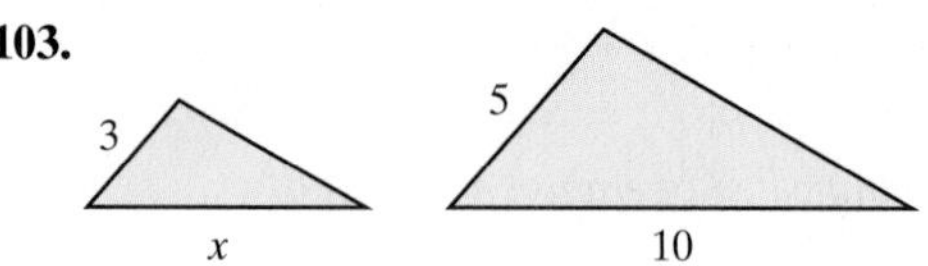

104.

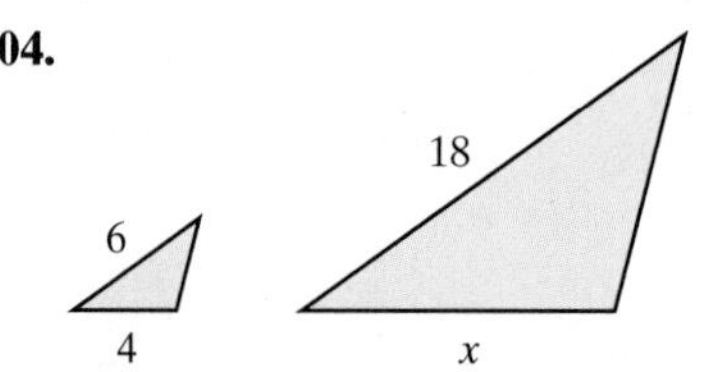

Simplify each complex fraction.

105. $\dfrac{\frac{1}{4}}{\frac{1}{3} + \frac{1}{2}}$

106. $\dfrac{4 + \frac{2}{x}}{6 + \frac{3}{x}}$

107. $\dfrac{y^{-2}}{1 - y^{-2}}$

108. $\dfrac{4 + x^{-1}}{3 + x^{-1}}$

Chapter 4 Test

MyMathLab®  

1. Find the domain of the rational function

$$g(x) = \frac{9x^2 - 9}{x^2 + 4x + 3}$$

2. For a certain computer desk, the average cost C (in dollars) per desk manufactured is

$$C = \frac{100x + 3000}{x}$$

where x is the number of desks manufactured.

a. Find the average cost per desk when manufacturing 200 computer desks.
b. Find the average cost per desk when manufacturing 1000 computer desks.

Simplify each rational expression.

3. $\dfrac{3x - 6}{5x - 10}$

4. $\dfrac{x + 6}{x^2 + 12x + 36}$

5. $\dfrac{x + 3}{x^3 + 27}$

6. $\dfrac{2m^3 - 2m^2 - 12m}{m^2 - 5m + 6}$

7. $\dfrac{ay + 3a + 2y + 6}{ay + 3a + 5y + 15}$

8. $\dfrac{y - x}{x^2 - y^2}$

Perform the indicated operation and simplify if possible.

9. $\dfrac{3}{x - 1} \cdot (5x - 5)$

10. $\dfrac{y^2 - 5y + 6}{2y + 4} \cdot \dfrac{y + 2}{2y - 6}$

11. $\dfrac{15x}{2x + 5} - \dfrac{6 - 4x}{2x + 5}$

12. $\dfrac{5a}{a^2 - a - 6} - \dfrac{2}{a - 3}$

13. $\dfrac{6}{x^2 - 1} + \dfrac{3}{x + 1}$

14. $\dfrac{x^2 - 9}{x^2 - 3x} \div \dfrac{xy + 5x + 3y + 15}{2x + 10}$

15. $\dfrac{x + 2}{x^2 + 11x + 18} + \dfrac{5}{x^2 - 3x - 10}$

Solve each equation.

16. $\dfrac{4}{y} - \dfrac{5}{3} = \dfrac{-1}{5}$

17. $\dfrac{5}{y + 1} = \dfrac{4}{y + 2}$

18. $\dfrac{a}{a - 3} = \dfrac{3}{a - 3} - \dfrac{3}{2}$

19. $x - \dfrac{14}{x - 1} = 4 - \dfrac{2x}{x - 1}$

20. $\dfrac{10}{x^2 - 25} = \dfrac{3}{x + 5} + \dfrac{1}{x - 5}$

Simplify each complex fraction.

21. $\dfrac{\frac{5x^2}{yz^2}}{\frac{10x}{z^3}}$

22. $\dfrac{5 - \frac{1}{y^2}}{\frac{1}{y} + \frac{2}{y^2}}$

23. $\dfrac{\frac{b}{a} - \frac{a}{b}}{\frac{1}{b} + \frac{1}{a}}$

24. In a sample of 85 fluorescent bulbs, 3 were found to be defective. At this rate, how many defective bulbs should be found in 510 bulbs?

25. One number plus five times its reciprocal is equal to six. Find the number.

26. A pleasure boat traveling down the Red River takes the same time to go 14 miles upstream as it takes to go 16 miles downstream. If the current of the river is 2 miles per hour, find the speed of the boat in still water.

27. An inlet pipe can fill a tank in 12 hours. A second pipe can fill the tank in 15 hours. If both pipes are used, find how long it takes to fill the tank.

28. Given that the two triangles are similar, find x.

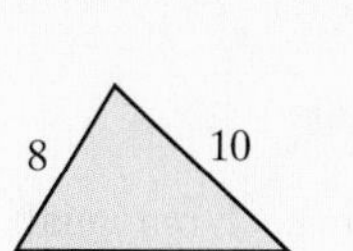

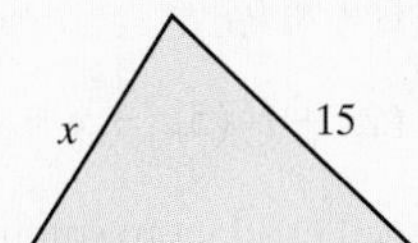

Chapter 4 Cumulative Review

TRANSLATING

1. Write each sentence as an equation or inequality. Let x represent the unknown number.
a. The quotient of 15 and a number is 4.
b. Three subtracted from 12 is a number.
c. Four times a number, added to 17, is not equal to 21.
d. Triple a number is less than 48.

2. Write each sentence as an equation. Let x represent the unknown number.
a. The difference of 12 and a number is -45.
b. The product of 12 and a number is -45.
c. A number less 10 is twice the number.

3. Rajiv Puri invested part of his \$20,000 inheritance in a mutual funds account that pays 7% simple interest yearly and the rest in a certificate of deposit that pays 9% simple interest yearly. At the end of one year, Rajiv's investments earned \$1550. Find the amount he invested at each rate.

4. The number of non-business bankruptcies has increased over the years. In 2002, the number of non-business bankruptcies was 80,000 less than twice the number in 1994. If the total of non-business bankruptcies for these two years is 2,290,000 find the number of non-business bankruptcies for each year. (*Source:* American Bankruptcy Institute)

5. Graph $x - 3y = 6$ by finding and plotting intercepts.

6. Find the slope of the line whose equation is $7x + 2y = 9$.

7. Use the product rule to simplify each expression.
a. $4^2 \cdot 4^5$ **b.** $x^4 \cdot x^6$
c. $y^3 \cdot y$ **d.** $y^3 \cdot y^2 \cdot y^7$
e. $(-5)^7 \cdot (-5)^8$ **f.** $a^2 \cdot b^2$

8. Simplify.
a. $\frac{x^9}{x^7}$ **b.** $\frac{x^{19}y^5}{xy}$
c. $(x^5y^2)^3$ **d.** $(-3a^2b)(5a^3b)$

9. Subtract $(5z - 7)$ from the sum of $(8z + 11)$ and $(9z - 2)$.

10. Subtract $(9x^2 - 6x + 2)$ from $(x + 1)$.

11. Multiply: $(3a + b)^3$

12. Multiply: $(2x + 1)(5x^2 - x + 2)$

13. Use a special product to square each binomial.
a. $(t + 2)^2$
b. $(p - q)^2$
c. $(2x + 5)^2$
d. $(x^2 - 7y)^2$

14. Multiply.
a. $(x + 9)^2$ **b.** $(2x + 1)(2x - 1)$
c. $8x(x^2 + 1)(x^2 - 1)$

15. Simplify each expression. Write results using positive exponents only.
a. $\frac{1}{x^{-3}}$ **b.** $\frac{1}{3^{-4}}$ **c.** $\frac{p^{-4}}{q^{-9}}$ **d.** $\frac{5^{-3}}{2^{-5}}$

16. Simplify. Write results with positive exponents only.
a. 5^{-3} **b.** $\frac{9}{x^{-7}}$ **c.** $\frac{11^{-1}}{7^{-2}}$

17. Divide: $\frac{4x^2 + 7 + 8x^3}{2x + 3}$

18. Divide $(4x^3 - 9x + 2)$ by $(x - 4)$.

19. Find the GCF of each list of numbers.
a. 28 and 40
b. 55 and 21
c. 15, 18, and 66

20. Find the GCF of $9x^2$, $6x^3$, and $21x^5$.

Factor.

21. $-9a^5 + 18a^2 - 3a$

22. $7x^6 - 7x^5 + 7x^4$

23. $3m^2 - 24m - 60$

24. $-2a^2 + 10a + 12$

25. $3x^2 + 11x + 6$

26. $10m^2 - 7m + 1$

27. $x^2 + 12x + 36$

28. $4x^2 + 12x + 9$

29. $x^2 + 4$

30. $x^2 - 4$

31. $x^3 + 8$

32. $27y^3 - 1$

33. $2x^3 + 3x^2 - 2x - 3$

34. $3x^3 + 5x^2 - 12x - 20$

35. $12m^2 - 3n^2$

36. $x^5 - x$

37. Solve: $x(2x - 7) = 4$

38. Solve: $3x^2 + 5x = 2$

39. Find the x-intercepts of the graph of $y = x^2 - 5x + 4$.

40. Find the x-intercepts of the graph of $y = x^2 - x - 6$.

41. The height of a triangular sail is 2 meters less than twice the length of the base. If the sail has an area of 30 square meters, find the length of its base and the height.

42. The height of a parallelogram is 5 feet more than three times its base. If the area of the parallelogram is 182 square feet, find the length of its base and height.

43. Simplify: $\dfrac{18 - 2x^2}{x^2 - 2x - 3}$

44. Simplify: $\dfrac{2x^2 - 50}{4x^4 - 20x^3}$

45. Divide: $\dfrac{6x + 2}{x^2 - 1} \div \dfrac{3x^2 + x}{x - 1}$

46. Multiply: $\dfrac{6x^2 - 18x}{3x^2 - 2x} \cdot \dfrac{15x - 10}{x^2 - 9}$

47. Simplify: $\dfrac{(2x)^{-1} + 1}{2x^{-1} - 1}$

48. Simplify: $\dfrac{\dfrac{m}{3} + \dfrac{n}{6}}{\dfrac{m + n}{12}}$

CHAPTER 5

Rational Exponents, Radicals, and Complex Numbers

In this chapter, radical notation is reviewed, and then rational exponents are introduced. As the name implies, rational exponents are exponents that are rational numbers. We present an interpretation of rational exponents that is consistent with the meaning and rules already established for integer exponents, and we present two forms of notation for roots: radical and exponent. We conclude this chapter with complex numbers, a natural extension of the real number system.

The Google Lunar X PRIZE is an international competition to safely land a robot on the surface of the moon, travel 500 meters over the lunar surface, and send images and data back to Earth. Teams needed to be registered by December 31, 2010. There are multiple prizes and bonuses, but the first team to land on the moon and complete the mission objectives by December 31, 2012, will be awarded \$20 million. After this time, the first prize drops to \$15 million. The deadline for winning the competition is December 31, 2014, and thus far, 20 teams are competing for the prize.

To reach the moon, these vehicles must first leave the gravity of Earth. In Exercises 115 and 116 of Section 5.1, you will calculate the escape velocity of Earth and the moon, the minimum speed an object must reach to escape the pull of a planet's gravity. (*Source:* X PRIZE Foundation)

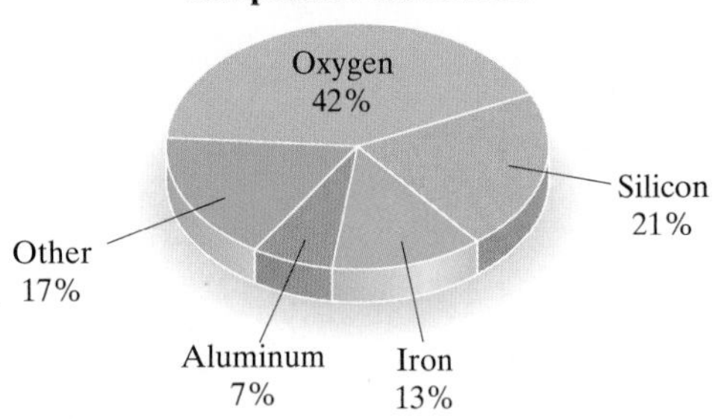

Why the moon? To name a few reasons:

- It is closest to Earth (1.3 seconds for light or radio) so that lunar machines can be directly controlled from Earth.
- It is also the closest source of materials to use for any other space project, and it is 22 times easier to launch from the moon than from Earth.
- The moon is 42% oxygen by weight (see the circle graph to the left) and oxygen is the main ingredient of rocket fuel.
- We can collect energy from the moon's surface and transmit it to Earth.

5.1 Radicals and Radical Functions 

OBJECTIVES

1. Find Square Roots.
2. Approximate Roots.
3. Find Cube Roots.
4. Find *n*th Roots.
5. Find $\sqrt[n]{a^n}$ Where *a* Is a Real Number.
6. Graph Square and Cube Root Functions.

OBJECTIVE

1 Finding Square Roots

To find a **square root** of a number *a*, we find a number that was squared to get *a*.

Thus, because

$$5^2 = 25 \quad \text{and} \quad (-5)^2 = 25,$$

both 5 and -5 are square roots of 25.

Recall that we denote the **nonnegative,** or **principal, square root** with the **radical sign.**

$$\sqrt{25} = 5$$

We denote the **negative square root** with the **negative radical sign.**

$$-\sqrt{25} = -5$$

An expression containing a radical sign is called a **radical expression.** An expression within, or "under," a radical sign is called a **radicand.**

radical expression: $\sqrt{a}$ (radical sign: $\sqrt{\ }$; radicand: a)

Principal and Negative Square Roots

If a is a nonnegative number, then

$\sqrt{a}$ is the **principal,** or **nonnegative, square root** of a

$-\sqrt{a}$ is the **negative square root** of a

EXAMPLE 1 Simplify. Assume that all variables represent positive numbers.

a. $\sqrt{36}$ **b.** $\sqrt{0}$ **c.** $\sqrt{\frac{4}{49}}$ **d.** $\sqrt{0.25}$

e. $\sqrt{x^6}$ **f.** $\sqrt{9x^{12}}$ **g.** $-\sqrt{81}$ **h.** $\sqrt{-81}$

Solution

a. $\sqrt{36} = 6$ because $6^2 = 36$ and 6 is not negative.

b. $\sqrt{0} = 0$ because $0^2 = 0$ and 0 is not negative.

c. $\sqrt{\frac{4}{49}} = \frac{2}{7}$ because $\left(\frac{2}{7}\right)^2 = \frac{4}{49}$ and $\frac{2}{7}$ is not negative.

d. $\sqrt{0.25} = 0.5$ because $(0.5)^2 = 0.25$.

e. $\sqrt{x^6} = x^3$ because $(x^3)^2 = x^6$.

f. $\sqrt{9x^{12}} = 3x^6$ because $(3x^6)^2 = 9x^{12}$.

g. $-\sqrt{81} = -9$. The negative in front of the radical indicates the negative square root of 81.

h. $\sqrt{-81}$ is not a real number. □

PRACTICE

1 Simplify. Assume that all variables represent positive numbers.

a. $\sqrt{49}$ **b.** $\sqrt{\frac{0}{1}}$ **c.** $\sqrt{\frac{16}{81}}$ **d.** $\sqrt{0.64}$

e. $\sqrt{z^8}$ **f.** $\sqrt{16b^4}$ **g.** $-\sqrt{36}$ **h.** $\sqrt{-36}$

Our discussion of the square root of a negative number. For example, can we simplify $\sqrt{-4}$? That is, can we find a real number whose square is -4? No, there is no real number whose square is -4, and we say that $\sqrt{-4}$ is not a real number. In general:

The square root of a negative number is not a real number.

> **Helpful Hint**
> - Remember: $\sqrt{0} = 0$.
> - Don't forget that the square root of a negative number is not a real number. For example,
>
> $$\sqrt{-9} \text{ is not a real number}$$
>
> because there is no real number that when multiplied by itself would give a product of -9. In Section 5.7, we will see what kind of a number $\sqrt{-9}$ is.

OBJECTIVE

2 Approximating Roots

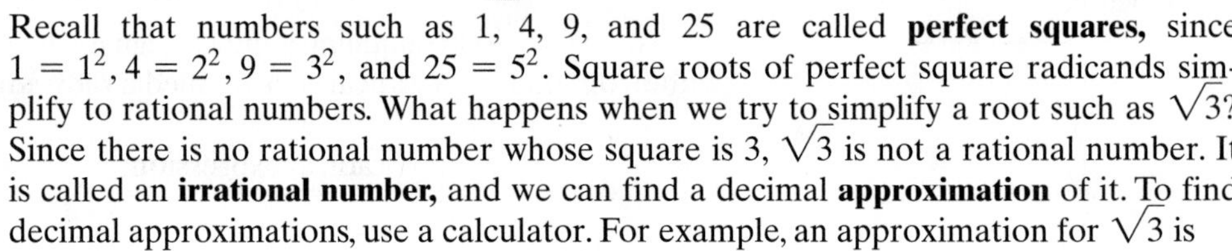

Recall that numbers such as 1, 4, 9, and 25 are called **perfect squares,** since $1 = 1^2, 4 = 2^2, 9 = 3^2$, and $25 = 5^2$. Square roots of perfect square radicands simplify to rational numbers. What happens when we try to simplify a root such as $\sqrt{3}$? Since there is no rational number whose square is 3, $\sqrt{3}$ is not a rational number. It is called an **irrational number,** and we can find a decimal **approximation** of it. To find decimal approximations, use a calculator. For example, an approximation for $\sqrt{3}$ is

$$\sqrt{3} \approx 1.732$$

↑
approximation symbol

To see if the approximation is reasonable, notice that since

$$1 < 3 < 4,$$
$$\sqrt{1} < \sqrt{3} < \sqrt{4}, \text{ or}$$
$$1 < \sqrt{3} < 2.$$

We found $\sqrt{3} \approx 1.732$, a number between 1 and 2, so our result is reasonable.

EXAMPLE 2 Use a calculator to approximate $\sqrt{20}$. Round the approximation to 3 decimal places and check to see that your approximation is reasonable.

$$\sqrt{20} \approx 4.472$$

Solution Is this reasonable? Since $16 < 20 < 25$, $\sqrt{16} < \sqrt{20} < \sqrt{25}$, or $4 < \sqrt{20} < 5$. The approximation is between 4 and 5 and thus is reasonable. □

PRACTICE

2 Use a calculator to approximate $\sqrt{45}$. Round the approximation to three decimal places and check to see that your approximation is reasonable.

OBJECTIVE

3 Finding Cube Roots

Finding roots can be extended to other roots such as cube roots. For example, since $2^3 = 8$, we call 2 the **cube root** of 8. In symbols, we write

$$\sqrt[3]{8} = 2$$

> **Cube Root**
>
> The **cube root** of a real number a is written as $\sqrt[3]{a}$, and
>
> $$\sqrt[3]{a} = b \text{ only if } b^3 = a$$

From this definition, we have

$$\sqrt[3]{64} = 4 \text{ since } 4^3 = 64$$
$$\sqrt[3]{-27} = -3 \text{ since } (-3)^3 = -27$$
$$\sqrt[3]{x^3} = x \text{ since } x^3 = x^3$$

Notice that, unlike with square roots, *it is possible to have a negative radicand when finding a cube root.* This is so because the *cube* of a negative number is a negative number. Therefore, the *cube root* of a negative number is a negative number.

EXAMPLE 3 Find the cube roots.

a. $\sqrt[3]{1}$ **b.** $\sqrt[3]{-64}$ **c.** $\sqrt[3]{\frac{8}{125}}$ **d.** $\sqrt[3]{x^6}$ **e.** $\sqrt[3]{-27x^9}$

Solution

a. $\sqrt[3]{1} = 1$ because $1^3 = 1$.

b. $\sqrt[3]{-64} = -4$ because $(-4)^3 = -64$.

c. $\sqrt[3]{\frac{8}{125}} = \frac{2}{5}$ because $\left(\frac{2}{5}\right)^3 = \frac{8}{125}$.

d. $\sqrt[3]{x^6} = x^2$ because $(x^2)^3 = x^6$.

e. $\sqrt[3]{-27x^9} = -3x^3$ because $(-3x^3)^3 = -27x^9$. □

PRACTICE 3 Find the cube roots.

a. $\sqrt[3]{-1}$ **b.** $\sqrt[3]{27}$ **c.** $\sqrt[3]{\frac{27}{64}}$ **d.** $\sqrt[3]{x^{12}}$ **e.** $\sqrt[3]{-8x^3}$

OBJECTIVE 4

Finding *n*th Roots

Just as we can raise a real number to powers other than 2 or 3, we can find roots other than square roots and cube roots. In fact, we can find the ***n*th root** of a number, where n is any natural number. In symbols, the nth root of a is written as $\sqrt[n]{a}$, where n is called the **index.** The index 2 is usually omitted for square roots.

Helpful Hint

If the index is even, such as $\sqrt{\ }$, $\sqrt[4]{\ }$, $\sqrt[6]{\ }$, and so on, the radicand must be nonnegative for the root to be a real number. For example,

$$\sqrt[4]{16} = 2, \text{ but } \sqrt[4]{-16} \text{ is not a real number.}$$
$$\sqrt[6]{64} = 2, \text{ but } \sqrt[6]{-64} \text{ is not a real number.}$$

If the index is odd, such as $\sqrt[3]{\ }$, $\sqrt[5]{\ }$, and so on, the radicand may be any real number. For example,

$$\sqrt[3]{64} = 4 \text{ and } \sqrt[3]{-64} = -4$$
$$\sqrt[5]{32} = 2 \text{ and } \sqrt[5]{-32} = -2$$

✓CONCEPT CHECK

Which one is not a real number?

a. $\sqrt[3]{-15}$ **b.** $\sqrt[4]{-15}$ **c.** $\sqrt[5]{-15}$ **d.** $\sqrt{(-15)^2}$

Answer to Concept Check: b

EXAMPLE 4 Simplify the following expressions.

a. $\sqrt[4]{81}$ **b.** $\sqrt[5]{-243}$ **c.** $-\sqrt{25}$ **d.** $\sqrt[4]{-81}$ **e.** $\sqrt[3]{64x^3}$

Solution

a. $\sqrt[4]{81} = 3$ because $3^4 = 81$ and 3 is positive.

b. $\sqrt[5]{-243} = -3$ because $(-3)^5 = -243$.

c. $-\sqrt{25} = -5$ because -5 is the opposite of $\sqrt{25}$.

d. $\sqrt[4]{-81}$ is not a real number. There is no real number that, when raised to the fourth power, is -81.

e. $\sqrt[3]{64x^3} = 4x$ because $(4x)^3 = 64x^3$. □

PRACTICE

4 Simplify the following expressions.

a. $\sqrt[4]{10{,}000}$ **b.** $\sqrt[5]{-1}$ **c.** $-\sqrt{81}$ **d.** $\sqrt[4]{-625}$ **e.** $\sqrt[3]{27x^9}$

OBJECTIVE

5 Finding $\sqrt[n]{a^n}$ Where a Is a Real Number

Recall that the notation $\sqrt{a^2}$ indicates the positive square root of a^2 only. For example,

$$\sqrt{(-7)^2} = \sqrt{49} = 7$$

When variables are present in the radicand and it is *unclear whether the variable represents a positive number or a negative number*, absolute value bars are sometimes needed to ensure that the result is a positive number. For example,

$$\sqrt{x^2} = |x|$$

This ensures that the result is positive. This same situation may occur when the index is any *even* positive integer. When the index is any *odd* positive integer, absolute value bars are not necessary.

Finding $\sqrt[n]{a^n}$

If n is an *even* positive integer, then $\sqrt[n]{a^n} = |a|$.

If n is an *odd* positive integer, then $\sqrt[n]{a^n} = a$.

EXAMPLE 5 Simplify.

a. $\sqrt{(-3)^2}$ **b.** $\sqrt{x^2}$ **c.** $\sqrt[4]{(x-2)^4}$ **d.** $\sqrt[3]{(-5)^3}$

e. $\sqrt[5]{(2x-7)^5}$ **f.** $\sqrt{25x^2}$ **g.** $\sqrt{x^2+2x+1}$

Solution

a. $\sqrt{(-3)^2} = |-3| = 3$ When the index is even, the absolute value bars ensure that our result is not negative.

b. $\sqrt{x^2} = |x|$

c. $\sqrt[4]{(x-2)^4} = |x-2|$

d. $\sqrt[3]{(-5)^3} = -5$

e. $\sqrt[5]{(2x-7)^5} = 2x-7$ Absolute value bars are not needed when the index is odd.

f. $\sqrt{25x^2} = 5|x|$

g. $\sqrt{x^2+2x+1} = \sqrt{(x+1)^2} = |x+1|$ □

PRACTICE

5 Simplify.

a. $\sqrt{(-4)^2}$ **b.** $\sqrt{x^{14}}$ **c.** $\sqrt[4]{(x+7)^4}$ **d.** $\sqrt[3]{(-7)^3}$

e. $\sqrt[5]{(3x-5)^5}$ **f.** $\sqrt{49x^2}$ **g.** $\sqrt{x^2+16x+64}$

OBJECTIVE

6 Graphing Square and Cube Root Functions 

Recall that an equation in x and y describes a function if each x-value is paired with exactly one y-value. With this in mind, does the equation

$$y = \sqrt{x}$$

describe a function? First, notice that replacement values for x must be nonnegative real numbers, since $\sqrt{x}$ is not a real number if $x < 0$. The notation $\sqrt{x}$ denotes the principal square root of x, so for every nonnegative number x, there is exactly one number, $\sqrt{x}$. Therefore, $y = \sqrt{x}$ describes a function, and we may write it as

$$f(x) = \sqrt{x}$$

In general, radical functions are functions of the form

$$f(x) = \sqrt[n]{x}.$$

Recall that the domain of a function in x is the set of all possible replacement values of x. This means that if n is even, the domain is the set of all nonnegative numbers, or $\{x|x \geq 0\}$ or $[0, \infty)$. If n is odd, the domain is the set of all real numbers, or $(-\infty, \infty)$. Keep this in mind as we find function values.

EXAMPLE 6 If $f(x) = \sqrt{x-4}$ and $g(x) = \sqrt[3]{x+2}$, find each function value.

a. $f(8)$ **b.** $f(6)$ **c.** $g(-1)$ **d.** $g(1)$

Solution

a. $f(8) = \sqrt{8-4} = \sqrt{4} = 2$ **b.** $f(6) = \sqrt{6-4} = \sqrt{2}$

c. $g(-1) = \sqrt[3]{-1+2} = \sqrt[3]{1} = 1$ **d.** $g(1) = \sqrt[3]{1+2} = \sqrt[3]{3}$ □

PRACTICE

6 If $f(x) = \sqrt{x+5}$ and $g(x) = \sqrt[3]{x-3}$, find each function value.

a. $f(11)$ **b.** $f(-1)$ **c.** $g(11)$ **d.** $g(-6)$

Helpful Hint

Notice that for the function $f(x) = \sqrt{x-4}$, the domain includes all real numbers that make the radicand ≥ 0. To see what numbers these are, solve $x - 4 \geq 0$ and find that $x \geq 4$. The domain is $\{x|x \geq 4\}$, or $[4, \infty)$.

The domain of the cube root function $g(x) = \sqrt[3]{x+2}$ is the set of real numbers, or $(-\infty, \infty)$.

EXAMPLE 7 Graph the square root function $f(x) = \sqrt{x}$.

Solution To graph, we identify the domain, evaluate the function for several values of x, plot the resulting points, and connect the points with a smooth curve. Since $\sqrt{x}$ represents the nonnegative square root of x, the domain of this function is the set of all nonnegative numbers, $\{x|x \geq 0\}$ or $[0, \infty)$. We have approximated $\sqrt{3}$ in the table on the next page to help us locate the point corresponding to $(3, \sqrt{3})$.

(Continued on next page)

x	$f(x) = \sqrt{x}$
0	0
1	1
3	$\sqrt{3} \approx 1.7$
4	2
9	3

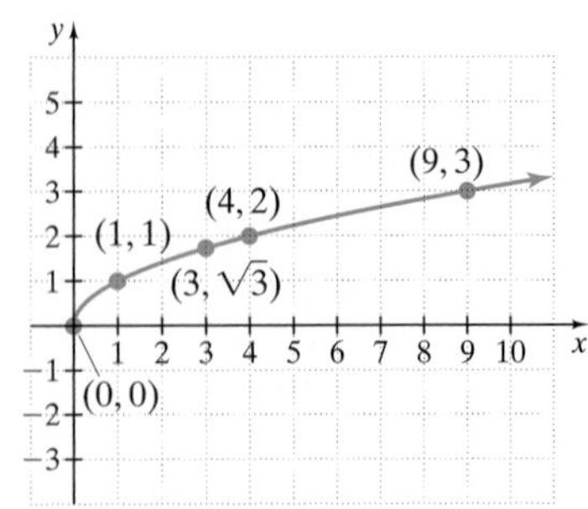

Notice that the graph of this function passes the vertical line test, as expected. □

PRACTICE

7 Graph the square root function $h(x) = \sqrt{x + 2}$.

The equation $f(x) = \sqrt[3]{x}$ also describes a function. Here, x may be any real number, so the domain of this function is the set of all real numbers, or $(-\infty, \infty)$. A few function values are given next.

$$f(0) = \sqrt[3]{0} = 0$$
$$f(1) = \sqrt[3]{1} = 1$$
$$f(-1) = \sqrt[3]{-1} = -1$$
$$f(6) = \sqrt[3]{6}$$
$$f(-6) = \sqrt[3]{-6}$$

Here, there is no rational number whose cube is 6. Thus, the radicals do not simplify to rational numbers.

$$f(8) = \sqrt[3]{8} = 2$$
$$f(-8) = \sqrt[3]{-8} = -2$$

EXAMPLE 8 Graph the function $f(x) = \sqrt[3]{x}$.

Solution To graph, we identify the domain, plot points, and connect the points with a smooth curve. The domain of this function is the set of all real numbers. The table comes from the function values obtained earlier. We have approximated $\sqrt[3]{6}$ and $\sqrt[3]{-6}$ for graphing purposes.

x	$f(x) = \sqrt[3]{x}$
0	0
1	1
−1	−1
6	$\sqrt[3]{6} \approx 1.8$
−6	$\sqrt[3]{-6} \approx -1.8$
8	2
−8	−2

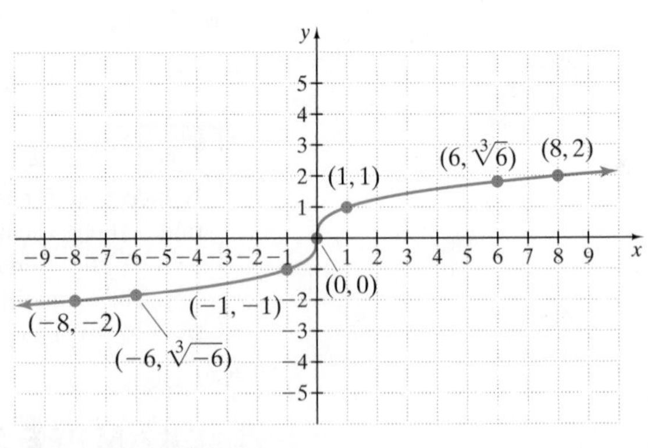

The graph of this function passes the vertical line test, as expected. □

PRACTICE

8 Graph the function $f(x) = \sqrt[3]{x} - 4$.

Vocabulary, Readiness & Video Check

Use the choices below to fill in each blank. Not all choices will be used.

is	cubes	$-\sqrt{a}$	radical sign	index
is not	squares	$\sqrt{-a}$	radicand	

1. In the expression $\sqrt[n]{a}$, the n is called the ________, the $\sqrt{\ }$ is called the ________, and a is called the ________.

2. If $\sqrt{a}$ is the positive square root of a, $a \neq 0$, then ________ is the negative square root of a.

3. The square root of a negative number ________ a real number.

4. Numbers such as 1, 4, 9, and 25 are called perfect ________, whereas numbers such as 1, 8, 27, and 125 are called perfect ________.

Fill in the blank.

5. The domain of the function $f(x) = \sqrt{x}$ is ________.

6. The domain of the function $f(x) = \sqrt[3]{x}$ is ________.

7. If $f(16) = 4$, the corresponding ordered pair is ________.

8. If $g(-8) = -2$, the corresponding ordered pair is ________.

Martin-Gay Interactive Videos

See Video 5.1

Watch the section lecture video and answer the following questions.

OBJECTIVE 1 — **9.** From Examples 5 and 6, when simplifying radicals containing variables with exponents, describe a shortcut you can use.

OBJECTIVE 2 — **10.** From Example 9, how can you determine a reasonable approximation for a non-perfect square root without using a calculator?

OBJECTIVE 3 — **11.** From Example 11, what is an important difference between the square root and the cube root of a negative number?

OBJECTIVE 4 — **12.** From Example 12, what conclusion is made about the even root of a negative number?

OBJECTIVE 5 — **13.** From the lecture before Example 17, why do you think no absolute value bars are used when n is odd?

OBJECTIVE 6 — **14.** In Example 19, the domain is found by looking at the graph. How can the domain be found by looking at the function?

5.1 Exercise Set

MyMathLab®

Simplify. Assume that variables represent positive real numbers. See Example 1.

1. $\sqrt{100}$ **2.** $\sqrt{400}$

3. $\sqrt{\frac{1}{4}}$ **4.** $\sqrt{\frac{9}{25}}$

5. $\sqrt{0.0001}$ **6.** $\sqrt{0.04}$

7. $-\sqrt{36}$ **8.** $-\sqrt{9}$

9. $\sqrt{x^{10}}$ **10.** $\sqrt{x^{16}}$

11. $\sqrt{16y^6}$ **12.** $\sqrt{64y^{20}}$

Use a calculator to approximate each square root to 3 decimal places. Check to see that each approximation is reasonable. See Example 2.

13. $\sqrt{7}$ **14.** $\sqrt{11}$

15. $\sqrt{38}$ **16.** $\sqrt{56}$

17. $\sqrt{200}$ **18.** $\sqrt{300}$

Find each cube root. See Example 3.

19. $\sqrt[3]{64}$ **20.** $\sqrt[3]{27}$

21. $\sqrt[3]{\frac{1}{8}}$ **22.** $\sqrt[3]{\frac{27}{64}}$

23. $\sqrt[3]{-1}$ **24.** $\sqrt[3]{-125}$

25. $\sqrt[3]{x^{12}}$ **26.** $\sqrt[3]{x^{15}}$

27. $\sqrt[3]{-27x^9}$ **28.** $\sqrt[3]{-64x^6}$

Find each root. Assume that all variables represent nonnegative real numbers. See Example 4.

29. $-\sqrt[4]{16}$

30. $\sqrt[5]{-243}$

31. $\sqrt[4]{-16}$

32. $\sqrt{-16}$

33. $\sqrt[5]{-32}$

34. $\sqrt[5]{-1}$

35. $\sqrt[5]{x^{20}}$

36. $\sqrt[4]{x^{20}}$

37. $\sqrt[6]{64x^{12}}$

38. $\sqrt[5]{-32x^{15}}$

39. $\sqrt{81x^4}$

40. $\sqrt[4]{81x^4}$

41. $\sqrt[4]{256x^8}$

42. $\sqrt{256x^8}$

Simplify. Assume that the variables represent any real number. See Example 5.

43. $\sqrt{(-8)^2}$

44. $\sqrt{(-7)^2}$

45. $\sqrt[3]{(-8)^3}$

46. $\sqrt[5]{(-7)^5}$

47. $\sqrt{4x^2}$

48. $\sqrt[4]{16x^4}$

49. $\sqrt[3]{x^3}$

50. $\sqrt[5]{x^5}$

51. $\sqrt{(x-5)^2}$

52. $\sqrt{(y-6)^2}$

53. $\sqrt{x^2+4x+4}$ (*Hint:* Factor the polynomial first.)

54. $\sqrt{x^2-8x+16}$ (*Hint:* Factor the polynomial first.)

MIXED PRACTICE

Simplify each radical. Assume that all variables represent positive real numbers.

55. $-\sqrt{121}$

56. $-\sqrt[3]{125}$

57. $\sqrt[3]{8x^3}$

58. $\sqrt{16x^8}$

59. $\sqrt{y^{12}}$

60. $\sqrt[3]{y^{12}}$

61. $\sqrt{25a^2b^{20}}$

62. $\sqrt{9x^4y^6}$

63. $\sqrt[3]{-27x^{12}y^9}$

64. $\sqrt[3]{-8a^{21}b^6}$

65. $\sqrt[4]{a^{16}b^4}$

66. $\sqrt[4]{x^8y^{12}}$

67. $\sqrt[5]{-32x^{10}y^5}$

68. $\sqrt[5]{-243x^5z^{15}}$

69. $\sqrt{\dfrac{25}{49}}$

70. $\sqrt{\dfrac{4}{81}}$

71. $\sqrt{\dfrac{x^{20}}{4y^2}}$

72. $\sqrt{\dfrac{y^{10}}{9x^6}}$

73. $-\sqrt[3]{\dfrac{z^{21}}{27x^3}}$

74. $-\sqrt[3]{\dfrac{64a^3}{b^9}}$

75. $\sqrt[4]{\dfrac{x^4}{16}}$

76. $\sqrt[4]{\dfrac{y^4}{81x^4}}$

If $f(x) = \sqrt{2x+3}$ and $g(x) = \sqrt[3]{x-8}$, find the following function values. See Example 6.

77. $f(0)$

78. $g(0)$

79. $g(7)$

80. $f(-1)$

81. $g(-19)$

82. $f(3)$

83. $f(2)$

84. $g(1)$

Identify the domain and then graph each function. See Example 7.

85. $f(x) = \sqrt{x} + 2$

86. $f(x) = \sqrt{x} - 2$

87. $f(x) = \sqrt{x-3}$; use the following table.

x	$f(x)$
3	
4	
7	
12	

88. $f(x) = \sqrt{x+1}$; use the following table.

x	$f(x)$
−1	
0	
3	
8	

Identify the domain and then graph each function. See Example 8.

89. $f(x) = \sqrt[3]{x} + 1$

90. $f(x) = \sqrt[3]{x} - 2$

91. $g(x) = \sqrt[3]{x-1}$; use the following table.

x	$g(x)$
1	
2	
0	
9	
−7	

92. $g(x) = \sqrt[3]{x+1}$; use the following table.

x	$g(x)$
−1	
0	
−2	
7	
−9	

REVIEW AND PREVIEW

Simplify each exponential expression.

93. $(-2x^3y^2)^5$

94. $(4y^6z^7)^3$

95. $(-3x^2y^3z^5)(20x^5y^7)$

96. $(-14a^5bc^2)(2abc^4)$

97. $\dfrac{7x^{-1}y}{14(x^5y^2)^{-2}}$

98. $\dfrac{(2a^{-1}b^2)^3}{(8a^2b)^{-2}}$

CONCEPT EXTENSIONS

Determine whether the following are real numbers. See the Concept Check in this section.

99. $\sqrt{-17}$

100. $\sqrt[3]{-17}$

101. $\sqrt[10]{-17}$

102. $\sqrt[15]{-17}$

Choose the correct letter or letters. No pencil is needed, just think your way through these.

103. Which radical is not a real number?

a. $\sqrt{3}$ **b.** $-\sqrt{11}$ **c.** $\sqrt[3]{-10}$ **d.** $\sqrt{-10}$

104. Which radical(s) simplify to 3?

a. $\sqrt{9}$ **b.** $\sqrt{-9}$ **c.** $\sqrt[3]{27}$ **d.** $\sqrt[3]{-27}$

105. Which radical(s) simplify to -3?

a. $\sqrt{9}$ **b.** $\sqrt{-9}$ **c.** $\sqrt[3]{27}$ **d.** $\sqrt[3]{-27}$

106. Which radical does not simplify to a whole number?

a. $\sqrt{64}$ **b.** $\sqrt[3]{64}$ **c.** $\sqrt{8}$ **d.** $\sqrt[3]{8}$

For Exercises 107 through 110, do not use a calculator.

107. $\sqrt{160}$ is closest to

a. 10 **b.** 13 **c.** 20 **d.** 40

108. $\sqrt{1000}$ is closest to

a. 10 **b.** 30 **c.** 100 **d.** 500

△ **109.** The perimeter of the triangle is closest to

a. 12 **b.** 18

c. 66 **d.** 132

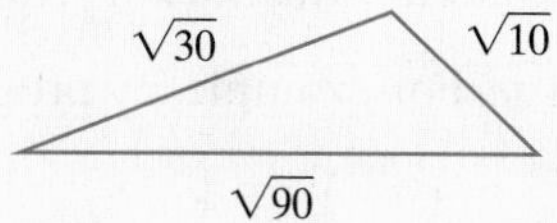

110. The length of the bent wire is closest to

a. 5 **b.** $\sqrt{28}$

c. 7 **d.** 14

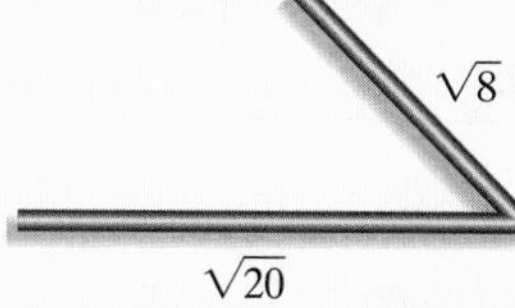

111. Explain why $\sqrt{-64}$ is not a real number.

112. Explain why $\sqrt[3]{-64}$ is a real number.

The Mosteller formula for calculating adult body surface area is $B = \sqrt{\dfrac{hw}{3131}}$, where B is an individual's body surface area in square meters, h is the individual's height in inches, and w is the individual's weight in pounds. Use this information to answer Exercises 113 and 114. Round answers to 2 decimal places.

△ **113.** Find the body surface area of an individual who is 66 inches tall and who weighs 135 pounds.

△ **114.** Find the body surface area of an individual who is 74 inches tall and who weighs 225 pounds.

115. Escape velocity is the minimum speed that an object must reach to escape the pull of a planet's gravity. Escape velocity v is given by the equation $v = \sqrt{\dfrac{2Gm}{r}}$, where m is the mass of the planet, r is its radius, and G is the universal gravitational constant, which has a value of $G = 6.67 \times 10^{-11}$ m^3/kg · s^2. The mass of Earth is 5.97×10^{24} kg, and its radius is 6.37×10^6 m. Use this information to find the escape velocity for Earth in meters per second. Round to the nearest whole number. (*Source:* National Space Science Data Center)

116. Use the formula from Exercise 115 to determine the escape velocity for the moon. The mass of the moon is 7.35×10^{22} kg, and its radius is 1.74×10^6 m. Round to the nearest whole number. (*Source*: National Space Science Data Center)

117. Suppose a classmate tells you that $\sqrt{13} \approx 5.7$. Without a calculator, how can you convince your classmate that he or she must have made an error?

118. Suppose a classmate tells you that $\sqrt[3]{10} \approx 3.2$. Without a calculator, how can you convince your friend that he or she must have made an error?

Use a graphing calculator to verify the domain of each function and its graph.

119. Exercise 85

120. Exercise 86

121. Exercise 89

122. Exercise 90

5.2 Rational Exponents

OBJECTIVES

1. Understand the Meaning of $a^{1/n}$.
2. Understand the Meaning of $a^{m/n}$.
3. Understand the Meaning of $a^{-m/n}$.
4. Use Rules for Exponents to Simplify Expressions That Contain Rational Exponents.
5. Use Rational Exponents to Simplify Radical Expressions.

OBJECTIVE

1 Understanding the Meaning of $a^{1/n}$

So far in this text, we have not defined expressions with rational exponents such as $3^{1/2}$, $x^{2/3}$, and $-9^{-1/4}$. We will define these expressions so that the rules for exponents will apply to these rational exponents as well.

Suppose that $x = 5^{1/3}$. Then

$$x^3 = (5^{1/3})^3 = 5^{1/3 \cdot 3} = 5^1 \text{ or } 5$$

using rules for exponents

Since $x^3 = 5$, x is the number whose cube is 5, or $x = \sqrt[3]{5}$. Notice that we also know that $x = 5^{1/3}$. This means

$$5^{1/3} = \sqrt[3]{5}$$

Definition of $a^{1/n}$

If n is a positive integer greater than 1 and $\sqrt[n]{a}$ is a real number, then

$$a^{1/n} = \sqrt[n]{a}$$

Notice that the denominator of the rational exponent corresponds to the index of the radical.

EXAMPLE 1 Use radical notation to write the following. Simplify if possible.

a. $4^{1/2}$ **b.** $64^{1/3}$ **c.** $x^{1/4}$ **d.** $0^{1/6}$ **e.** $-9^{1/2}$ **f.** $(81x^8)^{1/4}$ **g.** $5y^{1/3}$

Solution

a. $4^{1/2} = \sqrt{4} = 2$

b. $64^{1/3} = \sqrt[3]{64} = 4$

c. $x^{1/4} = \sqrt[4]{x}$

d. $0^{1/6} = \sqrt[6]{0} = 0$

e. $-9^{1/2} = -\sqrt{9} = -3$

f. $(81x^8)^{1/4} = \sqrt[4]{81x^8} = 3x^2$

g. $5y^{1/3} = 5\sqrt[3]{y}$ □

PRACTICE

1 Use radical notation to write the following. Simplify if possible.

a. $36^{1/2}$ **b.** $1000^{1/3}$ **c.** $x^{1/3}$ **d.** $1^{1/4}$

e. $-64^{1/2}$ **f.** $(125x^9)^{1/3}$ **g.** $3x^{1/4}$

OBJECTIVE

2 Understanding the Meaning of $a^{m/n}$

As we expand our use of exponents to include $\frac{m}{n}$, we define their meaning so that rules for exponents still hold true. For example, by properties of exponents,

$$8^{2/3} = (8^{1/3})^2 = (\sqrt[3]{8})^2 \quad \text{or}$$
$$8^{2/3} = (8^2)^{1/3} = \sqrt[3]{8^2}$$

Definition of $a^{m/n}$

If m and n are positive integers greater than 1 with $\frac{m}{n}$ in simplest form, then

$$a^{m/n} = \sqrt[n]{a^m} = (\sqrt[n]{a})^m$$

as long as $\sqrt[n]{a}$ is a real number.

Notice that the denominator n of the rational exponent corresponds to the index of the radical. The numerator m of the rational exponent indicates that the base is to be raised to the mth power. This means

$$8^{2/3} = \sqrt[3]{8^2} = \sqrt[3]{64} = 4 \qquad \text{or}$$
$$8^{2/3} = \left(\sqrt[3]{8}\right)^2 = 2^2 = 4$$

From simplifying $8^{2/3}$, can you see that it doesn't matter whether you raise to a power first and then take the nth root or you take the nth root first and then raise to a power?

> **Helpful Hint**
> Most of the time, $\left(\sqrt[n]{a}\right)^m$ will be easier to calculate than $\sqrt[n]{a^m}$.

EXAMPLE 2 Use radical notation to write the following. Then simplify if possible.

a. $4^{3/2}$ **b.** $-16^{3/4}$ **c.** $(-27)^{2/3}$

d. $\left(\frac{1}{9}\right)^{3/2}$ **e.** $(4x - 1)^{3/5}$

Solution

a. $4^{3/2} = \left(\sqrt{4}\right)^3 = 2^3 = 8$

b. $-16^{3/4} = -\left(\sqrt[4]{16}\right)^3 = -(2)^3 = -8$

c. $(-27)^{2/3} = \left(\sqrt[3]{-27}\right)^2 = (-3)^2 = 9$

d. $\left(\frac{1}{9}\right)^{3/2} = \left(\sqrt{\frac{1}{9}}\right)^3 = \left(\frac{1}{3}\right)^3 = \frac{1}{27}$

e. $(4x - 1)^{3/5} = \sqrt[5]{(4x - 1)^3}$ □

PRACTICE

2 Use radical notation to write the following. Simplify if possible.

a. $16^{3/2}$ **b.** $-1^{3/5}$ **c.** $-(81)^{3/4}$

d. $\left(\frac{1}{25}\right)^{3/2}$ **e.** $(3x + 2)^{5/9}$

> **Helpful Hint**
> The *denominator* of a rational exponent is the index of the corresponding radical. For example, $x^{1/5} = \sqrt[5]{x}$ and $z^{2/3} = \sqrt[3]{z^2}$, or $z^{2/3} = \left(\sqrt[3]{z}\right)^2$.

OBJECTIVE

3 Understanding the Meaning of $a^{-m/n}$

The rational exponents we have given meaning to exclude negative rational numbers. To complete the set of definitions, we define $a^{-m/n}$.

> **Definition of $a^{-m/n}$**
>
> $$a^{-m/n} = \frac{1}{a^{m/n}}$$
>
> as long as $a^{m/n}$ is a nonzero real number.

EXAMPLE 3 Write each expression with a positive exponent, and then simplify.

a. $16^{-3/4}$ **b.** $(-27)^{-2/3}$

Solution

a. $16^{-3/4} = \frac{1}{16^{3/4}} = \frac{1}{\left(\sqrt[4]{16}\right)^3} = \frac{1}{2^3} = \frac{1}{8}$

b. $(-27)^{-2/3} = \frac{1}{(-27)^{2/3}} = \frac{1}{\left(\sqrt[3]{-27}\right)^2} = \frac{1}{(-3)^2} = \frac{1}{9}$ □

(Continued on next page)

PRACTICE

3 Write each expression with a positive exponent; then simplify.

a. $9^{-3/2}$ **b.** $(-64)^{-2/3}$

Helpful Hint

If an expression contains a negative rational exponent, such as $9^{-3/2}$, you may want to first write the expression with a positive exponent and then interpret the rational exponent. Notice that the sign of the base is not affected by the sign of its exponent. For example,

$$9^{-3/2} = \frac{1}{9^{3/2}} = \frac{1}{(\sqrt{9})^3} = \frac{1}{27}$$

Also,

$$(-27)^{-1/3} = \frac{1}{(-27)^{1/3}} = -\frac{1}{3}$$

✓CONCEPT CHECK

Which one is correct?

a. $-8^{2/3} = \frac{1}{4}$ b. $8^{-2/3} = -\frac{1}{4}$ c. $8^{-2/3} = -4$ d. $-8^{-2/3} = -\frac{1}{4}$

OBJECTIVE

4 Using Rules for Exponents to Simplify Expressions 

It can be shown that the properties of integer exponents hold for rational exponents. By using these properties and definitions, we can now simplify expressions that contain rational exponents.

These rules are repeated here for review.

Note: For the remainder of this chapter, we will assume that variables represent positive real numbers. Since this is so, we need not insert absolute value bars when we simplify even roots.

Summary of Exponent Rules

If m and n are rational numbers, and a, b, and c are numbers for which the expressions below exist, then

Product rule for exponents: $a^m \cdot a^n = a^{m+n}$

Power rule for exponents: $(a^m)^n = a^{m \cdot n}$

Power rules for products and quotients: $(ab)^n = a^n b^n$ and

$\left(\frac{a}{c}\right)^n = \frac{a^n}{c^n}, c \neq 0$

Quotient rule for exponents: $\frac{a^m}{a^n} = a^{m-n}, a \neq 0$

Zero exponent: $a^0 = 1, a \neq 0$

Negative exponent: $a^{-n} = \frac{1}{a^n}, a \neq 0$

EXAMPLE 4 Use properties of exponents to simplify. Write results with only positive exponents.

a. $b^{1/3} \cdot b^{5/3}$ **b.** $x^{1/2}x^{1/3}$ **c.** $\frac{7^{1/3}}{7^{4/3}}$

d. $y^{-4/7} \cdot y^{6/7}$ **e.** $\frac{(2x^{2/5}y^{-1/3})^5}{x^2y}$

Answer to Concept Check: d

Solution

a. $b^{1/3} \cdot b^{5/3} = b^{(1/3+5/3)} = b^{6/3} = b^2$

b. $x^{1/2}x^{1/3} = x^{(1/2+1/3)} = x^{3/6+2/6} = x^{5/6}$ Use the product rule.

c. $\frac{7^{1/3}}{7^{4/3}} = 7^{1/3-4/3} = 7^{-3/3} = 7^{-1} = \frac{1}{7}$ Use the quotient rule.

d. $y^{-4/7} \cdot y^{6/7} = y^{-4/7+6/7} = y^{2/7}$ Use the product rule.

e. We begin by using the power rule $(ab)^m = a^m b^m$ to simplify the numerator.

$$\frac{(2x^{2/5}y^{-1/3})^5}{x^2y} = \frac{2^5(x^{2/5})^5(y^{-1/3})^5}{x^2y} = \frac{32x^2y^{-5/3}}{x^2y}$$ Use the power rule and simplify

$$= 32x^{2-2}y^{-5/3-3/3}$$ Apply the quotient rule.

$$= 32x^0y^{-8/3}$$

$$= \frac{32}{y^{8/3}}$$ □

PRACTICE 4 Use properties of exponents to simplify.

a. $y^{2/3} \cdot y^{8/3}$ **b.** $x^{3/5} \cdot x^{1/4}$ **c.** $\frac{9^{2/7}}{9^{9/7}}$

d. $b^{4/9} \cdot b^{-2/9}$ **e.** $\frac{(3x^{1/4}y^{-2/3})^4}{x^4y}$

EXAMPLE 5 Multiply.

a. $z^{2/3}(z^{1/3} - z^5)$ **b.** $(x^{1/3} - 5)(x^{1/3} + 2)$

Solution

a. $z^{2/3}(z^{1/3} - z^5) = z^{2/3}z^{1/3} - z^{2/3}z^5$ Apply the distributive property.

$= z^{(2/3+1/3)} - z^{(2/3+5)}$ Use the product rule.

$= z^{3/3} - z^{(2/3+15/3)}$

$= z - z^{17/3}$

b. $(x^{1/3} - 5)(x^{1/3} + 2) = x^{2/3} + 2x^{1/3} - 5x^{1/3} - 10$ Think of $(x^{1/3} - 5)$ and $(x^{1/3} + 2)$ as 2 binomials, and FOIL.

$= x^{2/3} - 3x^{1/3} - 10$ □

PRACTICE 5 Multiply.

a. $x^{3/5}(x^{1/3} - x^2)$ **b.** $(x^{1/2} + 6)(x^{1/2} - 2)$

EXAMPLE 6 Factor $x^{-1/2}$ from the expression $3x^{-1/2} - 7x^{5/2}$. Assume that all variables represent positive numbers.

Solution

$$3x^{-1/2} - 7x^{5/2} = (x^{-1/2})(3) - (x^{-1/2})(7x^{6/2})$$
$$= x^{-1/2}(3 - 7x^3)$$

To check, multiply $x^{-1/2}(3 - 7x^3)$ to see that the product is $3x^{-1/2} - 7x^{5/2}$. □

PRACTICE 6 Factor $x^{-1/5}$ from the expression $2x^{-1/5} - 7x^{4/5}$.

OBJECTIVE

5 Using Rational Exponents to Simplify Radical Expressions 

Some radical expressions are easier to simplify when we first write them with rational exponents. Use properties of exponents to simplify, and then convert back to radical notation.

EXAMPLE 7 Use rational exponents to simplify. Assume that variables represent positive numbers.

a. $\sqrt[8]{x^4}$ **b.** $\sqrt[6]{25}$ **c.** $\sqrt[4]{r^2s^6}$

Solution

a. $\sqrt[8]{x^4} = x^{4/8} = x^{1/2} = \sqrt{x}$

b. $\sqrt[6]{25} = 25^{1/6} = (5^2)^{1/6} = 5^{2/6} = 5^{1/3} = \sqrt[3]{5}$

c. $\sqrt[4]{r^2s^6} = (r^2s^6)^{1/4} = r^{2/4}s^{6/4} = r^{1/2}s^{3/2} = (rs^3)^{1/2} = \sqrt{rs^3}$ □

PRACTICE

7 Use rational exponents to simplify. Assume that the variables represent positive numbers.

a. $\sqrt[9]{x^3}$ **b.** $\sqrt[4]{36}$ **c.** $\sqrt[8]{a^4b^2}$

EXAMPLE 8 Use rational exponents to write as a single radical.

a. $\sqrt{x} \cdot \sqrt[4]{x}$ **b.** $\dfrac{\sqrt{x}}{\sqrt[3]{x}}$ **c.** $\sqrt[3]{3} \cdot \sqrt{2}$

Solution

a. $\sqrt{x} \cdot \sqrt[4]{x} = x^{1/2} \cdot x^{1/4} = x^{1/2+1/4}$

$= x^{3/4} = \sqrt[4]{x^3}$

b. $\dfrac{\sqrt{x}}{\sqrt[3]{x}} = \dfrac{x^{1/2}}{x^{1/3}} = x^{1/2-1/3} = x^{3/6-2/6}$

$= x^{1/6} = \sqrt[6]{x}$

c. $\sqrt[3]{3} \cdot \sqrt{2} = 3^{1/3} \cdot 2^{1/2}$ Write with rational exponents.

$= 3^{2/6} \cdot 2^{3/6}$ Write the exponents so that they have the same denominator.

$= (3^2 \cdot 2^3)^{1/6}$ Use $a^nb^n = (ab)^n$

$= \sqrt[6]{3^2 \cdot 2^3}$ Write with radical notation.

$= \sqrt[6]{72}$ Multiply $3^2 \cdot 2^3$. □

PRACTICE

8 Use rational expressions to write each of the following as a single radical.

a. $\sqrt[3]{x} \cdot \sqrt[4]{x}$ **b.** $\dfrac{\sqrt[3]{y}}{\sqrt[5]{y}}$ **c.** $\sqrt[3]{5} \cdot \sqrt{3}$

Vocabulary, Readiness & Video Check

Answer each true or false.

1. $9^{-1/2}$ is a positive number. __________

2. $9^{-1/2}$ is a whole number. __________

3. $\dfrac{1}{a^{-m/n}} = a^{m/n}$ (where $a^{m/n}$ is a nonzero real number). __________

Fill in the blank with the correct choice.

4. To simplify $x^{2/3} \cdot x^{1/5}$, ________ the exponents.
a. add **b.** subtract **c.** multiply **d.** divide

5. To simplify $(x^{2/3})^{1/5}$, ________ the exponents.
a. add **b.** subtract **c.** multiply **d.** divide

6. To simplify $\frac{x^{2/3}}{x^{1/5}}$, ________ the exponents.
a. add **b.** subtract **c.** multiply **d.** divide

Martin-Gay Interactive Videos

See Video 5.2

Watch the section lecture video and answer the following questions.

OBJECTIVE 1
7. From looking at Example 2, what is $-(3x)^{1/5}$ in radical notation?

OBJECTIVE 2
8. From Examples 3 and 4, in a fractional exponent, what do the numerator and denominator each represent in radical form?

OBJECTIVE 3
9. Based on Example 5, complete the following statements. A negative fractional exponent will move a base from the numerator to the ________ with the fractional exponent becoming ________.

OBJECTIVE 4
10. Based on Examples 7–9, complete the following statements. Assume you have an expression with fractional exponents. If applying the product rule of exponents, you ________ the exponents. If applying the quotient rule of exponents, you ________ the exponents. If applying the power rule of exponents, you ________ the exponents.

OBJECTIVE 5
11. From Example 10, describe a way to simplify a radical of a variable raised to a power if the index and the exponent have a common factor.

5.2 Exercise Set

MyMathLab®

Use radical notation to write each expression. Simplify if possible. See Example 1.

1. $49^{1/2}$
2. $64^{1/3}$
3. $27^{1/3}$
4. $8^{1/3}$
5. $\left(\frac{1}{16}\right)^{1/4}$
6. $\left(\frac{1}{64}\right)^{1/2}$
7. $169^{1/2}$
8. $81^{1/4}$
9. $2m^{1/3}$
10. $(2m)^{1/3}$
11. $(9x^4)^{1/2}$
12. $(16x^8)^{1/2}$
13. $(-27)^{1/3}$
14. $-64^{1/2}$
15. $-16^{1/4}$
16. $(-32)^{1/5}$

Use radical notation to write each expression. Simplify if possible. See Example 2.

17. $16^{3/4}$
18. $4^{5/2}$
19. $(-64)^{2/3}$
20. $(-8)^{4/3}$
21. $(-16)^{3/4}$
22. $(-9)^{3/2}$
23. $(2x)^{3/5}$
24. $2x^{3/5}$
25. $(7x + 2)^{2/3}$
26. $(x - 4)^{3/4}$
27. $\left(\frac{16}{9}\right)^{3/2}$
28. $\left(\frac{49}{25}\right)^{3/2}$

Write with positive exponents. Simplify if possible. See Example 3.

29. $8^{-4/3}$
30. $64^{-2/3}$
31. $(-64)^{-2/3}$
32. $(-8)^{-4/3}$
33. $(-4)^{-3/2}$
34. $(-16)^{-5/4}$
35. $x^{-1/4}$
36. $y^{-1/6}$
37. $\frac{1}{a^{-2/3}}$
38. $\frac{1}{n^{-8/9}}$
39. $\frac{5}{7x^{-3/4}}$
40. $\frac{2}{3y^{-5/7}}$

Use the properties of exponents to simplify each expression. Write with positive exponents. See Example 4.

41. $a^{2/3}a^{5/3}$
42. $b^{9/5}b^{8/5}$
43. $x^{-2/5} \cdot x^{7/5}$
44. $y^{4/3} \cdot y^{-1/3}$
45. $3^{1/4} \cdot 3^{3/8}$
46. $5^{1/2} \cdot 5^{1/6}$
47. $\frac{y^{1/3}}{y^{1/6}}$
48. $\frac{x^{3/4}}{x^{1/8}}$
49. $(4u^2)^{3/2}$
50. $(32^{1/5}x^{2/3})^3$
51. $\frac{b^{1/2}b^{3/4}}{-b^{1/4}}$
52. $\frac{a^{1/4}a^{-1/2}}{a^{2/3}}$
53. $\frac{(x^3)^{1/2}}{x^{7/2}}$
54. $\frac{y^{11/3}}{(y^5)^{1/3}}$

55. $\frac{(3x^{1/4})^3}{x^{1/12}}$

56. $\frac{(2x^{1/5})^4}{x^{3/10}}$

57. $\frac{(y^3z)^{1/6}}{y^{-1/2}z^{1/3}}$

58. $\frac{(m^2n)^{1/4}}{m^{-1/2}n^{5/8}}$

59. $\frac{(x^3y^2)^{1/4}}{(x^{-5}y^{-1})^{-1/2}}$

60. $\frac{(a^{-2}b^3)^{1/8}}{(a^{-3}b)^{-1/4}}$

Multiply. See Example 5.

61. $y^{1/2}(y^{1/2} - y^{2/3})$

62. $x^{1/2}(x^{1/2} + x^{3/2})$

63. $x^{2/3}(x - 2)$

64. $3x^{1/2}(x + y)$

65. $(2x^{1/3} + 3)(2x^{1/3} - 3)$

66. $(y^{1/2} + 5)(y^{1/2} + 5)$

Factor the given factor from the expression. See Example 6.

67. $x^{8/3}; x^{8/3} + x^{10/3}$

68. $x^{3/2}; x^{5/2} - x^{3/2}$

69. $x^{1/5}; x^{2/5} - 3x^{1/5}$

70. $x^{2/7}; x^{3/7} - 2x^{2/7}$

71. $x^{-1/3}; 5x^{-1/3} + x^{2/3}$

72. $x^{-3/4}; x^{-3/4} + 3x^{1/4}$

Use rational exponents to simplify each radical. Assume that all variables represent positive numbers. See Example 7.

73. $\sqrt[6]{x^3}$

74. $\sqrt[9]{a^3}$

75. $\sqrt[6]{4}$

76. $\sqrt[4]{36}$

77. $\sqrt[4]{16x^2}$

78. $\sqrt[8]{4y^2}$

79. $\sqrt[8]{x^4y^4}$

80. $\sqrt[9]{y^6z^3}$

81. $\sqrt[12]{a^8b^4}$

82. $\sqrt[10]{a^5b^5}$

83. $\sqrt[4]{(x + 3)^2}$

84. $\sqrt[8]{(y + 1)^4}$

Use rational expressions to write as a single radical expression. See Example 8.

85. $\sqrt[3]{y} \cdot \sqrt[5]{y^2}$

86. $\sqrt[3]{y^2} \cdot \sqrt[6]{y}$

87. $\frac{\sqrt[3]{b^2}}{\sqrt[4]{b}}$

88. $\frac{\sqrt[4]{a}}{\sqrt[5]{a}}$

89. $\sqrt[3]{x} \cdot \sqrt[4]{x} \cdot \sqrt[8]{x^3}$

90. $\sqrt[6]{y} \cdot \sqrt[3]{y} \cdot \sqrt[5]{y^2}$

91. $\frac{\sqrt[3]{a^2}}{\sqrt[6]{a}}$

92. $\frac{\sqrt[5]{b^2}}{\sqrt[10]{b^3}}$

93. $\sqrt{3} \cdot \sqrt[3]{4}$

94. $\sqrt[3]{5} \cdot \sqrt{2}$

95. $\sqrt[5]{7} \cdot \sqrt[3]{y}$

96. $\sqrt[4]{5} \cdot \sqrt[3]{x}$

97. $\sqrt{5r} \cdot \sqrt[3]{s}$

98. $\sqrt[3]{b} \cdot \sqrt[5]{4a}$

REVIEW AND PREVIEW

Write each integer as a product of two integers such that one of the factors is a perfect square. For example, write 18 as 9 · 2 because 9 is a perfect square.

99. 75

100. 20

101. 48

102. 45

Write each integer as a product of two integers such that one of the factors is a perfect cube. For example, write 24 as 8 · 3 because 8 is a perfect cube.

103. 16

104. 56

105. 54

106. 80

CONCEPT EXTENSIONS

Choose the correct letter for each exercise. Letters will be used more than once. No pencil is needed. Just think about the meaning of each expression.

A = 2, B = −2, C = not a real number

107. $4^{1/2}$ ______

108. $-4^{1/2}$ ______

109. $(-4)^{1/2}$ ______

110. $8^{1/3}$ ______

111. $-8^{1/3}$ ______

112. $(-8)^{1/3}$ ______

Basal metabolic rate (BMR) is the number of calories per day a person needs to maintain life. A person's basal metabolic rate $B(w)$ in calories per day can be estimated with the function $B(w) = 70w^{3/4}$, where w is the person's weight in kilograms. Use this information to answer Exercises 113 and 114.

113. Estimate the BMR for a person who weighs 60 kilograms. Round to the nearest calorie. (*Note:* 60 kilograms is approximately 132 pounds.)

114. Estimate the BMR for a person who weighs 90 kilograms. Round to the nearest calorie. (*Note:* 90 kilograms is approximately 198 pounds.)

The number of cell telephone subscribers in the United States from 1995–2010 can be modeled by $f(x) = 25x^{23/25}$, where $f(x)$ is the number of cellular telephone subscriptions in millions, x years after 1995. (Source: CTIA-Wireless Association, 1995–2010) Use this information to answer Exercises 115 and 116.

115. Use this model to estimate the number of cellular subscriptions in 2010. Round to the nearest tenth of a million.

116. Predict the number of cellular telephone subscriptions in 2015. Round to the nearest tenth of a million.

117. Explain how writing x^{-7} with positive exponents is similar to writing $x^{-1/4}$ with positive exponents.

118. Explain how writing $2x^{-5}$ with positive exponents is similar to writing $2x^{-3/4}$ with positive exponents.

Fill in each box with the correct expression.

119. $\square \cdot a^{2/3} = a^{3/3}$, or a

120. $\square \cdot x^{1/8} = x^{4/8}$, or $x^{1/2}$

121. $\dfrac{\square}{x^{-2/5}} = x^{3/5}$

122. $\dfrac{\square}{y^{-3/4}} = y^{4/4}$, or y

Use a calculator to write a four-decimal-place approximation of each number.

123. $8^{1/4}$

124. $20^{1/5}$

125. $18^{3/5}$

126. $76^{5/7}$

127. In physics, the speed of a wave traveling over a stretched string with tension t and density u is given by the expression $\dfrac{\sqrt{t}}{\sqrt{u}}$. Write this expression with rational exponents.

128. In electronics, the angular frequency of oscillations in a certain type of circuit is given by the expression $(LC)^{-1/2}$. Use radical notation to write this expression.

5.3 Simplifying Radical Expressions 

OBJECTIVES

1 Use the Product Rule for Radicals.

2 Use the Quotient Rule for Radicals.

3 Simplify Radicals.

4 Use the Distance and Midpoint Formulas.

OBJECTIVE

1 Using the Product Rule 

It is possible to simplify some radicals that do not evaluate to rational numbers. To do so, we use a product rule and a quotient rule for radicals. To discover the product rule, notice the following pattern.

$$\sqrt{9}\cdot\sqrt{4} = 3\cdot 2 = 6$$
$$\sqrt{9\cdot 4} = \sqrt{36} = 6$$

Since both expressions simplify to 6, it is true that

$$\sqrt{9}\cdot\sqrt{4} = \sqrt{9\cdot 4}$$

This pattern suggests the following product rule for radicals.

Product Rule for Radicals

If $\sqrt[n]{a}$ and $\sqrt[n]{b}$ are real numbers, then

$$\sqrt[n]{a}\cdot\sqrt[n]{b} = \sqrt[n]{ab}$$

Notice that the product rule is the relationship $a^{1/n}\cdot b^{1/n} = (ab)^{1/n}$ stated in radical notation.

EXAMPLE 1 Multiply.

a. $\sqrt{3}\cdot\sqrt{5}$ **b.** $\sqrt{21}\cdot\sqrt{x}$ **c.** $\sqrt[3]{4}\cdot\sqrt[3]{2}$

d. $\sqrt[4]{5y^2}\cdot\sqrt[4]{2x^3}$ **e.** $\sqrt{\dfrac{2}{a}}\cdot\sqrt{\dfrac{b}{3}}$

Solution

a. $\sqrt{3}\cdot\sqrt{5} = \sqrt{3\cdot 5} = \sqrt{15}$

b. $\sqrt{21}\cdot\sqrt{x} = \sqrt{21x}$

c. $\sqrt[3]{4}\cdot\sqrt[3]{2} = \sqrt[3]{4\cdot 2} = \sqrt[3]{8} = 2$

d. $\sqrt[4]{5y^2}\cdot\sqrt[4]{2x^3} = \sqrt[4]{5y^2\cdot 2x^3} = \sqrt[4]{10y^2x^3}$

e. $\sqrt{\dfrac{2}{a}}\cdot\sqrt{\dfrac{b}{3}} = \sqrt{\dfrac{2}{a}\cdot\dfrac{b}{3}} = \sqrt{\dfrac{2b}{3a}}$ □

PRACTICE

1 Multiply.

a. $\sqrt{5}\cdot\sqrt{7}$ **b.** $\sqrt{13}\cdot\sqrt{z}$ **c.** $\sqrt[4]{125}\cdot\sqrt[4]{5}$

d. $\sqrt[3]{5y}\cdot\sqrt[3]{3x^2}$ **e.** $\sqrt{\dfrac{5}{m}}\cdot\sqrt{\dfrac{t}{2}}$

OBJECTIVE

2 Using the Quotient Rule 

To discover a quotient rule for radicals, notice the following pattern.

$$\sqrt{\frac{4}{9}} = \frac{2}{3}$$

$$\frac{\sqrt{4}}{\sqrt{9}} = \frac{2}{3}$$

Since both expressions simplify to $\frac{2}{3}$, it is true that

$$\sqrt{\frac{4}{9}} = \frac{\sqrt{4}}{\sqrt{9}}$$

This pattern suggests the following quotient rule for radicals.

Quotient Rule for Radicals

If $\sqrt[n]{a}$ and $\sqrt[n]{b}$ are real numbers and $\sqrt[n]{b}$ is not zero, then

$$\sqrt[n]{\frac{a}{b}} = \frac{\sqrt[n]{a}}{\sqrt[n]{b}}$$

Notice that the quotient rule is the relationship $\left(\frac{a}{b}\right)^{1/n} = \frac{a^{1/n}}{b^{1/n}}$ stated in radical notation. We can use the quotient rule to simplify radical expressions by reading the rule from left to right or to divide radicals by reading the rule from right to left.

For example,

$$\sqrt{\frac{x}{16}} = \frac{\sqrt{x}}{\sqrt{16}} = \frac{\sqrt{x}}{4} \qquad \text{Using } \sqrt[n]{\frac{a}{b}} = \frac{\sqrt[n]{a}}{\sqrt[n]{b}}$$

$$\frac{\sqrt{75}}{\sqrt{3}} = \sqrt{\frac{75}{3}} = \sqrt{25} = 5 \qquad \text{Using } \frac{\sqrt[n]{a}}{\sqrt[n]{b}} = \sqrt[n]{\frac{a}{b}}$$

Note: *Recall that from Section 5.2 on, we assume that variables represent positive real numbers. Since this is so, we need not insert absolute value bars when we simplify even roots.*

EXAMPLE 2 Use the quotient rule to simplify.

a. $\sqrt{\frac{25}{49}}$ **b.** $\sqrt{\frac{x}{9}}$ **c.** $\sqrt[3]{\frac{8}{27}}$ **d.** $\sqrt[4]{\frac{3}{16y^4}}$

Solution

a. $\sqrt{\frac{25}{49}} = \frac{\sqrt{25}}{\sqrt{49}} = \frac{5}{7}$

b. $\sqrt{\frac{x}{9}} = \frac{\sqrt{x}}{\sqrt{9}} = \frac{\sqrt{x}}{3}$

c. $\sqrt[3]{\frac{8}{27}} = \frac{\sqrt[3]{8}}{\sqrt[3]{27}} = \frac{2}{3}$

d. $\sqrt[4]{\frac{3}{16y^4}} = \frac{\sqrt[4]{3}}{\sqrt[4]{16y^4}} = \frac{\sqrt[4]{3}}{2y}$ □

PRACTICE

2 Use the quotient rule to simplify.

a. $\sqrt{\frac{36}{49}}$ **b.** $\sqrt{\frac{z}{16}}$ **c.** $\sqrt[3]{\frac{125}{8}}$ **d.** $\sqrt[4]{\frac{5}{81x^8}}$

OBJECTIVE

3 Simplifying Radicals

Both the product and quotient rules can be used to simplify a radical. If the product rule is read from right to left, we have that

$$\sqrt[n]{ab} = \sqrt[n]{a} \cdot \sqrt[n]{b}.$$

This is used to simplify the following radicals.

EXAMPLE 3 Simplify the following.

a. $\sqrt{50}$ **b.** $\sqrt[3]{24}$ **c.** $\sqrt{26}$ **d.** $\sqrt[4]{32}$

Solution

a. Factor 50 such that one factor is the largest perfect square that divides 50. The largest perfect square factor of 50 is 25, so we write 50 as $25 \cdot 2$ and use the product rule for radicals to simplify.

$$\sqrt{50} = \sqrt{25 \cdot 2} = \sqrt{25} \cdot \sqrt{2} = 5\sqrt{2}$$

The largest perfect square factor of 50

> **Helpful Hint**
> Don't forget that, for example, $5\sqrt{2}$ means $5 \cdot \sqrt{2}$.

b. $\sqrt[3]{24} = \sqrt[3]{8 \cdot 3} = \sqrt[3]{8} \cdot \sqrt[3]{3} = 2\sqrt[3]{3}$

The largest perfect cube factor of 24

c. $\sqrt{26}$ The largest perfect square factor of 26 is 1, so $\sqrt{26}$ cannot be simplified further.

d. $\sqrt[4]{32} = \sqrt[4]{16 \cdot 2} = \sqrt[4]{16} \cdot \sqrt[4]{2} = 2\sqrt[4]{2}$

The largest fourth power factor of 32 □

PRACTICE

3 Simplify the following.

a. $\sqrt{98}$ **b.** $\sqrt[3]{54}$ **c.** $\sqrt{35}$ **d.** $\sqrt[4]{243}$

After simplifying a radical such as a square root, always check the radicand to see that it contains no other perfect square factors. It may, if the largest perfect square factor of the radicand was not originally recognized. For example,

$$\sqrt{200} = \sqrt{4 \cdot 50} = \sqrt{4} \cdot \sqrt{50} = 2\sqrt{50}$$

Notice that the radicand 50 still contains the perfect square factor 25. This is because 4 is not the largest perfect square factor of 200. We continue as follows.

$$2\sqrt{50} = 2\sqrt{25 \cdot 2} = 2 \cdot \sqrt{25} \cdot \sqrt{2} = 2 \cdot 5 \cdot \sqrt{2} = 10\sqrt{2}$$

The radical is now simplified since 2 contains no perfect square factors (other than 1).

> **Helpful Hint**
> To help you recognize largest perfect power factors of a radicand, it will help if you are familiar with some perfect powers. A few are listed below.

Perfect Squares	1,	4,	9,	16,	25,	36,	49,	64,	81,	100,	121,	144
	1^2	2^2	3^2	4^2	5^2	6^2	7^2	8^2	9^2	10^2	11^2	12^2
Perfect Cubes	1,	8,	27,	64,	125							
	1^3	2^3	3^3	4^3	5^3							
Perfect Fourth Powers	1,	16,	81,	256								
	1^4	2^4	3^4	4^4								

In general, we say that a radicand of the form $\sqrt[n]{a}$ is simplified when the radicand a contains no factors that are perfect nth powers (other than 1 or -1).

EXAMPLE 4 Use the product rule to simplify.

a. $\sqrt{25x^3}$ **b.** $\sqrt[3]{54x^6y^8}$ **c.** $\sqrt[4]{81z^{11}}$

Solution

a. $\sqrt{25x^3} = \sqrt{25x^2 \cdot x}$ Find the largest perfect square factor.

$= \sqrt{25x^2} \cdot \sqrt{x}$ Apply the product rule.

$= 5x\sqrt{x}$ Simplify.

b. $\sqrt[3]{54x^6y^8} = \sqrt[3]{27 \cdot 2 \cdot x^6 \cdot y^6 \cdot y^2}$ Factor the radicand and identify perfect cube factors.

$= \sqrt[3]{27x^6y^6 \cdot 2y^2}$

$= \sqrt[3]{27x^6y^6} \cdot \sqrt[3]{2y^2}$ Apply the product rule.

$= 3x^2y^2\sqrt[3]{2y^2}$ Simplify.

c. $\sqrt[4]{81z^{11}} = \sqrt[4]{81 \cdot z^8 \cdot z^3}$ Factor the radicand and identify perfect fourth power factors.

$= \sqrt[4]{81z^8} \cdot \sqrt[4]{z^3}$ Apply the product rule.

$= 3z^2\sqrt[4]{z^3}$ Simplify. □

PRACTICE 4 Use the product rule to simplify.

a. $\sqrt{36z^7}$ **b.** $\sqrt[3]{32p^4q^7}$ **c.** $\sqrt[4]{16x^{15}}$

EXAMPLE 5 Use the quotient rule to divide, and simplify if possible.

a. $\dfrac{\sqrt{20}}{\sqrt{5}}$ **b.** $\dfrac{\sqrt{50x}}{2\sqrt{2}}$ **c.** $\dfrac{7\sqrt[3]{48x^4y^8}}{\sqrt[3]{6y^2}}$ **d.** $\dfrac{2\sqrt[4]{32a^8b^6}}{\sqrt[4]{a^{-1}b^2}}$

Solution

a. $\dfrac{\sqrt{20}}{\sqrt{5}} = \sqrt{\dfrac{20}{5}}$ Apply the quotient rule.

$= \sqrt{4}$ Simplify.

$= 2$ Simplify.

b. $\dfrac{\sqrt{50x}}{2\sqrt{2}} = \dfrac{1}{2} \cdot \sqrt{\dfrac{50x}{2}}$ Apply the quotient rule.

$= \dfrac{1}{2} \cdot \sqrt{25x}$ Simplify.

$= \dfrac{1}{2} \cdot \sqrt{25} \cdot \sqrt{x}$ Factor $25x$.

$= \dfrac{1}{2} \cdot 5 \cdot \sqrt{x}$ Simplify.

$= \dfrac{5}{2}\sqrt{x}$

c. $\dfrac{7\sqrt[3]{48x^4y^8}}{\sqrt[3]{6y^2}} = 7 \cdot \sqrt[3]{\dfrac{48x^4y^8}{6y^2}}$ Apply the quotient rule.

$= 7 \cdot \sqrt[3]{8x^4y^6}$ Simplify.

$= 7\sqrt[3]{8x^3y^6 \cdot x}$ Factor.

$= 7 \cdot \sqrt[3]{8x^3y^6} \cdot \sqrt[3]{x}$ Apply the product rule.

$$= 7 \cdot 2xy^2 \cdot \sqrt[3]{x} \quad \text{Simplify.}$$
$$= 14xy^2\sqrt[3]{x}$$

d. $\dfrac{2\sqrt[4]{32a^8b^6}}{\sqrt[4]{a^{-1}b^2}} = 2\sqrt[4]{\dfrac{32a^8b^6}{a^{-1}b^2}} = 2\sqrt[4]{32a^9b^4} = 2\sqrt[4]{16 \cdot a^8 \cdot b^4 \cdot 2 \cdot a}$

$= 2\sqrt[4]{16a^8b^4} \cdot \sqrt[4]{2a} = 2 \cdot 2a^2b \cdot \sqrt[4]{2a} = 4a^2b\sqrt[4]{2a}$ □

PRACTICE

5 Use the quotient rule to divide and simplify.

a. $\dfrac{\sqrt{80}}{\sqrt{5}}$ **b.** $\dfrac{\sqrt{98z}}{3\sqrt{2}}$ **c.** $\dfrac{5\sqrt[3]{40x^5y^7}}{\sqrt[3]{5y}}$ **d.** $\dfrac{3\sqrt[5]{64x^9y^8}}{\sqrt[5]{x^{-1}y^2}}$

✓CONCEPT CHECK

Find and correct the error:

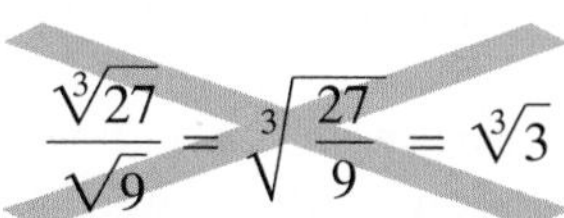

OBJECTIVE

4 Using the Distance and Midpoint Formulas 

Now that we know how to simplify radicals, we can derive and use the distance formula. The midpoint formula is often confused with the distance formula, so to clarify both, we will also review the midpoint formula.

The Cartesian coordinate system helps us visualize a distance between points. To find the distance between two points, we use the distance formula, which is derived from the Pythagorean theorem.

To find the distance d between two points (x_1, y_1) and (x_2, y_2) as shown to the left, notice that the length of leg a is $x_2 - x_1$ and that the length of leg b is $y_2 - y_1$.

Thus, the Pythagorean theorem tells us that

$$d^2 = a^2 + b^2$$

or

$$d^2 = (x_2 - x_1)^2 + (y_2 - y_1)^2$$

or

$$d = \sqrt{(x_2 - x_1)^2 + (y_2 - y_1)^2}$$

This formula gives us the distance between any two points on the real plane.

Distance Formula

The distance d between two points (x_1, y_1) and (x_2, y_2) is given by

$$d = \sqrt{(x_2 - x_1)^2 + (y_2 - y_1)^2}$$

EXAMPLE 6 Find the distance between $(2, -5)$ and $(1, -4)$. Give an exact distance and a three-decimal-place approximation.

Solution To use the distance formula, it makes no difference which point we call (x_1, y_1) and which point we call (x_2, y_2). We will let $(x_1, y_1) = (2, -5)$ and $(x_2, y_2) = (1, -4)$.

(Continued on next page)

Answer to Concept Check:
$\dfrac{\sqrt[3]{27}}{\sqrt{9}} = \dfrac{3}{3} = 1$

$$\begin{aligned} d &= \sqrt{(x_2 - x_1)^2 + (y_2 - y_1)^2} \\ &= \sqrt{(1 - 2)^2 + [-4 - (-5)]^2} \\ &= \sqrt{(-1)^2 + (1)^2} \\ &= \sqrt{1 + 1} \\ &= \sqrt{2} \approx 1.414 \end{aligned}$$

The distance between the two points is exactly $\sqrt{2}$ units, or approximately 1.414 units. □

PRACTICE

6 Find the distance between $(-3,7)$ and $(-2,3)$. Give an exact distance and a three-decimal-place approximation.

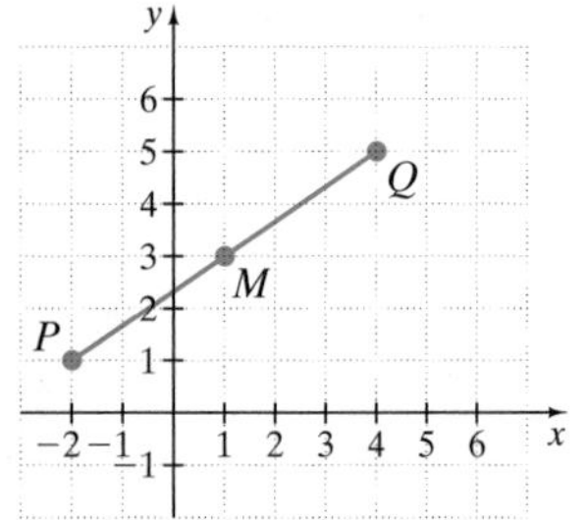

The **midpoint** of a line segment is the **point** located exactly halfway between the two endpoints of the line segment. On the graph to the left, the point M is the midpoint of line segment PQ. Thus, the distance between M and P equals the distance between M and Q.

Note: We usually need no knowledge of roots to calculate the midpoint of a line segment. We review midpoint here only because it is often confused with the distance between two points.

The x-coordinate of M is at half the distance between the x-coordinates of P and Q, and the y-coordinate of M is at half the distance between the y-coordinates of P and Q. That is, the x-coordinate of M is the average of the x-coordinates of P and Q; the y-coordinate of M is the average of the y-coordinates of P and Q.

Midpoint Formula

The midpoint of the line segment whose endpoints are (x_1, y_1) and (x_2, y_2) is the point with coordinates

$$\left(\frac{x_1 + x_2}{2}, \frac{y_1 + y_2}{2}\right)$$

EXAMPLE 7 Find the midpoint of the line segment that joins points $P(-3,3)$ and $Q(1,0)$.

Solution Use the midpoint formula. It makes no difference which point we call (x_1, y_1) or which point we call (x_2, y_2). Let $(x_1, y_1) = (-3,3)$ and $(x_2, y_2) = (1,0)$.

$$\begin{aligned} \text{midpoint} &= \left(\frac{x_1 + x_2}{2}, \frac{y_1 + y_2}{2}\right) \\ &= \left(\frac{-3 + 1}{2}, \frac{3 + 0}{2}\right) \\ &= \left(\frac{-2}{2}, \frac{3}{2}\right) \\ &= \left(-1, \frac{3}{2}\right) \end{aligned}$$

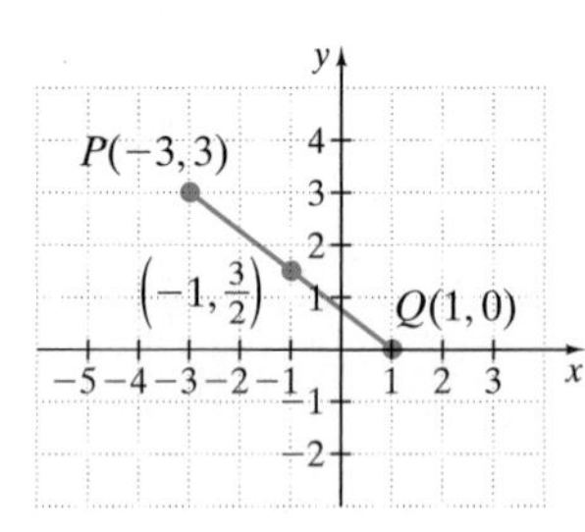

The midpoint of the segment is $\left(-1, \frac{3}{2}\right)$. □

PRACTICE

7 Find the midpoint of the line segment that joins points $P(5,-2)$ and $Q(8,-6)$.

Helpful Hint

The distance between two points is a distance. The midpoint of a line segment is the point halfway between the endpoints of the segment.

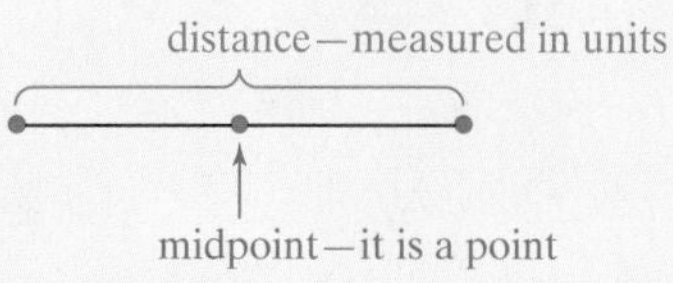

Vocabulary, Readiness & Video Check

Use the choices below to fill in each blank. Some choices may be used more than once.

distance   midpoint   point

1. The _______ of a line segment is a _______ exactly halfway between the two endpoints of the line segment.
2. The _______ between two points is a distance, measured in units.
3. The _______ formula is $d = \sqrt{(x_2 - x_1)^2 + (y_2 - y_1)^2}$.
4. The _______ formula is $\left(\frac{x_1 + x_2}{2}, \frac{y_1 + y_2}{2}\right)$.

Martin-Gay Interactive Videos

See Video 5.3

Watch the section lecture video and answer the following questions.

OBJECTIVE 1
5. From Example 1 and the lecture before, in order to apply the product rule for radicals, what must be true about the indexes of the radicals being multiplied?

OBJECTIVE 2
6. From Examples 2–6, when might you apply the quotient rule (in either direction) in order to simplify a fractional radical expression?

OBJECTIVE 3
7. From Example 8, we know that an even power of a variable is a perfect square factor of the variable, leaving no factor in the radicand once simplified. Therefore, what must be true about the power of any variable left in the radicand of a simplified square root? Explain.

OBJECTIVE 4
8. From Example 10, the formula uses the coordinates of two points similar to the slope formula. What caution should you take when replacing values in the formula?

OBJECTIVE 4
9. Based on Example 11, complete the following statement. The x-value of the midpoint is the _______ of the x-values of the endpoints and the y-value of the midpoint is the _______ of the y-values of the endpoints.

5.3 Exercise Set

MyMathLab®

Use the product rule to multiply. See Example 1.

1. $\sqrt{7} \cdot \sqrt{2}$
2. $\sqrt{11} \cdot \sqrt{10}$
3. $\sqrt[4]{8} \cdot \sqrt[4]{2}$
4. $\sqrt[4]{27} \cdot \sqrt[4]{3}$
5. $\sqrt[3]{4} \cdot \sqrt[3]{9}$
6. $\sqrt[3]{10} \cdot \sqrt[3]{5}$
7. $\sqrt{2} \cdot \sqrt{3x}$
8. $\sqrt{3y} \cdot \sqrt{5x}$
9. $\sqrt{\frac{7}{x}} \cdot \sqrt{\frac{2}{y}}$
10. $\sqrt{\frac{6}{m}} \cdot \sqrt{\frac{n}{5}}$
11. $\sqrt[4]{4x^3} \cdot \sqrt[4]{5}$
12. $\sqrt[4]{ab^2} \cdot \sqrt[4]{27ab}$

Use the quotient rule to simplify. See Examples 2 and 3.

13. $\sqrt{\frac{6}{49}}$
14. $\sqrt{\frac{8}{81}}$
15. $\sqrt{\frac{2}{49}}$
16. $\sqrt{\frac{5}{121}}$
17. $\sqrt[4]{\frac{x^3}{16}}$
18. $\sqrt[4]{\frac{y}{81x^4}}$
19. $\sqrt[3]{\frac{4}{27}}$
20. $\sqrt[3]{\frac{3}{64}}$

21. $\sqrt[4]{\frac{8}{x^8}}$

22. $\sqrt[4]{\frac{a^3}{81}}$

23. $\sqrt[3]{\frac{2x}{81y^{12}}}$

24. $\sqrt[3]{\frac{3}{8x^6}}$

25. $\sqrt{\frac{x^2y}{100}}$

26. $\sqrt{\frac{y^2z}{36}}$

27. $\sqrt{\frac{5x^2}{4y^2}}$

28. $\sqrt{\frac{y^{10}}{9x^6}}$

29. $-\sqrt[3]{\frac{z^7}{27x^3}}$

30. $-\sqrt[3]{\frac{64a}{b^9}}$

Simplify. See Examples 3 and 4.

31. $\sqrt{32}$

32. $\sqrt{27}$

33. $\sqrt[3]{192}$

34. $\sqrt[3]{108}$

35. $5\sqrt{75}$

36. $3\sqrt{8}$

37. $\sqrt{24}$

38. $\sqrt{20}$

39. $\sqrt{100x^5}$

40. $\sqrt{64y^9}$

41. $\sqrt[3]{16y^7}$

42. $\sqrt[3]{64y^9}$

43. $\sqrt[4]{a^8b^7}$

44. $\sqrt[5]{32z^{12}}$

45. $\sqrt{y^5}$

46. $\sqrt[3]{y^5}$

47. $\sqrt{25a^2b^3}$

48. $\sqrt{9x^5y^7}$

49. $\sqrt[5]{-32x^{10}y}$

50. $\sqrt[5]{-243z^9}$

51. $\sqrt[3]{50x^{14}}$

52. $\sqrt[3]{40y^{10}}$

53. $-\sqrt{32a^8b^7}$

54. $-\sqrt{20ab^6}$

55. $\sqrt{9x^7y^9}$

56. $\sqrt{12r^9s^{12}}$

57. $\sqrt[3]{125r^9s^{12}}$

58. $\sqrt[3]{8a^6b^9}$

59. $\sqrt[4]{32x^{12}y^5}$

60. $\sqrt[4]{162x^7y^{20}}$

Use the quotient rule to divide. Then simplify if possible. See Example 5.

61. $\frac{\sqrt{14}}{\sqrt{7}}$

62. $\frac{\sqrt{45}}{\sqrt{9}}$

63. $\frac{\sqrt[3]{24}}{\sqrt[3]{3}}$

64. $\frac{\sqrt[3]{10}}{\sqrt[3]{2}}$

65. $\frac{5\sqrt[4]{48}}{\sqrt[4]{3}}$

66. $\frac{7\sqrt[4]{162}}{\sqrt[4]{2}}$

67. $\frac{\sqrt{x^5y^3}}{\sqrt{xy}}$

68. $\frac{\sqrt{a^7b^6}}{\sqrt{a^3b^2}}$

69. $\frac{8\sqrt[3]{54m^7}}{\sqrt[3]{2m}}$

70. $\frac{\sqrt[3]{128x^3}}{-3\sqrt[3]{2x}}$

71. $\frac{3\sqrt{100x^2}}{2\sqrt{2x^{-1}}}$

72. $\frac{\sqrt{270y^2}}{5\sqrt{3y^{-4}}}$

73. $\frac{\sqrt[4]{96a^{10}b^3}}{\sqrt[4]{3a^2b^3}}$

74. $\frac{\sqrt[4]{160x^{10}y^5}}{\sqrt[4]{2x^2y^2}}$

75. $\frac{\sqrt[5]{64x^{10}y^3}}{\sqrt[5]{2x^3y^{-7}}}$

76. $\frac{\sqrt[5]{192x^6y^{12}}}{\sqrt[5]{2x^{-1}y^{-3}}}$

Find the distance between each pair of points. Give an exact distance and a three-decimal-place approximation. See Example 6.

77. $(5, 1)$ and $(8, 5)$

78. $(2, 3)$ and $(14, 8)$

79. $(-3, 2)$ and $(1, -3)$

80. $(3, -2)$ and $(-4, 1)$

81. $(-9, 4)$ and $(-8, 1)$

82. $(-5, -2)$ and $(-6, -6)$

83. $(0, -\sqrt{2})$ and $(\sqrt{3}, 0)$

84. $(-\sqrt{5}, 0)$ and $(0, \sqrt{7})$

85. $(1.7, -3.6)$ and $(-8.6, 5.7)$

86. $(9.6, 2.5)$ and $(-1.9, -3.7)$

Find the midpoint of the line segment whose endpoints are given. See Example 7.

87. $(6, -8), (2, 4)$

88. $(3, 9), (7, 11)$

89. $(-2, -1), (-8, 6)$

90. $(-3, -4), (6, -8)$

91. $(7, 3), (-1, -3)$

92. $(-2, 5), (-1, 6)$

93. $\left(\frac{1}{2}, \frac{3}{8}\right), \left(-\frac{3}{2}, \frac{5}{8}\right)$

94. $\left(-\frac{2}{5}, \frac{7}{15}\right), \left(-\frac{2}{5}, -\frac{4}{15}\right)$

95. $(\sqrt{2}, 3\sqrt{5}), (\sqrt{2}, -2\sqrt{5})$

96. $(\sqrt{8}, -\sqrt{12}), (3\sqrt{2}, 7\sqrt{3})$

97. $(4.6, -3.5), (7.8, -9.8)$

98. $(-4.6, 2.1), (-6.7, 1.9)$

REVIEW AND PREVIEW

Perform each indicated operation.

99. $6x + 8x$

100. $(6x)(8x)$

101. $(2x + 3)(x - 5)$

102. $(2x + 3) + (x - 5)$

103. $9y^2 - 8y^2$

104. $(9y^2)(-8y^2)$

105. $-3(x + 5)$

106. $-3 + x + 5$

107. $(x - 4)^2$

108. $(2x + 1)^2$

CONCEPT EXTENSIONS

Answer true or false. Assume all radicals represent nonzero real numbers.

109. $\sqrt[n]{a} \cdot \sqrt[n]{b} = \sqrt[n]{ab}$, ____

110. $\sqrt[3]{7} \cdot \sqrt[3]{11} = \sqrt[3]{18}$, ____

111. $\sqrt[3]{7} \cdot \sqrt{11} = \sqrt{77}$, ____

112. $\sqrt{x^7y^8} = \sqrt{x^7} \cdot \sqrt{y^8}$, ____

113. $\frac{\sqrt[n]{a}}{\sqrt[n]{b}} = \sqrt[n]{\frac{a}{b}}$, ____

114. $\frac{\sqrt[3]{12}}{\sqrt[3]{4}} = \sqrt[3]{8}$, ____

Find and correct the error. See the Concept Check in this section.

115. $\dfrac{\sqrt[3]{64}}{\sqrt{64}} = \sqrt[3]{\dfrac{64}{64}} = \sqrt[3]{1} = 1$

116. $\dfrac{\sqrt[4]{16}}{\sqrt{4}} = \sqrt[4]{\dfrac{16}{4}} = \sqrt[4]{4}$

Simplify. See the Concept Check in this section. Assume variables represent positive numbers.

117. $\sqrt[5]{x^{35}}$

118. $\sqrt[6]{y^{48}}$

119. $\sqrt[4]{a^{12}b^4c^{20}}$

120. $\sqrt[3]{a^9b^{21}c^3}$

121. $\sqrt[3]{z^{32}}$

122. $\sqrt[5]{x^{49}}$

123. $\sqrt[7]{q^{17}r^{40}s^7}$

124. $\sqrt[4]{p^{11}q^4r^{45}}$

125. The formula for the radius r of a sphere with surface area A is given by $r = \sqrt{\dfrac{A}{4\pi}}$. Calculate the radius of a standard zorb, whose outside surface area is 32.17 sq m. Round to the nearest tenth. (A zorb is a large inflated ball within a ball in which a person, strapped inside, may choose to roll down a hill. *Source:* Zorb, Ltd.)

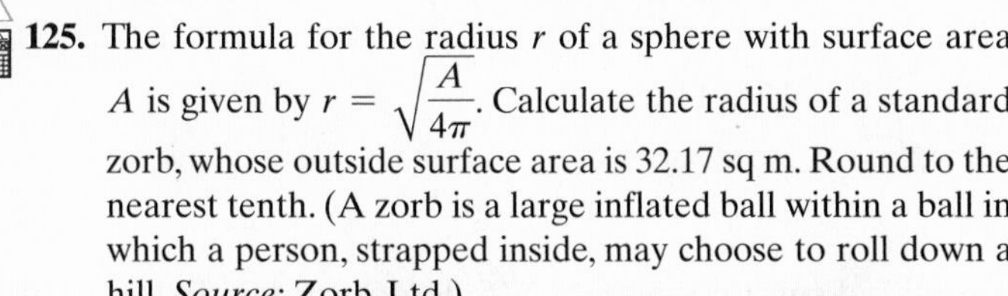

126. The owner of Knightime Classic Movie Rentals has determined that the demand equation for renting older released DVDs is $F(x) = 0.6\sqrt{49 - x^2}$, where x is the price in dollars per two-day rental and $F(x)$ is the number of times the DVD is demanded per week.

a. Approximate to one decimal place the demand per week of an older released DVD if the rental price is \$3 per two-day rental.

b. Approximate to one decimal place the demand per week of an older released DVD if the rental price is \$5 per two-day rental.

c. Explain how the owner of the store can use this equation to predict the number of copies of each DVD that should be in stock.

127. The formula for the lateral surface area A of a cone with height h and radius r is given by

$$A = \pi r\sqrt{r^2 + h^2}$$

a. Find the lateral surface area of a cone whose height is 3 centimeters and whose radius is 4 centimeters.

b. Approximate to two decimal places the lateral surface area of a cone whose height is 7.2 feet and whose radius is 6.8 feet.

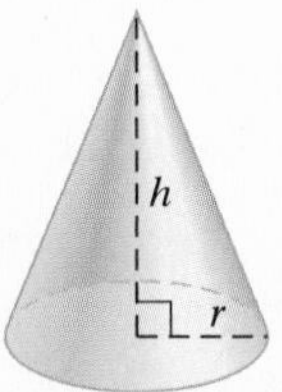

128. Before Mount Vesuvius, a volcano in Italy, erupted violently in 79 C.E., its height was 4190 feet. Vesuvius was roughly cone-shaped, and its base had a radius of approximately 25,200 feet. Use the formula for the lateral surface area of a cone, given in Exercise 127, to approximate the surface area this volcano had before it erupted. (*Source:* Global Volcanism Network)

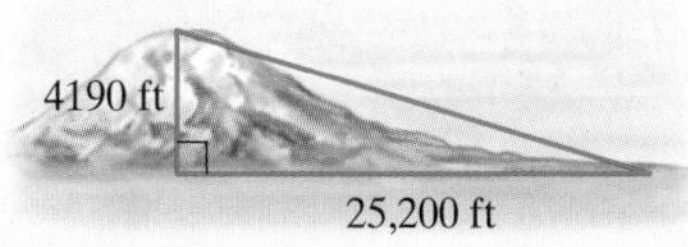

5.4 Adding, Subtracting, and Multiplying Radical Expressions 

OBJECTIVES

1 Add or Subtract Radical Expressions.

2 Multiply Radical Expressions.

OBJECTIVE

1 Adding or Subtracting Radical Expressions 

We have learned that sums or differences of like terms can be simplified. To simplify these sums or differences, we use the distributive property. For example,

$$2x + 3x = (2 + 3)x = 5x \quad \text{and} \quad 7x^2y - 4x^2y = (7 - 4)x^2y = 3x^2y$$

The distributive property can also be used to add **like radicals.**

Like Radicals

Radicals with the same index and the same radicand are like radicals.

For example, $2\sqrt{7} + 3\sqrt{7} = (2 + 3)\sqrt{7} = 5\sqrt{7}$. Also,

Like radicals

$$5\sqrt{3x} - 7\sqrt{3x} = (5 - 7)\sqrt{3x} = -2\sqrt{3x}$$

The expression $2\sqrt{7} + 2\sqrt[3]{7}$ cannot be simplified further since $2\sqrt{7}$ and $2\sqrt[3]{7}$ are not like radicals.

Unlike radicals

EXAMPLE 1 Add or subtract as indicated. Assume all variables represent positive real numbers.

a. $4\sqrt{11} + 8\sqrt{11}$ **b.** $5\sqrt[3]{3x} - 7\sqrt[3]{3x}$ **c.** $4\sqrt{5} + 4\sqrt[3]{5}$

Solution

a. $4\sqrt{11} + 8\sqrt{11} = (4 + 8)\sqrt{11} = 12\sqrt{11}$

b. $5\sqrt[3]{3x} - 7\sqrt[3]{3x} = (5 - 7)\sqrt[3]{3x} = -2\sqrt[3]{3x}$

c. $4\sqrt{5} + 4\sqrt[3]{5}$

This expression cannot be simplified since $4\sqrt{5}$ and $4\sqrt[3]{5}$ do not contain like radicals. □

PRACTICE

1 Add or subtract as indicated.

a. $3\sqrt{17} + 5\sqrt{17}$ **b.** $7\sqrt[3]{5z} - 12\sqrt[3]{5z}$ **c.** $3\sqrt{2} + 5\sqrt[3]{2}$

When adding or subtracting radicals, always check first to see whether any radicals can be simplified.

✓CONCEPT CHECK

True or false?

$$\sqrt{a} + \sqrt{b} = \sqrt{a + b}$$

Explain.

EXAMPLE 2 Add or subtract. Assume that variables represent positive real numbers.

a. $\sqrt{20} + 2\sqrt{45}$ **b.** $\sqrt[3]{54} - 5\sqrt[3]{16} + \sqrt[3]{2}$ **c.** $\sqrt{27x} - 2\sqrt{9x} + \sqrt{72x}$

d. $\sqrt[3]{98} + \sqrt{98}$ **e.** $\sqrt[3]{48y^4} + \sqrt[3]{6y^4}$

Solution First, simplify each radical. Then add or subtract any like radicals.

a.

$$\begin{aligned} \sqrt{20} + 2\sqrt{45} &= \sqrt{4 \cdot 5} + 2\sqrt{9 \cdot 5} && \text{Factor 20 and 45.} \\ &= \sqrt{4} \cdot \sqrt{5} + 2 \cdot \sqrt{9} \cdot \sqrt{5} && \text{Use the product rule.} \\ &= 2 \cdot \sqrt{5} + 2 \cdot 3 \cdot \sqrt{5} && \text{Simplify } \sqrt{4} \text{ and } \sqrt{9}. \\ &= 2\sqrt{5} + 6\sqrt{5} \\ &= 8\sqrt{5} && \text{Add like radicals.} \end{aligned}$$

b. $\sqrt[3]{54} - 5\sqrt[3]{16} + \sqrt[3]{2}$

$$\begin{aligned} &= \sqrt[3]{27} \cdot \sqrt[3]{2} - 5 \cdot \sqrt[3]{8} \cdot \sqrt[3]{2} + \sqrt[3]{2} && \text{Factor and use the product rule.} \\ &= 3 \cdot \sqrt[3]{2} - 5 \cdot 2 \cdot \sqrt[3]{2} + \sqrt[3]{2} && \text{Simplify } \sqrt[3]{27} \text{ and } \sqrt[3]{8}. \\ &= 3\sqrt[3]{2} - 10\sqrt[3]{2} + \sqrt[3]{2} && \text{Write } 5 \cdot 2 \text{ as 10.} \\ &= -6\sqrt[3]{2} && \text{Combine like radicals.} \end{aligned}$$

Answer to Concept Check:
false; answers may vary

c. $\sqrt{27x} - 2\sqrt{9x} + \sqrt{72x}$

$= \sqrt{9}\cdot\sqrt{3x} - 2\cdot\sqrt{9}\cdot\sqrt{x} + \sqrt{36}\cdot\sqrt{2x}$ Factor and use the product rule.

$= 3\cdot\sqrt{3x} - 2\cdot 3\cdot\sqrt{x} + 6\cdot\sqrt{2x}$ Simplify $\sqrt{9}$ and $\sqrt{36}$.

$= 3\sqrt{3x} - 6\sqrt{x} + 6\sqrt{2x}$ Write $2\cdot 3$ as 6.

Helpful Hint

None of these terms contain like radicals. We can simplify no further.

d. $\sqrt[3]{98} + \sqrt{98} = \sqrt[3]{98} + \sqrt{49}\cdot\sqrt{2}$ Factor and use the product rule.

$= \sqrt[3]{98} + 7\sqrt{2}$ No further simplification is possible.

e. $\sqrt[3]{48y^4} + \sqrt[3]{6y^4} = \sqrt[3]{8y^3}\cdot\sqrt[3]{6y} + \sqrt[3]{y^3}\cdot\sqrt[3]{6y}$ Factor and use the product rule.

$= 2y\sqrt[3]{6y} + y\sqrt[3]{6y}$ Simplify $\sqrt[3]{8y^3}$ and $\sqrt[3]{y^3}$.

$= 3y\sqrt[3]{6y}$ Combine like radicals. □

PRACTICE 2 Add or subtract.

a. $\sqrt{24} + 3\sqrt{54}$ **b.** $\sqrt[3]{24} - 4\sqrt[3]{81} + \sqrt[3]{3}$ **c.** $\sqrt{75x} - 3\sqrt{27x} + \sqrt{12x}$

d. $\sqrt{40} + \sqrt[3]{40}$ **e.** $\sqrt[3]{81x^4} + \sqrt[3]{3x^4}$

Let's continue to assume that variables represent positive real numbers.

EXAMPLE 3 Add or subtract as indicated.

a. $\dfrac{\sqrt{45}}{4} - \dfrac{\sqrt{5}}{3}$ **b.** $\sqrt[3]{\dfrac{7x}{8}} + 2\sqrt[3]{7x}$

Solution

a. $\dfrac{\sqrt{45}}{4} - \dfrac{\sqrt{5}}{3} = \dfrac{3\sqrt{5}}{4} - \dfrac{\sqrt{5}}{3}$ To subtract, notice that the LCD is 12.

$= \dfrac{3\sqrt{5}\cdot 3}{4\cdot 3} - \dfrac{\sqrt{5}\cdot 4}{3\cdot 4}$ Write each expression as an equivalent expression with a denominator of 12.

$= \dfrac{9\sqrt{5}}{12} - \dfrac{4\sqrt{5}}{12}$ Multiply factors in the numerator and the denominator.

$= \dfrac{5\sqrt{5}}{12}$ Subtract.

b. $\sqrt[3]{\dfrac{7x}{8}} + 2\sqrt[3]{7x} = \dfrac{\sqrt[3]{7x}}{\sqrt[3]{8}} + 2\sqrt[3]{7x}$ Apply the quotient rule for radicals.

$= \dfrac{\sqrt[3]{7x}}{2} + 2\sqrt[3]{7x}$ Simplify.

$= \dfrac{\sqrt[3]{7x}}{2} + \dfrac{2\sqrt[3]{7x}\cdot 2}{2}$ Write each expression as an equivalent expression with a denominator of 2.

$= \dfrac{\sqrt[3]{7x}}{2} + \dfrac{4\sqrt[3]{7x}}{2}$

$= \dfrac{5\sqrt[3]{7x}}{2}$ Add. □

PRACTICE 3 Add or subtract as indicated.

a. $\dfrac{\sqrt{28}}{3} - \dfrac{\sqrt{7}}{4}$ **b.** $\sqrt[3]{\dfrac{6y}{64}} + 3\sqrt[3]{6y}$

OBJECTIVE

2 Multiplying Radical Expressions 

We can multiply radical expressions by using many of the same properties used to multiply polynomial expressions. For instance, to multiply $\sqrt{2}(\sqrt{6} - 3\sqrt{2})$, we use the distributive property and multiply $\sqrt{2}$ by each term inside the parentheses.

$$\begin{aligned}\sqrt{2}(\sqrt{6} - 3\sqrt{2}) &= \sqrt{2}(\sqrt{6}) - \sqrt{2}(3\sqrt{2}) && \text{Use the distributive property.}\\ &= \sqrt{2 \cdot 6} - 3\sqrt{2 \cdot 2}\\ &= \sqrt{2 \cdot 2 \cdot 3} - 3 \cdot 2 && \text{Use the product rule for radicals.}\\ &= 2\sqrt{3} - 6\end{aligned}$$

EXAMPLE 4 Multiply.

a. $\sqrt{3}(5 + \sqrt{30})$ **b.** $(\sqrt{5} - \sqrt{6})(\sqrt{7} + 1)$ **c.** $(7\sqrt{x} + 5)(3\sqrt{x} - \sqrt{5})$

d. $(4\sqrt{3} - 1)^2$ **e.** $(\sqrt{2x} - 5)(\sqrt{2x} + 5)$ **f.** $(\sqrt{x - 3} + 5)^2$

Solution

a. $$\begin{aligned}\sqrt{3}(5 + \sqrt{30}) &= \sqrt{3}(5) + \sqrt{3}(\sqrt{30})\\ &= 5\sqrt{3} + \sqrt{3 \cdot 30}\\ &= 5\sqrt{3} + \sqrt{3 \cdot 3 \cdot 10}\\ &= 5\sqrt{3} + 3\sqrt{10}\end{aligned}$$

b. To multiply, we can use the FOIL method.

$$\begin{aligned}(\sqrt{5} - \sqrt{6})(\sqrt{7} + 1) &= \overset{\text{First}}{\sqrt{5} \cdot \sqrt{7}} + \overset{\text{Outer}}{\sqrt{5} \cdot 1} - \overset{\text{Inner}}{\sqrt{6} \cdot \sqrt{7}} - \overset{\text{Last}}{\sqrt{6} \cdot 1}\\ &= \sqrt{35} + \sqrt{5} - \sqrt{42} - \sqrt{6}\end{aligned}$$

c. $$\begin{aligned}(7\sqrt{x} + 5)(3\sqrt{x} - \sqrt{5}) &= 7\sqrt{x}(3\sqrt{x}) - 7\sqrt{x}(\sqrt{5}) + 5(3\sqrt{x}) - 5(\sqrt{5})\\ &= 21x - 7\sqrt{5x} + 15\sqrt{x} - 5\sqrt{5}\end{aligned}$$

d. $$\begin{aligned}(4\sqrt{3} - 1)^2 &= (4\sqrt{3} - 1)(4\sqrt{3} - 1)\\ &= 4\sqrt{3}(4\sqrt{3}) - 4\sqrt{3}(1) - 1(4\sqrt{3}) - 1(-1)\\ &= 16 \cdot 3 - 4\sqrt{3} - 4\sqrt{3} + 1\\ &= 48 - 8\sqrt{3} + 1\\ &= 49 - 8\sqrt{3}\end{aligned}$$

e. $$\begin{aligned}(\sqrt{2x} - 5)(\sqrt{2x} + 5) &= \sqrt{2x} \cdot \sqrt{2x} + 5\sqrt{2x} - 5\sqrt{2x} - 5 \cdot 5\\ &= 2x - 25\end{aligned}$$

f. $$\begin{aligned}(\underbrace{\sqrt{x - 3}}_{a} + \underbrace{5}_{b})^2 &= \underbrace{(\sqrt{x - 3})^2}_{a^2} \underbrace{+ 2 \cdot}_{+\,2\cdot} \underbrace{\sqrt{x - 3}}_{a} \underbrace{\cdot 5 + 5^2}_{\cdot b + b^2}\\ &= x - 3 + 10\sqrt{x - 3} + 25 && \text{Simplify.}\\ &= x + 22 + 10\sqrt{x - 3} && \text{Combine like terms.}\end{aligned}$$ □

PRACTICE

4 Multiply.

a. $\sqrt{5}(2 + \sqrt{15})$ **b.** $(\sqrt{2} - \sqrt{5})(\sqrt{6} + 2)$

c. $(3\sqrt{z} - 4)(2\sqrt{z} + 3)$ **d.** $(\sqrt{6} - 3)^2$

e. $(\sqrt{5x} + 3)(\sqrt{5x} - 3)$ **f.** $(\sqrt{x + 2} + 3)^2$

Vocabulary, Readiness & Video Check

Complete the table with "Like" or "Unlike."

	Terms	*Like or Unlike Radical Terms?*
1.	$\sqrt{7}, \sqrt[3]{7}$	
2.	$\sqrt[3]{x^2y}, \sqrt[3]{yx^2}$	
3.	$\sqrt[3]{abc}, \sqrt[3]{cba}$	
4.	$2x\sqrt{5}, 2x\sqrt{10}$	

Simplify. Assume that all variables represent positive real numbers.

5. $2\sqrt{3} + 4\sqrt{3} =$ ______
6. $5\sqrt{7} + 3\sqrt{7} =$ ______
7. $8\sqrt{x} - \sqrt{x} =$ ______
8. $3\sqrt{y} - \sqrt{y} =$ ______
9. $7\sqrt[3]{x} + \sqrt[3]{x} =$ ______
10. $8\sqrt[3]{z} + \sqrt[3]{z} =$ ______

Martin-Gay Interactive Videos

See Video 5.4

Watch the section lecture video and answer the following questions.

OBJECTIVE 1

11. From Examples 1 and 2, why should you always check to see if all terms in your expression are simplified before attempting to add or subtract radicals?

OBJECTIVE 2

12. In Example 4, what are you told to remember about the square root of a positive number?

5.4 Exercise Set

MyMathLab®

Add or subtract. See Examples 1 through 3.

1. $\sqrt{8} - \sqrt{32}$

2. $\sqrt{27} - \sqrt{75}$

3. $2\sqrt{2x^3} + 4x\sqrt{8x}$

4. $3\sqrt{45x^3} + x\sqrt{5x}$

5. $2\sqrt{50} - 3\sqrt{125} + \sqrt{98}$

6. $4\sqrt{32} - \sqrt{18} + 2\sqrt{128}$

7. $\sqrt[3]{16x} - \sqrt[3]{54x}$

8. $2\sqrt[3]{3a^4} - 3a\sqrt[3]{81a}$

9. $\sqrt{9b^3} - \sqrt{25b^3} + \sqrt{49b^3}$

10. $\sqrt{4x^7} + 9x^2\sqrt{x^3} - 5x\sqrt{x^5}$

11. $\dfrac{5\sqrt{2}}{3} + \dfrac{2\sqrt{2}}{5}$

12. $\dfrac{\sqrt{3}}{2} + \dfrac{4\sqrt{3}}{3}$

13. $\sqrt[3]{\dfrac{11}{8}} - \dfrac{\sqrt[3]{11}}{6}$

14. $\dfrac{2\sqrt[3]{4}}{7} - \dfrac{\sqrt[3]{4}}{14}$

15. $\dfrac{\sqrt{20x}}{9} + \sqrt{\dfrac{5x}{9}}$

16. $\dfrac{3x\sqrt{7}}{5} + \sqrt{\dfrac{7x^2}{100}}$

17. $7\sqrt{9} - 7 + \sqrt{3}$

18. $\sqrt{16} - 5\sqrt{10} + 7$

19. $2 + 3\sqrt{y^2} - 6\sqrt{y^2} + 5$

20. $3\sqrt{7} - \sqrt[3]{x} + 4\sqrt{7} - 3\sqrt[3]{x}$

21. $3\sqrt{108} - 2\sqrt{18} - 3\sqrt{48}$

22. $-\sqrt{75} + \sqrt{12} - 3\sqrt{3}$

23. $-5\sqrt[3]{625} + \sqrt[3]{40}$

24. $-2\sqrt[3]{108} - \sqrt[3]{32}$

25. $a^3\sqrt{9ab^3} - \sqrt{25a^7b^3} + \sqrt{16a^7b^3}$

26. $\sqrt{4x^7y^5} + 9x^2\sqrt{x^3y^5} - 5xy\sqrt{x^5y^3}$

27. $5y\sqrt{8y} + 2\sqrt{50y^3}$

28. $3\sqrt{8x^2y^3} - 2x\sqrt{32y^3}$

29. $\sqrt[3]{54xy^3} - 5\sqrt[3]{2xy^3} + y\sqrt[3]{128x}$

30. $2\sqrt[3]{24x^3y^4} + 4x\sqrt[3]{81y^4}$

31. $6\sqrt[3]{11} + 8\sqrt{11} - 12\sqrt{11}$

32. $3\sqrt[3]{5} + 4\sqrt{5} - 8\sqrt{5}$

33. $-2\sqrt[4]{x^7} + 3\sqrt[4]{16x^7} - x\sqrt[4]{x^3}$

34. $6\sqrt[3]{24x^3} - 2\sqrt[3]{81x^3} - x\sqrt[3]{3}$

35. $\frac{4\sqrt{3}}{3} - \frac{\sqrt{12}}{3}$

36. $\frac{\sqrt{45}}{10} + \frac{7\sqrt{5}}{10}$

37. $\frac{\sqrt[3]{8x^4}}{7} + \frac{3x\sqrt[3]{x}}{7}$

38. $\frac{\sqrt[4]{48}}{5x} - \frac{2\sqrt[4]{3}}{10x}$

39. $\sqrt{\frac{28}{x^2}} + \sqrt{\frac{7}{4x^2}}$

40. $\frac{\sqrt{99}}{5x} - \sqrt{\frac{44}{x^2}}$

41. $\sqrt[3]{\frac{16}{27}} - \frac{\sqrt[3]{54}}{6}$

42. $\frac{\sqrt[3]{3}}{10} + \sqrt[3]{\frac{24}{125}}$

43. $-\frac{\sqrt[3]{2x^4}}{9} + \sqrt[3]{\frac{250x^4}{27}}$

44. $\frac{\sqrt[3]{y^5}}{8} + \frac{5y\sqrt[3]{y^2}}{4}$

△ **45.** Find the perimeter of the trapezoid.

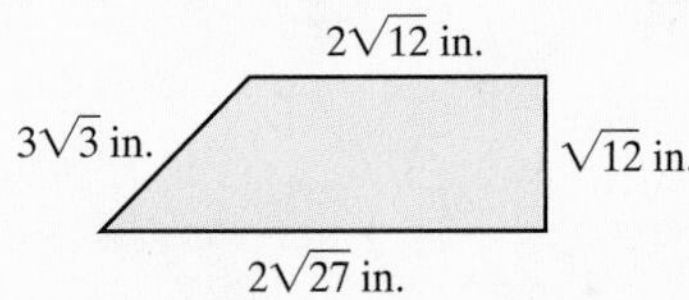

△ **46.** Find the perimeter of the triangle.

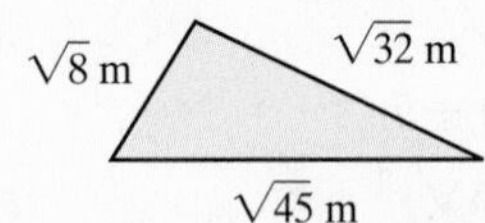

Multiply and then simplify if possible. See Example 4.

47. $\sqrt{7}(\sqrt{5} + \sqrt{3})$

48. $\sqrt{5}(\sqrt{15} - \sqrt{35})$

49. $(\sqrt{5} - \sqrt{2})^2$

50. $(3x - \sqrt{2})(3x - \sqrt{2})$

51. $\sqrt{3x}(\sqrt{3} - \sqrt{x})$

52. $\sqrt{5y}(\sqrt{y} + \sqrt{5})$

53. $(2\sqrt{x} - 5)(3\sqrt{x} + 1)$

54. $(8\sqrt{y} + z)(4\sqrt{y} - 1)$

55. $(\sqrt[3]{a} - 4)(\sqrt[3]{a} + 5)$

56. $(\sqrt[3]{a} + 2)(\sqrt[3]{a} + 7)$

57. $6(\sqrt{2} - 2)$

58. $\sqrt{5}(6 - \sqrt{5})$

59. $\sqrt{2}(\sqrt{2} + x\sqrt{6})$

60. $\sqrt{3}(\sqrt{3} - 2\sqrt{5x})$

61. $(2\sqrt{7} + 3\sqrt{5})(\sqrt{7} - 2\sqrt{5})$

62. $(\sqrt{6} - 4\sqrt{2})(3\sqrt{6} + \sqrt{2})$

63. $(\sqrt{x} - y)(\sqrt{x} + y)$

64. $(\sqrt{3x} + 2)(\sqrt{3x} - 2)$

65. $(\sqrt{3} + x)^2$

66. $(\sqrt{y} - 3x)^2$

67. $(\sqrt{5x} - 2\sqrt{3x})(\sqrt{5x} - 3\sqrt{3x})$

68. $(5\sqrt{7x} - \sqrt{2x})(4\sqrt{7x} + 6\sqrt{2x})$

69. $(\sqrt[3]{4} + 2)(\sqrt[3]{2} - 1)$

70. $(\sqrt[3]{3} + \sqrt[3]{2})(\sqrt[3]{9} - \sqrt[3]{4})$

71. $(\sqrt[3]{x} + 1)(\sqrt[3]{x^2} - \sqrt[3]{x} + 1)$

72. $(\sqrt[3]{3x} + 2)(\sqrt[3]{9x^2} - 2\sqrt[3]{3x} + 4)$

73. $(\sqrt{x - 1} + 5)^2$

74. $(\sqrt{3x + 1} + 2)^2$

75. $(\sqrt{2x + 5} - 1)^2$

76. $(\sqrt{x - 6} - 7)^2$

REVIEW AND PREVIEW

Factor each numerator and denominator. Then simplify if possible. See Section 4.1.

77. $\frac{2x - 14}{2}$

78. $\frac{8x - 24y}{4}$

79. $\frac{7x - 7y}{x^2 - y^2}$

80. $\frac{x^3 - 8}{4x - 8}$

81. $\frac{6a^2b - 9ab}{3ab}$

82. $\frac{14r - 28r^2s^2}{7rs}$

83. $\frac{-4 + 2\sqrt{3}}{6}$

84. $\frac{-5 + 10\sqrt{7}}{5}$

CONCEPT EXTENSIONS

△ **85.** Find the perimeter and area of the rectangle.

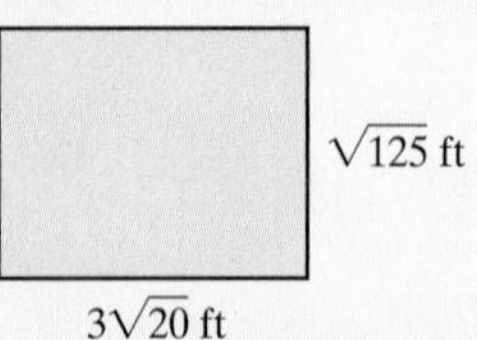

△ **86.** Find the area and perimeter of the trapezoid. (*Hint:* The area of a trapezoid is the product of half the height $6\sqrt{3}$ meters and the sum of the bases $2\sqrt{63}$ and $7\sqrt{7}$ meters.)

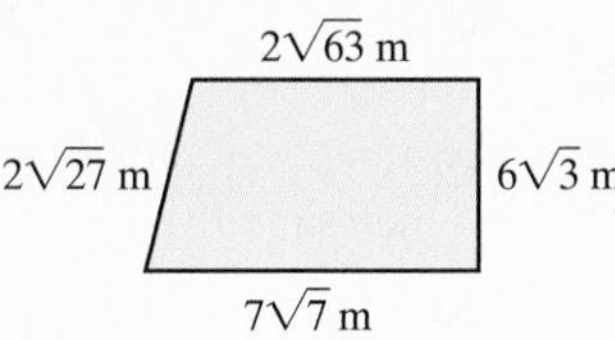

87. a. Add: $\sqrt{3} + \sqrt{3}$.

b. Multiply: $\sqrt{3} \cdot \sqrt{3}$.

c. Describe the differences in parts (a) and (b).

88. a. Add: $2\sqrt{5} + \sqrt{5}$

b. Multiply: $2\sqrt{5} \cdot \sqrt{5}$

c. Describe the differences in parts (a) and (b).

89. Multiply: $(\sqrt{2} + \sqrt{3} - 1)^2$.

90. Multiply: $(\sqrt{5} - \sqrt{2} + 1)^2$

91. Explain how simplifying $2x + 3x$ is similar to simplifying $2\sqrt{x} + 3\sqrt{x}$.

92. Explain how multiplying $(x - 2)(x + 3)$ is similar to multiplying $(\sqrt{x} - \sqrt{2})(\sqrt{x} + 3)$.

5.5 Rationalizing Denominators and Numerators of Radical Expressions

OBJECTIVES

1 Rationalize Denominators.

2 Rationalize Denominators Having Two Terms.

3 Rationalize Numerators.

OBJECTIVE

1 Rationalizing Denominators of Radical Expressions 

Often in mathematics, it is helpful to write a radical expression such as $\frac{\sqrt{3}}{\sqrt{2}}$ either without a radical in the denominator or without a radical in the numerator. The process of writing this expression as an equivalent expression but without a radical in the denominator is called **rationalizing the denominator.** To rationalize the denominator of $\frac{\sqrt{3}}{\sqrt{2}}$, we use the fundamental principle of fractions and multiply the numerator and the denominator by $\sqrt{2}$. Recall that this is the same as multiplying by $\frac{\sqrt{2}}{\sqrt{2}}$, which simplifies to 1.

$$\frac{\sqrt{3}}{\sqrt{2}} = \frac{\sqrt{3} \cdot \sqrt{2}}{\sqrt{2} \cdot \sqrt{2}} = \frac{\sqrt{6}}{\sqrt{4}} = \frac{\sqrt{6}}{2}$$

In this section, we continue to assume that variables represent positive real numbers.

EXAMPLE 1 Rationalize the denominator of each expression.

a. $\frac{2}{\sqrt{5}}$ **b.** $\frac{2\sqrt{16}}{\sqrt{9x}}$ **c.** $\sqrt[3]{\frac{1}{2}}$

Solution

a. To rationalize the denominator, we multiply the numerator and denominator by a factor that makes the radicand in the denominator a perfect square.

$$\frac{2}{\sqrt{5}} = \frac{2 \cdot \sqrt{5}}{\sqrt{5} \cdot \sqrt{5}} = \frac{2\sqrt{5}}{5} \quad \text{The denominator is now rationalized.}$$

b. First, we simplify the radicals and then rationalize the denominator.

$$\frac{2\sqrt{16}}{\sqrt{9x}} = \frac{2(4)}{3\sqrt{x}} = \frac{8}{3\sqrt{x}}$$

To rationalize the denominator, multiply the numerator and denominator by $\sqrt{x}$. Then

$$\frac{8}{3\sqrt{x}} = \frac{8 \cdot \sqrt{x}}{3\sqrt{x} \cdot \sqrt{x}} = \frac{8\sqrt{x}}{3x}$$

(Continued on next page)

c. $\sqrt[3]{\frac{1}{2}} = \frac{\sqrt[3]{1}}{\sqrt[3]{2}} = \frac{1}{\sqrt[3]{2}}$. Now we rationalize the denominator. Since $\sqrt[3]{2}$ is a cube root, we want to multiply by a value that will make the radicand 2 a perfect cube. If we multiply $\sqrt[3]{2}$ by $\sqrt[3]{2^2}$, we get $\sqrt[3]{2^3} = \sqrt[3]{8} = 2$.

$$\frac{1 \cdot \sqrt[3]{2^2}}{\sqrt[3]{2} \cdot \sqrt[3]{2^2}} = \frac{\sqrt[3]{4}}{\sqrt[3]{2^3}} = \frac{\sqrt[3]{4}}{2}$$ Multiply the numerator and denominator by $\sqrt[3]{2^2}$ and then simplify. □

PRACTICE 1 Rationalize the denominator of each expression.

a. $\frac{5}{\sqrt{3}}$ **b.** $\frac{3\sqrt{25}}{\sqrt{4x}}$ **c.** $\sqrt[3]{\frac{2}{9}}$

✓CONCEPT CHECK

Determine by which number both the numerator and denominator can be multiplied to rationalize the denominator of the radical expression.

a. $\frac{1}{\sqrt[3]{7}}$ **b.** $\frac{1}{\sqrt[4]{8}}$

EXAMPLE 2 Rationalize the denominator of $\sqrt{\frac{7x}{3y}}$.

Solution

$$\sqrt{\frac{7x}{3y}} = \frac{\sqrt{7x}}{\sqrt{3y}}$$ Use the quotient rule. No radical may be simplified further.

$$= \frac{\sqrt{7x} \cdot \sqrt{3y}}{\sqrt{3y} \cdot \sqrt{3y}}$$ Multiply numerator and denominator by $\sqrt{3y}$ so that the radicand in the denominator is a perfect square.

$$= \frac{\sqrt{21xy}}{3y}$$ Use the product rule in the numerator and denominator. Remember that $\sqrt{3y} \cdot \sqrt{3y} = 3y$. □

PRACTICE 2 Rationalize the denominator of $\sqrt{\frac{3z}{5y}}$.

EXAMPLE 3 Rationalize the denominator of $\frac{\sqrt[4]{x}}{\sqrt[4]{81y^5}}$.

Solution First, simplify each radical if possible.

$$\frac{\sqrt[4]{x}}{\sqrt[4]{81y^5}} = \frac{\sqrt[4]{x}}{\sqrt[4]{81y^4} \cdot \sqrt[4]{y}}$$ Use the product rule in the denominator.

$$= \frac{\sqrt[4]{x}}{3y\sqrt[4]{y}}$$ Write $\sqrt[4]{81y^4}$ as $3y$.

$$= \frac{\sqrt[4]{x} \cdot \sqrt[4]{y^3}}{3y\sqrt[4]{y} \cdot \sqrt[4]{y^3}}$$ Multiply numerator and denominator by $\sqrt[4]{y^3}$ so that the radicand in the denominator is a perfect fourth power.

$$= \frac{\sqrt[4]{xy^3}}{3y\sqrt[4]{y^4}}$$ Use the product rule in the numerator and denominator.

$$= \frac{\sqrt[4]{xy^3}}{3y^2}$$ In the denominator, $\sqrt[4]{y^4} = y$ and $3y \cdot y = 3y^2$. □

PRACTICE 3 Rationalize the denominator of $\frac{\sqrt[3]{z^2}}{\sqrt[3]{27x^4}}$.

Answer to Concept Check:

a. $\sqrt[3]{7^2}$ or $\sqrt[3]{49}$ **b.** $\sqrt[4]{2}$

OBJECTIVE

2 Rationalizing Denominators Having Two Terms 

Remember the product of the sum and difference of two terms?

$$(a + b)(a - b) = a^2 - b^2$$

These two expressions are called **conjugates** of each other.

To rationalize a numerator or denominator that is a sum or difference of two terms, we use conjugates. To see how and why this works, let's rationalize the denominator of the expression $\frac{5}{\sqrt{3} - 2}$. To do so, we multiply both the numerator and the denominator by $\sqrt{3} + 2$, the **conjugate** of the denominator $\sqrt{3} - 2$, and see what happens.

$$\frac{5}{\sqrt{3} - 2} = \frac{5(\sqrt{3} + 2)}{(\sqrt{3} - 2)(\sqrt{3} + 2)}$$

$$= \frac{5(\sqrt{3} + 2)}{(\sqrt{3})^2 - 2^2} \quad \text{Multiply the sum and difference of two terms: } (a + b)(a - b) = a^2 - b^2.$$

$$= \frac{5(\sqrt{3} + 2)}{3 - 4}$$

$$= \frac{5(\sqrt{3} + 2)}{-1}$$

$$= -5(\sqrt{3} + 2) \quad \text{or} \quad -5\sqrt{3} - 10$$

Notice in the denominator that the product of $(\sqrt{3} - 2)$ and its conjugate, $(\sqrt{3} + 2)$, is -1. In general, the product of an expression and its conjugate will contain no radical terms. This is why, when rationalizing a denominator or a numerator containing two terms, we multiply by its conjugate. Examples of conjugates are

$$\sqrt{a} - \sqrt{b} \quad \text{and} \quad \sqrt{a} + \sqrt{b}$$

$$x + \sqrt{y} \quad \text{and} \quad x - \sqrt{y}$$

EXAMPLE 4 Rationalize each denominator.

a. $\frac{2}{3\sqrt{2} + 4}$ **b.** $\frac{\sqrt{6} + 2}{\sqrt{5} - \sqrt{3}}$ **c.** $\frac{2\sqrt{m}}{3\sqrt{x} + \sqrt{m}}$

Solution

a. Multiply the numerator and denominator by the conjugate of the denominator, $3\sqrt{2} + 4$.

$$\frac{2}{3\sqrt{2} + 4} = \frac{2(3\sqrt{2} - 4)}{(3\sqrt{2} + 4)(3\sqrt{2} - 4)}$$

$$= \frac{2(3\sqrt{2} - 4)}{(3\sqrt{2})^2 - 4^2}$$

$$= \frac{2(3\sqrt{2} - 4)}{18 - 16}$$

$$= \frac{2(3\sqrt{2} - 4)}{2}, \quad \text{or} \quad 3\sqrt{2} - 4$$

It is often useful to leave a numerator in factored form to help determine whether the expression can be simplified.

(Continued on next page)

b. Multiply the numerator and denominator by the conjugate of $\sqrt{5} - \sqrt{3}$.

$$\frac{\sqrt{6} + 2}{\sqrt{5} - \sqrt{3}} = \frac{(\sqrt{6} + 2)(\sqrt{5} + \sqrt{3})}{(\sqrt{5} - \sqrt{3})(\sqrt{5} + \sqrt{3})}$$

$$= \frac{\sqrt{6}\sqrt{5} + \sqrt{6}\sqrt{3} + 2\sqrt{5} + 2\sqrt{3}}{(\sqrt{5})^2 - (\sqrt{3})^2}$$

$$= \frac{\sqrt{30} + \sqrt{18} + 2\sqrt{5} + 2\sqrt{3}}{5 - 3}$$

$$= \frac{\sqrt{30} + 3\sqrt{2} + 2\sqrt{5} + 2\sqrt{3}}{2}$$

c. Multiply by the conjugate of $3\sqrt{x} + \sqrt{m}$ to eliminate the radicals from the denominator.

$$\frac{2\sqrt{m}}{3\sqrt{x} + \sqrt{m}} = \frac{2\sqrt{m}(3\sqrt{x} - \sqrt{m})}{(3\sqrt{x} + \sqrt{m})(3\sqrt{x} - \sqrt{m})} = \frac{6\sqrt{mx} - 2m}{(3\sqrt{x})^2 - (\sqrt{m})^2}$$

$$= \frac{6\sqrt{mx} - 2m}{9x - m}$$

□

PRACTICE

4 Rationalize the denominator.

a. $\frac{5}{3\sqrt{5} + 2}$ **b.** $\frac{\sqrt{2} + 5}{\sqrt{3} - \sqrt{5}}$ **c.** $\frac{3\sqrt{x}}{2\sqrt{x} + \sqrt{y}}$

OBJECTIVE

3 Rationalizing Numerators

As mentioned earlier, it is also often helpful to write an expression such as $\frac{\sqrt{3}}{\sqrt{2}}$ as an equivalent expression without a radical in the numerator. This process is called **rationalizing the numerator.** To rationalize the numerator of $\frac{\sqrt{3}}{\sqrt{2}}$, we multiply the numerator and the denominator by $\sqrt{3}$.

$$\frac{\sqrt{3}}{\sqrt{2}} = \frac{\sqrt{3} \cdot \sqrt{3}}{\sqrt{2} \cdot \sqrt{3}} = \frac{\sqrt{9}}{\sqrt{6}} = \frac{3}{\sqrt{6}}$$

EXAMPLE 5 Rationalize the numerator of $\frac{\sqrt{7}}{\sqrt{45}}$.

Solution First we simplify $\sqrt{45}$.

$$\frac{\sqrt{7}}{\sqrt{45}} = \frac{\sqrt{7}}{\sqrt{9 \cdot 5}} = \frac{\sqrt{7}}{3\sqrt{5}}$$

Next we rationalize the numerator by multiplying the numerator and the denominator by $\sqrt{7}$.

$$\frac{\sqrt{7}}{3\sqrt{5}} = \frac{\sqrt{7} \cdot \sqrt{7}}{3\sqrt{5} \cdot \sqrt{7}} = \frac{7}{3\sqrt{5 \cdot 7}} = \frac{7}{3\sqrt{35}}$$

□

PRACTICE

5 Rationalize the numerator of $\frac{\sqrt{32}}{\sqrt{80}}$.

EXAMPLE 6 Rationalize the numerator of $\frac{\sqrt[3]{2x^2}}{\sqrt[3]{5y}}$.

Solution The numerator and the denominator of this expression are already simplified. To rationalize the numerator, $\sqrt[3]{2x^2}$, we multiply the numerator and denominator by a factor that will make the radicand a perfect cube. If we multiply $\sqrt[3]{2x^2}$ by $\sqrt[3]{4x}$, we get $\sqrt[3]{8x^3} = 2x$.

$$\frac{\sqrt[3]{2x^2}}{\sqrt[3]{5y}} = \frac{\sqrt[3]{2x^2} \cdot \sqrt[3]{4x}}{\sqrt[3]{5y} \cdot \sqrt[3]{4x}} = \frac{\sqrt[3]{8x^3}}{\sqrt[3]{20xy}} = \frac{2x}{\sqrt[3]{20xy}}$$ □

PRACTICE 6 Rationalize the numerator of $\frac{\sqrt[3]{5b}}{\sqrt[3]{2a}}$.

EXAMPLE 7 Rationalize the numerator of $\frac{\sqrt{x} + 2}{5}$.

Solution We multiply the numerator and the denominator by the conjugate of the numerator, $\sqrt{x} + 2$.

$$\frac{\sqrt{x} + 2}{5} = \frac{(\sqrt{x} + 2)(\sqrt{x} - 2)}{5(\sqrt{x} - 2)}$$ Multiply by $\sqrt{x} - 2$, the conjugate of $\sqrt{x} + 2$.

$$= \frac{(\sqrt{x})^2 - 2^2}{5(\sqrt{x} - 2)}$$ $(a + b)(a - b) = a^2 - b^2$

$$= \frac{x - 4}{5(\sqrt{x} - 2)}$$ □

PRACTICE 7 Rationalize the numerator of $\frac{\sqrt{x} - 3}{4}$.

Vocabulary, Readiness & Video Check

Use the choices below to fill in each blank. Not all choices will be used.

rationalizing the numerator	conjugate	$\frac{\sqrt{3}}{\sqrt{3}}$
rationalizing the denominator	$\frac{5}{5}$	

1. The ______________ of $a + b$ is $a - b$.
2. The process of writing an equivalent expression, but without a radical in the denominator, is called ______________.
3. The process of writing an equivalent expression, but without a radical in the numerator, is called ______________.
4. To rationalize the denominator of $\frac{5}{\sqrt{3}}$, we multiply by ______________.

Martin-Gay Interactive Videos

See Video 5.5

Watch the section lecture video and answer the following questions.

OBJECTIVE 1
5. From Examples 1–3, what is the goal of rationalizing a denominator?

OBJECTIVE 2
6. From Example 4, why will multiplying a denominator by its conjugate always rationalize the denominator?

OBJECTIVE 3
7. From Example 5, is the process of rationalizing a numerator any different from rationalizing a denominator?

5.5 Exercise Set

MyMathLab®

Rationalize each denominator. See Examples 1 through 3.

1. $\frac{\sqrt{2}}{\sqrt{7}}$

2. $\frac{\sqrt{3}}{\sqrt{2}}$

3. $\sqrt{\frac{1}{5}}$

4. $\sqrt{\frac{1}{2}}$

5. $\sqrt{\frac{4}{x}}$

6. $\sqrt{\frac{25}{y}}$

7. $\frac{4}{\sqrt[3]{3}}$

8. $\frac{6}{\sqrt[3]{9}}$

9. $\frac{3}{\sqrt{8x}}$

10. $\frac{5}{\sqrt{27a}}$

11. $\frac{3}{\sqrt[3]{4x^2}}$

12. $\frac{5}{\sqrt[3]{3y}}$

13. $\frac{9}{\sqrt{3a}}$

14. $\frac{x}{\sqrt{5}}$

15. $\frac{3}{\sqrt[3]{2}}$

16. $\frac{5}{\sqrt[3]{9}}$

17. $\frac{2\sqrt{3}}{\sqrt{7}}$

18. $\frac{-5\sqrt{2}}{\sqrt{11}}$

19. $\sqrt{\frac{2x}{5y}}$

20. $\sqrt{\frac{13a}{2b}}$

21. $\sqrt[3]{\frac{3}{5}}$

22. $\sqrt[3]{\frac{7}{10}}$

23. $\sqrt{\frac{3x}{50}}$

24. $\sqrt{\frac{11y}{45}}$

25. $\frac{1}{\sqrt{12z}}$

26. $\frac{1}{\sqrt{32x}}$

27. $\frac{\sqrt[3]{2y^2}}{\sqrt[3]{9x^2}}$

28. $\frac{\sqrt[3]{3x}}{\sqrt[3]{4y^4}}$

29. $\sqrt[4]{\frac{81}{8}}$

30. $\sqrt[4]{\frac{1}{9}}$

31. $\sqrt[4]{\frac{16}{9x^7}}$

32. $\sqrt[5]{\frac{32}{m^6n^{13}}}$

33. $\frac{5a}{\sqrt[5]{8a^9b^{11}}}$

34. $\frac{9y}{\sqrt[4]{4y^9}}$

Write the conjugate of each expression.

35. $\sqrt{2} + x$

36. $\sqrt{3} + y$

37. $5 - \sqrt{a}$

38. $6 - \sqrt{b}$

39. $-7\sqrt{5} + 8\sqrt{x}$

40. $-9\sqrt{2} - 6\sqrt{y}$

Rationalize each denominator. See Example 4.

41. $\frac{6}{2 - \sqrt{7}}$

42. $\frac{3}{\sqrt{7} - 4}$

43. $\frac{-7}{\sqrt{x} - 3}$

44. $\frac{-8}{\sqrt{y} + 4}$

45. $\frac{\sqrt{2} - \sqrt{3}}{\sqrt{2} + \sqrt{3}}$

46. $\frac{\sqrt{3} + \sqrt{4}}{\sqrt{2} - \sqrt{3}}$

47. $\frac{\sqrt{a} + 1}{2\sqrt{a} - \sqrt{b}}$

48. $\frac{2\sqrt{a} - 3}{2\sqrt{a} + \sqrt{b}}$

49. $\frac{8}{1 + \sqrt{10}}$

50. $\frac{-3}{\sqrt{6} - 2}$

51. $\frac{\sqrt{x}}{\sqrt{x} + \sqrt{y}}$

52. $\frac{2\sqrt{a}}{2\sqrt{x} - \sqrt{y}}$

53. $\frac{2\sqrt{3} + \sqrt{6}}{4\sqrt{3} - \sqrt{6}}$

54. $\frac{4\sqrt{5} + \sqrt{2}}{2\sqrt{5} - \sqrt{2}}$

Rationalize each numerator. See Examples 5 and 6.

55. $\sqrt{\frac{5}{3}}$

56. $\sqrt{\frac{3}{2}}$

57. $\sqrt{\frac{18}{5}}$

58. $\sqrt{\frac{12}{7}}$

59. $\frac{\sqrt{4x}}{7}$

60. $\frac{\sqrt{3x^5}}{6}$

61. $\frac{\sqrt[3]{5y^2}}{\sqrt[3]{4x}}$

62. $\frac{\sqrt[3]{4x}}{\sqrt[3]{z^4}}$

63. $\sqrt{\frac{2}{5}}$

64. $\sqrt{\frac{3}{7}}$

65. $\frac{\sqrt{2x}}{11}$

66. $\frac{\sqrt{y}}{7}$

67. $\sqrt[3]{\frac{7}{8}}$

68. $\sqrt[3]{\frac{25}{2}}$

69. $\frac{\sqrt[3]{3x^5}}{10}$

70. $\sqrt[3]{\frac{9y}{7}}$

71. $\sqrt{\frac{18x^4y^6}{3z}}$

72. $\sqrt{\frac{8x^5y}{2z}}$

Rationalize each numerator. See Example 7.

73. $\frac{2 - \sqrt{11}}{6}$

74. $\frac{\sqrt{15} + 1}{2}$

75. $\frac{2 - \sqrt{7}}{-5}$

76. $\frac{\sqrt{5} + 2}{\sqrt{2}}$

77. $\frac{\sqrt{x} + 3}{\sqrt{x}}$

78. $\frac{5 + \sqrt{2}}{\sqrt{2x}}$

79. $\frac{\sqrt{2} - 1}{\sqrt{2} + 1}$

80. $\frac{\sqrt{8} - \sqrt{3}}{\sqrt{2} + \sqrt{3}}$

81. $\frac{\sqrt{x} + 1}{\sqrt{x} - 1}$

82. $\frac{\sqrt{x} + \sqrt{y}}{\sqrt{x} - \sqrt{y}}$

REVIEW AND PREVIEW

Solve each equation. See Section 3.6.

83. $2x - 7 = 3(x - 4)$

84. $9x - 4 = 7(x - 2)$

85. $(x - 6)(2x + 1) = 0$

86. $(y + 2)(5y + 4) = 0$

87. $x^2 - 8x = -12$

88. $x^3 = x$

CONCEPT EXTENSIONS

△ **89.** The formula of the radius r of a sphere with surface area A is

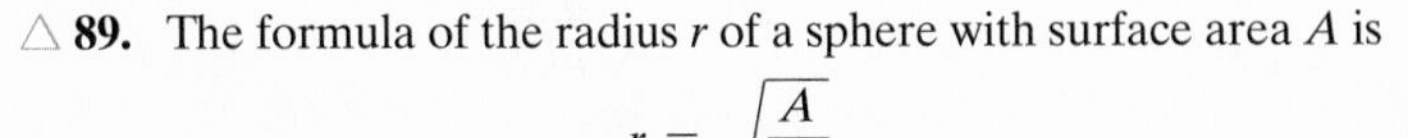

$$r = \sqrt{\frac{A}{4\pi}}$$

Rationalize the denominator of the radical expression in this formula.

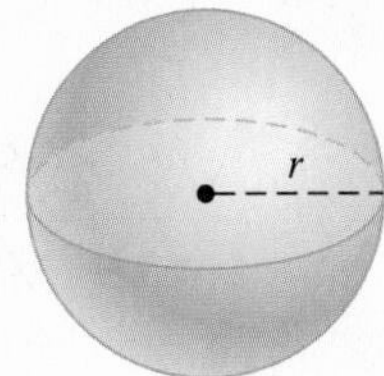

△ **90.** The formula for the radius r of a cone with height 7 centimeters and volume V is

$$r = \sqrt{\frac{3V}{7\pi}}$$

Rationalize the numerator of the radical expression in this formula.

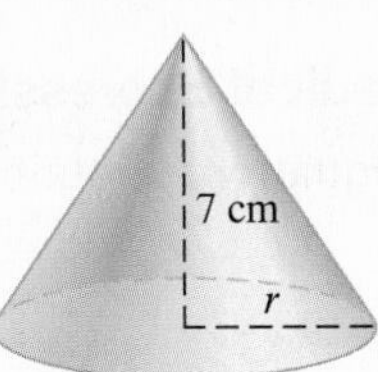

91. Given $\frac{\sqrt{5y^3}}{\sqrt{12x^3}}$, rationalize the denominator by following parts (a) and (b).

a. Multiply the numerator and denominator by $\sqrt{12x^3}$.

b. Multiply the numerator and denominator by $\sqrt{3x}$.

c. What can you conclude from parts (a) and (b)?

92. Given $\frac{\sqrt[3]{5y}}{\sqrt[3]{4}}$, rationalize the denominator by following parts (a) and (b).

a. Multiply the numerator and denominator by $\sqrt[3]{16}$.

b. Multiply the numerator and denominator by $\sqrt[3]{2}$.

c. What can you conclude from parts (a) and (b)?

Determine the smallest number both the numerator and denominator should be multiplied by to rationalize the denominator of the radical expression. See the Concept Check in this section.

93. $\frac{9}{\sqrt[3]{5}}$

94. $\frac{5}{\sqrt{27}}$

95. When rationalizing the denominator of $\frac{\sqrt{5}}{\sqrt{7}}$, explain why both the numerator and the denominator must be multiplied by $\sqrt{7}$.

96. When rationalizing the numerator of $\frac{\sqrt{5}}{\sqrt{7}}$, explain why both the numerator and the denominator must be multiplied by $\sqrt{5}$.

97. Explain why rationalizing the denominator does not change the value of the original expression.

98. Explain why rationalizing the numerator does not change the value of the original expression.

Integrated Review RADICALS AND RATIONAL EXPONENTS

Sections 5.1–5.5

Throughout this review, assume that all variables represent positive real numbers.

Find each root.

1. $\sqrt{81}$

2. $\sqrt[3]{-8}$

3. $\sqrt[4]{\frac{1}{16}}$

4. $\sqrt{x^6}$

5. $\sqrt[3]{y^9}$

6. $\sqrt{4y^{10}}$

7. $\sqrt[5]{-32y^5}$

8. $\sqrt[4]{81b^{12}}$

Use radical notation to write each expression. Simplify if possible.

9. $36^{1/2}$

10. $(3y)^{1/4}$

11. $64^{-2/3}$

12. $(x + 1)^{3/5}$

Use the properties of exponents to simplify each expression. Write with positive exponents.

13. $y^{-1/6} \cdot y^{7/6}$

14. $\frac{(2x^{1/3})^4}{x^{5/6}}$

15. $\frac{x^{1/4}x^{3/4}}{x^{-1/4}}$

16. $4^{1/3} \cdot 4^{2/5}$

Use rational exponents to simplify each radical.

17. $\sqrt[3]{8x^6}$

18. $\sqrt[12]{a^9b^6}$

Use rational exponents to write each as a single radical expression.

19. $\sqrt[4]{x} \cdot \sqrt{x}$ **20.** $\sqrt{5} \cdot \sqrt[3]{2}$

Simplify.

21. $\sqrt{40}$ **22.** $\sqrt[4]{16x^7y^{10}}$ **23.** $\sqrt[3]{54x^4}$ **24.** $\sqrt[5]{-64b^{10}}$

Multiply or divide. Then simplify if possible.

25. $\sqrt{5} \cdot \sqrt{x}$ **26.** $\sqrt[3]{8x} \cdot \sqrt[3]{8x^2}$ **27.** $\dfrac{\sqrt{98y^6}}{\sqrt{2y}}$ **28.** $\dfrac{\sqrt[4]{48a^9b^3}}{\sqrt[4]{ab^3}}$

Perform each indicated operation.

29. $\sqrt{20} - \sqrt{75} + 5\sqrt{7}$ **30.** $\sqrt[3]{54y^4} - y\sqrt[3]{16y}$ **31.** $\sqrt{3}(\sqrt{5} - \sqrt{2})$

32. $(\sqrt{7} + \sqrt{3})^2$ **33.** $(2x - \sqrt{5})(2x + \sqrt{5})$ **34.** $(\sqrt{x+1} - 1)^2$

Rationalize each denominator.

35. $\sqrt{\dfrac{7}{3}}$ **36.** $\dfrac{5}{\sqrt[3]{2x^2}}$ **37.** $\dfrac{\sqrt{3} - \sqrt{7}}{2\sqrt{3} + \sqrt{7}}$

Rationalize each numerator.

38. $\sqrt{\dfrac{7}{3}}$ **39.** $\sqrt[3]{\dfrac{9y}{11}}$ **40.** $\dfrac{\sqrt{x} - 2}{\sqrt{x}}$

5.6 Radical Equations and Problem Solving

OBJECTIVES

1. Solve Equations That Contain Radical Expressions.
2. Use the Pythagorean Theorem to Model Problems.

OBJECTIVE

1 Solving Equations That Contain Radical Expressions

In this section, we present techniques to solve equations containing radical expressions such as

$$\sqrt{2x - 3} = 9$$

We use the power rule to help us solve these radical equations.

Power Rule

If both sides of an equation are raised to the same power, **all** solutions of the original equation are **among** the solutions of the new equation.

This property *does not* say that raising both sides of an equation to a power yields an equivalent equation. A solution of the new equation *may or may not* be a solution of the original equation. For example, $(-2)^2 = 2^2$, but $-2 \neq 2$. Thus, *each solution of the new equation must be checked* to make sure it is a solution of the original equation. Recall that a proposed solution that is not a solution of the original equation is called an **extraneous solution**.

EXAMPLE 1 Solve: $\sqrt{2x - 3} = 9$.

Solution We use the power rule to square both sides of the equation to eliminate the radical.

$$\begin{aligned} \sqrt{2x - 3} &= 9 \\ (\sqrt{2x - 3})^2 &= 9^2 \\ 2x - 3 &= 81 \\ 2x &= 84 \\ x &= 42 \end{aligned}$$

Now we check the solution in the original equation.

Check:

$$\sqrt{2x - 3} = 9$$
$$\sqrt{2(42) - 3} \stackrel{?}{=} 9 \quad \text{Let } x = 42.$$
$$\sqrt{84 - 3} \stackrel{?}{=} 9$$
$$\sqrt{81} \stackrel{?}{=} 9$$
$$9 = 9 \quad \text{True}$$

The solution checks, so we conclude that the solution is 42, or the solution set is $\{42\}$. □

PRACTICE 1 Solve: $\sqrt{3x - 5} = 7$.

To solve a radical equation, first isolate a radical on one side of the equation.

EXAMPLE 2 Solve: $\sqrt{-10x - 1} + 3x = 0$.

Solution First, isolate the radical on one side of the equation. To do this, we subtract $3x$ from both sides.

$$\sqrt{-10x - 1} + 3x = 0$$
$$\sqrt{-10x - 1} + 3x - 3x = 0 - 3x$$
$$\sqrt{-10x - 1} = -3x$$

Next we use the power rule to eliminate the radical.

$$(\sqrt{-10x - 1})^2 = (-3x)^2$$
$$-10x - 1 = 9x^2$$

Since this is a quadratic equation, we can set the equation equal to 0 and try to solve by factoring.

$$9x^2 + 10x + 1 = 0$$
$$(9x + 1)(x + 1) = 0 \quad \text{Factor.}$$
$$9x + 1 = 0 \quad \text{or} \quad x + 1 = 0 \quad \text{Set each factor equal to 0.}$$
$$x = -\frac{1}{9} \quad \text{or} \quad x = -1$$

Check: Let $x = -\frac{1}{9}$.

$$\sqrt{-10x - 1} + 3x = 0$$
$$\sqrt{-10\left(-\frac{1}{9}\right) - 1} + 3\left(-\frac{1}{9}\right) \stackrel{?}{=} 0$$
$$\sqrt{\frac{10}{9} - \frac{9}{9}} - \frac{3}{9} \stackrel{?}{=} 0$$
$$\sqrt{\frac{1}{9}} - \frac{1}{3} \stackrel{?}{=} 0$$
$$\frac{1}{3} - \frac{1}{3} = 0 \quad \text{True}$$

Let $x = -1$.

$$\sqrt{-10x - 1} + 3x = 0$$
$$\sqrt{-10(-1) - 1} + 3(-1) \stackrel{?}{=} 0$$
$$\sqrt{10 - 1} - 3 \stackrel{?}{=} 0$$
$$\sqrt{9} - 3 \stackrel{?}{=} 0$$
$$3 - 3 = 0 \quad \text{True}$$

Both solutions check. The solutions are $-\frac{1}{9}$ and -1, or the solution set is $\left\{-\frac{1}{9}, -1\right\}$. □

PRACTICE 2 Solve: $\sqrt{16x - 3} - 4x = 0$.

The following steps may be used to solve a radical equation.

Solving a Radical Equation

Step 1. Isolate one radical on one side of the equation.

Step 2. Raise each side of the equation to a power equal to the index of the radical and simplify.

Step 3. If the equation still contains a radical term, repeat Steps 1 and 2. If not, solve the equation.

Step 4. Check all proposed solutions in the original equation.

EXAMPLE 3 Solve: $\sqrt[3]{x+1}+5=3$.

Solution First we isolate the radical by subtracting 5 from both sides of the equation.

$$\sqrt[3]{x+1}+5=3$$
$$\sqrt[3]{x+1}=-2$$

Next we raise both sides of the equation to the third power to eliminate the radical.

$$\left(\sqrt[3]{x+1}\right)^3=(-2)^3$$
$$x+1=-8$$
$$x=-9$$

The solution checks in the original equation, so the solution is -9. □

PRACTICE 3 Solve: $\sqrt[3]{x-2}+1=3$.

EXAMPLE 4 Solve: $\sqrt{4-x}=x-2$.

Solution

$$\sqrt{4-x}=x-2$$
$$\left(\sqrt{4-x}\right)^2=(x-2)^2$$
$$4-x=x^2-4x+4$$
$$x^2-3x=0 \quad \text{Write the quadratic equation in standard form.}$$
$$x(x-3)=0 \quad \text{Factor.}$$
$$x=0 \quad \text{or} \quad x-3=0 \quad \text{Set each factor equal to 0.}$$
$$x=3$$

Check:

$\sqrt{4-x}=x-2$	$\sqrt{4-x}=x-2$
$\sqrt{4-0}\stackrel{?}{=}0-2$ Let $x=0$.	$\sqrt{4-3}\stackrel{?}{=}3-2$ Let $x=3$.
$2=-2$ False	$1=1$ True

The proposed solution 3 checks, but 0 does not. Since 0 is an extraneous solution, the only solution is 3. □

PRACTICE 4 Solve: $\sqrt{16+x}=x-4$.

Helpful Hint

In Example 4, notice that $(x-2)^2=x^2-4x+4$. Make sure binomials are squared correctly.

✓CONCEPT CHECK
How can you immediately tell that the equation $\sqrt{2y+3} = -4$ has no real solution?

EXAMPLE 5 Solve: $\sqrt{2x+5} + \sqrt{2x} = 3$.

Solution We get one radical alone by subtracting $\sqrt{2x}$ from both sides.

$$\sqrt{2x+5} + \sqrt{2x} = 3$$
$$\sqrt{2x+5} = 3 - \sqrt{2x}$$

Now we use the power rule to begin eliminating the radicals. First we square both sides.

$$(\sqrt{2x+5})^2 = (3 - \sqrt{2x})^2$$
$$2x + 5 = 9 - 6\sqrt{2x} + 2x \quad \text{Multiply } (3 - \sqrt{2x})(3 - \sqrt{2x}).$$

There is still a radical in the equation, so we get a radical alone again. Then we square both sides.

$$2x + 5 = 9 - 6\sqrt{2x} + 2x$$
$$6\sqrt{2x} = 4 \quad \text{Get the radical alone.}$$
$$36(2x) = 16 \quad \text{Square both sides of the equation to eliminate the radical.}$$
$$72x = 16 \quad \text{Multiply.}$$
$$x = \frac{16}{72} \quad \text{Solve.}$$
$$x = \frac{2}{9} \quad \text{Simplify.}$$

The proposed solution, $\frac{2}{9}$, checks in the original equation. The solution is $\frac{2}{9}$. □

PRACTICE 5 Solve: $\sqrt{8x+1} + \sqrt{3x} = 2$.

Helpful Hint
Make sure expressions are squared correctly. In Example 5, we squared $(3 - \sqrt{2x})$ as

$$(3 - \sqrt{2x})^2 = (3 - \sqrt{2x})(3 - \sqrt{2x})$$
$$= 3 \cdot 3 - 3\sqrt{2x} - 3\sqrt{2x} + \sqrt{2x} \cdot \sqrt{2x}$$
$$= 9 - 6\sqrt{2x} + 2x$$

✓CONCEPT CHECK
What is wrong with the following solution?

$$\sqrt{2x+5} + \sqrt{4-x} = 8$$
$$(\sqrt{2x+5} + \sqrt{4-x})^2 = 8^2$$
$$(2x+5) + (4-x) = 64$$
$$x + 9 = 64$$
$$x = 55$$

Answers to Concept Checks:
answers may vary;
$(\sqrt{2x+5} + \sqrt{4-x})^2$ is not $(2x+5) + (4-x)$.

OBJECTIVE 2 **Using the Pythagorean Theorem** 

Recall that the Pythagorean theorem states that in a right triangle, the length of the hypotenuse squared equals the sum of the lengths of each of the legs squared.

Pythagorean Theorem

If a and b are the lengths of the legs of a right triangle and c is the length of the hypotenuse, then $a^2 + b^2 = c^2$.

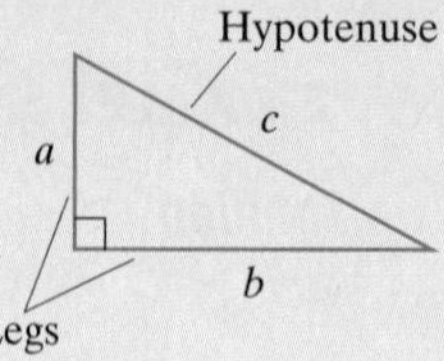

EXAMPLE 6 Find the length of the unknown leg of the right triangle.

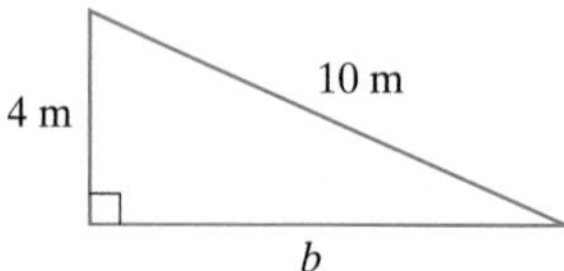

Solution In the formula $a^2 + b^2 = c^2$, c is the hypotenuse. Here, $c = 10$, the length of the hypotenuse, and $a = 4$. We solve for b. Then $a^2 + b^2 = c^2$ becomes

$$4^2 + b^2 = 10^2$$
$$16 + b^2 = 100$$
$$b^2 = 84 \quad \text{Subtract 16 from both sides.}$$
$$b = \pm\sqrt{84} = \pm\sqrt{4 \cdot 21} = \pm 2\sqrt{21}$$

Since b is a length and thus is positive, we will use the positive value only. The unknown leg of the triangle is $2\sqrt{21}$ meters long. □

PRACTICE
6 Find the length of the unknown leg of the right triangle.

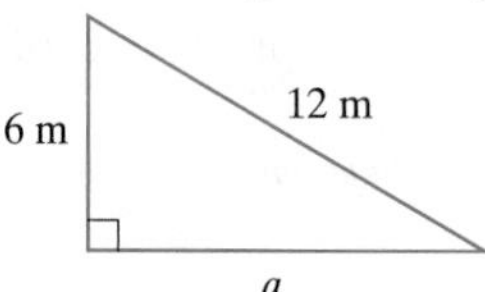

EXAMPLE 7 **Calculating Placement of a Wire**

A 50-foot supporting wire is to be attached to a 75-foot antenna. Because of surrounding buildings, sidewalks, and roadways, the wire must be anchored exactly 20 feet from the base of the antenna.

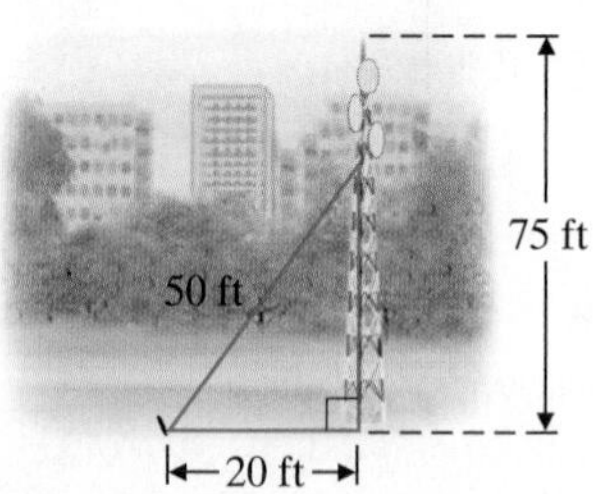

a. How high from the base of the antenna is the wire attached?

b. Local regulations require that a supporting wire be attached at a height no less than $\frac{3}{5}$ of the total height of the antenna. From part (a), have local regulations been met?

Solution

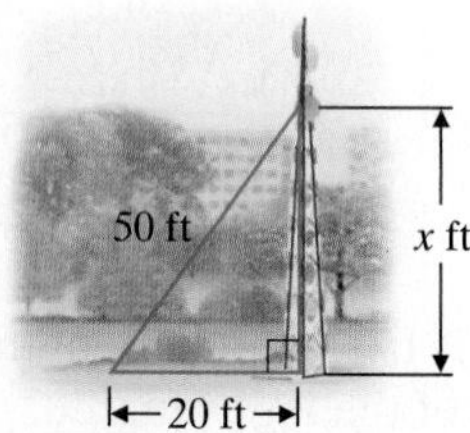

1. UNDERSTAND. Read and reread the problem. From the diagram, we notice that a right triangle is formed with hypotenuse 50 feet and one leg 20 feet. Let x be the height from the base of the antenna to the attached wire.

2. TRANSLATE. Use the Pythagorean theorem.

$$a^2 + b^2 = c^2$$
$$20^2 + x^2 = 50^2 \quad a = 20, c = 50$$

3. SOLVE.

$$20^2 + x^2 = 50^2$$
$$400 + x^2 = 2500$$
$$x^2 = 2100 \quad \text{Subtract 400 from both sides.}$$
$$x = \pm\sqrt{2100}$$
$$= \pm 10\sqrt{21}$$

4. INTERPRET. *Check* the work and *state* the solution.

Check: We will use only the positive value, $x = 10\sqrt{21}$, because x represents length. The wire is attached exactly $10\sqrt{21}$ feet from the base of the pole, or approximately 45.8 feet.

State: The supporting wire must be attached at a height no less than $\frac{3}{5}$ of the total height of the antenna. This height is $\frac{3}{5}$(75 feet), or 45 feet. Since we know from part (a) that the wire is to be attached at a height of approximately 45.8 feet, local regulations have been met. □

PRACTICE
7 Keith Robinson bought two Siamese fighting fish, but when he got home, he found he only had one rectangular tank that was 12 in. long, 7 in. wide, and 5 in. deep. Since the fish must be kept separated, he needed to insert a plastic divider in the diagonal of the tank. He already has a piece that is 5 in. in one dimension, but how long must it be to fit corner to corner in the tank?

Graphing Calculator Explorations

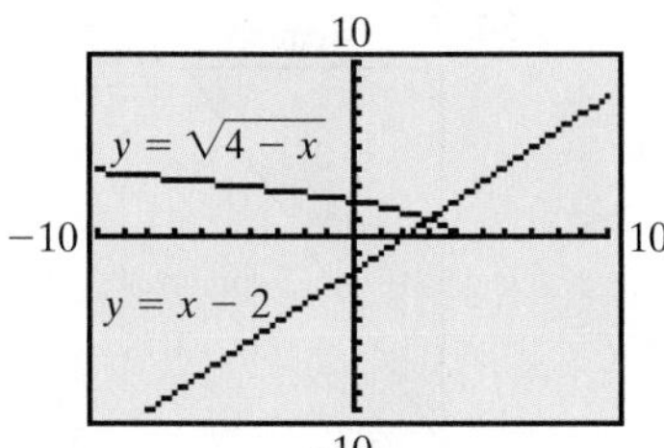

We can use a graphing calculator to solve radical equations. For example, to use a graphing calculator to approximate the solutions of the equation solved in Example 4, we graph the following.

$$Y_1 = \sqrt{4 - x} \quad \text{and} \quad Y_2 = x - 2$$

The x-value of the point of intersection is the solution. Use the Intersect feature or the Zoom and Trace features of your graphing calculator to see that the solution is 3.

Use a graphing calculator to solve each radical equation. Round all solutions to the nearest hundredth.

1. $\sqrt{x + 7} = x$

2. $\sqrt{3x + 5} = 2x$

3. $\sqrt{2x + 1} = \sqrt{2x + 2}$

4. $\sqrt{10x - 1} = \sqrt{-10x + 10} - 1$

5. $1.2x = \sqrt{3.1x + 5}$

6. $\sqrt{1.9x^2 - 2.2} = -0.8x + 3$

Vocabulary, Readiness & Video Check

Use the choices below to fill in each blank. Not all choices will be used.

hypotenuse	right	$x^2 + 25$	$16 - 8\sqrt{7x} + 7x$
extraneous solution	legs	$x^2 - 10x + 25$	$16 + 7x$

1. A proposed solution that is not a solution of the original equation is called a(n) ______________.

2. The Pythagorean theorem states that $a^2 + b^2 = c^2$ where a and b are the lengths of the ______________ of a(n) ______________ triangle and c is the length of the ______________.

3. The square of $x - 5$, or $(x - 5)^2 =$ ______________.
4. The square of $4 - \sqrt{7x}$, or $(4 - \sqrt{7x})^2 =$ ______________.

Martin-Gay Interactive Videos

See Video 5.6

Watch the section lecture video and answer the following questions.

OBJECTIVE 1

5. From Examples 1–4, why must you be careful and check your proposed solution(s) in the original equation?

OBJECTIVE 2

6. From Example 5, when solving problems using the Pythagorean theorem, what two things must you remember?

OBJECTIVE 2

7. What important reminder is given as the final answer to Example 5 is being found?

5.6 Exercise Set

MyMathLab®

Solve. See Examples 1 and 2.

1. $\sqrt{2x} = 4$
2. $\sqrt{3x} = 3$
3. $\sqrt{x - 3} = 2$
4. $\sqrt{x + 1} = 5$
5. $\sqrt{2x} = -4$
6. $\sqrt{5x} = -5$
7. $\sqrt{4x - 3} - 5 = 0$
8. $\sqrt{x - 3} - 1 = 0$
9. $\sqrt{2x - 3} - 2 = 1$
10. $\sqrt{3x + 3} - 4 = 8$

Solve. See Example 3.

11. $\sqrt[3]{6x} = -3$
12. $\sqrt[3]{4x} = -2$
13. $\sqrt[3]{x - 2} - 3 = 0$
14. $\sqrt[3]{2x - 6} - 4 = 0$

Solve. See Examples 4 and 5.

15. $\sqrt{13 - x} = x - 1$
16. $\sqrt{2x - 3} = 3 - x$
17. $x - \sqrt{4 - 3x} = -8$
18. $2x + \sqrt{x + 1} = 8$
19. $\sqrt{y + 5} = 2 - \sqrt{y - 4}$
20. $\sqrt{x + 3} + \sqrt{x - 5} = 3$
21. $\sqrt{x - 3} + \sqrt{x + 2} = 5$
22. $\sqrt{2x - 4} - \sqrt{3x + 4} = -2$

MIXED PRACTICE

Solve. See Examples 1 through 5.

23. $\sqrt{3x - 2} = 5$
24. $\sqrt{5x - 4} = 9$
25. $-\sqrt{2x} + 4 = -6$
26. $-\sqrt{3x + 9} = -12$
27. $\sqrt{3x + 1} + 2 = 0$
28. $\sqrt{3x + 1} - 2 = 0$
29. $\sqrt[4]{4x + 1} - 2 = 0$
30. $\sqrt[4]{2x - 9} - 3 = 0$
31. $\sqrt{4x - 3} = 7$
32. $\sqrt{3x + 9} = 6$
33. $\sqrt[3]{6x - 3} - 3 = 0$
34. $\sqrt[3]{3x} + 4 = 7$
35. $\sqrt[3]{2x - 3} - 2 = -5$
36. $\sqrt[3]{x - 4} - 5 = -7$
37. $\sqrt{x + 4} = \sqrt{2x - 5}$
38. $\sqrt{3y + 6} = \sqrt{7y - 6}$
39. $x - \sqrt{1 - x} = -5$
40. $x - \sqrt{x - 2} = 4$
41. $\sqrt[3]{-6x - 1} = \sqrt[3]{-2x - 5}$
42. $\sqrt[3]{-4x - 3} = \sqrt[3]{-x - 15}$
43. $\sqrt{5x - 1} - \sqrt{x} + 2 = 3$
44. $\sqrt{2x - 1} - 4 = -\sqrt{x - 4}$
45. $\sqrt{2x - 1} = \sqrt{1 - 2x}$
46. $\sqrt{7x - 4} = \sqrt{4 - 7x}$

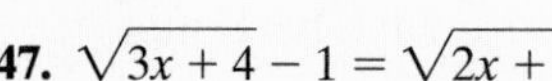

47. $\sqrt{3x + 4} - 1 = \sqrt{2x + 1}$
48. $\sqrt{x - 2} + 3 = \sqrt{4x + 1}$
49. $\sqrt{y + 3} - \sqrt{y - 3} = 1$
50. $\sqrt{x + 1} - \sqrt{x - 1} = 2$

Find the length of the unknown side of each triangle. See Example 6.

△ 51.

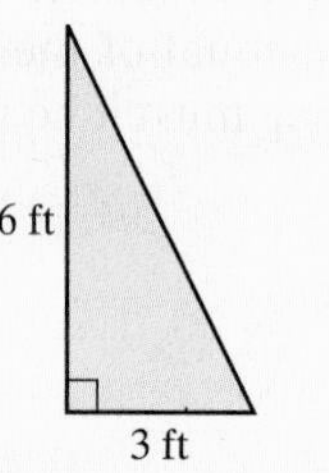

△ 52.

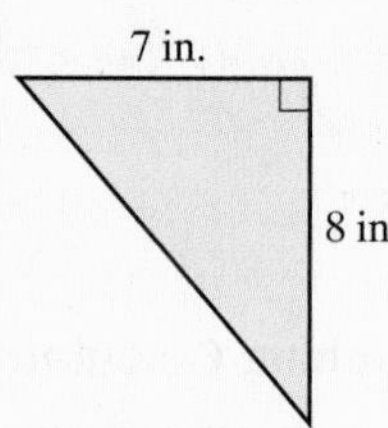

△ 53.

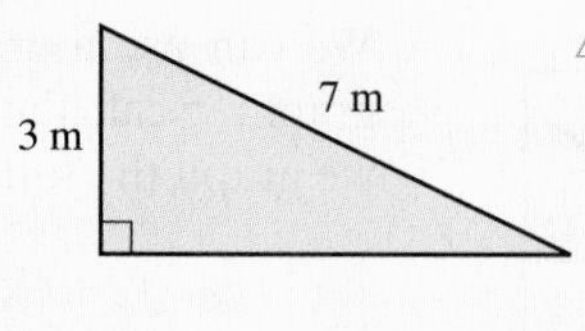

△ 54.

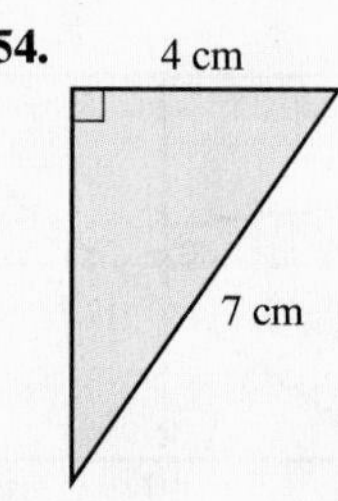

Find the length of the unknown side of each triangle. Give the exact length and a one-decimal-place approximation. See Example 6.

△ 55.

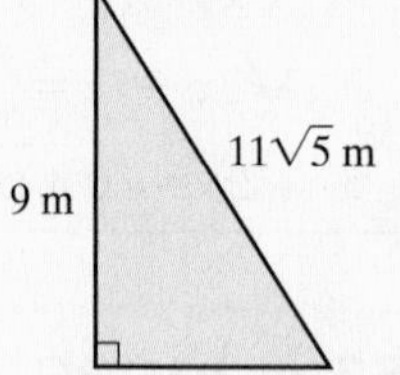

△ 56.

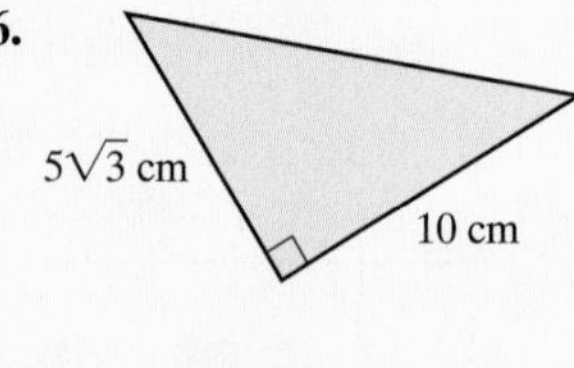

△ 57.

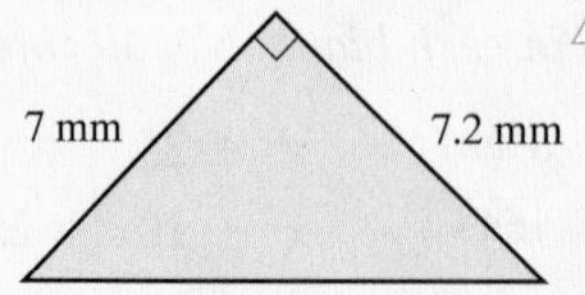

△ 58.

2.7 in.

2.3 in.

Solve. Give exact answers and two-decimal-place approximations where appropriate. For Exercises 59 and 60, the solutions have been started for you. See Example 7.

59. A wire is needed to support a vertical pole 15 feet tall. The cable will be anchored to a stake 8 feet from the base of the pole. How much cable is needed?

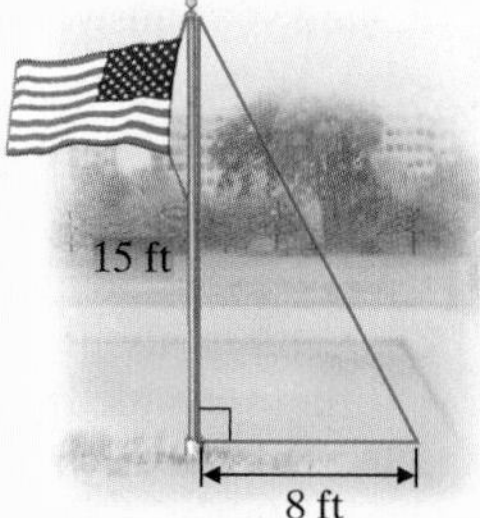

Start the solution:

1. UNDERSTAND the problem. Reread it as many times as needed. Notice that a right triangle is formed with legs of length 8 ft and 15 ft.
   Since we are looking for how much cable is needed, let

   $x =$ amount of cable needed

2. TRANSLATE into an equation. We use the Pythagorean theorem. (Fill in the blanks below.)

$$\begin{array}{ccccc} a^2 & + & b^2 & = & c^2 \\ \downarrow & & \downarrow & & \\ \_\_\_^2 & + & \_\_\_^2 & = & x^2 \end{array}$$

   Finish with:

3. SOLVE and **4.** INTERPRET

60. The tallest structure in the United States is a TV tower in Blanchard, North Dakota. Its height is 2063 feet. A 2382-foot length of wire is to be used as a guy wire attached to the top of the tower. Approximate to the nearest foot how far from the base of the tower the guy wire must be anchored. (*Source:* U.S. Geological Survey)

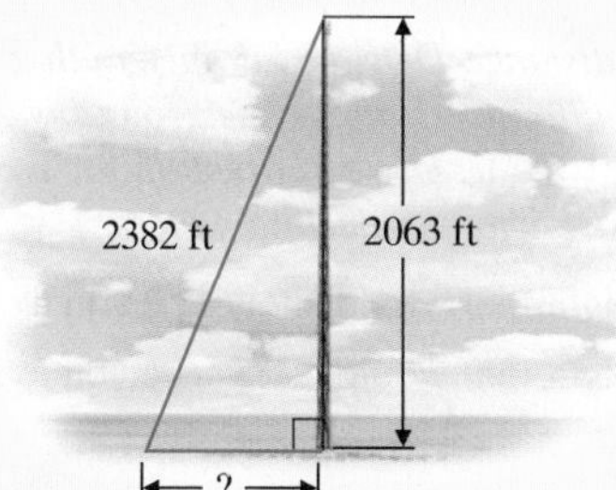

Start the solution:

1. UNDERSTAND the problem. Reread it as many times as needed. Notice that a right triangle is formed with hypotenuse 2382 ft and one leg 2063 ft.
   Since we are looking for how far from the base of the tower the guy wire is anchored, let

   $x =$ distance from base of tower to where guy wire is anchored.

2. TRANSLATE into an equation. We use the Pythagorean theorem. (Fill in the blanks below.)

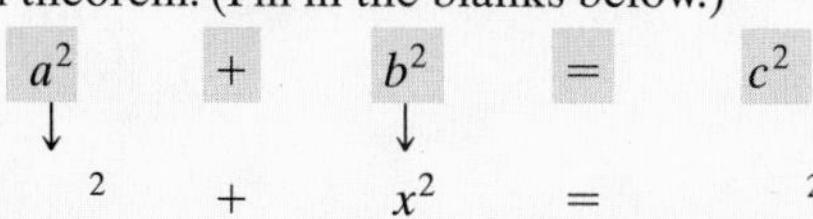

$$\begin{array}{ccccc} a^2 & + & b^2 & = & c^2 \\ \downarrow & & \downarrow & & \\ \_\_\_^2 & + & x^2 & = & \_\_\_^2 \end{array}$$

   Finish with:

3. SOLVE and **4.** INTERPRET

△ **61.** A spotlight is mounted on the eaves of a house 12 feet above the ground. A flower bed runs between the house and the sidewalk, so the closest a ladder can be placed to the house is 5 feet. How long of a ladder is needed so that an electrician can reach the place where the light is mounted?

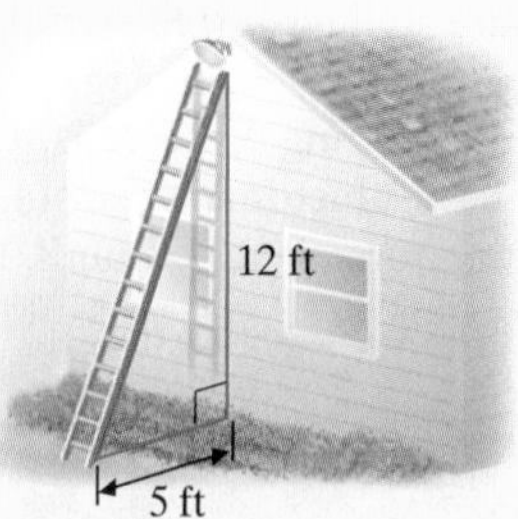

△ **62.** A wire is to be attached to support a telephone pole. Because of surrounding buildings, sidewalks, and roadways, the wire must be anchored exactly 15 feet from the base of the pole. Telephone company workers have only 30 feet of cable, and 2 feet of that must be used to attach the cable to the pole and to the stake on the ground. How high from the base of the pole can the wire be attached?

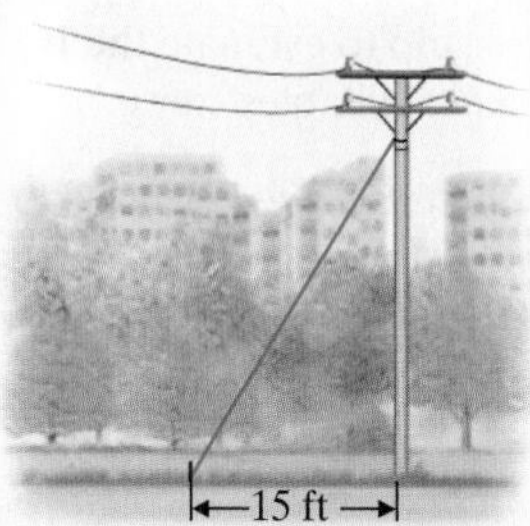

△ **63.** The radius of the moon is 1080 miles. Use the formula for the radius r of a sphere given its surface area A,

$$r = \sqrt{\frac{A}{4\pi}}$$

to find the surface area of the moon. Round to the nearest square mile. (*Source:* National Space Science Data Center)

64. Police departments find it very useful to be able to approximate the speed of a car when they are given the distance that the car skidded before it came to a stop. If the road surface is wet concrete, the function $S(x) = \sqrt{10.5x}$ is used, where $S(x)$ is the speed of the car in miles per hour and x is the distance skidded in feet. Find how fast a car was moving if it skidded 280 feet on wet concrete.

65. The formula $v = \sqrt{2gh}$ gives the velocity v, in feet per second, of an object when it falls h feet accelerated by gravity g, in feet per second squared. If g is approximately 32 feet per second squared, find how far an object has fallen if its velocity is 80 feet per second.

66. Two tractors are pulling a tree stump from a field. If two forces A and B pull at right angles (90°) to each other, the size of the resulting force R is given by the formula $R = \sqrt{A^2 + B^2}$. If tractor A is exerting 600 pounds of force and the resulting force is 850 pounds, find how much force tractor B is exerting.

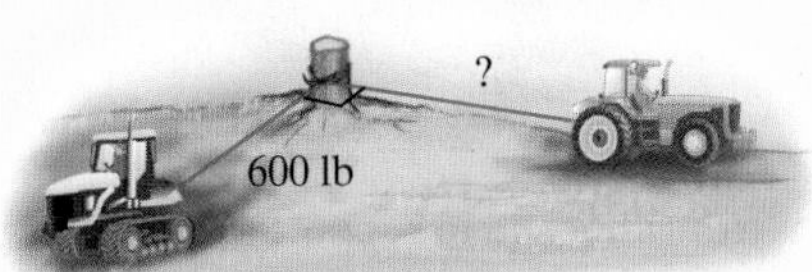

In psychology, it has been suggested that the number S of nonsense syllables that a person can repeat consecutively depends on his or her IQ score I according to the equation $S = 2\sqrt{I} - 9$.

67. Use this relationship to estimate the IQ of a person who can repeat 11 nonsense syllables consecutively.

68. Use this relationship to estimate the IQ of a person who can repeat 15 nonsense syllables consecutively.

The ***period*** *of a pendulum is the time it takes for the pendulum to make one full back-and-forth swing. The period of a pendulum depends on the length of the pendulum. The formula for the period P, in seconds, is* $P = 2\pi\sqrt{\frac{l}{32}}$, *where l is the length of the pendulum in feet. Use this formula for Exercises 69 through 74.*

69. Find the period of a pendulum whose length is 2 feet. Give an exact answer and a two-decimal-place approximation.

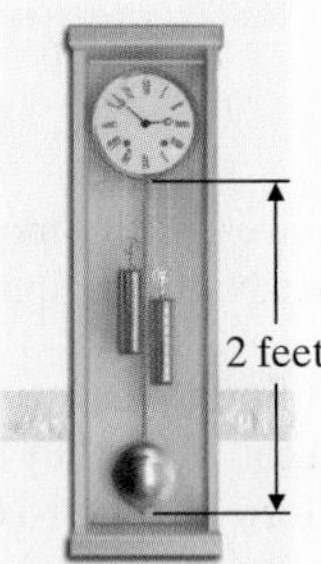

70. Klockit sells a 43-inch lyre pendulum. Find the period of this pendulum. Round your answer to 2 decimal places. (*Hint:* First convert inches to feet.)

71. Find the length of a pendulum whose period is 4 seconds. Round your answer to 2 decimal places.

72. Find the length of a pendulum whose period is 3 seconds. Round your answer to 2 decimal places.

73. Study the relationship between period and pendulum length in Exercises 69 through 72 and make a conjecture about this relationship.

74. Galileo experimented with pendulums. He supposedly made conjectures about pendulums of equal length with different bob weights. Try this experiment. Make two pendulums 3 feet long. Attach a heavy weight (lead) to one and a light weight (a cork) to the other. Pull both pendulums back the same angle measure and release. Make a conjecture from your observations.

If the three lengths of the sides of a triangle are known, Heron's formula can be used to find its area. If a, b, and c are the lengths of the three sides, Heron's formula for area is

$$A = \sqrt{s(s-a)(s-b)(s-c)}$$

where s is half the perimeter of the triangle, or $s = \frac{1}{2}(a + b + c)$.

Use this formula to find the area of each triangle. Give an exact answer and then a two-decimal-place approximation.

75. **76.**

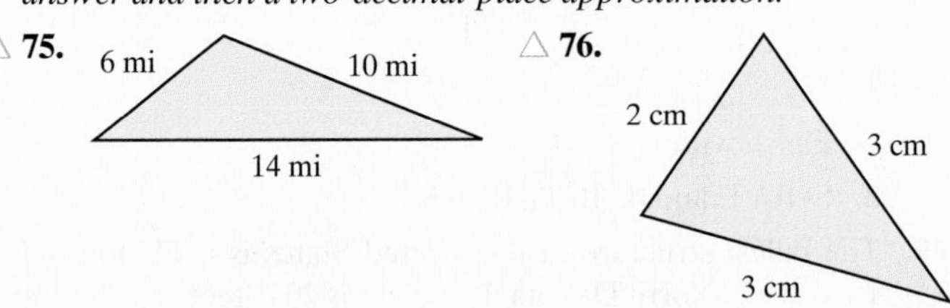

77. Describe when Heron's formula might be useful.

78. In your own words, explain why you think s in Heron's formula is called the *semiperimeter*.

The maximum distance D(h) in kilometers that a person can see from a height h kilometers above the ground is given by the function $D(h) = 111.7\sqrt{h}$. *Use this function for Exercises 79 and 80. Round your answers to two decimal places.*

79. Find the height that would allow a person to see 80 kilometers.

80. Find the height that would allow a person to see 40 kilometers.

REVIEW AND PREVIEW

Use the vertical line test to determine whether each graph represents the graph of a function.

81. **82.**

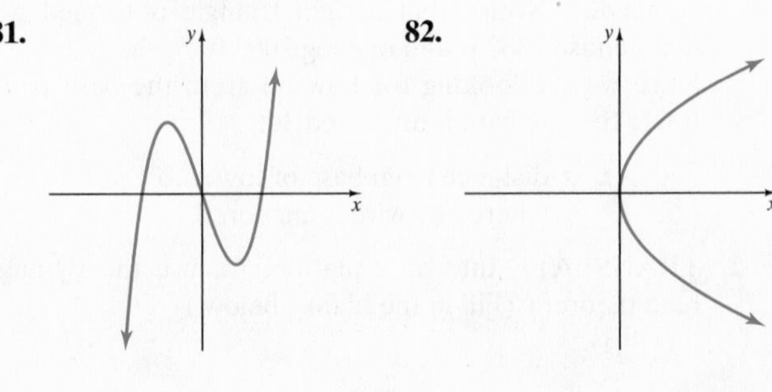

83.

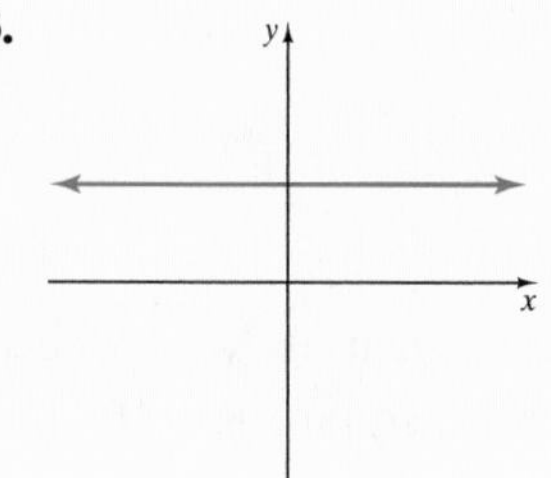

84.

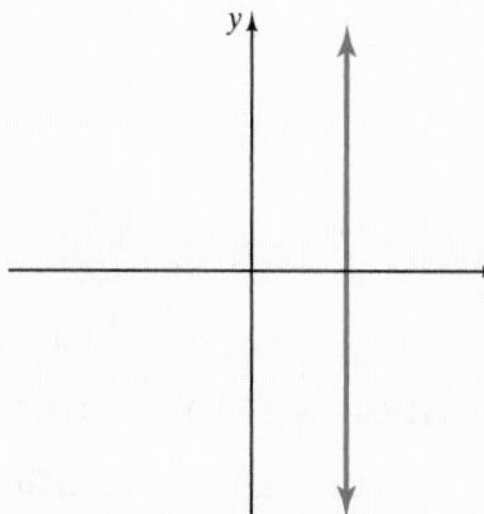

85.

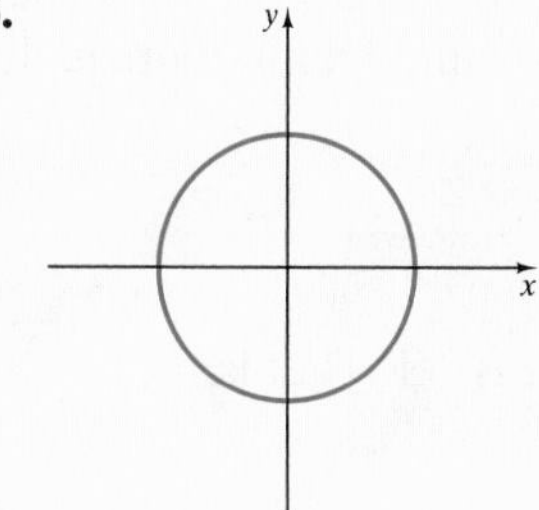

86.

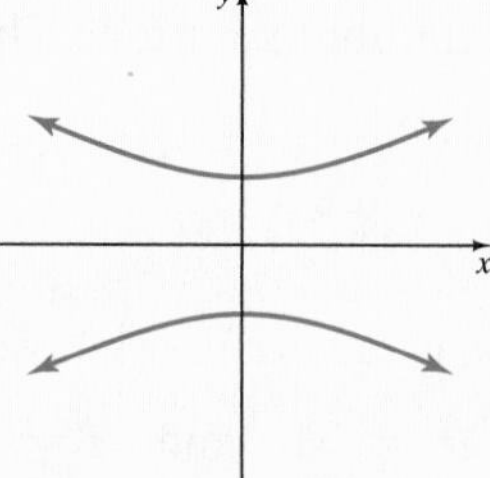

Simplify. See Section 4.7.

87. $\dfrac{\frac{x}{6}}{\frac{2x}{3}+\frac{1}{2}}$

88. $\dfrac{\frac{1}{y}+\frac{4}{5}}{-\frac{3}{20}}$

89. $\dfrac{\frac{z}{5}+\frac{1}{10}}{\frac{z}{20}-\frac{z}{5}}$

90. $\dfrac{\frac{1}{y}+\frac{1}{x}}{\frac{1}{y}-\frac{1}{x}}$

CONCEPT EXTENSIONS

Find the error in each solution and correct. See the second Concept Check in this section.

91.
$$\sqrt{5x-1}+4=7$$
$$(\sqrt{5x-1}+4)^2=7^2$$
$$5x-1+16=49$$
$$5x=34$$
$$x=\frac{34}{5}$$

92.
$$\sqrt{2x+3}+4=1$$
$$\sqrt{2x+3}=5$$
$$(\sqrt{2x+3})^2=5^2$$
$$2x+3=25$$
$$2x=22$$
$$x=11$$

93. Solve: $\sqrt{\sqrt{x+3}+\sqrt{x}}=\sqrt{3}$

94. The cost $C(x)$ in dollars per day to operate a small delivery service is given by $C(x) = 80\sqrt[3]{x} + 500$, where x is the number of deliveries per day. In July, the manager decides that it is necessary to keep delivery costs below $1620.00. Find the greatest number of deliveries this company can make per day and still keep overhead below $1620.00.

95. Consider the equations $\sqrt{2x} = 4$ and $\sqrt[3]{2x} = 4$.

a. Explain the difference in solving these equations.

b. Explain the similarity in solving these equations.

96. Explain why proposed solutions of radical equations must be checked.

Example

For Exercises 97 through 100, see the example below.

Solve $(t^2 - 3t) - 2\sqrt{t^2 - 3t} = 0$.

Solution

Substitution can be used to make this problem somewhat simpler. Since $t^2 - 3t$ occurs more than once, let $x = t^2 - 3t$.

$$(t^2-3t)-2\sqrt{t^2-3t}=0$$
$$x-2\sqrt{x}=0$$
$$x=2\sqrt{x}$$
$$x^2=(2\sqrt{x})^2$$
$$x^2=4x$$
$$x^2-4x=0$$
$$x(x-4)=0$$
$$x=0 \quad \text{or} \quad x-4=0$$
$$x=4$$

Now we "undo" the substitution.

$x = 0$ Replace x with $t^2 - 3t$.

$$t^2-3t=0$$
$$t(t-3)=0$$
$$t=0 \quad \text{or} \quad t-3=0$$
$$t=3$$

$x = 4$ Replace x with $t^2 - 3t$.

$$t^2-3t=4$$
$$t^2-3t-4=0$$
$$(t-4)(t+1)=0$$
$$t-4=0 \quad \text{or} \quad t+1=0$$
$$t=4 \qquad t=-1$$

In this problem, we have four possible solutions: 0, 3, 4, and -1. All four solutions check in the original equation, so the solutions are $-1, 0, 3, 4$.

Solve. See the preceding example.

97. $3\sqrt{x^2 - 8x} = x^2 - 8x$

98. $\sqrt{(x^2 - x) + 7} = 2(x^2 - x) - 1$

99. $7 - (x^2 - 3x) = \sqrt{(x^2 - 3x) + 5}$

100. $x^2 + 6x = 4\sqrt{x^2 + 6x}$

5.7 Complex Numbers 

OBJECTIVES

1 Write Square Roots of Negative Numbers in the Form *bi*.

2 Add or Subtract Complex Numbers.

3 Multiply Complex Numbers.

4 Divide Complex Numbers.

5 Raise *i* to Powers.

OBJECTIVE

1 Writing Numbers in the Form *bi* 

Our work with radical expressions has excluded expressions such as $\sqrt{-16}$ because $\sqrt{-16}$ is not a real number; there is no real number whose square is -16. In this section, we discuss a number system that includes roots of negative numbers. This number system is the **complex number system,** and it includes the set of real numbers as a subset. The complex number system allows us to solve equations such as $x^2 + 1 = 0$ that have no real number solutions. The set of complex numbers includes the **imaginary unit.**

Imaginary Unit

The imaginary unit, written i, is the number whose square is -1. That is,

$$i^2 = -1 \quad \text{and} \quad i = \sqrt{-1}$$

To write the square root of a negative number in terms of i, use the property that if a is a positive number, then

$$\sqrt{-a} = \sqrt{-1} \cdot \sqrt{a}$$
$$= i \cdot \sqrt{a}$$

Using i, we can write $\sqrt{-16}$ as

$$\sqrt{-16} = \sqrt{-1 \cdot 16} = \sqrt{-1} \cdot \sqrt{16} = i \cdot 4, \text{ or } 4i$$

EXAMPLE 1 Write with i notation.

a. $\sqrt{-36}$ **b.** $\sqrt{-5}$ **c.** $-\sqrt{-20}$

Solution

a. $\sqrt{-36} = \sqrt{-1 \cdot 36} = \sqrt{-1} \cdot \sqrt{36} = i \cdot 6, \text{ or } 6i$

b. $\sqrt{-5} = \sqrt{-1(5)} = \sqrt{-1} \cdot \sqrt{5} = i\sqrt{5}.$

c. $-\sqrt{-20} = -\sqrt{-1 \cdot 20} = -\sqrt{-1} \cdot \sqrt{4 \cdot 5} = -i \cdot 2\sqrt{5} = -2i\sqrt{5}$ □

Helpful Hint
Since $\sqrt{5}i$ can easily be confused with $\sqrt{5i}$, we write $\sqrt{5}i$ as $i\sqrt{5}$.

PRACTICE

1 Write with i notation.

a. $\sqrt{-4}$ **b.** $\sqrt{-7}$ **c.** $-\sqrt{-18}$

The product rule for radicals does not necessarily hold true for imaginary numbers. *To multiply square roots of negative numbers, first we write each number in terms of the imaginary unit i.* For example, to multiply $\sqrt{-4}$ and $\sqrt{-9}$, we first write each number in the form *bi*.

$$\sqrt{-4}\sqrt{-9} = 2i(3i) = 6i^2 = 6(-1) = -6 \quad \text{Correct}$$

We will also use this method to simplify quotients of square roots of negative numbers. Why? The product rule does not work for this example. In other words,

$$\sqrt{-4} \cdot \sqrt{-9} = \sqrt{(-4)(-9)} = \sqrt{36} = 6 \quad \text{Incorrect}$$

EXAMPLE 2 Multiply or divide as indicated.

a. $\sqrt{-3} \cdot \sqrt{-5}$ **b.** $\sqrt{-36} \cdot \sqrt{-1}$ **c.** $\sqrt{8} \cdot \sqrt{-2}$ **d.** $\dfrac{\sqrt{-125}}{\sqrt{5}}$

Solution

a. $\sqrt{-3} \cdot \sqrt{-5} = i\sqrt{3}(i\sqrt{5}) = i^2\sqrt{15} = -1\sqrt{15} = -\sqrt{15}$

b. $\sqrt{-36} \cdot \sqrt{-1} = 6i(i) = 6i^2 = 6(-1) = -6$

c. $\sqrt{8} \cdot \sqrt{-2} = 2\sqrt{2}(i\sqrt{2}) = 2i(\sqrt{2}\sqrt{2}) = 2i(2) = 4i$

d. $\dfrac{\sqrt{-125}}{\sqrt{5}} = \dfrac{i\sqrt{125}}{\sqrt{5}} = i\sqrt{25} = 5i$ □

PRACTICE

2 Multiply or divide as indicated.

a. $\sqrt{-5} \cdot \sqrt{-6}$ **b.** $\sqrt{-9} \cdot \sqrt{-1}$ **c.** $\sqrt{125} \cdot \sqrt{-5}$ **d.** $\dfrac{\sqrt{-27}}{\sqrt{3}}$

Now that we have practiced working with the imaginary unit, we define complex numbers.

Complex Numbers

A **complex number** is a number that can be written in the form $a + bi$, where a and b are real numbers.

Notice that the set of real numbers is a subset of the complex numbers since any real number can be written in the form of a complex number. For example,

$$16 = 16 + 0i$$

In general, a complex number $a + bi$ is a real number if $b = 0$. Also, a complex number is called a **pure imaginary number** or an imaginary number if $a = 0$ and $b \neq 0$. For example,

$$3i = 0 + 3i \quad \text{and} \quad i\sqrt{7} = 0 + i\sqrt{7}$$

are pure imaginary numbers.

The following diagram shows the relationship between complex numbers and their subsets.

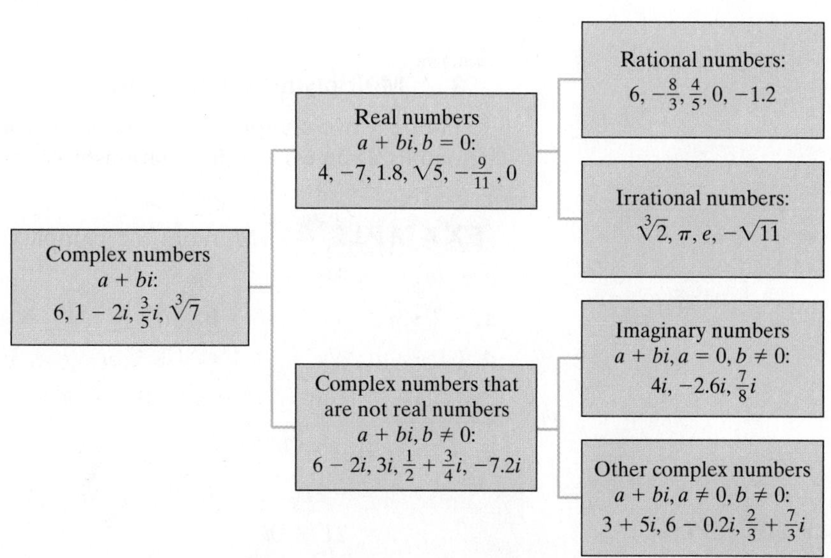

✓CONCEPT CHECK
True or false? Every complex number is also a real number.

OBJECTIVE
2 Adding or Subtracting Complex Numbers 

Two complex numbers $a + bi$ and $c + di$ are equal if and only if $a = c$ and $b = d$. Complex numbers can be added or subtracted by adding or subtracting their real parts and then adding or subtracting their imaginary parts.

Sum or Difference of Complex Numbers

If $a + bi$ and $c + di$ are complex numbers, then their sum is

$$(a + bi) + (c + di) = (a + c) + (b + d)i$$

Their difference is

$$(a + bi) - (c + di) = a + bi - c - di = (a - c) + (b - d)i$$

EXAMPLE 3 Add or subtract the complex numbers. Write the sum or difference in the form $a + bi$.

a. $(2 + 3i) + (-3 + 2i)$ **b.** $5i - (1 - i)$ **c.** $(-3 - 7i) - (-6)$

Solution

a. $(2 + 3i) + (-3 + 2i) = (2 - 3) + (3 + 2)i = -1 + 5i$

b. $5i - (1 - i) = 5i - 1 + i$
$= -1 + (5 + 1)i$
$= -1 + 6i$

c. $(-3 - 7i) - (-6) = -3 - 7i + 6$
$= (-3 + 6) - 7i$
$= 3 - 7i$ □

PRACTICE
3 Add or subtract the complex numbers. Write the sum or difference in the form $a + bi$.

a. $(3 - 5i) + (-4 + i)$ **b.** $4i - (3 - i)$ **c.** $(-5 - 2i) - (-8)$

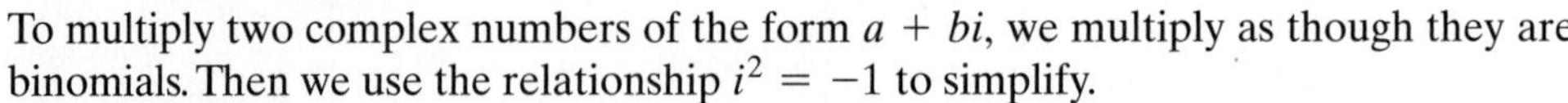

OBJECTIVE
3 Multiplying Complex Numbers

To multiply two complex numbers of the form $a + bi$, we multiply as though they are binomials. Then we use the relationship $i^2 = -1$ to simplify.

EXAMPLE 4 Multiply the complex numbers. Write the product in the form $a + bi$.

a. $-7i \cdot 3i$ **b.** $3i(2 - i)$ **c.** $(2 - 5i)(4 + i)$
d. $(2 - i)^2$ **e.** $(7 + 3i)(7 - 3i)$

Solution

a. $-7i \cdot 3i = -21i^2$
$= -21(-1)$ Replace i^2 with -1.
$= 21 + 0i$

Answer to Concept Check:
false

b. $3i(2 - i) = 3i \cdot 2 - 3i \cdot i$ Use the distributive property.
$= 6i - 3i^2$ Multiply.
$= 6i - 3(-1)$ Replace i^2 with -1.
$= 6i + 3$
$= 3 + 6i$

Use the FOIL order below. (First, Outer, Inner, Last)

c. $(2 - 5i)(4 + i) = \underset{\text{F}}{2(4)} + \underset{\text{O}}{2(i)} - \underset{\text{I}}{5i(4)} - \underset{\text{L}}{5i(i)}$
$= 8 + 2i - 20i - 5i^2$
$= 8 - 18i - 5(-1)$ $\quad i^2 = -1$
$= 8 - 18i + 5$
$= 13 - 18i$

d. $(2 - i)^2 = (2 - i)(2 - i)$
$= 2(2) - 2(i) - 2(i) + i^2$
$= 4 - 4i + (-1)$ $\quad i^2 = -1$
$= 3 - 4i$

e. $(7 + 3i)(7 - 3i) = 7(7) - 7(3i) + 3i(7) - 3i(3i)$
$= 49 - 21i + 21i - 9i^2$
$= 49 - 9(-1)$ $\quad i^2 = -1$
$= 49 + 9$
$= 58 + 0i$ □

PRACTICE

4 Multiply the complex numbers. Write the product in the form $a + bi$.

a. $-4i \cdot 5i$ **b.** $5i(2 + i)$ **c.** $(2 + 3i)(6 - i)$
d. $(3 - i)^2$ **e.** $(9 + 2i)(9 - 2i)$

Notice that if you add, subtract, or multiply two complex numbers, just like real numbers, the result is a complex number.

OBJECTIVE

4 Dividing Complex Numbers

From Example 4e, notice that the product of $7 + 3i$ and $7 - 3i$ is a real number. These two complex numbers are called **complex conjugates** of one another. In general, we have the following definition.

Complex Conjugates

The complex numbers $(a + bi)$ and $(a - bi)$ are called **complex conjugates** of each other, and

$$(a + bi)(a - bi) = a^2 + b^2.$$

To see that the product of a complex number $a + bi$ and its conjugate $a - bi$ is the real number $a^2 + b^2$, we multiply.

$$\begin{aligned}(a + bi)(a - bi) &= a^2 - abi + abi - b^2i^2 \\ &= a^2 - b^2(-1) \\ &= a^2 + b^2\end{aligned}$$

We use complex conjugates to divide by a complex number.

EXAMPLE 5 Divide. Write in the form $a + bi$.

a. $\frac{2 + i}{1 - i}$ **b.** $\frac{7}{3i}$

Solution

a. Multiply the numerator and denominator by the complex conjugate of $1 - i$ to eliminate the imaginary number in the denominator.

$$\frac{2+i}{1-i} = \frac{(2+i)(1+i)}{(1-i)(1+i)}$$
$$= \frac{2(1) + 2(i) + 1(i) + i^2}{1^2 - i^2}$$
$$= \frac{2 + 3i - 1}{1 + 1} \quad \text{Here, } i^2 = -1.$$
$$= \frac{1 + 3i}{2} \quad \text{or} \quad \frac{1}{2} + \frac{3}{2}i$$

b. Multiply the numerator and denominator by the conjugate of $3i$. Note that $3i = 0 + 3i$, so its conjugate is $0 - 3i$ or $-3i$.

$$\frac{7}{3i} = \frac{7(-3i)}{(3i)(-3i)} = \frac{-21i}{-9i^2} = \frac{-21i}{-9(-1)} = \frac{-21i}{9} = \frac{-7i}{3} \quad \text{or} \quad 0 - \frac{7}{3}i$$

□

PRACTICE

5 Divide. Write in the form $a + bi$.

a. $\frac{4 - i}{3 + i}$ **b.** $\frac{5}{2i}$

Helpful Hint

Recall that division can be checked by multiplication.

To check that $\frac{2+i}{1-i} = \frac{1}{2} + \frac{3}{2}i$, in Example 5a, multiply $\left(\frac{1}{2} + \frac{3}{2}i\right)(1 - i)$ to verify that the product is $2 + i$.

OBJECTIVE

5 Finding Powers of *i*

We can use the fact that $i^2 = -1$ to find higher powers of i. To find i^3, we rewrite it as the product of i^2 and i.

$$i^3 = i^2 \cdot i = (-1)i = -i$$
$$i^4 = i^2 \cdot i^2 = (-1) \cdot (-1) = 1$$

We continue this process and use the fact that $i^4 = 1$ and $i^2 = -1$ to simplify i^5 and i^6.

$$i^5 = i^4 \cdot i = 1 \cdot i = i$$
$$i^6 = i^4 \cdot i^2 = 1 \cdot (-1) = -1$$

If we continue finding powers of i, we generate the following pattern. Notice that the values i, -1, $-i$, and 1 repeat as i is raised to higher and higher powers.

$i^1 = i$	$i^5 = i$	$i^9 = i$
$i^2 = -1$	$i^6 = -1$	$i^{10} = -1$
$i^3 = -i$	$i^7 = -i$	$i^{11} = -i$
$i^4 = 1$	$i^8 = 1$	$i^{12} = 1$

This pattern allows us to find other powers of i. To do so, we will use the fact that $i^4 = 1$ and rewrite a power of i in terms of i^4. For example,

$$i^{22} = i^{20} \cdot i^2 = (i^4)^5 \cdot i^2 = 1^5 \cdot (-1) = 1 \cdot (-1) = -1.$$

EXAMPLE 6 Find the following powers of i.

a. i^7 **b.** i^{20} **c.** i^{46} **d.** i^{-12}

Solution

a. $i^7 = i^4 \cdot i^3 = 1(-i) = -i$

b. $i^{20} = (i^4)^5 = 1^5 = 1$

c. $i^{46} = i^{44} \cdot i^2 = (i^4)^{11} \cdot i^2 = 1^{11}(-1) = -1$

d. $i^{-12} = \dfrac{1}{i^{12}} = \dfrac{1}{(i^4)^3} = \dfrac{1}{(1)^3} = \dfrac{1}{1} = 1$ □

PRACTICE 6 Find the following powers of i.

a. i^9 **b.** i^{16} **c.** i^{34} **d.** i^{-24}

Vocabulary, Readiness & Video Check

Use the choices below to fill in each blank. Not all choices will be used.

-1	$\sqrt{-1}$	real	imaginary unit
1	$\sqrt{1}$	complex	pure imaginary

1. A __________ number is one that can be written in the form $a + bi$, where a and b are real numbers.
2. In the complex number system, i denotes the __________.
3. $i^2 =$ __________
4. $i =$ __________
5. A complex number, $a + bi$, is a __________ number if $b = 0$.
6. A complex number, $a + bi$, is a __________ number if $a = 0$ and $b \neq 0$.

Martin-Gay Interactive Videos

See Video 5.7

Watch the section lecture video and answer the following questions.

OBJECTIVE 1

7. From Example 4, with what rule must you be especially careful when working with imaginary numbers and why?

OBJECTIVE 2

8. In Examples 5 and 6, what is the process of adding and subtracting complex numbers compared to? What important reminder is given about i?

OBJECTIVE 3

9. In Examples 7 and 8, what part of the definition of the imaginary unit i may be used during the multiplication of complex numbers to help simplify products?

OBJECTIVE 4

10. In Example 9, using complex conjugates to divide complex numbers is compared to what process?

OBJECTIVE 5

11. From the lecture before Example 10, what are the first four powers of i whose values keep repeating?

5.7 Exercise Set

MyMathLab®

Simplify. See Example 1.

1. $\sqrt{-81}$
2. $\sqrt{-49}$
3. $\sqrt{-7}$
4. $\sqrt{-3}$
5. $-\sqrt{16}$
6. $-\sqrt{4}$
7. $\sqrt{-64}$
8. $\sqrt{-100}$

Write in terms of i. See Example 1.

9. $\sqrt{-24}$
10. $\sqrt{-32}$
11. $-\sqrt{-36}$
12. $-\sqrt{-121}$
13. $8\sqrt{-63}$
14. $4\sqrt{-20}$
15. $-\sqrt{54}$
16. $\sqrt{-63}$

Multiply or divide. See Example 2.

17. $\sqrt{-2}\cdot\sqrt{-7}$
18. $\sqrt{-11}\cdot\sqrt{-3}$
19. $\sqrt{-5}\cdot\sqrt{-10}$
20. $\sqrt{-2}\cdot\sqrt{-6}$
21. $\sqrt{16}\cdot\sqrt{-1}$
22. $\sqrt{3}\cdot\sqrt{-27}$
23. $\dfrac{\sqrt{-9}}{\sqrt{3}}$
24. $\dfrac{\sqrt{49}}{\sqrt{-10}}$
25. $\dfrac{\sqrt{-80}}{\sqrt{-10}}$
26. $\dfrac{\sqrt{-40}}{\sqrt{-8}}$

Add or subtract. Write the sum or difference in the form a + bi. See Example 3.

27. $(4 - 7i) + (2 + 3i)$
28. $(2 - 4i) - (2 - i)$
29. $(6 + 5i) - (8 - i)$
30. $(8 - 3i) + (-8 + 3i)$
31. $6 - (8 + 4i)$
32. $(9 - 4i) - 9$

Multiply. Write the product in the form a + bi. See Example 4.

33. $-10i\cdot -4i$
34. $-2i\cdot -11i$
35. $6i(2 - 3i)$
36. $5i(4 - 7i)$
37. $(\sqrt{3} + 2i)(\sqrt{3} - 2i)$
38. $(\sqrt{5} - 5i)(\sqrt{5} + 5i)$
39. $(4 - 2i)^2$
40. $(6 - 3i)^2$

Write each quotient in the form a + bi. See Example 5.

41. $\dfrac{4}{i}$
42. $\dfrac{5}{6i}$
43. $\dfrac{7}{4 + 3i}$
44. $\dfrac{9}{1 - 2i}$
45. $\dfrac{3 + 5i}{1 + i}$
46. $\dfrac{6 + 2i}{4 - 3i}$
47. $\dfrac{5 - i}{3 - 2i}$
48. $\dfrac{6 - i}{2 + i}$

MIXED PRACTICE

Perform each indicated operation. Write the result in the form a + bi.

49. $(7i)(-9i)$
50. $(-6i)(-4i)$
51. $(6 - 3i) - (4 - 2i)$
52. $(-2 - 4i) - (6 - 8i)$
53. $-3i(-1 + 9i)$
54. $-5i(-2 + i)$
55. $\dfrac{4 - 5i}{2i}$
56. $\dfrac{6 + 8i}{3i}$
57. $(4 + i)(5 + 2i)$
58. $(3 + i)(2 + 4i)$
59. $(6 - 2i)(3 + i)$
60. $(2 - 4i)(2 - i)$
61. $(8 - 3i) + (2 + 3i)$
62. $(7 + 4i) + (4 - 4i)$
63. $(1 - i)(1 + i)$
64. $(6 + 2i)(6 - 2i)$
65. $\dfrac{16 + 15i}{-3i}$
66. $\dfrac{2 - 3i}{-7i}$
67. $(9 + 8i)^2$
68. $(4 - 7i)^2$
69. $\dfrac{2}{3 + i}$
70. $\dfrac{5}{3 - 2i}$
71. $(5 - 6i) - 4i$
72. $(6 - 2i) + 7i$
73. $\dfrac{2 - 3i}{2 + i}$
74. $\dfrac{6 + 5i}{6 - 5i}$
75. $(2 + 4i) + (6 - 5i)$
76. $(5 - 3i) + (7 - 8i)$
77. $(\sqrt{6} + i)(\sqrt{6} - i)$
78. $(\sqrt{14} - 4i)(\sqrt{14} + 4i)$
79. $4(2 - i)^2$
80. $9(2 - i)^2$

Find each power of i. See Example 6.

81. i^8
82. i^{10}
83. i^{21}
84. i^{15}
85. i^{11}
86. i^{40}
87. i^{-6}
88. i^{-9}
89. $(2i)^6$
90. $(5i)^4$
91. $(-3i)^5$
92. $(-2i)^7$

REVIEW AND PREVIEW

Recall that the sum of the measures of the angles of a triangle is 180°. Find the unknown angle in each triangle.

△ 93.
△ 94.

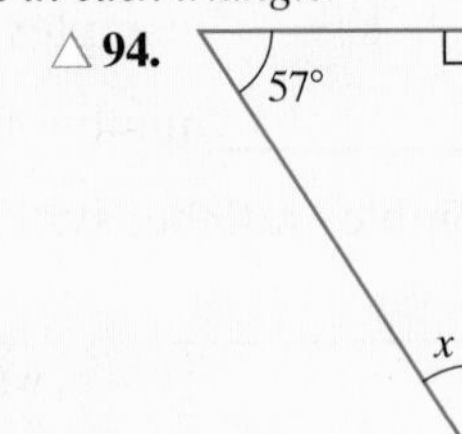

Use synthetic division to divide the following.

95. $(x^3 - 6x^2 + 3x - 4) \div (x - 1)$
96. $(5x^4 - 3x^2 + 2) \div (x + 2)$

Thirty people were recently polled about the average monthly balance in their checking accounts. The results of this poll are shown in the following histogram. Use this graph to answer Exercises 97 through 102. See Section 1.1.

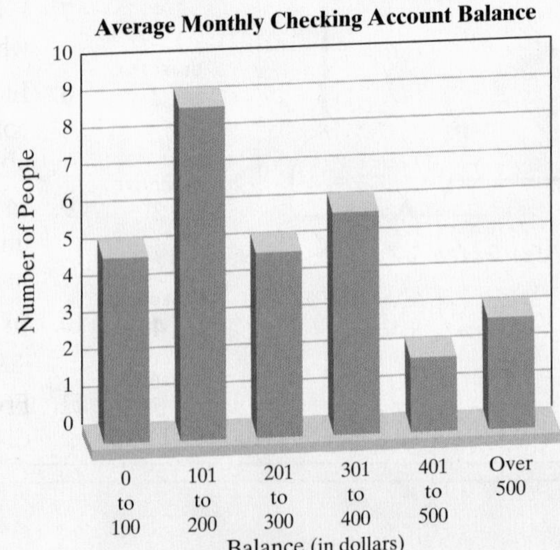

97. How many people polled reported an average checking balance of \$201 to \$300?

98. How many people polled reported an average checking balance of \$0 to \$100?

99. How many people polled reported an average checking balance of \$200 or less?

100. How many people polled reported an average checking balance of \$301 or more?

101. What percent of people polled reported an average checking balance of \$201 to \$300? Round to the nearest tenth of a percent.

102. What percent of people polled reported an average checking balance of \$0 to \$100? Round to the nearest tenth of a percent.

CONCEPT EXTENSIONS

Write in the form $a + bi$.

103. $i^3 - i^4$

104. $i^8 - i^7$

105. $i^6 + i^8$

106. $i^4 + i^{12}$

107. $2 + \sqrt{-9}$

108. $5 - \sqrt{-16}$

109. $\dfrac{6 + \sqrt{-18}}{3}$

110. $\dfrac{4 - \sqrt{-8}}{2}$

111. $\dfrac{5 - \sqrt{-75}}{10}$

112. $\dfrac{7 + \sqrt{-98}}{14}$

113. Describe how to find the conjugate of a complex number.

114. Explain why the product of a complex number and its complex conjugate is a real number.

Simplify.

115. $(8 - \sqrt{-3}) - (2 + \sqrt{-12})$

116. $(8 - \sqrt{-4}) - (2 + \sqrt{-16})$

117. Determine whether $2i$ is a solution of $x^2 + 4 = 0$.

118. Determine whether $-1 + i$ is a solution of $x^2 + 2x = -2$.

Chapter 5 Vocabulary Check

Fill in each blank with one of the words or phrases listed below.

index	rationalizing	conjugate	principal square root	cube root	midpoint
complex number	like radicals	radicand	imaginary unit	distance	

1. The __________ of $\sqrt{3} + 2$ is $\sqrt{3} - 2$.
2. The __________ of a nonnegative number a is written as $\sqrt{a}$.
3. The process of writing a radical expression as an equivalent expression but without a radical in the denominator is called __________ the denominator.
4. The __________, written i, is the number whose square is -1.
5. The __________ of a number is written as $\sqrt[3]{a}$.
6. In the notation $\sqrt[n]{a}$, n is called the __________ and a is called the __________.
7. Radicals with the same index and the same radicand are called __________.
8. A(n) __________ is a number that can be written in the form $a + bi$, where a and b are real numbers.
9. The __________ formula is $d = \sqrt{(x_2 - x_1)^2 + (y_2 - y_1)^2}$.
10. The __________ formula is $\left(\dfrac{x_1 + x_2}{2}, \dfrac{y_1 + y_2}{2}\right)$.

Chapter 5 Highlights

DEFINITIONS AND CONCEPTS	EXAMPLES
Section 5.1 Radicals and Radical Functions	
The **positive,** or **principal, square root** of a nonnegative number a is written as $\sqrt{a}$. $\sqrt{a} = b$ only if $b^2 = a$ and $b \ge 0$ The **negative square root of** a is written as $-\sqrt{a}$.	$\sqrt{36} = 6 \qquad \sqrt{\dfrac{9}{100}} = \dfrac{3}{10}$ $-\sqrt{36} = -6 \qquad -\sqrt{0.04} = -0.2$

(continued)

DEFINITIONS AND CONCEPTS	EXAMPLES
Section 5.1 Radicals and Radical Functions (continued)	
The **cube root** of a real number a is written as $\sqrt[3]{a}$. $\sqrt[3]{a} = b$ only if $b^3 = a$	$\sqrt[3]{27} = 3$ $\quad \sqrt[3]{-\frac{1}{8}} = -\frac{1}{2}$ $\sqrt[3]{y^6} = y^2$ $\quad \sqrt[3]{64x^9} = 4x^3$
If n is an even positive integer, then $\sqrt[n]{a^n} = \lvert a \rvert$.	$\sqrt{(-3)^2} = \lvert -3 \rvert = 3$
If n is an odd positive integer, then $\sqrt[n]{a^n} = a$.	$\sqrt[3]{(-7)^3} = -7$
A **radical function** in x is a function defined by an expression containing a root of x.	If $f(x) = \sqrt{x} + 2$, $f(1) = \sqrt{(1)} + 2 = 1 + 2 = 3$ $f(3) = \sqrt{(3)} + 2 \approx 3.73$
Section 5.2 Rational Exponents	
$a^{1/n} = \sqrt[n]{a}$ if $\sqrt[n]{a}$ is a real number.	$81^{1/2} = \sqrt{81} = 9$ $(-8x^3)^{1/3} = \sqrt[3]{-8x^3} = -2x$
If m and n are positive integers greater than 1 with $\frac{m}{n}$ in lowest terms and $\sqrt[n]{a}$ is a real number, then $a^{m/n} = (a^{1/n})^m = (\sqrt[n]{a})^m$	$4^{5/2} = (\sqrt{4})^5 = 2^5 = 32$ $27^{2/3} = (\sqrt[3]{27})^2 = 3^2 = 9$
$a^{-m/n} = \frac{1}{a^{m/n}}$ as long as $a^{m/n}$ is a nonzero number.	$16^{-3/4} = \frac{1}{16^{3/4}} = \frac{1}{(\sqrt[4]{16})^3} = \frac{1}{2^3} = \frac{1}{8}$
Exponent rules are true for rational exponents.	$x^{2/3} \cdot x^{-5/6} = x^{2/3-5/6} = x^{-1/6} = \frac{1}{x^{1/6}}$ $(8^4)^{1/2} = 8^2 = 64$ $\frac{a^{4/5}}{a^{-2/5}} = a^{4/5-(-2/5)} = a^{6/5}$
Section 5.3 Simplifying Radical Expressions	
Product and Quotient Rules If $\sqrt[n]{a}$ and $\sqrt[n]{b}$ are real numbers, $\sqrt[n]{a} \cdot \sqrt[n]{b} = \sqrt[n]{a \cdot b}$ $\frac{\sqrt[n]{a}}{\sqrt[n]{b}} = \sqrt[n]{\frac{a}{b}}$, provided $\sqrt[n]{b} \neq 0$	Multiply or divide as indicated: $\sqrt{11} \cdot \sqrt{3} = \sqrt{33}$ $\frac{\sqrt[3]{40x}}{\sqrt[3]{5x}} = \sqrt[3]{8} = 2$
A radical of the form $\sqrt[n]{a}$ is **simplified** when a contains no factors that are perfect nth powers.	$\sqrt{40} = \sqrt{4 \cdot 10} = 2\sqrt{10}$ $\sqrt{36x^5} = \sqrt{36x^4 \cdot x} = 6x^2\sqrt{x}$ $\sqrt[3]{24x^7y^3} = \sqrt[3]{8x^6y^3 \cdot 3x} = 2x^2y\sqrt[3]{3x}$
Distance Formula The distance d between two points (x_1, y_1) and (x_2, y_2) is given by $d = \sqrt{(x_2 - x_1)^2 + (y_2 - y_1)^2}$	Find the distance between points $(-1, 6)$ and $(-2, -4)$. Let $(x_1, y_1) = (-1, 6)$ and $(x_2, y_2) = (-2, -4)$. $d = \sqrt{(x_2 - x_1)^2 + (y_2 - y_1)^2}$ $= \sqrt{(-2 - (-1))^2 + (-4 - 6)^2}$ $= \sqrt{1 + 100} = \sqrt{101}$

DEFINITIONS AND CONCEPTS	EXAMPLES
Section 5.3 Simplifying Radical Expressions (continued)	
Midpoint Formula The midpoint of the line segment whose endpoints are (x_1, y_1) and (x_2, y_2) is the point with coordinates $\left(\frac{x_1 + x_2}{2}, \frac{y_1 + y_2}{2}\right)$	Find the midpoint of the line segment whose endpoints are $(-1, 6)$ and $(-2, -4)$. $\left(\frac{-1 + (-2)}{2}, \frac{6 + (-4)}{2}\right)$ The midpoint is $\left(-\frac{3}{2}, 1\right)$.
Section 5.4 Adding, Subtracting, and Multiplying Radical Expressions	
Radicals with the same index and the same radicand are **like radicals.**	$5\sqrt{6} + 2\sqrt{6} = (5 + 2)\sqrt{6} = 7\sqrt{6}$
The distributive property can be used to add like radicals.	$\sqrt[3]{3x} - 10\sqrt[3]{3x} + 3\sqrt[3]{10x}$ $= (-1 - 10)\sqrt[3]{3x} + 3\sqrt[3]{10x}$ $= -11\sqrt[3]{3x} + 3\sqrt[3]{10x}$
Radical expressions are multiplied by using many of the same properties used to multiply polynomials.	Multiply: $(\sqrt{5} - \sqrt{2x})(\sqrt{2} + \sqrt{2x})$ $= \sqrt{10} + \sqrt{10x} - \sqrt{4x} - 2x$ $= \sqrt{10} + \sqrt{10x} - 2\sqrt{x} - 2x$ $(2\sqrt{3} - \sqrt{8x})(2\sqrt{3} + \sqrt{8x})$ $= 4(3) - 8x = 12 - 8x$
Section 5.5 Rationalizing Denominators and Numerators of Radical Expressions	
The **conjugate** of $a + b$ is $a - b$.	The conjugate of $\sqrt{7} + \sqrt{3}$ is $\sqrt{7} - \sqrt{3}$.
The process of writing the denominator of a radical expression without a radical is called **rationalizing the denominator.**	Rationalize each denominator. $\frac{\sqrt{5}}{\sqrt{3}} = \frac{\sqrt{5} \cdot \sqrt{3}}{\sqrt{3} \cdot \sqrt{3}} = \frac{\sqrt{15}}{3}$ $\frac{6}{\sqrt{7} + \sqrt{3}} = \frac{6(\sqrt{7} - \sqrt{3})}{(\sqrt{7} + \sqrt{3})(\sqrt{7} - \sqrt{3})}$ $= \frac{6(\sqrt{7} - \sqrt{3})}{7 - 3}$ $= \frac{6(\sqrt{7} - \sqrt{3})}{4} = \frac{3(\sqrt{7} - \sqrt{3})}{2}$

(continued)

DEFINITIONS AND CONCEPTS	EXAMPLES
Section 5.5 Rationalizing Denominators and Numerators of Radical Expressions (continued)	
The process of writing the numerator of a radical expression without a radical is called **rationalizing the numerator.**	Rationalize each numerator: $\frac{\sqrt[3]{9}}{\sqrt[3]{5}} = \frac{\sqrt[3]{9}\cdot\sqrt[3]{3}}{\sqrt[3]{5}\cdot\sqrt[3]{3}} = \frac{\sqrt[3]{27}}{\sqrt[3]{15}} = \frac{3}{\sqrt[3]{15}}$ $\frac{\sqrt{9}+\sqrt{3x}}{12} = \frac{(\sqrt{9}+\sqrt{3x})(\sqrt{9}-\sqrt{3x})}{12(\sqrt{9}-\sqrt{3x})}$ $= \frac{9-3x}{12(\sqrt{9}-\sqrt{3x})}$ $= \frac{3(3-x)}{3\cdot 4(3-\sqrt{3x})} = \frac{3-x}{4(3-\sqrt{3x})}$
Section 5.6 Radical Equations and Problem Solving	
To Solve a Radical Equation	Solve: $x = \sqrt{4x+9} + 3$.
Step 1. Write the equation so that one radical is by itself on one side of the equation.	**1.** $x - 3 = \sqrt{4x+9}$
Step 2. Raise each side of the equation to a power equal to the index of the radical and simplify.	**2.** $(x-3)^2 = (\sqrt{4x+9})^2$ $x^2 - 6x + 9 = 4x + 9$
Step 3. If the equation still contains a radical, repeat Steps 1 and 2. If not, solve the equation.	**3.** $x^2 - 10x = 0$ $x(x-10) = 0$ $x = 0$ or $x = 10$
Step 4. Check all proposed solutions in the original equation.	**4.** The proposed solution 10 checks, but 0 does not. The solution is 10.
Section 5.7 Complex Numbers	
$i^2 = -1$ and $i = \sqrt{-1}$ A **complex number** is a number that can be written in the form $a + bi$, where a and b are real numbers.	Simplify: $\sqrt{-9}$. $\sqrt{-9} = \sqrt{-1\cdot 9} = \sqrt{-1}\cdot\sqrt{9} = i\cdot 3$ or $3i$ ***Complex Numbers*** — ***Written in Form a + bi*** 12 — $12 + 0i$ $-5i$ — $0 + (-5)i$ $-2 - 3i$ — $-2 + (-3)i$ Multiply. $\sqrt{-3}\cdot\sqrt{-7} = i\sqrt{3}\cdot i\sqrt{7}$ $= i^2\sqrt{21}$ $= -\sqrt{21}$
To add or subtract complex numbers, add or subtract their real parts and then add or subtract their imaginary parts.	Perform each indicated operation. $(-3+2i) - (7-4i) = -3 + 2i - 7 + 4i$ $= -10 + 6i$
To multiply complex numbers, multiply as though they are binomials.	$(-7-2i)(6+i) = -42 - 7i - 12i - 2i^2$ $= -42 - 19i - 2(-1)$ $= -42 - 19i + 2$ $= -40 - 19i$

DEFINITIONS AND CONCEPTS	EXAMPLES
Section 5.7 Complex Numbers (continued)	
The complex numbers $(a + bi)$ and $(a - bi)$ are called **complex conjugates.**	The complex conjugate of $(3 + 6i)$ is $(3 - 6i)$. Their product is a real number: $(3 - 6i)(3 + 6i) = 9 - 36i^2 = 9 - 36(-1) = 9 + 36 = 45$
To divide complex numbers, multiply the numerator and the denominator by the conjugate of the denominator.	Divide. $\frac{4}{2 - i} = \frac{4(2 + i)}{(2 - i)(2 + i)} = \frac{4(2 + i)}{4 - i^2} = \frac{4(2 + i)}{5} = \frac{8 + 4i}{5} = \frac{8}{5} + \frac{4}{5}i$

Chapter 5 Review

(5.1) Find the root. Assume that all variables represent positive numbers.

1. $\sqrt{81}$

2. $\sqrt[4]{81}$

3. $\sqrt[3]{-8}$

4. $\sqrt[4]{-16}$

5. $-\sqrt{\frac{1}{49}}$

6. $\sqrt{x^{64}}$

7. $-\sqrt{36}$

8. $\sqrt[3]{64}$

9. $\sqrt[3]{-a^6b^9}$

10. $\sqrt{16a^4b^{12}}$

11. $\sqrt[5]{32a^5b^{10}}$

12. $\sqrt[5]{-32x^{15}y^{20}}$

13. $\sqrt{\frac{x^{12}}{36y^2}}$

14. $\sqrt[3]{\frac{27y^3}{z^{12}}}$

Simplify. Use absolute value bars when necessary.

15. $\sqrt{(-x)^2}$

16. $\sqrt[4]{(x^2 - 4)^4}$

17. $\sqrt[3]{(-27)^3}$

18. $\sqrt[5]{(-5)^5}$

19. $-\sqrt[5]{x^5}$

20. $-\sqrt[3]{x^3}$

21. $\sqrt[4]{16(2y + z)^4}$

22. $\sqrt{25(x - y)^2}$

23. $\sqrt[5]{y^5}$

24. $\sqrt[6]{x^6}$

25. Let $f(x) = \sqrt{x} + 3$.

a. Find $f(0)$ and $f(9)$.

b. Find the domain of $f(x)$.

c. Graph $f(x)$.

26. Let $g(x) = \sqrt[3]{x} - 3$.

a. Find $g(11)$ and $g(20)$.

b. Find the domain of $g(x)$.

c. Graph $g(x)$.

(5.2) Evaluate.

27. $\left(\frac{1}{81}\right)^{1/4}$

28. $\left(-\frac{1}{27}\right)^{1/3}$

29. $(-27)^{-1/3}$

30. $(-64)^{-1/3}$

31. $-9^{3/2}$

32. $64^{-1/3}$

33. $(-25)^{5/2}$

34. $\left(\frac{25}{49}\right)^{-3/2}$

35. $\left(\frac{8}{27}\right)^{-2/3}$

36. $\left(-\frac{1}{36}\right)^{-1/4}$

Write with rational exponents.

37. $\sqrt[3]{x^2}$

38. $\sqrt[5]{5x^2y^3}$

Write using radical notation.

39. $y^{4/5}$

40. $5(xy^2z^5)^{1/3}$

41. $(x + 2)^{-1/3}$

42. $(x + 2y)^{-1/2}$

Simplify each expression. Assume that all variables represent positive real numbers. Write with only positive exponents.

43. $a^{1/3}a^{4/3}a^{1/2}$

44. $\frac{b^{1/3}}{b^{4/3}}$

45. $(a^{1/2}a^{-2})^3$

46. $(x^{-3}y^6)^{1/3}$

47. $\left(\frac{b^{3/4}}{a^{-1/2}}\right)^8$

48. $\frac{x^{1/4}x^{-1/2}}{x^{2/3}}$

49. $\left(\frac{49c^{5/3}}{a^{-1/4}b^{5/6}}\right)^{-1}$

50. $a^{-1/4}(a^{5/4} - a^{9/4})$

Use a calculator and write a three-decimal-place approximation of each number.

51. $\sqrt{20}$

52. $\sqrt[3]{-39}$

53. $\sqrt[4]{726}$

54. $56^{1/3}$

55. $-78^{3/4}$

56. $105^{-2/3}$

Use rational exponents to write each as a single radical.

57. $\sqrt[3]{2}\cdot\sqrt{7}$

58. $\sqrt[3]{3}\cdot\sqrt[4]{x}$

(5.3) Perform each indicated operation and then simplify if possible. Assume that all variables represent positive real numbers.

59. $\sqrt{3}\cdot\sqrt{8}$

60. $\sqrt[3]{7y}\cdot\sqrt[3]{x^2z}$

61. $\dfrac{\sqrt{44x^3}}{\sqrt{11x}}$

62. $\dfrac{\sqrt[4]{a^6b^{13}}}{\sqrt[4]{a^2b}}$

Simplify.

63. $\sqrt{60}$

64. $-\sqrt{75}$

65. $\sqrt[3]{162}$

66. $\sqrt[3]{-32}$

67. $\sqrt{36x^7}$

68. $\sqrt[3]{24a^5b^7}$

69. $\sqrt{\dfrac{p^{17}}{121}}$

70. $\sqrt[3]{\dfrac{y^5}{27x^6}}$

71. $\sqrt[4]{\dfrac{xy^6}{81}}$

72. $\sqrt{\dfrac{2x^3}{49y^4}}$

△ *The formula for the radius r of a circle of area A is* $r = \sqrt{\dfrac{A}{\pi}}$. *Use this for Exercises 73 and 74.*

73. Find the exact radius of a circle whose area is 25 square meters.

74. Approximate to two decimal places the radius of a circle whose area is 104 square inches.

Find the distance between each pair of points. Give an exact value and a three-decimal-place approximation.

75. $(-6, 3)$ and $(8, 4)$

76. $(-4, -6)$ and $(-1, 5)$

77. $(-1, 5)$ and $(2, -3)$

78. $(-\sqrt{2}, 0)$ and $(0, -4\sqrt{6})$

79. $(-\sqrt{5}, -\sqrt{11})$ and $(-\sqrt{5}, -3\sqrt{11})$

80. $(7.4, -8.6)$ and $(-1.2, 5.6)$

Find the midpoint of each line segment whose endpoints are given.

81. $(2, 6); (-12, 4)$

82. $(-6, -5); (-9, 7)$

83. $(4, -6); (-15, 2)$

84. $\left(0, -\dfrac{3}{8}\right); \left(\dfrac{1}{10}, 0\right)$

85. $\left(\dfrac{3}{4}, -\dfrac{1}{7}\right); \left(-\dfrac{1}{4}, -\dfrac{3}{7}\right)$

86. $(\sqrt{3}, -2\sqrt{6}); (\sqrt{3}, -4\sqrt{6})$

(5.4) Perform each indicated operation. Assume that all variables represent positive real numbers.

87. $\sqrt{20} + \sqrt{45} - 7\sqrt{5}$

88. $x\sqrt{75x} - \sqrt{27x^3}$

89. $\sqrt[3]{128} + \sqrt[3]{250}$

90. $3\sqrt[4]{32a^5} - a\sqrt[4]{162a}$

91. $\dfrac{5}{\sqrt{4}} + \dfrac{\sqrt{3}}{3}$

92. $\sqrt{\dfrac{8}{x^2}} - \sqrt{\dfrac{50}{16x^2}}$

93. $2\sqrt{50} - 3\sqrt{125} + \sqrt{98}$

94. $2a\sqrt[4]{32b^5} - 3b\sqrt[4]{162a^4b} + \sqrt[4]{2a^4b^5}$

Multiply and then simplify if possible. Assume that all variables represent positive real numbers.

95. $\sqrt{3}(\sqrt{27} - \sqrt{3})$

96. $(\sqrt{x} - 3)^2$

97. $(\sqrt{5} - 5)(2\sqrt{5} + 2)$

98. $(2\sqrt{x} - 3\sqrt{y})(2\sqrt{x} + 3\sqrt{y})$

99. $(\sqrt{a} + 3)(\sqrt{a} - 3)$

100. $(\sqrt[3]{a} + 2)^2$

101. $(\sqrt[3]{5x} + 9)(\sqrt[3]{5x} - 9)$

102. $(\sqrt[3]{a} + 4)(\sqrt[3]{a^2} - 4\sqrt[3]{a} + 16)$

(5.5) Rationalize each denominator. Assume that all variables represent positive real numbers.

103. $\dfrac{3}{\sqrt{7}}$

104. $\sqrt{\dfrac{x}{12}}$

105. $\dfrac{5}{\sqrt[3]{4}}$

106. $\sqrt{\dfrac{24x^5}{3y}}$

107. $\sqrt[3]{\dfrac{15x^6y^7}{z^2}}$

108. $\sqrt[4]{\dfrac{81}{8x^{10}}}$

109. $\dfrac{3}{\sqrt{y} - 2}$

110. $\dfrac{\sqrt{2} - \sqrt{3}}{\sqrt{2} + \sqrt{3}}$

Rationalize each numerator. Assume that all variables represent positive real numbers.

111. $\dfrac{\sqrt{11}}{3}$

112. $\sqrt{\dfrac{18}{y}}$

113. $\dfrac{\sqrt[3]{9}}{7}$

114. $\sqrt{\dfrac{24x^5}{3y^2}}$

115. $\sqrt[3]{\dfrac{xy^2}{10z}}$

116. $\dfrac{\sqrt{x} + 5}{-3}$

(5.6) Solve each equation.

117. $\sqrt{y - 7} = 5$

118. $\sqrt{2x} + 10 = 4$

119. $\sqrt[3]{2x - 6} = 4$

120. $\sqrt{x + 6} = \sqrt{x + 2}$

121. $2x - 5\sqrt{x} = 3$

122. $\sqrt{x + 9} = 2 + \sqrt{x - 7}$

Find each unknown length.

△ **123.**

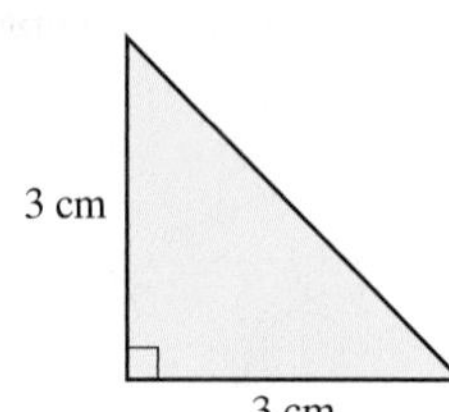

△ **124.**

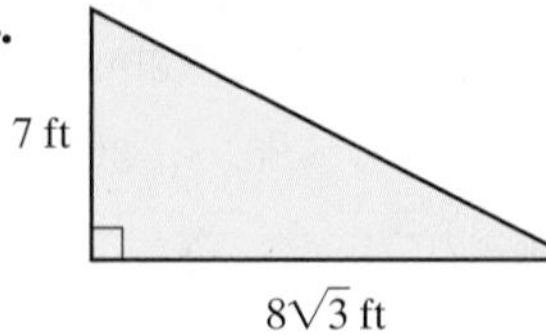

△ **125.** Craig and Daniel Cantwell want to determine the distance x across a pond on their property. They are able to measure the distances shown on the following diagram. Find how wide the pond is at the crossing point indicated by the triangle to the nearest tenth of a foot.

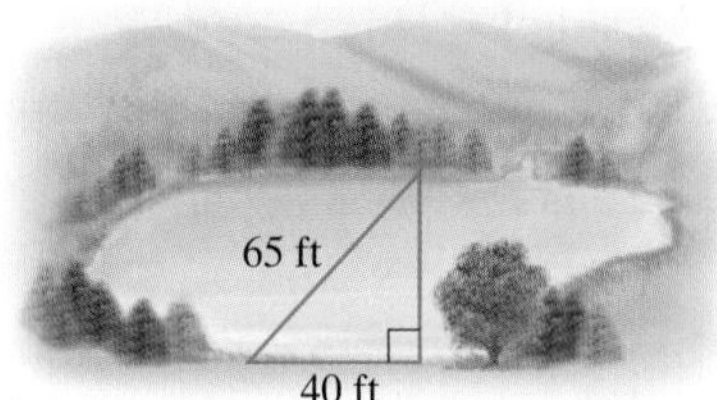

△ **126.** Andrea Roberts, a pipefitter, needs to connect two underground pipelines that are offset by 3 feet, as pictured in the diagram. Neglecting the joints needed to join the pipes, find the length of the shortest possible connecting pipe rounded to the nearest hundredth of a foot.

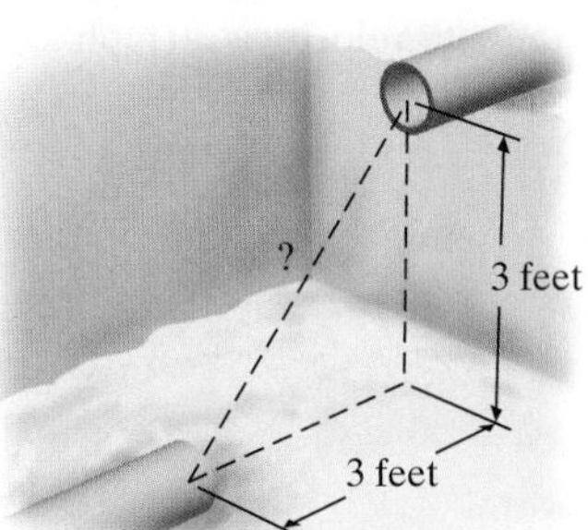

(5.7) *Perform each indicated operation and simplify. Write the results in the form $a + bi$.*

127. $\sqrt{-8}$

128. $-\sqrt{-6}$

129. $\sqrt{-4} + \sqrt{-16}$

130. $\sqrt{-2} \cdot \sqrt{-5}$

131. $(12 - 6i) + (3 + 2i)$

132. $(-8 - 7i) - (5 - 4i)$

133. $(2i)^6$

134. $(3i)^4$

135. $-3i(6 - 4i)$

136. $(3 + 2i)(1 + i)$

137. $(2 - 3i)^2$

138. $(\sqrt{6} - 9i)(\sqrt{6} + 9i)$

139. $\dfrac{2 + 3i}{2i}$

140. $\dfrac{1 + i}{-3i}$

MIXED REVIEW

Simplify. Use absolute value bars when necessary.

141. $\sqrt[3]{x^3}$

142. $\sqrt{(x + 2)^2}$

Simplify. Assume that all variables represent positive real numbers. If necessary, write answers with positive exponents only.

143. $-\sqrt{100}$

144. $\sqrt[3]{-x^{12}y^3}$

145. $\sqrt[4]{\dfrac{y^{20}}{16x^{12}}}$

146. $9^{1/2}$

147. $64^{-1/2}$

148. $\left(\dfrac{27}{64}\right)^{-2/3}$

149. $\dfrac{(x^{2/3}x^{-3})^3}{x^{-1/2}}$

150. $\sqrt{200x^9}$

151. $\sqrt{\dfrac{3n^3}{121m^{10}}}$

152. $3\sqrt{20} - 7x\sqrt[3]{40} + 3\sqrt[3]{5x^3}$

153. $(2\sqrt{x} - 5)^2$

154. Find the distance between $(-3, 5)$ and $(-8, 9)$.

155. Find the midpoint of the line segment joining $(-3, 8)$ and $(11, 24)$.

Rationalize each denominator.

156. $\dfrac{7}{\sqrt{13}}$

157. $\dfrac{2}{\sqrt{x} + 3}$

Solve.

158. $\sqrt{x} + 2 = x$

159. $\sqrt{2x - 1} + 2 = x$

Chapter 5 Test

Raise to the power or find the root. Assume that all variables represent positive numbers. Write with only positive exponents.

1. $\sqrt{216}$

2. $-\sqrt[4]{x^{64}}$

3. $\left(\dfrac{1}{125}\right)^{1/3}$

4. $\left(\dfrac{1}{125}\right)^{-1/3}$

5. $\left(\dfrac{8x^3}{27}\right)^{2/3}$

6. $\sqrt[3]{-a^{18}b^9}$

7. $\left(\dfrac{64c^{4/3}}{a^{-2/3}b^{5/6}}\right)^{1/2}$

8. $a^{-2/3}(a^{5/4} - a^3)$

Find the root. Use absolute value bars when necessary.

9. $\sqrt[4]{(4xy)^4}$

10. $\sqrt[3]{(-27)^3}$

Rationalize the denominator. Assume that all variables represent positive numbers.

11. $\sqrt{\dfrac{9}{y}}$

12. $\dfrac{4 - \sqrt{x}}{4 + 2\sqrt{x}}$

13. $\dfrac{\sqrt[3]{ab}}{\sqrt[3]{ab^2}}$

14. Rationalize the numerator of $\dfrac{\sqrt{6} + x}{8}$ and simplify.

Perform the indicated operations. Assume that all variables represent positive numbers.

15. $\sqrt{125x^3} - 3\sqrt{20x^3}$

16. $\sqrt{3}(\sqrt{16} - \sqrt{2})$

17. $(\sqrt{x} + 1)^2$

18. $(\sqrt{2} - 4)(\sqrt{3} + 1)$

19. $(\sqrt{5} + 5)(\sqrt{5} - 5)$

Use a calculator to approximate each to three decimal places.

20. $\sqrt{561}$

21. $386^{-2/3}$

Solve.

22. $x = \sqrt{x - 2} + 2$

23. $\sqrt{x^2 - 7} + 3 = 0$

24. $\sqrt[3]{x + 5} = \sqrt[3]{2x - 1}$

Perform the indicated operation and simplify. Write the result in the form $a + bi$.

25. $\sqrt{-2}$

26. $-\sqrt{-8}$

27. $(12 - 6i) - (12 - 3i)$

28. $(6 - 2i)(6 + 2i)$

29. $(4 + 3i)^2$

30. $\dfrac{1 + 4i}{1 - i}$

31. Find x.

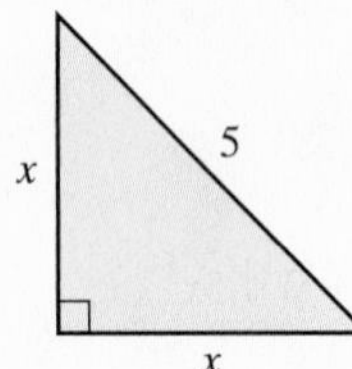

32. Identify the domain of $g(x)$. Then complete the accompanying table and graph $g(x)$.

$$g(x) = \sqrt{x + 2}$$

x	-2	-1	2	7
$g(x)$				

33. Find the distance between the points $(-6, 3)$ and $(-8, -7)$.

34. Find the distance between the points $(-2\sqrt{5}, \sqrt{10})$ and $(-\sqrt{5}, 4\sqrt{10})$.

35. Find the midpoint of the line segment whose endpoints are $(-2, -5)$ and $(-6, 12)$.

36. Find the midpoint of the line segment whose endpoints are $\left(-\frac{2}{3}, -\frac{1}{5}\right)$ and $\left(-\frac{1}{3}, \frac{4}{5}\right)$.

Solve.

37. The function $V(r) = \sqrt{2.5r}$ can be used to estimate the maximum safe velocity V in miles per hour at which a car can travel if it is driven along a curved road with a *radius of curvature* r in feet. To the nearest whole number, find the maximum safe speed if a cloverleaf exit on an expressway has a radius of curvature of 300 feet.

38. Use the formula from Exercise 37 to find the radius of curvature if the safe velocity is 30 mph.

Chapter 5 Cumulative Review

1. Simplify each expression.
   a. $-3 + [(-2 - 5) - 2]$
   b. $2^3 - |10| + [-6 - (-5)]$

2. Simplify each expression.
   a. $2(x - 3) + (5x + 3)$
   b. $4(3x + 2) - 3(5x - 1)$
   c. $7x + 2(x - 7) - 3x$

3. Solve: $\dfrac{x}{2} - 1 = \dfrac{2}{3}x - 3$

4. Solve: $\dfrac{a - 1}{2} + a = 2 - \dfrac{2a + 7}{8}$

5. A 48-inch balsa wood stick is to be cut into two pieces so that the longer piece is 3 times the shorter. Find the length of each piece.

6. The Smith family owns a lake house 121.5 miles from home. If it takes them $4\frac{1}{2}$ hours to drive round-trip from their house to their lake house, find their average speed.

7. Without graphing, determine the number of solutions of the system.
$$\begin{cases} 3x - y = 4 \\ x + 2y = 8 \end{cases}$$

8. Solve: $|3x - 2| + 5 = 5$

9. Solve the system: $\begin{cases} x + 2y = 7 \\ 2x + 2y = 13 \end{cases}$

10. Solve: $\left|\dfrac{x}{2} - 1\right| \le 0$.

11. Solve the system: $\begin{cases} 2x - y = 7 \\ 8x - 4y = 1 \end{cases}$

12. Graph $y = |x - 2|$.

13. Lynn Pike, a pharmacist, needs 70 liters of a 50% alcohol solution. She has available a 30% alcohol solution and an 80% alcohol solution. How many liters of each solution should she mix to obtain 70 liters of a 50% alcohol solution?

14. Find the domain and the range of each relation. Use the vertical line test to determine whether each graph is the graph of a function.

a.

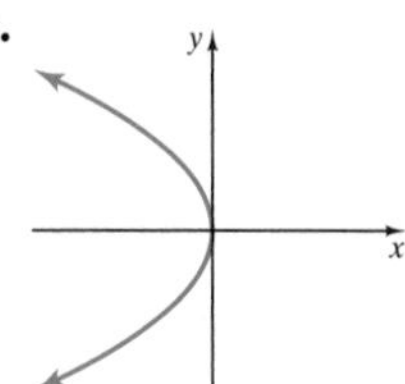

b.

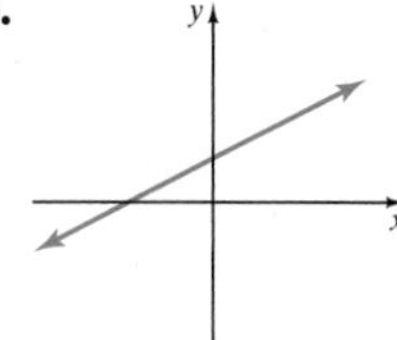

c.

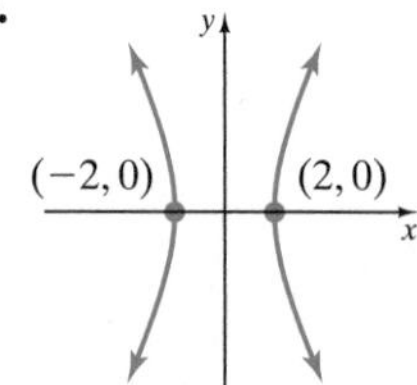

15. If $P(x) = 3x^2 - 2x - 5$, find the following.

a. $P(1)$ **b.** $P(-2)$

16. Graph $f(x) = -2$.

17. Divide $6m^2 + 2m$ by $2m$.

18. Find the slope of $y = -3$.

19. Use synthetic division to divide $2x^3 - x^2 - 13x + 1$ by $x - 3$.

20. Solve the system.

$$\begin{cases} \dfrac{x}{6} - \dfrac{y}{2} = 1 \\ \dfrac{x}{3} - \dfrac{y}{4} = 2 \end{cases}$$

21. Factor $40 - 13t + t^2$.

22. At a seasonal clearance sale, Nana Long spent \$33.75. She paid \$3.50 for tee-shirts and \$4.25 for shorts. If she bought 9 items, how many of each item did she buy?

23. Simplify each rational expression.

a. $\dfrac{x^3 + 8}{2 + x}$

b. $\dfrac{2y^2 + 2}{y^3 - 5y^2 + y - 5}$

24. Use scientific notation to simplify and write the answer in scientific notation. $\dfrac{0.0000035 \times 4000}{0.28}$

25. Solve: $|x - 3| = |5 - x|$

26. Subtract $(2x - 5)$ from the sum of $(5x^2 - 3x + 6)$ and $(4x^2 + 5x - 3)$.

27. Subtract: $\dfrac{3x^2 + 2x}{x - 1} - \dfrac{10x - 5}{x - 1}$

28. Multiply and simplify the product if possible.

a. $(y - 2)(3y + 4)$

b. $(3y - 1)(2y^2 + 3y - 1)$

29. Add: $1 + \dfrac{m}{m + 1}$

30. Factor. $x^3 - x^2 + 4x - 4$

31. Simply each complex fraction.

a. $\dfrac{\dfrac{5x}{x + 2}}{\dfrac{10}{x - 2}}$

b. $\dfrac{\dfrac{x}{y^2} + \dfrac{1}{y}}{\dfrac{y}{x^2} + \dfrac{1}{x}}$

32. Simplify each rational expression.

a. $\dfrac{a^3 - 8}{2 - a}$

b. $\dfrac{3a^2 - 3}{a^3 + 5a^2 - a - 5}$

33. Solve: $|5x + 1| + 1 \le 10$

34. Perform the indicated operations.

a. $\dfrac{3}{xy^2} - \dfrac{2}{3x^2y}$

b. $\dfrac{5x}{x + 3} - \dfrac{2x}{x - 3}$

c. $\dfrac{x}{x - 2} - \dfrac{5}{2 - x}$

35. If the following two triangles are similar, find the missing length x.

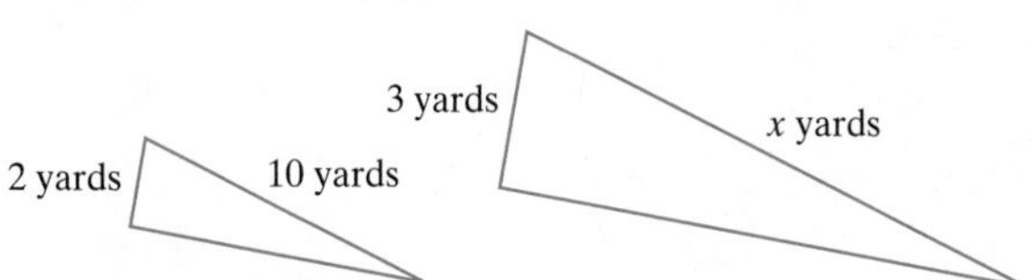

36. Simplify each complex fraction.

a. $\dfrac{\dfrac{y - 2}{16}}{\dfrac{2y + 3}{12}}$

b. $\dfrac{\dfrac{x}{16} - \dfrac{1}{x}}{1 - \dfrac{4}{x}}$

37. Find the cube roots.

a. $\sqrt[3]{1}$ **b.** $\sqrt[3]{-64}$

c. $\sqrt[3]{\dfrac{8}{125}}$ **d.** $\sqrt[3]{x^6}$

e. $\sqrt[3]{-27x^9}$

38. Divide $x^3 - 2x^2 + 3x - 6$ by $x - 2$.

39. Write each expression with a positive exponent, and then simplify.

a. $16^{-3/4}$

b. $(-27)^{-2/3}$

40. Use synthetic division to divide $4y^3 - 12y^2 - y + 12$ by $y - 3$.

41. Rationalize the numerator of $\dfrac{\sqrt{x} + 2}{5}$

42. Solve: $\dfrac{28}{9 - a^2} = \dfrac{2a}{a - 3} + \dfrac{6}{a + 3}$

43. Suppose that u varies inversely as w. If u is 3 when w is 5, find the constant of variation and the inverse variation equation.

44. Suppose that y varies directly as x. If $y = 0.51$ when $x = 3$, find the constant of variation and the direct variation equation.

CHAPTER 6

Quadratic Equations and Functions

An important part of the study of algebra is learning to model and solve problems. Often, the model of a problem is a quadratic equation or a function containing a second-degree polynomial. In this chapter, we continue the work begun in Chapter 3, when we solved polynomial equations in one variable by factoring. Two additional methods of solving quadratic equations are analyzed as well as methods of solving nonlinear inequalities in one variable.

Man has always desired to reach the stars, and some buildings seem to be trying to do just that. As populations expand and land becomes scarcer, ever taller and more spectacular buildings are being constructed. As of 2010, the tallest building in the world was the Burj Khalifa, in Dubai. In Exercise 80, Section 6.1, you will explore the height of the Burj Khalifa. (*Source:* Council on Tall Buildings and Urban Habitat, *Fast Company*)

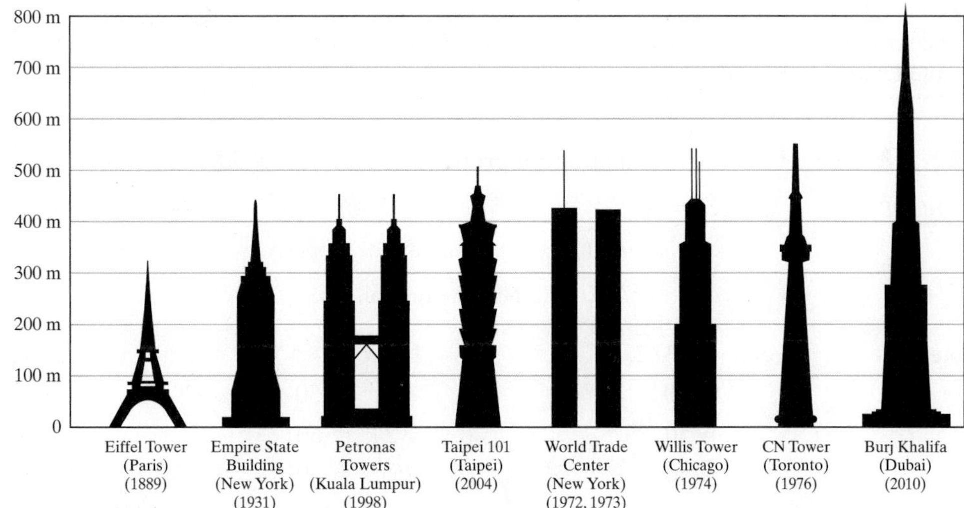

Source: Council on Tall Buildings and Urban Habitat, (*Fast Company*)

 6.1 Solving Quadratic Equations by Completing the Square 

OBJECTIVES

1. Use the Square Root Property to Solve Quadratic Equations.
2. Solve Quadratic Equations by Completing the Square.
3. Use Quadratic Equations to Solve Problems.

OBJECTIVE

1 Using the Square Root Property 

In Chapter 3, we solved quadratic equations by factoring. Recall that a **quadratic,** or **second-degree, equation** is an equation that can be written in the form $ax^2 + bx + c = 0$, where *a, b,* and *c* are real numbers and *a* is not 0. To solve a quadratic equation such as $x^2 = 9$ by factoring, we use the zero factor theorem. To use the zero factor theorem, the equation must first be written in standard form, $ax^2 + bx + c = 0$.

$$x^2 = 9$$
$$x^2 - 9 = 0 \quad \text{Subtract 9 from both sides.}$$
$$(x + 3)(x - 3) = 0 \quad \text{Factor.}$$
$$x + 3 = 0 \quad \text{or} \quad x - 3 = 0 \quad \text{Set each factor equal to 0.}$$
$$x = -3 \qquad x = 3 \quad \text{Solve.}$$

The solution set is $\{-3, 3\}$, the positive and negative square roots of 9. Not all quadratic equations can be solved by factoring, so we need to explore other methods. Notice that the solutions of the equation $x^2 = 9$ are two numbers whose square is 9.

$$3^2 = 9 \quad \text{and} \quad (-3)^2 = 9$$

Thus, we can solve the equation $x^2 = 9$ by taking the square root of both sides. Be sure to include both $\sqrt{9}$ and $-\sqrt{9}$ as solutions since both $\sqrt{9}$ and $-\sqrt{9}$ are numbers whose square is 9.

$$x^2 = 9$$
$$\sqrt{x^2} = \pm\sqrt{9} \quad \text{The notation } \pm\sqrt{9} \text{ (read as "plus or minus } \sqrt{9}\text{")}$$
$$x = \pm 3 \quad \text{indicates the pair of numbers } +\sqrt{9} \text{ and } -\sqrt{9}.$$

This illustrates the square root property.

Square Root Property

If b is a real number and if $a^2 = b$, then $a = \pm\sqrt{b}$.

Helpful Hint

The notation ± 3, for example, is read as "plus or minus 3." It is a shorthand notation for the pair of numbers +3 and −3.

EXAMPLE 1 Use the square root property to solve $x^2 = 50$.

Solution

$$x^2 = 50$$
$$x = \pm\sqrt{50} \quad \text{Use the square root property.}$$
$$x = \pm 5\sqrt{2} \quad \text{Simplify the radical.}$$

Check:

Let $x = 5\sqrt{2}$.

$$x^2 = 50$$
$$(5\sqrt{2})^2 \stackrel{?}{=} 50$$
$$25 \cdot 2 \stackrel{?}{=} 50$$
$$50 = 50 \quad \text{True}$$

Let $x = -5\sqrt{2}$.

$$x^2 = 50$$
$$(-5\sqrt{2})^2 \stackrel{?}{=} 50$$
$$25 \cdot 2 \stackrel{?}{=} 50$$
$$50 = 50 \quad \text{True}$$

The solutions are $5\sqrt{2}$ and $-5\sqrt{2}$, or the solution set is $\{-5\sqrt{2}, 5\sqrt{2}\}$. □

PRACTICE

1 Use the square root property to solve $x^2 = 32$.

EXAMPLE 2 Use the square root property to solve $2x^2 - 14 = 0$.

Solution First we get the squared variable alone on one side of the equation.

$$\begin{aligned} 2x^2 - 14 &= 0 \\ 2x^2 &= 14 && \text{Add 14 to both sides.} \\ x^2 &= 7 && \text{Divide both sides by 2.} \\ x &= \pm\sqrt{7} && \text{Use the square root property.} \end{aligned}$$

Check to see that the solutions are $\sqrt{7}$ and $-\sqrt{7}$, or the solution set is $\{-\sqrt{7}, \sqrt{7}\}$. □

PRACTICE
2 Use the square root property to solve $5x^2 - 50 = 0$.

EXAMPLE 3 Use the square root property to solve $(x + 1)^2 = 12$.

Solution

$$\begin{aligned} (x + 1)^2 &= 12 \\ x + 1 &= \pm\sqrt{12} && \text{Use the square root property.} \\ x + 1 &= \pm 2\sqrt{3} && \text{Simplify the radical.} \\ x &= -1 \pm 2\sqrt{3} && \text{Subtract 1 from both sides.} \end{aligned}$$

Helpful Hint
Don't forget that $-1 \pm 2\sqrt{3}$, for example, means $-1 + 2\sqrt{3}$ and $-1 - 2\sqrt{3}$. In other words, the equation in Example 3 has two solutions.

Check: Below is a check for $-1 + 2\sqrt{3}$. The check for $-1 - 2\sqrt{3}$ is almost the same and is left for you to do on your own.

$$\begin{aligned} (x + 1)^2 &= 12 \\ \left(-1 + 2\sqrt{3} + 1\right)^2 &\stackrel{?}{=} 12 \\ \left(2\sqrt{3}\right)^2 &\stackrel{?}{=} 12 \\ 4 \cdot 3 &\stackrel{?}{=} 12 \\ 12 &= 12 && \text{True} \end{aligned}$$

The solutions are $-1 + 2\sqrt{3}$ and $-1 - 2\sqrt{3}$. □

PRACTICE
3 Use the square root property to solve $(x + 3)^2 = 20$.

EXAMPLE 4 Use the square root property to solve $(2x - 5)^2 = -16$.

Solution

$$\begin{aligned} (2x - 5)^2 &= -16 \\ 2x - 5 &= \pm\sqrt{-16} && \text{Use the square root property.} \\ 2x - 5 &= \pm 4i && \text{Simplify the radical.} \\ 2x &= 5 \pm 4i && \text{Add 5 to both sides.} \\ x &= \frac{5 \pm 4i}{2} && \text{Divide both sides by 2.} \end{aligned}$$

The solutions are $\frac{5 + 4i}{2}$ and $\frac{5 - 4i}{2}$, or in standard form $a + bi$ for complex numbers, $\frac{5}{2} + 2i$ and $\frac{5}{2} - 2i$. □

PRACTICE
4 Use the square root property to solve $(5x - 2)^2 = -9$.

✓CONCEPT CHECK

How do you know just by looking that $(x - 2)^2 = -4$ has complex but not real solutions?

OBJECTIVE

2 Solving by Completing the Square 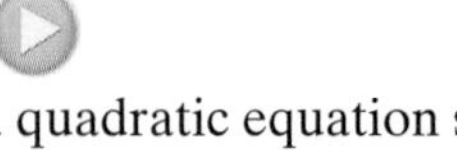

Notice from Examples 3 and 4 that, if we write a quadratic equation so that one side is the square of a binomial, we can solve by using the square root property. To write the square of a binomial, we write perfect square trinomials. Recall that a perfect square trinomial is a trinomial that can be factored into two identical binomial factors.

Perfect Square Trinomials	*Factored Form*
$x^2 + 8x + 16$	$(x + 4)^2$
$x^2 - 6x + 9$	$(x - 3)^2$
$x^2 + 3x + \frac{9}{4}$	$\left(x + \frac{3}{2}\right)^2$

Notice that for each perfect square trinomial in x, **the constant term of the trinomial is the square of half the coefficient of the x-term.** For example,

$$x^2 + 8x + 16 \qquad\qquad x^2 - 6x + 9$$

$$\frac{1}{2}(8) = 4 \text{ and } 4^2 = 16 \qquad \frac{1}{2}(-6) = -3 \text{ and } (-3)^2 = 9$$

The process of writing a quadratic equation so that one side is a perfect square trinomial is called **completing the square.**

EXAMPLE 5 Solve $p^2 + 2p = 4$ by completing the square.

Solution First, add the square of half the coefficient of p to both sides so that the resulting trinomial will be a perfect square trinomial. The coefficient of p is 2.

$$\frac{1}{2}(2) = 1 \quad \text{and} \quad 1^2 = 1$$

Add 1 to both sides of the original equation.

$$p^2 + 2p = 4$$

$$p^2 + 2p + 1 = 4 + 1 \quad \text{Add 1 to both sides.}$$

$$(p + 1)^2 = 5 \quad \text{Factor the trinomial; simplify the right side.}$$

We may now use the square root property and solve for p.

$$p + 1 = \pm\sqrt{5} \quad \text{Use the square root property.}$$

$$p = -1 \pm \sqrt{5} \quad \text{Subtract 1 from both sides.}$$

Notice that there are two solutions: $-1 + \sqrt{5}$ and $-1 - \sqrt{5}$. □

PRACTICE

5 Solve $b^2 + 4b = 3$ by completing the square.

EXAMPLE 6 Solve $m^2 - 7m - 1 = 0$ for m by completing the square.

Solution First, add 1 to both sides of the equation so that the left side has no constant term.

$$m^2 - 7m - 1 = 0$$

$$m^2 - 7m = 1$$

Answer to Concept Check:
answers may vary

Now find the constant term that makes the left side a perfect square trinomial by squaring half the coefficient of m. Add this constant to both sides of the equation.

$$\frac{1}{2}(-7) = -\frac{7}{2} \quad \text{and} \quad \left(-\frac{7}{2}\right)^2 = \frac{49}{4}$$

$$m^2 - 7m + \frac{49}{4} = 1 + \frac{49}{4}$$ Add $\frac{49}{4}$ to both sides of the equation.

$$\left(m - \frac{7}{2}\right)^2 = \frac{53}{4}$$ Factor the perfect square trinomial and simplify the right side.

$$m - \frac{7}{2} = \pm\sqrt{\frac{53}{4}}$$ Apply the square root property.

$$m = \frac{7}{2} \pm \frac{\sqrt{53}}{2}$$ Add $\frac{7}{2}$ to both sides and simplify $\sqrt{\frac{53}{4}}$.

$$m = \frac{7 \pm \sqrt{53}}{2}$$ Simplify.

The solutions are $\frac{7 + \sqrt{53}}{2}$ and $\frac{7 - \sqrt{53}}{2}$. □

PRACTICE 6 Solve $p^2 - 3p + 1 = 0$ by completing the square.

The following steps may be used to solve a quadratic equation such as $ax^2 + bx + c = 0$ by completing the square. This method may be used whether or not the polynomial $ax^2 + bx + c$ is factorable.

Solving a Quadratic Equation in x by Completing the Square

Step 1. If the coefficient of x^2 is 1, go to Step 2. Otherwise, divide both sides of the equation by the coefficient of x^2.

Step 2. Isolate all variable terms on one side of the equation.

Step 3. Complete the square for the resulting binomial by adding the square of half of the coefficient of x to both sides of the equation.

Step 4. Factor the resulting perfect square trinomial and write it as the square of a binomial.

Step 5. Use the square root property to solve for x.

EXAMPLE 7 Solve: $2x^2 - 8x + 3 = 0$.

Solution Our procedure for finding the constant term to complete the square works only if the coefficient of the squared variable term is 1. Therefore, to solve this equation, the first step is to divide both sides by 2, the coefficient of x^2.

$$2x^2 - 8x + 3 = 0$$

Step 1. $x^2 - 4x + \frac{3}{2} = 0$ Divide both sides by 2.

Step 2. $x^2 - 4x = -\frac{3}{2}$ Subtract $\frac{3}{2}$ from both sides.

Next find the square of half of -4.

$$\frac{1}{2}(-4) = -2 \quad \text{and} \quad (-2)^2 = 4$$

Add 4 to both sides of the equation to complete the square.

Step 3. $x^2 - 4x + 4 = -\frac{3}{2} + 4$

(Continued on next page)

Step 4. $(x-2)^2 = \frac{5}{2}$ Factor the perfect square and simplify the right side.

Step 5. $x - 2 = \pm\sqrt{\frac{5}{2}}$ Apply the square root property.

$x - 2 = \pm\frac{\sqrt{10}}{2}$ Rationalize the denominator.

$x = 2 \pm \frac{\sqrt{10}}{2}$ Add 2 to both sides.

$= \frac{4}{2} \pm \frac{\sqrt{10}}{2}$ Find a common denominator.

$= \frac{4 \pm \sqrt{10}}{2}$ Simplify.

The solutions are $\frac{4+\sqrt{10}}{2}$ and $\frac{4-\sqrt{10}}{2}$. □

PRACTICE
7 Solve: $3x^2 - 12x + 1 = 0$.

EXAMPLE 8 Solve $3x^2 - 9x + 8 = 0$ by completing the square.

Solution $3x^2 - 9x + 8 = 0$

Step 1. $x^2 - 3x + \frac{8}{3} = 0$ Divide both sides of the equation by 3.

Step 2. $x^2 - 3x = -\frac{8}{3}$ Subtract $\frac{8}{3}$ from both sides.

Since $\frac{1}{2}(-3) = -\frac{3}{2}$ and $\left(-\frac{3}{2}\right)^2 = \frac{9}{4}$, we add $\frac{9}{4}$ to both sides of the equation.

Step 3. $x^2 - 3x + \frac{9}{4} = \underbrace{-\frac{8}{3} + \frac{9}{4}}$

Step 4. $\left(x - \frac{3}{2}\right)^2 = -\frac{5}{12}$ Factor the perfect square trinomial.

Step 5. $x - \frac{3}{2} = \pm\sqrt{-\frac{5}{12}}$ Apply the square root property.

$x - \frac{3}{2} = \pm\frac{i\sqrt{5}}{2\sqrt{3}}$ Simplify the radical.

$x - \frac{3}{2} = \pm\frac{i\sqrt{15}}{6}$ Rationalize the denominator.

$x = \frac{3}{2} \pm \frac{i\sqrt{15}}{6}$ Add $\frac{3}{2}$ to both sides.

$= \frac{9}{6} \pm \frac{i\sqrt{15}}{6}$ Find a common denominator.

$= \frac{9 \pm i\sqrt{15}}{6}$ Simplify.

The solutions are $\frac{9+i\sqrt{15}}{6}$ and $\frac{9-i\sqrt{15}}{6}$, or in $a + bi$ form, $\frac{3}{2} + \frac{\sqrt{15}}{6}i$ and $\frac{3}{2} - \frac{\sqrt{15}}{6}i$. □

PRACTICE
8 Solve $2x^2 - 5x + 7 = 0$ by completing the square.

OBJECTIVE

3 Solving Problems Modeled by Quadratic Equations

Recall the **simple interest** formula $I = Prt$, where I is the interest earned, P is the principal, r is the rate of interest, and t is time in years. If \$100 is invested at a simple interest rate of 5% annually, at the end of 3 years the total interest I earned is

$$I = P \cdot r \cdot t$$

or

$$I = 100 \cdot 0.05 \cdot 3 = \$15$$

and the new principal is

$$\$100 + \$15 = \$115$$

Most of the time, the interest computed on money borrowed or money deposited is **compound interest.** Compound interest, unlike simple interest, is computed on original principal *and* on interest already earned. To see the difference between simple interest and compound interest, suppose that \$100 is invested at a rate of 5% compounded annually. To find the total amount of money at the end of 3 years, we calculate as follows.

$$I = P \cdot r \cdot t$$

First year: Interest $= \$100 \cdot 0.05 \cdot 1 = \$5.00$
New principal $= \$100.00 + \$5.00 = \$105.00$

Second year: Interest $= \$105.00 \cdot 0.05 \cdot 1 = \$5.25$
New principal $= \$105.00 + \$5.25 = \$110.25$

Third year: Interest $= \$110.25 \cdot 0.05 \cdot 1 \approx \$5.51$
New principal $= \$110.25 + \$5.51 = \$115.76$

At the end of the third year, the total compound interest earned is \$15.76, whereas the total simple interest earned is \$15.

It is tedious to calculate compound interest as we did above, so we use a compound interest formula. The formula for calculating the total amount of money when interest is compounded annually is

$$A = P(1 + r)^t$$

where P is the original investment, r is the interest rate per compounding period, and t is the number of periods. For example, the amount of money A at the end of 3 years if \$100 is invested at 5% compounded annually is

$$A = \$100(1 + 0.05)^3 \approx \$100(1.1576) = \$115.76$$

as we previously calculated.

EXAMPLE 9 **Finding Interest Rates**

Use the formula $A = P(1 + r)^t$ to find the interest rate r if \$2000 compounded annually grows to \$2420 in 2 years.

Solution

1. UNDERSTAND the problem. Since the \$2000 is compounded annually, we use the compound interest formula. For this example, make sure that you understand the formula for compounding interest annually.
2. TRANSLATE. We substitute the given values into the formula.

$$A = P(1 + r)^t$$

$$2420 = 2000(1 + r)^2 \quad \text{Let } A = 2420, P = 2000, \text{ and } t = 2.$$

(Continued on next page)

3. SOLVE. Solve the equation for r.

$$2420 = 2000(1 + r)^2$$

$$\frac{2420}{2000} = (1 + r)^2 \quad \text{Divide both sides by 2000.}$$

$$\frac{121}{100} = (1 + r)^2 \quad \text{Simplify the fraction.}$$

$$\pm\sqrt{\frac{121}{100}} = 1 + r \quad \text{Use the square root property.}$$

$$\pm\frac{11}{10} = 1 + r \quad \text{Simplify.}$$

$$-1 \pm \frac{11}{10} = r$$

$$-\frac{10}{10} \pm \frac{11}{10} = r$$

$$\frac{1}{10} = r \quad \text{or} \quad -\frac{21}{10} = r$$

4. INTERPRET. The rate cannot be negative, so we reject $-\frac{21}{10}$.

Check: $\frac{1}{10} = 0.10 = 10\%$ per year. If we invest \$2000 at 10% compounded annually, in 2 years the amount in the account would be $2000(1 + 0.10)^2 = 2420$ dollars, the desired amount.

State: The interest rate is 10% compounded annually. □

PRACTICE

9 Use the formula from Example 9 to find the interest rate r if \$5000 compounded annually grows to \$5618 in 2 years.

Graphing Calculator Explorations

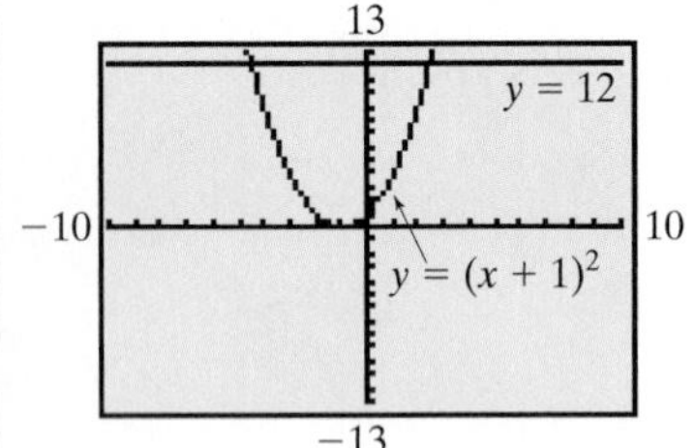

In Section 3.6, we showed how we can use a grapher to approximate real number solutions of a quadratic equation written in standard form. We can also use a grapher to solve a quadratic equation when it is not written in standard form. For example, to solve $(x + 1)^2 = 12$, the quadratic equation in Example 3, we graph the following on the same set of axes. Use Xmin $= -10$, Xmax $= 10$, Ymin $= -13$, and Ymax $= 13$.

$$Y_1 = (x + 1)^2 \quad \text{and} \quad Y_2 = 12$$

Use the Intersect feature or the Zoom and Trace features to locate the points of intersection of the graphs. (See your manuals for specific instructions.) The x-values of these points are the solutions of $(x + 1)^2 = 12$. The solutions, rounded to two decimal places, are 2.46 and −4.46.

Check to see that these numbers are approximations of the exact solutions $-1 \pm 2\sqrt{3}$.

Use a graphing calculator to solve each quadratic equation. Round all solutions to the nearest hundredth.

1. $x(x - 5) = 8$

2. $x(x + 2) = 5$

3. $x^2 + 0.5x = 0.3x + 1$

4. $x^2 - 2.6x = -2.2x + 3$

5. Use a graphing calculator and solve $(2x - 5)^2 = -16$, Example 4 in this section, using the window

$$\begin{aligned} \text{Xmin} &= -20 \\ \text{Xmax} &= 20 \\ \text{Xscl} &= 1 \\ \text{Ymin} &= -20 \\ \text{Ymax} &= 20 \\ \text{Yscl} &= 1 \end{aligned}$$

Explain the results. Compare your results with the solution found in Example 4.

6. What are the advantages and disadvantages of using a graphing calculator to solve quadratic equations?

Vocabulary, Readiness & Video Check

Use the choices below to fill in each blank. Not all choices will be used.

binomial	$\sqrt{b}$	$\pm\sqrt{b}$	b^2	9	25	completing the square
quadratic	$-\sqrt{b}$	$\frac{b}{2}$	$\left(\frac{b}{2}\right)^2$	3	5	

1. By the square root property, if b is a real number, and $a^2 = b$, then $a =$ ________________.
2. A ________________ equation can be written in the form $ax^2 + bx + c = 0, a \neq 0$.
3. The process of writing a quadratic equation so that one side is a perfect square trinomial is called ________________.
4. A perfect square trinomial is one that can be factored as a ________________ squared.
5. To solve $x^2 + 6x = 10$ by completing the square, add ________________ to both sides.
6. To solve $x^2 + bx = c$ by completing the square, add ________________ to both sides.

Martin-Gay Interactive Videos

See Video 6.1

Watch the section lecture video and answer the following questions.

OBJECTIVE 1

7. From Examples 2 and 3, explain a step you can perform so that you may easily apply the square root property to $2x^2 = 16$. Explain why you perform this step.

OBJECTIVE 2

8. In Example 5, why is the equation first divided through by 3?

OBJECTIVE 3

9. In Example 6, why is the negative solution not considered?

6.1 Exercise Set

MyMathLab®

Use the square root property to solve each equation. These equations have real number solutions. See Examples 1 through 3.

1. $x^2 = 16$
2. $x^2 = 49$
3. $x^2 - 7 = 0$
4. $x^2 - 11 = 0$
5. $x^2 = 18$
6. $y^2 = 20$
7. $3z^2 - 30 = 0$
8. $2x^2 - 4 = 0$
9. $(x + 5)^2 = 9$
10. $(y - 3)^2 = 4$
11. $(z - 6)^2 = 18$
12. $(y + 4)^2 = 27$
13. $(2x - 3)^2 = 8$
14. $(4x + 9)^2 = 6$

Use the square root property to solve each equation. See Examples 1 through 4.

15. $x^2 + 9 = 0$
16. $x^2 + 4 = 0$
17. $x^2 - 6 = 0$
18. $y^2 - 10 = 0$
19. $2z^2 + 16 = 0$
20. $3p^2 + 36 = 0$

21. $(3x - 1)^2 = -16$

22. $(4y + 2)^2 = -25$

23. $(z + 7)^2 = 5$

24. $(x + 10)^2 = 11$

25. $(x + 3)^2 + 8 = 0$

26. $(y - 4)^2 + 18 = 0$

Add the proper constant to each binomial so that the resulting trinomial is a perfect square trinomial. Then factor the trinomial.

27. $x^2 + 16x +$ ________

28. $y^2 + 2y +$ ________

29. $z^2 - 12z +$ ________

30. $x^2 - 8x +$ ________

31. $p^2 + 9p +$ ________

32. $n^2 + 5n +$ ________

33. $x^2 + x +$ ________

34. $y^2 - y +$ ________

MIXED PRACTICE

Solve each equation by completing the square. These equations have real number solutions. See Examples 5 through 7.

35. $x^2 + 8x = -15$

36. $y^2 + 6y = -8$

37. $x^2 + 6x + 2 = 0$

38. $x^2 - 2x - 2 = 0$

39. $x^2 + x - 1 = 0$

40. $x^2 + 3x - 2 = 0$

41. $x^2 + 2x - 5 = 0$

42. $x^2 - 6x + 3 = 0$

43. $y^2 + y - 7 = 0$

44. $x^2 - 7x - 1 = 0$

45. $3p^2 - 12p + 2 = 0$

46. $2x^2 + 14x - 1 = 0$

47. $4y^2 - 2 = 12y$

48. $6x^2 - 3 = 6x$

49. $2x^2 + 7x = 4$

50. $3x^2 - 4x = 4$

51. $x^2 + 8x + 1 = 0$

52. $x^2 - 10x + 2 = 0$

53. $3y^2 + 6y - 4 = 0$

54. $2y^2 + 12y + 3 = 0$

55. $2x^2 - 3x - 5 = 0$

56. $5x^2 + 3x - 2 = 0$

Solve each equation by completing the square. See Examples 5 through 8.

57. $y^2 + 2y + 2 = 0$

58. $x^2 + 4x + 6 = 0$

59. $y^2 + 6y - 8 = 0$

60. $y^2 + 10y - 26 = 0$

61. $2a^2 + 8a = -12$

62. $3x^2 + 12x = -14$

63. $5x^2 + 15x - 1 = 0$

64. $16y^2 + 16y - 1 = 0$

65. $2x^2 - x + 6 = 0$

66. $4x^2 - 2x + 5 = 0$

67. $x^2 + 10x + 28 = 0$

68. $y^2 + 8y + 18 = 0$

69. $z^2 + 3z - 4 = 0$

70. $y^2 + y - 2 = 0$

71. $2x^2 - 4x = -3$

72. $9x^2 - 36x = -40$

73. $3x^2 + 3x = 5$

74. $10y^2 - 30y = 2$

Use the formula $A = P(1 + r)^t$ to solve Exercises 75 through 78. See Example 9.

75. Find the rate r at which \$3000 compounded annually grows to \$4320 in 2 years.

76. Find the rate r at which \$800 compounded annually grows to \$882 in 2 years.

77. Find the rate at which \$15,000 compounded annually grows to \$16,224 in 2 years.

78. Find the rate at which \$2000 compounded annually grows to \$2880 in 2 years.

Neglecting air resistance, the distance $s(t)$ in feet traveled by a freely falling object is given by the function $s(t) = 16t^2$, where t is time in seconds. Use this formula to solve Exercises 79 through 82. Round answers to two decimal places.

79. The Petronas Towers in Kuala Lumpur, completed in 1998, are the tallest buildings in Malaysia. Each tower is 1483 feet tall. How long would it take an object to fall to the ground from the top of one of the towers? (*Source:* Council on Tall Buildings and Urban Habitat, Lehigh University)

80. The Burj Khalifa, the tallest building in the world, was completed in 2010 in Dubai. It is estimated to be 2717 feet tall. How long would it take an object to fall to the ground from the top of the building? (*Source:* Council on Tall Buildings and Urban Habitat)

81. The Rogun Dam in Tajikistan (part of the former USSR that borders Afghanistan) is the tallest dam in the world at 1100 feet. How long would it take an object to fall from the top to the base of the dam? (*Source:* U.S. Committee on Large Dams of the International Commission on Large Dams)

82. The Hoover Dam, located on the Colorado River on the border of Nevada and Arizona near Las Vegas, is 725 feet tall. How long would it take an object to fall from the top to the base of the dam? (*Source:* U.S. Committee on Large Dams of the International Commission on Large Dams)

Solve.

△ **83.** The area of a square room is 225 square feet. Find the dimensions of the room.

△ **84.** The area of a circle is 36π square inches. Find the radius of the circle.

△ **85.** An isosceles right triangle has legs of equal length. If the hypotenuse is 20 centimeters long, find the length of each leg.

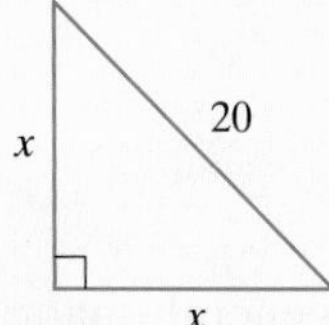

△ **86.** The top of a square coffee table has a diagonal that measures 30 inches. Find the length of each side of the top of the coffee table.

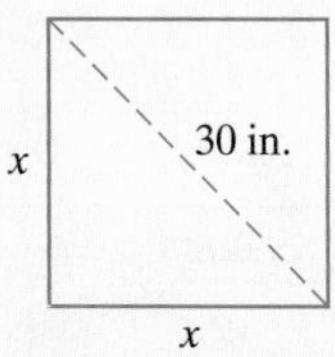

REVIEW AND PREVIEW

Simplify each expression. See Section 5.1

87. $\frac{1}{2} - \sqrt{\frac{9}{4}}$

88. $\frac{9}{10} - \sqrt{\frac{49}{100}}$

Simplify each expression. See Section 5.5.

89. $\frac{6 + 4\sqrt{5}}{2}$

90. $\frac{10 - 20\sqrt{3}}{2}$

91. $\frac{3 - 9\sqrt{2}}{6}$

92. $\frac{12 - 8\sqrt{7}}{16}$

Evaluate $\sqrt{b^2 - 4ac}$ *for each set of values. See Section 5.3.*

93. $a = 2, b = 4, c = -1$

94. $a = 1, b = 6, c = 2$

95. $a = 3, b = -1, c = -2$

96. $a = 1, b = -3, c = -1$

CONCEPT EXTENSIONS

Without solving, determine whether the solutions of each equation are real numbers or complex but not real numbers. See the Concept Check in this section.

97. $(x + 1)^2 = -1$

98. $(y - 5)^2 = -9$

99. $3z^2 = 10$

100. $4x^2 = 17$

101. $(2y - 5)^2 + 7 = 3$

102. $(3m + 2)^2 + 4 = 1$

Find two possible missing terms so that each is a perfect square trinomial.

103. $x^2 + \quad + 16$

104. $y^2 + \quad + 9$

105. $z^2 + \quad + \frac{25}{4}$

106. $x^2 + \quad + \frac{1}{4}$

107. In your own words, explain how to calculate the number that will complete the square on an expression such as $x^2 - 5x$.

108. In your own words, what is the difference between simple interest and compound interest?

109. If you are depositing money in an account that pays 4%, would you prefer the interest to be simple or compound? Explain your answer.

110. If you are borrowing money at a rate of 10%, would you prefer the interest to be simple or compound? Explain your answer.

A common equation used in business is a demand equation. It expresses the relationship between the unit price of some commodity and the quantity demanded. For Exercises 111 and 112, p represents the unit price and x represents the quantity demanded in thousands.

111. A manufacturing company has found that the demand equation for a certain type of scissors is given by the equation $p = -x^2 + 47$. Find the demand for the scissors if the price is \$11 per pair.

112. Acme, Inc., sells desk lamps and has found that the demand equation for a certain style of desk lamp is given by the equation $p = -x^2 + 15$. Find the demand for the desk lamp if the price is \$7 per lamp.

6.2 Solving Quadratic Equations by the Quadratic Formula 

OBJECTIVES

1 Solve Quadratic Equations by Using the Quadratic Formula.
2 Determine the Number and Type of Solutions of a Quadratic Equation by Using the Discriminant.
3 Solve Problems Modeled by Quadratic Equations.

OBJECTIVE

1 Solving Quadratic Equations by Using the Quadratic Formula 

Any quadratic equation can be solved by completing the square. Since the same sequence of steps is repeated each time we complete the square, let's complete the square for a general quadratic equation, $ax^2 + bx + c = 0, a \neq 0$. By doing so, we find a pattern for the solutions of a quadratic equation known as the **quadratic formula.**

Recall that to complete the square for an equation such as $ax^2 + bx + c = 0$, we first divide both sides by the coefficient of x^2.

$$ax^2 + bx + c = 0$$

$$x^2 + \frac{b}{a}x + \frac{c}{a} = 0 \quad \text{Divide both sides by } a \text{, the coefficient of } x^2.$$

$$x^2 + \frac{b}{a}x = -\frac{c}{a} \quad \text{Subtract the constant } \frac{c}{a} \text{ from both sides.}$$

Next, find the square of half $\frac{b}{a}$, the coefficient of x.

$$\frac{1}{2}\left(\frac{b}{a}\right) = \frac{b}{2a} \quad \text{and} \quad \left(\frac{b}{2a}\right)^2 = \frac{b^2}{4a^2}$$

Add this result to both sides of the equation.

$$x^2 + \frac{b}{a}x + \frac{b^2}{4a^2} = -\frac{c}{a} + \frac{b^2}{4a^2} \quad \text{Add } \frac{b^2}{4a^2} \text{ to both sides.}$$

$$x^2 + \frac{b}{a}x + \frac{b^2}{4a^2} = \frac{-c \cdot 4a}{a \cdot 4a} + \frac{b^2}{4a^2} \quad \text{Find a common denominator on the right side.}$$

$$x^2 + \frac{b}{a}x + \frac{b^2}{4a^2} = \frac{b^2 - 4ac}{4a^2} \quad \text{Simplify the right side.}$$

$$\left(x + \frac{b}{2a}\right)^2 = \frac{b^2 - 4ac}{4a^2} \quad \text{Factor the perfect square trinomial on the left side.}$$

$$x + \frac{b}{2a} = \pm\sqrt{\frac{b^2 - 4ac}{4a^2}} \quad \text{Apply the square root property.}$$

$$x + \frac{b}{2a} = \pm\frac{\sqrt{b^2 - 4ac}}{2a} \quad \text{Simplify the radical.}$$

$$x = -\frac{b}{2a} \pm \frac{\sqrt{b^2 - 4ac}}{2a} \quad \text{Subtract } \frac{b}{2a} \text{ from both sides.}$$

$$x = \frac{-b \pm \sqrt{b^2 - 4ac}}{2a} \quad \text{Simplify.}$$

This equation identifies the solutions of the general quadratic equation in standard form and is called the quadratic formula. It can be used to solve any equation written in standard form $ax^2 + bx + c = 0$ as long as a is not 0.

Quadratic Formula

A quadratic equation written in the form $ax^2 + bx + c = 0$ has the solutions

$$x = \frac{-b \pm \sqrt{b^2 - 4ac}}{2a}$$

EXAMPLE 1 Solve $3x^2 + 16x + 5 = 0$ for x.

Solution This equation is in standard form, so $a = 3$, $b = 16$, and $c = 5$. Substitute these values into the quadratic formula.

$$x = \frac{-b \pm \sqrt{b^2 - 4ac}}{2a} \qquad \text{Quadratic formula}$$

$$= \frac{-16 \pm \sqrt{16^2 - 4(3)(5)}}{2 \cdot 3} \qquad \text{Use } a = 3, b = 16, \text{ and } c = 5.$$

$$= \frac{-16 \pm \sqrt{256 - 60}}{6}$$

$$= \frac{-16 \pm \sqrt{196}}{6} = \frac{-16 \pm 14}{6}$$

$$x = \frac{-16 + 14}{6} = -\frac{1}{3} \quad \text{or} \quad x = \frac{-16 - 14}{6} = -\frac{30}{6} = -5$$

The solutions are $-\frac{1}{3}$ and -5, or the solution set is $\left\{-\frac{1}{3}, -5\right\}$. □

PRACTICE

1 Solve $3x^2 - 5x - 2 = 0$ for x.

Helpful Hint

To replace a, b, and c correctly in the quadratic formula, write the quadratic equation in standard form $ax^2 + bx + c = 0$.

EXAMPLE 2 Solve: $2x^2 - 4x = 3$.

Solution First write the equation in standard form by subtracting 3 from both sides.

$$2x^2 - 4x - 3 = 0$$

Now $a = 2$, $b = -4$, and $c = -3$. Substitute these values into the quadratic formula.

$$x = \frac{-b \pm \sqrt{b^2 - 4ac}}{2a}$$

$$= \frac{-(-4) \pm \sqrt{(-4)^2 - 4(2)(-3)}}{2 \cdot 2}$$

$$= \frac{4 \pm \sqrt{16 + 24}}{4}$$

$$= \frac{4 \pm \sqrt{40}}{4} = \frac{4 \pm 2\sqrt{10}}{4}$$

$$= \frac{2(2 \pm \sqrt{10})}{2 \cdot 2} = \frac{2 \pm \sqrt{10}}{2}$$

The solutions are $\frac{2 + \sqrt{10}}{2}$ and $\frac{2 - \sqrt{10}}{2}$, or the solution set is $\left\{\frac{2 - \sqrt{10}}{2}, \frac{2 + \sqrt{10}}{2}\right\}$. □

PRACTICE

2 Solve: $3x^2 - 8x = 2$.

Helpful Hint

To simplify the expression $\frac{4 \pm 2\sqrt{10}}{4}$ in the preceding example, note that 2 is factored out of both terms of the numerator *before* simplifying.

$$\frac{4 \pm 2\sqrt{10}}{4} = \frac{2(2 \pm \sqrt{10})}{2 \cdot 2} = \frac{2 \pm \sqrt{10}}{2}$$

> ✓**CONCEPT CHECK**
> For the quadratic equation $x^2 = 7$, which substitution is correct?
> **a.** $a = 1, b = 0$, and $c = -7$
> **b.** $a = 1, b = 0$, and $c = 7$
> **c.** $a = 0, b = 0$, and $c = 7$
> **d.** $a = 1, b = 1$, and $c = -7$

EXAMPLE 3 Solve: $\frac{1}{4}m^2 - m + \frac{1}{2} = 0$.

Solution We could use the quadratic formula with $a = \frac{1}{4}$, $b = -1$, and $c = \frac{1}{2}$. Instead, we find a simpler, equivalent standard form equation whose coefficients are not fractions.

Multiply both sides of the equation by the LCD 4 to clear fractions.

$$4\left(\frac{1}{4}m^2 - m + \frac{1}{2}\right) = 4 \cdot 0$$

$$m^2 - 4m + 2 = 0 \quad \text{Simplify.}$$

Substitute $a = 1, b = -4$, and $c = 2$ into the quadratic formula and simplify.

$$m = \frac{-(-4) \pm \sqrt{(-4)^2 - 4(1)(2)}}{2 \cdot 1} = \frac{4 \pm \sqrt{16 - 8}}{2}$$

$$= \frac{4 \pm \sqrt{8}}{2} = \frac{4 \pm 2\sqrt{2}}{2} = \frac{2(2 \pm \sqrt{2})}{2}$$

$$= 2 \pm \sqrt{2}$$

The solutions are $2 + \sqrt{2}$ and $2 - \sqrt{2}$. □

PRACTICE 3 Solve: $\frac{1}{8}x^2 - \frac{1}{4}x - 2 = 0$.

EXAMPLE 4 Solve: $x = -3x^2 - 3$.

Solution The equation in standard form is $3x^2 + x + 3 = 0$. Thus, let $a = 3, b = 1$, and $c = 3$ in the quadratic formula.

$$x = \frac{-1 \pm \sqrt{1^2 - 4(3)(3)}}{2 \cdot 3} = \frac{-1 \pm \sqrt{1 - 36}}{6} = \frac{-1 \pm \sqrt{-35}}{6} = \frac{-1 \pm i\sqrt{35}}{6}$$

The solutions are $\frac{-1 + i\sqrt{35}}{6}$ and $\frac{-1 - i\sqrt{35}}{6}$, or in the form $a + bi$, $-\frac{1}{6} + \frac{\sqrt{35}}{6}i$ and $-\frac{1}{6} - \frac{\sqrt{35}}{6}i$. □

PRACTICE 4 Solve: $x = -2x^2 - 2$.

> ✓**CONCEPT CHECK**
> What is the first step in solving $-3x^2 = 5x - 4$ using the quadratic formula?

In Example 1, the equation $3x^2 + 16x + 5 = 0$ had 2 real roots, $-\frac{1}{3}$ and -5. In Example 4, the equation $3x^2 + x + 3 = 0$ (written in standard form) had no real roots. How do their related graphs compare? Recall that the x-intercepts of

Answers to Concept Checks:
a
Write the equation in standard form.

$f(x) = 3x^2 + 16x + 5$ occur where $f(x) = 0$ or where $3x^2 + 16x + 5 = 0$. Since this equation has 2 real roots, the graph has 2 x-intercepts. Similarly, since the equation $3x^2 + x + 3 = 0$ has no real roots, the graph of $f(x) = 3x^2 + x + 3$ has no x-intercepts.

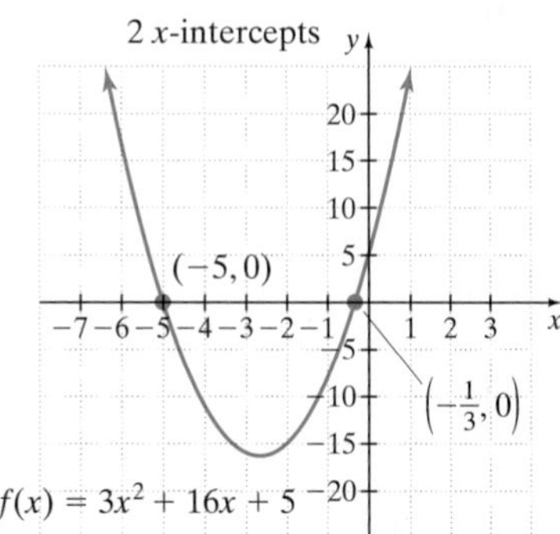

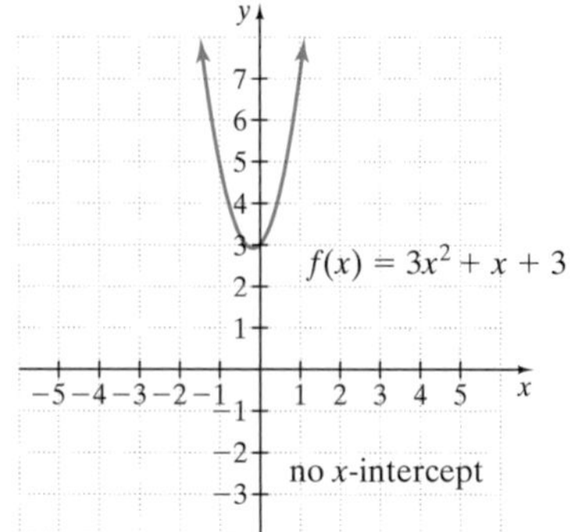

OBJECTIVE

2 Using the Discriminant

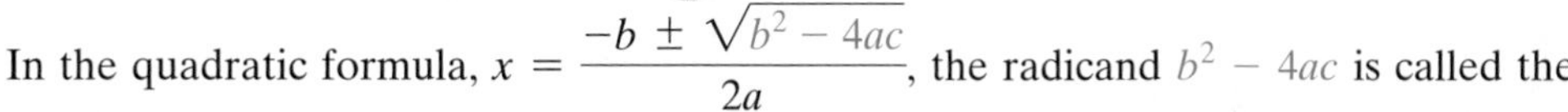

In the quadratic formula, $x = \dfrac{-b \pm \sqrt{b^2 - 4ac}}{2a}$, the radicand $b^2 - 4ac$ is called the **discriminant** because, by knowing its value, we can **discriminate** among the possible number and type of solutions of a quadratic equation. Possible values of the discriminant and their meanings are summarized next.

Discriminant

The following table corresponds the discriminant $b^2 - 4ac$ of a quadratic equation of the form $ax^2 + bx + c = 0$ with the number and type of solutions of the equation.

$b^2 - 4ac$	*Number and Type of Solutions*
Positive	Two real solutions
Zero	One real solution
Negative	Two complex but not real solutions

EXAMPLE 5 Use the discriminant to determine the number and type of solutions of each quadratic equation.

a. $x^2 + 2x + 1 = 0$ **b.** $3x^2 + 2 = 0$ **c.** $2x^2 - 7x - 4 = 0$

Solution

a. In $x^2 + 2x + 1 = 0$, $a = 1$, $b = 2$, and $c = 1$. Thus,

$$b^2 - 4ac = 2^2 - 4(1)(1) = 0$$

Since $b^2 - 4ac = 0$, this quadratic equation has one real solution.

b. In this equation, $a = 3$, $b = 0$, $c = 2$. Then $b^2 - 4ac = 0 - 4(3)(2) = -24$. Since $b^2 - 4ac$ is negative, the quadratic equation has two complex but not real solutions.

c. In this equation, $a = 2$, $b = -7$, and $c = -4$. Then

$$b^2 - 4ac = (-7)^2 - 4(2)(-4) = 81$$

Since $b^2 - 4ac$ is positive, the quadratic equation has two real solutions. □

PRACTICE

5 Use the discriminant to determine the number and type of solutions of each quadratic equation.

a. $x^2 - 6x + 9 = 0$ **b.** $x^2 - 3x - 1 = 0$ **c.** $7x^2 + 11 = 0$

The discriminant helps us determine the number and type of solutions of a quadratic equation, $ax^2 + bx + c = 0$. Recall that the solutions of this equation are the same as the x-intercepts of its related graph $f(x) = ax^2 + bx + c$. This means that the discriminant of $ax^2 + bx + c = 0$ also tells us the number of x-intercepts for the graph of $f(x) = ax^2 + bx + c$ or, equivalently, $y = ax^2 + bx + c$.

Graph of $f(x) = ax^2 + bx + c$ or $y = ax^2 + bx + c$

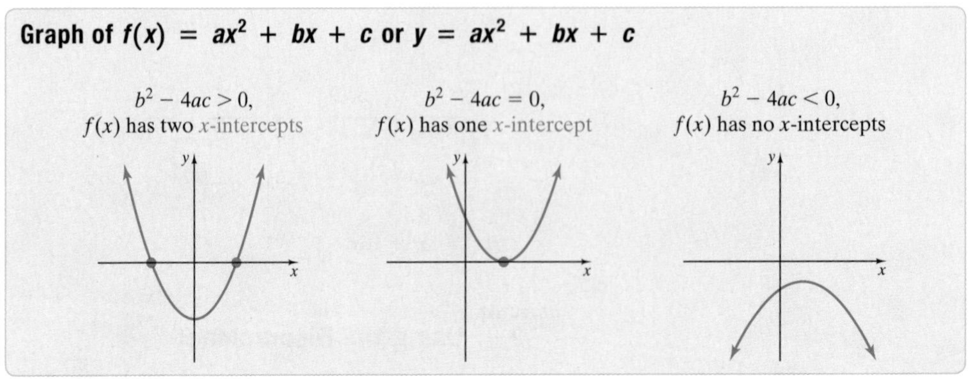

OBJECTIVE

3 Solving Problems Modeled by Quadratic Equations

The quadratic formula is useful in solving problems that are modeled by quadratic equations.

EXAMPLE 6 Calculating Distance Saved

At a local university, students often leave the sidewalk and cut across the lawn to save walking distance. Given the diagram below of a favorite place to cut across the lawn, approximate how many feet of walking distance a student saves by cutting across the lawn instead of walking on the sidewalk.

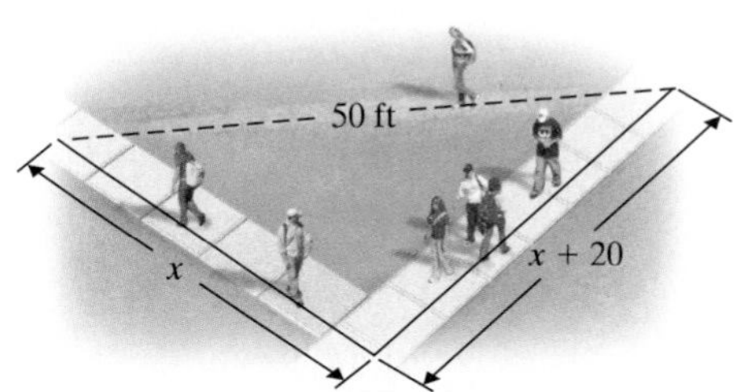

Solution

1. UNDERSTAND. Read and reread the problem. In the diagram, notice that a triangle is formed. Since the corner of the block forms a right angle, we use the Pythagorean theorem for right triangles. You may want to review this theorem.
2. TRANSLATE. By the Pythagorean theorem, we have

In words: $(\text{leg})^2 + (\text{leg})^2 = (\text{hypotenuse})^2$

Translate: $x^2 + (x + 20)^2 = 50^2$

3. SOLVE. Use the quadratic formula to solve.

$$x^2 + x^2 + 40x + 400 = 2500 \quad \text{Square } (x + 20) \text{ and } 50.$$
$$2x^2 + 40x - 2100 = 0 \quad \text{Set the equation equal to 0.}$$
$$x^2 + 20x - 1050 = 0 \quad \text{Divide by 2.}$$

Here, $a = 1, b = 20, c = -1050$. By the quadratic formula,

$$x = \frac{-20 \pm \sqrt{20^2 - 4(1)(-1050)}}{2 \cdot 1}$$

$$= \frac{-20 \pm \sqrt{400 + 4200}}{2} = \frac{-20 \pm \sqrt{4600}}{2}$$

$$= \frac{-20 \pm \sqrt{100 \cdot 46}}{2} = \frac{-20 \pm 10\sqrt{46}}{2}$$

$$= -10 \pm 5\sqrt{46} \quad \text{Simplify.}$$

4. INTERPRET

Check: Your calculations in the quadratic formula. The length of a side of a triangle can't be negative, so we reject $-10 - 5\sqrt{46}$. Since $-10 + 5\sqrt{46} \approx 24$ feet, the walking distance along the sidewalk is

$$x + (x + 20) \approx 24 + (24 + 20) = 68 \text{ feet.}$$

State: A student saves about $68 - 50$ or 18 feet of walking distance by cutting across the lawn. □

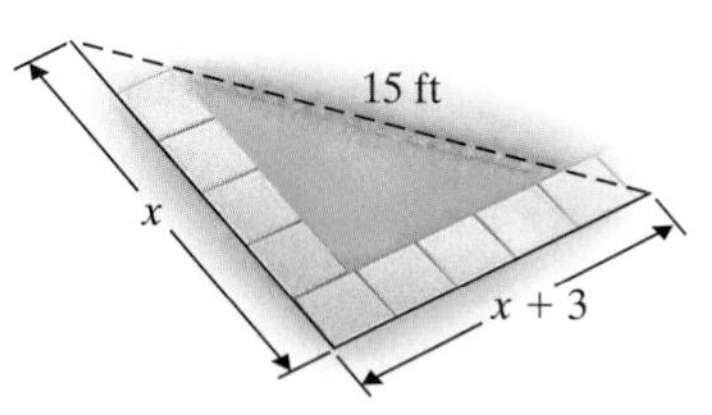

PRACTICE

6 Given the diagram, approximate to the nearest foot how many feet of walking distance a person can save by cutting across the lawn instead of walking on the sidewalk.

EXAMPLE 7 Calculating Landing Time

An object is thrown upward from the top of a 200-foot cliff with a velocity of 12 feet per second. The height h in feet of the object after t seconds is

$$h = -16t^2 + 12t + 200$$

How long after the object is thrown will it strike the ground? Round to the nearest tenth of a second.

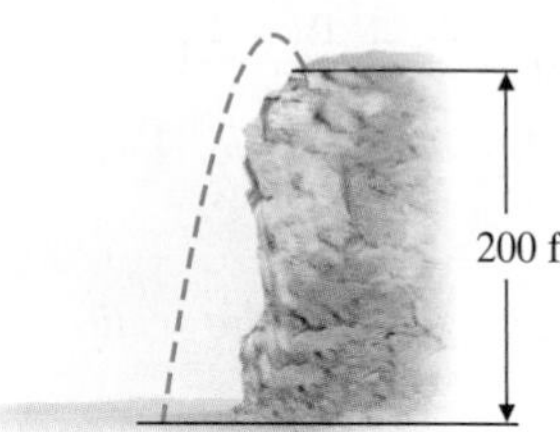

Solution

1. UNDERSTAND. Read and reread the problem.

2. TRANSLATE. Since we want to know when the object strikes the ground, we want to know when the height $h = 0$, or

$$0 = -16t^2 + 12t + 200$$

3. SOLVE. First we divide both sides of the equation by -4.

$$0 = 4t^2 - 3t - 50 \quad \text{Divide both sides by } -4.$$

Here, $a = 4, b = -3$, and $c = -50$. By the quadratic formula,

$$t = \frac{-(-3) \pm \sqrt{(-3)^2 - 4(4)(-50)}}{2 \cdot 4}$$

$$= \frac{3 \pm \sqrt{9 + 800}}{8}$$

$$= \frac{3 \pm \sqrt{809}}{8}$$

(Continued on next page)

4. INTERPRET.

Check: We check our calculations from the quadratic formula. Since the time won't be negative, we reject the proposed solution

$$\frac{3 - \sqrt{809}}{8}.$$

State: The time it takes for the object to strike the ground is exactly

$$\frac{3 + \sqrt{809}}{8} \text{ seconds} \approx 3.9 \text{ seconds}.$$ □

PRACTICE **7** A toy rocket is shot upward from the top of a building, 45 feet high, with an initial velocity of 20 feet per second. The height h in feet of the rocket after t seconds is

$$h = -16t^2 + 20t + 45$$

How long after the rocket is launched will it strike the ground? Round to the nearest tenth of a second.

Vocabulary, Readiness & Video Check

Fill in each blank.

1. The quadratic formula is ____________________.
2. For $2x^2 + x + 1 = 0$, if $a = 2$, then $b =$ _____ and $c =$ _____.
3. For $5x^2 - 5x - 7 = 0$, if $a = 5$, then $b =$ _____ and $c =$ _____.
4. For $7x^2 - 4 = 0$, if $a = 7$, then $b =$ _____ and $c =$ _____.
5. For $x^2 + 9 = 0$, if $c = 9$, then $a =$ _____ and $b =$ _____.
6. The correct simplified form of $\frac{5 \pm 10\sqrt{2}}{5}$ is ______________.

   a. $1 \pm 10\sqrt{2}$ **b.** $2\sqrt{2}$ **c.** $1 \pm 2\sqrt{2}$ **d.** $\pm 5\sqrt{2}$

Martin-Gay Interactive Videos

See Video 6.2

Watch the section lecture video and answer the following questions.

OBJECTIVE 1

7. Based on Examples 1–3, answer the following.
   a. Must a quadratic equation be written in standard form in order to use the quadratic formula? Why or why not?
   b. Must fractions be cleared from an equation before using the quadratic formula? Why or why not?

OBJECTIVE 2

8. Based on Example 4 and the lecture before, complete the following statements. The discriminant is the ________ in the quadratic formula and can be used to find the number and type of solutions of a quadratic equation without ________ the equation. To use the discriminant, the quadratic equation needs to be written in ________ form.

OBJECTIVE 3

9. In Example 5, the value of x is found, which is then used to find the dimensions of the triangle. Yet all this work still does solve the problem. Explain.

6.2 Exercise Set

MyMathLab®

Use the quadratic formula to solve each equation. These equations have real number solutions only. See Examples 1 through 3.

1. $m^2 + 5m - 6 = 0$
2. $p^2 + 11p - 12 = 0$
3. $2y = 5y^2 - 3$
4. $5x^2 - 3 = 14x$
5. $x^2 - 6x + 9 = 0$
6. $y^2 + 10y + 25 = 0$
7. $x^2 + 7x + 4 = 0$
8. $y^2 + 5y + 3 = 0$
9. $8m^2 - 2m = 7$
10. $11n^2 - 9n = 1$
11. $3m^2 - 7m = 3$
12. $x^2 - 13 = 5x$
13. $\frac{1}{2}x^2 - x - 1 = 0$
14. $\frac{1}{6}x^2 + x + \frac{1}{3} = 0$
15. $\frac{2}{5}y^2 + \frac{1}{5}y = \frac{3}{5}$
16. $\frac{1}{8}x^2 + x = \frac{5}{2}$
17. $\frac{1}{3}y^2 = y + \frac{1}{6}$
18. $\frac{1}{2}y^2 = y + \frac{1}{2}$
19. $x^2 + 5x = -2$
20. $y^2 - 8 = 4y$
21. $(m + 2)(2m - 6) = 5(m - 1) - 12$
22. $7p(p - 2) + 2(p + 4) = 3$

MIXED PRACTICE

Use the quadratic formula to solve each equation. These equations have real solutions and complex but not real solutions. See Examples 1 through 4.

23. $x^2 + 6x + 13 = 0$
24. $x^2 + 2x + 2 = 0$
25. $(x + 5)(x - 1) = 2$
26. $x(x + 6) = 2$
27. $6 = -4x^2 + 3x$
28. $2 = -9x^2 - x$
29. $\frac{x^2}{3} - x = \frac{5}{3}$
30. $\frac{x^2}{2} - 3 = -\frac{9}{2}x$
31. $10y^2 + 10y + 3 = 0$
32. $3y^2 + 6y + 5 = 0$
33. $x(6x + 2) = 3$
34. $x(7x + 1) = 2$
35. $\frac{2}{5}y^2 + \frac{1}{5}y + \frac{3}{5} = 0$
36. $\frac{1}{8}x^2 + x + \frac{5}{2} = 0$
37. $\frac{1}{2}y^2 = y - \frac{1}{2}$
38. $\frac{2}{3}x^2 - \frac{20}{3}x = -\frac{100}{6}$
39. $(n - 2)^2 = 2n$
40. $\left(p - \frac{1}{2}\right)^2 = \frac{p}{2}$

Use the discriminant to determine the number and types of solutions of each equation. See Example 5.

41. $x^2 - 5 = 0$
42. $x^2 - 7 = 0$
43. $4x^2 + 12x = -9$
44. $9x^2 + 1 = 6x$
45. $3x = -2x^2 + 7$
46. $3x^2 = 5 - 7x$
47. $6 = 4x - 5x^2$
48. $8x = 3 - 9x^2$
49. $9x - 2x^2 + 5 = 0$
50. $5 - 4x + 12x^2 = 0$

Solve. See Examples 7 and 8.

51. △ Nancy, Thelma, and John Varner live on a corner lot. Often, neighborhood children cut across their lot to save walking distance. Given the diagram below, approximate to the nearest foot how many feet of walking distance is saved by cutting across their property instead of walking around the lot.

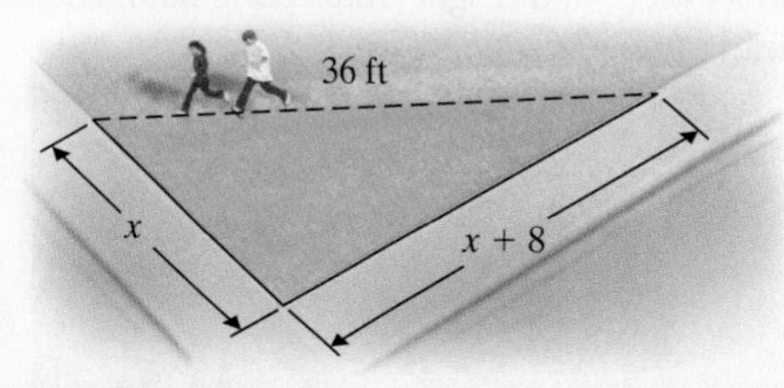

△ **52.** Given the diagram below, approximate to the nearest foot how many feet of walking distance a person saves by cutting across the lawn instead of walking on the sidewalk.

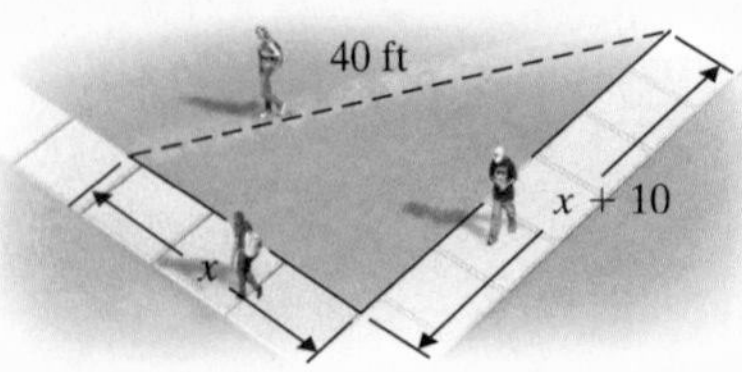

△ **53.** The hypotenuse of an isosceles right triangle is 2 centimeters longer than either of its legs. Find the exact length of each side. (*Hint:* An isosceles right triangle is a right triangle whose legs are the same length.)

△ **54.** The hypotenuse of an isosceles right triangle is one meter longer than either of its legs. Find the length of each side.

△ **55.** Bailey's rectangular dog pen for his Irish setter must have an area of 400 square feet. Also, the length must be 10 feet longer than the width. Find the dimensions of the pen.

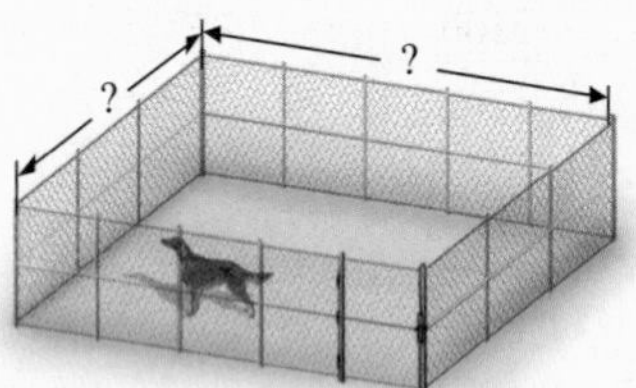

△ **56.** An entry in the Peach Festival Poster Contest must be rectangular and have an area of 1200 square inches. Furthermore, its length must be 20 inches longer than its width. Find the dimensions each entry must have.

△ **57.** A holding pen for cattle must be square and have a diagonal length of 100 meters.

a. Find the length of a side of the pen.

b. Find the area of the pen.

△ **58.** A rectangle is three times longer than it is wide. It has a diagonal of length 50 centimeters.

a. Find the dimensions of the rectangle.

b. Find the perimeter of the rectangle.

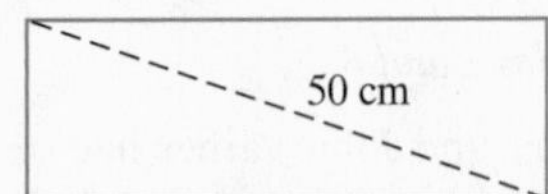

△ **59.** The heaviest reported door in the world is the 708.6 ton radiation shield door in the National Institute for Fusion Science at Toki, Japan. If the height of the door is 1.1 feet longer than its width, and its front area (neglecting depth) is 1439.9 square feet, find its width and height [Interesting note: The door is 6.6 feet thick.] (*Source: Guinness World Records*)

△ **60.** Christi and Robbie Wegmann are constructing a rectangular stained glass window whose length is 7.3 inches longer than its width. If the area of the window is 569.9 square inches, find its width and length.

△ **61.** The base of a triangle is four more than twice its height. If the area of the triangle is 42 square centimeters, find its base and height.

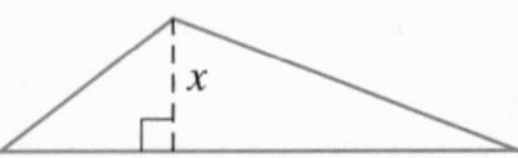

62. If a point B divides a line segment such that the smaller portion is to the larger portion as the larger is to the whole, the whole is the length of the *golden ratio*.

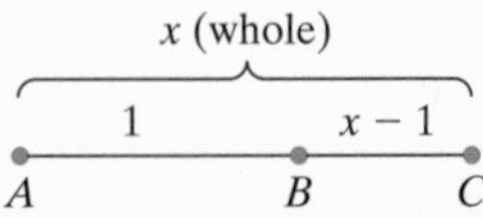

The golden ratio was thought by the Greeks to be the most pleasing to the eye, and many of their buildings contained numerous examples of the golden ratio. The value of the golden ratio is the positive solution of

$$\begin{matrix}\text{(smaller)} \\ \text{(larger)}\end{matrix} \quad \frac{x-1}{1} = \frac{1}{x} \quad \begin{matrix}\text{(larger)} \\ \text{(whole)}\end{matrix}$$

Find this value.

The Wollomombi Falls in Australia have a height of 1100 feet. A pebble is thrown upward from the top of the falls with an initial velocity of 20 feet per second. The height of the pebble h after t seconds is given by the equation $h = -16t^2 + 20t + 1100$*. Use this equation for Exercises 63 and 64.*

63. How long after the pebble is thrown will it hit the ground? Round to the nearest tenth of a second.

64. How long after the pebble is thrown will it be 550 feet from the ground? Round to the nearest tenth of a second.

A ball is thrown downward from the top of a 180-foot building with an initial velocity of 20 feet per second. The height of the ball h after t seconds is given by the equation $h = -16t^2 - 20t + 180$*. Use this equation to answer Exercises 65 and 66.*

65. How long after the ball is thrown will it strike the ground? Round the result to the nearest tenth of a second.

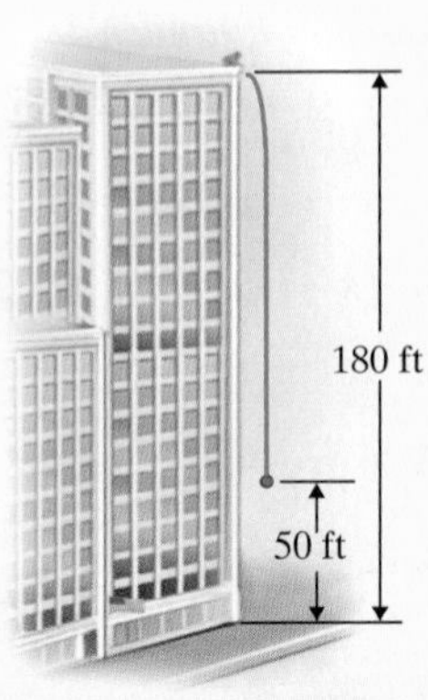

66. How long after the ball is thrown will it be 50 feet from the ground? Round the result to the nearest tenth of a second.

REVIEW AND PREVIEW

Solve each equation. See Sections 4.6 and 5.6.

67. $\sqrt{5x - 2} = 3$

68. $\sqrt{y + 2} + 7 = 12$

69. $\frac{1}{x} + \frac{2}{5} = \frac{7}{x}$

70. $\frac{10}{z} = \frac{5}{z} - \frac{1}{3}$

Factor. See Sections 3.3 through 3.5.

71. $x^4 + x^2 - 20$

72. $2y^4 + 11y^2 - 6$

73. $z^4 - 13z^2 + 36$

74. $x^4 - 1$

CONCEPT EXTENSIONS

For each quadratic equation, choose the correct substitution for a, b, and c in the standard form $ax^2 + bx + c = 0$.

75. $x^2 = -10$

a. $a = 1, b = 0, c = -10$

b. $a = 1, b = 0, c = 10$

c. $a = 0, b = 1, c = -10$

d. $a = 1, b = 1, c = 10$

76. $x^2 + 5 = -x$

a. $a = 1, b = 5, c = -1$

b. $a = 1, b = -1, c = 5$

c. $a = 1, b = 5, c = 1$

d. $a = 1, b = 1, c = 5$

77. Solve Exercise 1 by factoring. Explain the result.

78. Solve Exercise 2 by factoring. Explain the result.

Use the quadratic formula and a calculator to approximate each solution to the nearest tenth.

79. $2x^2 - 6x + 3 = 0$

80. $3.6x^2 + 1.8x - 4.3 = 0$

The accompanying graph shows the daily low temperatures for one week in New Orleans, Louisiana.

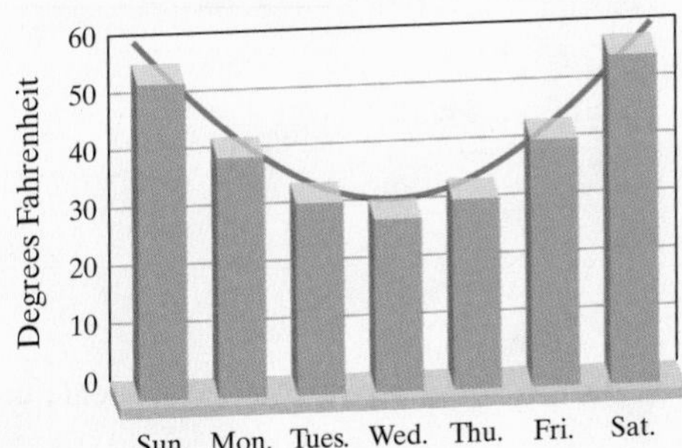

81. Between which days of the week was there the greatest decrease in the low temperature?

82. Between which days of the week was there the greatest increase in the low temperature?

83. Which day of the week had the lowest low temperature?

84. Use the graph to estimate the low temperature on Thursday.

Notice that the shape of the temperature graph is similar to the curve drawn. In fact, this graph can be modeled by the quadratic function $f(x) = 3x^2 - 18x + 56$, where $f(x)$ is the temperature in degrees Fahrenheit and x is the number of days from Sunday. (This graph is shown in blue.) Use this function to answer Exercises 85 and 86.

85. Use the quadratic function given to approximate the temperature on Thursday. Does your answer agree with the graph?

86. Use the function given and the quadratic formula to find when the temperature was 35° F. [*Hint:* Let $f(x) = 35$ and solve for x.] Round your answer to one decimal place and interpret your result. Does your answer agree with the graph?

87. The number of college students in the United States can be modeled by the quadratic function $f(x) = 22x^2 + 274x + 15{,}628$, where $f(x)$ is the number of college students in thousands of students, and x is the number of years after 2000. (*Source:* Based on data from the U.S. Department of Education)

a. Find the number of college students in the United States in 2010.

b. If the trend described by this model continues, find the year after 2000 in which the population of American college students reaches 24,500 students.

88. The projected number of Wi-Fi-enabled cell phones in the United States can be modeled by the quadratic function $c(x) = -0.4x^2 + 21x + 35$, where $c(x)$ is the projected number of Wi-Fi-enabled cell phones in millions and x is the number of years after 2009. Round to the nearest million. (*Source:* Techcrunchies.com)

a. Find the number of Wi-Fi-enabled cell phones in the United States in 2010.

b. Find the estimated number of Wi-Fi-enabled cell phones in the United States in 2012.

c. If the trend described by this model continues, find the year in which the projected number of Wi-Fi-enabled cell phones in the United States reaches 150 million.

89. The average total daily supply y of motor gasoline (in thousands of barrels per day) in the United States for the period 2000–2008 can be approximated by the equation $y = -10x^2 + 193x + 8464$, where x is the number of years after 2000. (*Source:* Based on data from the Energy Information Administration)

a. Find the average total daily supply of motor gasoline in 2004.

b. According to this model, in what year, from 2000 to 2008, was the average total daily supply of gasoline 9325 thousand barrels per day?

c. According to this model, in what year, from 2009 on, will the average total supply of gasoline be 9325 thousand barrels per day?

90. The relationship between body weight and the Recommended Dietary Allowance (RDA) for vitamin A in children up to age 10 is modeled by the quadratic equation $y = 0.149x^2 - 4.475x + 406.478$, where y is the RDA for vitamin A in micrograms for a child whose weight is x pounds. (*Source:* Based on data from the Food and Nutrition Board, National Academy of Sciences–Institute of Medicine, 1989)

a. Determine the vitamin A requirements of a child who weighs 35 pounds.

b. What is the weight of a child whose RDA of vitamin A is 600 micrograms? Round your answer to the nearest pound.

The solutions of the quadratic equation $ax^2 + bx + c = 0$ are $\dfrac{-b + \sqrt{b^2 - 4ac}}{2a}$ *and* $\dfrac{-b - \sqrt{b^2 - 4ac}}{2a}$.

91. Show that the sum of these solutions is $\dfrac{-b}{a}$.

92. Show that the product of these solutions is $\dfrac{c}{a}$.

Use the quadratic formula to solve each quadratic equation.

93. $3x^2 - \sqrt{12}x + 1 = 0$
(*Hint:* $a = 3, b = -\sqrt{12}, c = 1$)

94. $5x^2 + \sqrt{20}x + 1 = 0$

95. $x^2 + \sqrt{2}x + 1 = 0$

96. $x^2 - \sqrt{2}x + 1 = 0$

97. $2x^2 - \sqrt{3}x - 1 = 0$

98. $7x^2 + \sqrt{7}x - 2 = 0$

99. Use a graphing calculator to solve Exercises 63 and 65.

100. Use a graphing calculator to solve Exercises 64 and 66.

Recall that the discriminant also tells us the number of x-intercepts of the related function.

101. Check the results of Exercise 49 by graphing $y = 9x - 2x^2 + 5$.

102. Check the results of Exercise 50 by graphing $y = 5 - 4x + 12x^2$.

Chapter 6 Vocabulary Check

Fill in each blank with one of the words or phrases listed below.

quadratic formula	quadratic	discriminant	$\pm\sqrt{b}$
completing the square	quadratic inequality	(h, k)	$(0, k)$
$(h, 0)$	$\dfrac{-b}{2a}$		

1. The ________________ helps us find the number and type of solutions of a quadratic equation.

2. If $a^2 = b$, then $a =$ ________________.

3. The graph of $f(x) = ax^2 + bx + c$, where a is not 0, is a parabola whose vertex has x-value ________________.

4. A ________________ is an inequality that can be written so that one side is a quadratic expression and the other side is 0.

5. The process of writing a quadratic equation so that one side is a perfect square trinomial is called ________________.

6. The graph of $f(x) = x^2 + k$ has vertex ________________.

7. The graph of $f(x) = (x - h)^2$ has vertex ________________.

8. The graph of $f(x) = (x - h)^2 + k$ has vertex ________________.

9. The formula $x = \dfrac{-b \pm \sqrt{b^2 - 4ac}}{2a}$ is called the ________________.

10. A ________________ equation is one that can be written in the form $ax^2 + bx + c = 0$ where a, b, and c are real numbers and a is not 0.

Chapter 6 Highlights

DEFINITIONS AND CONCEPTS	EXAMPLES
Section 6.1 Solving Quadratic Equations by Completing the Square	
Square root property If b is a real number and if $a^2 = b$, then $a = \pm\sqrt{b}$.	Solve: $(x + 3)^2 = 14$. $x + 3 = \pm\sqrt{14}$ $x = -3 \pm \sqrt{14}$
To solve a quadratic equation in x by completing the square	Solve: $3x^2 - 12x - 18 = 0$.
Step 1. If the coefficient of x^2 is not 1, divide both sides of the equation by the coefficient of x^2.	**1.** $x^2 - 4x - 6 = 0$
Step 2. Isolate the variable terms.	**2.** $x^2 - 4x = 6$
Step 3. Complete the square by adding the square of half of the coefficient of x to both sides.	**3.** $\frac{1}{2}(-4) = -2$ and $(-2)^2 = 4$ $x^2 - 4x + 4 = 6 + 4$
Step 4. Write the resulting trinomial as the square of a binomial.	**4.** $(x - 2)^2 = 10$
Step 5. Apply the square root property and solve for x.	**5.** $x - 2 = \pm\sqrt{10}$ $x = 2 \pm \sqrt{10}$
Section 6.2 Solving Quadratic Equations by the Quadratic Formula	
A quadratic equation written in the form $ax^2 + bx + c = 0$ has solutions $x = \dfrac{-b \pm \sqrt{b^2 - 4ac}}{2a}$	Solve: $x^2 - x - 3 = 0$. $a = 1, b = -1, c = -3$ $x = \dfrac{-(-1) \pm \sqrt{(-1)^2 - 4(1)(-3)}}{2 \cdot 1}$ $x = \dfrac{1 \pm \sqrt{13}}{2}$

Chapter 6 Review

(6.1) *Solve by factoring.*

1. $x^2 - 15x + 14 = 0$

2. $7a^2 = 29a + 30$

Solve by using the square root property.

3. $4m^2 = 196$

4. $(5x - 2)^2 = 2$

Solve by completing the square.

5. $z^2 + 3z + 1 = 0$

6. $(2x + 1)^2 = x$

7. If P dollars are originally invested, the formula $A = P(1 + r)^2$ gives the amount A in an account paying interest rate r compounded annually after 2 years. Find the interest rate r such that \$2500 increases to \$2717 in 2 years. Round the result to the nearest hundredth of a percent.

△**8.** Two ships leave a port at the same time and travel at the same speed. One ship is traveling due north and the other due east. In a few hours, the ships are 150 miles apart. How many miles has each ship traveled? Give an exact answer and a one-decimal-place approximation.

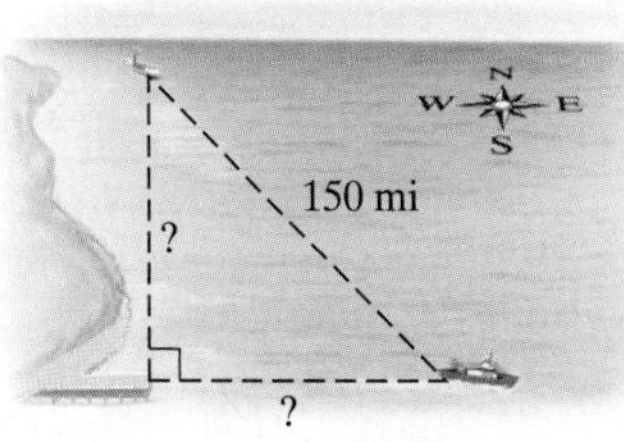

(6.2) *If the discriminant of a quadratic equation has the given value, determine the number and type of solutions of the equation.*

9. -8

10. 48

11. 100

12. 0

Solve by using the quadratic formula.

13. $x^2 - 16x + 64 = 0$

14. $x^2 + 5x = 0$

15. $2x^2 + 3x = 5$

16. $9x^2 + 4 = 2x$

17. $6x^2 + 7 = 5x$

18. $(2x - 3)^2 = x$

19. Cadets graduating from military school usually toss their hats high into the air at the end of the ceremony. One cadet threw his hat so that its distance $d(t)$ in feet above the ground t seconds after it was thrown was $d(t) = -16t^2 + 30t + 6$.

a. Find the distance above the ground of the hat 1 second after it was thrown.

b. Find the time it takes the hat to hit the ground. Give an exact time and a one-decimal-place approximation.

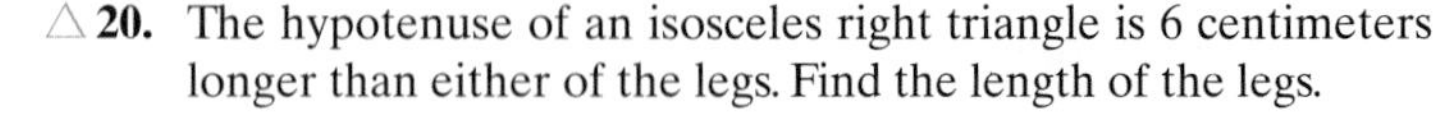

△ **20.** The hypotenuse of an isosceles right triangle is 6 centimeters longer than either of the legs. Find the length of the legs.

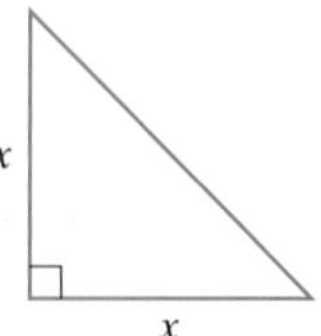

Chapter 6 Test

MyMathLab®  CHAPTER Test Prep VIDEOS  YouTube

Solve each equation.

1. $5x^2 - 2x = 7$

2. $(x + 1)^2 = 10$

3. $m^2 - m + 8 = 0$

4. $u^2 - 6u + 2 = 0$

5. $7x^2 + 8x + 1 = 0$

6. $y^2 - 3y = 5$

7. $\dfrac{4}{x + 2} + \dfrac{2x}{x - 2} = \dfrac{6}{x^2 - 4}$

8. $x^5 + 3x^4 = x + 3$

9. $x^6 + 1 = x^4 + x^2$

10. $(x + 1)^2 - 15(x + 1) + 56 = 0$

Solve by completing the square.

11. $x^2 - 6x = -2$

12. $2a^2 + 5 = 4a$

Solve each inequality for x. Write the solution set in interval notation.

13. $2x^2 - 7x > 15$

14. $(x^2 - 16)(x^2 - 25) \geq 0$

15. $\dfrac{5}{x + 3} < 1$

16. $\dfrac{7x - 14}{x^2 - 9} \leq 0$

Graph each function. Label the vertex.

17. $f(x) = 3x^2$

18. $G(x) = -2(x - 1)^2 + 5$

Graph each function. Find and label the vertex, y-intercept, and x-intercepts (if any).

19. $h(x) = x^2 - 4x + 4$

20. $F(x) = 2x^2 - 8x + 9$

21. Dave and Sandy Hartranft can paint a room together in 4 hours. Working alone, Dave can paint the room in 2 hours less time than Sandy can. Find how long it takes Sandy to paint the room alone.

22. A stone is thrown upward from a bridge. The stone's height in feet, $s(t)$, above the water t seconds after the stone is thrown is a function given by the equation $s(t) = -16t^2 + 32t + 256$.

a. Find the maximum height of the stone.

b. Find the time it takes the stone to hit the water. Round the answer to two decimal places.

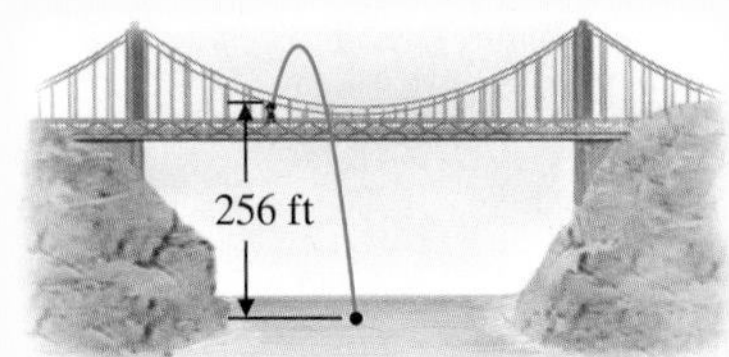

23. Given the diagram shown, approximate to the nearest tenth of a foot how many feet of walking distance a person saves by cutting across the lawn instead of walking on the sidewalk.

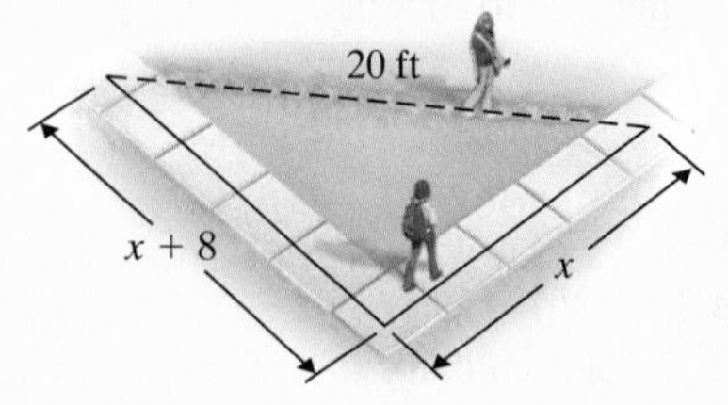

Chapter 6 Cumulative Review

1. Find the value of each expression when $x = 2$ and $y = -5$.

a. $\dfrac{x - y}{12 + x}$ **b.** $x^2 - 3y$

2. Solve $|3x - 2| = -5$.

3. Simplify each expression by combining like terms.

a. $2x + 3x + 5 + 2$

b. $-5a - 3 + a + 2$

c. $4y - 3y^2$

d. $2.3x + 5x - 6$

e. $-\dfrac{1}{2}b + b$

4. Use the addition method to solve the system.

$$\begin{cases} -6x + y = 5 \\ 4x - 2y = 6 \end{cases}$$

5. Solve the following system of equations by graphing.

$$\begin{cases} 2x + y = 7 \\ 2y = -4x \end{cases}$$

6. Simplify. Use positive exponents to write each answer.

a. $(a^{-2}bc^3)^{-3}$ **b.** $\left(\dfrac{a^{-4}b^2}{c^3}\right)^{-2}$

c. $\left(\dfrac{3a^8b^2}{12a^5b^5}\right)^{-2}$

7. Solve the system: $\begin{cases} 7x - 3y = -14 \\ -3x + y = 6 \end{cases}$

8. Multiply.

a. $(4a - 3)(7a - 2)$

b. $(2a + b)(3a - 5b)$

9. Simplify each quotient.

a. $\dfrac{x^5}{x^2}$ **b.** $\dfrac{4^7}{4^3}$

c. $\dfrac{(-3)^5}{(-3)^2}$ **d.** $\dfrac{s^2}{t^3}$

e. $\dfrac{2x^5y^2}{xy}$

10. Factor.

a. $9x^3 + 27x^2 - 15x$

b. $2x(3y - 2) - 5(3y - 2)$

c. $2xy + 6x - y - 3$

11. If $P(x) = 2x^3 - 4x^2 + 5$

a. Find $P(2)$ by substitution.

b. Use synthetic division to find the remainder when $P(x)$ is divided by $x - 2$.

12. Factor $x^2 - 2x - 48$.

13. Solve $(5x - 1)(2x^2 + 15x + 18) = 0$.

14. Factor. $2ax^2 - 12axy + 18ay^2$

15. Write the rational expression in lowest terms.

$$\frac{2x^2}{10x^3 - 2x^2}$$

16. Solve $2(a^2 + 2) - 8 = -2a(a - 2) - 5$.

17. Simplify. $\dfrac{x^{-1} + 2xy^{-1}}{x^{-2} - x^{-2}y^{-1}}$

18. Find the vertex and any intercepts of $f(x) = x^2 + x - 12$.

19. Factor $4m^4 - 4m^2 + 1$.

20. Simplify. $\dfrac{x^2 - 4x + 4}{2 - x}$

21. The square of a number plus three times the number is 70. Find the number.

22. Subtract. $\frac{a+1}{a^2-6a+8} - \frac{3}{16-a^2}$

23. Use the product rule to simplify.

a. $\sqrt{25x^3}$ **b.** $\sqrt[3]{54x^6y^8}$

c. $\sqrt[4]{81z^{11}}$

24. Simplify. $\frac{(2a)^{-1}+b^{-1}}{a^{-1}+(2b)^{-1}}$

25. Rationalize the denominator of each expression.

a. $\frac{2}{\sqrt{5}}$

b. $\frac{2\sqrt{16}}{\sqrt{9x}}$

c. $\sqrt[3]{\frac{1}{2}}$

26. Divide $x^3 - 3x^2 - 10x + 24$ by $x + 3$.

27. Solve $\sqrt{2x+5} + \sqrt{2x} = 3$.

28. If $P(x) = 4x^3 - 2x^2 + 3$,

a. Find $P(-2)$ by substitution.

b. Use synthetic division to find the remainder when $P(x)$ is divided by $x + 2$.

29. Solve $\frac{x}{2} + \frac{8}{3} = \frac{1}{6}$.

30. Solve $\frac{x+3}{x^2+5x+6} = \frac{3}{2x+4} - \frac{1}{x+3}$.

31. The quotient of a number and 6, minus $\frac{5}{3}$, is the quotient of the number and 2. Find the number.

32. Mr. Briley can roof his house in 24 hours. His son can roof the same house in 40 hours. If they work together, how long will it take to roof the house?

33. Suppose that y varies directly as x. If y is 5 when x is 30, find the constant of variation and the direct variation equation.

34. Suppose that y varies inversely as x. If y is 8 when x is 24, find the constant of variation and the inverse variation equation.

35. Simplify.

a. $\sqrt{(-3)^2}$ **b.** $\sqrt{x^2}$

c. $\sqrt[4]{(x-2)^4}$ **d.** $\sqrt[3]{(-5)^3}$

e. $\sqrt[5]{(2x-7)^5}$ **f.** $\sqrt{25x^2}$

g. $\sqrt{x^2+2x+1}$

36. Simplify. Assume that the variables represent any real number.

a. $\sqrt{(-2)^2}$

b. $\sqrt{y^2}$

c. $\sqrt[4]{(a-3)^4}$

d. $\sqrt[3]{(-6)^3}$

e. $\sqrt[5]{(3x-1)^5}$

37. Use rational exponents to simplify. Assume that variables represent positive numbers.

a. $\sqrt[8]{x^4}$

b. $\sqrt[6]{25}$

c. $\sqrt[4]{r^2s^6}$

38. Use rational exponents to simplify. Assume that variables represent positive numbers.

a. $\sqrt[4]{5^2}$

b. $\sqrt[12]{x^3}$

c. $\sqrt[6]{x^2y^4}$

39. Divide. Write in the form $a + bi$.

a. $\frac{2+i}{1-i}$

b. $\frac{7}{3i}$

40. Write each product in the form of $a + bi$.

a. $3i(5-2i)$

b. $(6-5i)^2$

c. $(\sqrt{3}+2i)(\sqrt{3}-2i)$

41. Use the square root property to solve $(x+1)^2 = 12$.

42. Use the square root property to solve $(y-1)^2 = 24$.

43. Solve $x - \sqrt{x} - 6 = 0$.

44. Use the quadratic formula to solve $m^2 = 4m + 8$.

Graphs, Equations, and Inequalities

Outline

Financing a Purchase

Whenever we make a major purchase, such as an automobile or a house, we often need to finance the purchase by borrowing money from a lending institution, such as a bank. Have you ever wondered how the bank determines the monthly payment? How much total interest will be paid over the course of the loan? What roles do the rate of interest and the length of the loan play?

—See the Internet-based Chapter Project I—

A LOOK AHEAD In this chapter, we use the rectangular coordinate system to graph equations. Then, we algebraically solve equations and use the rectangular coordinate system to visualize the solution. The idea of using a system of rectangular coordinates dates back to ancient times, when such a system was used for surveying and city planning. Apollonius of Perga, in 200 BC, used a form of rectangular coordinates in his work on conics, although this use does not stand out as clearly as it does in modern treatments. Sporadic use of rectangular coordinates continued until the 1600s. By that time, algebra had developed sufficiently so that René Descartes (1596–1650) and Pierre de Fermat (1601–1665) could take the crucial step, which was the use of rectangular coordinates to translate geometry problems into algebra problems, and vice versa. This step allowed both geometers and algebraists to gain new insights into their subjects, which previously had been regarded as separate, but now were seen to be connected in many important ways.

With the advent of modern technology, in particular, graphing utilities, not only are we able to visualize the dual roles of algebra and geometry, but we are also able to solve many problems that required advanced methods before this technology.

7.1 The Distance and Midpoint Formulas; Graphing Utilities; Introduction to Graphing Equations

Now Work the 'Are You Prepared?' problems on page 471.

OBJECTIVES

Rectangular Coordinates

Figure 1

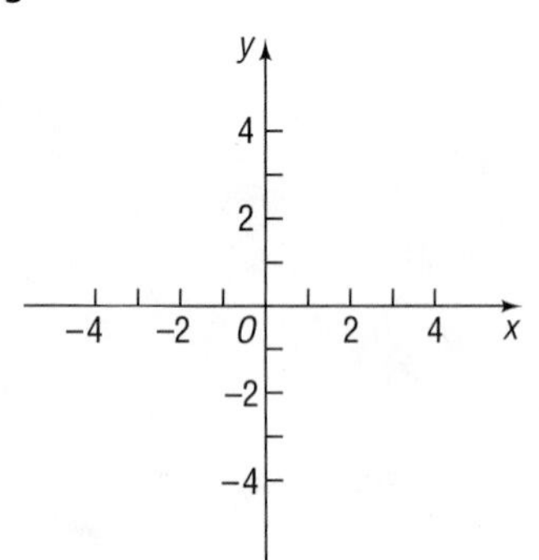

We locate a point on the real number line by assigning it a single real number, called the *coordinate of the point*. For work in a two-dimensional plane, points are located by using two numbers.

We begin with two real number lines located in the same plane: one horizontal and the other vertical. The horizontal line is called the ***x*-axis,** the vertical line the ***y*-axis,** and the point of intersection the **origin *O*.** See Figure 1. Assign coordinates to every point on these number lines using a convenient scale. Recall that the scale of a number line is the distance between 0 and 1. In mathematics, we usually use the same scale on each axis, but in applications, a different scale is often used.

The origin O has a value of 0 on both the x-axis and y-axis. Points on the x-axis to the right of O are associated with positive real numbers, and those to the left of O are associated with negative real numbers. Points on the y-axis above O are associated with positive real numbers, and those below O are associated with negative real numbers. In Figure 1, the x-axis and y-axis are labeled as x and y, respectively, and we have used an arrow at the end of each axis to denote the positive direction.

The coordinate system described here is called a **rectangular** or **Cartesian*** **coordinate system.** The plane formed by the x-axis and y-axis is sometimes called the ***xy*-plane,** and the x-axis and y-axis are referred to as the **coordinate axes.**

Any point P in the xy-plane can then be located by using an **ordered pair** (x, y) of real numbers. Let x denote the signed distance of P from the y-axis (*signed* means that, if P is to the right of the y-axis, then $x > 0$, and if P is to the left of the y-axis, then $x < 0$); and let y denote the signed distance of P from the x-axis. The ordered pair (x, y), also called the **coordinates** of P, then gives us enough information to locate the point P in the plane.

Figure 2

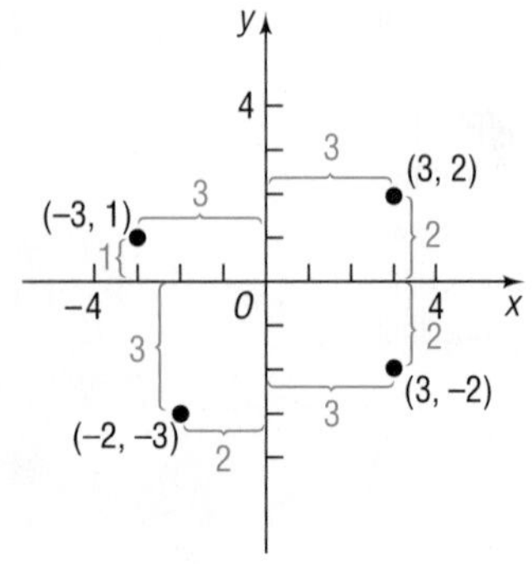

For example, to locate the point whose coordinates are $(-3, 1)$, go 3 units along the x-axis to the left of O and then go straight up 1 unit. We **plot** this point by placing a dot at this location. See Figure 2, in which the points with coordinates $(-3, 1)$, $(-2, -3)$, $(3, -2)$, and $(3, 2)$ are plotted.

The origin has coordinates $(0, 0)$. Any point on the x-axis has coordinates of the form $(x, 0)$, and any point on the y-axis has coordinates of the form $(0, y)$.

If (x, y) are the coordinates of a point P, then x is called the ***x*-coordinate,** or **abscissa,** of P and y is the ***y*-coordinate,** or **ordinate,** of P. We identify the point P by its coordinates (x, y) by writing $P = (x, y)$. Usually, we will simply say "the point (x, y)" rather than "the point whose coordinates are (x, y)."

*Named after René Descartes (1596–1650), a French mathematician, philosopher, and theologian.

Figure 3

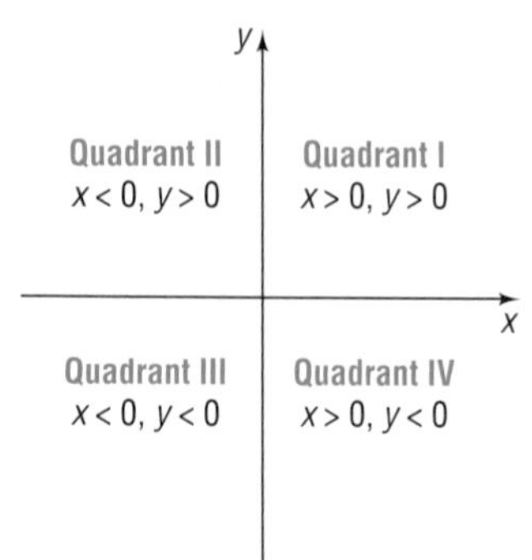

The coordinate axes divide the xy-plane into four sections called **quadrants,** as shown in Figure 3. In quadrant I, both the x-coordinate and the y-coordinate of all points are positive; in quadrant II, x is negative and y is positive; in quadrant III, both x and y are negative; and in quadrant IV, x is positive and y is negative. Points on the coordinate axes belong to no quadrant.

Now Work PROBLEM 13

Graphing Utilities

All graphing utilities (graphing calculators and computer software graphing packages) graph equations by plotting points on a screen. The screen itself actually consists of small rectangles, called **pixels.** The more pixels the screen has, the better the resolution. Most graphing calculators have 48 pixels per square inch; most computer screens have 32 to 108 pixels per square inch. When a point to be plotted lies inside a pixel, the pixel is turned on (lights up). The graph of an equation is a collection of lighted pixels. Figure 4 shows how the graph of $y = 2x$ looks on a TI-84 Plus graphing calculator.

Figure 4

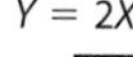

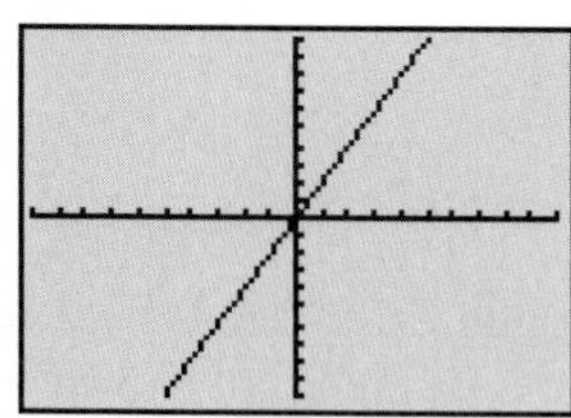

The screen of a graphing utility will display the coordinate axes of a rectangular coordinate system. However, you must set the scale on each axis. You must also include the smallest and largest values of x and y that you want included in the graph. This is called **setting the viewing rectangle** or **viewing window.** Figure 5 illustrates a typical viewing window.

Figure 5

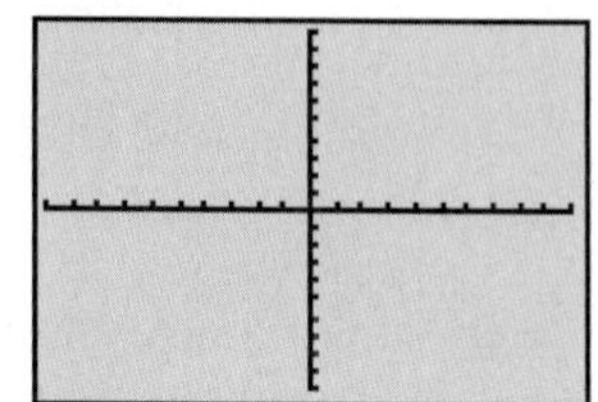

To select the viewing window, we must give values to the following expressions:

*X*min: the smallest value of x shown on the viewing window
*X*max: the largest value of x shown on the viewing window
*X*scl: the number of units per tick mark on the x-axis
*Y*min: the smallest value of y shown on the viewing window
*Y*max: the largest value of y shown on the viewing window
*Y*scl: the number of units per tick mark on the y-axis

Figure 6 illustrates these settings and their relation to the Cartesian coordinate system.

Figure 6

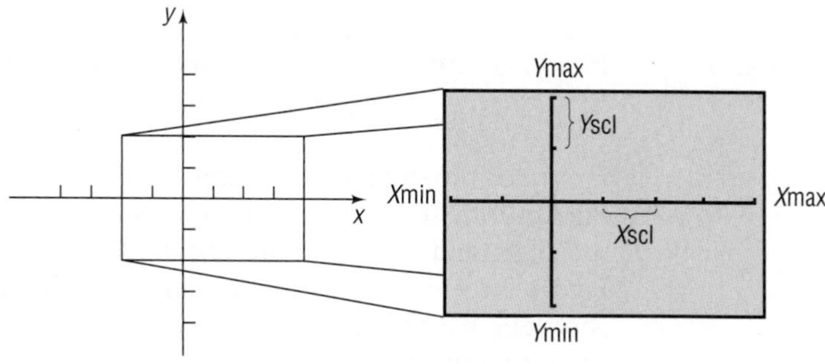

If the scale used on each axis is known, we can determine the minimum and maximum values of x and y shown on the screen by counting the tick marks. Look again at Figure 5. For a scale of 1 on each axis, the minimum and maximum values of x are -10 and 10, respectively; the minimum and maximum values of y are also -10 and 10. If the scale is 2 on each axis, then the minimum and maximum values of x are -20 and 20, respectively; and the minimum and maximum values of y are -20 and 20, respectively.

Conversely, if we know the minimum and maximum values of x and y, we can determine the scales being used by counting the tick marks displayed. We shall follow the practice of showing the minimum and maximum values of x and y in our illustrations so that you will know how the window was set. See Figure 7 from which we can determine the following window settings:

Figure 7

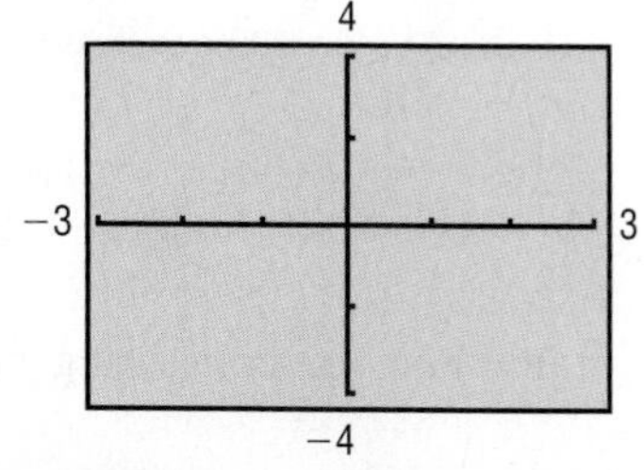

$$X\text{min} = -3 \qquad Y\text{min} = -4$$
$$X\text{max} = 3 \qquad Y\text{max} = 4$$
$$X\text{scl} = 1 \qquad Y\text{scl} = 2$$

EXAMPLE 1 **Finding the Coordinates of a Point Shown on a Graphing Utility Screen**

Find the coordinates of the point shown in Figure 8. Assume the coordinates are integers.

Figure 8

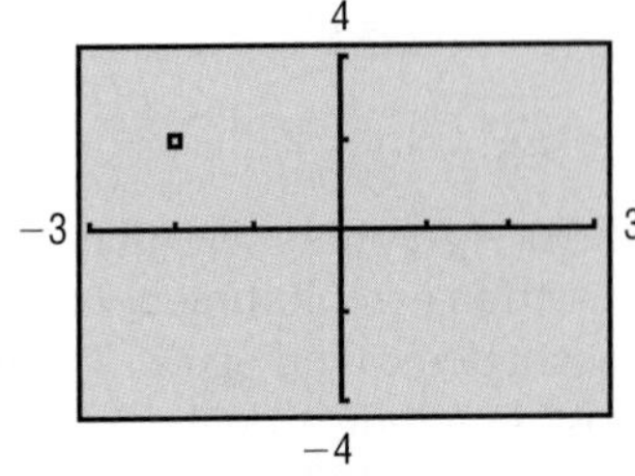

Solution First note that the viewing window used in Figure 8 is

$$Xmin = -3 \qquad Ymin = -4$$
$$Xmax = 3 \qquad Ymax = 4$$
$$Xscl = 1 \qquad Yscl = 2$$

The point shown is 2 tick units to the left on the horizontal axis (scale = 1) and 1 tick up on the vertical scale (scale = 2). The coordinates of the point shown are $(-2, 2)$. ■

Now Work PROBLEMS 17 AND 27

1 Use the Distance Formula

If the same units of measurement, such as inches, centimeters, and so on, are used for both the x-axis and y-axis, then all distances in the xy-plane can be measured using this unit of measurement.

EXAMPLE 2 **Finding the Distance between Two Points**

Find the distance d between the points $(1, 3)$ and $(5, 6)$.

Solution First plot the points $(1, 3)$ and $(5, 6)$ and connect them with a straight line. See Figure 9(a). To find the length d, begin by drawing a horizontal line from $(1, 3)$ to $(5, 3)$ and a vertical line from $(5, 3)$ to $(5, 6)$, forming a right triangle, as in Figure 9(b). One leg of the triangle is of length 4 (since $|5 - 1| = 4$) and the other is of length 3 (since $|6 - 3| = 3$). By the Pythagorean Theorem, the square of the distance d that we seek is

$$d^2 = 4^2 + 3^2 = 16 + 9 = 25$$
$$d = \sqrt{25} = 5$$

Figure 9

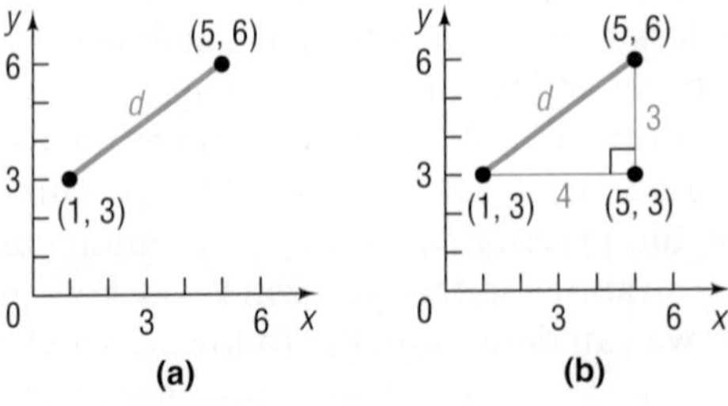

■

The **distance formula** provides a straightforward method for computing the distance between two points.

THEOREM

Distance Formula

The distance between two points $P_1 = (x_1, y_1)$ and $P_2 = (x_2, y_2)$, denoted by $d(P_1, P_2)$, is

$$d(P_1, P_2) = \sqrt{(x_2 - x_1)^2 + (y_2 - y_1)^2} \quad (1)$$

In Words

To compute the distance between two points, find the difference of the x-coordinates, square it, and add this to the square of the difference of the y-coordinates. The square root of this sum is the distance.

Figure 10 illustrates the theorem.

Figure 10

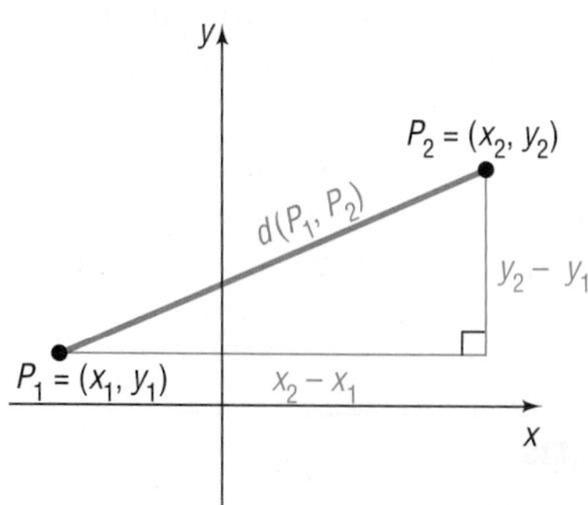

Proof of the Distance Formula Let (x_1, y_1) denote the coordinates of point P_1, and let (x_2, y_2) denote the coordinates of point P_2. Assume that the line joining P_1 and P_2 is neither horizontal nor vertical. Refer to Figure 11(a). The coordinates of P_3 are (x_2, y_1). The horizontal distance from P_1 to P_3 is the absolute value of the difference of the x-coordinates, $|x_2 - x_1|$. The vertical distance from P_3 to P_2 is the absolute value of the difference of the y-coordinates, $|y_2 - y_1|$. See Figure 11(b). The distance $d(P_1, P_2)$ that we seek is the length of the hypotenuse of the right triangle, so, by the Pythagorean Theorem, it follows that

$$\begin{aligned} [d(P_1, P_2)]^2 &= |x_2 - x_1|^2 + |y_2 - y_1|^2 \\ &= (x_2 - x_1)^2 + (y_2 - y_1)^2 \\ d(P_1, P_2) &= \sqrt{(x_2 - x_1)^2 + (y_2 - y_1)^2} \end{aligned}$$

Figure 11

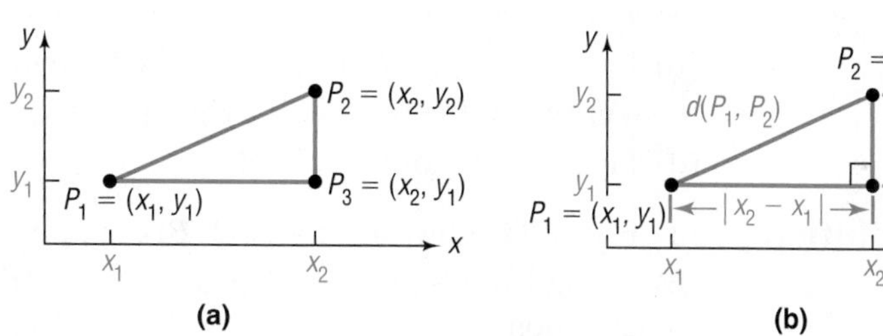

Now, if the line joining P_1 and P_2 is horizontal, then the y-coordinate of P_1 equals the y-coordinate of P_2; that is, $y_1 = y_2$. Refer to Figure 12(a). In this case, the distance formula (1) still works, because, for $y_1 = y_2$, it reduces to

$$d(P_1, P_2) = \sqrt{(x_2 - x_1)^2 + 0^2} = \sqrt{(x_2 - x_1)^2} = |x_2 - x_1|$$

Figure 12

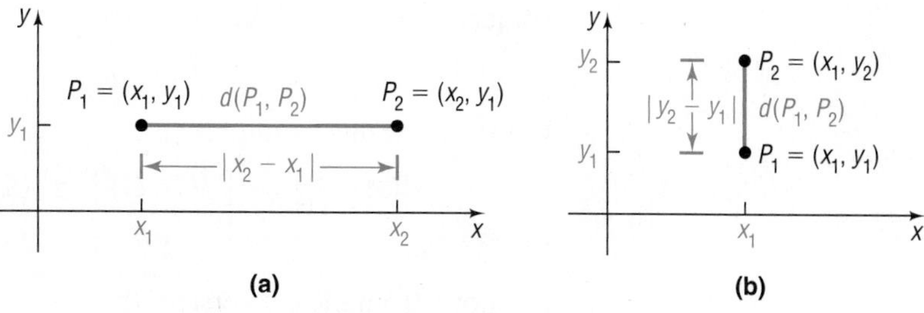

A similar argument holds if the line joining P_1 and P_2 is vertical. See Figure 12(b). ■

EXAMPLE 3 **Finding the Length of a Line Segment**

Find the length of the line segment shown in Figure 13 on page 464.

Solution The length of the line segment is the distance between the points $P_1 = (x_1, y_1) = (-4, 5)$ and $P_2 = (x_2, y_2) = (3, 2)$. Using the distance formula (1) with $x_1 = -4$, $y_1 = 5$, $x_2 = 3$, and $y_2 = 2$, the length d is

$$d = \sqrt{(x_2 - x_1)^2 + (y_2 - y_1)^2} = \sqrt{[3 - (-4)]^2 + (2 - 5)^2}$$
$$= \sqrt{7^2 + (-3)^2} = \sqrt{49 + 9} = \sqrt{58} \approx 7.62$$ ■

Figure 13

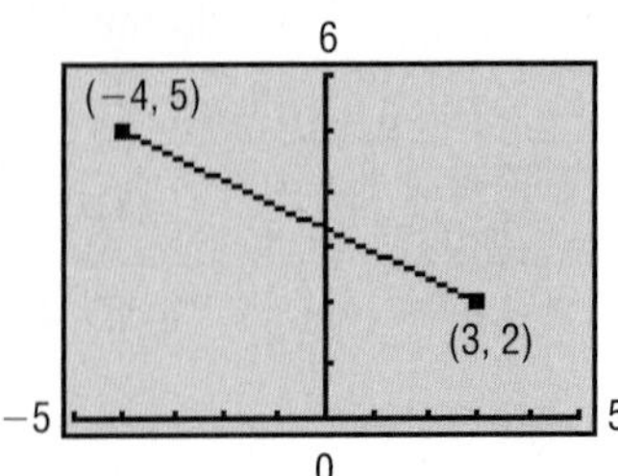

Now Work PROBLEM 33

The distance between two points $P_1 = (x_1, y_1)$ and $P_2 = (x_2, y_2)$ is never a negative number. Furthermore, the distance between two points is 0 only when the points are identical, that is, when $x_1 = x_2$ and $y_1 = y_2$. Also, because $(x_2 - x_1)^2 = (x_1 - x_2)^2$ and $(y_2 - y_1)^2 = (y_1 - y_2)^2$, it makes no difference whether the distance is computed from P_1 to P_2 or from P_2 to P_1; that is, $d(P_1, P_2) = d(P_2, P_1)$.

The introduction to this chapter mentioned that rectangular coordinates enable us to translate geometry problems into algebra problems, and vice versa. The next example shows how algebra (the distance formula) can be used to solve geometry problems.

EXAMPLE 4 Using Algebra to Solve Geometry Problems

Consider the three points $A = (-2, 1)$, $B = (2, 3)$, and $C = (3, 1)$.

(a) Plot each point and form the triangle ABC.
(b) Find the length of each side of the triangle.
(c) Verify that the triangle is a right triangle.
(d) Find the area of the triangle.

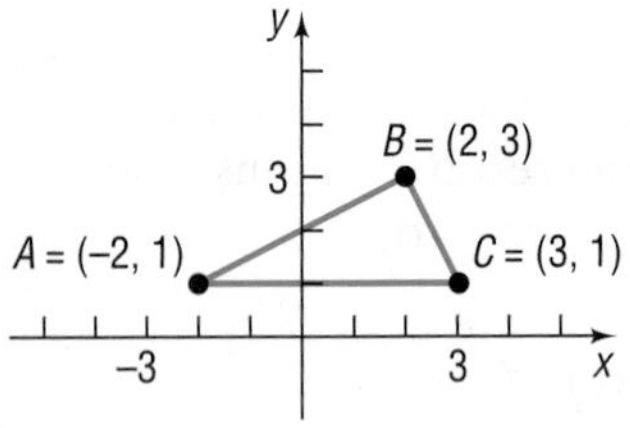

Solution

(a) Figure 14 shows the points A, B, C and the triangle ABC.

Figure 14

(b) To find the length of each side of the triangle, we use the distance formula, equation (1).

$$d(A, B) = \sqrt{[2 - (-2)]^2 + (3 - 1)^2} = \sqrt{16 + 4} = \sqrt{20} = 2\sqrt{5}$$
$$d(B, C) = \sqrt{(3 - 2)^2 + (1 - 3)^2} = \sqrt{1 + 4} = \sqrt{5}$$
$$d(A, C) = \sqrt{[3 - (-2)]^2 + (1 - 1)^2} = \sqrt{25 + 0} = 5$$

(c) To show that the triangle is a right triangle, we need to show that the sum of the squares of the lengths of two of the sides equals the square of the length of the third side. (Why is this sufficient?) Looking at Figure 14, it seems reasonable to conjecture that the right angle is at vertex B. We shall check to see whether

$$[d(A, B)]^2 + [d(B, C)]^2 = [d(A, C)]^2$$

Using the results from part (b),

$$[d(A, B)]^2 + [d(B, C)]^2 = (2\sqrt{5})^2 + (\sqrt{5})^2$$
$$= 20 + 5 = 25 = [d(A, C)]^2$$

It follows from the converse of the Pythagorean Theorem that triangle ABC is a right triangle.

(d) Because the right angle is at vertex B, the sides AB and BC form the base and height of the triangle. Its area is

$$\text{Area} = \frac{1}{2}(\text{Base})(\text{Height}) = \frac{1}{2}(2\sqrt{5})(\sqrt{5}) = 5 \text{ square units}$$ ■

Now Work PROBLEM 49

2 Use the Midpoint Formula

Figure 15

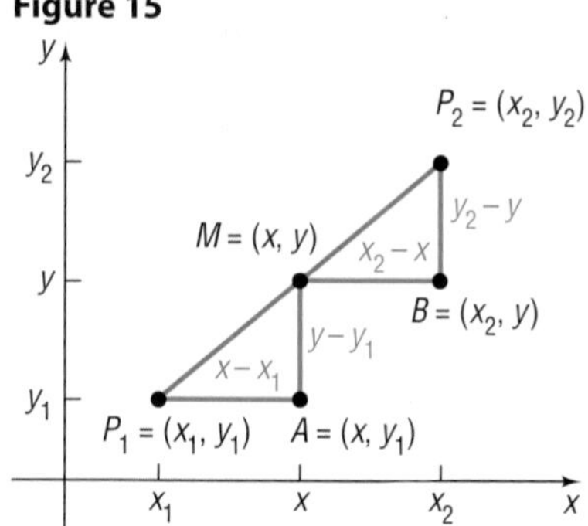

We now derive a formula for the coordinates of the **midpoint of a line segment.** Let $P_1 = (x_1, y_1)$ and $P_2 = (x_2, y_2)$ be the endpoints of a line segment, and let $M = (x, y)$ be the point on the line segment that is the same distance from P_1 as it is from P_2. See Figure 15. The triangles P_1AM and MBP_2 are congruent. [Do you see why? Angle AP_1M = angle BMP_2,* angle P_1MA = angle MP_2B, and $d(P_1, M) = d(M, P_2)$ is given. So, we have angle–side–angle.] Hence, corresponding sides are equal in length. That is,

$$x - x_1 = x_2 - x \quad \text{and} \quad y - y_1 = y_2 - y$$
$$2x = x_1 + x_2 \qquad 2y = y_1 + y_2$$
$$x = \frac{x_1 + x_2}{2} \qquad y = \frac{y_1 + y_2}{2}$$

THEOREM

Midpoint Formula

The midpoint $M = (x, y)$ of the line segment from $P_1 = (x_1, y_1)$ to $P_2 = (x_2, y_2)$ is

$$M = (x, y) = \left(\frac{x_1 + x_2}{2}, \frac{y_1 + y_2}{2}\right) \qquad \textbf{(2)}$$

In Words
To find the midpoint of a line segment, average the x-coordinates and average the y-coordinates of the endpoints.

EXAMPLE 5 Finding the Midpoint of a Line Segment

Find the midpoint of a line segment from $P_1 = (-5, 5)$ to $P_2 = (3, 1)$. Plot the points P_1 and P_2 and their midpoint.

Solution Apply the midpoint formula (2) using $x_1 = -5$, $y_1 = 5$, $x_2 = 3$, and $y_2 = 1$. Then the coordinates (x, y) of the midpoint M are

$$x = \frac{x_1 + x_2}{2} = \frac{-5 + 3}{2} = -1 \quad \text{and} \quad y = \frac{y_1 + y_2}{2} = \frac{5 + 1}{2} = 3$$

That is, $M = (-1, 3)$. See Figure 16. ■

Figure 16

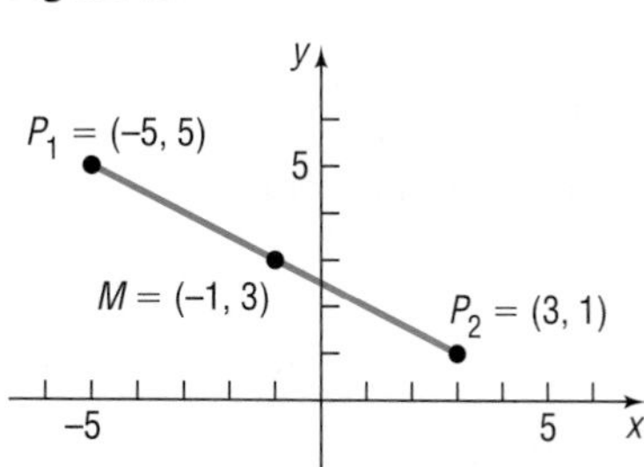

Now Work PROBLEM 55

3 Graph Equations by Hand by Plotting Points

An **equation in two variables,** say x and y, is a statement in which two expressions involving x and y are equal. The expressions are called the **sides** of the equation. Since an equation is a statement, it may be true or false, depending on the value of the variables. Any values of x and y that result in a true statement are said to **satisfy** the equation.

For example, the following are all equations in two variables x and y:

$$x^2 + y^2 = 5 \qquad 2x - y = 6 \qquad y = 2x + 5 \qquad x^2 = y$$

The first of these, $x^2 + y^2 = 5$, is satisfied for $x = 1, y = 2$, since $1^2 + 2^2 = 1 + 4 = 5$. Other choices of x and y also satisfy this equation. It is not satisfied for $x = 2$ and $y = 3$, since $2^2 + 3^2 = 4 + 9 = 13 \neq 5$.

*A postulate from geometry states that the transversal $\overline{P_1P_2}$ forms congruent corresponding angles with the parallel line segments $\overline{P_1A}$ and $\overline{MB}$.

The **graph of an equation in two variables** x and y consists of the set of points in the xy-plane whose coordinates (x, y) satisfy the equation.

Graphs play an important role in helping us to visualize the relationships that exist between two variables or quantities. Figure 17 shows the relation between the level of risk in a stock portfolio and the average annual rate of return. The graph shows that, when 30% of a portfolio of stocks is invested in foreign companies, risk is minimized.

Figure 17
Source: T. Rowe Price

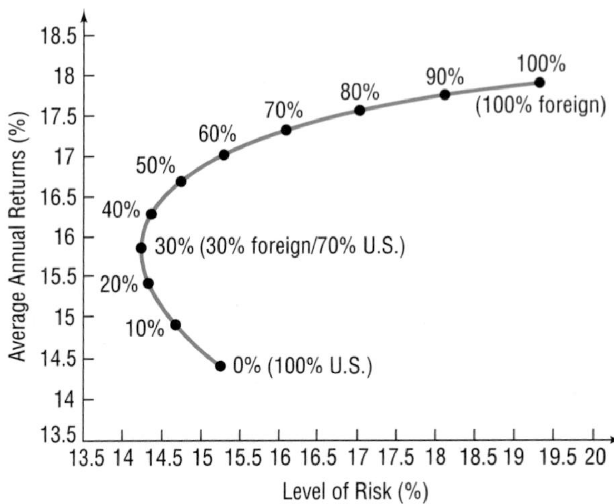

EXAMPLE 6 Determining Whether a Point Is on the Graph of an Equation

Determine if the following points are on the graph of the equation $2x - y = 6$.

(a) $(2, 3)$ (b) $(2, -2)$

Solution

(a) For the point $(2, 3)$, check to see if $x = 2, y = 3$ satisfies the equation $2x - y = 6$.

$$2x - y = 2(2) - 3 = 4 - 3 = 1 \neq 6$$

The equation is not satisfied, so the point $(2, 3)$ is not on the graph.

(b) For the point $(2, -2)$,

$$2x - y = 2(2) - (-2) = 4 + 2 = 6$$

The equation is satisfied, so the point $(2, -2)$ is on the graph. ■

Now Work PROBLEM 63

EXAMPLE 7 Graphing an Equation by Hand by Plotting Points

Graph the equation: $y = -2x + 3$

Step-by-Step Solution

Step 1 Find some points (x, y) that satisfy the equation. To determine these points, choose values of x and use the equation to find the corresponding values for y. See Table 1.

Table 1

x	$y = -2x + 3$	(x, y)
-2	$-2(-2) + 3 = 7$	$(-2, 7)$
-1	$-2(-1) + 3 = 5$	$(-1, 5)$
0	$-2(0) + 3 = 3$	$(0, 3)$
1	$-2(1) + 3 = 1$	$(1, 1)$
2	$-2(2) + 3 = -1$	$(2, -1)$

Step 2 Plot the points listed in the table as shown in Figure 18(a). Now connect the points to obtain the graph of the equation (a line), as shown in Figure 18(b).

Figure 18

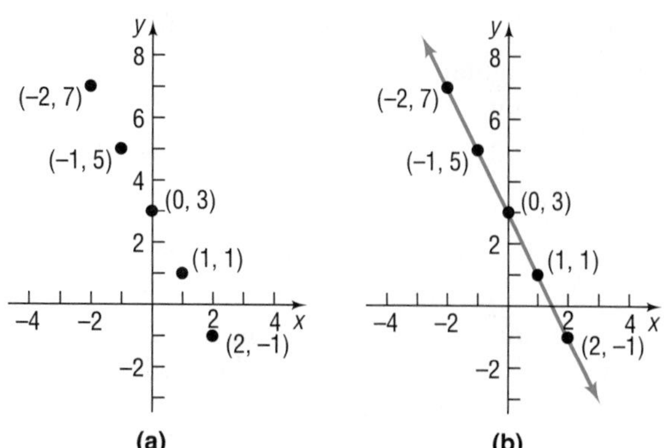

EXAMPLE 8 Graphing an Equation by Hand by Plotting Points

Graph the equation: $y = x^2$

Solution Table 2 provides several points on the graph. In Figure 19 we plot these points and connect them with a smooth curve to obtain the graph (a *parabola*).

Table 2

x	$y = x^2$	(x, y)
−4	16	(−4, 16)
−3	9	(−3, 9)
−2	4	(−2, 4)
−1	1	(−1, 1)
0	0	(0, 0)
1	1	(1, 1)
2	4	(2, 4)
3	9	(3, 9)
4	16	(4, 16)

Figure 19

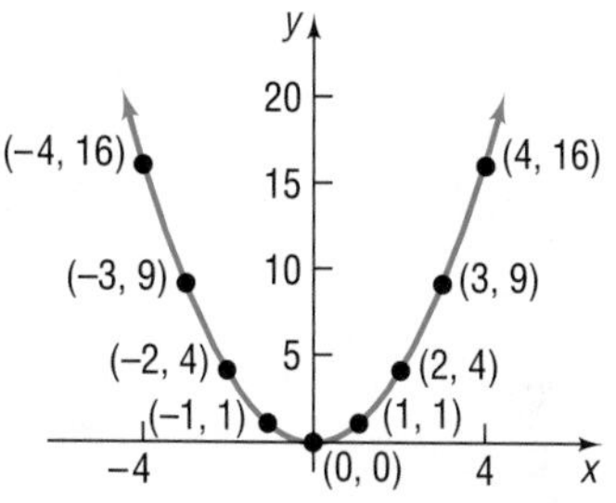

The graphs of the equations shown in Figures 18(b) and 19 do not show all the points that are on the graph. For example, in Figure 18(b), the point $(20, -37)$ is a part of the graph of $y = -2x + 3$, but it is not shown. Since the graph of $y = -2x + 3$ could be extended out as far as we please, we use arrows to indicate that the pattern shown continues. It is important when illustrating a graph to present enough of the graph so that any viewer of the illustration will "see" the rest of it as an obvious continuation of what is actually there. This is referred to as a **complete graph.**

One way to obtain a complete graph of an equation is to plot a sufficient number of points on the graph until a pattern becomes evident. Then connect these points with a smooth curve following the suggested pattern. But how many points are sufficient? Sometimes knowledge about the equation tells us. For example, we will learn in Section 8.2 that, if an equation is of the form $y = mx + b$, then its graph is a line. In this case, two points would suffice to obtain the graph.

One purpose of this book is to investigate the properties of equations in order to decide whether a graph is complete. Sometimes we shall graph equations by plotting a sufficient number of points on the graph until a pattern becomes evident and then connect these points with a smooth curve, following the suggested pattern. (Shortly, we shall investigate various techniques that will enable us to graph an equation without plotting so many points.) Other times we shall graph equations using a graphing utility.

4 Graph Equations Using a Graphing Utility

From Examples 7 and 8, we see that a graph can be obtained by plotting points in a rectangular coordinate system and connecting them. Graphing utilities perform these same steps when graphing an equation. For example, the TI-84 Plus determines 95 evenly spaced input values,* uses the equation to determine the output values, plots these points on the screen, and finally (if in the connected mode) draws a line between consecutive points.

To graph an equation in two variables x and y using a graphing utility requires that the equation be written in the form $y = \{\text{expression in } x\}$. If the original equation is not in this form, rewrite it using equivalent equations until the form $y = \{\text{expression in } x\}$ is obtained. In general, there are four ways to obtain equivalent equations.

Procedures That Result in Equivalent Equations

1. Interchange the two sides of the equation:

$$3x + 5 = y \quad \text{is equivalent to} \quad y = 3x + 5$$

2. Simplify the sides of the equation by combining like terms, eliminating parentheses, and so on:

$$2y + 2 + 6 = 2x + 5(x + 1) \quad \text{is equivalent to} \quad 2y + 8 = 7x + 5$$

3. Add or subtract the same expression on both sides of the equation:

$$y + 3x - 5 = 4 \quad \text{is equivalent to} \quad y + 3x - 5 + 5 = 4 + 5$$

4. Multiply or divide both sides of the equation by the same nonzero expression:

$$3y = 6 - 2x \quad \text{is equivalent to} \quad \frac{1}{3} \cdot 3y = \frac{1}{3}(6 - 2x)$$

EXAMPLE 9 **Expressing an Equation in the Form $y = \{\text{expression in } x\}$**

Solve for y: $2y + 3x - 5 = 4$

Solution We replace the original equation by a succession of equivalent equations.

$$2y + 3x - 5 = 4$$

$$2y + 3x - 5 + 5 = 4 + 5 \qquad \text{Add 5 to both sides.}$$

$$2y + 3x = 9 \qquad \text{Simplify.}$$

$$2y + 3x - 3x = 9 - 3x \qquad \text{Subtract } 3x \text{ from both sides.}$$

$$2y = 9 - 3x \qquad \text{Simplify.}$$

$$\frac{2y}{2} = \frac{9 - 3x}{2} \qquad \text{Divide both sides by 2.}$$

$$y = \frac{9 - 3x}{2} \qquad \text{Simplify.}$$

WARNING Be careful when entering the expression $\frac{9 - 3x}{2}$. Use parentheses as follows: (9 − 3x)/2.

Now we are ready to graph equations using a graphing utility.

*These input values depend on the values of Xmin and Xmax. For example, if Xmin = −10 and Xmax = 10, then the first input value will be −10 and the next input value will be $-10 + (10 - (-10))/94 = -9.7872$, and so on.

EXAMPLE 10

Graphing an Equation Using a Graphing Utility

Use a graphing utility to graph the equation: $6x^2 + 3y = 36$

Step-by-Step Solution

Step 1 Solve the equation for y in terms of x.

$$6x^2 + 3y = 36$$

$$3y = -6x^2 + 36 \quad \text{Subtract } 6x^2 \text{ from both sides of the equation.}$$

$$y = -2x^2 + 12 \quad \text{Divide both sides of the equation by 3 and simplify.}$$

Step 2 Enter the equation to be graphed into your graphing utility. Figure 20 shows the equation to be graphed entered on a TI-84 Plus.

Figure 20

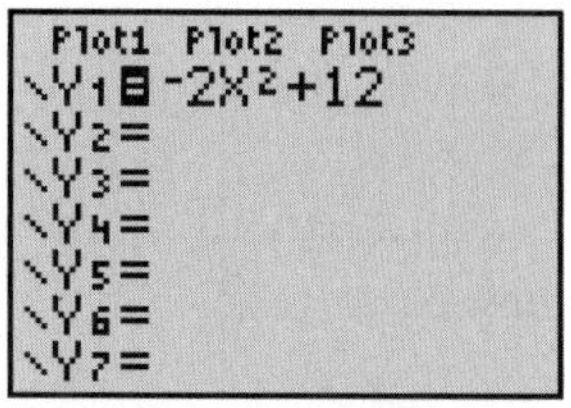

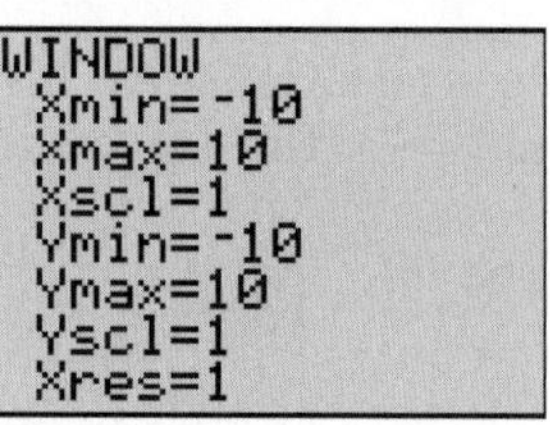

Step 3 Choose an initial viewing window. Without any knowledge about the behavior of the graph, it is common to choose the standard viewing window as the initial viewing window. The standard viewing window is

Xmin = −10 Ymin = −10

Xmax = 10 Ymax = 10

Xscl = 1 Yscl = 1

See Figure 21.

Figure 21

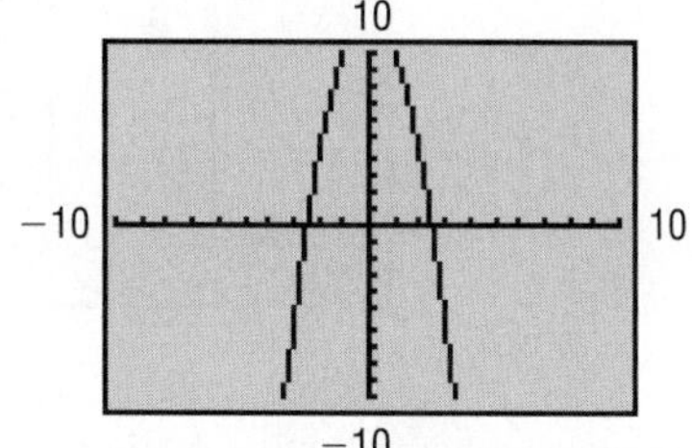

Step 4 Graph the equation. See Figure 22.

Figure 22

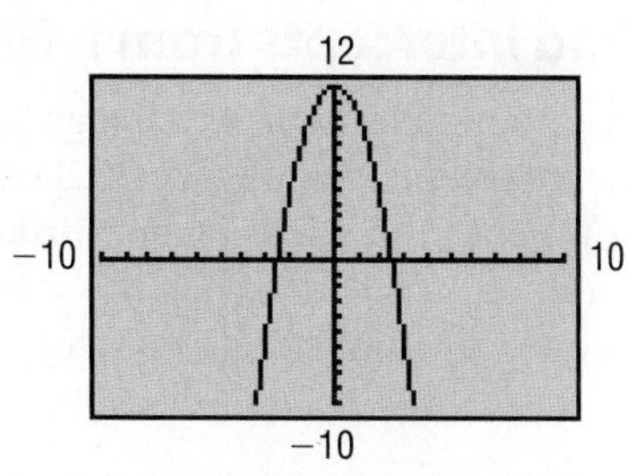

Step 5 Adjust the viewing window until a complete graph is obtained.

The graph of $y = -2x^2 + 12$ is not complete. The value of Ymax must be increased so that the top portion of the graph is visible. After increasing the value of Ymax to 12, we obtain the graph in Figure 23. The graph is now complete.

Figure 23

12

−10 10

−10

■

NOTE Some graphing utilities have a ZOOM-STANDARD feature that automatically sets the viewing window to the standard viewing window. In addition, some graphing utilities have a ZOOM-FIT feature that determines the appropriate Ymin and Ymax for a given Xmin and Xmax. Consult your owner's manual for the appropriate keystrokes. ■

Now Work PROBLEM 81

5 Use a Graphing Utility to Create Tables

In addition to graphing equations, graphing utilities can also be used to create a table of values that satisfy the equation. This feature is especially useful in determining an appropriate viewing window when graphing an equation.

EXAMPLE 11 Creating a Table Using a Graphing Utility

Create a table that displays the points on the graph of $6x^2 + 3y = 36$ for $x = -3, -2, -1, 0, 1, 2,$ and 3.

Step-by-Step Solution

Step 1 Solve the equation for y in terms of x.

We solved the equation for y in terms of x in Example 10 and obtained $y = -2x^2 + 12$.

Step 2 Enter the expression in x following the $Y =$ prompt of the graphing utility.

See Figure 20 on page 469.

Step 3 Set up the table. Graphing utilities typically have two modes for creating tables. In the AUTO mode, the user determines a starting point for the table (TblStart) and ΔTbl (pronounced "delta table"). The ΔTbl feature determines the increment for x in the table. The ASK mode requires the user to enter values of x, and then the utility determines the corresponding value of y.

Create a table using AUTO mode. The table we wish to create starts at -3, so TblStart = –3. The increment in x is 1, so $\Delta\text{Tbl} = 1$. See Figure 24.

Figure 24

Step 4 Create the table. See Table 3.

Table 3

X	Y1
-3	-6
-2	4
-1	10
0	12
1	10
2	4
3	-6

Y1=-2X²+12

The user can scroll within the table if it is created in AUTO mode. ■

In looking at Table 3, notice that $y = 12$ when $x = 0$. This information could have been used to help to create the initial viewing window by letting us know that Ymax needs to be at least 12 in order to get a complete graph.

6 Find Intercepts from a Graph

Figure 25

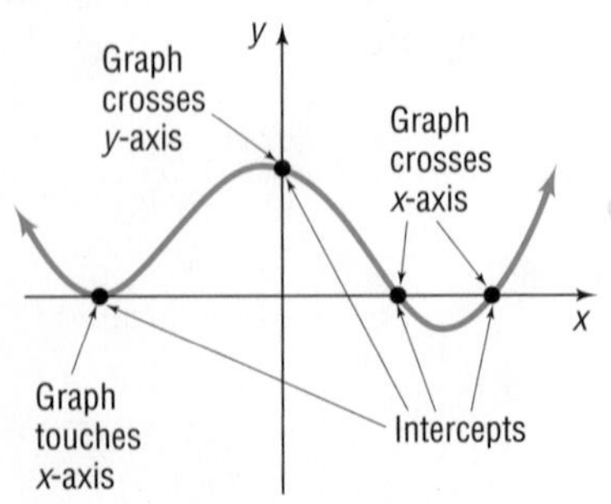

The points, if any, at which a graph crosses or touches the coordinate axes are called the **intercepts.** See Figure 25. The x-coordinate of a point at which the graph crosses or touches the x-axis is an ***x*-intercept,** and the y-coordinate of a point at which the graph crosses or touches the y-axis is a ***y*-intercept.** For a graph to be complete, all its intercepts must be displayed.

EXAMPLE 12 Finding Intercepts from a Graph

Find the intercepts of the graph in Figure 26. What are its x-intercepts? What are its y-intercepts?

Solution The intercepts of the graph are the points

Figure 26

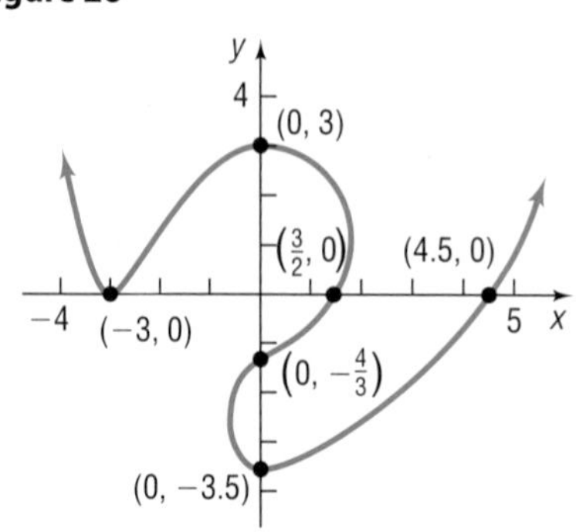

$$(-3, 0),\quad (0, 3),\quad \left(\frac{3}{2}, 0\right),\quad \left(0, -\frac{4}{3}\right),\quad (0, -3.5),\quad (4.5, 0)$$

The x-intercepts are -3, $\frac{3}{2}$, and 4.5; the y-intercepts are -3.5, $-\frac{4}{3}$, and 3. ■

In Example 12 notice the following usage: If the type of intercept is not specified (x- versus y-), then report the intercept as an ordered pair. However, if the type of intercept is specified, then report the coordinate of the specified intercept. For x-intercepts, report the x-coordinate of the intercept; for y-intercepts, report the y-coordinate of the intercept.

Now Work PROBLEM 69

7 Use a Graphing Utility to Approximate Intercepts

We can use a graphing utility to approximate the intercepts of the graph of an equation.

EXAMPLE 13 **Approximating Intercepts Using a Graphing Utility**

Use a graphing utility to approximate the intercepts of the equation $y = x^3 - 16$.

Solution Figure 27(a) shows the graph of $y = x^3 - 16$.

The eVALUEate feature of a TI-84 Plus graphing calculator accepts as input a value of x and determines the value of y. If we let $x = 0$, the y-intercept is found to be -16. See Figure 27(b).

The ZERO feature of a TI-84 Plus is used to find the x-intercept(s). See Figure 27(c). Rounded to two decimal places, the x-intercept is 2.52.

Figure 27

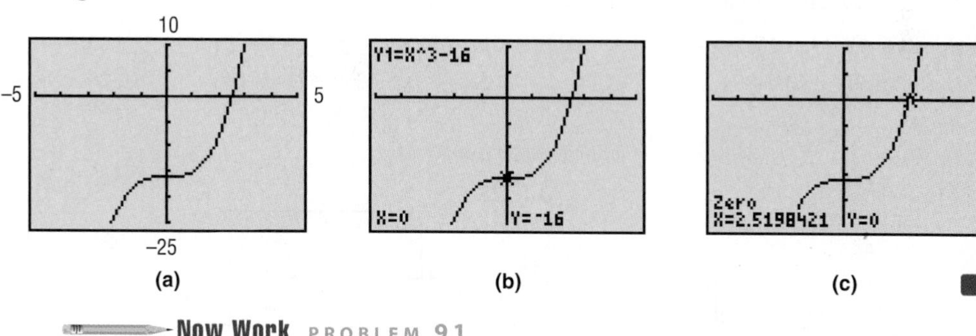

■

Now Work PROBLEM 91

To find the intercepts algebraically requires the ability to solve equations, the subject of the following four sections.

7.1 Assess Your Understanding

'Are You Prepared?' *Answers are given at the end of these exercises.*

1. On a real number line the origin is assigned the number ________.
2. If -3 and 5 are the coordinates of two points on the real number line, the distance between these points is ________.
3. If 3 and 4 are the legs of a right triangle, the hypotenuse is ________.
4. Use the converse of the Pythagorean Theorem to show that a triangle whose sides are of lengths 11, 60, and 61 is a right triangle.
5. The area of a triangle whose base is b and whose altitude is h is $A =$ ________.
6. ***True or False*** Two triangles are congruent if two angles and the included side of one equals two angles and the included side of the other.

Concepts and Vocabulary

7. If (x, y) are the coordinates of a point P in the xy-plane, then x is called the ___________ of P and y is the ________ of P.

8. The coordinate axes divide the xy-plane into four sections called _________.

9. If three distinct points P, Q, and R all lie on a line and if $d(P, Q) = d(Q, R)$, then Q is called the ________ of the line segment from P to R.

10. ***True or False*** The distance between two points is sometimes a negative number.

11. ***True or False*** The point $(-1, 4)$ lies in quadrant IV of the Cartesian plane.

12. ***True or False*** The midpoint of a line segment is found by averaging the x-coordinates and averaging the y-coordinates of the endpoints.

Skill Building

In Problems 13 and 14, plot each point in the xy-plane. Tell in which quadrant or on what coordinate axis each point lies.

13. (a) $A = (-3, 2)$ (b) $B = (6, 0)$ (c) $C = (-2, -2)$ (d) $D = (6, 5)$ (e) $E = (0, -3)$ (f) $F = (6, -3)$

14. (a) $A = (1, 4)$ (b) $B = (-3, -4)$ (c) $C = (-3, 4)$ (d) $D = (4, 1)$ (e) $E = (0, 1)$ (f) $F = (-3, 0)$

15. Plot the points $(2, 0)$, $(2, -3)$, $(2, 4)$, $(2, 1)$, and $(2, -1)$. Describe the set of all points of the form $(2, y)$, where y is a real number.

16. Plot the points $(0, 3)$, $(1, 3)$, $(-2, 3)$, $(5, 3)$, and $(-4, 3)$. Describe the set of all points of the form $(x, 3)$, where x is a real number.

In Problems 17–20, determine the coordinates of the points shown. Tell in which quadrant each point lies. Assume the coordinates are integers.

17.
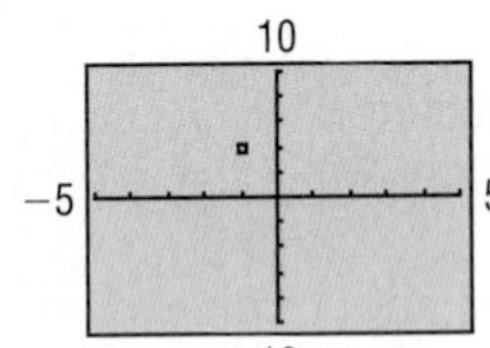

18.
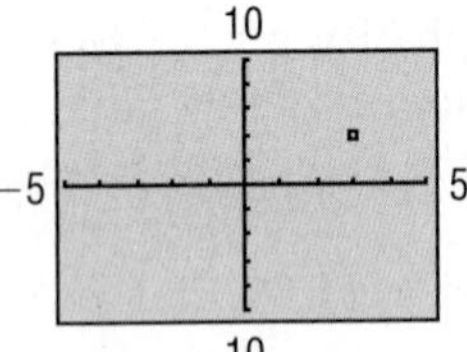

19.
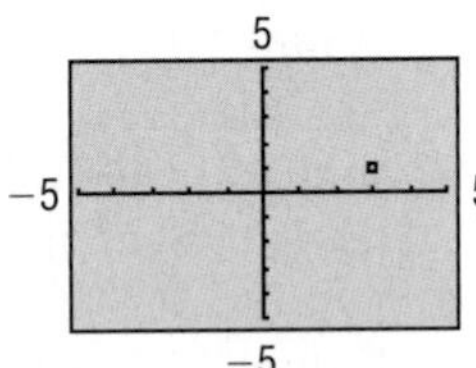

20.
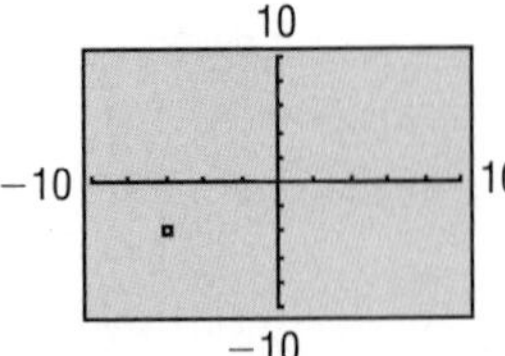

In Problems 21–26, select a setting so that each given point will lie within the viewing window.

21. $(-10, 5)$, $(3, -2)$, $(4, -1)$

22. $(5, 0)$, $(6, 8)$, $(-2, -3)$

23. $(40, 20)$, $(-20, -80)$, $(10, 40)$

24. $(-80, 60)$, $(20, -30)$, $(-20, -40)$

25. $(0, 0)$, $(100, 5)$, $(5, 150)$

26. $(0, -1)$, $(100, 50)$, $(-10, 30)$

In Problems 27–32, determine the viewing window used.

27.
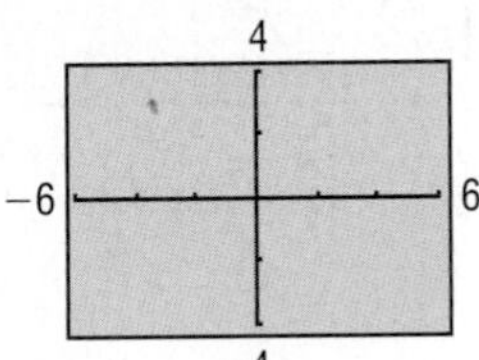

28.
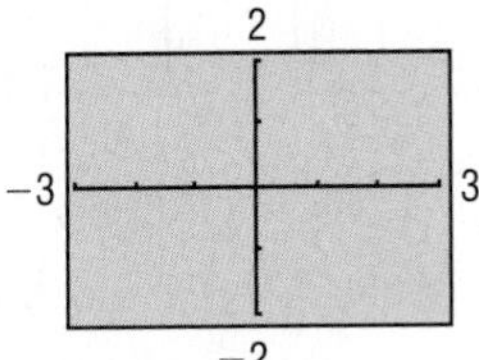

29.
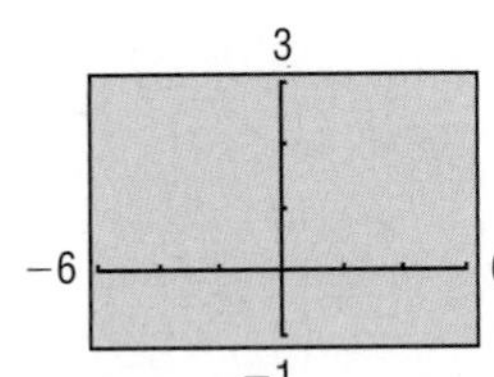

30.
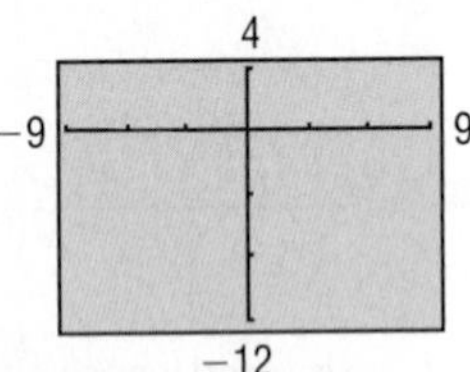

31.
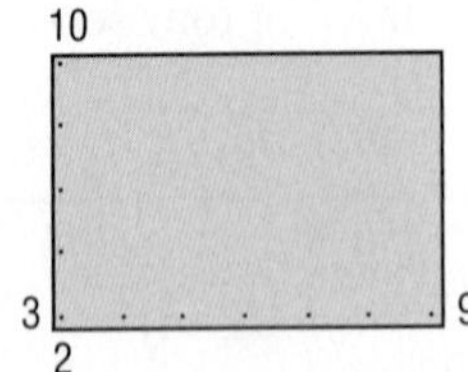

32.
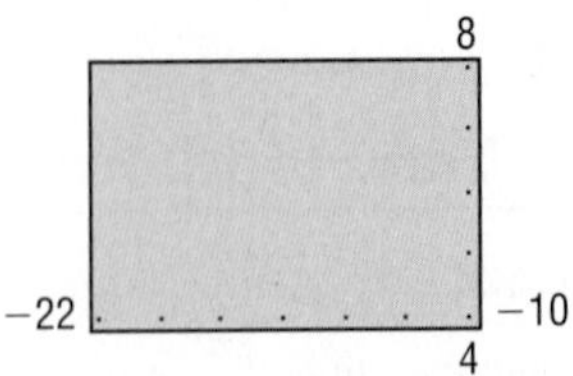

In Problems 33–44, find the distance $d(P_1, P_2)$ between the points P_1 and P_2.

33.
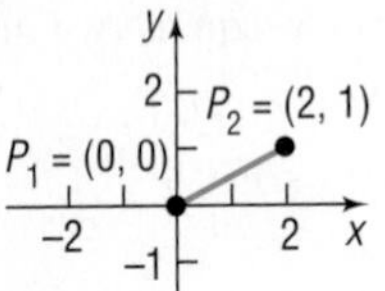

34.
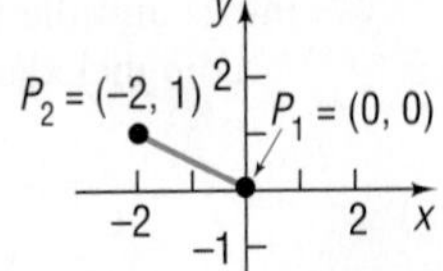

35.
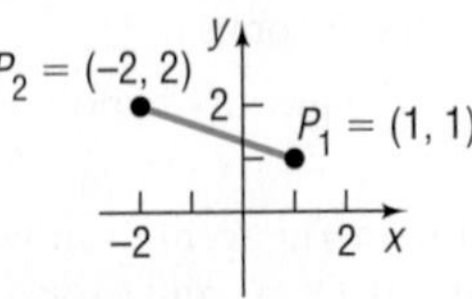

36.
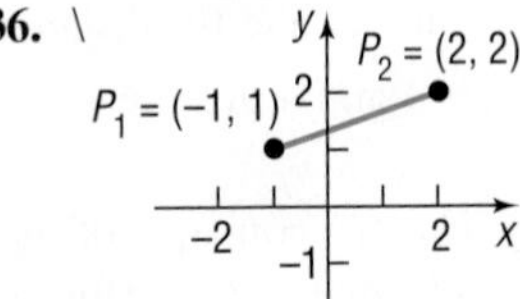

37. $P_1 = (3, -4);\ \ P_2 = (5, 4)$

38. $P_1 = (-1, 0);\ \ P_2 = (2, 4)$

39. $P_1 = (-5, -3);\ \ P_2 = (11, 9)$

40. $P_1 = (2, -3);\ \ P_2 = (10, 3)$

41. $P_1 = (4, -3);\ \ P_2 = (6, 4)$

42. $P_1 = (-4, -3);\ \ P_2 = (6, 2)$

43. $P_1 = (a, b);\ \ P_2 = (0, 0)$

44. $P_1 = (a, a);\ \ P_2 = (0, 0)$

In Problems 45–48, find the length of the line segment. Assume that the endpoints of each line segment have integer coordinates.

45.

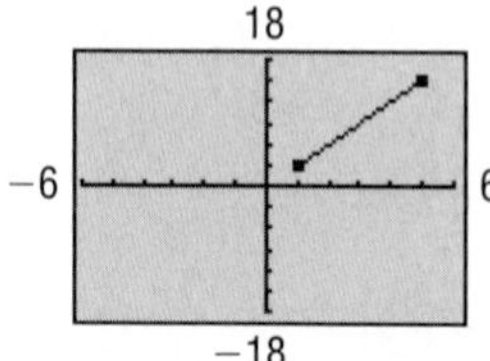

46.

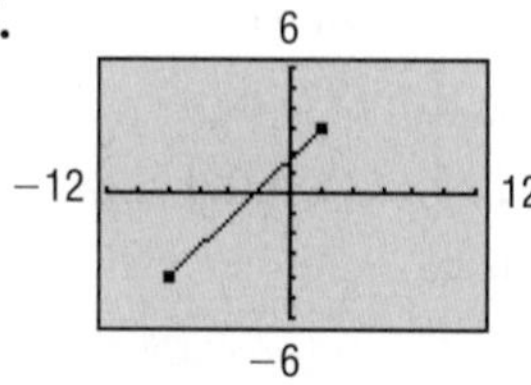

47.

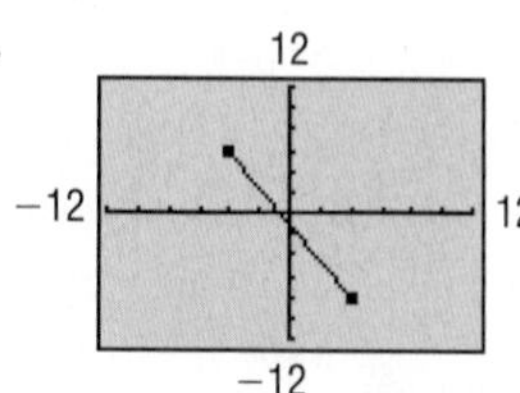

48.

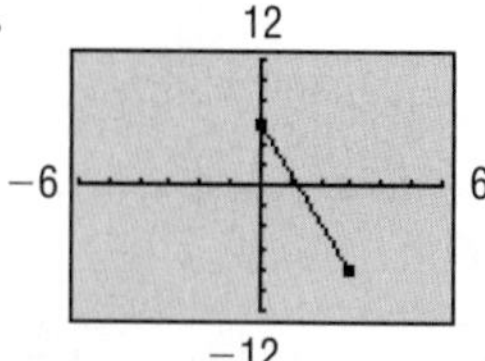

In Problems 49–54, plot each point and form the triangle ABC. Verify that the triangle is a right triangle. Find its area.

49. $A = (-2, 5);\ \ B = (1, 3);\ \ C = (-1, 0)$

50. $A = (-2, 5);\ \ B = (12, 3);\ \ C = (10, -11)$

51. $A = (-5, 3);\ \ B = (6, 0);\ \ C = (5, 5)$

52. $A = (-6, 3);\ \ B = (3, -5);\ \ C = (-1, 5)$

53. $A = (4, -3);\ \ B = (0, -3);\ \ C = (4, 2)$

54. $A = (4, -3);\ \ B = (4, 1);\ \ C = (2, 1)$

In Problems 55–62, find the midpoint of the line segment joining the points P_1 and P_2.

55. $P_1 = (3, -4);\ \ P_2 = (5, 4)$

56. $P_1 = (-2, 0);\ \ P_2 = (2, 4)$

57. $P_1 = (-5, -3);\ \ P_2 = (11, 9)$

58. $P_1 = (2, -3);\ \ P_2 = (10, 3)$

59. $P_1 = (4, -3);\ \ P_2 = (6, 1)$

60. $P_1 = (-4, -3);\ \ P_2 = (2, 2)$

61. $P_1 = (a, b);\ \ P_2 = (0, 0)$

62. $P_1 = (a, a);\ \ P_2 = (0, 0)$

In Problems 63–68, tell whether the given points are on the graph of the equation.

63. Equation: $y = x^4 - \sqrt{x}$
Points: $(0, 0); (1, 1); (-1, 0)$

64. Equation: $y = x^3 - 2\sqrt{x}$
Points: $(0, 0); (1, 1); (1, -1)$

65. Equation: $y^2 = x^2 + 9$
Points: $(0, 3); (3, 0); (-3, 0)$

66. Equation: $y^3 = x + 1$
Points: $(1, 2); (0, 1); (-1, 0)$

67. Equation: $x^2 + y^2 = 4$
Points: $(0, 2); (-2, 2); (\sqrt{2}, \sqrt{2})$

68. Equation: $x^2 + 4y^2 = 4$
Points: $(0, 1); (2, 0); \left(2, \frac{1}{2}\right)$

In Problems 69–76, the graph of an equation is given. List the intercepts of the graph.

69.

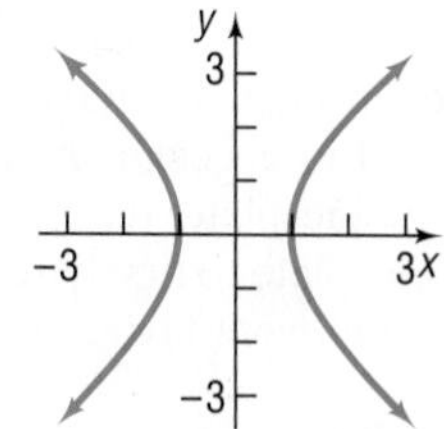

70.

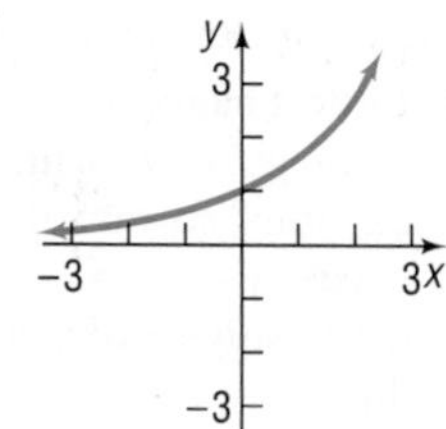

71.

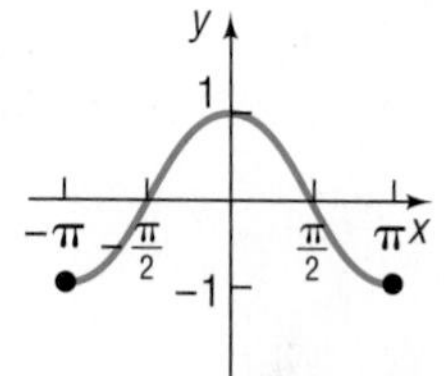

72.

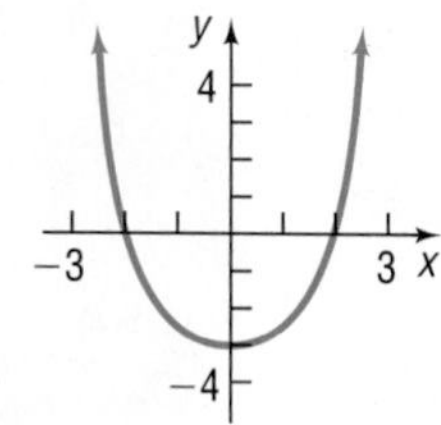

73.

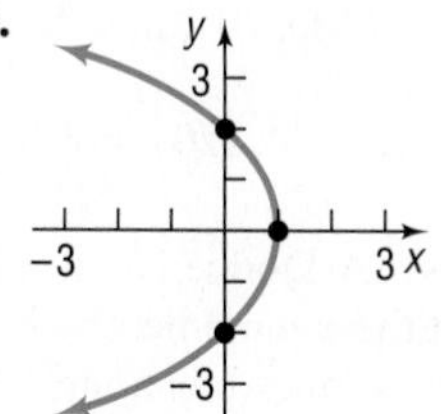

74.

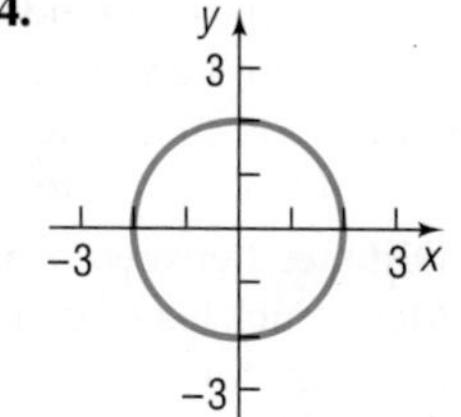

75.

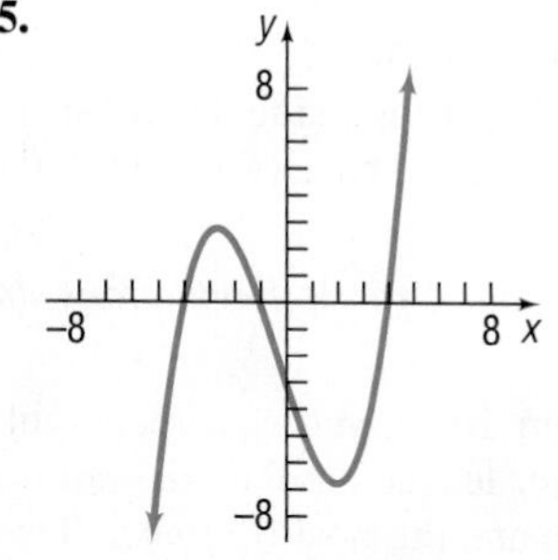

76.

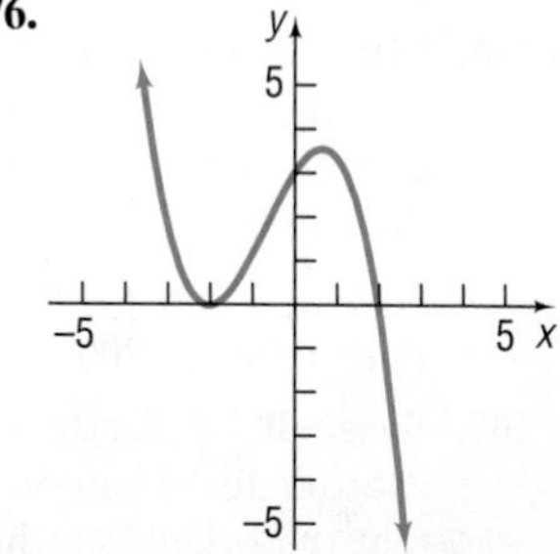

In Problems 77–88, graph each equation by hand by plotting points. Verify your results using a graphing utility.

77. $y = x + 2$
78. $y = x - 6$
79. $y = 2x + 8$
80. $y = 3x - 9$
81. $y = x^2 - 1$
82. $y = x^2 - 9$
83. $y = -x^2 + 4$
84. $y = -x^2 + 1$
85. $2x + 3y = 6$
86. $5x + 2y = 10$
87. $9x^2 + 4y = 36$
88. $4x^2 + y = 4$

In Problems 89–96, graph each equation using a graphing utility. Use a graphing utility to approximate the intercepts rounded to two decimal places. Use the TABLE feature to help to establish the viewing window.

89. $y = 2x - 13$
90. $y = -3x + 14$
91. $y = 2x^2 - 15$
92. $y = -3x^2 + 19$
93. $3x - 2y = 43$
94. $4x + 5y = 82$
95. $5x^2 + 3y = 37$
96. $2x^2 - 3y = 35$

97. If the point $(2, 5)$ is shifted 3 units right and 2 units down, what are its new coordinates?

98. If the point $(-1, 6)$ is shifted 2 units left and 4 units up, what are its new coordinates?

Applications and Extensions

99. The **medians** of a triangle are the line segments from each vertex to the midpoint of the opposite side (see the figure). Find the lengths of the medians of the triangle with vertices at $A = (0, 0)$, $B = (6, 0)$, and $C = (4, 4)$.

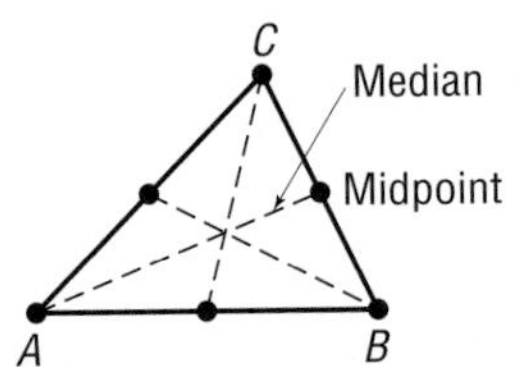

100. An **equilateral triangle** is one in which all three sides are of equal length. If two vertices of an equilateral triangle are $(0, 4)$ and $(0, 0)$, find the third vertex. How many of these triangles are possible?

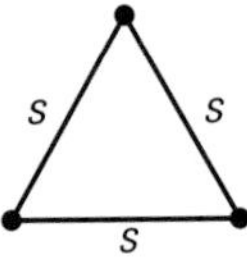

*In Problems 101–104, find the length of each side of the triangle determined by the three points P_1, P_2, and P_3. State whether the triangle is an isosceles triangle, a right triangle, neither of these, or both. (An **isosceles triangle** is one in which at least two of the sides are of equal length.)*

101. $P_1 = (2, 1)$; $P_2 = (-4, 1)$; $P_3 = (-4, -3)$
102. $P_1 = (-1, 4)$; $P_2 = (6, 2)$; $P_3 = (4, -5)$
103. $P_1 = (-2, -1)$; $P_2 = (0, 7)$; $P_3 = (3, 2)$
104. $P_1 = (7, 2)$; $P_2 = (-4, 0)$; $P_3 = (4, 6)$

105. Baseball A major league baseball "diamond" is actually a square, 90 feet on a side (see the figure). What is the distance directly from home plate to second base (the diagonal of the square)?

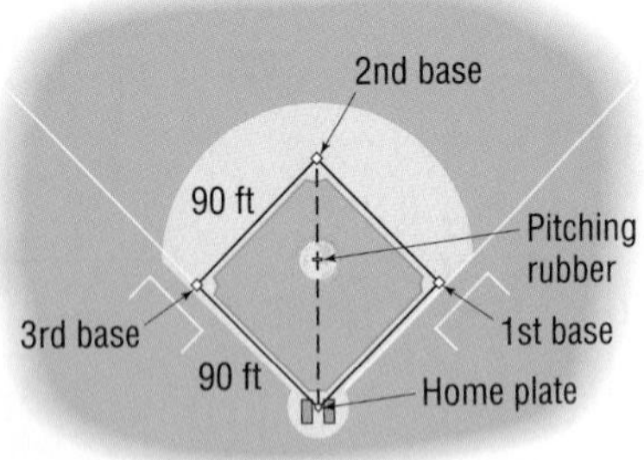

106. Little League Baseball The layout of a Little League playing field is a square, 60 feet on a side. How far is it directly from home plate to second base (the diagonal of the square)?

Source: Little League Baseball, Official Regulations and Playing Rules, 2007.

107. Baseball Refer to Problem 105. Overlay a rectangular coordinate system on a major league baseball diamond so that the origin is at home plate, the positive x-axis lies in the direction from home plate to first base, and the positive y-axis lies in the direction from home plate to third base.

(a) What are the coordinates of first base, second base, and third base? Use feet as the unit of measurement.

(b) If the right fielder is located at $(310, 15)$, how far is it from there to second base?

(c) If the center fielder is located at $(300, 300)$, how far is it from there to third base?

108. Little League Baseball Refer to Problem 106. Overlay a rectangular coordinate system on a Little League baseball diamond so that the origin is at home plate, the positive x-axis lies in the direction from home plate to first base, and the positive y-axis lies in the direction from home plate to third base.

(a) What are the coordinates of first base, second base, and third base? Use feet as the unit of measurement.

(b) If the right fielder is located at $(180, 20)$, how far is it from there to second base?

(c) If the center fielder is located at $(220, 220)$, how far is it from there to third base?

109. Distance between Moving Objects A Dodge Neon and a Mack truck leave an intersection at the same time. The Neon heads east at an average speed of 30 miles per hour, while the truck heads south at an average speed of 40 miles per hour. Find an expression for their distance apart d (in miles) at the end of t hours.

110. Distance of a Moving Object from a Fixed Point A hot-air balloon, headed due east at an average speed of 15 miles per hour at a constant altitude of 100 feet, passes over an intersection (see the figure). Find an expression for its distance d (measured in feet) from the intersection t seconds later.

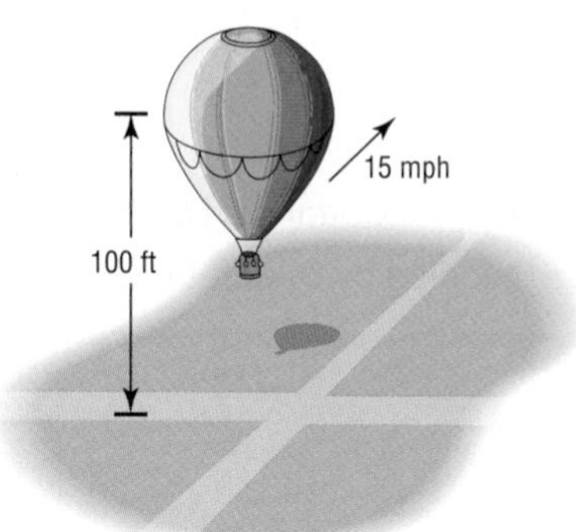

111. Drafting Error When a draftsman draws three lines that are to intersect at one point, the lines may not intersect as intended and subsequently will form an **error triangle.** If this error triangle is long and thin, one estimate for the location of the desired point is the midpoint of the shortest side. The figure shows one such error triangle.

(a) Find an estimate for the desired intersection point.
(b) Find the length of the median for the midpoint found in part (a). See Problem 99.

Source: www.uwgb.edu/dutchs/STRUCTGE/s100.htm

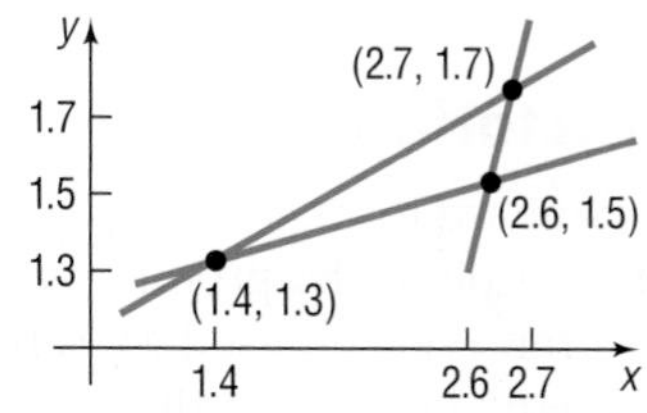

112. Net Sales The figure illustrates how net sales of Wal-Mart Stores, Inc., have grown from 2006 through 2010. Use the midpoint formula to estimate the net sales of Wal-Mart Stores, Inc., in 2008. How does your result compare to the reported value of \$374 billion?

Source: Wal-Mart Stores, Inc., 2010 Annual Report

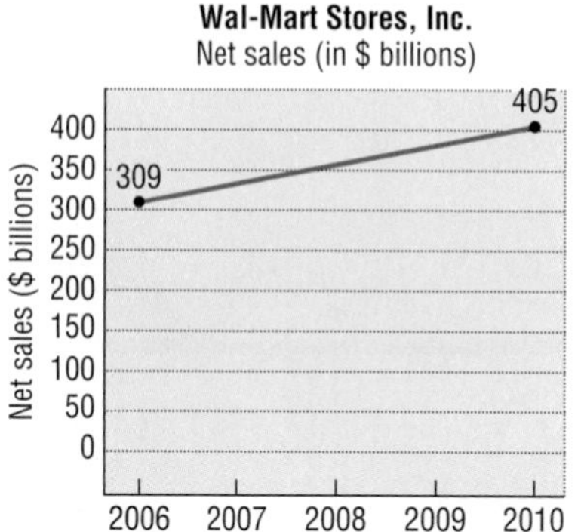

113. Poverty Threshold Poverty thresholds are determined by the U.S. Census Bureau. A poverty threshold represents the minimum annual household income for a family not to be considered poor. In 2001, the poverty threshold for a family of four with two children under the age of 18 years was \$17,960. In 2011, the poverty threshold for a family of four with two children under the age of 18 years was \$22,350. Assuming poverty thresholds increase in a straight-line fashion, use the midpoint formula to estimate the poverty threshold of a family of four with two children under the age of 18 in 2006. How does your result compare to the actual poverty threshold in 2006 of \$20,444?

Source: U.S. Census Bureau

114. Completing a Line Segment Plot the points $A = (-1, 8)$ and $M = (2, 3)$ in the xy-plane. If M is the midpoint of a line segment AB, find the coordinates of B.

Explaining Concepts: Discussion and Writing

In Problem 115, you may use a graphing utility, but it is not required.

115. (a) Graph $y = \sqrt{x^2}, y = x, y = |x|$, and $y = (\sqrt{x})^2$, noting which graphs are the same.
(b) Explain why the graphs of $y = \sqrt{x^2}$ and $y = |x|$ are the same.
(c) Explain why the graphs of $y = x$ and $y = (\sqrt{x})^2$ are not the same.
(d) Explain why the graphs of $y = \sqrt{x^2}$ and $y = x$ are not the same.

116. Make up an equation satisfied by the ordered pairs $(2, 0)$, $(4, 0)$, and $(0, 1)$. Compare your equation with a friend's equation. Comment on any similarities.

117. Draw a graph that contains the points $(-2, -1)$, $(0, 1)$, $(1, 3)$, and $(3, 5)$. Compare your graph with those of other students. Are most of the graphs almost straight lines? How many are "curved"? Discuss the various ways that these points might be connected.

118. Explain what is meant by a complete graph.

119. Write a paragraph that describes a Cartesian plane. Then write a second paragraph that describes how to plot points in the Cartesian plane. Your paragraphs should include the terms "coordinate axes," "ordered pair," "coordinates," "plot," "x-coordinate," and "y-coordinate."

'Are You Prepared?' Answers

1. 0 **2.** 8 **3.** 5 **4.** $11^2 + 60^2 = 61^2$ **5.** $\frac{1}{2}bh$ **6.** True

7.2 Quadratic Equations

Now Work the **'Are You Prepared?'** problems on page 483.

OBJECTIVES

Quadratic equations are equations such as

$$2x^2 + x + 8 = 0 \qquad 3x^2 - 5x = 0 \qquad x^2 - 9 = 0$$

A **quadratic equation** is an equation equivalent to one of the form

$$ax^2 + bx + c = 0 \tag{1}$$

where a, b, and c are real numbers and $a \neq 0$.

A quadratic equation written in the form $ax^2 + bx + c = 0$ is in **standard form.** Sometimes, a quadratic equation is called a **second-degree equation,** because the left side is a polynomial of degree 2. We shall discuss four algebraic ways of solving quadratic equations: by factoring, by the square root method, by completing the square, and by using the quadratic formula.

1 Solve Quadratic Equations by Factoring

When a quadratic equation is written in standard form, $ax^2 + bx + c = 0$, it may be possible to factor the expression on the left side as the product of two first-degree polynomials. The Zero-Product Property can then be used by setting each factor equal to 0 and solving the resulting linear equations. With this approach we obtain the *exact* solutions of the quadratic equation. This approach leads us to a basic premise in mathematics. Whenever a problem is encountered, use techniques that reduce the problem to one you already know how to solve. In this instance, we are reducing quadratic equations to linear equations using the technique of factoring.

Let's look at an example.

EXAMPLE 1 **Solving a Quadratic Equation by Factoring and by Graphing**

Solve the equation: $2x^2 - x - 3 = 0$

Algebraic Solution

The equation is in standard form. The left side may be factored as

$$2x^2 - x - 3 = 0$$

$$(2x - 3)(x + 1) = 0 \quad \text{Factor}$$

Graphing Solution

Graph $Y_1 = 2x^2 - x - 3$. See Figure 28(a) on the following page. From the graph it appears there are two solutions to the equation (since the graph crosses the x-axis in two places). Using ZERO, the x-intercepts, and therefore solutions to the equation, are -1 and 1.5. See Figures 34(b) and (c). The solution set is $\{-1, 1.5\}$.

Use the Zero-Product Property and set each factor equal to zero.

$$2x - 3 = 0 \quad \text{or} \quad x + 1 = 0$$
$$2x = 3 \quad \text{or} \quad x = -1$$
$$x = \frac{3}{2}$$

The solution set is $\left\{-1, \frac{3}{2}\right\}$.

Figure 28

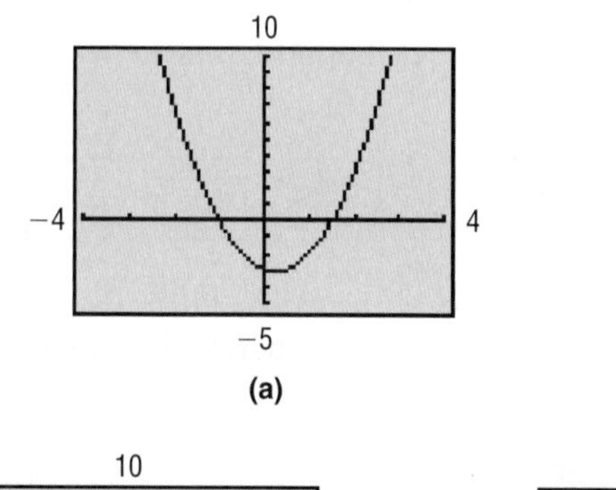

(a)

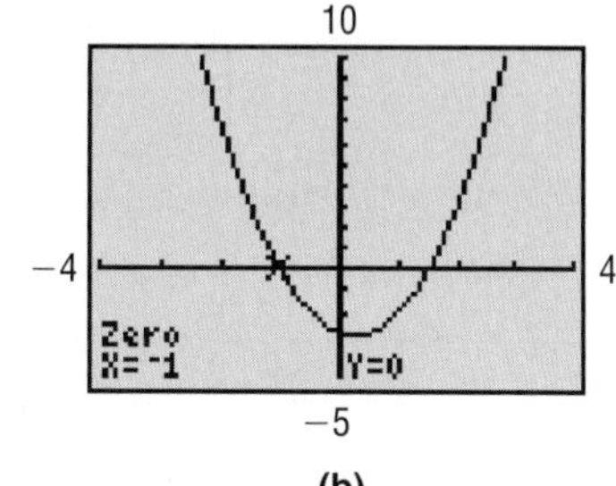

(b)

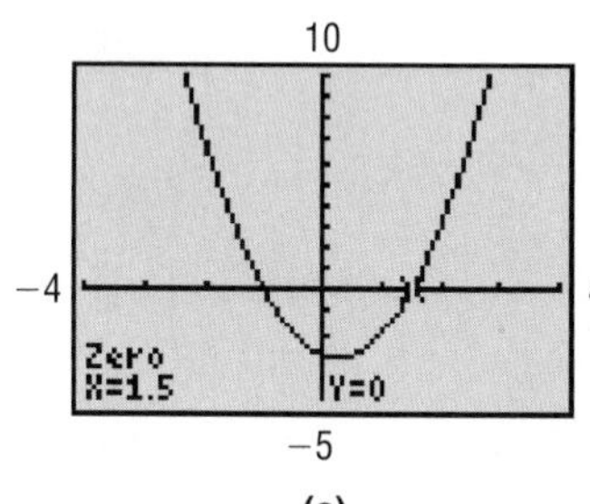

(c)

Now Work PROBLEM 13

When the left side factors into two linear equations with the same solution, the quadratic equation is said to have a **repeated solution.** This solution is also called a **root of multiplicity 2,** or a **double root.**

EXAMPLE 2 Solving a Quadratic Equation by Factoring and by Graphing

Solve the equation: $9x^2 + 1 = 6x$

Algebraic Solution

Put the equation in standard form by adding $-6x$ to each side.

$$9x^2 + 1 = 6x$$
$$9x^2 - 6x + 1 = 0$$

Factor the left side of the equation.

$$(3x - 1)(3x - 1) = 0$$
$$3x - 1 = 0 \quad \text{or} \quad 3x - 1 = 0 \qquad \text{Zero-Product Property}$$
$$x = \frac{1}{3} \quad \text{or} \quad x = \frac{1}{3}$$

The equation has only the repeated solution $\frac{1}{3}$.

The solution set is $\left\{\frac{1}{3}\right\}$.

Graphing Solution

Graph $Y_1 = 9x^2 + 1$ and $Y_2 = 6x$. See Figure 29. Using INTERSECT, the only point of intersection is (0.33, 2), so the solution of the equation is $x = 0.33$, rounded to two decimal places. The solution set is $\{0.33\}$. This solution is approximate.

Figure 29

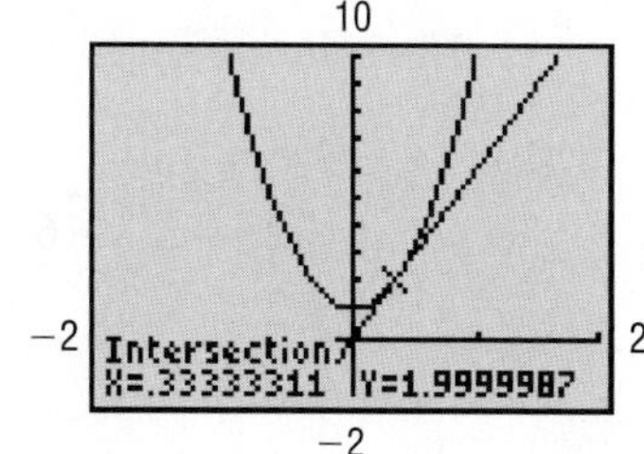

Now Work PROBLEM 23

2 Solve Quadratic Equations Using the Square Root Method

Suppose that we wish to solve the quadratic equation

$$x^2 = p \tag{2}$$

where p is a nonnegative number. Proceed as in the earlier examples:

$$x^2 - p = 0 \quad \text{Put in standard form.}$$
$$(x - \sqrt{p})(x + \sqrt{p}) = 0 \quad \text{Factor (over the real numbers).}$$
$$x = \sqrt{p} \quad \text{or} \quad x = -\sqrt{p} \quad \text{Solve.}$$

We have the following result:

$$\text{If } x^2 = p \text{ and } p \geq 0, \text{ then } x = \sqrt{p} \text{ or } x = -\sqrt{p}. \tag{3}$$

When statement (3) is used, it is called the **Square Root Method.** In statement (3), note that if $p > 0$ the equation $x^2 = p$ has two solutions, $x = \sqrt{p}$ and $x = -\sqrt{p}$. We usually abbreviate these solutions as $x = \pm\sqrt{p}$, read as "x equals plus or minus the square root of p." For example, the two solutions of the equation

$$x^2 = 4$$

are

$$x = \pm\sqrt{4}$$

and, since $\sqrt{4} = 2$, we have

$$x = \pm 2$$

The solution set is $\{-2, 2\}$.

EXAMPLE 3 **Solving Quadratic Equations by Using the Square Root Method**

Solve each equation: (a) $x^2 = 5$ (b) $(x - 2)^2 = 16$

Solution (a)

$$x^2 = 5$$
$$x = \pm\sqrt{5} \quad \text{Use the Square Root Method.}$$
$$x = \sqrt{5} \quad \text{or} \quad x = -\sqrt{5}$$

The solution set is $\{-\sqrt{5}, \sqrt{5}\}$.

(b) $(x - 2)^2 = 16$

$$x - 2 = \pm\sqrt{16} \quad \text{Use the Square Root Method.}$$
$$x - 2 = \sqrt{16} \quad \text{or} \quad x - 2 = -\sqrt{16}$$
$$x - 2 = 4 \qquad\qquad x - 2 = -4$$
$$x = 6 \qquad\qquad x = -2$$

The solution set is $\{-2, 6\}$.

Check: Verify the solutions using a graphing utility. Are the solutions provided by the utility exact? ■

Now Work PROBLEM 33

3 Solve Quadratic Equations by Completing the Square

EXAMPLE 4 **Solving a Quadratic Equation by Completing the Square**

Solve by completing the square: $x^2 + 5x + 4 = 0$

Solution Always begin this procedure by rearranging the equation so that the constant is on the right side.

$$x^2 + 5x + 4 = 0$$
$$x^2 + 5x = -4$$

Since the coefficient of x^2 is 1, we can complete the square on the left side by adding $\left(\frac{1}{2} \cdot 5\right)^2 = \frac{25}{4}$. Remember, in an equation, whatever is added to the left side must also be added to the right side. So add $\frac{25}{4}$ to *both* sides.

$$x^2 + 5x + \frac{25}{4} = -4 + \frac{25}{4} \qquad \text{Add } \frac{25}{4} \text{ to both sides.}$$
$$\left(x + \frac{5}{2}\right)^2 = \frac{9}{4} \qquad \text{Factor; simplify.}$$
$$x + \frac{5}{2} = \pm\sqrt{\frac{9}{4}} \qquad \text{Use the Square Root Method.}$$
$$x + \frac{5}{2} = \pm\frac{3}{2}$$
$$x = -\frac{5}{2} \pm \frac{3}{2}$$
$$x = -\frac{5}{2} + \frac{3}{2} = -1 \quad \text{or} \quad x = -\frac{5}{2} - \frac{3}{2} = -4$$

The solution set is $\{-4, -1\}$.

NOTE If the coefficient of the square term is not 1, divide through by the coefficient of the square term before attempting to complete the square. For example, to solve $2x^2 - 8x = 5$ by completing the square, divide both sides of the equation by 2 and obtain $x^2 - 4x = \frac{5}{2}$. ■

Check: Verify the solutions using a graphing utility. ■

The solution of the equation in Example 4 can also be obtained by factoring. Rework Example 4 using factoring.

Now Work PROBLEM 37

4 Solve Quadratic Equations Using the Quadratic Formula

We use the method of completing the square to obtain a general formula for solving the quadratic equation

$$ax^2 + bx + c = 0, \qquad a > 0$$

NOTE There is no loss in generality to assume that $a > 0$, since if $a < 0$ we can multiply both sides by -1 to obtain an equivalent equation with a positive leading coefficient. ■

As in Example 4, rearrange the terms as

$$ax^2 + bx = -c$$

Since $a > 0$, we can divide both sides by a to get

$$x^2 + \frac{b}{a}x = -\frac{c}{a}$$

Now the coefficient of x^2 is 1. To complete the square on the left side, add the square of $\frac{1}{2}$ of the coefficient of x; that is, add

$$\left(\frac{1}{2} \cdot \frac{b}{a}\right)^2 = \frac{b^2}{4a^2}$$

to each side. Then

$$x^2 + \frac{b}{a}x + \frac{b^2}{4a^2} = \frac{b^2}{4a^2} - \frac{c}{a}$$

$$\left(x + \frac{b}{2a}\right)^2 = \frac{b^2 - 4ac}{4a^2} \qquad \frac{b^2}{4a^2} - \frac{c}{a} = \frac{b^2}{4a^2} - \frac{4ac}{4a^2} = \frac{b^2 - 4ac}{4a^2} \tag{4}$$

Provided that $b^2 - 4ac \geq 0$, we now can use the Square Root Method to get

$$x + \frac{b}{2a} = \pm\sqrt{\frac{b^2 - 4ac}{4a^2}}$$

$$x + \frac{b}{2a} = \frac{\pm\sqrt{b^2 - 4ac}}{2a}$$ The square root of a quotient equals the quotient of the square roots. Also, $\sqrt{4a^2} = 2a$ since $a > 0$.

$$x = -\frac{b}{2a} \pm \frac{\sqrt{b^2 - 4ac}}{2a}$$ Add $-\frac{b}{2a}$ to both sides.

$$= \frac{-b \pm \sqrt{b^2 - 4ac}}{2a}$$ Combine the quotients on the right.

What if $b^2 - 4ac$ is negative? Then equation (4) states that the left expression (a real number squared) equals the right expression (a negative number). Since this occurrence is impossible for real numbers, we conclude that if $b^2 - 4ac < 0$ the quadratic equation has no *real* solution.*

THEOREM

Quadratic Formula

Consider the quadratic equation

$$ax^2 + bx + c = 0 \qquad a \neq 0$$

If $b^2 - 4ac < 0$, this equation has no real solution.
If $b^2 - 4ac \geq 0$, the real solution(s) of this equation is (are) given by the **quadratic formula.**

$$x = \frac{-b \pm \sqrt{b^2 - 4ac}}{2a}$$

The quantity $\boldsymbol{b^2 - 4ac}$ is called the **discriminant** of the quadratic equation, because its value tells us whether the equation has real solutions. In fact, it also tells us how many solutions to expect.

Discriminant of a Quadratic Equation

For a quadratic equation $ax^2 + bx + c = 0$:

1. If $b^2 - 4ac > 0$, there are two unequal real solutions.
2. If $b^2 - 4ac = 0$, there is a repeated real solution, a root of multiplicity 2.
3. If $b^2 - 4ac < 0$, there is no real solution.

When asked to find the real solutions, if any, of a quadratic equation, always evaluate the discriminant first to see if there are any real solutions.

*We consider quadratic equations where $b^2 - 4ac$ is negative in the next section.

EXAMPLE 5 **Solving a Quadratic Equation by Using the Quadratic Formula and by Graphing**

Find the real solutions, if any, of the equation $3x^2 - 5x + 1 = 0$.

Algebraic Solution

The equation is in standard form, so we compare it to $ax^2 + bx + c = 0$ to find a, b, and c.

$$3x^2 - 5x + 1 = 0$$

$$ax^2 + bx + c = 0 \quad a = 3, b = -5, c = 1$$

With $a = 3$, $b = -5$, and $c = 1$, evaluate the discriminant $b^2 - 4ac$.

$$b^2 - 4ac = (-5)^2 - 4(3)(1) = 25 - 12 = 13$$

Since $b^2 - 4ac > 0$, there are two real solutions.

Use the quadratic formula with $a = 3, b = -5, c = 1$, and $b^2 - 4ac = 13$.

$$x = \frac{-b \pm \sqrt{b^2 - 4ac}}{2a} = \frac{-(-5) \pm \sqrt{13}}{2(3)} = \frac{5 \pm \sqrt{13}}{6}$$

The solution set is $\left\{\frac{5 - \sqrt{13}}{6}, \frac{5 + \sqrt{13}}{6}\right\}$. These solutions are exact. ■

Graphing Solution

Figure 30 shows the graph of the equation

$$Y_1 = 3x^2 - 5x + 1$$

There are two x-intercepts: one between 0 and 1, the other between 1 and 2. Using ZERO (or ROOT), we find the solutions to the equation are 0.23 and 1.43, rounded to two decimal places. These solutions are approximate.

Figure 30

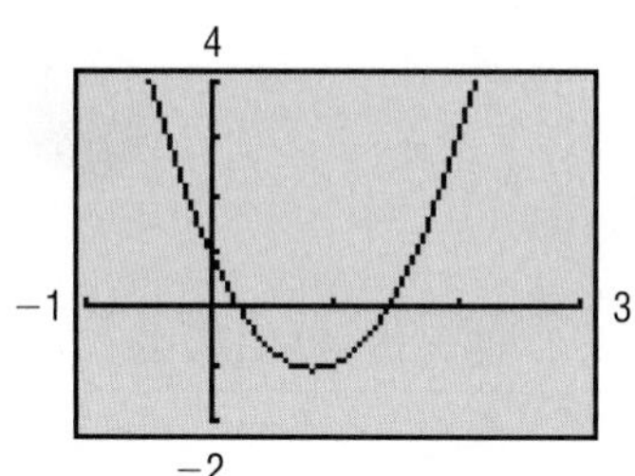

■

Now Work PROBLEM 43

EXAMPLE 6 **Solving a Quadratic Equation by Using the Quadratic Formula and by Graphing**

Find the real solutions, if any, of the equation $3x^2 + 2 = 4x$.

Algebraic Solution

The equation, as given, is not in standard form.

$$3x^2 + 2 = 4x$$

$$3x^2 - 4x + 2 = 0 \quad \text{Subtract } 4x \text{ from both sides to put the equation in standard form.}$$

$$ax^2 + bx + c = 0 \quad \text{Compare to standard form.}$$

With $a = 3$, $b = -4$, and $c = 2$, the discriminant is

$$b^2 - 4ac = (-4)^2 - 4(3)(2) = 16 - 24$$
$$= -8$$

Since $b^2 - 4ac < 0$, the equation has no real solution. ■

Graphing Solution

We use the standard form of the equation and graph

$$Y_1 = 3x^2 - 4x + 2$$

See Figure 31. We see that there are no x-intercepts, so the equation has no real solution, as expected based on the value of the discriminant.

Figure 31

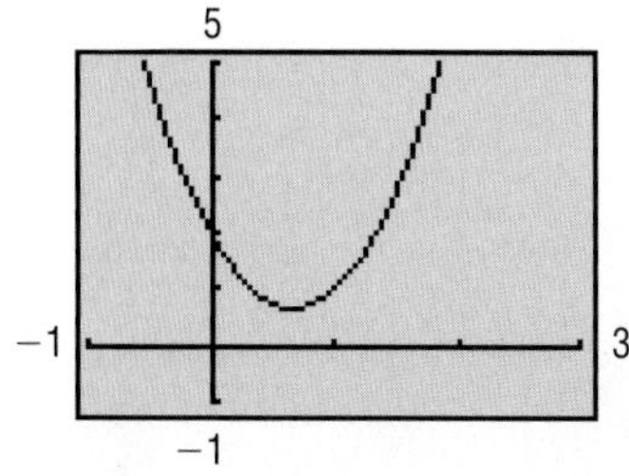

■

Now Work PROBLEM 49

SUMMARY

Procedure for Solving a Quadratic Equation Algebraically

To solve a quadratic equation algebraically, first put it in standard form:

$$ax^2 + bx + c = 0$$

Then:

STEP 1: Identify a, b, and c.

STEP 2: Evaluate the discriminant, $b^2 - 4ac$.

STEP 3: (a) If the discriminant is negative, the equation has no real solution.
(b) If the discriminant is zero, the equation has one real solution, a repeated root.
(c) If the discriminant is positive, the equation has two distinct real solutions.

If you can easily spot factors, use the factoring method to solve the equation. Otherwise, use the quadratic formula or the method of completing the square.

5 Solve Problems That Can Be Modeled by Quadratic Equations

Many applied problems require the solution of a quadratic equation. Let's look at one that you will probably see again in a slightly different form if you study calculus.

EXAMPLE 7 **Constructing a Box**

From each corner of a square piece of sheet metal, remove a square of side 9 centimeters. Turn up the edges to form an open box. If the box is to hold 144 cubic centimeters (cm^3), what should be the dimensions of the piece of sheet metal?

Solution Use Figure 32 as a guide. We have labeled the length of a side of the square piece of sheet metal, x. The box will be of height 9 centimeters, and its square base will have $x - 18$ as the length of a side. The volume (length $\times$ width $\times$ height) of the box is therefore

$$(x - 18)(x - 18) \cdot 9 = 9(x - 18)^2 \quad \text{The Model}$$

Figure 32

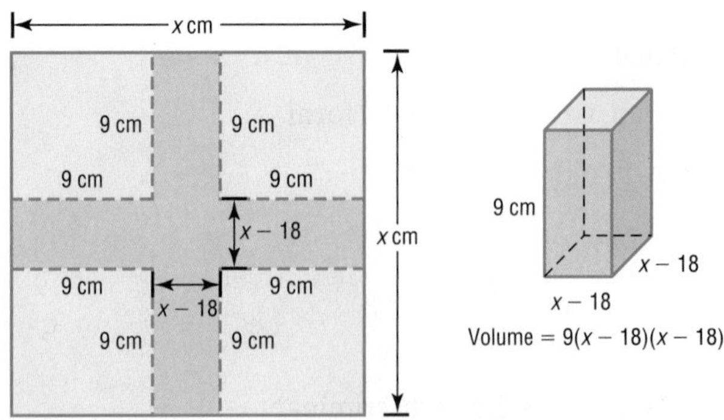

Since the volume of the box is to be 144 cm^3, we have

$$9(x - 18)^2 = 144$$

$$(x - 18)^2 = 16 \quad \text{Divide each side by 9.}$$

$$x - 18 = \pm 4 \quad \text{Use the Square Root Method.}$$

$$x = 18 \pm 4$$

$$x = 22 \quad \text{or} \quad x = 14$$

Discard the solution $x = 14$ (do you see why?) and conclude that the sheet metal should be 22 centimeters by 22 centimeters.

Check: If we begin with a piece of sheet metal 22 centimeters by 22 centimeters, cut out a 9-centimeter square from each corner, and fold up the edges, we get a box whose dimensions are 9 by 4 by 4, with volume $9 \times 4 \times 4 = 144 \text{ cm}^3$, as required. ■

Now Work PROBLEM 95

Historical Feature

Problems using quadratic equations are found in the oldest known mathematical literature. Babylonians and Egyptians were solving such problems before 1800 BC. Euclid solved quadratic equations geometrically in his *Data* (300 BC), and the Hindus and Arabs gave rules for solving any quadratic equation with real roots. Because negative numbers were not freely used before AD 1500, there were several different types of quadratic equations, each with its own rule. Thomas Harriot (1560–1621) introduced the method of factoring to obtain solutions, and François Viète (1540–1603) introduced a method that is essentially completing the square.

Until modern times it was usual to neglect the negative roots (if there were any), and equations involving square roots of negative quantities were regarded as unsolvable until the 1500s.

Historical Problems

1. *One solution of al-Khwǎtrizmi* Solve $x^2 + 12x = 85$ by drawing the square shown. The area of the four white rectangles and the yellow square is $x^2 + 12x$. We then set this expression equal to 85 to get the equation $x^2 + 12x = 85$. If we add the four blue squares, we will have a larger square of known area. Complete the solution.

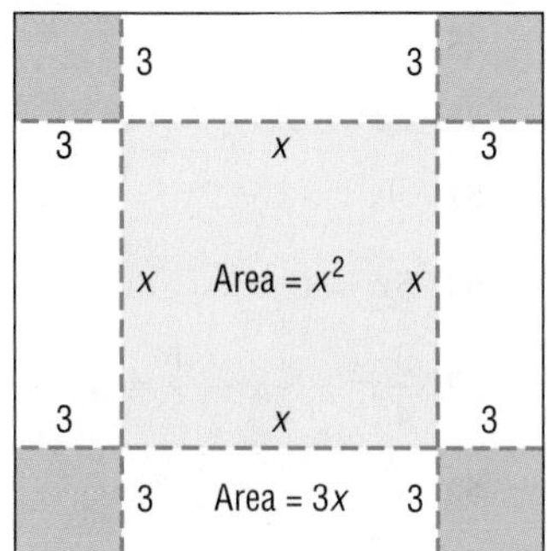

2. *Viète's method* Solve $x^2 + 12x - 85 = 0$ by letting $x = u + z$.
Then

$$(u + z)^2 + 12(u + z) - 85 = 0$$
$$u^2 + (2z + 12)u + (z^2 + 12z - 85) = 0$$

Now select z so that $2z + 12 = 0$ and finish the solution.

3. *Another method to get the quadratic formula* Look at equation (4) on page 480. Rewrite the right side as $\left(\dfrac{\sqrt{b^2 - 4ac}}{2a}\right)^2$ and then subtract it from each side. The right side is now 0 and the left side is a difference of two squares. If you factor this difference of two squares, you will easily be able to get the quadratic formula and, moreover, the quadratic expression is factored, which is sometimes useful.

7.2 Assess Your Understanding

'Are You Prepared?' *Answers are given at the end of these exercises.*

1. Factor: $x^2 - 5x - 6$
2. Factor: $2x^2 - x - 3$
3. The solution set of the equation $(x - 3)(3x + 5) = 0$ is ______.
4. Simplify: $\sqrt{8^2 - 4 \cdot 2 \cdot 3}$
5. Complete the square of the expression $x^2 + 5x$. Factor the new expression.

Concepts and Vocabulary

6. When a quadratic equation has a repeated solution, it is called a(n) ________ root or a root of __________ __________.
7. The quantity $b^2 - 4ac$ is called the ___________ of a quadratic equation. If it is __________, the equation has no real solution.

8. Quadratic equations are sometimes called _______-degree equations.

9. ***True or False*** Quadratic equations always have two real solutions.

10. ***True or False*** A quadratic equation that is in the form $ax^2 + bx + c = 0$ is said to be in standard form.

Skill Building

In Problems 11–30, solve each equation by factoring. Verify your solution using a graphing utility.

11. $x^2 - 9x = 0$
12. $x^2 + 4x = 0$
13. $x^2 - 25 = 0$
14. $x^2 - 9 = 0$
15. $z^2 + z - 6 = 0$
16. $v^2 + 7v + 6 = 0$
17. $2x^2 - 5x - 3 = 0$
18. $3x^2 + 5x + 2 = 0$
19. $3t^2 - 48 = 0$
20. $2y^2 - 50 = 0$
21. $x(x - 8) + 12 = 0$
22. $x(x + 4) = 12$
23. $4x^2 + 9 = 12x$
24. $25x^2 + 16 = 40x$
25. $6(p^2 - 1) = 5p$
26. $2(2u^2 - 4u) + 3 = 0$
27. $6x - 5 = \frac{6}{x}$
28. $x + \frac{12}{x} = 7$
29. $\frac{4(x-2)}{x-3} + \frac{3}{x} = \frac{-3}{x(x-3)}$
30. $\frac{5}{x+4} = 4 + \frac{3}{x-2}$

In Problems 31–36, solve each equation by the Square Root Method. Verify your solution using a graphing utility.

31. $x^2 = 25$
32. $x^2 = 36$
33. $(x - 1)^2 = 4$
34. $(x + 2)^2 = 1$
35. $(2y + 3)^2 = 9$
36. $(3z - 2)^2 = 4$

In Problems 37–42, solve each equation by completing the square. Verify your solution using a graphing utility.

37. $x^2 + 4x = 21$
38. $x^2 - 6x = 13$
39. $x^2 - \frac{1}{2}x - \frac{3}{16} = 0$
40. $x^2 + \frac{2}{3}x - \frac{1}{3} = 0$
41. $3x^2 + x - \frac{1}{2} = 0$
42. $2x^2 - 3x - 1 = 0$

In Problems 43–66, find the real solutions, if any, of each equation. Use the quadratic formula. Verify your solution using a graphing utility.

43. $x^2 - 4x + 2 = 0$
44. $x^2 + 4x + 2 = 0$
45. $x^2 - 4x - 1 = 0$
46. $x^2 + 6x + 1 = 0$
47. $2x^2 - 5x + 3 = 0$
48. $2x^2 + 5x + 3 = 0$
49. $4y^2 - y + 2 = 0$
50. $4t^2 + t + 1 = 0$
51. $4x^2 = 1 - 2x$
52. $2x^2 = 1 - 2x$
53. $4x^2 = 9x$
54. $5x = 4x^2$
55. $9t^2 - 6t + 1 = 0$
56. $4u^2 - 6u + 9 = 0$
57. $\frac{3}{4}x^2 - \frac{1}{4}x - \frac{1}{2} = 0$
58. $\frac{2}{3}x^2 - x - 3 = 0$
59. $\frac{5}{3}x^2 - x = \frac{1}{3}$
60. $\frac{3}{5}x^2 - x = \frac{1}{5}$
61. $2x(x + 2) = 3$
62. $3x(x + 2) = 1$
63. $4 - \frac{1}{x} - \frac{2}{x^2} = 0$
64. $4 + \frac{1}{x} - \frac{1}{x^2} = 0$
65. $\frac{3x}{x-2} + \frac{1}{x} = 4$
66. $\frac{2x}{x-3} + \frac{1}{x} = 4$

In Problems 67–72, use the discriminant to determine whether each quadratic equation has two unequal real solutions, a repeated real solution, or no real solution, without solving the equation.

67. $2x^2 - 6x + 7 = 0$
68. $x^2 + 4x + 7 = 0$
69. $9x^2 - 30x + 25 = 0$
70. $25x^2 - 20x + 4 = 0$
71. $3x^2 + 5x - 8 = 0$
72. $2x^2 - 3x - 7 = 0$

Mixed Practice

In Problems 73–88, find the real solutions, if any, of each equation. Use any method. Verify your solution using a graphing utility.

73. $x^2 - 5 = 0$
74. $x^2 - 6 = 0$
75. $16x^2 - 8x + 1 = 0$
76. $9x^2 - 12x + 4 = 0$
77. $10x^2 - 19x - 15 = 0$
78. $6x^2 + 7x - 20 = 0$
79. $2 + z = 6z^2$
80. $2 = y + 6y^2$
81. $3(x - 4) + 5 = 0$

82. $2(x+4)=3$

83. $x^2+x=4$

84. $x^2+x=1$

85. $5x(x-1)=-7x^2+2$

86. $10x(x+2)=-3x+5$

87. $\frac{x}{x-2}+\frac{2}{x+1}=\frac{7x+1}{x^2-x-2}$

88. $\frac{3x}{x+2}+\frac{1}{x-1}=\frac{4-7x}{x^2+x-2}$

Applications and Extensions

89. Pythagorean Theorem How many right triangles have a hypotenuse that measures $2x+3$ meters and legs that measure $2x-5$ meters and $x+7$ meters? What are the dimensions of the triangle(s)?

90. Pythagorean Theorem How many right triangles have a hypotenuse that measures $4x+5$ inches and legs that measure $3x+13$ inches and x inches? What are the dimensions of the triangle(s)?

91. Dimensions of a Window The area of the opening of a rectangular window is to be 143 square feet. If the length is to be 2 feet more than the width, what are the dimensions?

92. Dimensions of a Window The area of a rectangular window is to be 306 square centimeters. If the length exceeds the width by 1 centimeter, what are the dimensions?

93. Geometry Find the dimensions of a rectangle whose perimeter is 26 meters and whose area is 40 square meters.

94. Watering a Field An adjustable water sprinkler that sprays water in a circular pattern is placed at the center of a square field whose area is 1250 square feet (see the figure). What is the shortest radius setting that can be used if the field is to be completely enclosed within the circle?

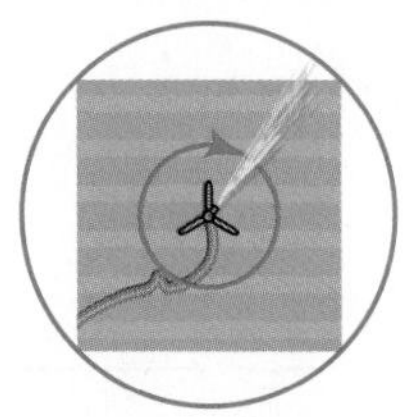

95. Constructing a Box An open box is to be constructed from a square piece of sheet metal by removing a square of side 1 foot from each corner and turning up the edges. If the box is to hold 4 cubic feet, what should be the dimensions of the sheet metal?

96. Constructing a Box Rework Problem 95 if the piece of sheet metal is a rectangle whose length is twice its width.

97. Physics A ball is thrown vertically upward from the top of a building 96 feet tall with an initial velocity of 80 feet per second. The distance s (in feet) of the ball from the ground after t seconds is $s=96+80t-16t^2$.

(a) After how many seconds does the ball strike the ground?

(b) After how many seconds will the ball pass the top of the building on its way down?

98. Physics An object is propelled vertically upward with an initial velocity of 20 meters per second. The distance s (in meters) of the object from the ground after t seconds is $s=-4.9t^2+20t$.

(a) When will the object be 15 meters above the ground?

(b) When will it strike the ground?

(c) Will the object reach a height of 100 meters?

99. Reducing the Size of a Candy Bar A jumbo chocolate bar with a rectangular shape measures 12 centimeters in length, 7 centimeters in width, and 3 centimeters in thickness. Due to escalating costs of cocoa, management decides to reduce the volume of the bar by 10%. To accomplish this reduction, management decides that the new bar should have the same 3 centimeter thickness, but the length and width of each should be reduced an equal number of centimeters. What should be the dimensions of the new candy bar?

100. Reducing the Size of a Candy Bar Rework Problem 99 if the reduction is to be 20%.

101. Constructing a Border around a Pool A circular pool measures 10 feet across. One cubic yard of concrete is to be used to create a circular border of uniform width around the pool. If the border is to have a depth of 3 inches, how wide will the border be? (1 cubic yard = 27 cubic feet) See the illustration.

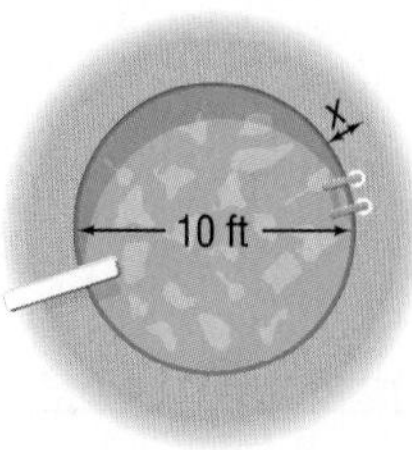

102. Constructing a Border around a Pool Rework Problem 101 if the depth of the border is 4 inches.

103. Constructing a Border around a Garden A landscaper, who just completed a rectangular flower garden measuring 6 feet by 10 feet, orders 1 cubic yard of premixed cement, all of which is to be used to create a border of uniform width around the garden. If the border is to have a depth of 3 inches, how wide will the border be? (1 cubic yard = 27 cubic feet)

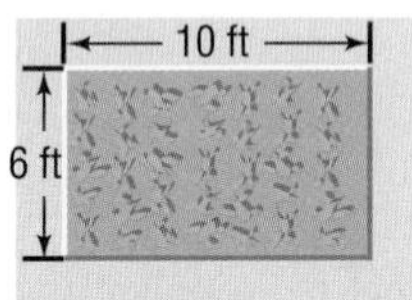

104. Dimensions of a Patio A contractor orders 8 cubic yards of premixed cement, all of which is to be used to pour a patio that will be 4 inches thick. If the length of the patio is specified to be twice the width, what will be the patio dimensions? (1 cubic yard = 27 cubic feet)

105. Comparing TVs The screen size of a television is determined by the length of the diagonal of the rectangular screen. Traditional TVs come in a 4 : 3 format, meaning the ratio of the length to the width of the rectangular screen is 4 to 3. What is the area of a 37-inch traditional TV screen? What is the area of a 37-inch LCD TV whose screen is in a 16 : 9 format? Which screen is larger?

[**Hint:** If x is the length of a 4 : 3 format screen, then $\frac{3}{4}x$ is the width.]

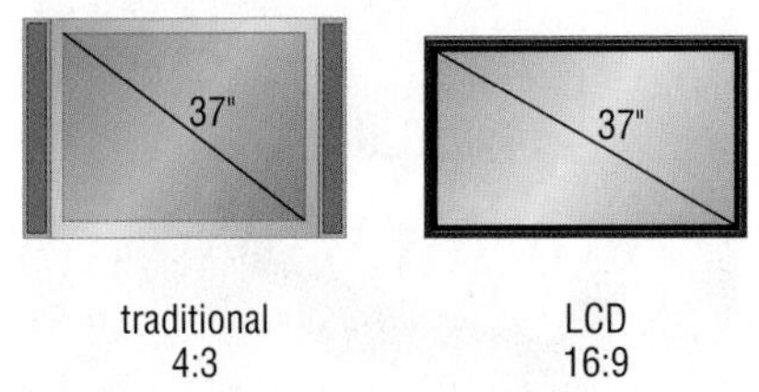

106. Comparing TVs Refer to Problem 105. Find the screen area of a traditional 50-inch TV and compare it with a 50-inch Plasma TV whose screen is in a 16 : 9 format. Which screen is larger?

107. The sum of the consecutive integers 1, 2, 3, … n is given by the formula $\frac{1}{2}n(n + 1)$. How many consecutive integers, starting with 1, must be added to get a sum of 666?

108. Geometry If a polygon of n sides has $\frac{1}{2}n(n - 3)$ diagonals, how many sides will a polygon with 65 diagonals have? Is there a polygon with 80 diagonals?

109. Show that the sum of the roots of a quadratic equation is $-\frac{b}{a}$.

110. Show that the product of the roots of a quadratic equation is $\frac{c}{a}$.

111. Find k such that the equation $kx^2 + x + k = 0$ has a repeated real solution.

112. Find k such that the equation $x^2 - kx + 4 = 0$ has a repeated real solution.

113. Show that the real solutions of the equation $ax^2 + bx + c = 0$ are the negatives of the real solutions of the equation $ax^2 - bx + c = 0$. Assume that $b^2 - 4ac \geq 0$.

114. Show that the real solutions of the equation $ax^2 + bx + c = 0$ are the reciprocals of the real solutions of the equation $cx^2 + bx + a = 0$. Assume that $b^2 - 4ac \geq 0$.

Explaining Concepts: Discussion and Writing

115. Which of the following pairs of equations are equivalent? Explain.

(a) $x^2 = 9$; $x = 3$ (b) $x = \sqrt{9}$; $x = 3$

(c) $(x - 1)(x - 2) = (x - 1)^2$; $x - 2 = x - 1$

116. Describe three ways that you might solve a quadratic equation. State your preferred method; explain why you chose it.

117. Explain the benefits of evaluating the discriminant of a quadratic equation before attempting to solve it.

118. Create three quadratic equations: one having two distinct solutions, one having no real solution, and one having exactly one real solution.

119. The word *quadratic* seems to imply four (*quad*), yet a quadratic equation is an equation that involves a polynomial of degree 2. Investigate the origin of the term *quadratic* as it is used in the expression *quadratic equation*. Write a brief essay on your findings.

'Are You Prepared?' Answers

1. $(x - 6)(x + 1)$ **2.** $(2x - 3)(x + 1)$ **3.** $\left\{-\frac{5}{3}, 3\right\}$ **4.** $2\sqrt{10}$ **5.** $x^2 + 5x + \frac{25}{4} = \left(x + \frac{5}{2}\right)^2$

7.3 Complex Numbers; Quadratic Equations in the Complex Number System

Now Work the **'Are You Prepared?'** problems on page 494.

OBJECTIVES 1 Add, Subtract, Multiply, and Divide Complex Numbers (p. 488)
2 Solve Quadratic Equations in the Complex Number System (p. 491)

Complex Numbers

One property of a real number is that its square is nonnegative (greater than or equal to 0). For example, there is no real number x for which

$$x^2 = -1$$

To remedy this situation, we introduce a number called the **imaginary unit,** which we denote by ***i***, whose square is -1; that is,

$$i^2 = -1$$

This should not surprise you. If our universe were to consist only of integers, there would be no number x for which $2x = 1$. This unfortunate circumstance was remedied by introducing numbers such as $\frac{1}{2}$ and $\frac{2}{3}$, the *rational numbers*. If our universe were to consist only of rational numbers, there would be no x whose square equals 2. That is, there would be no number x for which $x^2 = 2$. To remedy this, we introduced numbers such as $\sqrt{2}$ and $\sqrt[3]{5}$, the *irrational numbers*. The *real numbers,* you will recall, consist of the rational numbers and the irrational numbers. Now, if our universe were to consist only of real numbers, then there would be no number x whose square is -1. To remedy this, we introduce a number i, whose square is -1.

In the progression outlined, each time that we encountered a situation that was unsuitable, we introduced a new number system to remedy this situation. And each new number system contained the earlier number system as a subset. The number system that results from introducing the number i is called the **complex number system.**

Complex numbers are numbers of the form $\boldsymbol{a + bi}$, where a and b are real numbers. The real number a is called the **real part** of the number $a + bi$; the real number b is called the **imaginary part** of $a + bi$.

For example, the complex number $-5 + 6i$ has the real part -5 and the imaginary part 6.

When a complex number is written in the form $a + bi$, where a and b are real numbers, we say it is in **standard form.** However, if the imaginary part of a complex number is negative, such as in the complex number $3 + (-2)i$, we agree to write it instead in the form $3 - 2i$.

Also, the complex number $a + 0i$ is usually written simply as a. This serves to remind us that the real numbers are a subset of the complex numbers. The complex number $0 + bi$ is usually written as bi. Sometimes the complex number bi is called a **pure imaginary number.**

1 Add, Subtract, Multiply, and Divide Complex Numbers

Equality, addition, subtraction, and multiplication of complex numbers are defined so as to preserve the familiar rules of algebra for real numbers. Thus, two complex numbers are equal if and only if their real parts are equal and their imaginary parts are equal. That is,

Equality of Complex Numbers

$$a + bi = c + di \quad \text{if and only if} \quad a = c \text{ and } b = d \qquad \textbf{(1)}$$

Two complex numbers are added by forming the complex number whose real part is the sum of the real parts and whose imaginary part is the sum of the imaginary parts. That is,

Sum of Complex Numbers

$$(a + bi) + (c + di) = (a + c) + (b + d)i \qquad \textbf{(2)}$$

To subtract two complex numbers, use this rule:

Difference of Complex Numbers

$$(a + bi) - (c + di) = (a - c) + (b - d)i \qquad \textbf{(3)}$$

EXAMPLE 1 **Adding and Subtracting Complex Numbers**

(a) $(3 + 5i) + (-2 + 3i) = [3 + (-2)] + (5 + 3)i = 1 + 8i$

(b) $(6 + 4i) - (3 + 6i) = (6 - 3) + (4 - 6)i = 3 + (-2)i = 3 - 2i$ ■

Figure 33

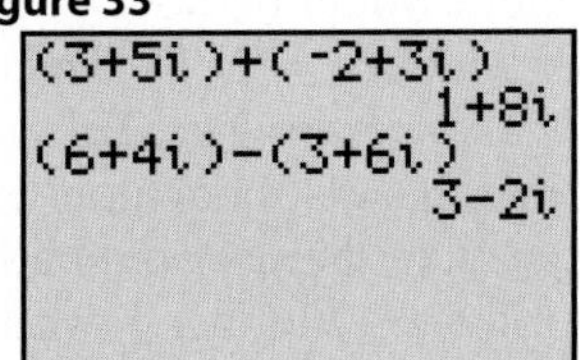

Some graphing calculators have the capability of handling complex numbers. For example, Figure 33 shows the results of Example 1 using a TI-84 Plus graphing calculator.

Now Work PROBLEM 13

Products of complex numbers are calculated as illustrated in Example 2.

EXAMPLE 2 **Multiplying Complex Numbers**

$$\begin{aligned}(5 + 3i)\cdot(2 + 7i) &= 5\cdot(2 + 7i) + 3i(2 + 7i) && \text{Distributive Property}\\ &= 10 + 35i + 6i + 21i^2 && \text{Distributive Property}\\ &= 10 + 41i + 21(-1) && i^2 = -1\\ &= -11 + 41i\end{aligned}$$ ■

Based on the procedure of Example 2, the **product** of two complex numbers is defined as follows:

Product of Complex Numbers

$$(a + bi)\cdot(c + di) = (ac - bd) + (ad + bc)i \qquad \textbf{(4)}$$

Figure 34

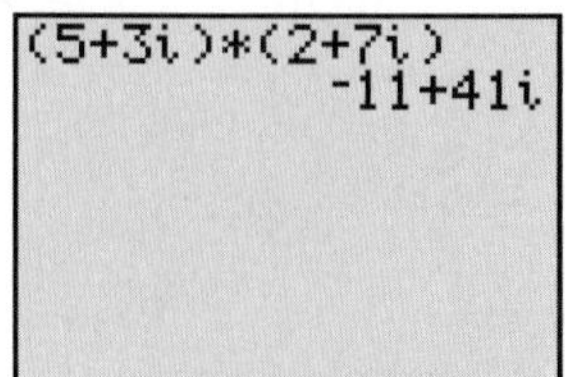

Do not bother to memorize formula (4). Instead, whenever it is necessary to multiply two complex numbers, follow the usual rules for multiplying two binomials, as in Example 2, remembering that $i^2 = -1$. For example,

$$(2i)(2i) = 4i^2 = -4$$
$$(2 + i)(1 - i) = 2 - 2i + i - i^2 = 3 - i$$

Graphing calculators may also be used to multiply complex numbers. Figure 34 shows the result obtained in Example 2 using a TI-84 Plus graphing calculator.

Now Work PROBLEM 19

Algebraic properties for addition and multiplication, such as the Commutative, Associative, and Distributive Properties, hold for complex numbers. However, the property that every nonzero complex number has a multiplicative inverse, or reciprocal, requires a closer look.

Conjugates

If $z = a + bi$ is a complex number, then its **conjugate,** denoted by $\bar{z}$, is defined as

$$\bar{z} = \overline{a + bi} = a - bi$$

For example, $\overline{2 + 3i} = 2 - 3i$ and $\overline{-6 - 2i} = -6 + 2i$.

EXAMPLE 3 Multiplying a Complex Number by Its Conjugate

Find the product of the complex number $z = 3 + 4i$ and its conjugate $\bar{z}$.

Solution Since $\bar{z} = 3 - 4i$, we have

$$z\bar{z} = (3 + 4i)(3 - 4i) = 9 - 12i + 12i - 16i^2 = 9 + 16 = 25$$ ■

The result obtained in Example 3 has an important generalization.

THEOREM

The product of a complex number and its conjugate is a nonnegative real number. That is, if $z = a + bi$, then

$$z\bar{z} = a^2 + b^2 \quad (5)$$

Proof If $z = a + bi$, then

$$z\bar{z} = (a + bi)(a - bi) = a^2 - abi + abi - (bi)^2 = a^2 - b^2i^2 = a^2 + b^2$$ ■

To express the reciprocal of a nonzero complex number z in standard form, multiply the numerator and denominator of $\frac{1}{z}$ by its conjugate $\bar{z}$. That is, if $z = a + bi$ is a nonzero complex number, then

$$\frac{1}{a + bi} = \frac{1}{z} = \frac{1}{z} \cdot \frac{\bar{z}}{\bar{z}} = \frac{\bar{z}}{z\bar{z}} \underset{\text{Use (5).}}{=} \frac{a - bi}{a^2 + b^2} = \frac{a}{a^2 + b^2} - \frac{b}{a^2 + b^2}i$$

EXAMPLE 4 Writing the Reciprocal of a Complex Number in Standard Form

Write $\frac{1}{3 + 4i}$ in standard form $a + bi$; that is, find the reciprocal of $3 + 4i$.

Solution Multiply the numerator and denominator of $\dfrac{1}{3+4i}$ by the conjugate of $3+4i$, the complex number $3-4i$. The result is

$$\frac{1}{3+4i} = \frac{1}{3+4i} \cdot \frac{3-4i}{3-4i} = \frac{3-4i}{9+16} = \frac{3}{25} - \frac{4}{25}i$$

Figure 35

A graphing calculator can be used to verify the result of Example 4. See Figure 35.

To express the quotient of two complex numbers in standard form, multiply the numerator and denominator of the quotient by the conjugate of the denominator.

EXAMPLE 5 Writing Quotients of Complex Numbers in Standard Form

Write each of the following in standard form.

(a) $\dfrac{1+4i}{5-12i}$ (b) $\dfrac{2-3i}{4-3i}$

Solution (a) $\dfrac{1+4i}{5-12i} = \dfrac{1+4i}{5-12i} \cdot \dfrac{5+12i}{5+12i} = \dfrac{5+12i+20i+48i^2}{25+144}$

$$= \frac{-43+32i}{169} = -\frac{43}{169} + \frac{32}{169}i$$

(b) $\dfrac{2-3i}{4-3i} = \dfrac{2-3i}{4-3i} \cdot \dfrac{4+3i}{4+3i} = \dfrac{8+6i-12i-9i^2}{16+9}$

$$= \frac{17-6i}{25} = \frac{17}{25} - \frac{6}{25}i$$

Now Work PROBLEM 27

EXAMPLE 6 Writing Other Expressions in Standard Form

If $z = 2-3i$ and $w = 5+2i$, write each of the following expressions in standard form.

(a) $\dfrac{z}{w}$ (b) $\overline{z+w}$ (c) $z+\bar{z}$

Solution (a) $\dfrac{z}{w} = \dfrac{z \cdot \bar{w}}{w \cdot \bar{w}} = \dfrac{(2-3i)(5-2i)}{(5+2i)(5-2i)} = \dfrac{10-4i-15i+6i^2}{25+4}$

$$= \frac{4-19i}{29} = \frac{4}{29} - \frac{19}{29}i$$

(b) $\overline{z+w} = \overline{(2-3i)+(5+2i)} = \overline{7-i} = 7+i$

(c) $z+\bar{z} = (2-3i)+(2+3i) = 4$

The conjugate of a complex number has certain general properties that we shall find useful later.

For a real number $a = a+0i$, the conjugate is $\bar{a} = \overline{a+0i} = a-0i = a$. That is,

THEOREM The conjugate of a real number is the real number itself.

Other properties that are direct consequences of the definition of the conjugate are given next. In each statement, z and w represent complex numbers.

THEOREM

The conjugate of the conjugate of a complex number is the complex number itself.

$$(\overline{\overline{z}}) = z \tag{6}$$

The conjugate of the sum of two complex numbers equals the sum of their conjugates.

$$\overline{z + w} = \overline{z} + \overline{w} \tag{7}$$

The conjugate of the product of two complex numbers equals the product of their conjugates.

$$\overline{z \cdot w} = \overline{z} \cdot \overline{w} \tag{8}$$

The proofs of equations (6), (7), and (8) are left as exercises. See Problems 88–90.

Powers of *i*

The powers of i follow a pattern that is useful to know.

$$i^1 = i \qquad i^5 = i^4 \cdot i = 1 \cdot i = i$$
$$i^2 = -1 \qquad i^6 = i^4 \cdot i^2 = -1$$
$$i^3 = i^2 \cdot i = -i \qquad i^7 = i^4 \cdot i^3 = -i$$
$$i^4 = i^2 \cdot i^2 = (-1)(-1) = 1 \qquad i^8 = i^4 \cdot i^4 = 1$$

And so on. The powers of i repeat with every fourth power.

EXAMPLE 7 **Evaluating Powers of *i***

(a) $i^{27} = i^{24} \cdot i^3 = (i^4)^6 \cdot i^3 = 1^6 \cdot i^3 = -i$

(b) $i^{101} = i^{100} \cdot i^1 = (i^4)^{25} \cdot i = 1^{25} \cdot i = i$ ■

EXAMPLE 8 **Writing the Power of a Complex Number in Standard Form**

Write $(2 + i)^3$ in standard form.

Solution We use the special product formula for $(a + b)^3$.

$$(a + b)^3 = a^3 + 3a^2b + 3ab^2 + b^3$$

Using this special product formula,

$$\begin{aligned}(2 + i)^3 &= 2^3 + 3 \cdot 2^2 \cdot i + 3 \cdot 2 \cdot i^2 + i^3 \\ &= 8 + 12i + 6(-1) + (-i) \\ &= 2 + 11i\end{aligned}$$ ■

NOTE If you did not remember the special product formula for $(a + b)^3$, you could find $(2 + i)^3$ by simplifying $(2 + i)^2(2 + i)$. ■

Now Work PROBLEMS 33 AND 41

2 Solve Quadratic Equations in the Complex Number System

Quadratic equations with a negative discriminant have no real number solution. However, if we extend our number system to allow complex numbers, quadratic equations will always have a solution. Since the solution to a quadratic equation involves the square root of the discriminant, we begin with a discussion of square roots of negative numbers.

DEFINITION

If N is a positive real number, we define the **principal square root of $-N$,** denoted by $\sqrt{-N}$, as

$$\sqrt{-N} = \sqrt{N}i$$

where i is the imaginary unit and $i^2 = -1$.

EXAMPLE 9 **Evaluating the Square Root of a Negative Number**

(a) $\sqrt{-1} = \sqrt{1}i = i$ (b) $\sqrt{-16} = \sqrt{16}i = 4i$

(c) $\sqrt{-8} = \sqrt{8}i = 2\sqrt{2}i$ ■

Now Work PROBLEM 49

EXAMPLE 10 **Using the Square Root Method in the Complex Number System**

Solve each equation in the complex number system.

(a) $x^2 = 4$ (b) $x^2 = -9$

Solution (a) $x^2 = 4$

$$x = \pm\sqrt{4} = \pm 2$$

The equation has the solution set $\{-2, 2\}$.

(b) $x^2 = -9$

$$x = \pm\sqrt{-9} = \pm\sqrt{9}i = \pm 3i$$

The equation has the solution set $\{-3i, 3i\}$. ■

WARNING When working with square roots of negative numbers, do not set the square root of a product equal to the product of the square roots (which can be done with positive numbers). To see why, look at this calculation: We know that $\sqrt{100} = 10$. However, it is also true that $100 = (-25)(-4)$, so

$$\begin{aligned} 10 &= \sqrt{100} \\ &= \sqrt{(-25)(-4)} \\ &\neq \sqrt{-25}\sqrt{-4} \end{aligned}$$

because

$$\begin{aligned} &\sqrt{-25} \cdot \sqrt{-4} \\ &= \left(\sqrt{25}i\right)\left(\sqrt{4}i\right) \\ &= (5i)(2i) \\ &= 10i^2 = -10 \end{aligned}$$ ■

Now Work PROBLEM 53

Because we have defined the square root of a negative number, we can now restate the quadratic formula without restriction.

THEOREM

Quadratic Formula

In the complex number system, the solutions of the quadratic equation $ax^2 + bx + c = 0$, where a, b, and c are real numbers and $a \neq 0$, are given by the formula

$$x = \frac{-b \pm \sqrt{b^2 - 4ac}}{2a} \quad \textbf{(9)}$$

EXAMPLE 11 **Solving a Quadratic Equation in the Complex Number System**

Solve the equation $x^2 - 4x + 8 = 0$ in the complex number system.

Solution Here $a = 1$, $b = -4$, $c = 8$, and $b^2 - 4ac = 16 - 4(1)(8) = -16$. Using equation (9),

$$x = \frac{-(-4) \pm \sqrt{-16}}{2(1)} = \frac{4 \pm \sqrt{16}i}{2} = \frac{4 \pm 4i}{2} = 2 \pm 2i$$

The equation has the solution set $\{2 - 2i, 2 + 2i\}$.

Check:

Figure 36

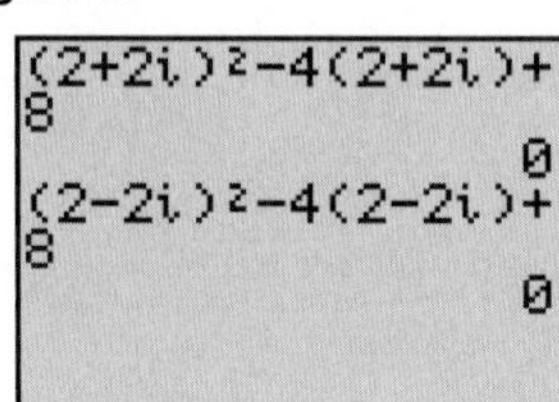

$$2 + 2i: \quad (2 + 2i)^2 - 4(2 + 2i) + 8 = 4 + 8i + 4i^2 - 8 - 8i + 8$$
$$= 4 - 4 = 0$$
$$2 - 2i: \quad (2 - 2i)^2 - 4(2 - 2i) + 8 = 4 - 8i + 4i^2 - 8 + 8i + 8$$
$$= 4 - 4 = 0$$

Figure 36 shows the check of the solution using a TI-84 Plus graphing calculator. Graph $Y_1 = x^2 - 4x + 8$. How many x-intercepts are there?

Now Work PROBLEM 59

The discriminant $b^2 - 4ac$ of a quadratic equation still serves as a way to determine the character of the solutions.

Character of the Solutions of a Quadratic Equation

In the complex number system, consider a quadratic equation $ax^2 + bx + c = 0$ with real coefficients.

1. If $b^2 - 4ac > 0$, the equation has two unequal real solutions.
2. If $b^2 - 4ac = 0$, the equation has a repeated real solution, a double root.
3. If $b^2 - 4ac < 0$, the equation has two complex solutions that are not real. The solutions are conjugates of each other.

The third conclusion in the display is a consequence of the fact that if $b^2 - 4ac = -N < 0$ then, by the quadratic formula, the solutions are

$$x = \frac{-b + \sqrt{b^2 - 4ac}}{2a} = \frac{-b + \sqrt{-N}}{2a} = \frac{-b + \sqrt{N}i}{2a} = \frac{-b}{2a} + \frac{\sqrt{N}}{2a}i$$

and

$$x = \frac{-b - \sqrt{b^2 - 4ac}}{2a} = \frac{-b - \sqrt{-N}}{2a} = \frac{-b - \sqrt{N}i}{2a} = \frac{-b}{2a} - \frac{\sqrt{N}}{2a}i$$

which are conjugates of each other.

EXAMPLE 12 **Determining the Character of the Solutions of a Quadratic Equation**

Without solving, determine the character of the solutions of each equation.

(a) $3x^2 + 4x + 5 = 0$ (b) $2x^2 + 4x + 1 = 0$
(c) $9x^2 - 6x + 1 = 0$

Solution

(a) Here $a = 3, b = 4,$ and $c = 5,$ so $b^2 - 4ac = 4^2 - 4(3)(5) = -44$. The solutions are two complex numbers that are not real and are conjugates of each other.

(b) Here $a = 2, b = 4,$ and $c = 1,$ so $b^2 - 4ac = 4^2 - 4(2)(1) = 8$. The solutions are two unequal real numbers.

(c) Here $a = 9, b = -6,$ and $c = 1,$ so $b^2 - 4ac = (-6)^2 - 4(9)(1) = 0$. The solution is a repeated real number, that is, a double root.

Now Work PROBLEM 73

7.3 Assess Your Understanding

'Are You Prepared?' *Answers are given at the end of these exercises.*

1. Name the integers and the rational numbers in the set $\left\{-3, 0, \sqrt{2}, \frac{6}{5}, \pi\right\}$.

2. ***True or False*** Rational numbers and irrational numbers are in the set of real numbers.

3. Rationalize the denominator of $\frac{3}{2 + \sqrt{3}}$.

Concepts and Vocabulary

4. In the complex number $5 + 2i$, the number 5 is called the _____ part; the number 2 is called the __________ part; the number i is called the ________________.

5. The equation $x^2 = -4$ has the solution set _______.

6. ***True or False*** The conjugate of $2 + 5i$ is $-2 - 5i$.

7. ***True or False*** All real numbers are complex numbers.

8. ***True or False*** If $2 - 3i$ is a solution of a quadratic equation with real coefficients, then $-2 + 3i$ is also a solution.

Skill Building

In Problems 9–46, write each expression in the standard form $a + bi$. Verify your results using a graphing utility.

9. $(2 - 3i) + (6 + 8i)$ **10.** $(4 + 5i) + (-8 + 2i)$ **11.** $(-3 + 2i) - (4 - 4i)$ **12.** $(3 - 4i) - (-3 - 4i)$

13. $(2 - 5i) - (8 + 6i)$ **14.** $(-8 + 4i) - (2 - 2i)$ **15.** $3(2 - 6i)$ **16.** $-4(2 + 8i)$

17. $2i(2 - 3i)$ **18.** $3i(-3 + 4i)$ **19.** $(3 - 4i)(2 + i)$ **20.** $(5 + 3i)(2 - i)$

21. $(-6 + i)(-6 - i)$ **22.** $(-3 + i)(3 + i)$ **23.** $\frac{10}{3 - 4i}$ **24.** $\frac{13}{5 - 12i}$

25. $\frac{2 + i}{i}$ **26.** $\frac{2 - i}{-2i}$ **27.** $\frac{6 - i}{1 + i}$ **28.** $\frac{2 + 3i}{1 - i}$

29. $\left(\frac{1}{2} + \frac{\sqrt{3}}{2}i\right)^2$ **30.** $\left(\frac{\sqrt{3}}{2} - \frac{1}{2}i\right)^2$ **31.** $(1 + i)^2$ **32.** $(1 - i)^2$

33. i^{23} **34.** i^{14} **35.** i^{-15} **36.** i^{-23}

37. $i^6 - 5$ **38.** $4 + i^3$ **39.** $6i^3 - 4i^5$ **40.** $4i^3 - 2i^2 + 1$

41. $(1 + i)^3$ **42.** $(3i)^4 + 1$ **43.** $i^7(1 + i^2)$ **44.** $2i^4(1 + i^2)$

45. $i^6 + i^4 + i^2 + 1$ **46.** $i^7 + i^5 + i^3 + i$

In Problems 47–52, perform the indicated operations and express your answer in the form $a + bi$.

47. $\sqrt{-4}$ **48.** $\sqrt{-9}$ **49.** $\sqrt{-25}$

50. $\sqrt{-64}$ **51.** $\sqrt{(3 + 4i)(4i - 3)}$ **52.** $\sqrt{(4 + 3i)(3i - 4)}$

In Problems 53–72, solve each equation in the complex number system. Check your results using a graphing utility.

53. $x^2 + 4 = 0$ **54.** $x^2 - 4 = 0$ **55.** $x^2 - 16 = 0$ **56.** $x^2 + 25 = 0$

57. $x^2 - 6x + 13 = 0$ **58.** $x^2 + 4x + 8 = 0$ **59.** $x^2 - 6x + 10 = 0$ **60.** $x^2 - 2x + 5 = 0$

61. $8x^2 - 4x + 1 = 0$ **62.** $10x^2 + 6x + 1 = 0$ **63.** $5x^2 + 1 = 2x$ **64.** $13x^2 + 1 = 6x$

65. $x^2 + x + 1 = 0$ **66.** $x^2 - x + 1 = 0$ **67.** $x^3 - 8 = 0$ **68.** $x^3 + 27 = 0$

69. $x^4 = 16$ **70.** $x^4 = 1$ **71.** $x^4 + 13x^2 + 36 = 0$ **72.** $x^4 + 3x^2 - 4 = 0$

In Problems 73–78, without solving, determine the character of the solutions of each equation in the complex number system. Verify your answer using a graphing utility.

73. $3x^2 - 3x + 4 = 0$ **74.** $2x^2 - 4x + 1 = 0$ **75.** $2x^2 + 3x = 4$

76. $x^2 + 6 = 2x$ **77.** $9x^2 - 12x + 4 = 0$ **78.** $4x^2 + 12x + 9 = 0$

79. $2 + 3i$ is a solution of a quadratic equation with real coefficients. Find the other solution.

80. $4 - i$ is a solution of a quadratic equation with real coefficients. Find the other solution.

In Problems 81–84, $z = 3 - 4i$ and $w = 8 + 3i$. Write each expression in the standard form $a + bi$.

81. $z + \bar{z}$ **82.** $w - \bar{w}$ **83.** $z\bar{z}$ **84.** $\overline{z - w}$

Applications and Extensions

85. **Electrical Circuits** The impedance Z, in ohms, of a circuit element is defined as the ratio of the phasor voltage V, in volts, across the element to the phasor current I, in amperes, through the elements. That is, $Z = \frac{V}{I}$. If the voltage across a circuit element is $18 + i$ volts and the current through the element is $3 - 4i$ amperes, determine the impedance.

86. **Parallel Circuits** In an ac circuit with two parallel pathways, the total impedance Z, in ohms, satisfies the formula $\frac{1}{Z} = \frac{1}{Z_1} + \frac{1}{Z_2}$, where Z_1 is the impedance of the first pathway and Z_2 is the impedance of the second pathway. Determine the total impedance if the impedances of the two pathways are $Z_1 = 2 + i$ ohms and $Z_2 = 4 - 3i$ ohms.

87. Use $z = a + bi$ to show that $z + \bar{z} = 2a$ and $z - \bar{z} = 2bi$.

88. Use $z = a + bi$ to show that $\bar{\bar{z}} = z$.

89. Use $z = a + bi$ and $w = c + di$ to show that $\overline{z + w} = \bar{z} + \bar{w}$.

90. Use $z = a + bi$ and $w = c + di$ to show that $\overline{z \cdot w} = \bar{z} \cdot \bar{w}$.

Explaining Concepts: Discussion and Writing

91. Explain to a friend how you would add two complex numbers and how you would multiply two complex numbers. Explain any differences in the two explanations.

92. Write a brief paragraph that compares the method used to rationalize denominators and the method used to write the quotient of two complex numbers in standard form.

93. Use an Internet search engine to investigate the origins of complex numbers. Write a paragraph describing what you find and present it to the class.

94. Explain how the method of multiplying two complex numbers is related to multiplying two binomials.

95. **What Went Wrong?** A student multiplied $\sqrt{-9}$ and $\sqrt{-9}$ as follows:

$$\begin{aligned}\sqrt{-9} \cdot \sqrt{-9} &= \sqrt{(-9)(-9)} \\ &= \sqrt{81} \\ &= 9\end{aligned}$$

The instructor marked the problem incorrect. Why?

'Are You Prepared?' Answers

1. Integers: $\{-3, 0\}$; rational numbers: $\left\{-3, 0, \frac{6}{5}\right\}$ 2. True 3. $3(2 - \sqrt{3})$

7.4 Radical Equations; Equations Quadratic in Form; Absolute Value Equations; Factorable Equations

Now Work the **'Are You Prepared?'** problems on page 501.

OBJECTIVES
1. Solve Radical Equations (p. 495)
2. Solve Equations Quadratic in Form (p. 497)
3. Solve Absolute Value Equations (p. 499)
4. Solve Equations by Factoring (p. 500)

1 Solve Radical Equations

When the variable in an equation occurs in a square root, cube root, and so on, that is, when it occurs in a radical, the equation is called a **radical equation.** Sometimes a suitable operation will change a radical equation to one that is linear or quadratic. A commonly used procedure is to isolate the most complicated radical on one side of the equation and then eliminate it by raising each side to a power equal to the index of the radical. Care must be taken, however, because apparent solutions that are not, in fact, solutions of the original equation may result. Recall that these are called extraneous solutions. In radical equations, extraneous solutions may occur when the index of the radical is even. Therefore, we need to check all answers when working with radical equations.

EXAMPLE 1 Solving a Radical Equation

Find the real solutions of the equation: $\sqrt[3]{2x-4} - 2 = 0$

Algebraic Solution

The equation contains a radical whose index is 3. We isolate it on the left side:

$$\sqrt[3]{2x-4} - 2 = 0$$
$$\sqrt[3]{2x-4} = 2$$

Because the index of the radical is 3, raise each side to the third power and solve.

$$(\sqrt[3]{2x-4})^3 = 2^3 \quad \text{Raise each side to the power 3.}$$
$$2x - 4 = 8 \quad \text{Simplify}$$
$$2x = 12 \quad \text{Add 4 to both sides.}$$
$$x = 6 \quad \text{Divide both sides by 2.}$$

Graphing Solution

Figure 37 shows the graph of the equation $Y_1 = \sqrt[3]{2x-4} - 2$. From the graph, we see one x-intercept near 6. Using ZERO (or ROOT), we find that the x-intercept is 6. The only solution is $x = 6$.

Figure 37

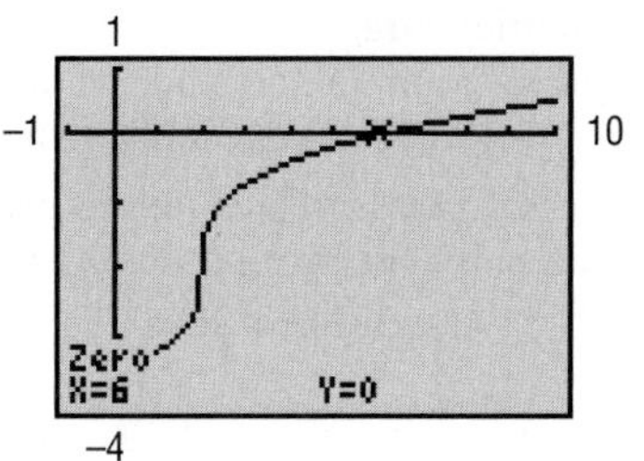

Check: $\sqrt[3]{2(6)-4} - 2 = \sqrt[3]{12-4} - 2 = \sqrt[3]{8} - 2 = 2 - 2 = 0$

The solution set is $\{6\}$. ■

Now Work PROBLEM 11

EXAMPLE 2 Solving a Radical Equation

Find the real solutions of the equation: $\sqrt{x-1} = x - 7$

Algebraic Solution

Square both sides since the index of a square root is 2.

$$\sqrt{x-1} = x - 7$$
$$\left(\sqrt{x-1}\right)^2 = (x-7)^2 \quad \text{Square both sides.}$$
$$x - 1 = x^2 - 14x + 49 \quad \text{Remove parentheses.}$$
$$x^2 - 15x + 50 = 0 \quad \text{Put in standard form.}$$
$$(x-10)(x-5) = 0 \quad \text{Factor}$$
$$x = 10 \quad \text{or} \quad x = 5 \quad \text{Apply the Zero-Product Property and solve.}$$

Graphing Solution

Graph $Y_1 = \sqrt{x-1}$ and $Y_2 = x - 7$. See Figure 38. From the graph, there is one point of intersection. Using INTERSECT, the point of intersection is $(10, 3)$, so the solution is $x = 10$.

Figure 38

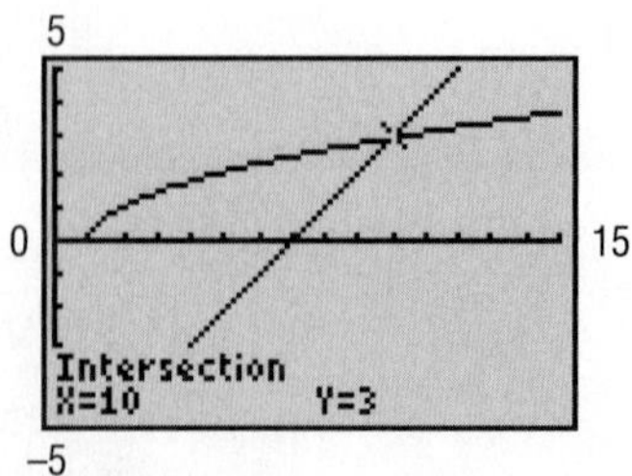

There is a discrepancy between the algebraic solution and graphing solution. Let's check the results of our algebraic solution.

Check: $x = 10$: $\sqrt{x-1} = \sqrt{10-1} = \sqrt{9} = 3$ and $x - 7 = 10 - 7 = 3$

$x = 5$: $\sqrt{x-1} = \sqrt{5-1} = \sqrt{4} = 2$ and $x - 7 = 5 - 7 = -2$

The apparent algebraic solution $x = 5$ is extraneous; the only solution of the equation is $x = 10$. The solution set is $\{10\}$. ■

Now Work PROBLEM 23

Sometimes, we need to raise each side to a power more than once in order to solve a radical equation algebraically.

EXAMPLE 3 **Solving a Radical Equation**

Find the real solutions of the equation: $\sqrt{2x+3} - \sqrt{x+2} = 2$

Algebraic Solution

First, isolate the more complicated radical expression (in this case, $\sqrt{2x+3}$) on the left side:

$$\sqrt{2x+3} = \sqrt{x+2} + 2$$

Now square both sides (the index of the radical is 2).

$$\left(\sqrt{2x+3}\right)^2 = \left(\sqrt{x+2} + 2\right)^2$$

$$2x + 3 = \left(\sqrt{x+2}\right)^2 + 4\sqrt{x+2} + 4 \quad \text{Remove parentheses.}$$

$$2x + 3 = x + 2 + 4\sqrt{x+2} + 4 \quad \text{Simplify}$$

$$2x + 3 = x + 6 + 4\sqrt{x+2} \quad \text{Combine like terms.}$$

Because the equation still contains a radical, isolate the remaining radical on the right side and again square both sides.

$$x - 3 = 4\sqrt{x+2} \quad \text{Isolate the radical on the right side.}$$

$$(x-3)^2 = 16(x+2) \quad \text{Square both sides.}$$

$$x^2 - 6x + 9 = 16x + 32 \quad \text{Remove parentheses.}$$

$$x^2 - 22x - 23 = 0 \quad \text{Put in standard form.}$$

$$(x-23)(x+1) = 0 \quad \text{Factor}$$

$$x = 23 \quad \text{or} \quad x = -1$$

Graphing Solution

Graph $Y_1 = \sqrt{2x+3} - \sqrt{x+2}$ and $Y_2 = 2$. See Figure 39. From the graph there is one point of intersection. Using INTERSECT, the point of intersection is $(23, 2)$, so the solution is $x = 23$.

Figure 39

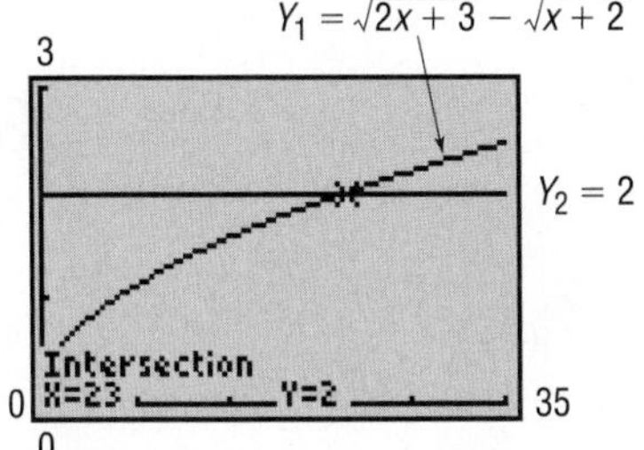

Check: $x = 23$: $\sqrt{2(23)+3} - \sqrt{23+2} = \sqrt{49} - \sqrt{25} = 7 - 5 = 2$

$x = -1$: $\sqrt{2(-1)+3} - \sqrt{-1+2} = \sqrt{1} - \sqrt{1} = 1 - 1 = 0$

The apparent solution $x = -1$ is extraneous; the only solution is $x = 23$. The solution set of the equation is $\{23\}$. ■

Now Work PROBLEM 31

2 Solve Equations Quadratic in Form

The equation $x^4 + x^2 - 12 = 0$ is not quadratic in x, but it is quadratic in x^2. That is, if we let $u = x^2$, we get $u^2 + u - 12 = 0$, a quadratic equation. This equation can be solved for u and, then, by using $u = x^2$, we can find the solutions x of the original equation.

In general, if an appropriate substitution u transforms an equation into one of the form

$$au^2 + bu + c = 0, \qquad a \neq 0$$

then the original equation is called an **equation of the quadratic type** or an **equation quadratic in form.**

The difficulty of solving such an equation lies in the determination that the equation is, in fact, quadratic in form. After you are told an equation is quadratic in form, it is easy enough to see it, but some practice is needed to enable you to recognize them on your own.

EXAMPLE 4

Solving an Equation That Is Quadratic in Form

Find the real solutions of the equation: $(x + 2)^2 + 11(x + 2) - 12 = 0$

Solution For this equation, let $u = x + 2$. Then $u^2 = (x + 2)^2$, and the original equation,

$$(x + 2)^2 + 11(x + 2) - 12 = 0$$

becomes

$$u^2 + 11u - 12 = 0 \quad \text{Let } u = x + 2.$$
$$(u + 12)(u - 1) = 0 \quad \text{Factor.}$$
$$u = -12 \quad \text{or} \quad u = 1 \quad \text{Solve}$$

But we want to solve for x. Because $u = x + 2$, we have

$$x + 2 = -12 \quad \text{or} \quad x + 2 = 1$$
$$x = -14 \qquad\qquad x = -1$$

✓**Check:** $x = -14$: $(-14 + 2)^2 + 11(-14 + 2) - 12$
$= (-12)^2 + 11(-12) - 12 = 144 - 132 - 12 = 0$

$x = -1$: $(-1 + 2)^2 + 11(-1 + 2) - 12 = 1 + 11 - 12 = 0$

The original equation has the solution set $\{-14, -1\}$. ■

✓**Check:** Verify the solution of Example 4 using a graphing utility.

EXAMPLE 5

Solving an Equation That Is Quadratic in Form

Find the real solutions of the equation: $x + 2\sqrt{x} - 3 = 0$

Solution For the equation $x + 2\sqrt{x} - 3 = 0$, let $u = \sqrt{x}$. Then $u^2 = x$, and the original equation,

$$x + 2\sqrt{x} - 3 = 0$$

becomes

$$u^2 + 2u - 3 = 0 \quad \text{Let } \;\; = \sqrt{x}.$$
$$(u + 3)(u - 1) = 0 \quad \text{Factor}$$
$$u = -3 \quad \text{or} \quad u = 1 \quad \text{Solve}$$

Since $u = \sqrt{x}$, we have $\sqrt{x} = -3$ or $\sqrt{x} = 1$. The first of these, $\sqrt{x} = -3$, has no real solution, since the square root of a real number is never negative. The second, $\sqrt{x} = 1$, has the solution $x = 1$.

✓**Check:** $1 + 2\sqrt{1} - 3 = 1 + 2 - 3 = 0$

The solution set of the original equation is $\{1\}$. ■

✓**Check:** Verify the solution to Example 5 using a graphing utility.

Another method for solving Example 5 would be to treat it as a radical equation. Solve it this way for practice.

The idea should now be clear. If an equation contains an expression and that same expression squared, make a substitution for the expression. You may get a quadratic equation.

Now Work PROBLEM 51

3 Solve Absolute Value Equations

Recall that, on the real number line, the absolute value of a equals the distance from the origin to the point whose coordinate is a. For example, there are two points whose distance from the origin is 5 units, -5 and 5. Thus the equation $|x| = 5$ will have the solution set $\{-5, 5\}$.

Another way to obtain this result is to use the algebraic definition of absolute value, $|a| = a$ if $a \geq 0$, $|a| = -a$ if $a < 0$. The equation $|u| = a$ leads to two equations depending on whether u is nonnegative (greater than or equal to zero) or negative.

$$|u| = a$$

If $u < 0$

$|u| = a$

$-u = a$ $\quad |u| = -u$ when $u < 0$

$u = -a$ $\quad$ Multiply both sides by -1.

If $u \geq 0$

$|u| = a$

$u = a$ $\quad |u| = u$ when $u \geq 0$

So we have the following result.

THEOREM

If a is a positive real number and if u is any algebraic expression, then

$$|u| = a \quad \text{is equivalent to} \quad u = a \quad \text{or} \quad u = -a \qquad (1)$$

EXAMPLE 6 **Solving an Equation Involving Absolute Value**

Solve the equation: $|2x - 3| + 2 = 7$

Algebraic Solution

$$|2x - 3| + 2 = 7$$

$$|2x - 3| = 5 \quad \text{Subtract 2 from each side.}$$

$$2x - 3 = 5 \quad \text{or} \quad 2x - 3 = -5 \quad \text{Apply statement (1).}$$

$$2x = 8 \quad \text{or} \quad 2x = -2$$

$$x = 4 \quad \text{or} \quad x = -1$$

The solution set is $\{-1, 4\}$. ■

Graphing Solution

For this equation, graph $Y_1 = |2x - 3| + 2$ and $Y_2 = 7$ on the same screen and find their point(s) of intersection, if any. See Figure 40. Using the INTERSECT command (twice), we find the points of intersection to be $(-1, 7)$ and $(4, 7)$. The solution set is $\{-1, 4\}$.

Figure 40

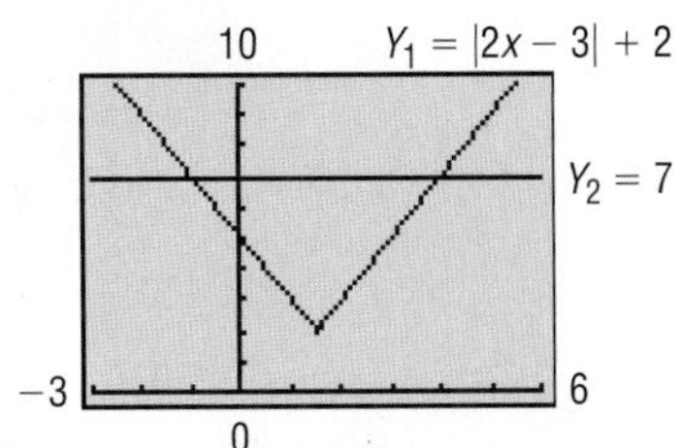

■

Now Work PROBLEM 67

4 Solve Equations by Factoring

We have already solved certain quadratic equations using factoring. Let's look at examples of other kinds of equations that can be solved by factoring.

EXAMPLE 7 Solving Equations by Factoring

Solve the equation: $x^4 = 4x^2$

Algebraic Solution

Begin by collecting all terms on one side. This results in 0 on one side and an expression to be factored on the other.

$$x^4 = 4x^2$$

$$x^4 - 4x^2 = 0$$

$$x^2(x^2 - 4) = 0 \quad \text{Factor}$$

$$x^2 = 0 \quad \text{or} \quad x^2 - 4 = 0 \quad \text{Apply the Zero-Product Property.}$$

$$x^2 = 4$$

$$x = 0 \quad \text{or} \quad x = -2 \quad \text{or} \quad x = 2 \quad \text{Use the Square Root Method.}$$

Graphing Solution

Graph $Y_1 = x^4$ and $Y_2 = 4x^2$ on the same screen and find their point(s) of intersection, if any. See Figure 41. Using the INTERSECT command (three times), we find the points of intersection to be $(-2, 16)$, $(0, 0)$, and $(2, 16)$. The solutions are $x = -2$, $x = 0$, or $x = 2$.

Figure 41

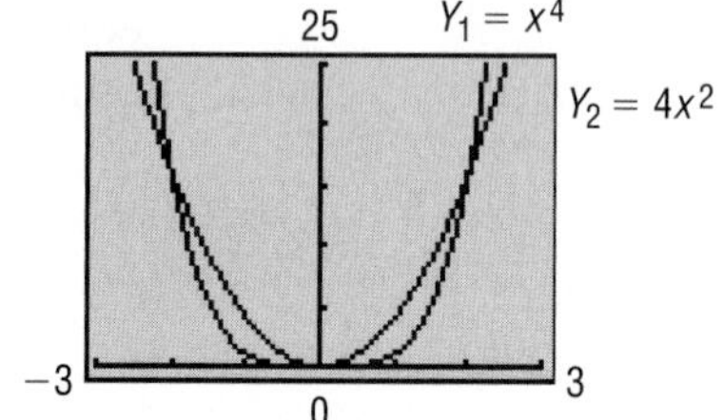

Check: $x = -2$: $(-2)^4 = 16$ and $4(-2)^2 = 16$ So −2 is a solution.

$x = 0$: $0^4 = 0$ and $4 \cdot 0^2 = 0$ So 0 is a solution.

$x = 2$: $2^4 = 16$ and $4 \cdot 2^2 = 16$ So 2 is a solution.

The solution set is $\{-2, 0, 2\}$. ■

EXAMPLE 8 Solving Equations by Factoring

Solve the equation: $x^3 - x^2 - 4x + 4 = 0$

Algebraic Solution

Group the terms of $x^3 - x^2 - 4x + 4 = 0$ as follows:

$$(x^3 - x^2) - (4x - 4) = 0$$

Factor out x^2 from the first grouping and 4 from the second.

$$x^2(x - 1) - 4(x - 1) = 0$$

This reveals the common factor $(x - 1)$, so we have

$$(x^2 - 4)(x - 1) = 0$$

$$(x - 2)(x + 2)(x - 1) = 0 \quad \text{Factor again.}$$

$$x - 2 = 0 \quad \text{or} \quad x + 2 = 0 \quad \text{or} \quad x - 1 = 0 \quad \text{Set each factor equal to 0.}$$

$$x = 2 \qquad x = -2 \qquad x = 1 \quad \text{Solve}$$

Graphing Solution

Graph $Y_1 = x^3 - x^2 - 4x + 4$. See Figure 42. Using ZERO (three times), the values of x for which $y = 0$ are −2, 1, and 2.

Figure 42

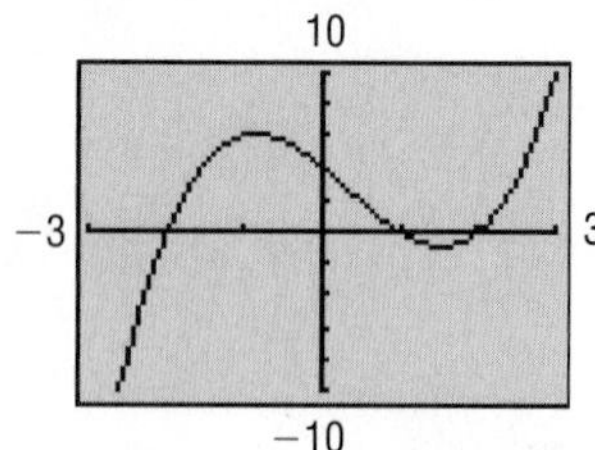

Check:

$x = -2$: $(-2)^3 - (-2)^2 - 4(-2) + 4 = -8 - 4 + 8 + 4 = 0$ −2 is a solution.

$x = 1$: $1^3 - 1^2 - 4(1) + 4 = 1 - 1 - 4 + 4 = 0$ 1 is a solution.

$x = 2$: $2^3 - 2^2 - 4(2) + 4 = 8 - 4 - 8 + 4 = 0$ 2 is a solution.

The solution set is $\{-2, 1, 2\}$. ■

Now Work PROBLEM 89

7.4 Assess Your Understanding

'Are You Prepared?' *Answers are given at the end of these exercises.*

1. ***True or False*** The principal square root of any nonnegative real number is always nonnegative.
2. $(\sqrt[3]{x})^3 =$ ______.
3. Factor $2x^2 - 7x - 4$.
4. Factor $x^3 + 4x^2 - 9x - 36$.
5. Use a real number line to describe why $|-4| = 4$.

Concepts and Vocabulary

6. When an apparent solution does not satisfy the original equation, it is called a(n)________ solution.
7. If u is an expression involving x, the equation $au^2 + bu + c = 0$, $a \neq 0$, is called a(n) equation ________________.
8. ***True or False*** Radical equations sometimes have no real solution.

Skill Building

In Problems 9–40, find the real solutions of each equation. Verify your results using a graphing utility.

9. $\sqrt{y+3} = 5$
10. $\sqrt{t-3} = 7$
11. $\sqrt{2t-1} = 1$
12. $\sqrt{3t+4} = 2$
13. $\sqrt{3t+4} = -6$
14. $\sqrt{5t+3} = -2$
15. $\sqrt[3]{1-2x} - 3 = 0$
16. $\sqrt[3]{1-2x} - 1 = 0$
17. $\sqrt[4]{5x-4} = 2$
18. $\sqrt[5]{2x-3} = -1$
19. $\sqrt[5]{x^2+2x} = -1$
20. $\sqrt[4]{x^2+16} = \sqrt{5}$
21. $x = 8\sqrt{x}$
22. $x = 3\sqrt{x}$
23. $\sqrt{15-2x} = x$
24. $\sqrt{12-x} = x$
25. $\sqrt{x^2-x-4} = x+2$
26. $\sqrt{x^2-x-8} = x+5$
27. $3 + \sqrt{3x+1} = x$
28. $2 + \sqrt{12-2x} = x$
29. $\sqrt{2x+3} - \sqrt{x+1} = 1$
30. $\sqrt{3x+7} + \sqrt{x+2} = 1$
31. $\sqrt{3x+1} - \sqrt{x-1} = 2$
32. $\sqrt{3x-5} - \sqrt{x+7} = 2$
33. $\sqrt{3-2\sqrt{x}} = \sqrt{x}$
34. $\sqrt{10+3\sqrt{x}} = \sqrt{x}$
35. $(3x+1)^{1/2} = 4$
36. $(3x-5)^{1/2} = 2$
37. $(5x-2)^{1/3} = 2$
38. $(2x+1)^{1/3} = -1$
39. $(x^2+9)^{1/2} = 5$
40. $(x^2-16)^{1/2} = 9$

In Problems 41–66, find the real solutions of each equation. Verify your results using a graphing utility.

41. $t^4 - 16 = 0$
42. $y^4 - 4 = 0$
43. $x^4 - 5x^2 + 4 = 0$
44. $x^4 - 10x^2 + 24 = 0$
45. $3x^4 - 2x^2 - 1 = 0$
46. $2x^4 - 5x^2 - 12 = 0$
47. $x^6 + 7x^3 - 8 = 0$
48. $x^6 - 7x^3 - 8 = 0$
49. $(x+2)^2 + 7(x+2) + 12 = 0$
50. $(2x+5)^2 - (2x+5) - 6 = 0$
51. $2(s+1)^2 - 5(s+1) = 3$
52. $3(1-y)^2 + 5(1-y) + 2 = 0$
53. $x - 4\sqrt{x} = 0$
54. $x - 8\sqrt{x} = 0$
55. $x + \sqrt{x} = 20$
56. $x + \sqrt{x} = 6$
57. $t^{1/2} - 2t^{1/4} + 1 = 0$
58. $z^{1/2} - 4z^{1/4} + 4 = 0$
59. $4x^{1/2} - 9x^{1/4} + 4 = 0$
60. $x^{1/2} - 3x^{1/4} + 2 = 0$
61. $\dfrac{1}{(x+1)^2} = \dfrac{1}{x+1} + 2$
62. $\dfrac{1}{(x-1)^2} + \dfrac{1}{x-1} = 12$
63. $3x^{-2} - 7x^{-1} - 6 = 0$
64. $2x^{-2} - 3x^{-1} - 4 = 0$
65. $2x^{2/3} - 5x^{1/3} - 3 = 0$
66. $3x^{4/3} + 5x^{2/3} - 2 = 0$

In Problems 67–84, solve each equation. Verify your results using a graphing utility.

67. $|2x+3| = 5$
68. $|3x-1| = 2$
69. $|1-4t| + 8 = 13$

70. $|1 - 2z| + 6 = 9$

71. $|-2x| = 8$

72. $|-x| = 1$

73. $4 - |2x| = 3$

74. $5 - \left|\frac{1}{2}x\right| = 3$

75. $\frac{2}{3}|x| = 9$

76. $\frac{3}{4}|x| = 9$

77. $\left|\frac{x}{3} + \frac{2}{5}\right| = 2$

78. $\left|\frac{x}{2} - \frac{1}{3}\right| = 1$

79. $|u - 2| = -\frac{1}{2}$

80. $|2 - v| = -1$

81. $|x^2 - 9| = 0$

82. $|x^2 - 16| = 0$

83. $|x^2 - 2x| = 3$

84. $|x^2 + x| = 12$

In Problems 85–94, find the real solutions of each equation by factoring. Verify your results using a graphing utility.

85. $x^3 - 9x = 0$

86. $x^4 - 81x^2 = 0$

87. $x^3 + x^2 - 20x = 0$

88. $x^3 + 6x^2 - 7x = 0$

89. $x^3 + x^2 - x - 1 = 0$

90. $x^3 + 4x^2 - x - 4 = 0$

91. $x^3 - 3x^2 - 4x + 12 = 0$

92. $x^3 - 3x^2 - x + 3 = 0$

93. $2x^3 + 4 = x^2 + 8x$

94. $3x^3 + 4x^2 = 27x + 36$

In Problems 95–98, find the real solutions of each equation. Use a calculator to express any solutions rounded to two decimal places.

95. $x - 4x^{1/2} + 2 = 0$

96. $x^{2/3} + 4x^{1/3} + 2 = 0$

97. $x^4 + \sqrt{3}x^2 - 3 = 0$

98. $x^4 + \sqrt{2}x^2 - 2 = 0$

Mixed Practice

In Problems 99–118, find the real solutions of each equation. Verify your results using a graphing utility.

99. $3x^2 + 7x - 20 = 0$

100. $2x^2 - 13x + 21 = 0$

101. $5a^3 - 45a = -2a^2 + 18$

102. $3z^3 - 12z = -5z^2 + 20$

103. $-3|5x - 2| + 9 = 0$

104. $\frac{1}{4}|2x - 3| = \frac{3}{2}$

105. $4(w - 3) = w + 3$

106. $6(k + 3) - 2k = 12$

107. $\left(\frac{v}{v+1}\right)^2 + \frac{2v}{v+1} = 8$

108. $\left(\frac{y}{y-1}\right)^2 = \frac{6y}{y-1} + 7$

109. $|-3x + 2| = x + 10$

110. $|4x - 3| = x + 2$

111. $\sqrt{2x + 5} - x = 1$

112. $\sqrt{3x + 1} - 2x = -6$

113. $3m^2 + 6m = -1$

114. $4y^2 - 8y = 3$

115. $|x^2 + x - 1| = 1$

116. $|x^2 + 3x - 2| = 2$

117. $\sqrt[4]{5x^2 - 6} = x$

118. $\sqrt[4]{4 - 3x^2} = x$

In Problems 119–122, find all complex solutions of each equation.

119. $t^4 - 16 = 0$

120. $y^4 - 81 = 0$

121. $x^6 - 9x^3 + 8 = 0$

122. $z^6 + 28z^3 + 27 = 0$

Applications and Extensions

123. If $k = \frac{x + 3}{x - 3}$ and $k^2 - k = 12$, find x.

124. If $k = \frac{x + 3}{x - 4}$ and $k^2 - 3k = 28$, find x.

125. Find all points having an x-coordinate of 2 whose distance from the point $(-2, -1)$ is 5.

126. Find all points having a y-coordinate of -3 whose distance from the point $(1, 2)$ is 13.

127. Find all points on the x-axis that are 5 units from the point $(4, -3)$.

128. Find all points on the y-axis that are 5 units from the point $(4, 4)$.

129. Physics: Using Sound to Measure Distance The distance to the surface of the water in a well can sometimes be found by dropping an object into the well and measuring the time elapsed until a sound is heard. If t_1 is the time (measured in seconds) that it takes for the object to strike the water, then t_1 will obey the equation $s = 16t_1^2$, where s is the distance (measured in feet). It follows that $t_1 = \frac{\sqrt{s}}{4}$. Suppose that t_2 is the time that it takes for the sound of the impact to reach your ears. Because sound travels at a speed of approximately 1100 feet per second, the time t_2 for the sound to travel the distance s will be $t_2 = \frac{s}{1100}$. See the illustration on the following page. Now $t_1 + t_2$ is the total time that elapses from the moment that the object is dropped to the moment that a sound is heard. We have the equation

$$\text{Total time elapsed} = \frac{\sqrt{s}}{4} + \frac{s}{1100}$$

Find the distance to the water's surface if the total time elapsed from dropping a rock to hearing it hit water is 4 seconds.

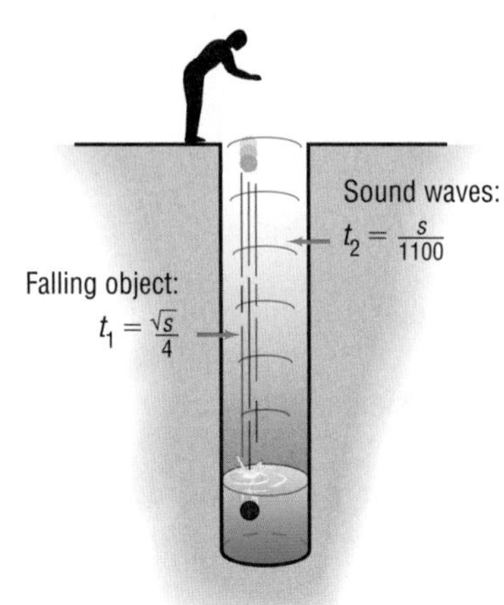

130. Crushing Load A civil engineer relates the thickness T, in inches, and height H, in feet, of a square wooden pillar to its crushing load L, in tons, using the model $T = \sqrt[4]{\frac{LH^2}{25}}$. If a square wooden pillar is 4 inches thick and 10 feet high, what is its crushing load?

131. Foucault's Pendulum The period of a pendulum is the time it takes the pendulum to make one full swing back and forth. The period T, in seconds, is given by the formula $T = 2\pi\sqrt{\frac{l}{32}}$, where l is the length, in feet, of the pendulum. In 1851, Jean-Bernard-Léon Foucault demonstrated the axial rotation accent of Earth using a large pendulum that he hung in the Panthéon in Paris. The period of Foucault's pendulum was approximately 16.5 seconds. What was its length?

Discussion and Writing

132. Make up a radical equation that has no solution.

133. Make up a radical equation that has an extraneous solution.

134. Discuss the step in the solving process for radical equations that leads to the possibility of extraneous solutions. Why is there no such possibility for linear and quadratic equations?

135. The equation $|x| = -2$ has no real solution. Why?

136. **What Went Wrong?** On an exam, Jane solved the equation $\sqrt{2x+3} - x = 0$ and wrote that the solution set was $\{-1, 3\}$. Jane received 3 out of 5 points for the problem. Jane asks you why she received 3 out of 5 points. Provide an explanation.

'Are You Prepared?' Answers

1. True **2.** x **3.** $(2x + 1)(x - 4)$ **4.** $(x - 3)(x + 3)(x + 4)$

5. The distance from the origin to -4 on a real number line is 4 units.

7.5 Solving Inequalities

Now Work the **'Are You Prepared?'** problems on page 511.

OBJECTIVES
1 Use Interval Notation (p. 504)
2 Use Properties of Inequalities (p. 505)
3 Solve Linear Inequalities Algebraically and Graphically (p. 507)
4 Solve Combined Inequalities Algebraically and Graphically (p. 508)
5 Solve Absolute Value Inequalities Algebraically and Graphically (p. 509)

Suppose that a and b are two real numbers and $a < b$. We use the notation $a < x < b$ to mean that x is a number *between* a and b. So, the expression $a < x < b$ is equivalent to the two inequalities $a < x$ and $x < b$. Similarly, the expression $a \leq x \leq b$ is equivalent to the two inequalities $a \leq x$ and $x \leq b$. The remaining two possibilities, $a \leq x < b$ and $a < x \leq b$, are defined similarly.

Although it is acceptable to write $3 \geq x \geq 2$, it is preferable to reverse the inequality symbols and write instead $2 \leq x \leq 3$ so that, as you read from left to right, the values go from smaller to larger.

A statement such as $2 \leq x \leq 1$ is false because there is no number x for which $2 \leq x$ and $x \leq 1$. Finally, never mix inequality symbols, as in $2 \leq x \geq 3$.

1 Use Interval Notation

Let a and b represent two real numbers with $a < b$:

In Words

The notation $[a, b]$ represents all real numbers between a and b, inclusive. The notation (a, b) represents all real numbers between a and b, not including either a or b.

A **closed interval,** denoted by $[a, b]$, consists of all real numbers x for which $a \leq x \leq b$.

An **open interval,** denoted by (a, b), consists of all real numbers x for which $a < x < b$.

The **half-open,** or **half-closed, intervals** are $(a, b]$, consisting of all real numbers x for which $a < x \leq b$, and $[a, b)$, consisting of all real numbers x for which $a \leq x < b$.

In each of these definitions, a is called the **left endpoint** and b the **right endpoint** of the interval.

The symbol ∞ (read as "infinity") is not a real number but a notational device used to indicate unboundedness in the positive direction. The symbol $-\infty$ (read as "minus infinity" or "negative infinity") also is not a real number but a notational device used to indicate unboundedness in the negative direction. Using the symbols ∞ and $-\infty$, we can define five other kinds of intervals:

$[a, \infty)$ consists of all real numbers x for which $x \geq a$

(a, ∞) consists of all real numbers x for which $x > a$

$(-\infty, a]$ consists of all real numbers x for which $x \leq a$

$(-\infty, a)$ consists of all real numbers x for which $x < a$

$(-\infty, \infty)$ consists of all real numbers x

Note that ∞ and $-\infty$ are never included as endpoints since they are not real numbers.

Table 4 summarizes interval notation, corresponding inequality notation, and their graphs.

Table 4

Interval	Inequality	Graph
The open interval (a, b)	$a < x < b$	a b
The closed interval $[a, b]$	$a \leq x \leq b$	a b
The half-open interval $[a, b)$	$a \leq x < b$	a b
The half-open interval $(a, b]$	$a < x \leq b$	a b
The interval $[a, \infty)$	$x \geq a$	a
The interval (a, ∞)	$x > a$	a
The interval $(-\infty, a]$	$x \leq a$	a
The interval $(-\infty, a)$	$x < a$	a
The interval $(-\infty, \infty)$	All real numbers	

EXAMPLE 1 **Writing Inequalities Using Interval Notation**

Write each inequality using interval notation.

(a) $1 \le x \le 3$
(b) $-4 < x < 0$
(c) $x > 5$
(d) $x \le 1$

Solution

(a) $1 \le x \le 3$ represents all numbers x between 1 and 3, inclusive. In interval notation, we write $[1, 3]$.
(b) In interval notation, $-4 < x < 0$ is written $(-4, 0)$.
(c) $x > 5$ consists of all numbers x greater than 5. In interval notation, we write $(5, \infty)$.
(d) In interval notation, $x \le 1$ is written $(-\infty, 1]$. ■

EXAMPLE 2 **Writing Intervals Using Inequality Notation**

Write each interval as an inequality involving x.

(a) $[1, 4)$
(b) $(2, \infty)$
(c) $[2, 3]$
(d) $(-\infty, -3]$

Solution

(a) $[1, 4)$ consists of all numbers x for which $1 \le x < 4$.
(b) $(2, \infty)$ consists of all numbers x for which $x > 2$.
(c) $[2, 3]$ consists of all numbers x for which $2 \le x \le 3$.
(d) $(-\infty, -3]$ consists of all numbers x for which $x \le -3$. ■

Now Work PROBLEMS 11, 21, AND 29

2 Use Properties of Inequalities

The product of two positive real numbers is positive, the product of two negative real numbers is positive, and the product of 0 and 0 is 0. For any real number a, the value of a^2 is 0 or positive; that is, a^2 is nonnegative. This is called the **nonnegative property.**

In Words
The square of a real number is never negative.

Nonnegative Property

For any real number a,

$$a^2 \ge 0 \qquad \textbf{(1)}$$

If we add the same number to both sides of an inequality, we obtain an equivalent inequality. For example, since $3 < 5$, then $3 + 4 < 5 + 4$ or $7 < 9$. This is called the **addition property** of inequalities.

In Words
The addition property states that the sense, or direction, of an inequality remains unchanged if the same number is added to each side.

Addition Property of Inequalities

For real numbers a, b, and c:

$$\text{If } a < b, \text{ then } a + c < b + c. \qquad \textbf{(2a)}$$

$$\text{If } a > b, \text{ then } a + c > b + c. \qquad \textbf{(2b)}$$

Figure 43 illustrates the addition property (2a). In Figure 43(a), we see that a lies to the left of b. If c is positive, then $a + c$ and $b + c$ each lie c units to the right of a and b, respectively. Consequently, $a + c$ must lie to the left of $b + c$; that is, $a + c < b + c$. Figure 43(b) illustrates the situation if c is negative.

Figure 43

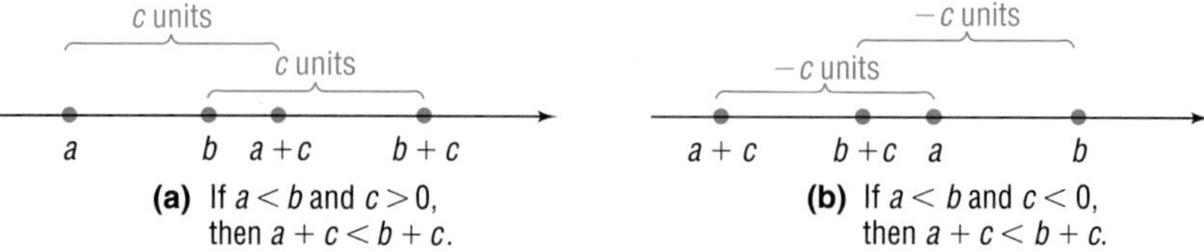

(a) If $a < b$ and $c > 0$, then $a + c < b + c$.
(b) If $a < b$ and $c < 0$, then $a + c < b + c$.

Draw an illustration similar to Figure 43 that illustrates the addition property (2b).

EXAMPLE 3 Addition Property of Inequalities

(a) If $x < -5$, then $x + 5 < -5 + 5$ or $x + 5 < 0$.
(b) If $x > 2$, then $x + (-2) > 2 + (-2)$ or $x - 2 > 0$. ■

Now Work PROBLEM 37

EXAMPLE 4 Multiplying an Inequality by a Positive Number

Express as an inequality the result of multiplying each side of the inequality $3 < 7$ by 2.

Solution Begin with

$$3 < 7$$

Multiplying each side by 2 yields the numbers 6 and 14, so we have

$$6 < 14$$
■

EXAMPLE 5 Multiplying an Inequality by a Negative Number

Express as an inequality the result of multiplying each side of the inequality $9 > 2$ by -4.

Solution Begin with

$$9 > 2$$

Multiplying each side by -4 yields the numbers -36 and -8, so we have

$$-36 < -8$$
■

Note that the effect of multiplying both sides of $9 > 2$ by the negative number -4 is that the direction of the inequality symbol is reversed.

Examples 4 and 5 illustrate the following general **multiplication properties** for inequalities:

In Words
The multiplication properties state that the sense, or direction, of an inequality remains the same if each side is multiplied by a positive real number, whereas the direction is reversed if each side is multiplied by a negative real number.

Multiplication Properties for Inequalities

For real numbers a, b, and c:

If $a < b$ and if $c > 0$, then $ac < bc$.
If $a < b$ and if $c < 0$, then $ac > bc$. **(3a)**

If $a > b$ and if $c > 0$, then $ac > bc$.
If $a > b$ and if $c < 0$, then $ac < bc$. **(3b)**

EXAMPLE 6 **Multiplication Property of Inequalities**

(a) If $2x < 6$, then $\frac{1}{2}(2x) < \frac{1}{2}(6)$ or $x < 3$.

(b) If $\frac{x}{-3} > 12$, then $-3\left(\frac{x}{-3}\right) < -3(12)$ or $x < -36$.

(c) If $-4x > -8$, then $\frac{-4x}{-4} < \frac{-8}{-4}$ or $x < 2$. ■

Now Work PROBLEM 43

3 Solve Linear Inequalities Algebraically and Graphically

An **inequality in one variable** is a statement involving two expressions, at least one containing the variable, separated by one of the inequality symbols, $<, \leq, >$, or $\geq$. To **solve an inequality** means to find all values of the variable for which the statement is true. These values are called **solutions** of the inequality.

For example, the following are all inequalities involving one variable, x:

$$x + 5 < 8 \qquad 2x - 3 \geq 4 \qquad x^2 - 1 \leq 3 \qquad \frac{x+1}{x-2} > 0$$

As with equations, one method for solving an inequality is to replace it by a series of equivalent inequalities until an inequality with an obvious solution, such as $x < 3$, is obtained. We obtain equivalent inequalities by applying some of the same operations as those used to find equivalent equations. The addition property and the multiplication properties form the basis for the following procedures.

Procedures That Leave the Inequality Symbol Unchanged

1. Simplify both sides of the inequality by combining like terms and eliminating parentheses:

$$x + 2 + 6 > 2x + 5(x + 1)$$

is equivalent to $\quad x + 8 > 7x + 5$

2. Add or subtract the same expression on both sides of the inequality:

$$3x - 5 < 4$$

is equivalent to $\quad (3x - 5) + 5 < 4 + 5$

3. Multiply or divide both sides of the inequality by the same *positive* expression:

$$4x > 16 \quad \text{is equivalent to} \quad \frac{4x}{4} > \frac{16}{4}$$

Procedures That Reverse the Sense or Direction of the Inequality Symbol

1. Interchange the two sides of the inequality:

$$3 < x \quad \text{is equivalent to} \quad x > 3$$

2. Multiply or divide both sides of the inequality by the same *negative* expression:

$$-2x > 6 \quad \text{is equivalent to} \quad \frac{-2x}{-2} < \frac{6}{-2}$$

To solve an inequality using a graphing utility, we follow these steps:

Steps for Solving Inequalities Graphically

STEP 1: Write the inequality in one of the following forms:

$$Y_1 < Y_2, \quad Y_1 > Y_2, \quad Y_1 \leq Y_2, \quad Y_1 \geq Y_2$$

STEP 2: Graph Y_1 and Y_2 on the same screen.

STEP 3: If the inequality is of the form $Y_1 < Y_2$, determine on what interval Y_1 is below Y_2.
If the inequality is of the form $Y_1 > Y_2$, determine on what interval Y_1 is above Y_2.
If the inequality is not strict ($\leq$ or $\geq$), include the x-coordinates of the points of intersection in the solution.

As the examples that follow illustrate, we solve linear inequalities using many of the same steps that we would use to solve linear equations. The goal is to get the variable on one side of the inequality and a constant on the other. In writing the solution of an inequality, we may use either set notation or interval notation, whichever is more convenient.

EXAMPLE 7 **Solving an Inequality Algebraically and Graphically**

Solve the inequality $4x + 7 \geq 2x - 3$, and graph the solution set.

Algebraic Solution

$4x + 7 \geq 2x - 3$

$4x + 7 - 7 \geq 2x - 3 - 7$ Subtract 7 from both sides.

$4x \geq 2x - 10$ Simplify.

$4x - 2x \geq 2x - 10 - 2x$ Subtract 2x from both sides.

$2x \geq -10$ Simplify.

$\frac{2x}{2} \geq \frac{-10}{2}$ Divide both sides by 2. (The direction of the inequality symbol is unchanged.)

$x \geq -5$ Simplify.

The solution set is $\{x \mid x \geq -5\}$ or, using interval notation, all numbers in the interval $[-5, \infty)$.

Graphing Solution

We graph $Y_1 = 4x + 7$ and $Y_2 = 2x - 3$ on the same screen. See Figure 44. Using the INTERSECT command, we find that Y_1 and Y_2 intersect at $x = -5$. The graph of Y_1 is above that of Y_2, $Y_1 > Y_2$, to the right of the point of intersection. Since the inequality is not strict, the solution set is $\{x \mid x \geq -5\}$ or, using interval notation, $[-5, \infty)$.

Figure 44

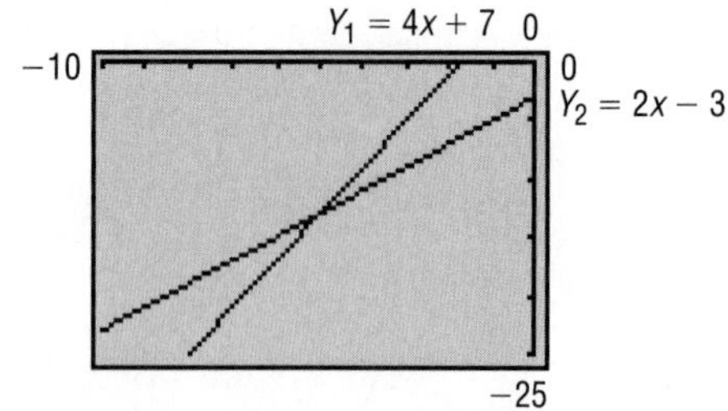

See Figure 45 for the graph of the solution set. ■

Figure 45

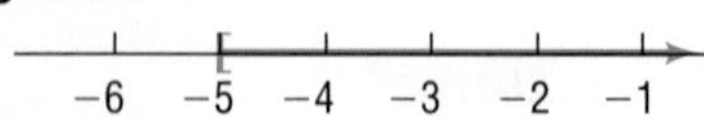

Now Work PROBLEM 49

4 Solve Combined Inequalities Algebraically and Graphically

EXAMPLE 8 **Solving a Combined Inequality Algebraically and Graphically**

Solve the inequality: $-1 \leq \frac{3 - 5x}{2} \leq 9$

Algebraic Solution

$$-1 \le \frac{3-5x}{2} \le 9$$

$$2(-1) \le 2\left(\frac{3-5x}{2}\right) \le 2(9)$$ Multiply each part by 2 to remove the denominator.

$$-2 \le 3-5x \le 18$$ Simplify.

$$-2-3 \le 3-5x-3 \le 18-3$$ Subtract 3 from each part to isolate the term containing x.

$$-5 \le -5x \le 15$$ Simplify.

$$\frac{-5}{-5} \ge \frac{-5x}{-5} \ge \frac{15}{-5}$$ Divide each part by -5 (reverse the sense of each inequality symbol).

$$1 \ge x \ge -3$$ Simplify.

$$-3 \le x \le 1$$ Reverse the order so the numbers get larger as you read from left to right.

The solution set is $\{x \mid -3 \le x \le 1\}$. In interval notation, the solution is $[-3, 1]$.

Graphing Solution

To solve a combined inequality graphically, we graph each part: $Y_1 = -1$, $Y_2 = \frac{3-5x}{2}$, $Y_3 = 9$. We seek the values of x for which the graph of Y_2 is between the graphs of Y_1 and Y_3. See Figure 46. The point of intersection of Y_1 and Y_2 is $(1, -1)$, and the point of intersection of Y_2 and Y_3 is $(-3, 9)$. The inequality is true for all values of x between these two intersection points. Since the inequality is nonstrict, the solution set is $\{x \mid -3 \le x \le 1\}$ or, using interval notation, $[-3, 1]$.

Figure 46

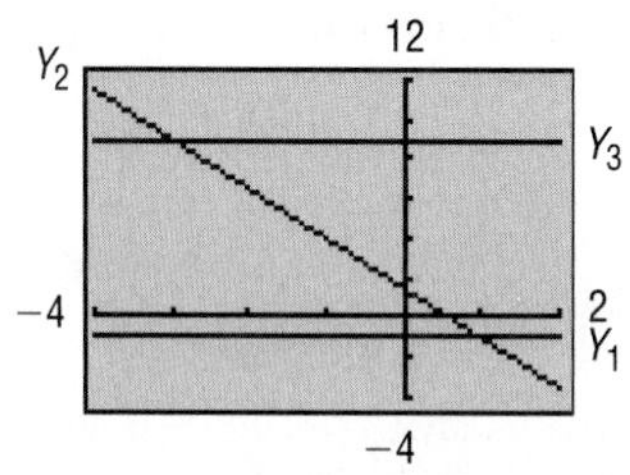

See Figure 47 for the graph of the solution set.

Figure 47

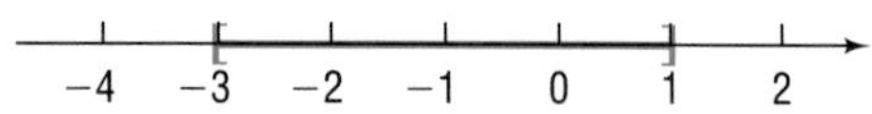

Now Work PROBLEM 65

5 Solve Absolute Value Inequalities Algebraically and Graphically

EXAMPLE 9 **Solving an Inequality Involving Absolute Value**

Solve the inequality: $|x| < 4$

Algebraic Solution

We are looking for all points whose coordinate x is a distance less than 4 units from the origin. See Figure 48 for an illustration.

Figure 48

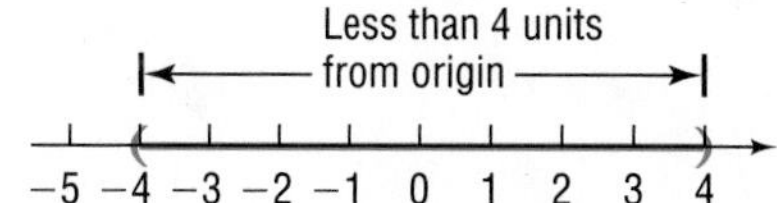

Because any x between -4 and 4 satisfies the condition $|x| < 4$, the solution set consists of all numbers x for which $-4 < x < 4$, that is, all x in the interval $(-4, 4)$.

Graphing Solution

Graph $Y_1 = |x|$ and $Y_2 = 4$ on the same screen. See Figure 49. Using the INTERSECT command (twice), we find that Y_1 and Y_2 intersect at $x = -4$ and at $x = 4$. The graph of Y_1 is below that of Y_2, $Y_1 < Y_2$, between the points of intersection. Since the inequality is strict, the solution set is $\{x \mid -4 < x < 4\}$ or, using interval notation, $(-4, 4)$.

Figure 49

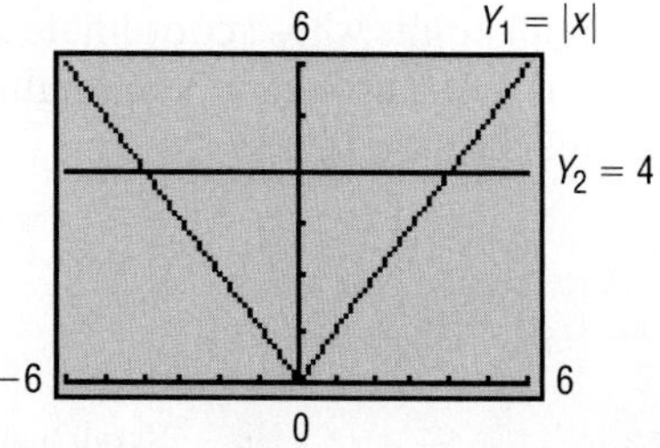

We are led to the following results:

THEOREM

If a is any positive number and if u is any algebraic expression, then

$\lvert u \rvert < a$	is equivalent to	$-a < u < a$	**(4)**
$\lvert u \rvert \le a$	is equivalent to	$-a \le u \le a$	**(5)**

In other words, $|u| < a$ is equivalent to $-a < u$ and $u < a$.

EXAMPLE 10 **Solving an Inequality Involving Absolute Value**

Solve the inequality $|2x + 4| \le 3$, and graph the solution set.

Algebraic Solution

$$|2x + 4| \le 3$$ This follows the form of statement (5); the expression $u = 2x + 4$ is inside the absolute value bars.

$$-3 \le 2x + 4 \le 3$$ Apply statement (5).

$$-3 - 4 \le 2x + 4 - 4 \le 3 - 4$$ Subtract 4 from each part.

$$-7 \le 2x \le -1$$ Simplify.

$$\frac{-7}{2} \le \frac{2x}{2} \le \frac{-1}{2}$$ Divide each part by 2.

$$-\frac{7}{2} \le x \le -\frac{1}{2}$$ Simplify.

The solution set is $\left\{x \middle| -\frac{7}{2} \le x \le -\frac{1}{2}\right\}$, that is, all x in the interval $\left[-\frac{7}{2}, -\frac{1}{2}\right]$.

Graphing Solution

We graph $Y_1 = |2x + 4|$ and $Y_2 = 3$ on the same screen. See Figure 50. Using the INTERSECT command (twice), we find that Y_1 and Y_2 intersect at $x = -3.5$ and at $x = -0.5$. The graph of Y_1 is below that of Y_2, $Y_1 < Y_2$, between the points of intersection. Since the inequality is not strict, the solution set is $\{x | -3.5 \le x \le -0.5\}$ or, using interval notation, $[-3.5, -0.5]$.

Figure 50

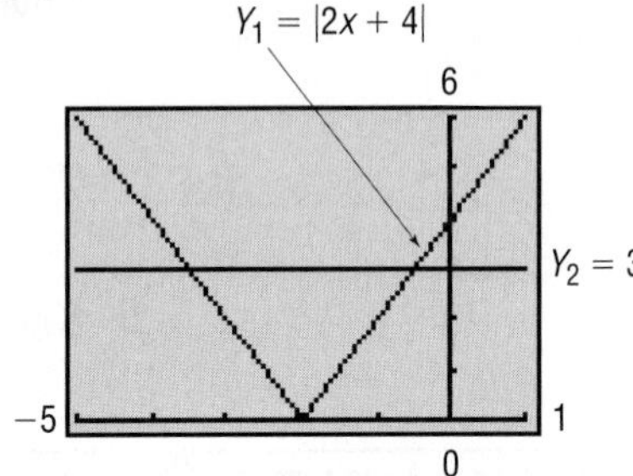

Figure 51

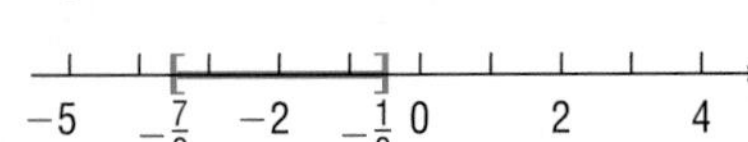

See Figure 51 for a graph of the solution set.

Now Work PROBLEM 77

EXAMPLE 11 **Solving an Inequality Involving Absolute Value**

Solve the inequality $|x| > 3$.

Algebraic Solution

We are looking for all points whose coordinate x is a distance greater than 3 units from the origin. Figure 52 illustrates the situation.

Figure 52

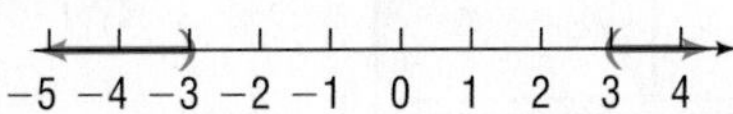

Graphing Solution

We graph $Y_1 = |x|$ and $Y_2 = 3$ on the same screen. See Figure 53. Using the INTERSECT command (twice), we find that Y_1 and Y_2 intersect at $x = -3$ and at $x = 3$. The graph of Y_1 is above that of Y_2, $Y_1 > Y_2$, to the left of $x = -3$ and to the right of $x = 3$. Since the inequality is strict, the solution set is $\{x | x < -3 \text{ or } x > 3\}$. Using interval notation, the solution is $(-\infty, -3) \cup (3, \infty)$.*

*Recall that the symbol $\cup$ represents the union of two sets and means "or".

We conclude that any x less than -3 or greater than 3 satisfies the condition $|x| > 3$. Consequently, the solution set is $\{x \mid x < -3 \text{ or } x > 3\}$. Using interval notation, the solution is $(-\infty, -3) \cup (3, \infty)$. ■

Figure 53

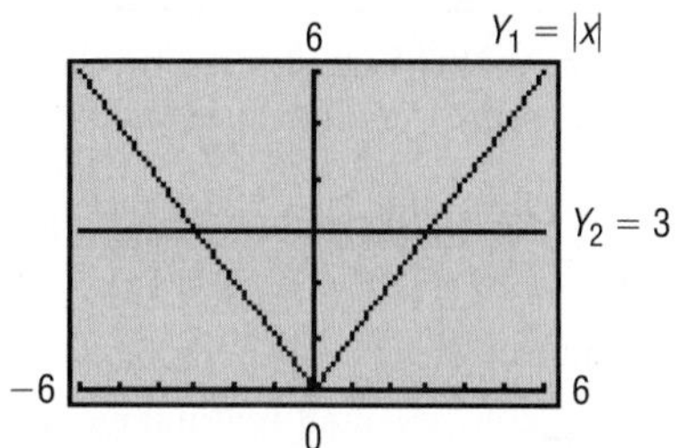

■

THEOREM

If a is any positive number and u is any algebraic expression, then

$\lvert u \rvert > a$	is equivalent to	$u < -a$ or $u > a$	**(6)**
$\lvert u \rvert \geq a$	is equivalent to	$u \leq -a$ or $u \geq a$	**(7)**

WARNING A common error to be avoided is to attempt to write the solution $x < 1$ or $x > 4$ as $1 > x > 4$, which is incorrect, since there are no numbers x for which $1 > x$ *and* $x > 4$. Another common error is to "mix" the symbols and write $1 < x > 4$, which makes no sense. ■

EXAMPLE 12 Solving an Inequality Involving Absolute Value

Solve the inequality $|2x - 5| > 3$, and graph the solution set.

Algebraic Solution

$|2x - 5| > 3$ This follows the form of statement (6); the expression $u = 2x - 5$ is inside the absolute value bars.

$2x - 5 < -3$	or	$2x - 5 > 3$	Apply statement (6).
$2x - 5 + 5 < -3 + 5$	or	$2x - 5 + 5 > 3 + 5$	Add 5 to each part.
$2x < 2$	or	$2x > 8$	Simplify.
$\frac{2x}{2} < \frac{2}{2}$	or	$\frac{2x}{2} > \frac{8}{2}$	Divide each part by 2.
$x < 1$	or	$x > 4$	Simplify.

The solution set is $\{x \mid x < 1 \text{ or } x > 4\}$. Using interval notation, the solution is $(-\infty, 1) \cup (4, \infty)$.

Figure 55

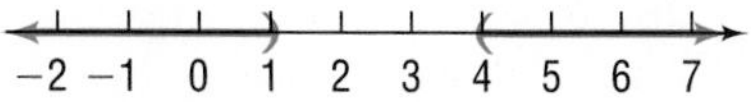

Graphing Solution

We graph $Y_1 = |2x - 5|$ and $Y_2 = 3$ on the same screen. See Figure 54. Using the INTERSECT command (twice), we find that Y_1 and Y_2 intersect at $x = 1$ and at $x = 4$. The graph of Y_1 is above that of Y_2, $Y_1 > Y_2$, to the left of $x = 1$ and to the right of $x = 4$. Since the inequality is strict, the solution set is $\{x \mid x < 1 \text{ or } x > 4\}$. Using interval notation, the solution is $(-\infty, 1) \cup (4, \infty)$.

Figure 54

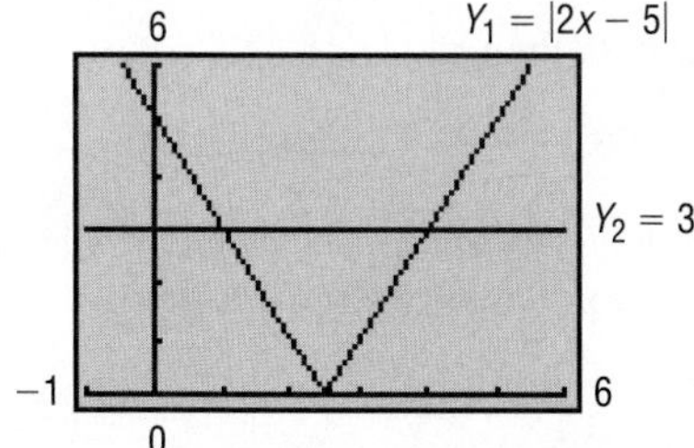

See Figure 55 for a graph of the solution set. ■

Now Work PROBLEM 79

7.5 Assess Your Understanding

'Are You Prepared?' *Answers are given at the end of these exercises.*

1. Graph the inequality: $x \geq -2$.
2. ***True or False*** The absolute value of a negative number is positive.
3. If $A = \{a, e, i, o, u\}$ and $B = \{a, b, c, d, e\}$, what is $A \cup B$?

Concepts and Vocabulary

4. If each side of an inequality is multiplied by a(n) _______ number, then the sense of the inequality symbol is reversed.

5. A(n) _______ _______, denoted $[a, b]$, consists of all real numbers x for which $a \le x \le b$.

6. $|u| \le a$ is equivalent to __________.

7. The interval _______ consists of all real numbers for which $x \le a$.

In Problems 8–10, assume that $a < b$ and $c < 0$.

8. ***True or False*** $a + c < b + c$

9. ***True or False*** $ac > bc$

10. ***True or False*** $\frac{a}{c} < \frac{b}{c}$

Skill Building

In Problems 11–16, express the graph shown in color using interval notation. Also express each as an inequality involving x.

11. 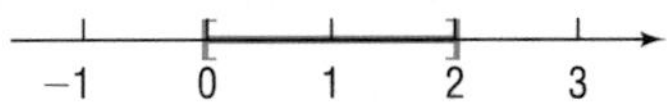

12. 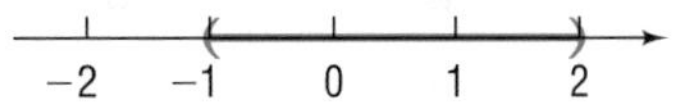

13. 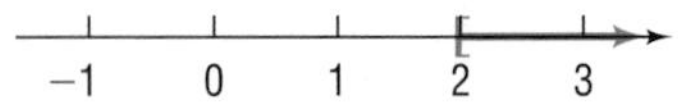

14. 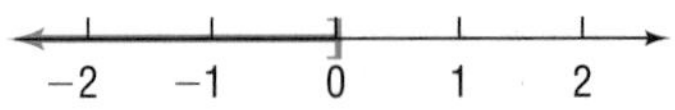

15. 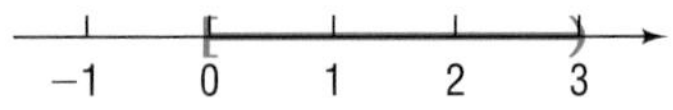

16. 

In Problems 17–20, an inequality is given. Write the inequality obtained by:

(a) Adding 3 to each side of the given inequality.
(b) Subtracting 5 from each side of the given inequality.
(c) Multiplying each side of the given inequality by 3.
(d) Multiplying each side of the given inequality by −2.

17. $3 < 5$ **18.** $2 > 1$ **19.** $2x + 1 < 2$ **20.** $1 - 2x > 5$

In Problems 21–28, write each inequality using interval notation, and illustrate each inequality using the real number line.

21. $0 \le x \le 4$ **22.** $-1 < x < 5$ **23.** $4 \le x < 6$ **24.** $-2 < x \le 0$
25. $x \ge 4$ **26.** $x \le 5$ **27.** $x < -4$ **28.** $x > 1$

In Problems 29–36, write each interval as an inequality involving x, and illustrate each inequality using the real number line.

29. $[2, 5]$ **30.** $(1, 2)$ **31.** $(-3, -2)$ **32.** $[0, 1)$
33. $[4, \infty)$ **34.** $(-\infty, 2]$ **35.** $(-\infty, -3)$ **36.** $(-8, \infty)$

In Problems 37–48, fill in the blank with the correct inequality symbol.

37. If $x < 5$, then $x - 5$ ________ 0.
38. If $x < -4$, then $x + 4$ ________ 0.
39. If $x > -4$, then $x + 4$ ________ 0.
40. If $x > 6$, then $x - 6$ ________ 0.
41. If $x \ge -4$, then $3x$ ________ -12.
42. If $x \le 3$, then $2x$ ________ 6.
43. If $x > 6$, then $-2x$ ________ -12.
44. If $x > -2$, then $-4x$ ________ 8.
45. If $2x < 6$, then x ________ 3.
46. If $3x \le 12$, then x ________ 4.
47. If $-\frac{1}{2}x \le 3$, then x ________ -6.
48. If $-\frac{1}{4}x > 1$, then x ________ -4.

In Problems 49–86, solve each inequality algebraically. Express your answer using set notation or interval notation. Graph the solution set. Verify your results using a graphing utility.

49. $3x - 7 > 2$ **50.** $2x + 5 > 1$ **51.** $1 - 2x \le 3$
52. $2 - 3x \le 5$ **53.** $3x - 1 \ge 3 + x$ **54.** $2x - 2 \ge 3 + x$
55. $-2(x + 3) < 8$ **56.** $-3(1 - x) < 12$ **57.** $4 - 3(1 - x) \le 3$
58. $8 - 4(2 - x) \le -2x$ **59.** $\frac{1}{2}(x - 4) > x + 8$ **60.** $3x + 4 > \frac{1}{3}(x - 2)$
61. $0 \le 2x - 6 \le 4$ **62.** $4 \le 2x + 2 \le 10$ **63.** $-5 \le 4 - 3x \le 2$
64. $-3 \le 3 - 2x \le 9$ **65.** $-3 < \frac{2x - 1}{4} < 0$ **66.** $0 < \frac{3x + 2}{2} < 4$
67. $1 < 1 - \frac{1}{2}x < 4$ **68.** $0 < 1 - \frac{1}{3}x < 1$ **69.** $(x + 2)(x - 3) > (x - 1)(x + 1)$
70. $(x - 1)(x + 1) > (x - 3)(x + 4)$ **71.** $|2x| < 8$ **72.** $|3x| < 15$
73. $|3x| > 12$ **74.** $|2x| > 6$ **75.** $|3t - 2| \le 4$

76. $|2u + 5| \le 7$

77. $|x - 2| + 2 < 3$

78. $|x + 4| + 3 < 5$

79. $|x - 3| \ge 2$

80. $|x + 4| \ge 2$

81. $|1 - 2x| > |-3|$

82. $|2 - 3x| > |-1|$

83. $|1 - 4x| - 7 < -2$

84. $|1 - 2x| - 4 < -1$

85. $|2x + 1| < -1$

86. $|3x - 4| \ge 0$

Mixed Practice

In Problems 87–106, solve each inequality algebraically. Express your answer using set notation or interval notation. Graph the solution set. Verify your results using a graphing utility.

87. $3 - 4x < 11$

88. $1 - 3x \le 7$

89. $|2x + 1| - 5 \ge -1$

90. $|5x + 2| - 3 > 9$

91. $\frac{x}{2} \ge 1 - \frac{x}{4}$

92. $\frac{x}{3} \ge 2 + \frac{x}{6}$

93. $-\frac{1}{3} \le \frac{x+1}{6} < \frac{4}{3}$

94. $-\frac{3}{2} < \frac{x-3}{4} \le \frac{5}{4}$

95. $x(4x + 3) \le (2x + 1)^2$

96. $x(9x - 5) \le (3x - 1)^2$

97. $|(3x - 2) - 7| < \frac{1}{2}$

98. $|(4x - 1) - 11)| < \frac{1}{4}$

99. $-3 < 5 - 2x \le 11$

100. $2 \le 3 - 2(x + 1) < 8$

101. $7 - |x - 1| > 4$

102. $9 - |x + 3| \ge 5$

103. $-3 < x + 5 < 2x$

104. $2 < x - 3 < 2x$

105. $x + 2 < 2x - 1 < 5x$

106. $2x - 1 < 3x + 5 < 5x - 7$

Applications and Extensions

107. Express the fact that x differs from 2 by less than $\frac{1}{2}$ as an inequality involving an absolute value. Solve for x.

108. Express the fact that x differs from -1 by less than 1 as an inequality involving an absolute value. Solve for x.

109. Express the fact that x differs from -3 by more than 2 as an inequality involving an absolute value. Solve for x.

110. Express the fact that x differs from 2 by more than 3 as an inequality involving an absolute value. Solve for x.

111. A young adult may be defined as someone older than 21 but less than 30 years of age. Express this statement using inequalities.

112. Middle-aged may be defined as being 40 or more and less than 60. Express this statement using inequalities.

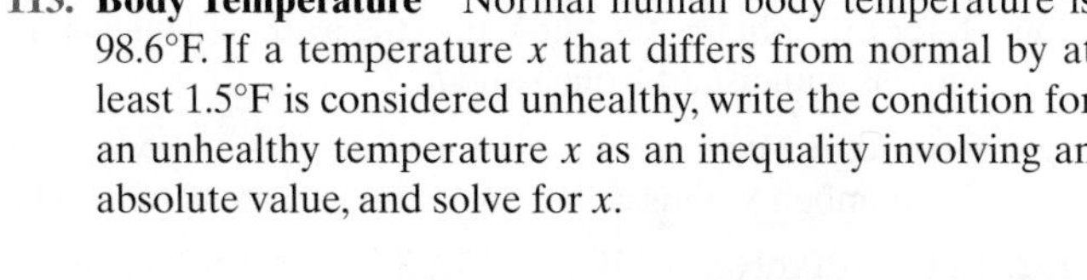

113. Body Temperature Normal human body temperature is 98.6°F. If a temperature x that differs from normal by at least 1.5°F is considered unhealthy, write the condition for an unhealthy temperature x as an inequality involving an absolute value, and solve for x.

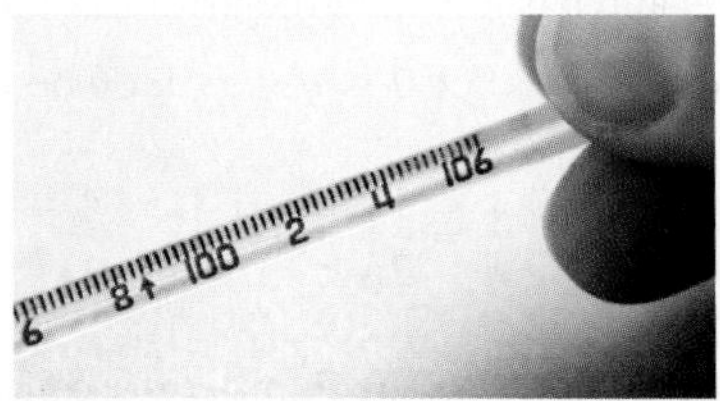

114. Household Voltage In the United States, normal household voltage is 115 volts. However, it is not uncommon for actual voltage to differ from normal voltage by at most 5 volts. Express this situation as an inequality involving an absolute value. Use x as the actual voltage and solve for x.

115. Life Expectancy The Social Security Administration determined that an average 30-year-old male in 2007 could expect to live at least 47.1 more years and an average 30-year-old female in 2007 could expect to live at least 51.5 more years.

(a) To what age can an average 30-year-old male expect to live? Express your answer as an inequality.

(b) To what age can an average 30-year-old female expect to live? Express your answer as an inequality.

(c) Who can expect to live longer, a male or a female? By how many years?

Source: National Vital Statistics Report, May 2010.

116. General Chemistry For a certain ideal gas, the volume V (in cubic centimeters) equals 20 times the temperature T in kelvin (K). If the temperature varies from 353 to 393 K, inclusive, what is the corresponding range of the volume of the gas?

117. Real Estate A real estate agent agrees to sell a large apartment complex according to the following commission schedule: \$45,000 plus 25% of the selling price in excess of \$900,000. Assuming that the complex will sell at some price between \$900,000 and \$1,100,000, inclusive, over what range does the agent's commission vary? How does the commission vary as a percent of selling price?

118. Sales Commission A used car salesperson is paid a commission of \$25 plus 40% of the selling price in excess of owner's cost. The owner claims that used cars typically sell for at least owner's cost plus \$70 and at most owner's cost plus \$300. For each sale made, over what range can the salesperson expect the commission to vary?

119. Federal Tax Withholding The percentage method of withholding for federal income tax (2011) states that a single person whose weekly wages, after subtracting withholding allowances, are over \$740, but not over \$1648, shall have \$91.40 plus 25% of the excess over \$740 withheld. Over what range does the amount withheld vary if the weekly wages vary from \$800 to \$1000, inclusive?

Source: Employer's Tax Guide. Department of the Treasury, Internal Revenue Service, 2011.

120. Exercising Sue wants to lose weight. For healthy weight loss, the American College of Sports Medicine (ACSM) recommends 200 to 300 minutes of exercise per week. For the first six days of the week, Sue exercised 40, 45, 0, 50, 25, and 35 minutes. How long should Sue exercise on the seventh day in order to stay within the ACSM guidelines?

121. Electricity Rates Commonwealth Edison Company's summer charge for electricity is 7.582¢ per kilowatt-hour. In addition, each monthly bill contains a customer charge of \$8.49. If last summer's bills ranged from a low of \$63.74 to a high of \$127.45, over what range did usage vary (in kilowatt-hours)?

Source: Commonwealth Edison Co., Chicago, Illinois, 2011.

122. Water Bills The Village of Oak Lawn charges homeowners \$37.62 per quarter-year plus \$3.86 per 1000 gallons for water usage in excess of 10,000 gallons. In 2010, one homeowner's quarterly bill ranged from a high of \$122.54 to a low of \$68.50. Over what range did water usage vary?

Source: Village of Oak Lawn, Illinois, 2010.

123. Markup of a Used Car The markup over dealer's cost of a used car ranges from 12% to 18%. If the sticker price is \$8800, over what range will the dealer's cost vary?

124. IQ Tests A standard intelligence test has an average score of 100. According to statistical theory, of the people who take the test, the 2.5% with the highest scores will have scores of more than 1.96σ above the average, where σ (sigma, a number called the *standard deviation*) depends on the nature of the test. If $\sigma = 12$ for this test and there is (in principle) no upper limit to the score possible on the test, write the interval of possible test scores of the people in the top 2.5%.

125. Computing Grades In your Economics 101 class, you have scores of 68, 82, 87, and 89 on the first four of five tests. To get a grade of B, the average of the first five test scores must be greater than or equal to 80 and less than 90.

(a) Find the range of the score that you need on the last test to get a B.

(b) What score do you need if the fifth test counts double?

126. "Light" Foods For food products to be labeled "light," the U.S. Food and Drug Administration requires that the altered product must either contain one-third or fewer calories than the regular product or it must contain one-half or less fat than the regular product. If a serving of Miracle Whip® Light contains 20 calories and 1.5 grams of fat, then what must be true about either the number of calories or the grams of fat in a serving of regular Miracle Whip®?

127. Reading Books A Gallup poll found that Americans read an average of 13.4 books per year. Gallup is 99% confident that the result from this poll is off by fewer than 1.35 books from the actual average x. Express this situation as an inequality involving absolute value, and solve the inequality for x to determine the interval in which the actual average is likely to fall.

[**Note:** In statistics, this interval is called a 99% **confidence interval.**]

128. Speed of Sound According to data from the Hill Aerospace Museum (Hill Air Force Base, Utah), the speed of sound varies depending on altitude, barometric pressure, and temperature. For example, at 20,000 feet, 13.75 inches of mercury, and $-12.3°$F, the speed of sound is about 707 miles per hour, but the speed can vary from this result by as much as 55 miles per hour as conditions change.

(a) Express this situation as an inequality involving an absolute value.

(b) Using x for the speed of sound, solve for x to find an interval for the speed of sound.

129. Arithmetic Mean If $a < b$, show that $a < \frac{a+b}{2} < b$. The number $\frac{a+b}{2}$ is called the **arithmetic mean** of a and b.

130. Refer to Problem 129. Show that the arithmetic mean of a and b is equidistant from a and b.

131. Geometric Mean If $0 < a < b$, show that $a < \sqrt{ab} < b$. The number $\sqrt{ab}$ is called the **geometric mean** of a and b.

132. Refer to Problems 129 and 131. Show that the geometric mean of a and b is less than the arithmetic mean of a and b.

133. Harmonic Mean For $0 < a < b$, let h be defined by

$$\frac{1}{h} = \frac{1}{2}\left(\frac{1}{a} + \frac{1}{b}\right)$$

Show that $a < h < b$. The number h is called the **harmonic mean** of a and b.

134. Refer to Problems 129, 131, and 133. Show that the harmonic mean of a and b equals the geometric mean squared divided by the arithmetic mean.

Explaining Concepts: Discussion and Writing

135. Make up an inequality that has no solution. Make up one that has exactly one solution.

136. How would you explain to a fellow student the underlying reason for the multiplication properties for inequalities (page 506); that is, the sense or direction of an inequality remains the same if each side is multiplied by a positive real number, while the direction is reversed if each side is multiplied by a negative real number.

137. The inequality $x^2 + 1 < -5$ has no solution. Explain why.

138. Do you prefer to use inequality notation or interval notation to express the solution to an inequality? Give your reasons. Are there particular circumstances when you prefer one to the other? Cite examples.

'Are You Prepared?' Answers

1. 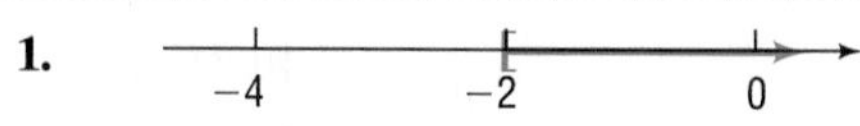

2. True

3. $A \cup B = \{a, b, c, d, e, i, o, u\}$

CHAPTER REVIEW

Things to Know

Formulas

Distance formula (p. 463)	$d = \sqrt{(x_2 - x_1)^2 + (y_2 - y_1)^2}$
Midpoint formula (p. 465)	$M = (x, y) = \left(\frac{x_1 + x_2}{2}, \frac{y_1 + y_2}{2}\right)$

Quadratic equation and quadratic formula

The real solutions of the equation $ax^2 + bx + c = 0$, $a \neq 0$, are given by $x = \frac{-b \pm \sqrt{b^2 - 4ac}}{2a}$, provided $b^2 - 4ac \geq 0$. If $b^2 - 4ac < 0$, there are no real solutions. (p. 480)

In the complex number system, the solutions of the equation $ax^2 + bx + c = 0$, $a \neq 0$, are given by $x = \frac{-b \pm \sqrt{b^2 - 4ac}}{2a}$. (p. 492)

Discriminant (pp. 480 and 493)

If $b^2 - 4ac > 0$, there are two unequal real solutions.

If $b^2 - 4ac = 0$, there is one repeated real solution, a root of multiplicity 2.

If $b^2 - 4ac < 0$, there are no real solutions, but there are two distinct complex solutions that are not real; the complex solutions are conjugates of each other.

Interval notation (p. 504)

$[a, b]$	$\{x \mid a \leq x \leq b\}$	(a, b)	$\{x \mid a < x < b\}$	$(-\infty, a]$	$\{x \mid x \leq a\}$
$[a, b)$	$\{x \mid a \leq x < b\}$	$[a, \infty)$	$\{x \mid x \geq a\}$	$(-\infty, a)$	$\{x \mid x < a\}$
$(a, b]$	$\{x \mid a < x \leq b\}$	(a, ∞)	$\{x \mid x > a\}$	$(-\infty, \infty)$	All real numbers

Properties of inequalities

Addition property (p. 505)
- If $a < b$, then $a + c < b + c$.
- If $a > b$, then $a + c > b + c$.

Multiplication properties (p. 506)
- (a) If $a < b$ and if $c > 0$, then $ac < bc$.
  If $a < b$ and if $c < 0$, then $ac > bc$.
- (b) If $a > b$ and if $c > 0$, then $ac > bc$.
  If $a > b$ and if $c < 0$, then $ac < bc$.

Absolute value

If $|u| = a$, $a > 0$, then $u = -a$ or $u = a$. (p. 499)

If $|u| \leq a$, $a > 0$, then $-a \leq u \leq a$. (p. 510)

If $|u| \geq a$, $a > 0$, then $u \leq -a$ or $u \geq a$. (p. 511)

Objectives

Section		You should be able to	Example(s)	Review Exercises
7.1	1	Use the distance formula (p. 462)	2, 3, 4	45(a)–47(a), 53, 54
	2	Use the midpoint formula (p. 465)	5	45(b)–47(b)
	3	Graph equations by hand by plotting points (p. 465)	6, 7, 8	50–52
	4	Graph equations using a graphing utility (p. 468)	9, 10	48, 50–52
	5	Use a graphing utility to create tables (p. 470)	11	48
	6	Find intercepts from a graph (p. 470)	12	49
	7	Use a graphing utility to approximate intercepts (p. 471)	13	50–52
7.2	1	Solve quadratic equations by factoring (p. 476)	1, 2	5, 7, 18, 19
	2	Solve quadratic equations using the Square Root Method (p. 478)	3	26
	3	Solve quadratic equations by completing the square (p. 479)	4	5, 7, 8, 10, 11, 18, 19
	4	Solve quadratic equations using the quadratic formula (p. 479)	5, 6	5, 7, 8, 10, 11, 18, 19
	5	Solve problems that can be modeled by quadratic equations (p. 482)	7	63, 67, 71, 72
7.3	1	Add, subtract, multiply, and divide complex numbers (p. 488)	1–8	36–40
	2	Solve quadratic equations in the complex number system (p. 491)	10, 11	41–44
7.4	1	Solve radical equations (p. 495)	1–3	9, 13–15, 20
	2	Solve equations quadratic in form (p. 497)	4, 5	12, 17
	3	Solve absolute value equations (p. 499)	6	21, 22
	4	Solve equations by factoring (p. 500)	7, 8	23, 24
7.5	1	Use interval notation (p. 504)	1, 2	29–35
	2	Use properties of inequalities (p. 505)	3–6	29–35
	3	Solve linear inequalities algebraically and graphically (p. 507)	7	29
	4	Solve combined inequalities algebraically and graphically (p. 508)	8	30, 31, 59
	5	Solve absolute value inequalities algebraically and graphically (p. 509)	9–12	32–35

Review Exercises

In Problems 1–26, find all the real solutions, if any, of each equation. (Where they appear, a, b, m, and n are positive constants.) When possible, verify your results using a graphing utility.

1. $2 - \frac{x}{3} = 8$

2. $-2(5 - 3x) + 8 = 4 + 5x$

3. $\frac{3x}{4} - \frac{x}{3} = \frac{1}{12}$

4. $\frac{x}{x-1} = \frac{6}{5}, \quad x \neq 1$

5. $x(1 - x) = 6$

6. $\frac{1-3x}{4} = \frac{x+6}{3} + \frac{1}{2}$

7. $(x - 1)(2x + 3) = 3$

8. $2x + 3 = 4x^2$

9. $\sqrt[3]{x^2 - 1} = 2$

10. $x(x + 1) + 2 = 0$

11. $3x^2 - x + 1 = 0$

12. $x^4 - 5x^2 + 4 = 0$

13. $\sqrt{2x - 3} + x = 3$

14. $\sqrt[4]{2x + 3} = 2$

15. $\sqrt{x+1} + \sqrt{x-1} = \sqrt{2x+1}$

16. $2x^{1/2} - 3 = 0$

17. $x^{-6} - 7x^{-3} - 8 = 0$

18. $x^2 + m^2 = 2mx + (nx)^2, \quad n \neq 1, n \neq -1$

19. $10a^2x^2 - 2abx - 36b^2 = 0$

20. $\sqrt{x^2 + 3x + 7} - \sqrt{x^2 - 3x + 9} + 2 = 0$

21. $|2x + 3| = 7$

22. $|2 - 3x| + 2 = 9$

23. $2x^3 = 3x^2$

24. $2x^3 + 5x^2 - 8x - 20 = 0$

25. $\frac{1}{x-1} + \frac{3}{x+2} = \frac{11}{x^2 + x - 2}$

26. $(x - 2)^2 = 9$

In Problems 27–28, use a graphing utility to approximate the solutions of each equation rounded to two decimal places. All solutions lie between −10 and 10.

27. $x^3 - 5x + 3 = 0$

28. $x^4 - 3 = 2x + 1$

In Problems 29–35, solve each inequality. Express your answer using set notation or interval notation. Graph the solution set. Verify your results using a graphing utility.

29. $\frac{2x-3}{5} + 2 \le \frac{x}{2}$

30. $-9 \le \frac{2x+3}{-4} \le 7$

31. $2 < \frac{3-3x}{12} < 6$

32. $|3x + 4| < \frac{1}{2}$

33. $|2x - 5| \ge 9$

34. $2 + |2 - 3x| \le 4$

35. $1 - |2 - 3x| < -4$

In Problems 36–40, use the complex number system and write each expression in the standard form $a + bi$.

36. $(6 + 3i) - (2 - 4i)$

37. $4(3 - i) + 3(-5 + 2i)$

38. $\frac{3}{3 + i}$

39. i^{50}

40. $(2 + 3i)^3$

In Problems 41–44, solve each equation in the complex number system.

41. $x^2 + x + 1 = 0$

42. $2x^2 + x - 2 = 0$

43. $x^2 + 3 = x$

44. $x(1 + x) = 2$

In Problems 45–47, find the following for each pair of points:
(a) *The distance between the points*
(b) *The midpoint of the line segment connecting the points*

45. $(0, 0)$; $(4, 2)$

46. $(1, -1)$; $(-2, 3)$

47. $(4, -4)$; $(4, 8)$

48. Graph $y = -x^2 + 15$ using a graphing utility. Create a table of values to determine a good initial viewing window.

49. List the intercepts of the following graph.

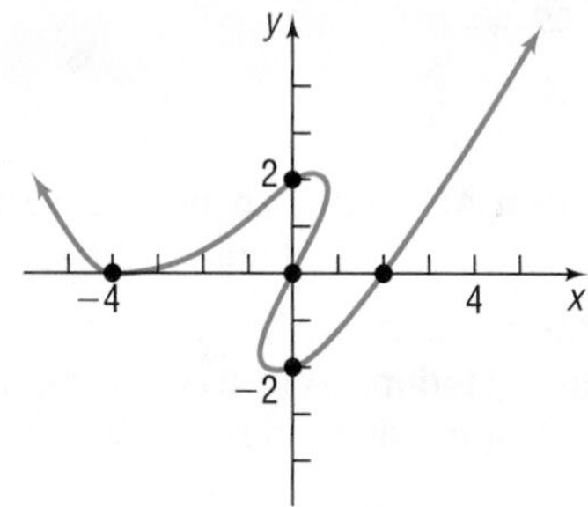

In Problems 50–52, graph each equation by hand by plotting points. Verify your results using a graphing utility. Approximate the intercepts using a graphing utility and label them on the graph.

50. $2x - 3y = 6$

51. $y = x^2 - 9$

52. $x^2 + 2y = 16$

53. Show that the points $A = (3, 4)$, $B = (1, 1)$, and $C = (-2, 3)$ are the vertices of an isosceles triangle.

54. Find two numbers y such that the distance from $(-3, 2)$ to $(5, y)$ is 10.

55. Translate the following statement into a mathematical expression: The perimeter p of a rectangle is the sum of two times the length l and two times the width w.

56. Banking A bank lends $9000 at 7% simple interest. At the end of 1 year, how much interest is owed on the loan?

57. Financial Planning Steve, a recent retiree, requires $5000 per year in extra income. He has $70,000 to invest and can invest in A-rated bonds paying 8% per year or in a certificate of deposit (CD) paying 5% per year. How much money should be invested in each to realize exactly $5000 in interest per year?

58. Lightning and Thunder A flash of lightning is seen, and the resulting thunderclap is heard 3 seconds later. If the speed of sound averages 1100 feet per second, how far away is the storm?

59. Physics: Intensity of Light The intensity I (in candlepower) of a certain light source obeys the equation $I = \frac{900}{x^2}$, where

x is the distance (in meters) from the light. Over what range of distances can an object be placed from this light source so that the range of intensity of light is from 1600 to 3600 candlepower, inclusive?

60. **Extent of Search and Rescue** A search plane has a cruising speed of 250 miles per hour and carries enough fuel for at most 5 hours of flying. If there is a wind that averages 30 miles per hour and the direction of the search is with the wind one way and against it the other, how far can the search plane travel before it has to turn back?

61. **Rescue at Sea** A life raft, set adrift from a sinking ship 150 miles offshore, travels directly toward a Coast Guard station at the rate of 5 miles per hour. At the time that the raft is set adrift, a rescue helicopter is dispatched from the Coast Guard station. If the helicopter's average speed is 90 miles per hour, how long will it take the helicopter to reach the life raft?

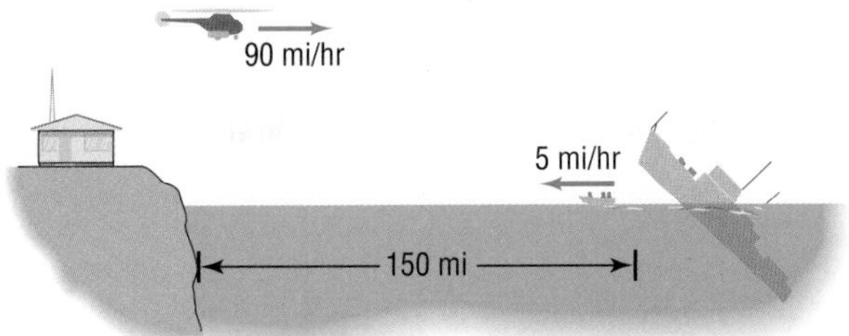

62. **Physics: Uniform Motion** Two bees leave two locations 150 meters apart and fly, without stopping, back and forth between these two locations at average speeds of 3 meters per second and 5 meters per second, respectively. How long is it until the bees meet for the first time? How long is it until they meet for the second time?

63. **Physics** An object is thrown down from the top of a building 1280 feet tall with an initial velocity of 32 feet per second. The distance s (in feet) of the object from the ground after t seconds is $s = 1280 - 32t - 16t^2$.
    (a) When will the object strike ground?
    (b) What is the height of the object after 4 seconds?

64. **Working Together to Get a Job Done** Clarissa and Shawna, working together, can paint the exterior of a house in 6 days. Clarissa by herself can complete this job in 5 days less than Shawna. How long will it take Clarissa to complete the job by herself?

65. **Business: Blending Coffee** A coffee house has 20 pounds of a coffee that sells for \$4 per pound. How many pounds of a coffee that sells for \$8 per pound should be mixed with the 20 pounds of \$4-per-pound coffee to obtain a blend that will sell for \$5 per pound? How much of the \$5-per-pound coffee is there to sell?

66. **Chemistry: Salt Solutions** How much water must be evaporated from 64 ounces of a 2% salt solution to make a 10% salt solution?

67. **Geometry** The hypotenuse of a right triangle measures 13 centimeters. Find the lengths of the legs if their sum is 17 centimeters.

68. **Physics: Uniform Motion** A man is walking at an average speed of 4 miles per hour alongside a railroad track. A freight train, going in the same direction at an average speed of 30 miles per hour, requires 5 seconds to pass the man. How long is the freight train? Give your answer in feet.

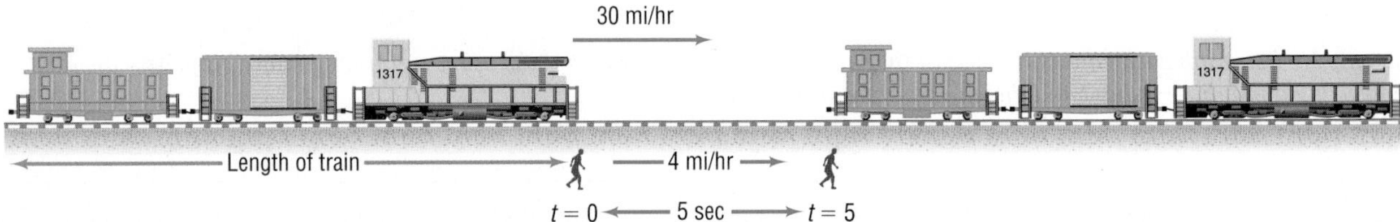

69. **Framing a Painting** An artist has 50 inches of oak trim to frame a painting. The frame is to have a border 3 inches wide surrounding the painting.
    (a) If the painting is square, what are its dimensions? What are the dimensions of the frame?
    (b) If the painting is rectangular with a length twice its width, what are the dimensions of the painting? What are the dimensions of the frame?

70. **Using Two Pumps** An 8-horsepower (hp) pump can fill a tank in 8 hours. A smaller, 3-hp pump fills the same tank in 12 hours. The pumps are used together to begin filling this tank. After 4 hours, the 8-hp pump breaks down. How long will it take the smaller pump to fill the tank?

71. **Pleasing Proportion** One formula stating the relationship between the length l and width w of a rectangle of "pleasing proportion" is $l^2 = w(l + w)$. How should a 4 foot by 8 foot sheet of plasterboard be cut so that the result is a rectangle of "pleasing proportion" with a width of 4 feet?

72. **Business: Determining the Cost of a Charter** A group of 20 senior citizens can charter a bus for a one-day excursion trip for \$15 per person. The charter company agrees to reduce the price of each ticket by 10¢ for each additional passenger in excess of 20 who goes on the trip, up to a maximum of 44 passengers (the capacity of the bus). If the final bill from the charter company was \$482.40, how many seniors went on the trip, and how much did each pay?

73. **Evening Up a Race** In a 100-meter race, Todd crosses the finish line 5 meters ahead of Scott. To even things up, Todd suggests to Scott that they race again, this time with Todd lining up 5 meters behind the start.
    (a) Assuming that Todd and Scott run at the same pace as before, does the second race end in a tie?
    (b) If not, who wins?
    (c) By how many meters does he win?
    (d) How far back should Todd start so that the race ends in a tie?

    After running the race a second time, Scott, to even things up, suggests to Todd that he (Scott) line up 5 meters in front of the start.
    (e) Assuming again that they run at the same pace as in the first race, does the third race result in a tie?
    (f) If not, who wins?
    (g) By how many meters?
    (h) How far up should Scott start so that the race ends in a tie?

74. Explain the differences among the following three problems. Are there any similarities in their solution?
(a) Write the expression as a single quotient:

$$\frac{x}{x-2}+\frac{x}{x^2-4}$$

(b) Solve: $\frac{x}{x-2}+\frac{x}{x^2-4}=0$

(c) Solve: $\frac{x}{x-2}+\frac{x}{x^2-4}<0$

CHAPTER TEST

The Chapter Test Prep Videos are step-by-step test solutions available in the Video Resources DVD, in MyMathLab, or on this text's YouTube Channel. Flip back to the Student Resources page to see the exact web address for this text's YouTube channel.

1. Suppose the points $(-2, -3)$ and $(4, 5)$ are the endpoints of a line segment.
(a) Find the distance between the two points.
(b) Find the midpoint of the line segment connecting the two points.

In Problems 2–9, solve each equation algebraically in the real number system. Answers should be exact.

2. $2x^2+6x=x-3$ **3.** $x+1=\sqrt{x+7}$

4. $2-\frac{3}{m}=\frac{2}{m+2}$ **5.** $5x-8=-4(x-1)+6$

6. $5|3-2b|-7=8$ **7.** $x^4+x^2=3x^2+8$

8. $x^2-4x+2=0$ **9.** $2x^2+x-1=x(x+7)+2$

In Problems 10 and 11, graph each equation by hand by plotting points. Use a graphing utility to approximate the intercepts and label them on the graph.

10. $2x-7y=21$ **11.** $y=x^2-5$

In Problems 12–14, use a graphing utility to approximate the real solutions of each equation rounded to two decimal places. All solutions lie between −10 and 10.

12. $2x^3-x^2-2x+1=0$

13. $x^4-5x^2-8=0$

14. $-x^3+7x-2=x^2+3x-3$

In Problems 15–18, solve each inequality. Express your answer in set-builder notation or interval notation. Graph the solution set.

15. $\frac{2x+3}{4}<-2$ **16.** $|2x+3|-4\geq 3$

17. $-7<3-5x\leq 8$ **18.** $|3x+4|<8$

In Problems 19–21, write each expression in the standard form $a+bi$.

19. $2(3-7i)-(4+11i)$ **20.** $(3+10i)(8+i)$

21. $\frac{2+i}{5-3i}$

22. Solve the equation $4x^2-4x+5=0$ in the complex number system.

23. Jamie is a cashier at a local supermarket. On average, she can check out a customer in 5 minutes. Scott, a cashier trainee, takes an average of 8.5 minutes to check out customers. How long would it take Jamie and Scott to check out 65 customers if they work together at different registers? Round to two decimal places if necessary.

24. A health food retailer sells a mixture of dried cherries, cranberries, and pecans for \$15.00 per pound and dried banana chips for \$2.25 per pound. The retailer decides to create a new mix by adding banana chips to the original mix. How many pounds of banana chips must be mixed with 40 pounds of the original mix to obtain a new mixture that sells for \$10.25 per pound with no loss in revenue? Round to two decimal places if necessary.

25. A Mountainsmith Auspex 4000 backpack originally sold for \$275.00 but is advertised at 42% off. What is the sale price of the backpack?

26. Glenn invests \$10,000 in a certificate of deposit (CD) that pays simple interest of 4% per annum. How much interest will Glenn earn after 3 months?

CHAPTER PROJECTS

Internet-based Project

I. Financing a Purchase At some point in your life you are likely going to need to borrow money to finance a purchase. For example, most of us will finance the purchase of a car or a home. What is the mathematics behind financing a purchase? When we borrow money from a bank, the bank uses a rather complex equation (or formula) to determine how much you need to pay each month to repay the loan. There are a number of variables that determine the monthly payment. These variables include the amount borrowed, the interest rate, and the length of the loan. The interest rate is determined based on current economic conditions, the length of the loan, the type of item being purchased, and your credit history. To learn how banks judge your credit worthiness, read the article "How Credit Scores Work" at *http://money.howstuffworks.com/personal-finance/debt-management/credit-score.htm*

The formula on the following page gives the monthly payment P required to pay off a loan amount L at an annual interest rate r, expressed as a decimal, but usually given as a percent. The time t, measured in months, is the length of the loan. For example, a 30-year loan requires $12 \times 30 = 360$ monthly payments.

$$P = L\left[\frac{\frac{r}{12}}{1-\left(1+\frac{r}{12}\right)^{-t}}\right]$$

P = monthly payment
L = loan amount
r = annual rate of interest, expressed as a decimal
t = length of loan, in months

1. Interest rates change daily. Many websites post current interest rates on loans. Go to *www.bankrate.com* (or some other website that posts lender's interest rates) and find the current best interest rate on a 48-month new car purchase loan. Use this rate to determine the monthly payment on a $20,000 automobile loan.
2. Determine the total amount paid for the loan by multiplying the loan payment by the term of the loan.
3. Determine the total amount of interest paid by subtracting the loan amount from the total amount paid from question 2.
4. More often than not, we decide how much of a payment we can afford and use that information to determine the loan amount. Suppose you can afford a monthly payment of $500. Use the interest rate from question 1 to determine the maximum amount you can borrow. If you have $5000 to put down on the car, what is the maximum value of a car you can purchase?
5. Repeat questions 1 through 4 using a 60-month new car purchase loan, a 48-month used car purchase loan, and a 60-month used car purchase loan.

---

6. We can use the power of a spreadsheet, such as Excel, to amortize the loan. A loan amortization schedule is a list of the monthly payments, a breakdown of interest and principal, along with a current loan balance. Create a loan amortization schedule for each of the four loan scenarios discussed above using the following as a guide. You may want to use an Internet search engine to research specific keystrokes for creating an amortization schedule in a spreadsheet. We supply a sample spreadsheet with formulas included as a guide. Use the spreadsheet to verify your results from questions 1 through 5.

Loan Information		**Payment Number**	**Payment Amount**	**Interest**	**Principal**	**Balance**	**Total Interest Paid**
Loan Amount	$20,000.00	1	=PMT($B$3/12,$B$5,−$B$2,0)	=B2*$B$3/12	=E2−F2	=B2−G2	=B2*$B$3/12
Annual Interest Rate	0.05	2	=PMT($B$3/12,$B$5,−$B$2,0)	=H2*$B$3/12	=E3−F3	=H2−G3	=I2+F3
Length of Loan (years)	4	3	=PMT($B$3/12,$B$5,−$B$2,0)	=H3*$B$3/12	=E4−F4	=H3−G4	=I3+F4
Number of Payments	=B4*12	.	.	.	.	.	.
		.	.	.	.	.	.
		.	.	.	.	.	.

7. Go to an online automobile website such as *www.cars.com*, *www.vehix.com*, or *www.autobytel.com*. Research the types of vehicles you can afford for a monthly payment of $500. Decide on a vehicle you would purchase based on your analysis in questions 1–6. Be sure to justify your decision and include the impact the term of the loan has on your decision. You might consider other factors in your decision such as expected maintenance costs and insurance costs.

Citations:

Obringer, Lee Ann. "How Credit Scores Work." 16 July 2002. HowStuffWorks.com. <http://money.howstuffworks.com/personal-finance/debt-management/credit-score.htm> 15 March 2010; Excel ©2010 Microsoft Corporation. Used with permission from Microsoft.

The following project is also available on the Instructor's Resource Center (IRC):

II. Project at Motorola How Many Cellular Phones Can I Make? An industrial engineer uses a model involving equations to be sure production levels meet customer demand.

Graphs

8

Outline

How to Value a House

Two things to consider in valuing a home are, first, how does it compare to similar homes that have sold recently? Is the asking price fair? And second, what value do you place on the advertised features and amenities? Yes, other people might value them highly, but do you?

Zestimate home valuation, RealestateABC.com, and Reply.com are among the many algorithmic (generated by a computer model) starting points in figuring out the value of a home. It shows you how the home is priced relative to other homes in the area, but you need to add in all the things that only someone who has seen the house knows. You can do that using My Estimator, and then you create your own estimate and see how it stacks up against the asking price.

Looking at "Comps"

Knowing whether an asking price is fair will be important when you're ready to make an offer on a house. It will be even more important when your mortgage lender hires an appraiser to determine whether the house is worth the loan you're after.

Check with your agent, Zillow.com, propertyshark.com, or other websites to see recent sales of homes in the area that are similar, or comparable, to what you're looking for. Print them out and keep these "comps" in a three-ring binder; you'll be referring to them quite a bit.

Note that "recent sales" usually means within the last six months. A sales price from a year ago may bear little or no relation to what is going on in your area right now. In fact, some lenders will not accept comps older than three months.

Market activity also determines how easy or difficult it is to find accurate comps. In a "hot" or busy market, with sales happening all the time, you're likely to have lots of comps to choose from. In a less active market, finding reasonable comps becomes harder. And if the home you're looking at has special design features, finding a comparable property is harder still. It's also necessary to know what's going on in a given sub-segment. Maybe large, high-end homes are selling like hotcakes, but owners of smaller houses are staying put, or vice versa.

Source: *http://realestate.yahoo.com/Homevalues/How_to_Value_a_House.html*

—See the Internet-based Chapter Project—

A LOOK BACK In Chapter 7 we introduced the Cartesian plane to graph equations in two variables and studied equations in one variable.

A LOOK AHEAD Now we will continue our discussion of the Cartesian plane by introducing additional techniques that can be used to obtain the graph of an equation with two variables. We also introduce two specific graphs: lines and circles. We conclude the chapter by looking at variation.

8.1 Intercepts; Symmetry; Graphing Key Equations

PREPARING FOR THIS SECTION *Before getting started, review the following:*

- Introduction to Graphing Equations (Section 7.1, pp. 465–469)
- Solving Quadratic Equations (Section 7.2, pp. 476–482)
- Finding Intercepts Using a Graphing Utility (Section 7.1, p. 471)
- Finding Intercepts from a Graph (Section 7.1, pp. 470–471)

Now Work the **'Are You Prepared?'** problems on page 527.

OBJECTIVES
1 Find Intercepts Algebraically from an Equation (p. 522)
2 Test an Equation for Symmetry (p. 523)
3 Know How to Graph Key Equations (p. 525)

1 Find Intercepts Algebraically from an Equation

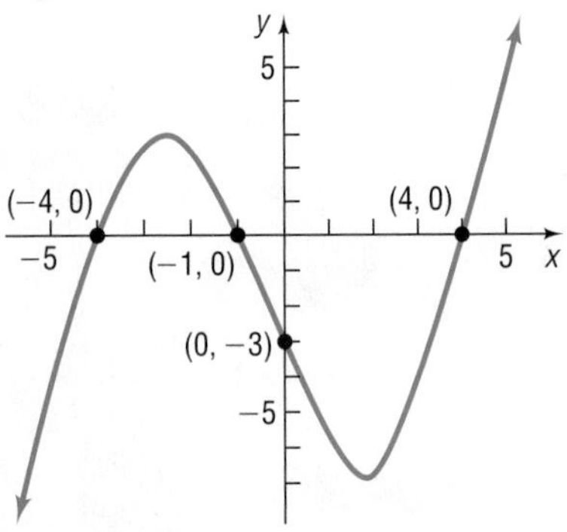

In Section 7.1, we discussed how to find intercepts from a graph and how to approximate intercepts from an equation using a graphing utility. Now we discuss how to find intercepts from an equation algebraically. To help understand the procedure, we present Figure 1. From the graph, we can see that the intercepts are $(-4, 0)$, $(-1, 0)$, $(4, 0)$, and $(0, -3)$. The x-intercepts are $-4, -1$, and 4. The y-intercept is -3. Notice that x-intercepts have y-coordinates that equal 0; y-intercepts have x-coordinates that equal 0. This leads to the following procedure for finding intercepts.

Figure 1

Procedure for Finding Intercepts

1. To find the x-intercept(s), if any, of the graph of an equation, let $y = 0$ in the equation and solve for x, where x is a real number.
2. To find the y-intercept(s), if any, of the graph of an equation, let $x = 0$ in the equation and solve for y, where y is a real number.

EXAMPLE 1 **Finding Intercepts from an Equation**

Find the x-intercept(s) and the y-intercept(s) of the graph of $y = x^2 - 4$. Then graph $y = x^2 - 4$ by plotting points.

Solution To find the x-intercept(s), let $y = 0$ and obtain the equation

$$x^2 - 4 = 0 \quad y = x^2 - 4 \text{ with } y = 0$$

$$(x + 2)(x - 2) = 0 \quad \text{Factor.}$$

$$x + 2 = 0 \quad \text{or} \quad x - 2 = 0 \quad \text{Zero-Product Property}$$

$$x = -2 \quad \text{or} \quad x = 2 \quad \text{Solve.}$$

The equation has two solutions, -2 and 2. The x-intercepts are -2 and 2.

To find the y-intercept(s), let $x = 0$ in the equation.

$$y = x^2 - 4$$
$$= 0^2 - 4 = -4$$

The y-intercept is -4.

Since $x^2 \geq 0$ for all x, we deduce from the equation $y = x^2 - 4$ that $y \geq -4$ for all x. This information, the intercepts, and the points from Table 1 enable us to graph $y = x^2 - 4$ by hand. See Figure 2.

Table 1

x	$y = x^2 - 4$	(x, y)
-3	$(-3)^2 - 4 = 5$	$(-3, 5)$
-1	-3	$(-1, -3)$
1	-3	$(1, -3)$
3	5	$(3, 5)$

Figure 2

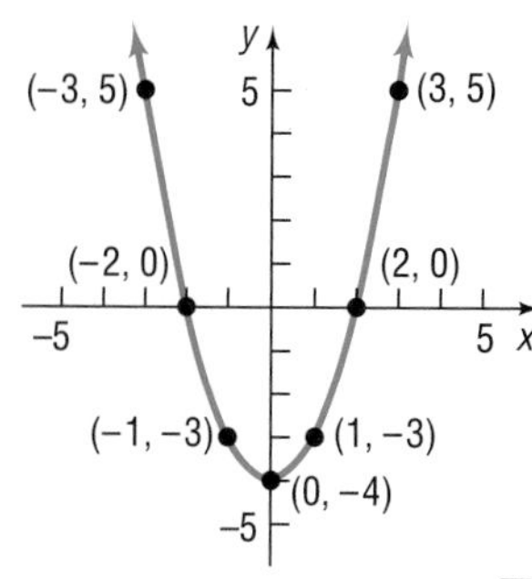

■

Now Work PROBLEM 15

2 Test an Equation for Symmetry

Another helpful tool for graphing equations by hand involves *symmetry,* particularly symmetry with respect to the x-axis, the y-axis, and the origin.

Symmetry often occurs in nature. Consider the picture of the butterfly. Do you see the symmetry?

DEFINITION

A graph is said to be **symmetric with respect to the x-axis** if, for every point (x, y) on the graph, the point $(x, -y)$ is also on the graph.

A graph is said to be **symmetric with respect to the y-axis** if, for every point (x, y) on the graph, the point $(-x, y)$ is also on the graph.

A graph is said to be **symmetric with respect to the origin** if, for every point (x, y) on the graph, the point $(-x, -y)$ is also on the graph.

Figure 3 illustrates the definition. Notice that, when a graph is symmetric with respect to the x-axis, the part of the graph above the x-axis is a reflection or mirror image of the part below it, and vice versa. When a graph is symmetric with respect to the y-axis, the part of the graph to the right of the y-axis is a reflection of the part to the left of it, and vice versa. Symmetry with respect to the origin may be viewed in two ways:

1. As a reflection about the y-axis, followed by a reflection about the x-axis
2. As a projection along a line through the origin so that the distances from the origin are equal

Figure 3

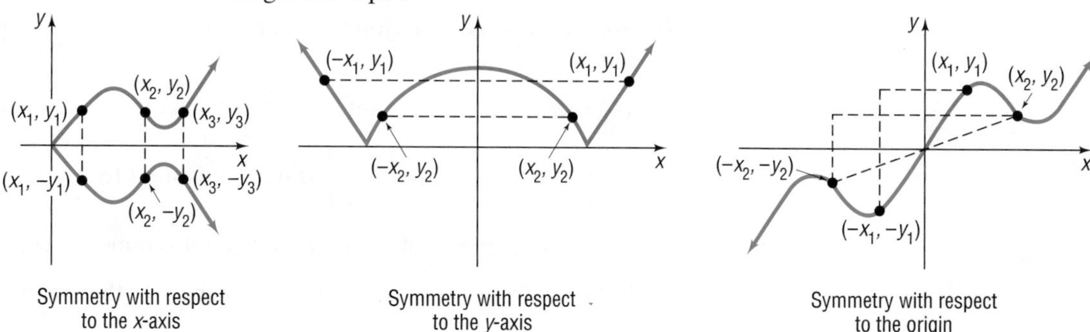

EXAMPLE 2 Symmetric Points

(a) If a graph is symmetric with respect to the x-axis and the point $(4, 2)$ is on the graph, then the point $(4, -2)$ is also on the graph.

(b) If a graph is symmetric with respect to the y-axis and the point $(4, 2)$ is on the graph, then the point $(-4, 2)$ is also on the graph.

(c) If a graph is symmetric with respect to the origin and the point $(4, 2)$ is on the graph, then the point $(-4, -2)$ is also on the graph. ■

Now Work PROBLEM 23

When the graph of an equation is symmetric with respect to the x-axis, the y-axis, or the origin, the number of points that you need to plot in order to see the pattern is reduced. For example, if the graph of an equation is symmetric with respect to the y-axis, then, once points to the right of the y-axis are plotted, an equal number of points on the graph can be obtained by reflecting them about the y-axis. Because of this, before we graph an equation, we first want to determine whether it has any symmetry. The following tests are used for this purpose.

Tests for Symmetry

To test the graph of an equation for symmetry with respect to the

x-Axis Replace y by $-y$ in the equation. If an equivalent equation results, the graph of the equation is symmetric with respect to the x-axis.

y-Axis Replace x by $-x$ in the equation. If an equivalent equation results, the graph of the equation is symmetric with respect to the y-axis.

Origin Replace x by $-x$ and y by $-y$ in the equation. If an equivalent equation results, the graph of the equation is symmetric with respect to the origin.

EXAMPLE 3 Finding Intercepts and Testing an Equation for Symmetry

For the equation $y = \dfrac{x^2 - 4}{x^2 + 1}$: (a) find the intercepts and (b) test for symmetry.

Solution (a) To obtain the x-intercept(s), let $y = 0$ in the equation and solve for x.

$$\frac{x^2 - 4}{x^2 + 1} = 0 \quad \text{Let } y = 0.$$

$$x^2 - 4 = 0 \quad \text{Multiply both sides by } x^2 + 1.$$

$$x = -2 \quad \text{or} \quad x = 2 \quad \text{Factor and use the Zero-Product Property.}$$

To obtain the y-intercept(s), let $x = 0$ in the equation and solve for y.

$$y = \frac{x^2 - 4}{x^2 + 1} = \frac{0^2 - 4}{0^2 + 1} = \frac{-4}{1} = -4$$

The x-intercepts are -2 and 2; the y-intercept is -4.

(b) We now test the equation for symmetry with respect to the x-axis, the y-axis, and the origin.

x-Axis: To test for symmetry with respect to the x-axis, replace y by $-y$. Since

$$-y = \frac{x^2 - 4}{x^2 + 1} \text{ is not equivalent to } y = \frac{x^2 - 4}{x^2 + 1}$$

the graph of the equation is not symmetric with respect to the x-axis.

y-Axis: To test for symmetry with respect to the y-axis, replace x by $-x$. Since

$$y = \frac{(-x)^2 - 4}{(-x)^2 + 1} = \frac{x^2 - 4}{x^2 + 1} \text{ is equivalent to } y = \frac{x^2 - 4}{x^2 + 1}$$

the graph of the equation is symmetric with respect to the y-axis.

Origin: To test for symmetry with respect to the origin, replace x by $-x$ and y by $-y$.

$$-y = \frac{(-x)^2 - 4}{(-x)^2 + 1} \quad \text{Replace } x \text{ by } -x \text{ and } y \text{ by } -y.$$

$$-y = \frac{x^2 - 4}{x^2 + 1} \quad \text{Simplify.}$$

Since the result is not equivalent to the original equation, the graph of the equation $y = \frac{x^2 - 4}{x^2 + 1}$ is not symmetric with respect to the origin. ■

Seeing the Concept

Figure 4

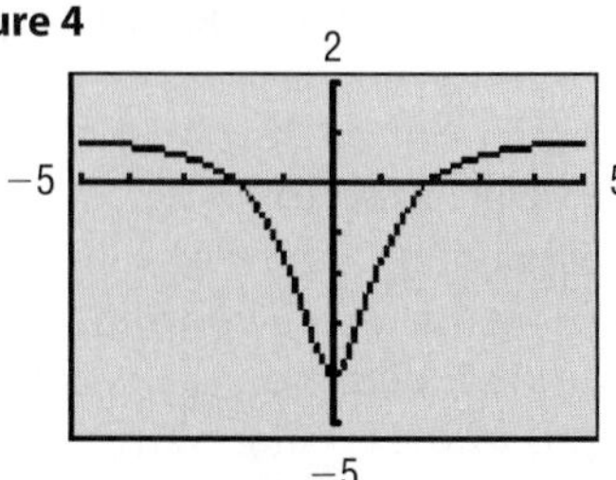

Figure 4 shows the graph of $y = \frac{x^2 - 4}{x^2 + 1}$ using a graphing utility. Do you see the symmetry with respect to the *y*-axis? Also, did you notice that the point (2, 0) is on the graph along with (−2, 0)? How could we have found the second *x*-intercept using symmetry?

Now Work PROBLEM 49

3 Know How to Graph Key Equations

There are certain equations whose graphs we should be able to easily visualize in our mind's eye. For example, you should know the graph of $y = x^2$ discussed in Example 8 in Section 7.1. The next three examples use intercepts, symmetry, and point plotting to obtain the graphs of additional key equations. It is important to know the graphs of these key equations because we use them later.

EXAMPLE 4 Graphing the Equation $y = x^3$ by Finding Intercepts and Checking for Symmetry

Graph the equation $y = x^3$ by hand by plotting points. Find any intercepts and check for symmetry first.

Solution First, find the intercepts of $y = x^3$. When $x = 0$, then $y = 0$; and when $y = 0$, then $x = 0$. The origin (0, 0) is the only intercept. Now test $y = x^3$ for symmetry.

x-Axis: Replace y by $-y$. Since $-y = x^3$ is not equivalent to $y = x^3$, the graph is not symmetric with respect to the *x*-axis.

y-Axis: Replace x by $-x$. Since $y = (-x)^3 = -x^3$ is not equivalent to $y = x^3$, the graph is not symmetric with respect to the *y*-axis.

Origin: Replace x by $-x$ and y by $-y$. Since $-y = (-x)^3 = -x^3$ is equivalent to $y = x^3$ (multiply both sides by −1), the graph is symmetric with respect to the origin.

Figure 5

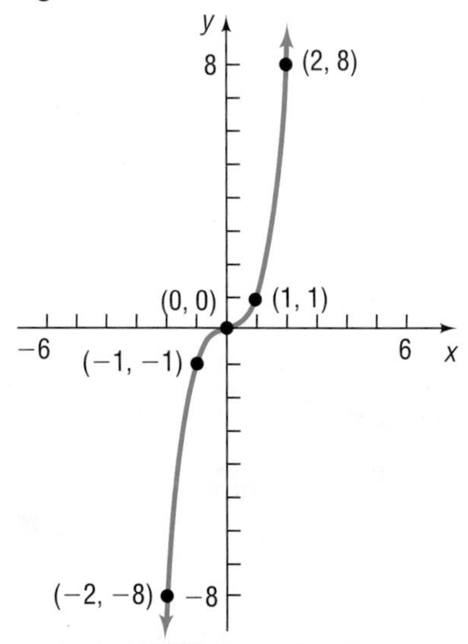

To graph by hand, use the equation to obtain several points on the graph. Because of the symmetry with respect to the origin, we only need to locate points on the graph for which $x \geq 0$. See Table 2. Points on the graph could also be obtained using the TABLE feature on a graphing utility. See Table 3. Do you see the symmetry with respect to the origin from the table? Figure 5 shows the graph.

Table 2

x	$y = x^3$	(x, y)
0	0	(0, 0)
1	1	(1, 1)
2	8	(2, 8)
3	27	(3, 27)

Table 3

X	Y1
-3	-27
-2	-8
-1	-1
0	0
1	1
2	8
3	27

Y1=X^3

■

EXAMPLE 5 Graphing the Equation $x = y^2$

(a) Graph the equation $x = y^2$. Find any intercepts and check for symmetry first.
(b) Graph $x = y^2$ where $y \geq 0$.

Solution (a) The lone intercept is $(0, 0)$. The graph is symmetric with respect to the x-axis since $x = (-y)^2$ is equivalent to $x = y^2$. The graph is not symmetric with respect to the y-axis or the origin.

To graph $x = y^2$ by hand, use the equation to obtain several points on the graph. Because the equation is solved for x, it is easier to assign values to y and use the equation to determine the corresponding values of x. Because of the symmetry, we can restrict ourselves to points whose y-coordinates are nonnegative. Then use the symmetry to find additional points on the graph. See Table 4. For example, since $(1, 1)$ is on the graph, so is $(1, -1)$. Since $(4, 2)$ is on the graph, so is $(4, -2)$, and so on. Plot these points and connect them with a smooth curve to obtain Figure 6.

Table 4

y	$x = y^2$	(x, y)
0	0	(0, 0)
1	1	(1, 1)
2	4	(4, 2)
3	9	(9, 3)

Figure 6

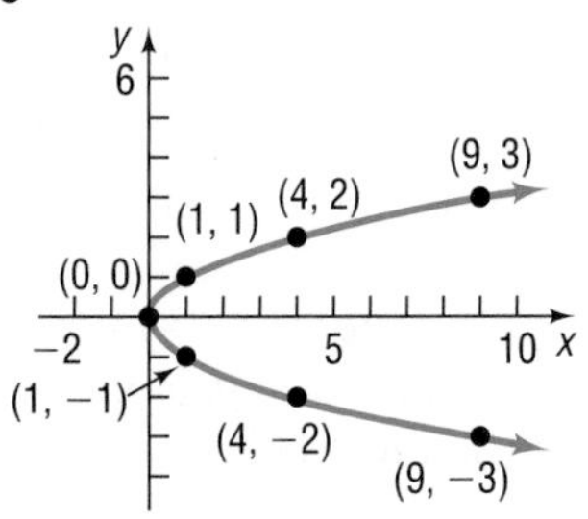

To graph the equation $x = y^2$ using a graphing utility, write the equation in the form $y = \{\text{expression in } x\}$. We proceed to solve for y.

$$x = y^2$$
$$y^2 = x$$
$$y = \pm\sqrt{x} \quad \text{Square Root Method}$$

To graph $x = y^2$, graph both $Y_1 = \sqrt{x}$ and $Y_2 = -\sqrt{x}$ on the same screen. Figure 7 shows the result. Table 5 shows various values of y for a given value of x when $Y_1 = \sqrt{x}$ and $Y_2 = -\sqrt{x}$. Notice that when $x < 0$ we get an error. Can you explain why?

Figure 7

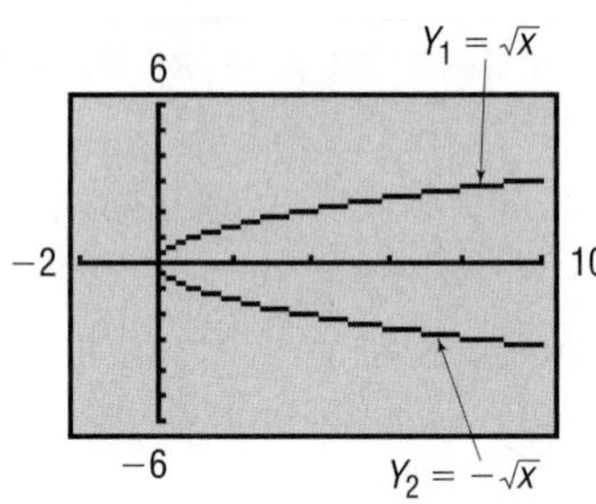

Table 5

X	Y1	Y2
-1	ERROR	ERROR
0	0	0
1	1	-1
2	1.4142	-1.414
3	1.7321	-1.732
4	2	-2
5	2.2361	-2.236

Y1=√(X)

(b) If we restrict y so that $y \geq 0$, the equation $x = y^2, y \geq 0$, may be written as $y = \sqrt{x}$. The portion of the graph of $x = y^2$ in quadrant I plus the origin is the graph of $y = \sqrt{x}$. See Figure 8.

Figure 8

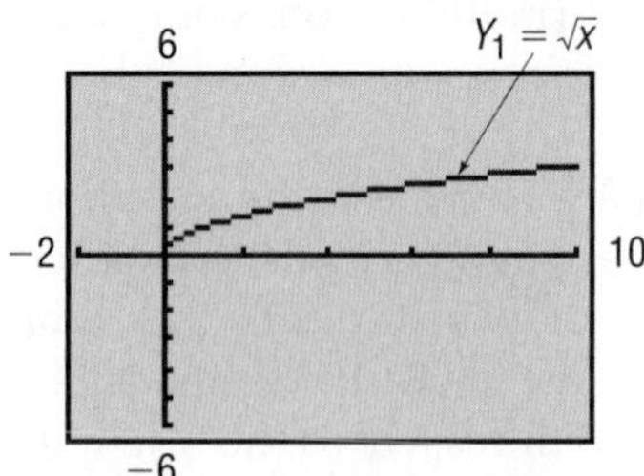

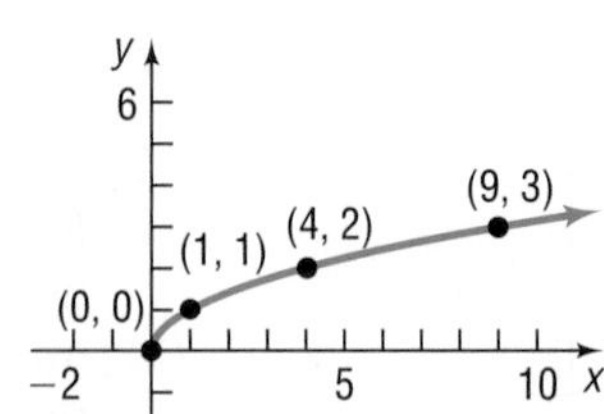

■

EXAMPLE 6 Graphing the Equation $y = \dfrac{1}{x}$

Graph the equation $y = \dfrac{1}{x}$. Find any intercepts and check for symmetry first.

Solution Check for intercepts first. If we let $x = 0$, we obtain a 0 in the denominator, which is not defined. We conclude that there is no y-intercept. If we let $y = 0$, we get the equation $\frac{1}{x} = 0$, which has no solution. We conclude that there is no x-intercept. The graph of $y = \frac{1}{x}$ does not cross or touch the coordinate axes.

Next check for symmetry.

x-Axis: Replacing y by $-y$ yields $-y = \frac{1}{x}$, which is not equivalent to $y = \frac{1}{x}$.

y-Axis: Replacing x by $-x$ yields $y = \frac{1}{-x} = -\frac{1}{x}$, which is not equivalent to $y = \frac{1}{x}$.

Origin: Replacing x by $-x$ and y by $-y$ yields $-y = -\frac{1}{x}$, which is equivalent to $y = \frac{1}{x}$. The graph is symmetric only with respect to the origin.

Table 6

x	$y = \frac{1}{x}$	(x, y)
$\frac{1}{10}$	10	$\left(\frac{1}{10}, 10\right)$
$\frac{1}{3}$	3	$\left(\frac{1}{3}, 3\right)$
$\frac{1}{2}$	2	$\left(\frac{1}{2}, 2\right)$
1	1	$(1, 1)$
2	$\frac{1}{2}$	$\left(2, \frac{1}{2}\right)$
3	$\frac{1}{3}$	$\left(3, \frac{1}{3}\right)$
10	$\frac{1}{10}$	$\left(10, \frac{1}{10}\right)$

Use the equation to form Table 6 and obtain some points on the graph. Because of symmetry, we only find points (x, y) for which x is positive. From Table 6 we infer that, if x is a large and positive number, then $y = \frac{1}{x}$ is a positive number close to 0. We also infer that if x is a positive number close to 0 then $y = \frac{1}{x}$ is a large and positive number. Armed with this information, we can graph the equation. Figure 9 illustrates some of these points and the graph of $y = \frac{1}{x}$. Observe how the absence of intercepts and the existence of symmetry with respect to the origin were utilized. Figure 10 confirms our algebraic analysis using a TI-84 Plus.

Figure 9

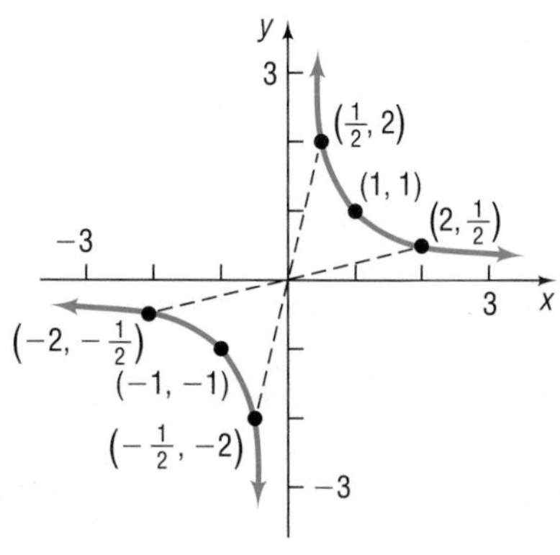

Figure 10

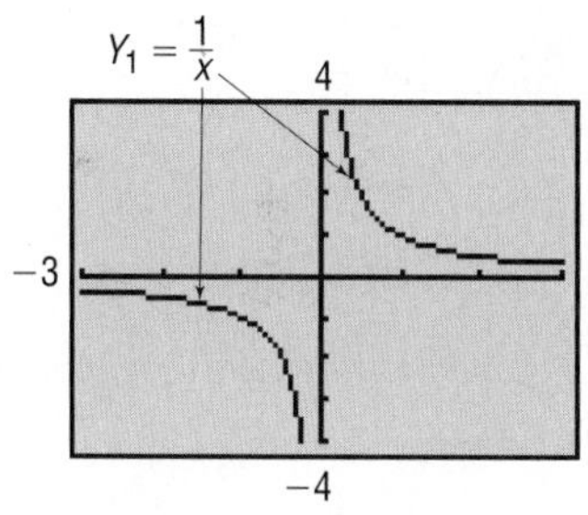

8.1 Assess Your Understanding

'Are You Prepared?' *Answers are given at the end of these exercises. If you get a wrong answer, read the pages listed in red.*

1. Graph $y = 2x - 4$ by plotting points. Based on the graph, determine the intercepts. (pp. 465–471)

2. Solve: $x^2 - 4x - 12 = 0$ (pp. 476–477)

Concepts and Vocabulary

3. The points, if any, at which a graph crosses or touches the coordinate axes are called ________.

4. The x-intercepts of the graph of an equation are those x-values for which ________.

5. If for every point (x, y) on the graph of an equation the point $(-x, y)$ is also on the graph, then the graph is symmetric with respect to the ________.

6. If the graph of an equation is symmetric with respect to the y-axis and -4 is an x-intercept of this graph, then ______ is also an x-intercept.

7. If the graph of an equation is symmetric with respect to the origin and $(3, -4)$ is a point on the graph, then ______ is also a point on the graph.

8. ***True or False*** To find the y-intercepts of the graph of an equation, let $x = 0$ and solve for y.

9. ***True or False*** The y-coordinate of a point at which the graph crosses or touches the x-axis is an x-intercept.

10. ***True or False*** If a graph is symmetric with respect to the x-axis, then it cannot be symmetric with respect to the y-axis.

Skill Building

In Problems 11–22, find the intercepts and graph each equation by plotting points. Be sure to label the intercepts.

11. $y = x + 2$ **12.** $y = x - 6$ **13.** $y = 2x + 8$ **14.** $y = 3x - 9$

15. $y = x^2 - 1$ **16.** $y = x^2 - 9$ **17.** $y = -x^2 + 4$ **18.** $y = -x^2 + 1$

19. $2x + 3y = 6$ **20.** $5x + 2y = 10$ **21.** $9x^2 + 4y = 36$ **22.** $4x^2 + y = 4$

In Problems 23–32, plot each point. Then plot the point that is symmetric to it with respect to (a) the x-axis; (b) the y-axis; (c) the origin.

23. $(3, 4)$ **24.** $(5, 3)$ **25.** $(-2, 1)$ **26.** $(4, -2)$ **27.** $(5, -2)$

28. $(-1, -1)$ **29.** $(-3, -4)$ **30.** $(4, 0)$ **31.** $(0, -3)$ **32.** $(-3, 0)$

In Problems 33–40, the graph of an equation is given. (a) Find the intercepts. (b) Indicate whether the graph is symmetric with respect to the x-axis, the y-axis, or the origin.

33.

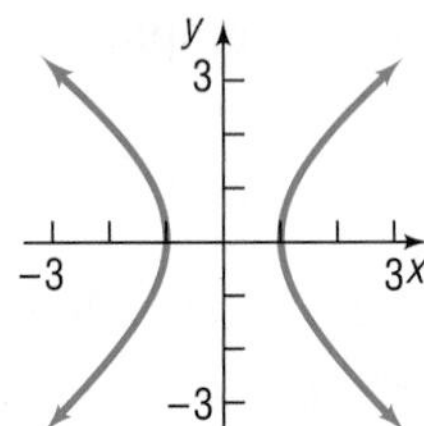

34.

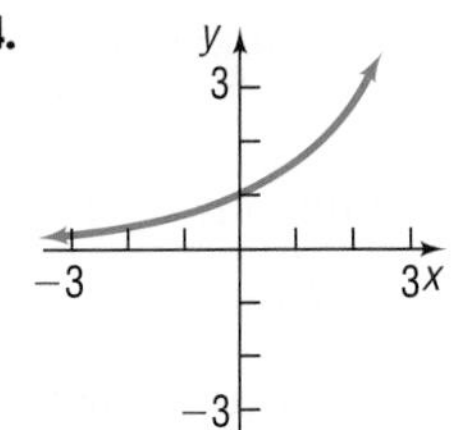

35.

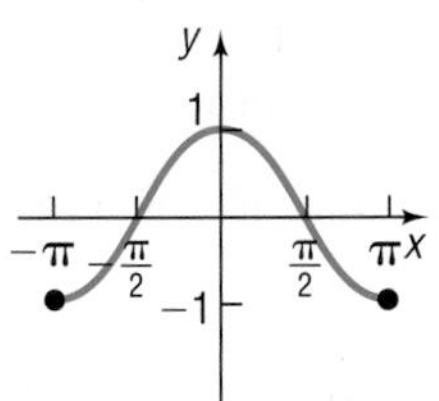

36.

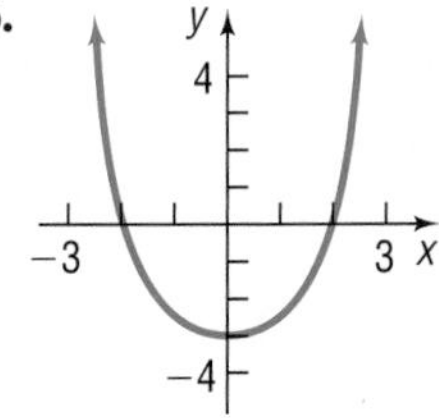

37.

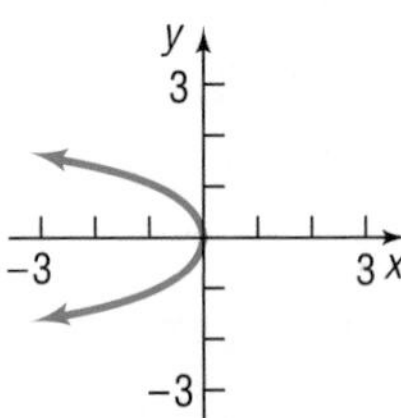

38.

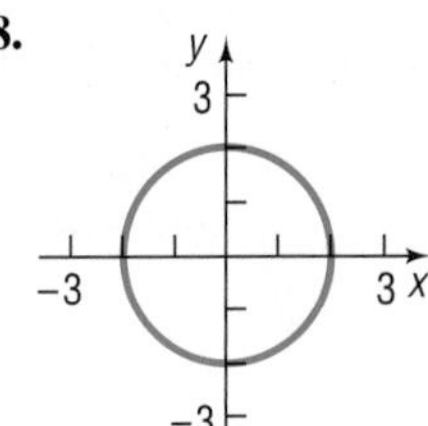

39.

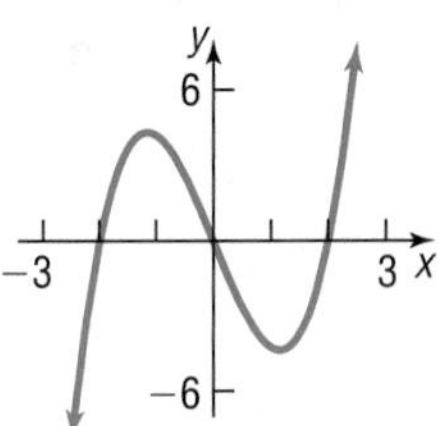

40.

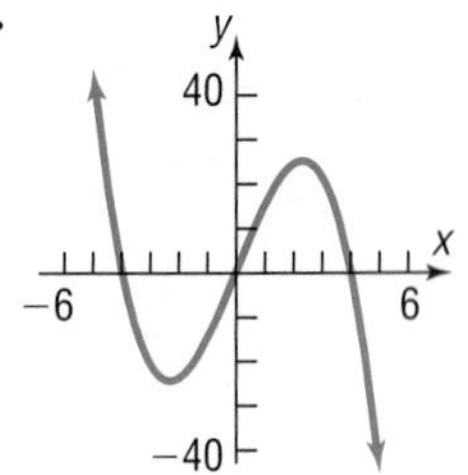

In Problems 41–44, draw a complete graph so that it has the type of symmetry indicated.

41. y-axis

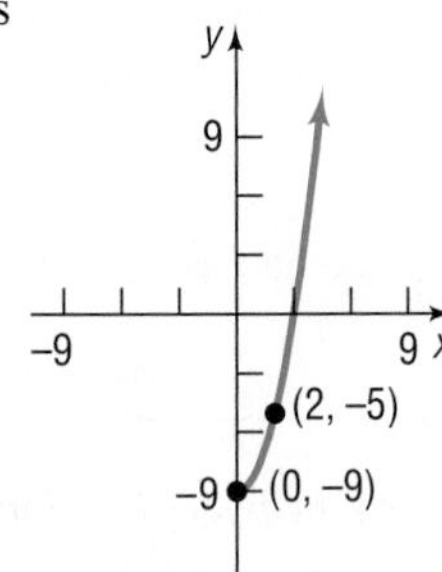

42. x-axis

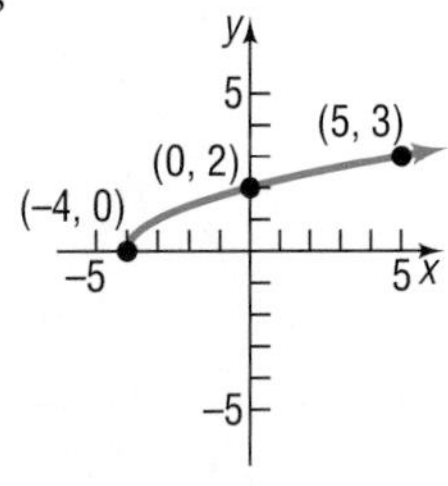

43. Origin

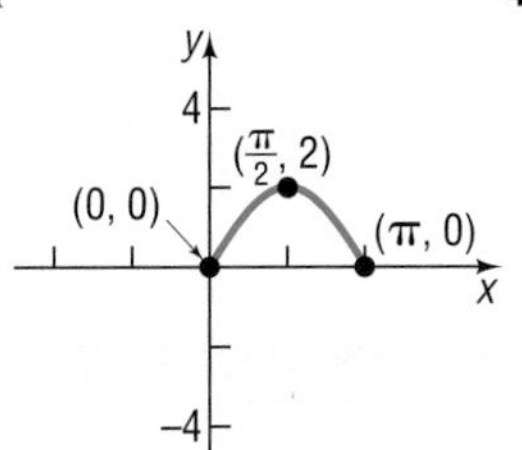

44. y-axis

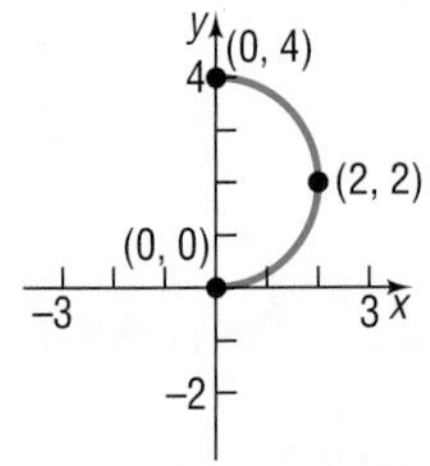

In Problems 45–60, list the intercepts and test for symmetry.

45. $y^2 = x + 4$ **46.** $y^2 = x + 9$ **47.** $y = \sqrt[3]{x}$ **48.** $y = \sqrt[5]{x}$

49. $y = x^4 - 8x^2 - 9$ **50.** $y = x^4 - 2x^2 - 8$ **51.** $9x^2 + 4y^2 = 36$ **52.** $4x^2 + y^2 = 4$

53. $y = x^3 - 27$ **54.** $y = x^4 - 1$ **55.** $y = x^2 - 3x - 4$ **56.** $y = x^2 + 4$

57. $y = \dfrac{3x}{x^2 + 9}$ **58.** $y = \dfrac{x^2 - 4}{2x}$ **59.** $y = \dfrac{-x^3}{x^2 - 9}$ **60.** $y = \dfrac{x^4 + 1}{2x^5}$

In Problems 61–64, draw a quick sketch of each equation.

61. $y = x^3$ **62.** $x = y^2$ **63.** $y = \sqrt{x}$ **64.** $y = \dfrac{1}{x}$

65. If $(3, b)$ is a point on the graph of $y = 4x + 1$, what is b?

66. If $(-2, b)$ is a point on the graph of $2x + 3y = 2$, what is b?

67. If $(a, 4)$ is a point on the graph of $y = x^2 + 3x$, what is a?

68. If $(a, -5)$ is a point on the graph of $y = x^2 + 6x$, what is a?

Mixed Practice

In Problems 69–76, (a) find the intercepts of each equation, (b) test each equation for symmetry with respect to the x-axis, the y-axis, and the origin, and (c) graph each equation by hand by plotting points. Be sure to label the intercepts on the graph and use any symmetry to assist in drawing the graph. Verify your results using a graphing utility.

69. $y = x^2 - 5$ **70.** $y = x^2 - 8$ **71.** $x - y^2 = -9$ **72.** $x + y^2 = 4$

73. $x^2 + y^2 = 9$ **74.** $x^2 + y^2 = 16$ **75.** $y = x^3 - 4x$ **76.** $y = x^3 - x$

Applications and Extensions

77. Given that the point $(1, 2)$ is on the graph of an equation that is symmetric with respect to the origin, what other point is on the graph?

78. If the graph of an equation is symmetric with respect to the y-axis and 6 is an x-intercept of this graph, name another x-intercept.

79. If the graph of an equation is symmetric with respect to the origin and -4 is an x-intercept of this graph, name another x-intercept.

80. If the graph of an equation is symmetric with respect to the x-axis and 2 is a y-intercept, name another y-intercept.

81. Microphones In studios and on stages, cardioid microphones are often preferred for the richness they add to voices and for their ability to reduce the level of sound from the sides and rear of the microphone. Suppose one such cardioid pattern is given by the equation $(x^2 + y^2 - x)^2 = x^2 + y^2$.

(a) Find the intercepts of the graph of the equation.

(b) Test for symmetry with respect to the x-axis, y-axis, and origin.

Source: www.notaviva.com

82. Solar Energy The solar electric generating systems at Kramer Junction, California, use parabolic troughs to heat a heat-transfer fluid to a high temperature. This fluid is used to generate steam that drives a power conversion system to produce electricity. For troughs 7.5 feet wide, an equation for the cross-section is $16y^2 = 120x - 225$.

(a) Find the intercepts of the graph of the equation.

(b) Test for symmetry with respect to the x-axis, y-axis, and origin.

Source: U.S. Department of Energy

Explaining Concepts: Discussion and Writing

83. (a) Graph $y = \sqrt{x^2}$, $y = x$, $y = |x|$, and $y = (\sqrt{x})^2$, noting which graphs are the same.

(b) Explain why the graphs of $y = \sqrt{x^2}$ and $y = |x|$ are the same.

(c) Explain why the graphs of $y = x$ and $y = (\sqrt{x})^2$ are not the same.

(d) Explain why the graphs of $y = \sqrt{x^2}$ and $y = x$ are not the same.

84. Explain what is meant by a complete graph.

85. Draw a graph of an equation that contains two x-intercepts; at one the graph crosses the x-axis, and at the other the graph touches the x-axis.

86. Make up an equation with the intercepts $(2, 0)$, $(4, 0)$, and $(0, 1)$. Compare your equation with a friend's equation. Comment on any similarities.

87. Draw a graph that contains the points $(-2, -1)$, $(0, 1)$, $(1, 3)$, and $(3, 5)$. Compare your graph with those of other students. Are most of the graphs almost straight lines? How many are "curved"? Discuss the various ways that these points might be connected.

88. An equation is being tested for symmetry with respect to the x-axis, the y-axis, and the origin. Explain why, if two of these symmetries are present, the remaining one must also be present.

89. Draw a graph that contains the points $(-2, 5)$, $(-1, 3)$, and $(0, 2)$ that is symmetric with respect to the y-axis. Compare your graph with those of other students; comment on any similarities. Can a graph contain these points and be symmetric with respect to the x-axis? the origin? Why or why not?

Interactive Exercises

Ask your instructor if the applets below are of interest to you.

90. y-axis Symmetry *Open the y-axis symmetry applet.* Move point A around the Cartesian plane with your mouse. How are the coordinates of point A and the coordinates of point B related?

91. x-axis Symmetry *Open the x-axis symmetry applet.* Move point A around the Cartesian plane with your mouse. How are the coordinates of point A and the coordinates of point B related?

92. Origin Symmetry *Open the origin symmetry applet.* Move point A around the Cartesian plane with your mouse. How are the coordinates of point A and the coordinates of point B related?

'Are You Prepared?' Answers

1.

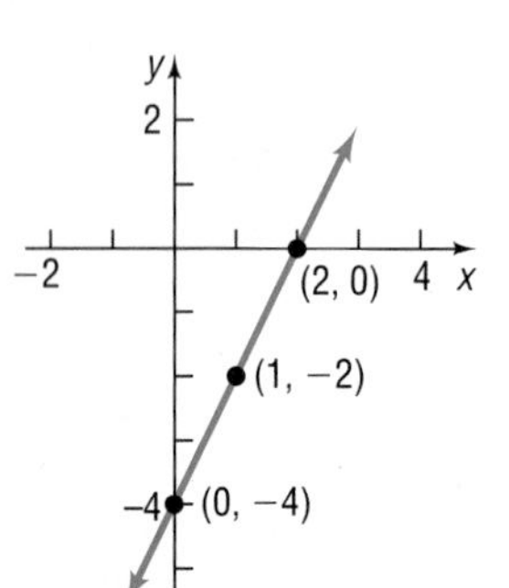

x-intercept: 2; y-intercept: −4

2. $\{-2, 6\}$

8.2 Lines

OBJECTIVES

1 Calculate and Interpret the Slope of a Line (p. 530)
2 Graph Lines Given a Point and the Slope (p. 533)
3 Find the Equation of a Vertical Line (p. 533)
4 Use the Point–Slope Form of a Line; Identify Horizontal Lines (p. 534)
5 Find the Equation of a Line Given Two Points (p. 535)
6 Write the Equation of a Line in Slope–Intercept Form (p. 535)
7 Identify the Slope and y-Intercept of a Line from Its Equation (p. 536)
8 Graph Lines Written in General Form Using Intercepts (p. 537)
9 Find Equations of Parallel Lines (p. 538)
10 Find Equations of Perpendicular Lines (p. 539)

In this section we study a certain type of equation that contains two variables, called a *linear equation,* and its graph, a *line.*

1 Calculate and Interpret the Slope of a Line

Figure 11

Consider the staircase illustrated in Figure 11. Each step contains exactly the same horizontal **run** and the same vertical **rise.** The ratio of the rise to the run, called the *slope*, is a numerical measure of the steepness of the staircase. For example, if the run is increased and the rise remains the same, the staircase becomes less steep. If the run is kept the same, but the rise is increased, the staircase becomes more steep. This important characteristic of a line is best defined using rectangular coordinates.

DEFINITION

Let $P = (x_1, y_1)$ and $Q = (x_2, y_2)$ be two distinct points. If $x_1 \neq x_2$, the **slope** ***m*** of the nonvertical line L containing P and Q is defined by the formula

$$m = \frac{y_2 - y_1}{x_2 - x_1} \qquad x_1 \neq x_2 \tag{1}$$

If $x_1 = x_2$, L is a **vertical line** and the slope m of L is **undefined** (since this results in division by 0).

Figure 12(a) provides an illustration of the slope of a nonvertical line; Figure 12(b) illustrates a vertical line.

Figure 12

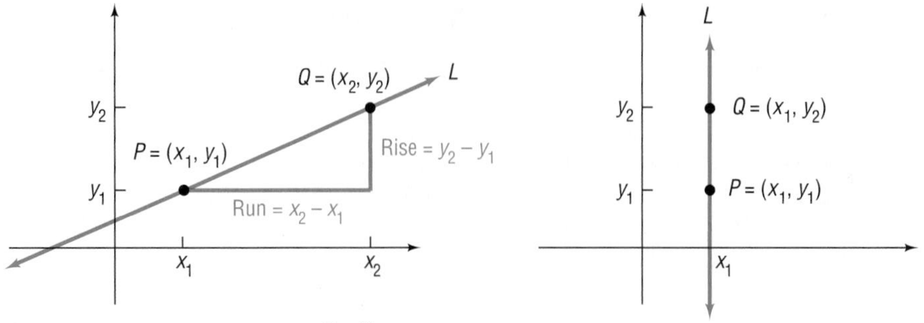

(a) Slope of L is $m = \dfrac{y_2 - y_1}{x_2 - x_1}$

(b) Slope is undefined; L is vertical

In Words

The symbol Δ is the Greek letter delta. In mathematics, we read Δ as "change in," so $\dfrac{\Delta y}{\Delta x}$ is read, "change in y divided by change in x."

As Figure 12(a) illustrates, the slope m of a nonvertical line may be viewed as

$$m = \frac{y_2 - y_1}{x_2 - x_1} = \frac{\text{Rise}}{\text{Run}} \quad \text{or} \quad m = \frac{y_2 - y_1}{x_2 - x_1} = \frac{\text{Change in } y}{\text{Change in } x} = \frac{\Delta y}{\Delta x}$$

That is, the slope m of a nonvertical line measures the amount y changes when x changes from x_1 to x_2. The expression $\dfrac{\Delta y}{\Delta x}$ is called the **average rate of change** of y, with respect to x.

Two comments about computing the slope of a nonvertical line may prove helpful:

1. Any two distinct points on the line can be used to compute the slope of the line. (See Figure 13 for justification.)

Figure 13

Triangles ABC and PQR are similar (equal angles), so ratios of corresponding sides are equal. Then

Slope using P and $Q = \dfrac{y_2 - y_1}{x_2 - x_1} = \dfrac{d(B, C)}{d(A, C)} =$ Slope using A and B

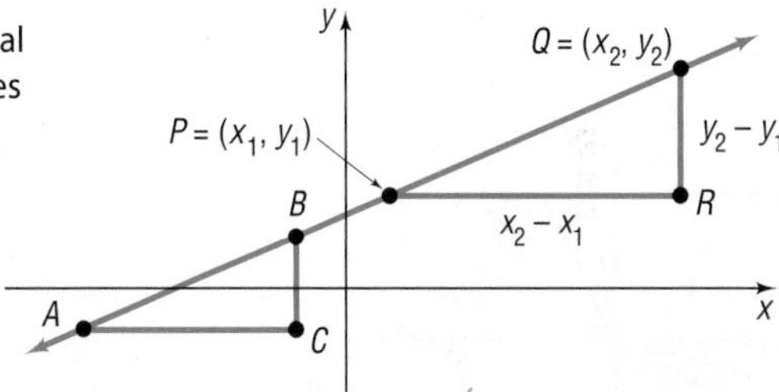

Since any two distinct points can be used to compute the slope of a line, the average rate of change of a line is always the same number.

2. The slope of a line may be computed from $P = (x_1, y_1)$ to $Q = (x_2, y_2)$ or from Q to P because

$$\frac{y_2 - y_1}{x_2 - x_1} = \frac{y_1 - y_2}{x_1 - x_2}$$

EXAMPLE 1 Finding and Interpreting the Slope of a Line Given Two Points

The slope m of the line containing the points $(1, 2)$ and $(5, -3)$ may be computed as

$$m = \frac{-3 - 2}{5 - 1} = \frac{-5}{4} = -\frac{5}{4} \quad \text{or as} \quad m = \frac{2 - (-3)}{1 - 5} = \frac{5}{-4} = -\frac{5}{4}$$

For every 4-unit change in x, y will change by -5 units. That is, if x increases by 4 units, then y will decrease by 5 units. The average rate of change of y with respect to x is $-\dfrac{5}{4}$. ■

Now Work PROBLEMS 11 AND 17

Figure 14

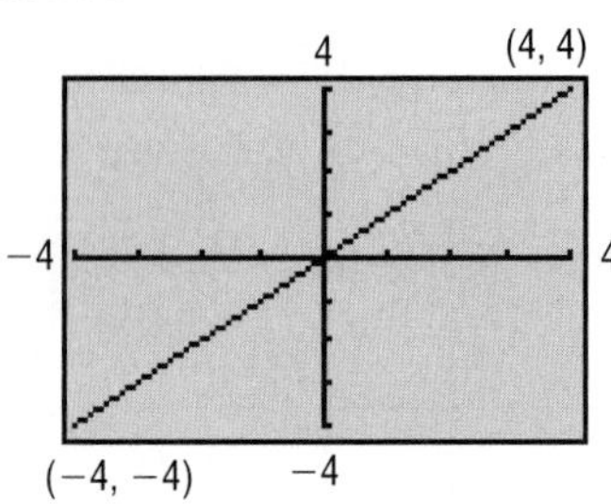

Square Screens

To get an undistorted view of slope, the same scale must be used on each axis. However, most graphing utilities have a rectangular screen. Because of this, using the same interval for both x and y will result in a distorted view. For example, Figure 14 shows the graph of the line $y = x$ connecting the points $(-4, -4)$ and $(4, 4)$. We expect the line to bisect the first and third quadrants, but it doesn't. We need to adjust the selections for Xmin, Xmax, Ymin, and Ymax so that a **square screen** results. On most graphing utilities, this is accomplished by setting the ratio of x to y at 3:2.*

Figure 15 shows the graph of the line $y = x$ on a square screen using a TI-84 Plus. Notice that the line now bisects the first and third quadrants. Compare this illustration to Figure 14.

Figure 15

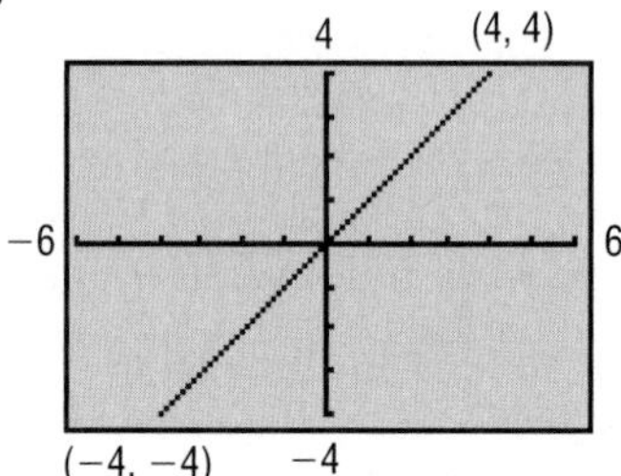

To get a better idea of the meaning of the slope m of a line, consider the following:

Exploration

Figure 16

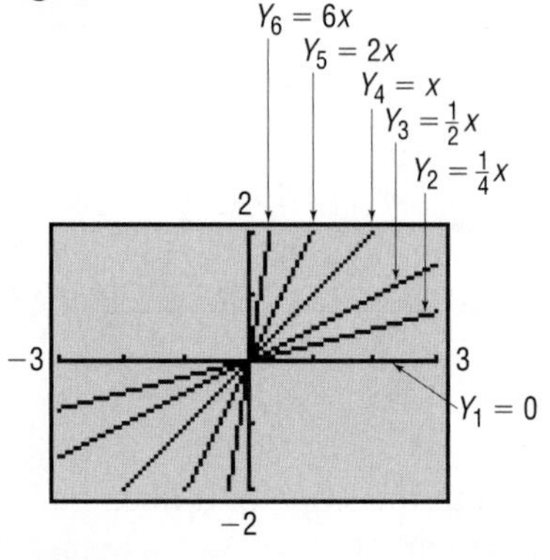

On the same square screen, graph the following equations:

$Y_1 = 0$ *Slope of line is 0.*

$Y_2 = \frac{1}{4}x$ *Slope of line is $\frac{1}{4}$.*

$Y_3 = \frac{1}{2}x$ *Slope of line is $\frac{1}{2}$.*

$Y_4 = x$ *Slope of line is 1.*

$Y_5 = 2x$ *Slope of line is 2.*

$Y_6 = 6x$ *Slope of line is 6.*

See Figure 16.

Exploration

Figure 17

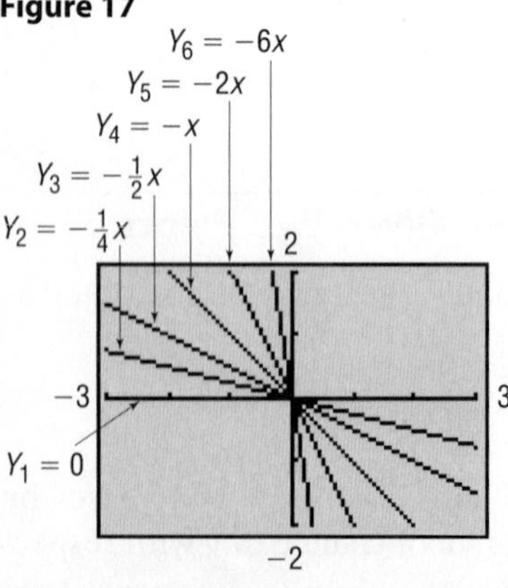

On the same square screen, graph the following equations:

$Y_1 = 0$ *Slope of line is 0.*

$Y_2 = -\frac{1}{4}x$ *Slope of line is $-\frac{1}{4}$.*

$Y_3 = -\frac{1}{2}x$ *Slope of line is $-\frac{1}{2}$.*

$Y_4 = -x$ *Slope of line is −1.*

$Y_5 = -2x$ *Slope of line is −2.*

$Y_6 = -6x$ *Slope of line is −6.*

See Figure 17.

*Most graphing utilities have a feature that automatically squares the viewing window. Consult your owner's manual for the appropriate keystrokes.

Figures 16 and 17 illustrate the following facts:

1. When the slope of a line is positive, the line slants upward from left to right.
2. When the slope of a line is negative, the line slants downward from left to right.
3. When the slope is 0, the line is horizontal.

Figures 16 and 17 also illustrate that the closer the line is to the vertical position, the greater the magnitude of the slope. So, a line with slope 6 is steeper than a line whose slope is 3.

2 Graph Lines Given a Point and the Slope

EXAMPLE 2 **Graphing a Line Given a Point and a Slope**

Draw a graph of the line that contains the point (3, 2) and has a slope of:

(a) $\frac{3}{4}$ (b) $-\frac{4}{5}$

Solution

(a) Slope $= \frac{\text{Rise}}{\text{Run}}$. The fact that the slope is $\frac{3}{4}$ means that for every horizontal movement (run) of 4 units to the right there will be a vertical movement (rise) of 3 units. If we start at the given point (3, 2) and move 4 units to the right and 3 units up, we reach the point (7, 5). By drawing the line through this point and the point (3, 2), we have the graph. See Figure 18.

Figure 18

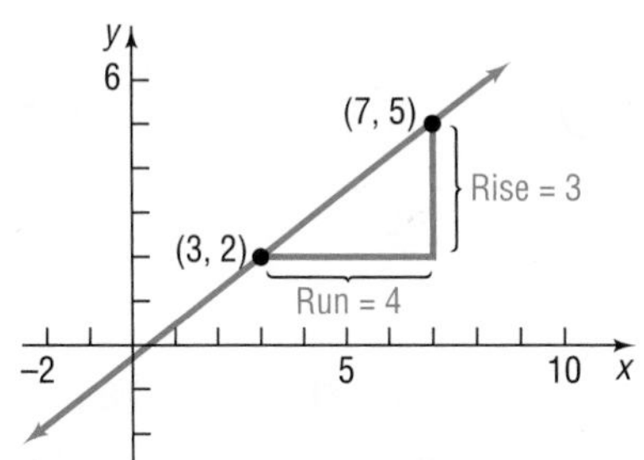

(b) The fact that the slope is

$$-\frac{4}{5} = \frac{-4}{5} = \frac{\text{Rise}}{\text{Run}}$$

means that for every horizontal movement of 5 units to the right there will be a corresponding vertical movement of −4 units (a downward movement of 4 units). If we start at the given point (3, 2) and move 5 units to the right and then 4 units down, we arrive at the point (8, −2). By drawing the line through these points, we have the graph. See Figure 19.

Figure 19

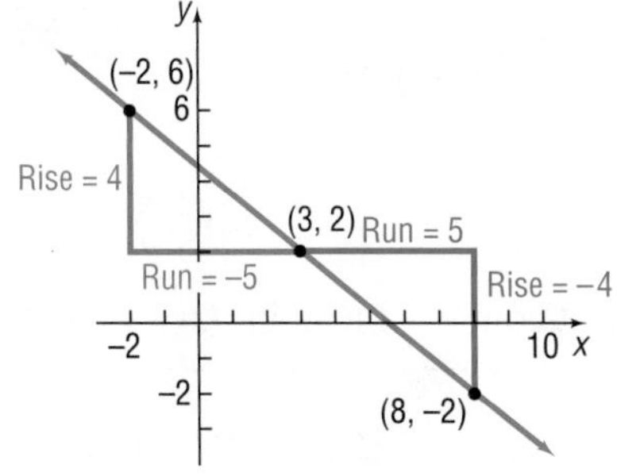

Alternatively, we can set

$$-\frac{4}{5} = \frac{4}{-5} = \frac{\text{Rise}}{\text{Run}}$$

so that for every horizontal movement of −5 units (a movement to the left of 5 units) there will be a corresponding vertical movement of 4 units (upward). This approach brings us to the point (−2, 6), which is also on the graph shown in Figure 19. ■

Now Work PROBLEM 23

3 Find the Equation of a Vertical Line

EXAMPLE 3 **Graphing a Line**

Graph the equation: $x = 3$

Solution To graph $x = 3$ by hand, find all points (x, y) in the plane for which $x = 3$. No matter what y-coordinate is used, the corresponding x-coordinate always equals 3. Consequently, the graph of the equation $x = 3$ is a vertical line with x-intercept 3 and undefined slope. See Figure 20(a) on the next page.

To use a graphing utility, we need to express the equation in the form $y = \{\text{expression in } x\}$. But $x = 3$ cannot be put into this form, so an alternative method must be used. Consult your manual to determine the methodology required to draw vertical lines. Figure 20(b) shows the graph that you should obtain.

Figure 20
$x = 3$

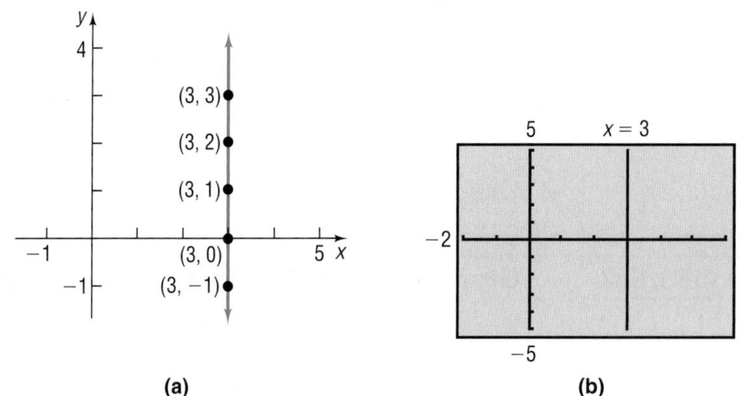

As suggested by Example 3, we have the following result:

THEOREM

Equation of a Vertical Line

A vertical line is given by an equation of the form

$$x = a$$

where a is the x-intercept.

Figure 21

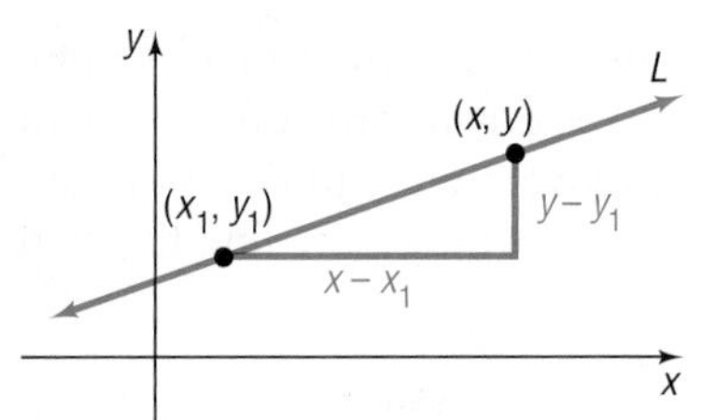

4 Use the Point–Slope Form of a Line; Identify Horizontal Lines

Let L be a nonvertical line with slope m and containing the point (x_1, y_1). See Figure 21. For any other point (x, y) on L, we have

$$m = \frac{y - y_1}{x - x_1} \quad \text{or} \quad y - y_1 = m(x - x_1)$$

THEOREM

Point–Slope Form of an Equation of a Line

An equation of a nonvertical line with slope m that contains the point (x_1, y_1) is

$$y - y_1 = m(x - x_1) \qquad \textbf{(2)}$$

EXAMPLE 4 **Using the Point–Slope Form of a Line**

An equation of the line with slope 4 and containing the point $(1, 2)$ can be found by using the point–slope form with $m = 4$, $x_1 = 1$, and $y_1 = 2$.

$$y - y_1 = m(x - x_1)$$

$$y - 2 = 4(x - 1) \qquad m = 4, x_1 = 1, y_1 = 2$$

$$y = 4x - 2 \qquad \text{Solve for } y.$$

Figure 22

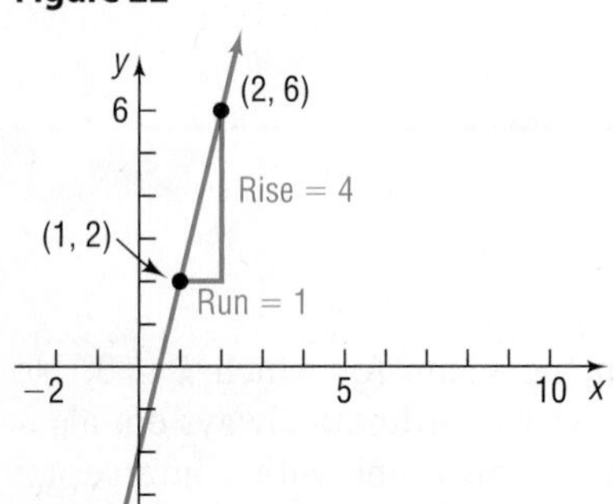

See Figure 22 for the graph.

Now Work PROBLEM 45

EXAMPLE 5 **Finding the Equation of a Horizontal Line**

Find an equation of the horizontal line containing the point (3, 2).

Solution Because all the y-values are equal on a horizontal line, the slope of a horizontal line is 0. To get an equation, use the point–slope form with $m = 0$, $x_1 = 3$, and $y_1 = 2$.

Figure 23

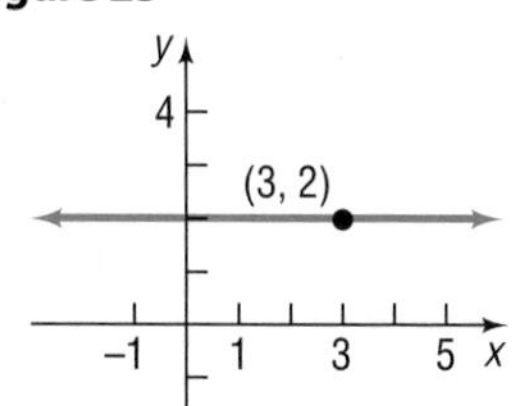

$$y - y_1 = m(x - x_1)$$

$$y - 2 = 0 \cdot (x - 3) \quad m = 0, x_1 = 3, \text{ and } y_1 = 2$$

$$y - 2 = 0$$

$$y = 2$$

See Figure 23 for the graph. ■

As suggested by Example 5, we have the following result:

THEOREM **Equation of a Horizontal Line**

A horizontal line is given by an equation of the form

$$y = b$$

where b is the y-intercept.

5 Find the Equation of a Line Given Two Points

EXAMPLE 6 **Finding an Equation of a Line Given Two Points**

Find an equation of the line containing the points (2, 3) and (−4, 5). Graph the line.

Solution First compute the slope of the line.

$$m = \frac{5 - 3}{-4 - 2} = \frac{2}{-6} = -\frac{1}{3}$$

Use the point (2, 3) and the slope $m = -\frac{1}{3}$ to get the point–slope form of the equation of the line.

Figure 24

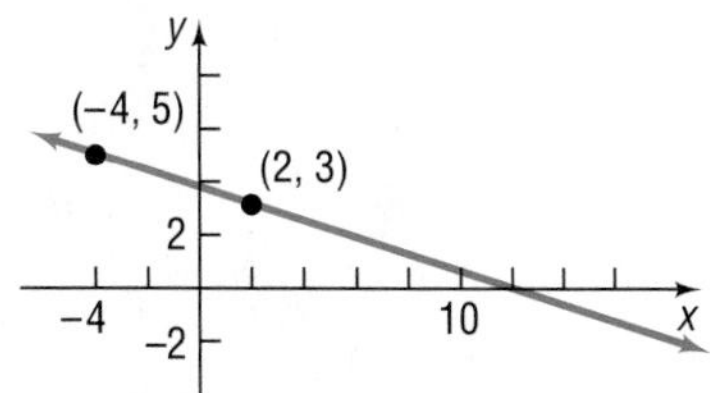

$$y - 3 = -\frac{1}{3}(x - 2)$$

See Figure 24 for the graph. ■

In the solution to Example 6, we could have used the other point, (−4, 5), instead of the point (2, 3). The equation that results, although it looks different, is equivalent to the equation obtained in the example. (Try it for yourself.)

Now Work PROBLEM 37

6 Write the Equation of a Line in Slope–Intercept Form

Another useful equation of a line is obtained when the slope m and y-intercept b are known. In this event, we know both the slope m of the line and the point $(0, b)$ on the line; then use the point–slope form, equation (2), to obtain the following equation:

$$y - b = m(x - 0) \quad \text{or} \quad y = mx + b$$

THEOREM

Slope–Intercept Form of an Equation of a Line

An equation of a line with slope m and y-intercept b is

$$y = mx + b \tag{3}$$

Now Work PROBLEM 51 (EXPRESS ANSWER IN SLOPE–INTERCEPT FORM)

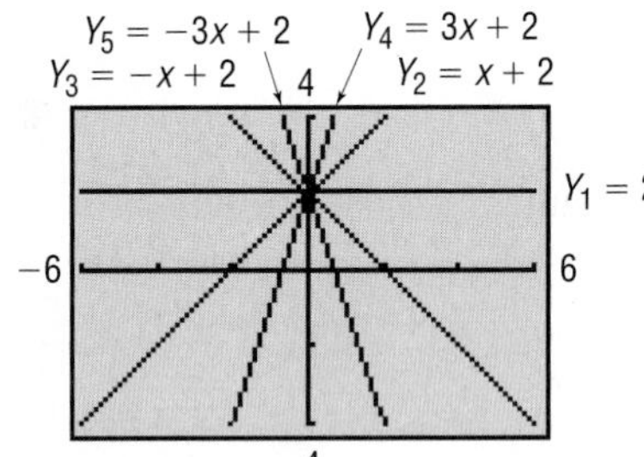

Figure 25 $y = mx + 2$

Seeing the Concept

To see the role that the slope m plays, graph the following lines on the same screen.

$$Y_1 = 2$$
$$Y_2 = x + 2$$
$$Y_3 = -x + 2$$
$$Y_4 = 3x + 2$$
$$Y_5 = -3x + 2$$

See Figure 25. What do you conclude about the lines $y = mx + 2$?

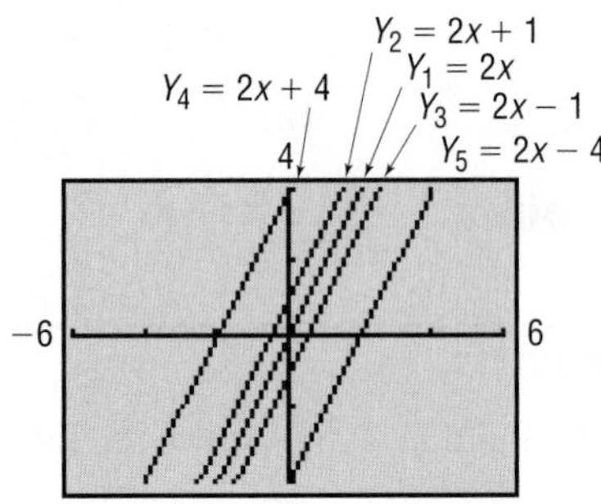

Figure 26 $y = 2x + b$

Seeing the Concept

To see the role of the y-intercept b, graph the following lines on the same screen.

$$Y_1 = 2x$$
$$Y_2 = 2x + 1$$
$$Y_3 = 2x - 1$$
$$Y_4 = 2x + 4$$
$$Y_5 = 2x - 4$$

See Figure 26. What do you conclude about the lines $y = 2x + b$?

7 Identify the Slope and y-Intercept of a Line from Its Equation

When the equation of a line is written in slope–intercept form, it is easy to find the slope m and y-intercept b of the line. For example, suppose that the equation of a line is

$$y = -2x + 7$$

Compare it to $y = mx + b$.

$$\begin{aligned} y &= -2x + 7 \\ &\quad\ \uparrow \qquad \uparrow \\ y &= \ \ mx + b \end{aligned}$$

The slope of this line is -2 and its y-intercept is 7.

Now Work PROBLEM 71

EXAMPLE 7 **Finding the Slope and y-Intercept**

Find the slope m and y-intercept b of the equation $2x + 4y = 8$. Graph the equation.

Solution To obtain the slope and y-intercept, write the equation in slope–intercept form by solving for y.

Figure 27

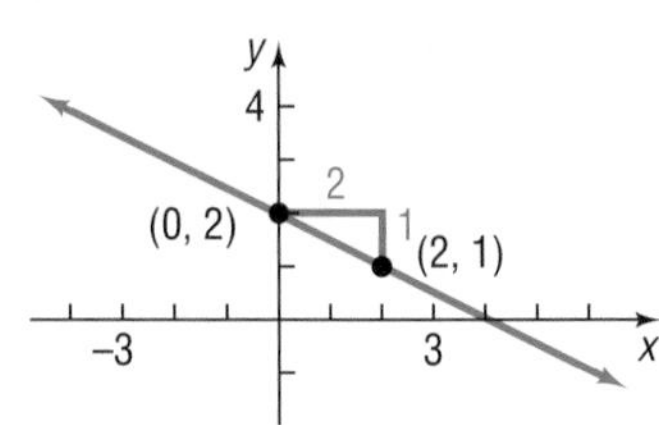

$$2x + 4y = 8$$

$$4y = -2x + 8$$

$$y = -\frac{1}{2}x + 2 \quad y = mx + b$$

The coefficient of x, $-\frac{1}{2}$, is the slope, and the y-intercept is 2. Graph the line using the fact that the y-intercept is 2 and the slope is $-\frac{1}{2}$. Then, starting at the point $(0, 2)$, go to the right 2 units and then down 1 unit to the point $(2, 1)$. See Figure 27. ■

Now Work PROBLEM 77

8 Graph Lines Written in General Form Using Intercepts

Refer to Example 7. The form of the equation of the line $2x + 4y = 8$ is called the *general form*.

DEFINITION The equation of a line is in **general form*** when it is written as

$$Ax + By = C \qquad (4)$$

where A, B, and C are real numbers and A and B are not both 0.

If $B = 0$ in (4), then $A \neq 0$ and the graph of the equation is a vertical line: $x = \frac{C}{A}$. If $B \neq 0$ in (4), then we can solve the equation for y and write the equation in slope–intercept form as we did in Example 7.

Another approach to graphing equation (4) would be to find its intercepts. Remember, the intercepts of the graph of an equation are the points where the graph crosses or touches a coordinate axis.

EXAMPLE 8 **Graphing an Equation in General Form Using Its Intercepts**

Graph the equation $2x + 4y = 8$ by finding its intercepts.

Solution To obtain the x-intercept, let $y = 0$ in the equation and solve for x.

$$2x + 4y = 8$$

$$2x + 4(0) = 8 \quad \text{Let } y = 0.$$

$$2x = 8$$

$$x = 4 \quad \text{Divide both sides by 2.}$$

The x-intercept is 4 and the point $(4, 0)$ is on the graph of the equation.

To obtain the y-intercept, let $x = 0$ in the equation and solve for y.

$$2x + 4y = 8$$

$$2(0) + 4y = 8 \quad \text{Let } x = 0.$$

$$4y = 8$$

$$y = 2 \quad \text{Divide both sides by 4.}$$

Figure 28

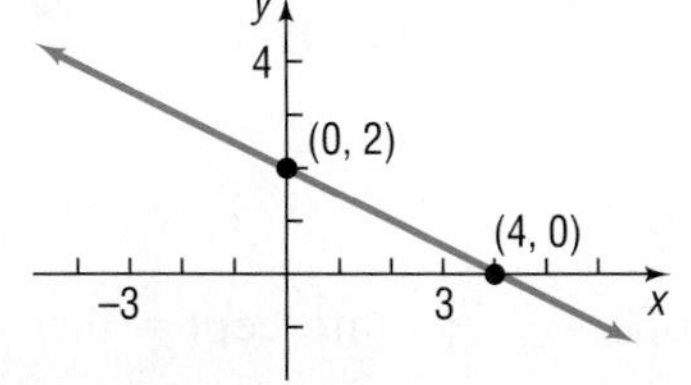

The y-intercept is 2 and the point $(0, 2)$ is on the graph of the equation.

Plot the points $(4, 0)$ and $(0, 2)$ and draw the line through the points. See Figure 28. ■

Now Work PROBLEM 91

*Some books use the term **standard form.**

Every line has an equation that is equivalent to an equation written in general form. For example, a vertical line whose equation is

$$x = a$$

can be written in the general form

$$1 \cdot x + 0 \cdot y = a \quad A = 1, B = 0, C = a$$

A horizontal line whose equation is

$$y = b$$

can be written in the general form

$$0 \cdot x + 1 \cdot y = b \quad A = 0, B = 1, C = b$$

Lines that are neither vertical nor horizontal have general equations of the form

$$Ax + By = C \quad A \neq 0 \text{ and } B \neq 0$$

Because the equation of every line can be written in general form, any equation equivalent to equation (4) is called a **linear equation.**

Figure 29

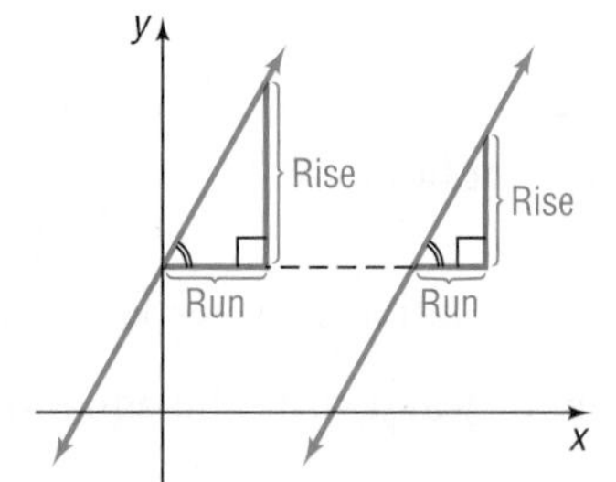

9 Find Equations of Parallel Lines

When two lines (in the plane) do not intersect (that is, they have no points in common), they are said to be **parallel.** Look at Figure 29. There we have drawn two parallel lines and have constructed two right triangles by drawing sides parallel to the coordinate axes. The right triangles are similar. (Do you see why? Two angles are equal.) Because the triangles are similar, the ratios of corresponding sides are equal.

THEOREM

Criterion for Parallel Lines

Two nonvertical lines are parallel if and only if their slopes are equal and they have different y-intercepts.

The use of the words "if and only if" in the preceding theorem means that actually two statements are being made, one the converse of the other.

If two nonvertical lines are parallel, then their slopes are equal and they have different y-intercepts.

If two nonvertical lines have equal slopes and they have different y-intercepts, then they are parallel.

EXAMPLE 9 **Showing That Two Lines Are Parallel**

Show that the lines given by the following equations are parallel:

$$L_1: \; 2x + 3y = 6, \qquad L_2: \; 4x + 6y = 0$$

Solution To determine whether these lines have equal slopes and different y-intercepts, write each equation in slope–intercept form:

$$L_1: \; 2x + 3y = 6 \qquad\qquad L_2: \; 4x + 6y = 0$$

$$3y = -2x + 6 \qquad\qquad 6y = -4x$$

$$y = -\frac{2}{3}x + 2 \qquad\qquad y = -\frac{2}{3}x$$

$$\text{Slope} = -\frac{2}{3};\; y\text{-intercept} = 2 \qquad\qquad \text{Slope} = -\frac{2}{3};\; y\text{-intercept} = 0$$

Because these lines have the same slope, $-\frac{2}{3}$, but different y-intercepts, the lines are parallel. See Figure 30.

Figure 30 Parallel lines

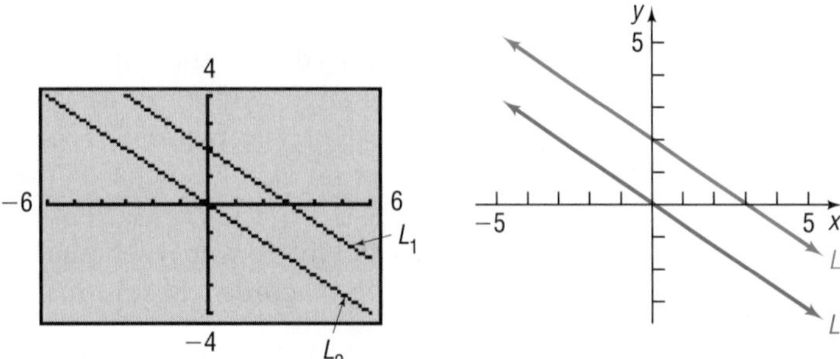

EXAMPLE 10 Finding a Line That Is Parallel to a Given Line

Find an equation for the line that contains the point $(2, -3)$ and is parallel to the line $2x + y = 6$.

Solution Since the two lines are to be parallel, the slope of the line that we seek equals the slope of the line $2x + y = 6$. Begin by writing the equation of the line $2x + y = 6$ in slope–intercept form.

Figure 31

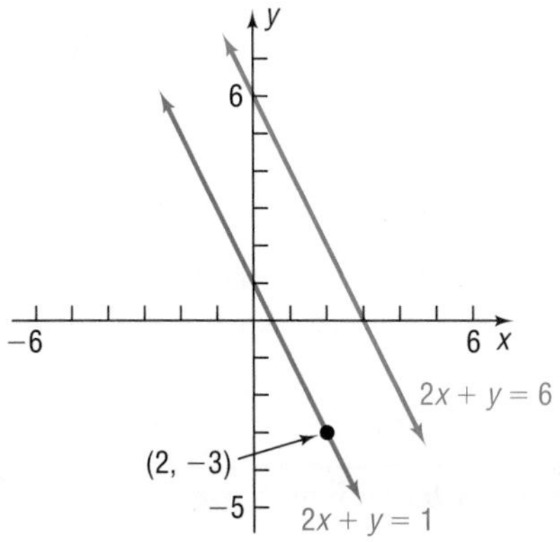

$$2x + y = 6$$
$$y = -2x + 6$$

The slope is -2. Since the line that we seek also has slope -2 and contains the point $(2, -3)$, use the point–slope form to obtain its equation.

$$y - y_1 = m(x - x_1) \quad \text{Point–slope form}$$
$$y - (-3) = -2(x - 2) \quad m = -2, x_1 = 2, y_1 = -3$$
$$y + 3 = -2x + 4 \quad \text{Simplify.}$$
$$y = -2x + 1 \quad \text{Slope–intercept form}$$
$$2x + y = 1 \quad \text{General form}$$

This line is parallel to the line $2x + y = 6$ and contains the point $(2, -3)$. See Figure 31. ■

Now Work PROBLEM 59

10 Find Equations of Perpendicular Lines

Figure 32

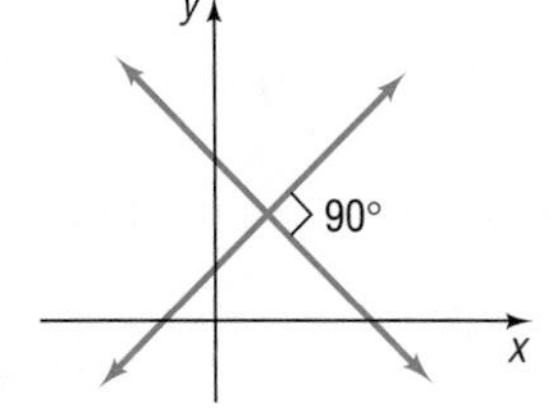

When two lines intersect at a right angle (90°), they are said to be **perpendicular.** See Figure 32.

The following result gives a condition, in terms of their slopes, for two lines to be perpendicular.

THEOREM

Criterion for Perpendicular Lines

Two nonvertical lines are perpendicular if and only if the product of their slopes is -1.

Here we shall prove the "only if" part of the statement:

If two nonvertical lines are perpendicular, then the product of their slopes is -1.

In Problem 128 you are asked to prove the "if" part of the theorem; that is:

If two nonvertical lines have slopes whose product is -1, then the lines are perpendicular.

Figure 33

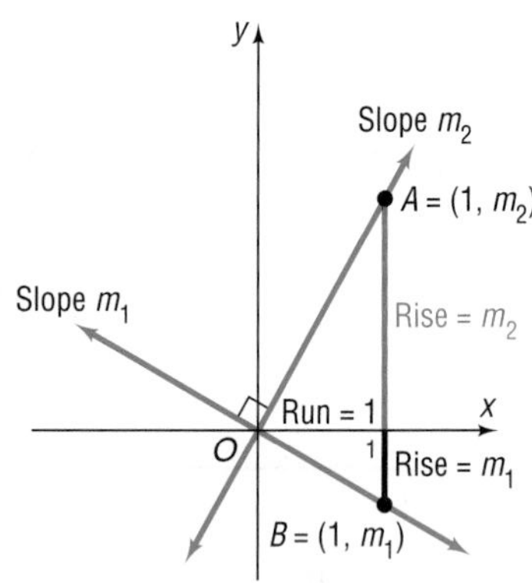

Proof Let m_1 and m_2 denote the slopes of the two lines. There is no loss in generality (that is, neither the angle nor the slopes are affected) if we situate the lines so that they meet at the origin. See Figure 33. The point $A = (1, m_2)$ is on the line having slope m_2, and the point $B = (1, m_1)$ is on the line having slope m_1. (Do you see why this must be true?)

Suppose that the lines are perpendicular. Then triangle OAB is a right triangle. As a result of the Pythagorean Theorem, it follows that

$$[d(O, A)]^2 + [d(O, B)]^2 = [d(A, B)]^2 \qquad \textbf{(5)}$$

Using the distance formula, the squares of these distances are

$$[d(O, A)]^2 = (1 - 0)^2 + (m_2 - 0)^2 = 1 + m_2^2$$

$$[d(O, B)]^2 = (1 - 0)^2 + (m_1 - 0)^2 = 1 + m_1^2$$

$$[d(A, B)]^2 = (1 - 1)^2 + (m_2 - m_1)^2 = m_2^2 - 2m_1m_2 + m_1^2$$

Using these facts in equation (5), we get

$$\left(1 + m_2^2\right) + \left(1 + m_1^2\right) = m_2^2 - 2m_1m_2 + m_1^2$$

which, upon simplification, can be written as

$$m_1m_2 = -1$$

If the lines are perpendicular, the product of their slopes is -1. ■

You may find it easier to remember the condition for two nonvertical lines to be perpendicular by observing that the equality $m_1m_2 = -1$ means that m_1 and m_2 are negative reciprocals of each other; that is, either $m_1 = -\dfrac{1}{m_2}$ or $m_2 = -\dfrac{1}{m_1}$.

EXAMPLE 11 **Finding the Slope of a Line Perpendicular to Another Line**

If a line has slope $\dfrac{3}{2}$, any line having slope $-\dfrac{2}{3}$ is perpendicular to it. ■

EXAMPLE 12 **Finding the Equation of a Line Perpendicular to a Given Line**

Find an equation of the line that contains the point $(1, -2)$ and is perpendicular to the line $x + 3y = 6$. Graph the two lines.

Solution First write the equation of the given line in slope–intercept form to find its slope.

$$x + 3y = 6$$

$$3y = -x + 6 \qquad \text{Proceed to solve for } y.$$

$$y = -\frac{1}{3}x + 2 \qquad \text{Place in the form } y = mx + b.$$

The given line has slope $-\dfrac{1}{3}$. Any line perpendicular to this line will have slope 3. Because we require the point $(1, -2)$ to be on this line with slope 3, use the point–slope form of the equation of a line.

$$y - y_1 = m(x - x_1) \qquad \text{Point–slope form}$$

$$y - (-2) = 3(x - 1) \qquad m = 3, x_1 = 1, y_1 = -2$$

To obtain other forms of the equation, proceed as follows:

$$y + 2 = 3(x - 1)$$
$$y + 2 = 3x - 3 \quad \text{Simplify.}$$
$$y = 3x - 5 \quad \text{Slope–intercept form}$$
$$3x - y = 5 \quad \text{General form}$$

Figure 34 shows the graphs.

Figure 34

WARNING Be sure to use a square screen when you graph perpendicular lines. Otherwise, the angle between the two lines will appear distorted. ■

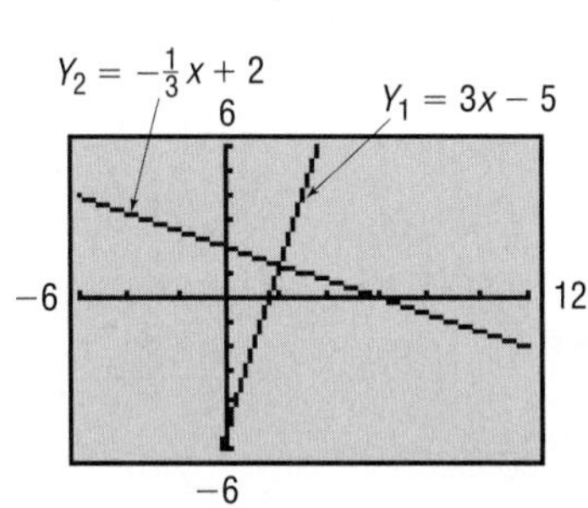

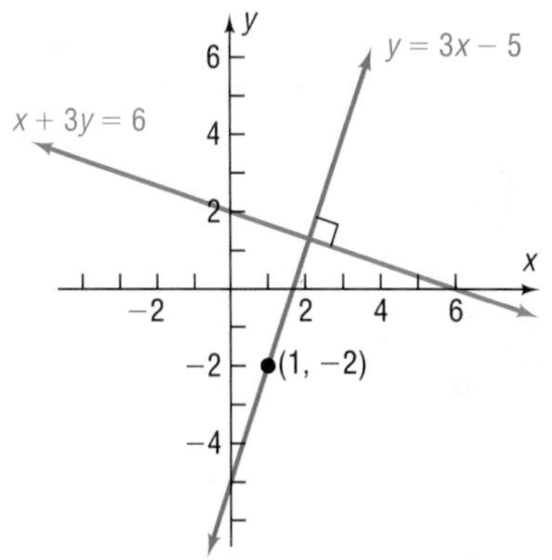

■

Now Work PROBLEM 65

8.2 Assess Your Understanding

Concepts and Vocabulary

1. The slope of a vertical line is __________; the slope of a horizontal line is _______.
2. For the line $2x + 3y = 6$, the x-intercept is _______ and the y-intercept is _______.
3. A horizontal line is given by an equation of the form _______, where b is the __________.
4. ***True or False*** Vertical lines have an undefined slope.
5. ***True or False*** The slope of the line $2y = 3x + 5$ is 3.
6. ***True or False*** The point $(1, 2)$ is on the line $2x + y = 4$.
7. Two nonvertical lines have slopes m_1 and m_2, respectively. The lines are parallel if __________ and the __________ are unequal; the lines are perpendicular if __________.
8. The lines $y = 2x + 3$ and $y = ax + 5$ are parallel if $a =$ _______.
9. The lines $y = 2x - 1$ and $y = ax + 2$ are perpendicular if $a =$ _______.
10. ***True or False*** Perpendicular lines have slopes that are reciprocals of one another.

Skill Building

In Problems 11–14, (a) find the slope of the line and (b) interpret the slope.

11.
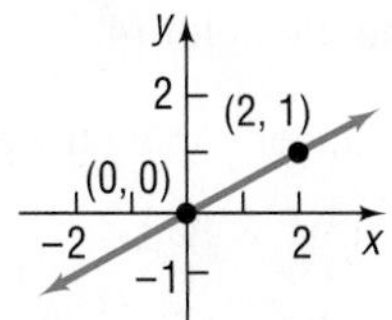

12.
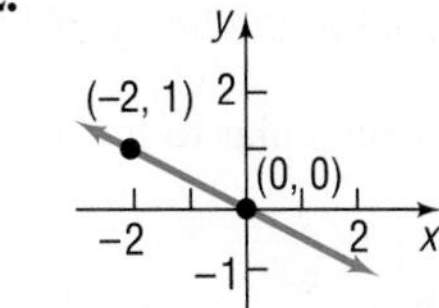

13.
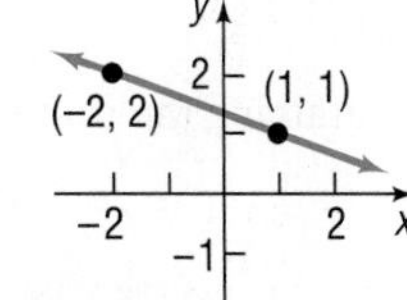

14.
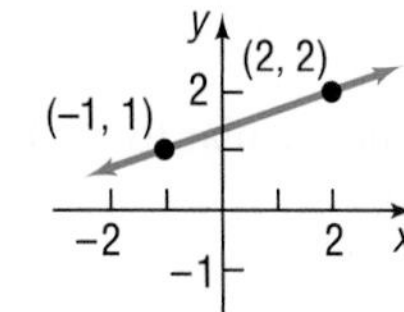

In Problems 15–22, plot each pair of points and determine the slope of the line containing them. Graph the line by hand.

15. $(2, 3); (4, 0)$
16. $(4, 2); (3, 4)$
17. $(-2, 3); (2, 1)$
18. $(-1, 1); (2, 3)$
19. $(-3, -1); (2, -1)$
20. $(4, 2); (-5, 2)$
21. $(-1, 2); (-1, -2)$
22. $(2, 0); (2, 2)$

In Problems 23–30, graph the line containing the point P and having slope m.

23. $P = (1, 2); m = 3$ **24.** $P = (2, 1); m = 4$ **25.** $P = (2, 4); m = -\frac{3}{4}$ **26.** $P = (1, 3); m = -\frac{2}{5}$

27. $P = (-1, 3); m = 0$ **28.** $P = (2, -4); m = 0$ **29.** $P = (0, 3)$; slope undefined **30.** $P = (-2, 0)$; slope undefined

In Problems 31–36, the slope and a point on a line are given. Use this information to locate three additional points on the line. Answers may vary.

[**Hint:** It is not necessary to find the equation of the line. See Example 2.]

31. Slope 4; point $(1, 2)$ **32.** Slope 2; point $(-2, 3)$ **33.** Slope $-\frac{3}{2}$; point $(2, -4)$

34. Slope $\frac{4}{3}$; point $(-3, 2)$ **35.** Slope -2; point $(-2, -3)$ **36.** Slope -1; point $(4, 1)$

In Problems 37–44, find an equation of the line L.

37.

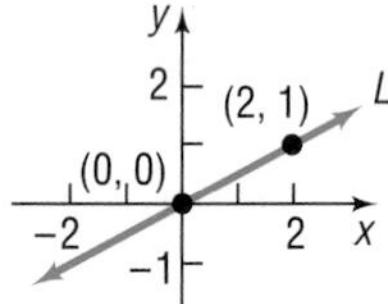

38.

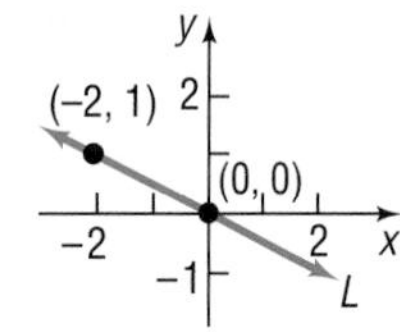

39.

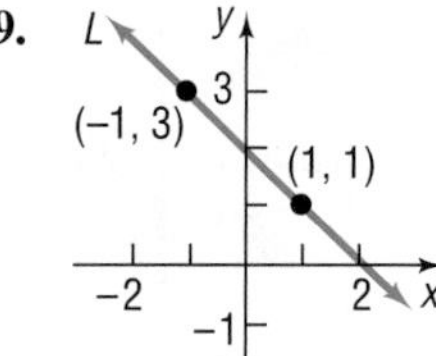

40.

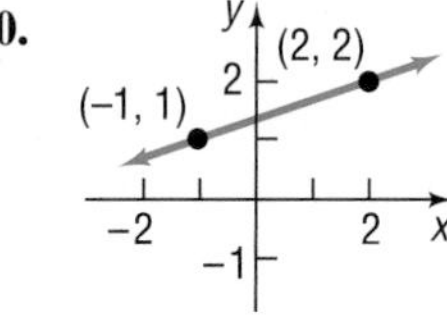

41.

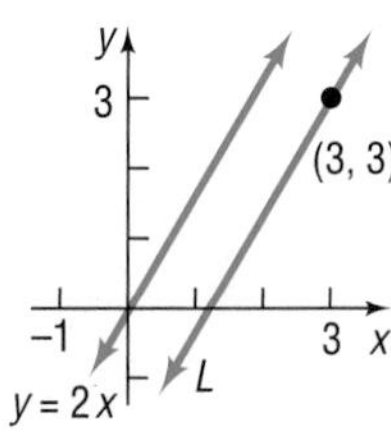

42.

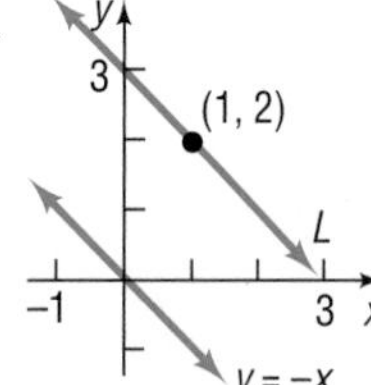

43.

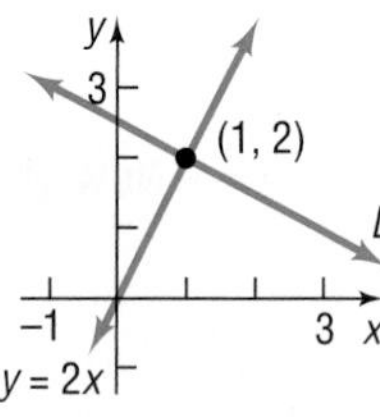

44.

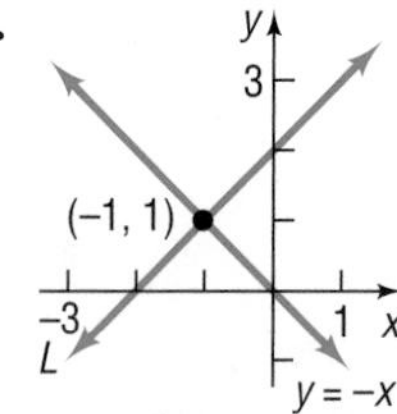

In Problems 45–70, find an equation for the line with the given properties. Express your answer using either the general form or the slope–intercept form of the equation of a line, whichever you prefer.

45. Slope $= 3$; containing the point $(-2, 3)$

46. Slope $= 2$; containing the point $(4, -3)$

47. Slope $= -\frac{2}{3}$; containing the point $(1, -1)$

48. Slope $= \frac{1}{2}$; containing the point $(3, 1)$

49. Containing the points $(1, 3)$ and $(-1, 2)$

50. Containing the points $(-3, 4)$ and $(2, 5)$

51. Slope $= -3$; y-intercept $= 3$

52. Slope $= -2$; y-intercept $= -2$

53. x-intercept $= 2$; y-intercept $= -1$

54. x-intercept $= -4$; y-intercept $= 4$

55. Slope undefined; containing the point $(2, 4)$

56. Slope undefined; containing the point $(3, 8)$

57. Horizontal; containing the point $(-3, 2)$

58. Vertical; containing the point $(4, -5)$

59. Parallel to the line $y = 2x$; containing the point $(-1, 2)$

60. Parallel to the line $y = -3x$; containing the point $(-1, 2)$

61. Parallel to the line $2x - y = -2$; containing the point $(0, 0)$

62. Parallel to the line $x - 2y = -5$; containing the point $(0, 0)$

63. Parallel to the line $x = 5$; containing the point $(4, 2)$

64. Parallel to the line $y = 5$; containing the point $(4, 2)$

65. Perpendicular to the line $y = \frac{1}{2}x + 4$; containing the point $(1, -2)$

66. Perpendicular to the line $y = 2x - 3$; containing the point $(1, -2)$

67. Perpendicular to the line $2x + y = 2$; containing the point $(-3, 0)$

68. Perpendicular to the line $x - 2y = -5$; containing the point $(0, 4)$

69. Perpendicular to the line $x = 8$; containing the point $(3, 4)$

70. Perpendicular to the line $y = 8$; containing the point $(3, 4)$

In Problems 71–90, find the slope and y-intercept of each line. Graph the line by hand. Verify your graph using a graphing utility.

71. $y = 2x + 3$ **72.** $y = -3x + 4$ **73.** $\frac{1}{2}y = x - 1$ **74.** $\frac{1}{3}x + y = 2$ **75.** $y = \frac{1}{2}x + 2$

76. $y = 2x + \frac{1}{2}$ **77.** $x + 2y = 4$ **78.** $-x + 3y = 6$ **79.** $2x - 3y = 6$ **80.** $3x + 2y = 6$

81. $x + y = 1$ **82.** $x - y = 2$ **83.** $x = -4$ **84.** $y = -1$ **85.** $y = 5$

86. $x = 2$ **87.** $y - x = 0$ **88.** $x + y = 0$ **89.** $2y - 3x = 0$ **90.** $3x + 2y = 0$

In Problems 91–100, (a) find the intercepts of the graph of each equation and (b) graph the equation.

91. $2x + 3y = 6$ **92.** $3x - 2y = 6$ **93.** $-4x + 5y = 40$ **94.** $6x - 4y = 24$

95. $7x + 2y = 21$ **96.** $5x + 3y = 18$ **97.** $\frac{1}{2}x + \frac{1}{3}y = 1$ **98.** $x - \frac{2}{3}y = 4$

99. $0.2x - 0.5y = 1$ **100.** $-0.3x + 0.4y = 1.2$

101. Find an equation of the x-axis. **102.** Find an equation of the y-axis.

In Problems 103–106, the equations of two lines are given. Determine if the lines are parallel, perpendicular, or neither.

103. $y = 2x - 3$
$y = 2x + 4$

104. $y = \frac{1}{2}x - 3$
$y = -2x + 4$

105. $y = 4x + 5$
$y = -4x + 2$

106. $y = -2x + 3$
$y = -\frac{1}{2}x + 2$

In Problems 107–110, write an equation of each line. Express your answer using either the general form or the slope–intercept form of the equation of a line, whichever you prefer.

107.

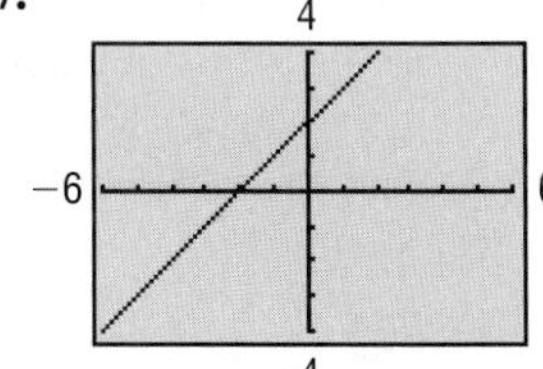

108.

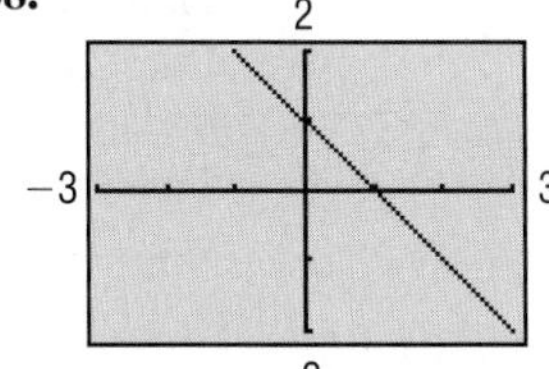

109.

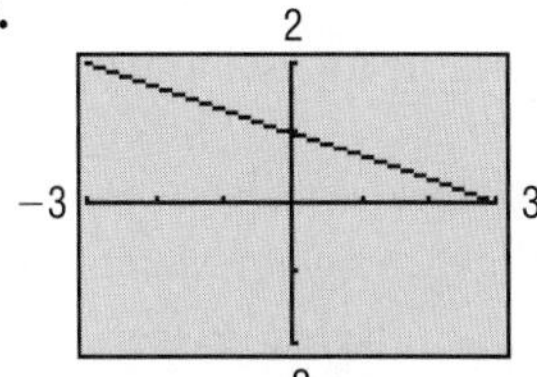

110.

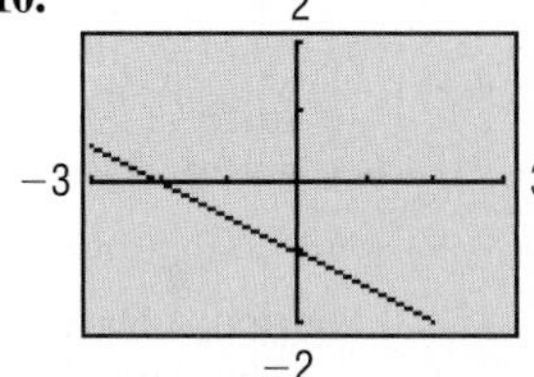

Applications and Extensions

111. Geometry Use slopes to show that the triangle whose vertices are $(-2, 5)$, $(1, 3)$, and $(-1, 0)$ is a right triangle.

112. Geometry Use slopes to show that the quadrilateral whose vertices are $(1, -1)$, $(4, 1)$, $(2, 2)$, and $(5, 4)$ is a parallelogram.

113. Geometry Use slopes to show that the quadrilateral whose vertices are $(-1, 0)$, $(2, 3)$, $(1, -2)$, and $(4, 1)$ is a rectangle.

114. Geometry Use slopes and the distance formula to show that the quadrilateral whose vertices are $(0, 0)$, $(1, 3)$, $(4, 2)$, and $(3, -1)$ is a square.

115. Truck Rentals A truck rental company rents a moving truck for one day by charging \$29 plus \$0.20 per mile. Write a linear equation that relates the cost C, in dollars, of renting the truck to the number x of miles driven. What is the cost of renting the truck if the truck is driven 110 miles? 230 miles?

116. Cost Equation The **fixed costs** of operating a business are the costs incurred regardless of the level of production. Fixed costs include rent, fixed salaries, and costs of leasing machinery. The **variable costs** of operating a business are the costs that change with the level of output. Variable costs include raw materials, hourly wages, and electricity. Suppose that a manufacturer of jeans has fixed daily costs of \$500 and variable costs of \$8 for each pair of jeans manufactured. Write a linear equation that relates the daily cost C, in dollars, of manufacturing the jeans to the number x of jeans manufactured. What is the cost of manufacturing 400 pairs of jeans? 740 pairs?

117. Cost of Driving a Car The annual fixed costs for owning a small sedan are \$1289, assuming the car is completely paid for. The cost to drive the car is approximately \$0.15 per mile. Write a linear equation that relates the cost C and the number x of miles driven annually.

Source: www.pacebus.com

118. Wages of a Car Salesperson Dan receives \$375 per week for selling new and used cars at a car dealership in Oak Lawn, Illinois. In addition, he receives 5% of the profit on any sales that he generates. Write a linear equation that represents Dan's weekly salary S when he has sales that generate a profit of x dollars.

119. **Electricity Rates in Illinois** Commonwealth Edison Company supplies electricity to residential customers for a monthly customer charge of \$11.47 plus 11 cents per kilowatt-hour for up to 600 kilowatt-hours.

(a) Write a linear equation that relates the monthly charge C, in dollars, to the number x of kilowatt-hours used in a month, $0 \le x \le 600$.
(b) Graph this equation.
(c) What is the monthly charge for using 200 kilowatt-hours?
(d) What is the monthly charge for using 500 kilowatt-hours?
(e) Interpret the slope of the line.

Source: Commonwealth Edison Company, March, 2011.

120. **Electricity Rates in Florida** Florida Power & Light Company supplies electricity to residential customers for a monthly customer charge of \$5.90 plus 8.81 cents per kilowatt-hour for up to 1000 kilowatt-hours.
(a) Write a linear equation that relates the monthly charge C, in dollars, to the number x of kilowatt-hours used in a month, $0 \le x \le 1000$.
(b) Graph this equation.
(c) What is the monthly charge for using 200 kilowatt-hours?
(d) What is the monthly charge for using 500 kilowatt-hours?
(e) Interpret the slope of the line.

Source: Florida Power & Light Company, March, 2011.

121. **Measuring Temperature** The relationship between Celsius (°C) and Fahrenheit (°F) degrees of measuring temperature is linear. Find a linear equation relating °C and °F if 0°C corresponds to 32°F and 100°C corresponds to 212°F. Use the equation to find the Celsius measure of 70°F.

122. **Measuring Temperature** The Kelvin (K) scale for measuring temperature is obtained by adding 273 to the Celsius temperature.
(a) Write a linear equation relating K and °C.
(b) Write a linear equation relating K and °F (see Problem 121).

123. **Access Ramp** A wooden access ramp is being built to reach a platform that sits 30 inches above the floor. The ramp drops 2 inches for every 25-inch run.

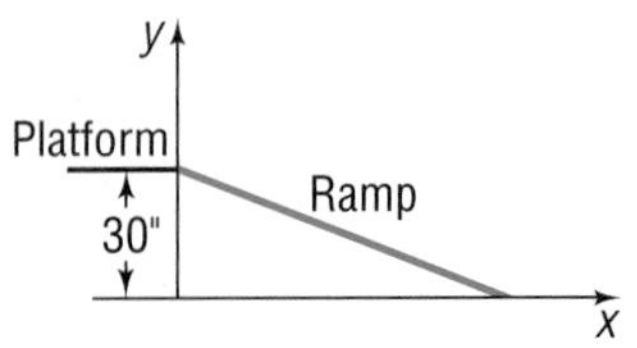

(a) Write a linear equation that relates the height y of the ramp above the floor to the horizontal distance x from the platform.
(b) Find and interpret the x-intercept of the graph of your equation.
(c) Design requirements stipulate that the maximum run be 30 feet and that the maximum slope be a drop of 1 inch for each 12 inches of run. Will this ramp meet the requirements? Explain.
(d) What slopes could be used to obtain the 30-inch rise and still meet design requirements?

Source: www.adaptiveaccess.com/wood_ramps.php

124. **Cigarette Use** A report in the Child Trends DataBase indicated that, in 2000, 20.6% of twelfth grade students reported daily use of cigarettes. In 2009, 11.2% of twelfth grade students reported daily use of cigarettes.
(a) Write a linear equation that relates the percent y of twelfth grade students who smoke cigarettes daily to the number x of years after 2000.
(b) Find the intercepts of the graph of your equation.
(c) Do the intercepts have any meaningful interpretation?
(d) Use your equation to predict the percent for the year 2025. Is this result reasonable?

Source: www.childtrendsdatabank.org

125. **Product Promotion** A cereal company finds that the number of people who will buy one of its products in the first month that it is introduced is linearly related to the amount of money it spends on advertising. If it spends \$40,000 on advertising, then 100,000 boxes of cereal will be sold, and if it spends \$60,000, then 200,000 boxes will be sold.
(a) Write a linear equation that relates the amount A spent on advertising to the number x of boxes the company aims to sell.
(b) How much advertising is needed to sell 300,000 boxes of cereal?
(c) Interpret the slope.

126. Show that the line containing the points (a, b) and (b, a), $a \neq b$, is perpendicular to the line $y = x$. Also show that the midpoint of (a, b) and (b, a) lies on the line $y = x$.

127. The equation $2x - y = C$ defines a **family of lines,** one line for each value of C. On one set of coordinate axes, graph the members of the family when $C = -4$, $C = 0$, and $C = 2$. Can you draw a conclusion from the graph about each member of the family?

128. Prove that if two nonvertical lines have slopes whose product is -1 then the lines are perpendicular. [**Hint:** Refer to Figure 33 and use the converse of the Pythagorean Theorem.]

Explaining Concepts: Discussion and Writing

129. Which of the following equations might have the graph shown? (More than one answer is possible.)
   (a) $2x + 3y = 6$
   (b) $-2x + 3y = 6$
   (c) $3x - 4y = -12$
   (d) $x - y = 1$
   (e) $x - y = -1$
   (f) $y = 3x - 5$
   (g) $y = 2x + 3$
   (h) $y = -3x + 3$

130. Which of the following equations might have the graph shown? (More than one answer is possible.)
   (a) $2x + 3y = 6$
   (b) $2x - 3y = 6$
   (c) $3x + 4y = 12$
   (d) $x - y = 1$
   (e) $x - y = -1$
   (f) $y = -2x - 1$
   (g) $y = -\frac{1}{2}x + 10$
   (h) $y = x + 4$

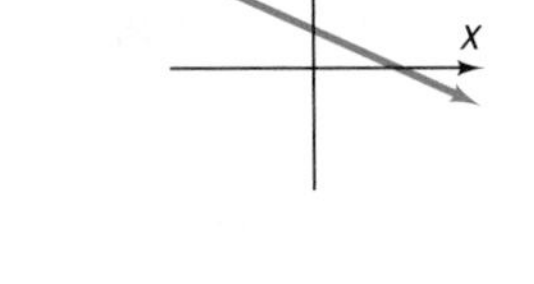

131. The figure shows the graph of two parallel lines. Which of the following pairs of equations might have such a graph?
   (a) $x - 2y = 3$
   $x + 2y = 7$
   (b) $x + y = 2$
   $x + y = -1$
   (c) $x - y = -2$
   $x - y = 1$
   (d) $x - y = -2$
   $2x - 2y = -4$
   (e) $x + 2y = 2$
   $x + 2y = -1$

132. The figure shows the graph of two perpendicular lines. Which of the following pairs of equations might have such a graph?
   (a) $y - 2x = 2$
   $y + 2x = -1$
   (b) $y - 2x = 0$
   $2y + x = 0$
   (c) $2y - x = 2$
   $2y + x = -2$
   (d) $y - 2x = 2$
   $x + 2y = -1$
   (e) $2x + y = -2$
   $2y + x = -2$

133. ***m* is for Slope** The accepted symbol used to denote the slope of a line is the letter m. Investigate the origin of this symbolism. Begin by consulting a French dictionary and looking up the French word *monter*. Write a brief essay on your findings.

134. **Grade of a Road** The term *grade* is used to describe the inclination of a road. How does this term relate to the notion of slope of a line? Is a 4% grade very steep? Investigate the grades of some mountainous roads and determine their slopes. Write a brief essay on your findings.

135. **Carpentry** Carpenters use the term *pitch* to describe the steepness of staircases and roofs. How does pitch relate to slope? Investigate typical pitches used for stairs and for roofs. Write a brief essay on your findings.

136. Can the equation of every line be written in slope–intercept form? Why?

137. Does every line have exactly one x-intercept and one y-intercept? Are there any lines that have no intercepts?

138. What can you say about two lines that have equal slopes and equal y-intercepts?

139. What can you say about two lines with the same x-intercept and the same y-intercept? Assume that the x-intercept is not 0.

140. If two distinct lines have the same slope, but different x-intercepts, can they have the same y-intercept?

141. If two distinct lines have the same y-intercept, but different slopes, can they have the same x-intercept?

142. Which form of the equation of a line do you prefer to use? Justify your position with an example that shows that your choice is better than another. Have reasons.

143. **What Went Wrong?** A student is asked to find the slope of the line joining $(-3, 2)$ and $(1, -4)$. He states that the slope is $\frac{3}{2}$. Is he correct? If not, what went wrong?

Interactive Exercise

Ask your instructor if the applet below is of interest to you.

144. **Slope** *Open the slope applet.* Move point B around the Cartesian plane with your mouse.
   (a) Move B to the point whose coordinates are $(2, 7)$. What is the slope of the line?
   (b) Move B to the point whose coordinates are $(3, 6)$. What is the slope of the line?

(c) Move B to the point whose coordinates are (4, 5). What is the slope of the line?
(d) Move B to the point whose coordinates are (4, 4). What is the slope of the line?
(e) Move B to the point whose coordinates are (4, 1). What is the slope of the line?
(f) Move B to the point whose coordinates are (3, −2). What is the slope of the line?
(g) Slowly move B to a point whose x-coordinate is 1. What happens to the value of the slope as the x-coordinate approaches 1?
(h) What can be said about a line whose slope is positive? What can be said about a line whose slope is negative? What can be said about a line whose slope is 0?
(i) Consider the results of parts (a)–(c). What can be said about the steepness of a line with positive slope as its slope increases?
(j) Move B to the point whose coordinates are (3, 5). What is the slope of the line? Move B to the point whose coordinates are (5, 6). What is the slope of the line? Move B to the point whose coordinates are (−1, 3). What is the slope of the line?

8.3 Circles

PREPARING FOR THIS SECTION *Before getting started, review the following:*

- Square Root Method (Section 7.2, p. 478)

Now Work the **'Are You Prepared?'** problems on page 550.

OBJECTIVES
1 Write the Standard Form of the Equation of a Circle (p. 546)
2 Graph a Circle by Hand and by Using a Graphing Utility (p. 547)
3 Work with the General Form of the Equation of a Circle (p. 549)

1 Write the Standard Form of the Equation of a Circle

One advantage of a coordinate system is that it enables us to translate a geometric statement into an algebraic statement, and vice versa. Consider, for example, the following geometric statement that defines a circle.

DEFINITION A **circle** is a set of points in the xy-plane that are a fixed distance r from a fixed point (h, k). The fixed distance r is called the **radius,** and the fixed point (h, k) is called the **center** of the circle.

Figure 35

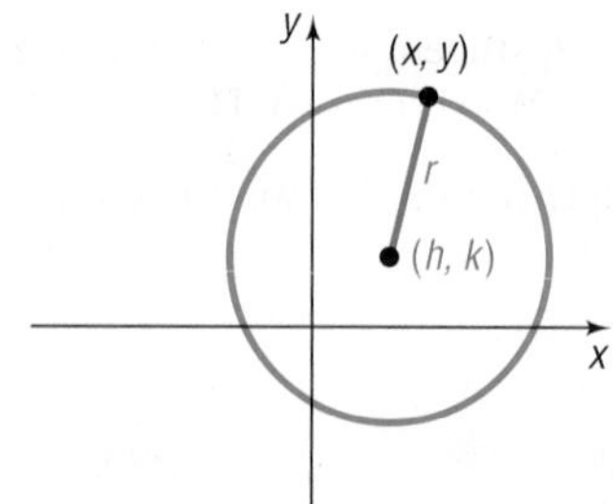

Figure 35 shows the graph of a circle. To find the equation, let (x, y) represent the coordinates of any point on a circle with radius r and center (h, k). Then the distance between the points (x, y) and (h, k) must always equal r. That is, by the distance formula

$$\sqrt{(x-h)^2 + (y-k)^2} = r$$

or, equivalently,

$$(x-h)^2 + (y-k)^2 = r^2$$

DEFINITION The **standard form of an equation of a circle** with radius r and center (h, k) is

$$(x-h)^2 + (y-k)^2 = r^2 \quad \textbf{(1)}$$

THEOREM

The standard form of an equation of a circle of radius r with center at the origin $(0, 0)$ is

$$x^2 + y^2 = r^2$$

DEFINITION

If the radius $r = 1$, the circle whose center is at the origin is called the **unit circle** and has the equation

$$x^2 + y^2 = 1$$

See Figure 36. Notice that the graph of the unit circle is symmetric with respect to the x-axis, the y-axis, and the origin.

Figure 36
Unit circle $x^2 + y^2 = 1$

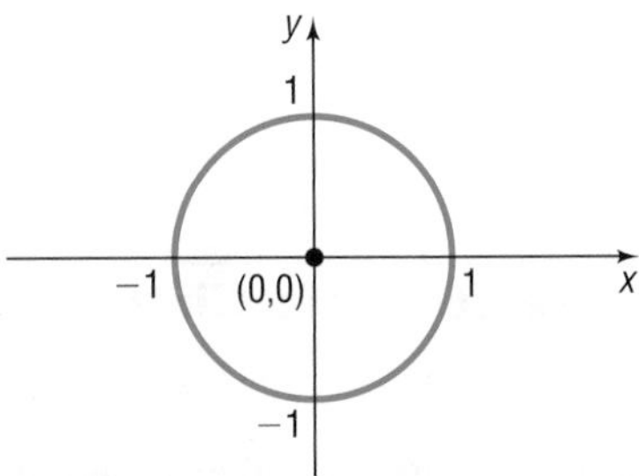

EXAMPLE 1 **Writing the Standard Form of the Equation of a Circle**

Write the standard form of the equation of the circle with radius 5 and center $(-3, 6)$.

Solution Using equation (1) and substituting the values $r = 5$, $h = -3$, and $k = 6$, we have

$$(x - h)^2 + (y - k)^2 = r^2$$
$$(x + 3)^2 + (y - 6)^2 = 25$$

■

Now Work PROBLEM 7

2 Graph a Circle by Hand and by Using a Graphing Utility

EXAMPLE 2 **Graphing a Circle by Hand and by Using a Graphing Utility**

Graph the equation: $(x + 3)^2 + (y - 2)^2 = 16$

Solution Since the equation is in the form of equation (1), its graph is a circle. To graph the equation by hand, compare the given equation to the standard form of the equation of a circle. The comparison yields information about the circle.

$$(x + 3)^2 + (y - 2)^2 = 16$$
$$(x - (-3))^2 + (y - 2)^2 = 4^2$$
$$\uparrow \qquad\qquad \uparrow \quad \uparrow$$
$$(x - h)^2 + (y - k)^2 = r^2$$

Figure 37

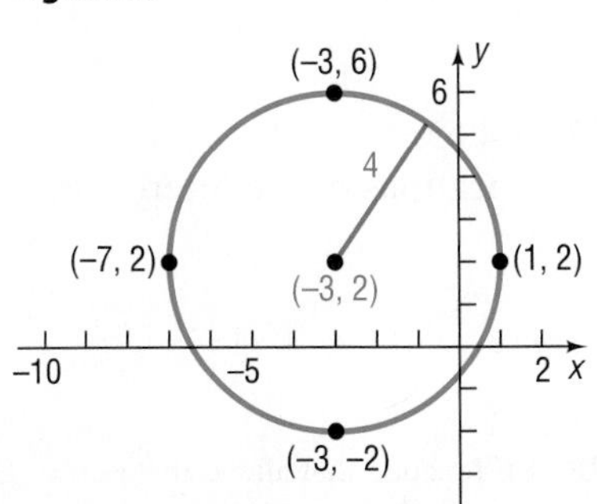

We see that $h = -3$, $k = 2$, and $r = 4$. The circle has center $(-3, 2)$ and a radius of 4 units. To graph this circle, first plot the center $(-3, 2)$. Since the radius is 4, locate four points on the circle by plotting points 4 units to the left, to the right, up, and down from the center. These four points can then be used as guides to obtain the graph. See Figure 37.

In Words

The symbol $\pm$ is read "plus or minus." It means to add and subtract the quantity following the $\pm$ symbol. For example, 5 ± 2 means $5 - 2 = 3$ or $5 + 2 = 7$.

To graph a circle on a graphing utility, we must write the equation in the form $y = \{\text{expression involving } x\}$.* We must solve for y in the equation

$$(x + 3)^2 + (y - 2)^2 = 16$$

$$(y - 2)^2 = 16 - (x + 3)^2 \quad \text{Subtract } (x + 3)^2 \text{ from both sides.}$$

$$y - 2 = \pm\sqrt{16 - (x + 3)^2} \quad \text{Use the Square Root Method.}$$

$$y = 2 \pm \sqrt{16 - (x + 3)^2} \quad \text{Add 2 to both sides.}$$

To graph the circle, we graph the top half

$$Y_1 = 2 + \sqrt{16 - (x + 3)^2}$$

and the bottom half

$$Y_2 = 2 - \sqrt{16 - (x + 3)^2}$$

Also, be sure to use a square screen. Otherwise, the circle will appear distorted. Figure 38 shows the graph on a TI-84 Plus. The graph is "disconnected" due to the resolution of the calculator. ■

Figure 38

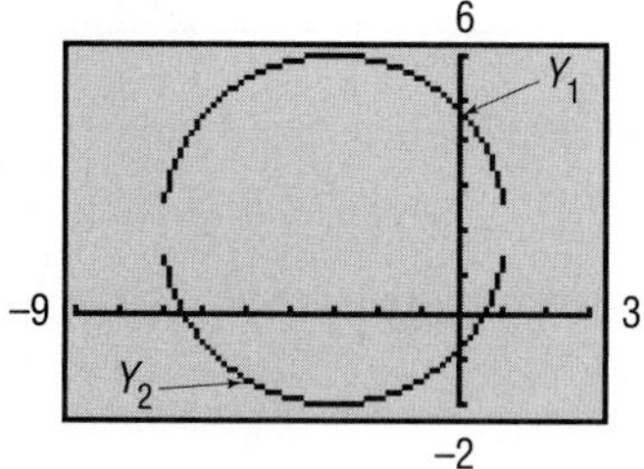

Now Work PROBLEMS 23(a) AND (b)

EXAMPLE 3 **Finding the Intercepts of a Circle**

For the circle $(x + 3)^2 + (y - 2)^2 = 16$, find the intercepts, if any, of its graph.

Solution This is the equation discussed and graphed in Example 2. To find the x-intercepts, if any, let $y = 0$ and solve for x. Then

$$(x + 3)^2 + (y - 2)^2 = 16$$

$$(x + 3)^2 + (0 - 2)^2 = 16 \quad y = 0$$

$$(x + 3)^2 + 4 = 16 \quad \text{Simplify.}$$

$$(x + 3)^2 = 12 \quad \text{Subtract 4 from both sides.}$$

$$x + 3 = \pm\sqrt{12} \quad \text{Apply the Square Root Method.}$$

$$x = -3 \pm 2\sqrt{3} \quad \text{Solve for x.}$$

The x-intercepts are $-3 - 2\sqrt{3} \approx -6.46$ and $-3 + 2\sqrt{3} \approx 0.46$.

To find the y-intercepts, if any, let $x = 0$ and solve for y. Then

$$(x + 3)^2 + (y - 2)^2 = 16$$

$$(0 + 3)^2 + (y - 2)^2 = 16 \quad x = 0$$

$$9 + (y - 2)^2 = 16$$

$$(y - 2)^2 = 7$$

$$y - 2 = \pm\sqrt{7} \quad \text{Apply the Square Root Method.}$$

$$y = 2 \pm \sqrt{7} \quad \text{Solve for y.}$$

The y-intercepts are $2 - \sqrt{7} \approx -0.65$ and $2 + \sqrt{7} \approx 4.65$.

Look back at Figure 37 to verify the approximate locations of the intercepts. ■

Now Work PROBLEM 23 (c)

*Some graphing utilities (e.g., TI-83, TI-84, and TI-86) have a CIRCLE function that allows the user to enter only the coordinates of the center of the circle and its radius to graph the circle.

3 Work with the General Form of the Equation of a Circle

If we eliminate the parentheses from the standard form of the equation of the circle given in Example 3, we get

$$(x + 3)^2 + (y - 2)^2 = 16$$
$$x^2 + 6x + 9 + y^2 - 4y + 4 = 16$$

which, upon simplifying, is equivalent to

$$x^2 + y^2 + 6x - 4y - 3 = 0$$

It can be shown that any equation of the form

$$x^2 + y^2 + ax + by + c = 0$$

has a graph that is a circle or a point, or has no graph at all. For example, the graph of the equation $x^2 + y^2 = 0$ is the single point $(0, 0)$. The equation $x^2 + y^2 + 5 = 0$, or $x^2 + y^2 = -5$, has no graph, because sums of squares of real numbers are never negative.

DEFINITION When its graph is a circle, the equation

$$x^2 + y^2 + ax + by + c = 0$$

is referred to as the **general form of the equation of a circle.**

If an equation of a circle is in the general form, we use the method of completing the square to put the equation in standard form so that we can identify its center and radius.

EXAMPLE 4 **Graphing a Circle Whose Equation Is in General Form**

Graph the equation $x^2 + y^2 + 4x - 6y + 12 = 0$.

Solution Group the expression involving x, group the expression involving y, and put the constant on the right side of the equation. The result is

$$(x^2 + 4x) + (y^2 - 6y) = -12$$

Next, complete the square of each expression in parentheses. Remember that any number added on the left side of the equation must be added on the right.

$$(x^2 + 4x + 4) + (y^2 - 6y + 9) = -12 + 4 + 9$$

$$\left(\frac{4}{2}\right)^2 = 4 \qquad \left(\frac{-6}{2}\right)^2 = 9$$

$$(x + 2)^2 + (y - 3)^2 = 1 \quad \text{Factor}$$

This equation is the standard form of the equation of a circle with radius 1 and center $(-2, 3)$. To graph the equation by hand, use the center $(-2, 3)$ and the radius 1. See Figure 39(a) on the following page.

To graph the equation using a graphing utility, solve for y.

$$(y - 3)^2 = 1 - (x + 2)^2$$
$$y - 3 = \pm\sqrt{1 - (x + 2)^2} \quad \text{Use the Square Root Method.}$$
$$y = 3 \pm\sqrt{1 - (x + 2)^2} \quad \text{Add 3 to both sides.}$$

Figure 39(b) illustrates the graph on a TI-84 Plus graphing calculator.

Figure 39

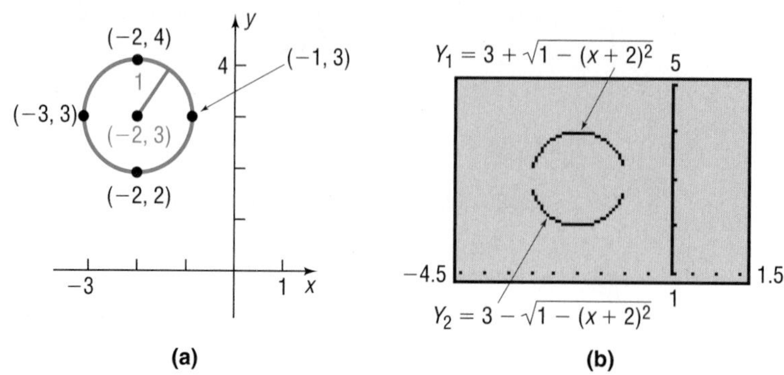

(a) (b)

Now Work PROBLEM 27

EXAMPLE 5 **Finding the General Equation of a Circle**

Find the general equation of the circle whose center is $(1, -2)$ and whose graph contains the point $(4, -2)$.

Solution To find the equation of a circle, we need to know its center and its radius. Here, the center is $(1, -2)$. Since the point $(4, -2)$ is on the graph, the radius r will equal the distance from $(4, -2)$ to the center $(1, -2)$. See Figure 40. Thus,

Figure 40

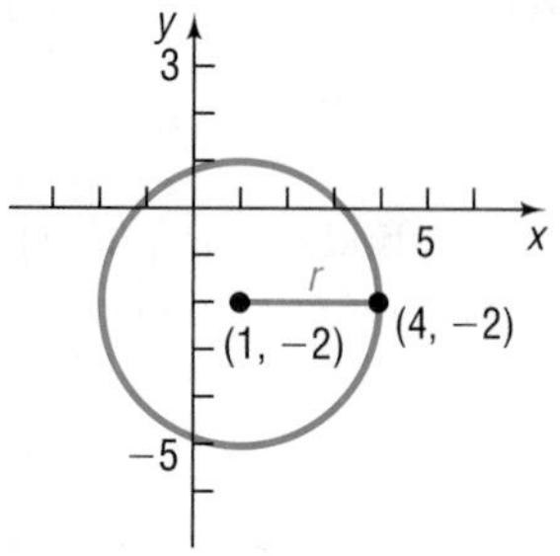

$$r = \sqrt{(4 - 1)^2 + [-2 - (-2)]^2}$$
$$= \sqrt{9} = 3$$

The standard form of the equation of the circle is

$$(x - 1)^2 + (y + 2)^2 = 9$$

Eliminate the parentheses and rearrange the terms to get the general equation

$$x^2 + y^2 - 2x + 4y - 4 = 0$$

Now Work PROBLEM 13

Overview

The discussion in Sections 8.2 and 8.3 about lines and circles dealt with two main types of problems that can be generalized as follows:

1. Given an equation, classify it and graph it.
2. Given a graph, or information about a graph, find its equation.

This text deals with both types of problems. We shall study various equations, classify them, and graph them. The second type of problem is usually more difficult to solve than the first. In many instances a graphing utility can be used to solve problems when information about the problem (such as data) is given.

8.3 Assess Your Understanding

'Are You Prepared?' *Answers are given at the end of these exercises. If you get a wrong answer, read the pages listed in red.*

1. To complete the square of $x^2 + 10x$, you would (*add/subtract*) the number ______.

2. Use the Square Root Method to solve the equation $(x - 2)^2 = 9$. (p. 478)

Concepts and Vocabulary

3. ***True or False*** Every equation of the form
$$x^2 + y^2 + ax + by + c = 0$$
has a circle as its graph.

4. For a circle, the ______ is the distance from the center to any point on the circle.

5. ***True or False*** The radius of the circle $x^2 + y^2 = 9$ is 3.

6. ***True or False*** The center of the circle
$$(x + 3)^2 + (y - 2)^2 = 13$$
is $(3, -2)$.

Skill Building

In Problems 7–10, find the center and radius of each circle. Write the standard form of the equation.

7.
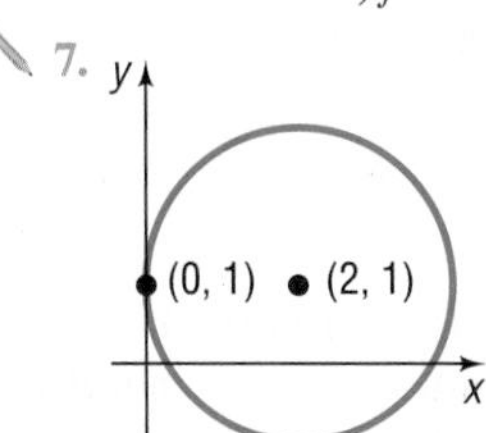

8.
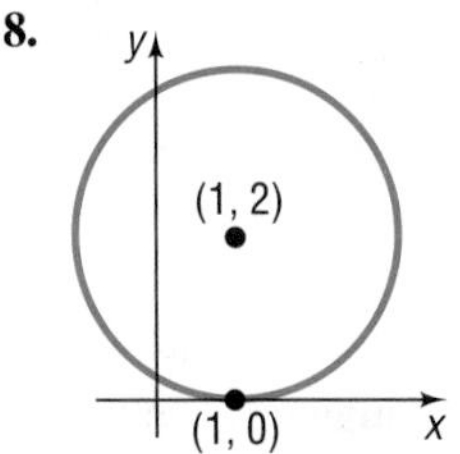

9.
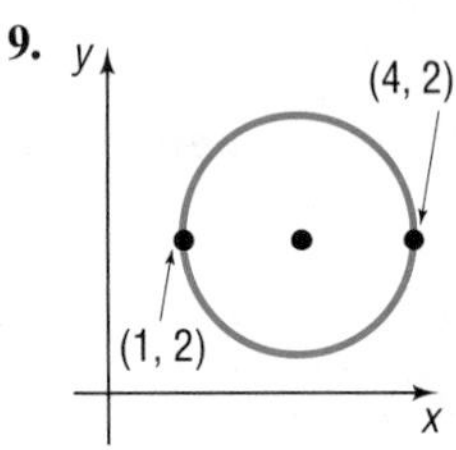

10.
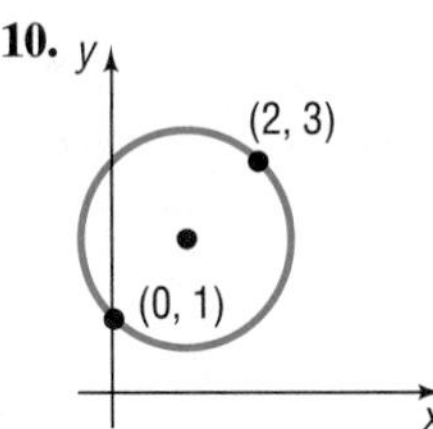

In Problems 11–20, write the standard form of the equation and the general form of the equation of each circle of radius r and center (h, k). Graph each circle.

11. $r = 2;\ (h, k) = (0, 0)$
12. $r = 3;\ (h, k) = (0, 0)$
13. $r = 2;\ (h, k) = (0, 2)$
14. $r = 3;\ (h, k) = (1, 0)$
15. $r = 5;\ (h, k) = (4, -3)$
16. $r = 4;\ (h, k) = (2, -3)$
17. $r = 4;\ (h, k) = (-2, 1)$
18. $r = 7;\ (h, k) = (-5, -2)$
19. $r = \frac{1}{2};\ (h, k) = \left(\frac{1}{2}, 0\right)$
20. $r = \frac{1}{2};\ (h, k) = \left(0, -\frac{1}{2}\right)$

In Problems 21–34, (a) find the center (h, k) and radius r of each circle; (b) graph each circle; (c) find the intercepts, if any.

21. $x^2 + y^2 = 4$
22. $x^2 + (y - 1)^2 = 1$
23. $2(x - 3)^2 + 2y^2 = 8$
24. $3(x + 1)^2 + 3(y - 1)^2 = 6$
25. $x^2 + y^2 - 2x - 4y - 4 = 0$
26. $x^2 + y^2 + 4x + 2y - 20 = 0$
27. $x^2 + y^2 + 4x - 4y - 1 = 0$
28. $x^2 + y^2 - 6x + 2y + 9 = 0$
29. $x^2 + y^2 - x + 2y + 1 = 0$
30. $x^2 + y^2 + x + y - \frac{1}{2} = 0$
31. $2x^2 + 2y^2 - 12x + 8y - 24 = 0$
32. $2x^2 + 2y^2 + 8x + 7 = 0$
33. $2x^2 + 8x + 2y^2 = 0$
34. $3x^2 + 3y^2 - 12y = 0$

In Problems 35–42, find the standard form of the equation of each circle.

35. Center at the origin and containing the point $(-2, 3)$
36. Center $(1, 0)$ and containing the point $(-3, 2)$
37. Center $(2, 3)$ and tangent to the x-axis
38. Center $(-3, 1)$ and tangent to the y-axis
39. With endpoints of a diameter at $(1, 4)$ and $(-3, 2)$
40. With endpoints of a diameter at $(4, 3)$ and $(0, 1)$
41. Center $(-1, 3)$ and tangent to the line $y = 2$
42. Center $(4, -2)$ and tangent to the line $x = 1$

In Problems 43–46, match each graph with the correct equation.

(a) $(x - 3)^2 + (y + 3)^2 = 9$ (b) $(x + 1)^2 + (y - 2)^2 = 4$ (c) $(x - 1)^2 + (y + 2)^2 = 4$ (d) $(x + 3)^2 + (y - 3)^2 = 9$

43.
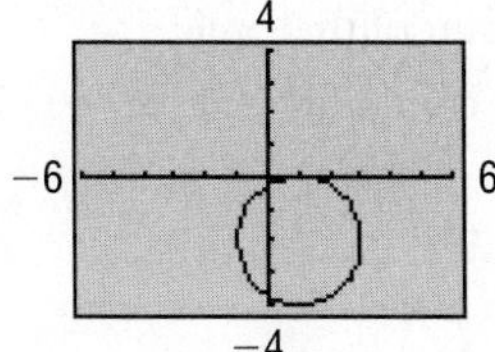

44.
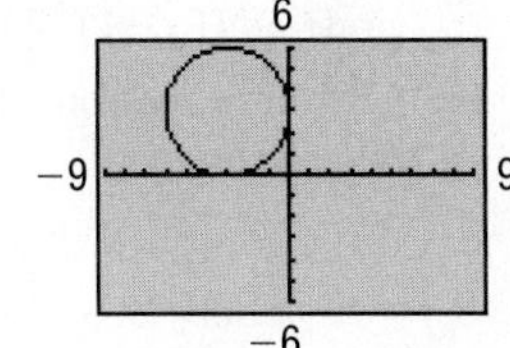

45.
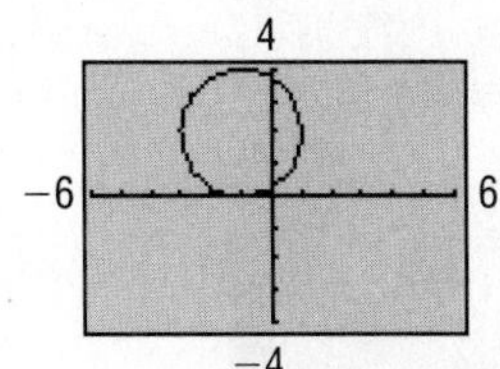

46.
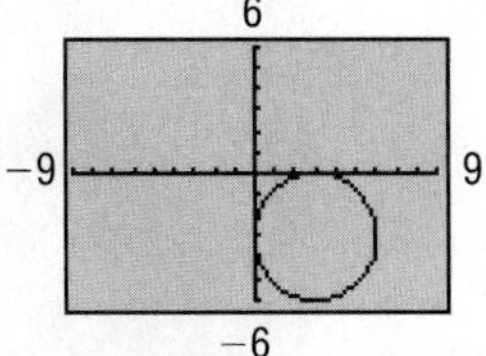

Applications and Extensions

47. Find the area of the square in the figure.

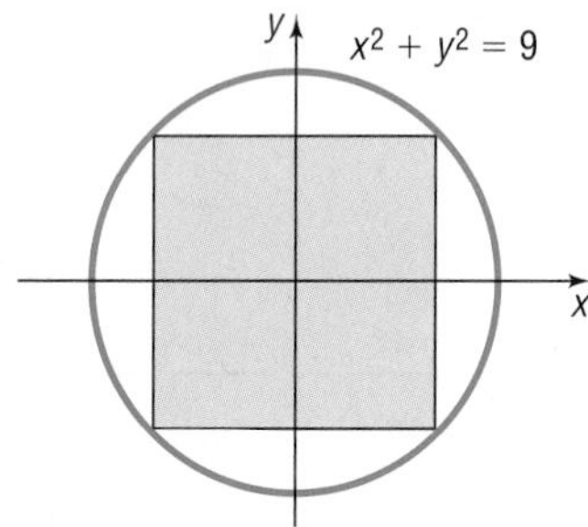

48. Find the area of the blue shaded region in the figure, assuming the quadrilateral inside the circle is a square.

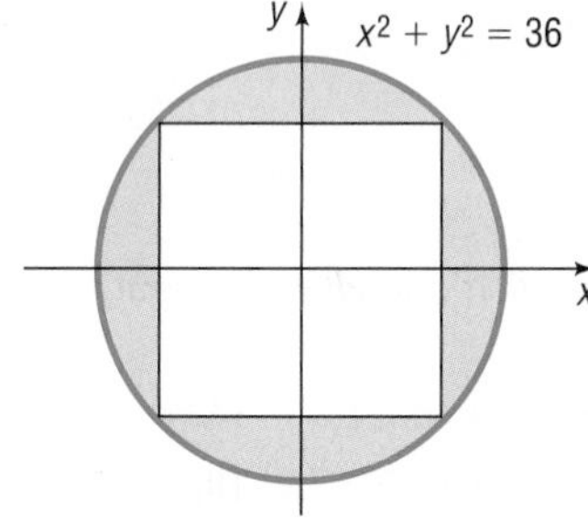

49. Ferris Wheel The original Ferris wheel was built in 1893 by Pittsburgh, Pennsylvania, bridge builder George W. Ferris. The Ferris wheel was originally built for the 1893 World's Fair in Chicago and was later reconstructed for the 1904 World's Fair in St. Louis. It had a maximum height of 264 feet and a wheel diameter of 250 feet. Find an equation for the wheel if the center of the wheel is on the y-axis.

Source: inventors.about.com

50. Ferris Wheel In 2008, the Singapore Flyer opened as the world's largest Ferris wheel. It has a maximum height of 165 meters and a diameter of 150 meters, with one full rotation taking approximately 30 minutes. Find an equation for the wheel if the center of the wheel is on the y-axis.

Source: Wikipedia

51. Weather Satellites Earth is represented on a map of a portion of the solar system so that its surface is the circle with equation $x^2 + y^2 + 2x + 4y - 4091 = 0$. A weather satellite circles 0.6 unit above Earth with the center of its circular orbit at the center of Earth. Find the equation for the orbit of the satellite on this map.

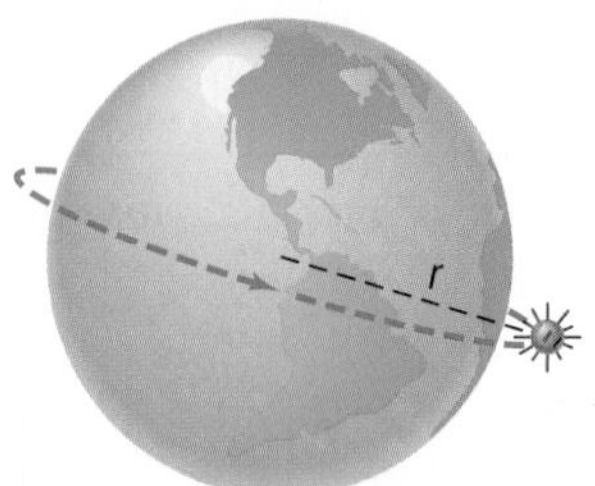

52. The **tangent line** to a circle may be defined as the line that intersects the circle in a single point, called the **point of tangency.** See the figure.

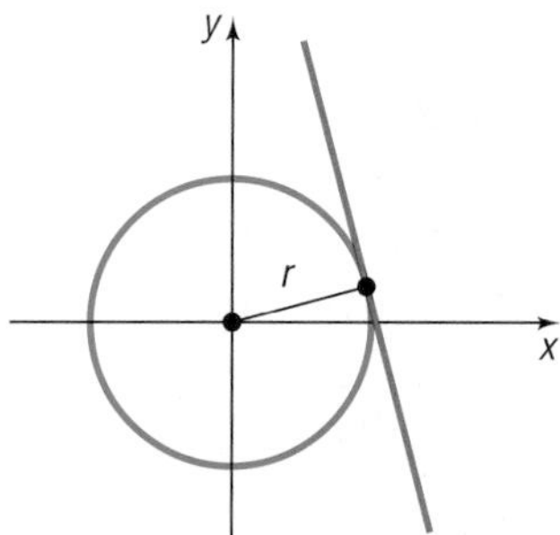

If the equation of the circle is $x^2 + y^2 = r^2$ and the equation of the tangent line is $y = mx + b$, show that:

(a) $r^2(1 + m^2) = b^2$
[**Hint:** The quadratic equation $x^2 + (mx + b)^2 = r^2$ has exactly one solution.]

(b) The point of tangency is $\left(\frac{-r^2 m}{b}, \frac{r^2}{b}\right)$.

(c) The tangent line is perpendicular to the line containing the center of the circle and the point of tangency.

53. The Greek Method The Greek method for finding the equation of the tangent line to a circle uses the fact that at any point on a circle the lines containing the center and the tangent line are perpendicular (see Problem 52). Use this method to find an equation of the tangent line to the circle $x^2 + y^2 = 9$ at the point $(1, 2\sqrt{2})$.

54. Use the Greek method described in Problem 53 to find an equation of the tangent line to the circle $x^2 + y^2 - 4x + 6y + 4 = 0$ at the point $(3, 2\sqrt{2} - 3)$.

55. Refer to Problem 52. The line $x - 2y + 4 = 0$ is tangent to a circle at $(0, 2)$. The line $y = 2x - 7$ is tangent to the same circle at $(3, -1)$. Find the center of the circle.

56. Find an equation of the line containing the centers of the two circles

$$x^2 + y^2 - 4x + 6y + 4 = 0$$

and

$$x^2 + y^2 + 6x + 4y + 9 = 0$$

57. If a circle of radius 2 is made to roll along the x-axis, what is an equation for the path of the center of the circle?

58. If the circumference of a circle is 6π, what is its radius?

Explaining Concepts: Discussion and Writing

59. Which of the following equations might have the graph shown? (More than one answer is possible.)
(a) $(x - 2)^2 + (y + 3)^2 = 13$
(b) $(x - 2)^2 + (y - 2)^2 = 8$
(c) $(x - 2)^2 + (y - 3)^2 = 13$
(d) $(x + 2)^2 + (y - 2)^2 = 8$
(e) $x^2 + y^2 - 4x - 9y = 0$
(f) $x^2 + y^2 + 4x - 2y = 0$
(g) $x^2 + y^2 - 9x - 4y = 0$
(h) $x^2 + y^2 - 4x - 4y = 4$

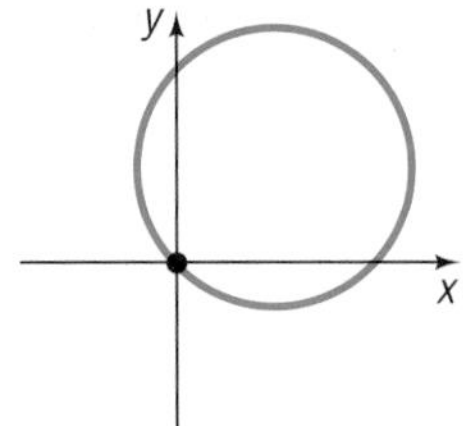

60. Which of the following equations might have the graph shown? (More than one answer is possible.)
(a) $(x - 2)^2 + y^2 = 3$
(b) $(x + 2)^2 + y^2 = 3$
(c) $x^2 + (y - 2)^2 = 3$
(d) $(x + 2)^2 + y^2 = 4$
(e) $x^2 + y^2 + 10x + 16 = 0$
(f) $x^2 + y^2 + 10x - 2y = 1$
(g) $x^2 + y^2 + 9x + 10 = 0$
(h) $x^2 + y^2 - 9x - 10 = 0$

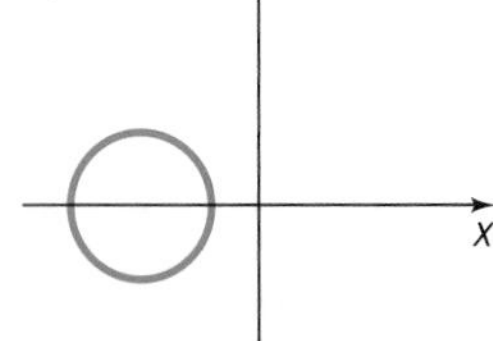

61. Explain how the center and radius of a circle can be used to graph the circle.

62. **What Went Wrong?** A student stated that the center and radius of the graph whose equation is $(x + 3)^2 + (y - 2)^2 = 16$ are $(3, -2)$ and 4, respectively. Why is this incorrect?

Interactive Exercises

Ask your instructor if the applets below are of interest to you.

63. **Center of a Circle** *Open the "Circle: the role of the center" applet.* Place the cursor on the center of the circle and hold the mouse button. Drag the center around the Cartesian plane and note how the equation of the circle changes.
(a) What is the radius of the circle?
(b) Draw a circle whose center is at $(1, 3)$. What is the equation of the circle?
(c) Draw a circle whose center is at $(-1, 3)$. What is the equation of the circle?
(d) Draw a circle whose center is at $(-1, -3)$. What is the equation of the circle?
(e) Draw a circle whose center is at $(1, -3)$. What is the equation of the circle?
(f) Write a few sentences explaining the role the center of the circle plays in the equation of the circle.

64. **Radius of a Circle** *Open the "Circle: the role of the radius" applet.* Place the cursor on point B, press and hold the mouse button. Drag B around the Cartesian plane.
(a) What is the center of the circle?
(b) Move B to a point in the Cartesian plane directly above the center such that the radius of the circle is 5.
(c) Move B to a point in the Cartesian plane such that the radius of the circle is 4.
(d) Move B to a point in the Cartesian plane such that the radius of the circle is 3.
(e) Find the coordinates of two points with integer coordinates in the fourth quadrant on the circle that result in a circle of radius 5 with center equal to that found in part (a).
(f) Use the concept of symmetry about the center, vertical line through the center of the circle, and horizontal line through the center of the circle to find three other points with integer coordinates in the other three quadrants that lie on the circle of radius 5 with center equal to that found in part (a).

'Are You Prepared?' Answers

1. add; 25 **2.** $\{-1, 5\}$

CHAPTER REVIEW

Things to Know

Formulas

Slope (p. 530)	$m = \dfrac{y_2 - y_1}{x_2 - x_1}$ if $x_1 \neq x_2$; undefined if $x_1 = x_2$
Parallel lines (p. 538)	Equal slopes ($m_1 = m_2$) and different y-intercepts ($b_1 \neq b_2$)
Perpendicular lines (p. 539)	Product of slopes is -1 ($m_1 \cdot m_2 = -1$)

Equations of Lines and Circles

Vertical line (p. 534)	$x = a$; a is the x-intercept
Horizontal line (p. 535)	$y = b$; b is the y-intercept
Point–slope form of the equation of a line (p. 534)	$y - y_1 = m(x - x_1)$; m is the slope of the line, (x_1, y_1) is a point on the line
Slope–intercept form of the equation of a line (p. 536)	$y = mx + b$; m is the slope of the line, b is the y-intercept
General form of the equation of a line (p. 537)	$Ax + By = C$; A, B not both 0

Standard form of the equation of a circle (p. 546)	$(x-h)^2+(y-k)^2=r^2$; r is the radius of the circle, (h,k) is the center of the circle
Equation of the unit circle (p. 547)	$x^2+y^2=1$
General form of the equation of a circle (p. 549)	$x^2+y^2+ax+by+c=0$, with restrictions on a, b, and c

Objectives

Section		You should be able to ...	Examples	Review Exercises
8.1	1	Find intercepts algebraically from an equation (p. 522)	1	5–9
	2	Test an equation for symmetry (p. 523)	2, 3	5–9
	3	Know how to graph key equations (p. 525)	4–6	27
8.2	1	Calculate and interpret the slope of a line (p. 530)	1	1–3, 29, 31
	2	Graph lines given a point and the slope (p. 533)	2	28
	3	Find the equation of a vertical line (p. 533)	3	17
	4	Use the point–slope form of a line; identify horizontal lines (p. 534)	4, 5	15, 16
	5	Find the equation of a line given two points (p. 535)	6	18–20
	6	Write the equation of a line in slope–intercept form (p. 535)	pg. 535	15, 16, 18–22
	7	Identify the slope and y-intercept of a line from its equation (p. 536)	7	23, 24
	8	Graph lines written in general form using intercepts (p. 537)	8	25, 26
	9	Find equations of parallel lines (p. 538)	9, 10	21
	10	Find equations of perpendicular lines (p. 539)	11, 12	22
8.3	1	Write the standard form of the equation of a circle (p. 546)	1	10, 11, 30
	2	Graph a circle by hand and by using a graphing utility (p. 547)	2, 3	12–14
	3	Work with the general form of the equation of a circle (p. 549)	4, 5	13, 14

Review Exercises

In Problems 1–4, find the following for each pair of points:
(a) The slope of the line containing the points
(b) Interpret the slope found in part (a)

1. $(0, 0); (4, 2)$
2. $(1, -1); (-2, 3)$
3. $(4, -4); (4, 8)$
4. $(-2, -1); (3, -1)$

In Problems 5–9, list the intercepts and test for symmetry with respect to the x-axis, the y-axis, and the origin.

5. $2x = 3y^2$
6. $x^2 + 4y^2 = 16$
7. $y = x^4 - 3x^2 - 4$
8. $y = x^3 - x$
9. $x^2 + x + y^2 + 2y = 0$

In Problems 10–11, find the standard form of the equation of the circle whose center and radius are given.

10. $(h, k) = (-2, 3); r = 4$
11. $(h, k) = (-1, -2); r = 1$

In Problems 12–14, find the center and radius of each circle. Graph each circle by hand. Find the intercepts, if any, of each circle.

12. $x^2 + (y-1)^2 = 4$
13. $x^2 + y^2 - 2x + 4y - 4 = 0$
14. $3x^2 + 3y^2 - 6x + 12y = 0$

In Problems 15–22, find an equation of the line having the given characteristics. Express your answer using either the general form or the slope–intercept form of the equation of a line, whichever you prefer.

15. Slope $= -2$; containing the point $(3, -1)$
16. Slope $= 0$; containing the point $(-5, 4)$
17. Vertical; containing the point $(-3, 4)$
18. x-intercept $= 2$; containing the point $(4, -5)$
19. y-intercept $= -2$; containing the point $(5, -3)$
20. Containing the points $(3, -4)$ and $(2, 1)$
21. Parallel to the line $2x - 3y = -4$; containing the point $(-5, 3)$
22. Perpendicular to the line $3x - y = -4$; containing the point $(-2, 4)$

In Problems 23–24, find the slope and y-intercept of each line. Graph the line, labeling any intercepts.

23. $4x - 5y = -20$

24. $\frac{1}{2}x - \frac{1}{3}y = -\frac{1}{6}$

In Problems 25–26, find the intercepts and graph each line.

25. $2x - 3y = 12$

26. $\frac{1}{2}x + \frac{1}{3}y = 2$

27. Sketch a graph of $y = x^3$.

28. Graph the line with slope $\frac{2}{3}$ containing the point $(1, 2)$.

29. Show that the points $A = (-2, 0)$, $B = (-4, 4)$, and $C = (8, 5)$ are the vertices of a right triangle by using the slopes of the lines joining the vertices.

30. The endpoints of the diameter of a circle are $(-3, 2)$ and $(5, -6)$. Find the center and radius of the circle. Write the standard equation of this circle.

31. Show that the points $A = (2, 5)$, $B = (6, 1)$, and $C = (8, -1)$ lie on a line by using slopes.

32. Mortgage Payments The monthly payment p on a mortgage varies directly with the amount borrowed B. If the monthly payment on a 30-year mortgage is \$854.00 when \$130,000 is borrowed, find an equation that relates the monthly payment p to the amount borrowed B for a mortgage with the same terms. Then find the monthly payment p when the amount borrowed B is \$165,000.

33. Weight of a Body The weight of a body varies inversely with the square of its distance from the center of Earth. Assuming that the radius of Earth is 3960 miles, how much would a man weigh at an altitude of 1 mile above Earth's surface if he weighs 200 pounds on Earth's surface?

---

34. Kepler's Third Law of Planetary Motion Kepler's Third Law of Planetary Motion states that the square of the period of revolution T of a planet varies directly with the cube of its mean distance a from the Sun. If the mean distance of Earth from the Sun is 93 million miles, what is the mean distance of the planet Mercury from the Sun, given that Mercury has a "year" of 88 days?

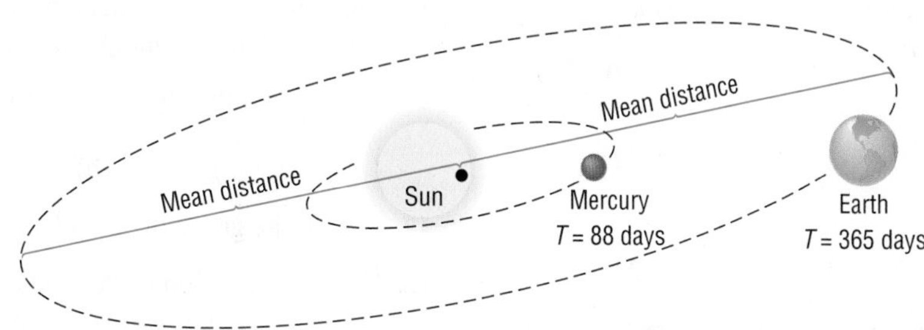

35. Create four problems that you might be asked to do given the two points $(-3, 4)$ and $(6, 1)$. Each problem should involve a different concept. Be sure that your directions are clearly stated.

36. Describe each of the following graphs in the xy-plane. Give justification.

(a) $x = 0$ (b) $y = 0$ (c) $x + y = 0$ (d) $xy = 0$ (e) $x^2 + y^2 = 0$

37. Suppose that you have a rectangular field that requires watering. Your watering system consists of an arm of variable length that rotates so that the watering pattern is a circle. Decide where to position the arm and what length it should be so that the entire field is watered most efficiently. When does it become desirable to use more than one arm?

[**Hint:** Use a rectangular coordinate system positioned as shown in the figures. Write equations for the circle(s) swept out by the watering arm(s).]

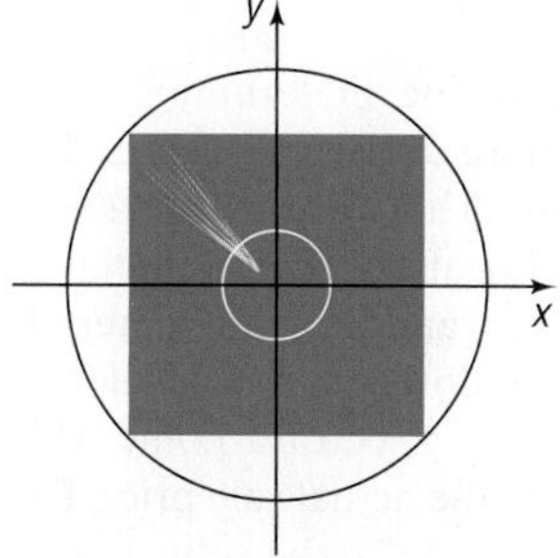

Square field

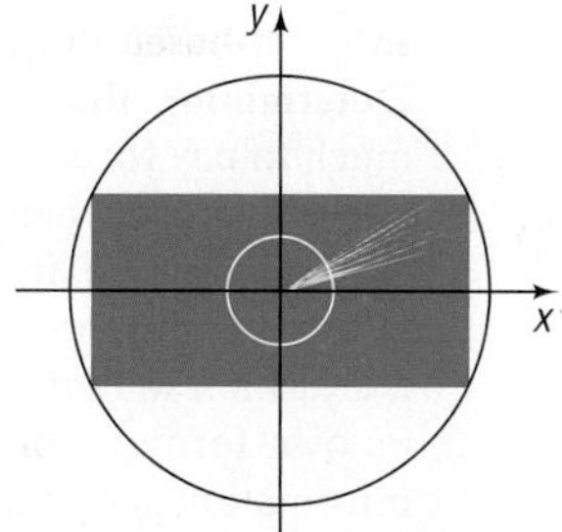

Rectangular field, one arm

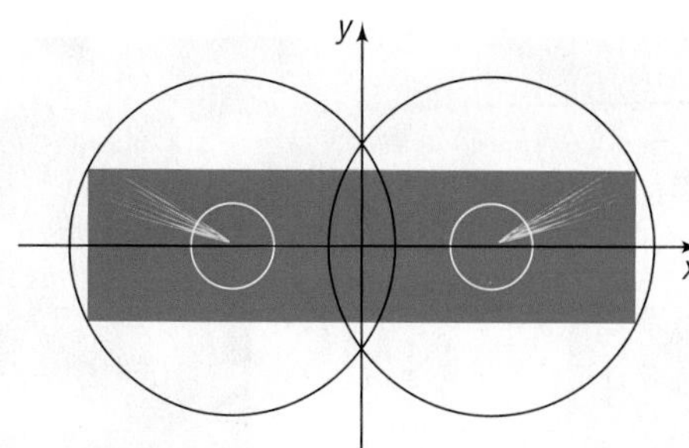

Rectangular field, two arms

CHAPTER TEST

The Chapter Test Prep Videos are step-by-step test solutions available in the Video Resources DVD, in MyMathLab, or on this text's YouTube Channel. Flip back to the Student Resources page to see the exact web address for this text's YouTube channel.

1. Use $P_1 = (-1, 3)$ and $P_2 = (5, -1)$.
   (a) Find the slope of the line containing P_1 and P_2.
   (b) Interpret this slope.
2. Graph $y = x^2 - 9$ by plotting points.
3. Sketch the graph of $y^2 = x$.
4. List the intercepts and test for symmetry: $x^2 + y = 9$.
5. Write the slope–intercept form of the line with slope -2 containing the point $(3, -4)$. Graph the line.
6. Find the slope and y-intercept: $2x + 3y = 9$.
7. Graph the line $3x - 4y = 24$ by finding the intercepts.
8. Write the general form of the circle with center $(4, -3)$ and radius 5.
9. Find the center and radius of the circle $x^2 + y^2 + 4x - 2y - 4 = 0$. Graph this circle.
10. For the line $2x + 3y = 6$, find a line parallel to it containing the point $(1, -1)$. Also find a line perpendicular to it containing the point $(0, 3)$.
11. **Resistance due to a Conductor** The resistance (in ohms) of a circular conductor varies directly with the length of the conductor and inversely with the square of the radius of the conductor. If 50 feet of wire with a radius of 6×10^{-3} inch has a resistance of 10 ohms, what would be the resistance of 100 feet of the same wire if the radius is increased to 7×10^{-3} inch?

CUMULATIVE REVIEW

In Problems 1–8, find the real solution(s) of each equation.

1. $3x - 5 = 0$
2. $x^2 - x - 12 = 0$
3. $2x^2 - 5x - 3 = 0$
4. $x^2 - 2x - 2 = 0$
5. $x^2 + 2x + 5 = 0$
6. $\sqrt{2x + 1} = 3$
7. $|x - 2| = 1$
8. $\sqrt{x^2 + 4x} = 2$

In Problems 9 and 10, solve each equation in the complex number system.

9. $x^2 = -9$
10. $x^2 - 2x + 5 = 0$

In Problems 11–14, solve each inequality. Graph the solution set.

11. $2x - 3 \leq 7$
12. $-1 < x + 4 < 5$
13. $|x - 2| \leq 1$
14. $|2 + x| > 3$
15. Find the distance between the points $P = (-1, 3)$ and $Q = (4, -2)$. Find the midpoint of the line segment from P to Q.
16. Which of the following points are on the graph of $y = x^3 - 3x + 1$?
    (a) $(-2, -1)$ (b) $(2, 3)$ (c) $(3, 1)$
17. Sketch the graph of $y = x^3$.
18. Find the equation of the line containing the points $(-1, 4)$ and $(2, -2)$. Express your answer in slope–intercept form.
19. Find the equation of the line perpendicular to the line $y = 2x + 1$ and containing the point $(3, 5)$. Express your answer in slope–intercept form and graph the line.
20. Graph the equation $x^2 + y^2 - 4x + 8y - 5 = 0$.

CHAPTER PROJECT

Internet-based Project

Determining the Selling Price of a Home Determining how much to pay for a home is one of the more difficult decisions that must be made when purchasing a home. There are many factors that play a role in a home's value. Location, size, number of bedrooms, number of bathrooms, lot size, and building materials are just a few. Fortunately, the website Zillow.com has developed its own formula for predicting the selling price of a home. This information is a great tool for predicting the actual sale price. For example, the data below show the "zestimate"—the selling price of a home as predicted by the folks at Zillow and the actual selling price of the home for homes in Oak Park, Illinois.

Zestimate (000s of dollars)	Sale Price (000s of dollars)
291.5	268
320	305
371.5	375
303.5	283
351.5	350
314	275
332.5	356
295	300
313	285
368	385

The graph below, called a scatter diagram, shows the points (291.5, 268), (320, 305), . . . , (368, 385) in a Cartesian plane. From the graph, it appears that the data follow a linear relation.

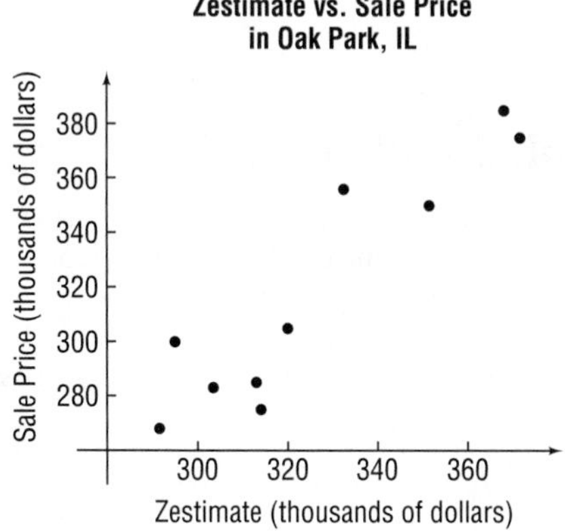

1. Imagine drawing a line through the data that appears to fit the data well. Do you believe the slope of the line would be positive, negative, or close to zero? Why?
2. Pick two points from the scatter diagram. Treat the zestimate as the value of x and treat the sale price as the corresponding value of y. Find the equation of the line through the two points you selected.
3. Interpret the slope of the line.
4. Use your equation to predict the selling price of a home whose zestimate is \$335,000.
5. Do you believe it would be a good idea to use the equation you found in part 2 if the zestimate is \$950,000? Why or why not?
6. Choose a location in which you would like to live. Go to www.zillow.com and randomly select at least ten homes that have recently sold.
   (a) Draw a scatter diagram of your data.
   (b) Select two points from the scatter diagram and find the equation of the line through the points.
   (c) Interpret the slope.
   (d) Find a home from the Zillow website that interests you under the "Make Me Move" option for which a zestimate is available. Use your equation to predict the sale price based on the estimate.

9 Functions and Their Graphs

Outline

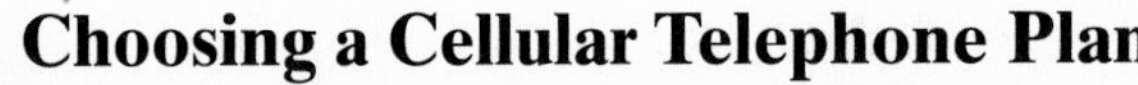

Choosing a Cellular Telephone Plan

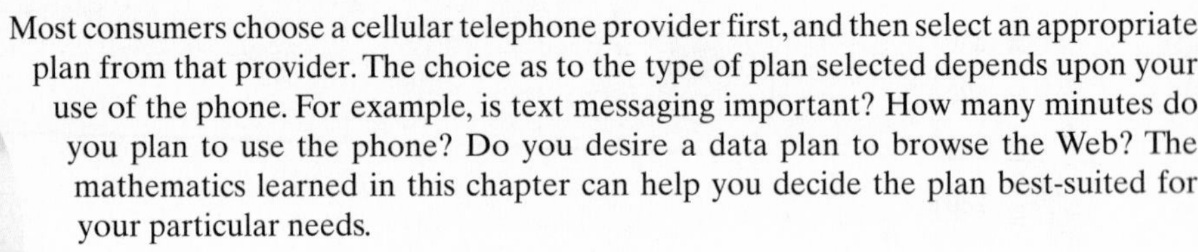

Most consumers choose a cellular telephone provider first, and then select an appropriate plan from that provider. The choice as to the type of plan selected depends upon your use of the phone. For example, is text messaging important? How many minutes do you plan to use the phone? Do you desire a data plan to browse the Web? The mathematics learned in this chapter can help you decide the plan best-suited for your particular needs.

—See the Internet-based Chapter Project— 

A LOOK BACK So far, our discussion has focused on techniques for graphing equations containing two variables.

A LOOK AHEAD In this chapter, we look at a special type of equation involving two variables called a *function*. This chapter deals with what a function is, how to graph functions, properties of functions, and how functions are used in applications. The word *function* apparently was introduced by René Descartes in 1637. For him, a function simply meant any positive integral power of a variable *x*. Gottfried Wilhelm Leibniz (1646–1716), who always emphasized the geometric side of mathematics, used the word *function* to denote any quantity associated with a curve, such as the coordinates of a point on the curve. Leonhard Euler (1707–1783) employed the word to mean any equation or formula involving variables and constants. His idea of a function is similar to the one most often seen in courses that precede calculus. Later, the use of functions in investigating heat flow equations led to a very broad definition, due to Lejeune Dirichlet (1805–1859), which describes a function as a correspondence between two sets. It is his definition that we use here.

9.1 Functions

PREPARING FOR THIS SECTION *Before getting started, review the following:*

- Intervals (Section 7.5, pp. 504–505)
- Solving Inequalities (Section 7.5, pp. 507–508)

Now Work the **'Are You Prepared?'** problems on page 569.

OBJECTIVES
1 Determine Whether a Relation Represents a Function (p. 559)
2 Find the Value of a Function (p. 562)
3 Find the Domain of a Function Defined by an Equation (p. 565)
4 Form the Sum, Difference, Product, and Quotient of Two Functions (p. 567)

1 Determine Whether a Relation Represents a Function

Often there are situations where one variable is somehow linked to the value of another variable. For example, an individual's level of education is linked to annual income. Engine size is linked to gas mileage. When the value of one variable is related to the value of a second variable, we have a *relation*. A **relation** is a correspondence between two sets. If x and y are two elements in these sets and if a relation exists between x and y, then we say that x **corresponds** to y or that y **depends on** x, and we write $x \rightarrow y$.

Figure 1

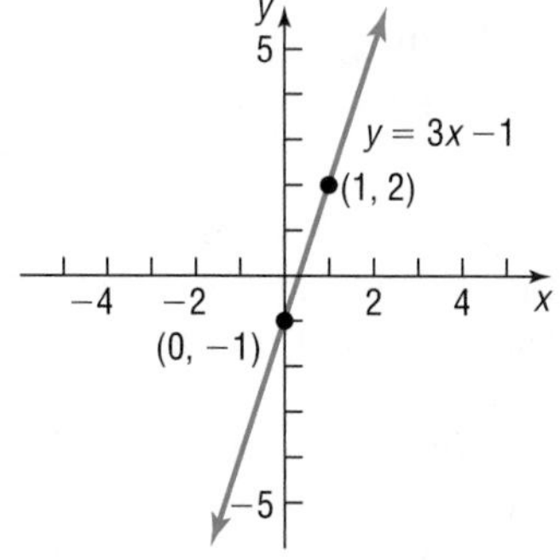

There are a number of ways to express relations between two sets. For example, the equation $y = 3x - 1$ shows a relation between x and y. It says that if we take some number x, multiply it by 3, and then subtract 1 we obtain the corresponding value of y. In this sense, x serves as the **input** to the relation and y is the **output** of the relation. We can also express this relation as a graph as shown in Figure 1.

Not only can a relation be expressed through an equation or graph, but we can also express a relation through a technique called *mapping*. A **map** illustrates a relation by using a set of inputs and drawing arrows to the corresponding element in the set of outputs. **Ordered pairs** can be used to represent $x \rightarrow y$ as (x, y).

EXAMPLE 1 **Maps and Ordered Pairs as Relations**

Figure 2 shows a relation between states and the number of representatives each state has in the House of Representatives. The relation might be named "number of representatives."

Figure 2

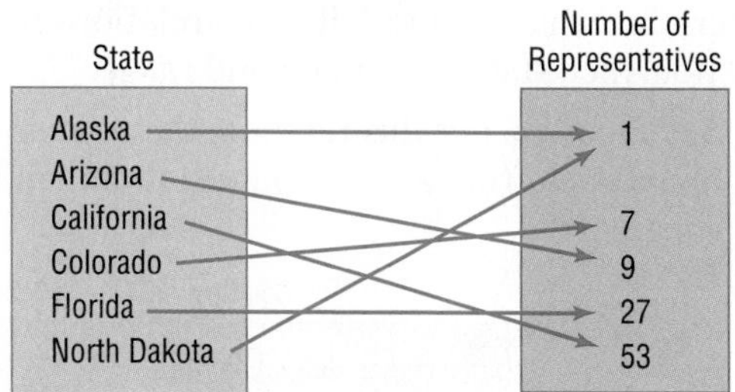

In this relation, Alaska corresponds to 1, Arizona corresponds to 9, and so on. Using ordered pairs, this relation would be expressed as

$$\{(\text{Alaska}, 1), (\text{Arizona}, 9), (\text{California}, 53), (\text{Colorado}, 7), (\text{Florida}, 27), (\text{North Dakota}, 1)\}$$

■

One of the most important concepts in algebra is the *function*. A function is a special type of relation. To understand the idea behind a function, let's revisit the relation presented in Example 1. If we were to ask, "How many representatives does Alaska have?," you would respond "1." In fact, each input *state* corresponds to a single output *number of representatives*.

Let's consider a second relation where we have a correspondence between four people and their phone numbers. See Figure 3. Notice that Colleen has two telephone numbers. If asked, "What is Colleen's phone number?" you cannot assign a single number to her.

Figure 3

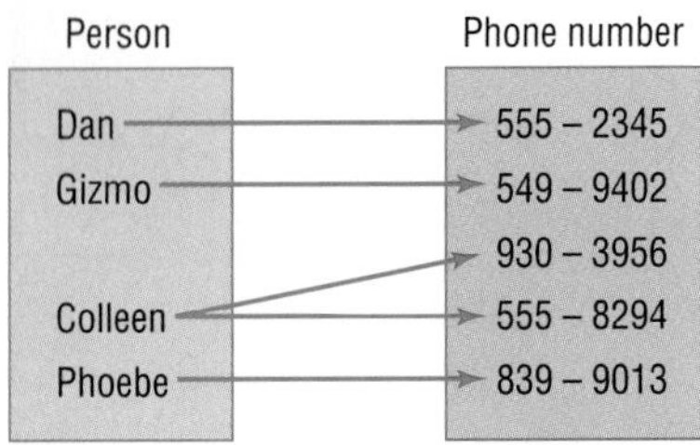

Let's look at one more relation. Figure 4 is a relation that shows a correspondence between *animals* and *life expectancy*. If asked to determine the life expectancy of a dog, we would all respond "11 years." If asked to determine the life expectancy of a rabbit, we would all respond "7 years."

Figure 4

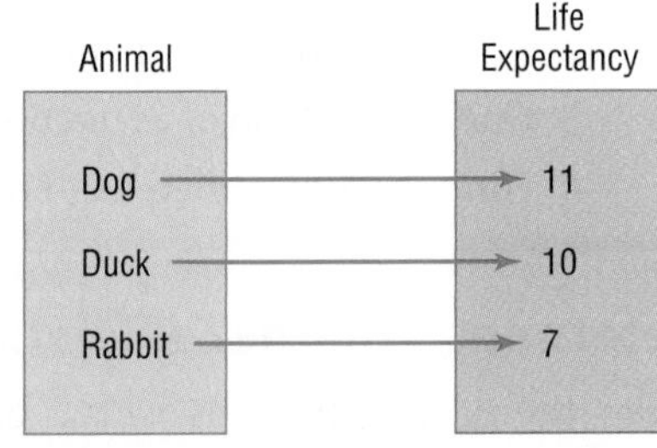

Notice that the relations presented in Figures 2 and 4 have something in common. What is it? The common link between these two relations is that each input corresponds to exactly one output. This leads to the definition of a *function*.

DEFINITION

Let X and Y be two nonempty sets.* A **function** from X into Y is a relation that associates with each element of X exactly one element of Y.

Figure 5

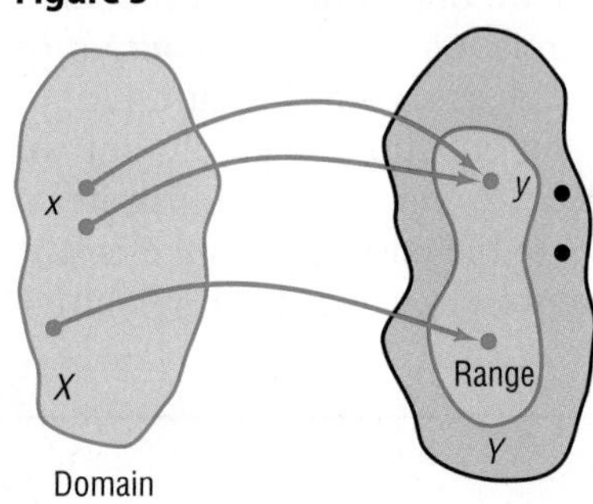

The set X is called the **domain** of the function. For each element x in X, the corresponding element y in Y is called the **value** of the function at x, or the **image** of x. The set of all images of the elements in the domain is called the **range** of the function. See Figure 5.

Since there may be some elements in Y that are not the image of some x in X, it follows that the range of a function may be a subset of Y, as shown in Figure 5. For example, consider the function $y = x^2$. Since $x^2 \geq 0$ for all real numbers x, the range of $y = x^2$ is $\{y \mid y \geq 0\}$, which is a subset of the set of all real numbers, Y.

Not all relations between two sets are functions. The next example shows how to determine whether a relation is a function.

EXAMPLE 2 Determining Whether a Relation Represents a Function

Determine which of the following relations represent a function. If the relation is a function, then state its domain and range.

(a) See Figure 6. For this relation, the domain represents the number of calories in a sandwich from a fast-food restaurant and the range represents the fat content (in grams).

Figure 6
Source: Each company's Web site.

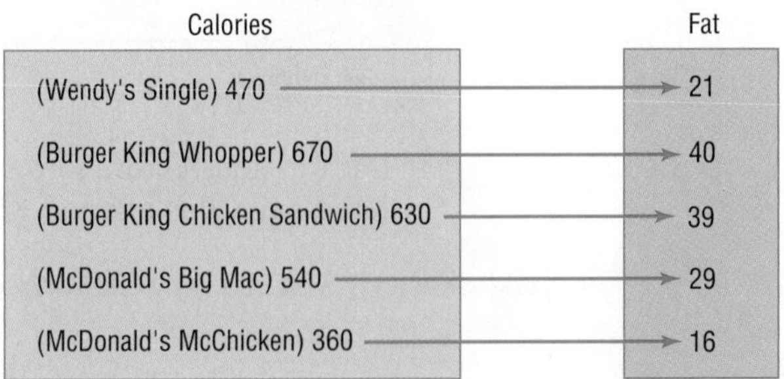

*The sets X and Y will usually be sets of real numbers, in which case a (real) function results. The two sets can also be sets of complex numbers, and then we have defined a complex function. In the broad definition (due to Lejeune Dirichlet), X and Y can be any two sets.

(b) See Figure 7. For this relation, the domain represents gasoline stations in Collier County, Florida, and the range represents the price per gallon of regular unleaded gasoline in July, 2011.

(c) See Figure 8. For this relation, the domain represents the weight (in carats) of pear-cut diamonds and the range represents the price (in dollars).

Figure 7

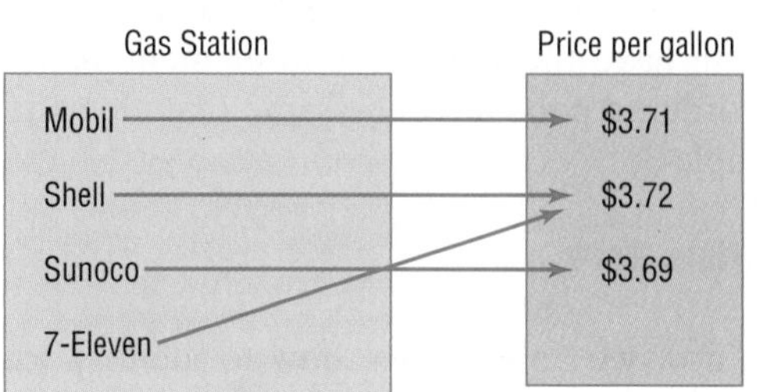

Figure 8

Source: Used with permission of Diamonds.com

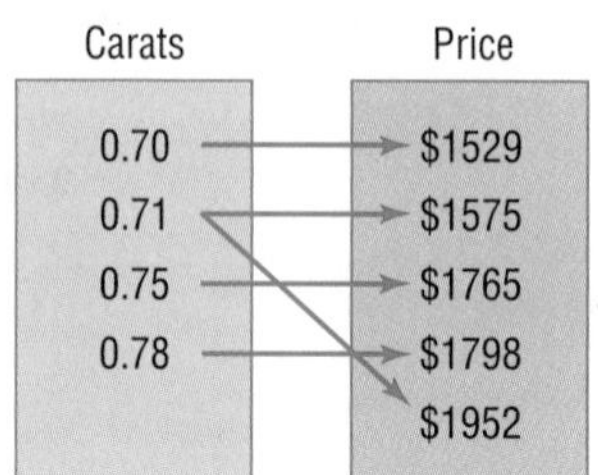

Solution (a) The relation in Figure 6 is a function because each element in the domain corresponds to exactly one element in the range. The domain of the function is $\{470, 670, 630, 540, 360\}$, and the range of the function is $\{21, 40, 39, 29, 16\}$.

(b) The relation in Figure 7 is a function because each element in the domain corresponds to exactly one element in the range. The domain of the function is {Mobil, Shell, Sunoco, 7-Eleven}. The range of the function is $\{3.69, 3.71, 3.72\}$. Notice that it is okay for more than one element in the domain to correspond to the same element in the range (Shell and 7-Eleven each sell gas for \$3.72 a gallon).

(c) The relation in Figure 8 is not a function because each element in the domain does not correspond to exactly one element in the range. If a 0.71-carat diamond is chosen from the domain, a single price cannot be assigned to it. ■

Now Work PROBLEM 15

The idea behind a function is its predictability. If the input is known, we can use the function to determine the output. With "nonfunctions," we don't have this predictability. Look back at Figure 6. If asked, "How many grams of fat are in a 470-calorie sandwich?" we can use the correspondence to answer "21." Now consider Figure 8. If asked, "What is the price of a 0.71-carat diamond?" we could not give a single response because two outputs result from the single input "0.71." For this reason, the relation in Figure 8 is not a function.

In Words

For a function, no input has more than one output. The domain of a function is the set of all inputs; the range is the set of all outputs.

We may also think of a function as a set of ordered pairs (x, y) in which no ordered pairs have the same first element and different second elements. The set of all first elements x is the domain of the function, and the set of all second elements y is its range. Each element x in the domain corresponds to exactly one element y in the range.

EXAMPLE 3 **Determining Whether a Relation Represents a Function**

Determine whether each relation represents a function. If it is a function, state the domain and range.

(a) $\{(1, 4), (2, 5), (3, 6), (4, 7)\}$

(b) $\{(1, 4), (2, 4), (3, 5), (6, 10)\}$

(c) $\{(-3, 9), (-2, 4), (0, 0), (1, 1), (-3, 8)\}$

Solution (a) This relation is a function because there are no ordered pairs with the same first element and different second elements. The domain of this function is $\{1, 2, 3, 4\}$, and its range is $\{4, 5, 6, 7\}$.

(b) This relation is a function because there are no ordered pairs with the same first element and different second elements. The domain of this function is $\{1, 2, 3, 6\}$, and its range is $\{4, 5, 10\}$.

(c) This relation is not a function because there are two ordered pairs, $(-3, 9)$ and $(-3, 8)$, that have the same first element and different second elements. ■

In Example 3(b), notice that 1 and 2 in the domain each have the same image in the range. This does not violate the definition of a function; two different first elements can have the same second element. A violation of the definition occurs when two ordered pairs have the same first element and different second elements, as in Example 3(c).

Now Work PROBLEM 19

Up to now we have shown how to identify when a relation is a function for relations defined by mappings (Example 2) and ordered pairs (Example 3). But relations can also be expressed as equations. The circumstances under which equations are functions are discussed next.

To determine whether an equation, where y depends on x, is a function, it is often easiest to solve the equation for y. If any value of x in the domain corresponds to more than one y, the equation does not define a function; otherwise, it does define a function.

EXAMPLE 4 **Determining Whether an Equation Is a Function**

Determine if the equation $y = 2x - 5$ defines y as a function of x.

Solution The equation tells us to take an input x, multiply it by 2, and then subtract 5. For any input x, these operations yield only one output y. For example, if $x = 1$, then $y = 2(1) - 5 = -3$. If $x = 3$, then $y = 2(3) - 5 = 1$. For this reason, the equation is a function. ■

EXAMPLE 5 **Determining Whether an Equation Is a Function**

Determine if the equation $x^2 + y^2 = 1$ defines y as a function of x.

Solution To determine whether the equation $x^2 + y^2 = 1$, which defines the unit circle, is a function, solve the equation for y.

$$x^2 + y^2 = 1$$
$$y^2 = 1 - x^2$$
$$y = \pm\sqrt{1 - x^2}$$

For values of x between -1 and 1, two values of y result. For example, if $x = 0$, then $y = \pm 1$, so two different outputs result from the same input. This means that the equation $x^2 + y^2 = 1$ does not define a function. ■

Now Work PROBLEM 33

2 Find the Value of a Function

Functions are often denoted by letters such as f, F, g, G, and others. If f is a function, then for each number x in its domain the corresponding image in the range is designated by the symbol $f(x)$, read as "f of x" or as "f at x." We refer to $f(x)$ as the **value of f at the number x**; $f(x)$ is the number that results when x is given and the function f is applied; $f(x)$ is the output corresponding to x or the image of x; $f(x)$ does *not* mean "f times x." For example, the function given in Example 4 may be written as $y = f(x) = 2x - 5$. Then $f\left(\frac{3}{2}\right) = -2$.

Figure 9 illustrates some other functions. Notice that, in every function, for each x in the domain there is one value in the range.

Figure 9

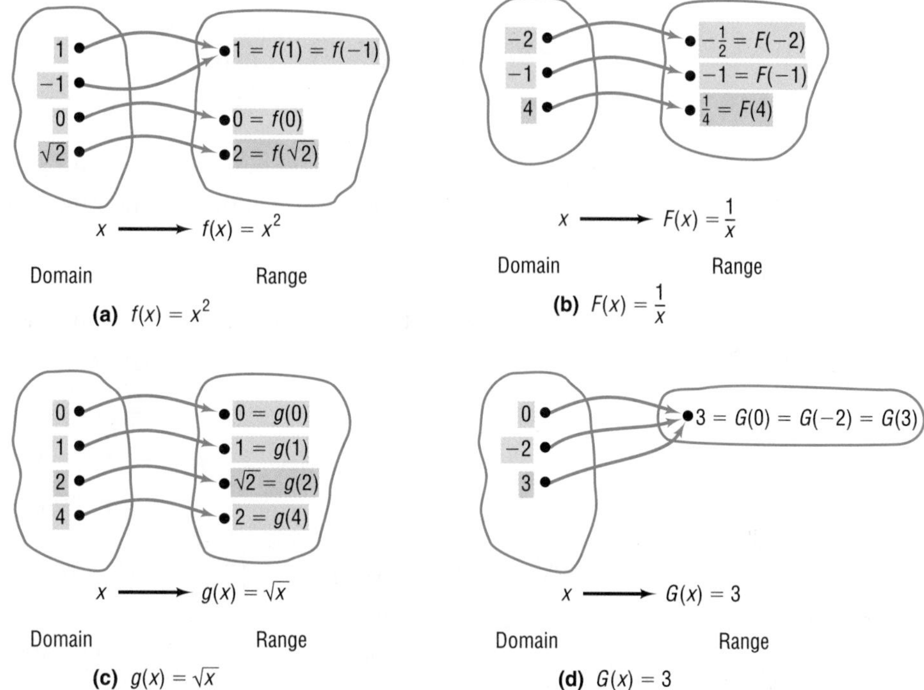

Figure 10

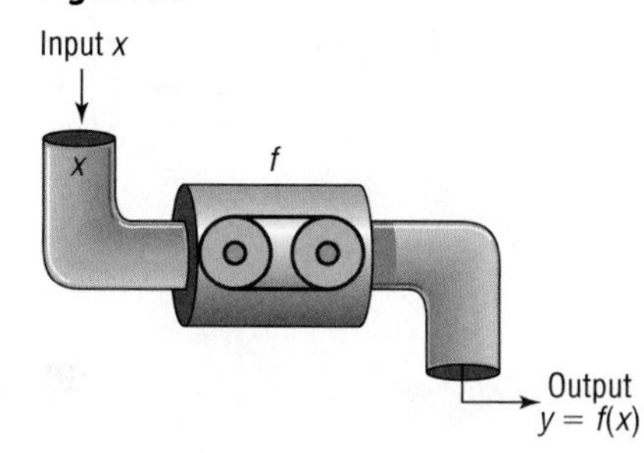

Sometimes it is helpful to think of a function f as a machine that receives as input a number from the domain, manipulates it, and outputs a value. See Figure 10. The restrictions on this input/output machine are as follows:

1. It only accepts numbers from the domain of the function.
2. For each input, there is exactly one output (which may be repeated for different inputs).

For a function $y = f(x)$, the variable x is called the **independent variable,** because it can be assigned any of the permissible numbers from the domain. The variable y is called the **dependent variable,** because its value depends on x.

Any symbols can be used to represent the independent and dependent variables. For example, if f is the *cube function,* then f can be given by $f(x) = x^3$ or $f(t) = t^3$ or $f(z) = z^3$. All three functions are the same. Each tells us to cube the independent variable to get the output. In practice, the symbols used for the independent and dependent variables are based on common usage, such as using C for cost in business.

The independent variable is also called the **argument** of the function. Thinking of the independent variable as an argument can sometimes make it easier to find the value of a function. For example, if f is the function defined by $f(x) = x^3$, then f tells us to cube the argument. Thus, $f(2)$ means to cube 2, $f(a)$ means to cube the number a, and $f(x + h)$ means to cube the quantity $x + h$.

EXAMPLE 6 Finding Values of a Function

For the function f defined by $f(x) = 2x^2 - 3x$, evaluate

(a) $f(3)$ (b) $f(x) + f(3)$ (c) $3f(x)$ (d) $f(-x)$

(e) $-f(x)$ (f) $f(3x)$ (g) $f(x + 3)$ (h) $\dfrac{f(x+h) - f(x)}{h}$ $h \neq 0$

Solution (a) Substitute 3 for x in the equation for f, $f(x) = 2x^2 - 3x$, to get

$$f(3) = 2(3)^2 - 3(3) = 18 - 9 = 9$$

The image of 3 is 9.

(b) $f(x) + f(3) = (2x^2 - 3x) + (9) = 2x^2 - 3x + 9$

(c) Multiply the equation for f by 3.

$$3f(x) = 3(2x^2 - 3x) = 6x^2 - 9x$$

(d) Substitute $-x$ for x in the equation for f and simplify.

$$f(-x) = 2(-x)^2 - 3(-x) = 2x^2 + 3x \quad \text{Notice the use of parentheses here.}$$

(e) $-f(x) = -(2x^2 - 3x) = -2x^2 + 3x$

(f) Substitute $3x$ for x in the equation for f and simplify.

$$f(3x) = 2(3x)^2 - 3(3x) = 2(9x^2) - 9x = 18x^2 - 9x$$

(g) Substitute $x + 3$ for x in the equation for f and simplify.

$$\begin{aligned} f(x+3) &= 2(x+3)^2 - 3(x+3) \\ &= 2(x^2 + 6x + 9) - 3x - 9 \\ &= 2x^2 + 12x + 18 - 3x - 9 \\ &= 2x^2 + 9x + 9 \end{aligned}$$

(h) $$\frac{f(x+h) - f(x)}{h} = \frac{[2(x+h)^2 - 3(x+h)] - [2x^2 - 3x]}{h}$$

$\uparrow$ $f(x+h) = 2(x+h)^2 - 3(x+h)$

$$\begin{aligned} &= \frac{2(x^2 + 2xh + h^2) - 3x - 3h - 2x^2 + 3x}{h} && \text{Simplify.} \\ &= \frac{2x^2 + 4xh + 2h^2 - 3h - 2x^2}{h} && \text{Distribute and combine like terms.} \\ &= \frac{4xh + 2h^2 - 3h}{h} && \text{Combine like terms.} \\ &= \frac{h(4x + 2h - 3)}{h} && \text{Factor out } h. \\ &= 4x + 2h - 3 && \text{Divide out the } h\text{'s.} \end{aligned}$$

■

Notice in this example that $f(x + 3) \neq f(x) + f(3)$, $f(-x) \neq -f(x)$, and $3f(x) \neq f(3x)$.

The expression in part (h) is called the **difference quotient** of f, an important expression in calculus.

Now Work PROBLEMS 39 AND 75

Most calculators have special keys that allow you to find the value of certain commonly used functions. For example, you should be able to find the square function $f(x) = x^2$, the square root function $f(x) = \sqrt{x}$, the reciprocal function $f(x) = \frac{1}{x} = x^{-1}$, and many others that will be discussed later in this book (such as $\ln x$ and $\log x$). Verify the results of Example 7, which follows, on your calculator.

EXAMPLE 7 Finding Values of a Function on a Calculator

(a) $f(x) = x^2$ $\qquad f(1.234) = 1.234^2 = 1.522756$

(b) $F(x) = \frac{1}{x}$ $\qquad F(1.234) = \frac{1}{1.234} \approx 0.8103727715$

(c) $g(x) = \sqrt{x}$ $\qquad g(1.234) = \sqrt{1.234} \approx 1.110855526$

■

COMMENT Graphing calculators can be used to evaluate any function that you wish. Figure 11 shows the result obtained in Example 6(a) on a TI-84 Plus graphing calculator with the function to be evaluated, $f(x) = 2x^2 - 3x$, in Y_1.

Figure 11

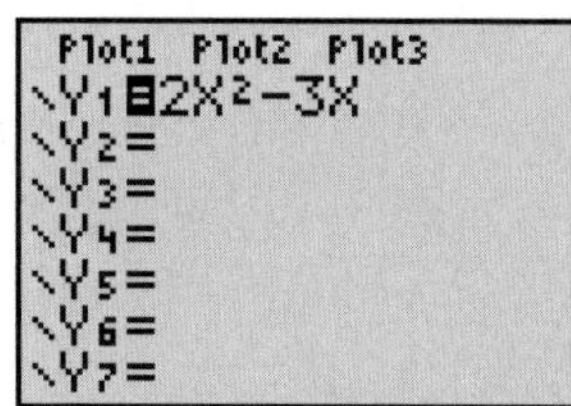

■

COMMENT The explicit form of a function is the form required by a graphing calculator. ■

Implicit Form of a Function

In general, when a function f is defined by an equation in x and y, we say that the function f is given **implicitly.** If it is possible to solve the equation for y in terms of x, then we write $y = f(x)$ and say that the function is given **explicitly.** For example,

Implicit Form	**Explicit Form**
$3x + y = 5$	$y = f(x) = -3x + 5$
$x^2 - y = 6$	$y = f(x) = x^2 - 6$
$xy = 4$	$y = f(x) = \dfrac{4}{x}$

SUMMARY
Important Facts about Functions

(a) For each x in the domain of a function f, there is exactly one image $f(x)$ in the range; however, an element in the range can result from more than one x in the domain.

(b) f is the symbol that we use to denote the function. It is symbolic of the equation (rule) that we use to get from an x in the domain to $f(x)$ in the range.

(c) If $y = f(x)$, then x is called the independent variable or argument of f, and y is called the dependent variable or the value of f at x.

3 Find the Domain of a Function Defined by an Equation

Often the domain of a function f is not specified; instead, only the equation defining the function is given. In such cases, we agree that the **domain of f** is the largest set of real numbers for which the value $f(x)$ is a real number. The domain of a function f is the same as the domain of the variable x in the expression $f(x)$.

EXAMPLE 8 **Finding the Domain of a Function**

Find the domain of each of the following functions:

(a) $f(x) = x^2 + 5x$ (b) $g(x) = \dfrac{3x}{x^2 - 4}$

(c) $h(t) = \sqrt{4 - 3t}$ (d) $F(x) = \dfrac{\sqrt{3x + 12}}{x - 5}$

Solution (a) The function tells us to square a number and then add five times the number. Since these operations can be performed on any real number, we conclude that the domain of f is the set of all real numbers.

(b) The function g tells us to divide $3x$ by $x^2 - 4$. Since division by 0 is not defined, the denominator $x^2 - 4$ can never be 0, so x can never equal -2 or 2. The domain of the function g is $\{x | x \neq -2, x \neq 2\}$.

In Words

The domain of g found in Example 8(b) is $\{x \mid x \neq -2, x \neq 2\}$. This notation is read, "The domain of the function g is the set of all real numbers x such that x does not equal -2 and x does not equal 2."

(c) The function h tells us to take the square root of $4 - 3t$. But only nonnegative numbers have real square roots, so the expression under the square root (the radicand) must be nonnegative (greater than or equal to zero). This requires that

$$4 - 3t \geq 0$$
$$-3t \geq -4$$
$$t \leq \frac{4}{3}$$

The domain of h is $\left\{t \middle| t \leq \frac{4}{3}\right\}$ or the interval $\left(-\infty, \frac{4}{3}\right]$.

(d) The function F tells us to take the square root of $3x + 12$ and divide this result by $x - 5$. This requires that $3x + 12 \geq 0$, so $x \geq -4$, and that $x - 5 \neq 0$, so $x \neq 5$. Combining these two restrictions, the domain of F is $\{x \mid x \geq -4, x \neq 5\}$. ■

For the functions that we will encounter in this book, the following steps may prove helpful for finding the domain of a function that is defined by an equation and whose domain is a subset of the real numbers.

Finding the Domain of a Function Defined by an Equation

1. Start with the domain as the set of real numbers.
2. If the equation has a denominator, exclude any numbers that give a zero denominator.
3. If the equation has a radical of even index, exclude any numbers that cause the expression inside the radical to be negative.

Now Work PROBLEM 51

If x is in the domain of a function f, we shall say that **f is defined at x,** or **$f(x)$ exists.** If x is not in the domain of f, we say that **f is not defined at x,** or **$f(x)$ does not exist.** For example, if $f(x) = \frac{x}{x^2 - 1}$, then $f(0)$ exists, but $f(1)$ and $f(-1)$ do not exist. (Do you see why?)

We will say more about finding the range when we look at the graph of a function in the next section. When a function is defined by an equation, it can be difficult to find the range. Therefore, we shall usually be content to find just the domain of a function when the function is defined by an equation. We shall express the domain of a function using inequalities, interval notation, set notation, or words, whichever is most convenient.

When we use functions in applications, the domain may be restricted by physical or geometric considerations. For example, the domain of the function f defined by $f(x) = x^2$ is the set of all real numbers. However, if f is used to obtain the area of a square when the length x of a side is known, then we must restrict the domain of f to the positive real numbers, since the length of a side can never be 0 or negative.

EXAMPLE 9 **Finding the Domain in an Application**

Express the area of a circle as a function of its radius. Find the domain.

Solution See Figure 12. The formula for the area A of a circle of radius r is $A = \pi r^2$. If we use r to represent the independent variable and A to represent the dependent variable, the function expressing this relationship is

Figure 12

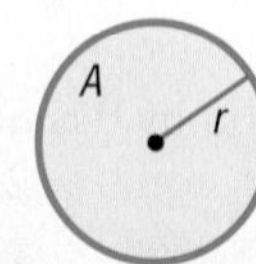

$$A(r) = \pi r^2$$

In this setting, the domain is $\{r \mid r > 0\}$. (Do you see why?) ■

Observe in the solution to Example 9 that the symbol A is used in two ways: It is used to name the function, and it is used to symbolize the dependent variable. This double use is common in applications and should not cause any difficulty.

Now Work PROBLEM 89

4 Form the Sum, Difference, Product, and Quotient of Two Functions

Next we introduce some operations on functions. We shall see that functions, like numbers, can be added, subtracted, multiplied, and divided. For example, if $f(x) = x^2 + 9$ and $g(x) = 3x + 5$, then

$$f(x) + g(x) = (x^2 + 9) + (3x + 5) = x^2 + 3x + 14$$

The new function $y = x^2 + 3x + 14$ is called the *sum function* $f + g$. Similarly,

$$f(x) \cdot g(x) = (x^2 + 9)(3x + 5) = 3x^3 + 5x^2 + 27x + 45$$

The new function $y = 3x^3 + 5x^2 + 27x + 45$ is called the *product function* $f \cdot g$.

The general definitions are given next.

DEFINITION

If f and g are functions:

The **sum** $\boldsymbol{f + g}$ is the function defined by

$$(f + g)(x) = f(x) + g(x)$$

In Words

Remember, the symbol $\cap$ stands for intersection. It means you should find the elements that are common to two sets.

The domain of $f + g$ consists of the numbers x that are in the domains of both f and g. That is, domain of $f + g$ = domain of $f \cap$ domain of g.

DEFINITION

The **difference** $\boldsymbol{f - g}$ is the function defined by

$$(f - g)(x) = f(x) - g(x)$$

The domain of $f - g$ consists of the numbers x that are in the domains of both f and g. That is, domain of $f - g$ = domain of $f \cap$ domain of g.

DEFINITION

The **product** $\boldsymbol{f \cdot g}$ is the function defined by

$$(f \cdot g)(x) = f(x) \cdot g(x)$$

The domain of $f \cdot g$ consists of the numbers x that are in the domains of both f and g. That is, domain of $f \cdot g$ = domain of $f \cap$ domain of g.

DEFINITION

The **quotient** $\boldsymbol{\frac{f}{g}}$ is the function defined by

$$\left(\frac{f}{g}\right)(x) = \frac{f(x)}{g(x)} \qquad g(x) \neq 0$$

The domain of $\frac{f}{g}$ consists of the numbers x for which $g(x) \neq 0$ and that are in the domains of both f and g. That is,

$$\text{domain of } \frac{f}{g} = \{x \mid g(x) \neq 0\} \cap \text{domain of } f \cap \text{domain of } g$$

EXAMPLE 10 **Operations on Functions**

Let f and g be two functions defined as

$$f(x) = \frac{1}{x+2} \quad \text{and} \quad g(x) = \frac{x}{x-1}$$

Find the following, and determine the domain in each case.

(a) $(f+g)(x)$ (b) $(f-g)(x)$ (c) $(f \cdot g)(x)$ (d) $\left(\frac{f}{g}\right)(x)$

Solution The domain of f is $\{x \mid x \neq -2\}$ and the domain of g is $\{x \mid x \neq 1\}$.

(a) $$(f+g)(x) = f(x) + g(x) = \frac{1}{x+2} + \frac{x}{x-1}$$
$$= \frac{x-1}{(x+2)(x-1)} + \frac{x(x+2)}{(x+2)(x-1)} = \frac{x^2+3x-1}{(x+2)(x-1)}$$

The domain of $f+g$ consists of those numbers x that are in the domains of both f and g. Therefore, the domain of $f+g$ is $\{x \mid x \neq -2, x \neq 1\}$.

(b) $$(f-g)(x) = f(x) - g(x) = \frac{1}{x+2} - \frac{x}{x-1}$$
$$= \frac{x-1}{(x+2)(x-1)} - \frac{x(x+2)}{(x+2)(x-1)} = \frac{-(x^2+x+1)}{(x+2)(x-1)}$$

The domain of $f-g$ consists of those numbers x that are in the domains of both f and g. Therefore, the domain of $f-g$ is $\{x \mid x \neq -2, x \neq 1\}$.

(c) $$(f \cdot g)(x) = f(x) \cdot g(x) = \frac{1}{x+2} \cdot \frac{x}{x-1} = \frac{x}{(x+2)(x-1)}$$

The domain of $f \cdot g$ consists of those numbers x that are in the domains of both f and g. Therefore, the domain of $f \cdot g$ is $\{x \mid x \neq -2, x \neq 1\}$.

(d) $$\left(\frac{f}{g}\right)(x) = \frac{f(x)}{g(x)} = \frac{\frac{1}{x+2}}{\frac{x}{x-1}} = \frac{1}{x+2} \cdot \frac{x-1}{x} = \frac{x-1}{x(x+2)}$$

The domain of $\frac{f}{g}$ consists of the numbers x for which $g(x) \neq 0$ and that are in the domains of both f and g. Since $g(x) = 0$ when $x = 0$, we exclude 0 as well as -2 and 1 from the domain. The domain of $\frac{f}{g}$ is $\{x \mid x \neq -2, x \neq 0, x \neq 1\}$. ■

Now Work PROBLEM 63

In calculus, it is sometimes helpful to view a complicated function as the sum, difference, product, or quotient of simpler functions. For example,

$F(x) = x^2 + \sqrt{x}$ is the sum of $f(x) = x^2$ and $g(x) = \sqrt{x}$.

$H(x) = \frac{x^2-1}{x^2+1}$ is the quotient of $f(x) = x^2 - 1$ and $g(x) = x^2 + 1$.

SUMMARY

Function A relation between two sets of real numbers so that each number x in the first set, the domain, has corresponding to it exactly one number y in the second set.

A set of ordered pairs (x, y) or $(x, f(x))$ in which no first element is paired with two different second elements.

The range is the set of y values of the function that are the images of the x values in the domain.

A function f may be defined implicitly by an equation involving x and y or explicitly by writing $y = f(x)$.

Unspecified domain If a function f is defined by an equation and no domain is specified, then the domain will be taken to be the largest set of real numbers for which the equation defines a real number.

Function notation $y = f(x)$

f is a symbol for the function.

x is the independent variable or argument.

y is the dependent variable.

$f(x)$ is the value of the function at x, or the image of x.

9.1 Assess Your Understanding

'Are You Prepared?' *Answers are given at the end of these exercises. If you get a wrong answer, read the pages listed in red.*

1. The inequality $-1 < x < 3$ can be written in interval notation as________. (pp. 504–505)

2. If $x = -2$, the value of the expression $3x^2 - 5x + \frac{1}{x}$ is ______.

3. The domain of the variable in the expression $\frac{x-3}{x+4}$ is ________.

4. Solve the inequality: $3 - 2x > 5$. Graph the solution set. (pp. 507–508)

Concepts and Vocabulary

5. If f is a function defined by the equation $y = f(x)$, then x is called the ________ variable and y is the ________ variable.

6. The set of all images of the elements in the domain of a function is called the ________.

7. If the domain of f is all real numbers in the interval $[0, 7]$ and the domain of g is all real numbers in the interval $[-2, 5]$, the domain of $f + g$ is all real numbers in the interval ________.

8. The domain of $\frac{f}{g}$ consists of numbers x for which $g(x)$ ____ 0 that are in the domains of both ____ and ____.

9. If $f(x) = x + 1$ and $g(x) = x^3$, then________ $=$ $x^3 - (x + 1)$.

10. ***True or False*** Every relation is a function.

11. ***True or False*** The domain of $(f \cdot g)(x)$ consists of the numbers x that are in the domains of both f and g.

12. ***True or False*** The independent variable is sometimes referred to as the argument of the function.

13. ***True or False*** If no domain is specified for a function f, then the domain of f is taken to be the set of real numbers.

14. ***True or False*** The domain of the function $f(x) = \frac{x^2 - 4}{x}$ is $\{x | x \neq \pm 2\}$.

Skill Building

In Problems 15–26, determine whether each relation represents a function. For each function, state the domain and range.

15.

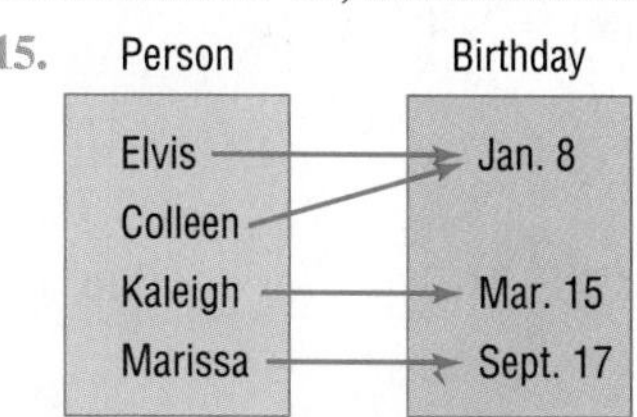

16.

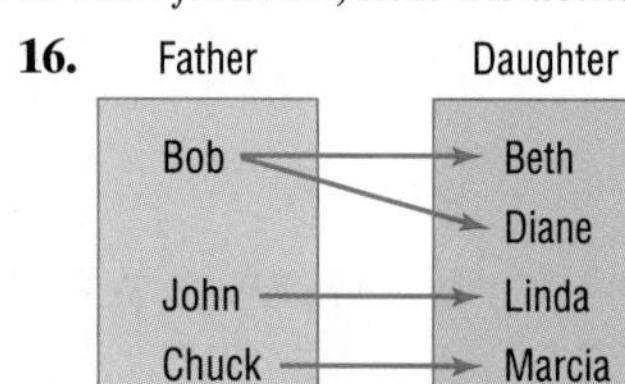

17. 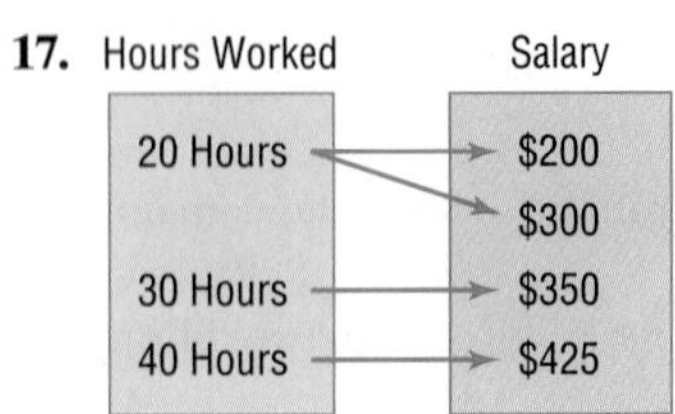

18. 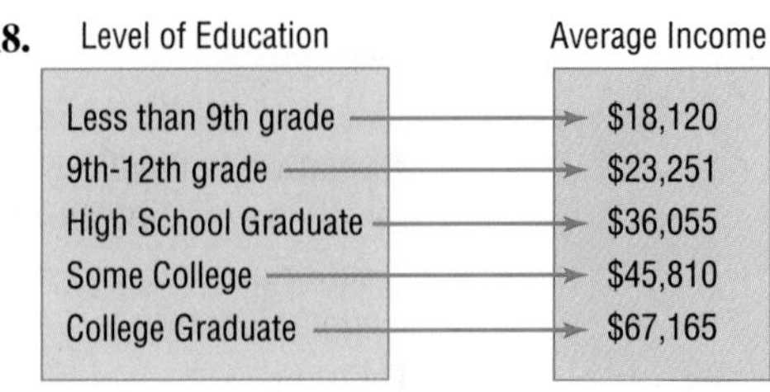

19. $\{(2, 6), (-3, 6), (4, 9), (2, 10)\}$

20. $\{(-2, 5), (-1, 3), (3, 7), (4, 12)\}$

21. $\{(1, 3), (2, 3), (3, 3), (4, 3)\}$

22. $\{(0, -2), (1, 3), (2, 3), (3, 7)\}$

23. $\{(-2, 4), (-2, 6), (0, 3), (3, 7)\}$

24. $\{(-4, 4), (-3, 3), (-2, 2), (-1, 1), (-4, 0)\}$

25. $\{(-2, 4), (-1, 1), (0, 0), (1, 1)\}$

26. $\{(-2, 16), (-1, 4), (0, 3), (1, 4)\}$

In Problems 27–38, determine whether the equation defines y as a function of x.

27. $y = x^2$

28. $y = x^3$

29. $y = \frac{1}{x}$

30. $y = |x|$

31. $y^2 = 4 - x^2$

32. $y = \pm\sqrt{1 - 2x}$

33. $x = y^2$

34. $x + y^2 = 1$

35. $y = 2x^2 - 3x + 4$

36. $y = \frac{3x - 1}{x + 2}$

37. $2x^2 + 3y^2 = 1$

38. $x^2 - 4y^2 = 1$

In Problems 39–46, find the following for each function:

(a) $f(0)$ (b) $f(1)$ (c) $f(-1)$ (d) $f(-x)$ (e) $-f(x)$ (f) $f(x + 1)$ (g) $f(2x)$ (h) $f(x + h)$

39. $f(x) = 3x^2 + 2x - 4$

40. $f(x) = -2x^2 + x - 1$

41. $f(x) = \frac{x}{x^2 + 1}$

42. $f(x) = \frac{x^2 - 1}{x + 4}$

43. $f(x) = |x| + 4$

44. $f(x) = \sqrt{x^2 + x}$

45. $f(x) = \frac{2x + 1}{3x - 5}$

46. $f(x) = 1 - \frac{1}{(x + 2)^2}$

In Problems 47–62, find the domain of each function.

47. $f(x) = -5x + 4$

48. $f(x) = x^2 + 2$

49. $f(x) = \frac{x}{x^2 + 1}$

50. $f(x) = \frac{x^2}{x^2 + 1}$

51. $g(x) = \frac{x}{x^2 - 16}$

52. $h(x) = \frac{2x}{x^2 - 4}$

53. $F(x) = \frac{x - 2}{x^3 + x}$

54. $G(x) = \frac{x + 4}{x^3 - 4x}$

55. $h(x) = \sqrt{3x - 12}$

56. $G(x) = \sqrt{1 - x}$

57. $f(x) = \frac{4}{\sqrt{x - 9}}$

58. $f(x) = \frac{x}{\sqrt{x - 4}}$

59. $p(x) = \sqrt{\frac{2}{x - 1}}$

60. $q(x) = \sqrt{-x - 2}$

61. $P(t) = \frac{\sqrt{t - 4}}{3t - 21}$

62. $h(z) = \frac{\sqrt{z + 3}}{z - 2}$

In Problems 63–72, for the given functions f and g, find the following. For parts (a)–(d), also find the domain.

(a) $(f + g)(x)$ (b) $(f - g)(x)$ (c) $(f \cdot g)(x)$ (d) $\left(\frac{f}{g}\right)(x)$

(e) $(f + g)(3)$ (f) $(f - g)(4)$ (g) $(f \cdot g)(2)$ (h) $\left(\frac{f}{g}\right)(1)$

63. $f(x) = 3x + 4;\ g(x) = 2x - 3$

64. $f(x) = 2x + 1;\ g(x) = 3x - 2$

65. $f(x) = x - 1;\ g(x) = 2x^2$

66. $f(x) = 2x^2 + 3;\ g(x) = 4x^3 + 1$

67. $f(x) = \sqrt{x};\ g(x) = 3x - 5$

68. $f(x) = |x|;\ g(x) = x$

69. $f(x) = 1 + \frac{1}{x};\ g(x) = \frac{1}{x}$

70. $f(x) = \sqrt{x - 1};\ g(x) = \sqrt{4 - x}$

71. $f(x) = \frac{2x + 3}{3x - 2};\ g(x) = \frac{4x}{3x - 2}$

72. $f(x) = \sqrt{x + 1};\ g(x) = \frac{2}{x}$

73. Given $f(x) = 3x + 1$ and $(f + g)(x) = 6 - \frac{1}{2}x$, find the function g.

74. Given $f(x) = \frac{1}{x}$ and $\left(\frac{f}{g}\right)(x) = \frac{x + 1}{x^2 - x}$, find the function g.

In Problems 75–82, find the difference quotient of f; that is, find $\dfrac{f(x+h)-f(x)}{h}$, $h \neq 0$, *for each function. Be sure to simplify.*

75. $f(x) = 4x + 3$

76. $f(x) = -3x + 1$

77. $f(x) = x^2 - x + 4$

78. $f(x) = 3x^2 - 2x + 6$

79. $f(x) = \dfrac{1}{x^2}$

80. $f(x) = \dfrac{1}{x+3}$

81. $f(x) = \sqrt{x}$ [**Hint:** Rationalize the numerator.]

82. $f(x) = \sqrt{x+1}$

Applications and Extensions

83. If $f(x) = 2x^3 + Ax^2 + 4x - 5$ and $f(2) = 5$, what is the value of A?

84. If $f(x) = 3x^2 - Bx + 4$ and $f(-1) = 12$, what is the value of B?

85. If $f(x) = \dfrac{3x+8}{2x-A}$ and $f(0) = 2$, what is the value of A?

86. If $f(x) = \dfrac{2x-B}{3x+4}$ and $f(2) = \dfrac{1}{2}$, what is the value of B?

87. If $f(x) = \dfrac{2x-A}{x-3}$ and $f(4) = 0$, what is the value of A? Where is f not defined?

88. If $f(x) = \dfrac{x-B}{x-A}$, $f(2) = 0$ and $f(1)$ is undefined, what are the values of A and B?

89. **Geometry** Express the area A of a rectangle as a function of the length x if the length of the rectangle is twice its width.

90. **Geometry** Express the area A of an isosceles right triangle as a function of the length x of one of the two equal sides.

91. **Constructing Functions** Express the gross salary G of a person who earns \$10 per hour as a function of the number x of hours worked.

92. **Constructing Functions** Tiffany, a commissioned sales person, earns \$100 base pay plus \$10 per item sold. Express her gross salary G as a function of the number x of items sold.

93. **Population as a Function of Age** The function

$$P(a) = 0.015a^2 - 4.962a + 290.580$$

represents the population P (in millions) of Americans that are a years of age or older.

(a) Identify the dependent and independent variables.
(b) Evaluate $P(20)$. Provide a verbal explanation of the meaning of $P(20)$.
(c) Evaluate $P(0)$. Provide a verbal explanation of the meaning of $P(0)$.

94. **Number of Rooms** The function

$$N(r) = -1.44r^2 + 14.52r - 14.96$$

represents the number N of housing units (in millions) that have r rooms, where r is an integer and $2 \le r \le 9$.

(a) Identify the dependent and independent variables.
(b) Evaluate $N(3)$. Provide a verbal explanation of the meaning of $N(3)$.

95. **Effect of Gravity on Earth** If a rock falls from a height of 20 meters on Earth, the height H (in meters) after x seconds is approximately

$$H(x) = 20 - 4.9x^2$$

(a) What is the height of the rock when $x = 1$ second? $x = 1.1$ seconds? $x = 1.2$ seconds? $x = 1.3$ seconds?
(b) When is the height of the rock 15 meters? When is it 10 meters? When is it 5 meters?
(c) When does the rock strike the ground?

96. **Effect of Gravity on Jupiter** If a rock falls from a height of 20 meters on the planet Jupiter, its height H (in meters) after x seconds is approximately

$$H(x) = 20 - 13x^2$$

(a) What is the height of the rock when $x = 1$ second? $x = 1.1$ seconds? $x = 1.2$ seconds?
(b) When is the height of the rock 15 meters? When is it 10 meters? When is it 5 meters?
(c) When does the rock strike the ground?

97. **Cost of Trans-Atlantic Travel** A Boeing 747 crosses the Atlantic Ocean (3000 miles) with an airspeed of 500 miles per hour. The cost C (in dollars) per passenger is given by

$$C(x) = 100 + \frac{x}{10} + \frac{36{,}000}{x}$$

where x is the ground speed (airspeed $\pm$ wind).

(a) What is the cost per passenger for quiescent (no wind) conditions?
(b) What is the cost per passenger with a head wind of 50 miles per hour?
(c) What is the cost per passenger with a tail wind of 100 miles per hour?
(d) What is the cost per passenger with a head wind of 100 miles per hour?

98. **Cross-sectional Area** The cross-sectional area of a beam cut from a log with radius 1 foot is given by the function $A(x) = 4x\sqrt{1 - x^2}$, where x represents the length, in feet, of half the base of the beam. See the figure. Determine the cross-sectional area of the beam if the length of half the base of the beam is as follows:

(a) One-third of a foot
(b) One-half of a foot
(c) Two-thirds of a foot

$A(x) = 4x\sqrt{1 - x^2}$

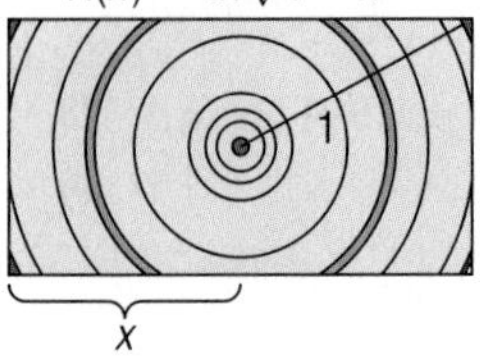

99. **Economics** The **participation rate** is the number of people in the labor force divided by the civilian population (excludes military). Let $L(x)$ represent the size of the labor force in year x and $P(x)$ represent the civilian population in year x. Determine a function that represents the participation rate R as a function of x.

100. **Crimes** Suppose that $V(x)$ represents the number of violent crimes committed in year x and $P(x)$ represents the number of property crimes committed in year x. Determine a function T that represents the combined total of violent crimes and property crimes in year x.

101. **Health Care** Suppose that $P(x)$ represents the percentage of income spent on health care in year x and $I(x)$ represents income in year x. Determine a function H that represents total health care expenditures in year x.

102. **Income Tax** Suppose that $I(x)$ represents the income of an individual in year x before taxes and $T(x)$ represents the individual's tax bill in year x. Determine a function N that represents the individual's net income (income after taxes) in year x.

103. **Profit Function** Suppose that the revenue R, in dollars, from selling x cell phones, in hundreds, is $R(x) = -1.2x^2 + 220x$. The cost C, in dollars, of selling x cell phones is $C(x) = 0.05x^3 - 2x^2 + 65x + 500$.
   (a) Find the profit function, $P(x) = R(x) - C(x)$.
   (b) Find the profit if $x = 15$ hundred cell phones are sold.
   (c) Interpret $P(15)$.

104. **Profit Function** Suppose that the revenue R, in dollars, from selling x clocks is $R(x) = 30x$. The cost C, in dollars, of selling x clocks is $C(x) = 0.1x^2 + 7x + 400$.
   (a) Find the profit function, $P(x) = R(x) - C(x)$.
   (b) Find the profit if $x = 30$ clocks are sold.
   (c) Interpret $P(30)$.

105. Some functions f have the property that $f(a + b) = f(a) + f(b)$ for all real numbers a and b. Which of the following functions have this property?
   (a) $h(x) = 2x$ (b) $g(x) = x^2$
   (c) $F(x) = 5x - 2$ (d) $G(x) = \dfrac{1}{x}$

Explaining Concepts: Discussion and Writing

106. Are the functions $f(x) = x - 1$ and $g(x) = \dfrac{x^2 - 1}{x + 1}$ the same? Explain.

107. Investigate when, historically, the use of the function notation $y = f(x)$ first appeared.

108. Find a function H that multiplies a number x by 3, then subtracts the cube of x and divides the result by your age.

'Are You Prepared?' Answers

1. $(-1, 3)$ **2.** 21.5 **3.** $\{x \mid x \neq -4\}$ **4.** $\{x \mid x < -1\}$

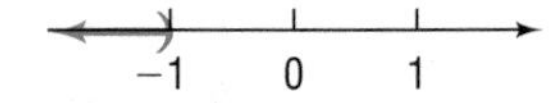

9.2 The Graph of a Function

PREPARING FOR THIS SECTION *Before getting started, review the following:*

- Graphs of Equations (Section 7.1, pp. 465–469)
- Intercepts (Section 8.1, pp. 522–523)

Now Work the **'Are You Prepared?'** problems on page 577.

OBJECTIVES
1 Identify the Graph of a Function (p. 573)
2 Obtain Information from or about the Graph of a Function (p. 574)

In applications, a graph often demonstrates more clearly the relationship between two variables than, say, an equation or table would. For example, Table 1 on the next page shows the average price of gasoline at a particular gas station in Texas (for the years 1981–2010 adjusted for inflation, based on 2008 dollars). If we plot these data and then connect the points, we obtain Figure 13 (also on the next page).

Table 1

Year	Price	Year	Price	Year	Price
1981	3.26	1991	1.90	2001	1.40
1982	3.15	1992	1.82	2002	1.86
1983	2.51	1993	1.70	2003	1.79
1984	2.51	1994	1.85	2004	2.13
1985	2.46	1995	1.68	2005	2.60
1986	1.63	1996	1.87	2006	2.62
1987	1.90	1997	1.65	2007	3.29
1988	1.77	1998	1.50	2008	2.10
1989	1.83	1999	1.73	2009	2.45
1990	2.25	2000	1.85	2010	3.18

Source: http://www.randomuseless.info/gasprice/gasprice.html

Figure 13 Average retail price of gasoline (2008 dollars)

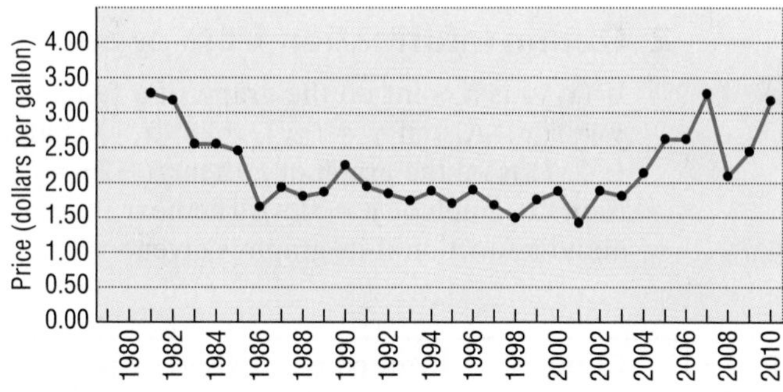

Source: http://www.randomuseless.info/gasprice/gasprice.html

We can see from the graph that the price of gasoline (adjusted for inflation) fell from 1981 to 1986 and rose rapidly from 2003 to 2007. The graph also shows that the lowest price occurred in 2001. To learn information such as this from an equation requires that some calculations be made.

Look again at Figure 13. The graph shows that for each date on the horizontal axis there is only one price on the vertical axis. The graph represents a function, although the exact rule for getting from date to price is not given.

When a function is defined by an equation in x and y, the **graph of the function** is the graph of the equation, that is, the set of points (x, y) in the xy-plane that satisfy the equation.

1 Identify the Graph of a Function

> **In Words**
> If any vertical line intersects a graph at more than one point, the graph is not the graph of a function.

Not every collection of points in the xy-plane represents the graph of a function. Remember, for a function, each number x in the domain has exactly one image y in the range. This means that the graph of a function cannot contain two points with the same x-coordinate and different y-coordinates. Therefore, the graph of a function must satisfy the following **vertical-line test.**

THEOREM

Vertical-line Test

A set of points in the xy-plane is the graph of a function if and only if every vertical line intersects the graph in at most one point.

EXAMPLE 1 **Identifying the Graph of a Function**

Which of the graphs in Figure 14 are graphs of functions?

Figure 14

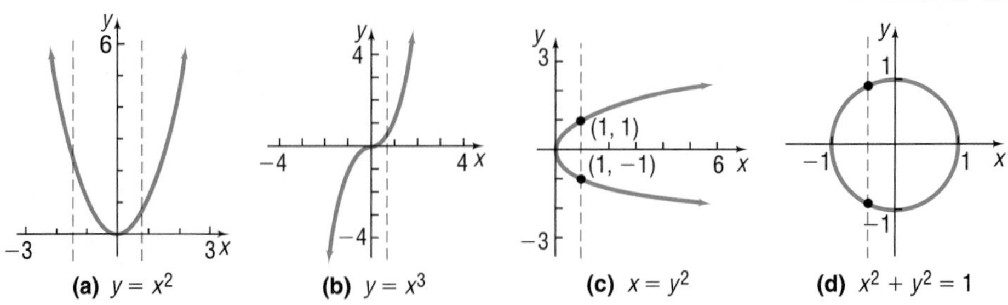

Solution The graphs in Figures 14(a) and 14(b) are graphs of functions, because every vertical line intersects each graph in at most one point. The graphs in Figures 14(c) and 14(d) are not graphs of functions, because there is a vertical line that intersects each graph in more than one point. Notice in Figure 14(c) that the input 1 corresponds to two outputs, -1 and 1. This is why the graph does not represent a function. ■

Now Work PROBLEM 15

2 Obtain Information from or about the Graph of a Function

If (x, y) is a point on the graph of a function f, then y is the value of f at x; that is, $y = f(x)$. Also if $y = f(x)$, then (x, y) is a point on the graph of f. For example, if $(-2, 7)$ is on the graph of f, then $f(-2) = 7$, and if $f(5) = 8$, then the point $(5, 8)$ is on the graph of $y = f(x)$. The next example illustrates how to obtain information about a function if its graph is given.

EXAMPLE 2 Obtaining Information from the Graph of a Function

Figure 15

Let f be the function whose graph is given in Figure 15. (The graph of f might represent the distance y that the bob of a pendulum is from its *at-rest* position at time x. Negative values of y mean that the pendulum is to the left of the at-rest position, and positive values of y mean that the pendulum is to the right of the at-rest position.)

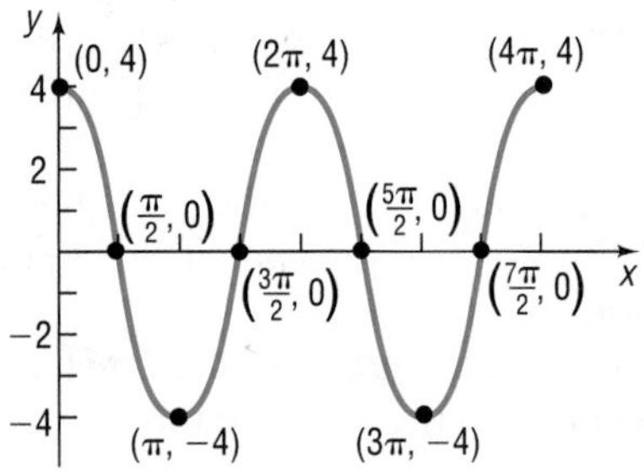

(a) What are $f(0)$, $f\left(\frac{3\pi}{2}\right)$, and $f(3\pi)$?

(b) What is the domain of f?

(c) What is the range of f?

(d) List the intercepts. (Recall that these are the points, if any, where the graph crosses or touches the coordinate axes.)

(e) How many times does the line $y = 2$ intersect the graph?

(f) For what values of x does $f(x) = -4$?

(g) For what values of x is $f(x) > 0$?

Solution (a) Since $(0, 4)$ is on the graph of f, the y-coordinate 4 is the value of f at the x-coordinate 0; that is, $f(0) = 4$. In a similar way, we find that when $x = \frac{3\pi}{2}$, then $y = 0$, so $f\left(\frac{3\pi}{2}\right) = 0$. When $x = 3\pi$, then $y = -4$, so $f(3\pi) = -4$.

(b) To determine the domain of f, we notice that the points on the graph of f have x-coordinates between 0 and 4π, inclusive; and for each number x between 0 and 4π, there is a point $(x, f(x))$ on the graph. The domain of f is $\{x | 0 \le x \le 4\pi\}$ or the interval $[0, 4\pi]$.

(c) The points on the graph all have y-coordinates between -4 and 4, inclusive; and for each such number y, there is at least one corresponding number x in the domain. The range of f is $\{y | -4 \le y \le 4\}$ or the interval $[-4, 4]$.

(d) The intercepts are the points

$$(0, 4), \left(\frac{\pi}{2}, 0\right), \left(\frac{3\pi}{2}, 0\right), \left(\frac{5\pi}{2}, 0\right), \quad \text{and} \quad \left(\frac{7\pi}{2}, 0\right)$$

(e) If we draw the horizontal line $y = 2$ on the graph in Figure 15, we find that it intersects the graph four times.

(f) Since $(\pi, -4)$ and $(3\pi, -4)$ are the only points on the graph for which $y = f(x) = -4$, we have $f(x) = -4$ when $x = \pi$ and $x = 3\pi$.

(g) To determine where $f(x) > 0$, look at Figure 15 and determine the x-values from 0 to 4π for which the y-coordinate is positive. This occurs on $\left[0, \frac{\pi}{2}\right) \cup \left(\frac{3\pi}{2}, \frac{5\pi}{2}\right) \cup \left(\frac{7\pi}{2}, 4\pi\right]$. Using inequality notation, $f(x) > 0$ for $0 \le x < \frac{\pi}{2}$ or $\frac{3\pi}{2} < x < \frac{5\pi}{2}$ or $\frac{7\pi}{2} < x \le 4\pi$. ■

When the graph of a function is given, its domain may be viewed as the shadow created by the graph on the x-axis by vertical beams of light. Its range can be viewed as the shadow created by the graph on the y-axis by horizontal beams of light. Try this technique with the graph given in Figure 15.

Now Work PROBLEMS 9 AND 13

EXAMPLE 3 Obtaining Information about the Graph of a Function

Consider the function: $f(x) = \dfrac{x + 1}{x + 2}$

(a) Find the domain of f.

(b) Is the point $\left(1, \frac{1}{2}\right)$ on the graph of f?

(c) If $x = 2$, what is $f(x)$? What point is on the graph of f?

(d) If $f(x) = 2$, what is x? What point is on the graph of f?

(e) What are the x-intercepts of the graph of f (if any)? What point(s) are on the graph of f?

Solution (a) The domain of f is $\{x \mid x \neq -2\}$, since $x = -2$ results in division by 0.

(b) When $x = 1$,

$$f(x) = \frac{x + 1}{x + 2}$$

$$f(1) = \frac{1 + 1}{1 + 2} = \frac{2}{3}$$

The point $\left(1, \frac{2}{3}\right)$ is on the graph of f; the point $\left(1, \frac{1}{2}\right)$ is not.

(c) If $x = 2$,

$$f(x) = \frac{x + 1}{x + 2}$$

$$f(2) = \frac{2 + 1}{2 + 2} = \frac{3}{4}$$

The point $\left(2, \frac{3}{4}\right)$ is on the graph of f.

(d) If $f(x) = 2$, then

$$f(x) = 2$$
$$\frac{x+1}{x+2} = 2$$
$$x + 1 = 2(x+2) \quad \text{Multiply both sides by } x+2.$$
$$x + 1 = 2x + 4 \quad \text{Remove parentheses.}$$
$$x = -3 \quad \text{Solve for } x.$$

If $f(x) = 2$, then $x = -3$. The point $(-3, 2)$ is on the graph of f.

(e) The x-intercepts of the graph of f are the real solutions of the equation $f(x) = 0$ that are in the domain of f. The only real solution of the equation $f(x) = \frac{x+1}{x+2} = 0$, is $x = -1$, so -1 is the only x-intercept. Since $f(-1) = 0$, the point $(-1, 0)$ is on the graph of f. ■

Now Work PROBLEM 25

EXAMPLE 4 **Average Cost Function**

The average cost $\overline{C}$ of manufacturing x computers per day is given by the function

$$\overline{C}(x) = 0.56x^2 - 34.39x + 1212.57 + \frac{20{,}000}{x}$$

Determine the average cost of manufacturing:

(a) 30 computers in a day
(b) 40 computers in a day
(c) 50 computers in a day
(d) Graph the function $\overline{C} = \overline{C}(x)$, $0 < x \le 80$.
(e) Create a TABLE with TblStart = 1 and ΔTbl = 1. Which value of x minimizes the average cost?

Solution (a) The average cost of manufacturing $x = 30$ computers is

$$\overline{C}(30) = 0.56(30)^2 - 34.39(30) + 1212.57 + \frac{20{,}000}{30} = \$1351.54$$

(b) The average cost of manufacturing $x = 40$ computers is

$$\overline{C}(40) = 0.56(40)^2 - 34.39(40) + 1212.57 + \frac{20{,}000}{40} = \$1232.97$$

(c) The average cost of manufacturing $x = 50$ computers is

$$\overline{C}(50) = 0.56(50)^2 - 34.39(50) + 1212.57 + \frac{20{,}000}{50} = \$1293.07$$

(d) See Figure 16 for the graph of $\overline{C} = \overline{C}(x)$.

(e) With the function $\overline{C} = \overline{C}(x)$ in Y_1, we create Table 2. We scroll down until we find a value of x for which Y_1 is smallest. Table 3 shows that manufacturing $x = 41$ computers minimizes the average cost at \$1231.74 per computer.

Figure 16

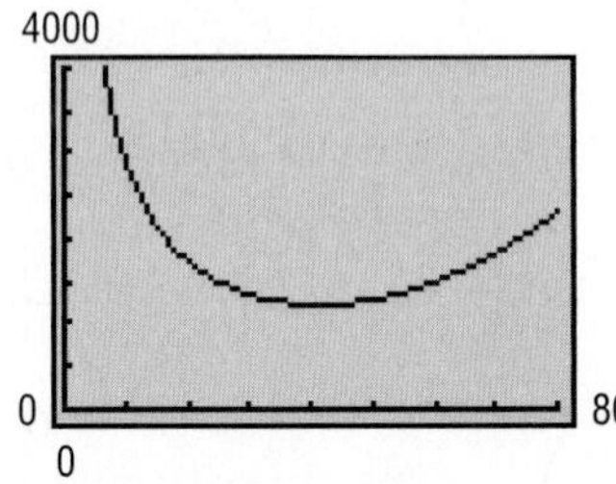

Table 2

X	Y1
1	21179
2	11146
3	7781.1
4	6084
5	5054.6
6	4359.7
7	3856.4

Y1=.56X²-34.39X...

Table 3

X	Y1
38	1240.7
39	1235.9
40	1233
41	1231.7
42	1232.2
43	1234.4
44	1238.1

Y1=1231.74487805

■

Now Work PROBLEM 31

SUMMARY

Graph of a Function The collection of points (x, y) that satisfies the equation $y = f(x)$.

Vertical Line Test A collection of points is the graph of a function provided that every vertical line intersects the graph in at most one point.

9.2 Assess Your Understanding

'Are You Prepared?' *Answers are given at the end of these exercises. If you get a wrong answer, read the pages listed in red.*

1. The intercepts of the equation $x^2 + 4y^2 = 16$ are ____________________. (pp. 522–523)

2. ***True or False*** The point $(-2, -6)$ is on the graph of the equation $x = 2y - 2$. (p. 466)

Concepts and Vocabulary

3. A set of points in the xy-plane is the graph of a function if and only if every ________ line intersects the graph in at most one point.

4. If the point $(5, -3)$ is a point on the graph of f, then $f(\_\_\_) = \_\_\_\_\_$.

5. Find a so that the point $(-1, 2)$ is on the graph of $f(x) = ax^2 + 4$.

6. ***True or False*** A function can have more than one y-intercept.

7. ***True or False*** The graph of a function $y = f(x)$ always crosses the y-axis.

8. ***True or False*** The y-intercept of the graph of the function $y = f(x)$, whose domain is all real numbers, is $f(0)$.

Skill Building

9. Use the given graph of the function f to answer parts (a)–(n).

(a) Find $f(0)$ and $f(-6)$.
(b) Find $f(6)$ and $f(11)$.
(c) Is $f(3)$ positive or negative?
(d) Is $f(-4)$ positive or negative?
(e) For what values of x is $f(x) = 0$?
(f) For what values of x is $f(x) > 0$?
(g) What is the domain of f?
(h) What is the range of f?
(i) What are the x-intercepts?
(j) What is the y-intercept?
(k) How often does the line $y = \frac{1}{2}$ intersect the graph?
(l) How often does the line $x = 5$ intersect the graph?
(m) For what values of x does $f(x) = 3$?
(n) For what values of x does $f(x) = -2$?

10. Use the given graph of the function f to answer parts (a)–(n).

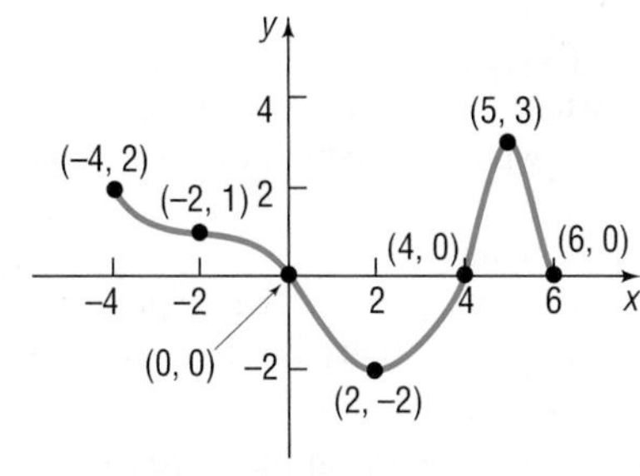

(a) Find $f(0)$ and $f(6)$.
(b) Find $f(2)$ and $f(-2)$.
(c) Is $f(3)$ positive or negative?
(d) Is $f(-1)$ positive or negative?
(e) For what values of x is $f(x) = 0$?
(f) For what values of x is $f(x) < 0$?
(g) What is the domain of f?
(h) What is the range of f?
(i) What are the x-intercepts?
(j) What is the y-intercept?
(k) How often does the line $y = -1$ intersect the graph?
(l) How often does the line $x = 1$ intersect the graph?
(m) For what value of x does $f(x) = 3$?
(n) For what value of x does $f(x) = -2$?

In Problems 11–22, determine whether the graph is that of a function by using the vertical-line test. If it is, use the graph to find:
(a) The domain and range (b) The intercepts, if any
(c) Any symmetry with respect to the x-axis, the y-axis, or the origin

11.

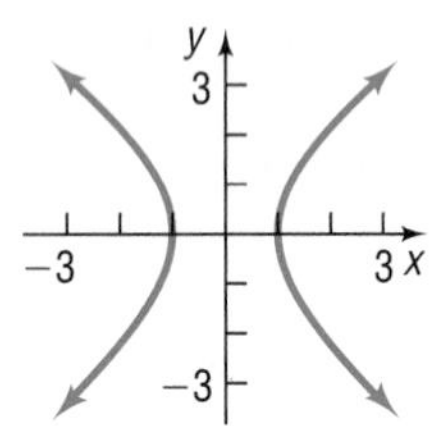

12.

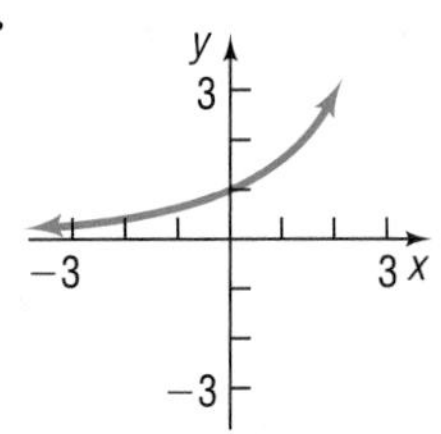

13.

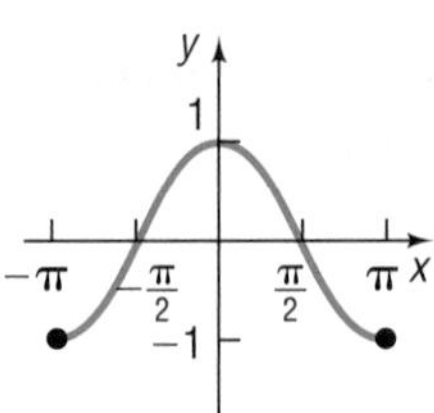

14.

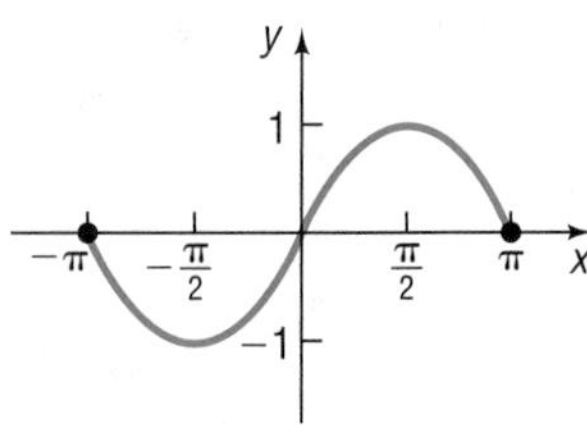

15.

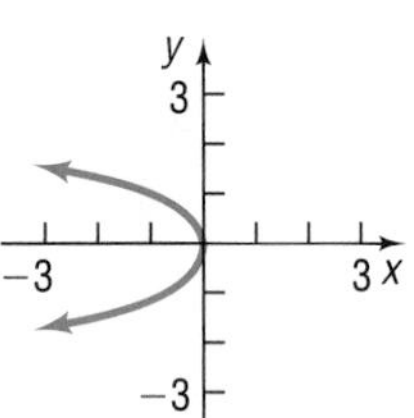

16.

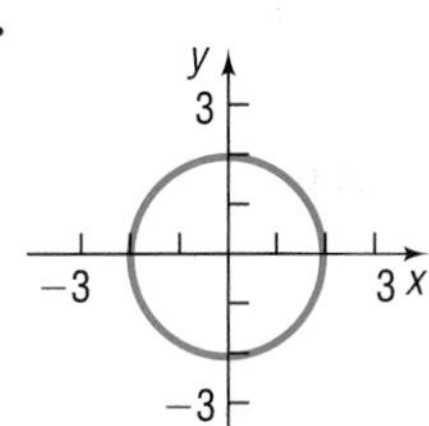

17.

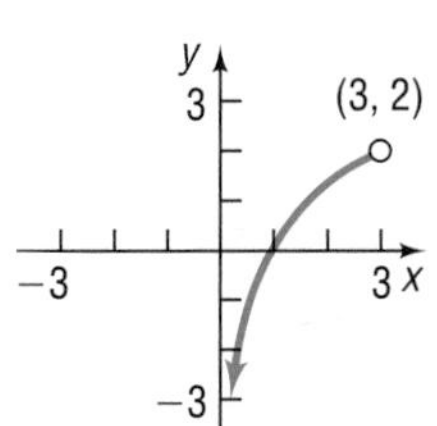

18.

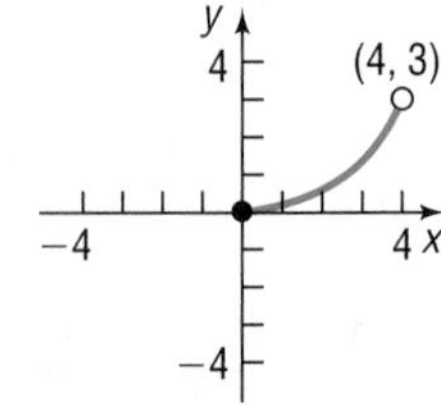

19.

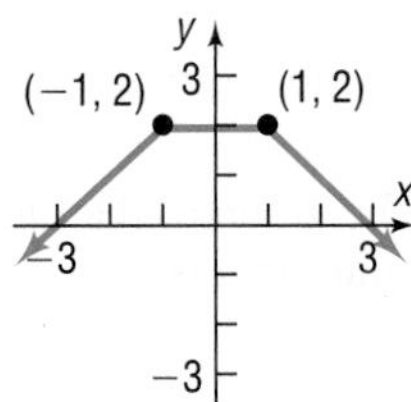

20.

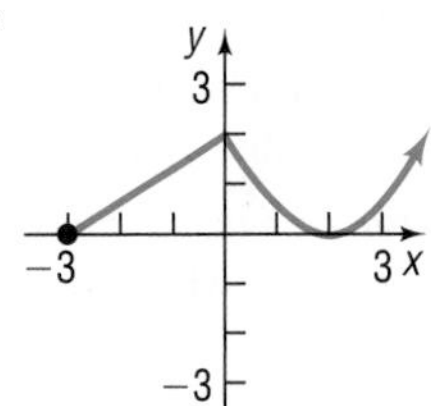

21.

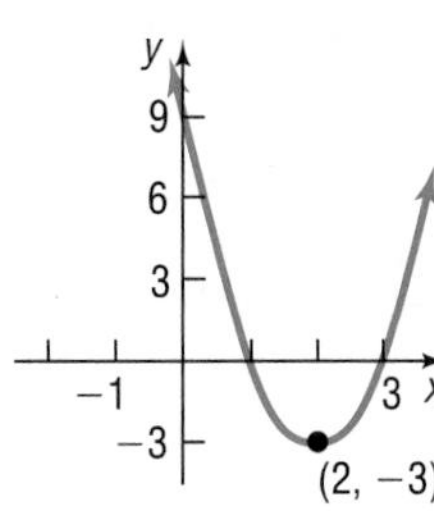

22.

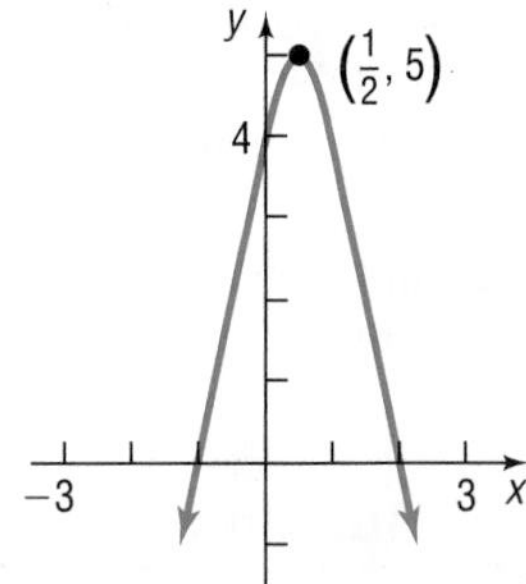

In Problems 23–28, answer the questions about the given function.

23. $f(x) = 2x^2 - x - 1$
(a) Is the point $(-1, 2)$ on the graph of f?
(b) If $x = -2$, what is $f(x)$? What point is on the graph of f?
(c) If $f(x) = -1$, what is x? What point(s) are on the graph of f?
(d) What is the domain of f?
(e) List the x-intercepts, if any, of the graph of f.
(f) List the y-intercept, if there is one, of the graph of f.

24. $f(x) = -3x^2 + 5x$
(a) Is the point $(-1, 2)$ on the graph of f?
(b) If $x = -2$, what is $f(x)$? What point is on the graph of f?
(c) If $f(x) = -2$, what is x? What point(s) are on the graph of f?
(d) What is the domain of f?
(e) List the x-intercepts, if any, of the graph of f.
(f) List the y-intercept, if there is one, of the graph of f.

25. $f(x) = \dfrac{x+2}{x-6}$
(a) Is the point $(3, 14)$ on the graph of f?
(b) If $x = 4$, what is $f(x)$? What point is on the graph of f?
(c) If $f(x) = 2$, what is x? What point(s) are on the graph of f?
(d) What is the domain of f?
(e) List the x-intercepts, if any, of the graph of f.
(f) List the y-intercept, if there is one, of the graph of f.

26. $f(x) = \dfrac{x^2+2}{x+4}$
(a) Is the point $\left(1, \dfrac{3}{5}\right)$ on the graph of f?
(b) If $x = 0$, what is $f(x)$? What point is on the graph of f?
(c) If $f(x) = \dfrac{1}{2}$, what is x? What point(s) are on the graph of f?
(d) What is the domain of f?
(e) List the x-intercepts, if any, of the graph of f.
(f) List the y-intercept, if there is one, of the graph of f.

27. $f(x) = \dfrac{2x^2}{x^4+1}$
(a) Is the point $(-1, 1)$ on the graph of f?
(b) If $x = 2$, what is $f(x)$? What point is on the graph of f?
(c) If $f(x) = 1$, what is x? What point(s) are on the graph of f?
(d) What is the domain of f?
(e) List the x-intercepts, if any, of the graph of f.
(f) List the y-intercept, if there is one, of the graph of f.

28. $f(x) = \dfrac{2x}{x-2}$
(a) Is the point $\left(\dfrac{1}{2}, -\dfrac{2}{3}\right)$ on the graph of f?
(b) If $x = 4$, what is $f(x)$? What point is on the graph of f?
(c) If $f(x) = 1$, what is x? What point(s) are on the graph of f?
(d) What is the domain of f?
(e) List the x-intercepts, if any, of the graph of f.
(f) List the y-intercept, if there is one, of the graph of f.

Applications and Extensions

29. Free-throw Shots According to physicist Peter Brancazio, the key to a successful foul shot in basketball lies in the arc of the shot. Brancazio determined the optimal angle of the arc from the free-throw line to be 45 degrees. The arc also depends on the velocity with which the ball is shot. If a player shoots a foul shot, releasing the ball at a 45-degree angle from a position 6 feet above the floor, then the path of the ball can be modeled by the function

$$h(x) = -\frac{44x^2}{v^2} + x + 6$$

where h is the height of the ball above the floor, x is the forward distance of the ball in front of the foul line, and v is the initial velocity with which the ball is shot in feet per second. Suppose a player shoots a ball with an initial velocity of 28 feet per second.

(a) Determine the height of the ball after it has traveled 8 feet in front of the foul line.

(b) Determine $h(12)$. What does this value represent?

(c) Find additional points and graph the path of the basketball.

(d) The center of the hoop is 10 feet above the floor and 15 feet in front of the foul line. Will the ball go through the hoop? Why or why not? If not, with what initial velocity must the ball be shot in order for the ball to go through the hoop?

Source: The Physics of Foul Shots, Discover, *Vol. 21, No. 10, October 2000*

30. Granny Shots The last player in the NBA to use an underhand foul shot (a "granny" shot) was Hall of Fame forward Rick Barry who retired in 1980. Barry believes that current NBA players could increase their free-throw percentage if they were to use an underhand shot. Since underhand shots are released from a lower position, the angle of the shot must be increased. If a player shoots an underhand foul shot, releasing the ball at a 70-degree angle from a position 3.5 feet above the floor, then the path of the ball can be modeled by the function $h(x) = -\frac{136x^2}{v^2} + 2.7x + 3.5$, where h is the height of the ball above the floor, x is the forward distance of the ball in front of the foul line, and v is the initial velocity with which the ball is shot in feet per second.

(a) The center of the hoop is 10 feet above the floor and 15 feet in front of the foul line. Determine the initial velocity with which the ball must be shot in order for the ball to go through the hoop.

(b) Write the function for the path of the ball using the velocity found in part (a).

(c) Determine $h(9)$. What does this value represent?

(d) Find additional points and graph the path of the basketball.

Source: The Physics of Foul Shots, Discover, *Vol. 21, No. 10, October 2000*

31. Motion of a Golf Ball A golf ball is hit with an initial velocity of 130 feet per second at an inclination of 45° to the horizontal. In physics, it is established that the height h of the golf ball is given by the function

$$h(x) = \frac{-32x^2}{130^2} + x$$

where x is the horizontal distance that the golf ball has traveled.

(a) Determine the height of the golf ball after it has traveled 100 feet.

(b) What is the height after it has traveled 300 feet?

(c) What is $h(500)$? Interpret this value.

(d) How far was the golf ball hit?

(e) Use a graphing utility to graph the function $h = h(x)$.

(f) Use a graphing utility to determine the distance that the ball has traveled when the height of the ball is 90 feet.

(g) Create a TABLE with TblStart = 0 and ΔTbl = 25. To the nearest 25 feet, how far does the ball travel before it reaches a maximum height? What is the maximum height?

(h) Adjust the value of ΔTbl until you determine the distance, to within 1 foot, that the ball travels before it reaches a maximum height.

32. Cross-sectional Area The cross-sectional area of a beam cut from a log with radius 1 foot is given by the function $A(x) = 4x\sqrt{1 - x^2}$, where x represents the length, in feet, of half the base of the beam. See the figure.

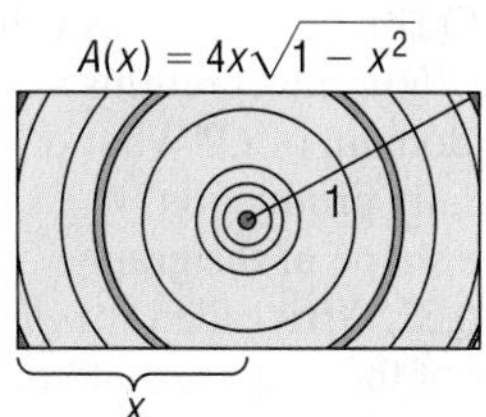

(a) Find the domain of A.

(b) Use a graphing utility to graph the function $A = A(x)$.

(c) Create a TABLE with TblStart = 0 and ΔTbl = 0.1. Which value of x in the domain found in part (a) maximizes the cross-sectional area? What should be the length of the base of the beam to maximize the cross-sectional area?

33. Cost of Trans-Atlantic Travel A Boeing 747 crosses the Atlantic Ocean (3000 miles) with an airspeed of 500 miles per hour. The cost C (in dollars) per passenger is given by

$$C(x) = 100 + \frac{x}{10} + \frac{36{,}000}{x}$$

where x is the ground speed (airspeed $\pm$ wind).

(a) Use a graphing utility to graph the function $C = C(x)$.
(b) Create a TABLE with TblStart = 0 and ΔTbl = 50.
(c) To the nearest 50 miles per hour, what ground speed minimizes the cost per passenger?

34. Effect of Elevation on Weight If an object weighs m pounds at sea level, then its weight W (in pounds) at a height of h miles above sea level is given approximately by

$$W(h) = m\left(\frac{4000}{4000 + h}\right)^2$$

(a) If Amy weighs 120 pounds at sea level, how much will she weigh on Pike's Peak, which is 14,110 feet above sea level?
(b) Use a graphing utility to graph the function $W = W(h)$. Use $m = 120$ pounds.
(c) Create a TABLE with TblStart = 0 and ΔTbl = 0.5 to see how the weight W varies as h changes from 0 to 5 miles.
(d) At what height will Amy weigh 119.95 pounds?
(e) Does your answer to part (d) seem reasonable? Explain.

35. The graph of two functions, f and g, is illustrated. Use the graph to answer parts (a)–(f).

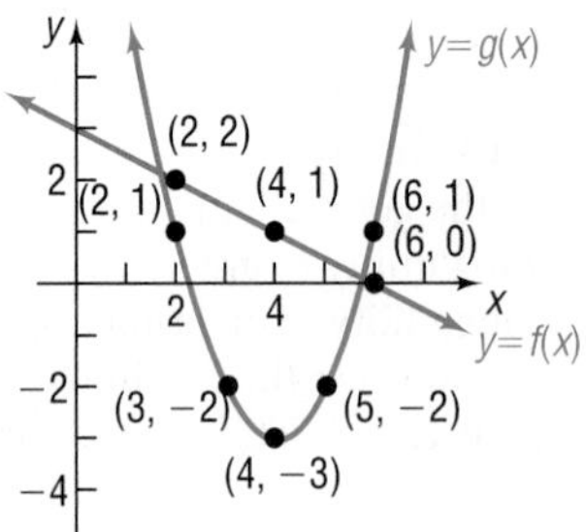

(a) $(f + g)(2)$
(b) $(f + g)(4)$
(c) $(f - g)(6)$
(d) $(g - f)(6)$
(e) $(f \cdot g)(2)$
(f) $\left(\frac{f}{g}\right)(4)$

36. Reading and Interpreting Graphs Let C be the function whose graph is given in the next column. This graph represents the cost C of manufacturing q computers in a day.

(a) Determine $C(0)$. Interpret this value.
(b) Determine $C(10)$. Interpret this value.
(c) Determine $C(50)$. Interpret this value.
(d) What is the domain of C? What does this domain imply in terms of daily production?
(e) Describe the shape of the graph.
(f) The point (30,32000) is called an *inflection point*. Describe the behavior of the graph around the inflection point.

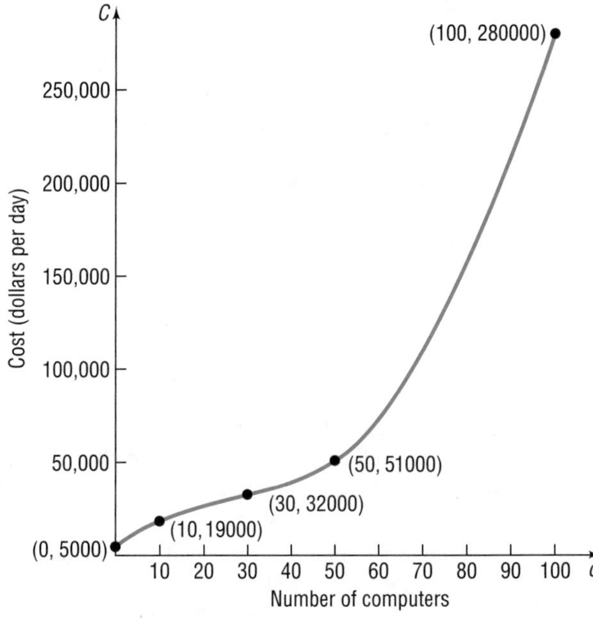

37. Reading and Interpreting Graphs Let C be the function whose graph is given below. This graph represents the cost C of using m anytime cell phone minutes in a month for a five-person family plan.

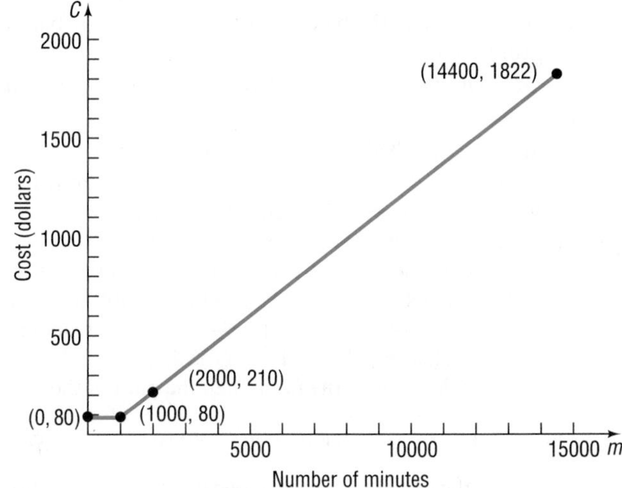

(a) Determine $C(0)$. Interpret this value.
(b) Determine $C(1000)$. Interpret this value.
(c) Determine $C(2000)$. Interpret this value.
(d) What is the domain of C? What does this domain imply in terms of the number of anytime minutes?
(e) Describe the shape of the graph.

Explaining Concepts: Discussion and Writing

38. Describe how you would proceed to find the domain and range of a function if you were given its graph. How would your strategy change if you were given the equation defining the function instead of its graph?

39. How many x-intercepts can the graph of a function have? How many y-intercepts can the graph of a function have?

40. Is a graph that consists of a single point the graph of a function? Can you write the equation of such a function?

41. Match each of the following functions with the graph on the next page that best describes the situation.
(a) The cost of building a house as a function of its square footage
(b) The height of an egg dropped from a 300-foot building as a function of time
(c) The height of a human as a function of time
(d) The demand for Big Macs as a function of price
(e) The height of a child on a swing as a function of time?

(I) (II) (III) (IV) (V)

42. Match each of the following functions with the graph that best describes the situation.
    (a) The temperature of a bowl of soup as a function of time
    (b) The number of hours of daylight per day over a 2-year period
    (c) The population of Texas as a function of time
    (d) The distance traveled by a car going at a constant velocity as a function of time
    (e) The height of a golf ball hit with a 7-iron as a function of time

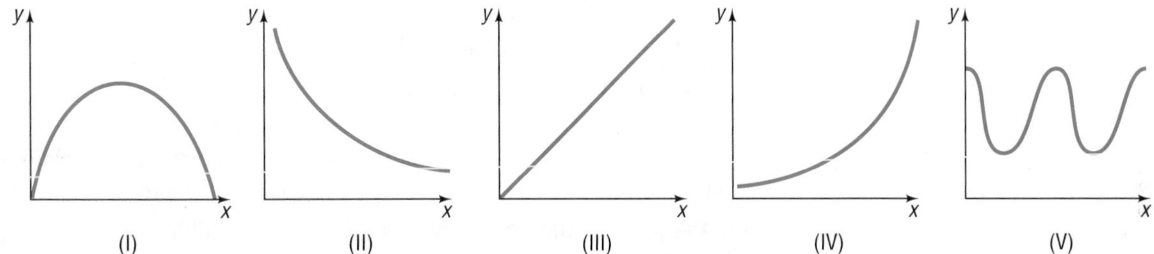

43. Consider the following scenario: Barbara decides to take a walk. She leaves home, walks 2 blocks in 5 minutes at a constant speed, and realizes that she forgot to lock the door. So Barbara runs home in 1 minute. While at her doorstep, it takes her 1 minute to find her keys and lock the door. Barbara walks 5 blocks in 15 minutes and then decides to jog home. It takes her 7 minutes to get home. Draw a graph of Barbara's distance from home (in blocks) as a function of time.

44. Consider the following scenario: Jayne enjoys riding her bicycle through the woods. At the forest preserve, she gets on her bicycle and rides up a 2000-foot incline in 10 minutes. She then travels down the incline in 3 minutes. The next 5000 feet is level terrain and she covers the distance in 20 minutes. She rests for 15 minutes. Jayne then travels 10,000 feet in 30 minutes. Draw a graph of Jayne's distance traveled (in feet) as a function of time.

45. The following sketch represents the distance d (in miles) that Kevin was from home as a function of time t (in hours). Answer the questions based on the graph. In parts (a)–(g), how many hours elapsed and how far was Kevin from home during this time?

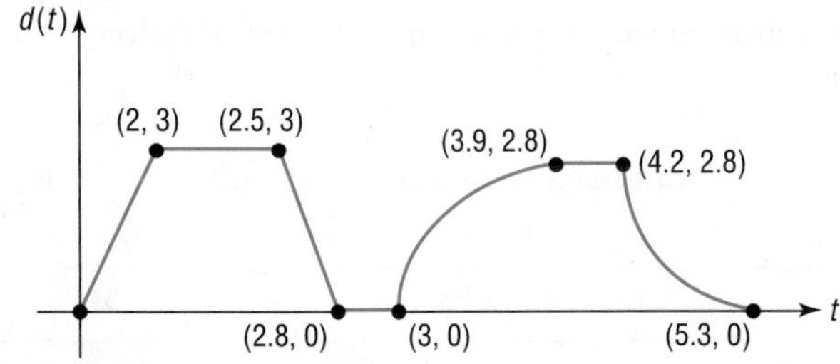

    (a) From $t = 0$ to $t = 2$
    (b) From $t = 2$ to $t = 2.5$
    (c) From $t = 2.5$ to $t = 2.8$
    (d) From $t = 2.8$ to $t = 3$
    (e) From $t = 3$ to $t = 3.9$
    (f) From $t = 3.9$ to $t = 4.2$
    (g) From $t = 4.2$ to $t = 5.3$
    (h) What is the farthest distance that Kevin was from home?
    (i) How many times did Kevin return home?

46. The following sketch represents the speed v (in miles per hour) of Michael's car as a function of time t (in minutes).

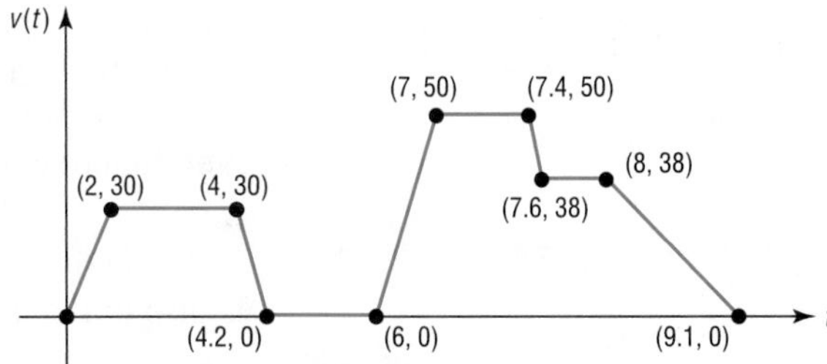

    (a) Over what interval of time was Michael traveling fastest?
    (b) Over what interval(s) of time was Michael's speed zero?
    (c) What was Michael's speed between 0 and 2 minutes?
    (d) What was Michael's speed between 4.2 and 6 minutes?
    (e) What was Michael's speed between 7 and 7.4 minutes?
    (f) When was Michael's speed constant?

47. Draw the graph of a function whose domain is $\{x \mid -3 \le x \le 8, x \ne 5\}$ and whose range is $\{y \mid -1 \le y \le 2, y \ne 0\}$. What point(s) in the rectangle $-3 \le x \le 8, -1 \le y \le 2$ cannot be on the graph? Compare your graph with those of other students. What differences do you see?

48. Is there a function whose graph is symmetric with respect to the x-axis? Explain.

'Are You Prepared?' Answers

1. $(-4, 0), (4, 0), (0, -2), (0, 2)$ **2.** False

9.3 Properties of Functions

PREPARING FOR THIS SECTION *Before getting started, review the following:*

- Intervals (Section 7.5, pp. 504–505)
- Intercepts (Section 8.1, pp. 522–523)
- Slope of a Line (Section 8.2, pp. 530–533)
- Point–Slope Form of a Line (Section 8.2, p. 534)
- Symmetry (Section 8.1, pp. 523–525)

Now Work the **'Are You Prepared?'** problems on page 590.

OBJECTIVES
1 Determine Even and Odd Functions from a Graph (p. 582)
2 Identify Even and Odd Functions from the Equation (p. 583)
3 Use a Graph to Determine Where a Function is Increasing, Decreasing, or Constant (p. 584)
4 Use a Graph to Locate Local Maxima and Local Minima (p. 585)
5 Use a Graph to Locate the Absolute Maximum and the Absolute Minimum (p. 586)
6 Use a Graphing Utility to Approximate Local Maxima and Local Minima and to Determine Where a Function is Increasing or Decreasing (p. 587)
7 Find the Average Rate of Change of a Function (p. 588)

To obtain the graph of a function $y = f(x)$, it is often helpful to know certain properties that the function has and the impact of these properties on the way that the graph will look.

1 Determine Even and Odd Functions from a Graph

The words *even* and *odd,* when applied to a function f, describe the symmetry that exists for the graph of the function.

A function f is even, if and only if, whenever the point (x, y) is on the graph of f then the point $(-x, y)$ is also on the graph. Using function notation, we define an even function as follows:

DEFINITION

A function f is **even** if, for every number x in its domain, the number $-x$ is also in the domain and

$$f(-x) = f(x)$$

A function f is odd, if and only if, whenever the point (x, y) is on the graph of f then the point $(-x, -y)$ is also on the graph. Using function notation, we define an odd function as follows:

DEFINITION

A function f is **odd** if, for every number x in its domain, the number $-x$ is also in the domain and

$$f(-x) = -f(x)$$

Refer to page 524, where the tests for symmetry are listed. The following results are then evident.

THEOREM

A function is even if and only if its graph is symmetric with respect to the y-axis. A function is odd if and only if its graph is symmetric with respect to the origin.

EXAMPLE 1 **Determining Even and Odd Functions from the Graph**

Determine whether each graph given in Figure 17 is the graph of an even function, an odd function, or a function that is neither even nor odd.

Figure 17

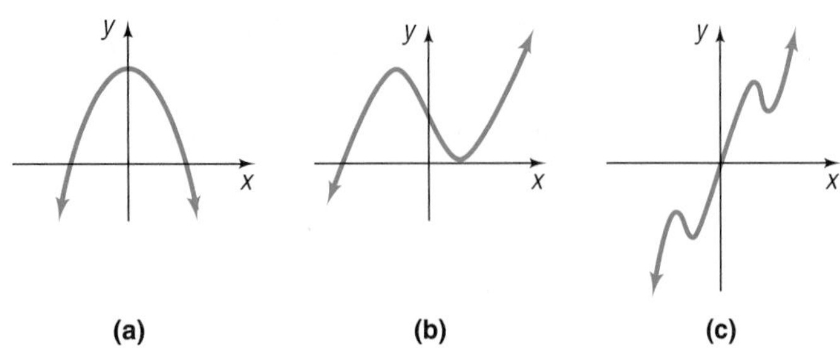

Solution

(a) The graph in Figure 17(a) is that of an even function, because the graph is symmetric with respect to the y-axis.

(b) The function whose graph is given in Figure 17(b) is neither even nor odd, because the graph is neither symmetric with respect to the y-axis nor symmetric with respect to the origin.

(c) The function whose graph is given in Figure 17(c) is odd, because the graph is symmetric with respect to the origin. ■

Now Work PROBLEMS 21(a), (b), AND (d)

2 Identify Even and Odd Functions from the Equation

A graphing utility can be used to conjecture whether a function is even, odd, or neither. Remember that, when the graph of an even function contains the point (x, y), it must also contain the point $(-x, y)$. Therefore, if the graph shows evidence of symmetry with respect to the y-axis, we would conjecture that the function is even. In addition, if the graph shows evidence of symmetry with respect to the origin, we would conjecture that the function is odd.

EXAMPLE 2 **Identifying Even and Odd Functions**

Use a graphing utility to conjecture whether each of the following functions is even, odd, or neither. Then algebraically determine whether the graph is symmetric with respect to the y-axis or with respect to the origin.

(a) $f(x) = x^2 - 5$ (b) $g(x) = x^3 - 1$ (c) $h(x) = 5x^3 - x$

Figure 18

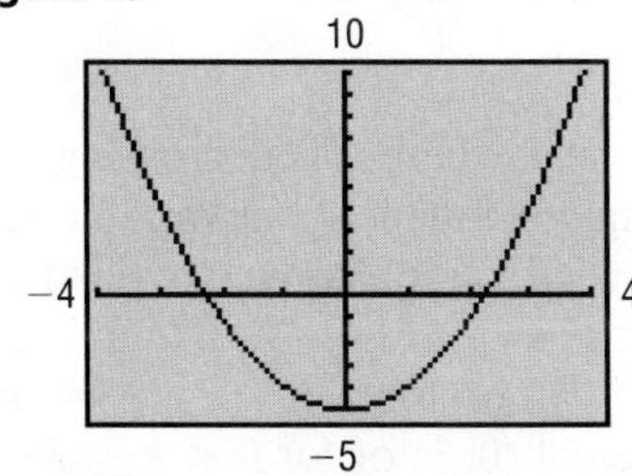

Figure 19

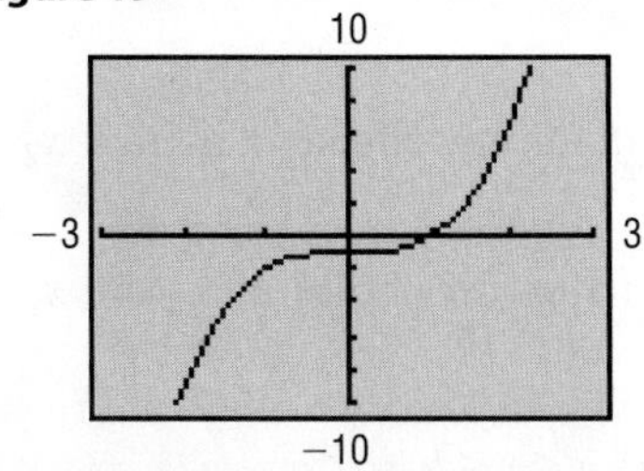

Solution

(a) Graph the function. See Figure 18. It appears that the graph is symmetric with respect to the y-axis. We conjecture that the function is even.

To algebraically verify the conjecture, replace x by $-x$ in $f(x) = x^2 - 5$. Then

$$f(-x) = (-x)^2 - 5 = x^2 - 5 = f(x)$$

Since $f(-x) = f(x)$, we conclude that f is an even function and that the graph is symmetric with respect to the y-axis.

(b) Graph the function. See Figure 19. It appears that there is no symmetry. We conjecture that the function is neither even nor odd.

To algebraically verify that the function is not even, find $g(-x)$ and compare the result with $g(x)$.

$$g(-x) = (-x)^3 - 1 = -x^3 - 1; \quad g(x) = x^3 - 1$$

Since $g(-x) \neq g(x)$, the function is not even.

To algebraically verify that the function is not odd, find $-g(x)$ and compare the result with $g(-x)$.

$$-g(x) = -(x^3 - 1) = -x^3 + 1; \quad g(-x) = -x^3 - 1$$

Since $g(-x) \neq -g(x)$, the function is not odd. The graph is not symmetric with respect to the y-axis nor is it symmetric with respect to the origin.

(c) Graph the function. See Figure 20. It appears that there is symmetry with respect to the origin. We conjecture that the function is odd.

To algebraically verify the conjecture, replace x by $-x$ in $h(x) = 5x^3 - x$. Then

$$h(-x) = 5(-x)^3 - (-x) = -5x^3 + x = -(5x^3 - x) = -h(x)$$

Since $h(-x) = -h(x)$, h is an odd function and the graph of h is symmetric with respect to the origin. ■

Figure 20

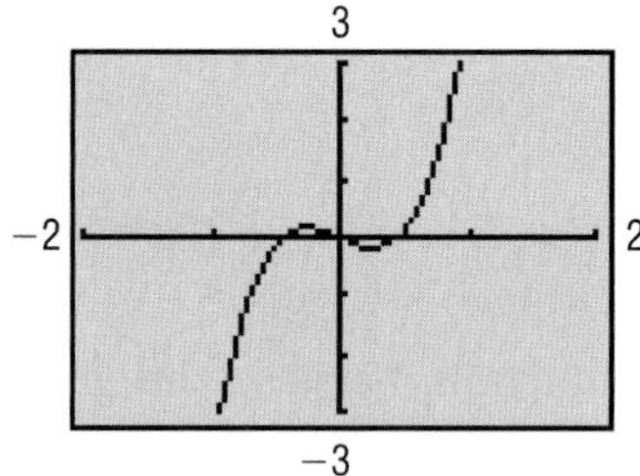

Now Work PROBLEM 33

3 Use a Graph to Determine Where a Function Is Increasing, Decreasing, or Constant

Consider the graph given in Figure 21. If you look from left to right along the graph of the function, you will notice that parts of the graph are going up, parts are going down, and parts are horizontal. In such cases, the function is described as *increasing, decreasing,* or *constant,* respectively.

Figure 21

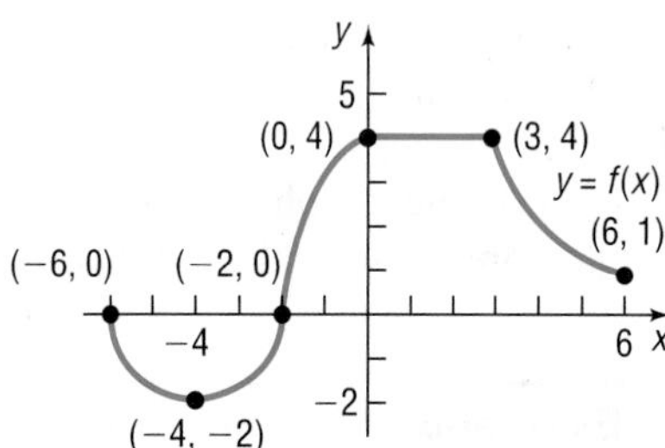

EXAMPLE 3

Determining Where a Function Is Increasing, Decreasing, or Constant from Its Graph

Where is the function in Figure 21 increasing? Where is it decreasing? Where is it constant?

Solution To answer the question of where a function is increasing, where it is decreasing, and where it is constant, we use strict inequalities involving the independent variable x, or we use open intervals* of x-coordinates. The function whose graph is given in Figure 21 is increasing on the open interval $(-4, 0)$ or for $-4 < x < 0$. The function is decreasing on the open intervals $(-6, -4)$ and $(3, 6)$ or for $-6 < x < -4$ and $3 < x < 6$. The function is constant on the open interval $(0, 3)$ or for $0 < x < 3$. ■

WARNING We describe the behavior of a graph in terms of its x-values. Do not say the graph in Figure 21 is increasing from the point $(-4, -2)$ to the point $(0, 4)$. Rather, say it is increasing on the interval $(-4, 0)$. ■

More precise definitions follow:

DEFINITIONS

A function f is **increasing** on an open interval I if, for any choice of x_1 and x_2 in I, with $x_1 < x_2$, we have $f(x_1) < f(x_2)$.

A function f is **decreasing** on an open interval I if, for any choice of x_1 and x_2 in I, with $x_1 < x_2$, we have $f(x_1) > f(x_2)$.

* The open interval (a, b) consists of all real numbers x for which $a < x < b$.

In Words

If a function is decreasing, then, as the values of x get bigger, the values of the function get smaller. If a function is increasing, then, as the values of x get bigger, the values of the function also get bigger. If a function is constant, then, as the values of x get bigger, the values of the function remain unchanged.

A function f is **constant** on an open interval I if, for all choices of x in I, the values of $f(x)$ are equal.

Figure 22 illustrates the definitions. Graphs are read like a book—from left to right. So, the graph of an increasing function goes up from left to right, the graph of a decreasing function goes down from left to right, and the graph of a constant function remains at a fixed height.

Figure 22

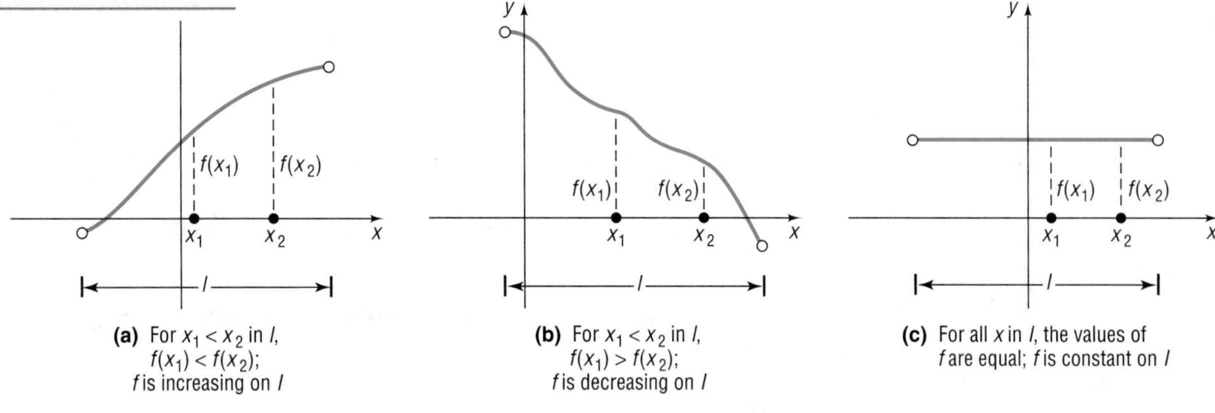

(a) For $x_1 < x_2$ in I, $f(x_1) < f(x_2)$; f is increasing on I

(b) For $x_1 < x_2$ in I, $f(x_1) > f(x_2)$; f is decreasing on I

(c) For all x in I, the values of f are equal; f is constant on I

Now Work PROBLEMS 11, 13, 15, AND 21(c)

4 Use a Graph to Locate Local Maxima and Local Minima

Suppose f is a function defined on an open interval containing c. If the value of f at c is greater than or equal to the values of f on I, then f has a *local maximum* at c*. See Figure 23(a).

If the value of f at c is less than or equal to the values of f on I, then f has a *local minimum* at c. See Figure 23(b).

Figure 23

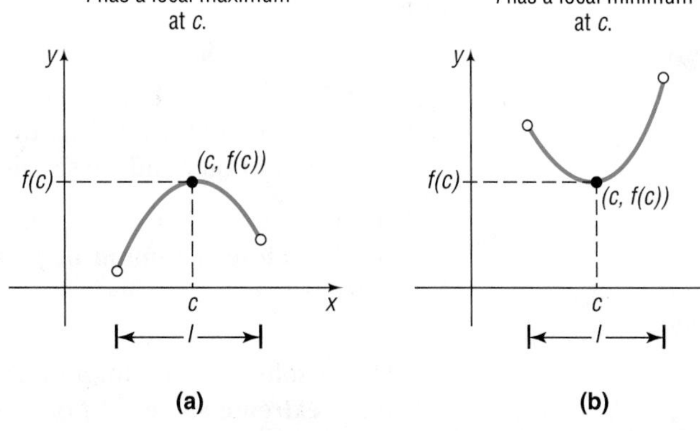

(a) (b)

DEFINITIONS

A function f has a **local maximum** at c if there is an open interval I containing c so that for all x in I, $f(x) \leq f(c)$. We call $f(c)$ a **local maximum value of *f*.**

A function f has a **local minimum** at c if there is an open interval I containing c so that, for all x in I, $f(x) \geq f(c)$. We call $f(c)$ a **local minimum value of *f*.**

If f has a local maximum at c, then the value of f at c is greater than or equal to the values of f near c. If f has a local minimum at c, then the value of f at c is less than or equal to the values of f near c. The word *local* is used to suggest that it is only near c, that is, in some open interval containing c, that the value $f(c)$ has these properties.

*Some texts use the term *relative* instead of *local*.

EXAMPLE 4 **Finding Local Maxima and Local Minima from the Graph of a Function and Determining Where the Function Is Increasing, Decreasing, or Constant**

Figure 24

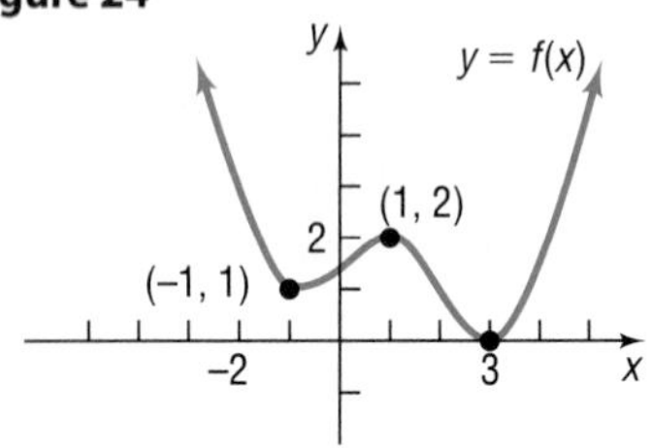

Figure 24 shows the graph of a function f.

(a) At what value(s) of x, if any, does f have a local maximum? List the local maximum values.

(b) At what value(s) of x, if any, does f have a local minimum? List the local minimum values.

(c) Find the intervals on which f is increasing. Find the intervals on which f is decreasing.

Solution The domain of f is the set of real numbers.

(a) f has a local maximum at 1, since for all x close to 1, we have $f(x) \leq f(1)$. The local maximum value is $f(1) = 2$.

(b) f has local minima at -1 and at 3. The local minimum values are $f(-1) = 1$ and $f(3) = 0$.

(c) The function whose graph is given in Figure 24 is increasing for all values of x between -1 and 1 and for all values of x greater than 3. That is, the function is increasing on the intervals $(-1, 1)$ and $(3, \infty)$ or for $-1 < x < 1$ and $x > 3$. The function is decreasing for all values of x less than -1 and for all values of x between 1 and 3. That is, the function is decreasing on the intervals $(-\infty, -1)$ and $(1, 3)$ or for $x < -1$ and $1 < x < 3$. ■

WARNING The y-value is the local maximum value or local minimum value and it occurs at some x-value. For example, in Figure 24, we say f has a local maximum at 1 and the local maximum value is 2. ■

Now Work PROBLEMS 17 AND 19

5 Use a Graph to Locate the Absolute Maximum and the Absolute Minimum

Look at the graph of the function f given in Figure 25. The domain of f is the closed interval $[a, b]$. Also, the largest value of f is $f(u)$ and the smallest value of f is $f(v)$. These are called, respectively, the *absolute maximum* and the *absolute minimum* of f on $[a, b]$.

Figure 25

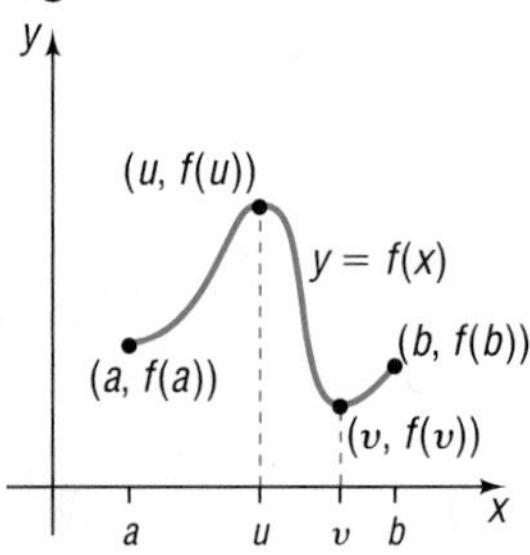

domain: $[a, b]$
for all x in $[a, b]$, $f(x) \leq f(u)$
for all x in $[a, b]$, $f(x) \geq f(v)$
absolute maximum: $f(u)$
absolute minimum: $f(v)$

DEFINITION Let f denote a function defined on some interval I. If there is a number u in I for which $f(x) \leq f(u)$ for all x in I, then $f(u)$ is the **absolute maximum of f** on I and we say **the absolute maximum of f occurs at u.**

If there is a number v in I for which $f(x) \geq f(v)$ for all x in I, then $f(v)$ is the **absolute minimum of f** on I and we say **the absolute minimum of f occurs at v.**

The absolute maximum and absolute minimum of a function f are sometimes called the **extreme values** of f on I.

The absolute maximum or absolute minimum of a function f may not exist. Let's look at some examples.

EXAMPLE 5 **Finding the Absolute Maximum and the Absolute Minimum from the Graph of a Function**

For each graph of a function $y = f(x)$ in Figure 26 on the following page, find the absolute maximum and the absolute minimum, if they exist.

Solution (a) The function f whose graph is given in Figure 26(a) has the closed interval $[0, 5]$ as its domain. The largest value of f is $f(3) = 6$, the absolute maximum. The smallest value of f is $f(0) = 1$, the absolute minimum.

Figure 26

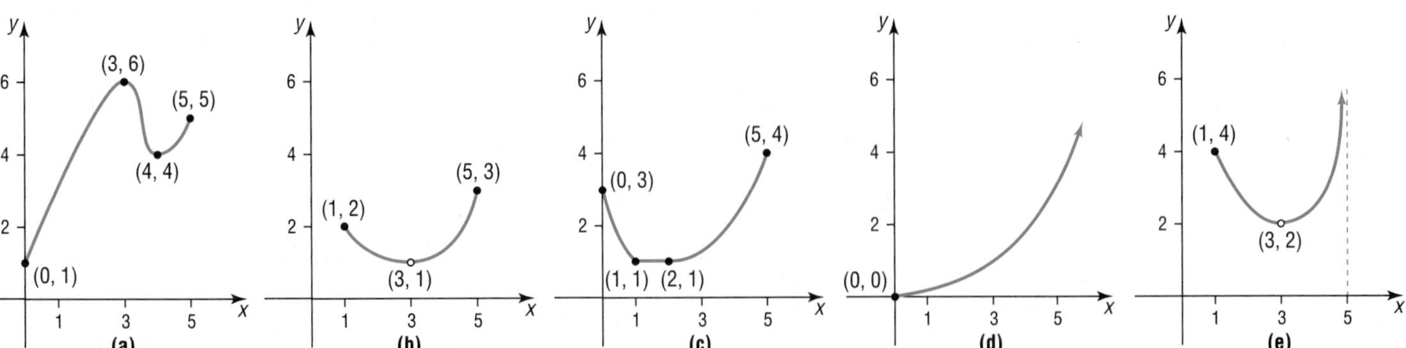

(b) The function f whose graph is given in Figure 26(b) has the domain $\{x|1 \le x \le 5, x \ne 3\}$. Note that we exclude 3 from the domain because of the "hole" at $(3, 1)$. The largest value of f on its domain is $f(5) = 3$, the absolute maximum. There is no absolute minimum. Do you see why? As you trace the graph, getting closer to the point $(3, 1)$, there is no single smallest value. [As soon as you claim a smallest value, we can trace closer to $(3, 1)$ and get a smaller value!]

(c) The function f whose graph is given in Figure 26(c) has the interval $[0, 5]$ as its domain. The absolute maximum of f is $f(5) = 4$. The absolute minimum is 1. Notice that the absolute minimum 1 occurs at any number in the interval $[1, 2]$.

(d) The graph of the function f given in Figure 26(d) has the interval $[0, \infty)$ as its domain. The function has no absolute maximum; the absolute minimum is $f(0) = 0$.

(e) The graph of the function f in Figure 26(e) has the domain $\{x|1 \le x < 5, x \ne 3\}$. The function f has no absolute maximum and no absolute minimum. Do you see why? ■

In calculus, there is a theorem with conditions that guarantee a function will have an absolute maximum and an absolute minimum.

THEOREM

Extreme Value Theorem

If f is a continuous function* whose domain is a closed interval $[a, b]$, then f has an absolute maximum and an absolute minimum on $[a, b]$.

Now Work PROBLEM 45

6 Use a Graphing Utility to Approximate Local Maxima and Local Minima and to Determine Where a Function Is Increasing or Decreasing

To locate the exact value at which a function f has a local maximum or a local minimum usually requires calculus. However, a graphing utility may be used to approximate these values by using the MAXIMUM and MINIMUM features.

EXAMPLE 6

Using a Graphing Utility to Approximate Local Maxima and Minima and to Determine Where a Function Is Increasing or Decreasing

(a) Use a graphing utility to graph $f(x) = 6x^3 - 12x + 5$ for $-2 < x < 2$. Approximate where f has a local maximum and where f has a local minimum.

(b) Determine where f is increasing and where it is decreasing.

*Although it requires calculus for a precise definition, we'll agree for now that a continuous function is one whose graph has no gaps or holes and can be traced without lifting the pencil from the paper.

Solution (a) Graphing utilities have a feature that finds the maximum or minimum point of a graph within a given interval. Graph the function f for $-2 < x < 2$. The MAXIMUM and MINIMUM commands require us to first determine the open interval I. The graphing utility will then approximate the maximum or minimum value in the interval. Using MAXIMUM we find that the local maximum is 11.53 and it occurs at $x = -0.82$, rounded to two decimal places. See Figure 27(a). Using MINIMUM, we find that the local minimum is -1.53 and it occurs at $x = 0.82$, rounded to two decimal places. See Figure 27(b).

Figure 27

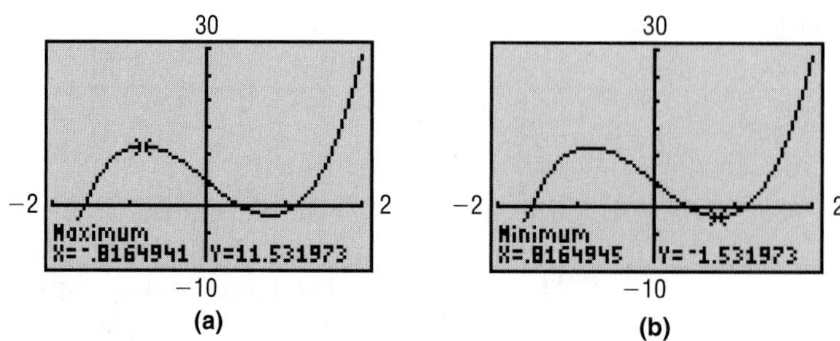

(b) Looking at Figures 27(a) and (b), we see that the graph of f is increasing from $x = -2$ to $x = -0.82$ and from $x = 0.82$ to $x = 2$, so f is increasing on the intervals $(-2, -0.82)$ and $(0.82, 2)$ or for $-2 < x < -0.82$ and $0.82 < x < 2$. The graph is decreasing from $x = -0.82$ to $x = 0.82$, so f is decreasing on the interval $(-0.82, 0.82)$ or for $-0.82 < x < 0.82$. ■

Now Work PROBLEM 53

7 Find the Average Rate of Change of a Function

In Section 8.2, we said that the slope of a line could be interpreted as the average rate of change. To find the average rate of change of a function between any two points on its graph, calculate the slope of the line containing the two points.

DEFINITION If a and b, $a \neq b$, are in the domain of a function $y = f(x)$, the **average rate of change of f from a to b** is defined as

$$\text{Average rate of change} = \frac{\Delta y}{\Delta x} = \frac{f(b) - f(a)}{b - a} \qquad a \neq b \qquad \textbf{(1)}$$

The symbol Δy in (1) is the "change in y," and Δx is the "change in x." The average rate of change of f is the change in y divided by the change in x.

EXAMPLE 7 **Finding the Average Rate of Change**

Find the average rate of change of $f(x) = 3x^2$:

(a) From 1 to 3 (b) From 1 to 5 (c) From 1 to 7

Solution (a) The average rate of change of $f(x) = 3x^2$ from 1 to 3 is

$$\frac{\Delta y}{\Delta x} = \frac{f(3) - f(1)}{3 - 1} = \frac{27 - 3}{3 - 1} = \frac{24}{2} = 12$$

(b) The average rate of change of $f(x) = 3x^2$ from 1 to 5 is

$$\frac{\Delta y}{\Delta x} = \frac{f(5) - f(1)}{5 - 1} = \frac{75 - 3}{5 - 1} = \frac{72}{4} = 18$$

(c) The average rate of change of $f(x) = 3x^2$ from 1 to 7 is

$$\frac{\Delta y}{\Delta x} = \frac{f(7) - f(1)}{7 - 1} = \frac{147 - 3}{7 - 1} = \frac{144}{6} = 24$$

■

See Figure 28 for a graph of $f(x) = 3x^2$. The function f is increasing for $x > 0$. The fact that the average rate of change is positive for any $x_1, x_2, x_1 \neq x_2$ in the interval $(1, 7)$ indicates that the graph is increasing on $1 < x < 7$. Further, the average rate of change is consistently getting larger for $1 < x < 7$, indicating that the graph is increasing at an increasing rate.

Figure 28

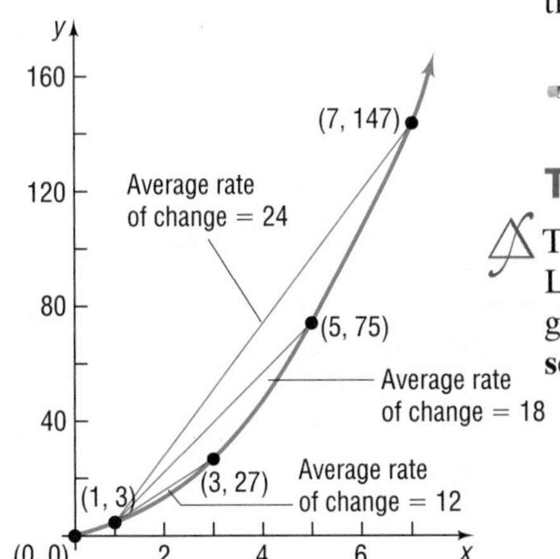

Now Work PROBLEM 61

The Secant Line

The average rate of change of a function has an important geometric interpretation. Look at the graph of $y = f(x)$ in Figure 29. We have labeled two points on the graph: $(a, f(a))$ and $(b, f(b))$. The line containing these two points is called the **secant line;** its slope is

$$m_{\text{sec}} = \frac{f(b) - f(a)}{b - a} = \frac{f(a + h) - f(a)}{h}$$

Figure 29

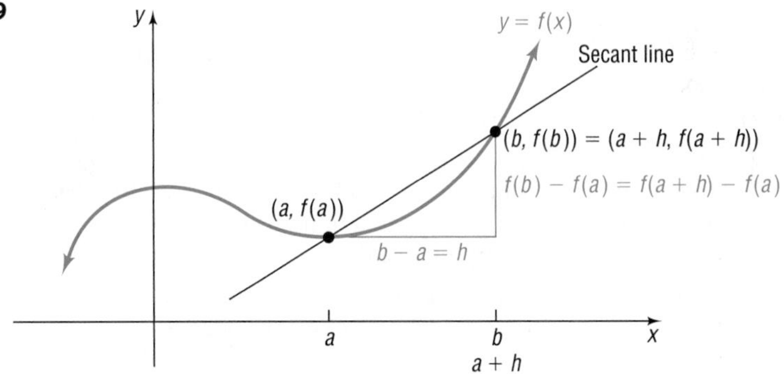

THEOREM

Slope of the Secant Line

The average rate of change of a function f from a to b equals the slope of the secant line containing the two points $(a, f(a))$ and $(b, f(b))$ on its graph.

EXAMPLE 8

Finding the Equation of a Secant Line

Suppose that $g(x) = 3x^2 - 2x + 3$.

(a) Find the average rate of change of g from -2 to 1.
(b) Find an equation of the secant line containing $(-2, g(-2))$ and $(1, g(1))$.
(c) Using a graphing utility, draw the graph of g and the secant line obtained in part (b) on the same screen.

Solution (a) The average rate of change of $g(x) = 3x^2 - 2x + 3$ from -2 to 1 is

$$\text{Average rate of change} = \frac{g(1) - g(-2)}{1 - (-2)}$$

$$= \frac{4 - 19}{3} \qquad g(1) = 3(1)^2 - 2(1) + 3 = 4 \quad g(-2) = 3(-2)^2 - 2(-2) + 3 = 19$$

$$= -\frac{15}{3} = -5$$

(b) The slope of the secant line containing $(-2, g(-2)) = (-2, 19)$ and $(1, g(1)) = (1, 4)$ is $m_{\text{sec}} = -5$. We use the point–slope form to find an equation of the secant line.

Figure 30

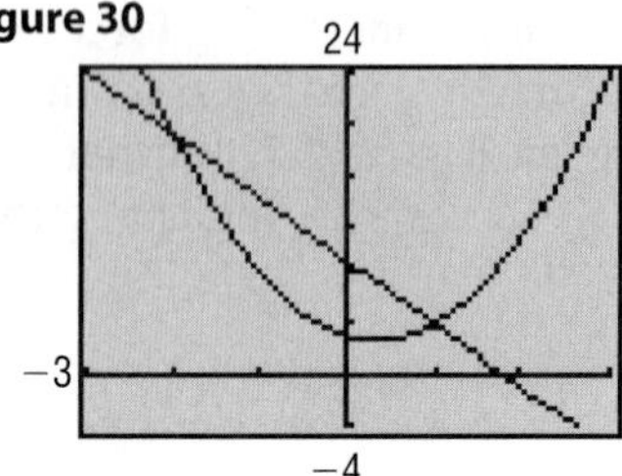

$$y - y_1 = m_{sec}(x - x_1) \quad \text{Point–slope form of the secant line}$$
$$y - 19 = -5(x - (-2)) \quad x_1 = -2, y_1 = g(-2) = 19, m_{sec} = -5$$
$$y - 19 = -5x - 10 \quad \text{Simplify.}$$
$$y = -5x + 9 \quad \text{Slope–intercept form of the secant line}$$

(c) Figure 30 shows the graph of g along with the secant line $y = -5x + 9$. ■

Now Work PROBLEM 67

9.3 Assess Your Understanding

'Are You Prepared?' *Answers are given at the end of these exercises. If you get a wrong answer, read the pages listed in red.*

1. The interval (2, 5) can be written as the inequality ________. (pp. 504–505)
2. The slope of the line containing the points (−2, 3) and (3, 8) is ______. (pp. 530–531)
3. Test the equation $y = 5x^2 - 1$ for symmetry with respect to the x-axis, the y-axis, and the origin. (pp. 523–525)
4. Write the point–slope form of the line with slope 5 containing the point (3, −2). (p. 534)
5. The intercepts of the equation $y = x^2 - 9$ are ________________. (pp. 522–523)

Concepts and Vocabulary

6. A function f is ________ on an open interval I if, for any choice of x_1 and x_2 in I, with $x_1 < x_2$, we have $f(x_1) < f(x_2)$.
7. A(n) _____ function f is one for which $f(-x) = f(x)$ for every x in the domain of f; a(n) ______ function f is one for which $f(-x) = -f(x)$ for every x in the domain of f.
8. ***True or False*** A function f is decreasing on an open interval I if, for any choice of x_1 and x_2 in I, with $x_1 < x_2$, we have $f(x_1) > f(x_2)$.
9. ***True or False*** A function f has a local maximum at c if there is an open interval I containing c so that for all x in I, $f(x) \le f(c)$.
10. ***True or False*** Even functions have graphs that are symmetric with respect to the origin.

Skill Building

In Problems 11–20, use the graph of the function f given.

11. Is f increasing on the interval (−8, −2)?
12. Is f decreasing on the interval (−8, −4)?
13. Is f increasing on the interval (2, 10)?
14. Is f decreasing on the interval (2, 5)?
15. List the interval(s) on which f is increasing.
16. List the interval(s) on which f is decreasing.
17. Is there a local maximum value at 2? If yes, what is it?
18. Is there a local maximum value at 5? If yes, what is it?
19. List the number(s) at which f has a local maximum. What are the local maximum values?
20. List the number(s) at which f has a local minimum. What are the local minimum values?

In Problems 21–28, the graph of a function is given. Use the graph to find:
(a) The intercepts, if any
(b) The domain and range
(c) The intervals on which it is increasing, decreasing, or constant
(d) Whether it is even, odd, or neither

21.
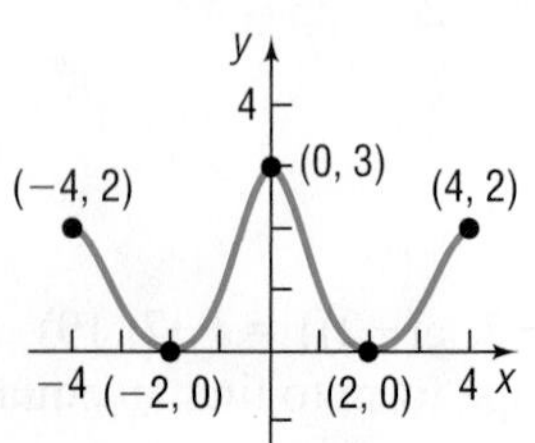

22.
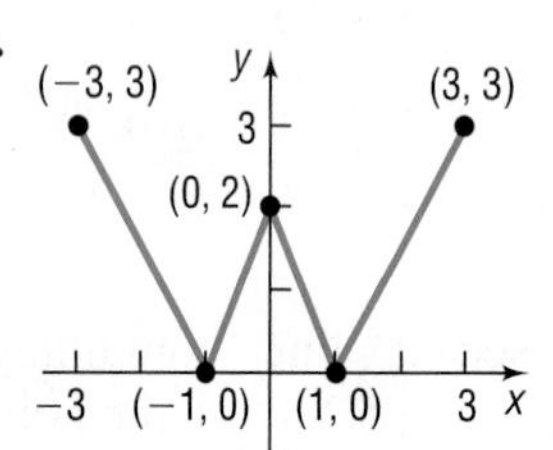

23.
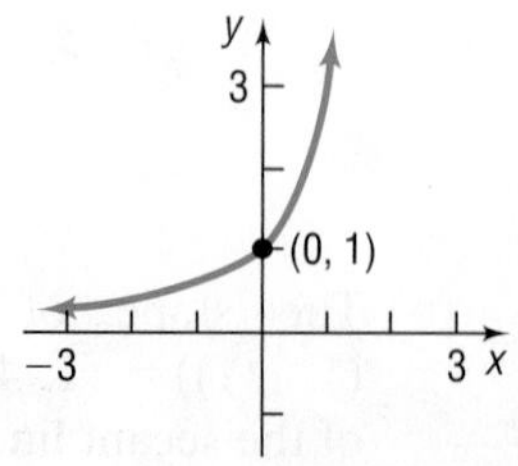

24.
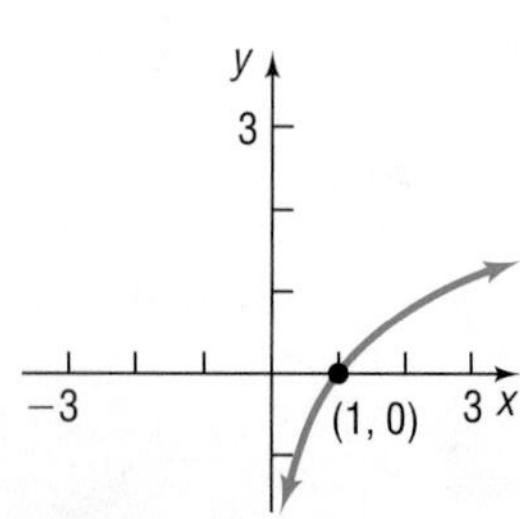

25.
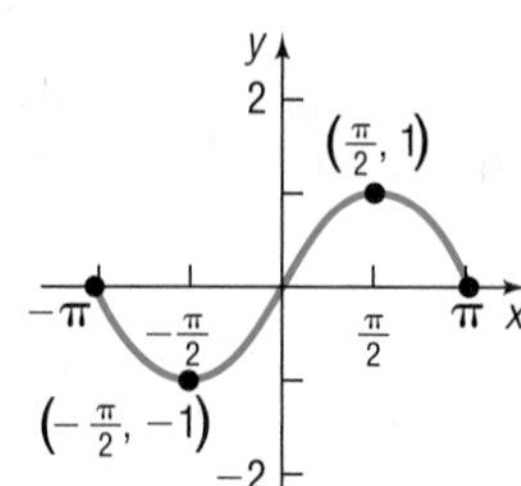

26.
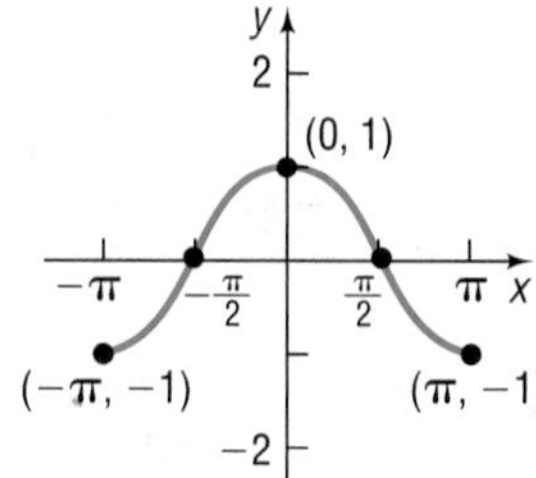

27.
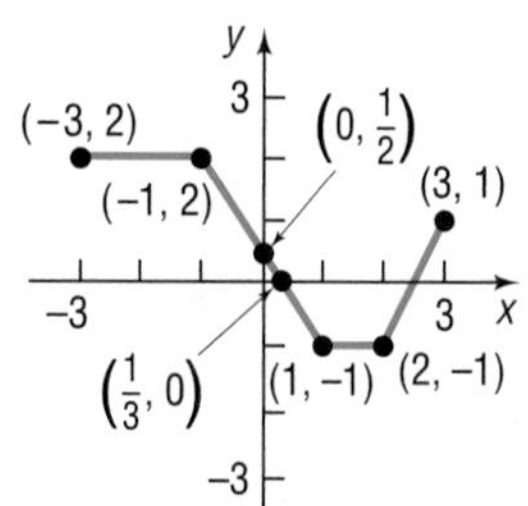

28.
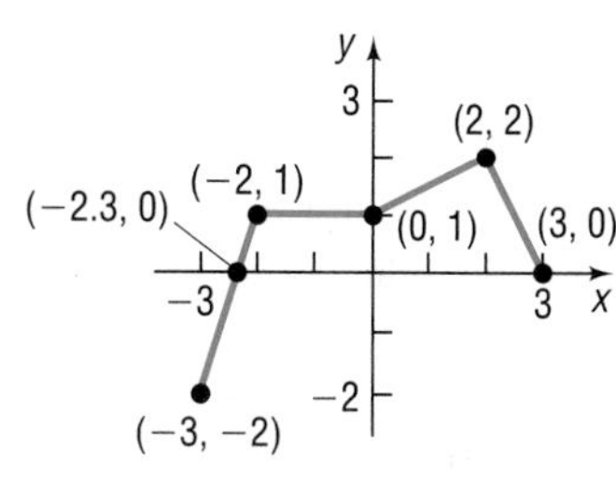

In Problems 29–32, the graph of a function f is given. Use the graph to find:
(a) The numbers, if any, at which f has a local maximum value. What are the local maximum values?
(b) The numbers, if any, at which f has a local minimum value. What are the local minimum values?

29.
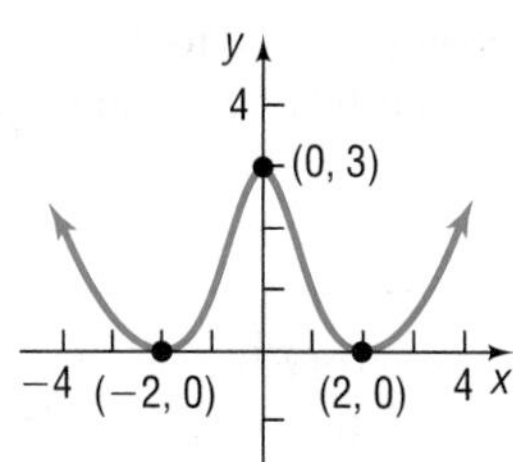

30.
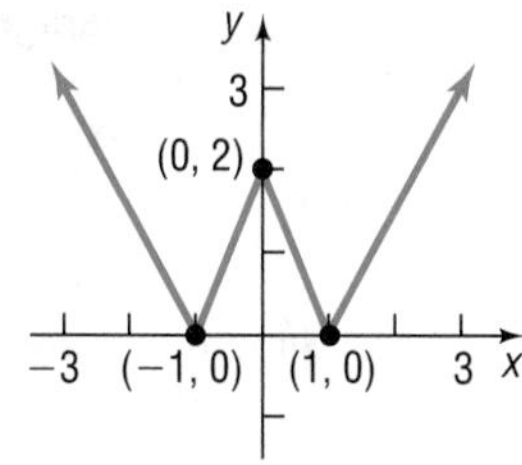

31.
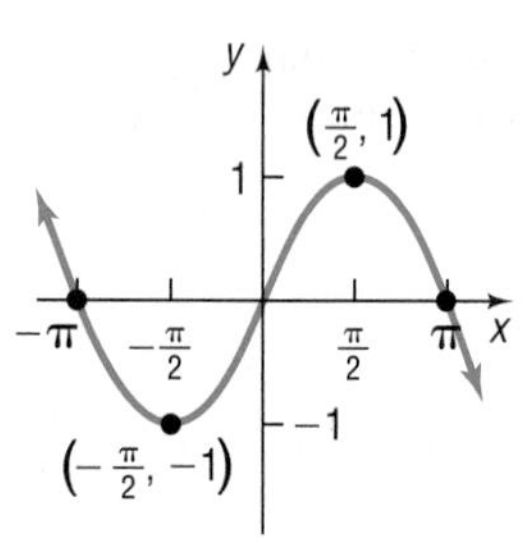

32.
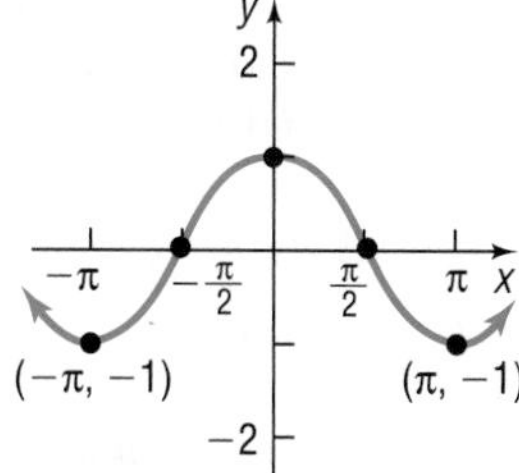

In Problems 33–44, determine algebraically whether each function is even, odd, or neither.

33. $f(x) = 4x^3$
34. $f(x) = 2x^4 - x^2$
35. $g(x) = -3x^2 - 5$
36. $h(x) = 3x^3 + 5$
37. $F(x) = \sqrt[3]{x}$
38. $G(x) = \sqrt{x}$
39. $f(x) = x + |x|$
40. $f(x) = \sqrt[3]{2x^2 + 1}$
41. $g(x) = \dfrac{x^2 + 3}{x^2 - 1}$
42. $h(x) = \dfrac{x}{x^2 - 1}$
43. $h(x) = \dfrac{-x^3}{3x^2 - 9}$
44. $F(x) = \dfrac{2x}{|x|}$

In Problems 45–52, for each graph of a function $y = f(x)$, find the absolute maximum and the absolute minimum, if they exist.

45.
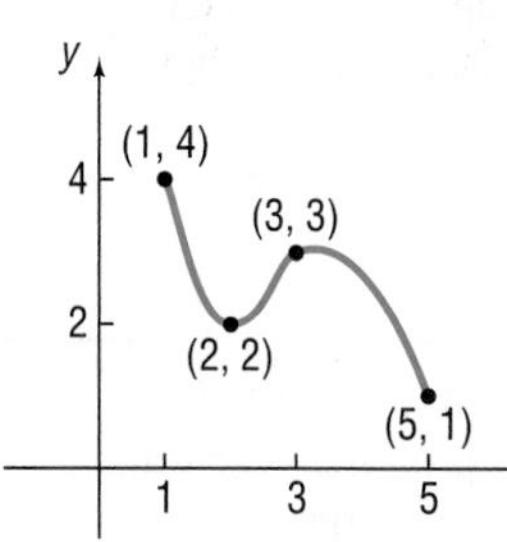

46.
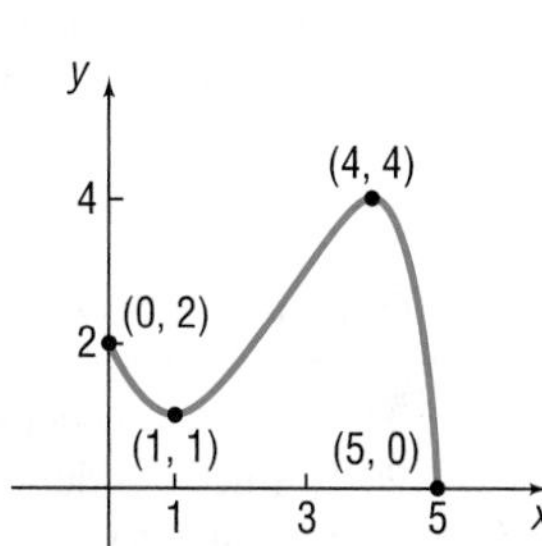

47.
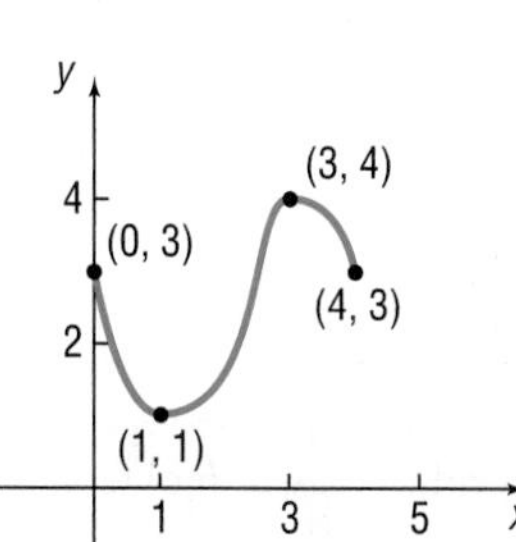

48.
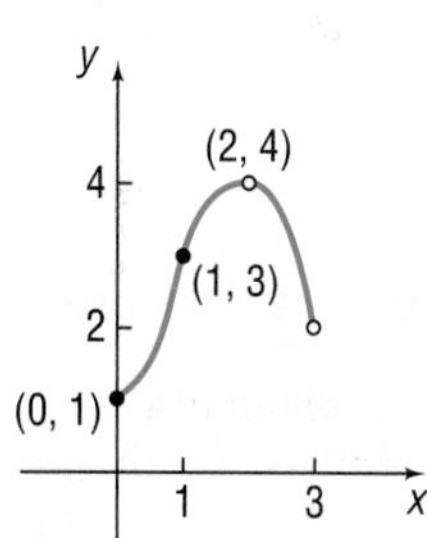

49.
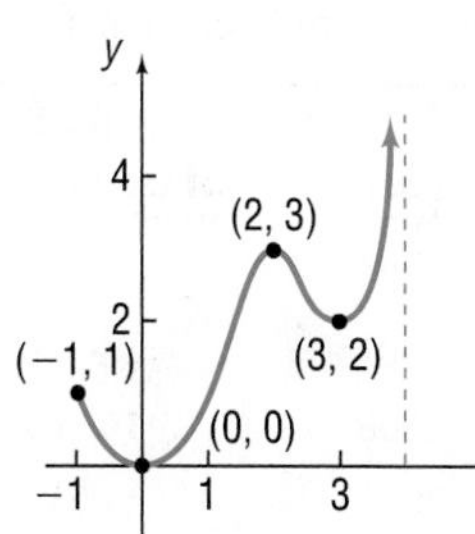

50.
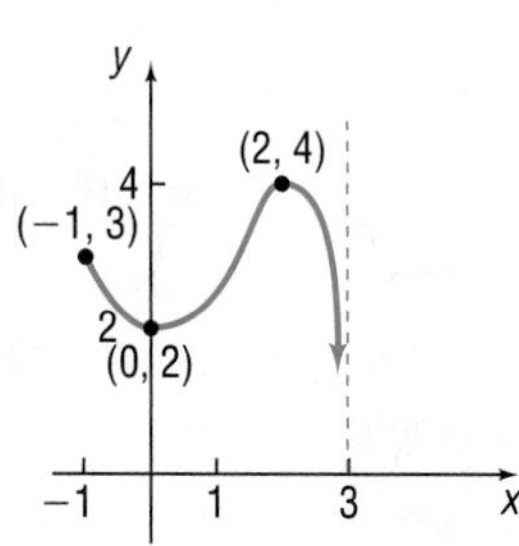

51.
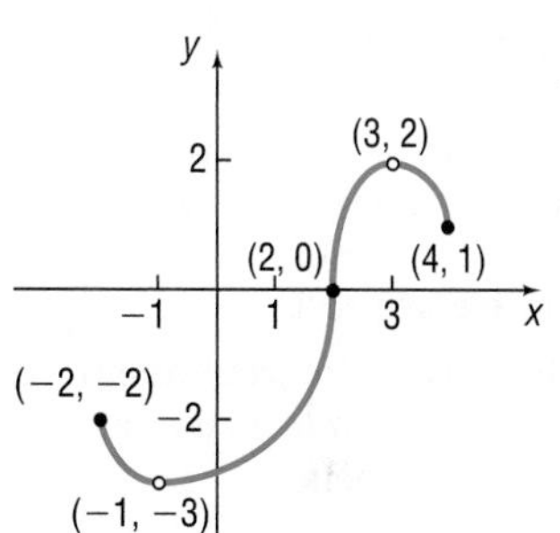

52.
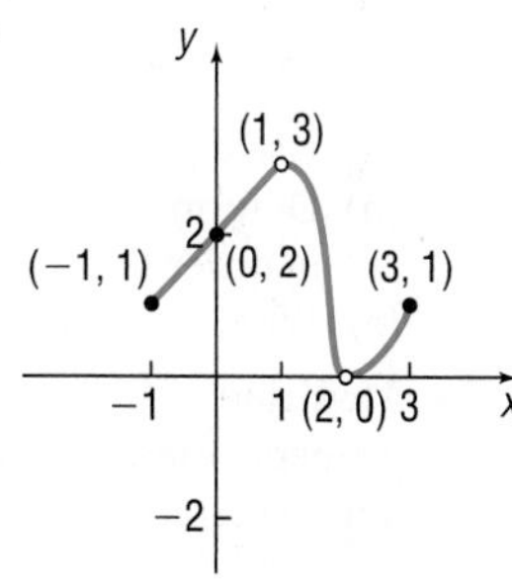

In Problems 53–60, use a graphing utility to graph each function over the indicated interval and approximate any local maximum values and local minimum values. Determine where the function is increasing and where it is decreasing. Round answers to two decimal places.

53. $f(x) = x^3 - 3x + 2 \quad (-2, 2)$
54. $f(x) = x^3 - 3x^2 + 5 \quad (-1, 3)$
55. $f(x) = x^5 - x^3 \quad (-2, 2)$
56. $f(x) = x^4 - x^2 \quad (-2, 2)$
57. $f(x) = -0.2x^3 - 0.6x^2 + 4x - 6 \quad (-6, 4)$
58. $f(x) = -0.4x^3 + 0.6x^2 + 3x - 2 \quad (-4, 5)$
59. $f(x) = 0.25x^4 + 0.3x^3 - 0.9x^2 + 3 \quad (-3, 2)$
60. $f(x) = -0.4x^4 - 0.5x^3 + 0.8x^2 - 2 \quad (-3, 2)$

61. Find the average rate of change of $f(x) = -2x^2 + 4$
(a) From 0 to 2
(b) From 1 to 3
(c) From 1 to 4

62. Find the average rate of change of $f(x) = -x^3 + 1$
(a) From 0 to 2
(b) From 1 to 3
(c) From −1 to 1

63. Find the average rate of change of $g(x) = x^3 - 2x + 1$
(a) From -3 to -2
(b) From -1 to 1
(c) From 1 to 3

64. Find the average rate of change of $h(x) = x^2 - 2x + 3$
(a) From -1 to 1
(b) From 0 to 2
(c) From 2 to 5

65. $f(x) = 5x - 2$
(a) Find the average rate of change from 1 to 3.
(b) Find an equation of the secant line containing $(1, f(1))$ and $(3, f(3))$.

66. $f(x) = -4x + 1$
(a) Find the average rate of change from 2 to 5.
(b) Find an equation of the secant line containing $(2, f(2))$ and $(5, f(5))$.

67. $g(x) = x^2 - 2$
(a) Find the average rate of change from -2 to 1.
(b) Find an equation of the secant line containing $(-2, g(-2))$ and $(1, g(1))$.

68. $g(x) = x^2 + 1$
(a) Find the average rate of change from -1 to 2.
(b) Find an equation of the secant line containing $(-1, g(-1))$ and $(2, g(2))$.

69. $h(x) = x^2 - 2x$
(a) Find the average rate of change from 2 to 4.
(b) Find an equation of the secant line containing $(2, h(2))$ and $(4, h(4))$.

70. $h(x) = -2x^2 + x$
(a) Find the average rate of change from 0 to 3.
(b) Find an equation of the secant line containing $(0, h(0))$ and $(3, h(3))$.

Mixed Practice

71. $g(x) = x^3 - 27x$
(a) Determine whether g is even, odd, or neither.
(b) There is a local minimum value of -54 at 3. Determine the local maximum value.

72. $f(x) = -x^3 + 12x$
(a) Determine whether f is even, odd, or neither.
(b) There is a local maximum value of 16 at 2. Determine the local minimum value.

73. $F(x) = -x^4 + 8x^2 + 8$
(a) Determine whether F is even, odd, or neither.
(b) There is a local maximum value of 24 at $x = 2$. Determine a second local maximum value.
(c) Suppose the area under the graph of F between $x = 0$ and $x = 3$ that is bounded below by the x-axis is 47.4 square units. Using the result from part (a), determine the area under the graph of F between $x = -3$ and $x = 0$ bounded below by the x-axis.

74. $G(x) = -x^4 + 32x^2 + 144$
(a) Determine whether G is even, odd, or neither.
(b) There is a local maximum value of 400 at $x = 4$. Determine a second local maximum value.
(c) Suppose the area under the graph of G between $x = 0$ and $x = 6$ that is bounded below by the x-axis is 1612.8 square units. Using the result from part (a), determine the area under the graph of G between $x = -6$ and $x = 0$ bounded below by the x-axis.

Applications and Extensions

75. **Minimum Average Cost** The average cost per hour in dollars, $\overline{C}$, of producing x riding lawn mowers can be modeled by the function

$$\overline{C}(x) = 0.3x^2 + 21x - 251 + \frac{2500}{x}$$

(a) Use a graphing utility to graph $\overline{C} = \overline{C}(x)$.
(b) Determine the number of riding lawn mowers to produce in order to minimize average cost.
(c) What is the minimum average cost?

76. **Medicine Concentration** The concentration C of a medication in the bloodstream t hours after being administered is modeled by the function

$$C(t) = -0.002t^4 + 0.039t^3 - 0.285t^2 + 0.766t + 0.085$$

(a) After how many hours will the concentration be highest?
(b) A woman nursing a child must wait until the concentration is below 0.5 before she can feed him. After taking the medication, how long must she wait before feeding her child?

77. **National Debt** The size of the total debt owed by the United States federal government has been growing over the past few years. In fact, according to the Department of the Treasury, the debt per person living in the United States is approximately \$45,000 (or over \$300,000 per U.S. household).

The data below represent the U.S. debt for the years 2000–2010. Since the debt D depends on the year y and each input corresponds to exactly one output, the debt is a function of the year; so $D(y)$ represents the debt for each year y.

Year	Debt (Billions of Dollars)	Year	Debt (Billions of Dollars)
2000	5674	2006	8507
2001	5807	2007	9008
2002	6228	2008	10,025
2003	6783	2009	11,910
2004	7379	2010	13,562
2005	7933		

Source: www.treasurydirect.gov

(a) Plot the points (2000, 5.7), (2001, 5.8), and so on in a Cartesian plane.
(b) Draw a line segment from the point (2000, 5.7) to (2002, 6.2). What does the slope of this line segment represent?
(c) Find the average rate of change of the debt from 2000 to 2002.
(d) Find the average rate of change of the debt from 2004 to 2006.

(e) Find the average rate of change of the debt from 2008 to 2010.
(f) What is happening to the average rate of change as time passes?

78. *E. coli* Growth A strain of *E. coli* Beu 397-recA441 is placed into a nutrient broth at 30° Celsius and allowed to grow. The data shown in the table are collected. The population is measured in grams and the time in hours. Since population P depends on time t and each input corresponds to exactly one output, we can say that population is a function of time; so $P(t)$ represents the population at time t.

Time (hours), t	Population (grams), P
0	0.09
2.5	0.18
3.5	0.26
4.5	0.35
6	0.50

(a) Plot the points (0, 0.09), (2.5, 0.18), and so on in a Cartesian plane.
(b) Draw a line segment from the point (0,0.09) to (2.5,0.18). What does the slope of this line segment represent?
(c) Find the average rate of change of the population from 0 to 2.5 hours.
(d) Find the average rate of change of the population from 4.5 to 6 hours.
(e) What is happening to the average rate of change as time passes?

79. For the function $f(x) = x^2$, compute each average rate of change:
(a) From 0 to 1
(b) From 0 to 0.5
(c) From 0 to 0.1
(d) From 0 to 0.01
(e) From 0 to 0.001
(f) Use a graphing utility to graph each of the secant lines along with f.
(g) What do you think is happening to the secant lines?
(h) What is happening to the slopes of the secant lines? Is there some number that they are getting closer to? What is that number?

80. For the function $f(x) = x^2$, compute each average rate of change:
(a) From 1 to 2
(b) From 1 to 1.5
(c) From 1 to 1.1
(d) From 1 to 1.01
(e) From 1 to 1.001
(f) Use a graphing utility to graph each of the secant lines along with f.
(g) What do you think is happening to the secant lines?
(h) What is happening to the slopes of the secant lines? Is there some number that they are getting closer to? What is that number?

Problems 81–88 require the following discussion of a secant line. The slope of the secant line containing the two points $(x, f(x))$ and $(x + h, f(x + h))$ on the graph of a function $y = f(x)$ may be given as

$$m_{sec} = \frac{f(x+h) - f(x)}{(x+h) - x} = \frac{f(x+h) - f(x)}{h} \qquad h \neq 0$$

In calculus, this expression is called the ***difference quotient of f.***
(a) Express the slope of the secant line of each function in terms of x and h. Be sure to simplify your answer.
(b) Find m_{sec} for $h = 0.5$, 0.1, and 0.01 at $x = 1$. What value does m_{sec} approach as h approaches 0?
(c) Find the equation for the secant line at $x = 1$ with $h = 0.01$.
(d) Use a graphing utility to graph f and the secant line found in part (c) on the same viewing window.

81. $f(x) = 2x + 5$
82. $f(x) = -3x + 2$
83. $f(x) = x^2 + 2x$
84. $f(x) = 2x^2 + x$
85. $f(x) = 2x^2 - 3x + 1$
86. $f(x) = -x^2 + 3x - 2$
87. $f(x) = \frac{1}{x}$
88. $f(x) = \frac{1}{x^2}$

Explaining Concepts: Discussion and Writing

89. Draw the graph of a function that has the following properties: domain: all real numbers; range: all real numbers; intercepts: $(0, -3)$ and $(3, 0)$; a local maximum value of -2 is at -1; a local minimum value of -6 is at 2. Compare your graph with those of others. Comment on any differences.

90. Redo Problem 89 with the following additional information: increasing on $(-\infty, -1), (2, \infty)$; decreasing on $(-1, 2)$. Again compare your graph with others and comment on any differences.

91. How many x-intercepts can a function defined on an interval have if it is increasing on that interval? Explain.

92. Suppose that a friend of yours does not understand the idea of increasing and decreasing functions. Provide an explanation, complete with graphs, that clarifies the idea.

93. Can a function be both even and odd? Explain.

94. Using a graphing utility, graph $y = 5$ on the interval $(-3, 3)$. Use MAXIMUM to find the local maximum values on $(-3, 3)$. Comment on the result provided by the calculator.

95. A function f has a positive average rate of change on the interval $[2, 5]$. Is f increasing on $[2, 5]$? Explain.

96. Show that a constant function $f(x) = b$ has an average rate of change of 0. Compute the average rate of change of $y = \sqrt{4 - x^2}$ on the interval $[-2, 2]$. Explain how this can happen.

Interactive Exercises

Ask your instructor if the applets below are of interest to you.

97. Open the *Secant Line Not Min Point* applet.
(a) Grab point B and move it just below the x-axis. Verify the slope of the secant line reported in the applet.
(b) Move point B closer to point A. What happens to the value of the slope of the secant line?
(c) Move point B as close as you can to point A. Describe the secant line as point B approaches point A. Find the equation of the secant line where point B is as close as possible to point A.

98. Open the *Secant Line Min Point* applet. In the applet, a local minimum is -7.33 at $x = 3$ (labeled as point A).
(a) Grab point B and move it just below the x-axis. Verify the slope of the secant line reported in the applet.
(b) Move point B closer to point A, so that the x-coordinate of point B remains greater than the x-coordinate of point A. What happens to the value of the slope of the secant line? Specifically, what is the sign of the slope of the secant line?
(c) Move point B so that the x-coordinate of point B is less than the x-coordinate of point A. What happens to the value of the slope of the secant line? Specifically, what is the sign of the slope of the secant line?
(d) As point B moves from the left of point A to the right of point A, note the slope of the secant line. Conjecture the value of the slope of the line tangent to the function at point A.

'Are You Prepared?' Answers

1. $2 < x < 5$ **2.** 1 **3.** symmetric with respect to the y-axis **4.** $y + 2 = 5(x - 3)$ **5.** $(-3, 0), (3, 0), (0, -9)$

9.4 Library of Functions; Piecewise-defined Functions

PREPARING FOR THIS SECTION *Before getting started, review the following:*

- Intercepts (Section 8.1, pp. 522–523)
- Graphs of Key Equations (Section 8.1: Example 4, p. 525; Example 5, p. 526; Example 6, p. 526)

Now Work the **'Are You Prepared?'** problems on page 601.

OBJECTIVES 1 Graph the Functions Listed in the Library of Functions (p. 594)
2 Graph Piecewise-defined Functions (p. 599)

1 Graph the Functions Listed in the Library of Functions

First we introduce a few more functions, beginning with the *square root function*.

On page 526, we graphed the equation $y = \sqrt{x}$. Figure 31 shows a graph of the function $f(x) = \sqrt{x}$. Based on the graph, we have the following properties:

Figure 31

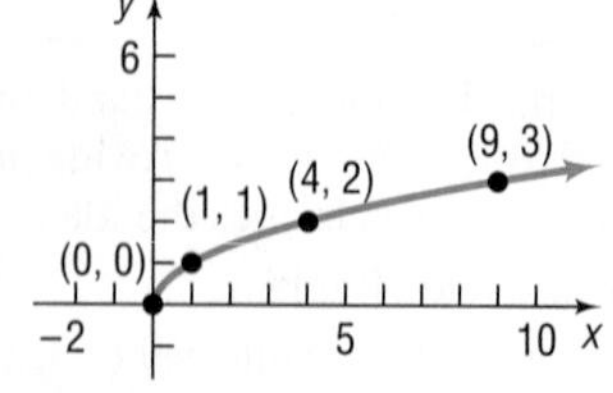

Properties of $f(x) = \sqrt{x}$

1. The domain and the range are the set of nonnegative real numbers.
2. The x-intercept of the graph of $f(x) = \sqrt{x}$ is 0. The y-intercept of the graph of $f(x) = \sqrt{x}$ is also 0.
3. The function is neither even nor odd.
4. The function is increasing on the interval $(0, \infty)$.
5. The function has an absolute minimum of 0 at $x = 0$.

EXAMPLE 1 **Graphing the Cube Root Function**

(a) Determine whether $f(x) = \sqrt[3]{x}$ is even, odd, or neither. State whether the graph of f is symmetric with respect to the y-axis or symmetric with respect to the origin.
(b) Determine the intercepts, if any, of the graph of $f(x) = \sqrt[3]{x}$.
(c) Graph $f(x) = \sqrt[3]{x}$.

Solution (a) Because

$$f(-x) = \sqrt[3]{-x} = -\sqrt[3]{x} = -f(x)$$

the function is odd. The graph of f is symmetric with respect to the origin.

(b) The y-intercept is $f(0) = \sqrt[3]{0} = 0$. The x-intercept is found by solving the equation $f(x) = 0$.

$$\begin{aligned} f(x) &= 0 \\ \sqrt[3]{x} &= 0 \quad f(x) = \sqrt[3]{x} \\ x &= 0 \quad \text{Cube both sides of the equation.} \end{aligned}$$

The x-intercept is also 0.

(c) Use the function to form Table 4 and obtain some points on the graph. Because of the symmetry with respect to the origin, we find only points (x, y) for which $x \geq 0$. Figure 32 shows the graph of $f(x) = \sqrt[3]{x}$.

Table 4

x	$y = f(x) = \sqrt[3]{x}$	(x, y)
0	0	(0, 0)
$\frac{1}{8}$	$\frac{1}{2}$	$\left(\frac{1}{8}, \frac{1}{2}\right)$
1	1	(1, 1)
2	$\sqrt[3]{2} \approx 1.26$	$(2, \sqrt[3]{2})$
8	2	(8, 2)

Figure 32

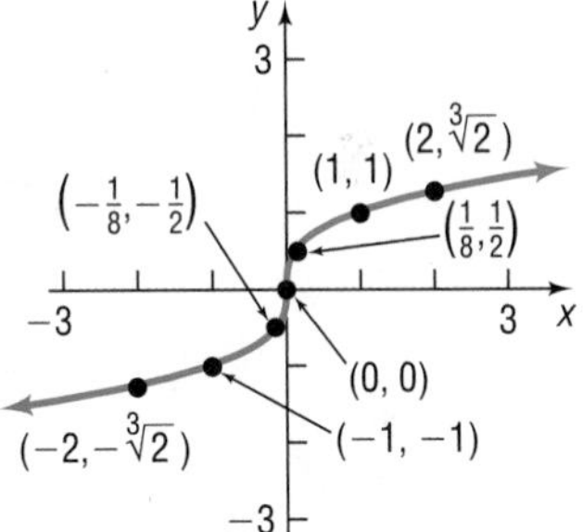

From the results of Example 1 and Figure 32, we have the following properties of the cube root function.

Properties of $f(x) = \sqrt[3]{x}$

1. The domain and the range are the set of all real numbers.
2. The x-intercept of the graph of $f(x) = \sqrt[3]{x}$ is 0. The y-intercept of the graph of $f(x) = \sqrt[3]{x}$ is also 0.
3. The graph is symmetric with respect to the origin. The function is odd.
4. The function is increasing on the interval $(-\infty, \infty)$.
5. The function does not have any local minima or any local maxima.

EXAMPLE 2 Graphing the Absolute Value Function

(a) Determine whether $f(x) = |x|$ is even, odd, or neither. State whether the graph of f is symmetric with respect to the y-axis or symmetric with respect to the origin.

(b) Determine the intercepts, if any, of the graph of $f(x) = |x|$.

(c) Graph $f(x) = |x|$.

Solution (a) Because

$$\begin{aligned} f(-x) &= |-x| \\ &= |x| = f(x) \end{aligned}$$

the function is even. The graph of f is symmetric with respect to the y-axis.

(b) The y-intercept is $f(0) = |0| = 0$. The x-intercept is found by solving the equation $f(x) = 0$ or $|x| = 0$. So the x-intercept is 0.

(c) Use the function to form Table 5 and obtain some points on the graph. Because of the symmetry with respect to the y-axis, we need to find only points (x, y) for which $x \geq 0$. Figure 33 shows the graph of $f(x) = |x|$.

Table 5

x	$y = f(x) = \|x\|$	(x, y)
0	0	(0, 0)
1	1	(1, 1)
2	2	(2, 2)
3	3	(3, 3)

Figure 33

From the results of Example 2 and Figure 33, we have the following properties of the absolute value function.

Properties of $f(x) = |x|$

1. The domain is the set of all real numbers. The range of f is $\{y \mid y \geq 0\}$.
2. The x-intercept of the graph of $f(x) = |x|$ is 0. The y-intercept of the graph of $f(x) = |x|$ is also 0.
3. The graph is symmetric with respect to the y-axis. The function is even.
4. The function is decreasing on the interval $(-\infty, 0)$. It is increasing on the interval $(0, \infty)$.
5. The function has an absolute minimum of 0 at $x = 0$.

Seeing the Concept

Graph $y = |x|$ on a square screen and compare what you see with Figure 33. Note that some graphing calculators use abs(x) for absolute value.

Below is a list of the key functions that we have discussed. In going through this list, pay special attention to the properties of each function, particularly to the shape of each graph. Knowing these graphs along with key points on each graph will lay the foundation for further graphing techniques.

Figure 34 Constant Function

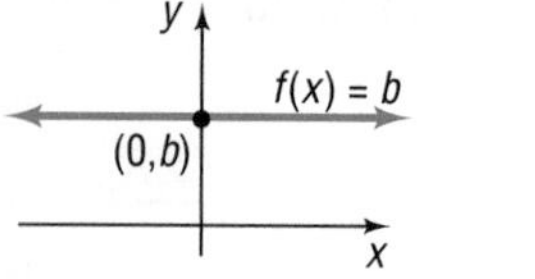

Constant Function

$$f(x) = b \qquad b \text{ is a real number}$$

See Figure 34.

The domain of a **constant function** is the set of all real numbers; its range is the set consisting of a single number b. Its graph is a horizontal line whose y-intercept is b. The constant function is an even function.

Figure 35 Identity Function

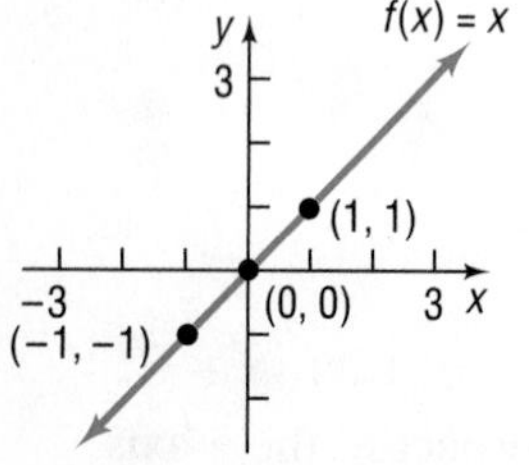

Identity Function

$$f(x) = x$$

See Figure 35.

The domain and the range of the **identity function** are the set of all real numbers. Its graph is a line whose slope is 1 and whose y-intercept is 0. The line consists of all points for which the x-coordinate equals the y-coordinate. The identity function is an odd function that is increasing over its domain. Note that the graph bisects quadrants I and III.

Figure 36 Square Function

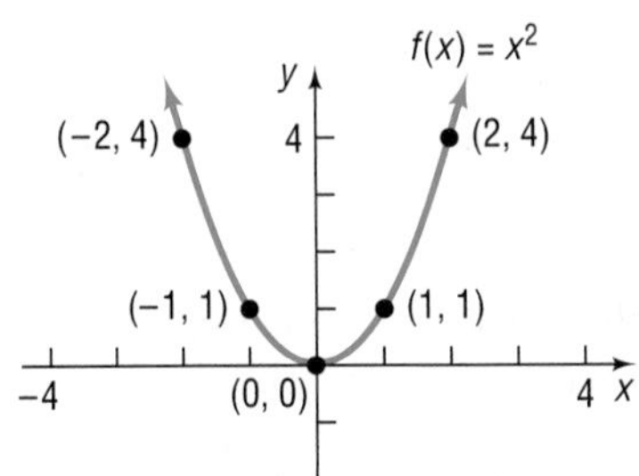

Square Function

$$f(x) = x^2$$

See Figure 36.

The domain of the **square function** f is the set of all real numbers; its range is the set of nonnegative real numbers. The graph of this function is a parabola whose vertex is at $(0, 0)$, which is also the only intercept. The square function is an even function that is decreasing on the interval $(-\infty, 0)$ and increasing on the interval $(0, \infty)$.

Figure 37 Cube Function

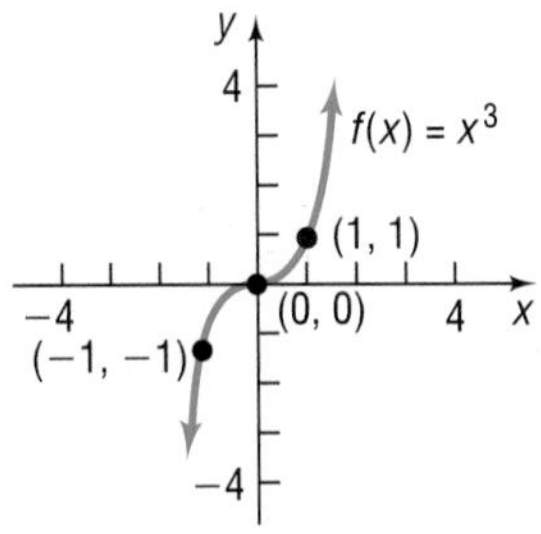

Cube Function

$$f(x) = x^3$$

See Figure 37.

The domain and the range of the **cube function** are the set of all real numbers. The intercept of the graph is at $(0, 0)$. The cube function is odd and is increasing on the interval $(-\infty, \infty)$.

Figure 38 Square Root Function

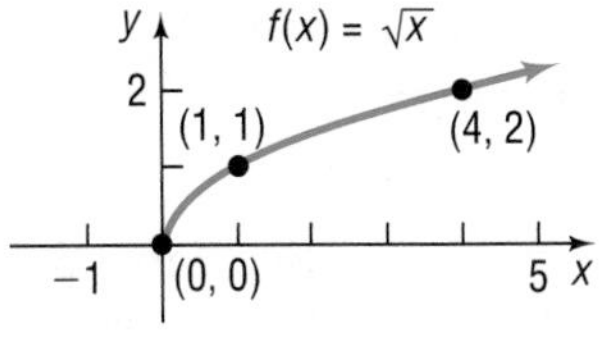

Square Root Function

$$f(x) = \sqrt{x}$$

See Figure 38.

The domain and the range of the **square root function** are the set of nonnegative real numbers. The intercept of the graph is at $(0, 0)$. The square root function is neither even nor odd and is increasing on the interval $(0, \infty)$.

Figure 39 Cube Root Function

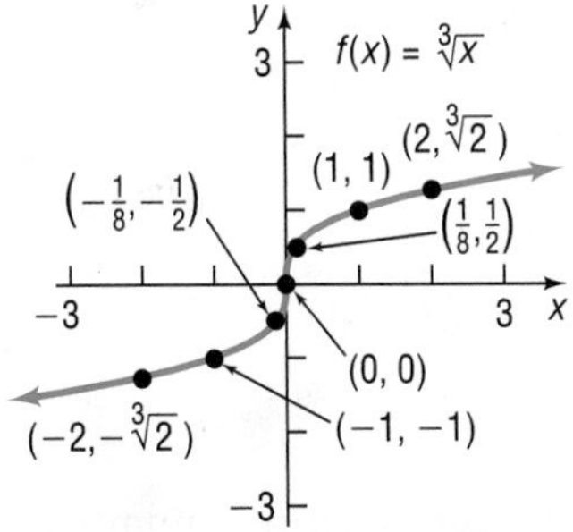

Cube Root Function

$$f(x) = \sqrt[3]{x}$$

See Figure 39.

The domain and the range of the **cube root function** are the set of all real numbers. The intercept of the graph is at $(0, 0)$. The cube root function is an odd function that is increasing on the interval $(-\infty, \infty)$.

Figure 40 Reciprocal Function

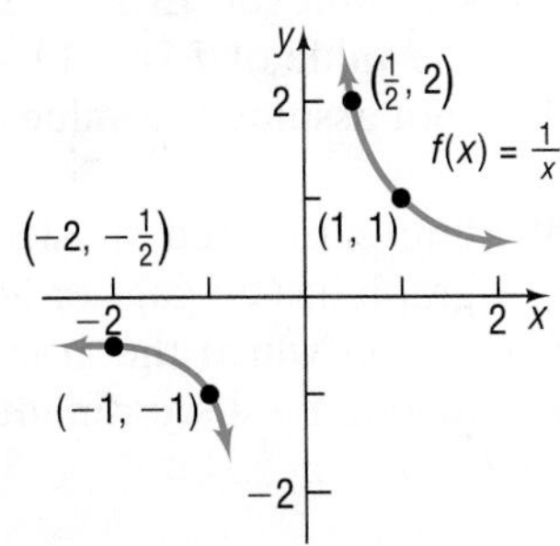

Reciprocal Function

$$f(x) = \frac{1}{x}$$

Refer to Example 6, page 526, for a discussion of the equation $y = \frac{1}{x}$. See Figure 40.

The domain and the range of the **reciprocal function** are the set of all nonzero real numbers. The graph has no intercepts. The reciprocal function is decreasing on the intervals $(-\infty, 0)$ and $(0, \infty)$ and is an odd function.

Absolute Value Function

$$f(x) = |x|$$

Figure 41 Absolute Value Function

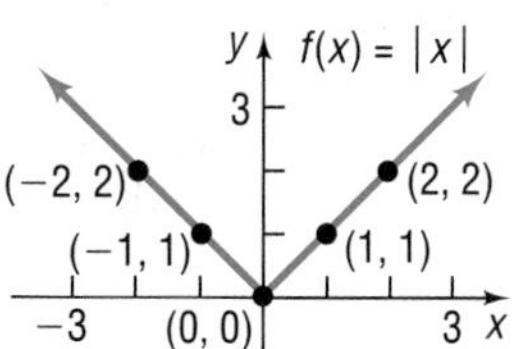

See Figure 41.

The domain of the **absolute value function** is the set of all real numbers; its range is the set of nonnegative real numbers. The intercept of the graph is at $(0, 0)$. If $x \geq 0$, then $f(x) = x$, and this part of the graph of f is the line $y = x$; if $x < 0$, then $f(x) = -x$, and this part of the graph of f is the line $y = -x$. The absolute value function is an even function; it is decreasing on the interval $(-\infty, 0)$ and increasing on the interval $(0, \infty)$.

The notation $\text{int}(x)$ stands for the largest integer less than or equal to x. For example,

$$\text{int}(1) = 1, \quad \text{int}(2.5) = 2, \quad \text{int}\left(\frac{1}{2}\right) = 0, \quad \text{int}\left(-\frac{3}{4}\right) = -1, \quad \text{int}(\pi) = 3$$

This type of correspondence occurs frequently enough in mathematics that we give it a name.

DEFINITION

Greatest Integer Function

$$f(x) = \text{int}(x)^* = \text{greatest integer less than or equal to } x$$

Table 6

x	$y = f(x) = \text{int}(x)$	(x, y)
-1	-1	$(-1, -1)$
$-\frac{1}{2}$	-1	$\left(-\frac{1}{2}, -1\right)$
$-\frac{1}{4}$	-1	$\left(-\frac{1}{4}, -1\right)$
0	0	$(0, 0)$
$\frac{1}{4}$	0	$\left(\frac{1}{4}, 0\right)$
$\frac{1}{2}$	0	$\left(\frac{1}{2}, 0\right)$
$\frac{3}{4}$	0	$\left(\frac{3}{4}, 0\right)$

We obtain the graph of $f(x) = \text{int}(x)$ by plotting several points. See Table 6. For values of x, $-1 \leq x < 0$, the value of $f(x) = \text{int}(x)$ is -1; for values of x, $0 \leq x < 1$, the value of f is 0. See Figure 42 for the graph.

Figure 42 Greatest Integer Function

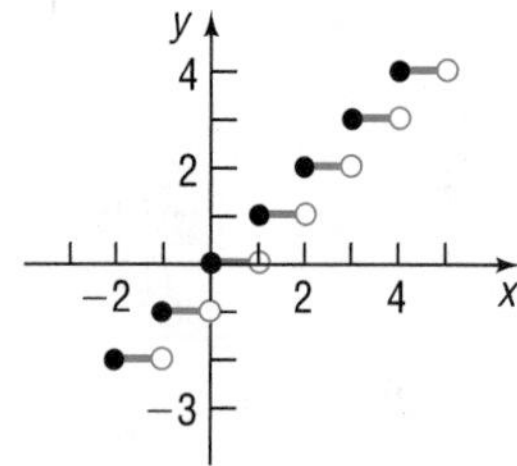

The domain of the **greatest integer function** is the set of all real numbers; its range is the set of integers. The y-intercept of the graph is 0. The x-intercepts lie in the interval $[0, 1)$. The greatest integer function is neither even nor odd. It is constant on every interval of the form $[k, k + 1)$, for k an integer. In Figure 42, we use a solid dot to indicate, for example, that at $x = 1$ the value of f is $f(1) = 1$; we use an open circle to illustrate that the function does not assume the value of 0 at $x = 1$.

Although a precise definition requires the idea of a limit, discussed in calculus, in a rough sense, a function is said to be **continuous** if its graph has no gaps or holes and can be drawn without lifting a pencil from the paper on which the graph is drawn. We contrast this with a *discontinuous* function. A function is **discontinuous** if

*Some books use the notation $f(x) = [x]$ instead of $\text{int}(x)$.

its graph has gaps or holes so that its graph cannot be drawn without lifting a pencil from the paper.

From the graph of the greatest integer function, we can see why it is also called a **step function.** At $x = 0, x = \pm 1, x = \pm 2$, and so on, this function is discontinuous because, at integer values, the graph suddenly "steps" from one value to another without taking on any of the intermediate values. For example, to the immediate left of $x = 3$, the y-coordinates of the points on the graph are 2, and at $x = 3$ and to the immediate right of $x = 3$, the y-coordinates of the points on the graph are 3. So, the graph has gaps in it.

Figure 43 $f(x) = \text{int}(x)$.

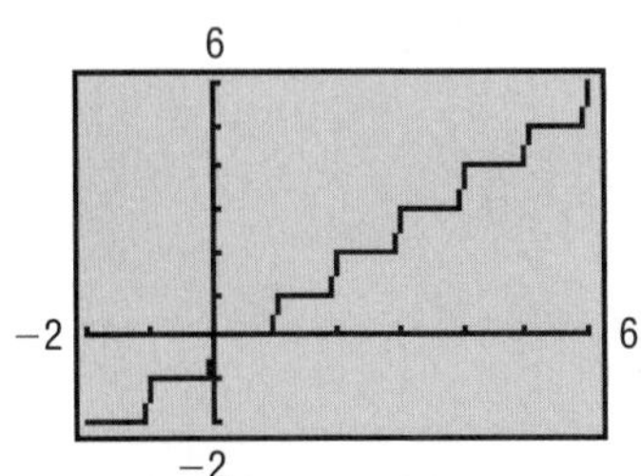

(a) Connected mode

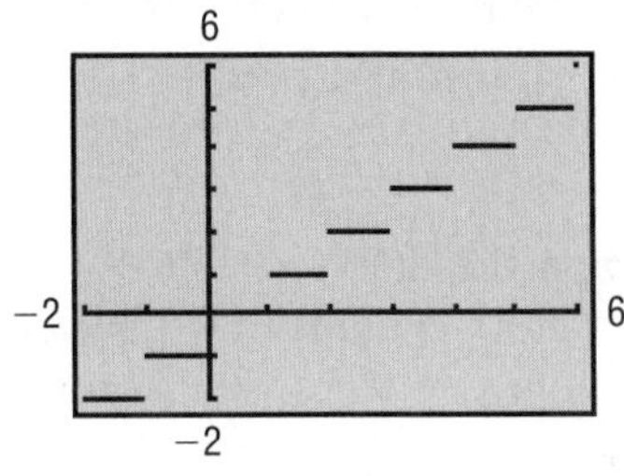

(b) Dot mode

COMMENT When graphing a function using a graphing utility, you can choose either the **connected mode,** in which points plotted on the screen are connected, making the graph appear without any breaks, or the **dot mode,** in which only the points plotted appear. When graphing the greatest integer function with a graphing utility, it may be necessary to be in the dot mode. This is to prevent the utility from "connecting the dots" when $f(x)$ changes from one integer value to the next. See Figure 43. ■

The functions discussed so far are basic. Whenever you encounter one of them, you should see a mental picture of its graph. For example, if you encounter the function $f(x) = x^2$, you should see in your mind's eye a picture like Figure 36.

Now Work PROBLEMS 9 THROUGH 16

2 Graph Piecewise-defined Functions

Sometimes a function is defined using different equations on different parts of its domain. For example, the absolute value function $f(x) = |x|$ is actually defined by two equations: $f(x) = x$ if $x \geq 0$ and $f(x) = -x$ if $x < 0$. For convenience, these equations are generally combined into one expression as

$$f(x) = |x| = \begin{cases} x & \text{if } x \geq 0 \\ -x & \text{if } x < 0 \end{cases}$$

When a function is defined by different equations on different parts of its domain, it is called a **piecewise-defined** function.

EXAMPLE 3 **Analyzing a Piecewise-defined Function**

The function f is defined as

$$f(x) = \begin{cases} -2x + 1 & \text{if } -3 \leq x < 1 \\ 2 & \text{if } x = 1 \\ x^2 & \text{if } x > 1 \end{cases}$$

(a) Find $f(-2), f(1)$, and $f(2)$.
(b) Determine the domain of f.
(c) Locate any intercepts.
(d) Graph f.
(e) Use the graph to find the range of f.
(f) Is f continuous on its domain?

Solution

(a) To find $f(-2)$, observe that when $x = -2$ the equation for f is given by $f(x) = -2x + 1$. So

$$f(-2) = -2(-2) + 1 = 5$$

When $x = 1$, the equation for f is $f(x) = 2$. That is,

$$f(1) = 2$$

When $x = 2$, the equation for f is $f(x) = x^2$. So

$$f(2) = 2^2 = 4$$

(b) To find the domain of f, look at its definition. Since f is defined for all x greater than or equal to -3, the domain of f is $\{x \mid x \geq -3\}$, or the interval $[-3, \infty)$.

(c) The y-intercept of the graph of the function is $f(0)$. Because the equation for f when $x = 0$ is $f(x) = -2x + 1$, the y-intercept is $f(0) = -2(0) + 1 = 1$. The

x-intercepts of the graph of a function f are the real solutions to the equation $f(x) = 0$. To find the x-intercepts of f, solve $f(x) = 0$ for each "piece" of the function and then determine if the values of x, if any, satisfy the condition that defines the piece.

$$\begin{aligned} f(x) &= 0 \\ -2x + 1 &= 0 \quad -3 \le x < 1 \\ -2x &= -1 \\ x &= \frac{1}{2} \end{aligned} \qquad \begin{aligned} f(x) &= 0 \\ 2 &= 0 \quad x = 1 \\ &\text{No solution} \end{aligned} \qquad \begin{aligned} f(x) &= 0 \\ x^2 &= 0 \quad x > 1 \\ x &= 0 \end{aligned}$$

The first potential x-intercept, $x = \frac{1}{2}$, satisfies the condition $-3 \le x < 1$, so $x = \frac{1}{2}$ is an x-intercept. The second potential x-intercept, $x = 0$, does not satisfy the condition $x > 1$, so $x = 0$ is not an x-intercept. The only x-intercept is $\frac{1}{2}$. The intercepts are $(0, 1)$ and $\left(\frac{1}{2}, 0\right)$.

Figure 44

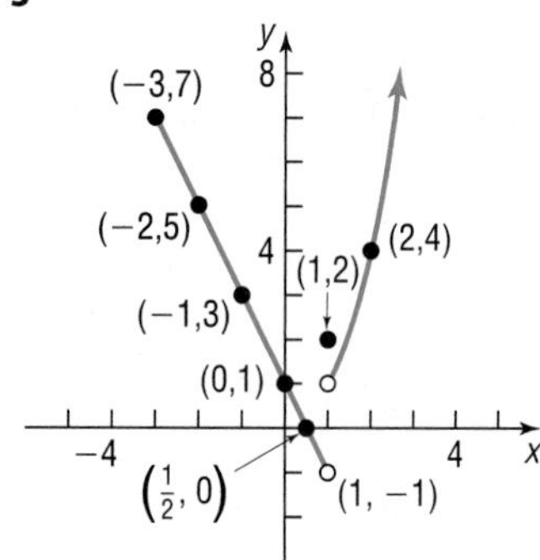

(d) To graph f, we graph "each piece." First we graph the line $y = -2x + 1$ and keep only the part for which $-3 \le x < 1$. Then we plot the point $(1, 2)$ because, when $x = 1$, $f(x) = 2$. Finally, we graph the parabola $y = x^2$ and keep only the part for which $x > 1$. See Figure 44.

(e) From the graph, we conclude that the range of f is $\{y \mid y > -1\}$, or the interval $(-1, \infty)$.

(f) The function f is not continuous because there is a "jump" in the graph at $x = 1$. ■

Now Work PROBLEM 29

EXAMPLE 4 Cost of Electricity

In the summer of 2011, Duke Energy supplied electricity to residences in Ohio for a monthly customer charge of \$5.50 plus 6.4471¢ per kilowatt-hour (kWhr) for the first 1000 kWhr supplied in the month and 7.8391¢ per kWhr for all usage over 1000 kWhr in the month.

(a) What is the charge for using 300 kWhr in a month?
(b) What is the charge for using 1500 kWhr in a month?
(c) If C is the monthly charge for x kWhr, develop a model relating the monthly charge and kilowatt-hours used. That is, express C as a function of x.

Source: Duke Energy, 2011.

Solution

(a) For 300 kWhr, the charge is \$5.50 plus 6.4471¢ = \$0.064471 per kWhr. That is,

$$\text{Charge} = \$5.50 + \$0.064471(300) = \$24.84$$

(b) For 1500 kWhr, the charge is \$5.50 plus 6.4471¢ per kWhr for the first 1000 kWhr plus 7.8391¢ per kWhr for the 500 kWhr in excess of 1000. That is,

$$\text{Charge} = \$5.50 + \$0.064471(1000) + \$0.078391(500) = \$109.17$$

(c) Let x represent the number of kilowatt-hours used. If $0 \le x \le 1000$, the monthly charge C (in dollars) can be found by multiplying x times \$0.064471 and adding the monthly customer charge of \$5.50. So, if $0 \le x \le 1000$, then $C(x) = 0.064471x + 5.50$.

For $x > 1000$, the charge is $0.064471(1000) + 5.50 + 0.078391(x - 1000)$, since $x - 1000$ equals the usage in excess of 1000 kWhr, which costs \$0.078391 per kWhr. That is, if $x > 1000$, then

$$\begin{aligned} C(x) &= 0.064471(1000) + 5.50 + 0.078391(x - 1000) \\ &= 69.971 + 0.078391(x - 1000) \\ &= 0.078391x - 8.42 \end{aligned}$$

Figure 45

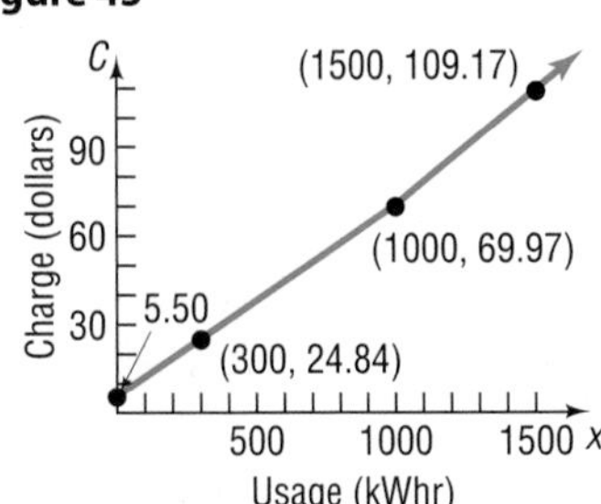

The rule for computing C follows two equations:

$$C(x) = \begin{cases} 0.064471x + 5.50 & \text{if } 0 \le x \le 1000 \\ 0.078391x - 8.42 & \text{if } x > 1000 \end{cases}$$ The Model

See Figure 45 for the graph. ■

9.4 Assess Your Understanding

'Are You Prepared?' *Answers are given at the end of these exercises. If you get a wrong answer, read the pages listed in red.*

1. Sketch the graph of $y = \sqrt{x}$. (p. 526)
2. Sketch the graph of $y = \dfrac{1}{x}$. (pp. 526–527)
3. List the intercepts of the equation $y = x^3 - 8$. (pp. 522–523)

Concepts and Vocabulary

4. The function $f(x) = x^2$ is decreasing on the interval ________.
5. When functions are defined by more than one equation, they are called ________________ functions.
6. ***True or False*** The cube function is odd and is increasing on the interval $(-\infty, \infty)$.
7. ***True or False*** The cube root function is odd and is decreasing on the interval $(-\infty, \infty)$.
8. ***True or False*** The domain and the range of the reciprocal function are the set of all real numbers.

Skill Building

In Problems 9–16, match each graph to its function.

A. Constant function *B. Identity function* *C. Square function* *D. Cube function*
E. Square root function *F. Reciprocal function* *G. Absolute value function* *H. Cube root function*

9. 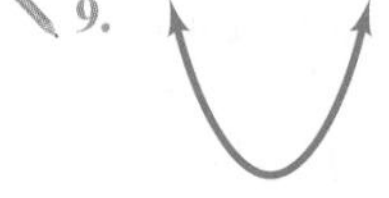

10. 

11. 

12. 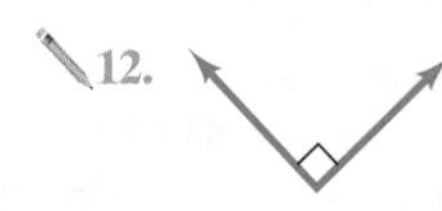

13. 

14. 

15. 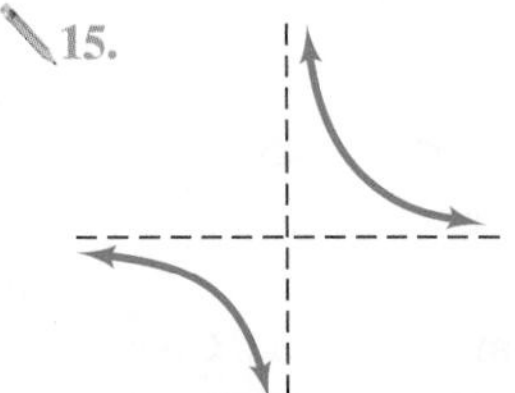

16. 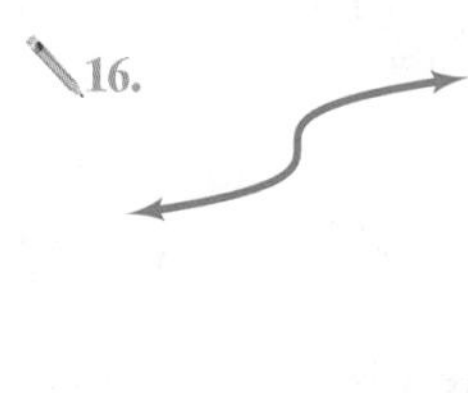

In Problems 17–24, sketch the graph of each function. Be sure to label three points on the graph.

17. $f(x) = x$
18. $f(x) = x^2$
19. $f(x) = x^3$
20. $f(x) = \sqrt{x}$
21. $f(x) = \dfrac{1}{x}$
22. $f(x) = |x|$
23. $f(x) = \sqrt[3]{x}$
24. $f(x) = 3$

25. If $f(x) = \begin{cases} x^2 & \text{if } x < 0 \\ 2 & \text{if } x = 0 \\ 2x + 1 & \text{if } x > 0 \end{cases}$

find: (a) $f(-2)$ (b) $f(0)$ (c) $f(2)$

26. If $f(x) = \begin{cases} -3x & \text{if } x < -1 \\ 0 & \text{if } x = -1 \\ 2x^2 + 1 & \text{if } x > -1 \end{cases}$

find: (a) $f(-2)$ (b) $f(-1)$ (c) $f(0)$

27. If $f(x) = \begin{cases} 2x - 4 & \text{if } -1 \le x \le 2 \\ x^3 - 2 & \text{if } 2 < x \le 3 \end{cases}$

find: (a) $f(0)$ (b) $f(1)$ (c) $f(2)$ (d) $f(3)$

28. If $f(x) = \begin{cases} x^3 & \text{if } -2 \le x < 1 \\ 3x + 2 & \text{if } 1 \le x \le 4 \end{cases}$

find: (a) $f(-1)$ (b) $f(0)$ (c) $f(1)$ (d) $f(3)$

In Problems 29–40:

(a) *Find the domain of each function.* (b) *Locate any intercepts.* (c) *Graph each function.*
(d) *Based on the graph, find the range.* (e) *Is f continuous on its domain?*

29. $f(x) = \begin{cases} 2x & \text{if } x \neq 0 \\ 1 & \text{if } x = 0 \end{cases}$

30. $f(x) = \begin{cases} 3x & \text{if } x \neq 0 \\ 4 & \text{if } x = 0 \end{cases}$

31. $f(x) = \begin{cases} -2x + 3 & \text{if } x < 1 \\ 3x - 2 & \text{if } x \geq 1 \end{cases}$

32. $f(x) = \begin{cases} x + 3 & \text{if } x < -2 \\ -2x - 3 & \text{if } x \geq -2 \end{cases}$

33. $f(x) = \begin{cases} x + 3 & \text{if } -2 \leq x < 1 \\ 5 & \text{if } x = 1 \\ -x + 2 & \text{if } x > 1 \end{cases}$

34. $f(x) = \begin{cases} 2x + 5 & \text{if } -3 \leq x < 0 \\ -3 & \text{if } x = 0 \\ -5x & \text{if } x > 0 \end{cases}$

35. $f(x) = \begin{cases} 1 + x & \text{if } x < 0 \\ x^2 & \text{if } x \geq 0 \end{cases}$

36. $f(x) = \begin{cases} \dfrac{1}{x} & \text{if } x < 0 \\ \sqrt[3]{x} & \text{if } x \geq 0 \end{cases}$

37. $f(x) = \begin{cases} |x| & \text{if } -2 \leq x < 0 \\ x^3 & \text{if } x > 0 \end{cases}$

38. $f(x) = \begin{cases} 2 - x & \text{if } -3 \leq x < 1 \\ \sqrt{x} & \text{if } x > 1 \end{cases}$

39. $f(x) = 2\,\text{int}(x)$

40. $f(x) = \text{int}(2x)$

In Problems 41–44, the graph of a piecewise-defined function is given. Write a definition for each function.

41.

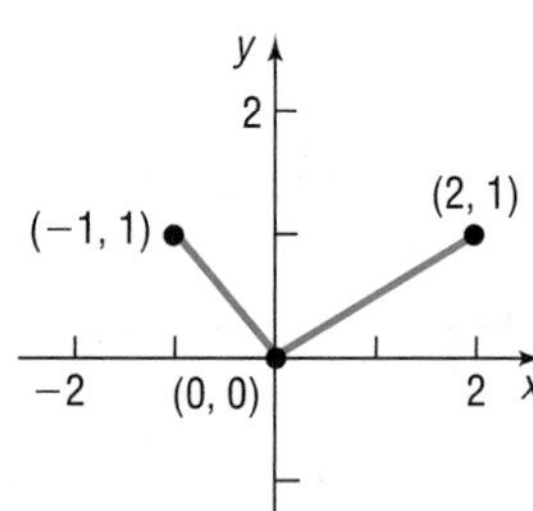

42.

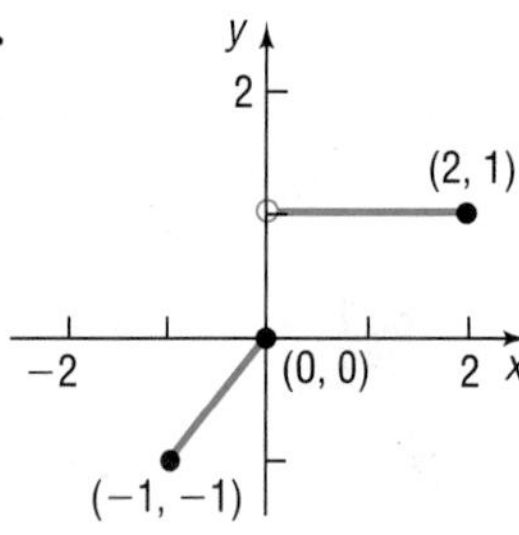

43.

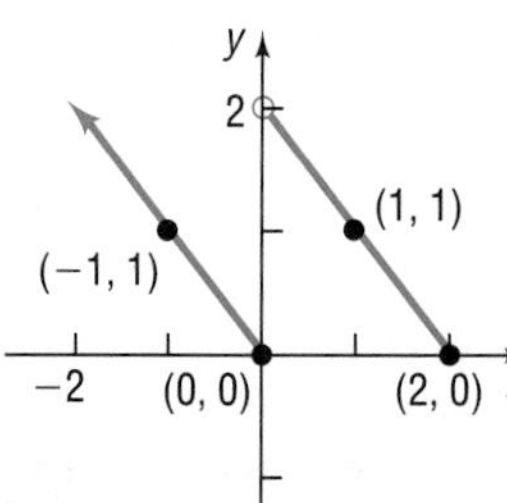

44.

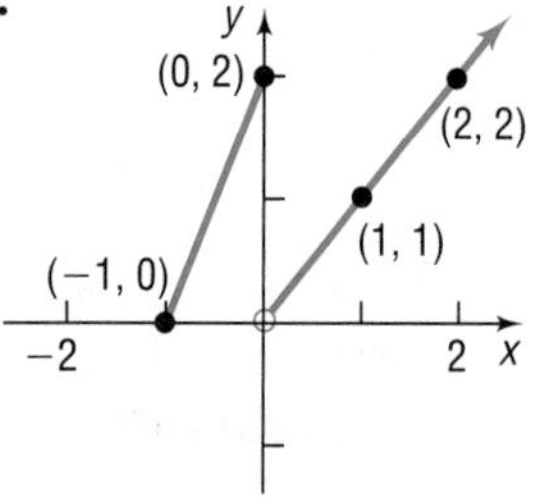

45. If $f(x) = \text{int}(2x)$, find
(a) $f(1.2)$ (b) $f(1.6)$ (c) $f(-1.8)$

46. If $f(x) = \text{int}\left(\dfrac{x}{2}\right)$, find
(a) $f(1.2)$ (b) $f(1.6)$ (c) $f(-1.8)$

Applications and Extensions

47. **Cell Phone Service** Sprint PCS offers a monthly cellular phone plan for \$39.99. It includes 450 anytime minutes and charges \$0.45 per minute for additional minutes. The following function is used to compute the monthly cost for a subscriber:

$$C(x) = \begin{cases} 39.99 & \text{if } 0 \leq x \leq 450 \\ 0.45x - 162.51 & \text{if } x > 450 \end{cases}$$

where x is the number of anytime minutes used. Compute the monthly cost of the cellular phone for use of the following number of anytime minutes:
(a) 200 (b) 465 (c) 451
Source: Sprint PCS

48. **Parking at O'Hare International Airport** The short-term (no more than 24 hours) parking fee F (in dollars) for parking x hours at O'Hare International Airport's main parking garage can be modeled by the function

$$F(x) = \begin{cases} 2 & \text{if } 0 < x \leq 1 \\ 4 & \text{if } 1 < x \leq 3 \\ 10 & \text{if } 3 < x \leq 4 \\ 5\,\text{int}(x + 1) + 2 & \text{if } 4 < x < 9 \\ 51 & \text{if } 9 \leq x \leq 24 \end{cases}$$

Determine the fee for parking in the short-term parking garage for
(a) 2 hours (b) 7 hours (c) 15 hours
(d) 8 hours and 24 minutes
Source: O'Hare International Airport

49. **Cost of Natural Gas** In March 2011, Peoples Energy had the following rate schedule for natural gas usage in single-family residences:

Monthly service charge	\$18.95
Per therm service charge	
1st 50 therms	\$0.33372/therm
Over 50 therms	\$0.12360/therm
Gas charge	\$0.5038/therm

(a) What is the charge for using 50 therms in a month?
(b) What is the charge for using 500 therms in a month?
(c) Develop a model that relates the monthly charge C for x therms of gas.
(d) Graph the function found in part (c).
Source: Peoples Energy, Chicago, Illinois, 2011

50. **Cost of Natural Gas** In March 2011, Nicor Gas had the following rate schedule for natural gas usage in single-family residences:

Monthly customer charge	\$13.55
Distribution charge	
1st 20 therms	\$0.1473/therm
Next 30 therms	\$0.0579/therm
Over 50 therms	\$0.0519/therm
Gas supply charge	\$0.51/therm

(a) What is the charge for using 40 therms in a month?

(b) What is the charge for using 150 therms in a month?

(c) Develop a model that gives the monthly charge C for x therms of gas.

(d) Graph the function found in part (c).

Source: Nicor Gas, Aurora, Illinois, 2011

51. **Federal Income Tax** Two 2011 Tax Rate Schedules are given in the table below. If x equals taxable income and y equals the tax due, construct a function $y = f(x)$ for Schedule X.

52. **Federal Income Tax** Refer to the revised 2011 tax rate schedules. If x equals taxable income and y equals the tax due, construct a function $y = f(x)$ for Schedule Y-1.

REVISED 2011 TAX RATE SCHEDULES

Schedule X—Single						Schedule Y-1—Married Filing Jointly or Qualifying Widow(er)					
If Taxable Income Is Over	But Not Over	The Tax Is This Amount		Plus This %	Of the Excess Over	If Taxable Income Is Over	But Not Over	The Tax Is This Amount		Plus This %	Of The Excess Over
\$0	\$8,500	–	+	10%	\$0	\$0	\$17,000	–	+	10%	\$0
8,500	34,500	\$850.00	+	15%	8,500	17,000	69,000	\$1,700.00	+	15%	17,000
34,500	83,600	4,750.00	+	25%	34,500	69,000	139,350	9,500.00	+	25%	69,000
83,600	174,400	17,025.00	+	28%	83,600	139,350	212,300	27,087.50	+	28%	139,350
174,400	379,150	42,449.00	+	33%	174,400	212,300	379,150	47,513.50	+	33%	212,300
379,150	–	110,016.50	+	35%	379,150	379,150	–	102,574.00	+	35%	379,150

Source: Internal Revenue Service

53. **Cost of Transporting Goods** A trucking company transports goods between Chicago and New York, a distance of 960 miles. The company's policy is to charge, for each pound, \$0.50 per mile for the first 100 miles, \$0.40 per mile for the next 300 miles, \$0.25 per mile for the next 400 miles, and no charge for the remaining 160 miles.

(a) Graph the relationship between the cost of transportation in dollars and mileage over the entire 960-mile route.

(b) Find the cost as a function of mileage for hauls between 100 and 400 miles from Chicago.

(c) Find the cost as a function of mileage for hauls between 400 and 800 miles from Chicago.

54. **Car Rental Costs** An economy car rented in Florida from National Car Rental® on a weekly basis costs \$95 per week. Extra days cost \$24 per day until the day rate exceeds the weekly rate, in which case the weekly rate applies. Also, any part of a day used counts as a full day. Find the cost C of renting an economy car as a function of the number x of days used, where $7 \le x \le 14$. Graph this function.

55. **Mortgage Fees** Fannie Mae charges an adverse market delivery charge on all mortgages, which represents a fee homebuyers seeking a loan must pay. The rate paid depends on the credit score of the borrower, the amount borrowed, and the loan-to-value (LTV) ratio. The LTV ratio is the ratio of amount borrowed to appraised value of the home. For example, a homebuyer who wishes to borrow \$250,000 with a credit score of 730 and an LTV ratio of 80% will pay 0.5% (0.005) of \$250,000 or \$1250. The table shows the adverse delivery charge for various credit scores and an LTV ratio of 80%.

Credit Score	Adverse Market Delivery Charge Rate
≤ 659	3.25%
660–679	2.75%
680–699	1.5%
700–719	1%
720–739	0.5%
≥ 740	0.25%

Source: Fannie Mae.

(a) Construct a function $C = C(s)$ where C is the adverse market delivery charge and s is the credit score of an individual who wishes to borrow \$300,000 with an 80% LTV ratio.

(b) What is the adverse market delivery charge on a \$300,000 loan with an 80% LTV ratio for a borrower whose credit score is 725?

(c) What is the adverse market delivery charge on a \$300,000 loan with an 80% LTV ratio for a borrower whose credit score is 670?

56. **Minimum Payments for Credit Cards** Holders of credit cards issued by banks, department stores, oil companies, and so on, receive bills each month that state minimum

amounts that must be paid by a certain due date. The minimum due depends on the total amount owed. One such credit card company uses the following rules: For a bill of less than \$10, the entire amount is due. For a bill of at least \$10 but less than \$500, the minimum due is \$10. A minimum of \$30 is due on a bill of at least \$500 but less than \$1000, a minimum of \$50 is due on a bill of at least \$1000 but less than \$1500, and a minimum of \$70 is due on bills of \$1500 or more. Find the function f that describes the minimum payment due on a bill of x dollars. Graph f.

57. Wind Chill The wind chill factor represents the equivalent air temperature at a standard wind speed that would produce the same heat loss as the given temperature and wind speed. One formula for computing the equivalent temperature is

$$W = \begin{cases} t & 0 \le v < 1.79 \\ 33 - \dfrac{(10.45 + 10\sqrt{v} - v)(33 - t)}{22.04} & 1.79 \le v \le 20 \\ 33 - 1.5958(33 - t) & v > 20 \end{cases}$$

where v represents the wind speed (in meters per second) and t represents the air temperature (°C). Compute the wind chill for the following:

(a) An air temperature of 10°C and a wind speed of 1 meter per second (m/sec)

(b) An air temperature of 10°C and a wind speed of 5 m/sec

(c) An air temperature of 10°C and a wind speed of 15 m/sec

(d) An air temperature of 10°C and a wind speed of 25 m/sec

(e) Explain the physical meaning of the equation corresponding to $0 \le v < 1.79$.

(f) Explain the physical meaning of the equation corresponding to $v > 20$.

58. Wind Chill Redo Problem 57(a)–(d) for an air temperature of −10°C.

59. First-class Mail In 2011 the U.S. Postal Service charged \$0.88 postage for first-class mail retail flats (such as an 8.5″ by 11″ envelope) weighing up to 1 ounce, plus \$0.17 for each additional ounce up to 13 ounces. First-class rates do not apply to flats weighing more than 13 ounces. Develop a model that relates C, the first-class postage charged, for a flat weighing x ounces. Graph the function.

Source: United States Postal Service

Explaining Concepts: Discussion and Writing

In Problems 60–67, use a graphing utility.

60. **Exploration** Graph $y = x^2$. Then on the same screen graph $y = x^2 + 2$, followed by $y = x^2 + 4$, followed by $y = x^2 - 2$. What pattern do you observe? Can you predict the graph of $y = x^2 - 4$? Of $y = x^2 + 5$?

61. **Exploration** Graph $y = x^2$. Then on the same screen graph $y = (x - 2)^2$, followed by $y = (x - 4)^2$, followed by $y = (x + 2)^2$. What pattern do you observe? Can you predict the graph of $y = (x + 4)^2$? Of $y = (x - 5)^2$?

62. **Exploration** Graph $y = |x|$. Then on the same screen graph $y = 2|x|$, followed by $y = 4|x|$, followed by $y = \frac{1}{2}|x|$. What pattern do you observe? Can you predict the graph of $y = \frac{1}{4}|x|$? Of $y = 5|x|$?

63. **Exploration** Graph $y = x^2$. Then on the same screen graph $y = -x^2$. What pattern do you observe? Now try $y = |x|$ and $y = -|x|$. What do you conclude?

64. **Exploration** Graph $y = \sqrt{x}$. Then on the same screen graph $y = \sqrt{-x}$. What pattern do you observe? Now try $y = 2x + 1$ and $y = 2(-x) + 1$. What do you conclude?

65. **Exploration** Graph $y = x^3$. Then on the same screen graph $y = (x - 1)^3 + 2$. Could you have predicted the result?

66. **Exploration** Graph $y = x^2$, $y = x^4$, and $y = x^6$ on the same screen. What do you notice is the same about each graph? What do you notice that is different?

67. **Exploration** Graph $y = x^3$, $y = x^5$, and $y = x^7$ on the same screen. What do you notice is the same about each graph? What do you notice that is different?

68. Consider the equation

$$y = \begin{cases} 1 & \text{if } x \text{ is rational} \\ 0 & \text{if } x \text{ is irrational} \end{cases}$$

Is this a function? What is its domain? What is its range? What is its y-intercept, if any? What are its x-intercepts, if any? Is it even, odd, or neither? How would you describe its graph?

69. Define some functions that pass through $(0, 0)$ and $(1, 1)$ and are increasing for $x \ge 0$. Begin your list with $y = \sqrt{x}$, $y = x$, and $y = x^2$. Can you propose a general result about such functions?

'Are You Prepared?' Answers

1.

2.

3. $(0, -8), (2, 0)$

9.5 Graphing Techniques: Transformations

OBJECTIVES
1 Graph Functions Using Vertical and Horizontal Shifts (p. 605)
2 Graph Functions Using Compressions and Stretches (p. 607)
3 Graph Functions Using Reflections about the x-Axis or y-Axis (p. 609)

At this stage, if you were asked to graph any of the functions defined by $y = x$, $y = x^2$, $y = x^3$, $y = \sqrt{x}$, $y = \sqrt[3]{x}$, $y = |x|$, or $y = \frac{1}{x}$, your response should be, "Yes, I recognize these functions and know the general shapes of their graphs." (If this is not your answer, review the previous section, Figures 35 through 41.)

Sometimes we are asked to graph a function that is "almost" like one that we already know how to graph. In this section, we develop techniques for graphing such functions. Collectively, these techniques are referred to as **transformations.** We introduce the method of transformations because it is a more efficient method of graphing than point-plotting.

1 Graph Functions Using Vertical and Horizontal Shifts

Exploration

On the same screen, graph each of the following functions:

$$Y_1 = x^2$$
$$Y_2 = x^2 + 2$$
$$Y_3 = x^2 - 2$$

What do you observe? Now create a table of values for Y_1, Y_2, and Y_3. What do you observe?

Figure 46

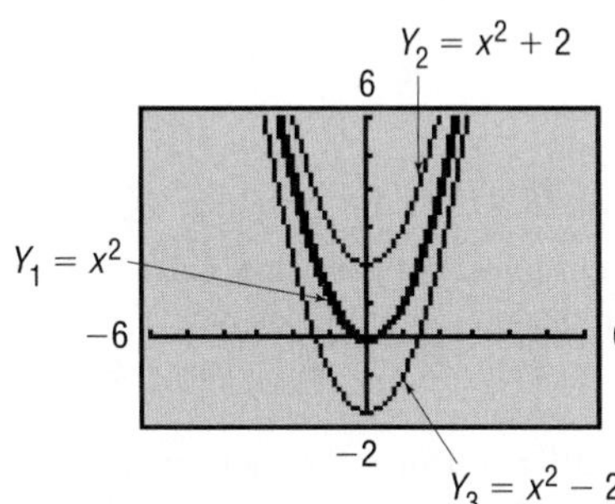

Result Figure 46 illustrates the graphs. You should have observed a general pattern. With $Y_1 = x^2$ on the screen, the graph of $Y_2 = x^2 + 2$ is identical to that of $Y_1 = x^2$, except that it is shifted vertically up 2 units. The graph of $Y_3 = x^2 - 2$ is identical to that of $Y_1 = x^2$, except that it is shifted vertically down 2 units. From Table 7(a), we see that the y-coordinates on $Y_2 = x^2 + 2$ are 2 units larger than the y-coordinates on $Y_1 = x^2$ for any given x-coordinate. From Table 7(b), we see that the y-coordinates on $Y_3 = x^2 - 2$ are 2 units smaller than the y-coordinates on $Y_1 = x^2$ for any given x-coordinate.

Notice a vertical shift only affects the range of a function, not the domain. For example, the range of Y_1 is $[0, \infty)$ while the range of Y_2 is $[2, \infty)$. The domain of both functions is all real numbers.

Table 7

X	Y1	Y2
-2	4	6
-1	1	3
0	0	2
1	1	3
2	4	6
3	9	11
4	16	18

Y2=X²+2

(a)

X	Y1	Y3
-2	4	2
-1	1	-1
0	0	-2
1	1	-1
2	4	2
3	9	7
4	16	14

Y3=X²−2

(b)

We are led to the following conclusions:

If a positive real number k is added to the outputs of a function $y = f(x)$, the graph of the new function $y = f(x) + k$ is the graph of f **shifted vertically up** k units.

If a positive real number k is subtracted from the outputs of a function $y = f(x)$, the graph of the new function $y = f(x) - k$ is the graph of f **shifted vertically down** k units.

EXAMPLE 1 **Vertical Shift Down**

Use the graph of $f(x) = x^2$ to obtain the graph of $h(x) = x^2 - 4$. Find the domain and range of h.

Solution Table 8 lists some points on the graphs of $Y_1 = f(x) = x^2$ and $Y_2 = h(x) = f(x) - 4 = x^2 - 4$. Notice that each y-coordinate of h is 4 units less than the corresponding y-coordinate of f.

Table 8

X	Y1	Y2
-3	9	5
-2	4	0
-1	1	-3
0	0	-4
1	1	-3
2	4	0
3	9	5

Y2 = X²−4

To obtain the graph of h from the graph of f, subtract 4 from each y-coordinate on the graph of f. The graph of h is identical to that of f, except that it is shifted down 4 units. See Figure 47.

Figure 47

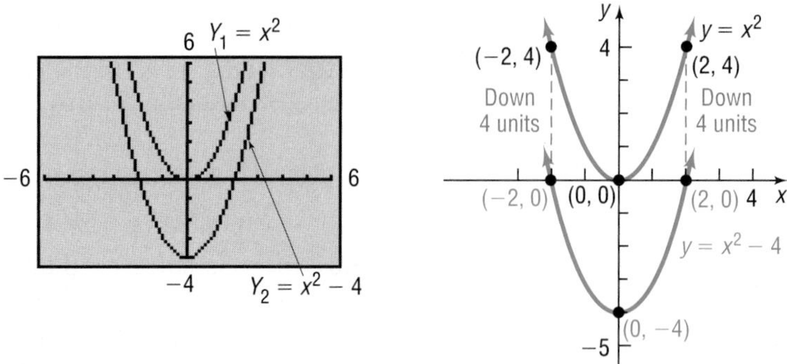

The domain of h is the set of all real numbers. The range of h is $[-4, \infty)$. ■

Now Work PROBLEM 39

Exploration

On the same screen, graph each of the following functions:

$$Y_1 = x^2$$
$$Y_2 = (x - 3)^2$$
$$Y_3 = (x + 2)^2$$

What do you observe?

Figure 48

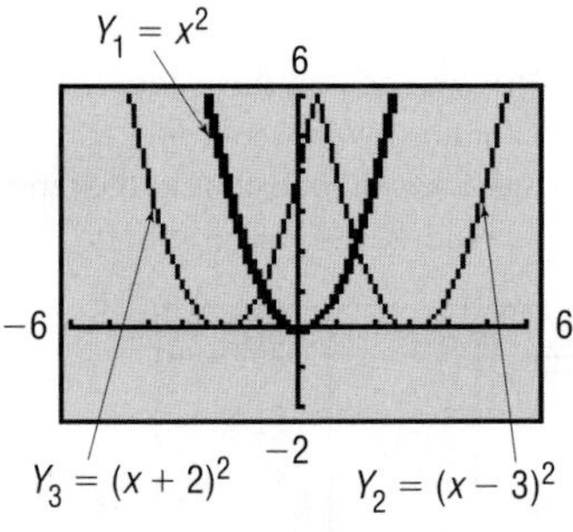

Result Figure 48 illustrates the graphs. You should have observed the following pattern. With the graph of $Y_1 = x^2$ on the screen, the graph of $Y_2 = (x - 3)^2$ is identical to that of $Y_1 = x^2$, except it is shifted horizontally to the right 3 units. The graph of $Y_3 = (x + 2)^2$ is identical to that of $Y_1 = x^2$, except it is shifted horizontally to the left 2 units.

From Table 9(a), we see the x-coordinates on $Y_2 = (x - 3)^2$ are 3 units larger than they are for $Y_1 = x^2$ for any given y-coordinate. For example, when $Y_1 = 0$, then $x = 0$, and when $Y_2 = 0$, then $x = 3$. Also, when $Y_1 = 1$, then $x = -1$ or 1, and when $Y_2 = 1$, then $x = 2$ or 4. From Table 9(b), we see the x-coordinates on $Y_3 = (x + 2)^2$ are 2 units smaller than they are for $Y_1 = x^2$ for any given y-coordinate. For example, when $Y_1 = 0$, then $x = 0$, and when $Y_3 = 0$, then $x = -2$. Also, when $Y_1 = 4$, then $x = -2$ or 2, and when $Y_3 = 4$, then $x = -4$ or 0.

Table 9

X	Y1	Y2
-1	1	16
0	0	9
1	1	4
2	4	1
3	9	0
4	16	1
5	25	4

Y2 = (X−3)²

(a)

X	Y1	Y3
-4	16	4
-3	9	1
-2	4	0
-1	1	1
0	0	4
1	1	9
2	4	16

Y3 = (X+2)²

(b)

We are led to the following conclusions:

If the argument x of a function f is replaced by $x - h$, $h > 0$, the graph of the new function $y = f(x - h)$ is the graph of f **shifted horizontally right** h units.

If the argument x of a function f is replaced by $x + h$, $h > 0$, the graph of the new function $y = f(x + h)$ is the graph of f **shifted horizontally left** h units.

Now Work PROBLEM 43

NOTE Vertical shifts result when adding or subtracting a real number k after performing the operation suggested by the basic function, while horizontal shifts result when adding or subtracting a real number h to or from x before performing the operation suggested by the basic function. For example, the graph of $f(x) = \sqrt{x} + 3$ is obtained by shifting the graph of $y = \sqrt{x}$ up 3 units, because we evaluate the square root function first and then add 3. The graph of $g(x) = \sqrt{x + 3}$ is obtained by shifting the graph of $y = \sqrt{x}$ left 3 units, because we first add 3 to x before we evaluate the square root function. ■

Vertical and horizontal shifts are sometimes combined.

EXAMPLE 2 **Combining Vertical and Horizontal Shifts**

Graph the function $f(x) = (x + 3)^2 - 5$. Find the domain and range of f.

Solution We graph f in steps. First, notice that the rule for f is basically a square function, so we begin with the graph of $y = x^2$ as shown in Figure 49(a). To get the graph of $y = (x + 3)^2$, shift the graph of $y = x^2$ horizontally 3 units to the left. See Figure 49(b). Finally, to get the graph of $y = (x + 3)^2 - 5$, shift the graph of $y = (x + 3)^2$ vertically down 5 units. See Figure 49(c). Note the points plotted on each graph. Using key points can be helpful in keeping track of the transformation that has taken place. The domain of f is the set of all real numbers. The range of f is $[-5, \infty)$.

Figure 49

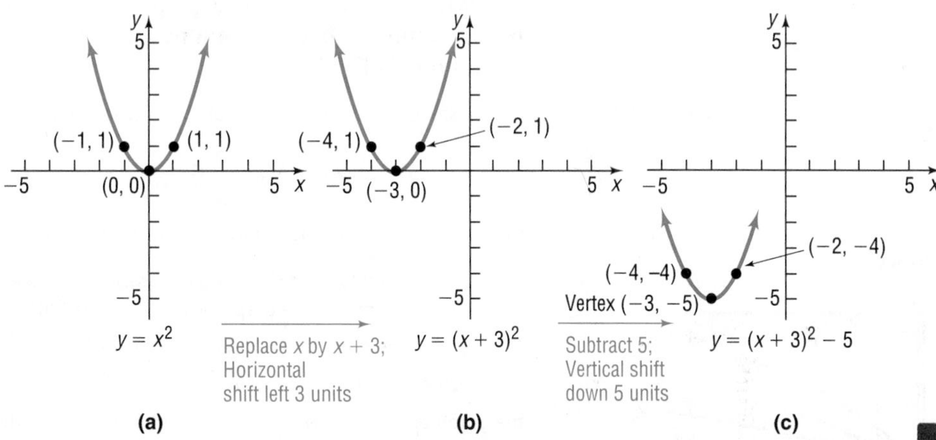

■

Check: Graph $Y_1 = f(x) = (x + 3)^2 - 5$ and compare the graph to Figure 49(c).

In Example 2, if the vertical shift had been done first, followed by the horizontal shift, the final graph would have been the same. (Try it for yourself.)

Now Work PROBLEMS 45 AND 77

2 Graph Functions Using Compressions and Stretches

Exploration On the same screen, graph each of the following functions:

$$Y_1 = |x|$$
$$Y_2 = 2|x|$$
$$Y_3 = \frac{1}{2}|x|$$

Then create a table of values and compare the y-coordinates for any given x-coordinate.

Figure 50

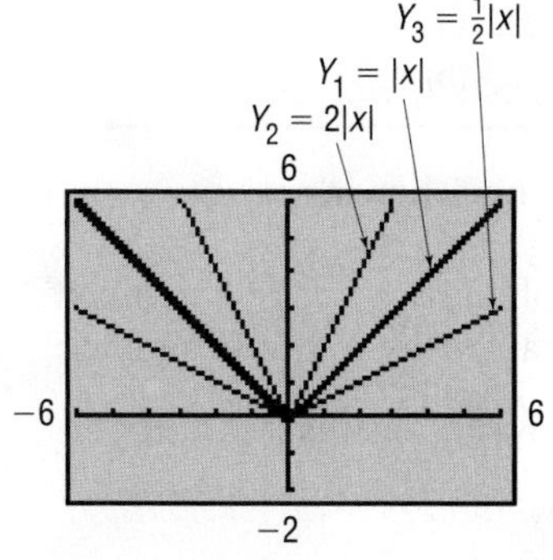

Result Figure 50 illustrates the graphs.

Now look at Table 10, where $Y_1 = |x|$ and $Y_2 = 2|x|$. Notice that the values for Y_2 are two times the values of Y_1 for each x-value. This means that the graph of $Y_2 = 2|x|$ can be obtained from the graph of $Y_1 = |x|$ by multiplying each y-coordinate of $Y_1 = |x|$ by 2. Therefore, the graph of Y_2 will be the graph of Y_1 vertically *stretched* by a factor of 2.

Look at Table 11 where $Y_1 = |x|$ and $Y_3 = \frac{1}{2}|x|$. The values of Y_3 are half the values of Y_1 for each x-value. So, the graph of $Y_3 = \frac{1}{2}|x|$ can be obtained from the graph of $Y_1 = |x|$ by multiplying each y-coordinate by $\frac{1}{2}$. Therefore, the graph of Y_3 will be the graph of Y_1 vertically *compressed* by a factor of $\frac{1}{2}$.

Table 10

X	Y_1	Y_2
-2	2	4
-1	1	2
0	0	0
1	1	2
2	2	4
3	3	6
4	4	8

$Y_2 = 2abs(X)$

Table 11

X	Y_1	Y_3
-2	2	1
-1	1	.5
0	0	0
1	1	.5
2	2	1
3	3	1.5
4	4	2

$Y_3 = .5abs(X)$

Based on the Exploration, we have the following result:

When the right side of a function $y = f(x)$ is multiplied by a positive number a, the graph of the new function $y = af(x)$ is obtained by multiplying each y-coordinate on the graph of $y = f(x)$ by a. The new graph is a **vertically compressed** (if $0 < a < 1$) or a **vertically stretched** (if $a > 1$) version of the graph of $y = f(x)$.

Now Work PROBLEM 47

What happens if the argument x of a function $y = f(x)$ is multiplied by a positive number a, creating a new function $y = f(ax)$? To find the answer, look at the following Exploration.

Exploration

On the same screen, graph each of the following functions:

$$Y_1 = f(x) = \sqrt{x} \qquad Y_2 = f(2x) = \sqrt{2x} \qquad Y_3 = f\left(\frac{1}{2}x\right) = \sqrt{\frac{1}{2}x} = \sqrt{\frac{x}{2}}$$

Create a table of values to explore the relation between the x- and y-coordinates of each function.

Figure 51

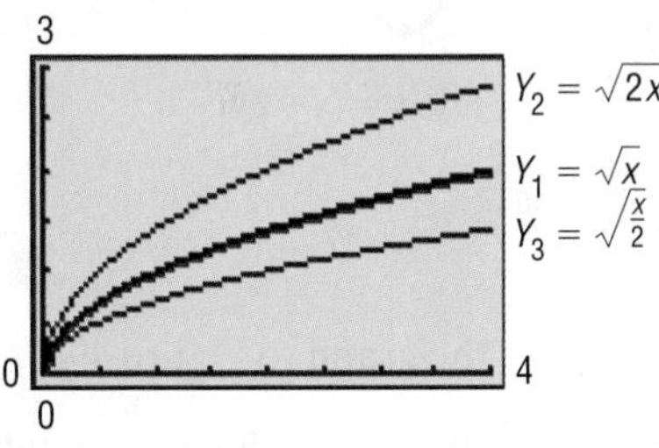

Result You should have obtained the graphs in Figure 51. Look at Table 12(a). Notice that (1, 1), (4, 2), and (9, 3) are points on the graph of $Y_1 = \sqrt{x}$. Also, (0.5, 1), (2, 2), and (4.5, 3) are points on the graph of $Y_2 = \sqrt{2x}$. For a given y-coordinate, the x-coordinate on the graph of Y_2 is $\frac{1}{2}$ of the x-coordinate on Y_1. We conclude that the graph of $Y_2 = \sqrt{2x}$ is obtained by multiplying the x-coordinate of each point on the graph of $Y_1 = \sqrt{x}$ by $\frac{1}{2}$. The graph of $Y_2 = \sqrt{2x}$ is the graph of $Y_1 = \sqrt{x}$ *compressed* horizontally.

Look at Table 12(b). Notice that (1, 1), (4, 2), and (9, 3) are points on the graph of $Y_1 = \sqrt{x}$. Also notice that (2, 1), (8, 2), and (18, 3) are points on the graph of $Y_3 = \sqrt{\frac{x}{2}}$. For a given y-coordinate, the x-coordinate on the graph of Y_3 is 2 times the x-coordinate on Y_1. We conclude that the graph of $Y_3 = \sqrt{\frac{x}{2}}$ is obtained by multiplying the x-coordinate of each point on the graph of $Y_1 = \sqrt{x}$ by 2. The graph of $Y_3 = \sqrt{\frac{x}{2}}$ is the graph of $Y_1 = \sqrt{x}$ *stretched* horizontally.

Table 12

X	Y_1	Y_2
0	0	0
.5	.70711	1
1	1	1.4142
2	1.4142	2
4	2	2.8284
4.5	2.1213	3
9	3	4.2426

$Y_2 = \sqrt{(2X)}$

(a)

X	Y_1	Y_3
0	0	0
1	1	.70711
2	1.4142	1
4	2	1.4142
8	2.8284	2
9	3	2.1213
18	4.2426	3

$Y_3 = \sqrt{(X/2)}$

(b)

Based on the results of the Exploration, we have the following result:

If the argument x of a function $y = f(x)$ is multiplied by a positive number a, the graph of the new function $y = f(ax)$ is obtained by multiplying each x-coordinate of $y = f(x)$ by $\frac{1}{a}$. A **horizontal compression** results if $a > 1$, and a **horizontal stretch** occurs if $0 < a < 1$.

Let's look at an example.

EXAMPLE 3 Graphing Using Stretches and Compressions

The graph of $y = f(x)$ is given in Figure 52. Use this graph to find the graphs of

(a) $y = 2f(x)$ (b) $y = f(3x)$

Figure 52

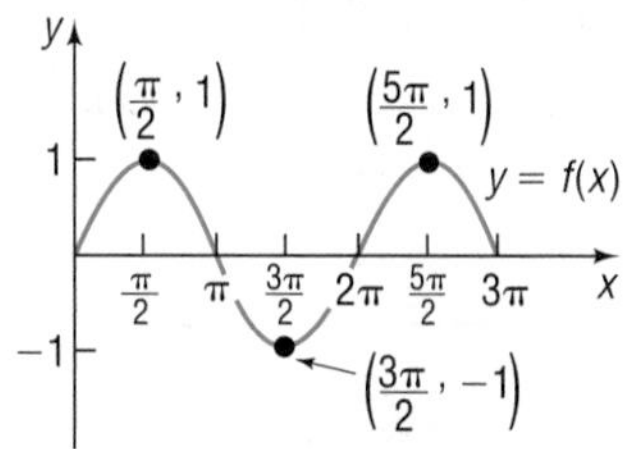

Solution (a) The graph of $y = 2f(x)$ is obtained by multiplying each y-coordinate of $y = f(x)$ by 2. See Figure 53.

(b) The graph of $y = f(3x)$ is obtained from the graph of $y = f(x)$ by multiplying each x-coordinate of $y = f(x)$ by $\frac{1}{3}$. See Figure 54.

Figure 53

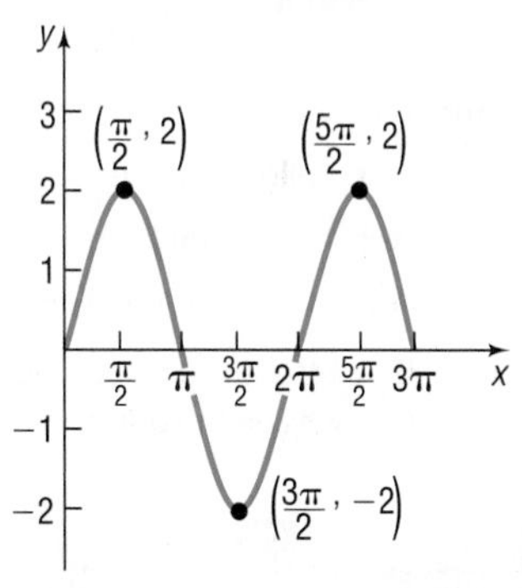

$y = 2f(x)$

Figure 54

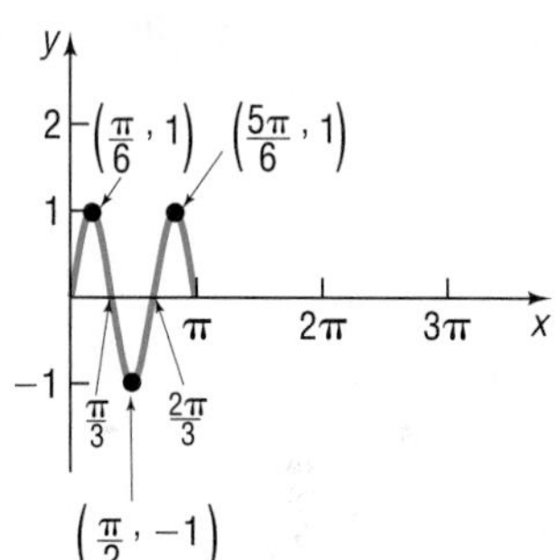

$y = f(3x)$

Now Work PROBLEM 69 (e) AND (g)

3 Graph Functions Using Reflections about the x-Axis or y-Axis

Exploration

Reflection about the x-axis:

(a) Graph and create a table of $Y_1 = x^2$ and $Y_2 = -x^2$.

(b) Graph and create a table of $Y_1 = |x|$ and $Y_2 = -|x|$.

(c) Graph and create a table of $Y_1 = x^2 - 4$ and $Y_2 = -(x^2 - 4) = -x^2 + 4$.

Result See Tables 13(a), (b), and (c) and Figures 55(a), (b), and (c). For each point (x, y) on the graph of Y_1, the point $(x, -y)$ is on the graph of Y_2. Put another way, Y_2 is the reflection about the x-axis of Y_1.

Table 13

X	Y1	Y2
-3	9	-9
-2	4	-4
-1	1	-1
0	0	0
1	1	-1
2	4	-4
3	9	-9

Y2■-X²

(a)

X	Y1	Y2
-3	3	-3
-2	2	-2
-1	1	-1
0	0	0
1	1	-1
2	2	-2
3	3	-3

Y2■-abs(X)

(b)

X	Y1	Y2
-3	5	-5
-2	0	0
-1	-3	3
0	-4	4
1	-3	3
2	0	0
3	5	-5

Y2■-X²+4

(c)

Figure 55

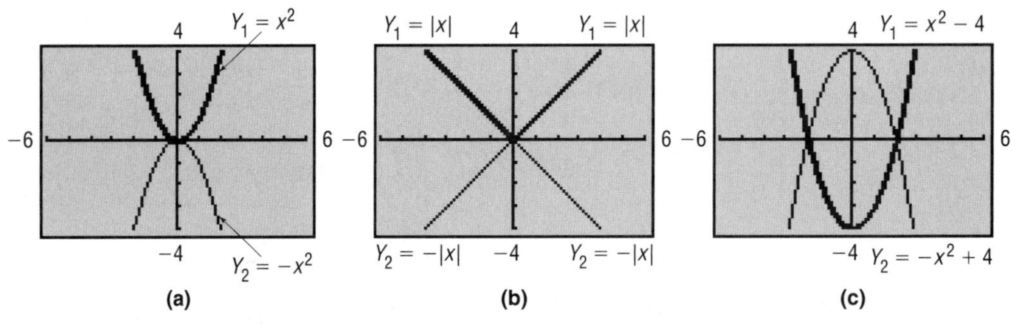

The results of the previous Exploration lead to the following result.

When the right side of the function $y = f(x)$ is multiplied by -1, the graph of the new function $y = -f(x)$ is the **reflection about the x-axis** of the graph of the function $y = f(x)$.

Now Work PROBLEM 51

Exploration

Reflection about the y-axis:

(a) Graph $Y_1 = \sqrt{x}$, followed by $Y_2 = \sqrt{-x}$.

(b) Graph $Y_1 = x + 1$, followed by $Y_2 = -x + 1$.

(c) Graph $Y_1 = x^4 + x$, followed by $Y_2 = (-x)^4 + (-x) = x^4 - x$.

Result See Tables 14(a), (b), and (c) and Figures 56(a), (b), and (c). For each point (x, y) on the graph of Y_1, the point $(-x, y)$ is on the graph of Y_2. Put another way, Y_2 is the reflection about the y-axis of Y_1.

Table 14

X	Y1	Y2
-3	ERROR	1.7321
-2	ERROR	1.4142
-1	ERROR	1
0	0	0
1	1	ERROR
2	1.4142	ERROR
3	1.7321	ERROR

Y2=√(-X)

(a)

X	Y1	Y2
-3	-2	4
-2	-1	3
-1	0	2
0	1	1
1	2	0
2	3	-1
3	4	-2

Y2=-X+1

(b)

X	Y1	Y2
-3	78	84
-2	14	18
-1	0	2
0	0	0
1	2	0
2	18	14
3	84	78

Y2=X^4-X

(c)

Figure 56

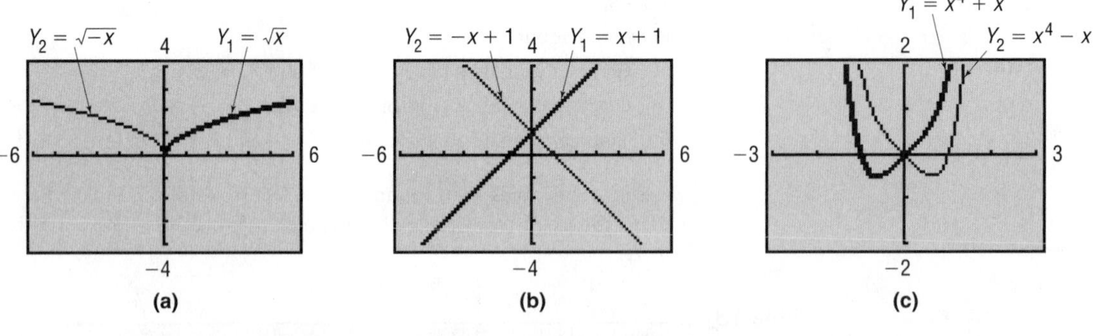

The results of the previous Exploration lead to the following result.

When the graph of the function $y = f(x)$ is known, the graph of the new function $y = f(-x)$ is the **reflection about the y-axis** of the graph of the function $y = f(x)$.

SUMMARY OF GRAPHING TECHNIQUES

To Graph:	Draw the Graph of f and:	Functional Change to $f(x)$
Vertical shifts		
$y = f(x) + k, \quad k > 0$	Raise the graph of f by k units.	Add k to $f(x)$.
$y = f(x) - k, \quad k > 0$	Lower the graph of f by k units.	Subtract k from $f(x)$.
Horizontal shifts		
$y = f(x + h), \quad h > 0$	Shift the graph of f to the left h units.	Replace x by $x + h$.
$y = f(x - h), \quad h > 0$	Shift the graph of f to the right h units.	Replace x by $x - h$.
Compressing or stretching		
$y = af(x), \quad a > 0$	Multiply each y-coordinate of $y = f(x)$ by a. Stretch the graph of f vertically if $a > 1$. Compress the graph of f vertically if $0 < a < 1$.	Multiply $f(x)$ by a.
$y = f(ax), \quad a > 0$	Multiply each x-coordinate of $y = f(x)$ by $\frac{1}{a}$. Stretch the graph of f horizontally if $0 < a < 1$. Compress the graph of f horizontally if $a > 1$.	Replace x by ax.
Reflection about the x-axis		
$y = -f(x)$	Reflect the graph of f about the x-axis.	Multiply $f(x)$ by -1.
Reflection about the y-axis		
$y = f(-x)$	Reflect the graph of f about the y-axis.	Replace x by $-x$.

EXAMPLE 4 **Determining the Function Obtained from a Series of Transformations**

Find the function that is finally graphed after the following three transformations are applied to the graph of $y = |x|$.

1. Shift left 2 units.
2. Shift up 3 units.
3. Reflect about the y-axis.

Solution

1. Shift left 2 units: Replace x by $x + 2$. $\quad y = |x + 2|$
2. Shift up 3 units: Add 3. $\quad y = |x + 2| + 3$
3. Reflect about the y-axis: Replace x by $-x$. $\quad y = |-x + 2| + 3$ ■

Now Work PROBLEM 27

EXAMPLE 5 **Combining Graphing Procedures**

Graph the function $f(x) = \dfrac{3}{x - 2} + 1$. Find the domain and the range of f.

Solution It is helpful to write f as $f(x) = 3\left(\dfrac{1}{x - 2}\right) + 1$. Now use the following steps to obtain the graph of f:

STEP 1: $y = \dfrac{1}{x}$ — Reciprocal function

STEP 2: $y = 3 \cdot \left(\dfrac{1}{x}\right) = \dfrac{3}{x}$ — Multiply by 3; vertical stretch of the graph of $y = \dfrac{1}{x}$ by a

STEP 3: $y = \dfrac{3}{x-2}$ factor of 3.

STEP 4: $y = \dfrac{3}{x-2} + 1$ Replace x by x − 2; horizontal shift to the right 2 units.

See Figure 57. Add 1; vertical shift up 1 unit.

Figure 57

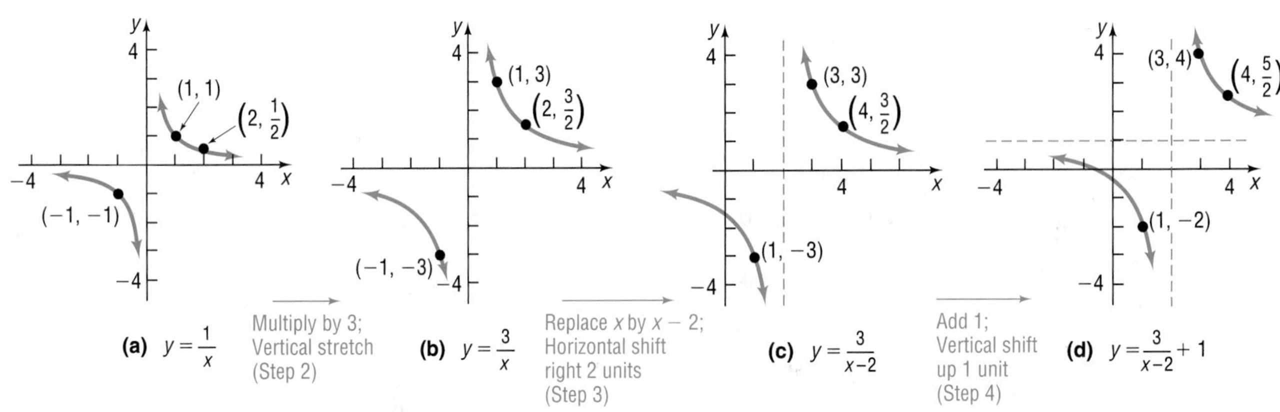

The domain of $y = \dfrac{1}{x}$ is $\{x \mid x \neq 0\}$ and its range is $\{y \mid y \neq 0\}$. Because we shifted right 2 units and up 1 unit to obtain f, the domain of f is $\{x \mid x \neq 2\}$ and its range is $\{y \mid y \neq 1\}$. ■

HINT Although the order in which transformations are performed can be altered, you may consider using the following order for consistency:

1. Reflections
2. Compressions and stretches
3. Shifts ■

Other ordering of the steps shown in Example 5 would also result in the graph of f. For example, try this one:

STEP 1: $y = \dfrac{1}{x}$ Reciprocal function

STEP 2: $y = \dfrac{1}{x-2}$ Replace x by x − 2; horizontal shift to the right 2 units.

STEP 3: $y = \dfrac{3}{x-2}$ Multiply by 3; vertical stretch of the graph of $y = \dfrac{1}{x-2}$ by a factor of 3.

STEP 4: $y = \dfrac{3}{x-2} + 1$ Add 1; vertical shift up 1 unit.

EXAMPLE 6 Combining Graphing Procedures

Graph the function $f(x) = \sqrt{1 - x} + 2$. Find the domain and the range of f.

Solution Because horizontal shifts require the form $x - h$, begin by rewriting $f(x)$ as $f(x) = \sqrt{1 - x} + 2 = \sqrt{-(x - 1)} + 2$. Now use the following steps:

STEP 1: $y = \sqrt{x}$ Square root function

STEP 2: $y = \sqrt{-x}$ Replace x by −x; reflect about the y-axis.

STEP 3: $y = \sqrt{-(x-1)} = \sqrt{1 - x}$ Replace x by x − 1; horizontal shift to the right 1 unit.

STEP 4: $y = \sqrt{1 - x} + 2$ Add 2; vertical shift up 2 units.

See Figure 58.

Figure 58

(a) $y = \sqrt{x}$ — Replace x by $-x$; Reflect about y-axis (Step 2) → (b) $y = \sqrt{-x}$ — Replace x by $x - 1$; Horizontal shift right 1 unit (Step 3) → (c) $y = \sqrt{-(x-1)} = \sqrt{-x+1} = \sqrt{1-x}$ — Add 2; Vertical shift up 2 units (Step 4) → (d) $y = \sqrt{1-x} + 2$

The domain of f is $(-\infty, 1]$ and its range is $[2, \infty)$. ■

Now Work PROBLEM 61

9.5 Assess Your Understanding

Concepts and Vocabulary

1. Suppose that the graph of a function f is known. Then the graph of $y = f(x - 2)$ may be obtained by a(n)__________ shift of the graph of f to the ________ a distance of 2 units.
2. Suppose that the graph of a function f is known. Then the graph of $y = f(-x)$ may be obtained by a reflection about the ________-axis of the graph of the function $y = f(x)$.
3. Suppose that the graph of a function g is known. The graph of $y = g(x) + 2$ may be obtained by a________ shift of the graph of g ________ a distance of 2 units.
4. ***True or False*** The graph of $y = -f(x)$ is the reflection about the x-axis of the graph of $y = f(x)$.
5. ***True or False*** To obtain the graph of $f(x) = \sqrt{x + 2}$, shift the graph of $y = \sqrt{x}$ horizontally to the right 2 units.
6. ***True or False*** To obtain the graph of $f(x) = x^3 + 5$, shift the graph of $y = x^3$ vertically up 5 units.

Skill Building

In Problems 7–18, match each graph to one of the following functions:

A. $y = x^2 + 2$	B. $y = -x^2 + 2$	C. $y = \lvert x\rvert + 2$	D. $y = -\lvert x\rvert + 2$
E. $y = (x - 2)^2$	F. $y = -(x + 2)^2$	G. $y = \lvert x - 2\rvert$	H. $y = -\lvert x + 2\rvert$
I. $y = 2x^2$	J. $y = -2x^2$	K. $y = 2\lvert x\rvert$	L. $y = -2\lvert x\rvert$

7.
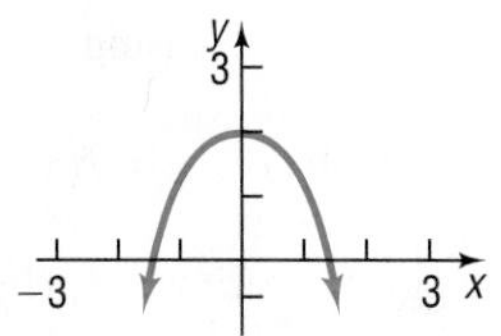

8.
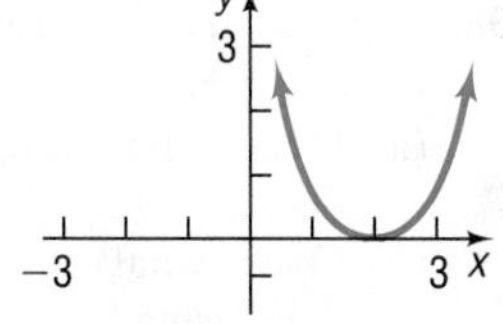

9.
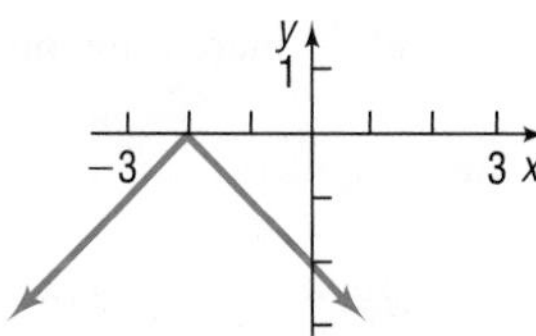

10.
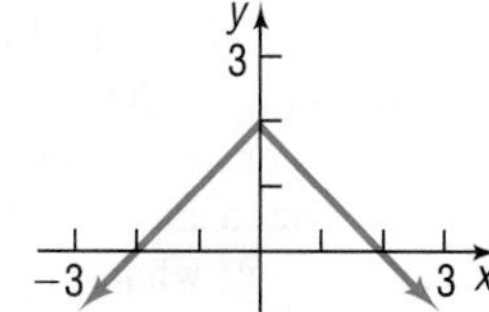

11.
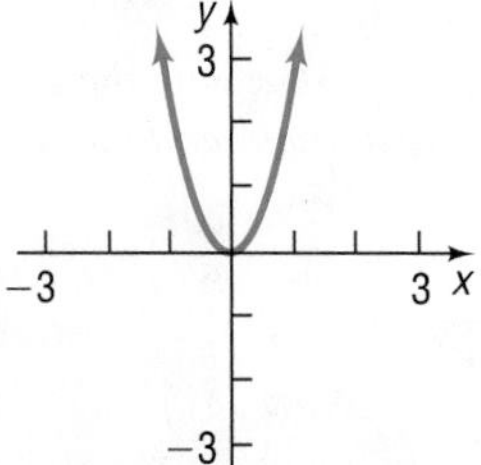

12.
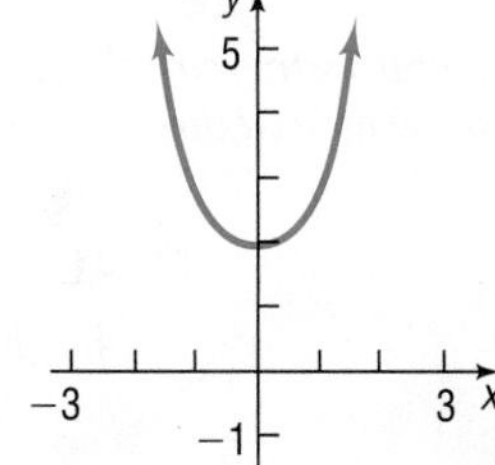

13.
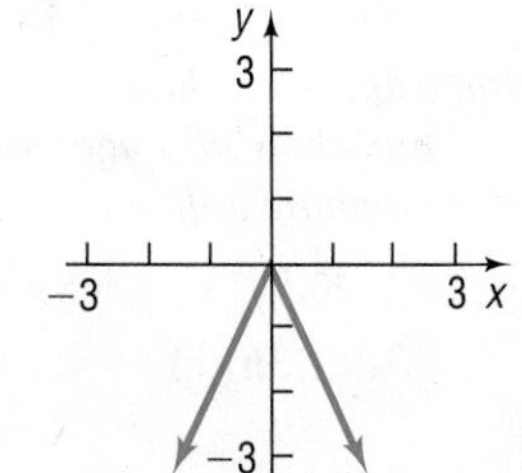

14.
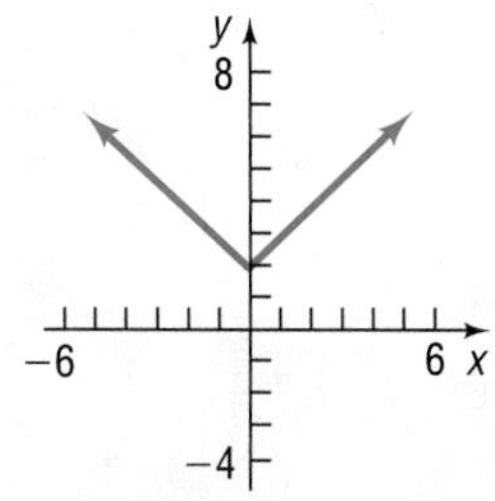

15.

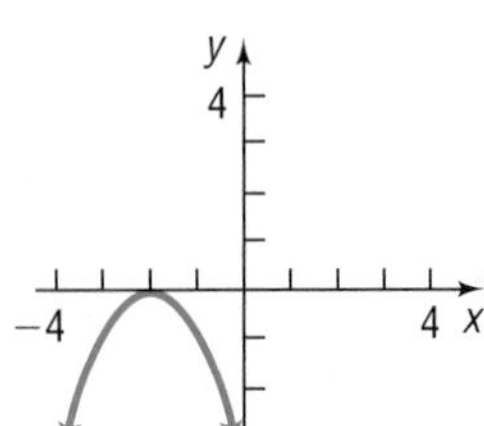

16.

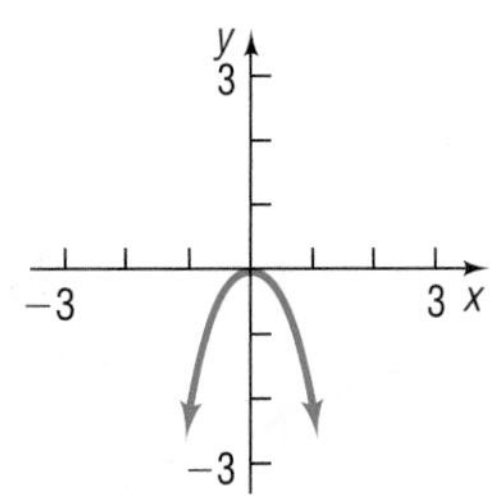

17.

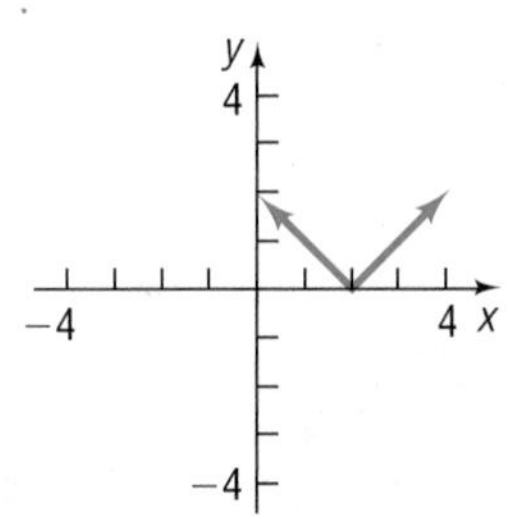

18.

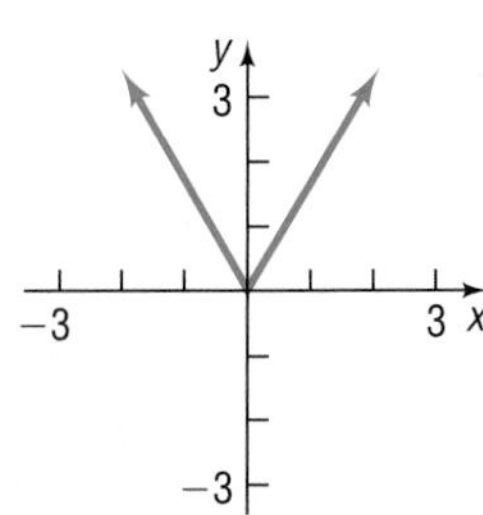

In Problems 19–26, write the function whose graph is the graph of $y = x^3$, but is:

19. Shifted to the right 4 units

20. Shifted to the left 4 units

21. Shifted up 4 units

22. Shifted down 4 units

23. Reflected about the y-axis

24. Reflected about the x-axis

25. Vertically stretched by a factor of 4

26. Horizontally stretched by a factor of 4

In Problems 27–30, find the function that is finally graphed after each of the following transformations is applied to the graph of $y = \sqrt{x}$ in the order stated.

27. (1) Shift up 2 units
(2) Reflect about the x-axis
(3) Reflect about the y-axis

28. (1) Reflect about the x-axis
(2) Shift right 3 units
(3) Shift down 2 units

29. (1) Reflect about the x-axis
(2) Shift up 2 units
(3) Shift left 3 units

30. (1) Shift up 2 units
(2) Reflect about the y-axis
(3) Shift left 3 units

31. If $(3, 6)$ is a point on the graph of $y = f(x)$, which of the following points must be on the graph of $y = -f(x)$?
(a) $(6, 3)$ (b) $(6, -3)$
(c) $(3, -6)$ (d) $(-3, 6)$

32. If $(3, 6)$ is a point on the graph of $y = f(x)$, which of the following points must be on the graph of $y = f(-x)$?
(a) $(6, 3)$ (b) $(6, -3)$
(c) $(3, -6)$ (d) $(-3, 6)$

33. If $(1, 3)$ is a point on the graph of $y = f(x)$, which of the following points must be on the graph of $y = 2f(x)$?
(a) $\left(1, \frac{3}{2}\right)$ (b) $(2, 3)$
(c) $(1, 6)$ (d) $\left(\frac{1}{2}, 3\right)$

34. If $(4, 2)$ is a point on the graph of $y = f(x)$, which of the following points must be on the graph of $y = f(2x)$?
(a) $(4, 1)$ (b) $(8, 2)$
(c) $(2, 2)$ (d) $(4, 4)$

35. Suppose that the x-intercepts of the graph of $y = f(x)$ are -5 and 3.
(a) What are the x-intercepts of the graph of $y = f(x + 2)$?
(b) What are the x-intercepts of the graph of $y = f(x - 2)$?
(c) What are the x-intercepts of the graph of $y = 4f(x)$?
(d) What are the x-intercepts of the graph of $y = f(-x)$?

36. Suppose that the x-intercepts of the graph of $y = f(x)$ are -8 and 1.
(a) What are the x-intercepts of the graph of $y = f(x + 4)$?
(b) What are the x-intercepts of the graph of $y = f(x - 3)$?
(c) What are the x-intercepts of the graph of $y = 2f(x)$?
(d) What are the x-intercepts of the graph of $y = f(-x)$?

37. Suppose that the function $y = f(x)$ is increasing on the interval $(-1, 5)$.
(a) Over what interval is the graph of $y = f(x + 2)$ increasing?
(b) Over what interval is the graph of $y = f(x - 5)$ increasing?
(c) What can be said about the graph of $y = -f(x)$?
(d) What can be said about the graph of $y = f(-x)$?

38. Suppose that the function $y = f(x)$ is decreasing on the interval $(-2, 7)$.
(a) Over what interval is the graph of $y = f(x + 2)$ decreasing?
(b) Over what interval is the graph of $y = f(x - 5)$ decreasing?
(c) What can be said about the graph of $y = -f(x)$?
(d) What can be said about the graph of $y = f(-x)$?

In Problems 39–68, graph each function using the techniques of shifting, compressing, stretching, and/or reflecting. Start with the graph of the basic function (for example, $y = x^2$) and show all stages. Be sure to show at least three key points. Find the domain and the range of each function. Verify your results using a graphing utility.

39. $f(x) = x^2 - 1$

40. $f(x) = x^2 + 4$

41. $g(x) = x^3 + 1$

42. $g(x) = x^3 - 1$

43. $h(x) = \sqrt{x - 2}$

44. $h(x) = \sqrt{x + 1}$

45. $f(x) = (x-1)^3 + 2$ | 46. $f(x) = (x+2)^3 - 3$ | 47. $g(x) = 4\sqrt{x}$

48. $g(x) = \frac{1}{2}\sqrt{x}$ | 49. $h(x) = \frac{1}{2x}$ | 50. $h(x) = \sqrt[3]{2x}$

51. $f(x) = -\sqrt[3]{x}$ | 52. $f(x) = -\sqrt{x}$ | 53. $g(x) = \sqrt[3]{-x}$

54. $g(x) = \frac{1}{-x}$ | 55. $h(x) = -x^3 + 2$ | 56. $h(x) = \frac{1}{-x} + 2$

57. $f(x) = 2(x+1)^2 - 3$ | 58. $f(x) = 3(x-2)^2 + 1$ | 59. $g(x) = 2\sqrt{x-2} + 1$

60. $g(x) = 3|x+1| - 3$ | 61. $h(x) = \sqrt{-x} - 2$ | 62. $h(x) = \frac{4}{x} + 2$

63. $f(x) = -(x+1)^3 - 1$ | 64. $f(x) = -4\sqrt{x-1}$ | 65. $g(x) = 2|1-x|$

66. $g(x) = 4\sqrt{2-x}$ | 67. $h(x) = 2\text{ int}(x-1)$ | 68. $h(x) = \text{int}(-x)$

In Problems 69–72, the graph of a function f is illustrated. Use the graph of f as the first step toward graphing each of the following functions:

(a) $F(x) = f(x) + 3$ *(b)* $G(x) = f(x+2)$ *(c)* $P(x) = -f(x)$ *(d)* $H(x) = f(x+1) - 2$

(e) $Q(x) = \frac{1}{2}f(x)$ *(f)* $g(x) = f(-x)$ *(g)* $h(x) = f(2x)$

69.

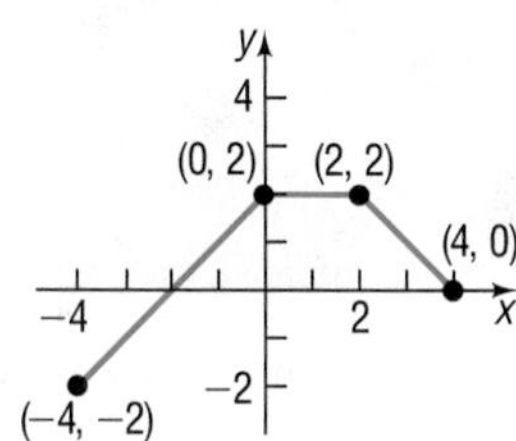

70.

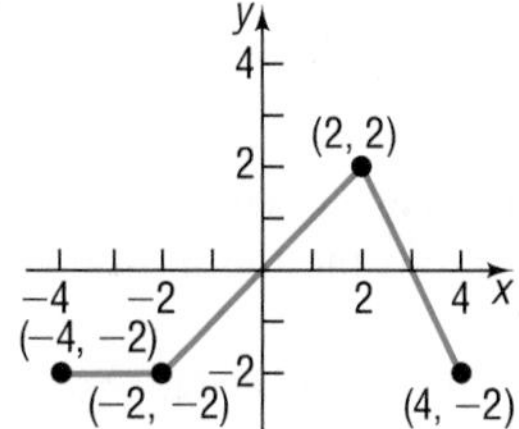

71.

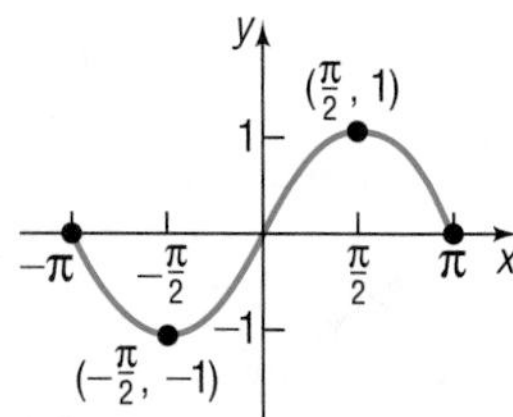

72.

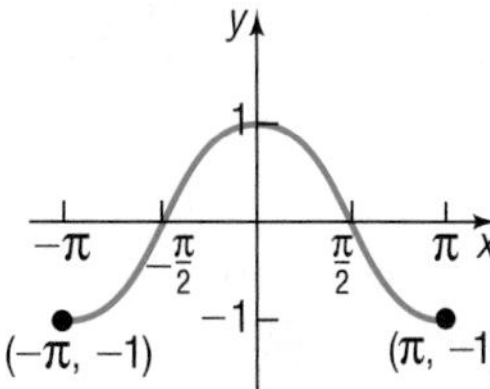

Mixed Practice

73. (a) Using a graphing utility, graph $f(x) = x^3 - 9x$ for $-4 < x < 4$.
(b) Find the x-intercepts of the graph of f.
(c) Approximate any local maxima and local minima.
(d) Determine where f is increasing and where it is decreasing.
(e) Without using a graphing utility, repeat parts (b)–(d) for $y = f(x+2)$.
(f) Without using a graphing utility, repeat parts (b)–(d) for $y = 2f(x)$.
(g) Without using a graphing utility, repeat parts (b)–(d) for $y = f(-x)$.

74. (a) Using a graphing utility, graph $f(x) = x^3 - 4x$ for $-3 < x < 3$.
(b) Find the x-intercepts of the graph of f.
(c) Approximate any local maxima and local minima.
(d) Determine where f is increasing and where it is decreasing.
(e) Without using a graphing utility, repeat parts (b)–(d) for $y = f(x-4)$.
(f) Without using a graphing utility, repeat parts (b)–(d) for $y = f(2x)$.
(g) Without using a graphing utility, repeat parts (b)–(d) for $y = -f(x)$.

In Problems 75–82, complete the square of each quadratic expression. Then graph each function using the technique of shifting.

75. $f(x) = x^2 + 2x$ | 76. $f(x) = x^2 - 6x$ | 77. $f(x) = x^2 - 8x + 1$ | 78. $f(x) = x^2 + 4x + 2$

79. $f(x) = 2x^2 - 12x + 19$ | 80. $f(x) = 3x^2 + 6x + 1$ | 81. $f(x) = -3x^2 - 12x - 17$ | 82. $f(x) = -2x^2 - 12x - 13$

Applications and Extensions

83. The equation $y = (x-c)^2$ defines a *family of parabolas,* one parabola for each value of c. On one set of coordinate axes, graph the members of the family for $c = 0$, $c = 3$, and $c = -2$.

84. Repeat Problem 83 for the family of parabolas $y = x^2 + c$.

85. Thermostat Control Energy conservation experts estimate that homeowners can save 5% to 10% on winter heating bills by programming their thermostats 5 to 10 degrees lower while sleeping. In the given graph, the temperature T (in degrees Fahrenheit) of a home is given as a function of time t (in hours after midnight) over a 24-hour period.

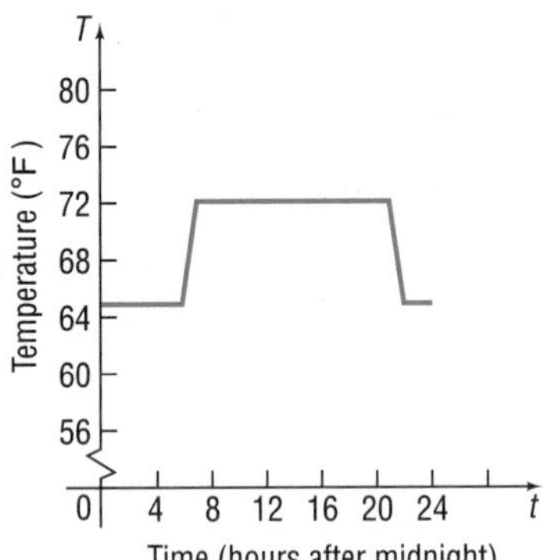

(a) At what temperature is the thermostat set during daytime hours? At what temperature is the thermostat set overnight?

(b) The homeowner reprograms the thermostat to $y = T(t) - 2$. Explain how this affects the temperature in the house. Graph this new function.

(c) The homeowner reprograms the thermostat to $y = T(t + 1)$. Explain how this affects the temperature in the house. Graph this new function.

Source: Roger Albright, *547 Ways to Be Fuel Smart,* 2000

86. Digital Music Revenues The total projected worldwide digital music revenues R, in millions of dollars, for the years 2005 through 2010 can be estimated by the function

$$R(x) = 170.7x^2 + 1373x + 1080$$

where x is the number of years after 2005.

(a) Find $R(0)$, $R(3)$, and $R(5)$ and explain what each value represents.

(b) Find $r = R(x - 5)$.

(c) Find $r(5)$, $r(8)$, and $r(10)$ and explain what each value represents.

(d) In the model r, what does x represent?

(e) Would there be an advantage in using the model r when estimating the projected revenues for a given year instead of the model R?

Source: eMarketer.com, May 2006

87. Temperature Measurements The relationship between the Celsius (°C) and Fahrenheit (°F) scales for measuring temperature is given by the equation

$$F = \frac{9}{5}C + 32$$

The relationship between the Celsius (°C) and Kelvin (K) scales is $K = C + 273$. Graph the equation $F = \frac{9}{5}C + 32$ using degrees Fahrenheit on the y-axis and degrees Celsius on the x-axis. Use the techniques introduced in this section to obtain the graph showing the relationship between Kelvin and Fahrenheit temperatures.

88. Period of a Pendulum The period T (in seconds) of a simple pendulum is a function of its length l (in feet) defined by the equation

$$T = 2\pi\sqrt{\frac{l}{g}}$$

where $g \approx 32.2$ feet per second per second is the acceleration of gravity.

(a) Use a graphing utility to graph the function $T = T(l)$.

(b) Now graph the functions $T = T(l + 1)$, $T = T(l + 2)$, and $T = T(l + 3)$.

(c) Discuss how adding to the length l changes the period T.

(d) Now graph the functions $T = T(2l)$, $T = T(3l)$, and $T = T(4l)$.

(e) Discuss how multiplying the length l by factors of 2, 3, and 4 changes the period T.

89. Cigar Company Profits The daily profits of a cigar company from selling x cigars are given by

$$p(x) = -0.05x^2 + 100x - 2000$$

The government wishes to impose a tax on cigars (sometimes called a *sin tax*) that gives the company the option of either paying a flat tax of \$10,000 per day or a tax of 10% on profits. As chief financial officer (CFO) of the company, you need to decide which tax is the better option for the company.

(a) On the same screen, graph $Y_1 = p(x) - 10{,}000$ and $Y_2 = (1 - 0.10)p(x)$.

(b) Based on the graph, which option would you select? Why?

(c) Using the terminology learned in this section, describe each graph in terms of the graph of $p(x)$.

(d) Suppose that the government offered the options of a flat tax of \$4800 or a tax of 10% on profits. Which would you select? Why?

90. The graph of a function f is illustrated in the figure.

(a) Draw the graph of $y = |f(x)|$.

(b) Draw the graph of $y = f(|x|)$.

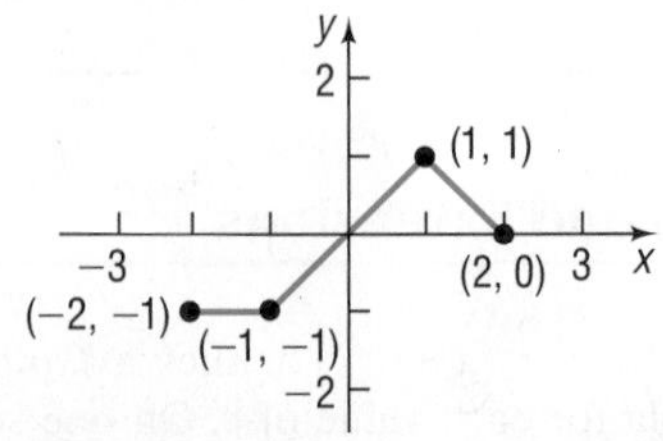

91. The graph of a function f is illustrated in the figure.
(a) Draw the graph of $y = |f(x)|$.
(b) Draw the graph of $y = f(|x|)$.

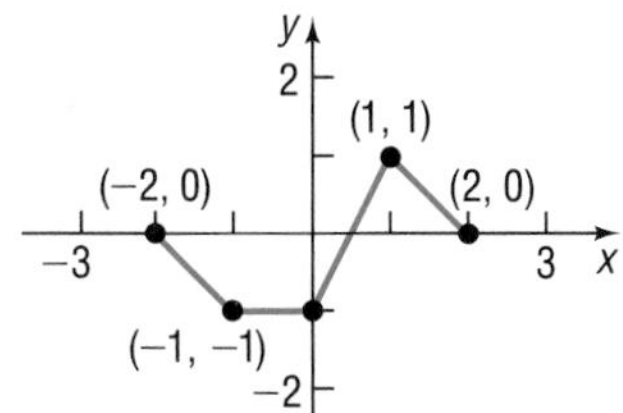

92. Suppose $(1, 3)$ is a point on the graph of $y = f(x)$.
(a) What point is on the graph of $y = f(x+3) - 5$?
(b) What point is on the graph of $y = -2f(x-2) + 1$?
(c) What point is on the graph of $y = f(2x + 3)$?

93. Suppose $(-3, 5)$ is a point on the graph of $y = g(x)$.
(a) What point is on the graph of $y = g(x+1) - 3$?
(b) What point is on the graph of $y = -3g(x-4) + 3$?
(c) What point is on the graph of $y = g(3x + 9)$?

Explaining Concepts: Discussion and Writing

94. Suppose that the graph of a function f is known. Explain how the graph of $y = 4f(x)$ differs from the graph of $y = f(4x)$.

95. Suppose that the graph of a function f is known. Explain how the graph of $y = f(x) - 2$ differs from the graph of $y = f(x - 2)$.

96. The area under the curve $y = \sqrt{x}$ bounded below by the x-axis and on the right by $x = 4$ is $\frac{16}{3}$ square units. Using the ideas presented in this section, what do you think is the area under the curve of $y = \sqrt{-x}$ bounded below by the x-axis and on the left by $x = -4$? Justify your answer.

97. Explain how the range of a function $y = f(x) = x^2$ compares to $y = g(x) = f(x) + k$.

98. Explain how the domain of $y = g(x) = \sqrt{x}$ compares to $y = g(x - k), k \geq 0$.

Interactive Exercises: Exploring Transformations

Ask your instructor if the applets below are of interest to you.

99. Vertical Shifts *Open the vertical shift applet.* Use your mouse to grab the slider and change the value of k. Note the role k plays in the graph of $g(x) = f(x) + k$, where $f(x) = x^2$.

100. Horizontal Shifts *Open the horizontal shift applet.* Use your mouse to grab the slider and change the value of h. Note the role h plays in the graph of $g(x) = f(x - h)$, where $f(x) = x^2$.

101. Vertical Stretches *Open the vertical stretch applet.* Use your mouse to grab the slider and change the value of a. Note the role a plays in the graph of $g(x) = af(x)$, where $f(x) = |x|$.

102. Horizontal Stretches *Open the horizontal stretch applet.*
(a) Use your mouse to grab the slider and change the value of a. Note the role a plays in the graph of $g(x) = f(ax) = \sqrt{ax}$, where $f(x) = \sqrt{x}$. What happens to the points on the graph of g when $0 < a < 1$? What happens to the points on the graph when $a > 1$?
(b) To further understand the concept of horizontal compressions, fill in the spreadsheet to the right of the graph as follows:
(i) What x-coordinate is required on the graph of $g(x) = \sqrt{2x}$, if the y-coordinate is to be 1?
(ii) What x-coordinate is required on the graph of $g(x) = \sqrt{2x}$, if the y-coordinate is to be 2?
(iii) What x-coordinate is required on the graph of $g(x) = \sqrt{2x}$, if the y-coordinate is to be 3?
(iv) What x-coordinate is required on the graph of $g(x) = \sqrt{\frac{1}{2}x}$, if the y-coordinate is to be 1?
(v) What x-coordinate is required on the graph of $g(x) = \sqrt{\frac{1}{2}x}$, if the y-coordinate is to be 2?
(vi) What x-coordinate is required on the graph of $g(x) = \sqrt{\frac{1}{2}x}$, if the y-coordinate is to be 3?

103. Reflection about the y-axis *Open the reflection about the y-axis applet.* Move your mouse to grab the slider and change the value of a from 1 to -1.

104. Reflection about the x-axis *Open the reflection about the x-axis applet.* Move your mouse to grab the slider and change the value of a from 1 to -1.

9.6 Mathematical Models: Building Functions

OBJECTIVE **1** Build and Analyze Functions (p. 617)

1 Build and Analyze Functions

Real-world problems often result in mathematical models that involve functions. These functions need to be constructed or built based on the information given. In building functions, we must be able to translate the verbal description into the language of mathematics. We do this by assigning symbols to represent the independent and dependent variables and then by finding the function or rule that relates these variables.

EXAMPLE 1

Finding the Distance from the Origin to a Point on a Graph

Let $P = (x, y)$ be a point on the graph of $y = x^2 - 1$.

(a) Express the distance d from P to the origin O as a function of x.

(b) What is d if $x = 0$?

(c) What is d if $x = 1$?

(d) What is d if $x = \dfrac{\sqrt{2}}{2}$?

(e) Use a graphing utility to graph the function $d = d(x)$, $x \geq 0$. Rounded to two decimal places, find the value(s) of x at which d has a local minimum. [This gives the point(s) on the graph of $y = x^2 - 1$ closest to the origin.]

Solution

Figure 59

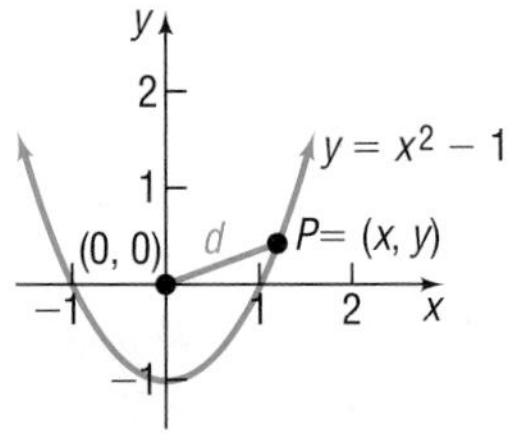

(a) Figure 59 illustrates the graph of $y = x^2 - 1$. The distance d from P to O is

$$d = \sqrt{(x-0)^2 + (y-0)^2} = \sqrt{x^2 + y^2}$$

Since P is a point on the graph of $y = x^2 - 1$, substitute $x^2 - 1$ for y. Then

$$d(x) = \sqrt{x^2 + (x^2-1)^2} = \sqrt{x^4 - x^2 + 1}$$

The distance d is expressed as a function of x.

(b) If $x = 0$, the distance d is

$$d(0) = \sqrt{0^4 - 0^2 + 1} = \sqrt{1} = 1$$

(c) If $x = 1$, the distance d is

$$d(1) = \sqrt{1^4 - 1^2 + 1} = 1$$

(d) If $x = \dfrac{\sqrt{2}}{2}$, the distance d is

$$d\left(\frac{\sqrt{2}}{2}\right) = \sqrt{\left(\frac{\sqrt{2}}{2}\right)^4 - \left(\frac{\sqrt{2}}{2}\right)^2 + 1} = \sqrt{\frac{1}{4} - \frac{1}{2} + 1} = \frac{\sqrt{3}}{2}$$

Figure 60

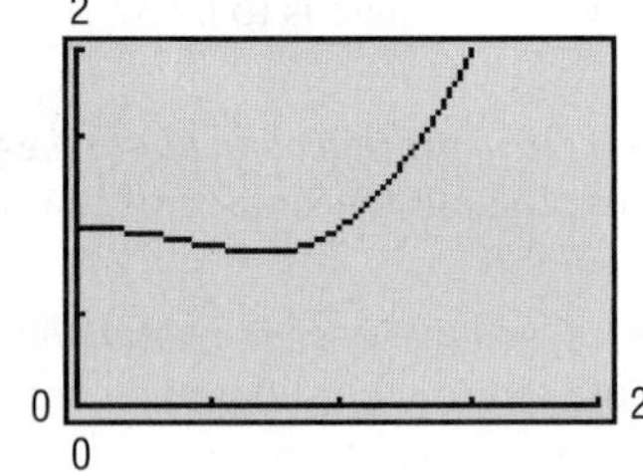

(e) Figure 60 shows the graph of $Y_1 = \sqrt{x^4 - x^2 + 1}$. Using the MINIMUM feature on a graphing utility, we find that when $x \approx 0.71$ the value of d is smallest. The local minimum is $d \approx 0.87$ rounded to two decimal places. Since $d(x)$ is even, by symmetry, it follows that when $x \approx -0.71$ the value of d is also a local minimum. Since $(\pm 0.71)^2 - 1 \approx -0.50$, the points $(-0.71, -0.50)$ and $(0.71, -0.50)$ on the graph of $y = x^2 - 1$ are closest to the origin. ■

Now Work PROBLEM 1

EXAMPLE 2

Area of a Rectangle

A rectangle has one corner in quadrant I on the graph of $y = 25 - x^2$, another at the origin, a third on the positive y-axis, and the fourth on the positive x-axis. See Figure 61 on the next page.

(a) Express the area A of the rectangle as a function of x.

(b) What is the domain of A?

(c) Graph $A = A(x)$.

(d) For what value of x is the area largest?

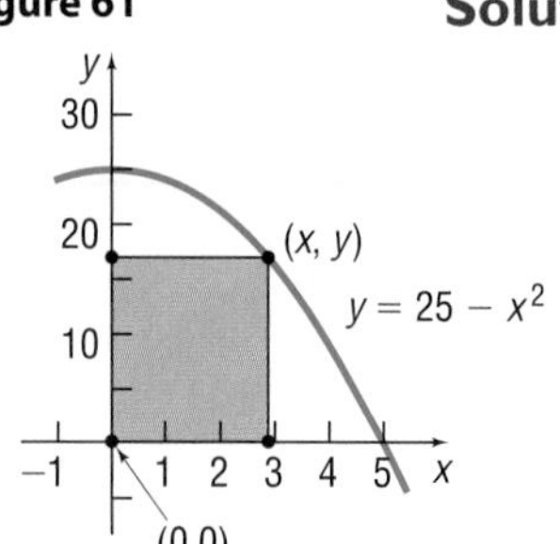

Figure 61

Solution

(a) The area A of the rectangle is $A = xy$, where $y = 25 - x^2$. Substituting this expression for y, we obtain $A(x) = x(25 - x^2) = 25x - x^3$.

(b) Since (x, y) is in quadrant I, we have $x > 0$. Also, $y = 25 - x^2 > 0$, which implies that $x^2 < 25$, so $-5 < x < 5$. Combining these restrictions, we have the domain of A as $\{x \mid 0 < x < 5\}$, or $(0, 5)$ using interval notation.

(c) See Figure 62 for the graph of $A = A(x)$.

(d) Using MAXIMUM, we find that the maximum area is 48.11 square units at $x = 2.89$ units, each rounded to two decimal places. See Figure 63.

Figure 62

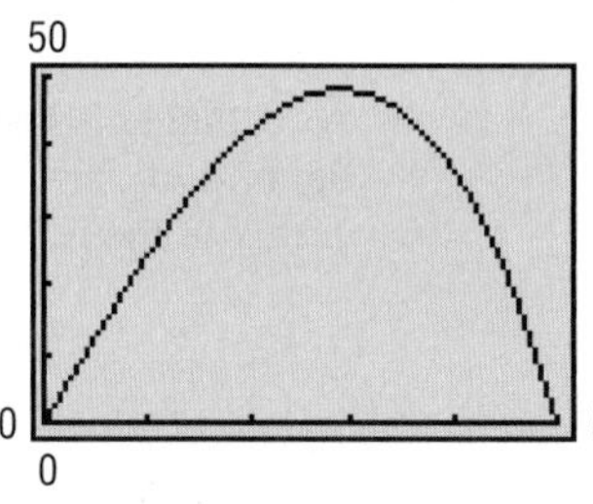

Figure 63

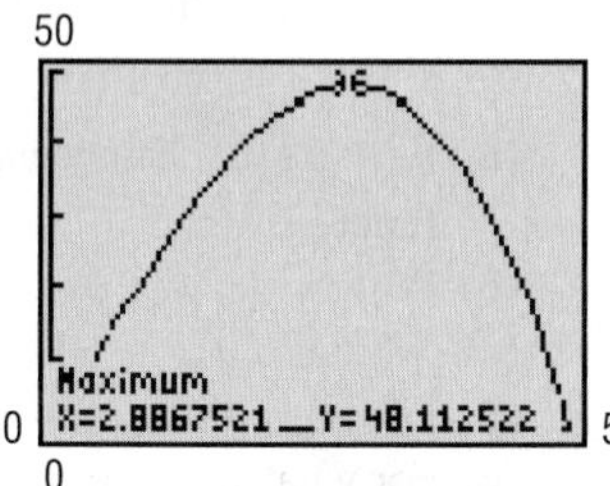

Now Work PROBLEM 7

EXAMPLE 3 Close Call?

Suppose two planes flying at the same altitude are headed toward each other. One plane is flying due South at a groundspeed of 400 miles per hour and is 600 miles from the potential intersection point of the planes. The other plane is flying due West with a groundspeed of 250 miles per hour and is 400 miles from the potential intersection point of the planes. See Figure 64.

(a) Build a model that expresses the distance d between the planes as a function of time t.

(b) Use a graphing utility to graph $d = d(t)$. How close do the planes come to each other? At what time are the planes closest?

Solution

(a) Refer to Figure 64. The distance d between the two planes is the hypotenuse of a right triangle. At any time t the length of the North/South leg of the triangle is $600 - 400t$. At any time t, the length of the East/West leg of the triangle is $400 - 250t$. Using the Pythagorean Theorem, the square of the distance between the two planes is

$$d^2 = (600 - 400t)^2 + (400 - 250t)^2$$

Therefore, the distance between the two planes as a function of time is given by the model

$$d(t) = \sqrt{(600 - 400t)^2 + (400 - 250t)^2}$$

(b) Figure 65(a) shows the graph of $d = d(t)$. Using MINIMUM, the minimum distance between the planes is 21.20 miles and the time at which the planes are closest is after 1.53 hours, each rounded to two decimal places. See Figure 65(b).

Figure 64

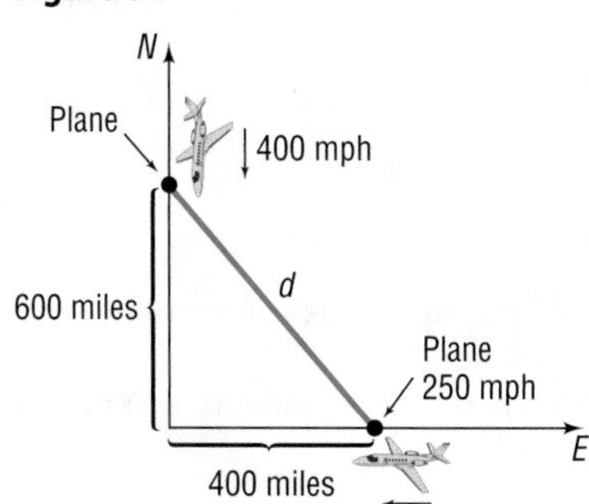

Figure 65

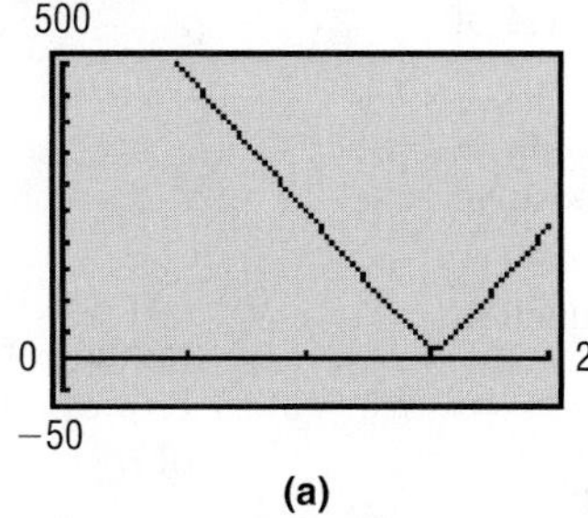

(a)

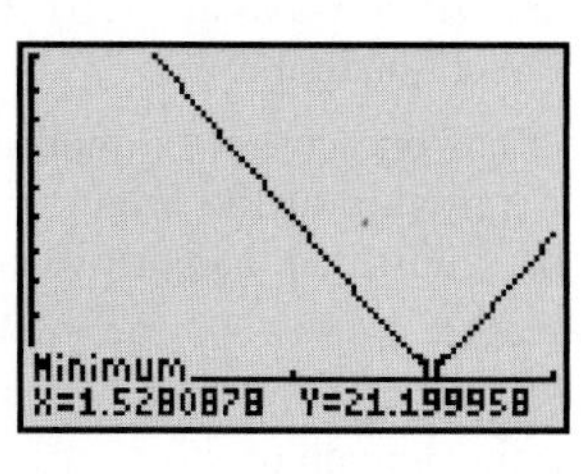

(b)

9.6 Assess Your Understanding

Applications and Extensions

1. Let $P = (x, y)$ be a point on the graph of $y = x^2 - 8$.
   (a) Express the distance d from P to the origin as a function of x.
   (b) What is d if $x = 0$?
   (c) What is d if $x = 1$?
   (d) Use a graphing utility to graph $d = d(x)$.
   (e) For what values of x is d smallest?

2. Let $P = (x, y)$ be a point on the graph of $y = x^2 - 8$.
   (a) Express the distance d from P to the point $(0, -1)$ as a function of x.
   (b) What is d if $x = 0$?
   (c) What is d if $x = -1$?
   (d) Use a graphing utility to graph $d = d(x)$.
   (e) For what values of x is d smallest?

3. Let $P = (x, y)$ be a point on the graph of $y = \sqrt{x}$.
   (a) Express the distance d from P to the point $(1, 0)$ as a function of x.
   (b) Use a graphing utility to graph $d = d(x)$.
   (c) For what values of x is d smallest?

4. Let $P = (x, y)$ be a point on the graph of $y = \frac{1}{x}$.
   (a) Express the distance d from P to the origin as a function of x.
   (b) Use a graphing utility to graph $d = d(x)$.
   (c) For what values of x is d smallest?

5. A right triangle has one vertex on the graph of $y = x^3, x > 0$, at (x, y), another at the origin, and the third on the positive y-axis at $(0, y)$, as shown in the figure. Express the area A of the triangle as a function of x.

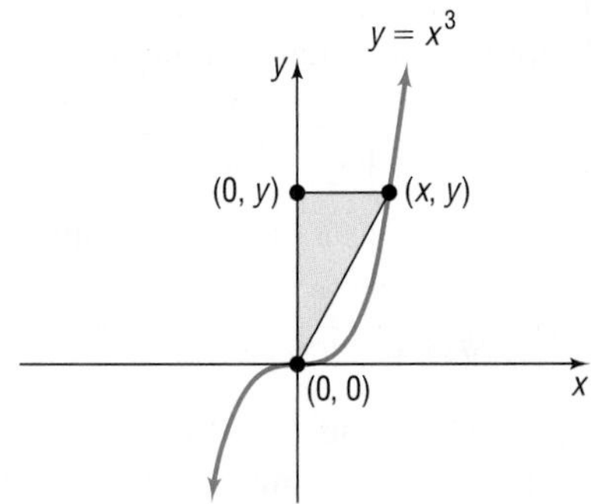

6. A right triangle has one vertex on the graph of $y = 9 - x^2, x > 0$, at (x, y), another at the origin, and the third on the positive x-axis at $(x, 0)$. Express the area A of the triangle as a function of x.

7. A rectangle has one corner in quadrant I on the graph of $y = 16 - x^2$, another at the origin, a third on the positive y-axis, and the fourth on the positive x-axis. See the figure.
   (a) Express the area A of the rectangle as a function of x.
   (b) What is the domain of A?
   (c) Graph $A = A(x)$. For what value of x is A largest?

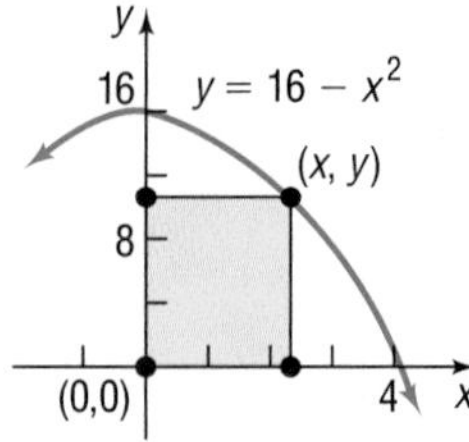

8. A rectangle is inscribed in a semicircle of radius 2. See the figure. Let $P = (x, y)$ be the point in quadrant I that is a vertex of the rectangle and is on the circle.

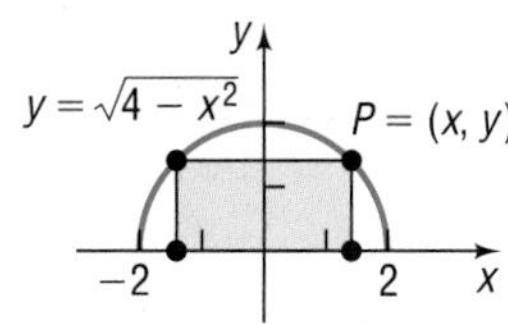

   (a) Express the area A of the rectangle as a function of x.
   (b) Express the perimeter p of the rectangle as a function of x.
   (c) Graph $A = A(x)$. For what value of x is A largest?
   (d) Graph $p = p(x)$. For what value of x is p largest?

9. A rectangle is inscribed in a circle of radius 2. See the figure. Let $P = (x, y)$ be the point in quadrant I that is a vertex of the rectangle and is on the circle.

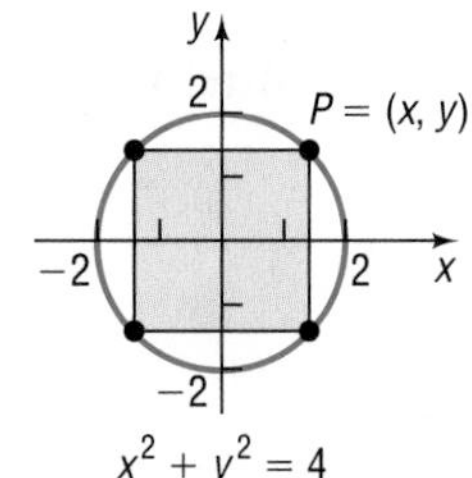

   (a) Express the area A of the rectangle as a function of x.
   (b) Express the perimeter p of the rectangle as a function of x.
   (c) Graph $A = A(x)$. For what value of x is A largest?
   (d) Graph $p = p(x)$. For what value of x is p largest?

10. A circle of radius r is inscribed in a square. See the figure.

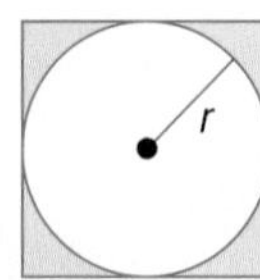

   (a) Express the area A of the square as a function of the radius r of the circle.
   (b) Express the perimeter p of the square as a function of r.

11. **Geometry** A wire 10 meters long is to be cut into two pieces. One piece will be shaped as a square, and the other piece will be shaped as a circle. See the figure.

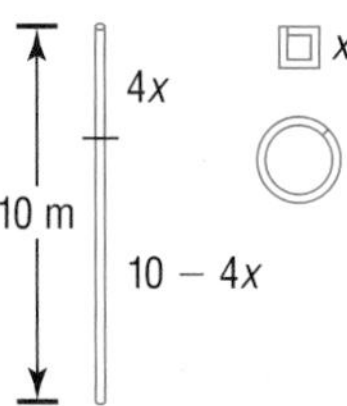

(a) Express the total area A enclosed by the pieces of wire as a function of the length x of a side of the square.
(b) What is the domain of A?
(c) Graph $A = A(x)$. For what value of x is A smallest?

12. **Geometry** A wire 10 meters long is to be cut into two pieces. One piece will be shaped as an equilateral triangle, and the other piece will be shaped as a circle.
(a) Express the total area A enclosed by the pieces of wire as a function of the length x of a side of the equilateral triangle.
(b) What is the domain of A?
(c) Graph $A = A(x)$. For what value of x is A smallest?

13. A wire of length x is bent into the shape of a circle.
(a) Express the circumference C of the circle as a function of x.
(b) Express the area A of the circle as a function of x.

14. A wire of length x is bent into the shape of a square.
(a) Express the perimeter p of the square as a function of x.
(b) Express the area A of the square as a function of x.

15. **Geometry** A semicircle of radius r is inscribed in a rectangle so that the diameter of the semicircle is the length of the rectangle. See the figure.

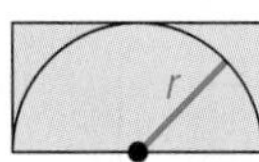

(a) Express the area A of the rectangle as a function of the radius r of the semicircle.
(b) Express the perimeter p of the rectangle as a function of r.

16. **Geometry** An equilateral triangle is inscribed in a circle of radius r. See the figure. Express the circumference C of the circle as a function of the length x of a side of the triangle.

[**Hint:** First show that $r^2 = \frac{x^2}{3}$.]

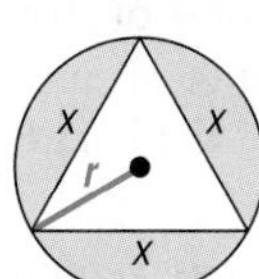

17. **Geometry** An equilateral triangle is inscribed in a circle of radius r. See the figure in Problem 16. Express the area A within the circle, but outside the triangle, as a function of the length x of a side of the triangle.

18. **Uniform Motion** Two cars leave an intersection at the same time. One is headed south at a constant speed of 30 miles per hour, and the other is headed west at a constant speed of 40 miles per hour (see the figure). Build a model that expresses the distance d between the cars as a function of the time t.

[**Hint:** At $t = 0$, the cars leave the intersection.]

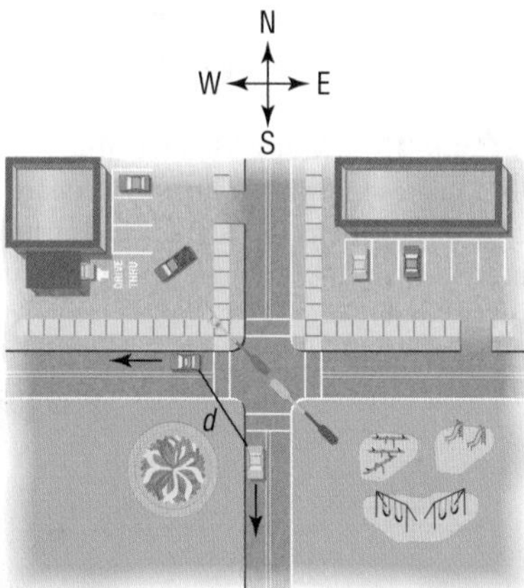

19. **Uniform Motion** Two cars are approaching an intersection. One is 2 miles south of the intersection and is moving at a constant speed of 30 miles per hour. At the same time, the other car is 3 miles east of the intersection and is moving at a constant speed of 40 miles per hour.
(a) Build a model that expresses the distance d between the cars as a function of time t.
[**Hint:** At $t = 0$, the cars are 2 miles south and 3 miles east of the intersection, respectively.]
(b) Use a graphing utility to graph $d = d(t)$. For what value of t is d smallest?

20. **Inscribing a Cylinder in a Sphere** Inscribe a right circular cylinder of height h and radius r in a sphere of fixed radius R. See the illustration. Express the volume V of the cylinder as a function of h.

[**Hint:** $V = \pi r^2 h$. Note also the right triangle.]

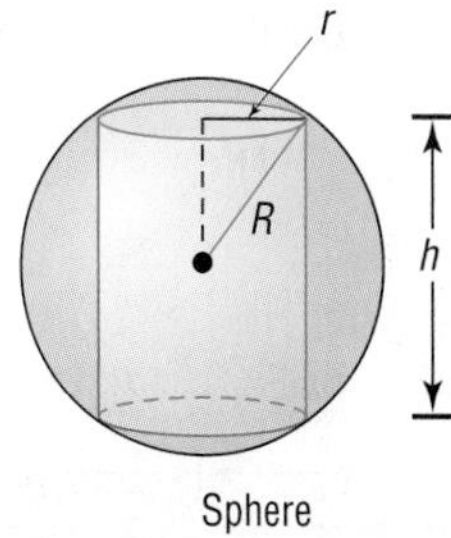

21. **Inscribing a Cylinder in a Cone** Inscribe a right circular cylinder of height h and radius r in a cone of fixed radius R and fixed height H. See the illustration. Express the volume V of the cylinder as a function of r.

[**Hint:** $V = \pi r^2 h$. Note also the similar triangles.]

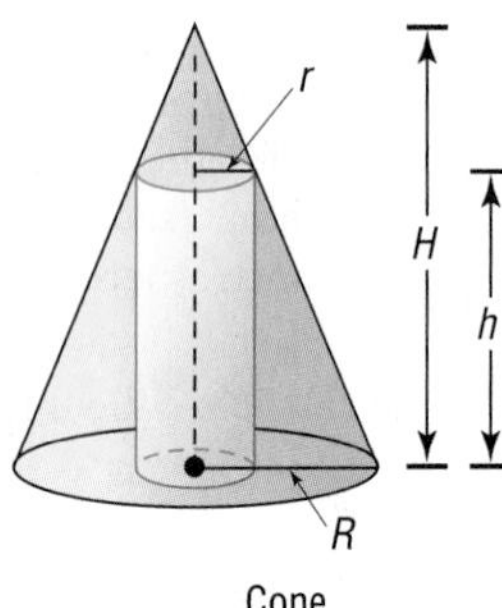

Cone

22. **Installing Cable TV** MetroMedia Cable is asked to provide service to a customer whose house is located 2 miles from the road along which the cable is buried. The nearest connection box for the cable is located 5 miles down the road. See the figure.

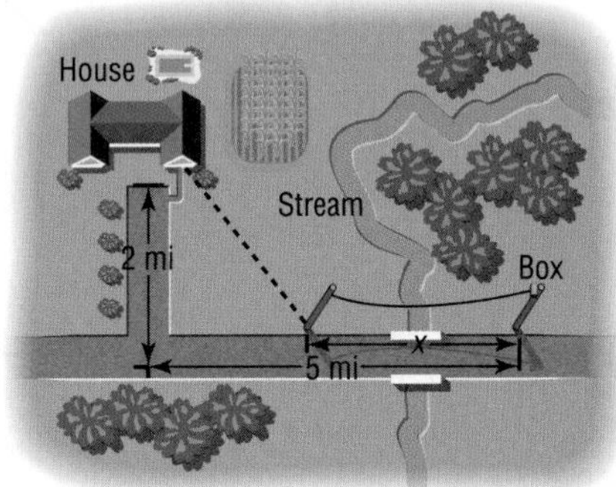

(a) If the installation cost is \$500 per mile along the road and \$700 per mile off the road, build a model that expresses the total cost C of installation as a function of the distance x (in miles) from the connection box to the point where the cable installation turns off the road. Give the domain.
(b) Compute the cost if $x = 1$ mile.
(c) Compute the cost if $x = 3$ miles.
(d) Graph the function $C = C(x)$. Use TRACE to see how the cost C varies as x changes from 0 to 5.
(e) What value of x results in the least cost?

23. **Time Required to Go from an Island to a Town** An island is 2 miles from the nearest point P on a straight shoreline. A town is 12 miles down the shore from P. See the illustration.

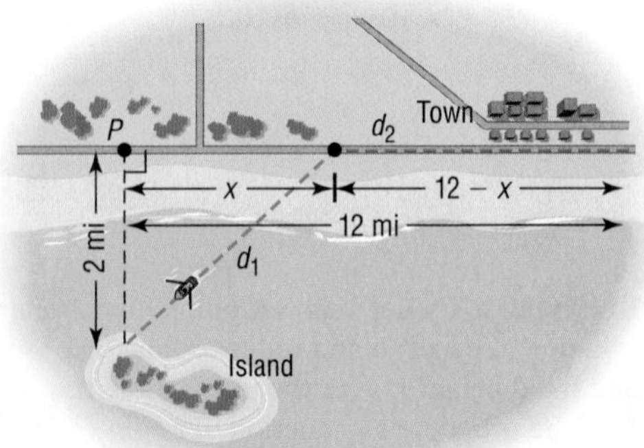

(a) If a person can row a boat at an average speed of 3 miles per hour and the same person can walk 5 miles per hour, build a model that expresses the time T that it takes to go from the island to town as a function of the distance x from P to where the person lands the boat.
(b) What is the domain of T?
(c) How long will it take to travel from the island to town if the person lands the boat 4 miles from P?
(d) How long will it take if the person lands the boat 8 miles from P?

24. **Filling a Conical Tank** Water is poured into a container in the shape of a right circular cone with radius 4 feet and height 16 feet. See the figure. Express the volume V of the water in the cone as a function of the height h of the water.

[**Hint:** The volume V of a cone of radius r and height h is $V = \frac{1}{3}\pi r^2 h$.]

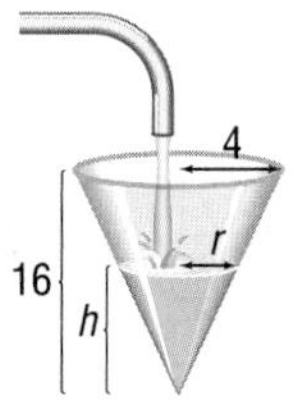

25. **Constructing an Open Box** An open box with a square base is to be made from a square piece of cardboard 24 inches on a side by cutting out a square from each corner and turning up the sides. See the figure.

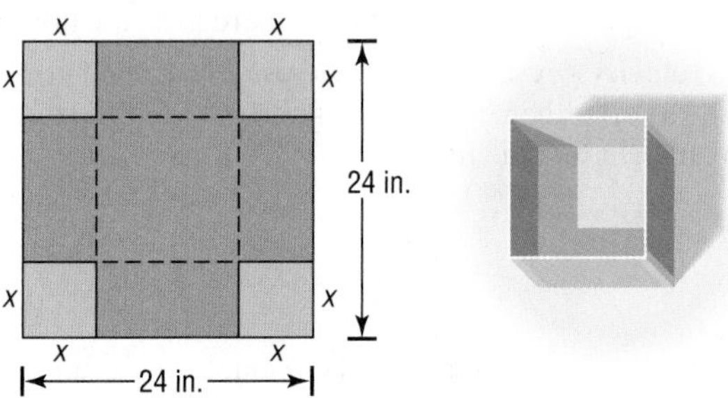

(a) Express the volume V of the box as a function of the length x of the side of the square cut from each corner.
(b) What is the volume if a 3-inch square is cut out?
(c) What is the volume if a 10-inch square is cut out?
(d) Graph $V = V(x)$. For what value of x is V largest?

26. **Constructing an Open Box** An open box with a square base is required to have a volume of 10 cubic feet.
(a) Express the amount A of material used to make such a box as a function of the length x of a side of the square base.
(b) How much material is required for a base 1 foot by 1 foot?
(c) How much material is required for a base 2 feet by 2 feet?
(d) Use a graphing utility to graph $A = A(x)$. For what value of x is A smallest?

CHAPTER REVIEW

Library of Functions

Constant function (p. 596)

$f(x) = b$

The graph is a horizontal line with y-intercept b.

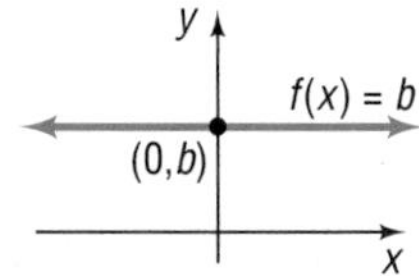

Identity function (p. 596)

$f(x) = x$

The graph is a line with slope 1 and y-intercept 0.

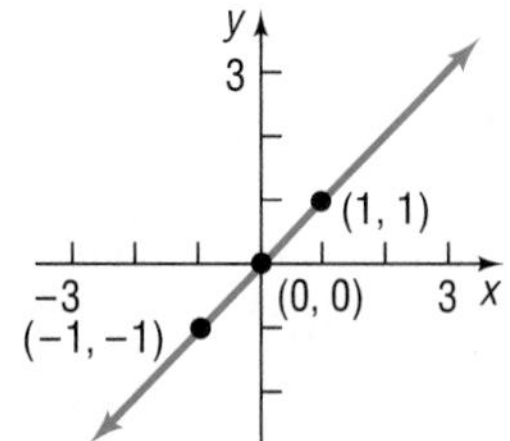

Square function (p. 597)

$f(x) = x^2$

The graph is a parabola with intercept at (0, 0).

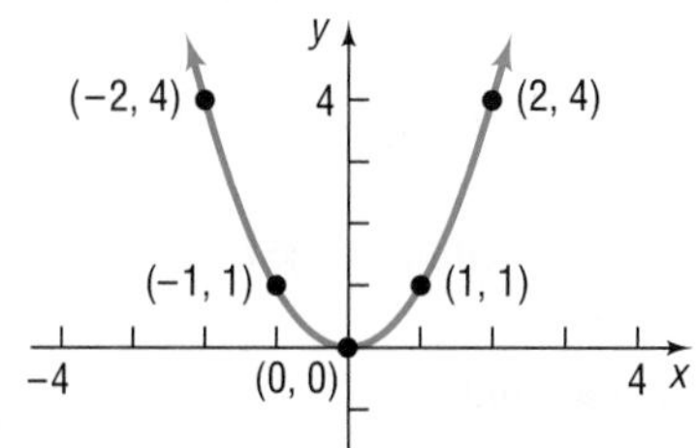

Cube function (p. 597)

$f(x) = x^3$

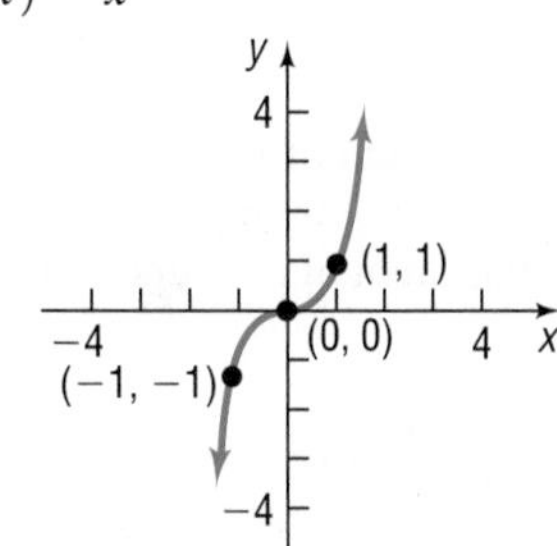

Square root function (pp. 594 and 597)

$f(x) = \sqrt{x}$

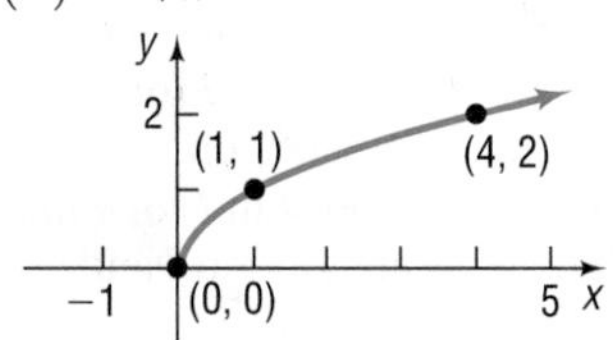

Cube root function (pp. 595 and 597)

$f(x) = \sqrt[3]{x}$

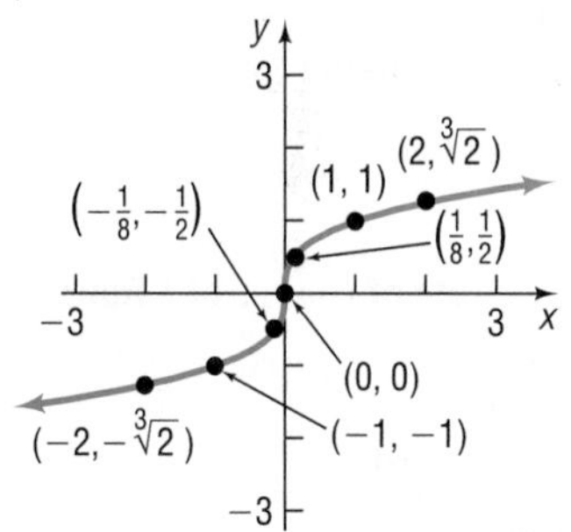

Reciprocal function (p. 597)

$f(x) = \dfrac{1}{x}$

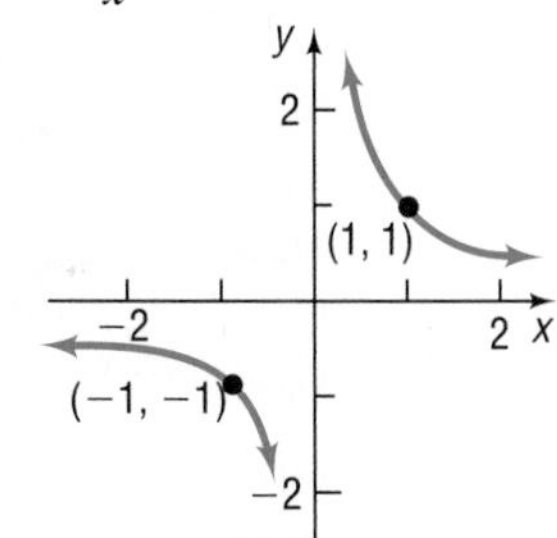

Absolute value function (p. 598)

$f(x) = |x|$

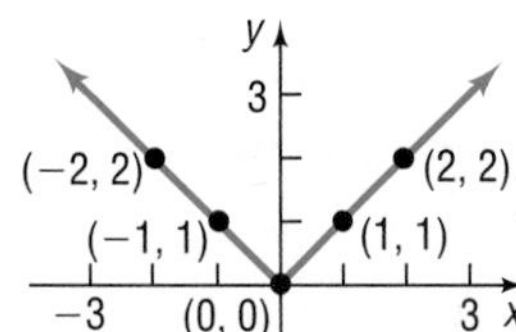

Greatest integer function (p. 598)

$f(x) = \text{int}(x)$

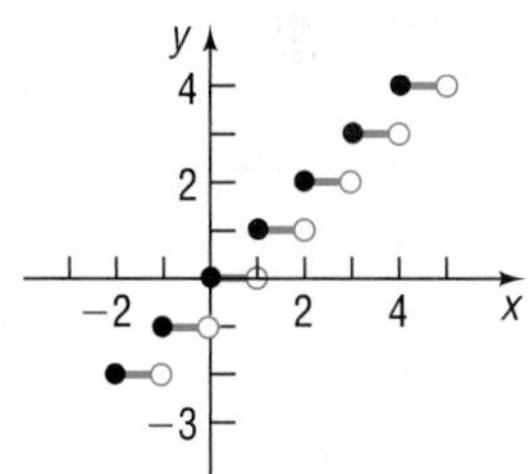

Things to Know

Function (pp. 559–562)

A relation between two sets so that each element x in the first set, the domain, has corresponding to it exactly one element y in the second set. The range is the set of y values of the function for the x values in the domain.

A function can also be characterized as a set of ordered pairs (x, y) in which no first element is paired with two different second elements.

Function notation (pp. 562–565)

$y = f(x)$

f is a symbol for the function.

x is the argument, or independent variable.

y is the dependent variable.

$f(x)$ is the value of the function at x, or the image of x.

A function f may be defined implicitly by an equation involving x and y or explicitly by writing $y = f(x)$.

Difference quotient of f (pp. 564 and 593)

$$\frac{f(x+h) - f(x)}{h} \quad h \neq 0$$

Domain (pp. 565–566)	If unspecified, the domain of a function f defined by an equation is the largest set of real numbers for which $f(x)$ is a real number.
Vertical-line test (p. 573)	A set of points in the plane is the graph of a function if and only if every vertical line intersects the graph in at most one point.
Even function f (p. 582)	$f(-x) = f(x)$ for every x in the domain ($-x$ must also be in the domain).
Odd function f (p. 582)	$f(-x) = -f(x)$ for every x in the domain ($-x$ must also be in the domain).
Increasing function (p. 584)	A function f is increasing on an open interval I if, for any choice of x_1 and x_2 in I, with $x_1 < x_2$, we have $f(x_1) < f(x_2)$.
Decreasing function (p. 584)	A function f is decreasing on an open interval I if, for any choice of x_1 and x_2 in I, with $x_1 < x_2$, we have $f(x_1) > f(x_2)$.
Constant function (p. 585)	A function f is constant on an open interval I if, for all choices of x in I, the values of $f(x)$ are equal.
Local maximum (p. 585)	A function f has a local maximum at c if there is an open interval I containing c so that, for all x in I, $f(x) \le f(c)$.
Local minimum (p. 585)	A function f has a local minimum at c if there is an open interval I containing c so that, for all x in I, $f(x) \ge f(c)$.
Absolute maximum and Absolute minimum (p. 586)	Let f denote a function defined on some interval I. If there is a number u in I for which $f(x) \le f(u)$ for all x in I, then $f(u)$ is the absolute maximum of f on I and we say the absolute maximum of f occurs at u. If there is a number v in I for which $f(x) \ge f(v)$, for all x in I, then $f(v)$ is the absolute minimum of f on I and we say the absolute minimum of f occurs at v.
Average rate of change of a function (p. 588)	The average rate of change of f from a to b is $\frac{\Delta y}{\Delta x} = \frac{f(b) - f(a)}{b - a} \quad a \neq b$

Objectives

Section		You should be able to ...	Examples	Review Exercises
9.1	1	Determine whether a relation represents a function (p. 559)	1–5	1, 2
	2	Find the value of a function (p. 562)	6, 7	3–5, 15, 39
	3	Find the domain of a function defined by an equation (p. 565)	8, 9	6–11
	4	Form the sum, difference, product, and quotient of two functions (p. 567)	10	12–14
9.2	1	Identify the graph of a function (p. 573)	1	27, 28
	2	Obtain information from or about the graph of a function (p. 574)	2–4	16(a)–(e), 17(a), 17(e), 17(g)
9.3	1	Determine even and odd functions from a graph (p. 582)	1	17(f)
	2	Identify even and odd functions from the equation (p. 583)	2	18–21
	3	Use a graph to determine where a function is increasing, decreasing, or constant (p. 584)	3	17(b)
	4	Use a graph to locate local maxima and local minima (p. 585)	4	17(c)
	5	Use a graph to locate the absolute maximum and the absolute minimum (p. 586)	5	17(d)
	6	Use a graphing utility to approximate local maxima and local minima and to determine where a function is increasing or decreasing (p. 587)	6	22, 23, 40(d), 41(b)
	7	Find the average rate of change of a function (p. 588)	7, 8	24–26
9.4	1	Graph the functions listed in the library of functions (p. 594)	1, 2	29, 30
	2	Graph piecewise-defined functions (p. 599)	3, 4	37, 38
9.5	1	Graph functions using vertical and horizontal shifts (p. 605)	1, 2, 5, 6	16(f), 31, 33, 34, 35, 36
	2	Graph functions using compressions and stretches (p. 607)	3, 5, 6	16(g), 32, 36
	3	Graph functions using reflections about the x-axis or y-axis (p. 609)	6	16(h), 32, 34, 36
9.6	1	Build and analyze functions (p. 617)	1–3	40, 41

Review Exercises

In Problems 1 and 2, determine whether each relation represents a function. For each function, state the domain and range.

1. $\{(-1, 0), (2, 3), (4, 0)\}$

2. $\{(4, -1), (2, 1), (4, 2)\}$

In Problems 3–5, find the following for each function:

(a) $f(2)$ (b) $f(-2)$ (c) $f(-x)$ (d) $-f(x)$ (e) $f(x-2)$ (f) $f(2x)$

3. $f(x) = \dfrac{3x}{x^2 - 1}$

4. $f(x) = \sqrt{x^2 - 4}$

5. $f(x) = \dfrac{x^2 - 4}{x^2}$

In Problems 6–11, find the domain of each function.

6. $f(x) = \dfrac{x}{x^2 - 9}$

7. $f(x) = \sqrt{2 - x}$

8. $g(x) = \dfrac{|x|}{x}$

9. $f(x) = \dfrac{x}{x^2 + 2x - 3}$

10. $f(x) = \dfrac{\sqrt{x + 1}}{x^2 - 4}$

11. $g(x) = \dfrac{x}{\sqrt{x + 8}}$

In Problems 12–14, find $f + g$, $f - g$, $f \cdot g$, and $\dfrac{f}{g}$ for each pair of functions. State the domain of each of these functions.

12. $f(x) = 2 - x;\ \ g(x) = 3x + 1$

13. $f(x) = 3x^2 + x + 1;\ \ g(x) = 3x$

14. $f(x) = \dfrac{x + 1}{x - 1};\ \ g(x) = \dfrac{1}{x}$

15. Find the difference quotient of $f(x) = -2x^2 + x + 1$; that is, find $\dfrac{f(x + h) - f(x)}{h}$, $h \neq 0$.

16. Using the graph of the function f shown to find:

(a) Find the domain and the range of f.
(b) List the intercepts.
(c) Find $f(-2)$.
(d) Find the value(s) of x for which $f(x) = -3$.
(e) Solve $f(x) > 0$.
(f) Graph $y = f(x - 3)$.
(g) Graph $y = f\left(\dfrac{1}{2}x\right)$.
(h) Graph $y = -f(x)$.

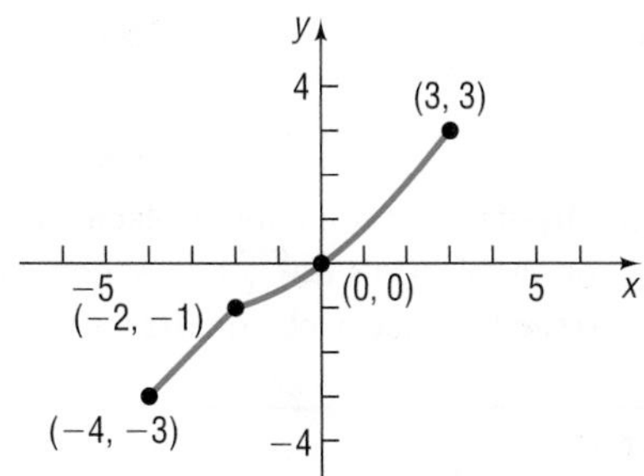

17. Use the graph of the function f shown to find:
(a) The domain and the range of f.
(b) The intervals on which f is increasing, decreasing, or constant.
(c) The local minimum values and local maximum values.
(d) The absolute maximum and absolute minimum.
(e) Whether the graph is symmetric with respect to the x-axis, the y-axis, or the origin.
(f) Whether the function is even, odd, or neither.
(g) The intercepts, if any.

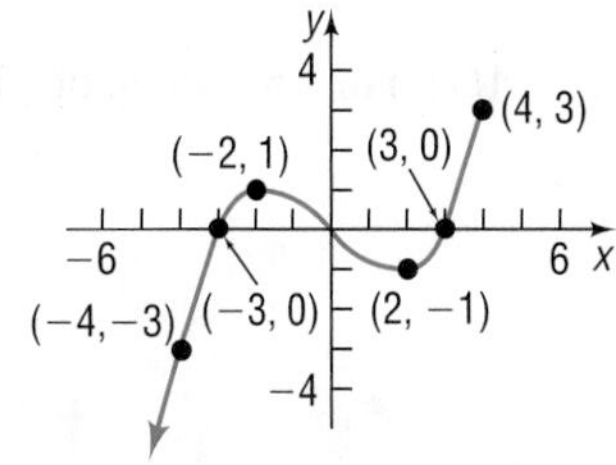

In Problems 18–21, determine (algebraically) whether the given function is even, odd, or neither.

18. $f(x) = x^3 - 4x$

19. $g(x) = \dfrac{4 + x^2}{1 + x^4}$

20. $G(x) = 1 - x + x^3$

21. $f(x) = \dfrac{x}{1 + x^2}$

In Problems 22 and 23, use a graphing utility to graph each function over the indicated interval. Approximate any local maximum values and local minimum values. Determine where the function is increasing and where it is decreasing.

22. $f(x) = 2x^3 - 5x + 1 \quad (-3, 3)$

23. $f(x) = 2x^4 - 5x^3 + 2x + 1 \quad (-2, 3)$

24. Find the average rate of change of $f(x) = 8x^2 - x$.
(a) From 1 to 2 (b) From 0 to 1 (c) From 2 to 4

In Problems 25 and 26, find the average rate of change from 2 to 3 for each function f. Be sure to simplify.

25. $f(x) = 2 - 5x$

26. $f(x) = 3x - 4x^2$

In Problems 27 and 28, is the graph shown the graph of a function?

27.

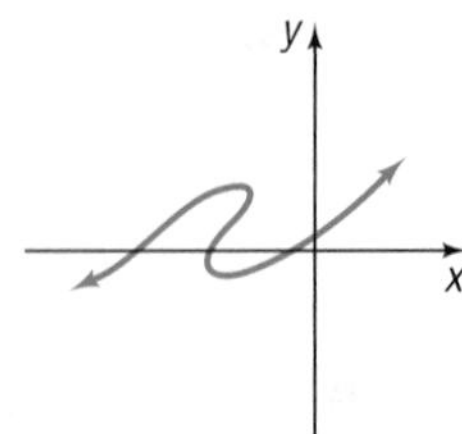

28.

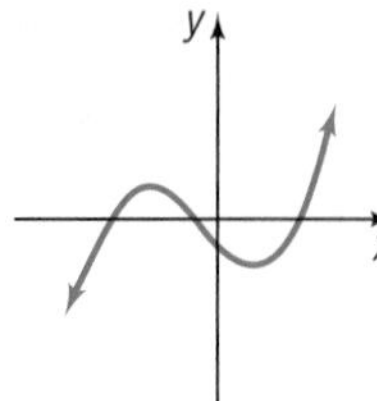

In Problems 29 and 30, sketch the graph of each function. Be sure to label at least three points.

29. $f(x) = |x|$

30. $f(x) = \sqrt{x}$

In Problems 31–36, graph each function using the techniques of shifting, compressing or stretching, and reflections. Identify any intercepts on the graph. State the domain and, based on the graph, find the range.

31. $F(x) = |x| - 4$

32. $g(x) = -2|x|$

33. $h(x) = \sqrt{x - 1}$

34. $f(x) = \sqrt{1 - x}$

35. $h(x) = (x - 1)^2 + 2$

36. $g(x) = -2(x + 2)^3 - 8$

In Problems 37 and 38,

(a) Find the domain of each function. *(b) Locate any intercepts.* *(c) Graph each function.*
(d) Based on the graph, find the range. *(e) Is f continuous on its domain?*

37. $f(x) = \begin{cases} 3x & \text{if } -2 < x \leq 1 \\ x + 1 & \text{if } x > 1 \end{cases}$

38. $f(x) = \begin{cases} x & \text{if } -4 \leq x < 0 \\ 1 & \text{if } x = 0 \\ 3x & \text{if } x > 0 \end{cases}$

39. A function f is defined by

$$f(x) = \frac{Ax + 5}{6x - 2}$$

If $f(1) = 4$, find A.

40. Constructing a Closed Box A closed box with a square base is required to have a volume of 10 cubic feet.

(a) Build a model that expresses the amount A of material used to make such a box as a function of the length x of a side of the square base.

(b) How much material is required for a base 1 foot by 1 foot?

(c) How much material is required for a base 2 feet by 2 feet?

(d) Graph $A = A(x)$. For what value of x is A smallest?

41. A rectangle has one vertex in quadrant I on the graph of $y = 10 - x^2$, another at the origin, one on the positive x-axis, and one on the positive y-axis.

(a) Express the area A of the rectangle as a function of x.

(b) Find the largest area A that can be enclosed by the rectangle.

CHAPTER TEST

The Chapter Test Prep Videos are step-by-step test solutions available in the Video Resources DVD, in MyMathLab, or on this text's YouTube Channel. Flip back to the Student Resources page to see the exact web address for this text's YouTube channel.

1. Determine whether each relation represents a function. For each function, state the domain and the range.

(a) $\{(2, 5), (4, 6), (6, 7), (8, 8)\}$

(b) $\{(1, 3), (4, -2), (-3, 5), (1, 7)\}$

(c)

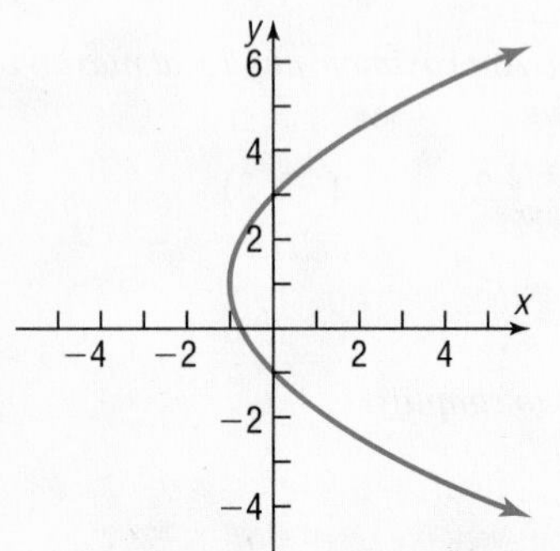

(d)

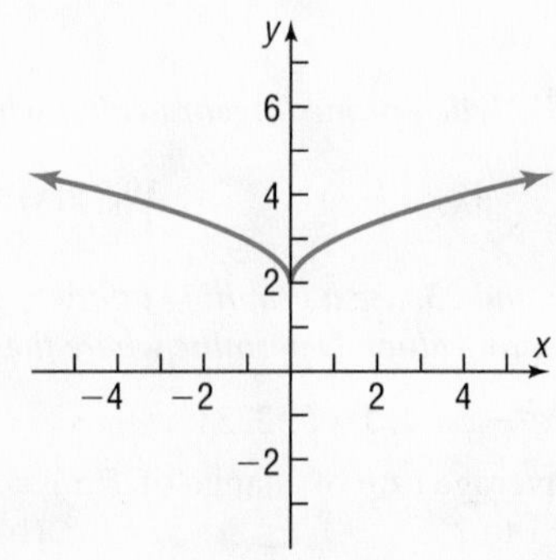

In Problems 2–4, find the domain of each function and evaluate each function at $x = -1$.

2. $f(x) = \sqrt{4 - 5x}$ **3.** $g(x) = \dfrac{x + 2}{|x + 2|}$

4. $h(x) = \dfrac{x - 4}{x^2 + 5x - 36}$

5. Using the graph of the function f:

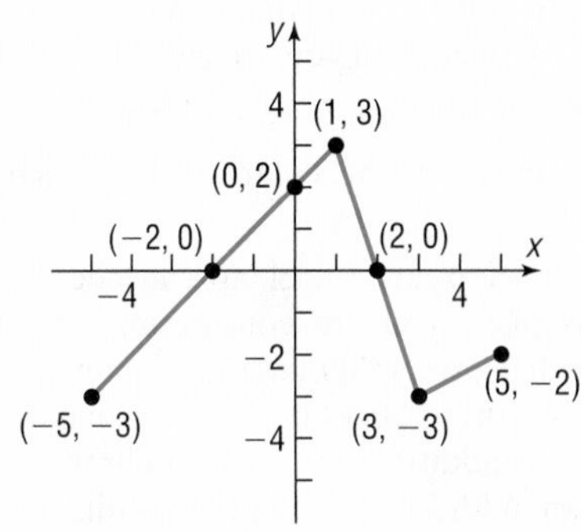

(a) Find the domain and the range of f.
(b) List the intercepts.
(c) Find $f(1)$.
(d) For what value(s) of x does $f(x) = -3$?
(e) Solve $f(x) < 0$.

6. Use a graphing utility to graph the function $f(x) = -x^4 + 2x^3 + 4x^2 - 2$ on the interval $(-5, 5)$. Approximate any local maximum values and local minimum values rounded to two decimal places. Determine where the function is increasing and where it is decreasing.

7. Consider the function $g(x) = \begin{cases} 2x + 1 & \text{if } x < -1 \\ x - 4 & \text{if } x \geq -1 \end{cases}$
(a) Graph the function.
(b) List the intercepts.
(c) Find $g(-5)$.
(d) Find $g(2)$.

8. For the function $f(x) = 3x^2 - 2x + 4$, find the average rate of change of f from 3 to 4.

9. For the functions $f(x) = 2x^2 + 1$ and $g(x) = 3x - 2$, find the following and simplify:
(a) $f - g$
(b) $f \cdot g$
(c) $f(x + h) - f(x)$

10. Graph each function using the techniques of shifting, compressing or stretching, and reflections. Start with the graph of the basic function and show all stages.
(a) $h(x) = -2(x + 1)^3 + 3$
(b) $g(x) = |x + 4| + 2$

11. The variable interest rate on a student loan changes each July 1 based on the bank prime loan rate. For the years 1992–2007, this rate can be approximated by the model $r(x) = -0.115x^2 + 1.183x + 5.623$, where x is the number of years since 1992 and r is the interest rate as a percent.
(a) Use a graphing utility to estimate the highest rate during this time period. During which year was the interest rate the highest?
(b) Use the model to estimate the rate in 2010. Does this value seem reasonable?

Source: U.S. Federal Reserve

12. A community skating rink is in the shape of a rectangle with semicircles attached at the ends. The length of the rectangle is 20 feet less than twice the width. The thickness of the ice is 0.75 inch.
(a) Build a model that expresses the ice volume, V, as a function of the width, x.
(b) How much ice is in the rink if the width is 90 feet?

CUMULATIVE REVIEW

In Problems 1–6, find the real solutions of each equation.

1. $3x - 8 = 10$ **2.** $3x^2 - x = 0$

3. $x^2 - 8x - 9 = 0$ **4.** $6x^2 - 5x + 1 = 0$

5. $|2x + 3| = 4$ **6.** $\sqrt{2x + 3} = 2$

In Problems 7–9, solve each inequality. Graph the solution set.

7. $2 - 3x > 6$ **8.** $|2x - 5| < 3$ **9.** $|4x + 1| \geq 7$

10. (a) Find the distance from $P_1 = (-2, -3)$ to $P_2 = (3, -5)$.
(b) What is the midpoint of the line segment from P_1 to P_2?
(c) What is the slope of the line containing the points P_1 and P_2?

In Problems 11–14, graph each equation.

11. $3x - 2y = 12$ **12.** $x = y^2$

13. $x^2 + (y - 3)^2 = 16$ **14.** $y = \sqrt{x}$

15. For the equation $3x^2 - 4y = 12$, find the intercepts and check for symmetry.

16. Find the slope–intercept form of the equation of the line containing the points $(-2, 4)$ and $(6, 8)$.

In Problems 17–19, graph each function.

17. $f(x) = (x + 2)^2 - 3$

18. $f(x) = \dfrac{1}{x}$

19. $f(x) = \begin{cases} 2 - x & \text{if } x \leq 2 \\ |x| & \text{if } x > 2 \end{cases}$

CHAPTER PROJECTS

Internet-based Project

I. Choosing a Cellular Telephone Plan Collect information from your family, friends, or consumer agencies such as Consumer Reports. Then decide on a cellular telephone provider, choosing the company that you feel offers the best service. Once you have selected a service provider, research the various types of individual plans offered by the company by visiting the provider's website.

1. Suppose you expect to use 400 anytime minutes without a texting or data plan. What would be the monthly cost of each plan you are considering?
2. Suppose you expect to use 600 anytime minutes with unlimited texting, but no data plan. What would be the monthly cost of each plan you are considering?
3. Suppose you expect to use 500 anytime minutes with unlimited texting and an unlimited data plan. What would be the monthly cost of each plan you are considering?
4. Suppose you expect to use 500 anytime minutes with unlimited texting and 20 MB of data. What would be the monthly cost of each plan you are considering?
5. Build a model that describes the monthly cost C as a function of the number of anytime minutes used m assuming unlimited texting and 20 MB of data each month for each plan you are considering.
6. Graph each function from Problem 5.
7. Based on your particular usage, which plan is best for you?
8. Now, develop an Excel spreadsheet to analyze the various plans you are considering. Suppose you want a plan that offers 700 anytime minutes with additional minutes costing \$0.40 per minute that costs \$39.99 per month. In addition, you want unlimited texting, which costs an additional \$20 per month, and a data plan that offers up to 25 MB of data each month, with each additional MB costing \$0.20. Because cellular telephone plans' cost structure is based on piecewise-defined functions, we need "if-then" statements within Excel to analyze the cost of the plan. Use the Excel spreadsheet below as a guide in developing your worksheet. Enter into your spreadsheet a variety of possible minutes and data used to help arrive at a decision regarding which plan is best for you.
9. Write a paragraph supporting the choice in plans that best meets your needs.
10. How are "if/then" loops similar to a piecewise-defined function?

Citation: Excel © 2010 Microsoft Corporation. Used with permission from Microsoft.

	A	B	C	D
1				
2	Monthly Fee	$ 39.99		
3	Alloted number of anytime minutes	700		
4	Number of anytime minutes used:	700		
5	Cost per additional minute	$ 0.40		
6	Monthly cost of text messaging:	$ 20.00		
7	Monthly cost of data plan	$ 9.99		
8	Alloted data per month (MB)	25		
9	Data used	30		
10	Cost per additional MB of data	$ 0.20		
11				
12	Cost of phone minutes	=IF(B4<B3,B2,B2+B5*(B4-B3))		
13	Cost of data	=IF(B9<B8,B7,B7+B10*(B9-B8))		
14				
15	Total Cost	=B6+B12+B13		
16				

The following projects are available on the Instructor's Resource Center (IRC):

II. Project at Motorola: *Wireless Internet Service* Use functions and their graphs to analyze the total cost of various wireless Internet service plans.

III. Cost of Cable When government regulations and customer preference influence the path of a new cable line, the Pythagorean Theorem can be used to assess the cost of installation.

IV. Oil Spill Functions are used to analyze the size and spread of an oil spill from a leaking tanker.

10 Linear and Quadratic Functions

Outline

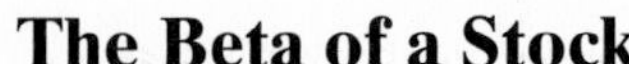

The Beta of a Stock

Investing in the stock market can be rewarding and fun, but how does one go about selecting which stocks to purchase? Financial investment firms hire thousands of analysts who track individual stocks (equities) and assess the value of the underlying company. One measure the analysts consider is the *beta* of the stock. **Beta** measures the relative risk of an individual company's equity to that of a market basket of stocks, such as the Standard & Poor's 500. But how is beta computed?

—See the Internet-based Chapter Project— 

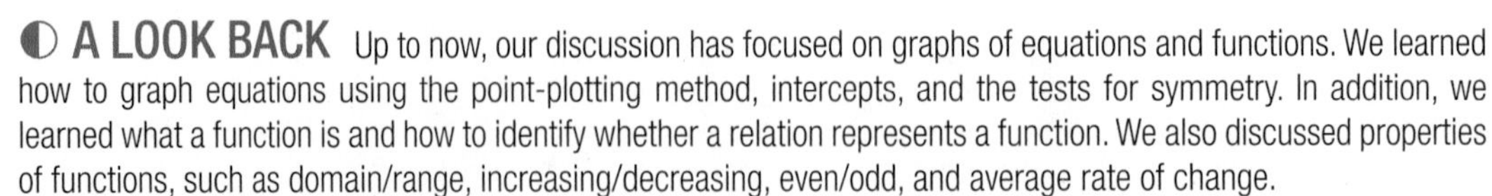

A LOOK BACK Up to now, our discussion has focused on graphs of equations and functions. We learned how to graph equations using the point-plotting method, intercepts, and the tests for symmetry. In addition, we learned what a function is and how to identify whether a relation represents a function. We also discussed properties of functions, such as domain/range, increasing/decreasing, even/odd, and average rate of change.

A LOOK AHEAD Going forward, we will look at classes of functions. In this chapter, we focus on linear and quadratic functions, their properties, and applications.

10.1 Linear Functions and Their Properties

PREPARING FOR THIS SECTION *Before getting started, review the following:*

- Lines (Section 8.2, pp. 530–541)
- Graphs of Equations in Two Variables; Intercepts; Symmetry (Section 8.1, pp. 522–527)
- Functions (Section 9.1, pp. 559–569)
- The Graph of a Function (Section 9.2, pp. 572–577)
- Properties of Functions (Section 9.3, pp. 582–590)

Now Work the **'Are You Prepared?'** problems on page 637.

OBJECTIVES
1 Graph Linear Functions (p. 631)
2 Use Average Rate of Change to Identify Linear Functions (p. 631)
3 Determine Whether a Linear Function Is Increasing, Decreasing, or Constant (p. 634)
4 Build Linear Models from Verbal Descriptions (p. 635)

1 Graph Linear Functions

In Section 8.2 we discussed lines. In particular, for nonvertical lines we developed the slope–intercept form of the equation of a line $y = mx + b$. When we write the slope–intercept form of a line using function notation, we have a *linear function*.

DEFINITION

A **linear function** is a function of the form

$$f(x) = mx + b$$

The graph of a linear function is a line with slope m and y-intercept b. Its domain is the set of all real numbers.

Functions that are not linear are said to be **nonlinear.**

EXAMPLE 1 **Graphing a Linear Function**

Graph the linear function: $f(x) = -3x + 7$

Solution This is a linear function with slope $m = -3$ and y-intercept $b = 7$. To graph this function, we plot the point $(0, 7)$, the y-intercept, and use the slope to find an additional point by moving right 1 unit and down 3 units. See Figure 1. ■

Figure 1

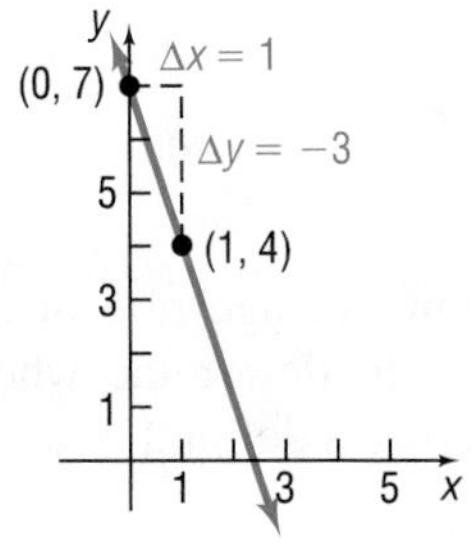

Alternatively, we could have found an additional point by evaluating the function at some $x \neq 0$. For $x = 1$, we find $f(1) = -3(1) + 7 = 4$ and obtain the point $(1, 4)$ on the graph.

Now Work PROBLEMS 13(a) AND (b)

2 Use Average Rate of Change to Identify Linear Functions

Look at Table 1, which shows certain values of the independent variable x and corresponding values of the dependent variable y for the function $f(x) = -3x + 7$. Notice that as the value of the independent variable, x, increases by 1 the value of the dependent variable y decreases by 3. That is, the average rate of change of y with respect to x is a constant, -3.

Table 1

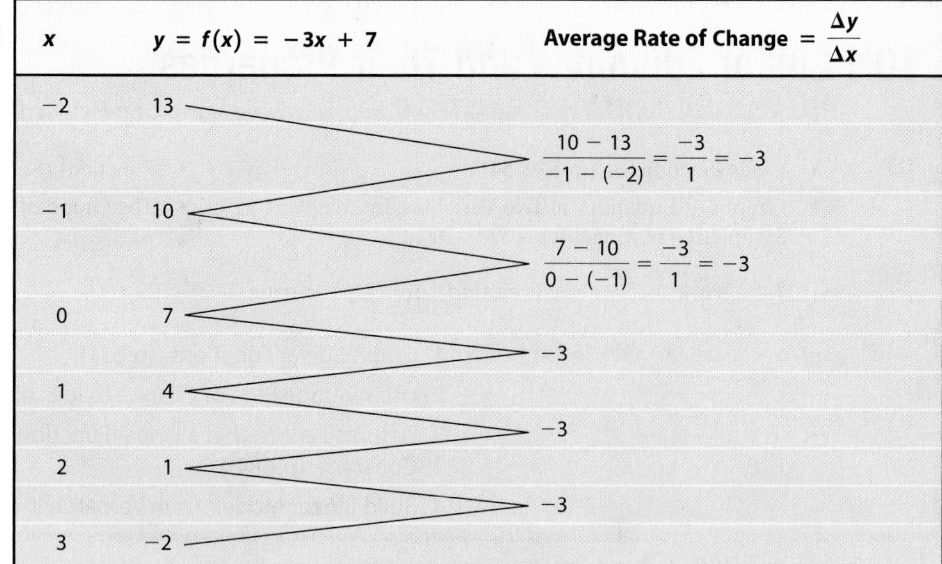

x	$y = f(x) = -3x + 7$	Average Rate of Change $= \dfrac{\Delta y}{\Delta x}$
-2	13	
		$\dfrac{10 - 13}{-1 - (-2)} = \dfrac{-3}{1} = -3$
-1	10	
		$\dfrac{7 - 10}{0 - (-1)} = \dfrac{-3}{1} = -3$
0	7	
		-3
1	4	
		-3
2	1	
		-3
3	-2	

It is not a coincidence that the average rate of change of the linear function $f(x) = -3x + 7$ is the slope of the linear function. That is, $\dfrac{\Delta y}{\Delta x} = m = -3$. The following theorem states this fact.

THEOREM

Average Rate of Change of a Linear Function

Linear functions have a constant average rate of change. That is, the average rate of change of a linear function $f(x) = mx + b$ is

$$\frac{\Delta y}{\Delta x} = m$$

Proof The average rate of change of $f(x) = mx + b$ from x_1 to x_2, $x_1 \neq x_2$, is

$$\frac{\Delta y}{\Delta x} = \frac{f(x_2) - f(x_1)}{x_2 - x_1} = \frac{(mx_2 + b) - (mx_1 + b)}{x_2 - x_1}$$

$$= \frac{mx_2 - mx_1}{x_2 - x_1} = \frac{m(x_2 - x_1)}{x_2 - x_1} = m \quad \blacksquare$$

Based on the theorem just proved, the average rate of change of the function $g(x) = -\frac{2}{5}x + 5$ is $-\frac{2}{5}$.

Now Work PROBLEM 13(c)

As it turns out, only linear functions have a constant average rate of change. Because of this, we can use the average rate of change to determine whether a function is linear or not. This is especially useful if the function is defined by a data set.

EXAMPLE 2 Using the Average Rate of Change to Identify Linear Functions

(a) A strain of *E. coli* Beu 397-recA441 is placed into a Petri dish at 30° Celsius and allowed to grow. The data shown in Table 2 on page 633 are collected. The population is measured in grams and the time in hours. Plot the ordered pairs (x, y) in the Cartesian plane and use the average rate of change to determine whether the function is linear.

(b) The data in Table 3 represent the maximum number of heartbeats that a healthy individual should have during a 15-second interval of time while exercising for different ages. Plot the ordered pairs (x, y) in the Cartesian plane, and use the average rate of change to determine whether the function is linear.

Table 2

Time (hours), x	Population (grams), y	(x, y)
0	0.09	(0, 0.09)
1	0.12	(1, 0.12)
2	0.16	(2, 0.16)
3	0.22	(3, 0.22)
4	0.29	(4, 0.29)
5	0.39	(5, 0.39)

Table 3

Age, x	Maximum Number of Heartbeats, y	(x, y)
20	50	(20, 50)
30	47.5	(30, 47.5)
40	45	(40, 45)
50	42.5	(50, 42.5)
60	40	(60, 40)
70	37.5	(70, 37.5)

Source: American Heart Association

Solution Compute the average rate of change of each function. If the average rate of change is constant, the function is linear. If the average rate of change is not constant, the function is nonlinear.

(a) Figure 2 shows the points listed in Table 2 plotted in the Cartesian plane. Notice that it is impossible to draw a straight line that contains all the points. Table 4 displays the average rate of change of the population.

Figure 2

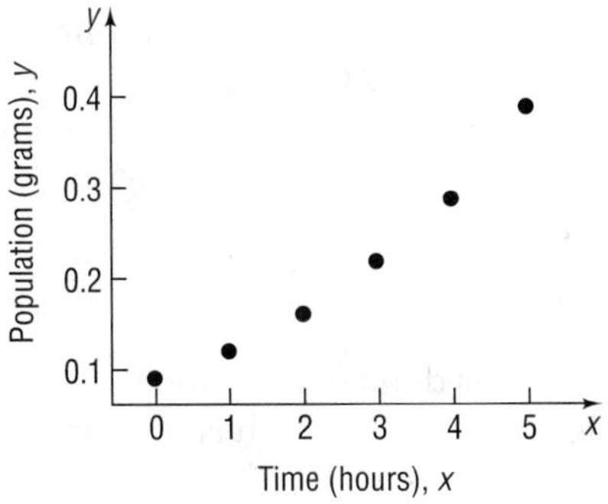

Table 4

Time (hours), x	Population (grams), y	Average Rate of Change $= \dfrac{\Delta y}{\Delta x}$
0	0.09	
		$\dfrac{0.12 - 0.09}{1 - 0} = 0.03$
1	0.12	
		0.04
2	0.16	
		0.06
3	0.22	
		0.07
4	0.29	
		0.10
5	0.39	

Because the average rate of change is not constant, we know that the function is not linear. In fact, because the average rate of change is increasing as the value of the independent variable increases, the function is increasing at an increasing rate. So not only is the population increasing over time, but it is also growing more rapidly as time passes.

(b) Figure 3 shows the points listed in Table 3 plotted in the Cartesian plane. We can see that the data in Figure 3 lie on a straight line. Table 5 contains the average rate of change of the maximum number of heartbeats. The average rate of change of the heartbeat data is constant, -0.25 beat per year, so the function is linear. We can find the linear function using the point-slope formula with $x_1 = 20$, $y_1 = 50$, and $m = -0.25$.

$$y - 50 = -0.25(x - 20) \quad y - y_1 = m(x - x_1)$$
$$y - 50 = -0.25x + 5$$
$$y = -0.25x + 55$$

Table 5

Age, x	Maximum Number of Heartbeats, y	Average Rate of Change $= \frac{\Delta y}{\Delta x}$
20	50	
		$\frac{47.5 - 50}{30 - 20} = -0.25$
30	47.5	
		-0.25
40	45	
		-0.25
50	42.5	
		-0.25
60	40	
		-0.25
70	37.5	

Figure 3

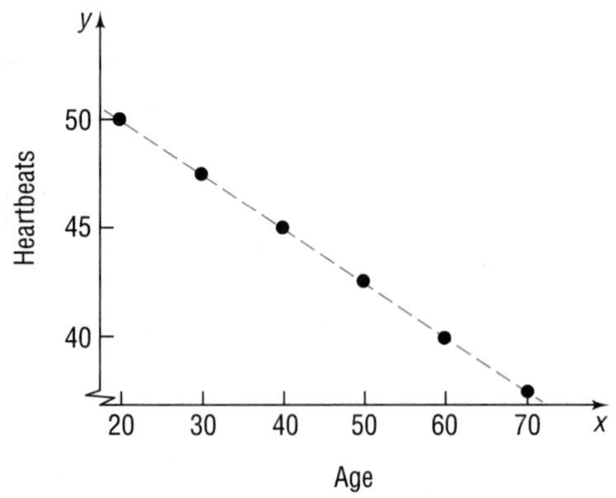

Now Work PROBLEM 21

3 Determine Whether a Linear Function Is Increasing, Decreasing, or Constant

Look back at the Seeing the Concept on page 532. When the slope m of a linear function is positive ($m > 0$), the line slants upward from left to right. When the slope m of a linear function is negative ($m < 0$), the line slants downward from left to right. When the slope m of a linear function is zero ($m = 0$), the line is horizontal.

THEOREM

Increasing, Decreasing, and Constant Linear Functions

A linear function $f(x) = mx + b$ is increasing over its domain if its slope, m, is positive. It is decreasing over its domain if its slope, m, is negative. It is constant over its domain if its slope, m, is zero.

EXAMPLE 3 **Determining Whether a Linear Function Is Increasing, Decreasing, or Constant**

Determine whether the following linear functions are increasing, decreasing, or constant.

(a) $f(x) = 5x - 2$ (b) $g(x) = -2x + 8$

(c) $s(t) = \frac{3}{4}t - 4$ (d) $h(z) = 7$

Solution

(a) For the linear function $f(x) = 5x - 2$, the slope is 5, which is positive. The function f is increasing on the interval $(-\infty, \infty)$.

(b) For the linear function $g(x) = -2x + 8$, the slope is -2, which is negative. The function g is decreasing on the interval $(-\infty, \infty)$.

(c) For the linear function $s(t) = \frac{3}{4}t - 4$, the slope is $\frac{3}{4}$, which is positive. The function s is increasing on the interval $(-\infty, \infty)$.

(d) We can write the linear function h as $h(z) = 0z + 7$. Because the slope is 0, the function h is constant on the interval $(-\infty, \infty)$. ■

Now Work PROBLEM 13(d)

4 Build Linear Models from Verbal Descriptions

When the average rate of change of a function is constant, we can use a linear function to model the relation between the two variables. For example, if your phone company charges you \$0.07 per minute to talk regardless of the number of minutes used, we can model the relation between the cost C and minutes used x as the linear function $C(x) = 0.07x$, with slope $m = \dfrac{0.07\text{ dollar}}{1\text{ minute}}$.

Modeling with a Linear Function

If the average rate of change of a function is a constant m, a linear function f can be used to model the relation between the two variables as follows:

$$f(x) = mx + b$$

where b is the value of f at 0, that is, $b = f(0)$.

EXAMPLE 4 **Straight-line Depreciation**

Book value is the value of an asset that a company uses to create its balance sheet. Some companies depreciate their assets using straight-line depreciation so that the value of the asset declines by a fixed amount each year. The amount of the decline depends on the useful life that the company places on the asset. Suppose that a company just purchased a fleet of new cars for its sales force at a cost of \$28,000 per car. The company chooses to depreciate each vehicle using the straight-line method over 7 years. This means that each car will depreciate by $\dfrac{\$28{,}000}{7} = \$4000$ per year.

(a) Write a linear function that expresses the book value V of each car as a function of its age, x.

(b) Graph the linear function.

(c) What is the book value of each car after 3 years?

(d) Interpret the slope.

(e) When will the book value of each car be \$8000?
[**Hint:** Solve the equation $V(x) = 8000$.]

Solution

(a) If we let $V(x)$ represent the value of each car after x years, then $V(0)$ represents the original value of each car, so $V(0) = \$28{,}000$. The y-intercept of the linear function is \$28,000. Because each car depreciates by \$4000 per year, the slope of the linear function is -4000. The linear function that represents the book value V of each car after x years is

$$V(x) = -4000x + 28{,}000$$

Figure 4

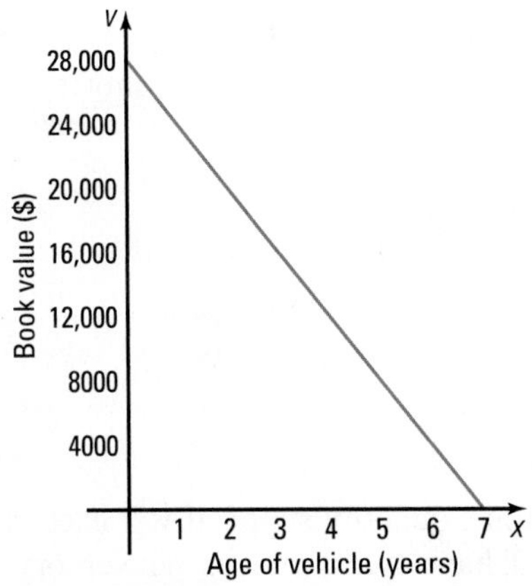

(b) Figure 4 shows the graph of V.

(c) The book value of each car after 3 years is

$$V(3) = -4000(3) + 28{,}000$$
$$= \$16{,}000$$

(d) Since the slope of $V(x) = -4000x + 28{,}000$ is -4000, the average rate of change of book value is $-\$4000$/year. So for each additional year that passes the book value of the car decreases by \$4000.

(e) To find when the book value will be \$8000, solve the equation

$$\begin{aligned} V(x) &= 8000 \\ -4000x + 28{,}000 &= 8000 \\ -4000x &= -20{,}000 && \text{Subtract 28,000 from each side.} \\ x &= \frac{-20{,}000}{-4000} = 5 && \text{Divide by } -4000. \end{aligned}$$

The car will have a book value of \$8000 when it is 5 years old. ■

Now Work PROBLEM 45

EXAMPLE 5

Supply and Demand

The **quantity supplied** of a good is the amount of a product that a company is willing to make available for sale at a given price. The **quantity demanded** of a good is the amount of a product that consumers are willing to purchase at a given price. Suppose that the quantity supplied, S, and quantity demanded, D, of cellular telephones each month are given by the following functions:

$$S(p) = 60p - 900$$
$$D(p) = -15p + 2850$$

where p is the price (in dollars) of the telephone.

(a) The **equilibrium price** of a product is defined as the price at which quantity supplied equals quantity demanded. That is, the equilibrium price is the price at which $S(p) = D(p)$. Find the equilibrium price of cellular telephones. What is the **equilibrium quantity,** the amount demanded (or supplied) at the equilibrium price?

(b) Determine the prices for which quantity supplied is greater than quantity demanded. That is, solve the inequality $S(p) > D(p)$.

(c) Graph $S = S(p)$, $D = D(p)$ and label the equilibrium point.

Solution

(a) To find the equilibrium price, solve the equation $S(p) = D(p)$.

$$\begin{aligned} 60p - 900 &= -15p + 2850 && S(p) = 60p - 900;\ D(p) = -15p + 2850 \\ 60p &= -15p + 3750 && \text{Add 900 to each side.} \\ 75p &= 3750 && \text{Add } 15p \text{ to each side.} \\ p &= 50 && \text{Divide each side by 75.} \end{aligned}$$

The equilibrium price is \$50 per cellular phone. To find the equilibrium quantity, evaluate either $S(p)$ or $D(p)$ at $p = 50$.

$$S(50) = 60(50) - 900 = 2100$$

The equilibrium quantity is 2100 cellular phones. At a price of \$50 per phone, the company will produce and sell 2100 phones each month and have no shortages or excess inventory.

(b) The inequality $S(p) > D(p)$ is

$$\begin{aligned} 60p - 900 &> -15p + 2850 && S(p) > D(p) \\ 60p &> -15p + 3750 && \text{Add 900 to each side.} \\ 75p &> 3750 && \text{Add } 15p \text{ to each side.} \\ p &> 50 && \text{Divide each side by 75.} \end{aligned}$$

If the company charges more than \$50 per phone, quantity supplied will exceed quantity demanded. In this case the company will have excess phones in inventory.

(c) Figure 5 shows the graphs of $S = S(p)$ and $D = D(p)$ with the equilibrium point labeled.

Figure 5

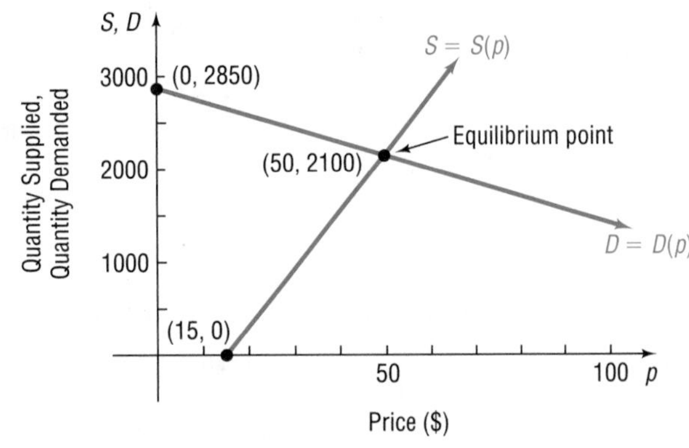

Now Work PROBLEM 39

10.1 Assess Your Understanding

'Are You Prepared?' *Answers are given at the end of these exercises. If you get a wrong answer, read the pages listed in red.*

1. Graph $y = 2x - 3$. (pp. 533–537)
2. Find the slope of the line joining the points $(2, 5)$ and $(-1, 3)$. (pp. 530–531)
3. Find the average rate of change of $f(x) = 3x^2 - 2$, from 2 to 4. (pp. 588–590)
4. Solve: $60x - 900 = -15x + 2850$.
5. If $f(x) = x^2 - 4$, find $f(-2)$. (pp. 562–565)
6. ***True or False*** The graph of the function $f(x) = x^2$ is increasing on the interval $(0, \infty)$. (pp. 584–585)

Concepts and Vocabulary

7. For the graph of the linear function $f(x) = mx + b$, m is the _____ and b is the __________.
8. For the graph of the linear function $H(z) = -4z + 3$, the slope is ______ and the y-intercept is _____.
9. If the slope m of the graph of a linear function is _______, the function is increasing over its domain.
10. ***True or False*** The slope of a nonvertical line is the average rate of change of the linear function.
11. ***True or False*** If the average rate of change of a linear function is $\frac{2}{3}$, then if y increases by 3, x will increase by 2.
12. ***True or False*** The average rate of change of $f(x) = 2x + 8$ is 8.

Skill Building

In Problems 13–20, a linear function is given.

(a) Determine the slope and y-intercept of each function.

(b) Use the slope and y-intercept to graph the linear function.

(c) Determine the average rate of change of each function.

(d) Determine whether the linear function is increasing, decreasing, or constant.

13. $f(x) = 2x + 3$
14. $g(x) = 5x - 4$
15. $h(x) = -3x + 4$
16. $p(x) = -x + 6$
17. $f(x) = \frac{1}{4}x - 3$
18. $h(x) = -\frac{2}{3}x + 4$
19. $F(x) = 4$
20. $G(x) = -2$

In Problems 21–28, determine whether the given function is linear or nonlinear. If it is linear, determine the equation of the line.

21.

x	y = f(x)
−2	4
−1	1
0	−2
1	−5
2	−8

22.

x	y = f(x)
−2	1/4
−1	1/2
0	1
1	2
2	4

23.

x	y = f(x)
−2	−8
−1	−3
0	0
1	1
2	0

24.

x	y = f(x)
−2	−4
−1	0
0	4
1	8
2	12

25.

x	$y = f(x)$
−2	−26
−1	−4
0	2
1	−2
2	−10

26.

x	$y = f(x)$
−2	−4
−1	−3.5
0	−3
1	−2.5
2	−2

27.

x	$y = f(x)$
−2	8
−1	8
0	8
1	8
2	8

28.

x	$y = f(x)$
−2	0
−1	1
0	4
1	9
2	16

Applications and Extensions

29. Suppose that $f(x) = 4x - 1$ and $g(x) = -2x + 5$.
(a) Solve $f(x) = 0$.
(b) Solve $f(x) > 0$.
(c) Solve $f(x) = g(x)$.
(d) Solve $f(x) \leq g(x)$.
(e) Graph $y = f(x)$ and $y = g(x)$ and label the point that represents the solution to the equation $f(x) = g(x)$.

30. Suppose that $f(x) = 3x + 5$ and $g(x) = -2x + 15$.
(a) Solve $f(x) = 0$.
(b) Solve $f(x) < 0$.
(c) Solve $f(x) = g(x)$.
(d) Solve $f(x) \geq g(x)$.
(e) Graph $y = f(x)$ and $y = g(x)$ and label the point that represents the solution to the equation $f(x) = g(x)$.

31. In parts (a)–(f), use the following figure.

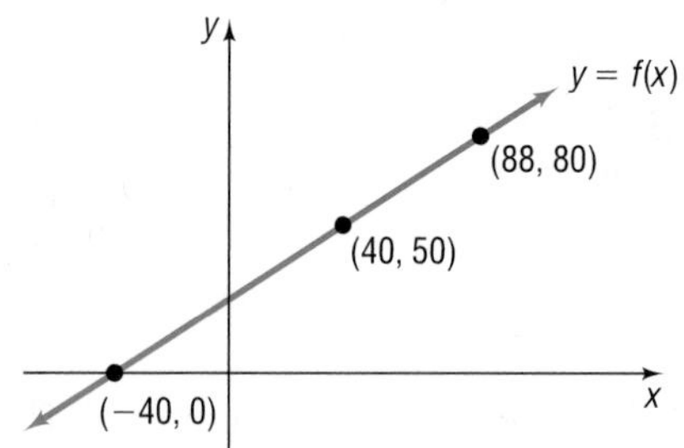

(a) Solve $f(x) = 50$.
(b) Solve $f(x) = 80$.
(c) Solve $f(x) = 0$.
(d) Solve $f(x) > 50$.
(e) Solve $f(x) \leq 80$.
(f) Solve $0 < f(x) < 80$.

32. In parts (a)–(f), use the following figure.

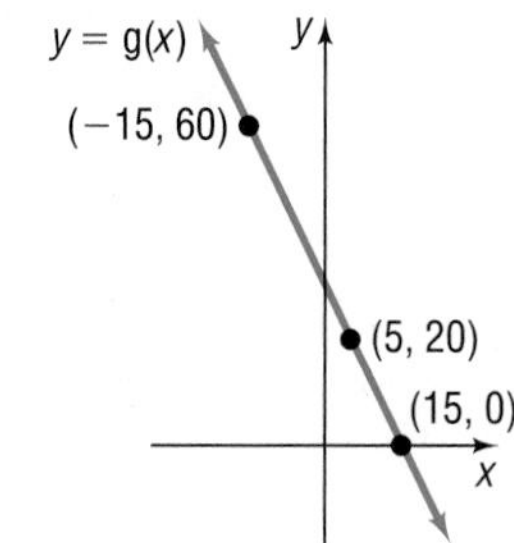

(a) Solve $g(x) = 20$.
(b) Solve $g(x) = 60$.
(c) Solve $g(x) = 0$.
(d) Solve $g(x) > 20$.
(e) Solve $g(x) \leq 60$.
(f) Solve $0 < g(x) < 60$.

33. In parts (a) and (b) use the following figure.

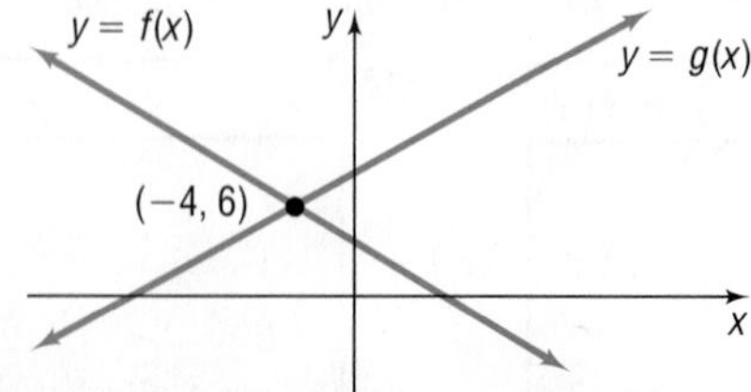

(a) Solve the equation: $f(x) = g(x)$.
(b) Solve the inequality: $f(x) > g(x)$.

34. In parts (a) and (b), use the following figure.

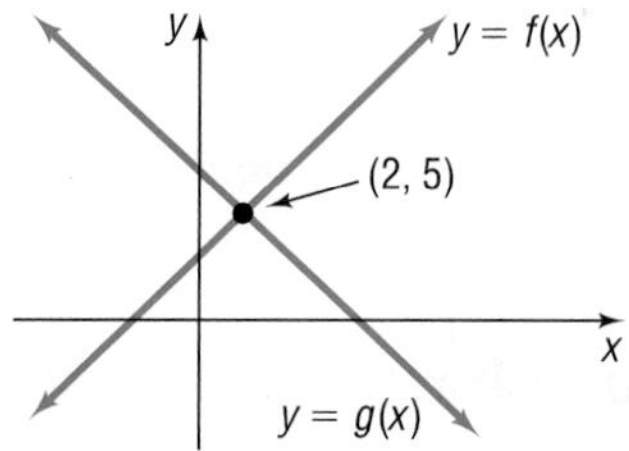

(a) Solve the equation: $f(x) = g(x)$.
(b) Solve the inequality: $f(x) \leq g(x)$.

35. In parts (a) and (b), use the following figure.

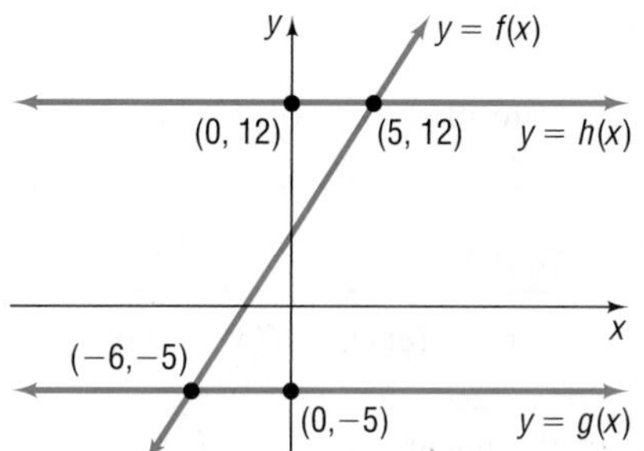

(a) Solve the equation: $f(x) = g(x)$.
(b) Solve the inequality: $g(x) \leq f(x) < h(x)$.

36. In parts (a) and (b), use the following figure.

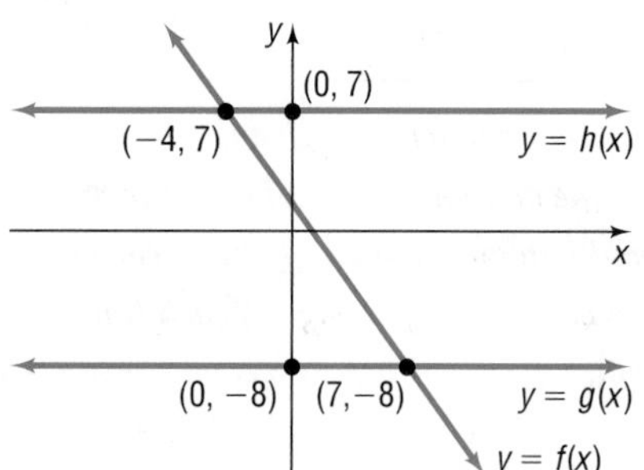

(a) Solve the equation: $f(x) = g(x)$.
(b) Solve the inequality: $g(x) < f(x) \leq h(x)$.

37. Car Rentals The cost C, in dollars, of renting a moving truck for a day is modeled by the function $C(x) = 0.25x + 35$, where x is the number of miles driven.
(a) What is the cost if you drive $x = 40$ miles?
(b) If the cost of renting the moving truck is \$80, how many miles did you drive?
(c) Suppose that you want the cost to be no more than \$100. What is the maximum number of miles that you can drive?
(d) What is the implied domain of C?

(e) Interpret the slope.
(f) Interpret the y-intercept.

38. Phone Charges The monthly cost C, in dollars, for international calls on a certain cellular phone plan is modeled by the function $C(x) = 0.38x + 5$, where x is the number of minutes used.

(a) What is the cost if you talk on the phone for $x = 50$ minutes?
(b) Suppose that your monthly bill is \$29.32. How many minutes did you use the phone?
(c) Suppose that you budget yourself \$60 per month for the phone. What is the maximum number of minutes that you can talk?
(d) What is the implied domain of C if there are 30 days in the month?
(e) Interpret the slope.
(f) Interpret the y-intercept.

39. Supply and Demand Suppose that the quantity supplied S and quantity demanded D of T-shirts at a concert are given by the following functions:

$$S(p) = -200 + 50p$$
$$D(p) = 1000 - 25p$$

where p is the price of a T-shirt.

(a) Find the equilibrium price for T-shirts at this concert. What is the equilibrium quantity?
(b) Determine the prices for which quantity demanded is greater than quantity supplied.
(c) What do you think will eventually happen to the price of T-shirts if quantity demanded is greater than quantity supplied?

40. Supply and Demand Suppose that the quantity supplied S and quantity demanded D of hot dogs at a baseball game are given by the following functions:

$$S(p) = -2000 + 3000p$$
$$D(p) = 10{,}000 - 1000p$$

where p is the price of a hot dog.

(a) Find the equilibrium price for hot dogs at the baseball game. What is the equilibrium quantity?
(b) Determine the prices for which quantity demanded is less than quantity supplied.
(c) What do you think will eventually happen to the price of hot dogs if quantity demanded is less than quantity supplied?

41. Taxes The function $T(x) = 0.15(x - 8350) + 835$ represents the tax bill T of a single person whose adjusted gross income is x dollars for income between \$8350 and \$33,950, inclusive, in 2009.

Source: Internal Revenue Service

(a) What is the domain of this linear function?
(b) What is a single filer's tax bill if adjusted gross income is \$20,000?
(c) Which variable is independent and which is dependent?
(d) Graph the linear function over the domain specified in part (a).
(e) What is a single filer's adjusted gross income if the tax bill is \$3707.50?
(f) Interpret the slope.

42. Luxury Tax In 2002, major league baseball signed a labor agreement with the players. In this agreement, any team whose payroll exceeded \$136.5 million in 2006 had to pay a luxury tax of 40% (for second offenses). The linear function $T(p) = 0.40(p - 136.5)$ describes the luxury tax T of a team whose payroll was p (in millions of dollars).

Source: Major League Baseball

(a) What is the implied domain of this linear function?
(b) What was the luxury tax for the New York Yankees whose 2006 payroll was \$171.1 million?
(c) Graph the linear function.
(d) What is the payroll of a team that pays a luxury tax of \$11.7 million?
(e) Interpret the slope.

The point at which a company's profits equal zero is called the company's ***break-even point.*** *For Problems 43 and 44, let R represent a company's revenue, let C represent the company's costs, and let x represent the number of units produced and sold each day.*

(a) Find the firm's break-even point; that is, find x so that R = C.
(b) Find the values of x such that R(x) > C(x). This represents the number of units that the company must sell to earn a profit.

43. $R(x) = 8x$
$C(x) = 4.5x + 17{,}500$

44. $R(x) = 12x$
$C(x) = 10x + 15{,}000$

45. Straight-line Depreciation Suppose that a company has just purchased a new computer for \$3000. The company chooses to depreciate the computer using the straight-line method over 3 years.

(a) Write a linear model that expresses the book value V of the computer as a function of its age x.
(b) What is the implied domain of the function found in part (a)?
(c) Graph the linear function.
(d) What is the book value of the computer after 2 years?
(e) When will the computer have a book value of \$2000?

46. Straight-line Depreciation Suppose that a company has just purchased a new machine for its manufacturing facility for \$120,000. The company chooses to depreciate the machine using the straight-line method over 10 years.

(a) Write a linear model that expresses the book value V of the machine as a function of its age x.
(b) What is the implied domain of the function found in part (a)?
(c) Graph the linear function.
(d) What is the book value of the machine after 4 years?
(e) When will the machine have a book value of \$72,000?

47. Cost Function The simplest cost function is the linear cost function, $C(x) = mx + b$, where the y-intercept b represents the fixed costs of operating a business and the slope m represents the cost of each item produced. Suppose that a small bicycle manufacturer has daily fixed costs of \$1800 and each bicycle costs \$90 to manufacture.

(a) Write a linear model that expresses the cost C of manufacturing x bicycles in a day.
(b) Graph the model.
(c) What is the cost of manufacturing 14 bicycles in a day?
(d) How many bicycles could be manufactured for \$3780?

48. Cost Function Refer to Problem 47. Suppose that the landlord of the building increases the bicycle manufacturer's rent by \$100 per month.

(a) Assuming that the manufacturer is open for business 20 days per month, what are the new daily fixed costs?
(b) Write a linear model that expresses the cost C of manufacturing x bicycles in a day with the higher rent.
(c) Graph the model.
(d) What is the cost of manufacturing 14 bicycles in a day?
(e) How many bicycles can be manufactured for \$3780?

49. Truck Rentals A truck rental company rents a truck for one day by charging \$29 plus \$0.07 per mile.
(a) Write a linear model that relates the cost C, in dollars, of renting the truck to the number x of miles driven.
(b) What is the cost of renting the truck if the truck is driven 110 miles? 230 miles?

50. Long Distance A phone company offers a domestic long distance package by charging \$5 plus \$0.05 per minute.
(a) Write a linear model that relates the cost C, in dollars, of talking x minutes.
(b) What is the cost of talking 105 minutes? 180 minutes?

Mixed Practice

51. Developing a Linear Model from Data The following data represent the price p and quantity demanded per day q of 24" LCD monitors.

Price, p (in dollars)	Quantity Demanded, q
150	100
200	80
250	60
300	40

(a) Plot the ordered pairs (p, q) in a Cartesian plane.
(b) Show that quantity demanded q is a linear function of the price p.
(c) Determine the linear function that describes the relation between p and q.
(d) What is the implied domain of the linear function?
(e) Graph the linear function in the Cartesian plane drawn in part (a).
(f) Interpret the slope.
(g) Interpret the values of the intercepts.

52. Developing a Linear Model from Data The following data represent the various combinations of soda and hot dogs that Yolanda can buy at a baseball game with \$60.

Soda, s	Hot Dogs, h
20	0
15	3
10	6
5	9

(a) Plot the ordered pairs (s, h) in a Cartesian plane.
(b) Show that the number of hot dogs purchased h is a linear function of the number of sodas purchased s.
(c) Determine the linear function that describes the relation between s and h.
(d) What is the implied domain of the linear function?
(e) Graph the linear function in the Cartesian plane drawn in part (a).
(f) Interpret the slope.
(g) Interpret the values of the intercepts.

Explaining Concepts: Discussion and Writing

53. Which of the following functions might have the graph shown? (More than one answer is possible.)
(a) $f(x) = 2x - 7$
(b) $g(x) = -3x + 4$
(c) $H(x) = 5$
(d) $F(x) = 3x + 4$
(e) $G(x) = \frac{1}{2}x + 2$

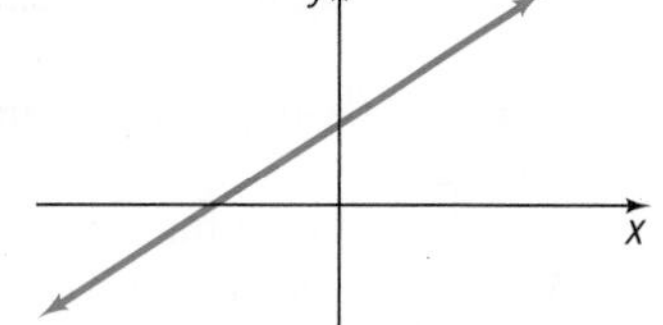

54. Which of the following functions might have the graph shown? (More than one answer is possible.)
(a) $f(x) = 3x + 1$
(b) $g(x) = -2x + 3$
(c) $H(x) = 3$
(d) $F(x) = -4x - 1$
(e) 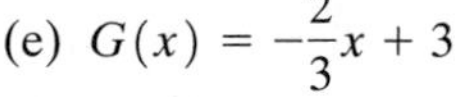 $G(x) = -\frac{2}{3}x + 3$

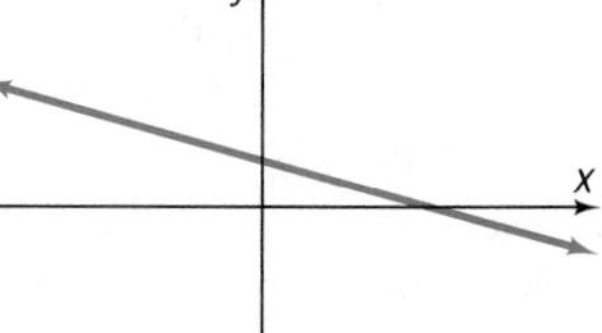

55. Under what circumstances is a linear function $f(x) = mx + b$ odd? Can a linear function ever be even?

56. Explain how the graph of $f(x) = mx + b$ can be used to solve $mx + b > 0$.

'Are You Prepared?' Answers

1.

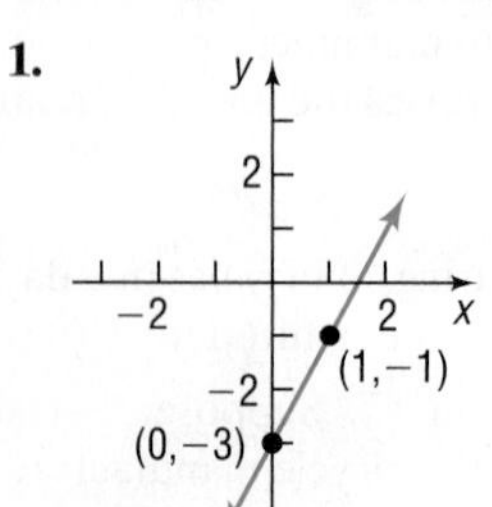

2. $\frac{2}{3}$ **3.** 18 **4.** $\{50\}$ **5.** 0 **6.** True

10.2 Linear Models: Building Linear Functions from Data

PREPARING FOR THIS SECTION *Before getting started, review the following:*

- Rectangular Coordinates (Section 7.1, pp. 460–462)
- Functions (Section 9.1, pp. 559–569)
- Lines (Section 8.2, pp. 530–541)

Now Work the **'Are You Prepared?'** problems on page 644.

OBJECTIVES
1 Draw and Interpret Scatter Diagrams (p. 641)
2 Distinguish between Linear and Nonlinear Relations (p. 642)
3 Use a Graphing Utility to Find the Line of Best Fit (p. 643)

1 Draw and Interpret Scatter Diagrams

In Section 10.1, we built linear models from verbal descriptions. Linear models can also be constructed by fitting a linear function to data. The first step is to plot the ordered pairs using rectangular coordinates. The resulting graph is called a **scatter diagram.**

EXAMPLE 1 Drawing and Interpreting a Scatter Diagram

In baseball, the on-base percentage for a team represents the percentage of time that the players safely reach base. The data given in Table 6 represent the number of runs scored y and the on-base percentage x for teams in the National League during the 2010 baseball season.

Table 6

Team	On-base Percentage, x	Runs Scored, y	(x, y)
Arizona	32.5	713	(32.5, 713)
Atlanta	33.9	738	(33.9, 738)
Chicago Cubs	32.0	685	(32.0, 685)
Cincinnati	33.8	790	(33.8, 790)
Colorado	33.6	770	(33.6, 770)
Florida	32.1	719	(32.1, 719)
Houston	30.3	611	(30.3, 611)
LA Dodgers	32.2	667	(32.2, 667)
Milwaukee	33.5	750	(33.5, 750)
NY Mets	31.4	656	(31.4, 656)
Philadelphia	33.2	772	(33.2, 772)
Pittsburgh	30.4	587	(30.4, 587)
San Diego	31.7	665	(31.7, 665)
San Francisco	32.1	697	(32.1, 697)
St. Louis	33.2	736	(33.2, 736)
Washington	31.8	655	(31.8, 655)

Source: espn.com

(a) Draw a scatter diagram of the data, treating on-base percentage as the independent variable.
(b) Use a graphing utility to draw a scatter diagram.
(c) Describe what happens to runs scored as the on-base percentage increases.

Solution

(a) To draw a scatter diagram, plot the ordered pairs listed in Table 6, with the on-base percentage as the x-coordinate and the runs scored as the y-coordinate. See Figure 6(a). Notice that the points in the scatter diagram are not connected.
(b) Figure 6(b) shows a scatter diagram using a TI-84 Plus graphing calculator.

(c) We see from the scatter diagrams that, as the on-base percentage increases, the trend is that the number of runs scored also increases.

Figure 6

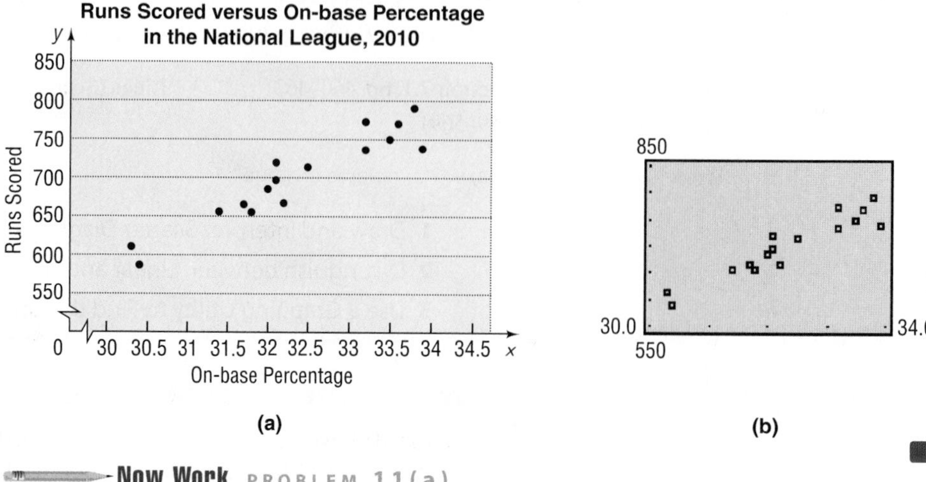

(a) (b)

Now Work PROBLEM 11(a)

2 Distinguish between Linear and Nonlinear Relations

Notice that the points in Figure 6 do not follow a perfect linear relation (as they do in Figure 3 in Section 10.1). However, the data do exhibit a linear pattern. There are numerous explanations as to why the data are not perfectly linear, but one easy explanation is the fact that other variables besides on-base percentage play a role in determining runs scored, such as number of home runs hit.

Scatter diagrams are used to help us see the type of relation that exists between two variables. In this text, we will discuss a variety of different relations that may exist between two variables. For now, we concentrate on distinguishing between linear and nonlinear relations. See Figure 7.

Figure 7

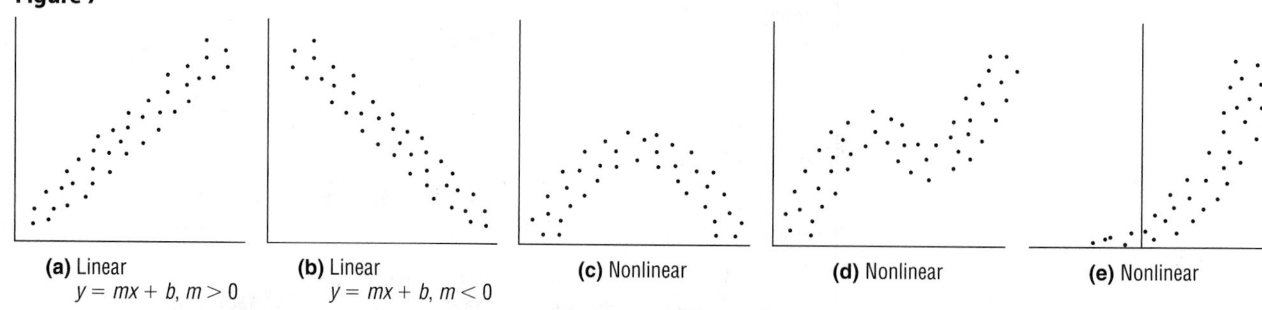

(a) Linear $y = mx + b, m > 0$ (b) Linear $y = mx + b, m < 0$ (c) Nonlinear (d) Nonlinear (e) Nonlinear

EXAMPLE 2 Distinguishing between Linear and Nonlinear Relations

Determine whether the relation between the two variables in Figure 8 is linear or nonlinear.

Figure 8

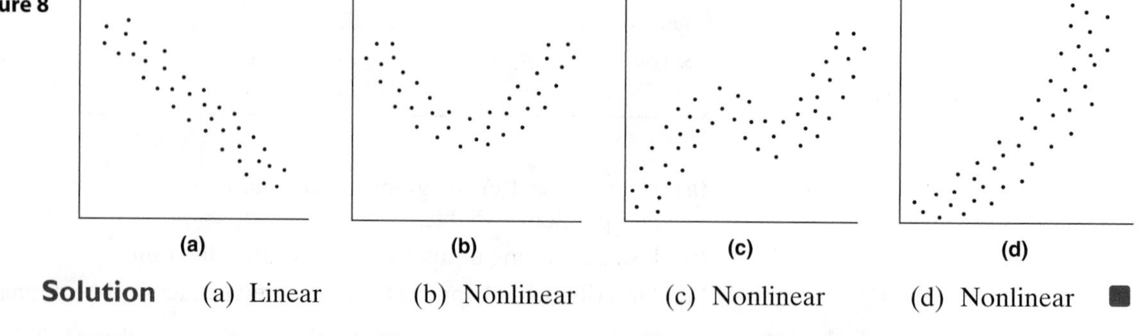

(a) (b) (c) (d)

Solution (a) Linear (b) Nonlinear (c) Nonlinear (d) Nonlinear

Now Work PROBLEM 5

In this section we study data whose scatter diagrams imply that a linear relation exists between the two variables.

Suppose that the scatter diagram of a set of data appears to be linearly related as in Figure 7(a) or (b). We might want to model the data by finding an equation of a line that relates the two variables. One way to obtain a model for such data is to draw a line through two points on the scatter diagram and determine the equation of the line.

EXAMPLE 3 **Finding a Model for Linearly Related Data**

Use the data in Table 6 from Example 1 to:

(a) Select two points and find an equation of the line containing the points.
(b) Graph the line on the scatter diagram obtained in Example 1(a).

Solution (a) Select two points, say (31.4, 656) and (33.6, 770). The slope of the line joining the points (31.4, 656) and (33.6, 770) is

$$m = \frac{770 - 656}{33.6 - 31.4} = \frac{114}{2.2} = 51.82$$

The equation of the line with slope 51.82 and passing through (31.4, 656) is found using the point–slope form with $m = 51.82$, $x_1 = 31.4$, and $y_1 = 656$.

$$y - y_1 = m(x - x_1) \quad \text{Point–slope form of a line}$$

$$y - 656 = 51.82(x - 31.4) \quad x_1 = 31.4,\ y_1 = 656,\ m = 51.82$$

$$y - 656 = 51.82x - 1627.148$$

$$y = 51.82x - 971.148 \quad \text{The Model}$$

(b) Figure 9 shows the scatter diagram with the graph of the line found in part (a).

Figure 9

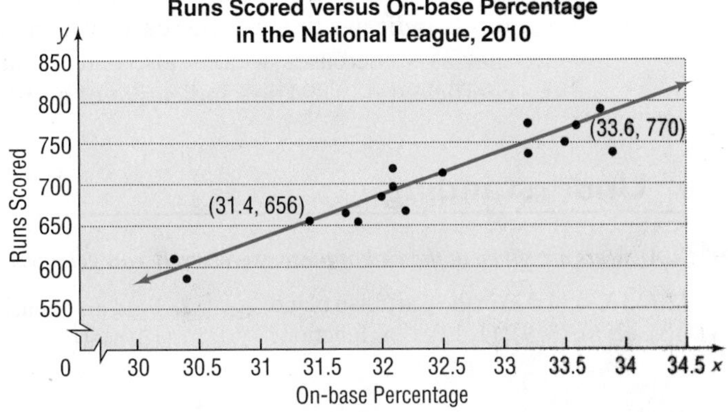

Select two other points and complete the solution. Graph the line on the scatter diagram obtained in Figure 6.

Now Work PROBLEM 11(b) AND (c)

3 Use a Graphing Utility to Find the Line of Best Fit

The model obtained in Example 3 depends on the selection of points, which will vary from person to person. So the model that we found might be different from the model you found. Although the model in Example 3 appears to fit the data well, there may be a model that "fits it better." Do you think your model fits the data better? Is there a *line of best fit*? As it turns out, there is a method for finding a model that best fits linearly related data (called the **line of best fit**).*

EXAMPLE 4 **Finding a Model for Linearly Related Data**

Use the data in Table 6 from Example 1.

(a) Use a graphing utility to find the line of best fit that models the relation between on-base percentage and runs scored.

(b) Graph the line of best fit on the scatter diagram obtained in Example 1(b).

(c) Interpret the slope.

(d) Use the line of best fit to predict the number of runs a team will score if their on-base percentage is 34.1.

Solution

Figure 10

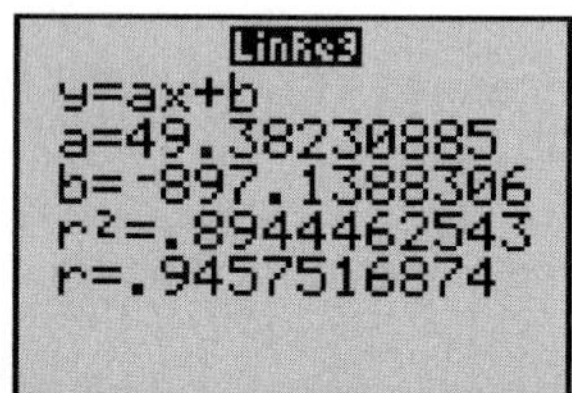

(a) Graphing utilities contain built-in programs that find the line of best fit for a collection of points in a scatter diagram. Upon executing the LINear REGression program, we obtain the results shown in Figure 10. The output that the utility provides shows us the equation $y = ax + b$, where a is the slope of the line and b is the y-intercept. The line of best fit that relates on-base percentage to runs scored may be expressed as the line

$$y = 49.38x - 897.14 \quad \text{The Model}$$

Figure 11

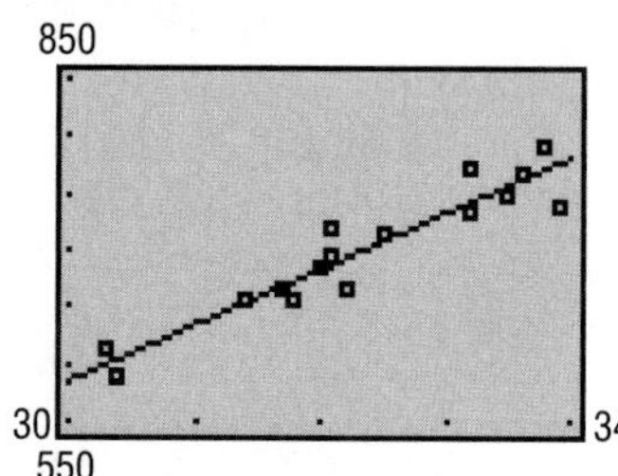

(b) Figure 11 shows the graph of the line of best fit, along with the scatter diagram.

(c) The slope of the line of best fit is 49.38, which means that, for every 1 percent increase in the on-base percentage, runs scored increase 49.38, on average.

(d) Letting $x = 34.1$ in the equation of the line of best fit, we obtain $y = 49.38(34.1) - 897.14 \approx 787$ runs. ■

Does the line of best fit appear to be a good fit? In other words, does the line appear to accurately describe the relation between on-base percentage and runs scored?

And just how "good" is this line of best fit? Look again at Figure 10. The last line of output is $r = 0.894$. This number, called the **correlation coefficient**, $r, -1 \le r \le 1$, is a measure of the strength of the linear relation that exists between two variables. The closer that $|r|$ is to 1, the more perfect the linear relationship is. If r is close to 0, there is little or no linear relationship between the variables. A negative value of r, $r < 0$, indicates that as x increases y decreases; a positive value of r, $r > 0$, indicates that as x increases y does also. The data given in Table 6, having a correlation coefficient of 0.894, are indicative of a linear relationship with positive slope.

10.2 Assess Your Understanding

'Are You Prepared?' *Answers are given at the end of these exercises. If you get a wrong answer, read the pages listed in red.*

1. Plot the points $(1,5), (2,6), (3,9), (1,12)$ in the Cartesian plane. Is the relation $\{(1,5), (2,6), (3,9), (1,12)\}$ a function? Why? (pp. 460 and 559–562)

2. Find an equation of the line containing the points $(1,4)$ and $(3,8)$. (p. 535)

Concepts and Vocabulary

3. A ______________ is used to help us to see the type of relation, if any, that may exist between two variables.

4. If the independent variable in a line of best fit $y = -0.008x + 14$ is credit score, and the dependent variable is the interest rate on a used car loan, then the slope is interpreted as "if credit score increases by 1 point, the interest rate will ________ (increase/decrease) by _____ percent, on average.

Skill Building

In Problems 5–10, examine the scatter diagram and determine whether the type of relation is linear or nonlinear.

5.

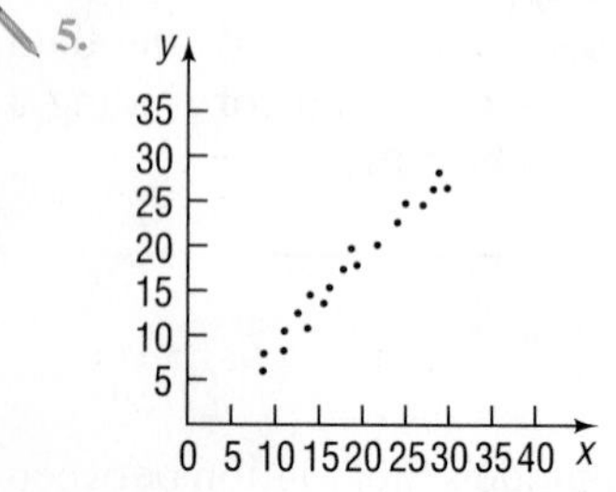

6.

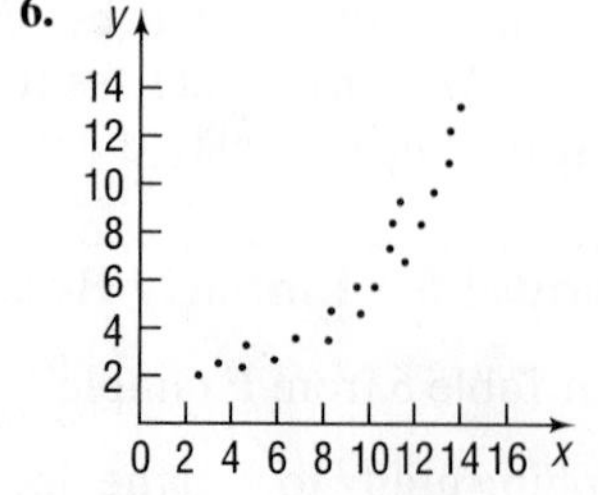

7.

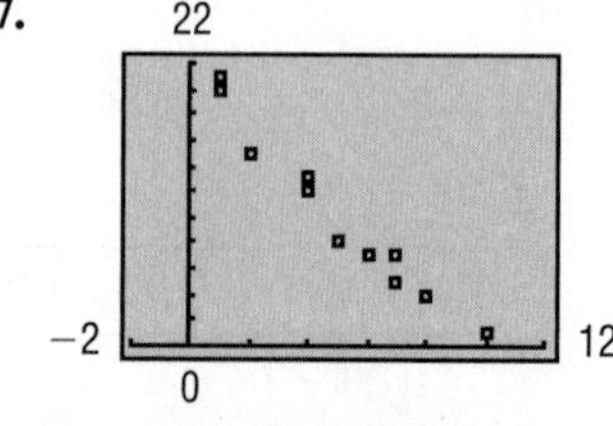

*We shall not discuss the underlying mathematics of lines of best fit in this book.

8. 50

5 20 30

9.

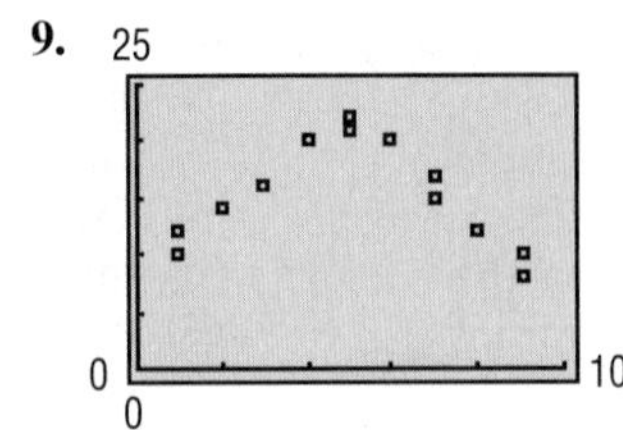

10.

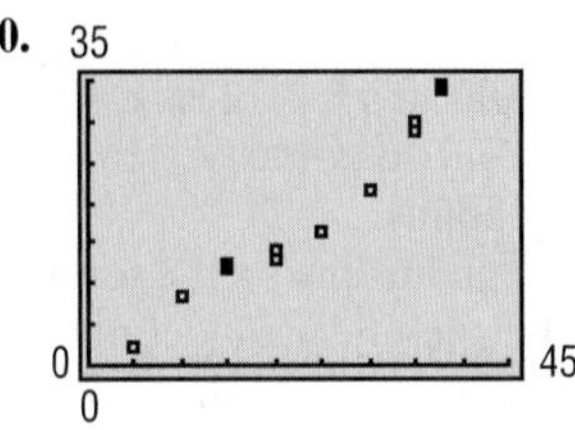

In Problems 11–16,

(a) Draw a scatter diagram.
(b) Select two points from the scatter diagram and find the equation of the line containing the points selected.
(c) Graph the line found in part (b) on the scatter diagram.
(d) Use a graphing utility to find the line of best fit.
(e) Use a graphing utility to draw the scatter diagram and graph the line of best fit on it.

11.

x	3	4	5	6	7	8	9
y	4	6	7	10	12	14	16

12.

x	3	5	7	9	11	13
y	0	2	3	6	9	11

13.

x	−2	−1	0	1	2
y	−4	0	1	4	5

14.

x	−2	−1	0	1	2
y	7	6	3	2	0

15.

x	−20	−17	−15	−14	−10
y	100	120	118	130	140

16.

x	−30	−27	−25	−20	−14
y	10	12	13	13	18

Applications and Extensions

17. Candy The following data represent the weight (in grams) of various candy bars and the corresponding number of calories.

Candy Bar	Weight, x	Calories, y
Hershey's Milk Chocolate®	44.28	230
Nestle's Crunch®	44.84	230
Butterfinger®	61.30	270
Baby Ruth®	66.45	280
Almond Joy®	47.33	220
Twix® (with Caramel)	58.00	280
Snickers®	61.12	280
Heath®	39.52	210

Source: Megan Pocius, Student at Joliet Junior College

(a) Draw a scatter diagram of the data treating weight as the independent variable.
(b) What type of relation appears to exist between the weight of a candy bar and the number of calories?
(c) Select two points and find a linear model that contains the points.
(d) Graph the line on the scatter diagram drawn in part (a).
(e) Use the linear model to predict the number of calories in a candy bar that weighs 62.3 grams.
(f) Interpret the slope of the line found in part (c).

18. Raisins The following data represent the weight (in grams) of a box of raisins and the number of raisins in the box.

Weight (in grams), w	Number of Raisins, N
42.3	87
42.7	91
42.8	93
42.4	87
42.6	89
42.4	90
42.3	82
42.5	86
42.7	86
42.5	86

Source: Jennifer Maxwell, Student at Joliet Junior College

(a) Draw a scatter diagram of the data treating weight as the independent variable.

(b) What type of relation appears to exist between the weight of a box of raisins and the number of raisins?
(c) Select two points and find a linear model that contains the points.
(d) Graph the line on the scatter diagram drawn in part (b).
(e) Use the linear model to predict the number of raisins in a box that weighs 42.5 grams.
(f) Interpret the slope of the line found in part (c).

19. Video Games and Grade-Point Average Professor Grant Alexander wanted to find a linear model that relates the number of hours a student plays video games each week, h, to the cumulative grade-point average, G, of the student. He obtained a random sample of 10 full-time students at his college and asked each student to disclose the number of hours spent playing video games and the student's cumulative grade-point average.

Hours of Video Games per Week, *h*	Grade-Point Average, *G*
0	3.49
0	3.05
2	3.24
3	2.82
3	3.19
5	2.78
8	2.31
8	2.54
10	2.03
12	2.51

(a) Explain why the number of hours spent playing video games is the independent variable and cumulative grade-point average is the dependent variable.
(b) Use a graphing utility to draw a scatter diagram.
(c) Use a graphing utility to find the line of best fit that models the relation between number of hours of video game playing each week and grade-point average. Express the model using function notation.
(d) Interpret the slope.
(e) Predict the grade-point average of a student who plays video games for 8 hours each week.
(f) How many hours of video game playing do you think a student plays whose grade-point average is 2.40?

20. Height versus Head Circumference A pediatrician wanted to find a linear model that relates a child's height, H, to head circumference, C. She randomly selects nine children from her practice, measures their height and head circumference, and obtains the data shown. Let H represent the independent variable and C the dependent variable.

Height, *H* (inches)	Head Circumference, *C* (inches)
25.25	16.4
25.75	16.9
25	16.9
27.75	17.6
26.5	17.3
27	17.5
26.75	17.3
26.75	17.5
27.5	17.5

Source: Denise Slucki, Student at Joliet Junior College

(a) Use a graphing utility to draw a scatter diagram.
(b) Use a graphing utility to find the line of best fit that models the relation between height and head circumference. Express the model using function notation.
(c) Interpret the slope.
(d) Predict the head circumference of a child that is 26 inches tall.
(e) What is the height of a child whose head circumference is 17.4 inches?

Mixed Practice

21. Demand for Jeans The marketing manager at Levi-Strauss wishes to find a function that relates the demand D for men's jeans and p, the price of the jeans. The following data were obtained based on a price history of the jeans.

Price ($/Pair), *p*	Demand (Pairs of Jeans Sold per Day), *D*
20	60
22	57
23	56
23	53
27	52
29	49
30	44

(a) Does the relation defined by the set of ordered pairs (p, D) represent a function?
(b) Draw a scatter diagram of the data.
(c) Using a graphing utility, find the line of best fit that models the relation between price and quantity demanded.
(d) Interpret the slope.
(e) Express the relationship found in part (c) using function notation.
(f) What is the domain of the function?
(g) How many jeans will be demanded if the price is $28 a pair?

22. **Advertising and Sales Revenue** A marketing firm wishes to find a function that relates the sales S of a product and A, the amount spent on advertising the product. The data are obtained from past experience. Advertising and sales are measured in thousands of dollars.

Advertising Expenditures, A	Sales, S
20	335
22	339
22.5	338
24	343
24	341
27	350
28.3	351

(a) Does the relation defined by the set of ordered pairs (A, S) represent a function?
(b) Draw a scatter diagram of the data.
(c) Using a graphing utility, find the line of best fit that models the relation between advertising expenditures and sales.
(d) Interpret the slope.
(e) Express the relationship found in part (c) using function notation.
(f) What is the domain of the function?
(g) Predict sales if advertising expenditures are \$25,000.

Explaining Concepts: Discussion and Writing

23. **Maternal Age versus Down Syndrome** A biologist would like to know how the age of the mother affects the incidence rate of Down syndrome. The data to the right represent the age of the mother and the incidence rate of Down syndrome per 1000 pregnancies.

Draw a scatter diagram treating age of the mother as the independent variable. Would it make sense to find the line of best fit for these data? Why or why not?

Age of Mother, x	Incidence of Down Syndrome, y
33	2.4
34	3.1
35	4
36	5
37	6.7
38	8.3
39	10
40	13.3
41	16.7
42	22.2
43	28.6
44	33.3
45	50

Source: Hook, E.B., *Journal of the American Medical Association*, 249, 2034–2038, 1983.

24. Explain why it does not make sense to interpret the y-intercept in Problem 17.

25. Refer to Problem 19. Solve $G(h) = 0$. Provide an interpretation of this result. Find $G(0)$. Provide an interpretation of this result.

'Are You Prepared' Answers

1.
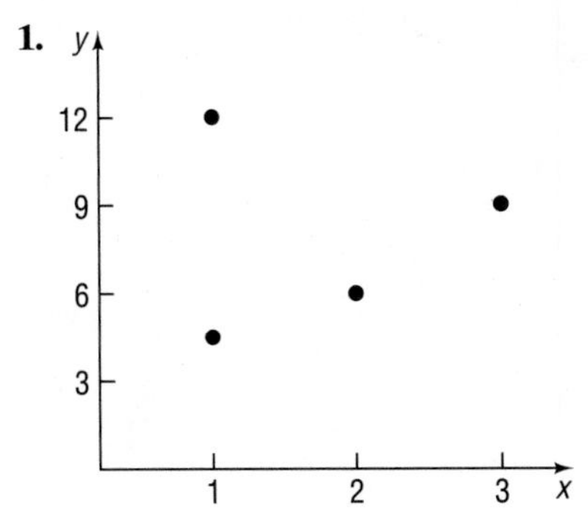

No, because the input, 1, corresponds to two different outputs.

2. $y = 2x + 2$

10.3 Quadratic Functions and Their Properties

PREPARING FOR THIS SECTION *Before getting started, review the following:*

- Intercepts (Section 8.1, pp. 522–523)
- Graphing Techniques: Transformations (Section 9.5, pp. 605–613)
- Quadratic Equations (Section 7.3, pp. 476–482)

Now Work the **'Are You Prepared?'** problems on page 656.

OBJECTIVES

Quadratic Functions

Here are some examples of quadratic functions.

$$F(x) = 3x^2 - 5x + 1 \quad g(x) = -6x^2 + 1 \quad H(x) = \frac{1}{2}x^2 + \frac{2}{3}x$$

DEFINITION

A **quadratic function** is a function of the form

$$f(x) = ax^2 + bx + c$$

where a, b, and c are real numbers and $a \neq 0$. The domain of a quadratic function is the set of all real numbers.

In Words

A quadratic function is a function defined by a second-degree polynomial in one variable.

Many applications require a knowledge of quadratic functions. For example, suppose that Texas Instruments collects the data shown in Table 7, which relate the number of calculators sold to the price p (in dollars) per calculator. Since the price of a product determines the quantity that will be purchased, we treat price as the independent variable. The relationship between the number x of calculators sold and the price p per calculator is given by the linear equation

$$x = 21{,}000 - 150p$$

Table 7

Price per Calculator, p (Dollars)	Number of Calculators, x
60	12,000
65	11,250
70	10,500
75	9,750
80	9,000
85	8,250
90	7,500

Then the revenue R derived from selling x calculators at the price p per calculator is equal to the unit selling price p of the calculator times the number x of

Figure 12

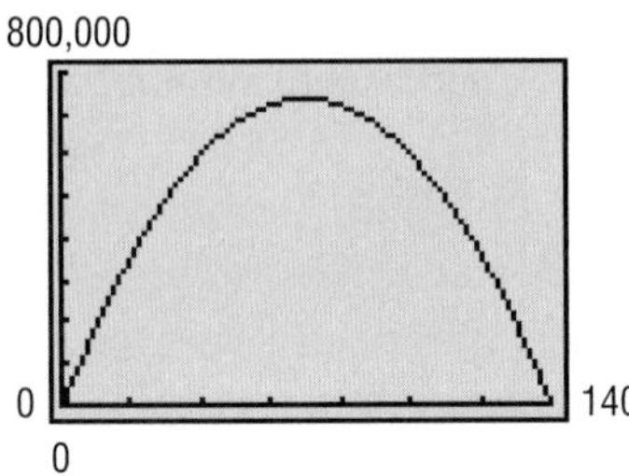

units actually sold. That is,

$$R = xp$$
$$R(p) = (21{,}000 - 150p)p \quad x = 21{,}000 - 150p$$
$$= -150p^2 + 21{,}000p$$

So the revenue R is a quadratic function of the price p. Figure 12 illustrates the graph of this revenue function, whose domain is $0 \le p \le 140$, since both x and p must be nonnegative.

A second situation in which a quadratic function appears involves the motion of a projectile. Based on Newton's Second Law of Motion (force equals mass times acceleration, $F = ma$), it can be shown that, ignoring air resistance, the path of a projectile propelled upward at an inclination to the horizontal is the graph of a quadratic function. See Figure 13 for an illustration.

Figure 13
Path of a cannonball

1 Graph a Quadratic Function Using Transformations

We know how to graph the square function $f(x) = x^2$. Figure 14 shows the graph of three functions of the form $f(x) = ax^2, a > 0$, for $a = 1, a = \frac{1}{2}$, and $a = 3$. Notice that the larger the value of a, the "narrower" the graph is, and the smaller the value of a, the "wider" the graph is.

Figure 15 shows the graphs of $f(x) = ax^2$ for $a < 0$. Notice that these graphs are reflections about the x-axis of the graphs in Figure 14. Based on the results of these two figures, we can draw some general conclusions about the graph of $f(x) = ax^2$. First, as $|a|$ increases, the graph becomes "taller" (a vertical stretch), and as $|a|$ gets closer to zero, the graph gets "shorter" (a vertical compression). Second, if a is positive, the graph opens "up," and if a is negative, the graph opens "down."

Figure 14

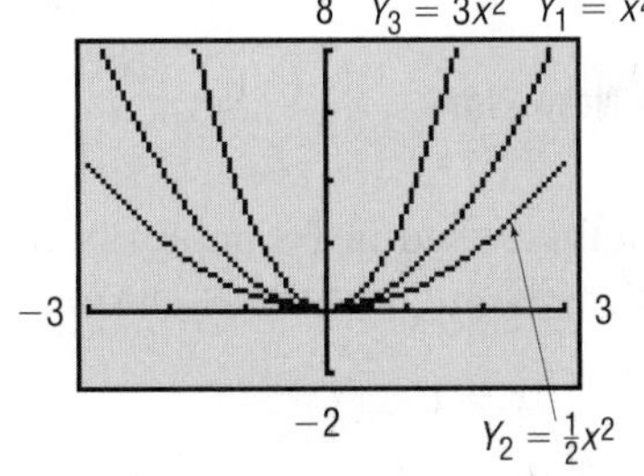

Figure 15

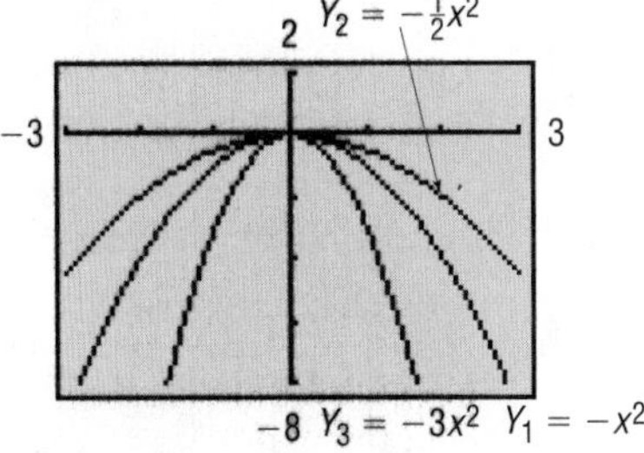

The graphs in Figures 14 and 15 are typical of the graphs of all quadratic functions, which we call **parabolas.*** Refer to Figure 16, where two parabolas are pictured. The one on the left **opens up** and has a lowest point; the one on the right **opens down** and has a highest point. The lowest or highest point of a parabola is called the **vertex.** The vertical line passing through the vertex in each parabola in Figure 16 is called the **axis of symmetry** (usually abbreviated to **axis**) of the parabola. Because the parabola is symmetric about its axis, the axis of symmetry of a parabola can be used to find additional points on the parabola.

Figure 16
Graphs of a quadratic function, $f(x) = ax^2 + bx + c, a \neq 0$

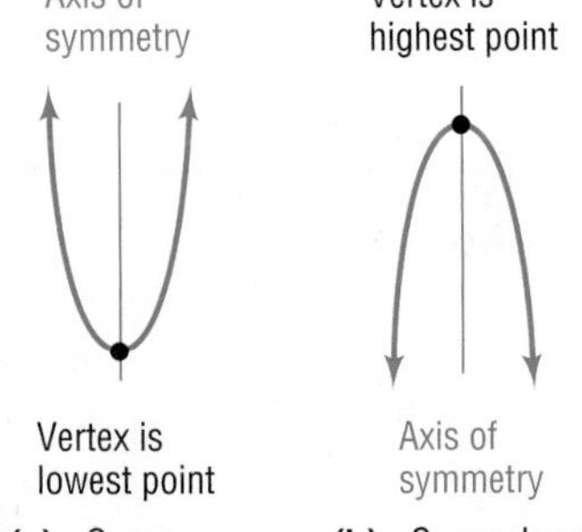

The parabolas shown in Figure 16 are the graphs of a quadratic function $f(x) = ax^2 + bx + c, a \neq 0$. Notice that the coordinate axes are not included in the figure. Depending on the values of a, b, and c, the axes could be placed anywhere. The important fact is that the shape of the graph of a quadratic function will look like one of the parabolas in Figure 16.

In the following example, we use techniques from Section 9.5 to graph a quadratic function $f(x) = ax^2 + bx + c, a \neq 0$. In so doing, we shall complete the square and write the function f in the form $f(x) = a(x - h)^2 + k$.

* We shall study parabolas using a geometric definition later in this book.

EXAMPLE 1 **Graphing a Quadratic Function Using Transformations**

Graph the function $f(x) = 2x^2 + 8x + 5$. Find the vertex and axis of symmetry.

Solution Begin by completing the square on the right side.

$$\begin{aligned} f(x) &= 2x^2 + 8x + 5 \\ &= 2(x^2 + 4x) + 5 && \text{Factor out the 2 from } 2x^2 + 8x. \\ &= 2(x^2 + 4x + 4) + 5 - 8 && \text{Complete the square of } x^2 + 4x \text{ by adding 4.} \\ &= 2(x + 2)^2 - 3 && \text{Notice that the factor of 2 requires that 8 be added and subtracted.} \end{aligned}$$

The graph of f can be obtained from the graph of $y = x^2$ in three stages, as shown in Figure 17. Now compare this graph to the graph in Figure 16(a). The graph of $f(x) = 2x^2 + 8x + 5$ is a parabola that opens up and has its vertex (lowest point) at $(-2, -3)$. Its axis of symmetry is the line $x = -2$.

Figure 17

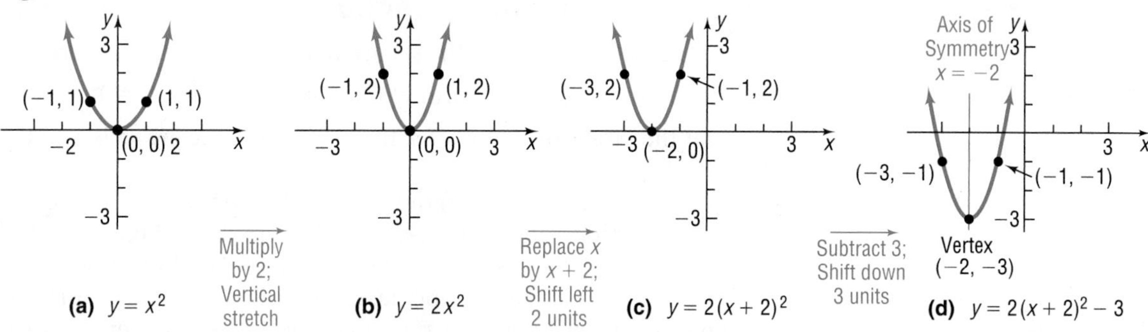

(a) $y = x^2$ **(b)** $y = 2x^2$ **(c)** $y = 2(x + 2)^2$ **(d)** $y = 2(x + 2)^2 - 3$

✓**Check:** Use a graphing utility to graph $Y_1 = f(x) = 2x^2 + 8x + 5$ and use the MINIMUM command to locate its vertex. ■

Now Work PROBLEM 23

The method used in Example 1 can be used to graph any quadratic function $f(x) = ax^2 + bx + c$, $a \neq 0$, as follows:

$$\begin{aligned} f(x) &= ax^2 + bx + c \\ &= a\left(x^2 + \frac{b}{a}x\right) + c && \text{Factor out } a \text{ from } ax^2 + bx. \\ &= a\left(x^2 + \frac{b}{a}x + \frac{b^2}{4a^2}\right) + c - a\left(\frac{b^2}{4a^2}\right) && \text{Complete the square by adding } \frac{b^2}{4a^2}. \text{ Look closely at this step!} \\ &= a\left(x + \frac{b}{2a}\right)^2 + c - \frac{b^2}{4a} && \text{Factor.} \\ &= a\left(x + \frac{b}{2a}\right)^2 + \frac{4ac - b^2}{4a} && c - \frac{b^2}{4a} = c\cdot\frac{4a}{4a} - \frac{b^2}{4a} = \frac{4ac - b^2}{4a} \end{aligned}$$

Based on these results, we conclude the following:

If $h = -\dfrac{b}{2a}$ and $k = \dfrac{4ac - b^2}{4a}$, then

$$f(x) = ax^2 + bx + c = a(x - h)^2 + k \qquad (1)$$

The graph of $f(x) = a(x - h)^2 + k$ is the parabola $y = ax^2$ shifted horizontally h units (replace x by $x - h$) and vertically k units (add k). As a result, the vertex is at (h, k), and the graph opens up if $a > 0$ and down if $a < 0$. The axis of symmetry is the vertical line $x = h$.

For example, compare equation (1) with the solution given in Example 1.

$$\begin{aligned} f(x) &= 2(x+2)^2 - 3 \\ &= 2(x-(-2))^2 + (-3) \\ &= a(x-h)^2 + k \end{aligned}$$

We conclude that $a = 2$, so the graph opens up. Also, we find that $h = -2$ and $k = -3$, so its vertex is at $(-2, -3)$.

2 Identify the Vertex and Axis of Symmetry of a Quadratic Function

We do not need to complete the square to obtain the vertex. In almost every case, it is easier to obtain the vertex of a quadratic function f by remembering that its x-coordinate is $h = -\dfrac{b}{2a}$. The y-coordinate k can then be found by evaluating f at $-\dfrac{b}{2a}$. That is, $k = f\left(-\dfrac{b}{2a}\right)$.

Properties of the Graph of a Quadratic Function

$$f(x) = ax^2 + bx + c \qquad a \neq 0$$

$$\text{Vertex} = \left(-\frac{b}{2a}, f\left(-\frac{b}{2a}\right)\right) \qquad \text{Axis of symmetry: the line } x = -\frac{b}{2a} \qquad \textbf{(2)}$$

Parabola opens up if $a > 0$; the vertex is a minimum point.
Parabola opens down if $a < 0$; the vertex is a maximum point.

EXAMPLE 2 **Locating the Vertex without Graphing**

Without graphing, locate the vertex and axis of symmetry of the parabola defined by $f(x) = -3x^2 + 6x + 1$. Does it open up or down?

Solution For this quadratic function, $a = -3$, $b = 6$, and $c = 1$. The x-coordinate of the vertex is

$$h = -\frac{b}{2a} = -\frac{6}{-6} = 1$$

The y-coordinate of the vertex is

$$k = f\left(-\frac{b}{2a}\right) = f(1) = -3 + 6 + 1 = 4$$

The vertex is located at the point $(1, 4)$. The axis of symmetry is the line $x = 1$. Because $a = -3 < 0$, the parabola opens down. ■

3 Graph a Quadratic Function Using Its Vertex, Axis, and Intercepts

The location of the vertex and intercepts of a quadratic function, $f(x) = ax^2 + bx + c$, $a \neq 0$, along with knowledge as to whether the graph opens up or down, usually provides enough information to graph it.

The y-intercept is the value of f at $x = 0$; that is, the y-intercept is $f(0) = c$. The x-intercepts, if there are any, are found by solving the quadratic equation

$$ax^2 + bx + c = 0$$

This equation has two, one, or no real solutions, depending on whether the discriminant $b^2 - 4ac$ is positive, 0, or negative. Depending on the value of the discriminant, the graph of f has x-intercepts, as follows:

The x-Intercepts of a Quadratic Function

1. If the discriminant $b^2 - 4ac > 0$, the graph of $f(x) = ax^2 + bx + c$ has two distinct x-intercepts so it crosses the x-axis in two places.
2. If the discriminant $b^2 - 4ac = 0$, the graph of $f(x) = ax^2 + bx + c$ has one x-intercept so it touches the x-axis at its vertex.
3. If the discriminant $b^2 - 4ac < 0$, the graph of $f(x) = ax^2 + bx + c$ has no x-intercepts so it does not cross or touch the x-axis.

Figure 18 illustrates these possibilities for parabolas that open up.

Figure 18
$f(x) = ax^2 + bx + c, a > 0$

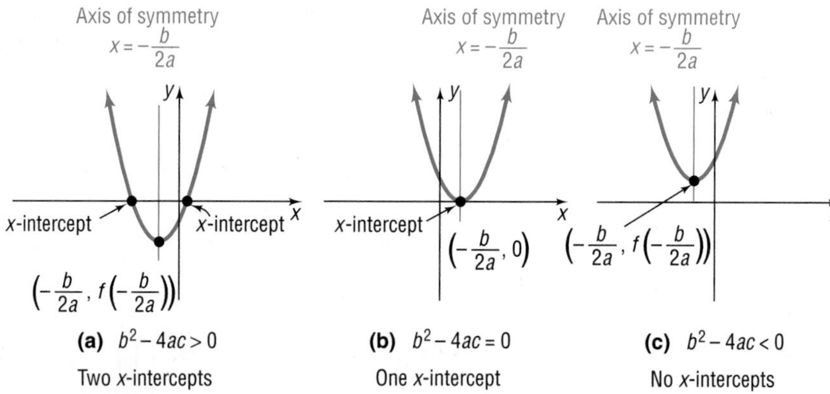

EXAMPLE 3

How to Graph a Quadratic Function by Hand Using Its Properties

Graph $f(x) = -3x^2 + 6x + 1$ using its properties. Determine the domain and the range of f. Determine where f is increasing and where it is decreasing.

Step-by-Step Solution

Step 1 Determine whether the graph of f opens up or down.

In Example 2, we determined that the graph of $f(x) = -3x^2 + 6x + 1$ opens down because $a = -3 < 0$.

Step 2 Determine the vertex and axis of symmetry of the graph of f.

In Example 2, we found the vertex to be at the point whose coordinates are $(1, 4)$. The axis of symmetry is the line $x = 1$.

Step 3 Determine the intercepts of the graph of f.

The y-intercept is found by letting $x = 0$. The y-intercept is $f(0) = 1$. The x-intercepts are found by solving the equation $f(x) = 0$.

$$f(x) = 0$$
$$-3x^2 + 6x + 1 = 0 \quad a = -3, b = 6, c = 1$$

The discriminant $b^2 - 4ac = (6)^2 - 4(-3)(1) = 36 + 12 = 48 > 0$, so the equation has two real solutions and the graph has two x-intercepts. Using the quadratic formula, we find that

$$x = \frac{-b + \sqrt{b^2 - 4ac}}{2a} = \frac{-6 + \sqrt{48}}{2(-3)} = \frac{-6 + 4\sqrt{3}}{-6} \approx -0.15$$

and

$$x = \frac{-b - \sqrt{b^2 - 4ac}}{2a} = \frac{-6 - \sqrt{48}}{2(-3)} = \frac{-6 - 4\sqrt{3}}{-6} \approx 2.15$$

The x-intercepts are approximately -0.15 and 2.15.

Step 4 Use the information in Steps 1 through 3 to graph f.

The graph is illustrated in Figure 19. Notice how we use the y-intercept and the axis of symmetry, $x = 1$, to obtain the additional point $(2, 1)$ on the graph.

Figure 19

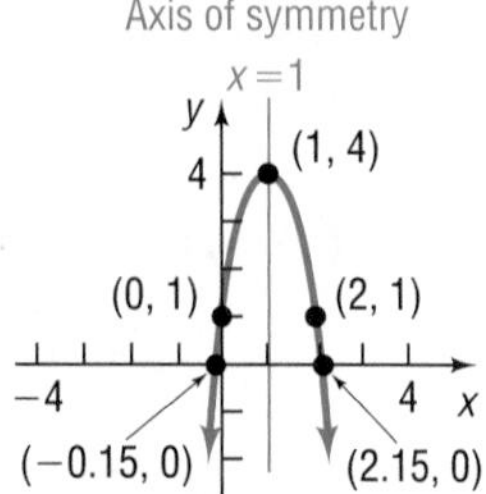

The domain of f is the set of all real numbers. Based on the graph, the range of f is the interval $(-\infty, 4]$. The function f is increasing on the interval $(-\infty, 1)$ and decreasing on the interval $(1, \infty)$. ■

Graph the function in Example 3 by completing the square and using transformations. Which method do you prefer?

Now Work PROBLEM 31

If the graph of a quadratic function has only one x-intercept or no x-intercepts, it is usually necessary to plot an additional point to obtain the graph.

EXAMPLE 4 Graphing a Quadratic Function Using Its Vertex, Axis, and Intercepts

(a) Graph $f(x) = x^2 - 6x + 9$ by determining whether the graph opens up or down and by finding its vertex, axis of symmetry, y-intercept, and x-intercepts, if any.

(b) Determine the domain and the range of f.

(c) Determine where f is increasing and where it is decreasing.

Solution (a) **Step 1:** For $f(x) = x^2 - 6x + 9$, we have $a = 1, b = -6$, and $c = 9$. Since $a = 1 > 0$, the parabola opens up.

Step 2: The x-coordinate of the vertex is

$$h = -\frac{b}{2a} = -\frac{-6}{2(1)} = 3$$

The y-coordinate of the vertex is

$$k = f(3) = (3)^2 - 6(3) + 9 = 0$$

So the vertex is at $(3, 0)$. The axis of symmetry is the line $x = 3$.

Step 3: The y-intercept is $f(0) = 9$. Since the vertex $(3, 0)$ lies on the x-axis, the graph touches the x-axis at the x-intercept.

Step 4: By using the axis of symmetry and the y-intercept at $(0, 9)$, we can locate the additional point $(6, 9)$ on the graph. See Figure 20.

Figure 20

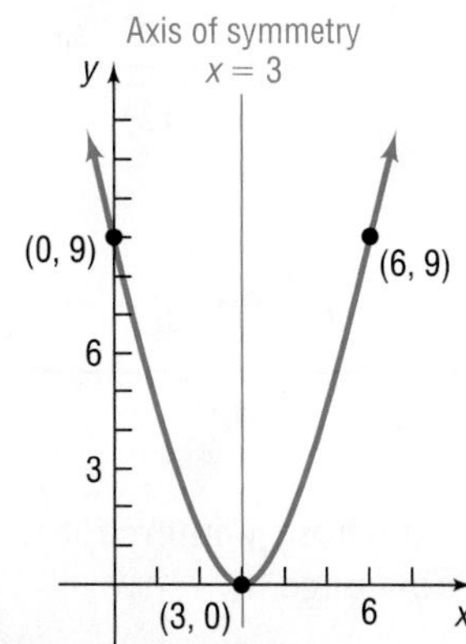

(b) The domain of f is the set of all real numbers. Based on the graph, the range of f is the interval $[0, \infty)$.

(c) The function f is decreasing on the interval $(-\infty, 3)$ and increasing on the interval $(3, \infty)$. ■

Now Work PROBLEM 37

EXAMPLE 5 **Graphing a Quadratic Function Using Its Vertex, Axis, and Intercepts**

(a) Graph $f(x) = 2x^2 + x + 1$ by determining whether the graph opens up or down and by finding its vertex, axis of symmetry, y-intercept, and x-intercepts, if any.

(b) Determine the domain and the range of f.

(c) Determine where f is increasing and where it is decreasing.

Solution (a) **STEP 1:** For $f(x) = 2x^2 + x + 1$, we have $a = 2, b = 1$, and $c = 1$. Since $a = 2 > 0$, the parabola opens up.

STEP 2: The x-coordinate of the vertex is

$$h = -\frac{b}{2a} = -\frac{1}{4}$$

The y-coordinate of the vertex is

$$k = f\left(-\frac{1}{4}\right) = 2\left(\frac{1}{16}\right) + \left(-\frac{1}{4}\right) + 1 = \frac{7}{8}$$

So the vertex is at $\left(-\frac{1}{4}, \frac{7}{8}\right)$. The axis of symmetry is the line $x = -\frac{1}{4}$.

NOTE In Example 5, since the vertex is above the x-axis and the parabola opens up, we can conclude that the graph of the quadratic function will have no x-intercepts. ■

STEP 3: The y-intercept is $f(0) = 1$. The x-intercept(s), if any, obey the equation $2x^2 + x + 1 = 0$. Since the discriminant $b^2 - 4ac = (1)^2 - 4(2)(1) = -7 < 0$, this equation has no real solutions, and, therefore, the graph has no x-intercepts.

Figure 21

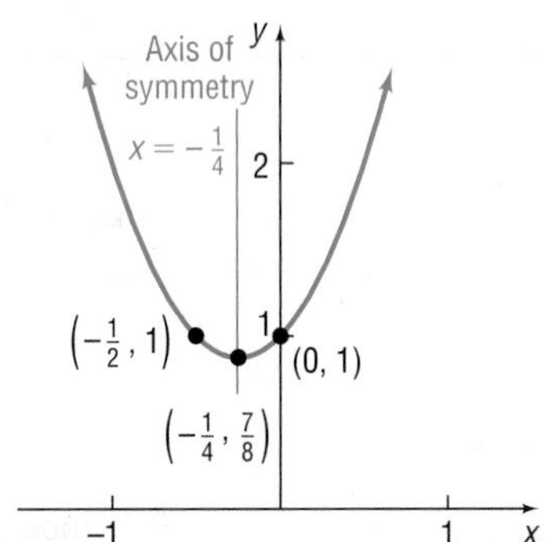

STEP 4: We use the point (0, 1) and the axis of symmetry $x = -\frac{1}{4}$ to locate the additional point $\left(-\frac{1}{2}, 1\right)$ on the graph. See Figure 21.

(b) The domain of f is the set of all real numbers. Based on the graph, the range of f is the interval $\left[\frac{7}{8}, \infty\right)$.

(c) The function f is decreasing on the interval $\left(-\infty, -\frac{1}{4}\right)$ and is increasing on the interval $\left(-\frac{1}{4}, \infty\right)$. ■

Now Work PROBLEM 41

4 Find a Quadratic Function Given Its Vertex and One Other Point

Given the vertex (h, k) and one additional point on the graph of a quadratic function $f(x) = ax^2 + bx + c, a \neq 0$, we can use

$$f(x) = a(x - h)^2 + k \qquad (3)$$

to obtain the quadratic function.

EXAMPLE 6 **Finding the Quadratic Function Given Its Vertex and One Other Point**

Determine the quadratic function whose vertex is $(1, -5)$ and whose y-intercept is -3. The graph of the parabola is shown in Figure 22 on the next page.

Figure 22

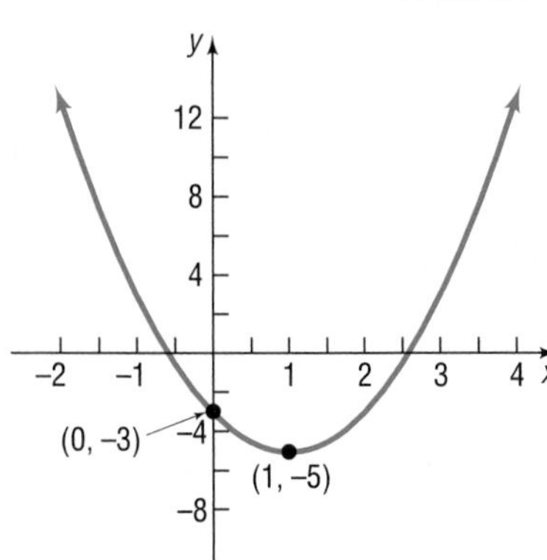

Solution The vertex is $(1, -5)$, so $h = 1$ and $k = -5$. Substitute these values into equation (3).

$$f(x) = a(x - h)^2 + k \quad \text{Equation (3)}$$
$$f(x) = a(x - 1)^2 - 5 \quad h = 1, k = -5$$

To determine the value of a, we use the fact that $f(0) = -3$ (the y-intercept).

$$f(x) = a(x - 1)^2 - 5$$
$$-3 = a(0 - 1)^2 - 5 \quad x = 0, y = f(0) = -3$$
$$-3 = a - 5$$
$$a = 2$$

The quadratic function whose graph is shown in Figure 22 is

$$f(x) = a(x - h)^2 + k = 2(x - 1)^2 - 5 = 2x^2 - 4x - 3$$

Figure 23

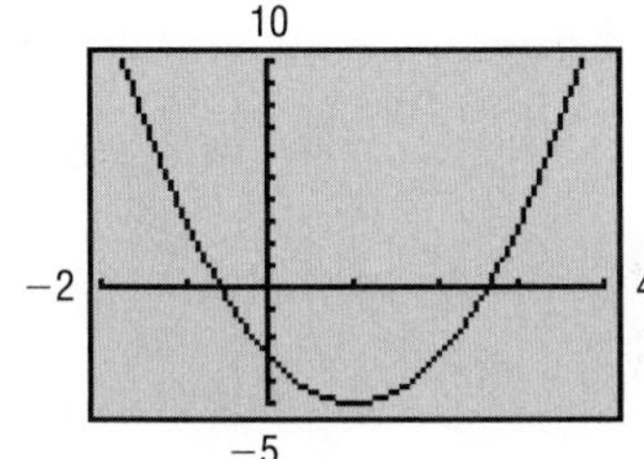

✓**Check:** Figure 23 shows the graph of $f(x) = 2x^2 - 4x - 3$ using a graphing utility. ■

Now Work PROBLEM 47

5 Find the Maximum or Minimum Value of a Quadratic Function

The graph of a quadratic function

$$f(x) = ax^2 + bx + c \qquad a \neq 0$$

is a parabola with vertex at $\left(-\frac{b}{2a}, f\left(-\frac{b}{2a}\right)\right)$. This vertex is the highest point on the graph if $a < 0$ and the lowest point on the graph if $a > 0$. If the vertex is the highest point ($a < 0$), then $f\left(-\frac{b}{2a}\right)$ is the **maximum value** of f. If the vertex is the lowest point ($a > 0$), then $f\left(-\frac{b}{2a}\right)$ is the **minimum value** of f.

EXAMPLE 7 **Finding the Maximum or Minimum Value of a Quadratic Function**

Determine whether the quadratic function

$$f(x) = x^2 - 4x - 5$$

has a maximum or minimum value. Then find the maximum or minimum value.

Solution Compare $f(x) = x^2 - 4x - 5$ to $f(x) = ax^2 + bx + c$. Then $a = 1, b = -4$, and $c = -5$. Since $a > 0$, the graph of f opens up, so the vertex is a minimum point. The minimum value occurs at

$$x = -\frac{b}{2a} \underset{\substack{\uparrow \\ a = 1, b = -4}}{=} -\frac{-4}{2(1)} = \frac{4}{2} = 2$$

The minimum value is

$$f\left(-\frac{b}{2a}\right) = f(2) = 2^2 - 4(2) - 5 = 4 - 8 - 5 = -9$$

✓**Check:** Graph $Y_1 = f(x) = x^2 - 4x - 5$. Use MINIMUM to verify the vertex is $(2, -9)$. ■

Now Work PROBLEM 55

SUMMARY

Steps for Graphing a Quadratic Function $f(x) = ax^2 + bx + c, a \neq 0$

Option 1

Step 1: Complete the square in x to write the quadratic function in the form $f(x) = a(x - h)^2 + k$.

Step 2: Graph the function in stages using transformations.

Option 2

Step 1: Determine whether the parabola opens up ($a > 0$) or down ($a < 0$).

Step 2: Determine the vertex $\left(-\frac{b}{2a}, f\left(-\frac{b}{2a}\right)\right)$.

Step 3: Determine the axis of symmetry, $x = -\frac{b}{2a}$.

Step 4: Determine the y-intercept, $f(0)$, and the x-intercepts, if any.

(a) If $b^2 - 4ac > 0$, the graph of the quadratic function has two x-intercepts, which are found by solving the equation $ax^2 + bx + c = 0$.

(b) If $b^2 - 4ac = 0$, the vertex is the x-intercept.

(c) If $b^2 - 4ac < 0$, there are no x-intercepts.

Step 5: Determine an additional point by using the y-intercept and the axis of symmetry.

Step 6: Plot the points and draw the graph.

10.3 Assess Your Understanding

'Are You Prepared?' *Answers are given at the end of these exercises. If you get a wrong answer, read the pages listed in red.*

1. List the intercepts of the equation $y = x^2 - 9$. (pp. 522–523)
2. Find the real solutions of the equation $2x^2 + 7x - 4 = 0$. (pp. 476–482)
3. To complete the square of $x^2 - 5x$, you add the number ______.
4. To graph $y = (x - 4)^2$, you shift the graph of $y = x^2$ to the ______ a distance of ______ units. (pp. 605–607)

Concepts and Vocabulary

5. The graph of a quadratic function is called a(n) ________.
6. The vertical line passing through the vertex of a parabola is called the ____________.
7. The x-coordinate of the vertex of $f(x) = ax^2 + bx + c$, $a \neq 0$, is ________.
8. ***True or False*** The graph of $f(x) = 2x^2 + 3x - 4$ opens up.
9. ***True or False*** The y-coordinate of the vertex of $f(x) = -x^2 + 4x + 5$ is $f(2)$.
10. ***True or False*** If the discriminant $b^2 - 4ac = 0$, the graph of $f(x) = ax^2 + bx + c, a \neq 0$, will touch the x-axis at its vertex.

Skill Building

In Problems 11–18, match each graph to one the following functions.

11. $f(x) = x^2 - 1$
12. $f(x) = -x^2 - 1$
13. $f(x) = x^2 - 2x + 1$
14. $f(x) = x^2 + 2x + 1$
15. $f(x) = x^2 - 2x + 2$
16. $f(x) = x^2 + 2x$
17. $f(x) = x^2 - 2x$
18. $f(x) = x^2 + 2x + 2$

A
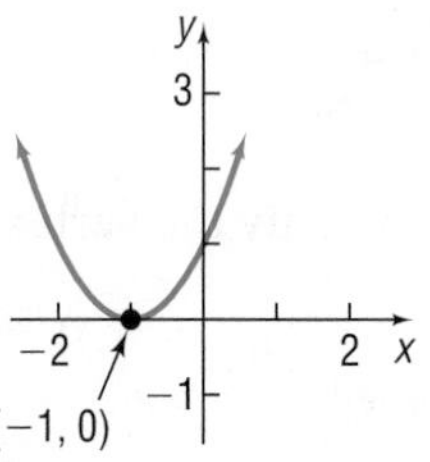

B
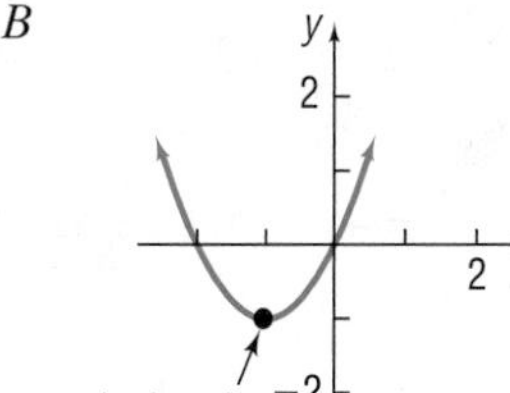

C
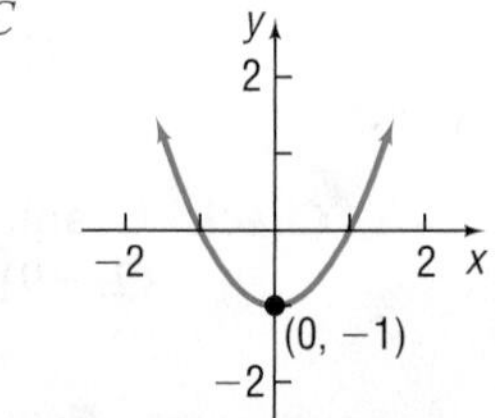

D
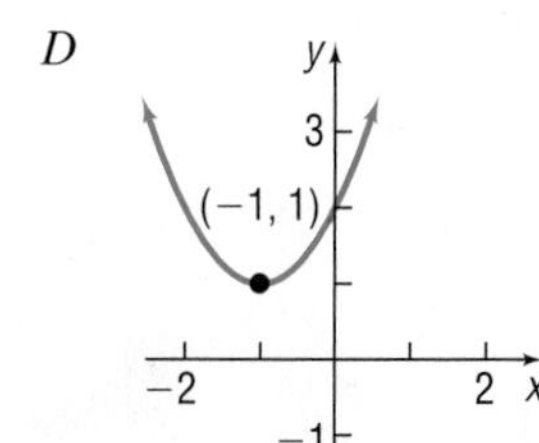

E

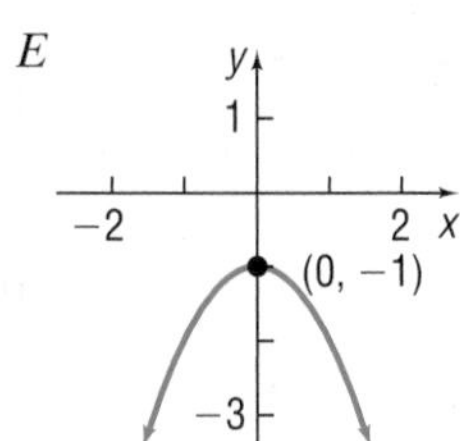

F

G

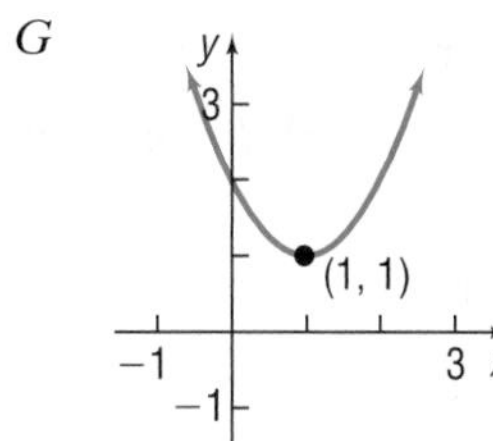

H

In Problems 19–30, graph the function f by starting with the graph of $y = x^2$ and using transformations (shifting, compressing, stretching, and/or reflection). Verify your results using a graphing utility.

[**Hint:** If necessary, write f in the form $f(x) = a(x - h)^2 + k$.]

19. $f(x) = \frac{1}{4}x^2$ **20.** $f(x) = 2x^2 + 4$ **21.** $f(x) = (x + 2)^2 - 2$ **22.** $f(x) = (x - 3)^2 - 10$

23. $f(x) = x^2 + 4x + 2$ **24.** $f(x) = x^2 - 6x - 1$ **25.** $f(x) = 2x^2 - 4x + 1$ **26.** $f(x) = 3x^2 + 6x$

27. $f(x) = -x^2 - 2x$ **28.** $f(x) = -2x^2 + 6x + 2$ **29.** $f(x) = \frac{1}{2}x^2 + x - 1$ **30.** $f(x) = \frac{2}{3}x^2 + \frac{4}{3}x - 1$

In Problems 31–46, (a) graph each quadratic function by determining whether its graph opens up or down and by finding its vertex, axis of symmetry, y-intercept, and x-intercepts, if any. (b) Determine the domain and the range of the function. (c) Determine where the function is increasing and where it is decreasing. Verify your results using a graphing utility.

31. $f(x) = x^2 + 2x$ **32.** $f(x) = x^2 - 4x$ **33.** $f(x) = -x^2 - 6x$ **34.** $f(x) = -x^2 + 4x$

35. $f(x) = x^2 + 2x - 8$ **36.** $f(x) = x^2 - 2x - 3$ 37. $f(x) = x^2 + 2x + 1$ **38.** $f(x) = x^2 + 6x + 9$

39. $f(x) = 2x^2 - x + 2$ **40.** $f(x) = 4x^2 - 2x + 1$ 41. $f(x) = -2x^2 + 2x - 3$ **42.** $f(x) = -3x^2 + 3x - 2$

43. $f(x) = 3x^2 + 6x + 2$ **44.** $f(x) = 2x^2 + 5x + 3$ **45.** $f(x) = -4x^2 - 6x + 2$ **46.** $f(x) = 3x^2 - 8x + 2$

In Problems 47–52, determine the quadratic function whose graph is given.

47.

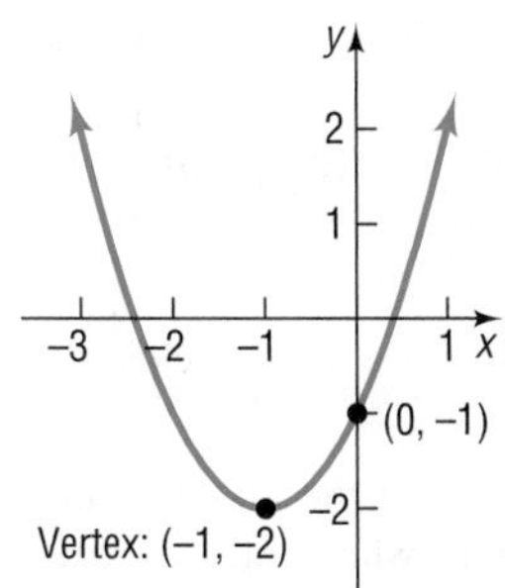

48.

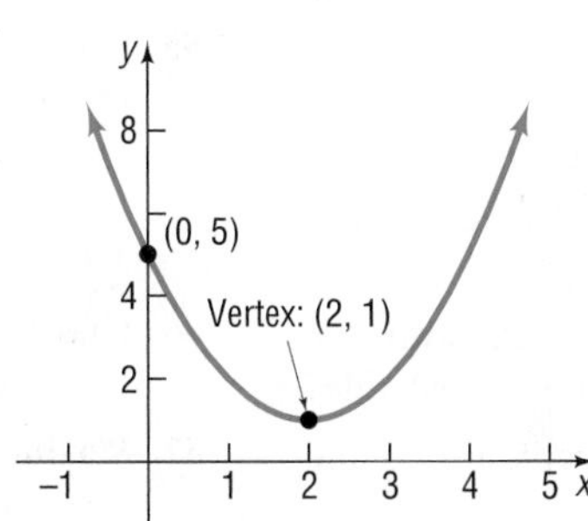

49.

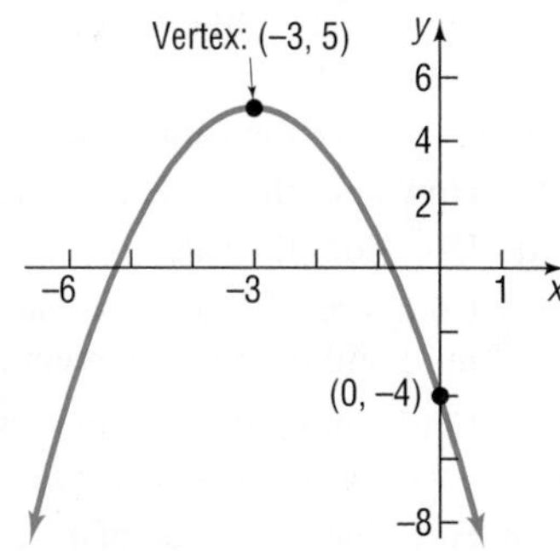

50.

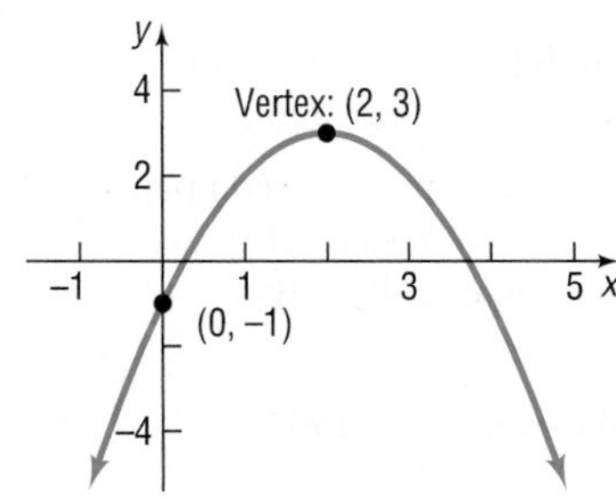

51.

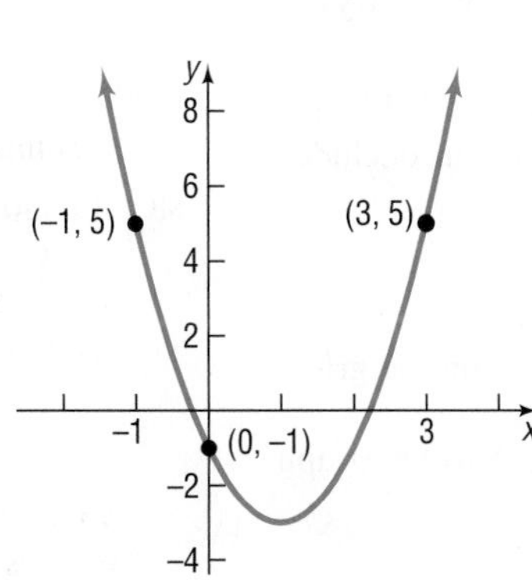

52.

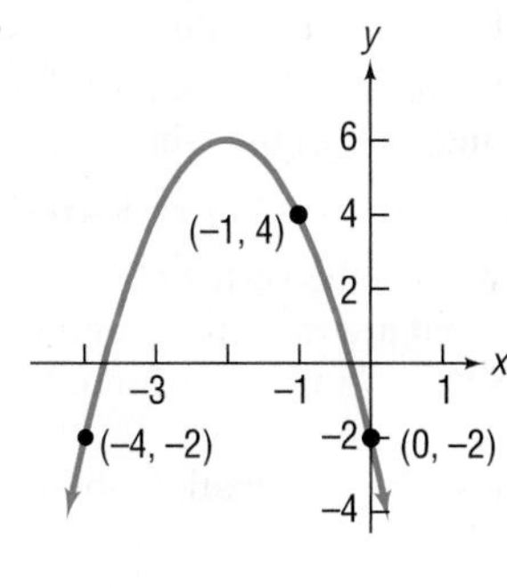

In Problems 53–60, determine, without graphing, whether the given quadratic function has a maximum value or a minimum value and then find the value.

53. $f(x) = 2x^2 + 12x$ **54.** $f(x) = -2x^2 + 12x$ 55. $f(x) = 2x^2 + 12x - 3$ **56.** $f(x) = 4x^2 - 8x + 3$

57. $f(x) = -x^2 + 10x - 4$ **58.** $f(x) = -2x^2 + 8x + 3$ **59.** $f(x) = -3x^2 + 12x + 1$ **60.** $f(x) = 4x^2 - 4x$

Mixed Practice

In Problems 61–72, (a) graph each function, (b) determine the domain and the range of the function, and (c) determine where the function is increasing and where it is decreasing.

61. $f(x) = x^2 - 2x - 15$ **62.** $g(x) = x^2 - 2x - 8$ **63.** $F(x) = 2x - 5$ **64.** $f(x) = \frac{3}{2}x - 2$

65. $g(x) = -2(x - 3)^2 + 2$ **66.** $h(x) = -3(x + 1)^2 + 4$ **67.** $f(x) = 2x^2 + x + 1$ **68.** $G(x) = 3x^2 + 2x + 5$

69. $h(x) = -\frac{2}{5}x + 4$ **70.** $f(x) = -3x + 2$ **71.** $H(x) = -4x^2 - 4x - 1$ **72.** $F(x) = -4x^2 + 20x - 25$

Applications and Extensions

73. The graph of the function $f(x) = ax^2 + bx + c$ has vertex at $(0, 2)$ and passes through the point $(1, 8)$. Find a, b, and c.

74. The graph of the function $f(x) = ax^2 + bx + c$ has vertex at $(1, 4)$ and passes through the point $(-1, -8)$. Find a, b, and c.

In Problems 75–80, for the given functions f and g,

(a) *Graph f and g on the same Cartesian plane.*
(b) *Solve $f(x) = g(x)$.*
(c) *Use the result of part (b) to label the points of intersection of the graphs of f and g.*
(d) *Shade the region for which $f(x) > g(x)$, that is, the region below f and above g.*

75. $f(x) = 2x - 1;\ g(x) = x^2 - 4$

76. $f(x) = -2x - 1;\ g(x) = x^2 - 9$

77. $f(x) = -x^2 + 4;\ g(x) = -2x + 1$

78. $f(x) = -x^2 + 9;\ g(x) = 2x + 1$

79. $f(x) = -x^2 + 5x;\ g(x) = x^2 + 3x - 4$

80. $f(x) = -x^2 + 7x - 6;\ g(x) = x^2 + x - 6$

Answer Problems 81 and 82 using the following: A quadratic function of the form $f(x) = ax^2 + bx + c$ with $b^2 - 4ac > 0$ may also be written in the form $f(x) = a(x - r_1)(x - r_2)$, where r_1 and r_2 are the x-intercepts of the graph of the quadratic function.

81. (a) Find a quadratic function whose x-intercepts are -3 and 1 with $a = 1; a = 2; a = -2; a = 5$.
(b) How does the value of a affect the intercepts?
(c) How does the value of a affect the axis of symmetry?
(d) How does the value of a affect the vertex?
(e) Compare the x-coordinate of the vertex with the midpoint of the x-intercepts. What might you conclude?

82. (a) Find a quadratic function whose x-intercepts are -5 and 3 with $a = 1; a = 2; a = -2; a = 5$.
(b) How does the value of a affect the intercepts?
(c) How does the value of a affect the axis of symmetry?
(d) How does the value of a affect the vertex?
(e) Compare the x-coordinate of the vertex with the midpoint of the x-intercepts. What might you conclude?

83. Suppose that $f(x) = x^2 + 4x - 21$.
(a) What is the vertex of f?
(b) What are the x-intercepts of the graph of f?
(c) Solve $f(x) = -21$ for x. What points are on the graph of f?
(d) Use the information obtained in parts (a)–(c) to graph $f(x) = x^2 + 4x - 21$.

84. Suppose that $f(x) = x^2 + 2x - 8$.
(a) What is the vertex of f?
(b) What are the x-intercepts of the graph of f?
(c) Solve $f(x) = -8$ for x. What points are on the graph of f?
(d) Use the information obtained in parts (a)–(c) to graph $f(x) = x^2 + 2x - 8$.

85. Find the point on the line $y = x$ that is closest to the point $(3, 1)$.

[**Hint:** Express the distance d from the point to the line as a function of x, and then find the minimum value of $[d(x)]^2$.]

86. Find the point on the line $y = x + 1$ that is closest to the point $(4, 1)$.

87. Maximizing Revenue Suppose that the manufacturer of a gas clothes dryer has found that, when the unit price is p dollars, the revenue R (in dollars) is

$$R(p) = -4p^2 + 4000p$$

What unit price should be established for the dryer to maximize revenue? What is the maximum revenue?

88. Maximizing Revenue The John Deere company has found that the revenue, in dollars, from sales of riding mowers is a function of the unit price p, in dollars, that it charges. If the revenue R is

$$R(p) = -\frac{1}{2}p^2 + 1900p$$

what unit price p should be charged to maximize revenue? What is the maximum revenue?

89. Minimizing Marginal Cost The **marginal cost** of a product can be thought of as the cost of producing one additional unit of output. For example, if the marginal cost of producing the 50th product is \$6.20, it cost \$6.20 to increase production from 49 to 50 units of output. Suppose the marginal cost C

(in dollars) to produce x thousand mp3 players is given by the function

$$C(x) = x^2 - 140x + 7400$$

(a) How many players should be produced to minimize the marginal cost?

(b) What is the minimum marginal cost?

90. Minimizing Marginal Cost (See Problem 89.) The marginal cost C (in dollars) of manufacturing x cell phones (in thousands) is given by

$$C(x) = 5x^2 - 200x + 4000$$

(a) How many cell phones should be manufactured to minimize the marginal cost?

(b) What is the minimum marginal cost?

91. Business The monthly revenue R achieved by selling x wristwatches is figured to be $R(x) = 75x - 0.2x^2$. The monthly cost C of selling x wristwatches is $C(x) = 32x + 1750$.

(a) How many wristwatches must the firm sell to maximize revenue? What is the maximum revenue?

(b) Profit is given as $P(x) = R(x) - C(x)$. What is the profit function?

(c) How many wristwatches must the firm sell to maximize profit? What is the maximum profit?

(d) Provide a reasonable explanation as to why the answers found in parts (a) and (c) differ. Explain why a quadratic function is a reasonable model for revenue.

92. Business The daily revenue R achieved by selling x boxes of candy is figured to be $R(x) = 9.5x - 0.04x^2$. The daily cost C of selling x boxes of candy is $C(x) = 1.25x + 250$.

(a) How many boxes of candy must the firm sell to maximize revenue? What is the maximum revenue?

(b) Profit is given as $P(x) = R(x) - C(x)$. What is the profit function?

(c) How many boxes of candy must the firm sell to maximize profit? What is the maximum profit?

(d) Provide a reasonable explanation as to why the answers found in parts (a) and (c) differ. Explain why a quadratic function is a reasonable model for revenue.

93. Stopping Distance An accepted relationship between stopping distance, d (in feet), and the speed of a car, v (in mph), is $d = 1.1v + 0.06v^2$ on dry, level concrete.

(a) How many feet will it take a car traveling 45 mph to stop on dry, level concrete?

(b) If an accident occurs 200 feet ahead of you, what is the maximum speed you can be traveling to avoid being involved?

(c) What might the term $1.1v$ represent?

Source: www2.nsta.org/Energy/fn_braking.html

94. Birthrate of Unmarried Women In the United States, the birthrate B of unmarried women (births per 1000 unmarried women) for women whose age is a is modeled by the function $B(a) = -0.27a^2 + 14.23a - 120.16$.

(a) What is the age of unmarried women with the highest birthrate?

(b) What is the highest birthrate of unmarried women?

(c) Evaluate and interpret $B(40)$.

Source: United States Statistical Abstract, 2009

95. Find a quadratic function whose x-intercepts are -4 and 2 and whose range is $[-18, \infty)$.

96. Find a quadratic function whose x-intercepts are -1 and 5 and whose range is $(-\infty, 9]$.

97. Let $f(x) = ax^2 + bx + c$, where a, b, and c are odd integers. If x is an integer, show that $f(x)$ must be an odd integer.
[**Hint:** x is either an even integer or an odd integer.]

Explaining Concepts: Discussion and Writing

98. Make up a quadratic function that opens down and has only one x-intercept. Compare yours with others in the class. What are the similarities? What are the differences?

99. On one set of coordinate axes, graph the family of parabolas $f(x) = x^2 + 2x + c$ for $c = -3$, $c = 0$, and $c = 1$. Describe the characteristics of a member of this family.

100. On one set of coordinate axes, graph the family of parabolas $f(x) = x^2 + bx + 1$ for $b = -4$, $b = 0$, and $b = 4$. Describe the general characteristics of this family.

101. State the circumstances that cause the graph of a quadratic function $f(x) = ax^2 + bx + c$ to have no x-intercepts.

102. Why does the graph of a quadratic function open up if $a > 0$ and down if $a < 0$?

103. Can a quadratic function have a range of $(-\infty, \infty)$? Justify your answer.

104. What are the possibilities for the number of times the graphs of two different quadratic functions intersect?

'Are You Prepared?' Answers

1. $(0, -9), (-3, 0), (3, 0)$ **2.** $\left\{-4, \frac{1}{2}\right\}$ **3.** $\frac{25}{4}$ **4.** right; 4

10.4 Build Quadratic Models from Verbal Descriptions and from Data

PREPARING FOR THIS SECTION *Before getting started, review the following:*

- Linear Models: Building Linear Functions from Data (Section 10.2, pp. 641–644)

Now Work the **'Are You Prepared?'** problems on page 665.

OBJECTIVES 1 Build Quadratic Models from Verbal Descriptions (p. 660)
2 Build Quadratic Models from Data (p. 664)

In this section we will first discuss models in the form of a quadratic function when a verbal description of the problem is given. We end the section by fitting a quadratic function to data, which is another form of modeling.

When a mathematical model is in the form of a quadratic function, the properties of the graph of the quadratic function can provide important information about the model. In particular, we can use the quadratic function to determine the maximum or minimum value of the function. The fact that the graph of a quadratic function has a maximum or minimum value enables us to answer questions involving **optimization,** that is, finding the maximum or minimum values in models.

1 Build Quadratic Models from Verbal Descriptions

In economics, revenue R, in dollars, is defined as the amount of money received from the sale of an item and is equal to the unit selling price p, in dollars, of the item times the number x of units actually sold. That is,

$$R = xp$$

The Law of Demand states that p and x are related: As one increases, the other decreases. The equation that relates p and x is called the **demand equation.** When the demand equation is linear, the revenue model is a quadratic function.

EXAMPLE 1 **Maximizing Revenue**

The marketing department at Texas Instruments has found that, when certain calculators are sold at a price of p dollars per unit, the number x of calculators sold is given by the demand equation

$$x = 21{,}000 - 150p$$

(a) Find a model that expresses the revenue R as a function of the price p.
(b) What is the domain of R?
(c) What unit price should be used to maximize revenue?
(d) If this price is charged, what is the maximum revenue?
(e) How many units are sold at this price?
(f) Graph R.
(g) What price should Texas Instruments charge to collect at least \$675,000 in revenue?

Solution (a) The revenue R is $R = xp$, where $x = 21{,}000 - 150p$.

$$R = xp = (21{,}000 - 150p)p = -150p^2 + 21{,}000p \quad \text{The Model}$$

(b) Because x represents the number of calculators sold, we have $x \geq 0$, so $21{,}000 - 150p \geq 0$. Solving this linear inequality, we find that $p \leq 140$. In addition, Texas Instruments will only charge a positive price for the calculator, so $p > 0$. Combining these inequalities, the domain of R is $\{p \mid 0 < p \leq 140\}$.

(c) The function R is a quadratic function with $a = -150$, $b = 21{,}000$, and $c = 0$. Because $a < 0$, the vertex is the highest point on the parabola. The revenue R is a maximum when the price p is

$$p = -\frac{b}{2a} \underset{\uparrow}{=} -\frac{21{,}000}{2(-150)} = -\frac{21{,}000}{-300} = \$70.00$$

$a = -150$, $b = 21{,}000$

(d) The maximum revenue R is

$$R(70) = -150(70)^2 + 21{,}000(70) = \$735{,}000$$

(e) The number of calculators sold is given by the demand equation $x = 21{,}000 - 150p$. At a price of $p = \$70$,

$$x = 21{,}000 - 150(70) = 10{,}500$$

calculators are sold.

(f) To graph R, plot the intercept (140, 0) and the vertex (70, 735,000). See Figure 24 for the graph.

Figure 24

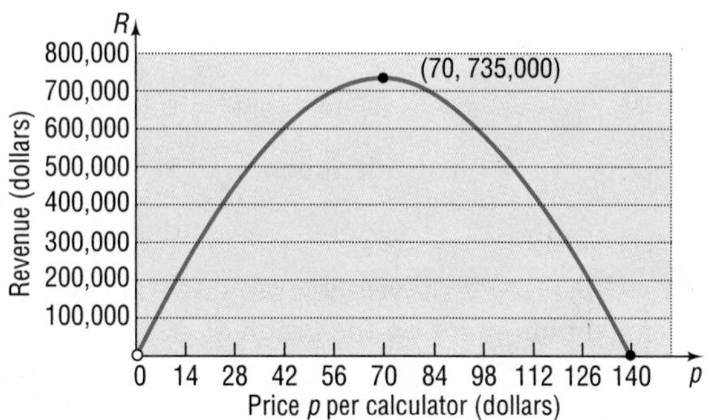

(g) Graph $R = 675{,}000$ and $R(p) = -150p^2 + 21{,}000p$ on the same Cartesian plane. See Figure 25. We find where the graphs intersect by solving

$$\begin{aligned} 675{,}000 &= -150p^2 + 21{,}000p \\ 150p^2 - 21{,}000p + 675{,}000 &= 0 && \text{Add } 150p^2 - 21{,}000p \text{ to both sides.} \\ p^2 - 140p + 4500 &= 0 && \text{Divide both sides by 150.} \\ (p - 50)(p - 90) &= 0 && \text{Factor.} \\ p = 50 \text{ or } p &= 90 && \text{Use the Zero-Product Property.} \end{aligned}$$

Figure 25

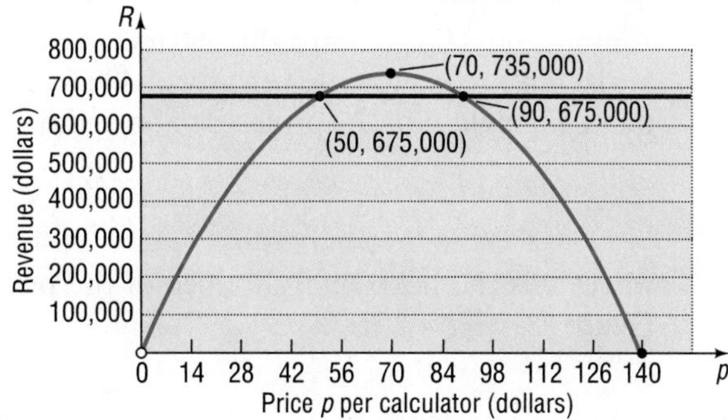

The graphs intersect at (50, 675,000) and (90, 675,000). Based on the graph in Figure 25, Texas Instruments should charge between \$50 and \$90 to earn at least \$675,000 in revenue. ■

Now Work PROBLEM 3

EXAMPLE 2 Maximizing the Area Enclosed by a Fence

A farmer has 2000 yards of fence to enclose a rectangular field. What are the dimensions of the rectangle that encloses the most area?

Solution Figure 26 illustrates the situation. The available fence represents the perimeter of the rectangle. If x is the length and w is the width, then

Figure 26

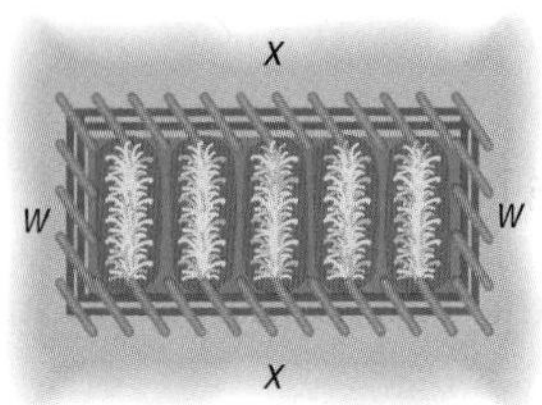

$$2x + 2w = 2000 \qquad \textbf{(1)}$$

The area A of the rectangle is

$$A = xw$$

To express A in terms of a single variable, solve equation (1) for w and substitute the result in $A = xw$. Then A involves only the variable x. [You could also solve equation (1) for x and express A in terms of w alone. Try it!]

$$\begin{aligned} 2x + 2w &= 2000 \\ 2w &= 2000 - 2x \\ w &= \frac{2000 - 2x}{2} = 1000 - x \end{aligned}$$

Then the area A is

$$A = xw = x(1000 - x) = -x^2 + 1000x$$

Now, A is a quadratic function of x.

$$A(x) = -x^2 + 1000x \quad a = -1, b = 1000, c = 0$$

Figure 27 shows the graph of $A(x) = -x^2 + 1000x$. Since $a < 0$, the vertex is a maximum point on the graph of A. The maximum value occurs at

$$x = -\frac{b}{2a} = -\frac{1000}{2(-1)} = 500$$

The maximum value of A is

Figure 27

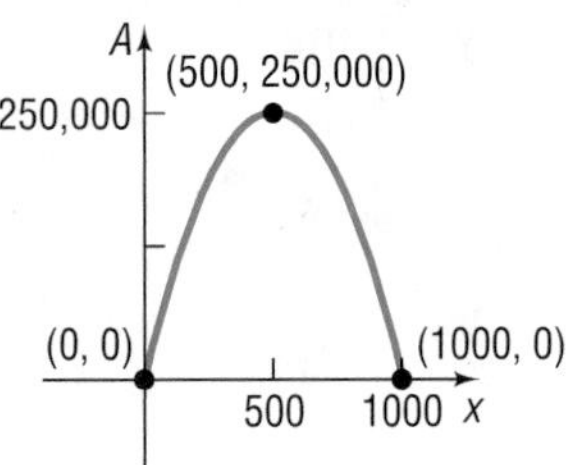

$$A\left(-\frac{b}{2a}\right) = A(500) = -500^2 + 1000(500) = -250{,}000 + 500{,}000 = 250{,}000$$

The largest rectangle that can be enclosed by 2000 yards of fence has an area of 250,000 square yards. Its dimensions are 500 yards by 500 yards. ■

Now Work PROBLEM 7

EXAMPLE 3 Analyzing the Motion of a Projectile

A projectile is fired from a cliff 500 feet above the water at an inclination of 45° to the horizontal, with a muzzle velocity of 400 feet per second. In physics, it is established that the height h of the projectile above the water can be modeled by

$$h(x) = \frac{-32x^2}{(400)^2} + x + 500$$

where x is the horizontal distance of the projectile from the base of the cliff. See Figure 28.

Figure 28

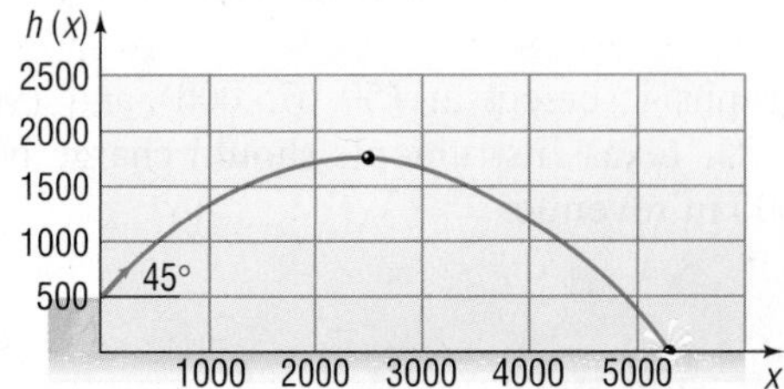

(a) Find the maximum height of the projectile.

(b) How far from the base of the cliff will the projectile strike the water?

Solution (a) The height of the projectile is given by a quadratic function.

$$h(x) = \frac{-32x^2}{(400)^2} + x + 500 = \frac{-1}{5000}x^2 + x + 500$$

We are looking for the maximum value of h. Since $a < 0$, the maximum value is obtained at the vertex, whose x-coordinate is

$$x = -\frac{b}{2a} = -\frac{1}{2\left(-\frac{1}{5000}\right)} = \frac{5000}{2} = 2500$$

The maximum height of the projectile is

$$h(2500) = \frac{-1}{5000}(2500)^2 + 2500 + 500 = -1250 + 2500 + 500 = 1750 \text{ ft}$$

(b) The projectile will strike the water when the height is zero. To find the distance x traveled, solve the equation

$$h(x) = \frac{-1}{5000}x^2 + x + 500 = 0$$

The discriminant of this quadratic equation is

$$b^2 - 4ac = 1^2 - 4\left(\frac{-1}{5000}\right)(500) = 1.4$$

Then

$$x = \frac{-b \pm \sqrt{b^2 - 4ac}}{2a} = \frac{-1 \pm \sqrt{1.4}}{2\left(-\frac{1}{5000}\right)} \approx \begin{cases} -458 \\ 5458 \end{cases}$$

Discard the negative solution. The projectile will strike the water at a distance of about 5458 feet from the base of the cliff. ■

Seeing the Concept

Graph

$$h(x) = \frac{-1}{5000}x^2 + x + 500$$
$$0 \le x \le 5500$$

Use MAXIMUM to find the maximum height of the projectile, and use ROOT or ZERO to find the distance from the base of the cliff to where it strikes the water. Compare your results with those obtained in Example 3.

Now Work PROBLEM 11

EXAMPLE 4 The Golden Gate Bridge

The Golden Gate Bridge, a suspension bridge, spans the entrance to San Francisco Bay. Its 746-foot-tall towers are 4200 feet apart. The bridge is suspended from two huge cables more than 3 feet in diameter; the 90-foot-wide roadway is 220 feet above the water. The cables are parabolic in shape* and touch the road surface at the center of the bridge. Find the height of the cable above the road at a distance of 1000 feet from the center.

Solution See Figure 29 on the next page. Begin by choosing the placement of the coordinate axes so that the x-axis coincides with the road surface and the origin coincides with the center of the bridge. As a result, the twin towers will be vertical (height $746 - 220 = 526$ feet above the road) and located 2100 feet from the center. Also, the cable, which has the shape of a parabola, will extend from the towers, open up, and have its vertex at $(0, 0)$. The choice of placement of the axes enables us to identify the equation of the parabola as $y = ax^2, a > 0$. Notice that the points $(-2100, 526)$ and $(2100, 526)$ are on the graph.

*A cable suspended from two towers is in the shape of a **catenary**, but when a horizontal roadway is suspended from the cable, the cable takes the shape of a parabola.

Figure 29

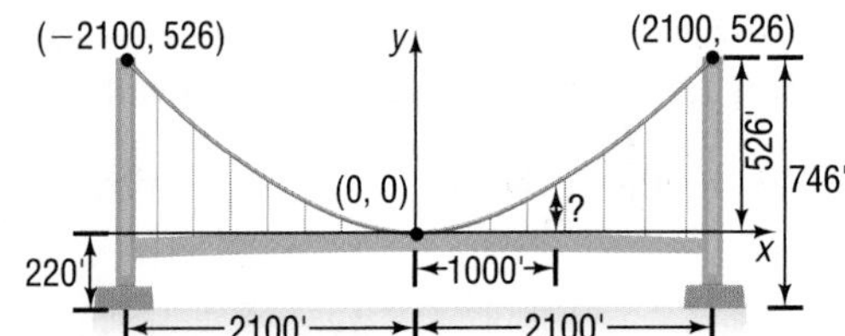

Based on these facts, we can find the value of a in $y = ax^2$.

$$y = ax^2$$
$$526 = a(2100)^2 \quad x = 2100,\ y = 526$$
$$a = \frac{526}{(2100)^2}$$

The equation of the parabola is

$$y = \frac{526}{(2100)^2}x^2$$

The height of the cable when $x = 1000$ is

$$y = \frac{526}{(2100)^2}(1000)^2 \approx 119.3 \text{ feet}$$

The cable is 119.3 feet above the road at a distance of 1000 feet from the center of the bridge. ■

Now Work PROBLEM 13

2 Build Quadratic Models from Data

In Section 10.2, we found the line of best fit for data that appeared to be linearly related. It was noted that data may also follow a nonlinear relation. Figures 30(a) and (b) show scatter diagrams of data that follow a quadratic relation.

Figure 30

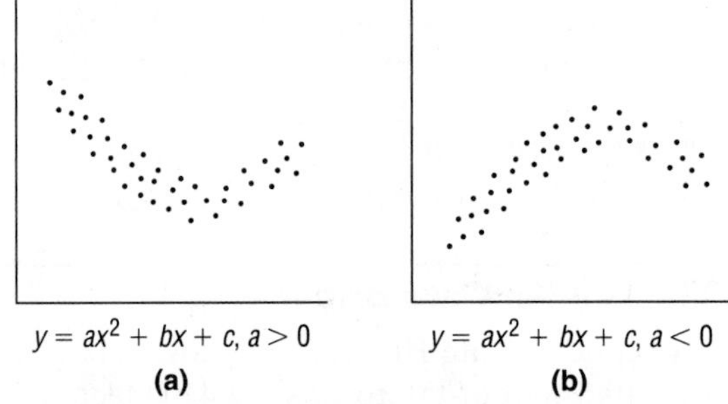

EXAMPLE 5 **Fitting a Quadratic Function to Data**

The data in Table 8 on the next page represent the percentage D of the population that is divorced for various ages x in 2007.

(a) Draw a scatter diagram of the data treating age as the independent variable. Comment on the type of relation that may exist between age and percentage of the population divorced.
(b) Use a graphing utility to find the quadratic function of best fit that models the relation between age and percentage of the population divorced.
(c) Use the model found in part (b) to approximate the age at which the percentage of the population divorced is greatest.
(d) Use the model found in part (b) to approximate the highest percentage of the population that is divorced.
(e) Use a graphing utility to draw the quadratic function of best fit on the scatter diagram.

Table 8

Age, x	Percentage Divorced, D
22	0.8
27	2.8
32	6.4
37	8.7
42	12.3
50	14.5
60	13.8
70	9.6
80	4.9

Source: United States Statistical Abstract, 2009

Figure 31

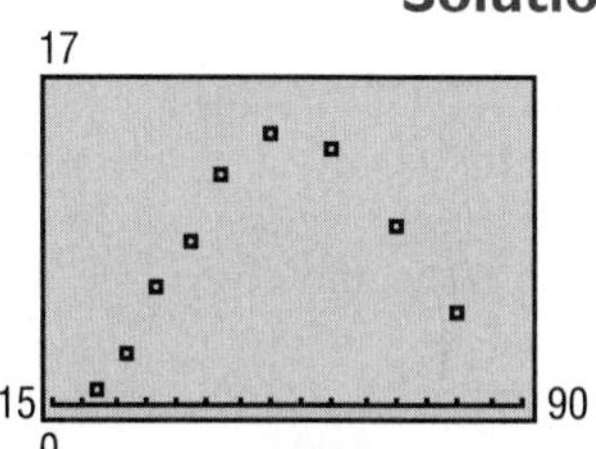

Solution

(a) Figure 31 shows the scatter diagram, from which it appears the data follow a quadratic relation, with $a < 0$.

(b) Upon executing the QUADratic REGression program, we obtain the results shown in Figure 32. The output of the utility shows us the equation $y = ax^2 + bx + c$. The quadratic function of best fit that models the relation between age and percentage divorced is

$$D(x) = -0.0136x^2 + 1.4794x - 26.3412 \quad \text{The Model}$$

where a represents age and D represents the percentage divorced.

Figure 32

(c) Based on the quadratic function of best fit, the age with the greatest percentage divorced is

$$-\frac{b}{2a} = -\frac{1.4794}{2(-0.0136)} \approx 54 \text{ years}$$

(d) Evaluate the function $D(x)$ at $x = 54$.

Figure 33

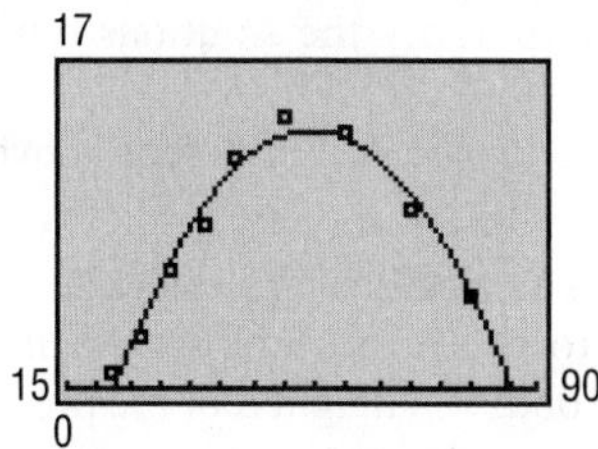

$$D(54) = -0.0136(54)^2 + 1.4794(54) - 26.3412 \approx 13.9 \text{ percent}$$

According to the model, 54-year-olds have the highest percentage divorced at 13.9 percent.

(e) Figure 33 shows the graph of the quadratic function found in part (b) drawn on the scatter diagram. ■

Now Work PROBLEM 25

10.4 Assess Your Understanding

'Are You Prepared?' *Answers are given at the end of these exercises. If you get a wrong answer, read the pages listed in red.*

1. Translate the following sentence into a mathematical equation: The total revenue R from selling x hot dogs is \$3 times the number of hot dogs sold. (pp. 503–504)

2. Use a graphing utility to find the line of best fit for the following data: (pp. 643–644)

x	3	5	5	6	7	8
y	10	13	12	15	16	19

Applications and Extensions

3. **Maximizing Revenue** The price p (in dollars) and the quantity x sold of a certain product obey the demand equation

$$p = -\frac{1}{6}x + 100$$

(a) Find a model that expresses the revenue R as a function of x. (Remember, $R = xp$.)

(b) What is the domain of R?

(c) What is the revenue if 200 units are sold?

(d) What quantity x maximizes revenue? What is the maximum revenue?
(e) What price should the company charge to maximize revenue?

4. Maximizing Revenue The price p (in dollars) and the quantity x sold of a certain product obey the demand equation

$$p = -\frac{1}{3}x + 100$$

(a) Find a model that expresses the revenue R as a function of x.
(b) What is the domain of R?
(c) What is the revenue if 100 units are sold?
(d) What quantity x maximizes revenue? What is the maximum revenue?
(e) What price should the company charge to maximize revenue?

5. Maximizing Revenue The price p (in dollars) and the quantity x sold of a certain product obey the demand equation

$$x = -5p + 100 \qquad 0 < p \le 20$$

(a) Express the revenue R as a function of x.
(b) What is the revenue if 15 units are sold?
(c) What quantity x maximizes revenue? What is the maximum revenue?
(d) What price should the company charge to maximize revenue?
(e) What price should the company charge to earn at least \$480 in revenue?

6. Maximizing Revenue The price p (in dollars) and the quantity x sold of a certain product obey the demand equation

$$x = -20p + 500 \qquad 0 < p \le 25$$

(a) Express the revenue R as a function of x.
(b) What is the revenue if 20 units are sold?
(c) What quantity x maximizes revenue? What is the maximum revenue?
(d) What price should the company charge to maximize revenue?
(e) What price should the company charge to earn at least \$3000 in revenue?

7. Enclosing a Rectangular Field David has 400 yards of fencing and wishes to enclose a rectangular area.
(a) Express the area A of the rectangle as a function of the width w of the rectangle.
(b) For what value of w is the area largest?
(c) What is the maximum area?

8. Enclosing a Rectangular Field Beth has 3000 feet of fencing available to enclose a rectangular field.
(a) Express the area A of the rectangle as a function of x, where x is the length of the rectangle.
(b) For what value of x is the area largest?
(c) What is the maximum area?

9. Enclosing the Most Area with a Fence A farmer with 4000 meters of fencing wants to enclose a rectangular plot that borders on a river. If the farmer does not fence the side along the river, what is the largest area that can be enclosed? (See the figure in the next column.)

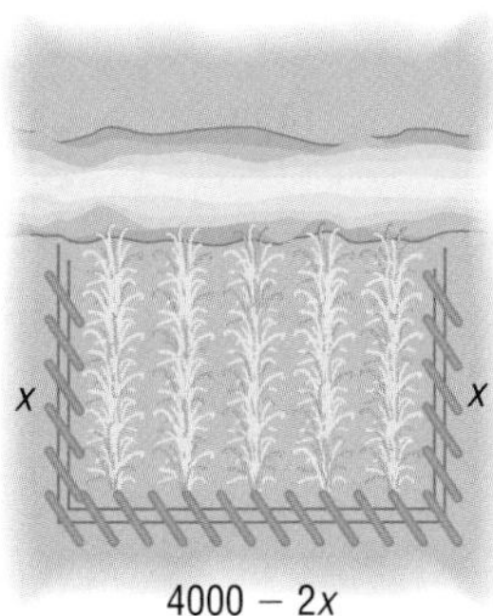

10. Enclosing the Most Area with a Fence A farmer with 2000 meters of fencing wants to enclose a rectangular plot that borders on a straight highway. If the farmer does not fence the side along the highway, what is the largest area that can be enclosed?

11. Analyzing the Motion of a Projectile A projectile is fired from a cliff 200 feet above the water at an inclination of 45° to the horizontal, with a muzzle velocity of 50 feet per second. The height h of the projectile above the water is modeled by

$$h(x) = \frac{-32x^2}{(50)^2} + x + 200$$

where x is the horizontal distance of the projectile from the face of the cliff.
(a) At what horizontal distance from the face of the cliff is the height of the projectile a maximum?
(b) Find the maximum height of the projectile.
(c) At what horizontal distance from the face of the cliff will the projectile strike the water?
(d) Using a graphing utility, graph the function h, $0 \le x \le 200$.
(e) Use a graphing utility to verify the solutions found in parts (b) and (c).
(f) When the height of the projectile is 100 feet above the water, how far is it from the cliff?

12. Analyzing the Motion of a Projectile A projectile is fired at an inclination of 45° to the horizontal, with a muzzle velocity of 100 feet per second. The height h of the projectile is modeled by

$$h(x) = \frac{-32x^2}{(100)^2} + x$$

where x is the horizontal distance of the projectile from the firing point.
(a) At what horizontal distance from the firing point is the height of the projectile a maximum?
(b) Find the maximum height of the projectile.
(c) At what horizontal distance from the firing point will the projectile strike the ground?
(d) Using a graphing utility, graph the function h, $0 \le x \le 350$.
(e) Use a graphing utility to verify the results obtained in parts (b) and (c).
(f) When the height of the projectile is 50 feet above the ground, how far has it traveled horizontally?

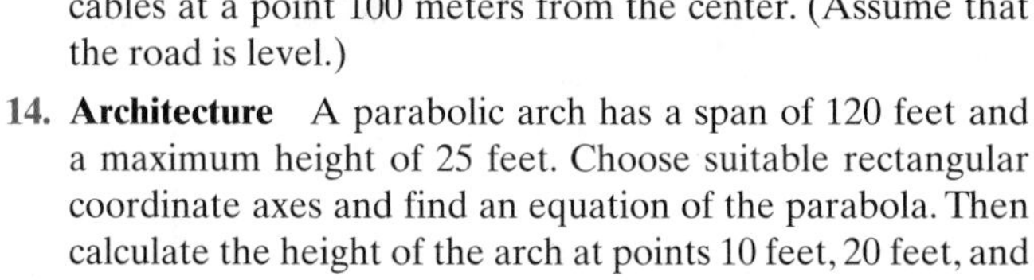

13. **Suspension Bridge** A suspension bridge with weight uniformly distributed along its length has twin towers that extend 75 meters above the road surface and are 400 meters apart. The cables are parabolic in shape and are suspended from the tops of the towers. The cables touch the road surface at the center of the bridge. Find the height of the cables at a point 100 meters from the center. (Assume that the road is level.)

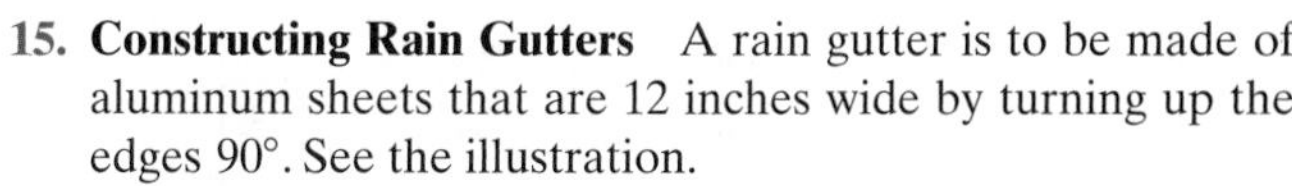

14. **Architecture** A parabolic arch has a span of 120 feet and a maximum height of 25 feet. Choose suitable rectangular coordinate axes and find an equation of the parabola. Then calculate the height of the arch at points 10 feet, 20 feet, and 40 feet from the center.

15. **Constructing Rain Gutters** A rain gutter is to be made of aluminum sheets that are 12 inches wide by turning up the edges 90°. See the illustration.
   (a) What depth will provide maximum cross-sectional area and hence allow the most water to flow?
   (b) What depths will allow at least 16 square inches of water to flow?

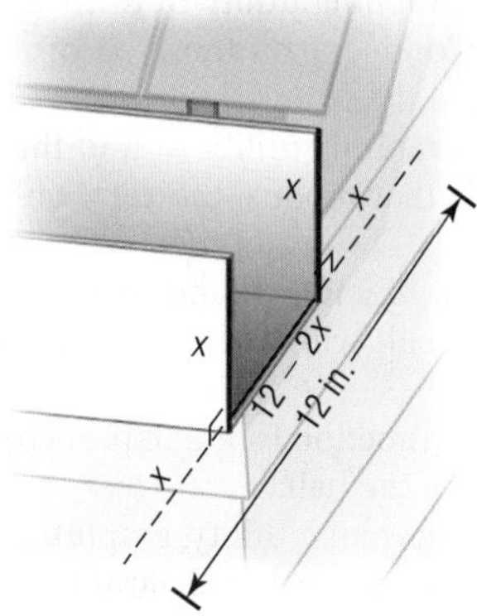

16. **Norman Windows** A **Norman window** has the shape of a rectangle surmounted by a semicircle of diameter equal to the width of the rectangle. See the figure. If the perimeter of the window is 20 feet, what dimensions will admit the most light (maximize the area)?

[**Hint:** Circumference of a circle $= 2\pi r$; area of a circle $= \pi r^2$, where r is the radius of the circle.]

17. **Constructing a Stadium** A track and field playing area is in the shape of a rectangle with semicircles at each end. See the figure. The inside perimeter of the track is to be 1500 meters. What should the dimensions of the rectangle be so that the area of the rectangle is a maximum?

18. **Architecture** A special window has the shape of a rectangle surmounted by an equilateral triangle. See the figure. If the perimeter of the window is 16 feet, what dimensions will admit the most light?

[**Hint:** Area of an equilateral triangle $= \left(\frac{\sqrt{3}}{4}\right)x^2$, where x is the length of a side of the triangle.]

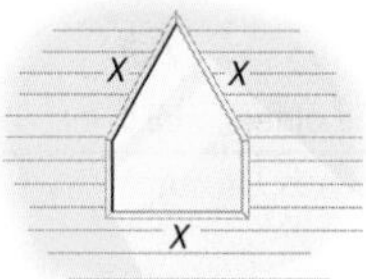

19. **Chemical Reactions** A self-catalytic chemical reaction results in the formation of a compound that causes the formation ratio to increase. If the reaction rate V is modeled by

$$V(x) = kx(a - x), \qquad 0 \le x \le a$$

where k is a positive constant, a is the initial amount of the compound, and x is the variable amount of the compound, for what value of x is the reaction rate a maximum?

20. **Calculus: Simpson's Rule** The figure shows the graph of $y = ax^2 + bx + c$. Suppose that the points $(-h, y_0)$, $(0, y_1)$, and (h, y_2) are on the graph. It can be shown that the area enclosed by the parabola, the x-axis, and the lines $x = -h$ and $x = h$ is

$$\text{Area} = \frac{h}{3}(2ah^2 + 6c)$$

Show that this area may also be given by

$$\text{Area} = \frac{h}{3}(y_0 + 4y_1 + y_2)$$

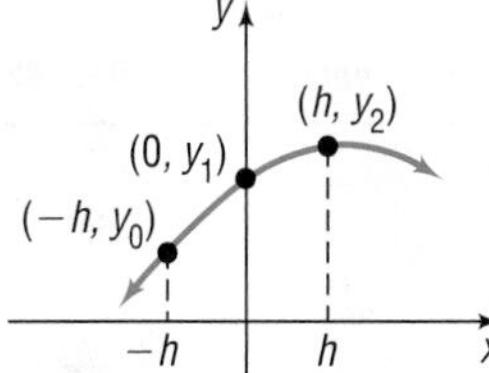

21. Use the result obtained in Problem 20 to find the area enclosed by $f(x) = -5x^2 + 8$, the x-axis, and the lines $x = -1$ and $x = 1$.

22. Use the result obtained in Problem 20 to find the area enclosed by $f(x) = 2x^2 + 8$, the x-axis, and the lines $x = -2$ and $x = 2$.

23. Use the result obtained in Problem 20 to find the area enclosed by $f(x) = x^2 + 3x + 5$, the x-axis, and the lines $x = -4$ and $x = 4$.

24. Use the result obtained in Problem 20 to find the area enclosed by $f(x) = -x^2 + x + 4$, the x-axis, and the lines $x = -1$ and $x = 1$.

25. **Life Cycle Hypothesis** An individual's income varies with his or her age. The following table shows the median income I of males of different age groups within the United States for 2009. For each age group, let the class midpoint represent the independent variable, x. For the class "65 years and older," we will assume that the class midpoint is 69.5.

Age	Class Midpoint, x	Median Income, I
15–24 years	19.5	$10,778
25–34 years	29.5	$33,415
35–44 years	39.5	$44,189
45–54 years	49.5	$45,540
55–64 years	59.5	$41,757
65 years and older	69.5	$25,503

Source: U.S. Census Bureau

(a) Use a graphing utility to draw a scatter diagram of the data. Comment on the type of relation that may exist between the two variables.
(b) Use a graphing utility to find the quadratic function of best fit that models the relation between age and median income.
(c) Use the function found in part (b) to determine the age at which an individual can expect to earn the most income. ≈
(d) Use the function found in part (b) to predict the peak income earned. ≈
(e) With a graphing utility, graph the quadratic function of best fit on the scatter diagram.

26. **Height of a Ball** A shot-putter throws a ball at an inclination of 45° to the horizontal. The following data represent the height of the ball h at the instant that it has traveled x feet horizontally.

Distance, x	Height, h
20	25
40	40
60	55
80	65
100	71
120	77
140	77
160	75
180	71
200	64

(a) Use a graphing utility to draw a scatter diagram of the data. Comment on the type of relation that may exist between the two variables.
(b) Use a graphing utility to find the quadratic function of best fit that models the relation between distance and height.
(c) Use the function found in part (b) to determine how far the ball will travel before it reaches its maximum height.
(d) Use the function found in part (b) to find the maximum height of the ball.
(e) With a graphing utility, graph the quadratic function of best fit on the scatter diagram.

Mixed Practice

27. **Which Model?** The following data represent the square footage and rents (dollars per month) for apartments in the Del Mar area of San Diego, California.

Square Footage, x	Rent per Month, R
686	1600
770	1665
817	1750
800	1685
809	1700
901	1770
803	1725

Source: apartments.com

(a) Using a graphing utility, draw a scatter diagram of the data treating square footage as the independent variable. What type of relation appears to exist between square footage and rent?
(b) Based on your response to part (a), find either a linear or quadratic model that describes the relation between square footage and rent.
(c) Use your model to predict the rent of an apartment in San Diego that is 850 square feet.

28. **Which Model?** An engineer collects the following data showing the speed s of a Toyota Camry and its average miles per gallon, M.

Speed, s	Miles per Gallon, M
30	18
35	20
40	23
40	25
45	25
50	28
55	30
60	29
65	26
65	25
70	25

(a) Using a graphing utility, draw a scatter diagram of the data treating speed as the independent variable. What type of relation appears to exist between speed and miles per gallon?
(b) Based on your response to part (a), find either a linear or quadratic model that describes the relation between speed and miles per gallon.
(c) Use your model to predict the miles per gallon for a Camry that is traveling 63 miles per hour.

29. Which Model? The following data represent the birth rate (births per 1000 population) for women whose age is x, in 2007.

Age, a	Birth Rate, B
12	0.6
17	42.5
22	106.4
27	117.6
32	99.9
37	47.5
42	9.5

Source: Statistical Abstract, 2011

(a) Using a graphing utility, draw a scatter diagram of the data treating age as the independent variable. What type of relation appears to exist between age and birth rate?
(b) Based on your response to part (a), find either a linear or quadratic model that describes the relation between age and birth rate.
(c) Use your model to predict the birth rate of 35-year-old women.

30. Which Model? A cricket makes a chirping noise by sliding its wings together rapidly. Perhaps you have noticed that the number of chirps seems to increase with the temperature. The following data list the temperature (in degrees Fahrenheit) and the number of chirps per second for the striped ground cricket.

Temperature, x	Chirps per Second, C
88.6	20.0
93.3	19.8
80.6	17.1
69.7	14.7
69.4	15.4
79.6	15.0
80.6	16.0
76.3	14.4
75.2	15.5

Source: Pierce, George W. *The Songs of Insects*. Cambridge, MA Harvard University Press, 1949, pp. 12 – 21

(a) Using a graphing utility, draw a scatter diagram of the data treating temperature as the independent variable. What type of relation appears to exist between temperature and chirps per second?
(b) Based on your response to part (a), find either a linear or quadratic model that best describes the relation between temperature and chirps per second.
(c) Use your model to predict the chirps per second if the temperature is 80°F.

Explaining Concepts: Discussion and Writing

31. Refer to Example 1 on page 660. Notice that if the price charged for the calculators is \$0 or \$140 the revenue is \$0. It is easy to explain why revenue would be \$0 if the price charged is \$0, but how can revenue be \$0 if the price charged is \$140?

'Are You Prepared?' Answers

1. $R = 3x$ **2.** $y = 1.7826x + 4.0652$

10.5 Inequalities Involving Quadratic Functions

PREPARING FOR THIS SECTION *Before getting started, review the following:*

- Solve Inequalities (Section 7.5, pp. 507–511)
- Use Interval Notation (Section 7.5, pp. 504–505)

Now Work the **'Are You Prepared?'** problems on page 672.

OBJECTIVE 1 Solve Inequalities Involving a Quadratic Function (p.670)

1 Solve Inequalities Involving a Quadratic Function

In this section we solve inequalities that involve quadratic functions. We will do this by using their graphs. For example, to solve the inequality

$$ax^2 + bx + c > 0 \qquad a \neq 0$$

graph the function $f(x) = ax^2 + bx + c$ and, from the graph, determine where it is above the x-axis, that is, where $f(x) > 0$. To solve the inequality $ax^2 + bx + c < 0$, $a \neq 0$, graph the function $f(x) = ax^2 + bx + c$ and determine where the graph is below the x-axis. If the inequality is not strict, include the x-intercepts in the solution.

EXAMPLE 1 Solving an Inequality

Solve the inequality $x^2 - 4x - 12 \leq 0$ and graph the solution set.

By Hand Solution

Graph the function $f(x) = x^2 - 4x - 12$. The intercepts are

y-intercept: $f(0) = -12$ Evaluate f at 0.

x-intercepts (if any): $x^2 - 4x - 12 = 0$ Solve $f(x) = 0$.

$(x - 6)(x + 2) = 0$ Factor.

$x - 6 = 0$ or $x + 2 = 0$ Apply the Zero-Product Property.

$x = 6$ or $x = -2$

The y-intercept is -12; the x-intercepts are -2 and 6.

The vertex is at $x = -\frac{b}{2a} = -\frac{-4}{2(1)} = 2$. Since $f(2) = -16$, the vertex is $(2, -16)$. See Figure 34 for the graph.

Figure 34

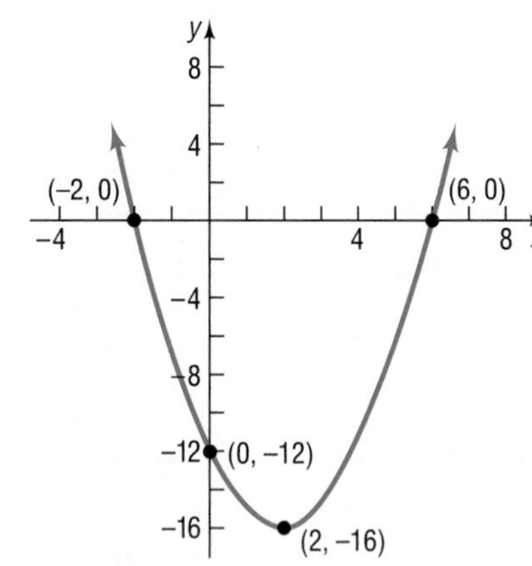

The graph is below the x-axis for $-2 < x < 6$. Since the original inequality is not strict, include the x-intercepts. The solution set is $\{x \mid -2 \leq x \leq 6\}$ or, using interval notation, $[-2, 6]$.

Graphing Utility Solution

Graph $Y_1 = x^2 - 4x - 12$. See Figure 35. Using the ZERO command, we find that the x-intercepts of Y_1 are -2 and 6. Since the inequality is not strict, the solution set is $\{x \mid -2 \leq x \leq 6\}$ or, using interval notation, $[-2, 6]$.

Figure 35

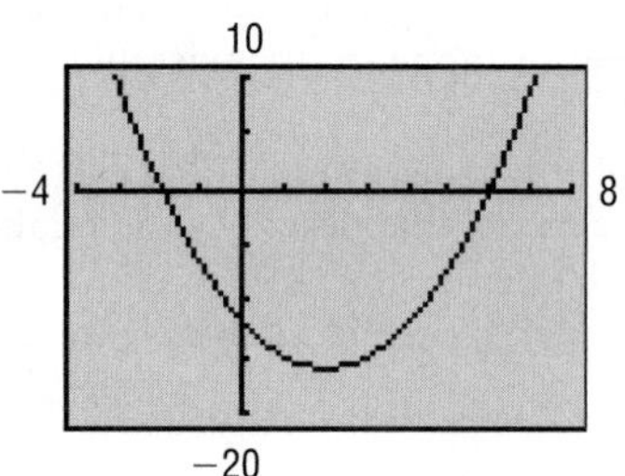

See Figure 36 for the graph of the solution set. ■

Figure 36

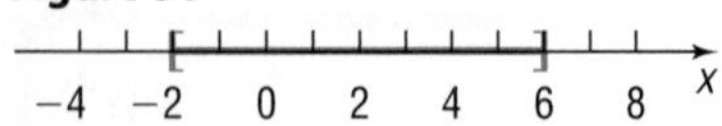

Now Work PROBLEM 9

EXAMPLE 2 Solving an Inequality

Solve the inequality $2x^2 < x + 10$ and graph the solution set.

Solution **Method 1** Rearrange the inequality so that 0 is on the right side.

$$2x^2 < x + 10$$

$$2x^2 - x - 10 < 0 \qquad \text{Subtract } x + 10 \text{ from both sides.}$$

This inequality is equivalent to the one that we want to solve.

Next graph the function $f(x) = 2x^2 - x - 10$ to find where $f(x) < 0$. The intercepts are

y-intercept:	$f(0) = -10$	Evaluate f at 0.
x-intercepts (if any):	$2x^2 - x - 10 = 0$	Solve $f(x) = 0$.
	$(2x - 5)(x + 2) = 0$	Factor.
	$2x - 5 = 0$ or $x + 2 = 0$	Apply the Zero-Product Property.
	$x = \frac{5}{2}$ or $x = -2$	

Figure 37

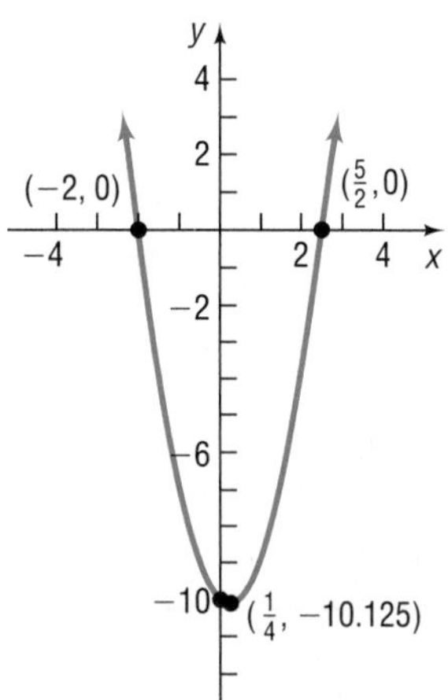

The y-intercept is -10; the x-intercepts are -2 and $\frac{5}{2}$.

The vertex is at $x = -\frac{b}{2a} = -\frac{-1}{2(2)} = \frac{1}{4}$. Since $f\left(\frac{1}{4}\right) = -10.125$, the vertex is $\left(\frac{1}{4}, -10.125\right)$. See Figure 37 for the graph.

The graph is below the x-axis $(f(x) < 0)$ between $x = -2$ and $x = \frac{5}{2}$. Since the inequality is strict, the solution set is $\left\{x \middle| -2 < x < \frac{5}{2}\right\}$ or, using interval notation, $\left(-2, \frac{5}{2}\right)$.

✓**Check:** Verify the result of Method 1 by graphing $Y_1 = 2x^2 - x - 10$ and using the ZERO feature.

Figure 38

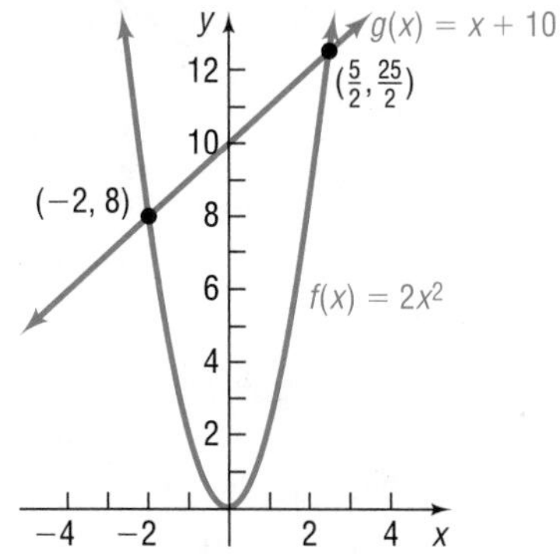

Method 2 If $f(x) = 2x^2$ and $g(x) = x + 10$, the inequality that we want to solve is $f(x) < g(x)$. Graph the functions $f(x) = 2x^2$ and $g(x) = x + 10$. See Figure 38. The graphs intersect where $f(x) = g(x)$. Then

$2x^2 = x + 10$	$f(x) = g(x)$
$2x^2 - x - 10 = 0$	
$(2x - 5)(x + 2) = 0$	Factor.
$2x - 5 = 0$ or $x + 2 = 0$	Apply the Zero-Product Property.
$x = \frac{5}{2}$ or $x = -2$	

The graphs intersect at the points $(-2, 8)$ and $\left(\frac{5}{2}, \frac{25}{2}\right)$. To solve $f(x) < g(x)$, we need to find where the graph of f is below that of g. This happens between the points of intersection. Since the inequality is strict, the solution set is $\left\{x \middle| -2 < x < \frac{5}{2}\right\}$ or, using interval notation, $\left(-2, \frac{5}{2}\right)$.

✓**Check:** Verify the result of Method 2 by graphing $Y_1 = 2x^2$ and $Y_2 = x + 10$ on the same screen. Use INTERSECT to find the x-coordinates of the points of intersection. Determine where Y_1 is below Y_2 to solve $Y_1 < Y_2$. ■

Figure 39

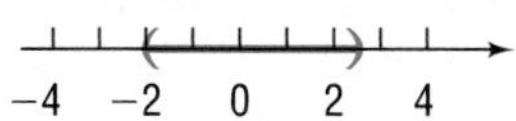

See Figure 39 for the graph of the solution set.

Now Work PROBLEMS 5 AND 13

EXAMPLE 3 **Solving an Inequality**

Solve the inequality $x^2 + x + 1 > 0$ and graph the solution set.

Solution Graph the function $f(x) = x^2 + x + 1$. The y-intercept is 1; there are no x-intercepts (Do you see why? Check the discriminant). The vertex is at $x = -\frac{b}{2a} = -\frac{1}{2}$. Since

Figure 40

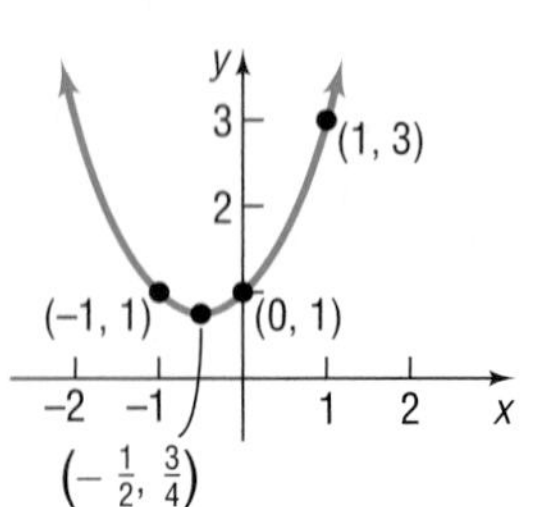

$f\left(-\frac{1}{2}\right) = \frac{3}{4}$, the vertex is at $\left(-\frac{1}{2}, \frac{3}{4}\right)$. The points $(1, 3)$ and $(-1, 1)$ are also on the graph. See Figure 40.

The graph of f lies above the x-axis for all x. The solution set is the set of all real numbers. See Figure 41.

Figure 41 −4 −2 0 2 4

Now Work PROBLEM 17

10.5 Assess Your Understanding

'Are You Prepared?' *Answers are given at the end of these exercises. If you get a wrong answer, read the pages listed in red.*

1. Solve the inequality $-3x - 2 < 7$. (pp. 508–509)

2. Write $(-2, 7]$ using inequality notation. (pp. 505–506)

Skill Building

In Problems 3–6, use the figure to solve each inequality.

3.

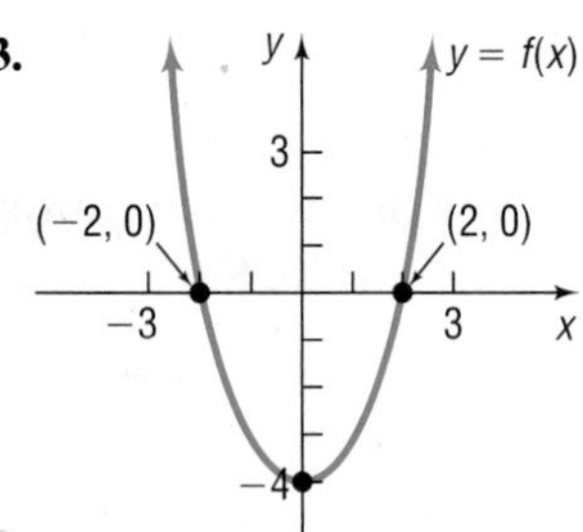

(a) $f(x) > 0$
(b) $f(x) \le 0$

4.

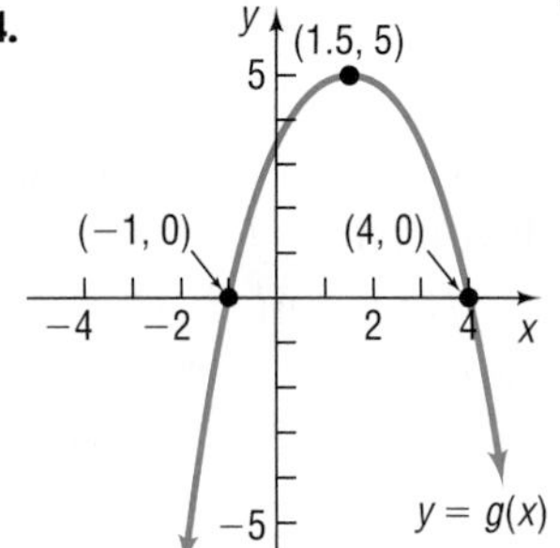

(a) $g(x) < 0$
(b) $g(x) \ge 0$

5.

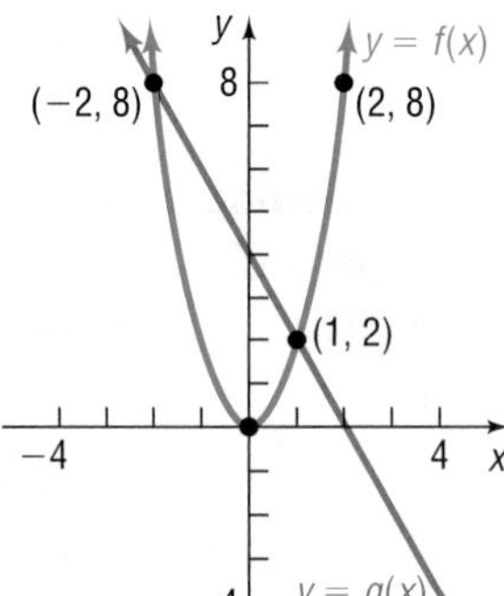

(a) $g(x) \ge f(x)$
(b) $f(x) > g(x)$

6.

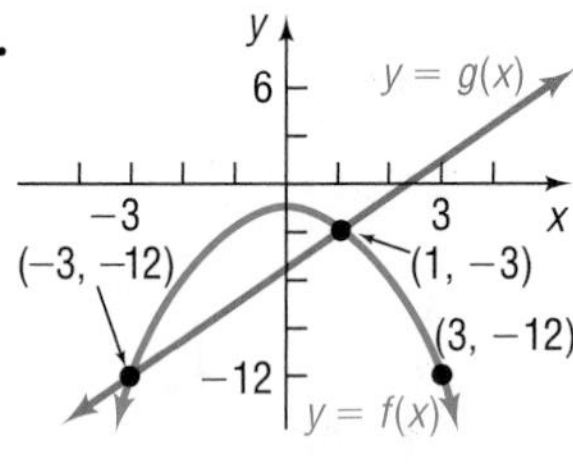

(a) $f(x) < g(x)$
(b) $f(x) \ge g(x)$

In Problems 7–22, solve each inequality.

7. $x^2 - 3x - 10 < 0$ **8.** $x^2 + 3x - 10 > 0$ **9.** $x^2 - 4x > 0$ **10.** $x^2 + 8x > 0$

11. $x^2 - 9 < 0$ **12.** $x^2 - 1 < 0$ **13.** $x^2 + x > 12$ **14.** $x^2 + 7x < -12$

15. $2x^2 < 5x + 3$ **16.** $6x^2 < 6 + 5x$ **17.** $x^2 - x + 1 \le 0$ **18.** $x^2 + 2x + 4 > 0$

19. $4x^2 + 9 < 6x$ **20.** $25x^2 + 16 < 40x$ **21.** $6(x^2 - 1) > 5x$ **22.** $2(2x^2 - 3x) > -9$

Mixed Practice

23. What is the domain of the function $f(x) = \sqrt{x^2 - 16}$?

24. What is the domain of the function $f(x) = \sqrt{x - 3x^2}$?

In Problems 25–32, use the given functions f and g.

(a) Solve $f(x) = 0$. *(b) Solve $g(x) = 0$.* *(c) Solve $f(x) = g(x)$.* *(d) Solve $f(x) > 0$.*
(e) Solve $g(x) \le 0$. *(f) Solve $f(x) > g(x)$.* *(g) Solve $f(x) \ge 1$.*

25. $f(x) = x^2 - 1$, $g(x) = 3x + 3$

26. $f(x) = -x^2 + 3$, $g(x) = -3x + 3$

27. $f(x) = -x^2 + 1$, $g(x) = 4x + 1$

28. $f(x) = -x^2 + 4$, $g(x) = -x - 2$

29. $f(x) = x^2 - 4$, $g(x) = -x^2 + 4$

30. $f(x) = x^2 - 2x + 1$, $g(x) = -x^2 + 1$

31. $f(x) = x^2 - x - 2$, $g(x) = x^2 + x - 2$

32. $f(x) = -x^2 - x + 1$, $g(x) = -x^2 + x + 6$

Applications and Extensions

33. **Physics** A ball is thrown vertically upward with an initial velocity of 80 feet per second. The distance s (in feet) of the ball from the ground after t seconds is $s(t) = 80t - 16t^2$.

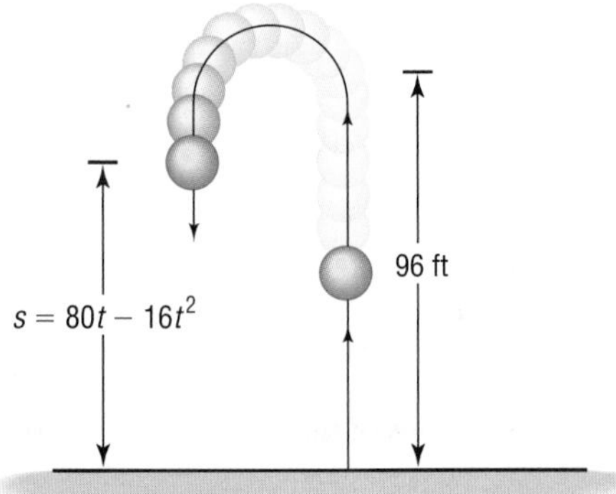

(a) At what time t will the ball strike the ground?
(b) For what time t is the ball more than 96 feet above the ground?

34. **Physics** A ball is thrown vertically upward with an initial velocity of 96 feet per second. The distance s (in feet) of the ball from the ground after t seconds is $s(t) = 96t - 16t^2$.
(a) At what time t will the ball strike the ground?
(b) For what time t is the ball more than 128 feet above the ground?

35. **Revenue** Suppose that the manufacturer of a gas clothes dryer has found that, when the unit price is p dollars, the revenue R (in dollars) is

$$R(p) = -4p^2 + 4000p$$

(a) At what prices p is revenue zero?
(b) For what range of prices will revenue exceed $800,000?

36. **Revenue** The John Deere company has found that the revenue from sales of heavy-duty tractors is a function of the unit price p, in dollars, that it charges. If the revenue R, in dollars, is

$$R(p) = -\frac{1}{2}p^2 + 1900p$$

(a) At what prices p is revenue zero?
(b) For what range of prices will revenue exceed $1,200,000?

37. **Artillery** A projectile fired from the point $(0, 0)$ at an angle to the positive x-axis has a trajectory given by

$$y = cx - (1 + c^2)\left(\frac{g}{2}\right)\left(\frac{x}{v}\right)^2$$

where

x = horizontal distance in meters
y = height in meters
v = initial muzzle velocity in meters per second (m/sec)
g = acceleration due to gravity = 9.81 meters per second squared (m/sec^2)
$c > 0$ is a constant determined by the angle of elevation.

A howitzer fires an artillery round with a muzzle velocity of 897 m/sec.
(a) If the round must clear a hill 200 meters high at a distance of 2000 meters in front of the howitzer, what c values are permitted in the trajectory equation?
(b) If the goal in part (a) is to hit a target on the ground 75 kilometers away, is it possible to do so? If so, for what values of c? If not, what is the maximum distance the round will travel?

Source: *www.answers.com*

38. **Runaway Car** Using Hooke's Law, we can show that the *work* done in compressing a spring a distance of x feet from its at-rest position is $W = \frac{1}{2}kx^2$, where k is a stiffness constant depending on the spring. It can also be shown that the work done by a body in motion before it comes to rest is given by $\widetilde{W} = \frac{w}{2g}v^2$, where w = weight of the object (lb), g = acceleration due to gravity (32.2 ft/sec^2), and v = object's velocity (in ft/sec). A parking garage has a spring shock absorber at the end of a ramp to stop runaway cars. The spring has a stiffness constant $k = 9450$ lb/ft and must be able to stop a 4000-lb car traveling at 25 mph. What is the least compression required of the spring? Express your answer using feet to the nearest tenth.
[**Hint:** Solve $W > \widetilde{W}, x \geq 0$].

Source: *www.sciforums.com*

Explaining Concepts: Discussion and Writing

39. Show that the inequality $(x - 4)^2 \leq 0$ has exactly one solution.

40. Show that the inequality $(x - 2)^2 > 0$ has one real number that is not a solution.

41. Explain why the inequality $x^2 + x + 1 > 0$ has all real numbers as the solution set.

42. Explain why the inequality $x^2 - x + 1 < 0$ has the empty set as solution set.

43. Explain the circumstances under which the x-intercepts of the graph of a quadratic function are included in the solution set of a quadratic inequality.

'Are You Prepared?' Answers

1. $\{x | x > -3\}$ or $(-3, \infty)$ **2.** $-2 < x \leq 7$

CHAPTER REVIEW

Things to Know

Linear function (p. 631)

$f(x) = mx + b$

Average rate of change $= m$

The graph is a line with slope m and y-intercept b.

Quadratic function (pp. 648–649)

$f(x) = ax^2 + bx + c, a \neq 0$

The graph is a parabola that opens up if $a > 0$ and opens down if $a < 0$.

Vertex: $\left(-\frac{b}{2a}, f\left(-\frac{b}{2a}\right)\right)$

Axis of symmetry: $x = -\frac{b}{2a}$

y-intercept: $f(0) = c$

x-intercept(s): If any, found by finding the real solutions of the equation $ax^2 + bx + c = 0$

Objectives

Section		You should be able to ...	Examples	Review Exercises
10.1	1	Graph linear functions (p. 631)	1	1(a)–3(a), 1(c)–3(c)
	2	Use average rate of change to identify linear functions (p. 631)	2	4, 5
	3	Determine whether a linear function is increasing, decreasing, or constant (p. 634)	3	1(d)–3(d)
	4	Build linear models from verbal descriptions (p. 635)	4, 5	22
10.2	1	Draw and interpret scatter diagrams (p. 641)	1	28(a), 29(a)
	2	Distinguish between linear and nonlinear relations (p. 642)	2	28(b), 29(a)
	3	Use a graphing utility to find the line of best fit (p. 643)	4	28(c)
10.3	1	Graph a quadratic function using transformations (p. 649)	1	6–8
	2	Identify the vertex and axis of symmetry of a quadratic function (p. 651)	2	9–14
	3	Graph a quadratic function using its vertex, axis, and intercepts (p. 651)	3–5	9–14
	4	Find a quadratic function given its vertex and one other point (p. 654)	6	20, 21
	5	Find the maximum or minimum value of a quadratic function (p. 655)	7	15–17, 23–26
10.4	1	Build quadratic models from verbal descriptions (p. 660)	1–4	23–27
	2	Build quadratic models from data (p. 664)	5	29
10.5	1	Solve inequalities involving a quadratic function (p. 670)	1–3	18, 19

Review Exercises

In Problems 1–3:
(a) Determine the slope and y-intercept of each linear function.
(b) Find the average rate of change of each function.
(c) Graph each function. Label the intercepts.
(d) Determine whether the function is increasing, decreasing, or constant.

1. $f(x) = 2x - 5$ **2.** $F(x) = -\frac{1}{3}x + 1$ **3.** $G(x) = 4$

In Problems 4 and 5, determine whether the function is linear or nonlinear. If the function is linear, find the equation of the line.

4.

x	$y = f(x)$
−1	−2
0	3
1	8
2	13
3	18

5.

x	$y = g(x)$
−1	−3
0	4
1	7
2	6
3	1

In Problems 6–8, graph each quadratic function using transformations (shifting, compressing, stretching, and/or reflecting).

6. $f(x) = (x - 2)^2 + 2$ **7.** $f(x) = -(x - 4)^2$ **8.** $f(x) = 2(x + 1)^2 + 4$

In Problems 9–14, (a) graph each quadratic function by determining whether its graph opens up or down and by finding its vertex, axis of symmetry, y-intercept, and x-intercepts, if any. (b) Determine the domain and the range of the function. (c) Determine where the function is increasing and where it is decreasing.

9. $f(x) = x^2 - 4x + 6$ **10.** $f(x) = -\frac{1}{2}x^2 + 2$ **11.** $f(x) = -4x^2 + 4x$

12. $f(x) = 9x^2 + 6x + 1$ **13.** $f(x) = -x^2 + x + \frac{1}{2}$ **14.** $f(x) = 3x^2 + 4x - 1$

In Problems 15–17, determine whether the given quadratic function has a maximum value or a minimum value, and then find the value.

15. $f(x) = 3x^2 - 6x + 4$ **16.** $f(x) = -x^2 + 8x - 4$ **17.** $f(x) = -2x^2 + 4$

In Problems 18–19, solve each quadratic inequality.

18. $x^2 + 6x - 16 < 0$ **19.** $3x^2 \geq 14x + 5$

In Problems 20 and 21, find the quadratic function for which:

20. Vertex is $(-1, 2)$; contains the points $(1, 6)$

21. Contains the points $(0, 5)$, $(1, 2)$, and $(3, 2)$

22. Comparing Phone Companies Marissa must decide between one of two companies as her long-distance phone provider. Company A charges a monthly fee of \$7.00 plus \$0.06 per minute, while Company B does not have a monthly fee, but charges \$0.08 per minute.

(a) Find a linear function that relates cost, C, to total minutes on the phone, x, for each company.
(b) Determine the number of minutes x for which the bill from Company A will equal the bill from Company B.
(c) Over what interval of minutes x will the bill from Company B be less than the bill from Company A?

23. Demand Equation The price p (in dollars) and the quantity x sold of a certain product obey the demand equation

$$p = -\frac{1}{10}x + 150 \quad 0 \leq x \leq 1500$$

(a) Express the revenue R as a function of x.
(b) What is the revenue if 100 units are sold?
(c) What quantity x maximizes revenue? What is the maximum revenue?
(d) What price should the company charge to maximize revenue?

24. Enclosing the Most Area with a Fence A farmer with 10,000 meters of fencing wants to enclose a rectangular field and then divide it into two plots with a fence parallel to one of the sides. See the figure. What is the largest area that can be enclosed?

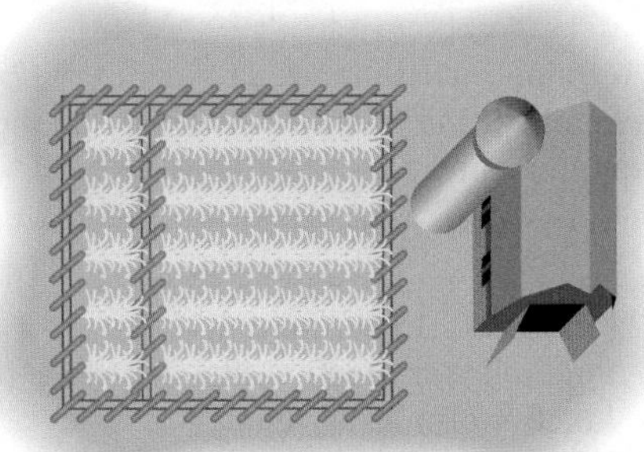

25. Minimizing Marginal Cost Callaway Golf Company has determined that the marginal cost C of manufacturing x Big Bertha golf clubs may be expressed by the quadratic function

$$C(x) = 4.9x^2 - 617.4x + 19{,}600$$

(a) How many clubs should be manufactured to minimize the marginal cost?
(b) At this level of production, what is the marginal cost?

26. A rectangle has one vertex on the line $y = 10 - x$, $x > 0$, another at the origin, one on the positive x-axis, and one on the positive y-axis. Express the area A of the rectangle as a function of x. Find the largest area A that can be enclosed by the rectangle.

27. Parabolic Arch Bridge A horizontal bridge is in the shape of a parabolic arch. Given the information shown in the figure, what is the height h of the arch 2 feet from shore?

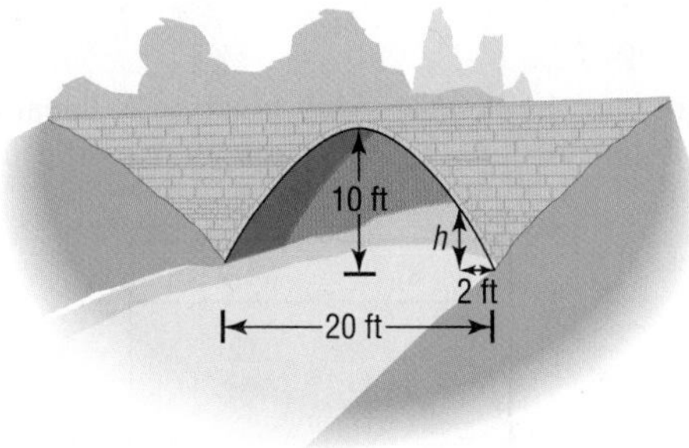

28. Bone Length Research performed at NASA, led by Dr. Emily R. Morey-Holton, measured the lengths of the right humerus and right tibia in 11 rats that were sent to space on Spacelab Life Sciences 2. The data on page 676 were collected.

(a) Draw a scatter diagram of the data treating length of the right humerus as the independent variable.
(b) Based on the scatter diagram, do you think that there is a linear relation between the length of the right humerus and the length of the right tibia?
(c) Use a graphing utility to find the line of best fit relating length of the right humerus and length of the right tibia.
(d) Predict the length of the right tibia on a rat whose right humerus is 26.5 millimeters (mm).

Right Humerus (mm), x	Right Tibia (mm), y
24.80	36.05
24.59	35.57
24.59	35.57
24.29	34.58
23.81	34.20
24.87	34.73
25.90	37.38
26.11	37.96
26.63	37.46
26.31	37.75
26.84	38.50

Source: NASA Life Sciences Data Archive

29. **Advertising** A small manufacturing firm collected the following data on advertising expenditures A (in thousands of dollars) and total revenue R (in thousands of dollars).

(a) Draw a scatter diagram of the data. Comment on the type of relation that may exist between the two variables.

(b) The quadratic function of best fit to these data is

$$R(A) = -7.76A^2 + 411.88A + 942.72$$

Use this function to determine the optimal level of advertising.

(c) Use the function to predict the total revenue when the optimal level of advertising is spent.

(d) Use a graphing utility to verify that the function given in part (b) is the quadratic function of best fit.

(e) Use a graphing utility to draw a scatter diagram of the data and then graph the quadratic function of best fit on the scatter diagram.

ADVERTISE HERE

Advertising	Total Revenue
20	\$6101
22	\$6222
25	\$6350
25	\$6378
27	\$6453
28	\$6423
29	\$6360
31	\$6231

CHAPTER TEST

The Chapter Test Prep Videos are step-by-step test solutions available in the Video Resources DVD, in *MyMathLab*, or on this text's YouTube Channel. Flip back to the Student Resources page to see the exact web address for this text's YouTube channel.

1. For the linear function $f(x) = -4x + 3$,
   (a) Find the slope and y-intercept.
   (b) Determine whether f is increasing, decreasing, or constant.
   (c) Graph f.

2. Determine whether the given function is linear or nonlinear. If it is linear, determine the equation of the line.

x	y
−2	12
−1	7
0	2
1	−3
2	−8

3. Graph $f(x) = (x - 3)^2 - 2$ using transformations.

In Problems 4 and 5,

(a) Determine whether the graph opens up or down.
(b) Determine the vertex of the graph of the quadratic function.
(c) Determine the axis of symmetry of the graph of the quadratic function.
(d) Determine the intercepts of the graph of the quadratic function.
(e) Use the information in parts (a)–(d) to graph the quadratic function.
(f) Based on the graph, determine the domain and the range of the quadratic function.
(g) Based on the graph, determine where the function is increasing and where it is decreasing.

4. $f(x) = 3x^2 - 12x + 4$
5. $g(x) = -2x^2 + 4x - 5$
6. Determine the quadratic function for the given graph.

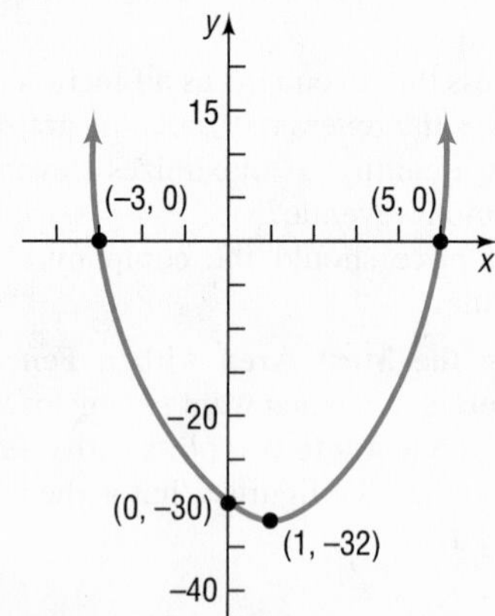

7. Determine whether $f(x) = -2x^2 + 12x + 3$ has a maximum or minimum value. Then find the maximum or minimum value.

8. Solve $x^2 - 10x + 24 \geq 0$.

9. The weekly rental cost of a 20-foot recreational vehicle is \$129.50 plus \$0.15 per mile.
   (a) Find a linear function that expresses the cost C as a function of miles driven m.
   (b) What is the rental cost if 860 miles are driven?
   (c) How many miles were driven if the rental cost is \$213.80?

10. The price p (in dollars) and the quantity x sold of a certain product obey the demand equation $p = -\frac{1}{10}x + 1000$.
(a) Find a model that expresses the revenue R as a function of x.
(b) What is the revenue if 400 units are sold?
(c) What quantity x maximizes revenue? What is the maximum revenue?
(d) What price should the company charge to maximize revenue?

11. Consider these two data sets:

Set A

x	−2	−1	0	0	1	2	2
y	5	2	1	−3	−8	−12	−10

Set B

x	−2	−1	0	0	1	2	2
y	10	4	2	3	5	10	12

One data set follows a linear pattern and one data set follows a quadratic relation.
(a) Draw a scatter diagram of each data set. Determine which is linear and which is quadratic. For the linear data, indicate whether the relation shows a positive or negative slope. For the quadratic relation, indicate whether the quadratic function of best fit will open up or down.
(b) For the linear data set, find the line of best fit.
(c) For the quadratic data set, find the quadratic function of best fit.

CUMULATIVE REVIEW

1. Find the distance between the points $P = (-1, 3)$ and $Q = (4, -2)$. Find the midpoint of the line segment from P to Q.

2. Which of the following points are on the graph of $y = x^3 - 3x + 1$?
(a) $(-2, -1)$
(b) $(2, 3)$
(c) $(3, 1)$

3. Solve the inequality $5x + 3 \geq 0$ and graph the solution set.

4. Find the equation of the line containing the points $(-1, 4)$ and $(2, -2)$. Express your answer in slope–intercept form and graph the line.

5. Find the equation of the line perpendicular to the line $y = 2x + 1$ and containing the point $(3, 5)$. Express your answer in slope–intercept form and graph the line.

6. Graph the equation $x^2 + y^2 - 4x + 8y - 5 = 0$.

7. Does the following relation represent a function? $\{(-3, 8), (1, 3), (2, 5), (3, 8)\}$.

8. For the function f defined by $f(x) = x^2 - 4x + 1$, find:
(a) $f(2)$
(b) $f(x) + f(2)$
(c) $f(-x)$
(d) $-f(x)$
(e) $f(x + 2)$
(f) $\frac{f(x + h) - f(x)}{h}$ $h \neq 0$

9. Find the domain of $h(z) = \frac{3z - 1}{6z - 7}$.

10. Is the following graph the graph of a function?

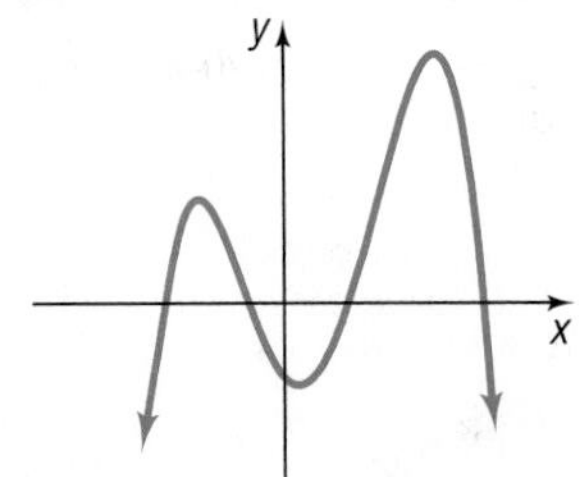

11. Consider the function $f(x) = \frac{x}{x + 4}$.
(a) Is the point $\left(1, \frac{1}{4}\right)$ on the graph of f?
(b) If $x = -2$, what is $f(x)$? What point is on the graph of f?
(c) If $f(x) = 2$, what is x? What point is on the graph of f?

12. Is the function $f(x) = \frac{x^2}{2x + 1}$ even, odd, or neither?

13. Approximate the local maximum values and local minimum values of $f(x) = x^3 - 5x + 1$ on $(-4, 4)$. Determine where the function is increasing and where it is decreasing.

14. If $f(x) = 3x + 5$ and $g(x) = 2x + 1$,
(a) Solve $f(x) = g(x)$.
(b) Solve $f(x) > g(x)$.

15. For the graph of the function f,

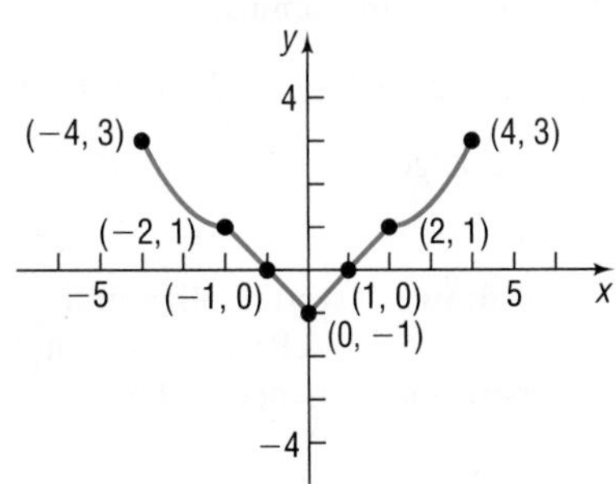

(a) Find the domain and the range of f.
(b) Find the intercepts.
(c) Is the graph of f symmetric with respect to the x-axis, the y-axis, or the origin?
(d) Find $f(2)$.
(e) For what value(s) of x is $f(x) = 3$?
(f) Solve $f(x) < 0$.
(g) Graph $y = f(x) + 2$.
(h) Graph $y = f(-x)$.
(i) Graph $y = 2f(x)$.
(j) Is f even, odd, or neither?
(k) Find the interval(s) on which f is increasing.

CHAPTER PROJECTS

Internet-based Project

I. **The Beta of a Stock** You want to invest in the stock market but are not sure which stock to purchase. Information is the key to making an informed investment decision. One piece of information that many stock analysts use is the beta of the stock. Go to Wikipedia (*http://en.wikipedia.org/wiki/Beta_%28finance%29*) and research what beta measures and what it represents.

1. **Approximating the beta of a stock.** Choose a well-known company such as Google or Coca-Cola. Go to a website such as Yahoo! Finance (*http://finance.yahoo.com/*) and find the weekly closing price of the company's stock for the past year. Then find the closing price of the Standard & Poor's 500 (S&P500) for the same time period. To get the historical prices in Yahoo! Finance click the price graph, choose Basic Chart, then scroll down and select Historical Prices. Choose the appropriate time period and select Weekly. Finally, select Download to Spreadsheet. Repeat this for the S&P500, and copy the data into the same spreadsheet. Finally, rearrange the data in chronological order. Be sure to expand the selection to sort all the data. Now, using the adjusted close price, compute the percentage change in price for each week using the formula $\%\text{change} = \dfrac{P_1 - P_o}{P_o}$. For example, if week 1 price is in cell D1 and week 2 price is in cell D2, then $\%\text{change} = \dfrac{D2 - D1}{D1}$. Repeat this for the S&P500 data.

2. **Using Excel to draw a scatter diagram.** Treat the percentage change in the S&P500 as the independent variable and the percentage change in the stock you chose as the dependent variable. The easiest way to draw a scatter diagram in Excel is to place the two columns of data next to each other (for example, have the percentage change in the S&P500 in column F and the percentage change in the stock you chose in column G). Then highlight the data and select the Scatter Diagram icon under Insert. Comment on the type of relation that appears to exist between the two variables.

3. **Finding beta.** To find beta requires that we find the line of best fit using least-squares regression. The easiest approach is to click inside the scatter diagram. Across the top of the screen you will see an option entitled "Chart Layouts." Select the option with a line drawn on the scatter diagram and *fx* labeled on the graph. The line of best fit appears on the scatter diagram. See below.

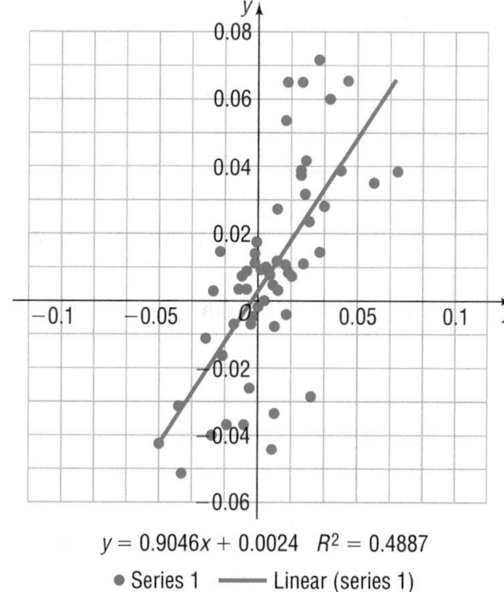

The line of best fit for this data is $y = 0.9046x + 0.0024$. You may click on Chart Title or either axis title and insert the appropriate names. The beta is the slope of the line of best fit, 0.9046. We interpret this by saying if the S&P500 increases by 1%, this stock will increase by 0.9%, on average. Find the beta of your stock and provide an interpretation. NOTE: Another way to use Excel to find the line of best fit requires using the Data Analysis Tool Pack under add-ins.

The following projects are available on the Instructor's Resource Center (IRC):

II. **Cannons** A battery commander uses the weight of a missile, its initial velocity, and the position of its gun to determine where the missile will travel.

III. **First and Second Differences** Finite differences provide a numerical method that is used to estimate the graph of an unknown function.

IV. **CBL Experiment** Computer simulation is used to study the physical properties of a bouncing ball.

Polynomial and Rational Functions

11

Outline

Day Length

Day length refers to the time each day from the moment the upper limb of the sun's disk appears above the horizon during sunrise to the moment when the upper limb disappears below the horizon during sunset. The length of a day depends upon the day of the year as well as the latitude of the location. Latitude gives the location of a point on Earth north or south of the equator. In the Internet Project at the end of this chapter, we use information from the chapter to investigate the relation between the length of day and latitude for a specific day of the year.

—*See the Internet-based Chapter Project I*—

◐ **A LOOK BACK** In Chapter 9, we began our discussion of functions. We defined domain, range, and independent and dependent variables, found the value of a function, and graphed functions. We continued our study of functions by listing the properties that a function might have, such as being even or odd, and created a library of functions, naming key functions and listing their properties, including their graphs.

In Chapter 10, we discussed linear functions and quadratic functions, which belong to the class of *polynomial functions*.

◑ **A LOOK AHEAD** In this chapter, we look at two general classes of functions, polynomial functions and rational functions, and examine their properties. Polynomial functions are arguably the simplest expressions in algebra. For this reason, they are often used to approximate other, more complicated functions. Rational functions are ratios of polynomial functions.

11.1 Polynomial Functions and Models

PREPARING FOR THIS SECTION *Before getting started, review the following:*

- Using a Graphing Utility to Approximate Local Maxima and Local Minima (Section 9.3, pp. 587–588)
- Intercepts of a Function (Section 9.2, pp. 574–576)
- Graphing Techniques: Transformations (Section 9.5, pp. 605–613)
- Intercepts (Section 8.1, pp. 522–523)

Now Work the **'Are You Prepared?'** problems on page 694.

OBJECTIVES
1. Identify Polynomial Functions and Their Degree (p. 680)
2. Graph Polynomial Functions Using Transformations (p. 683)
3. Identify the Real Zeros of a Polynomial Function and Their Multiplicity (p. 684)
4. Analyze the Graph of a Polynomial Function (p. 690)
5. Build Cubic Models from Data (p. 693)

1 Identify Polynomial Functions and Their Degree

In Chapter 10, we studied the linear function $f(x) = mx + b$, which can be written as

$$f(x) = a_1x + a_0$$

and the quadratic function $f(x) = ax^2 + bx + c, a \neq 0$, which can be written as

$$f(x) = a_2x^2 + a_1x + a_0 \qquad a_2 \neq 0$$

Each of these functions is an example of a *polynomial function.*

DEFINITION

A **polynomial function** is a function of the form

$$f(x) = a_nx^n + a_{n-1}x^{n-1} + \cdots + a_1x + a_0 \qquad (1)$$

where $a_n, a_{n-1}, \ldots, a_1, a_0$ are real numbers and n is a nonnegative integer. The domain of a polynomial function is the set of all real numbers.

In Words
A polynomial function is the sum of monomials.

A polynomial function is a function whose rule is given by a polynomial in one variable. The **degree** of a polynomial function is the largest power of x that appears. The zero polynomial function $f(x) = 0 + 0x + 0x^2 + \cdots + 0x^n$ is not assigned a degree.

Polynomial functions are among the simplest expressions in algebra. They are easy to evaluate: only addition and repeated multiplication are required. Because of this, they are often used to approximate other, more complicated functions. In this section, we investigate properties of this important class of functions.

EXAMPLE 1 **Identifying Polynomial Functions**

Determine which of the following are polynomial functions. For those that are, state the degree; for those that are not, tell why not.

(a) $f(x) = 2 - 3x^4$ (b) $g(x) = \sqrt{x}$ (c) $h(x) = \dfrac{x^2 - 2}{x^3 - 1}$

(d) $F(x) = 0$ (e) $G(x) = 8$ (f) $H(x) = -2x^3(x - 1)^2$

Solution
(a) f is a polynomial function of degree 4.
(b) g is not a polynomial function because $g(x) = \sqrt{x} = x^{\frac{1}{2}}$, so the variable x is raised to the $\frac{1}{2}$ power, which is not a nonnegative integer.

(c) h is not a polynomial function. It is the ratio of two distinct polynomials, and the polynomial in the denominator is of positive degree.

(d) F is the zero polynomial function; it is not assigned a degree.

(e) G is a nonzero constant function. It is a polynomial function of degree 0 since $G(x) = 8 = 8x^0$.

(f) $H(x) = -2x^3(x-1)^2 = -2x^3(x^2 - 2x + 1) = -2x^5 + 4x^4 - 2x^3$. So H is a polynomial function of degree 5. Do you see a way to find the degree of H without multiplying out? ■

Now Work PROBLEMS 15 AND 19

We have already discussed in detail polynomial functions of degrees 0, 1, and 2. See Table 1 for a summary of the properties of the graphs of these polynomial functions.

Table 1

Degree	Form	Name	Graph
No degree	$f(x) = 0$	Zero function	The x-axis
0	$f(x) = a_0, \quad a_0 \neq 0$	Constant function	Horizontal line with y-intercept a_0
1	$f(x) = a_1x + a_0, \quad a_1 \neq 0$	Linear function	Nonvertical, nonhorizontal line with slope a_1 and y-intercept a_0
2	$f(x) = a_2x^2 + a_1x + a_0, \quad a_2 \neq 0$	Quadratic function	Parabola: graph opens up if $a_2 > 0$; graph opens down if $a_2 < 0$

One objective of this section is to analyze the graph of a polynomial function. If you take a course in calculus, you will learn that the graph of every polynomial function is both smooth and continuous. By **smooth,** we mean that the graph contains no sharp corners or cusps; by **continuous,** we mean that the graph has no gaps or holes and can be drawn without lifting pencil from paper. See Figures 1(a) and (b).

Figure 1

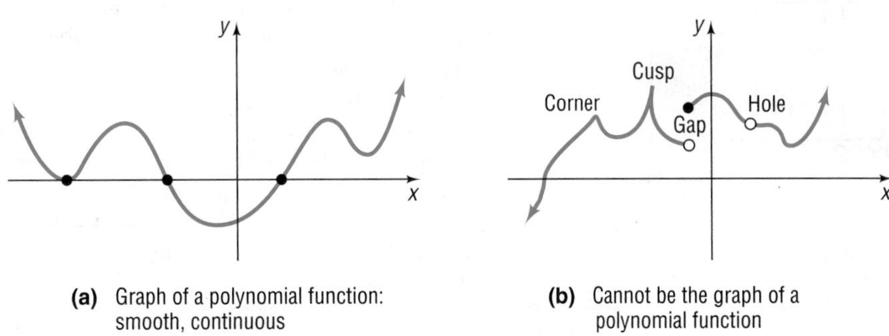

(a) Graph of a polynomial function: smooth, continuous

(b) Cannot be the graph of a polynomial function

Power Functions

We begin the analysis of the graph of a polynomial function by discussing *power functions,* a special kind of polynomial function.

DEFINITION

A **power function of degree n** is a monomial function of the form

$$f(x) = ax^n \tag{2}$$

where a is a real number, $a \neq 0$, and $n > 0$ is an integer.

In Words

A power function is defined by a single monomial.

Examples of power functions are

$$f(x) = 3x \qquad f(x) = -5x^2 \qquad f(x) = 8x^3 \qquad f(x) = -5x^4$$

degree 1 degree 2 degree 3 degree 4

The graph of a power function of degree 1, $f(x) = ax$, is a straight line, with slope a, that passes through the origin. The graph of a power function of degree 2, $f(x) = ax^2$, is a parabola, with vertex at the origin, that opens up if $a > 0$ and down if $a < 0$.

If we know how to graph a power function of the form $f(x) = x^n$, a compression or stretch and, perhaps, a reflection about the x-axis will enable us to obtain the graph of $g(x) = ax^n$. Consequently, we shall concentrate on graphing power functions of the form $f(x) = x^n$.

We begin with power functions of even degree of the form $f(x) = x^n$, $n \geq 2$ and *n even.*

Exploration

Using your graphing utility and the viewing window $-2 \leq x \leq 2, -4 \leq y \leq 16$, graph the function $Y_1 = f(x) = x^4$. On the same screen, graph $Y_2 = g(x) = x^8$. Now, also on the same screen, graph $Y_3 = h(x) = x^{12}$. What do you notice about the graphs as the magnitude of the exponent increases? Repeat this procedure for the viewing window $-1 \leq x \leq 1, 0 \leq y \leq 1$. What do you notice?

Result See Figures 2(a) and (b).

Figure 2

$Y_1 = x^4$ $Y_2 = x^8$ $Y_3 = x^{12}$ 16 −2 2 −4

(a)

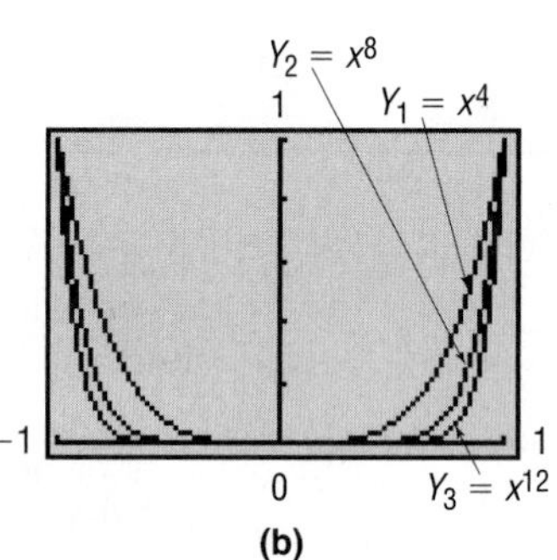

(b)

Table 2

X	Y2	Y3
-1	1	1
1	1	1
.5	.00391	2.4E-4
.1	1E-8	1E-12
.01	1E-16	1E-24
.001	1E-24	1E-36
0	0	0

Y2=X^8

NOTE Don't forget how graphing calculators express scientific notation. In Table 2, 1E −8 means 1×10^{-8}. ■

The domain of $f(x) = x^n, n \geq 2$ and n even, is the set of all real numbers, and the range is the set of nonnegative real numbers. Such a power function is an even function (do you see why?), so its graph is symmetric with respect to the y-axis. Its graph always contains the origin $(0, 0)$ and the points $(-1, 1)$ and $(1, 1)$.

If $n = 2$, the graph is the parabola $y = x^2$ that opens up, with vertex at the origin. For large n, it appears that the graph coincides with the x-axis near the origin, but it does not; the graph actually touches the x-axis only at the origin. See Table 2, where $Y_2 = x^8$ and $Y_3 = x^{12}$. For x close to 0, the values of y are positive and close to 0. Also, for large n, it may appear that for $x < -1$ or for $x > 1$ the graph is vertical, but it is not; it is only increasing very rapidly. If you TRACE along one of the graphs, these distinctions will be clear.

To summarize:

Properties of Power Functions, $f(x) = x^n$, n Is an Even Integer

1. f is an even function, so its graph is symmetric with respect to the y-axis.
2. The domain is the set of all real numbers. The range is the set of nonnegative real numbers.
3. The graph always contains the points $(-1, 1)$, $(0, 0)$, and $(1, 1)$.
4. As the exponent n increases in magnitude, the graph increases more rapidly when $x < -1$ or $x > 1$; but for x near the origin, the graph tends to flatten out and lie closer to the x-axis.

Now we consider power functions of odd degree of the form $f(x) = x^n$, *n odd.*

Exploration

Using your graphing utility and the viewing window $-2 \leq x \leq 2, -16 \leq y \leq 16$, graph the function $Y_1 = f(x) = x^3$. On the same screen, graph $Y_2 = g(x) = x^7$ and $Y_3 = h(x) = x^{11}$. What do you notice about the graphs as the magnitude of the exponent increases? Repeat this procedure for the viewing window $-1 \leq x \leq 1, -1 \leq y \leq 1$. What do you notice?

Result The graphs on your screen should look like Figures 3(a) and (b).

Figure 3

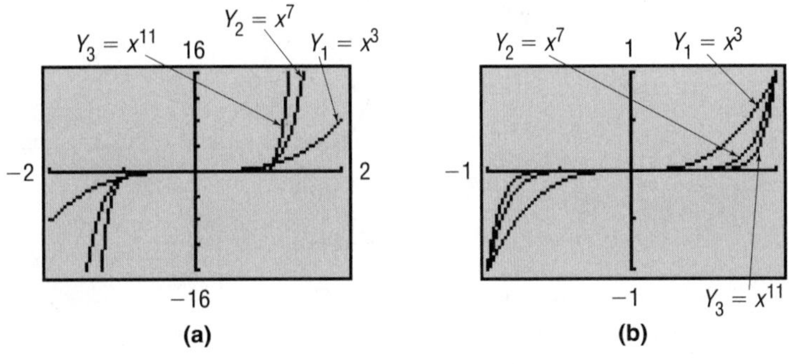

The domain and the range of $f(x) = x^n, n \geq 3$ and n odd, are the set of real numbers. Such a power function is an odd function (do you see why?), so its graph is symmetric with respect to the origin. Its graph always contains the origin (0, 0) and the points $(-1, -1)$ and $(1, 1)$.

It appears that the graph coincides with the x-axis near the origin, but it does not; the graph actually crosses the x-axis only at the origin. Also, it appears that as x increases the graph is vertical, but it is not; it is increasing very rapidly. TRACE along the graphs to verify these distinctions.

To summarize:

Properties of Power Functions, $f(x) = x^n$, n Is an Odd Integer

1. f is an odd function, so its graph is symmetric with respect to the origin.
2. The domain and the range are the set of all real numbers.
3. The graph always contains the points $(-1, -1)$, $(0, 0)$, and $(1, 1)$.
4. As the exponent n increases in magnitude, the graph increases more rapidly when $x < -1$ or $x > 1$, but for x near the origin, the graph tends to flatten out and lie closer to the x-axis.

2 Graph Polynomial Functions Using Transformations

The methods of shifting, compression, stretching, and reflection studied in Section 9.5, when used with the facts just presented, enable us to graph polynomial functions that are transformations of power functions.

EXAMPLE 2 **Graphing a Polynomial Function Using Transformations**

Graph: $f(x) = 1 - x^5$

Solution It is helpful to rewrite f as $f(x) = -x^5 + 1$. Figure 4 shows the required stages.

Figure 4

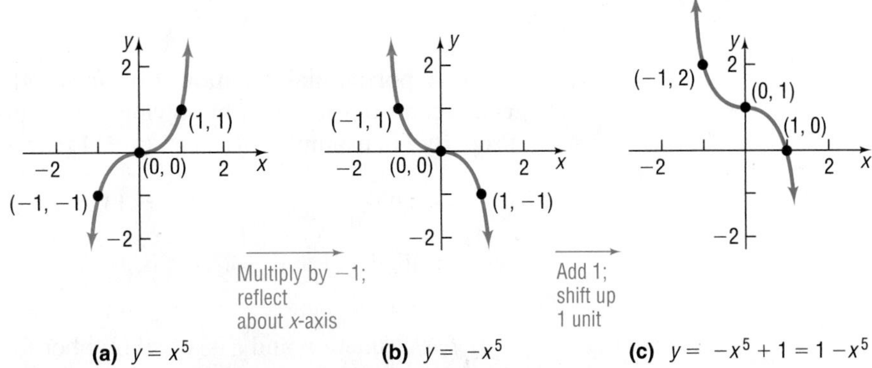

(a) $y = x^5$ (b) $y = -x^5$ (c) $y = -x^5 + 1 = 1 - x^5$

Check: Verify the graph of f by graphing $Y_1 = 1 - x^5$. ■

EXAMPLE 3 Graphing a Polynomial Function Using Transformations

Graph: $f(x) = \frac{1}{2}(x - 1)^4$

Solution Figure 5 shows the required stages.

Figure 5

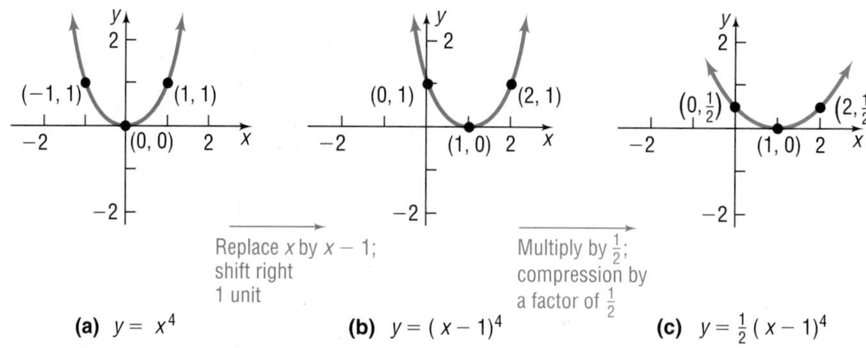

✓**Check:** Verify the graph of f by graphing $Y_1 = \frac{1}{2}(x - 1)^4$. ■

Now Work PROBLEMS 27 AND 33

3 Identify the Real Zeros of a Polynomial Function and Their Multiplicity

Figure 6 shows the graph of a polynomial function with four x-intercepts. Notice that at the x-intercepts the graph must either cross the x-axis or touch the x-axis. Consequently, between consecutive x-intercepts the graph is either above the x-axis or below the x-axis.

Figure 6

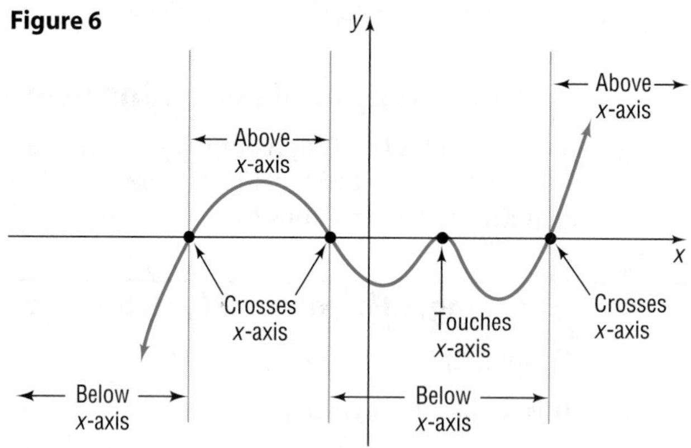

If a polynomial function f is factored completely, it is easy to locate the x-intercepts of the graph by solving the equation $f(x) = 0$ using the Zero-Product Property. For example, if $f(x) = (x - 1)^2(x + 3)$, then the solutions of the equation

$$f(x) = (x - 1)^2(x + 3) = 0$$

are identified as 1 and -3. That is, $f(1) = 0$ and $f(-3) = 0$.

DEFINITION If f is a function and r is a real number for which $f(r) = 0$, then r is called a **real zero** of f.

As a consequence of this definition, the following statements are equivalent.

1. r is a real zero of a polynomial function f.
2. r is an x-intercept of the graph of f.
3. $x - r$ is a factor of f.
4. r is a solution to the equation $f(x) = 0$.

So the real zeros of a polynomial function are the x-intercepts of its graph, and they are found by solving the equation $f(x) = 0$.

EXAMPLE 4 Finding a Polynomial Function from Its Zeros

(a) Find a polynomial of degree 3 whose zeros are -3, 2, and 5.

(b) Use a graphing utility to graph the polynomial found in part (a) to verify your result.

Solution (a) If r is a real zero of a polynomial function f, then $x - r$ is a factor of f. This means that $x - (-3) = x + 3$, $x - 2$, and $x - 5$ are factors of f. As a result, any polynomial function of the form

$$f(x) = a(x + 3)(x - 2)(x - 5)$$

where a is a nonzero real number, qualifies. The value of a causes a stretch, compression, or reflection, but does not affect the x-intercepts of the graph. Do you know why?

(b) We choose to graph f with $a = 1$. Then

$$f(x) = (x + 3)(x - 2)(x - 5) = x^3 - 4x^2 - 11x + 30$$

Figure 7 shows the graph of f. Notice that the x-intercepts are -3, 2, and 5. ■

Figure 7

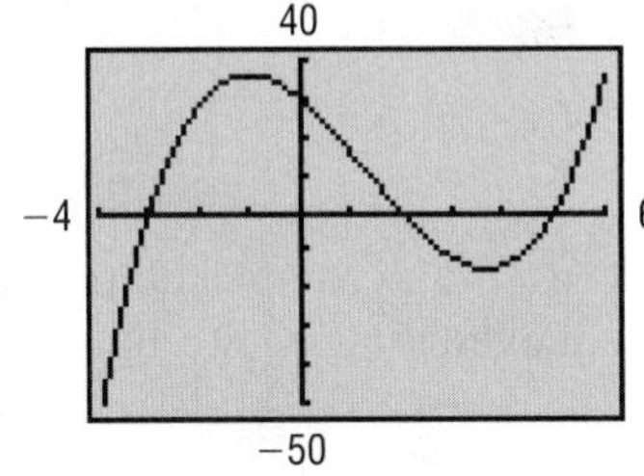

Seeing the Concept

Graph the function found in Example 4 for $a = 2$ and $a = -1$. Does the value of a affect the zeros of f? How does the value of a affect the graph of f?

Now Work PROBLEM 41

If the same factor $x - r$ occurs more than once, r is called a **repeated,** or **multiple, zero of f.** More precisely, we have the following definition.

DEFINITION If $(x - r)^m$ is a factor of a polynomial f and $(x - r)^{m+1}$ is not a factor of f, then r is called a **zero of multiplicity m of f.***

EXAMPLE 5 Identifying Zeros and Their Multiplicities

For the polynomial function

$$f(x) = 5(x - 2)(x + 3)^2\left(x - \frac{1}{2}\right)^4$$

2 is a zero of multiplicity 1 because the exponent on the factor $x - 2$ is 1.

-3 is a zero of multiplicity 2 because the exponent on the factor $x + 3$ is 2.

$\frac{1}{2}$ is a zero of multiplicity 4 because the exponent on the factor $x - \frac{1}{2}$ is 4. ■

Now Work PROBLEM 49(a)

*Some books use the terms **multiple root** and **root of multiplicity m**.

In Example 5 notice that, if you add the multiplicities $(1 + 2 + 4 = 7)$, you obtain the degree of the polynomial function.

Suppose that it is possible to factor completely a polynomial function and, as a result, locate all the x-intercepts of its graph (the real zeros of the function). The following example illustrates the role that the multiplicity of an x-intercept plays.

EXAMPLE 6 **Investigating the Role of Multiplicity**

For the polynomial function $f(x) = (x + 1)^2(x - 2)$:

(a) Find the x- and y-intercepts of the graph of f.
(b) Using a graphing utility, graph the polynomial function.
(c) For each x-intercept, determine whether it is of odd or even multiplicity.

Solution

(a) The y-intercept is $f(0) = (0 + 1)^2\,(0 - 2) = -2$. The x-intercepts satisfy the equation

$$f(x) = (x + 1)^2(x - 2) = 0$$

from which we find that

$$(x + 1)^2 = 0 \quad \text{or} \quad x - 2 = 0$$
$$x = -1 \quad \text{or} \quad x = 2$$

The x-intercepts are -1 and 2.

Figure 8

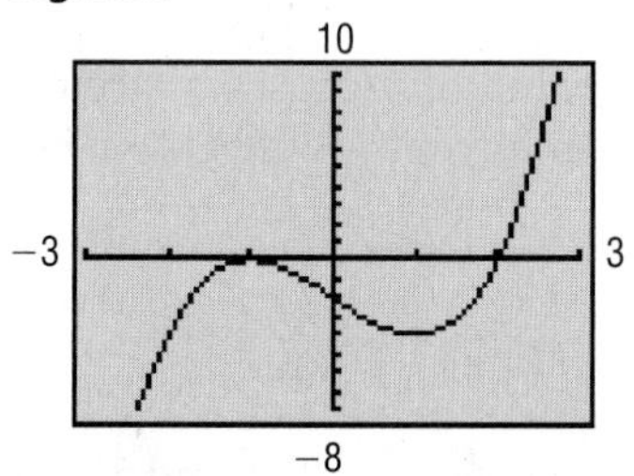

(b) See Figure 8 for the graph of f.

(c) We can see from the factored form of f that -1 is a zero or root of multiplicity 2, and 2 is a zero or root of multiplicity 1; so -1 is of even multiplicity and 2 is of odd multiplicity. ■

Table 3

X	Y1
-3	-20
-2	-4
-1	0
0	-2
1	-4
2	0
3	16

Y1=(X+1)²(X−2)

We can use a TABLE to further analyze the graph. See Table 3. The sign of $f(x)$ is the same on each side of $x = -1$, and the graph of f just *touches* the x-axis at $x = -1$ (a zero of *even* multiplicity). The sign of $f(x)$ changes from one side of $x = 2$ to the other, and the graph of f *crosses* the x-axis at $x = 2$ (a zero of *odd* multiplicity). These observations suggest the following result:

If r Is a Zero of Even Multiplicity

Sign of $f(x)$ does not change from one side of r to the other side of r. Graph **touches** x-axis at r.

If r Is a Zero of Odd Multiplicity

Sign of $f(x)$ changes from one side of r to the other side of r. Graph **crosses** x-axis at r.

Now Work PROBLEM 49(b)

Turning Points

Points on the graph where the graph changes from an increasing function to a decreasing function, or vice versa, are called **turning points**.*

*Graphing utilities can be used to approximate turning points. Calculus is needed to find the exact location of turning points.

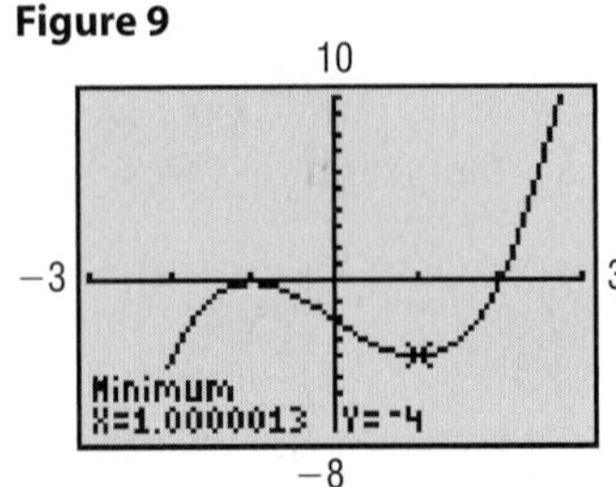

Figure 9

Look at Figure 9. The graph of $f(x) = (x+1)^2(x-2) = x^3 - 3x - 2$ has a turning point at $(-1, 0)$. After utilizing MINIMUM, we find that the graph also has a turning point at $(1, -4)$.

Exploration

Graph $Y_1 = x^3, Y_2 = x^3 - x$, and $Y_3 = x^3 + 3x^2 + 4$. How many turning points do you see? Graph $Y_1 = x^4, Y_2 = x^4 - \frac{4}{3}x^3$, and $Y_3 = x^4 - 2x^2$. How many turning points do you see? How does the number of turning points compare to the degree?

The following theorem from calculus supplies the answer to the question posed in the Exploration.

THEOREM

Turning Points

If f is a polynomial function of degree n, then f has at most $n - 1$ turning points.

If the graph of a polynomial function f has $n - 1$ turning points, the degree of f is at least n.

Based on the first part of the theorem, a polynomial function of degree 5 will have at most $5 - 1 = 4$ turning points. Based on the second part of the theorem, if a polynomial function has 3 turning points, then its degree must be at least 4.

EXAMPLE 7 Identifying the Graph of a Polynomial Function

Which of the graphs in Figure 10 could be the graph of a polynomial function? For those that could, list the real zeros and state the least degree the polynomial function can have. For those that could not, say why not.

Figure 10

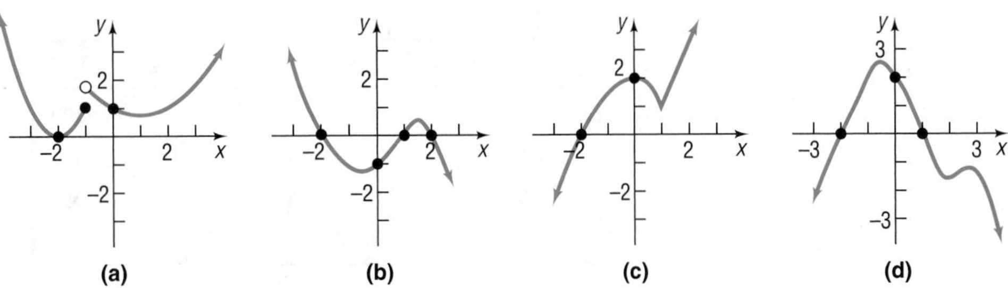

Solution

(a) The graph in Figure 10(a) cannot be the graph of a polynomial function because of the gap that occurs at $x = -1$. Remember, the graph of a polynomial function is continuous—no gaps or holes.

(b) The graph in Figure 10(b) could be the graph of a polynomial function. It has three real zeros, at -2, 1, and 2. Since the graph has two turning points, the degree of the polynomial function must be at least 3.

(c) The graph in Figure 10(c) cannot be the graph of a polynomial function because of the cusp at $x = 1$. Remember, the graph of a polynomial function is smooth.

(d) The graph in Figure 10(d) could be the graph of a polynomial function. It has two real zeros, at -2 and 1. Since the graph has three turning points, the degree of the polynomial function is at least 4. ■

Now Work PROBLEMS 49(c) AND 61

End Behavior

One last remark about Figure 8. For very large values of x, either positive or negative, the graph of $f(x) = (x + 1)^2(x - 2)$ looks like the graph of $y = x^3$. To see why, write f in the form

$$f(x) = (x + 1)^2(x - 2) = x^3 - 3x - 2 = x^3\left(1 - \frac{3}{x^2} - \frac{2}{x^3}\right)$$

Now, for large values of x, either positive or negative, the terms $\frac{3}{x^2}$ and $\frac{2}{x^3}$ are close to 0, so for large values of x

$$f(x) = x^3 - 3x - 2 = x^3\left(1 - \frac{3}{x^2} - \frac{2}{x^3}\right) \approx x^3$$

The behavior of the graph of a function for large values of x, either positive or negative, is referred to as its **end behavior.**

THEOREM

End Behavior

For large values of x, either positive or negative, the graph of the polynomial function

$$f(x) = a_n x^n + a_{n-1}x^{n-1} + \cdots + a_1 x + a_0$$

resembles the graph of the power function

$$y = a_n x^n$$

In Words

The end behavior of a polynomial function resembles that of its leading term.

For example, if $f(x) = -2x^3 + 5x^2 + x - 4$, then the graph of f will behave like the graph of $y = -2x^3$ for very large values of x, either positive or negative. We can see that the graphs of f and $y = -2x^3$ "behave" the same by considering Table 4 and Figure 11.

Table 4

x	f(x)	$y = -2x^3$
10	−1494	−2000
100	−1,949,904	−2,000,000
500	−248,749,504	−250,000,000
1000	−1,994,999,004	−2,000,000,000

Figure 11

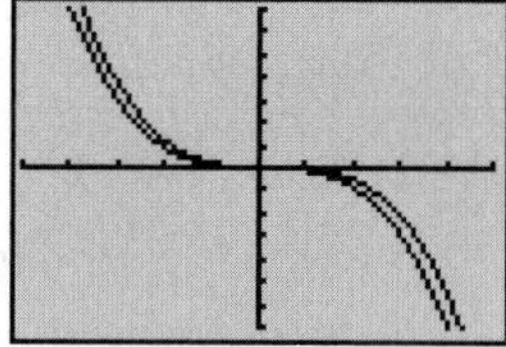

Notice that, as x becomes a larger and larger positive number, the values of f become larger and larger negative numbers. When this happens, we say that f is **unbounded in the negative direction.** Rather than using words to describe the behavior of the graph of the function, we explain its behavior using notation. We can symbolize "the value of f becomes a larger and larger negative number as x becomes a larger and larger positive number" by writing $f(x) \to -\infty$ as $x \to \infty$ (read "the values of f approach negative infinity as x approaches infinity"). In calculus, **limits** are used to convey these ideas. There we use the symbolism $\lim_{x \to \infty} f(x) = -\infty$ read "the limit of $f(x)$ as x approaches infinity equals negative infinity," to mean that $f(x) \to -\infty$ as $x \to \infty$.

When the value of a limit equals infinity, we mean that the values of the function are unbounded in the positive or negative direction and call the limit an **infinite limit.** When we discuss limits as x becomes unbounded in the negative direction or unbounded in the positive direction, we are discussing **limits at infinity.**

Look back at Figures 2 and 3. Based on the preceding theorem and the previous discussion on power functions, the end behavior of a polynomial function can only be of four types. See Figure 12.

Figure 12

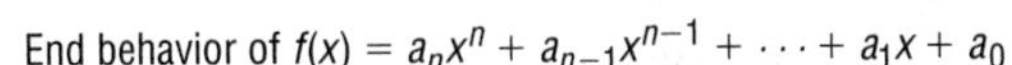

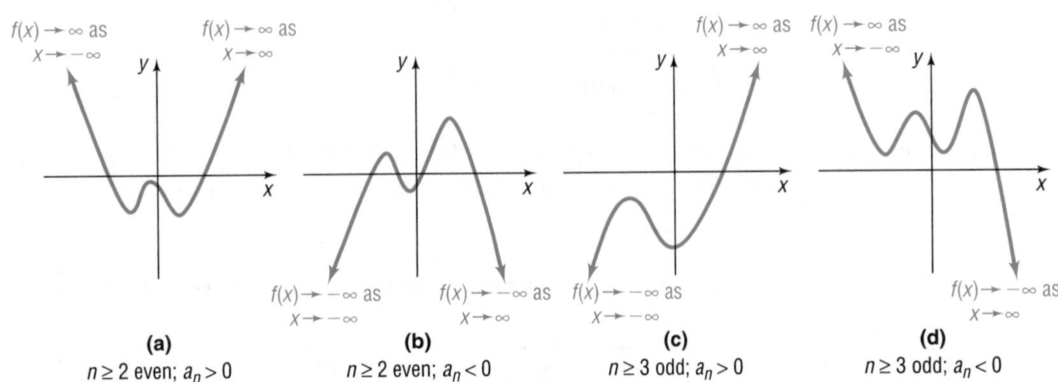

(a) $n \geq 2$ even; $a_n > 0$ (b) $n \geq 2$ even; $a_n < 0$ (c) $n \geq 3$ odd; $a_n > 0$ (d) $n \geq 3$ odd; $a_n < 0$

For example, if $f(x) = -2x^4 + x^3 + 4x^2 - 7x + 1$, the graph of f will resemble the graph of the power function $y = -2x^4$ for large $|x|$. The graph of f will behave like Figure 12(b) for large $|x|$.

Now Work PROBLEM 49(d)

EXAMPLE 8 Identifying the Graph of a Polynomial Function

Which of the graphs in Figure 13 could be the graph of

$$f(x) = x^4 + ax^3 + bx^2 - 5x - 6$$

where $a > 0, b > 0$?

Figure 13

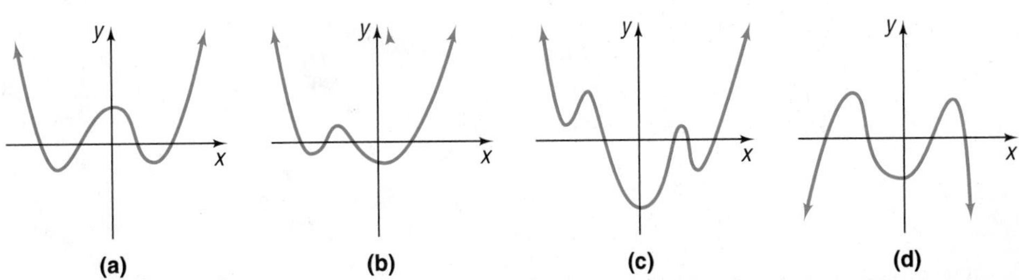

(a) (b) (c) (d)

Solution The y-intercept of f is $f(0) = -6$. We can eliminate the graph in Figure 13(a), whose y-intercept is positive.

We are not able to solve $f(x) = 0$ to find the x-intercepts of f, so we move on to investigate the turning points of each graph. Since f is of degree 4, the graph of f has at most 3 turning points. We eliminate the graph in Figure 13(c) since that graph has 5 turning points.

Now we look at end behavior. For large values of $|x|$, the graph of f will behave like the graph of $y = x^4$. This eliminates the graph in Figure 13(d), whose end behavior is like the graph of $y = -x^4$.

Only the graph in Figure 13(b) could be the graph of

$$f(x) = x^4 + ax^3 + bx^2 - 5x - 6$$

where $a > 0, b > 0$. ■

Now Work PROBLEM 65

SUMMARY

Graph of a Polynomial Function $f(x) = a_n x^n + a_{n-1}x^{n-1} + \cdots + a_1 x + a_0 \quad a_n \neq 0$

Degree of the polynomial function f: n
Graph is smooth and continuous.
Maximum number of turning points: $n - 1$
At a zero of even multiplicity: The graph of f touches the x-axis.
At a zero of odd multiplicity: The graph of f crosses the x-axis.
Between zeros, the graph of f is either above or below the x-axis.
End behavior: For large $|x|$, the graph of f behaves like the graph of $y = a_n x^n$.

4 Analyze the Graph of a Polynomial Function

EXAMPLE 9 **How to Analyze the Graph of a Polynomial Function**

Analyze the graph of the polynomial function $f(x) = (2x + 1)(x - 3)^2$.

Step-by-Step Solution

Step 1 Determine the end behavior of the graph of the function.

Expand the polynomial function to write it in the form

$$f(x) = a_n x^n + a_{n-1}x^{n-1} + \cdots + a_1 x + a_0$$

$$\begin{aligned} f(x) &= (2x + 1)(x - 3)^2 \\ &= (2x + 1)(x^2 - 6x + 9) \\ &= 2x^3 - 12x^2 + 18x + x^2 - 6x + 9 && \text{Multiply.} \\ &= 2x^3 - 11x^2 + 12x + 9 && \text{Combine like terms.} \end{aligned}$$

The polynomial function f is of degree 3. The graph of f behaves like $y = 2x^3$ for large values of $|x|$.

Step 2 Find the x- and y-intercepts of the graph of the function.

The y-intercept is $f(0) = 9$. To find the x-intercepts, solve $f(x) = 0$.

$$\begin{aligned} f(x) &= 0 \\ (2x + 1)(x - 3)^2 &= 0 \\ 2x + 1 = 0 \quad &\text{or} \quad (x - 3)^2 = 0 \\ x = -\frac{1}{2} \quad &\text{or} \quad x - 3 = 0 \\ & \qquad\quad x = 3 \end{aligned}$$

The x-intercepts are $-\frac{1}{2}$ and 3.

Step 3 Determine the zeros of the function and their multiplicity. Use this information to determine whether the graph crosses or touches the x-axis at each x-intercept.

The zeros of f are $-\frac{1}{2}$ and 3. The zero $-\frac{1}{2}$ is a zero of multiplicity 1, so the graph of f crosses the x-axis at $x = -\frac{1}{2}$. The zero 3 is a zero of multiplicity 2, so the graph of f touches the x-axis at $x = 3$.

Step 4 Use a graphing utility to graph the function.

See Figure 14 for the graph of f.

Figure 14

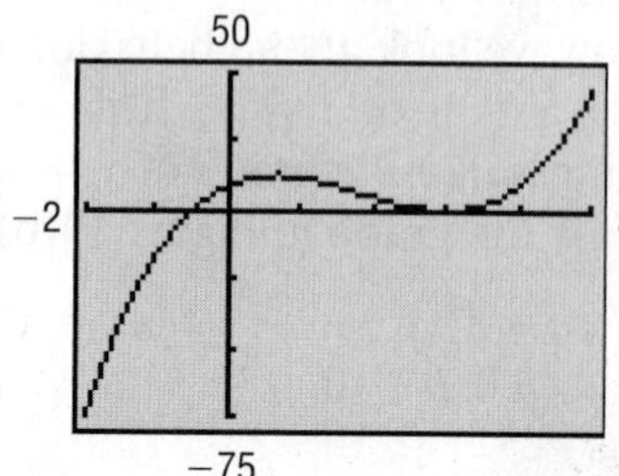

Step 5 Approximate the turning points of the graph.

From the graph of f shown in Figure 14, we see that f has two turning points. Using MAXIMUM, one turning point is at (0.67, 12.70), rounded to two decimal places. Using MINIMUM, the other turning point is at (3, 0).

Step 6 Use the information in Steps 1 to 5 to draw a complete graph of the function by hand.

Figure 15 shows a graph of f using the information in Steps 1 through 5.

Figure 15

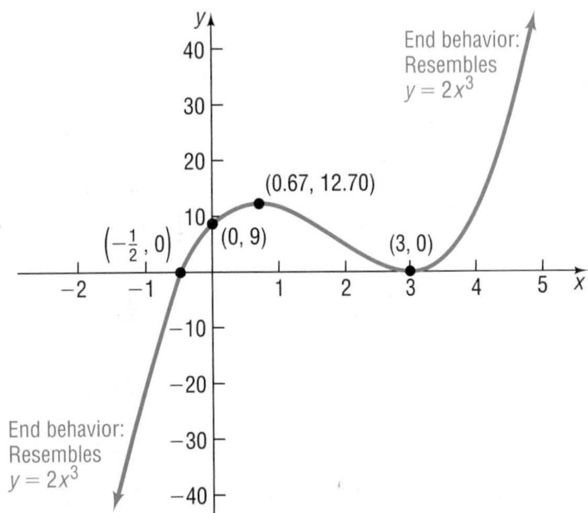

Step 7 Find the domain and the range of the function.

The domain and the range of f is the set of all real numbers.

Step 8 Use the graph to determine where the function is increasing and where it is decreasing.

Based on the graph, f is increasing on the intervals $(-\infty, 0.67)$ and $(3, \infty)$. Also, f is decreasing on the interval $(0.67, 3)$. ■

SUMMARY

Analyzing the Graph of a Polynomial Function

STEP 1: Determine the end behavior of the graph of the function.
STEP 2: Find the x- and y-intercepts of the graph of the function.
STEP 3: Determine the zeros of the function and their multiplicity. Use this information to determine whether the graph crosses or touches the x-axis at each x-intercept.
STEP 4: Use a graphing utility to graph the function.
STEP 5: Approximate the turning points of the graph.
STEP 6: Use the information in Steps 1 through 5 to draw a complete graph of the function by hand.
STEP 7: Find the domain and the range of the function.
STEP 8: Use the graph to determine where the function is increasing and where it is decreasing.

Now Work PROBLEM 69

For polynomial functions that have noninteger coefficients and for polynomials that are not easily factored, we utilize the graphing utility early in the analysis. This is because the amount of information that can be obtained from algebraic analysis is limited.

EXAMPLE 10 How to Use a Graphing Utility to Analyze the Graph of a Polynomial Function

Analyze the graph of the polynomial function

Step-by-Step Solution

$$f(x) = x^3 + 2.48x^2 - 4.3155x + 2.484406$$

Step 1 Determine the end behavior of the graph of the function.

The polynomial function f is of degree 3. The graph of f behaves like $y = x^3$ for large values of $|x|$.

Step 2 Graph the function using a graphing utility.

See Figure 16 for the graph of f.

Figure 16

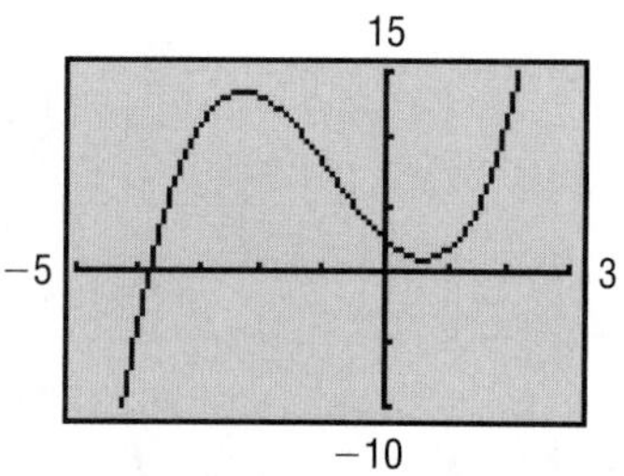

Step 3 Use a graphing utility to approximate the x- and y-intercepts of the graph.

The y-intercept is $f(0) = 2.484406$. In Example 9 the polynomial function was factored, so it was easy to find the x-intercepts algebraically. However, it is not readily apparent how to factor f in this example. Therefore, we use a graphing utility's ZERO (or ROOT or SOLVE) feature and find the lone x-intercept to be −3.79, rounded to two decimal places.

Step 4 Use a graphing utility to create a TABLE to find points on the graph around each x-intercept.

Table 5 shows values of x around the x-intercept. The points (−4, −4.57) and (−2, 13.04) are on the graph.

Table 5

X	Y1
-4	-4.574
-2	13.035

Y1=X^3+2.48X²−4...

Step 5 Approximate the turning points of the graph.

From the graph of f shown in Figure 16, we see that f has two turning points. Using MAXIMUM, one turning point is at (−2.28, 13.36), rounded to two decimal places. Using MINIMUM, the other turning point is at (0.63, 1), rounded to two decimal places.

Step 6 Use the information in Steps 1 through 5 to draw a complete graph of the function by hand.

Figure 17 shows a graph of f using the information in Steps 1 to 5.

Figure 17

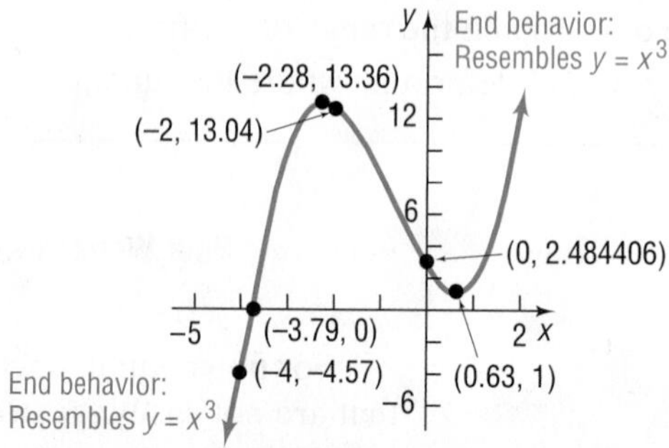

Step 7 Find the domain and the range of the function.

The domain and the range of f are the set of all real numbers.

Step 8 Use the graph to determine where the function is increasing and where it is decreasing.

Based on the graph, f is increasing on the intervals $(-\infty, -2.28)$ and $(0.63, \infty)$. Also, f is decreasing on the interval $(-2.28, 0.63)$. ■

SUMMARY

Using a Graphing Utility to Analyze the Graph of a Polynomial Function

STEP 1: Determine the end behavior of the graph of the function.
STEP 2: Graph the function using a graphing utility.
STEP 3: Use a graphing utility to approximate the x- and y-intercepts of the graph.
STEP 4: Use a graphing utility to create a TABLE to find points on the graph around each x-intercept.
STEP 5: Approximate the turning points of the graph.
STEP 6: Use the information in Steps 1 through 5 to draw a complete graph of the function by hand.
STEP 7: Find the domain and the range of the function.
STEP 8: Use the graph to determine where the function is increasing and where it is decreasing.

Now Work PROBLEM 87

5 Build Cubic Models from Data

In Section 10.2 we found the line of best fit from data, and in Section 10.4 we found the quadratic function of best fit. It is also possible to find polynomial functions of best fit. However, most statisticians do not recommend finding polynomial functions of best fit of degree higher than 3.

Data that follow a cubic relation should look like Figure 18(a) or 18(b).

Figure 18

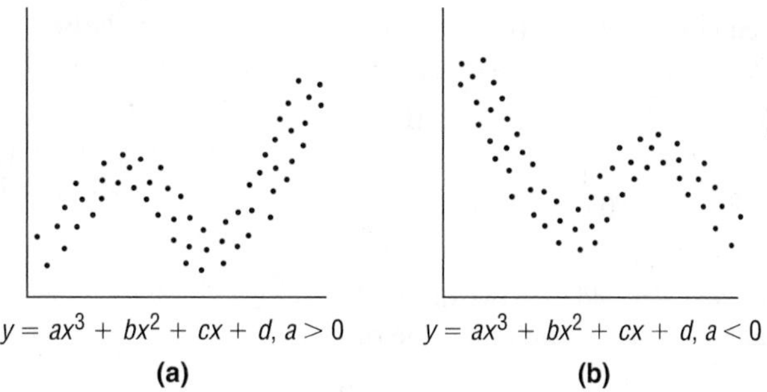

EXAMPLE 11 A Cubic Function of Best Fit

The data in Table 6 represent the weekly cost C (in thousands of dollars) of printing x thousand textbooks.

(a) Draw a scatter diagram of the data using x as the independent variable and C as the dependent variable. Comment on the type of relation that may exist between the two variables x and C.
(b) Using a graphing utility, find the cubic function of best fit $C = C(x)$ that models the relation between number of texts and cost.
(c) Graph the cubic function of best fit on your scatter diagram.
(d) Use the function found in part (b) to predict the cost of printing 22 thousand texts per week.

Table 6

Number of Textbooks, x	Cost, C
0	100
5	128.1
10	144
13	153.5
17	161.2
18	162.6
20	166.3
23	178.9
25	190.2
27	221.8

Solution

(a) Figure 19 shows the scatter diagram. A cubic relation may exist between the two variables.

(b) Upon executing the CUBIC REGression program, we obtain the results shown in Figure 20. The output the utility provides shows us the equation $y = ax^3 + bx^2 + cx + d$. The cubic function of best fit to the data is $C(x) = 0.0155x^3 - 0.5951x^2 + 9.1502x + 98.4327$.

(c) Figure 21 shows the graph of the cubic function of best fit on the scatter diagram. The function fits the data reasonably well.

Figure 19

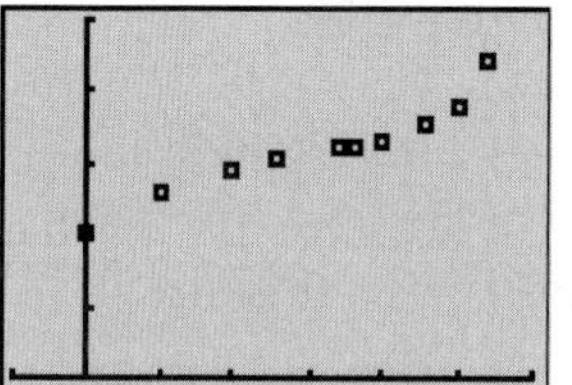

Figure 20

Figure 21

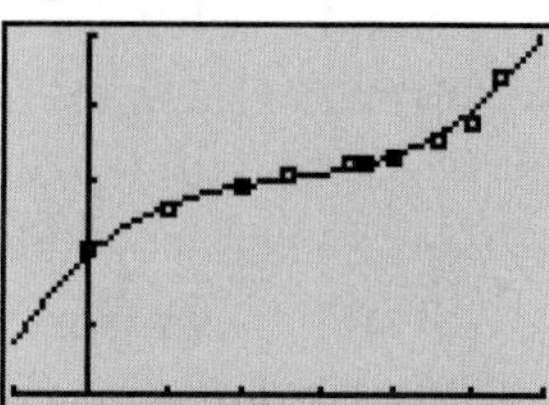

(d) Evaluate the function $C(x)$ at $x = 22$.

$$C(22) = 0.0155(22)^3 - 0.5951(22)^2 + 9.1502(22) + 98.4327 \approx 176.8$$

The model predicts that the cost of printing 22 thousand textbooks in a week will be 176.8 thousand dollars, that is $176,800. ■

11.1 Assess Your Understanding

'Are You Prepared' *Answers are given at the end of these exercises. If you get a wrong answer, read the pages listed in red.*

1. The intercepts of the equation $9x^2 + 4y = 36$ are ________. (pp. 522–523)

2. Is the expression $4x^3 - 3.6x^2 - \sqrt{2}$ a polynomial? If so, what is its degree?

3. To graph $y = x^2 - 4$, you would shift the graph of $y = x^2$ ______ a distance of ______ units. (pp. 605–606)

4. Use a graphing utility to approximate (rounded to two decimal places) the local maximum value and local minimum value of $f(x) = x^3 - 2x^2 - 4x + 5$, for $-3 < x < 3$. (pp. 587–588)

5. ***True or False*** The x-intercepts of the graph of a function $y = f(x)$ are the real solutions of the equation $f(x) = 0$. (pp. 574–576)

6. If $g(5) = 0$, what point is on the graph of g? What is the corresponding x-intercept of the graph of g? (pp. 574–575)

Concepts and Vocabulary

7. The graph of every polynomial function is both ______ and ________.

8. If r is a real zero of even multiplicity of a function f, then the graph of f ______ (crosses/touches) the x-axis at r.

9. The graphs of power functions of the form $f(x) = x^n$, where $n \geq 2$ is an even integer, always contain the points ______, ______, and ______.

10. If r is a solution to the equation $f(x) = 0$, name three additional statements that can be made about f and r assuming f is a polynomial function.

11. The points at which a graph changes direction (from increasing to decreasing or decreasing to increasing) are called __________.

12. The graph of the function $f(x) = 3x^4 - x^3 + 5x^2 - 2x - 7$ will behave like the graph of ______ for large values of $|x|$.

13. If $f(x) = -2x^5 + x^3 - 5x^2 + 7$, then $\lim_{x \to -\infty} f(x) =$ ______ and $\lim_{x \to \infty} f(x) =$ ______.

14. Explain what the notation $\lim_{x \to \infty} f(x) = -\infty$ means.

Skill Building

In Problems 15–26, determine which functions are polynomial functions. For those that are, state the degree. For those that are not, tell why not.

15. $f(x) = 4x + x^3$
16. $f(x) = 5x^2 + 4x^4$
17. $g(x) = \dfrac{1 - x^2}{2}$
18. $h(x) = 3 - \dfrac{1}{2}x$
19. $f(x) = 1 - \dfrac{1}{x}$
20. $f(x) = x(x - 1)$
21. $g(x) = x^{3/2} - x^2 + 2$
22. $h(x) = \sqrt{x}(\sqrt{x} - 1)$
23. $F(x) = 5x^4 - \pi x^3 + \dfrac{1}{2}$
24. $F(x) = \dfrac{x^2 - 5}{x^3}$
25. $G(x) = 2(x - 1)^2(x^2 + 1)$
26. $G(x) = -3x^2(x + 2)^3$

In Problems 27–40, use transformations of the graph of $y = x^4$ or $y = x^5$ to graph each function. Verify your results using a graphing utility.

27. $f(x) = (x + 1)^4$
28. $f(x) = (x - 2)^5$
29. $f(x) = x^5 - 3$
30. $f(x) = x^4 + 2$
31. $f(x) = \dfrac{1}{2}x^4$
32. $f(x) = 3x^5$
33. $f(x) = -x^5$
34. $f(x) = -x^4$
35. $f(x) = (x - 1)^5 + 2$
36. $f(x) = (x + 2)^4 - 3$
37. $f(x) = 2(x + 1)^4 + 1$
38. $f(x) = \dfrac{1}{2}(x - 1)^5 - 2$
39. $f(x) = 4 - (x - 2)^5$
40. $f(x) = 3 - (x + 2)^4$

In Problems 41–48, form a polynomial function whose real zeros and degree are given. Answers will vary depending on the choice of a leading coefficient.

41. Zeros: $-1, 1, 3$; degree 3
42. Zeros: $-2, 2, 3$; degree 3
43. Zeros: $-3, 0, 4$; degree 3
44. Zeros: $-4, 0, 2$; degree 3
45. Zeros: $-4, -1, 2, 3$; degree 4
46. Zeros: $-3, -1, 2, 5$; degree 4
47. Zeros: -1, multiplicity 1; 3, multiplicity 2; degree 3
48. Zeros: -2, multiplicity 2; 4, multiplicity 1; degree 3

In Problems 49–60, for each polynomial function:
(a) List each real zero and its multiplicity.
(b) Determine whether the graph crosses or touches the x-axis at each x-intercept.
(c) Determine the maximum number of turning points on the graph.
(d) Determine the end behavior; that is, find the power function that the graph of f resembles for large values of $|x|$.

49. $f(x) = 3(x - 7)(x + 3)^2$
50. $f(x) = 4(x + 4)(x + 3)^3$
51. $f(x) = 4(x^2 + 1)(x - 2)^3$
52. $f(x) = 2(x - 3)(x^2 + 4)^3$
53. $f(x) = -2\left(x + \dfrac{1}{2}\right)^2(x + 4)^3$
54. $f(x) = \left(x - \dfrac{1}{3}\right)^2(x - 1)^3$
55. $f(x) = (x - 5)^3(x + 4)^2$
56. $f(x) = \left(x + \sqrt{3}\right)^2(x - 2)^4$
57. $f(x) = 3(x^2 + 8)(x^2 + 9)^2$
58. $f(x) = -2(x^2 + 3)^3$
59. $f(x) = -2x^2(x^2 - 2)$
60. $f(x) = 4x(x^2 - 3)$

In Problems 61–64, identify which of the graphs could be the graph of a polynomial function. For those that could, list the real zeros and state the least degree the polynomial function can have. For those that could not, say why not.

61.
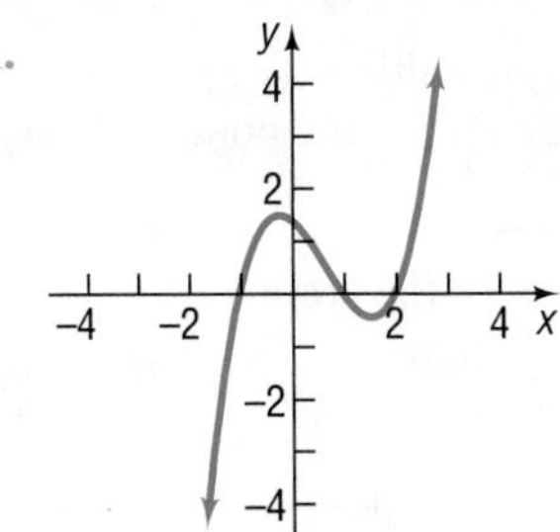

62.
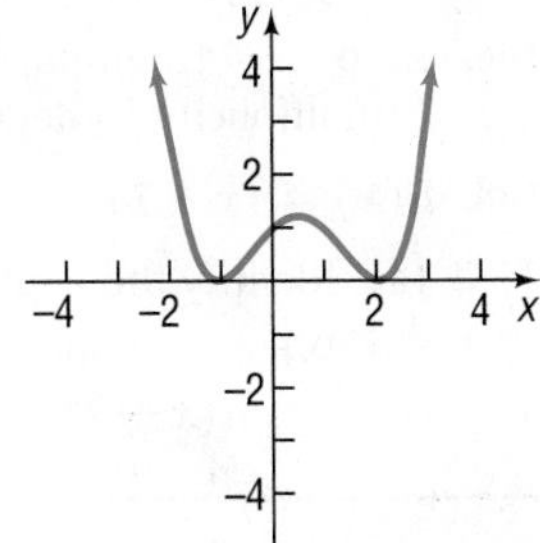

63.
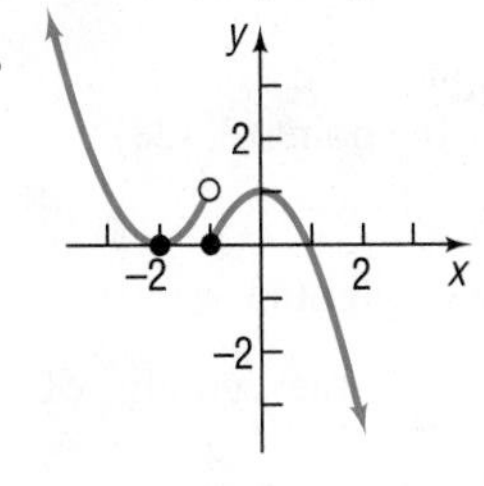

64.
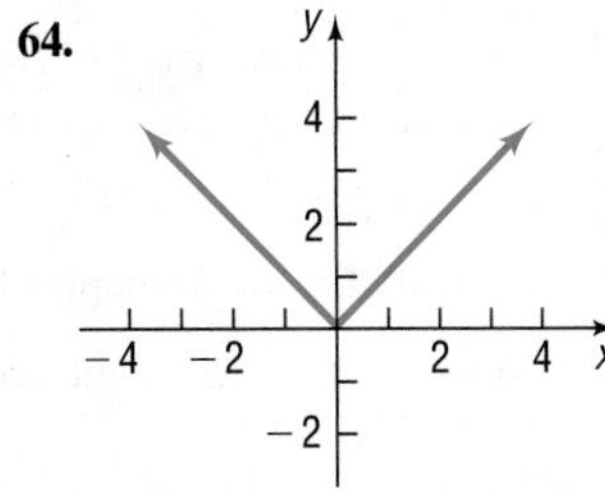

In Problems 65–68, construct a polynomial function that might have the given graph. (More than one answer may be possible.)

65. 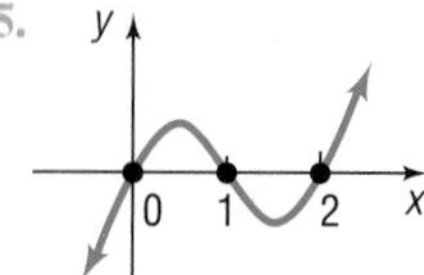

66. 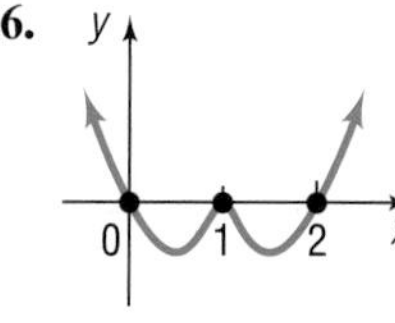

67. 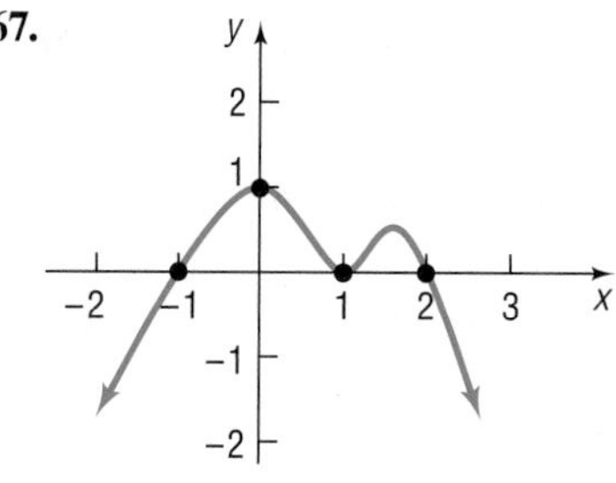

68. 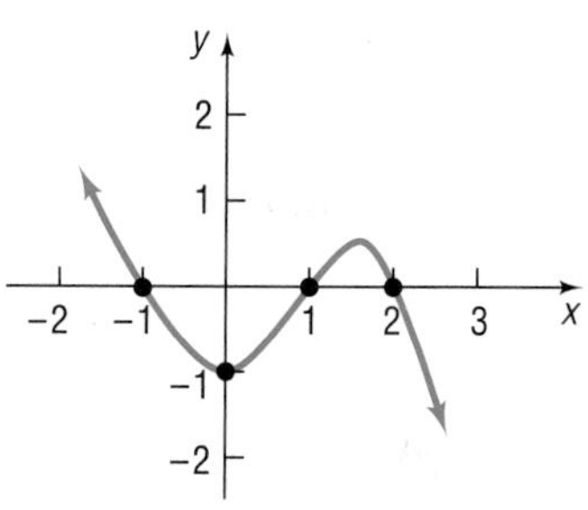

In Problems 69–86, analyze each polynomial function by following Steps 1 through 8 on page 691.

69. $f(x) = x^2(x - 3)$

70. $f(x) = x(x + 2)^2$

71. $f(x) = (x + 4)(x - 2)^2$

72. $f(x) = (x - 1)(x + 3)^2$

73. $f(x) = -2(x + 2)(x - 2)^3$

74. $f(x) = -\frac{1}{2}(x + 4)(x - 1)^3$

75. $f(x) = (x + 1)(x - 2)(x + 4)$

76. $f(x) = (x - 1)(x + 4)(x - 3)$

77. $f(x) = x^2(x - 2)(x + 2)$

78. $f(x) = x^2(x - 3)(x + 4)$

79. $f(x) = (x + 1)^2(x - 2)^2$

80. $f(x) = (x + 1)^3(x - 3)$

81. $f(x) = x^2(x - 3)(x + 1)$

82. $f(x) = x^2(x - 3)(x - 1)$

83. $f(x) = (x + 2)^2(x - 4)^2$

84. $f(x) = (x - 2)^2(x + 2)(x + 4)$

85. $f(x) = x^2(x - 2)(x^2 + 3)$

86. $f(x) = x^2(x^2 + 1)(x + 4)$

In Problems 87–94, analyze each polynomial function f by following Steps 1 through 8 on page 693.

87. $f(x) = x^3 + 0.2x^2 - 1.5876x - 0.31752$

88. $f(x) = x^3 - 0.8x^2 - 4.6656x + 3.73248$

89. $f(x) = x^3 + 2.56x^2 - 3.31x + 0.89$

90. $f(x) = x^3 - 2.91x^2 - 7.668x - 3.8151$

91. $f(x) = x^4 - 2.5x^2 + 0.5625$

92. $f(x) = x^4 - 18.5x^2 + 50.2619$

93. $f(x) = 2x^4 - \pi x^3 + \sqrt{5}x - 4$

94. $f(x) = -1.2x^4 + 0.5x^2 - \sqrt{3}x + 2$

Mixed Practice

In Problems 95–102, analyze each polynomial function by following Steps 1 through 8 on page 691.
[**Hint:** You will need to first factor the polynomial.]

95. $f(x) = 4x - x^3$

96. $f(x) = x - x^3$

97. $f(x) = x^3 + x^2 - 12x$

98. $f(x) = x^3 + 2x^2 - 8x$

99. $f(x) = 2x^4 + 12x^3 - 8x^2 - 48x$

100. $f(x) = 4x^3 + 10x^2 - 4x - 10$

101. $f(x) = -x^5 - x^4 + x^3 + x^2$

102. $f(x) = -x^5 + 5x^4 + 4x^3 - 20x^2$

In Problems 103–106, construct a polynomial function f with the given characteristics.

103. Zeros: $-3, 1, 4$; degree 3; y-intercept: 36

104. Zeros: $-4, -1, 2$; degree 3; y-intercept: 16

105. Zeros: -5 (multiplicity 2); 2 (multiplicity 1); 4 (multiplicity 1); degree 4; contains the point $(3, 128)$

106. Zeros: -4 (multiplicity 1); 0 (multiplicity 3); 2 (multiplicity 1); degree 5; contains the point $(-2, 64)$

107. $G(x) = (x + 3)^2(x - 2)$
   (a) Identify the x-intercepts of the graph of G.
   (b) What are the x-intercepts of the graph of $y = G(x + 3)$?

108. $h(x) = (x + 2)(x - 4)^3$
   (a) Identify the x-intercepts of the graph of h.
   (b) What are the x-intercepts of the graph of $y = h(x - 2)$?

Applications and Extensions

109. Hurricanes In 2005, Hurricane Katrina struck the Gulf Coast of the United States, killing 1289 people and causing an estimated $200 billion in damage. The following data represent the number of major hurricane strikes in the Atlantic Basin (category 3, 4, or 5) each decade from 1921 to 2010.

Decade, x	Major Hurricanes Striking Atlantic Basin, H
1921–1930, 1	17
1931–1940, 2	16
1941–1950, 3	29
1951–1960, 4	33
1961–1970, 5	27
1971–1980, 6	16
1981–1990, 7	16
1991–2000, 8	27
2001–2010, 9	33

Source: National Oceanic & Atmospheric Administration

(a) Draw a scatter diagram of the data. Comment on the type of relation that may exist between the two variables.
(b) Use a graphing utility to find the cubic function of best fit that models the relation between decade and number of major hurricanes.
(c) Use the model found in part (b) to predict the number of major hurricanes that struck the Atlantic Basin between 1961 and 1970.
(d) With a graphing utility, draw a scatter diagram of the data and then graph the cubic function of best fit on the scatter diagram.
(e) Concern has risen about the increase in the number and intensity of hurricanes, but some scientists believe this is just a natural fluctuation that could last another decade or two. Use your model to predict the number of major hurricanes that will strike the Atlantic Basin between 2011 and 2020. Is your result reasonable?

110. Cost of Manufacturing The following data represent the cost C (in thousands of dollars) of manufacturing Chevy Cobalts and the number x of Cobalts produced.

Number of Cobalts Produced, x	Cost, C
0	10
1	23
2	31
3	38
4	43
5	50
6	59
7	70
8	85
9	105
10	135

(a) Draw a scatter diagram of the data using x as the independent variable and C as the dependent variable. Comment on the type of relation that may exist between the two variables C and x.
(b) Use a graphing utility to find the cubic function of best fit $C = C(x)$.
(c) Graph the cubic function of best fit on the scatter diagram.
(d) Use the function found in part (b) to predict the cost of manufacturing 11 Cobalts.
(e) Interpret the y-intercept.

111. Temperature The following data represent the temperature T (Fahrenheit) in Kansas City, Missouri, x hours after midnight on May 15, 2010.

Hours after Midnight, x	Temperature (°F), T
3	45.0
6	44.1
9	51.1
12	57.9
15	63.0
18	63.0
21	59.0
24	54.0

Source: The Weather Underground

(a) Draw a scatter diagram of the data. Comment on the type of relation that may exist between the two variables.
(b) Find the average rate of change in temperature from 9 AM to 12 noon.
(c) What is the average rate of change in temperature from 3 PM to 6 PM?
(d) Decide on a function of best fit to these data (linear, quadratic, or cubic) and use this function to predict the temperature at 5 PM.
(e) With a graphing utility, draw a scatter diagram of the data and then graph the function of best fit on the scatter diagram.
(f) Interpret the y-intercept.

112. Future Value of Money Suppose that you make deposits of $500 at the beginning of every year into an Individual Retirement Account (IRA) earning interest r. At the beginning of the first year, the value of the account will be $500; at the beginning of the second year, the value of the account, will be

$$\$500 + \$500r + \$500 = \$500(1 + r) + \$500 = \$500r + \$1000$$

(a) Verify that the value of the account at the beginning of the third year is $T(r) = 500r^2 + 1500r + 1500$.

(b) The account value at the beginning of the fourth year is $F(r) = 500r^3 + 2000r^2 + 3000r + 2000$. If the annual rate of interest is $5\% = 0.05$, what will be the value of the account at the beginning of the fourth year?

113. A Geometric Series In calculus, you will learn that certain functions can be approximated by polynomial functions. We will explore one such function now.

(a) Using a graphing utility, create a table of values with $Y_1 = f(x) = \dfrac{1}{1-x}$ and $Y_2 = g_2(x) = 1 + x + x^2 + x^3$ for $-1 < x < 1$ with $\Delta\text{Tbl} = 0.1$.

(b) Using a graphing utility, create a table of values with $Y_1 = f(x) = \dfrac{1}{1-x}$ and $Y_2 = g_3(x) = 1 + x + x^2 + x^3 + x^4$ for $-1 < x < 1$ with $\Delta\text{Tbl} = 0.1$.

(c) Using a graphing utility, create a table of values with $Y_1 = f(x) = \dfrac{1}{1-x}$ and $Y_2 = g_4(x) = 1 + x + x^2 + x^3 + x^4 + x^5$ for $-1 < x < 1$ with $\Delta\text{Tbl} = 0.1$.

(d) What do you notice about the values of the function as more terms are added to the polynomial? Are there some values of x for which the approximations are better?

Explaining Concepts: Discussion and Writing

114. Can the graph of a polynomial function have no y-intercept? Can it have no x-intercepts? Explain.

115. Write a few paragraphs that provide a general strategy for graphing a polynomial function. Be sure to mention the following: degree, intercepts, end behavior, and turning points.

116. Make up a polynomial function that has the following characteristics: crosses the x-axis at -1 and 4, touches the x-axis at 0 and 2, and is above the x-axis between 0 and 2. Give your polynomial function to a fellow classmate and ask for a written critique.

117. Make up two polynomial functions, not of the same degree, with the following characteristics: crosses the x-axis at -2, touches the x-axis at 1, and is above the x-axis between -2 and 1. Give your polynomial functions to a fellow classmate and ask for a written critique.

118. The graph of a polynomial function is always smooth and continuous. Name a function studied earlier that is smooth and not continuous. Name one that is continuous but not smooth.

119. Which of the following statements are true regarding the graph of the cubic polynomial function $f(x) = x^3 + bx^2 + cx + d$? (Give reasons for your conclusions.)

(a) It intersects the y-axis in one and only one point.
(b) It intersects the x-axis in at most three points.
(c) It intersects the x-axis at least once.
(d) For $|x|$ very large, it behaves like the graph of $y = x^3$.
(e) It is symmetric with respect to the origin.
(f) It passes through the origin.

120. The illustration shows the graph of a polynomial function.

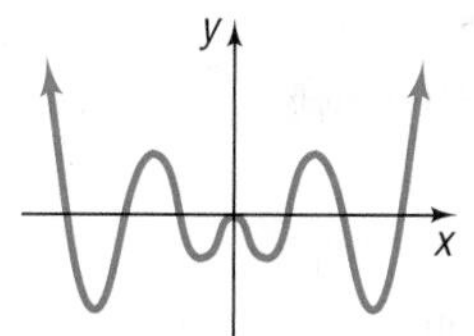

(a) Is the degree of the polynomial even or odd?
(b) Is the leading coefficient positive or negative?
(c) Is the function even, odd, or neither?
(d) Why is x^2 necessarily a factor of the polynomial?
(e) What is the minimum degree of the polynomial?
(f) Formulate five different polynomial functions whose graphs could look like the one shown. Compare yours to those of other students. What similarities do you see? What differences?

121. Design a polynomial function with the following characteristics: degree 6; four distinct real zeros, one of multiplicity 3; y-intercept 3; behaves like $y = -5x^6$ for large values of $|x|$. Is this polynomial function unique? Compare your polynomial function with those of other students. What terms will be the same as everyone else's? Add some more characteristics, such as symmetry or naming the real zeros. How does this modify the polynomial function?

Interactive Exercises

Ask your instructor if the applet exercise below is of interest to you.

Multiplicity and Turning Points *Open the Multiplicity applet. On the screen you will see the graph of* $f(x) = (x+2)^a x^b (x-2)^c$ *where* $a \in \{1, 2, 3\}$, $b \in \{1, 2, 3\}$, and $c \in \{1, 2, 3, 4\}$.

122. Grab the slider for the exponent a and move it from 1 to 2 to 3. What happens to the graph as the value of a changes? In particular, describe the behavior of the graph around the zero -2.

123. On the same graph, grab the slider for the exponent a and move it to 1. Grab the slider for the exponent b and move it from 1 to 2 to 3. What happens to the graph as the value of b changes? In particular, describe the behavior of the graph around the zero 0.

124. On the same graph, grab the slider for the exponent b and move it to 1. Grab the slider for the exponent c and move it from 1 to 2 to 3 to 4. What happens to the graph as the value of c changes? In particular, describe the behavior of the graph around the zero 2.

125. Experiment with the graph by adjusting a, b, and c. Based on your experiences, conjecture the role the exponent plays in the behavior of the graph around each zero of the function.

126. Obtain a graph of the function for the various values of a, b, and c in the following table. Conjecture a relation between the degree of a polynomial function and the number of turning points after completing the table. In the table, a can be 1, 2, or 3; b can be 1, 2, or 3; and c can be 1, 2, 3, or 4.

Values of *a*, *b*, and *c*	Degree	Turning Points	Values of *a*, *b*, and *c*	Degree	Turning Points
$a = 1, b = 1, c = 1$	3		$a = 1, b = 3, c = 3$		
$a = 1, b = 1, c = 2$	4		$a = 1, b = 3, c = 4$		
$a = 1, b = 1, c = 3$	5		$a = 2, b = 1, c = 1$		
$a = 1, b = 1, c = 4$			$a = 2, b = 1, c = 2$		
$a = 1, b = 2, c = 1$			$a = 2, b = 1, c = 3$		
$a = 1, b = 2, c = 2$			$a = 2, b = 1, c = 4$		
$a = 1, b = 2, c = 3$			$a = 2, b = 2, c = 1$		
$a = 1, b = 2, c = 4$			$a = 2, b = 2, c = 2$		
$a = 1, b = 3, c = 1$			$a = 3, b = 3, c = 4$		
$a = 1, b = 3, c = 2$			and so on		

'Are You Prepared?' Answers

1. $(-2,0)$, $(2,0)$, $(0,9)$ **2.** Yes; 3 **3.** Down; 4 **4.** Local maximum value 6.48 at $x = -0.67$; local minimum value -3 at $x = 2$
5. True **6.** $(5,0)$; 5

11.2 The Real Zeros of a Polynomial Function

PREPARING FOR THIS SECTION *Before getting started, review the following:*

- Evaluating Functions (Section 9.1 pp. 562–565)
- Intercepts of a Quadratic Function (Section 10.3, pp. 651–652)

Now Work the **'Are You Prepared?'** problems on page 710.

OBJECTIVES
1 Use the Remainder and Factor Theorems (p. 700)
2 Use the Rational Zeros Theorem to List the Potential Rational Zeros of a Polynomial Function (p. 702)
3 Find the Real Zeros of a Polynomial Function (p. 703)
4 Solve Polynomial Equations (p. 705)
5 Use the Theorem for Bounds on Zeros (p. 706)
6 Use the Intermediate Value Theorem (p. 708)

In Section 11.1, we were able to identify the real zeros of a polynomial function because either the polynomial function was in factored form or it could be easily factored. But how do we find the real zeros of a polynomial function if it is not factored or cannot be easily factored?

Recall that if r is a real zero of a polynomial function f then $f(r) = 0$, r is an x-intercept of the graph of f, $x - r$ is a factor of f, and r is a solution of the equation $f(x) = 0$. For example, if $x - 4$ is a factor of f, then 4 is a real zero of f and 4 is a solution to the equation $f(x) = 0$. For polynomial functions, we have seen the importance of the real zeros for graphing. In most cases, however, the real zeros of a polynomial function are difficult to find using algebraic methods. No nice formulas like the quadratic formula are available to help us find zeros for polynomial functions of degree 3 or higher. Formulas do exist for solving any third- or fourth-degree polynomial equation, but they are somewhat complicated. No general formulas exist for polynomial equations of degree 5 or higher. Refer to the Historical Feature at the end of this section for more information.

1 Use the Remainder and Factor Theorems

When we divide one polynomial (the dividend) by another (the divisor), we obtain a quotient polynomial and a remainder, the remainder being either the zero polynomial or a polynomial whose degree is less than the degree of the divisor. To check our work, we verify that

$$(\text{Quotient})(\text{Divisor}) + \text{Remainder} = \text{Dividend}$$

This checking routine is the basis for a famous theorem called the **division algorithm* for polynomials,** which we now state without proof.

THEOREM

Division Algorithm for Polynomials

If $f(x)$ and $g(x)$ denote polynomial functions and if $g(x)$ is a polynomial function whose degree is greater than zero, then there are unique polynomial functions $q(x)$ and $r(x)$ such that

$$\frac{f(x)}{g(x)} = q(x) + \frac{r(x)}{g(x)} \quad \text{or} \quad \underset{\text{dividend}}{f(x)} = \underset{\text{quotient}}{q(x)}\underset{\text{divisor}}{g(x)} + \underset{\text{remainder}}{r(x)} \tag{1}$$

where $r(x)$ is either the zero polynomial or a polynomial function of degree less than that of $g(x)$.

In equation (1), $f(x)$ is the **dividend,** $g(x)$ is the **divisor,** $q(x)$ is the **quotient,** and $r(x)$ is the **remainder.**

If the divisor $g(x)$ is a first-degree polynomial function of the form

$$g(x) = x - c \quad c \text{ a real number}$$

then the remainder $r(x)$ is either the zero polynomial or a polynomial function of degree 0. As a result, for such divisors, the remainder is some number, say R, and

$$f(x) = (x - c)q(x) + R \tag{2}$$

This equation is an identity in x and is true for all real numbers x. Suppose that $x = c$. Then equation (2) becomes

$$f(c) = (c - c)q(c) + R$$
$$f(c) = R$$

Substitute $f(c)$ for R in equation (2) to obtain

$$f(x) = (x - c)q(x) + f(c) \tag{3}$$

We have now proved the **Remainder Theorem.**

REMAINDER THEOREM

Let f be a polynomial function. If $f(x)$ is divided by $x - c$, then the remainder is $f(c)$.

*A systematic process in which certain steps are repeated a finite number of times is called an **algorithm.** For example, long division is an algorithm.

EXAMPLE 1 Using the Remainder Theorem

Find the remainder if $f(x) = x^3 - 4x^2 - 5$ is divided by

(a) $x - 3$ (b) $x + 2$

Solution (a) We could use long division or synthetic division, but it is easier to use the Remainder Theorem, which says that the remainder is $f(3)$.

$$f(3) = (3)^3 - 4(3)^2 - 5 = 27 - 36 - 5 = -14$$

The remainder is -14.

(b) To find the remainder when $f(x)$ is divided by $x + 2 = x - (-2)$, evaluate $f(-2)$.

$$f(-2) = (-2)^3 - 4(-2)^2 - 5 = -8 - 16 - 5 = -29$$

The remainder is -29. ■

Figure 22

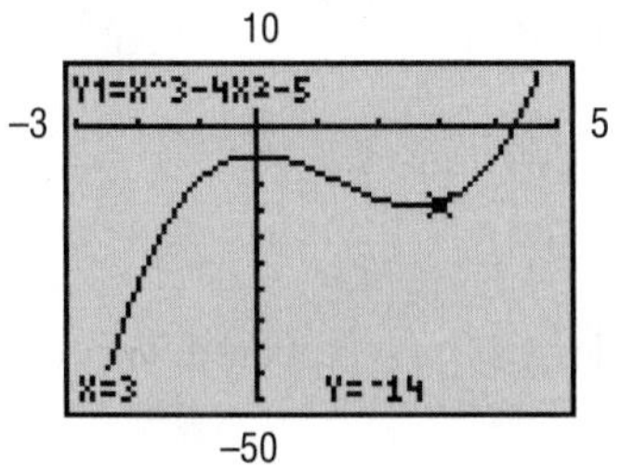

10

Y1=X^3-4X²-5

−3 5

X=3 Y=-14

−50

Compare the method used in Example 1(a) with the method used in Example 1 of Chapter R, Section R.6. Which method do you prefer? Give reasons.

COMMENT A graphing utility provides another way to find the value of a function using the eVALUEate feature. Consult your manual for details. See Figure 22 for the result of Example 1(a). ■

An important and useful consequence of the Remainder Theorem is the **Factor Theorem.**

FACTOR THEOREM

Let f be a polynomial function. Then $x - c$ is a factor of $f(x)$ if and only if $f(c) = 0$.

The Factor Theorem actually consists of two separate statements:

1. If $f(c) = 0$, then $x - c$ is a factor of $f(x)$.
2. If $x - c$ is a factor of $f(x)$, then $f(c) = 0$.

The proof requires two parts.

Proof

1. Suppose that $f(c) = 0$. Then, by equation (3), we have

$$f(x) = (x - c)q(x)$$

for some polynomial function $q(x)$. That is, $x - c$ is a factor of $f(x)$.

2. Suppose that $x - c$ is a factor of $f(x)$. Then there is a polynomial function q such that

$$f(x) = (x - c)q(x)$$

Replacing x by c, we find that

$$f(c) = (c - c)q(c) = 0 \cdot q(c) = 0$$

This completes the proof. ■

EXAMPLE 2 Using the Factor Theorem

Use the Factor Theorem to determine whether the function

$$f(x) = 2x^3 - x^2 + 2x - 3$$

has the factor

(a) $x - 1$ (b) $x + 2$

Solution The Factor Theorem states that if $f(c) = 0$ then $x - c$ is a factor.

(a) Because $x - 1$ is of the form $x - c$ with $c = 1$, we find the value of $f(1)$. We choose to use substitution.

$$f(1) = 2(1)^3 - (1)^2 + 2(1) - 3 = 2 - 1 + 2 - 3 = 0$$

See also Figure 23(a). By the Factor Theorem, $x - 1$ is a factor of $f(x)$.

(b) To test the factor $x + 2$, we first need to write it in the form $x - c$. Since $x + 2 = x - (-2)$, we find the value of $f(-2)$. See Figure 23(b). Because $f(-2) = -27 \neq 0$, we conclude from the Factor Theorem that $x - (-2) = x + 2$ is not a factor of $f(x)$. ■

Figure 23

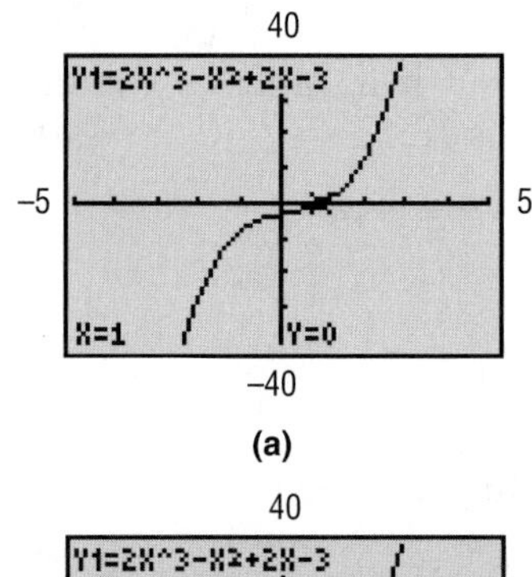

(a)

(b)

Now Work PROBLEM 11

In Example 2(a), we found that $x - 1$ is a factor of f. To write f in factored form, use long division or synthetic division. Using synthetic division,

$$\begin{array}{r|rrrr} 1 & 2 & -1 & 2 & -3 \\ & & 2 & 1 & 3 \\ \hline & 2 & 1 & 3 & 0 \end{array}$$

The quotient is $q(x) = 2x^2 + x + 3$ with a remainder of 0, as expected. Write f in factored form as

$$f(x) = 2x^3 - x^2 + 2x - 3 = (x - 1)(2x^2 + x + 3)$$

The next theorem concerns the number of real zeros that a polynomial function may have. In counting the zeros of a polynomial function, we count each zero as many times as its multiplicity.

THEOREM **Number of Real Zeros**

A polynomial function cannot have more real zeros than its degree.

Proof The proof is based on the Factor Theorem. If r is a real zero of a polynomial function f, then $f(r) = 0$ and, hence, $x - r$ is a factor of $f(x)$. Each real zero corresponds to a factor of degree 1. Because f cannot have more first-degree factors than its degree, the result follows. ■

2 Use the Rational Zeros Theorem to List the Potential Rational Zeros of a Polynomial Function

The next result, called the **Rational Zeros Theorem,** provides information about the rational zeros of a polynomial function *with integer coefficients*.

THEOREM **Rational Zeros Theorem**

Let f be a polynomial function of degree 1 or higher of the form

$$f(x) = a_n x^n + a_{n-1}x^{n-1} + \cdots + a_1 x + a_0 \quad a_n \neq 0, \quad a_0 \neq 0$$

where each coefficient is an integer. If $\frac{p}{q}$, in lowest terms, is a rational zero of f, then p must be a factor of a_0 and q must be a factor of a_n.

EXAMPLE 3 **Listing Potential Rational Zeros**

List the potential rational zeros of

$$f(x) = 2x^3 + 11x^2 - 7x - 6$$

Solution Because f has integer coefficients, we may use the Rational Zeros Theorem. First, list all the integers p that are factors of the constant term $a_0 = -6$ and all the integers q that are factors of the leading coefficient $a_3 = 2$.

$$p: \pm 1, \pm 2, \pm 3, \pm 6 \quad \text{Factors of } -6$$
$$q: \pm 1, \pm 2 \quad \text{Factors of } 2$$

Now form all possible ratios $\frac{p}{q}$.

$$\frac{p}{q}: \pm 1, \pm 2, \pm 3, \pm 6, \pm\frac{1}{2}, \pm\frac{3}{2}$$

If f has a rational zero, it will be found in this list, which contains 12 possibilities. ■

Now Work PROBLEM 21

> **In Words**
> For the polynomial function
> $f(x) = 2x^3 + 11x^2 - 7x - 6$,
> we know 5 is not a zero, because 5 is not in the list of potential rational zeros. However, -1 may or may not be a zero.

Be sure that you understand what the Rational Zeros Theorem says: For a polynomial function with integer coefficients, *if* there is a rational zero, it is one of those listed. It may be the case that the function does not have any rational zeros.

The Rational Zeros Theorem provides a list of potential rational zeros of a function f. If we graph f, we can get a better sense of the location of the x-intercepts and test to see if they are rational. We can also use the potential rational zeros to select our initial viewing window to graph f and then adjust the window based on the results. The graphs shown throughout the text will be those obtained after setting the final viewing window.

3 Find the Real Zeros of a Polynomial Function

EXAMPLE 4 **How to Find the Real Zeros of a Polynomial Function**

Find the real zeros of the polynomial function $f(x) = 2x^3 + 11x^2 - 7x - 6$. Write f in factored form.

Step-by-Step Solution

Step 1 Use the degree of the polynomial function to determine the maximum number of zeros.

Since f is a polynomial function of degree 3, there are at most three real zeros.

Step 2 If the polynomial function has integer coefficients, use the Rational Zeros Theorem to identify those rational numbers that potentially can be zeros.

List the potential rational zeros obtained in Example 3:

$$\pm 1, \pm 2, \pm 3, \pm 6, \pm\frac{1}{2}, \pm\frac{3}{2}$$

Step 3 Using a graphing utility, graph the polynomial function.

Figure 24 shows the graph of f. We see that f has three zeros: one near -6, one between -1 and 0, and one near 1.

Figure 24

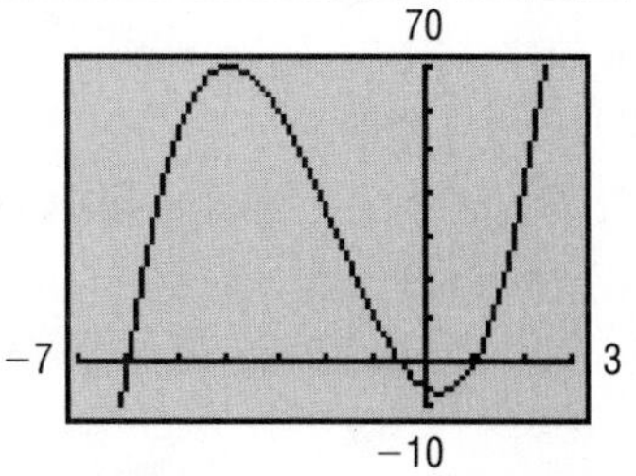

Step 4 Use the Factor Theorem to determine if the potential rational zero is a zero. If it is, use synthetic division or long division to factor the polynomial function. Repeat Step 4 until all the zeros of the polynomial function have been identified and the polynomial function is completely factored.

From our list of potential rational zeros, we test -6 to determine if it is a zero of f. Because

$$\begin{aligned} f(-6) &= 2(-6)^3 + 11(-6)^2 - 7(-6) - 6 \\ &= 2(-216) + 11(36) + 42 - 6 \\ &= -432 + 396 + 36 \\ &= 0 \end{aligned}$$

we know that -6 is a zero and $x - (-6) = x + 6$ is a factor of f. Use long division or synthetic division to factor f. (We will not show the division here, but you are encouraged to verify the results shown.) After dividing f by $x + 6$, the quotient is $2x^2 - x - 1$, so

$$\begin{aligned} f(x) &= 2x^3 + 11x^2 - 7x - 6 \\ &= (x + 6)(2x^2 - x - 1) \end{aligned}$$

Now any solution of the equation $2x^2 - x - 1 = 0$ will be a zero of f. Because of this, we call the equation $2x^2 - x - 1 = 0$ a **depressed equation** of f. Because any solution to the equation $2x^2 - x - 1 = 0$ is a zero of f, we work with the depressed equation to find the remaining zeros of f.

The depressed equation $2x^2 - x - 1 = 0$ is a quadratic equation with discriminant $b^2 - 4ac = (-1)^2 - 4(2)(-1) = 9 > 0$. The equation has two real solutions, which can be found by factoring.

$$2x^2 - x - 1 = (2x + 1)(x - 1) = 0$$

$$2x + 1 = 0 \quad \text{or} \quad x - 1 = 0$$

$$x = -\frac{1}{2} \quad \text{or} \quad x = 1$$

The zeros of f are -6, $-\frac{1}{2}$, and 1.

Factor f completely as follows:

$$f(x) = 2x^3 + 11x^2 - 7x - 6 = (x + 6)(2x^2 - x - 1) = (x + 6)(2x + 1)(x - 1)$$

Notice that the three zeros of f are in the list of potential rational zeros in Step 2. ■

SUMMARY

Steps for Finding the Real Zeros of a Polynomial Function

STEP 1: Use the degree of the polynomial function to determine the maximum number of zeros.

STEP 2: If the polynomial function has integer coefficients, use the Rational Zeros Theorem to identify those rational numbers that potentially can be zeros.

STEP 3: Graph the polynomial function using a graphing utility to find the best choice of potential rational zeros to test.

STEP 4: Use the Factor Theorem to determine if the potential rational zero is a zero. If it is, use synthetic division or long division to factor the polynomial function. Each time that a zero (and thus a factor) is found, repeat Step 4 on the depressed equation. In attempting to find the zeros, remember to use (if possible) the factoring techniques that you already know (special products, factoring by grouping, and so on).

EXAMPLE 5 Finding the Real Zeros of a Polynomial Function

Find the real zeros of $f(x) = x^5 - x^4 - 4x^3 + 8x^2 - 32x + 48$. Write f in factored form.

Solution

STEP 1: There are at most five real zeros.

STEP 2: To obtain the list of potential rational zeros, write the factors p of $a_0 = 48$ and the factors q of the leading coefficient $a_5 = 1$.

$$p: \quad \pm 1, \pm 2, \pm 3, \pm 4, \pm 6, \pm 8, \pm 12, \pm 16, \pm 24, \pm 48$$

$$q: \quad \pm 1$$

The potential rational zeros consist of all possible quotients $\frac{p}{q}$:

$$\frac{p}{q}: \quad \pm 1, \pm 2, \pm 3, \pm 4, \pm 6, \pm 8, \pm 12, \pm 16, \pm 24, \pm 48$$

Figure 25

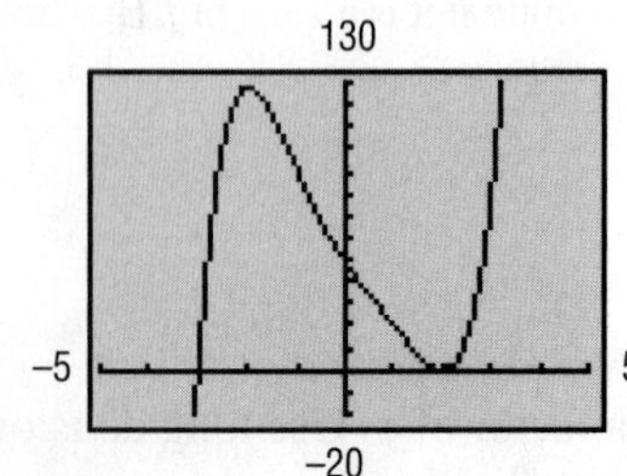

STEP 3: Figure 25 shows the graph of f. The graph has the characteristics expected of the given polynomial function of degree 5: no more than four turning points, y-intercept 48, and it behaves like $y = x^5$ for large $|x|$.

STEP 4: Since -3 appears to be a zero and -3 is a potential rational zero, evaluate $f(-3)$ and find that $f(-3) = 0$. By the Factor Theorem, $x + 3$ is a factor of f. We use synthetic division to factor f.

$$\begin{array}{r|rrrrrr} -3 & 1 & -1 & -4 & 8 & -32 & 48 \\ & & -3 & 12 & -24 & 48 & -48 \\ \hline & 1 & -4 & 8 & -16 & 16 & 0 \end{array}$$

Factor f as

$$f(x) = x^5 - x^4 - 4x^3 + 8x^2 - 32x + 48 = (x + 3)(x^4 - 4x^3 + 8x^2 - 16x + 16)$$

Now work with the first depressed equation:

$$q_1(x) = x^4 - 4x^3 + 8x^2 - 16x + 16 = 0$$

Repeat Step 4: In looking back at Figure 25, it appears that 2 might be a zero of even multiplicity. Check the potential rational zero 2 using synthetic division.

$$\begin{array}{r|rrrrr} 2 & 1 & -4 & 8 & -16 & 16 \\ & & 2 & -4 & 8 & -16 \\ \hline & 1 & -2 & 4 & -8 & 0 \end{array}$$

Since $f(2) = 0$, then $x - 2$ is a factor and

$$f(x) = (x + 3)(x - 2)(x^3 - 2x^2 + 4x - 8)$$

Repeat Step 4: The depressed equation $q_2(x) = x^3 - 2x^2 + 4x - 8 = 0$ can be factored by grouping.

$$\begin{aligned} x^3 - 2x^2 + 4x - 8 = (x^3 - 2x^2) + (4x - 8) &= x^2(x - 2) + 4(x - 2) \\ &= (x - 2)(x^2 + 4) = 0 \\ x - 2 = 0 \quad &\text{or} \quad x^2 + 4 = 0 \\ x = 2 \quad & \end{aligned}$$

Since $x^2 + 4 = 0$ has no real solutions, the real zeros of f are -3 and 2, with 2 being a zero of multiplicity 2. The factored form of f is

$$\begin{aligned} f(x) &= x^5 - x^4 - 4x^3 + 8x^2 - 32x + 48 \\ &= (x + 3)(x - 2)^2(x^2 + 4) \end{aligned}$$

■

Now Work PROBLEM 39

4 Solve Polynomial Equations

EXAMPLE 6 **Solving a Polynomial Equation**

Solve the equation: $x^5 - x^4 - 4x^3 + 8x^2 - 32x + 48 = 0$

Solution The solutions of this equation are the zeros of the polynomial function

$$f(x) = x^5 - x^4 - 4x^3 + 8x^2 - 32x + 48$$

Using the result of Example 5, the real zeros are -3 and 2. These are the real solutions of the equation $x^5 - x^4 - 4x^3 + 8x^2 - 32x + 48 = 0$. ■

Now Work PROBLEM 63

In Example 5, the quadratic factor $x^2 + 4$ that appears in the factored form of $f(x)$ is called *irreducible,* because the polynomial $x^2 + 4$ cannot be factored over the real numbers. In general, a quadratic factor $ax^2 + bx + c$ is **irreducible** if it cannot be factored over the real numbers, that is, if it is prime over the real numbers.

Refer back to Examples 4 and 5. The polynomial function of Example 4 has three real zeros, and its factored form contains three linear factors. The polynomial function of Example 5 has two distinct real zeros, and its factored form contains two distinct linear factors and one irreducible quadratic factor.

THEOREM

Every polynomial function (with real coefficients) can be uniquely factored into a product of linear factors and/or irreducible quadratic factors.

We prove this result in Section 11.3, and, in fact, shall draw several additional conclusions about the zeros of a polynomial function. One conclusion is worth noting now. If a polynomial function (with real coefficients) is of odd degree, then it must contain at least one linear factor. (Do you see why?) This means that it must have at least one real zero.

COROLLARY

A polynomial function (with real coefficients) of odd degree has at least one real zero.

5 Use the Theorem for Bounds on Zeros

One challenge in using a graphing utility is to set the viewing window so that a complete graph is obtained. The next theorem is a tool that can be used to find bounds on the zeros. This will assure that the function does not have any zeros outside these bounds. Then using these bounds to set *X*min and *X*max assures that all the x-intercepts appear in the viewing window.

A positive number M is a **bound** on the zeros of a polynomial function if every zero r lies between $-M$ and M, inclusive. That is, M is a bound to the zeros of a polynomial function f if

$$-M \leq \text{any zero of } f \leq M$$

THEOREM

Bounds on Zeros

Let f denote a polynomial function whose leading coefficient is 1.

$$f(x) = x^n + a_{n-1}x^{n-1} + \cdots + a_1x + a_0$$

A bound M on the real zeros of f is the smaller of the two numbers

$$\text{Max}\{1, |a_0| + |a_1| + \cdots + |a_{n-1}|\}, 1 + \text{Max}\{|a_0|, |a_1|, \ldots, |a_{n-1}|\} \quad \textbf{(4)}$$

where Max { } means "choose the largest entry in { }."

EXAMPLE 7 **Using the Theorem for Finding Bounds on Zeros**

Find a bound to the zeros of each polynomial function.

(a) $f(x) = x^5 + 3x^3 - 9x^2 + 5$ (b) $g(x) = 4x^5 - 2x^3 + 2x^2 + 1$

Solution (a) The leading coefficient of f is 1.

$$f(x) = x^5 + 3x^3 - 9x^2 + 5 \quad a_4 = 0, a_3 = 3, a_2 = -9, a_1 = 0, a_0 = 5$$

Evaluate the expressions in formula (4).

$$\begin{aligned} \text{Max}\{1, |a_0| + |a_1| + \cdots + |a_{n-1}|\} &= \text{Max}\{1, |5| + |0| + |-9| + |3| + |0|\} \\ &= \text{Max}\{1, 17\} = 17 \\ 1 + \text{Max}\{|a_0|, |a_1|, \ldots, |a_{n-1}|\} &= 1 + \text{Max}\{|5|, |0|, |-9|, |3|, |0|\} \\ &= 1 + 9 = 10 \end{aligned}$$

The smaller of the two numbers, 10, is the bound. Every real zero of f lies between -10 and 10.

(b) First factor the leading coefficient of g out.

$$g(x) = 4x^5 - 2x^3 + 2x^2 + 1 = 4\left(x^5 - \frac{1}{2}x^3 + \frac{1}{2}x^2 + \frac{1}{4}\right)$$

Next evaluate the two expressions in formula (4) with $a_4 = 0$, $a_3 = -\frac{1}{2}$, $a_2 = \frac{1}{2}$, $a_1 = 0$, and $a_0 = \frac{1}{4}$.

$$\begin{aligned}\text{Max}\{1, |a_0| + |a_1| + \cdots + |a_{n-1}|\} &= \text{Max}\left\{1, \left|\frac{1}{4}\right| + |0| + \left|\frac{1}{2}\right| + \left|-\frac{1}{2}\right| + |0|\right\}\\ &= \text{Max}\left\{1, \frac{5}{4}\right\} = \frac{5}{4}\end{aligned}$$

$$\begin{aligned}1 + \text{Max}\{|a_0|, |a_1|, \ldots, |a_{n-1}|\} &= 1 + \text{Max}\left\{\left|\frac{1}{4}\right|, |0|, \left|\frac{1}{2}\right|, \left|-\frac{1}{2}\right|, |0|\right\}\\ &= 1 + \frac{1}{2} = \frac{3}{2}\end{aligned}$$

The smaller of the two numbers, $\frac{5}{4}$, is the bound. Every zero of g lies between $-\frac{5}{4}$ and $\frac{5}{4}$. ■

EXAMPLE 8 Obtaining Graphs Using Bounds on Zeros

Obtain a graph for each polynomial function.

(a) $f(x) = x^5 + 3x^3 - 9x^2 + 5$ (b) $g(x) = 4x^5 - 2x^3 + 2x^2 + 1$

Solution (a) Based on Example 7(a), every zero lies between -10 and 10. Using $X\text{min} = -10$ and $X\text{max} = 10$, we graph $Y_1 = f(x) = x^5 + 3x^3 - 9x^2 + 5$. Figure 26(a) shows the graph obtained using ZOOM-FIT. Figure 26(b) shows the graph after adjusting the viewing window to improve the graph.

Figure 26

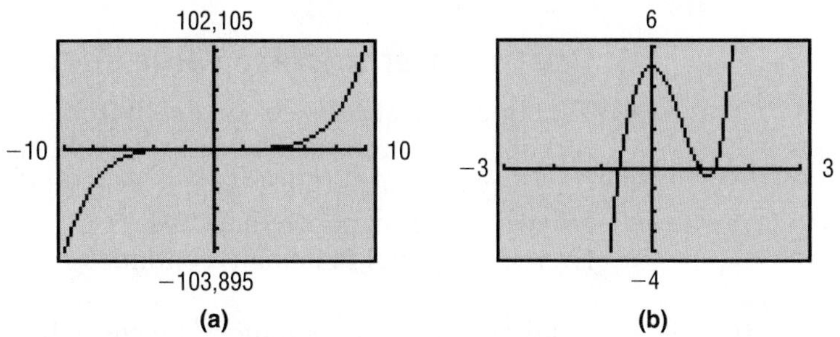

(b) Based on Example 7(b), every zero lies between $-\frac{5}{4}$ and $\frac{5}{4}$. Using $X\text{min} = -\frac{5}{4}$ and $X\text{max} = \frac{5}{4}$, we graph $Y_1 = g(x) = 4x^5 - 2x^3 + 2x^2 + 1$. Figure 27 shows the graph after using ZOOM-FIT. Here no adjustment of the viewing window is needed. ■

Figure 27

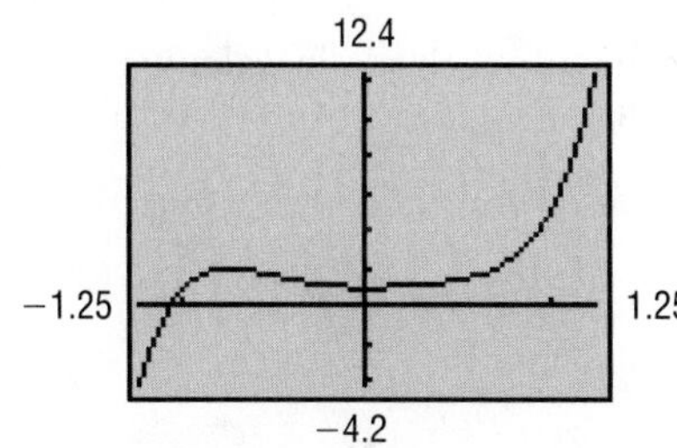

Now Work PROBLEM 33

The next example shows how to proceed when some of the coefficients of the polynomial are not integers.

EXAMPLE 9 Finding the Real Zeros of a Polynomial Function

Find all the real zeros of the polynomial function

$$f(x) = x^5 - 1.8x^4 - 17.79x^3 + 31.672x^2 + 37.95x - 8.7121$$

Round answers to two decimal places.

Solution **Step 1:** There are at most five real zeros.

Step 2: Since there are noninteger coefficients, the Rational Zeros Theorem does not apply.

Step 3: Determine the bounds on the zeros of f. The leading coefficient of f is 1 with $a_4 = -1.8$, $a_3 = -17.79$, $a_2 = 31.672$, $a_1 = 37.95$, and $a_0 = -8.7121$. Evaluate the expressions using formula (4).

$$\text{Max}\{1, |-8.7121| + |37.95| + |31.672| + |-17.79| + |-1.8|\} = \text{Max}\{1, 97.9241\} = 97.9241$$

$$1 + \text{Max}\{|-8.7121|, |37.95|, |31.672|, |-17.79|, |-1.8|\} = 1 + 37.95 = 38.95$$

Figure 28

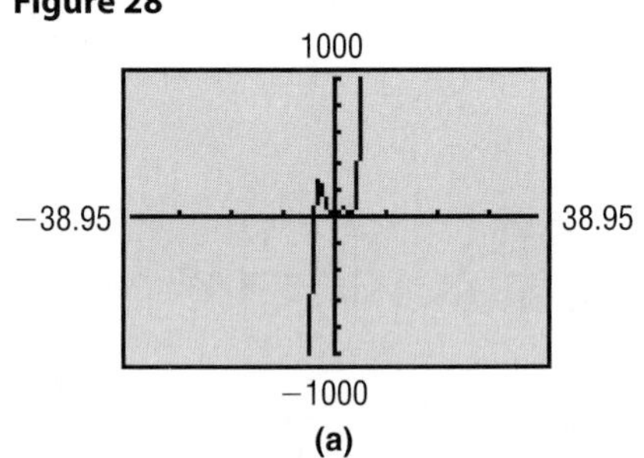

(a)

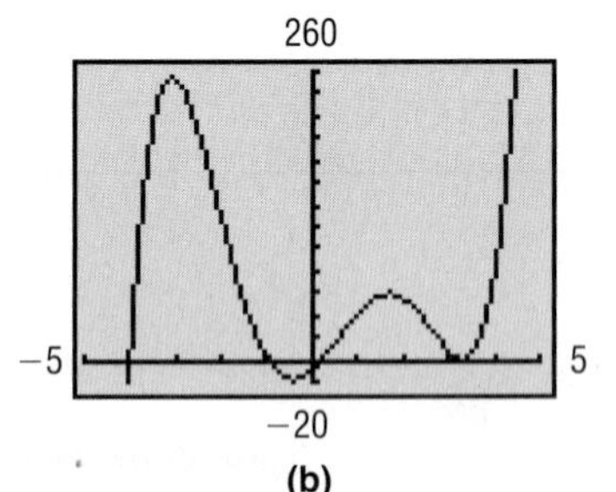

(b)

The smaller of the two numbers, 38.95, is the bound. Every real zero of f lies between -38.95 and 38.95. Figure 28(a) shows the graph of f with $X\text{min} = -38.95$ and $X\text{max} = 38.95$. Figure 28(b) shows a graph of f after adjusting the viewing window to improve the graph.

Step 4: From Figure 28(b), we see that f appears to have four x-intercepts: one near -4, one near -1, one between 0 and 1, and one near 3. The x-intercept near 3 might be a zero of even multiplicity since the graph seems to touch the x-axis at that point.

Use the Factor Theorem to determine if -4 and -1 are zeros. Since $f(-4) = f(-1) = 0$, -4 and -1 are zeros. Using ZERO (or ROOT), we find that the remaining zeros are 0.20 and 3.30, rounded to two decimal places.

There are no real zeros on the graph that have not already been identified. So either 3.30 is a zero of multiplicity 2 or there are two distinct zeros, each of which is 3.30, rounded to two decimal places. (Example 10 will explain how to determine which is true.) ■

Now Work PROBLEM 57

6 Use the Intermediate Value Theorem

The Intermediate Value Theorem requires that the function be *continuous*. Although calculus is needed to explain the meaning precisely, we have already said that, very basically, a function f is continuous when its graph can be drawn without lifting pencil from paper, that is, when the graph contains no holes or jumps or gaps. Every polynomial function is continuous.

INTERMEDIATE VALUE THEOREM

Let f denote a continuous function. If $a < b$ and if $f(a)$ and $f(b)$ are of opposite sign, then f has at least one zero between a and b.

Although the proof of this result requires advanced methods in calculus, it is easy to "see" why the result is true. Look at Figure 29.

Figure 29

If $f(a) < 0$ and $f(b) > 0$ and if f is continuous, there is at least one zero between a and b.

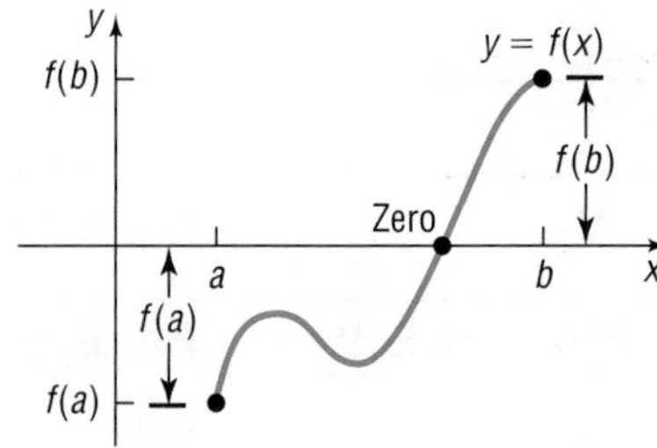

The Intermediate Value Theorem together with the TABLE feature of a graphing utility provides a basis for finding zeros.

EXAMPLE 10 Using the Intermediate Value Theorem and a Graphing Utility to Locate Zeros

Continue working with Example 9 to determine whether there is a repeated zero or two distinct zeros near 3.30.

Solution Use the TABLE feature of a graphing utility. See Table 7. Since $f(3.29) = 0.00956 > 0$ and $f(3.30) = -0.0001 < 0$, by the Intermediate Value Theorem there is a zero between 3.29 and 3.30. Similarly, since $f(3.30) = -0.0001 < 0$ and $f(3.31) = 0.0097 > 0$, there is another zero between 3.30 and 3.31. Now we know that the five zeros of f are distinct. ■

Table 7

X	Y1
3.27	.08567
3.28	.03829
3.29	.00956
3.3	-1E-4
3.31	.0097
3.32	.03936
3.33	.08931

Y1=X^5-1.8X^4-1...

Now Work PROBLEM 75

There are many other numerical techniques for approximating the zeros of a polynomial function. The one outlined in Examples 9 and 10 (a variation of the *bisection method*) has the advantages that it will always work, it can be programmed rather easily on a computer, and each time it is used another decimal place of accuracy is achieved. See Problem 99 for the bisection method, which places the zero in a succession of intervals, with each new interval being half the length of the preceding one.

Historical Feature

Formulas for the solution of third- and fourth-degree polynomial equations exist, and, while not very practical, they do have an interesting history.

In the 1500s in Italy, mathematical contests were a popular pastime, and persons possessing methods for solving problems kept them secret. (Solutions that were published were already common knowledge.) Niccolo of Brescia (1499–1557), commonly referred to as Tartaglia ("the stammerer"), had the secret for solving cubic (third-degree) equations, which gave him a decided advantage in the contests. Girolamo Cardano (1501–1576) found out that Tartaglia had the secret, and, being interested in cubics, he requested it from Tartaglia. The reluctant Tartaglia hesitated for some time, but finally, swearing Cardano to secrecy with midnight oaths by candlelight, told him the secret. Cardano then published the solution in his book *Ars Magna* (1545), giving Tartaglia the credit but rather compromising the secrecy. Tartaglia exploded into bitter recriminations, and each wrote pamphlets that reflected on the other's mathematics, moral character, and ancestry.

The quartic (fourth-degree) equation was solved by Cardano's student Lodovico Ferrari, and this solution also was included, with credit and this time with permission, in the *Ars Magna*.

Attempts were made to solve the fifth-degree equation in similar ways, all of which failed. In the early 1800s, P. Ruffini, Niels Abel, and Evariste Galois all found ways to show that it is not possible to solve fifth-degree equations by formula, but the proofs required the introduction of new methods. Galois's methods eventually developed into a large part of modern algebra.

Historical Problems

Problems 1–8 develop the Tartaglia–Cardano solution of the cubic equation and show why it is not altogether practical.

1. Show that the general cubic equation $y^3 + by^2 + cy + d = 0$ can be transformed into an equation of the form $x^3 + px + q = 0$ by using the substitution $y = x - \frac{b}{3}$.
2. In the equation $x^3 + px + q = 0$, replace x by $H + K$. Let $3HK = -p$, and show that $H^3 + K^3 = -q$.
3. Based on Problem 2, we have the two equations
$$3HK = -p \quad and \quad H^3 + K^3 = -q$$
Solve for K in $3HK = -p$ and substitute into $H^3 + K^3 = -q$. Then show that
$$H = \sqrt[3]{\frac{-q}{2} + \sqrt{\frac{q^2}{4} + \frac{p^3}{27}}}$$
[**Hint:** Look for an equation that is quadratic in form.]
4. Use the solution for H from Problem 3 and the equation $H^3 + K^3 = -q$ to show that
$$K = \sqrt[3]{\frac{-q}{2} - \sqrt{\frac{q^2}{4} + \frac{p^3}{27}}}$$
5. Use the results from Problems 2 to 4 to show that the solution of $x^3 + px + q = 0$ is
$$x = \sqrt[3]{\frac{-q}{2} + \sqrt{\frac{q^2}{4} + \frac{p^3}{27}}} + \sqrt[3]{\frac{-q}{2} - \sqrt{\frac{q^2}{4} + \frac{p^3}{27}}}$$
6. Use the result of Problem 5 to solve the equation $x^3 - 6x - 9 = 0$.
7. Use a calculator and the result of Problem 5 to solve the equation $x^3 + 3x - 14 = 0$.
8. Use the methods of this section to solve the equation $x^3 + 3x - 14 = 0$.

11.2 Assess Your Understanding

'Are You Prepared?' *Answers are given at the end of these exercises. If you get a wrong answer, read the pages listed in red.*

1. Find $f(-1)$ if $f(x) = 2x^2 - x$. (pp. 563–564)
2. Factor the expression $6x^2 + x - 2$.
3. Find the quotient and remainder if $3x^4 - 5x^3 + 7x - 4$ is divided by $x - 3$.
4. Find the zeros of $f(x) = x^2 + x - 3$. (pp. 651–653)

Concepts and Vocabulary

5. In the process of polynomial division, (Divisor)(Quotient) + ________ = ________.
6. When a polynomial function f is divided by $x - c$, the remainder is ________.
7. If a function f, whose domain is all real numbers, is even and if 4 is a zero of f, then ________ is also a zero.
8. ***True or False*** Every polynomial function of degree 3 with real coefficients has exactly three real zeros.
9. If f is a polynomial function and $x - 4$ is a factor of f, then $f(4) =$ ________.
10. ***True or False*** If f is a polynomial function of degree 4 and if $f(2) = 5$, then
$$\frac{f(x)}{x-2} = p(x) + \frac{5}{x-2}$$
where $p(x)$ is a polynomial function of degree 3.

Skill Building

In Problems 11–20, use the Remainder Theorem to find the remainder when $f(x)$ is divided by $x - c$. Then use the Factor Theorem to determine whether $x - c$ is a factor of $f(x)$.

11. $f(x) = 4x^3 - 3x^2 - 8x + 4; x - 2$
12. $f(x) = -4x^3 + 5x^2 + 8; \quad x + 3$
13. $f(x) = 3x^4 - 6x^3 - 5x + 10; x - 2$
14. $f(x) = 4x^4 - 15x^2 - 4; x - 2$
15. $f(x) = 3x^6 + 82x^3 + 27; x + 3$
16. $f(x) = 2x^6 - 18x^4 + x^2 - 9; x + 3$
17. $f(x) = 4x^6 - 64x^4 + x^2 - 15; x + 4$
18. $f(x) = x^6 - 16x^4 + x^2 - 16; x + 4$
19. $f(x) = 2x^4 - x^3 + 2x - 1; x - \frac{1}{2}$
20. $f(x) = 3x^4 + x^3 - 3x + 1; x + \frac{1}{3}$

In Problems 21–32, determine the maximum number of real zeros that each polynomial function may have. Then list the potential rational zeros of each polynomial function. Do not attempt to find the zeros.

21. $f(x) = 3x^4 - 3x^3 + x^2 - x + 1$
22. $f(x) = x^5 - x^4 + 2x^2 + 3$
23. $f(x) = x^5 - 6x^2 + 9x - 3$
24. $f(x) = 2x^5 - x^4 - x^2 + 1$
25. $f(x) = -4x^3 - x^2 + x + 2$
26. $f(x) = 6x^4 - x^2 + 2$
27. $f(x) = 6x^4 - x^2 + 9$
28. $f(x) = -4x^3 + x^2 + x + 6$
29. $f(x) = 2x^5 - x^3 + 2x^2 + 12$
30. $f(x) = 3x^5 - x^2 + 2x + 18$
31. $f(x) = 6x^4 + 2x^3 - x^2 + 20$
32. $f(x) = -6x^3 - x^2 + x + 10$

In Problems 33–38, find the bounds to the zeros of each polynomial function. Use the bounds to obtain a complete graph of f.

33. $f(x) = 2x^3 + x^2 - 1$
34. $f(x) = 3x^3 - 2x^2 + x + 4$
35. $f(x) = x^3 - 5x^2 - 11x + 11$
36. $f(x) = 2x^3 - x^2 - 11x - 6$
37. $f(x) = x^4 + 3x^3 - 5x^2 + 9$
38. $f(x) = 4x^4 - 12x^3 + 27x^2 - 54x + 81$

In Problems 39–56, find the real zeros of f. Use the real zeros to factor f.

39. $f(x) = x^3 + 2x^2 - 5x - 6$
40. $f(x) = x^3 + 8x^2 + 11x - 20$
41. $f(x) = 2x^3 - 13x^2 + 24x - 9$
42. $f(x) = 2x^3 - 5x^2 - 4x + 12$
43. $f(x) = 3x^3 + 4x^2 + 4x + 1$
44. $f(x) = 3x^3 - 7x^2 + 12x - 28$
45. $f(x) = x^3 - 8x^2 + 17x - 6$
46. $f(x) = x^3 + 6x^2 + 6x - 4$
47. $f(x) = x^4 + x^3 - 3x^2 - x + 2$
48. $f(x) = x^4 - x^3 - 6x^2 + 4x + 8$
49. $f(x) = 2x^4 + 17x^3 + 35x^2 - 9x - 45$
50. $f(x) = 4x^4 - 15x^3 - 8x^2 + 15x + 4$
51. $f(x) = 2x^4 - 3x^3 - 21x^2 - 2x + 24$
52. $f(x) = 2x^4 + 11x^3 - 5x^2 - 43x + 35$
53. $f(x) = 4x^4 + 7x^2 - 2$
54. $f(x) = 4x^4 + 15x^2 - 4$
55. $f(x) = 4x^5 - 8x^4 - x + 2$
56. $f(x) = 4x^5 + 12x^4 - x - 3$

In Problems 57–62, find the real zeros of f. If necessary, round to two decimal places.

57. $f(x) = x^3 + 3.2x^2 - 16.83x - 5.31$

58. $f(x) = x^3 + 3.2x^2 - 7.25x - 6.3$

59. $f(x) = x^4 - 1.4x^3 - 33.71x^2 + 23.94x + 292.41$

60. $f(x) = x^4 + 1.2x^3 - 7.46x^2 - 4.692x + 15.2881$

61. $f(x) = x^3 + 19.5x^2 - 1021x + 1000.5$

62. $f(x) = x^3 + 42.2x^2 - 664.8x + 1490.4$

In Problems 63–72, find the real solutions of each equation.

63. $x^4 - x^3 + 2x^2 - 4x - 8 = 0$

64. $2x^3 + 3x^2 + 2x + 3 = 0$

65. $3x^3 + 4x^2 - 7x + 2 = 0$

66. $2x^3 - 3x^2 - 3x - 5 = 0$

67. $3x^3 - x^2 - 15x + 5 = 0$

68. $2x^3 - 11x^2 + 10x + 8 = 0$

69. $x^4 + 4x^3 + 2x^2 - x + 6 = 0$

70. $x^4 - 2x^3 + 10x^2 - 18x + 9 = 0$

71. $x^3 - \frac{2}{3}x^2 + \frac{8}{3}x + 1 = 0$

72. $x^3 - \frac{2}{3}x^2 + 3x - 2 = 0$

In Problems 73–78, use the Intermediate Value Theorem to show that each function has a zero in the given interval. Approximate the zero rounded to two decimal places.

73. $f(x) = 8x^4 - 2x^2 + 5x - 1;\ [0, 1]$

74. $f(x) = x^4 + 8x^3 - x^2 + 2;\ [-1, 0]$

75. $f(x) = 2x^3 + 6x^2 - 8x + 2;\ [-5, -4]$

76. $f(x) = 3x^3 - 10x + 9;\ [-3, -2]$

77. $f(x) = x^5 - x^4 + 7x^3 - 7x^2 - 18x + 18;\ [1.4, 1.5]$

78. $f(x) = x^5 - 3x^4 - 2x^3 + 6x^2 + x + 2;\ [1.7, 1.8]$

Mixed Practice

In Problems 79–86, analyze each polynomial function using Steps 1 through 8 on page 691 in Section 11.1.

79. $f(x) = x^3 + 2x^2 - 5x - 6$
[**Hint:** See Problem 39.]

80. $f(x) = x^3 + 8x^2 + 11x - 20$
[**Hint:** See Problem 40.]

81. $f(x) = x^4 + x^3 - 3x^2 - x + 2$
[**Hint:** See Problem 47.]

82. $f(x) = x^4 - x^3 - 6x^2 + 4x + 8$
[**Hint:** See Problem 48.]

83. $f(x) = 4x^5 - 8x^4 - x + 2$
[**Hint:** See Problem 55.]

84. $f(x) = 4x^5 + 12x^4 - x - 3$
[**Hint:** See Problem 56.]

85. $f(x) = 6x^4 - 37x^3 + 58x^2 + 3x - 18$

86. $f(x) = 20x^4 + 73x^3 + 46x^2 - 52x - 24$

Applications and Extensions

87. Find k such that $f(x) = x^3 - kx^2 + kx + 2$ has the factor $x - 2$.

88. Find k such that $f(x) = x^4 - kx^3 + kx^2 + 1$ has the factor $x + 2$.

89. What is the remainder when $f(x) = 2x^{20} - 8x^{10} + x - 2$ is divided by $x - 1$?

90. What is the remainder when $f(x) = -3x^{17} + x^9 - x^5 + 2x$ is divided by $x + 1$?

91. Use the Factor Theorem to prove that $x - c$ is a factor of $x^n - c^n$ for any positive integer n.

92. Use the Factor Theorem to prove that $x + c$ is a factor of $x^n + c^n$ if $n \geq 1$ is an odd integer.

93. One solution of the equation $x^3 - 8x^2 + 16x - 3 = 0$ is 3. Find the sum of the remaining solutions.

94. One solution of the equation $x^3 + 5x^2 + 5x - 2 = 0$ is -2. Find the sum of the remaining solutions.

95. **Geometry** What is the length of the edge of a cube if, after a slice 1 inch thick is cut from one side, the volume remaining is 294 cubic inches?

96. **Geometry** What is the length of the edge of a cube if its volume could be doubled by an increase of 6 centimeters in one edge, an increase of 12 centimeters in a second edge, and a decrease of 4 centimeters in the third edge?

97. Let $f(x)$ be a polynomial function whose coefficients are integers. Suppose that r is a real zero of f and that the leading coefficient of f is 1. Use the Rational Zeros Theorem to show that r is either an integer or an irrational number.

98. Prove the Rational Zeros Theorem.
[**Hint:** Let $\frac{p}{q}$, where p and q have no common factors except 1 and -1, be a zero of the polynomial function

$$f(x) = a_n x^n + a_{n-1}x^{n-1} + \cdots + a_1 x + a_0$$

whose coefficients are all integers. Show that

$$a_n p^n + a_{n-1}p^{n-1}q + \cdots + a_1 p q^{n-1} + a_0 q^n = 0$$

Now, because p is a factor of the first n terms of this equation, p must also be a factor of the term $a_0 q^n$. Since p is not a factor of q (why?), p must be a factor of a_0. Similarly, q must be a factor of a_n.]

99. **Bisection Method for Approximating Zeros of a Function f** We begin with two consecutive integers, a and $a + 1$, such that $f(a)$ and $f(a + 1)$ are of opposite sign. Evaluate f at the midpoint m_1 of a and $a + 1$. If $f(m_1) = 0$, then m_1 is the zero of f, and we are finished. Otherwise, $f(m_1)$ is of opposite sign to either $f(a)$ or $f(a + 1)$. Suppose that it

is $f(a)$ and $f(m_1)$ that are of opposite sign. Now evaluate f at the midpoint m_2 of a and m_1. Repeat this process until the desired degree of accuracy is obtained. Note that each iteration places the zero in an interval whose length is half that of the previous interval. Use the bisection method to approximate the zero of $f(x) = 8x^4 - 2x^2 + 5x - 1$ in the interval $[0, 1]$ correct to three decimal places. Verify your result using a graphing utility.

[**Hint:** The process ends when both endpoints agree to the desired number of decimal places.]

Discussion and Writing

100. Is $\frac{1}{3}$ a zero of $f(x) = 2x^3 + 3x^2 - 6x + 7$? Explain.
101. Is $\frac{1}{3}$ a zero of $f(x) = 4x^3 - 5x^2 - 3x + 1$? Explain.
102. Is $\frac{3}{5}$ a zero of $f(x) = 2x^6 - 5x^4 + x^3 - x + 1$? Explain.
103. Is $\frac{2}{3}$ a zero of $f(x) = x^7 + 6x^5 - x^4 + x + 2$? Explain.

'Are You Prepared' Answers

1. 3 **2.** $(3x + 2)(2x - 1)$ **3.** Quotient: $3x^3 + 4x^2 + 12x + 43$; remainder: 125 **4.** $\left\{\frac{-1 - \sqrt{13}}{2}, \frac{-1 + \sqrt{13}}{2}\right\}$

11.3 Complex Zeros; Fundamental Theorem of Algebra

PREPARING FOR THIS SECTION *Before getting started, review the following:*

- Complex Numbers (Section 7.3, pp. 487–491)
- Complex Solutions of a Quadratic Equation (Section 7.3, pp. 491–493)

Now Work the **'Are You Prepared?'** problems on page 716.

OBJECTIVES
1 Use the Conjugate Pairs Theorem (p. 713)
2 Find a Polynomial Function with Specified Zeros (p. 714)
3 Find the Complex Zeros of a Polynomial Function (p. 715)

In Section 7.3, we found the real solutions of a quadratic equation. That is, we found the real zeros of a polynomial function of degree 2. Then, in Section 7.4 we found the complex solutions of a quadratic equation. That is, we found the complex zeros of a polynomial function of degree 2.

In Section 11.2, we found the real zeros of polynomial functions of degree 3 or higher. In this section we will find the *complex zeros* of polynomial functions of degree 3 or higher.

DEFINITION

A variable in the complex number system is referred to as a **complex variable.** A **complex polynomial function** f of degree n is a function of the form

$$f(x) = a_n x^n + a_{n-1}x^{n-1} + \cdots + a_1 x + a_0 \qquad (1)$$

where $a_n, a_{n-1}, \ldots, a_1, a_0$ are complex numbers, $a_n \neq 0$, n is a nonnegative integer, and x is a complex variable. As before, a_n is called the **leading coefficient** of f. A complex number r is called a **complex zero** of f if $f(r) = 0$.

In most of our work the coefficients in (1) will be real numbers.

We have learned that some quadratic equations have no real solutions, but that in the complex number system every quadratic equation has a solution, either real or complex. The next result, proved by Karl Friedrich Gauss (1777–1855) when he was 22 years old,* extends this idea to polynomial equations of degree 3 or higher. In fact, this result is so important and useful that it has become known as the **Fundamental Theorem of Algebra.**

*In all, Gauss gave four different proofs of this theorem, the first one in 1799 being the subject of his doctoral dissertation.

FUNDAMENTAL THEOREM OF ALGEBRA

Every complex polynomial function $f(x)$ of degree $n \geq 1$ has at least one complex zero.

We shall not prove this result, as the proof is beyond the scope of this book. However, using the Fundamental Theorem of Algebra and the Factor Theorem, we can prove the following result:

THEOREM

Every complex polynomial function $f(x)$ of degree $n \geq 1$ can be factored into n linear factors (not necessarily distinct) of the form

$$f(x) = a_n(x - r_1)(x - r_2) \cdot \cdots \cdot (x - r_n) \quad \textbf{(2)}$$

where $a_n, r_1, r_2, \ldots, r_n$ are complex numbers. That is, every complex polynomial function of degree $n \geq 1$ has exactly n complex zeros, some of which may repeat.

Proof Let

$$f(x) = a_n x^n + a_{n-1}x^{n-1} + \cdots + a_1 x + a_0$$

By the Fundamental Theorem of Algebra, f has at least one zero, say r_1. Then, by the Factor Theorem, $x - r_1$ is a factor, and

$$f(x) = (x - r_1)q_1(x)$$

where $q_1(x)$ is a complex polynomial function of degree $n - 1$ whose leading coefficient is a_n. Repeating this argument n times, we arrive at

$$f(x) = (x - r_1)(x - r_2) \cdot \cdots \cdot (x - r_n)q_n(x)$$

where $q_n(x)$ is a complex polynomial function of degree $n - n = 0$ whose leading coefficient is a_n. That is, $q_n(x) = a_n x^0 = a_n$, and so

$$f(x) = a_n(x - r_1)(x - r_2) \cdot \cdots \cdot (x - r_n)$$

We conclude that every complex polynomial function $f(x)$ of degree $n \geq 1$ has exactly n (not necessarily distinct) zeros. ■

1 Use the Conjugate Pairs Theorem

We can use the Fundamental Theorem of Algebra to obtain valuable information about the complex zeros of polynomial functions whose coefficients are real numbers.

CONJUGATE PAIRS THEOREM

Let $f(x)$ be a polynomial function whose coefficients are real numbers. If $r = a + bi$ is a zero of f, the complex conjugate $\bar{r} = a - bi$ is also a zero of f.

In other words, for polynomial functions whose coefficients are real numbers, the complex zeros occur in conjugate pairs. This result should not be all that surprising since the complex zeros of a quadratic function occurred in conjugate pairs.

Proof Let

$$f(x) = a_n x^n + a_{n-1}x^{n-1} + \cdots + a_1 x + a_0$$

where $a_n, a_{n-1}, \ldots, a_1, a_0$ are real numbers and $a_n \neq 0$. If $r = a + bi$ is a zero of f, then $f(r) = f(a + bi) = 0$, so

$$a_n r^n + a_{n-1}r^{n-1} + \cdots + a_1 r + a_0 = 0$$

Take the conjugate of both sides to get

$$\overline{a_n r^n + a_{n-1}r^{n-1} + \cdots + a_1 r + a_0} = \overline{0}$$

$$\overline{a_n r^n} + \overline{a_{n-1}r^{n-1}} + \cdots + \overline{a_1 r} + \overline{a_0} = \overline{0}$$

The conjugate of a sum equals the sum of the conjugates (see Section 7.4).

$$\overline{a_n}(\bar{r})^n + \overline{a_{n-1}}(\bar{r})^{n-1} + \cdots + \overline{a_1}\bar{r} + \overline{a_0} = \overline{0}$$ The conjugate of a product equals the product of the conjugates.

$$a_n(\bar{r})^n + a_{n-1}(\bar{r})^{n-1} + \cdots + a_1\bar{r} + a_0 = 0$$ The conjugate of a real number equals the real number.

This last equation states that $f(\bar{r}) = 0$; that is, $\bar{r} = a - bi$ is a zero of f. ■

The importance of this result should be clear. Once we know that, say, $3 + 4i$ is a zero of a polynomial function with real coefficients, then we know that $3 - 4i$ is also a zero. This result has an important corollary.

COROLLARY A polynomial function f of odd degree with real coefficients has at least one real zero.

Proof Because complex zeros occur as conjugate pairs in a polynomial function with real coefficients, there will always be an even number of zeros that are not real numbers. Consequently, since f is of odd degree, one of its zeros has to be a real number. ■

For example, the polynomial function $f(x) = x^5 - 3x^4 + 4x^3 - 5$ has at least one zero that is a real number, since f is of degree 5 (odd) and has real coefficients.

EXAMPLE 1 **Using the Conjugate Pairs Theorem**

A polynomial function f of degree 5 whose coefficients are real numbers has the zeros 1, $5i$, and $1 + i$. Find the remaining two zeros.

Solution Since f has coefficients that are real numbers, complex zeros appear as conjugate pairs. It follows that $-5i$, the conjugate of $5i$, and $1 - i$, the conjugate of $1 + i$, are the two remaining zeros. ■

Now Work PROBLEM 7

2 Find a Polynomial Function with Specified Zeros

EXAMPLE 2 **Finding a Polynomial Function Whose Zeros Are Given**

(a) Find a polynomial function f of degree 4 whose coefficients are real numbers and that has the zeros 1, 1, and $-4 + i$.
(b) Graph the function found in part (a) to verify your result.

Solution (a) Since $-4 + i$ is a zero, by the Conjugate Pairs Theorem, $-4 - i$ must also be a zero of f. Because of the Factor Theorem, if $f(c) = 0$, then $x - c$ is a factor of $f(x)$. So we can now write f as

$$f(x) = a(x-1)(x-1)[x-(-4+i)][x-(-4-i)]$$

where a is any real number. If we let $a = 1$, we obtain

$$\begin{aligned} f(x) &= (x-1)(x-1)[x-(-4+i)][x-(-4-i)] \\ &= (x^2-2x+1)[x^2-(-4+i)x-(-4-i)x+(-4+i)(-4-i)] \\ &= (x^2-2x+1)(x^2+4x-ix+4x+ix+16+4i-4i-i^2) \\ &= (x^2-2x+1)(x^2+8x+17) \\ &= x^4+8x^3+17x^2-2x^3-16x^2-34x+x^2+8x+17 \\ &= x^4+6x^3+2x^2-26x+17 \end{aligned}$$

(b) A quick analysis of the polynomial function f tells us what to expect:

At most three turning points
For large $|x|$, the graph behaves like $y = x^4$.

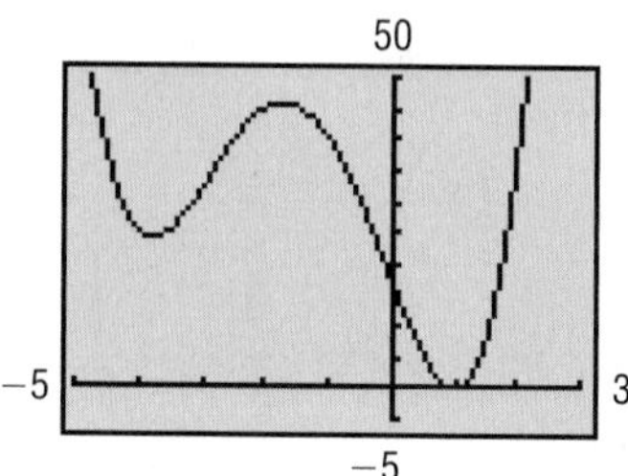

Figure 30

A repeated real zero at 1 so the graph touches the x-axis at 1
The only x-intercept is at 1.

Figure 30 shows the complete graph. (Do you see why? The graph has exactly three turning points and the degree of the polynomial function is 4.) ■

Now Work PROBLEM 17

Now we can prove the theorem we conjectured earlier in Section 11.2.

THEOREM Every polynomial function with real coefficients can be uniquely factored over the real numbers into a product of linear factors and/or irreducible quadratic factors.

Exploration

Graph the function found in Example 2 for $a = 2$ and $a = -1$. Does the value of a affect the zeros of f? How does the value of a affect the graph of f?

Proof Every complex polynomial function f of degree n has exactly n zeros and can be factored into a product of n linear factors. If its coefficients are real, then those zeros that are complex numbers always occur as conjugate pairs. As a result, if $r = a + bi$ is a complex zero, then so is $\bar{r} = a - bi$. Consequently, when the linear factors $x - r$ and $x - \bar{r}$ of f are multiplied, we have

$$(x - r)(x - \bar{r}) = x^2 - (r + \bar{r})x + r\bar{r} = x^2 - 2ax + a^2 + b^2$$

This second-degree polynomial has real coefficients and is irreducible (over the real numbers). Thus, the factors of f are either linear or irreducible quadratic factors. ■

3 Find the Complex Zeros of a Polynomial Function

The steps for finding the complex zeros of a polynomial function are the same as those for finding the real zeros.

EXAMPLE 3 Finding the Complex Zeros of a Polynomial Function

Find the complex zeros of the polynomial function

$$f(x) = 3x^4 + 5x^3 + 25x^2 + 45x - 18$$

Write f in factored form.

Solution

STEP 1: The degree of f is 4. So f has four complex zeros.

STEP 2: The Rational Zeros Theorem provides information about the potential rational zeros of polynomial functions with integer coefficients. For this polynomial function (which has integer coefficients), the potential rational zeros are

$$\pm\frac{1}{3},\ \pm\frac{2}{3},\ \pm 1,\ \pm 2,\ \pm 3,\ \pm 6,\ \pm 9,\ \pm 18$$

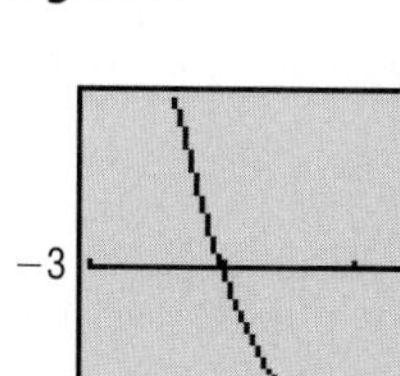

Figure 31

STEP 3: Figure 31 shows the graph of f. The graph has the characteristics expected of this polynomial function of degree 4: It behaves like $y = 3x^4$ for large $|x|$ and has y-intercept -18. There are x-intercepts near -2 and between 0 and 1.

STEP 4: Because $f(-2) = 0$, we know that -2 is a zero of f and $x - (-2) = x + 2$ is a factor of f. Use long division or synthetic division to factor f. Using synthetic division,

$$\begin{array}{r|rrrrr} -2 & 3 & 5 & 25 & 45 & -18 \\ & & -6 & 2 & -54 & 18 \\ \hline & 3 & -1 & 27 & -9 & 0 \end{array}$$

So $f(x) = (x + 2)(3x^3 - x^2 + 27x - 9)$. The depressed equation is

$$q_1(x) = 3x^3 - x^2 + 27x - 9 = 0$$

Repeat Step 4: The depressed equation $3x^3 - x^2 + 27x - 9 = 0$ can be factored by grouping.

$$3x^3 - x^2 + 27x - 9 = 0$$

$$x^2(3x - 1) + 9(3x - 1) = 0 \quad \text{Factor } x^2 \text{ from } 3x^3 - x^2 \text{ and 9 from } 27x - 9.$$

$$(x^2 + 9)(3x - 1) = 0 \quad \text{Factor out the common factor } 3x - 1.$$

$$x^2 + 9 = 0 \quad \text{or} \quad 3x - 1 = 0 \quad \text{Apply the Zero-Product Property.}$$

$$x^2 = -9 \quad \text{or} \quad 3x = 1$$

$$x = -3i, \; x = 3i \quad \text{or} \quad x = \frac{1}{3}$$

The four complex zeros of f are $\left\{-3i, 3i, -2, \frac{1}{3}\right\}$.

The factored form of f is

$$\begin{aligned} f(x) &= 3x^4 + 5x^3 + 25x^2 + 45x - 18 \\ &= (x + 3i)(x - 3i)(x + 2)(3x - 1) \\ &= 3(x + 3i)(x - 3i)(x + 2)\left(x - \frac{1}{3}\right) \end{aligned}$$

■

Now Work PROBLEM 33

11.3 Assess Your Understanding

'Are You Prepared?' *Answers are given at the end of these exercises. If you get a wrong answer, read the pages listed in red.*

1. Find the sum and the product of the complex numbers $3 - 2i$ and $-3 + 5i$. (pp. 488–489)
2. In the complex number system, find the complex solutions of the equation $x^2 + 2x + 2 = 0$. (pp. 492–493)

Concepts and Vocabulary

3. Every polynomial function of odd degree with real coefficients has at least _______ real zero(s).
4. If $3 + 4i$ is a zero of a polynomial function of degree 5 with real coefficients, then so is _______.
5. ***True or False*** A polynomial function of degree n with real coefficients has exactly n complex zeros. At most n of them are real zeros.
6. ***True or False*** A polynomial function of degree 4 with real coefficients could have $-3, 2 + i, 2 - i$, and $-3 + 5i$ as its zeros.

Skill Building

In Problems 7–16, information is given about a polynomial function $f(x)$ whose coefficients are real numbers. Find the remaining zeros of f.

7. Degree 3; zeros: $3, 4 - i$
8. Degree 3; zeros: $4, 3 + i$
9. Degree 4; zeros: $i, 1 + i$
10. Degree 4; zeros: $1, 2, 2 + i$
11. Degree 5; zeros: $1, i, 2i$
12. Degree 5; zeros: $0, 1, 2, i$
13. Degree 4; zeros: $i, 2, -2$
14. Degree 4; zeros: $2 - i, -i$
15. Degree 6; zeros: $2, 2 + i, -3 - i, 0$
16. Degree 6; zeros: $i, 3 - 2i, -2 + i$

In Problems 17–22, form a polynomial function f(x) with real coefficients having the given degree and zeros. Answers will vary depending on the choice of the leading coefficient. Use a graphing utility to graph the function and verify the result.

17. Degree 4; zeros: $3 + 2i$; 4, multiplicity 2
18. Degree 4; zeros: i; $1 + 2i$
19. Degree 5; zeros: 2; $-i$; $1 + i$
20. Degree 6; zeros: i; $4 - i$; $2 + i$
21. Degree 4; zeros: 3, multiplicity 2; $-i$
22. Degree 5; zeros: 1, multiplicity 3; $1 + i$

In Problems 23–30, use the given zero to find the remaining zeros of each function.

23. $f(x) = x^3 - 4x^2 + 4x - 16$; zero: $2i$
24. $g(x) = x^3 + 3x^2 + 25x + 75$; zero: $-5i$
25. $f(x) = 2x^4 + 5x^3 + 5x^2 + 20x - 12$; zero: $-2i$
26. $h(x) = 3x^4 + 5x^3 + 25x^2 + 45x - 18$; zero: $3i$
27. $h(x) = x^4 - 9x^3 + 21x^2 + 21x - 130$; zero: $3 - 2i$
28. $f(x) = x^4 - 7x^3 + 14x^2 - 38x - 60$; zero: $1 + 3i$
29. $h(x) = 3x^5 + 2x^4 + 15x^3 + 10x^2 - 528x - 352$; zero: $-4i$
30. $g(x) = 2x^5 - 3x^4 - 5x^3 - 15x^2 - 207x + 108$; zero: $3i$

In Problems 31–40, find the complex zeros of each polynomial function. Write f in factored form.

31. $f(x) = x^3 - 1$

32. $f(x) = x^4 - 1$

33. $f(x) = x^3 - 8x^2 + 25x - 26$

34. $f(x) = x^3 + 13x^2 + 57x + 85$

35. $f(x) = x^4 + 5x^2 + 4$

36. $f(x) = x^4 + 13x^2 + 36$

37. $f(x) = x^4 + 2x^3 + 22x^2 + 50x - 75$

38. $f(x) = x^4 + 3x^3 - 19x^2 + 27x - 252$

39. $f(x) = 3x^4 - x^3 - 9x^2 + 159x - 52$

40. $f(x) = 2x^4 + x^3 - 35x^2 - 113x + 65$

Explaining Concepts: Discussion and Writing

In Problems 41 and 42, explain why the facts given are contradictory.

41. $f(x)$ is a polynomial function of degree 3 whose coefficients are real numbers; its zeros are $4 + i$, $4 - i$, and $2 + i$.

42. $f(x)$ is a polynomial function of degree 3 whose coefficients are real numbers; its zeros are 2, i, and $3 + i$.

43. $f(x)$ is a polynomial function of degree 4 whose coefficients are real numbers; three of its zeros are 2, $1 + 2i$, and $1 - 2i$. Explain why the remaining zero must be a real number.

44. $f(x)$ is a polynomial function of degree 4 whose coefficients are real numbers; two of its zeros are -3 and $4 - i$. Explain why one of the remaining zeros must be a real number. Write down one of the missing zeros.

'Are You Prepared?' Answers

1. Sum: $3i$; product: $1 + 21i$ **2.** $-1 - i, -1 + i$

11.4 Properties of Rational Functions

PREPARING FOR THIS SECTION *Before getting started, review the following:*

- Graph of $f(x) = \frac{1}{x}$ (Section 8.1, Example 6, pp. 526–527)
- Graphing Techniques: Transformations (Section 9.5, pp. 605–613)

Now Work the **'Are You Prepared?'** problems on page 725.

OBJECTIVES
1 Find the Domain of a Rational Function (p. 717)
2 Find the Vertical Asymptotes of a Rational Function (p. 721)
3 Find the Horizontal or Oblique Asymptote of a Rational Function (p. 722)

Ratios of integers are called *rational numbers*. Similarly, ratios of polynomial functions are called *rational functions*. Examples of rational functions are

$$R(x) = \frac{x^2 - 4}{x^2 + x + 1} \qquad F(x) = \frac{x^3}{x^2 - 4} \qquad G(x) = \frac{3x^2}{x^4 - 1}$$

DEFINITION

A **rational function** is a function of the form

$$R(x) = \frac{p(x)}{q(x)}$$

where p and q are polynomial functions and q is not the zero polynomial. The domain of a rational function is the set of all real numbers except those for which the denominator q is 0.

1 Find the Domain of a Rational Function

EXAMPLE 1 **Finding the Domain of a Rational Function**

(a) The domain of $R(x) = \frac{2x^2 - 4}{x + 5}$ is the set of all real numbers x except -5; that is, the domain is $\{x | x \neq -5\}$.

(b) The domain of $R(x) = \dfrac{1}{x^2 - 4}$ is the set of all real numbers x except -2 and 2; that is, the domain is $\{x | x \neq -2, x \neq 2\}$.

(c) The domain of $R(x) = \dfrac{x^3}{x^2 + 1}$ is the set of all real numbers.

(d) The domain of $R(x) = \dfrac{x^2 - 1}{x - 1}$ is the set of all real numbers x except 1; that is, the domain is $\{x \mid x \neq 1\}$. ■

Although $\dfrac{x^2 - 1}{x - 1}$ reduces to $x + 1$, it is important to observe that the functions

$$R(x) = \frac{x^2 - 1}{x - 1} \quad \text{and} \quad f(x) = x + 1$$

are not equal, since the domain of R is $\{x \mid x \neq 1\}$ and the domain of f is the set of all real numbers. Notice in Table 8 there is an error message for $Y_1 = R(x) = \dfrac{x^2 - 1}{x - 1}$, but there is no error message for $Y_2 = f(x) = x + 1$.

Table 8

X	Y1	Y2
-3	-2	-2
-2	-1	-1
-1	0	0
0	1	1
1	ERROR	2
2	3	3
3	4	4

$Y_1 = (X^2-1)/(X-1)$

Now Work PROBLEM 15

If $R(x) = \dfrac{p(x)}{q(x)}$ is a rational function and if p and q have no common factors, then the rational function R is said to be in **lowest terms.** For a rational function $R(x) = \dfrac{p(x)}{q(x)}$ in lowest terms, the real zeros, if any, of the numerator in the domain of R are the x-intercepts of the graph of R and so play a major role in the graph of R. The real zeros of the denominator of R [that is, the numbers x, if any, for which $q(x) = 0$], although not in the domain of R, also play a major role in the graph of R.

We have already discussed the properties of the rational function $y = \dfrac{1}{x}$. (Refer to Example 6, page 526.) The next rational function that we take up is $H(x) = \dfrac{1}{x^2}$.

EXAMPLE 2 Graphing $y = \dfrac{1}{x^2}$

Analyze the graph of $H(x) = \dfrac{1}{x^2}$.

Solution The domain of $H(x) = \dfrac{1}{x^2}$ consists of all real numbers x except 0. The graph has no y-intercept, because x can never equal 0. The graph has no x-intercept because the equation $H(x) = 0$ has no solution. Therefore, the graph of H will not cross either coordinate axis.

Because

$$H(-x) = \frac{1}{(-x)^2} = \frac{1}{x^2} = H(x)$$

Figure 32

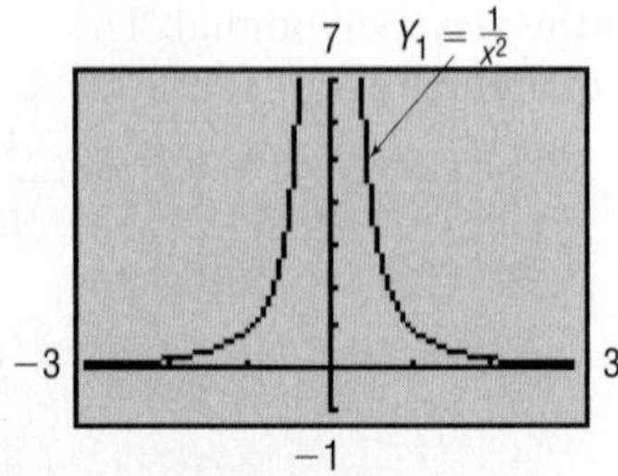

H is an even function, so its graph is symmetric with respect to the y-axis.

See Figure 32. Notice that the graph confirms the conclusions just reached. But what happens to the graph as the values of x get closer and closer to 0? We use a TABLE to answer the question. See Table 9 on the following page. The first four rows show that as the values of x approach (get closer to) 0 the values of $H(x)$ become larger and larger positive numbers. When this happens, we say that $H(x)$ is **unbounded in the positive direction.** We symbolize this by writing $H(x) \to \infty$ [read as "$H(x)$ **approaches infinity**"]. In calculus, we use limit notation, $\lim_{x \to 0} H(x) = \infty$, read as "the limit of $H(x)$ as x approaches 0 is infinity," to mean that $H(x) \to \infty$ as $x \to 0$.

Table 9

X	Y_1
.1	100
.01	10000
.001	1E6
1E-4	1E8
10	.01
100	1E-4
1000	1E-6

$Y_1 = 1/X^2$

Look at the last three rows of Table 9. As $x \to \infty$, the values of $H(x)$ approach 0 (the end behavior of the graph). This is symbolized in calculus by writing $\lim_{x\to\infty} H(x) = 0$. Remember, on the calculator 1E−4 means 1×10^{-4} or 0.0001.

Figure 33 shows the graph of $H(x) = \dfrac{1}{x^2}$ drawn by hand. Notice the use of red dashed lines to convey the ideas discussed.

Figure 33

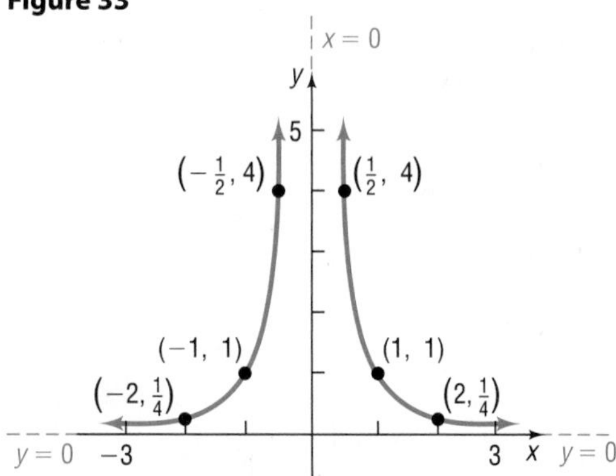

EXAMPLE 3 Using Transformations to Graph a Rational Function

Graph the rational function: $R(x) = \dfrac{1}{(x-2)^2} + 1$

Solution The domain of R is the set of all real numbers except $x = 2$. To graph R, start with the graph of $y = \dfrac{1}{x^2}$. See Figure 34 for the stages.

Figure 34

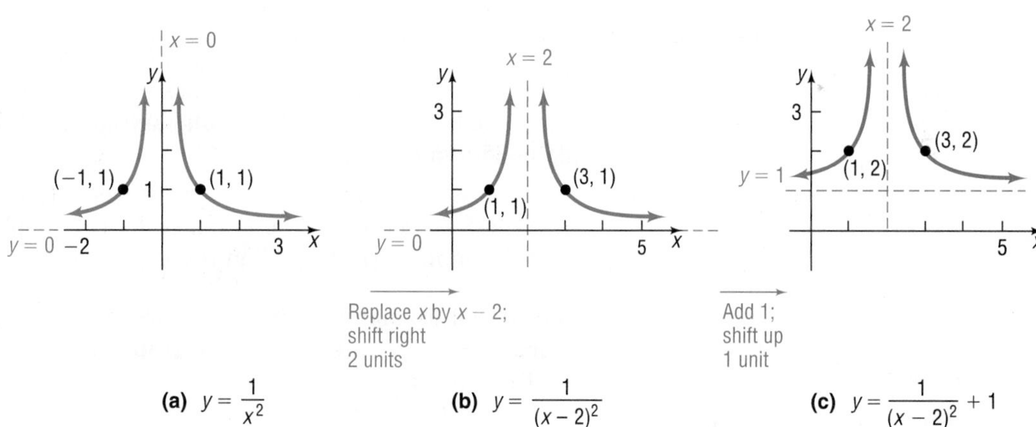

(a) $y = \dfrac{1}{x^2}$ (b) $y = \dfrac{1}{(x-2)^2}$ (c) $y = \dfrac{1}{(x-2)^2} + 1$

✓Check: Graph $Y_1 = \dfrac{1}{(x-2)^2} + 1$ using a graphing utility to verify the graph obtained in Figure 34(c). ■

Now Work PROBLEM 33

Asymptotes

Notice that the y-axis in Figure 34(a) is transformed into the vertical line $x = 2$ in Figure 34(c), and the x-axis in Figure 34(a) is transformed into the horizontal line $y = 1$ in Figure 34(c). The **Exploration** that follows will help us analyze the role of these lines.

Exploration

(a) Using a graphing utility and the TABLE feature, evaluate the function $H(x) = \dfrac{1}{(x-2)^2} + 1$ at $x = 10, 100, 1000$, and 10,000. What happens to the values of H as x becomes unbounded in the positive direction, symbolized by $\lim_{x\to\infty} H(x)$?

(b) Evaluate H at $x = -10, -100, -1000$, and $-10{,}000$. What happens to the values of H as x becomes unbounded in the negative direction, symbolized by $\lim_{x\to-\infty} H(x)$?

(c) Evaluate H at $x = 1.5, 1.9, 1.99, 1.999$, and 1.9999. What happens to the values of H as x approaches 2, $x < 2$, symbolized by $\lim_{x \to 2^-} H(x)$?

(d) Evaluate H at $x = 2.5, 2.1, 2.01, 2.001$, and 2.0001. What happens to the values of H as x approaches 2, $x > 2$, symbolized by $\lim_{x \to 2^+} H(x)$?

Result

(a) Table 10 shows the values of $Y_1 = H(x)$ as x approaches ∞. Notice that the values of H are approaching 1, so $\lim_{x \to \infty} H(x) = 1$.

(b) Table 11 shows the values of $Y_1 = H(x)$ as x approaches $-\infty$. Again the values of H are approaching 1, so $\lim_{x \to -\infty} H(x) = 1$.

(c) From Table 12 we see that, as x approaches 2, $x < 2$, the values of H are increasing without bound, so $\lim_{x \to 2^-} H(x) = \infty$.

(d) Finally, Table 13 reveals that, as x approaches 2, $x > 2$, the values of H are increasing without bound, so $\lim_{x \to 2^+} H(x) = \infty$.

Table 10

X	Y1
10	1.0156
100	1.0001
1000	1
10000	1

Y1=1/(X−2)²+1

Table 11

X	Y1
−10	1.0069
−100	1.0001
−1000	1
−10000	1

Y1=1/(X−2)²+1

Table 12

X	Y1
1.5	5
1.9	101
1.99	10001
1.999	1E6
1.9999	1E8

Y1=1/(X−2)²+1

Table 13

X	Y1
2.5	5
2.1	101
2.01	10001
2.001	1E6
2.0001	1E8

Y1=1/(X−2)²+1

The results of the Exploration reveal an important property of rational functions. The vertical line $x = 2$ and the horizontal line $y = 1$ in Figure 34(c) are called *asymptotes* of the graph of H.

DEFINITION

Let R denote a function:

If, as $x \to -\infty$ or as $x \to \infty$, the values of $R(x)$ approach some fixed number L, then the line $y = L$ is a **horizontal asymptote** of the graph of R. [Refer to Figures 35(a) and (b).]

If, as x approaches some number c, the values $|R(x)| \to \infty$, then the line $x = c$ is a **vertical asymptote** of the graph of R. The graph of R never intersects a vertical asymptote. [Refer to Figures 35(c) and (d).]

A horizontal asymptote, when it occurs, describes the end behavior of the graph as $x \to \infty$ or as $x \to -\infty$. **The graph of a function may intersect a horizontal asymptote.**

Figure 35

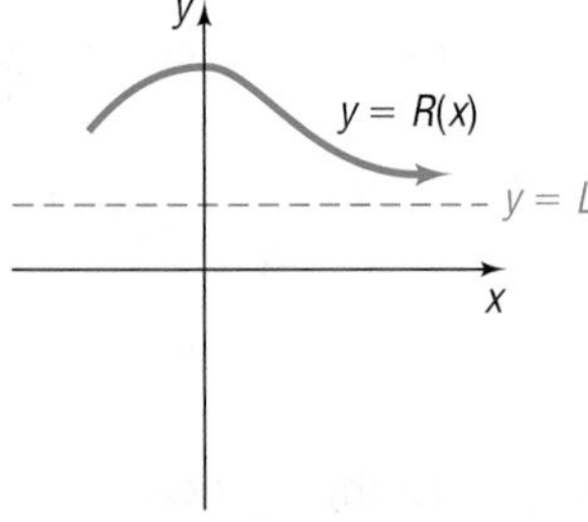

(a) End behavior: As $x \to \infty$, the values of $R(x)$ approach L [symbolized by $\lim_{x \to \infty} R(x) = L$]. That is, the points on the graph of R are getting closer to the line $y = L$; $y = L$ is a horizontal asymptote.

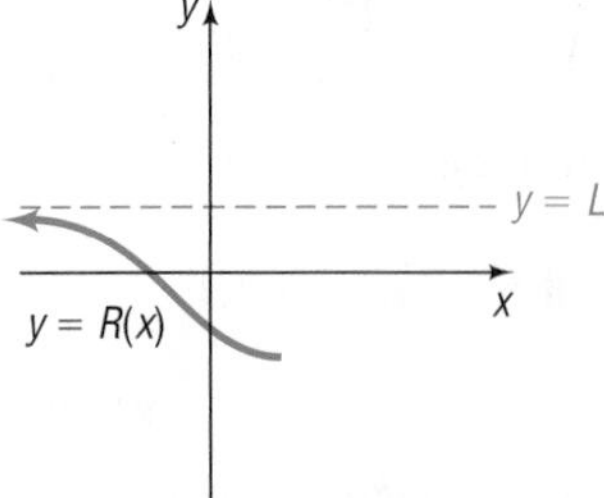

(b) End behavior: As $x \to -\infty$, the values of $R(x)$ approach L [symbolized by $\lim_{x \to -\infty} R(x) = L$]. That is, the points on the graph of R are getting closer to the line $y = L$; $y = L$ is a horizontal asymptote.

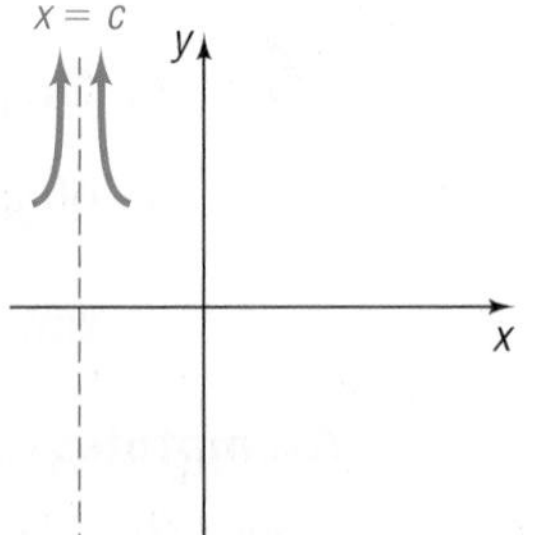

(c) As x approaches c, the values of $R(x) \to \infty$ [for $x < c$, this is symbolized by $\lim_{x \to c^-} R(x) = \infty$; for $x > c$, this is symbolized by $\lim_{x \to c^+} R(x) = \infty$]. That is, the points on the graph of R are getting closer to the line $x = c$; $x = c$ is a vertical asymptote.

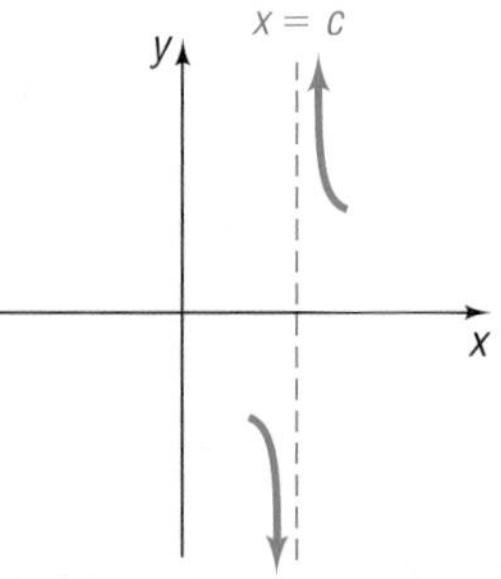

(d) As x approaches c, the values of $|R(x)| \to \infty$ [for $x < c$, this is symbolized by $\lim_{x \to c^-} R(x) = -\infty$; for $x > c$, this is symbolized by $\lim_{x \to c^+} R(x) = \infty$]. That is, the points on the graph of R are getting closer to the line $x = c$; $x = c$ is a vertical asymptote.

Figure 36

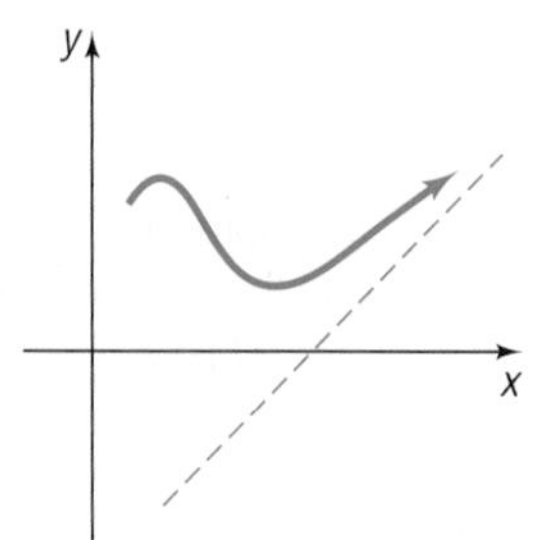

A vertical asymptote, when it occurs, describes the behavior of the graph when x is close to some number c. **The graph of a function will never intersect a vertical asymptote.**

There is a third possibility. If, as $x \to -\infty$ or as $x \to \infty$, the value of a rational function $R(x)$ approaches a linear expression $ax + b$, $a \neq 0$, then the line $y = ax + b, a \neq 0$, is an **oblique asymptote** of R. Figure 36 shows an oblique asymptote. An oblique asymptote, when it occurs, describes the end behavior of the graph. **The graph of a function may intersect an oblique asymptote.**

Now Work PROBLEM 25

2 Find the Vertical Asymptotes of a Rational Function

The vertical asymptotes of a rational function $R(x) = \dfrac{p(x)}{q(x)}$, in lowest terms, are located at the real zeros of the denominator, $q(x)$. Suppose that r is a real zero of q, so $x - r$ is a factor of q. As x approaches r, symbolized as $x \to r$, the values of $x - r$ approach 0, causing the ratio to become unbounded; that is, $|R(x)| \to \infty$. Based on the definition, we conclude that the line $x = r$ is a vertical asymptote.

THEOREM

Locating Vertical Asymptotes

A rational function $R(x) = \dfrac{p(x)}{q(x)}$, *in lowest terms,* will have a vertical asymptote $x = r$ if r is a real zero of the denominator q. That is, if $x - r$ is a factor of the denominator q of a rational function $R(x) = \dfrac{p(x)}{q(x)}$, in lowest terms, R will have the vertical asymptote $x = r$.

WARNING If a rational function is not in lowest terms, an application of this theorem may result in an incorrect listing of vertical asymptotes. ■

EXAMPLE 4 Finding Vertical Asymptotes

Find the vertical asymptotes, if any, of the graph of each rational function.

(a) $F(x) = \dfrac{x + 3}{x - 1}$ (b) $R(x) = \dfrac{x}{x^2 - 4}$

(c) $H(x) = \dfrac{x^2}{x^2 + 1}$ (d) $G(x) = \dfrac{x^2 - 9}{x^2 + 4x - 21}$

Solution

(a) F is in lowest terms, and the only zero of the denominator is 1. The line $x = 1$ is the vertical asymptote of the graph of F.

(b) R is in lowest terms, and the zeros of the denominator $x^2 - 4$ are -2 and 2. The lines $x = -2$ and $x = 2$ are the vertical asymptotes of the graph of R.

(c) H is in lowest terms, and the denominator has no real zeros, because the equation $x^2 + 1$ has no real solutions. The graph of H has no vertical asymptotes.

(d) Factor $G(x)$ to determine if it is in lowest terms.

$$G(x) = \frac{x^2 - 9}{x^2 + 4x - 21} = \frac{(x + 3)(x - 3)}{(x + 7)(x - 3)} = \frac{x + 3}{x + 7} \qquad x \neq 3$$

The only zero of the denominator of $G(x)$ in lowest terms is -7. The line $x = -7$ is the only vertical asymptote of the graph of G. ■

WARNING In Example 4(b), the vertical asymptotes are $x = -2$ and $x = 2$. Do not say that the vertical asymptotes are -2 and 2. ■

As Example 4 points out, rational functions can have no vertical asymptotes, one vertical asymptote, or more than one vertical asymptote.

Exploration

Graph each of the following rational functions:

$$R(x) = \frac{1}{x-1} \quad R(x) = \frac{1}{(x-1)^2} \quad R(x) = \frac{1}{(x-1)^3} \quad R(x) = \frac{1}{(x-1)^4}$$

Each has the vertical asymptote $x = 1$. What happens to the value of $R(x)$ as x approaches 1 from the right side of the vertical asymptote; that is, what is $\lim_{x \to 1^+} R(x)$? What happens to the value of $R(x)$ as x approaches 1 from the left side of the vertical asymptote; that is, what is $\lim_{x \to 1^-} R(x)$? How does the multiplicity of the zero in the denominator affect the graph of R?

Now graph

$$R(x) = \frac{1}{x-1} \quad R(x) = \frac{3x-3}{x-1} \quad R(x) = \frac{x^2-5x+4}{x-1}$$

Use a table to explore the behavior of each function as $x \to 1$.

Now Work PROBLEM 47 (FIND THE VERTICAL ASYMPTOTES, IF ANY)

3 Find the Horizontal or Oblique Asymptote of a Rational Function

The procedure for finding horizontal and oblique asymptotes is somewhat more involved. To find such asymptotes, we need to know how the value of a function behaves as $x \to -\infty$ or as $x \to \infty$. That is, we need to learn the end behavior of the function.

If a rational function $R(x)$ is **proper,** that is, if the degree of the numerator is less than the degree of the denominator, then as $x \to -\infty$ or as $x \to \infty$ the value of $R(x)$ approaches 0. Consequently, the line $y = 0$ (the x-axis) is a horizontal asymptote of the graph.

THEOREM If a rational function is proper, the line $y = 0$ is a horizontal asymptote of its graph.

EXAMPLE 5 **Finding a Horizontal Asymptote**

Find the horizontal asymptote, if one exists, of the graph of

$$R(x) = \frac{x-12}{4x^2+x+1}$$

Solution Since the degree of the numerator, 1, is less than the degree of the denominator, 2, the rational function R is proper. The line $y = 0$ is a horizontal asymptote of the graph of R. ■

To see why $y = 0$ is a horizontal asymptote of the function R in Example 5, we investigate the behavior of R as $x \to -\infty$ and $x \to \infty$. When $|x|$ is unbounded, the numerator of R, which is $x - 12$, can be approximated by the power function $y = x$, while the denominator of R, which is $4x^2 + x + 1$, can be approximated by the power function $y = 4x^2$. Applying these ideas to $R(x)$, we find

$$R(x) = \frac{x-12}{4x^2+x+1} \approx \frac{x}{4x^2} = \frac{1}{4x} \to 0$$

For $|x|$ unbounded   As $x \to -\infty$ or $x \to \infty$

Table 14

X	Y1
-10	-.0563
-100	-.0028
-1000	-3E-4
-10000	-3E-5
-1E5	-3E-6
-1E6	-3E-7
-1E7	-3E-8

Y1=(X-12)/(4X²+...

(a)

X	Y1
10	-.0049
100	.00219
1000	2.5E-4
10000	2.5E-5
100000	2.5E-6
1E6	2.5E-7
1E7	2.5E-8

Y1=(X-12)/(4X²+...

(b)

This shows that the line $y = 0$ is a horizontal asymptote of the graph of R.

We verify these results in Tables 14(a) and (b). Notice, as $x \to -\infty$ [Table 14(a)] or $x \to \infty$ [Table 14(b)], respectively, that the value of $R(x)$ approaches 0.

If a rational function $R(x) = \frac{p(x)}{q(x)}$ is **improper,** that is, if the degree of the numerator is greater than or equal to the degree of the denominator, we write the rational function as the sum of a polynomial function $f(x)$ plus a proper rational function $\frac{r(x)}{q(x)}$ using long division. That is, we write

$$R(x) = \frac{p(x)}{q(x)} = f(x) + \frac{r(x)}{q(x)}$$

where $f(x)$ is a polynomial function and $\frac{r(x)}{q(x)}$ is a proper rational function. Since $\frac{r(x)}{q(x)}$ is proper, then $\frac{r(x)}{q(x)} \to 0$ as $x \to -\infty$ or as $x \to \infty$. As a result,

$$R(x) = \frac{p(x)}{q(x)} \to f(x), \qquad \text{as } x \to -\infty \text{ or as } x \to \infty$$

The possibilities are listed next.

1. If $f(x) = b$, a constant, then the line $y = b$ is a horizontal asymptote of the graph of R.
2. If $f(x) = ax + b$, $a \neq 0$, then the line $y = ax + b$ is an oblique asymptote of the graph of R.
3. In all other cases, the graph of R approaches the graph of f, and there are no horizontal or oblique asymptotes.

   We illustrate each of these possibilities in Examples 6, 7, and 8.

EXAMPLE 6 Finding a Horizontal or Oblique Asymptote

Find the horizontal or oblique asymptote, if one exists, of the graph of

$$H(x) = \frac{3x^4 - x^2}{x^3 - x^2 + 1}$$

Solution Since the degree of the numerator, 4, is larger than the degree of the denominator, 3, the rational function H is improper. To find any horizontal or oblique asymptotes, we use long division.

$$\begin{array}{r l}
 & 3x + 3 \\
x^3 - x^2 + 1 \,\big)\!\!\! & \overline{3x^4 \qquad\qquad - x^2} \\
 & \underline{3x^4 - 3x^3 \qquad\quad + 3x} \\
 & \quad 3x^3 - x^2 - 3x \\
 & \quad \underline{3x^3 - 3x^2 \qquad + 3} \\
 & \qquad\quad 2x^2 - 3x - 3
\end{array}$$

As a result,

$$H(x) = \frac{3x^4 - x^2}{x^3 - x^2 + 1} = 3x + 3 + \frac{2x^2 - 3x - 3}{x^3 - x^2 + 1}$$

As $x \to -\infty$ or as $x \to \infty$,

$$\frac{2x^2 - 3x - 3}{x^3 - x^2 + 1} \approx \frac{2x^2}{x^3} = \frac{2}{x} \to 0$$

As $x \to -\infty$ or as $x \to \infty$, we have $H(x) \to 3x + 3$. The graph of the rational function H has an oblique asymptote $y = 3x + 3$. Put another way, as $x \to \pm\infty$, the graph of H will behave like the graph of $y = 3x + 3$.

We verify these results in Tables 15(a) and (b) with $Y_1 = H(x)$ and $Y_2 = 3x + 3$. As $x \to -\infty$ or $x \to \infty$, the difference in the values between Y_1 and Y_2 is indistinguishable.

Table 15

X	Y1	Y2
-10	-27.21	-27
-100	-297	-297
-1000	-2997	-2997
-10000	-29997	-29997
-1E5	-3E5	-3E5
-1E6	-3E6	-3E6
-1E7	-3E7	-3E7

Y1=(3X^4-X²)/(X...

(a)

X	Y1	Y2
10	33.185	33
100	303.02	303
1000	3003	3003
10000	30003	30003
100000	300003	300003
1E6	3E6	3E6
1E7	3E7	3E7

Y1=(3X^4-X²)/(X...

(b)

■

EXAMPLE 7 **Finding a Horizontal or Oblique Asymptote**

Find the horizontal or oblique asymptote, if one exists, of the graph of

$$R(x) = \frac{8x^2 - x + 2}{4x^2 - 1}$$

Solution Since the degree of the numerator, 2, equals the degree of the denominator, 2, the rational function R is improper. To find a horizontal or oblique asymptote, use long division.

$$\begin{array}{r} 2 \\ 4x^2 - 1 \overline{)8x^2 - x + 2} \\ \underline{8x^2 - 2} \\ -x + 4 \end{array}$$

As a result,

$$R(x) = \frac{8x^2 - x + 2}{4x^2 - 1} = 2 + \frac{-x + 4}{4x^2 - 1}$$

Then, as $x \to -\infty$ or as $x \to \infty$,

$$\frac{-x + 4}{4x^2 - 1} \approx \frac{-x}{4x^2} = \frac{-1}{4x} \to 0$$

As $x \to -\infty$ or as $x \to \infty$, we have $R(x) \to 2$. We conclude that $y = 2$ is a horizontal asymptote of the graph. The graph of R will behave like $y = 2$ as $x \to \pm\infty$.

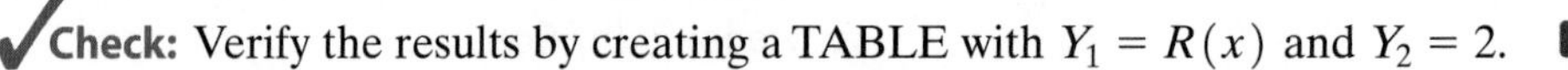

Check: Verify the results by creating a TABLE with $Y_1 = R(x)$ and $Y_2 = 2$. ■

In Example 7, notice that the quotient 2 obtained by long division is the quotient of the leading coefficients of the numerator polynomial and the denominator polynomial $\left(\frac{8}{4}\right)$. This means that we can avoid the long division process for rational functions whose numerator and denominator *are of the same degree* and conclude that the quotient of the leading coefficients gives us the horizontal asymptote.

Now Work PROBLEMS 43 AND 45

EXAMPLE 8 **Finding a Horizontal or Oblique Asymptote**

Find the horizontal or oblique asymptote, if one exists, of the graph of

$$G(x) = \frac{2x^5 - x^3 + 2}{x^3 - 1}$$

Solution Since the degree of the numerator, 5, is greater than the degree of the denominator, 3, the rational function G is improper. To find a horizontal or oblique asymptote, use long division.

$$\begin{array}{r} 2x^2 - 1 \\ x^3 - 1 \overline{)2x^5 - x^3 + 2} \\ \underline{2x^5 - 2x^2 } \\ -x^3 + 2x^2 + 2 \\ \underline{-x^3 + 1} \\ 2x^2 + 1 \end{array}$$

As a result,

$$G(x) = \frac{2x^5 - x^3 + 2}{x^3 - 1} = 2x^2 - 1 + \frac{2x^2 + 1}{x^3 - 1}$$

Then, as $x \to -\infty$ or as $x \to \infty$,

$$\frac{2x^2 + 1}{x^3 - 1} \approx \frac{2x^2}{x^3} = \frac{2}{x} \to 0$$

As $x \to -\infty$ or as $x \to \infty$, we have $G(x) \to 2x^2 - 1$. We conclude that, for large values of $|x|$, the graph of G approaches the graph of $y = 2x^2 - 1$. That is, the graph of G looks like the graph of $y = 2x^2 - 1$ as $x \to -\infty$ or $x \to \infty$. Since $y = 2x^2 - 1$ is not a linear function, G has no horizontal or oblique asymptote. ■

SUMMARY

Finding a Horizontal or Oblique Asymptote of a Rational Function

Consider the rational function

$$R(x) = \frac{p(x)}{q(x)} = \frac{a_n x^n + a_{n-1}x^{n-1} + \cdots + a_1 x + a_0}{b_m x^m + b_{m-1}x^{m-1} + \cdots + b_1 x + b_0}$$

in which the degree of the numerator is n and the degree of the denominator is m.

1. If $n < m$ (the degree of the numerator is less than the degree of the denominator), then R is a proper rational function, and the graph of R will have the horizontal asymptote $y = 0$ (the x-axis).
2. If $n \geq m$ (the degree of the numerator is greater than or equal to the degree of the denominator), then R is improper. Here long division is used.
   (a) If $n = m$ (the degree of the numerator equals the degree of the denominator), the quotient obtained will be the number $\frac{a_n}{b_m}$, and the line $y = \frac{a_n}{b_m}$ is a horizontal asymptote.
   (b) If $n = m + 1$ (the degree of the numerator is one more than the degree of the denominator), the quotient obtained is of the form $ax + b$ (a polynomial of degree 1), and the line $y = ax + b$ is an oblique asymptote.
   (c) If $n \geq m + 2$ (the degree of the numerator is two or more greater than the degree of the denominator), the quotient obtained is a polynomial of degree 2 or higher, and R has neither a horizontal nor an oblique asymptote. In this case, for very large values of $|x|$, the graph of R will behave like the graph of the quotient.

Note: The graph of a rational function either has one horizontal or one oblique asymptote or else has no horizontal and no oblique asymptote. ■

11.4 Assess Your Understanding

'Are You Prepared?' *Answers are given at the end of these exercises. If you get a wrong answer, read the pages listed in red.*

1. ***True or False*** The quotient of two polynomial expressions is a rational expression.
2. What are the quotient and remainder when $3x^4 - x^2$ is divided by $x^3 - x^2 + 1$?
3. Graph $y = \frac{1}{x}$. (pp. 526–527)
4. Graph $y = 2(x + 1)^2 - 3$ using transformations. (pp. 605–613)

Concepts and Vocabulary

5. ***True or False*** The domain of every rational function is the set of all real numbers.
6. If, as $x \to -\infty$ or as $x \to \infty$, the values of $R(x)$ approach some fixed number L, then the line $y = L$ is a ________ ________ of the graph of R.
7. If, as x approaches some number c, the values of $|R(x)| \to \infty$, then the line $x = c$ is a ________ ________ of the graph of R.
8. For a rational function R, if the degree of the numerator is less than the degree of the denominator, then R is ________.
9. ***True or False*** The graph of a rational function may intersect a horizontal asymptote.
10. ***True or False*** The graph of a rational function may intersect a vertical asymptote.
11. If a rational function is proper, then ______ is a horizontal asymptote.
12. ***True or False*** If the degree of the numerator of a rational function equals the degree of the denominator, then the ratio of the leading coefficients gives rise to the horizontal asymptote.

Skill Building

In Problems 13–24, find the domain of each rational function.

13. $R(x) = \dfrac{4x}{x - 3}$ **14.** $R(x) = \dfrac{5x^2}{3 + x}$ **15.** $H(x) = \dfrac{-4x^2}{(x - 2)(x + 4)}$

16. $G(x) = \dfrac{6}{(x + 3)(4 - x)}$ **17.** $F(x) = \dfrac{3x(x - 1)}{2x^2 - 5x - 3}$ **18.** $Q(x) = \dfrac{-x(1 - x)}{3x^2 + 5x - 2}$

19. $R(x) = \dfrac{x}{x^3 - 8}$ **20.** $R(x) = \dfrac{x}{x^4 - 1}$ **21.** $H(x) = \dfrac{3x^2 + x}{x^2 + 4}$

22. $G(x) = \dfrac{x - 3}{x^4 + 1}$ **23.** $R(x) = \dfrac{3(x^2 - x - 6)}{4(x^2 - 9)}$ **24.** $F(x) = \dfrac{-2(x^2 - 4)}{3(x^2 + 4x + 4)}$

In Problems 25–30, use the graph shown to find
(a) *The domain and range of each function* (b) *The intercepts, if any* (c) *Horizontal asymptote, if one exists*
(d) *Vertical asymptotes, if any* (e) *Oblique asymptote, if one exists*

25.

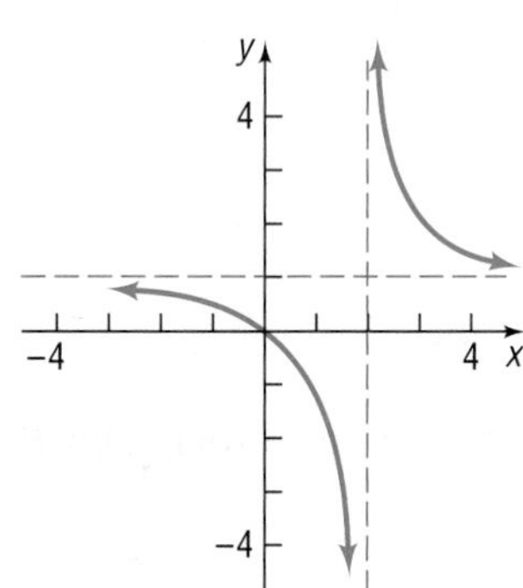

26.

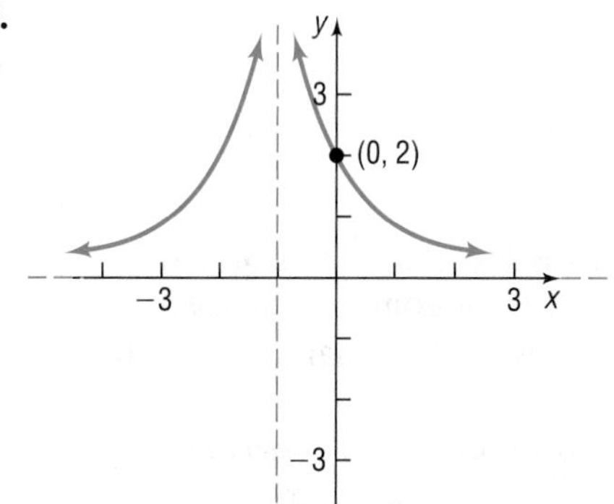

27.

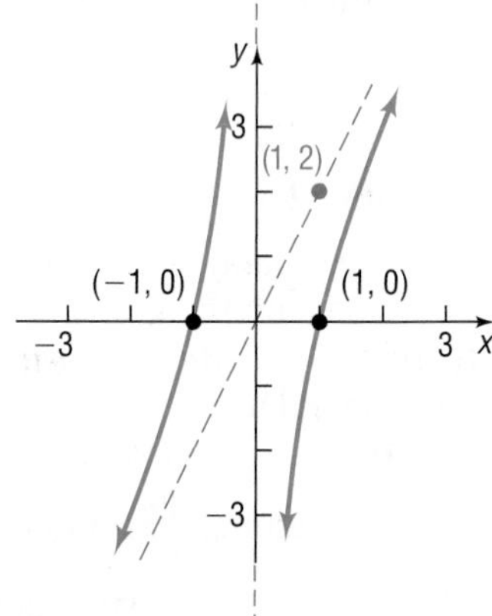

28.

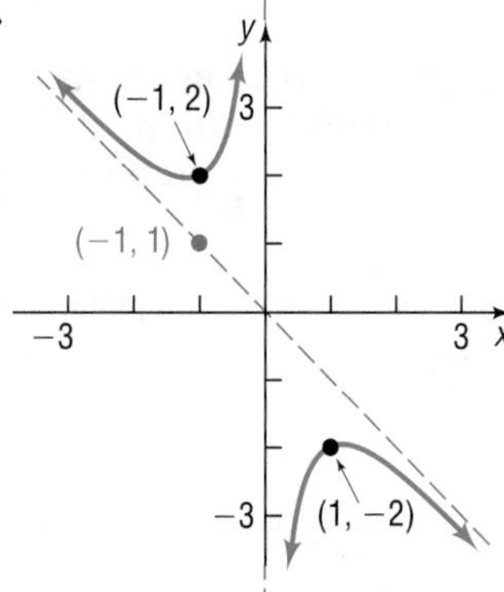

29.

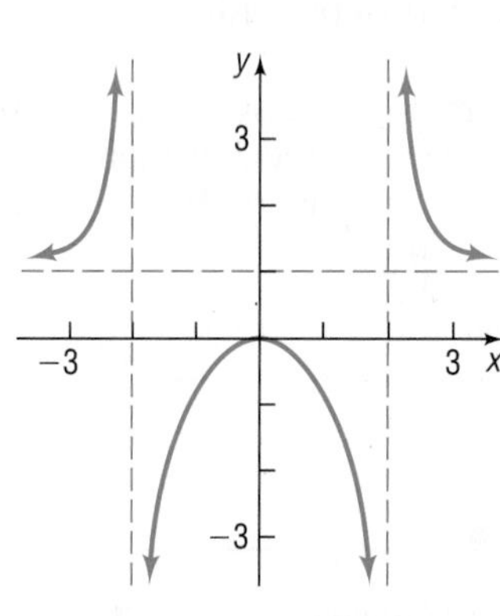

30.

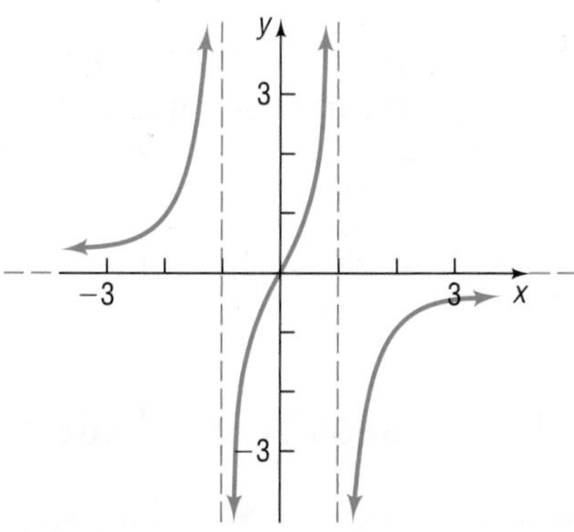

In Problems 31–42, graph each rational function using transformations.

31. $F(x) = 2 + \dfrac{1}{x}$ **32.** $Q(x) = 3 + \dfrac{1}{x^2}$ **33.** $R(x) = \dfrac{1}{(x - 1)^2}$ **34.** $R(x) = \dfrac{3}{x}$

35. $H(x) = \dfrac{-2}{x + 1}$ **36.** $G(x) = \dfrac{2}{(x + 2)^2}$ **37.** $R(x) = \dfrac{-1}{x^2 + 4x + 4}$ **38.** $R(x) = \dfrac{1}{x - 1} + 1$

39. $G(x) = 1 + \dfrac{2}{(x - 3)^2}$ **40.** $F(x) = 2 - \dfrac{1}{x + 1}$ **41.** $R(x) = \dfrac{x^2 - 4}{x^2}$ **42.** $R(x) = \dfrac{x - 4}{x}$

In Problems 43–54, find the vertical, horizontal, and oblique asymptotes, if any, of each rational function.

43. $R(x) = \dfrac{3x}{x + 4}$ **44.** $R(x) = \dfrac{3x + 5}{x - 6}$ **45.** $H(x) = \dfrac{x^3 - 8}{x^2 - 5x + 6}$ **46.** $G(x) = \dfrac{x^3 + 1}{x^2 - 5x - 14}$

47. $T(x) = \dfrac{x^3}{x^4 - 1}$ **48.** $P(x) = \dfrac{4x^2}{x^3 - 1}$ **49.** $Q(x) = \dfrac{2x^2 - 5x - 12}{3x^2 - 11x - 4}$ **50.** $F(x) = \dfrac{x^2 + 6x + 5}{2x^2 + 7x + 5}$

51. $R(x) = \dfrac{6x^2 + 7x - 5}{3x + 5}$ **52.** $R(x) = \dfrac{8x^2 + 26x - 7}{4x - 1}$ **53.** $G(x) = \dfrac{x^4 - 1}{x^2 - x}$ **54.** $F(x) = \dfrac{x^4 - 16}{x^2 - 2x}$

Applications and Extensions

55. Gravity In physics, it is established that the acceleration due to gravity, g (in meters/sec^2), at a height h meters above sea level is given by

$$g(h) = \frac{3.99 \times 10^{14}}{(6.374 \times 10^6 + h)^2}$$

where 6.374×10^6 is the radius of Earth in meters.

(a) What is the acceleration due to gravity at sea level?
(b) The Willis Tower in Chicago, Illinois, is 443 meters tall. What is the acceleration due to gravity at the top of the Willis Tower?
(c) The peak of Mount Everest is 8848 meters above sea level. What is the acceleration due to gravity on the peak of Mount Everest?
(d) Find the horizontal asymptote of $g(h)$.
(e) Solve $g(h) = 0$. How do you interpret your answer?

56. Population Model A rare species of insect was discovered in the Amazon Rain Forest. To protect the species, environmentalists declared the insect endangered and transplanted the insect into a protected area. The population P of the insect t months after being transplanted is

$$P(t) = \frac{50(1 + 0.5t)}{2 + 0.01t}$$

(a) How many insects were discovered? In other words, what was the population when $t = 0$?
(b) What will the population be after 5 years?
(c) Determine the horizontal asymptote of $P(t)$. What is the largest population that the protected area can sustain?

57. Resistance in Parallel Circuits From Ohm's law for circuits, it follows that the total resistance R_{tot} of two components connected in parallel is given by the equation

$$R_{tot} = \frac{R_1 R_2}{R_1 + R_2}$$

where R_1 and R_2 are the individual resistances.

(a) Let $R_1 = 10$ ohms, and graph R_{tot} as a function of R_2.
(b) Find and interpret any asymptotes of the graph obtained in part (a).
(c) If $R_2 = 2\sqrt{R_1}$, what value of R_1 will yield an R_{tot} of 17 ohms?

Source: en.wikipedia.org/wiki/Series_and_parallel_circuits

58. Newton's Method In calculus you will learn that, if

$$p(x) = a_n x^n + a_{n-1}x^{n-1} + \cdots + a_1 x + a_0$$

is a polynomial function, then the *derivative* of $p(x)$ is

$$p'(x) = na_n x^{n-1} + (n-1)a_{n-1}x^{n-2} + \cdots + 2a_2 x + a_1$$

Newton's Method is an efficient method for approximating the x-intercepts (or real zeros) of a function, such as $p(x)$. The following steps outline Newton's Method.

STEP 1: Select an initial value x_0 that is somewhat close to the x-intercept being sought.

STEP 2: Find values for x using the relation

$$x_{n+1} = x_n - \frac{p(x_n)}{p'(x_n)} \qquad n = 1, 2, \ldots$$

until you get two consecutive values x_n and x_{n+1} that agree to whatever decimal place accuracy you desire.

STEP 3: The approximate zero will be x_{n+1}.

Consider the polynomial function $p(x) = x^3 - 7x - 40$.

(a) Evaluate $p(5)$ and $p(-3)$.
(b) What might we conclude about a zero of p? Explain.
(c) Use Newton's Method to approximate an x-intercept, r, $-3 < r < 5$, of $p(x)$ to four decimal places.
(d) Use a graphing utility to graph $p(x)$ and verify your answer in part (c).
(e) Using a graphing utility, evaluate $p(r)$ to verify your result.

Explaining Concepts: Discussion and Writing

59. If the graph of a rational function R has the vertical asymptote $x = 4$, the factor $x - 4$ must be present in the denominator of R. Explain why.

60. If the graph of a rational function R has the horizontal asymptote $y = 2$, the degree of the numerator of R equals the degree of the denominator of R. Explain why.

61. Can the graph of a rational function have both a horizontal and an oblique asymptote? Explain.

62. Make up a rational function that has $y = 2x + 1$ as an oblique asymptote. Explain the methodology that you used.

'Are You Prepared?' Answers

1. True **2.** Quotient: $3x + 3$; remainder: $2x^2 - 3x - 3$ **3.** **4.**

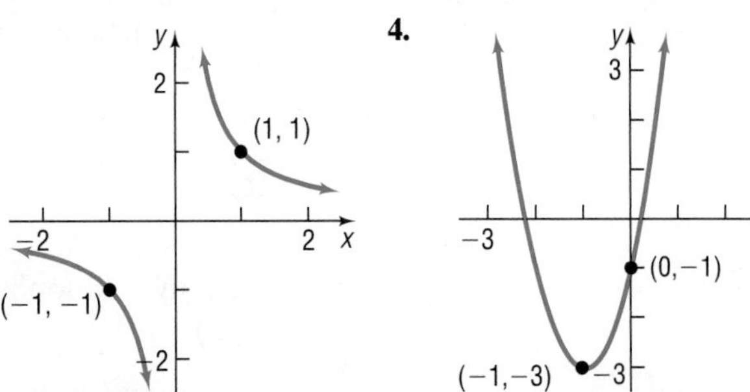

11.5 The Graph of a Rational Function

PREPARING FOR THIS SECTION *Before getting started, review the following:*

- Finding Intercepts (Section 8.1, pp. 522–523)

Now Work the **'Are You Prepared?'** problem on page 735.

OBJECTIVES
1 Analyze the Graph of a Rational Function (p. 728)
2 Solve Applied Problems Involving Rational Functions (p. 734)

1 Analyze the Graph of a Rational Function

Graphing utilities make the task of graphing rational functions less time consuming. However, the results of algebraic analysis must be taken into account before drawing conclusions based on the graph provided by the utility. In the next example we illustrate how to use the information collected in the last section in conjunction with the graphing utility to analyze the graph of a rational function $R(x) = \frac{p(x)}{q(x)}$.

EXAMPLE 1 **How to Analyze the Graph of a Rational Function**

Analyze the graph of the rational function: $R(x) = \frac{x - 1}{x^2 - 4}$

Step-by-Step Solution

Step 1 Factor the numerator and denominator of R. Find the domain of the rational function.

$$R(x) = \frac{x - 1}{x^2 - 4} = \frac{x - 1}{(x + 2)(x - 2)}$$

The domain of R is $\{x \mid x \neq -2, x \neq 2\}$.

Step 2 Write R in lowest terms.

Because there are no common factors between the numerator and denominator, R is in lowest terms.

Step 3 Locate the intercepts of the graph.

The x-intercepts are found by determining the real zeros of the numerator of R written in lowest terms. By solving $x - 1 = 0$, the only real zero of the numerator is 1. So the only x-intercept of the graph of R is 1. Since 0 is in the domain of R, the y-intercept is $R(0) = \frac{1}{4}$.

Step 4 Locate the vertical asymptotes.

To locate the vertical asymptotes, find the zeros of the denominator with the rational function in lowest terms. With R written in lowest terms, we find that the graph of R has two vertical asymptotes: the lines $x = -2$ and $x = 2$.

Step 5 Locate the horizontal or oblique asymptote. Determine points, if any, at which the graph of R intersects this asymptote.

Because the degree of the numerator is less than the degree of the denominator, R is proper and the line $y = 0$ (the x-axis) is a horizontal asymptote of the graph. To determine if the graph of R intersects the horizontal asymptote, solve the equation $R(x) = 0$:

$$\frac{x - 1}{x^2 - 4} = 0$$
$$x - 1 = 0$$
$$x = 1$$

The only solution is $x = 1$, so the graph of R intersects the horizontal asymptote at $(1, 0)$.

Step 6 Graph R using a graphing utility.

The analysis in Steps 1 through 5 helps us to determine an appropriate viewing window to obtain a complete graph. Figure 37 shows the graph of $R(x) = \dfrac{x-1}{x^2-4}$. You should confirm that all the algebraic conclusions that we came to in Steps 1 through 5 are part of the graph. For example, the graph has a horizontal asymptote at $y = 0$ and vertical asymptotes at $x = -2$ and $x = 2$. The y-intercept is $\dfrac{1}{4}$ and the x-intercept is 1.

Figure 37

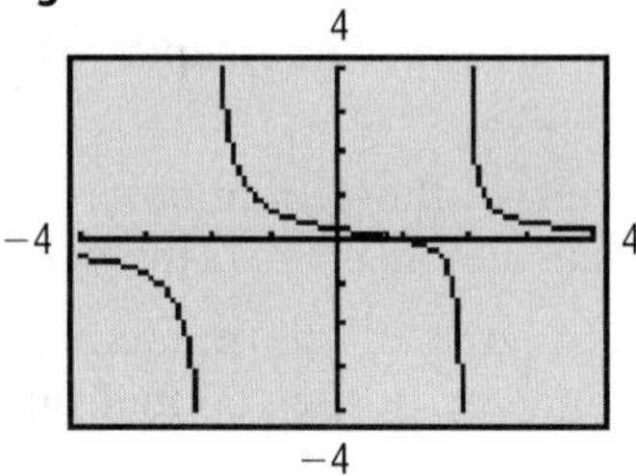

Step 7 Use the results obtained in Steps 1 through 6 to graph R by hand.

Figure 38 shows the graph of R.

Figure 38

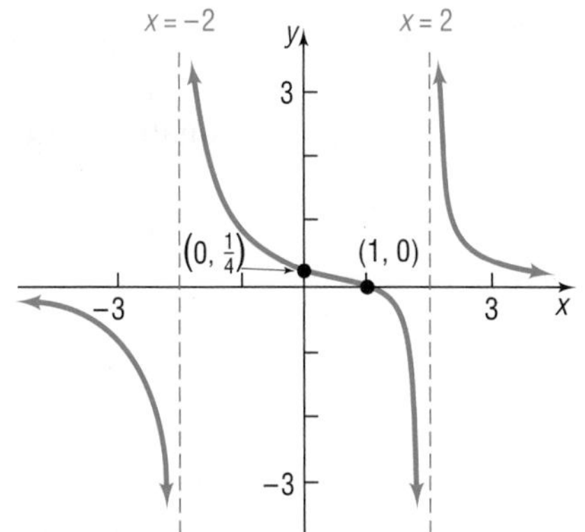

■

SUMMARY

Analyzing the Graph of a Rational Function

STEP 1: Factor the numerator and denominator of R. Find the domain of the rational function.

STEP 2: Write R in lowest terms.

STEP 3: Locate the intercepts of the graph. The x-intercepts, if any, of $R(x) = \dfrac{p(x)}{q(x)}$ in lowest terms satisfy the equation $p(x) = 0$. The y-intercept, if there is one, is $R(0)$.

STEP 4: Locate the vertical asymptotes. The vertical asymptotes, if any, of $R(x) = \dfrac{p(x)}{q(x)}$ in lowest terms are found by identifying the real zeros of $q(x)$. Each zero of the denominator gives rise to a vertical asymptote.

STEP 5: Locate the horizontal or oblique asymptote, if one exists, using the procedure given in Section 11.4. Determine points, if any, at which the graph of R intersects this asymptote.

STEP 6: Graph R using a graphing utility.

STEP 7: Use the results obtained in Steps 1 through 6 to graph R by hand.

Now Work PROBLEM 7

EXAMPLE 2 Analyzing the Graph of a Rational Function

Analyze the graph of the rational function: $R(x) = \frac{x^2 - 1}{x}$

Solution

Step 1: $R(x) = \frac{x^2 - 1}{x} = \frac{(x + 1)(x - 1)}{x}$

The domain of R is $\{x | x \neq 0\}$.

Step 2: R is in lowest terms.

Step 3: The graph has two x-intercepts: -1 and 1. There is no y-intercept, since x cannot equal 0.

Step 4: The real zero of the denominator with R in lowest terms is 0, so the graph of $R(x)$ has the line $x = 0$ (the y-axis) as a vertical asymptote.

Step 5: Since the degree of the numerator, 2, is one more than the degree of the denominator, 1, the rational function R is improper and will have an oblique asymptote. To find the oblique asymptote, use long division.

$$\begin{array}{r} x \\ x\overline{)x^2 - 1} \\ \underline{x^2 \quad\quad} \\ -1 \end{array}$$

NOTE Because the denominator of the rational function is a monomial, we can also find the oblique asymptote as follows:

$$\frac{x^2 - 1}{x} = \frac{x^2}{x} - \frac{1}{x} = x - \frac{1}{x}$$

Since $\frac{1}{x} \to 0$ as $x \to \infty$, $y = x$ is an oblique asymptote. ■

The quotient is x, so the line $y = x$ is an oblique asymptote of the graph. To determine whether the graph of R intersects the asymptote $y = x$, solve the equation $R(x) = x$.

$$R(x) = \frac{x^2 - 1}{x} = x$$
$$x^2 - 1 = x^2$$
$$-1 = 0 \quad \text{Impossible}$$

We conclude that the equation $\frac{x^2 - 1}{x} = x$ has no solution, so the graph of $R(x)$ does not intersect the line $y = x$.

Figure 39

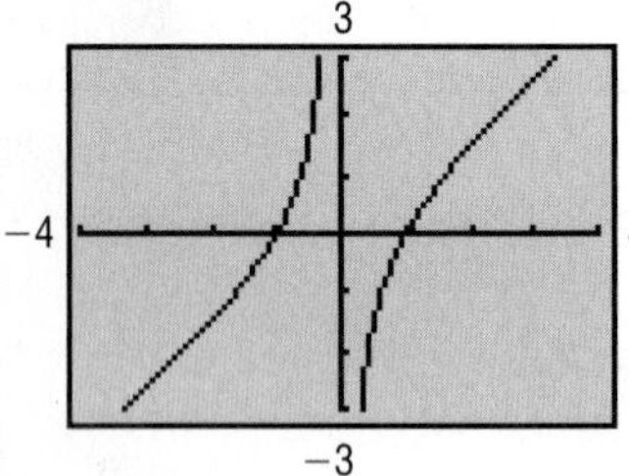

Step 6: See Figure 39. We see from the graph that there is no y-intercept and there are two x-intercepts, -1 and 1. We can also see that there is a vertical asymptote at $x = 0$.

Step 7: Using the information gathered in Steps 1 through 6, we obtain the graph of R shown in Figure 40. Notice how the oblique asymptote is used as a guide in graphing the rational function by hand.

Figure 40

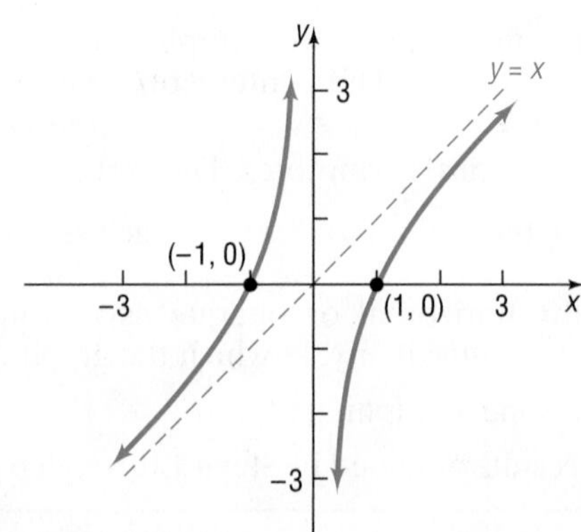

■

Now Work PROBLEM 15

EXAMPLE 3 Analyzing the Graph of a Rational Function

Analyze the graph of the rational function: $R(x) = \dfrac{3x^2 - 3x}{x^2 + x - 12}$

Solution

Step 1: Factor R to get

$$R(x) = \frac{3x(x-1)}{(x+4)(x-3)}$$

The domain of R is $\{x \mid x \neq -4, x \neq 3\}$.

Step 2: R is in lowest terms.

Step 3: The graph has two x-intercepts: 0 and 1. The y-intercept is $R(0) = 0$.

Step 4: The real zeros of the denominator of R with R in lowest terms are -4 and 3. So the graph of R has two vertical asymptotes: $x = -4$ and $x = 3$.

Step 5: Since the degree of the numerator equals the degree of the denominator, the graph has a horizontal asymptote. To find it, we form the quotient of the leading coefficient of the numerator, 3, and the leading coefficient of the denominator, 1. The graph of R has the horizontal asymptote $y = 3$. To find out whether the graph of R intersects the asymptote, solve the equation $R(x) = 3$.

$$R(x) = \frac{3x^2 - 3x}{x^2 + x - 12} = 3$$
$$3x^2 - 3x = 3x^2 + 3x - 36$$
$$-6x = -36$$
$$x = 6$$

The graph intersects the line $y = 3$ at $x = 6$, and $(6, 3)$ is a point on the graph of R.

Figure 41

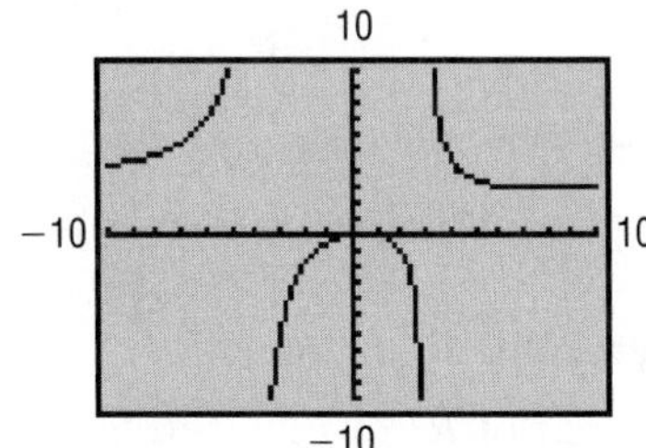

Step 6: Figure 41 shows the graph of R.

Step 7: Figure 41 does not clearly show the graph between the two x-intercepts, 0 and 1. Because the zeros in the numerator, 0 and 1, are of odd multiplicity (both are multiplicity 1), we know that the graph of R crosses the x-axis at 0 and 1. Therefore, the graph of R is above the x-axis for $0 < x < 1$. To see this part better, we graph R for $-1 \leq x \leq 2$ in Figure 42. Using MAXIMUM, we approximate the turning point to be $(0.52, 0.07)$, rounded to two decimal places.

Figure 42

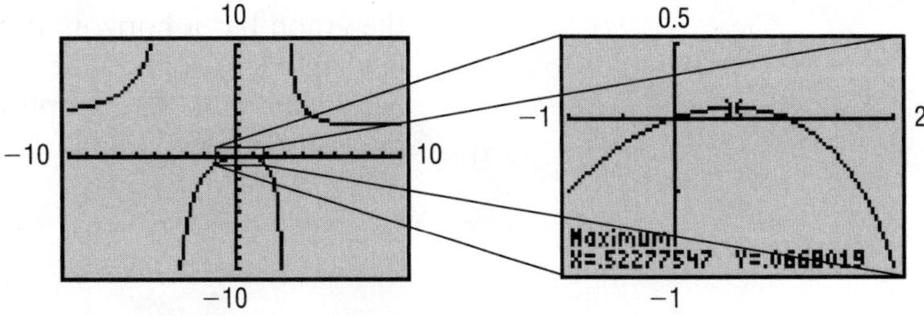

Figure 41 also does not display the graph of R crossing the horizontal asymptote at $(6, 3)$. To see this part better, we graph R for $4 \leq x \leq 60$ in Figure 43. Using MINIMUM, we approximate the turning point to be $(11.48, 2.75)$, rounded to two decimal places.

Figure 43

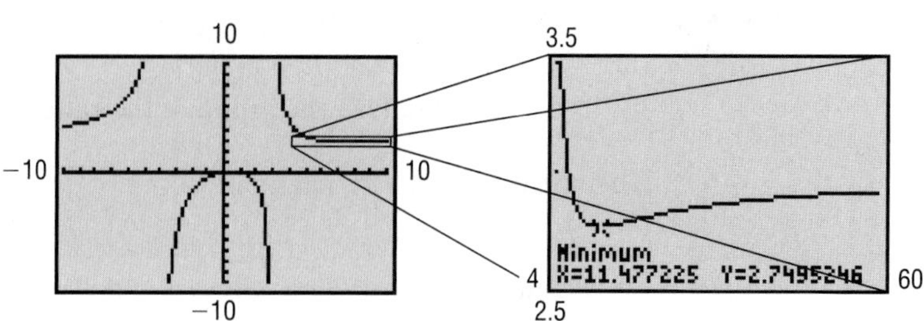

Using this information along with the information gathered in Steps 1 through 6, we obtain the graph of R shown in Figure 44.

Figure 44

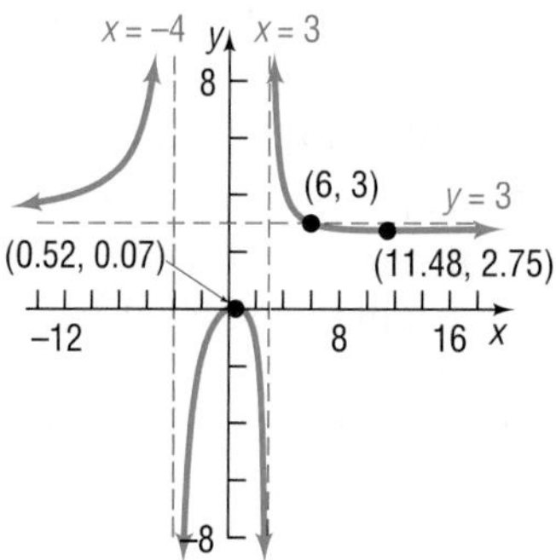

■

EXAMPLE 4 Analyzing the Graph of a Rational Function with a Hole

Analyze the graph of the rational function: $R(x) = \dfrac{2x^2 - 5x + 2}{x^2 - 4}$

Solution

Step 1: Factor R and obtain

$$R(x) = \frac{(2x - 1)(x - 2)}{(x + 2)(x - 2)}$$

The domain of R is $\{x \mid x \neq -2, x \neq 2\}$.

Step 2: In lowest terms,

$$R(x) = \frac{2x - 1}{x + 2} \qquad x \neq 2$$

Step 3: The graph has one x-intercept: 0.5. The y-intercept is $R(0) = -0.5$.

Step 4: Since $x + 2$ is the only factor of the denominator of $R(x)$ *in lowest terms*, the graph has one vertical asymptote, $x = -2$. However, the rational function is undefined at both $x = 2$ and $x = -2$.

Step 5: Since the degree of the numerator equals the degree of the denominator, the graph has a horizontal asymptote. To find it, form the quotient of the leading coefficient of the numerator, 2, and the leading coefficient of the denominator, 1. The graph of R has the horizontal asymptote $y = 2$. To find whether the graph of R intersects the asymptote, solve the equation $R(x) = 2$.

$$\begin{aligned} R(x) = \frac{2x - 1}{x + 2} &= 2 \\ 2x - 1 &= 2(x + 2) \\ 2x - 1 &= 2x + 4 \\ -1 &= 4 \qquad \text{Impossible} \end{aligned}$$

The graph does not intersect the line $y = 2$.

Figure 45

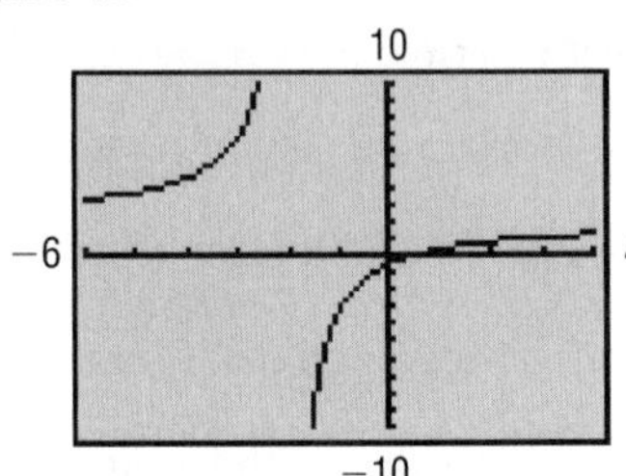

STEP 6: Figure 45 shows the graph of $R(x)$. Notice that the graph has one vertical asymptote at $x = -2$. Also, the function appears to be continuous at $x = 2$.

STEP 7: The analysis presented thus far does not explain the behavior of the graph at $x = 2$. We use the TABLE feature of our graphing utility to determine the behavior of the graph of R as x approaches 2. See Table 16. From the table, we conclude that the value of R approaches 0.75 as x approaches 2. This result is further verified by evaluating R in lowest terms at $x = 2$. We conclude that there is a hole in the graph at $(2, 0.75)$. Using the information gathered in Steps 1 through 6, we obtain the graph of R shown in Figure 46.

Table 16

X	Y1
1.99	.74687
1.999	.74969
1.9999	.74997
2	ERROR
2.0001	.75003
2.001	.75031
2.01	.75312

Y1■(2X²−5X+2)/(...

Figure 46

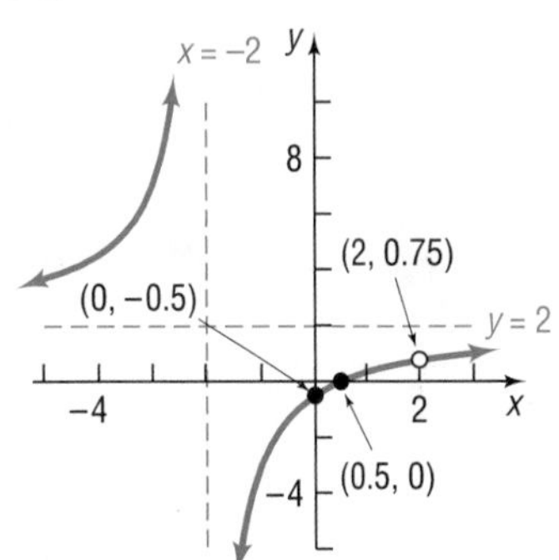

■

As Example 4 shows, **the values excluded from the domain of a rational function give rise to either vertical asymptotes or holes.**

Now Work PROBLEM 33

EXAMPLE 5 Constructing a Rational Function from Its Graph

Make up a rational function that might have the graph shown in Figure 47.

Figure 47

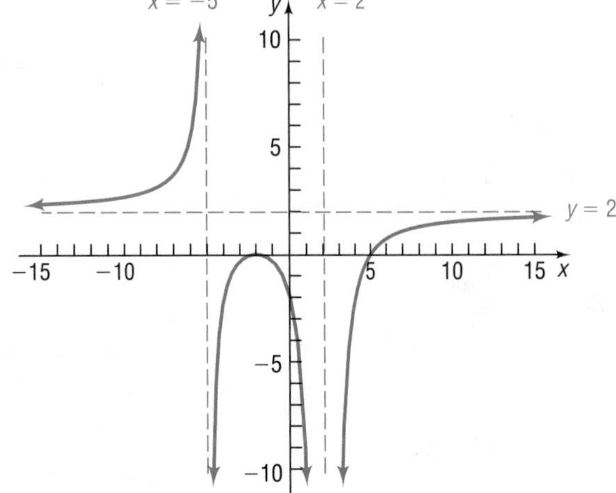

Solution The numerator of a rational function $R(x) = \dfrac{p(x)}{q(x)}$ in lowest terms determines the x-intercepts of its graph. The graph shown in Figure 47 has x-intercepts -2 (even multiplicity; graph touches the x-axis) and 5 (odd multiplicity; graph crosses the x-axis). So one possibility for the numerator is $p(x) = (x + 2)^2(x - 5)$.

The denominator of a rational function in lowest terms determines the vertical asymptotes of its graph. The vertical asymptotes of the graph are $x = -5$ and $x = 2$. Since $R(x)$ approaches ∞ from the left of $x = -5$ and $R(x)$ approaches $-\infty$ from the right of $x = -5$, we know that $(x + 5)$ is a factor of odd multiplicity in $q(x)$.

Figure 48

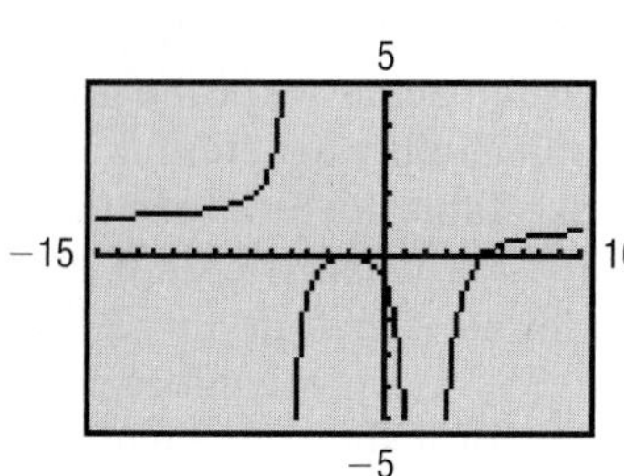

Also, $R(x)$ approaches $-\infty$ from both sides of $x = 2$, so $(x - 2)$ is a factor of even multiplicity in $q(x)$. A possibility for the denominator is $q(x) = (x + 5)(x - 2)^2$.

So far we have $R(x) = \dfrac{(x+2)^2(x-5)}{(x+5)(x-2)^2}$. The horizontal asymptote of the graph given in Figure 47 is $y = 2$, so we know that the degree of the numerator must equal the degree of the denominator, and the quotient of leading coefficients must be $\dfrac{2}{1}$. This leads to $R(x) = \dfrac{2(x+2)^2(x-5)}{(x+5)(x-2)^2}$. Figure 48 shows the graph of R drawn on a graphing utility. Since Figure 48 looks similar to Figure 47, we have found a rational function R for the graph in Figure 47. ■

Now Work PROBLEM 45

2 Solve Applied Problems Involving Rational Functions

EXAMPLE 6 **Finding the Least Cost of a Can**

Reynolds Metal Company manufactures aluminum cans in the shape of a cylinder with a capacity of 500 cubic centimeters (cm^3), or $\frac{1}{2}$ liter. The top and bottom of the can are made of a special aluminum alloy that costs 0.05¢/per square centimeter (cm^2). The sides of the can are made of material that costs 0.02¢/cm^2.

(a) Express the cost of material for the can as a function of the radius r of the can.
(b) Use a graphing utility to graph the function $C = C(r)$.
(c) What value of r will result in the least cost?
(d) What is this least cost?

Solution (a) Figure 49 illustrates the situation. Notice that the material required to produce a cylindrical can of height h and radius r consists of a rectangle of area $2\pi rh$ and two circles, each of area πr^2. The total cost C (in cents) of manufacturing the can is therefore

Figure 49

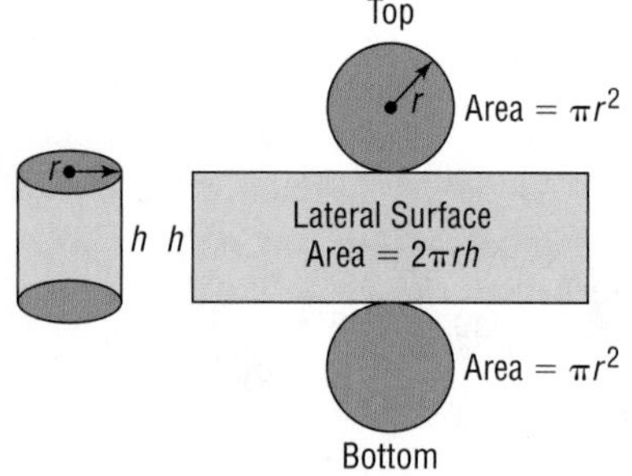

$$\begin{aligned} C &= \text{Cost of the top and bottom} + \text{Cost of the side} \\ &= \underbrace{2(\pi r^2)}_{\substack{\text{Total area}\\\text{of top and}\\\text{bottom}}} \underbrace{(0.05)}_{\substack{\text{Cost/unit}\\\text{area}}} + \underbrace{(2\pi rh)}_{\substack{\text{Total}\\\text{area of}\\\text{side}}} \underbrace{(0.02)}_{\substack{\text{Cost/unit}\\\text{area}}} \\ &= 0.10\pi r^2 + 0.04\pi rh \end{aligned}$$

But there is the additional restriction that the height h and radius r must be chosen so that the volume V of the can is 500 cm^3. Since $V = \pi r^2 h$,

$$500 = \pi r^2 h \quad \text{or} \quad h = \frac{500}{\pi r^2}$$

Figure 50

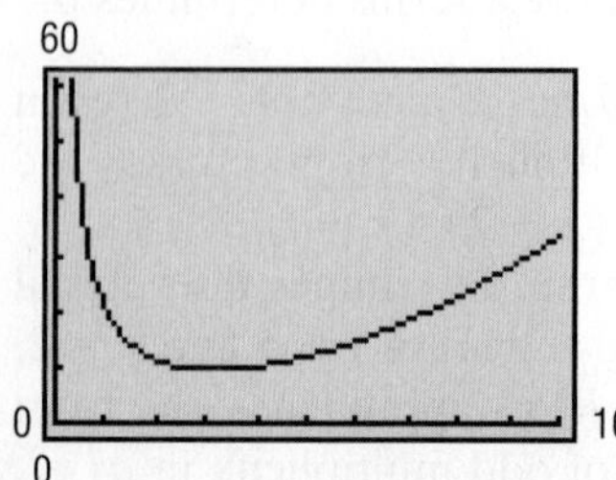

Substituting this expression for h, the cost C, in cents, as a function of the radius r, is

$$C(r) = 0.10\pi r^2 + 0.04\pi r \frac{500}{\pi r^2} = 0.10\pi r^2 + \frac{20}{r} = \frac{0.10\pi r^3 + 20}{r}$$

(b) See Figure 50 for the graph of $C = C(r)$.
(c) Using the MINIMUM command, the cost is least for a radius of about 3.17 cm.
(d) The least cost is $C(3.17) \approx 9.47$¢. ■

Now Work PROBLEM 55

11.5 Assess Your Understanding

'Are You Prepared?' *The answer is given at the end of these exercises. If you get a wrong answer, read the pages listed in red.*

1. Find the intercepts of the graph of the equation $y = \dfrac{x^2 - 1}{x^2 - 4}$. (pp. 522–523)

Concepts and Vocabulary

2. If the numerator and the denominator of a rational function have no common factors, the rational function is ___ _______ _____.

3. The graph of a rational function never intersects a _______ asymptote.

4. ***True or False*** The graph of a rational function sometimes intersects an oblique asymptote.

5. ***True or False*** The graph of a rational function sometimes has a hole.

6. $R(x) = \dfrac{x(x-2)^2}{x-2}$
   (a) Find the domain of R.
   (b) Find the x-intercepts of R.

Skill Building

In Problems 7–44, follow Steps 1 through 7 on page 729 to analyze the graph of each function.

7. $R(x) = \dfrac{x+1}{x(x+4)}$

8. $R(x) = \dfrac{x}{(x-1)(x+2)}$

9. $R(x) = \dfrac{3x+3}{2x+4}$

10. $R(x) = \dfrac{2x+4}{x-1}$

11. $R(x) = \dfrac{3}{x^2-4}$

12. $R(x) = \dfrac{6}{x^2-x-6}$

13. $P(x) = \dfrac{x^4+x^2+1}{x^2-1}$

14. $Q(x) = \dfrac{x^4-1}{x^2-4}$

15. $H(x) = \dfrac{x^3-1}{x^2-9}$

16. $G(x) = \dfrac{x^3+1}{x^2+2x}$

17. $R(x) = \dfrac{x^2}{x^2+x-6}$

18. $R(x) = \dfrac{x^2+x-12}{x^2-4}$

19. $G(x) = \dfrac{x}{x^2-4}$

20. $G(x) = \dfrac{3x}{x^2-1}$

21. $R(x) = \dfrac{3}{(x-1)(x^2-4)}$

22. $R(x) = \dfrac{-4}{(x+1)(x^2-9)}$

23. $H(x) = \dfrac{x^2-1}{x^4-16}$

24. $H(x) = \dfrac{x^2+4}{x^4-1}$

25. $F(x) = \dfrac{x^2-3x-4}{x+2}$

26. $F(x) = \dfrac{x^2+3x+2}{x-1}$

27. $R(x) = \dfrac{x^2+x-12}{x-4}$

28. $R(x) = \dfrac{x^2-x-12}{x+5}$

29. $F(x) = \dfrac{x^2+x-12}{x+2}$

30. $G(x) = \dfrac{x^2-x-12}{x+1}$

31. $R(x) = \dfrac{x(x-1)^2}{(x+3)^3}$

32. $R(x) = \dfrac{(x-1)(x+2)(x-3)}{x(x-4)^2}$

33. $R(x) = \dfrac{x^2+x-12}{x^2-x-6}$

34. $R(x) = \dfrac{x^2+3x-10}{x^2+8x+15}$

35. $R(x) = \dfrac{6x^2-7x-3}{2x^2-7x+6}$

36. $R(x) = \dfrac{8x^2+26x+15}{2x^2-x-15}$

37. $R(x) = \dfrac{x^2+5x+6}{x+3}$

38. $R(x) = \dfrac{x^2+x-30}{x+6}$

39. $f(x) = x + \dfrac{1}{x}$

40. $f(x) = 2x + \dfrac{9}{x}$

41. $f(x) = x^2 + \dfrac{1}{x}$

42. $f(x) = 2x^2 + \dfrac{16}{x}$

43. $f(x) = x + \dfrac{1}{x^3}$

44. $f(x) = 2x + \dfrac{9}{x^3}$

In Problems 45–48, find a rational function that might have the given graph. (More than one answer might be possible.)

45.

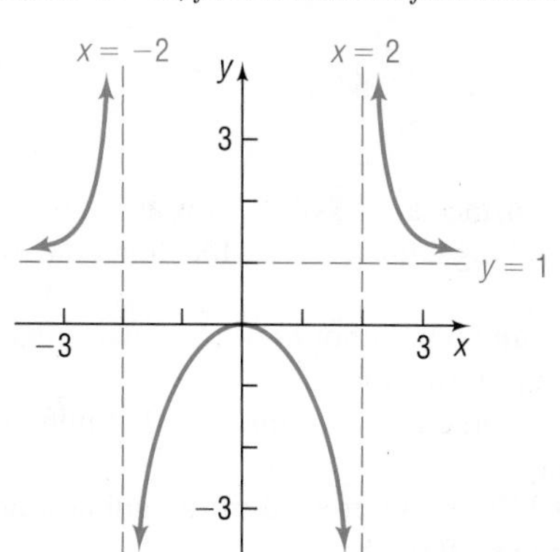

46.

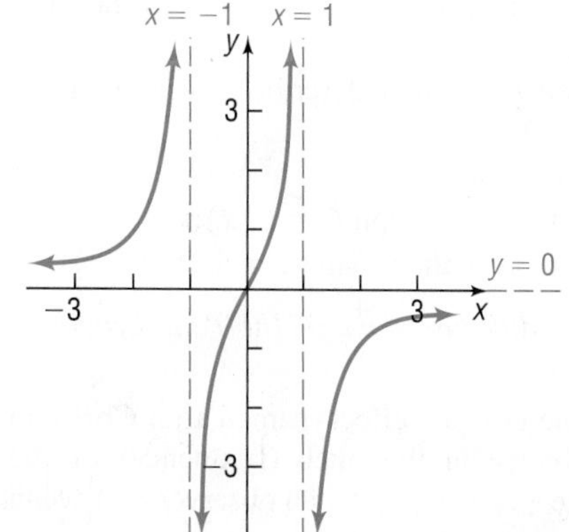

47.

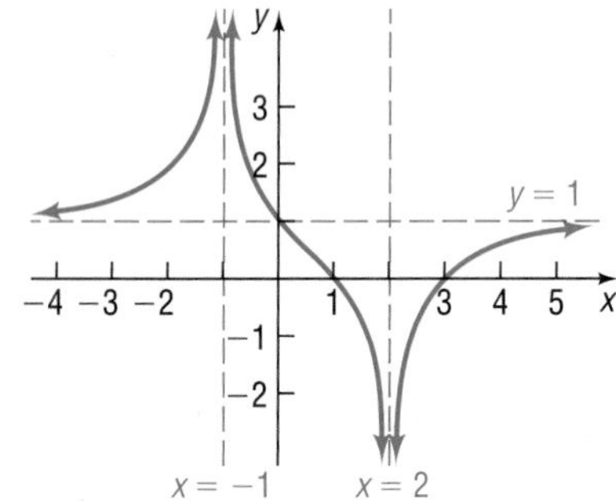

48.

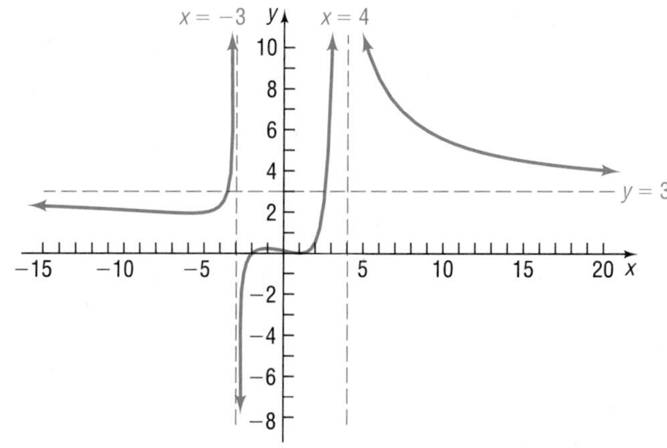

Applications and Extensions

49. **Drug Concentration** The concentration C of a certain drug in a patient's bloodstream t hours after injection is given by

$$C(t) = \frac{t}{2t^2 + 1}$$

(a) Find the horizontal asymptote of $C(t)$. What happens to the concentration of the drug as t increases?
(b) Using your graphing utility, graph $C = C(t)$.
(c) Determine the time at which the concentration is highest.

50. **Drug Concentration** The concentration C of a certain drug in a patient's bloodstream t minutes after injection is given by

$$C(t) = \frac{50t}{t^2 + 25}$$

(a) Find the horizontal asymptote of $C(t)$. What happens to the concentration of the drug as t increases?
(b) Using your graphing utility, graph $C = C(t)$.
(c) Determine the time at which the concentration is highest.

51. **Minimum Cost** A rectangular area adjacent to a river is to be fenced in; no fence is needed on the river side. The enclosed area is to be 1000 square feet. Fencing for the side parallel to the river is \$5 per linear foot, and fencing for the other two sides is \$8 per linear foot; the four corner posts are \$25 apiece. Let x be the length of one of the sides perpendicular to the river.
(a) Write a function $C(x)$ that describes the cost of the project.
(b) What is the domain of C?
(c) Use a graphing utility to graph $C = C(x)$.
(d) Find the dimensions of the cheapest enclosure.

Source: www.uncwil.edu/courses/math111hb/PandR/rational/rational.html

52. **Doppler Effect** The Doppler effect (named after Christian Doppler) is the change in the pitch (frequency) of the sound from a source (s) as heard by an observer (o) when one or both are in motion. If we assume both the source and the observer are moving in the same direction, the relationship is

$$f' = f_a\left(\frac{v - v_o}{v - v_s}\right)$$

where f' = perceived pitch by the observer
f_a = actual pitch of the source
v = speed of sound in air (assume 772.4 mph)
v_o = speed of the observer
v_s = speed of the source

Suppose that you are traveling down the road at 45 mph and you hear an ambulance (with siren) coming toward you from the rear. The actual pitch of the siren is 600 hertz (Hz).
(a) Write a function $f'(v_s)$ that describes this scenario.
(b) If $f' = 620$ Hz, find the speed of the ambulance.
(c) Use a graphing utility to graph the function.
(d) Verify your answer from part (b).

Source: www.kettering.edu/~drussell/

53. **Minimizing Surface Area** United Parcel Service has contracted you to design a closed box with a square base that has a volume of 10,000 cubic inches. See the illustration.

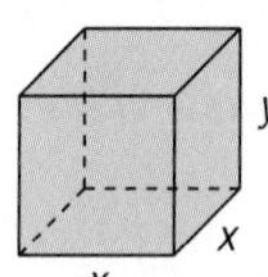

(a) Express the surface area S of the box as a function of x.
(b) Using a graphing utility, graph the function found in part (a).
(c) What is the minimum amount of cardboard that can be used to construct the box?
(d) What are the dimensions of the box that minimize the surface area?
(e) Why might UPS be interested in designing a box that minimizes the surface area?

54. **Minimizing Surface Area** United Parcel Service has contracted you to design an open box with a square base that has a volume of 5000 cubic inches. See the illustration.

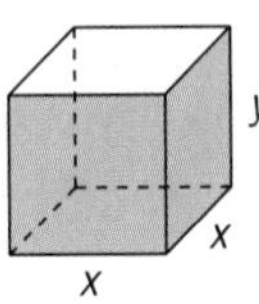

(a) Express the surface area S of the box as a function of x.
(b) Using a graphing utility, graph the function found in part (a).
(c) What is the minimum amount of cardboard that can be used to construct the box?
(d) What are the dimensions of the box that minimize the surface area?
(e) Why might UPS be interested in designing a box that minimizes the surface area?

55. **Cost of a Can** A can in the shape of a right circular cylinder is required to have a volume of 500 cubic centimeters. The top and bottom are made of material that costs 0.06¢ per square centimeter, while the sides are made of material that costs 0.04¢ per square centimeter.
(a) Express the total cost C of the material as a function of the radius r of the cylinder. (Refer to Figure 49.)
(b) Graph $C = C(r)$. For what value of r is the cost C a minimum?

56. **Material Needed to Make a Drum** A steel drum in the shape of a right circular cylinder is required to have a volume of 100 cubic feet.

(a) Express the amount A of material required to make the drum as a function of the radius r of the cylinder.
(b) How much material is required if the drum's radius is 3 feet?
(c) How much material is required if the drum's radius is 4 feet?
(d) How much material is required if the drum's radius is 5 feet?
(e) Graph $A = A(r)$. For what value of r is A smallest?

Explaining Concepts: Discussion and Writing

57. Graph each of the following functions:

$$y = \frac{x^2 - 1}{x - 1} \qquad y = \frac{x^3 - 1}{x - 1}$$

$$y = \frac{x^4 - 1}{x - 1} \qquad y = \frac{x^5 - 1}{x - 1}$$

Is $x = 1$ a vertical asymptote? Why not? What is happening for $x = 1$? What do you conjecture about $y = \dfrac{x^n - 1}{x - 1}$, $n \geq 1$ an integer, for $x = 1$?

58. Graph each of the following functions:

$$y = \frac{x^2}{x - 1} \qquad y = \frac{x^4}{x - 1} \qquad y = \frac{x^6}{x - 1} \qquad y = \frac{x^8}{x - 1}$$

What similarities do you see? What differences?

59. Write a few paragraphs that provide a general strategy for graphing a rational function. Be sure to mention the following: proper, improper, intercepts, and asymptotes.

60. Create a rational function that has the following characteristics: crosses the x-axis at 2; touches the x-axis at -1; one vertical asymptote at $x = -5$ and another at $x = 6$; and one horizontal asymptote, $y = 3$. Compare your function to a fellow classmate's. How do they differ? What are their similarities?

61. Create a rational function that has the following characteristics: crosses the x-axis at 3; touches the x-axis at -2; one vertical asymptote, $x = 1$; and one horizontal asymptote, $y = 2$. Give your rational function to a fellow classmate and ask for a written critique of your rational function.

62. Create a rational function with the following characteristics: three real zeros, one of multiplicity 2; y-intercept 1; vertical asymptotes, $x = -2$ and $x = 3$; oblique asymptote, $y = 2x + 1$. Is this rational function unique? Compare your function with those of other students. What will be the same as everyone else's? Add some more characteristics, such as symmetry or naming the real zeros. How does this modify the rational function?

63. Explain the circumstances under which the graph of a rational function will have a hole.

'Are You Prepared?' Answer

1. $\left(0, \frac{1}{4}\right)$, $(1, 0)$, $(-1, 0)$

11.6 Polynomial and Rational Inequalities

PREPARING FOR THIS SECTION *Before getting started, review the following:*

- Solving Linear Inequalities (Section 7.5, pp. 507–508)
- Solving Quadratic Inequalities (Section 10.5, pp. 669–672)

Now Work the **'Are You Prepared?'** problems on page 742.

OBJECTIVES
1. Solve Polynomial Inequalities Algebraically and Graphically (p. 738)
2. Solve Rational Inequalities Algebraically and Graphically (p. 739)

1 Solve Polynomial Inequalities Algebraically and Graphically

In this section we solve inequalities that involve polynomials of degree 3 and higher, along with inequalities that involve rational functions. To help understand the algebraic procedure for solving such inequalities, we use the information obtained in Sections 11.1, 11.2, and 11.5 about the graphs of polynomial and rational functions. The approach follows the same logic used to solve inequalities involving quadratic functions.

EXAMPLE 1 **Solving a Polynomial Inequality Using Its Graph**

Solve $(x + 3)(x - 1)^2 > 0$ by graphing $f(x) = (x + 3)(x - 1)^2$.

By Hand Graphical Solution

We graph $f(x) = (x + 3)(x - 1)^2$ and determine the intervals of x for which the graph is above the x-axis. Do you see why? These values of x result in $f(x)$ being positive. Using Steps 1 through 8 on page 691, we obtain the graph shown in Figure 51.

Figure 51

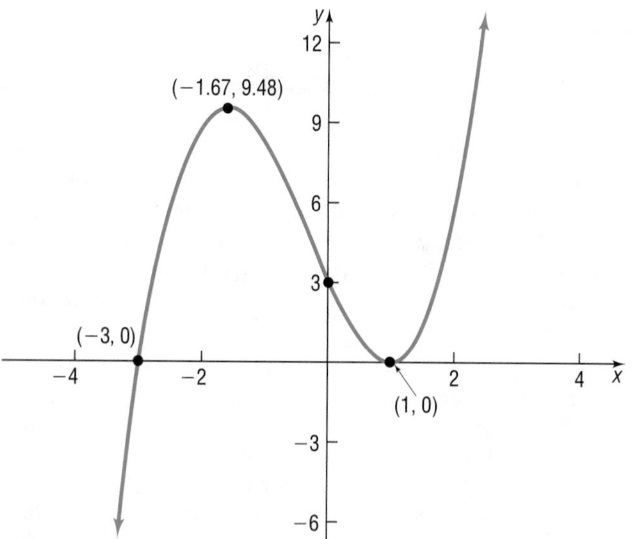

From the graph, we can see that $f(x) > 0$ for $-3 < x < 1$ or $x > 1$. The solution set is $\{x \mid -3 < x < 1 \text{ or } x > 1\}$ or, using interval notation, $(-3, 1) \cup (1, \infty)$. ■

Graphing Utility Solution

We graph $Y_1 = (x + 3)(x - 1)^2$. See Figure 52. Using the ZERO command, we find that the x-intercepts of the graph of Y_1 are -3 and 1. The graph of Y_1 is above the x-axis (and therefore f is positive) for $-3 < x < 1$ or $x > 1$. Therefore, the solution set is $\{x \mid -3 < x < 1 \text{ or } x > 1\}$ or, using interval notation, $(-3, 1) \cup (1, \infty)$.

Figure 52

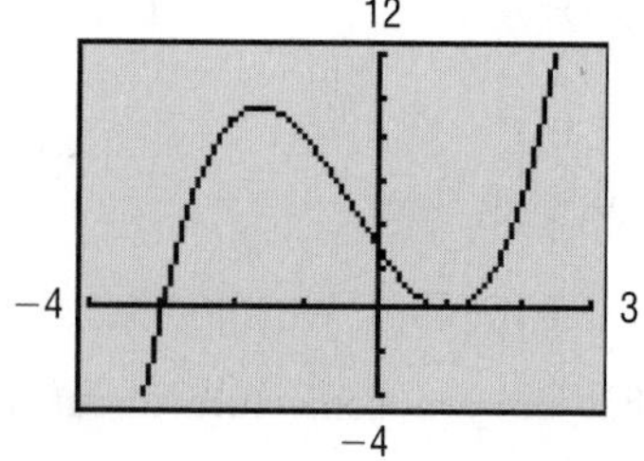

■

Now Work PROBLEM 9

The results of Example 1 lead to the following approach to solving polynomial inequalities algebraically. Suppose that the polynomial inequality is in one of the forms

$$f(x) < 0 \qquad f(x) > 0 \qquad f(x) \le 0 \qquad f(x) \ge 0$$

Locate the zeros (x-intercepts of the graph) of the polynomial function f. We know that the sign of f can change on either side of an x-intercept, so we use these zeros to divide the real number line into intervals. Then we know that on each interval the graph of f is either above $[f(x) > 0]$ or below $[f(x) < 0]$ the x-axis.

EXAMPLE 2

How to Solve a Polynomial Inequality Algebraically

Solve the inequality $x^4 > x$ algebraically, and graph the solution set.

Step-by-Step Solution

Step 1 Write the inequality so that a polynomial expression f is on the left side and zero is on the right side.

Rearrange the inequality so that 0 is on the right side.

$$x^4 > x$$

$$x^4 - x > 0 \quad \text{Subtract } x \text{ from both sides of the inequality.}$$

This inequality is equivalent to the one we wish to solve.

Step 2 Determine the real zeros (x-intercepts of the graph) of f.

Find the zeros of $f(x) = x^4 - x$ by solving $x^4 - x = 0$.

$$x^4 - x = 0$$

$$x(x^3 - 1) = 0 \quad \text{Factor out } x.$$

$$x(x - 1)(x^2 + x + 1) = 0 \quad \text{Factor the difference of two cubes.}$$

$$x = 0 \quad \text{or} \quad x - 1 = 0 \quad \text{or} \quad x^2 + x + 1 = 0 \quad \text{Set each factor equal to zero and solve}$$

$$x = 0 \quad \text{or} \quad x = 1$$

The equation $x^2 + x + 1 = 0$ has no real solutions. Do you see why?

Step 3 Use the zeros found in Step 2 to divide the real number line into intervals.

Use the zeros to separate the real number line into three intervals:

$$(-\infty, 0) \qquad (0, 1) \qquad (1, \infty)$$

Step 4 Select a number in each interval, evaluate f at the number, and determine whether f is positive or negative. If f is positive, all values of f in the interval are positive. If f is negative, all values of f in the interval are negative.

NOTE If the inequality is not strict ($\le$ or $\ge$), include the solutions of $f(x) = 0$ in the solution set.

Select a test number in each interval found in Step 3 and evaluate $f(x) = x^4 - x$ at each number to determine if $f(x)$ is positive or negative. See Table 17.

Table 17

	0	1	→ x
Interval	$(-\infty, 0)$	$(0, 1)$	$(1, \infty)$
Number chosen	-1	$\frac{1}{2}$	2
Value of f	$f(-1) = 2$	$f\left(\frac{1}{2}\right) = -\frac{7}{16}$	$f(2) = 14$
Conclusion	Positive	Negative	Positive

Since we want to know where $f(x)$ is positive, we conclude that $f(x) > 0$ for all numbers x for which $x < 0$ or $x > 1$. Because the original inequality is strict, numbers x that satisfy the equation $x^4 = x$ are not solutions. The solution set of the inequality $x^4 > x$ is $\{x \mid x < 0 \text{ or } x > 1\}$ or, using interval notation, $(-\infty, 0) \cup (1, \infty)$.

Figure 53 shows the graph of the solution set.

Figure 53 −2 −1 0 1 2

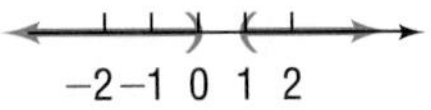

✓Check: Graph $Y_1 = x^4$ and $Y_2 = x$ on the same screen. Use INTERSECT to find where $Y_1 = Y_2$. Then determine where $Y_1 > Y_2$. ■

Now Work PROBLEM 21

2 Solve Rational Inequalities Algebraically and Graphically

Just as we presented a graphical approach to help understand the algebraic procedure for solving inequalities involving polynomials, we present a graphical approach to help understand the algebraic procedure for solving inequalities involving rational expressions.

EXAMPLE 3 Solving a Rational Inequality Using Its Graph

Solve $\frac{x-1}{x^2-4} \geq 0$ by graphing $R(x) = \frac{x-1}{x^2-4}$.

By Hand Graphical Solution

Graph $R(x) = \frac{x-1}{x^2-4}$ and determine the intervals of x such that the graph is above or on the x-axis. Do you see why? These values of x result in $R(x)$ being positive or zero. We graphed $R(x) = \frac{x-1}{x^2-4}$ in Example 1 from Section 11.5 (p. 728). We reproduce the graph in Figure 54.

Figure 54

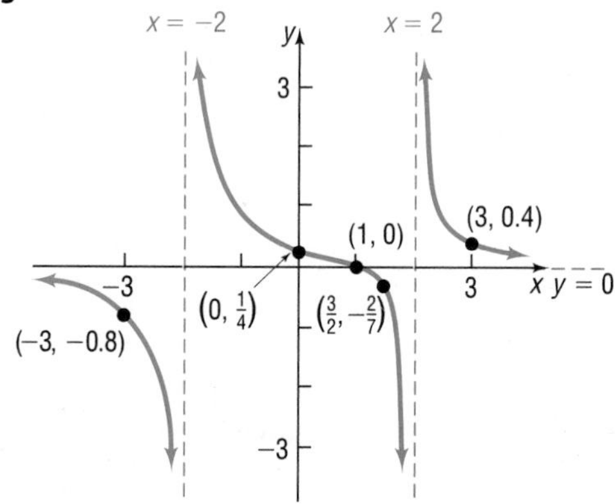

From the graph, we can see that $R(x) \geq 0$ for $-2 < x \leq 1$ or $x > 2$. The solution set is $\{x \mid -2 < x \leq 1 \text{ or } x > 2\}$ or, using interval notation, $(-2, 1] \cup (2, \infty)$.

Graphing Utility Solution

We graph $Y_1 = \frac{x-1}{x^2-4}$. See Figure 55. Using the ZERO command, we find that the x-intercept of the graph of Y_1 is 1. The graph of Y_1 is above the x-axis (and, therefore, R is positive) for $-2 < x < 1$ or $x > 2$. Since the inequality is not strict, we include 1 in the solution set. Therefore, the solution set is $\{x \mid -2 < x \leq 1 \text{ or } x > 2\}$ or, using interval notation, $(-2, 1] \cup (2, \infty)$.

Figure 55

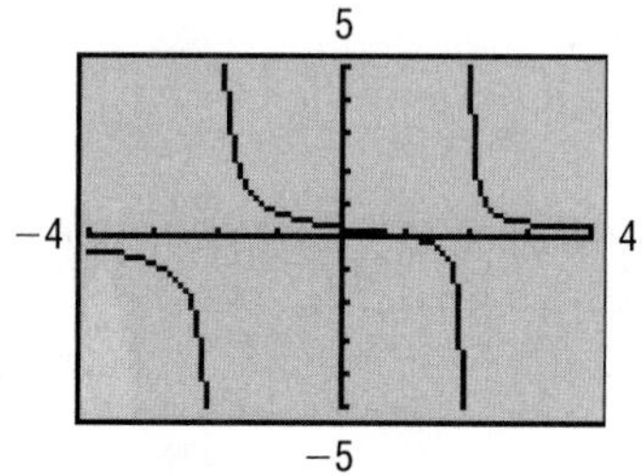

Now Work PROBLEM 33

To solve a rational inequality algebraically, we follow the same approach that we used to solve a polynomial inequality graphically. However, we must also identify the zeros of the denominator of the rational function, because the sign of a rational function may change on either side of a vertical asymptote. Convince yourself of this by looking at Figure 54. Notice the function values are negative for $x < -2$ and are positive for $x > -2$ (but less than 1).

EXAMPLE 4 How to Solve a Rational Inequality Algebraically

Solve the inequality $\frac{4x+5}{x+2} \geq 3$ algebraically, and graph the solution set.

Step-by-Step Solution

Step 1 Write the inequality so that a rational expression f is on the left side and zero is on the right side.

Rearrange the inequality so that 0 is on the right side.

$$\frac{4x+5}{x+2} \geq 3$$

$$\frac{4x+5}{x+2} - 3 \geq 0 \quad \text{Subtract 3 from both sides of the inequality.}$$

$$\frac{4x+5}{x+2} - 3 \cdot \frac{x+2}{x+2} \geq 0 \quad \text{Multiply 3 by } \frac{x+2}{x+2}.$$

$$\frac{4x+5-3x-6}{x+2} \geq 0 \quad \text{Write as a single quotient.}$$

$$\frac{x-1}{x+2} \geq 0 \quad \text{Combine like terms.}$$

Step 2 Determine the real zeros (x-intercepts of the graph) of f and the real numbers for which f is undefined.

The zero of $f(x) = \dfrac{x-1}{x+2}$ is 1. Also, f is undefined for $x = -2$.

Step 3 Use the zeros and undefined values found in Step 2 to divide the real number line into intervals.

Use the zero and the value for which f is undefined to separate the real number line into three intervals:

$$(-\infty, -2) \qquad (-2, 1) \qquad (1, \infty)$$

Step 4 Select a number in each interval, evaluate f at the number, and determine whether f is positive or negative. If f is positive, all values of f in the interval are positive. If f is negative, all values of f in the interval are negative.

NOTE If the inequality is not strict ($\leq$ or $\geq$), include the solutions of $f(x) = 0$ in the solution set.

Select a test number in each interval found in Step 3 and evaluate $f(x) = \dfrac{x-1}{x+2}$ at each number to determine if $f(x)$ is positive or negative. See Table 18.

Table 18

	−2	1	→ x
Interval	$(-\infty, -2)$	$(-2, 1)$	$(1, \infty)$
Number chosen	−3	0	2
Value of f	$f(-3) = 4$	$f(0) = -\frac{1}{2}$	$f(2) = \frac{1}{4}$
Conclusion	Positive	Negative	Positive

Since we want to know where $f(x)$ is positive or zero, we conclude that $f(x) \geq 0$ for all numbers x for which $x < -2$ or $x \geq 1$. Notice we do not include -2 in the solution because -2 is not in the domain of f. The solution set of the inequality $\dfrac{4x+5}{x+2} \geq 3$ is $\{x \mid x < -2 \text{ or } x \geq 1\}$ or, using interval notation, $(-\infty, -2) \cup [1, \infty)$.

Figure 56

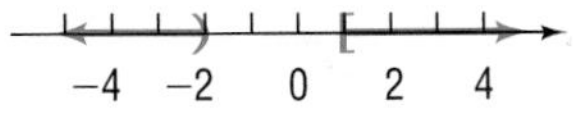

Figure 56 shows the graph of the solution set.

✓**Check:** Graph $Y_1 = \dfrac{4x+5}{x+2}$ and $Y_2 = 3$ on the same screen. Use INTERSECT to find where $Y_1 = Y_2$. Then determine where $Y_1 \geq Y_2$. ■

Now Work PROBLEM 39

SUMMARY

Steps for Solving Polynomial and Rational Inequalities Algebraically

STEP 1: Write the inequality so that a polynomial or rational expression f is on the left side and zero is on the right side in one of the following forms:

$$f(x) > 0 \qquad f(x) \geq 0 \qquad f(x) < 0 \qquad f(x) \leq 0$$

For rational expressions, be sure that the left side is written as a single quotient and find the domain of f.

STEP 2: Determine the real numbers at which the expression f equals zero and, if the expression is rational, the real numbers at which the expression f is undefined.

STEP 3: Use the numbers found in Step 2 to separate the real number line into intervals.

STEP 4: Select a number in each interval and evaluate f at the number.
(a) If the value of f is positive, then $f(x) > 0$ for all numbers x in the interval.
(b) If the value of f is negative, then $f(x) < 0$ for all numbers x in the interval.
If the inequality is not strict ($\geq$ or $\leq$), include the solutions of $f(x) = 0$ that are in the domain of f in the solution set. Be careful to exclude values of x where f is undefined.

11.6 Assess Your Understanding

'Are You Prepared?' *Answers are given at the end of these exercises. If you get a wrong answer, read the pages listed in red.*

1. Solve the inequality $3 - 4x > 5$. Graph the solution set. (pp. 507–508)

2. Solve the inequality $x^2 - 5x \leq 24$. Graph the solution set. (pp. 669–672)

Concepts and Vocabulary

3. ***True or False*** A test number for the interval $-2 < x < 5$ could be 4.

4. ***True or False*** The graph of $f(x) = \dfrac{x}{x-3}$ is above the x-axis for $x < 0$ or $x > 3$, so the solution set of the inequality $\dfrac{x}{x-3} \geq 0$ is $\{x \mid x \leq 0 \text{ or } x \geq 3\}$.

Skill Building

In Problems 5–8, use the graph of the function f to solve the inequality.

5. (a) $f(x) > 0$
(b) $f(x) \leq 0$

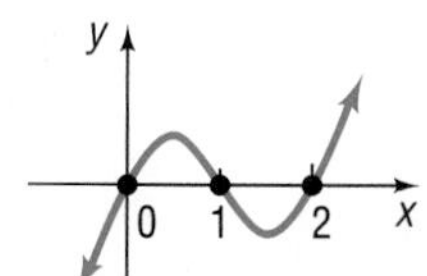

6. (a) $f(x) < 0$
(b) $f(x) \geq 0$

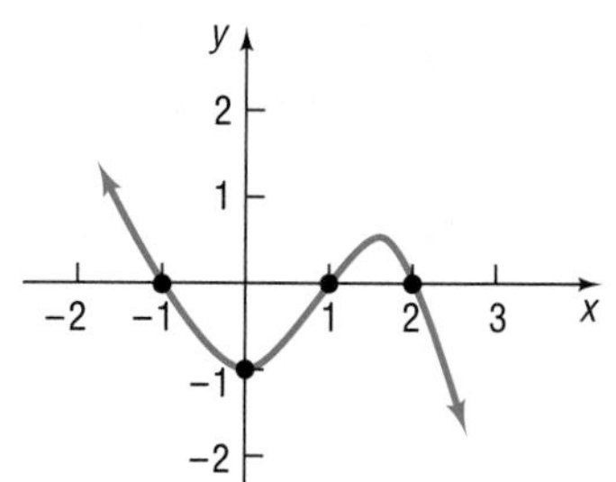

7. (a) $f(x) < 0$
(b) $f(x) \geq 0$

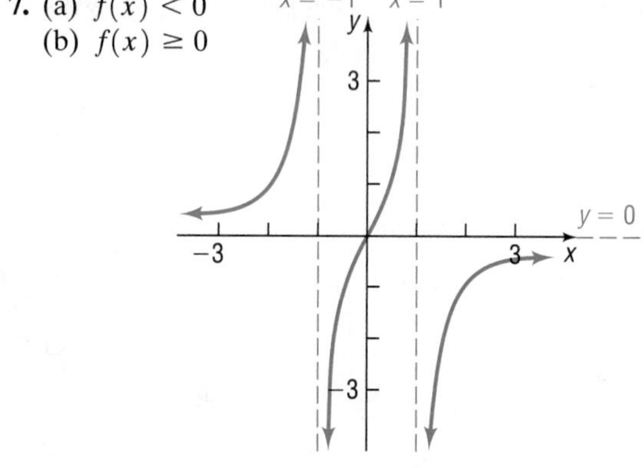

8. (a) $f(x) > 0$
(b) $f(x) \leq 0$

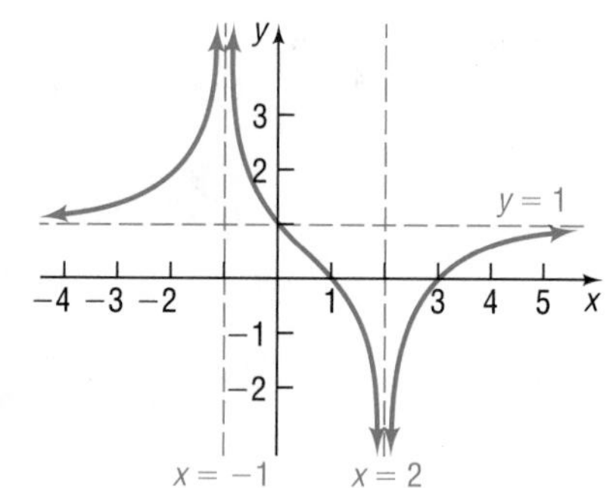

In Problems 9–14, solve the inequality by using the graph of the function.
[Hint: The graphs were drawn in Problems 69–74 of Section 11.1.]

9. Solve $f(x) < 0$, where $f(x) = x^2(x-3)$.

10. Solve $f(x) \leq 0$, where $f(x) = x(x+2)^2$.

11. Solve $f(x) \geq 0$, where $f(x) = (x+4)(x-2)^2$.

12. Solve $f(x) > 0$, where $f(x) = (x-1)(x+3)^2$.

13. Solve $f(x) \leq 0$, where $f(x) = -2(x+2)(x-2)^3$.

14. Solve $f(x) < 0$, where $f(x) = -\frac{1}{2}(x+4)(x-1)^3$.

In Problems 15–18, solve the inequality by using the graph of the function.
[Hint: The graphs were drawn in Problems 7–10 of Section 11.5.]

15. Solve $R(x) > 0$, where $R(x) = \dfrac{x+1}{x(x+4)}$.

16. Solve $R(x) < 0$, where $R(x) = \dfrac{x}{(x-1)(x+2)}$.

17. Solve $R(x) \leq 0$, where $R(x) = \dfrac{3x+3}{2x+4}$.

18. Solve $R(x) \geq 0$, where $R(x) = \dfrac{2x+4}{x-1}$.

In Problems 19–48, solve each inequality algebraically.

19. $(x-5)^2(x+2) < 0$

20. $(x-5)(x+2)^2 > 0$

21. $x^3 - 4x^2 > 0$

22. $x^3 + 8x^2 < 0$

23. $2x^3 > -8x^2$

24. $3x^3 < -15x^2$

25. $(x-1)(x-2)(x-3) \leq 0$

26. $(x+1)(x+2)(x+3) \leq 0$

27. $x^3 - 2x^2 - 3x > 0$

28. $x^3 + 2x^2 - 3x > 0$

29. $x^4 > x^2$

30. $x^4 < 9x^2$

31. $x^4 > 1$

32. $x^3 > 1$

33. $\dfrac{x+1}{x-1} > 0$

34. $\dfrac{x-3}{x+1} > 0$

35. $\dfrac{(x-1)(x+1)}{x} \le 0$

36. $\dfrac{(x-3)(x+2)}{x-1} \le 0$

37. $\dfrac{(x-2)^2}{x^2-1} \ge 0$

38. $\dfrac{(x+5)^2}{x^2-4} \ge 0$

39. $\dfrac{x+4}{x-2} \le 1$

40. $\dfrac{x+2}{x-4} \ge 1$

41. $\dfrac{3x-5}{x+2} \le 2$

42. $\dfrac{x-4}{2x+4} \ge 1$

43. $\dfrac{1}{x-2} < \dfrac{2}{3x-9}$

44. $\dfrac{5}{x-3} > \dfrac{3}{x+1}$

45. $\dfrac{x^2(3+x)(x+4)}{(x+5)(x-1)} \ge 0$

46. $\dfrac{x(x^2+1)(x-2)}{(x-1)(x+1)} \ge 0$

47. $\dfrac{(3-x)^3(2x+1)}{x^3-1} < 0$

48. $\dfrac{(2-x)^3(3x-2)}{x^3+1} < 0$

Mixed Practice

In Problems 49–60, solve each inequality algebraically.

49. $(x+1)(x-3)(x-5) > 0$

50. $(2x-1)(x+2)(x+5) < 0$

51. $7x - 4 \ge -2x^2$

52. $x^2 + 3x \ge 10$

53. $\dfrac{x+1}{x-3} \le 2$

54. $\dfrac{x-1}{x+2} \ge -2$

55. $3(x^2-2) < 2(x-1)^2 + x^2$

56. $(x-3)(x+2) < x^2 + 3x + 5$

57. $6x - 5 < \dfrac{6}{x}$

58. $x + \dfrac{12}{x} < 7$

59. $x^3 - 9x \le 0$

60. $x^3 - x \ge 0$

In Problems 61 and 62 (a) find the zeros of each function, (b) factor each function over the real numbers, (c) graph each function by hand, and (d) solve $f(x) < 0$.

61. $f(x) = 2x^4 + 11x^3 - 11x^2 - 104x - 48$

62. $f(x) = 4x^5 - 19x^4 + 32x^3 - 31x^2 + 28x - 12$

In Problems 63–66, (a) graph each function by hand, and (b) solve $f(x) \ge 0$.

63. $f(x) = \dfrac{x^2+5x-6}{x^2-4x+4}$

64. $f(x) = \dfrac{2x^2+9x+9}{x^2-4}$

65. $f(x) = \dfrac{x^3+2x^2-11x-12}{x^2-x-6}$

66. $f(x) = \dfrac{x^3-6x^2+9x-4}{x^2+x-20}$

Applications and Extensions

67. For what positive numbers will the cube of a number exceed four times its square?

68. For what positive numbers will the cube of a number be less than the number?

69. What is the domain of the function $f(x) = \sqrt{x^4 - 16}$?

70. What is the domain of the function $f(x) = \sqrt{x^3 - 3x^2}$?

71. What is the domain of the function $f(x) = \sqrt{\dfrac{x-2}{x+4}}$?

72. What is the domain of the function $f(x) = \sqrt{\dfrac{x-1}{x+4}}$?

In Problems 73–76, determine where the graph of f is below the graph of g by solving the inequality $f(x) \le g(x)$. Graph f and g together.

73. $f(x) = x^4 - 1$
$g(x) = -2x^2 + 2$

74. $f(x) = x^4 - 1$
$g(x) = x - 1$

75. $f(x) = x^4 - 4$
$g(x) = 3x^2$

76. $f(x) = x^4$
$g(x) = 2 - x^2$

77. **Average Cost** Suppose that the daily cost C of manufacturing bicycles is given by $C(x) = 80x + 5000$. Then the average daily cost $\overline{C}$ is given by $\overline{C}(x) = \dfrac{80x + 5000}{x}$. How many bicycles must be produced each day for the average daily cost to be no more than \$100?

78. **Average Cost** See Problem 77. Suppose that the government imposes a \$1000 per day tax on the bicycle manufacturer so that the daily cost C of manufacturing x bicycles is now given by $C(x) = 80x + 6000$. Now the average daily cost $\overline{C}$ is given by $\overline{C}(x) = \dfrac{80x + 6000}{x}$. How many bicycles must be produced each day for the daily average cost to be no more than \$100?

79. **Bungee Jumping** Originating on Pentecost Island in the Pacific, the practice of a person jumping from a high place harnessed to a flexible attachment was introduced to western culture in 1979 by the Oxford University Dangerous Sport Club. One important parameter to know before attempting a bungee jump is the amount the cord will stretch at the

bottom of the fall. The stiffness of the cord is related to the amount of stretch by the equation

$$K = \frac{2W(S + L)}{S^2}$$

where W = weight of the jumper (pounds)
K = cord's stiffness (pounds per foot)
L = free length of the cord (feet)
S = stretch (feet)

(a) A 150-pound person plans to jump off a ledge attached to a cord of length 42 feet. If the stiffness of the cord is no less than 16 pounds per foot, how much will the cord stretch?

(b) If safety requirements will not permit the jumper to get any closer than 3 feet to the ground, what is the minimum height required for the ledge in part (a)?

Source: American Institute of Physics, Physics News Update, No. 150, November 5, 1993.

80. **Gravitational Force** According to Newton's Law of universal gravitation, the attractive force F between two bodies is given by

$$F = G\frac{m_1 m_2}{r^2}$$

where m_1, m_2 = the masses of the two bodies
r = distance between the two bodies
G = gravitational constant = 6.6742×10^{-11} newtons meter^2 kilogram^{-2}

Suppose an object is traveling directly from Earth to the moon. The mass of Earth is 5.9742×10^{24} kilograms, the mass of the moon is 7.349×10^{22} kilograms, and the mean distance from Earth to the moon is 384,400 kilometers. For an object between Earth and the moon, how far from Earth is the force on the object due to the moon greater than the force on the object due to Earth?

Source: www.solarviews.com;en.wikipedia.org

81. **Field Trip** Mrs. West has decided to take her fifth grade class to a play. The manager of the theater agreed to discount the regular \$40 price of the ticket by \$0.20 for each ticket sold. The cost of the bus, \$500, will be split equally among each of the students. How many students must attend to keep the cost per student at or below \$40?

Explaining Concepts: Discussion and Writing

82. Make up an inequality that has no solution. Make up one that has exactly one solution.

83. The inequality $x^4 + 1 < -5$ has no solution. Explain why.

84. A student attempted to solve the inequality $\frac{x+4}{x-3} \le 0$ by multiplying both sides of the inequality by $x - 3$ to get $x + 4 \le 0$. This led to a solution of $\{x \mid x \le -4\}$. Is the student correct? Explain.

85. Write a rational inequality whose solution set is $\{x \mid -3 < x \le 5\}$.

'Are You Prepared?' Answers

1. $\left\{x \,\middle|\, x < -\frac{1}{2}\right\}$ or $\left(-\infty, -\frac{1}{2}\right)$

−2 −1 $-\frac{1}{2}$ 0 1

2. $\{x \mid -3 \le x \le 8\}$ or $[-3, 8]$

−3 0 8

CHAPTER REVIEW

Things to Know

Power function (pp. 681–683)

$f(x) = x^n$, $n \ge 2$ even	Domain: all real numbers Range: nonnegative real numbers Passes through $(-1, 1)$, $(0, 0)$, $(1, 1)$ Even function Decreasing on $(-\infty, 0)$, increasing on $(0, \infty)$
$f(x) = x^n$, $n \ge 3$ odd	Domain: all real numbers Range: all real numbers Passes through $(-1, -1)$, $(0, 0)$, $(1, 1)$ Odd function Increasing on $(-\infty, \infty)$

Polynomial function (pp. 680–690)

$f(x) = a_n x^n + a_{n-1}x^{n-1} + \cdots + a_1 x + a_0$, $a_n \ne 0$	Domain: all real numbers At most $n - 1$ turning points End behavior: Behaves like $y = a_n x^n$ for large $\lvert x \rvert$
Real zeros of a polynomial function *f* (p. 684)	Real numbers for which $f(x) = 0$; the real zeros of f are the x-intercepts of the graph of f
Remainder Theorem (p. 700)	If a polynomial function $f(x)$ is divided by $x - c$, then the remainder is $f(c)$.

Factor Theorem (p. 701)	$x - c$ is a factor of a polynomial function $f(x)$ if and only if $f(c) = 0$.
Rational Zeros Theorem (p. 702)	Let f be a polynomial function of degree 1 or higher of the form $f(x) = a_n x^n + a_{n-1}x^{n-1} + \cdots + a_1 x + a_0 \quad a_n \neq 0, a_0 \neq 0$ where each coefficient is an integer. If $\frac{p}{q}$, in lowest terms, is a rational zero of f, then p must be a factor of a_0, and q must be a factor of a_n.
Intermediate Value Theorem (p. 708)	Let f be a continuous function. If $a < b$ and $f(a)$ and $f(b)$ are of opposite sign, then there is at least one real zero of f between a and b.
Fundamental Theorem of Algebra (p. 713)	Every complex polynomial function $f(x)$ of degree $n \geq 1$ has at least one complex zero.
Conjugate Pairs Theorem (p. 713)	Let $f(x)$ be a polynomial function whose coefficients are real numbers. If $r = a + bi$ is a zero of f, then its complex conjugate $\bar{r} = a - bi$ is also a zero of f.
Rational function (pp. 717–725)	
$R(x) = \frac{p(x)}{q(x)}$	Domain: $\{x \mid q(x) \neq 0\}$
p, q are polynomial functions and q is not the zero polynomial.	Vertical asymptotes: With $R(x)$ in lowest terms, if $q(r) = 0$ for some real number, then $x = r$ is a vertical asymptote.
	Horizontal or oblique asymptote: See the summary on page 725.

Objectives

Section		You should be able to . . .	Example(s)	Review Exercises
11.1	1	Identify polynomial functions and their degree (p. 680)	1	1–4
	2	Graph polynomial functions using transformations (p. 683)	2, 3	5–7
	3	Identify the real zeros of a polynomial function and their multiplicity (p. 684)	4–6	8–11
	4	Analyze the graph of a polynomial function (p. 690)	9, 10	8–11
	5	Build cubic models from data (p. 693)	11	47
11.2	1	Use the Remainder and Factor Theorems (p. 700)	1, 2	12–14
	2	Use the Rational Zeros Theorem to list the potential rational zeros of a polynomial function (p. 702)	3	15–18
	3	Find the real zeros of a polynomial function (p. 703)	4, 5	16–18
	4	Solve polynomial equations (p. 705)	6	19–20
	5	Use the Theorem for Bounds on Zeros (p. 706)	7, 8, 9	21–22
	6	Use the Intermediate Value Theorem (p. 708)	10	23–24
11.3	1	Use the Conjugate Pairs Theorem (p. 713)	1	25–26
	2	Find a polynomial function with specified zeros (p. 714)	2	25–26
	3	Find the complex zeros of a polynomial function (p. 715)	3	27–30
11.4	1	Find the domain of a rational function (p. 717)	1	31, 32
	2	Find the vertical asymptotes of a rational function (p. 721)	4	31, 32, 40
	3	Find the horizontal or oblique asymptote of a rational function (p. 722)	5–8	31, 32, 40
11.5	1	Analyze the graph of a rational function (p. 728)	1–4	33–38
	2	Solve applied problems involving rational functions (p. 734)	6	46
11.6	1	Solve polynomial inequalities algebraically and graphically (p. 738)	1, 2	39, 41
	2	Solve rational inequalities algebraically and graphically (p. 739)	3, 4	40, 42–45

Review Exercises

In Problems 1–4, determine whether the function is a polynomial function, rational function, or neither. For those that are polynomial functions, state the degree. For those that are not polynomial functions, tell why not.

1. $f(x) = 4x^5 - 3x^2 + 5x - 2$

2. $f(x) = \dfrac{3x^5}{2x + 1}$

3. $f(x) = 3x^2 + 5x^{1/2} - 1$

4. $f(x) = 3$

In Problems 5–7, graph each function using transformations (shifting, compressing, stretching, and reflection). Show all the stages.

5. $f(x) = (x+2)^3$ **6.** $f(x) = -(x-1)^4$ **7.** $f(x) = (x-1)^4 + 2$

In Problems 8–11, analyze each polynomial function by following Steps 1 through 8 on page 691.

8. $f(x) = x(x+2)(x+4)$ **9.** $f(x) = (x-2)^2(x+4)$

10. $f(x) = -2x^3 + 4x^2$ **11.** $f(x) = (x-1)^2(x+3)(x+1)$

In Problems 12 and 13, find the remainder R when $f(x)$ is divided by $g(x)$. Is g a factor of f?

12. $f(x) = 8x^3 - 3x^2 + x + 4;\ \ g(x) = x - 1$ **13.** $f(x) = x^4 - 2x^3 + 15x - 2;\ \ g(x) = x + 2$

14. Find the value of $f(x) = 12x^6 - 8x^4 + 1$ at $x = 4$.

15. List all the potential rational zeros of $f(x) = 12x^8 - x^7 + 6x^4 - x^3 + x - 3$.

In Problems 16–18, use the Rational Zeros Theorem to find all the real zeros of each polynomial function. Use the zeros to factor f over the real numbers.

16. $f(x) = x^3 - 3x^2 - 6x + 8$ **17.** $f(x) = 4x^3 + 4x^2 - 7x + 2$ **18.** $f(x) = x^4 - 4x^3 + 9x^2 - 20x + 20$

In Problems 19 and 20, solve each equation in the real number system.

19. $2x^4 + 2x^3 - 11x^2 + x - 6 = 0$ **20.** $2x^4 + 7x^3 + x^2 - 7x - 3 = 0$

In Problems 21 and 22, find bounds to the real zeros of each polynomial function. Obtain a complete graph of f using a graphing utility.

21. $f(x) = x^3 - x^2 - 4x + 2$ **22.** $f(x) = 2x^3 - 7x^2 - 10x + 35$

In Problems 23 and 24, use the Intermediate Value Theorem to show that each polynomial function has a zero in the given interval.

23. $f(x) = 3x^3 - x - 1;\ [0, 1]$ **24.** $f(x) = 8x^4 - 4x^3 - 2x - 1;\ [0, 1]$

In Problems 25 and 26, information is given about a complex polynomial function f(x) whose coefficients are real numbers. Find the remaining zeros of f. Then find a polynomial function with real coefficients that has the zeros.

25. Degree 3; zeros: $4 + i, 6$ **26.** Degree 4; zeros: $i, 1 + i$

In Problems 27–30, find the complex zeros of each polynomial function $f(x)$. Write f in factored form.

27. $f(x) = x^3 - 3x^2 - 6x + 8$ **28.** $f(x) = 4x^3 + 4x^2 - 7x + 2$

29. $f(x) = x^4 - 4x^3 + 9x^2 - 20x + 20$ **30.** $f(x) = 2x^4 + 2x^3 - 11x^2 + x - 6$

In Problems 31 and 32, find the domain of each rational function. Find any horizontal, vertical, or oblique asymptotes.

31. $R(x) = \dfrac{x+2}{x^2-9}$ **32.** $R(x) = \dfrac{x^2+3x+2}{(x+2)^2}$

In Problems 33–38, discuss each rational function following Steps 1–7 given on page 729.

33. $R(x) = \dfrac{2x-6}{x}$ **34.** $H(x) = \dfrac{x+2}{x(x-2)}$ **35.** $R(x) = \dfrac{x^2+x-6}{x^2-x-6}$

36. $F(x) = \dfrac{x^3}{x^2-4}$ **37.** $R(x) = \dfrac{2x^4}{(x-1)^2}$ **38.** $G(x) = \dfrac{x^2-4}{x^2-x-2}$

39. Use the graph below of a polynomial function $y = f(x)$ to solve (a) $f(x) = 0$, (b) $f(x) > 0$, (c) $f(x) \le 0$, and (d) determine f.

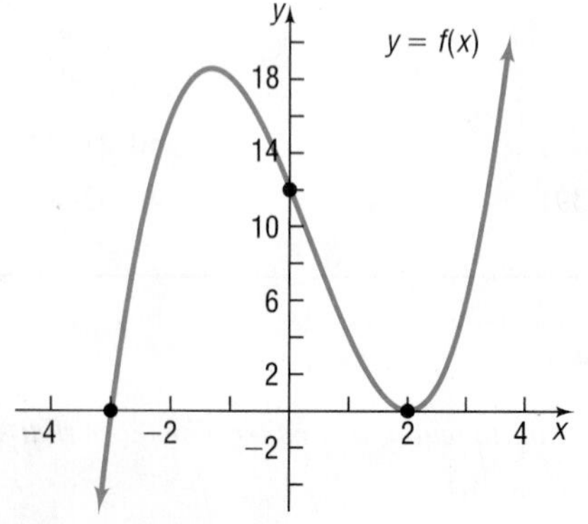

40. Use the graph below of a rational function $y = R(x)$ to (a) identify the horizontal asymptote of R, (b) identify the vertical asymptotes of R, (c) solve $R(x) < 0$, (d) solve $R(x) \ge 0$, and (e) determine R.

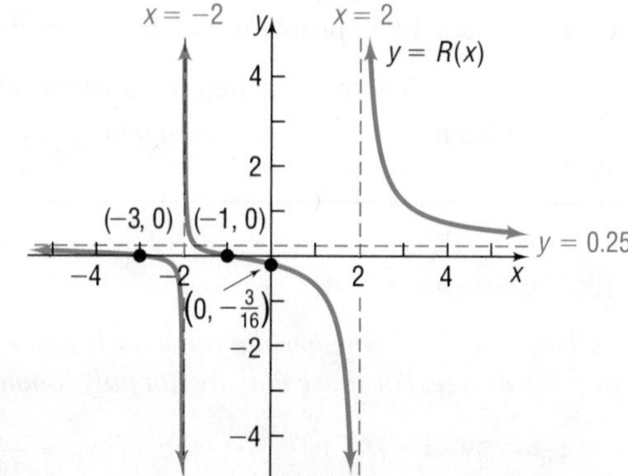

In Problems 41–45, solve each inequality. Graph the solution set.

41. $x^3 + x^2 < 4x + 4$

42. $\dfrac{6}{x+3} \geq 1$

43. $\dfrac{2x-6}{1-x} < 2$

44. $\dfrac{(x-2)(x-1)}{x-3} \geq 0$

45. $\dfrac{x^2 - 8x + 12}{x^2 - 16} > 0$

46. Making a Can A can in the shape of a right circular cylinder is required to have a volume of 250 cubic centimeters.

(a) Express the amount A of material to make the can as a function of the radius r of the cylinder.

(b) How much material is required if the can is of radius 3 centimeters?

(c) How much material is required if the can is of radius 5 centimeters?

(d) Graph $A = A(r)$. For what value of r is A smallest?

47. Model It: Poverty Rates The following data represent the percentage of persons in the United States whose income is below the poverty level.

Year, *t*	Percent below Poverty Level, *p*
1990, 1	13.5
1991, 2	14.2
1992, 3	14.8
1993, 4	15.1
1994, 5	14.5
1995, 6	13.8
1996, 7	13.7
1997, 8	13.3
1998, 9	12.7
1999, 10	11.9
2000, 11	11.3
2001, 12	11.7
2002, 13	12.1
2003, 14	12.5
2004, 15	12.7
2005, 16	12.6
2006, 17	12.3
2007, 18	12.5
2008, 19	13.3
2009, 20	14.3

Source: U.S. Census Bureau

(a) With a graphing utility, draw a scatter diagram of the data. Comment on the type of relation that appears to exist between the two variables.

(b) Decide on a function of best fit to these data (linear, quadratic, or cubic), and use this function to predict the percentage of persons that were below the poverty level in 2010 ($t = 21$).

(c) Draw the function of best fit on the scatter diagram drawn in part (a).

48. Design a polynomial function with the following characteristics: degree 6; four real zeros, one of multiplicity 3; y-intercept 3; behaves like $y = -5x^6$ for large values of $|x|$. Is this polynomial function unique? Compare your polynomial function with those of other students. What terms will be the same as everyone else's? Add some more characteristics, such as symmetry or naming the real zeros. How does this modify the polynomial function?

49. Design a rational function with the following characteristics: three real zeros, one of multiplicity 2; y-intercept 1; vertical asymptotes $x = -2$ and $x = 3$; oblique asymptote $y = 2x + 1$. Is this rational function unique? Compare yours with those of other students. What will be the same as everyone else's? Add some more characteristics, such as symmetry or naming the real zeros. How does this modify the rational function?

50. The illustration shows the graph of a polynomial function.

(a) Is the degree of the polynomial even or odd?

(b) Is the leading coefficient positive or negative?

(c) Is the function even, odd, or neither?

(d) Why is x^2 necessarily a factor of the polynomial?

(e) What is the minimum degree of the polynomial?

(f) Formulate five different polynomial functions whose graphs could look like the one shown. Compare yours to those of other students. What similarities do you see? What differences?

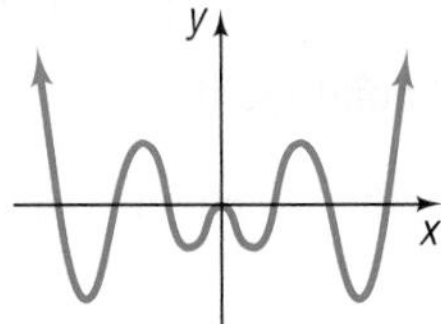

CHAPTER TEST

The Chapter Test Prep Videos are step-by-step test solutions available in the Video Resources DVD, in MyMathLab, or on this text's YouTube Channel. Flip back to the Student Resources page to see the exact web address for this text's YouTube channel.

1. Graph $f(x) = (x-3)^4 - 2$ using transformations.

2. For the polynomial function $g(x) = 2x^3 + 5x^2 - 28x - 15$,

(a) Determine the maximum number of real zeros that the function may have.

(b) Find bounds to the zeros of the function.

(c) List the potential rational zeros.

(d) Determine the real zeros of g. Factor g over the reals.

(e) Find the x- and y-intercepts of the graph of g.

(f) Determine whether the graph crosses or touches the x-axis at each x-intercept.

(g) Find the power function that the graph of g resembles for large values of $|x|$.

(h) Approximate the turning points on the graph of g.

(i) Put all the information together to obtain the graph of g.

3. Find the complex zeros of $f(x) = x^3 - 4x^2 + 25x - 100$.

4. Solve $3x^3 + 2x - 1 = 8x^2 - 4$ in the complex number system.

In Problems 5 and 6, find the domain of each function. Find any horizontal, vertical, or oblique asymptotes.

5. $g(x) = \dfrac{2x^2 - 14x + 24}{x^2 + 6x - 40}$

6. $r(x) = \dfrac{x^2 + 2x - 3}{x + 1}$

7. Sketch the graph of the function in Problem 6. Label all intercepts, vertical asymptotes, horizontal asymptotes, and oblique asymptotes.

In Problems 8 and 9, write a function that meets the given conditions.

8. Fourth-degree polynomial function with real coefficients; zeros: $-2, 0, 3 + i$.

9. Rational function; asymptotes: $y = 2, x = 4$; domain: $\{x | x \neq 4, x \neq 9\}$.

10. Use the Intermediate Value Theorem to show that the function $f(x) = -2x^2 - 3x + 8$ has at least one real zero on the interval $[0, 4]$.

11. Solve: $\dfrac{x + 2}{x - 3} < 2$

CUMULATIVE REVIEW

1. Find the distance between the points $P = (1, 3)$ and $Q = (-4, 2)$.

2. Solve the inequality $x^2 \geq x$ and graph the solution set.

3. Solve the inequality $x^2 - 3x < 4$ and graph the solution set.

4. Find a linear function with slope -3 that contains the point $(-1, 4)$. Graph the function.

5. Find the equation of the line parallel to the line $y = 2x + 1$ and containing the point $(3, 5)$. Express your answer in slope–intercept form and graph the line.

6. Graph the equation $y = x^3$.

7. Does the relation $\{(3, 6), (1, 3), (2, 5), (3, 8)\}$ represent a function? Why or why not?

8. Solve the equation $x^3 - 6x^2 + 8x = 0$.

9. Solve the inequality $3x + 2 \leq 5x - 1$ and graph the solution set.

10. Find the center and radius of the circle $x^2 + 4x + y^2 - 2y - 4 = 0$. Graph the circle.

11. For the equation $y = x^3 - 9x$, determine the intercepts and test for symmetry.

12. Find an equation of the line perpendicular to $3x - 2y = 7$ that contains the point $(1, 5)$.

13. Is the following the graph of a function? Why or why not?

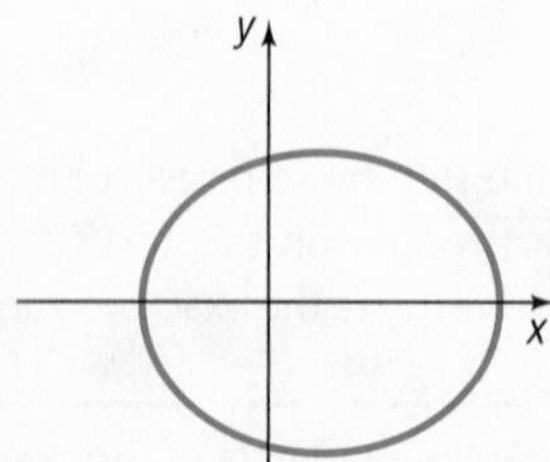

14. For the function $f(x) = x^2 + 5x - 2$, find

(a) $f(3)$ (b) $f(-x)$

(c) $-f(x)$ (d) $f(3x)$

(e) $\dfrac{f(x + h) - f(x)}{h}$ $h \neq 0$

15. Answer the following questions regarding the function

$$f(x) = \frac{x + 5}{x - 1}$$

(a) What is the domain of f?

(b) Is the point $(2, 6)$ on the graph of f?

(c) If $x = 3$, what is $f(x)$? What point is on the graph of f?

(d) If $f(x) = 9$, what is x? What point is on the graph of f?

(e) Is f a polynomial or rational function?

16. Graph the function $f(x) = -3x + 7$.

17. Graph $f(x) = 2x^2 - 4x + 1$ by determining whether its graph opens up or down and by finding its vertex, axis of symmetry, y-intercept, and x-intercepts, if any.

18. Find the average rate of change of $f(x) = x^2 + 3x + 1$ from 1 to 2. Use this result to find the equation of the secant line containing $(1, f(1))$ and $(2, f(2))$.

19. In parts (a) to (f), use the following graph.

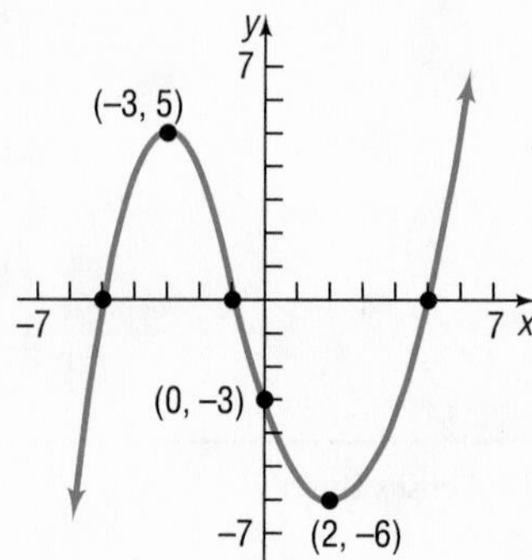

(a) Determine the intercepts.

(b) Based on the graph, tell whether the graph is symmetric with respect to the x-axis, the y-axis, and/or the origin.

(c) Based on the graph, tell whether the function is even, odd, or neither.

(d) List the intervals on which f is increasing. List the intervals on which f is decreasing.

(e) List the numbers, if any, at which f has a local maximum value. What are these local maxima values?

(f) List the numbers, if any, at which f has a local minimum value. What are these local minima values?

20. Determine algebraically whether the function

$$f(x) = \frac{5x}{x^2 - 9}$$

is even, odd, or neither.

21. For the function $f(x) = \begin{cases} 2x + 1 & \text{if } -3 < x < 2 \\ -3x + 4 & \text{if } x \geq 2 \end{cases}$

(a) Find the domain of f.
(b) Locate any intercepts.
(c) Graph the function.
(d) Based on the graph, find the range.

22. Graph the function $f(x) = -3(x + 1)^2 + 5$ using transformations.

23. Suppose that $f(x) = x^2 - 5x + 1$ and $g(x) = -4x - 7$.
(a) Find $f + g$ and state its domain.
(b) Find $\frac{f}{g}$ and state its domain.

24. Demand Equation The price p (in dollars) and the quantity x sold of a certain product obey the demand equation

$$p = -\frac{1}{10}x + 150, \qquad 0 \leq x \leq 1500$$

(a) Express the revenue R as a function of x.
(b) What is the revenue if 100 units are sold?
(c) What quantity x maximizes revenue? What is the maximum revenue?
(d) What price should the company charge to maximize revenue?

CHAPTER PROJECTS

Internet-based Project

I. Length of Day Go to *http://en.wikipedia.org/wiki/Latitude* and read about latitude through the subhead "Effect of Latitude". Now go to *http://www.orchidculture.com/COD/daylength.html*.

1. For a particular day of the year, record in a table the length of day for the equator (0°N), 5°N, 10°N, . . . , 60°N. Enter the data into an Excel spreadsheet, TI graphing calculator, or some other spreadsheet capable of finding linear, quadratic, and cubic functions of best fit.
2. Draw a scatter diagram of the data with latitude as the independent variable and length of day as the dependent variable using Excel, a TI graphing calculator, or some other spreadsheet. The Chapter 10 project describes how to draw a scatter diagram in Excel.
3. Determine the linear function of best fit. Graph the linear function of best fit on the scatter diagram. To do this in Excel, click on any data point in the scatter diagram. Now click the Layout menu, select Trendline within the Analysis region, select More Trendline Options. Select the Linear radio button and select Display Equation on Chart. See Figure 57. Move the Trendline Options window off to the side and you will see the linear function of best fit displayed on the scatter diagram. Do you think the function accurately describes the relation between latitude and length of the day?

Figure 57

Format Trendline
Trendline Options | Line Color | Line Style | Shadow
Trendline Options
Trend/Regression Type
Exponential
Linear
Logarithmic
Polynomial Order: 2
Power
Moving Average Period: 2
Trendline Name
Automatic: Linear (Length)
Custom:
Forecast
Forward: 0.0 periods
Backward: 0.0 periods
Set Intercept = 0.0
Display Equation on chart
Display R-squared value on chart
Close

4. Determine the quadratic function of best fit. Graph the quadratic function of best fit on the scatter diagram. To do this in Excel, click on any data point in the scatter diagram. Now click the Layout menu, select Trendline within the Analysis region, select More Trendline Options. Select the Polynomial radio button with Order set to 2. Select Display Equation on Chart. Move the Trendline Options window off to the side and you will see the quadratic function of best fit displayed on the scatter diagram. Do you think the function accurately describes the relation between latitude and length of the day?

5. Determine the cubic function of best fit. Graph the cubic function of best fit on the scatter diagram. To do this in Excel, click on any data point in the scatter diagram. Now click the Layout menu, select Trendline within the Analysis region, select More Trendline Options. Select the Polynomial radio button with Order set to 3. Select Display Equation on Chart. Move the Trendline Options window off to the side and you will see the cubic function of best fit displayed on the scatter diagram. Do you think the function accurately describes the relation between latitude and length of the day?
6. Which of the three models seems to fit the data best? Explain your reasoning.
7. Use your model to predict the hours of daylight on the day you selected for Chicago (41.85 degrees north latitude). Go to the Old Farmer's Almanac or other website (such as *http://astro.unl.edu/classaction/animations/coordsmotion/daylighthoursexplorer.html*) to determine the hours of daylight in Chicago for the day you selected. How do the two compare?

The following project is available at the Instructor's Resource Center (IRC):

II. **Theory of Equations** The coefficients of a polynomial function can be found if its zeros are known, an advantage of using polynomials in modeling.

Exponential and Logarithmic Functions

Outline

Depreciation of Cars

You are ready to buy that first new car. You know that cars lose value over time due to depreciation and that different cars have different rates of depreciation. So you will research the depreciation rates for the cars you are thinking of buying. After all, the lower the depreciation rate is, the more the car will be worth each year.

—See the Internet-based Chapter Project I— 

A LOOK BACK Until now, our study of functions has concentrated on polynomial and rational functions. These functions belong to the class of **algebraic functions,** that is, functions that can be expressed in terms of sums, differences, products, quotients, powers, or roots of polynomials. Functions that are not algebraic are called **transcendental** (they transcend, or go beyond, algebraic functions).

A LOOK AHEAD In this chapter, we study two transcendental functions: the exponential function and the logarithmic function. These functions occur frequently in a wide variety of applications, such as biology, chemistry, economics, and psychology.

The chapter begins with a discussion of composite, one-to-one, and inverse functions, concepts needed to see the relationship between exponential and logarithmic functions.

12.1 Composite Functions

PREPARING FOR THIS SECTION *Before getting started, review the following:*

- Find the Value of a Function (Section 9.1, pp. 562–565)
- Domain of a Function (Section 9.1, pp. 565–566)

Now Work the **'Are You Prepared?'** problems on page 757.

OBJECTIVES
1 Form a Composite Function (p. 752)
2 Find the Domain of a Composite Function (p. 753)

1 Form a Composite Function

Suppose that an oil tanker is leaking oil and you want to determine the area of the circular oil patch around the ship. See Figure 1. It is determined that the oil is leaking from the tanker in such a way that the radius of the circular patch of oil around the ship is increasing at a rate of 3 feet per minute. Therefore, the radius r of the oil patch at any time t, in minutes, is given by $r(t) = 3t$. So after 20 minutes the radius of the oil patch is $r(20) = 3(20) = 60$ feet.

Figure 1

The area A of a circle as a function of the radius r is given by $A(r) = \pi r^2$. The area of the circular patch of oil after 20 minutes is $A(60) = \pi(60)^2 = 3600\pi$ square feet. Notice that $60 = r(20)$, so $A(60) = A(r(20))$. The argument of the function A is the output a function!

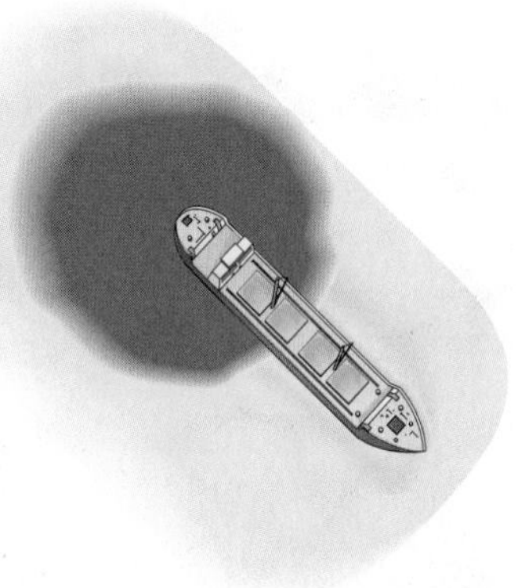

In general, we can find the area of the oil patch as a function of time t by evaluating $A(r(t))$ and obtaining $A(r(t)) = A(3t) = \pi(3t)^2 = 9\pi t^2$. The function $A(r(t))$ is a special type of function called a *composite function.*

As another example, consider the function $y = (2x + 3)^2$. If we write $y = f(u) = u^2$ and $u = g(x) = 2x + 3$, then, by a substitution process, we can obtain the original function: $y = f(u) = f(g(x)) = (2x + 3)^2$.

In general, suppose that f and g are two functions and that x is a number in the domain of g. By evaluating g at x, we get $g(x)$. If $g(x)$ is in the domain of f, then we may evaluate f at $g(x)$ and obtain the expression $f(g(x))$. The correspondence from x to $f(g(x))$ is called a *composite function* $f \circ g$.

DEFINITION

Given two functions f and g, the **composite function,** denoted by $f \circ g$ (read as "f composed with g"), is defined by

$$(f \circ g)(x) = f(g(x))$$

The domain of $f \circ g$ is the set of all numbers x in the domain of g such that $g(x)$ is in the domain of f.

Look carefully at Figure 2. Only those values of x in the domain of g for which $g(x)$ is in the domain of f can be in the domain of $f \circ g$. The reason is that if $g(x)$ is not in the domain of f then $f(g(x))$ is not defined. Because of this, the domain of $f \circ g$ is a subset of the domain of g; the range of $f \circ g$ is a subset of the range of f.

Figure 2

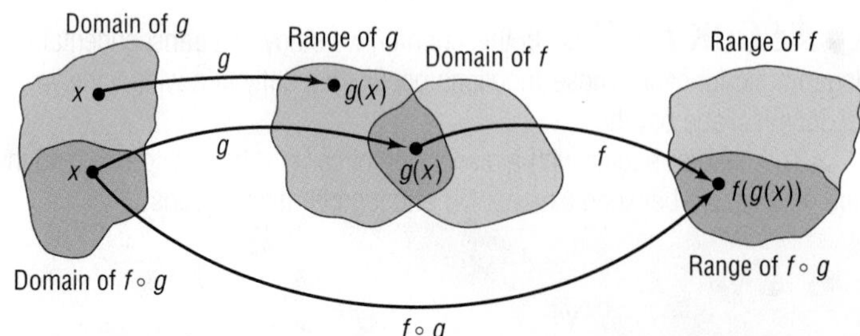

Figure 3 provides a second illustration of the definition. Here x is the input to the function g, yielding $g(x)$. Then $g(x)$ is the input to the function f, yielding $f(g(x))$. Notice that the "inside" function g in $f(g(x))$ is done first.

Figure 3

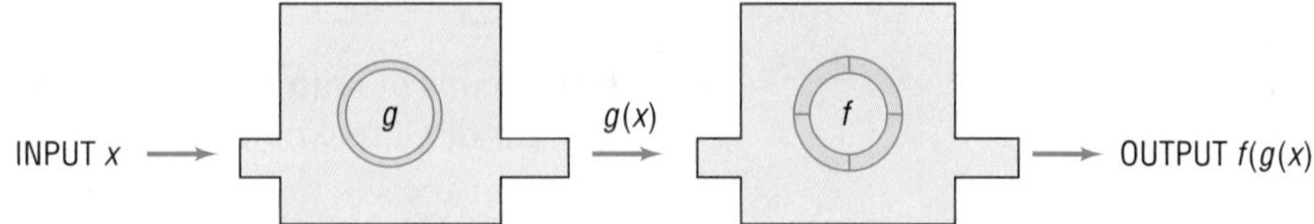

EXAMPLE 1 **Evaluating a Composite Function**

Suppose that $f(x) = 2x^2 - 3$ and $g(x) = 4x$. Find:

(a) $(f \circ g)(1)$ (b) $(g \circ f)(1)$ (c) $(f \circ f)(-2)$ (d) $(g \circ g)(-1)$

Solution (a) $(f \circ g)(1) = f(g(1)) = f(4) = 2 \cdot 4^2 - 3 = 29$

$\uparrow$ $g(x) = 4x$, $g(1) = 4$; $\uparrow$ $f(x) = 2x^2 - 3$

(b) $(g \circ f)(1) = g(f(1)) = g(-1) = 4 \cdot (-1) = -4$

$\uparrow$ $f(x) = 2x^2 - 3$, $f(1) = -1$; $\uparrow$ $g(x) = 4x$

(c) $(f \circ f)(-2) = f(f(-2)) = f(5) = 2 \cdot 5^2 - 3 = 47$

$\uparrow$ $f(-2) = 2(-2)^2 - 3 = 5$

(d) $(g \circ g)(-1) = g(g(-1)) = g(-4) = 4 \cdot (-4) = -16$

$\uparrow$ $g(-1) = -4$

■

Figure 4

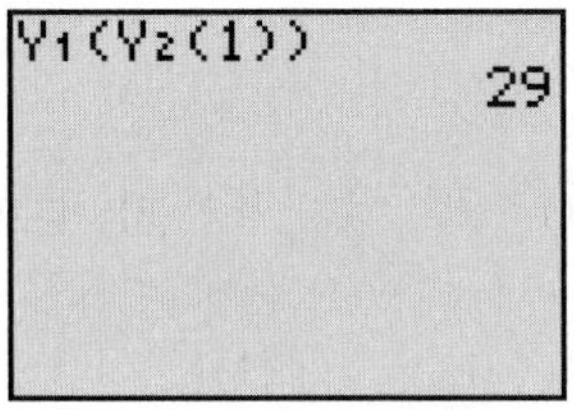

Y1(Y2(1))
29

COMMENT Graphing calculators can be used to evaluate composite functions.* Let $Y_1 = f(x) = 2x^2 - 3$ and $Y_2 = g(x) = 4x$. Then, using a TI-84 Plus graphing calculator, $(f \circ g)(1)$ is found as shown in Figure 4. Notice that this is the result obtained in Example 1(a). ■

Now Work PROBLEM 11

2 Find the Domain of a Composite Function

EXAMPLE 2 **Finding a Composite Function and Its Domain**

Suppose that $f(x) = x^2 + 3x - 1$ and $g(x) = 2x + 3$.

Find: (a) $f \circ g$ (b) $g \circ f$

Then find the domain of each composite function.

Solution The domain of f and the domain of g are the set of all real numbers.

(a) $(f \circ g)(x) = f(g(x)) = f(2x + 3) = (2x + 3)^2 + 3(2x + 3) - 1$

$\uparrow$ $f(x) = x^2 + 3x - 1$

$= 4x^2 + 12x + 9 + 6x + 9 - 1 = 4x^2 + 18x + 17$

Since the domains of both f and g are the set of all real numbers, the domain of $f \circ g$ is the set of all real numbers.

*Consult your owner's manual for the appropriate keystrokes.

(b) $(g \circ f)(x) = g(f(x)) = g(x^2 + 3x - 1) = 2(x^2 + 3x - 1) + 3$

$\uparrow$ $g(x) = 2x + 3$

$= 2x^2 + 6x - 2 + 3 = 2x^2 + 6x + 1$

Since the domains of both f and g are the set of all real numbers, the domain of $g \circ f$ is the set of all real numbers. ■

Look back at Figure 2 on page 752. In determining the domain of the composite function $(f \circ g)(x) = f(g(x))$, keep the following two thoughts in mind about the input x.

1. Any x not in the domain of g must be excluded.
2. Any x for which $g(x)$ is not in the domain of f must be excluded.

EXAMPLE 3 Finding the Domain of $f \circ g$

Find the domain of $f \circ g$ if $f(x) = \dfrac{1}{x + 2}$ and $g(x) = \dfrac{4}{x - 1}$.

Solution For $(f \circ g)(x) = f(g(x))$, first note that the domain of g is $\{x | x \neq 1\}$, so exclude 1 from the domain of $f \circ g$. Next note that the domain of f is $\{x | x \neq -2\}$, which means that $g(x)$ cannot equal -2. Solve the equation $g(x) = -2$ to determine what additional value(s) of x to exclude.

$$\begin{aligned} \frac{4}{x-1} &= -2 && g(x) = -2 \\ 4 &= -2(x - 1) \\ 4 &= -2x + 2 \\ 2x &= -2 \\ x &= -1 \end{aligned}$$

Also exclude -1 from the domain of $f \circ g$.
The domain of $f \circ g$ is $\{x | x \neq -1, x \neq 1\}$.

✓**Check:** For $x = 1$, $g(x) = \dfrac{4}{x - 1}$ is not defined, so $(f \circ g)(x) = f(g(x))$ is not defined.

For $x = -1$, $g(-1) = \dfrac{4}{-2} = -2$, and $(f \circ g)(-1) = f(g(-1)) = f(-2)$ is not defined. ■

Now Work PROBLEM 21

EXAMPLE 4 Finding a Composite Function and Its Domain

Suppose that $f(x) = \dfrac{1}{x + 2}$ and $g(x) = \dfrac{4}{x - 1}$.

Find: (a) $f \circ g$ (b) $f \circ f$

Then find the domain of each composite function.

Solution The domain of f is $\{x | x \neq -2\}$ and the domain of g is $\{x | x \neq 1\}$.

(a) $$(f \circ g)(x) = f(g(x)) = f\left(\frac{4}{x-1}\right) = \frac{1}{\dfrac{4}{x-1} + 2} = \frac{x-1}{4 + 2(x-1)} = \frac{x-1}{2x+2} = \frac{x-1}{2(x+1)}$$

$\uparrow$ $f(x) = \dfrac{1}{x+2}$ $\quad\uparrow$ Multiply by $\dfrac{x-1}{x-1}$.

In Example 3, we found the domain of $f \circ g$ to be $\{x | x \neq -1, x \neq 1\}$.

We could also find the domain of $f \circ g$ by first looking at the domain of g: $\{x \mid x \neq 1\}$. We exclude 1 from the domain of $f \circ g$ as a result. Then we look at $f \circ g$ and notice that x cannot equal -1, since $x = -1$ results in division by 0. So we also exclude -1 from the domain of $f \circ g$. Therefore, the domain of $f \circ g$ is $\{x \mid x \neq -1, x \neq 1\}$.

(b) $$(f \circ f)(x) = f(f(x)) = f\left(\frac{1}{x+2}\right) \underset{\substack{\uparrow \\ f(x) = \frac{1}{x+2}}}{=} \frac{1}{\frac{1}{x+2} + 2} \underset{\substack{\uparrow \\ \text{Multiply by } \frac{x+2}{x+2}.}}{=} \frac{x+2}{1 + 2(x+2)} = \frac{x+2}{2x+5}$$

The domain of $f \circ f$ consists of those x in the domain of f, $\{x \mid x \neq -2\}$, for which

$$f(x) = \frac{1}{x+2} \neq -2 \qquad \begin{aligned} \frac{1}{x+2} &= -2 \\ 1 &= -2(x+2) \\ 1 &= -2x - 4 \\ 2x &= -5 \\ x &= -\frac{5}{2} \end{aligned}$$

or, equivalently,

$$x \neq -\frac{5}{2}$$

The domain of $f \circ f$ is $\left\{x \,\middle|\, x \neq -\frac{5}{2}, x \neq -2\right\}$.

We could also find the domain of $f \circ f$ by recognizing that -2 is not in the domain of f and so should be excluded from the domain of $f \circ f$. Then, looking at $f \circ f$, we see that x cannot equal $-\frac{5}{2}$. Do you see why? Therefore, the domain of $f \circ f$ is $\left\{x \,\middle|\, x \neq -\frac{5}{2}, x \neq -2\right\}$. ■

Now Work PROBLEMS 33 AND 35

Look back at Example 2, which illustrates that, in general, $f \circ g \neq g \circ f$. Sometimes $f \circ g$ does equal $g \circ f$, as shown in the next example.

EXAMPLE 5 Showing That Two Composite Functions Are Equal

If $f(x) = 3x - 4$ and $g(x) = \frac{1}{3}(x + 4)$, show that

$$(f \circ g)(x) = (g \circ f)(x) = x$$

for every x in the domain of $f \circ g$ and $g \circ f$.

Solution

$$\begin{aligned} (f \circ g)(x) &= f(g(x)) \\ &= f\left(\frac{x+4}{3}\right) && g(x) = \frac{1}{3}(x+4) = \frac{x+4}{3} \\ &= 3\left(\frac{x+4}{3}\right) - 4 && \text{Substitute } g(x) \text{ into the rule for } f,\ f(x) = 3x - 4. \\ &= x + 4 - 4 = x \end{aligned}$$

Seeing the Concept
Using a graphing calculator, let

$Y_1 = f(x) = 3x - 4$

$Y_2 = g(x) = \frac{1}{3}(x + 4)$

$Y_3 = f \circ g, Y_4 = g \circ f$

Using the viewing window $-3 \le x \le 3$, $-2 \le y \le 2$, graph only Y_3 and Y_4. What do you see? TRACE to verify that $Y_3 = Y_4$.

$$\begin{aligned}(g \circ f)(x) &= g(f(x))\\ &= g(3x - 4) && f(x) = 3x - 4\\ &= \frac{1}{3}[(3x - 4) + 4] && \text{Substitute } f(x) \text{ into the rule for } g, g(x) = \frac{1}{3}(x + 4).\\ &= \frac{1}{3}(3x) = x\end{aligned}$$

We conclude that $(f \circ g)(x) = (g \circ f)(x) = x$. 

In Section 12.2, we shall see that there is an important relationship between functions f and g for which $(f \circ g)(x) = (g \circ f)(x) = x$.

Now Work PROBLEM 45

Calculus Application

Some techniques in calculus require that we be able to determine the components of a composite function. For example, the function $H(x) = \sqrt{x + 1}$ is the composition of the functions f and g, where $f(x) = \sqrt{x}$ and $g(x) = x + 1$, because $H(x) = (f \circ g)(x) = f(g(x)) = f(x + 1) = \sqrt{x + 1}$.

EXAMPLE 6 Finding the Components of a Composite Function

Find functions f and g such that $f \circ g = H$ if $H(x) = (x^2 + 1)^{50}$.

Solution The function H takes $x^2 + 1$ and raises it to the power 50. A natural way to decompose H is to raise the function $g(x) = x^2 + 1$ to the power 50. If we let $f(x) = x^{50}$ and $g(x) = x^2 + 1$, then

$$\begin{aligned}(f \circ g)(x) &= f(g(x))\\ &= f(x^2 + 1)\\ &= (x^2 + 1)^{50} = H(x)\end{aligned}$$

Figure 5

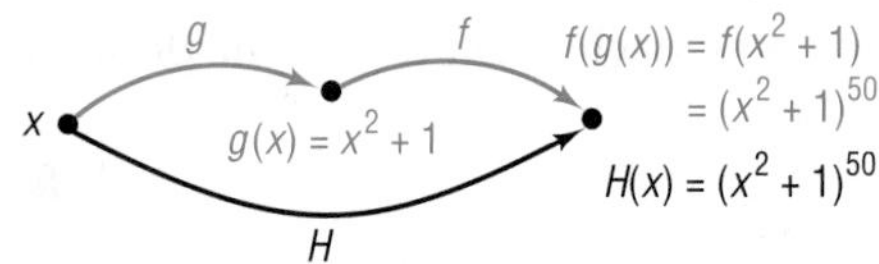

See Figure 5.

Other functions f and g may be found for which $f \circ g = H$ in Example 6. For example, if $f(x) = x^2$ and $g(x) = (x^2 + 1)^{25}$, then

$$(f \circ g)(x) = f(g(x)) = f((x^2 + 1)^{25}) = [(x^2 + 1)^{25}]^2 = (x^2 + 1)^{50}$$

Although the functions f and g found as a solution to Example 6 are not unique, there is usually a "natural" selection for f and g that comes to mind first.

EXAMPLE 7 Finding the Components of a Composite Function

Find functions f and g such that $f \circ g = H$ if $H(x) = \frac{1}{x + 1}$.

Solution Here H is the reciprocal of $g(x) = x + 1$. If we let $f(x) = \frac{1}{x}$ and $g(x) = x + 1$, we find that

$$(f \circ g)(x) = f(g(x)) = f(x + 1) = \frac{1}{x + 1} = H(x)$$

Now Work PROBLEM 53

12.1 Assess Your Understanding

'Are You Prepared?' *Answers are given at the end of these exercises. If you get a wrong answer, read the pages listed in red.*

1. Find $f(3)$ if $f(x) = -4x^2 + 5x$. (pp. 562–565)

2. Find $f(3x)$ if $f(x) = 4 - 2x^2$. (pp. 562–565)

3. Find the domain of the function $f(x) = \dfrac{x^2 - 1}{x^2 - 25}$. (pp. 565–566)

Concepts and Vocabulary

4. Given two functions f and g, the ________ ________, denoted $f \circ g$, is defined by $(f \circ g)(x) =$ ________.

5. ***True or False*** $f(g(x)) = f(x) \cdot g(x)$.

6. ***True or False*** The domain of the composite function $(f \circ g)(x)$ is the same as the domain of $g(x)$.

Skill Building

In Problems 7 and 8, evaluate each expression using the values given in the table.

7.

x	−3	−2	−1	0	1	2	3
$f(x)$	−7	−5	−3	−1	3	5	7
$g(x)$	8	3	0	−1	0	3	8

(a) $(f \circ g)(1)$ (b) $(f \circ g)(-1)$
(c) $(g \circ f)(-1)$ (d) $(g \circ f)(0)$
(e) $(g \circ g)(-2)$ (f) $(f \circ f)(-1)$

8.

x	−3	−2	−1	0	1	2	3
$f(x)$	11	9	7	5	3	1	−1
$g(x)$	−8	−3	0	1	0	−3	−8

(a) $(f \circ g)(1)$ (b) $(f \circ g)(2)$
(c) $(g \circ f)(2)$ (d) $(g \circ f)(3)$
(e) $(g \circ g)(1)$ (f) $(f \circ f)(3)$

In Problems 9 and 10, evaluate each expression using the graphs of $y = f(x)$ and $y = g(x)$ shown in the figure.

9. (a) $(g \circ f)(-1)$ (b) $(g \circ f)(0)$
(c) $(f \circ g)(-1)$ (d) $(f \circ g)(4)$

10. (a) $(g \circ f)(1)$ (b) $(g \circ f)(5)$
(c) $(f \circ g)(0)$ (d) $(f \circ g)(2)$

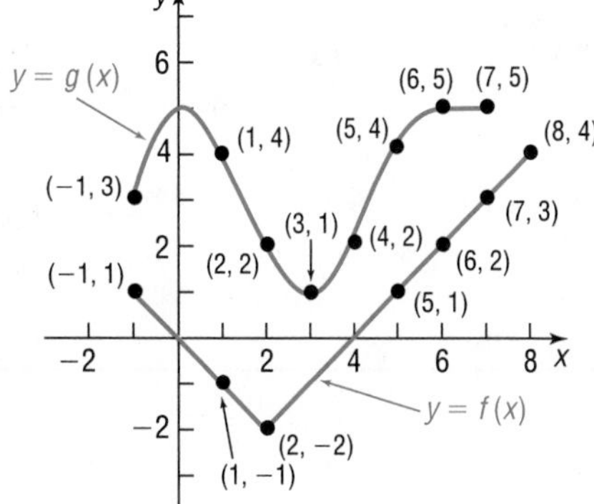

In Problems 11–20, for the given functions f and g, find:

(a) $(f \circ g)(4)$ *(b)* $(g \circ f)(2)$ *(c)* $(f \circ f)(1)$ *(d)* $(g \circ g)(0)$

11. $f(x) = 2x$; $g(x) = 3x^2 + 1$

12. $f(x) = 3x + 2$; $g(x) = 2x^2 - 1$

13. $f(x) = 4x^2 - 3$; $g(x) = 3 - \frac{1}{2}x^2$

14. $f(x) = 2x^2$; $g(x) = 1 - 3x^2$

15. $f(x) = \sqrt{x}$; $g(x) = 2x$

16. $f(x) = \sqrt{x + 1}$; $g(x) = 3x$

17. $f(x) = |x|$; $g(x) = \dfrac{1}{x^2 + 1}$

18. $f(x) = |x - 2|$; $g(x) = \dfrac{3}{x^2 + 2}$

19. $f(x) = \dfrac{3}{x + 1}$; $g(x) = \sqrt[3]{x}$

20. $f(x) = x^{3/2}$; $g(x) = \dfrac{2}{x + 1}$

In Problems 21–28, find the domain of the composite function $f \circ g$.

21. $f(x) = \dfrac{3}{x - 1}$; $g(x) = \dfrac{2}{x}$

22. $f(x) = \dfrac{1}{x + 3}$; $g(x) = -\dfrac{2}{x}$

23. $f(x) = \dfrac{x}{x-1}$; $g(x) = -\dfrac{4}{x}$

24. $f(x) = \dfrac{x}{x+3}$; $g(x) = \dfrac{2}{x}$

25. $f(x) = \sqrt{x}$; $g(x) = 2x + 3$

26. $f(x) = x - 2$; $g(x) = \sqrt{1 - x}$

27. $f(x) = x^2 + 1$; $g(x) = \sqrt{x - 1}$

28. $f(x) = x^2 + 4$; $g(x) = \sqrt{x - 2}$

In Problems 29–44, for the given functions f and g, find:
(a) $f \circ g$ *(b)* $g \circ f$ *(c)* $f \circ f$ *(d)* $g \circ g$

State the domain of each composite function.

29. $f(x) = 2x + 3$; $g(x) = 3x$

30. $f(x) = -x$; $g(x) = 2x - 4$

31. $f(x) = 3x + 1$; $g(x) = x^2$

32. $f(x) = x + 1$; $g(x) = x^2 + 4$

33. $f(x) = x^2$; $g(x) = x^2 + 4$

34. $f(x) = x^2 + 1$; $g(x) = 2x^2 + 3$

35. $f(x) = \dfrac{3}{x-1}$; $g(x) = \dfrac{2}{x}$

36. $f(x) = \dfrac{1}{x+3}$; $g(x) = -\dfrac{2}{x}$

37. $f(x) = \dfrac{x}{x-1}$; $g(x) = -\dfrac{4}{x}$

38. $f(x) = \dfrac{x}{x+3}$; $g(x) = \dfrac{2}{x}$

39. $f(x) = \sqrt{x}$; $g(x) = 2x + 3$

40. $f(x) = \sqrt{x - 2}$; $g(x) = 1 - 2x$

41. $f(x) = x^2 + 1$; $g(x) = \sqrt{x - 1}$

42. $f(x) = x^2 + 4$; $g(x) = \sqrt{x - 2}$

43. $f(x) = \dfrac{x-5}{x+1}$; $g(x) = \dfrac{x+2}{x-3}$

44. $f(x) = \dfrac{2x-1}{x-2}$; $g(x) = \dfrac{x+4}{2x-5}$

In Problems 45–52, show that $(f \circ g)(x) = (g \circ f)(x) = x$.

45. $f(x) = 2x$; $g(x) = \dfrac{1}{2}x$

46. $f(x) = 4x$; $g(x) = \dfrac{1}{4}x$

47. $f(x) = x^3$; $g(x) = \sqrt[3]{x}$

48. $f(x) = x + 5$; $g(x) = x - 5$

49. $f(x) = 2x - 6$; $g(x) = \dfrac{1}{2}(x + 6)$

50. $f(x) = 4 - 3x$; $g(x) = \dfrac{1}{3}(4 - x)$

51. $f(x) = ax + b$; $g(x) = \dfrac{1}{a}(x - b)$ $a \neq 0$

52. $f(x) = \dfrac{1}{x}$; $g(x) = \dfrac{1}{x}$

In Problems 53–58, find functions f and g so that $f \circ g = H$.

53. $H(x) = (2x + 3)^4$

54. $H(x) = (1 + x^2)^3$

55. $H(x) = \sqrt{x^2 + 1}$

56. $H(x) = \sqrt{1 - x^2}$

57. $H(x) = |2x + 1|$

58. $H(x) = |2x^2 + 3|$

Applications and Extensions

59. If $f(x) = 2x^3 - 3x^2 + 4x - 1$ and $g(x) = 2$, find $(f \circ g)(x)$ and $(g \circ f)(x)$.

60. If $f(x) = \dfrac{x+1}{x-1}$, find $(f \circ f)(x)$.

61. If $f(x) = 2x^2 + 5$ and $g(x) = 3x + a$, find a so that the graph of $f \circ g$ crosses the y-axis at 23.

62. If $f(x) = 3x^2 - 7$ and $g(x) = 2x + a$, find a so that the graph of $f \circ g$ crosses the y-axis at 68.

In Problems 63 and 64, use the functions f and g to find:
(a) $f \circ g$ *(b)* $g \circ f$
(c) the domain of $f \circ g$ *and of* $g \circ f$
(d) the conditions for which $f \circ g = g \circ f$

63. $f(x) = ax + b$; $g(x) = cx + d$

64. $f(x) = \dfrac{ax+b}{cx+d}$; $g(x) = mx$

65. Surface Area of a Balloon The surface area S (in square meters) of a hot-air balloon is given by

$$S(r) = 4\pi r^2$$

where r is the radius of the balloon (in meters). If the radius r is increasing with time t (in seconds) according to the formula $r(t) = \frac{2}{3}t^3$, $t \geq 0$, find the surface area S of the balloon as a function of the time t.

66. Volume of a Balloon The volume V (in cubic meters) of the hot-air balloon described in Problem 65 is given by $V(r) = \frac{4}{3}\pi r^3$. If the radius r is the same function of t as in Problem 65, find the volume V as a function of the time t.

67. Automobile Production The number N of cars produced at a certain factory in one day after t hours of operation is given by $N(t) = 100t - 5t^2$, $0 \leq t \leq 10$. If the cost C (in dollars) of producing N cars is $C(N) = 15{,}000 + 8000N$, find the cost C as a function of the time t of operation of the factory.

68. Environmental Concerns The spread of oil leaking from a tanker is in the shape of a circle. If the radius r (in feet) of the spread after t hours is $r(t) = 200\sqrt{t}$, find the area A of the oil slick as a function of the time t.

69. Production Cost The price p, in dollars, of a certain product and the quantity x sold obey the demand equation

$$p = -\frac{1}{4}x + 100 \quad 0 \le x \le 400$$

Suppose that the cost C, in dollars, of producing x units is

$$C = \frac{\sqrt{x}}{25} + 600$$

Assuming that all items produced are sold, find the cost C as a function of the price p.

[**Hint:** Solve for x in the demand equation and then form the composite.]

70. Cost of a Commodity The price p, in dollars, of a certain commodity and the quantity x sold obey the demand equation

$$p = -\frac{1}{5}x + 200 \quad 0 \le x \le 1000$$

Suppose that the cost C, in dollars, of producing x units is

$$C = \frac{\sqrt{x}}{10} + 400$$

Assuming that all items produced are sold, find the cost C as a function of the price p.

71. Volume of a Cylinder The volume V of a right circular cylinder of height h and radius r is $V = \pi r^2 h$. If the height is twice the radius, express the volume V as a function of r.

72. Volume of a Cone The volume V of a right circular cone is $V = \frac{1}{3}\pi r^2 h$. If the height is twice the radius, express the volume V as a function of r.

73. Foreign Exchange Traders often buy foreign currency in hope of making money when the currency's value changes. For example, on March 22, 2011, one U.S. dollar could purchase 0.7045 Euros, and one Euro could purchase 114.9278 yen. Let $f(x)$ represent the number of Euros you can buy with x dollars, and let $g(x)$ represent the number of yen you can buy with x Euros.

(a) Find a function that relates dollars to Euros.

(b) Find a function that relates Euros to yen.

(c) Use the results of parts (a) and (b) to find a function that relates dollars to yen. That is, find $(g \circ f)(x) = g(f(x))$.

(d) What is $g(f(1000))$? Interpret this result.

74. Temperature Conversion The function $C(F) = \frac{5}{9}(F - 32)$ converts a temperature in degrees Fahrenheit, F, to a temperature in degrees Celsius, C. The function $K(C) = C + 273$ converts a temperature in degrees Celsius to a temperature in kelvins, K.

(a) Find a function that converts a temperature in degrees Fahrenheit to a temperature in kelvins.

(b) Determine 80 degrees Fahrenheit in kelvins.

75. Discounts The manufacturer of a computer is offering two discounts on last year's model computer. The first discount is a \$200 rebate and the second discount is 20% off the regular price, p.

(a) Write a function f that represents the sale price if only the rebate applies.

(b) Write a function g that represents the sale price if only the 20% discount applies.

(c) Find $f \circ g$ and $g \circ f$. What does each of these functions represent? Which combination of discounts represents a better deal for the consumer? Why?

76. If f and g are odd functions, show that the composite function $f \circ g$ is also odd.

77. If f is an odd function and g is an even function, show that the composite functions $f \circ g$ and $g \circ f$ are both even.

'Are You Prepared?' Answers

1. -21 **2.** $4 - 18x^2$ **3.** $\{x \mid x \neq -5, x \neq 5\}$

12.2 One-to-One Functions; Inverse Functions

PREPARING FOR THIS SECTION *Before getting started, review the following:*

- Functions (Section 9.1, pp. 559–569)
- Increasing/Decreasing Functions (Section 9.3, pp. 584–585)

Now Work the **'Are You Prepared?'** problems on page 768.

OBJECTIVES
1. Determine Whether a Function Is One-to-One (p. 760)
2. Determine the Inverse of a Function Defined by a Map or a Set of Ordered Pairs (p. 762)
3. Obtain the Graph of the Inverse Function from the Graph of the Function (p. 764)
4. Find the Inverse of a Function Defined by an Equation (p. 765)

1 Determine Whether a Function Is One-to-One

In Section 9.1, we presented four different ways to represent a function: (1) a map, (2) a set of ordered pairs, (3) a graph, and (4) an equation. For example, Figures 6 and 7 illustrate two different functions represented as mappings. The function in Figure 6 shows the correspondence between states and their population (in millions). The function in Figure 7 shows a correspondence between animals and life expectancy (in years).

Figure 6

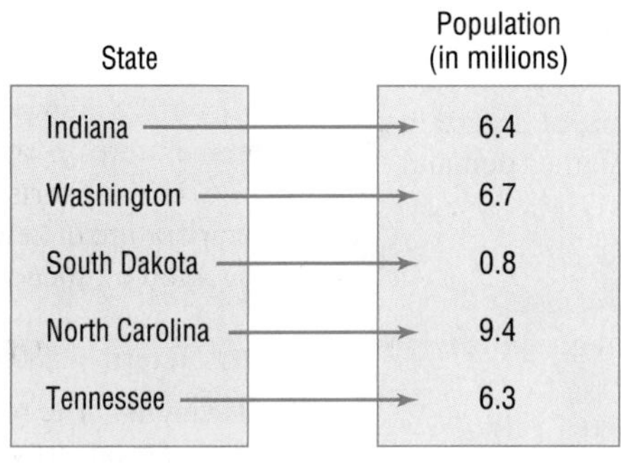

Figure 7

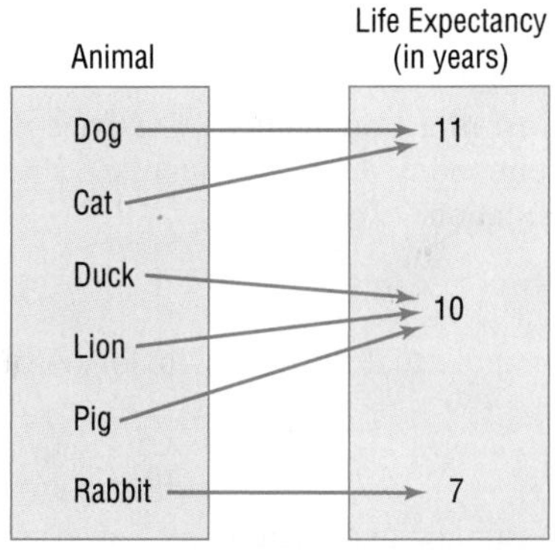

Suppose we asked a group of people to name the state that has a population of 0.8 million based on the function in Figure 6. Everyone in the group would respond South Dakota. Now, if we asked the same group of people to name the animal whose life expectancy is 11 years based on the function in Figure 7, some would respond dog, while others would respond cat. What is the difference between the functions in Figures 6 and 7? In Figure 6, we can see that no two elements in the domain correspond to the same element in the range. In Figure 7, this is not the case: two different elements in the domain correspond to the same element in the range. Functions such as the one in Figure 6 are given a special name.

DEFINITION

A function is **one-to-one** if any two different inputs in the domain correspond to two different outputs in the range. That is, if x_1 and x_2 are two different inputs of a function f, then f is one-to-one if $f(x_1) \neq f(x_2)$.

In Words
A function is not one-to-one if two different inputs correspond to the same output.

Put another way, a function f is one-to-one if no y in the range is the image of more than one x in the domain. A function is not one-to-one if two different elements in the domain correspond to the same element in the range. So the function in Figure 7 is not one-to-one because two different elements in the domain, *dog* and *cat*, both correspond to 11. Figure 8 illustrates the distinction among one-to-one functions, functions that are not one-to-one, and relations that are not functions.

Figure 8

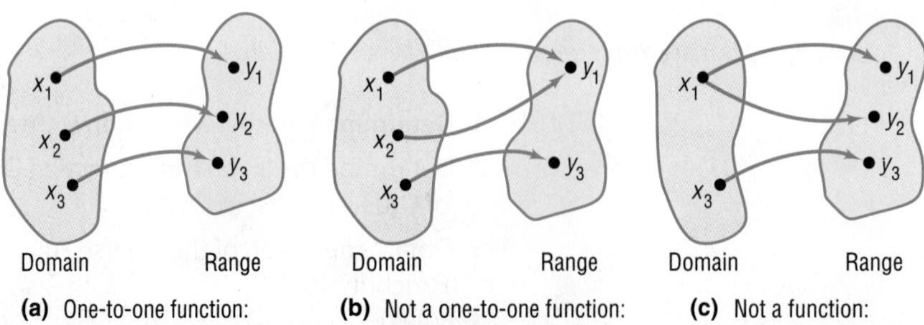

(a) One-to-one function: Each x in the domain has one and only one image in the range.

(b) Not a one-to-one function: y_1 is the image of both x_1 and x_2.

(c) Not a function: x_1 has two images, y_1 and y_2.

EXAMPLE 1 Determining Whether a Function Is One-to-One

Determine whether the following functions are one-to-one.

(a) For the following function, the domain represents the age of five males and the range represents their HDL (good) cholesterol (mg/dL).

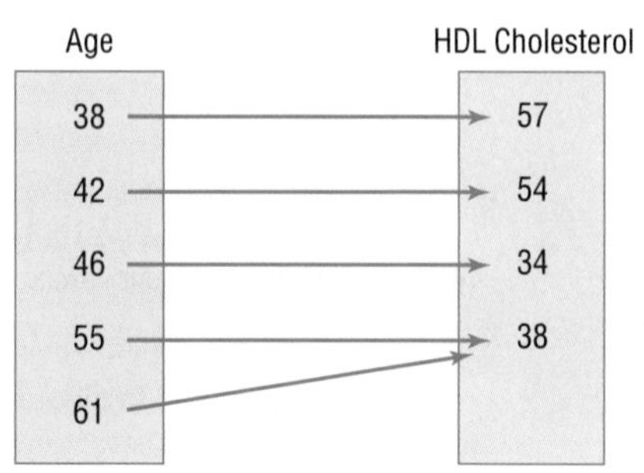

(b) $\{(-2, 6), (-1, 3), (0, 2), (1, 5), (2, 8)\}$

Solution (a) The function is not one-to-one because there are two different inputs, 55 and 61, that correspond to the same output, 38.

(b) The function is one-to-one because there are no two distinct inputs that correspond to the same output. ■

Now Work PROBLEMS 11 AND 15

For functions defined by an equation $y = f(x)$ and for which the graph of f is known, there is a simple test, called the **horizontal-line test,** to determine whether f is one-to-one.

THEOREM

Horizontal-line Test

If every horizontal line intersects the graph of a function f in at most one point, then f is one-to-one.

Figure 9
$f(x_1) = f(x_2) = h$ and $x_1 \neq x_2$; f is not a one-to-one function.

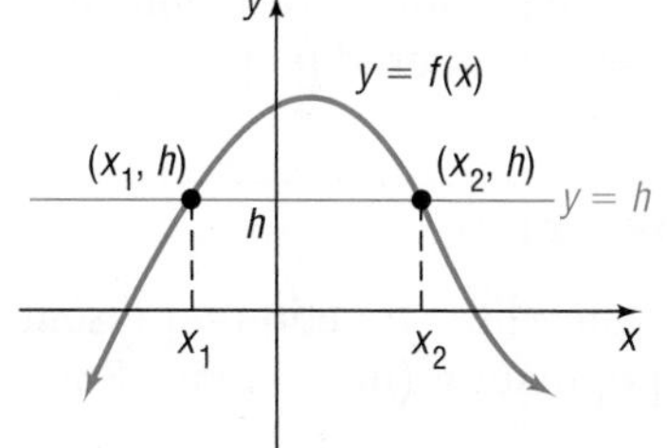

The reason that this test works can be seen in Figure 9, where the horizontal line $y = h$ intersects the graph at two distinct points, (x_1, h) and (x_2, h). Since h is the image of both x_1 and x_2 and $x_1 \neq x_2$, f is not one-to-one. Based on Figure 9, we can state the horizontal-line test in another way: If the graph of any horizontal line intersects the graph of a function f at more than one point, then f is not one-to-one.

EXAMPLE 2 Using the Horizontal-line Test

For each function, use its graph to determine whether the function is one-to-one.

(a) $f(x) = x^2$ (b) $g(x) = x^3$

Solution (a) Figure 10(a) illustrates the horizontal-line test for $f(x) = x^2$. The horizontal line $y = 1$ intersects the graph of f twice, at $(1, 1)$ and at $(-1, 1)$, so f is not one-to-one.

(b) Figure 10(b) illustrates the horizontal-line test for $g(x) = x^3$. Because every horizontal line intersects the graph of g exactly once, it follows that g is one-to-one.

Figure 10

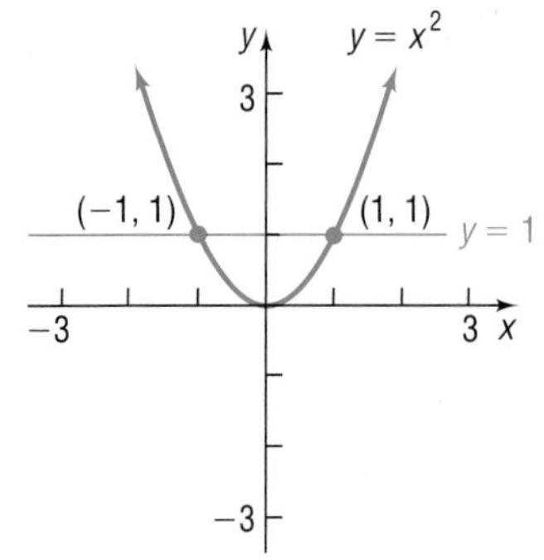

(a) A horizontal line intersects the graph twice; f is not one-to-one

(b) Every horizontal line intersects the graph exactly once; g is one-to-one

Now Work PROBLEM 19

Look more closely at the one-to-one function $g(x) = x^3$. This function is an increasing function. Because an increasing (or decreasing) function will always have different y-values for unequal x-values, it follows that a function that is increasing (or decreasing) over its domain is also a one-to-one function.

THEOREM

A function that is increasing on an interval I is a one-to-one function on I.
A function that is decreasing on an interval I is a one-to-one function on I.

2 Determine the Inverse of a Function Defined by a Map or a Set of Ordered Pairs

DEFINITION

Suppose that f is a one-to-one function. Then, to each x in the domain of f, there is exactly one y in the range (because f is a function); and to each y in the range of f, there is exactly one x in the domain (because f is one-to-one). The correspondence from the range of f back to the domain of f is called the **inverse function of *f*.** The symbol f^{-1} is used to denote the inverse of f.

In Words

Suppose that we have a one-to-one function f where the input 5 corresponds to the output 10. In the inverse function f^{-1}, the input 10 would correspond to the output 5.

We will discuss how to find inverses for all four representations of functions: (1) maps, (2) sets of ordered pairs, (3) graphs, and (4) equations. We begin with finding inverses of functions represented by maps or sets of ordered pairs.

EXAMPLE 3 **Finding the Inverse of a Function Defined by a Map**

Find the inverse of the following function. Let the domain of the function represent certain states, and let the range represent the state's population (in millions). State the domain and the range of the inverse function.

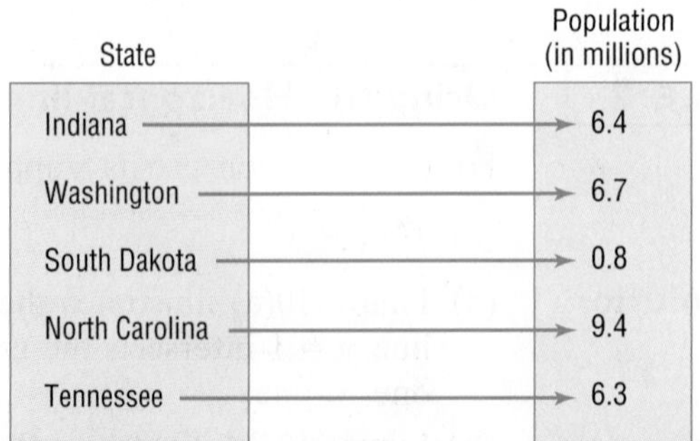

Solution The function is one-to-one. To find the inverse function, we interchange the elements in the domain with the elements in the range. For example, the function receives as

input Indiana and outputs 6.4 million. So the inverse receives as input 6.4 million and outputs Indiana. The inverse function is shown next.

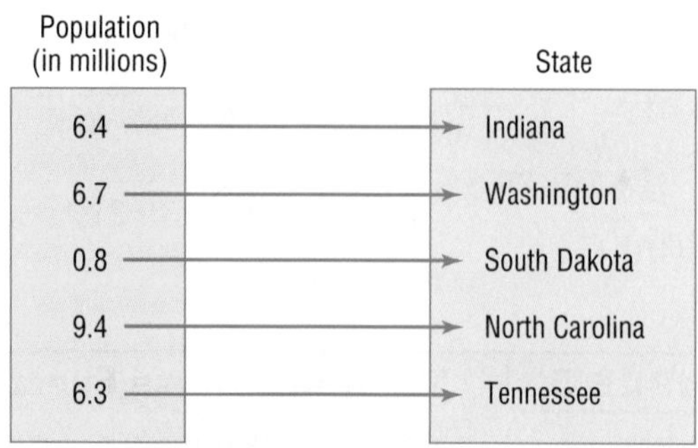

The domain of the inverse function is {6.4, 6.7, 0.8, 9.4, 6.3}. The range of the inverse function is {Indiana, Washington, South Dakota, North Carolina, Tennessee}. ■

If the function f is a set of ordered pairs (x, y), then the inverse of f, denoted f^{-1}, is the set of ordered pairs (y, x).

EXAMPLE 4 **Finding the Inverse of a Function Defined by a Set of Ordered Pairs**

Find the inverse of the following one-to-one function:

$$\{(-3, -27), (-2, -8), (-1, -1), (0, 0), (1, 1), (2, 8), (3, 27)\}$$

State the domain and the range of the function and its inverse.

Solution The inverse of the given function is found by interchanging the entries in each ordered pair and so is given by

$$\{(-27, -3), (-8, -2), (-1, -1), (0, 0), (1, 1), (8, 2), (27, 3)\}$$

The domain of the function is $\{-3, -2, -1, 0, 1, 2, 3\}$. The range of the function is $\{-27, -8, -1, 0, 1, 8, 27\}$. The domain of the inverse function is $\{-27, -8, -1, 0, 1, 8, 27\}$. The range of the inverse function is $\{-3, -2, -1, 0, 1, 2, 3\}$. ■

Now Work PROBLEMS 25 AND 29

Remember, if f is a one-to-one function, it has an inverse function, f^{-1}. See Figure 11.

The results of Example 4 and Figure 11 suggest two facts about a one-to-one function f and its inverse f^{-1}.

Figure 11

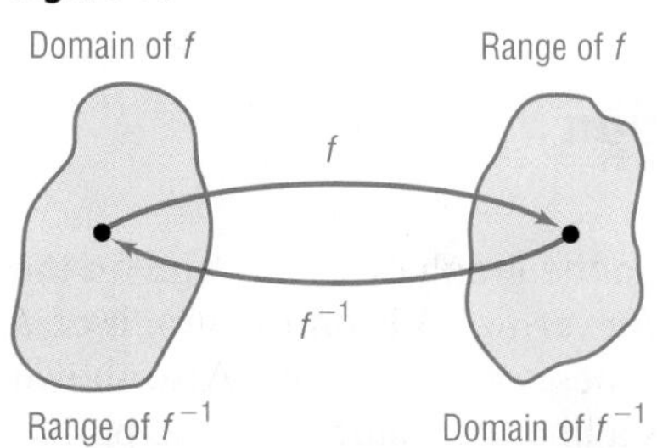

WARNING Be careful! f^{-1} is a symbol for the inverse function of f. The -1 used in f^{-1} is not an exponent. That is, f^{-1} does not mean the reciprocal of f; $f^{-1}(x)$ is not equal to $\dfrac{1}{f(x)}$. ■

Domain of f = Range of f^{-1} Range of f = Domain of f^{-1}

Look again at Figure 11 to visualize the relationship. If we start with x, apply f, and then apply f^{-1}, we get x back again. If we start with x, apply f^{-1}, and then apply f, we get the number x back again. To put it simply, what f does, f^{-1} undoes, and vice versa. See the illustration that follows.

Input x from domain of f $\xrightarrow{\text{Apply } f}$ $f(x)$ $\xrightarrow{\text{Apply } f^{-1}}$ $f^{-1}(f(x)) = x$

Input x from domain of f^{-1} $\xrightarrow{\text{Apply } f^{-1}}$ $f^{-1}(x)$ $\xrightarrow{\text{Apply } f}$ $f(f^{-1}(x)) = x$

In other words,

$$f^{-1}(f(x)) = x \text{ where } x \text{ is in the domain of } f$$
$$f(f^{-1}(x)) = x \text{ where } x \text{ is in the domain of } f^{-1}$$

Consider the function $f(x) = 2x$, which multiplies the argument x by 2. The inverse function f^{-1} undoes whatever f does. So the inverse function of f is $f^{-1}(x) = \frac{1}{2}x$, which divides the argument by 2. For example, $f(3) = 2(3) = 6$ and $f^{-1}(6) = \frac{1}{2}(6) = 3$, so f^{-1} undoes what f did. We can verify this by showing that

$$f^{-1}(f(x)) = f^{-1}(2x) = \frac{1}{2}(2x) = x \quad \text{and} \quad f(f^{-1}(x)) = f\left(\frac{1}{2}x\right) = 2\left(\frac{1}{2}x\right) = x$$

See Figure 12.

Figure 12

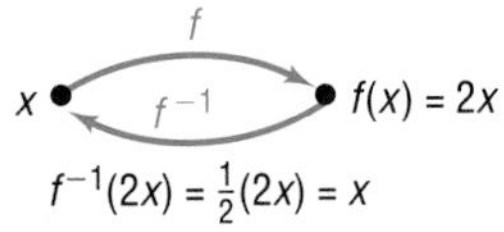

x —f→ $f(x) = 2x$; $f(x) = 2x$ —f^{-1}→ x

$f^{-1}(2x) = \frac{1}{2}(2x) = x$

EXAMPLE 5 **Verifying Inverse Functions**

(a) Verify that the inverse of $g(x) = x^3$ is $g^{-1}(x) = \sqrt[3]{x}$.

(b) Verify that the inverse of $f(x) = 2x + 3$ is $f^{-1}(x) = \frac{1}{2}(x - 3)$.

Solution

(a) $g^{-1}(g(x)) = g^{-1}(x^3) = \sqrt[3]{x^3} = x$ for all x in the domain of g

$g(g^{-1}(x)) = g(\sqrt[3]{x}) = (\sqrt[3]{x})^3 = x$ for all x in the domain of g^{-1}

(b) $f^{-1}(f(x)) = f^{-1}(2x + 3) = \frac{1}{2}[(2x + 3) - 3] = \frac{1}{2}(2x) = x$ for all x in the domain of f

$f(f^{-1}(x)) = f\left(\frac{1}{2}(x - 3)\right) = 2\left[\frac{1}{2}(x - 3)\right] + 3 = (x - 3) + 3 = x$ for all x in the domain of f^{-1}

■

EXAMPLE 6 **Verifying Inverse Functions**

Verify that the inverse of $f(x) = \frac{1}{x - 1}$ is $f^{-1}(x) = \frac{1}{x} + 1$. For what values of x is $f^{-1}(f(x)) = x$? For what values of x is $f(f^{-1}(x)) = x$?

Solution The domain of f is $\{x | x \neq 1\}$ and the domain of f^{-1} is $\{x | x \neq 0\}$. Now

$$f^{-1}(f(x)) = f^{-1}\left(\frac{1}{x - 1}\right) = \frac{1}{\frac{1}{x - 1}} + 1 = x - 1 + 1 = x \quad \text{provided } x \neq 1$$

$$f(f^{-1}(x)) = f\left(\frac{1}{x} + 1\right) = \frac{1}{\frac{1}{x} + 1 - 1} = \frac{1}{\frac{1}{x}} = x \quad \text{provided } x \neq 0$$

■

Now Work PROBLEM 33

Exploration

Simultaneously graph $Y_1 = x$, $Y_2 = x^3$, and $Y_3 = \sqrt[3]{x}$ on a square screen with $-3 \le x \le 3$. What do you observe about the graphs of $Y_2 = x^3$, its inverse $Y_3 = \sqrt[3]{x}$, and the line $Y_1 = x$?

Repeat this experiment by simultaneously graphing $Y_1 = x$, $Y_2 = 2x + 3$, and $Y_3 = \frac{1}{2}(x - 3)$ on a square screen with $-6 \le x \le 3$. Do you see the symmetry of the graph of Y_2 and its inverse Y_3 with respect to the line $Y_1 = x$?

3 Obtain the Graph of the Inverse Function from the Graph of the Function

For the functions in Example 5(b), we list points on the graph of $f = Y_1$ and on the graph of $f^{-1} = Y_2$ in Table 1. We notice that whenever (a, b) is on the graph of f then (b, a) is on the graph of f^{-1}. Figure 13 shows these points plotted. Also shown is the graph of $y = x$, which you should observe is a line of symmetry of the points.

Table 1

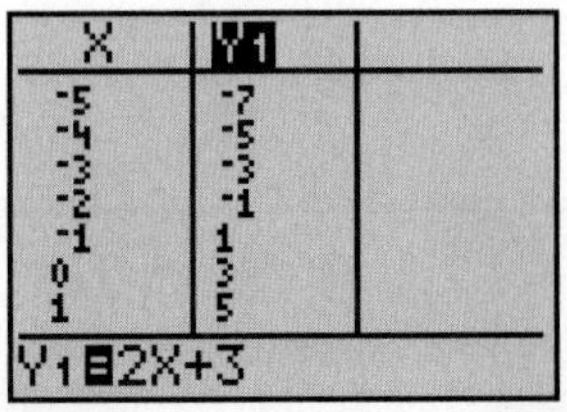

X	Y1
-5	-7
-4	-5
-3	-3
-2	-1
-1	1
0	3
1	5

Y1=2X+3

X	Y2
-7	-5
-5	-4
-3	-3
-1	-2
1	-1
3	0
5	1

Y2=(1/2)(X-3)

Figure 13

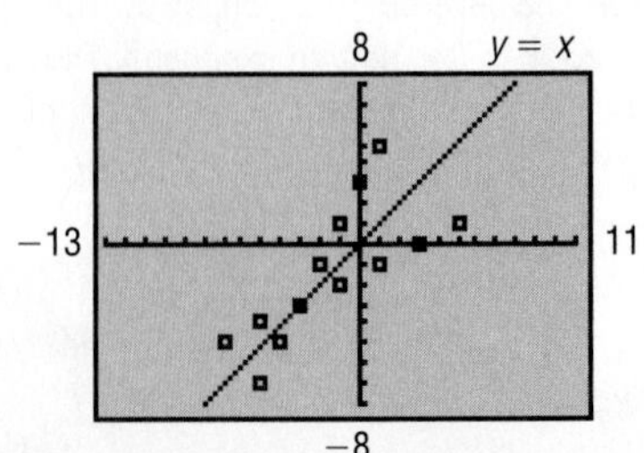

Figure 14

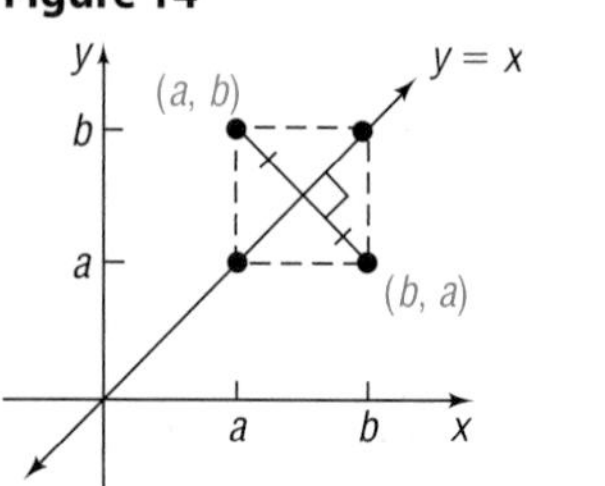

Suppose that (a, b) is a point on the graph of a one-to-one function f defined by $y = f(x)$. Then $b = f(a)$. This means that $a = f^{-1}(b)$, so (b, a) is a point on the graph of the inverse function f^{-1}. The relationship between the point (a, b) on f and the point (b, a) on f^{-1} is shown in Figure 14. The line segment with endpoints (a, b) and (b, a) is perpendicular to the line $y = x$ and is bisected by the line $y = x$. (Do you see why?) It follows that the point (b, a) on f^{-1} is the reflection about the line $y = x$ of the point (a, b) on f.

THEOREM

The graph of a one-to-one function f and the graph of its inverse f^{-1} are symmetric with respect to the line $y = x$.

Figure 15 illustrates this result. Notice that, once the graph of f is known, the graph of f^{-1} may be obtained by reflecting the graph of f about the line $y = x$.

Figure 15

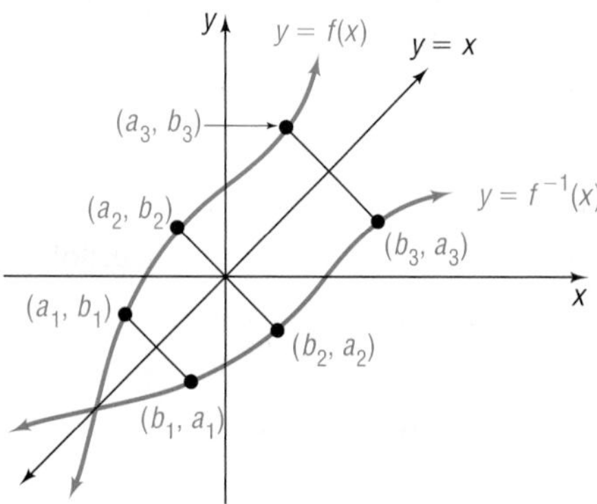

EXAMPLE 7 **Graphing the Inverse Function**

The graph in Figure 16(a) is that of a one-to-one function $y = f(x)$. Draw the graph of its inverse.

Solution Begin by adding the graph of $y = x$ to Figure 16(a). Since the points $(-2, -1)$, $(-1, 0)$, and $(2, 1)$ are on the graph of f, the points $(-1, -2)$, $(0, -1)$, and $(1, 2)$ must be on the graph of f^{-1}. Keeping in mind that the graph of f^{-1} is the reflection about the line $y = x$ of the graph of f, draw f^{-1}. See Figure 16(b).

Figure 16

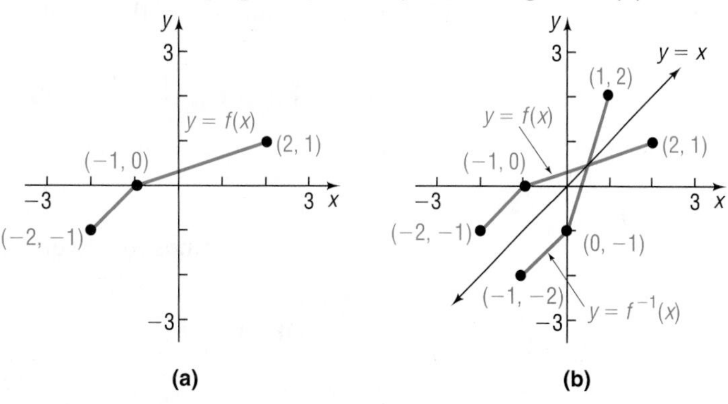

Now Work PROBLEM 43

4 Find the Inverse of a Function Defined by an Equation

The fact that the graphs of a one-to-one function f and its inverse function f^{-1} are symmetric with respect to the line $y = x$ tells us more. It says that we can obtain f^{-1} by interchanging the roles of x and y in f. Look again at Figure 15. If f is defined by the equation

$$y = f(x)$$

then f^{-1} is defined by the equation

$$x = f(y)$$

The equation $x = f(y)$ defines f^{-1} *implicitly*. If we can solve this equation for y, we will have the *explicit* form of f^{-1}, that is,

$$y = f^{-1}(x)$$

Let's use this procedure to find the inverse of $f(x) = 2x + 3$. (Since f is a linear function and is increasing, we know that f is one-to-one and so has an inverse function.)

EXAMPLE 8

How to Find the Inverse Function

Find the inverse of $f(x) = 2x + 3$. Graph f and f^{-1} on the same coordinate axes.

Step-by-Step Solution

Step 1 Replace $f(x)$ with y. In $y = f(x)$, interchange the variables x and y to obtain $x = f(y)$. This equation defines the inverse function f^{-1} implicitly.

Replace $f(x)$ with y in $f(x) = 2x + 3$ and obtain $y = 2x + 3$. Now interchange the variables x and y to obtain

$$x = 2y + 3$$

This equation defines the inverse f^{-1} implicitly.

Step 2 If possible, solve the implicit equation for y in terms of x to obtain the explicit form of f^{-1}, $y = f^{-1}(x)$.

To find the explicit form of the inverse, solve $x = 2y + 3$ for y.

$$x = 2y + 3$$

$$2y + 3 = x \quad \text{Reflexive Property; If } a = b, \text{ then } b = a.$$

$$2y = x - 3 \quad \text{Subtract 3 from both sides.}$$

$$y = \frac{1}{2}(x - 3) \quad \text{Divide both sides by 2.}$$

The explicit form of the inverse f^{-1} is

$$f^{-1}(x) = \frac{1}{2}(x - 3)$$

Step 3 Check the result by showing that $f^{-1}(f(x)) = x$ and $f(f^{-1}(x)) = x$.

We verified that f and f^{-1} are inverses in Example 5(b).

The graphs of $f(x) = 2x + 3$ and its inverse $f^{-1}(x) = \frac{1}{2}(x - 3)$ are shown in Figure 17. Note the symmetry of the graphs with respect to the line $y = x$. ■

Figure 17

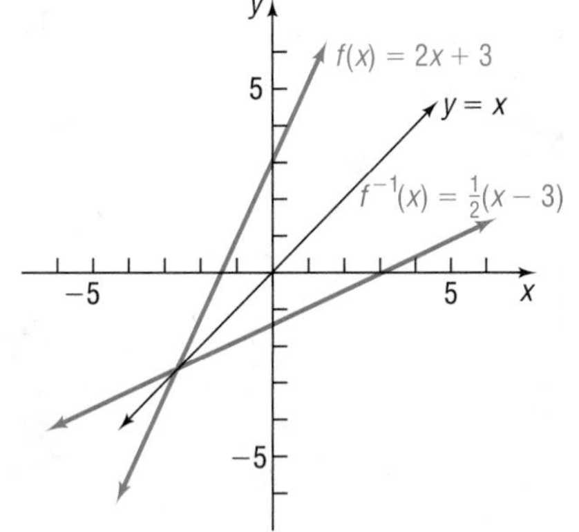

Procedure for Finding the Inverse of a One-to-One Function

STEP 1: In $y = f(x)$, interchange the variables x and y to obtain

$$x = f(y)$$

This equation defines the inverse function f^{-1} implicitly.

STEP 2: If possible, solve the implicit equation for y in terms of x to obtain the explicit form of f^{-1}:

$$y = f^{-1}(x)$$

STEP 3: Check the result by showing that

$$f^{-1}(f(x)) = x \quad \text{and} \quad f(f^{-1}(x)) = x$$

EXAMPLE 9

Finding the Inverse Function

The function

$$f(x) = \frac{2x + 1}{x - 1} \quad x \neq 1$$

is one-to-one. Find its inverse and check the result.

Solution **STEP 1:** Replace $f(x)$ with y and interchange the variables x and y in

$$y = \frac{2x + 1}{x - 1}$$

to obtain

$$x = \frac{2y + 1}{y - 1}$$

STEP 2: Solve for y.

$$x = \frac{2y + 1}{y - 1}$$

$$x(y - 1) = 2y + 1 \quad \text{Multiply both sides by } y - 1.$$

$$xy - x = 2y + 1 \quad \text{Apply the Distributive Property.}$$

$$xy - 2y = x + 1 \quad \text{Subtract } 2y \text{ from both sides; add } x \text{ to both sides.}$$

$$(x - 2)y = x + 1 \quad \text{Factor.}$$

$$y = \frac{x + 1}{x - 2} \quad \text{Divide by } x - 2.$$

The inverse is

$$f^{-1}(x) = \frac{x + 1}{x - 2} \quad x \neq 2 \quad \text{Replace } y \text{ by } f^{-1}(x).$$

STEP 3: ✓**Check:**

$$f^{-1}(f(x)) = f^{-1}\left(\frac{2x + 1}{x - 1}\right) = \frac{\frac{2x + 1}{x - 1} + 1}{\frac{2x + 1}{x - 1} - 2} = \frac{2x + 1 + x - 1}{2x + 1 - 2(x - 1)} = \frac{3x}{3} = x \quad x \neq 1$$

$$f(f^{-1}(x)) = f\left(\frac{x + 1}{x - 2}\right) = \frac{2\left(\frac{x + 1}{x - 2}\right) + 1}{\frac{x + 1}{x - 2} - 1} = \frac{2(x + 1) + x - 2}{x + 1 - (x - 2)} = \frac{3x}{3} = x \quad x \neq 2$$

■

Exploration

In Example 9, we found that, if $f(x) = \frac{2x + 1}{x - 1}$, then $f^{-1}(x) = \frac{x + 1}{x - 2}$. Compare the vertical and horizontal asymptotes of f and f^{-1}.

Result The vertical asymptote of f is $x = 1$, and the horizontal asymptote is $y = 2$. The vertical asymptote of f^{-1} is $x = 2$, and the horizontal asymptote is $y = 1$.

Now Work PROBLEMS 51 AND 65

If a function is not one-to-one, it has no inverse function. Sometimes, though, an appropriate restriction on the domain of such a function will yield a new function that is one-to-one. Then the function defined on the restricted domain has an inverse function. Let's look at an example of this common practice.

EXAMPLE 10 Finding the Inverse of a Domain-restricted Function

Find the inverse of $y = f(x) = x^2$ if $x \geq 0$. Graph f and f^{-1}.

Solution The function $y = x^2$ is not one-to-one. [Refer to Example 2(a).] However, if we restrict the domain of this function to $x \geq 0$, as indicated, we have a new function that is increasing and, therefore, is one-to-one. As a result, the function defined by $y = f(x) = x^2, x \geq 0$, has an inverse function, f^{-1}.

Follow the steps given previously to find f^{-1}.

Figure 18

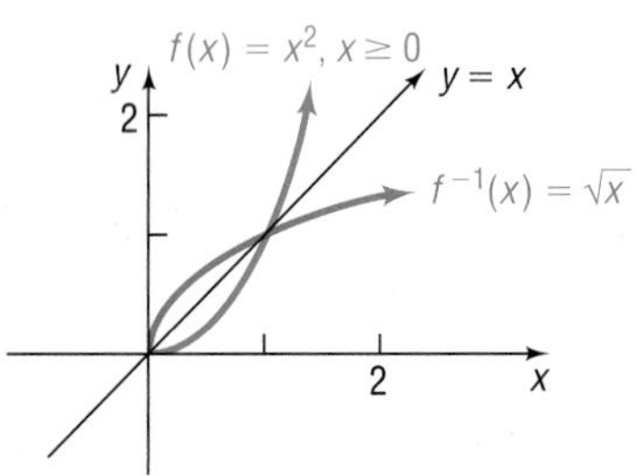

STEP 1: In the equation $y = x^2$, $x \geq 0$, interchange the variables x and y. The result is

$$x = y^2 \qquad y \geq 0$$

This equation defines (implicitly) the inverse function.

STEP 2: Solve for y to get the explicit form of the inverse. Since $y \geq 0$, only one solution for y is obtained: $y = \sqrt{x}$. So $f^{-1}(x) = \sqrt{x}$.

STEP 3: ✓**Check:** $f^{-1}(f(x)) = f^{-1}(x^2) = \sqrt{x^2} = |x| = x$ since $x \geq 0$

$$f(f^{-1}(x)) = f(\sqrt{x}) = (\sqrt{x})^2 = x$$

Figure 18 illustrates the graphs of $f(x) = x^2$, $x \geq 0$, and $f^{-1}(x) = \sqrt{x}$. Note that the domain of f = range of $f^{-1} = [0, \infty)$ and the domain of f^{-1} = range of $f = [0, \infty)$.

SUMMARY

1. If a function f is one-to-one, then it has an inverse function f^{-1}.
2. Domain of f = Range of f^{-1}; Range of f = Domain of f^{-1}.
3. To verify that f^{-1} is the inverse of f, show that $f^{-1}(f(x)) = x$ for every x in the domain of f and $f(f^{-1}(x)) = x$ for every x in the domain of f^{-1}.
4. The graphs of f and f^{-1} are symmetric with respect to the line $y = x$.

12.2 Assess Your Understanding

'Are You Prepared?' *Answers are given at the end of these exercises. If you get a wrong answer, read the pages listed in red.*

1. Is the set of ordered pairs $\{(1, 3), (2, 3), (-1, 2)\}$ a function? Why or why not? (pp. 559–562)
2. Where is the function $f(x) = x^2$ increasing? Where is it decreasing? (pp. 584–585)
3. What is the domain of $f(x) = \dfrac{x + 5}{x^2 + 3x - 18}$? (pp. 565–566)
4. Simplify: $\dfrac{\dfrac{1}{x} + 1}{\dfrac{1}{x^2} - 1}$

Concepts and Vocabulary

5. If x_1 and x_2 are two different inputs of a function f, then f is one-to-one if _______________.
6. If every horizontal line intersects the graph of a function f at no more than one point, f is a(n) ______________ function.
7. If f is a one-to-one function and $f(3) = 8$, then $f^{-1}(8) =$ _____.
8. If f^{-1} denotes the inverse of a function f, then the graphs of f and f^{-1} are symmetric with respect to the line _________.
9. If the domain of a one-to-one function f is $[4, \infty)$, the range of its inverse, f^{-1}, is __________.
10. ***True or False*** If f and g are inverse functions, the domain of f is the same as the range of g.

Skill Building

In Problems 11–18, determine whether the function is one-to-one.

11.

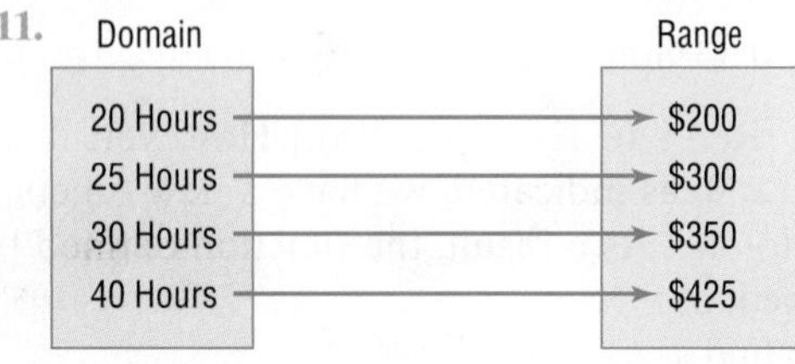

12.

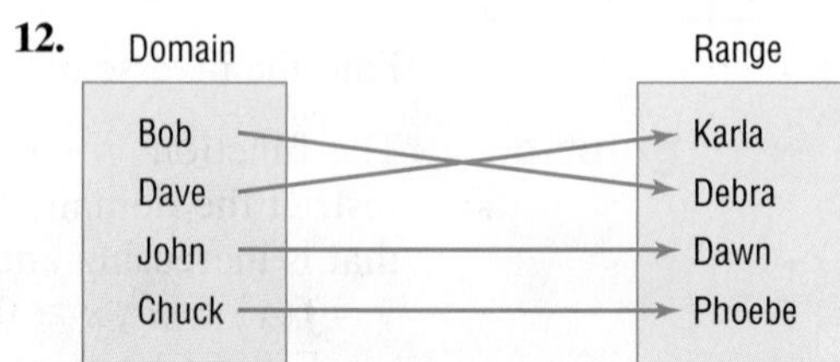

13.

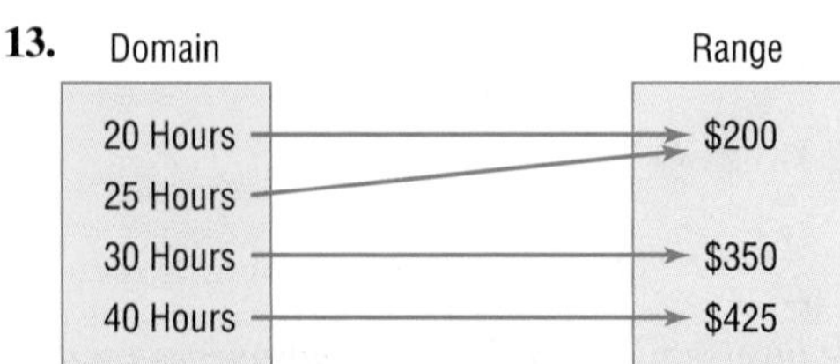

14.

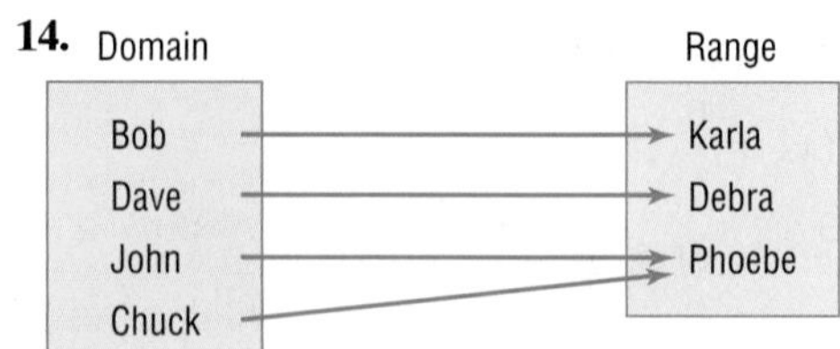

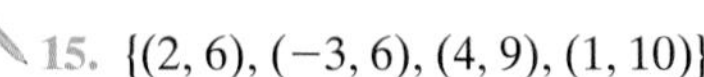
15. $\{(2, 6), (-3, 6), (4, 9), (1, 10)\}$

16. $\{(-2, 5), (-1, 3), (3, 7), (4, 12)\}$

17. $\{(0, 0), (1, 1), (2, 16), (3, 81)\}$

18. $\{(1, 2), (2, 8), (3, 18), (4, 32)\}$

In Problems 19–24, the graph of a function f is given. Use the horizontal-line test to determine whether f is one-to-one.

19.

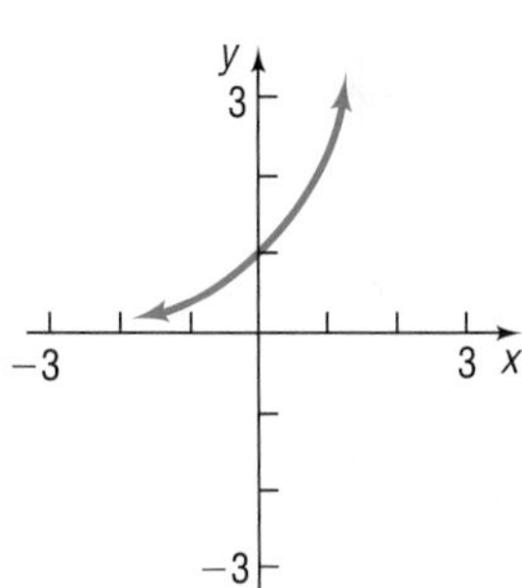

20.

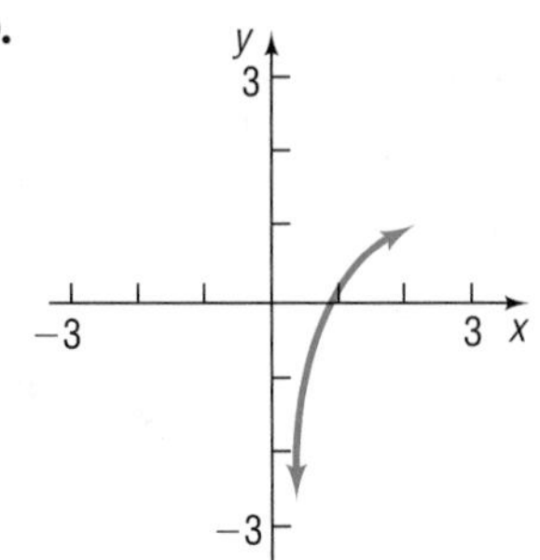

21.

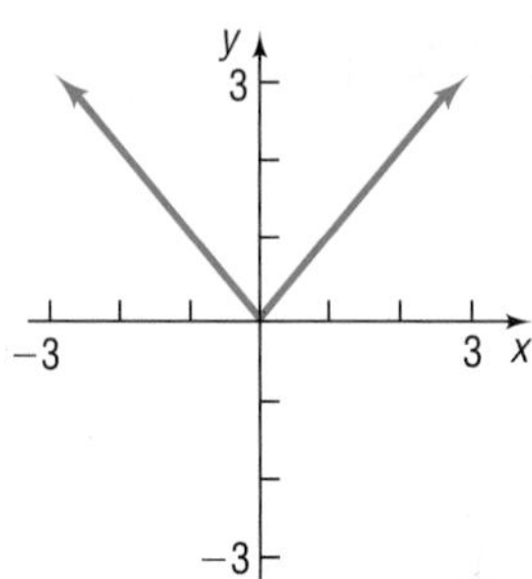

22.

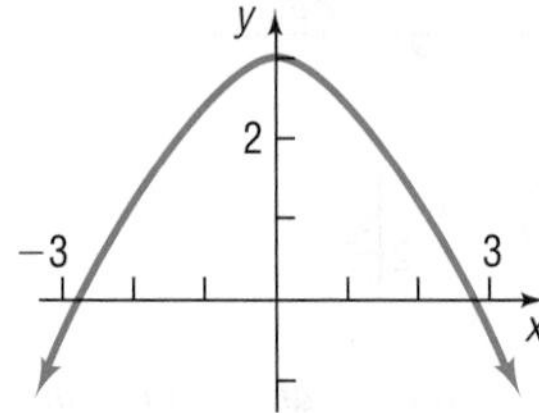

23.

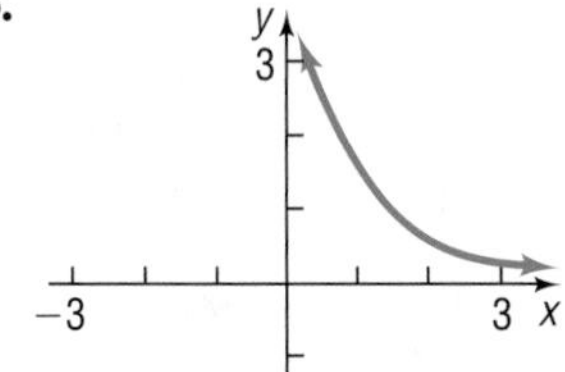

24.

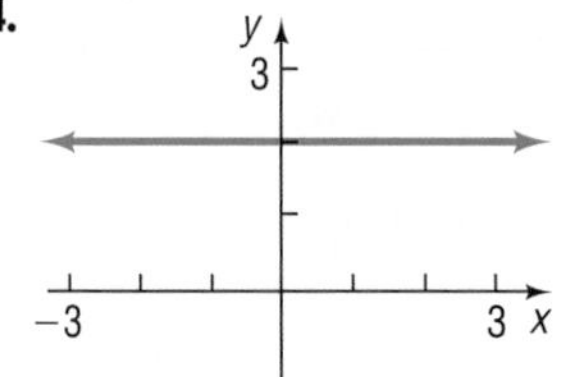

In Problems 25–32, find the inverse of each one-to-one function. State the domain and the range of each inverse function.

25.

Location	Annual Rainfall (inches)
Mt Waialeale, Hawaii	460.00
Monrovia, Liberia	202.01
Pago Pago, American Samoa	196.46
Moulmein, Burma	191.02
Lae, Papua New Guinea	182.87

Source: *Information Please Almanac*

26.

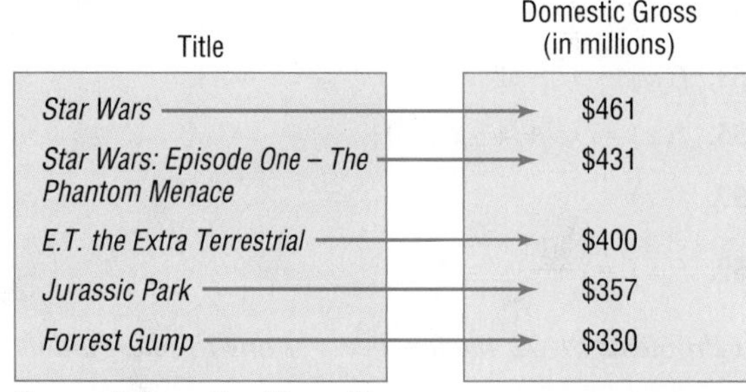

Source: *Information Please Almanac*

27.

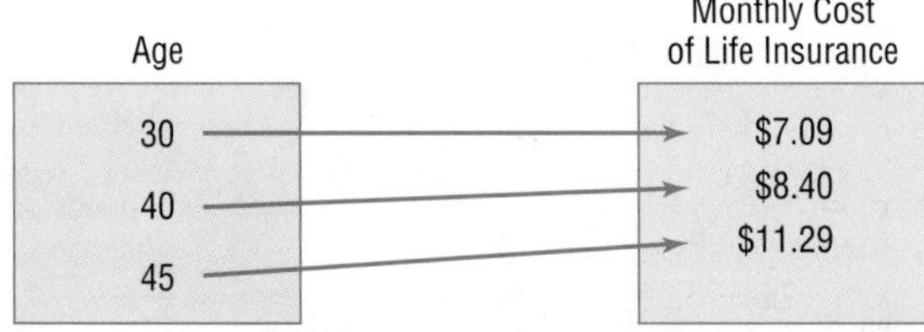

Source: eterm.com

28.

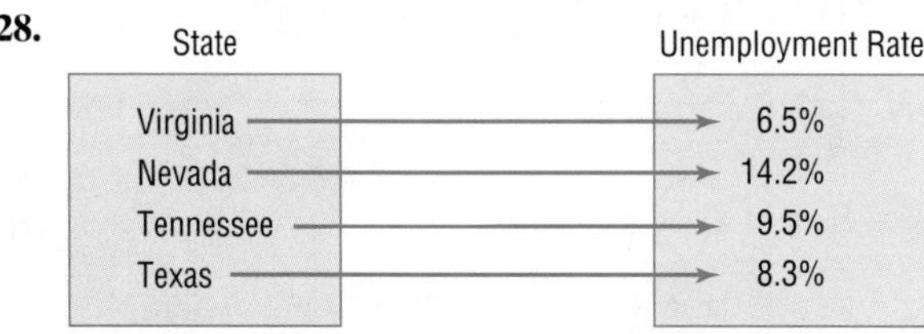

Source: United States Bureau of Labor Statistics

29. $\{(-3, 5), (-2, 9), (-1, 2), (0, 11), (1, -5)\}$

30. $\{(-2, 2), (-1, 6), (0, 8), (1, -3), (2, 9)\}$

31. $\{(-2, 1), (-3, 2), (-10, 0), (1, 9), (2, 4)\}$

32. $\{(-2, -8), (-1, -1), (0, 0), (1, 1), (2, 8)\}$

In Problems 33–42, verify that the functions f and g are inverses of each other by showing that $f(g(x)) = x$ and $g(f(x)) = x$. Give any values of x that need to be excluded from the domain of f and the domain of g.

33. $f(x) = 3x + 4;\quad g(x) = \frac{1}{3}(x - 4)$

34. $f(x) = 3 - 2x;\quad g(x) = -\frac{1}{2}(x - 3)$

35. $f(x) = 4x - 8;\quad g(x) = \frac{x}{4} + 2$

36. $f(x) = 2x + 6;\quad g(x) = \frac{1}{2}x - 3$

37. $f(x) = x^3 - 8;\ g(x) = \sqrt[3]{x + 8}$

38. $f(x) = (x - 2)^2, x \geq 2;\ g(x) = \sqrt{x} + 2$

39. $f(x) = \frac{1}{x};\ g(x) = \frac{1}{x}$

40. $f(x) = x;\ g(x) = x$

41. $f(x) = \frac{2x + 3}{x + 4};\ g(x) = \frac{4x - 3}{2 - x}$

42. $f(x) = \frac{x - 5}{2x + 3};\ g(x) = \frac{3x + 5}{1 - 2x}$

In Problems 43–48, the graph of a one-to-one function f is given. Draw the graph of the inverse function f^{-1}. For convenience (and as a hint), the graph of y = x is also given.

43.

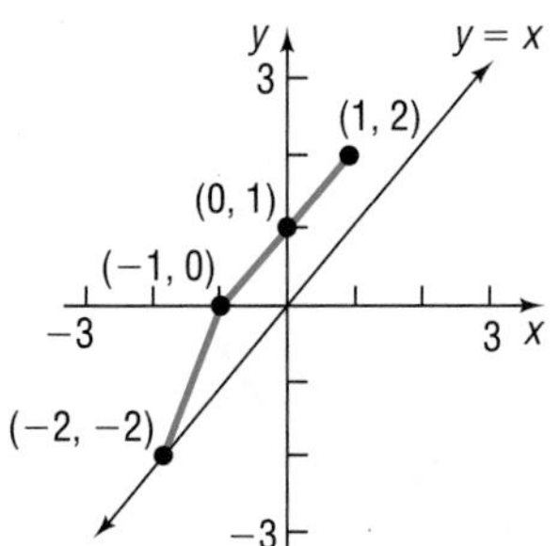

44.

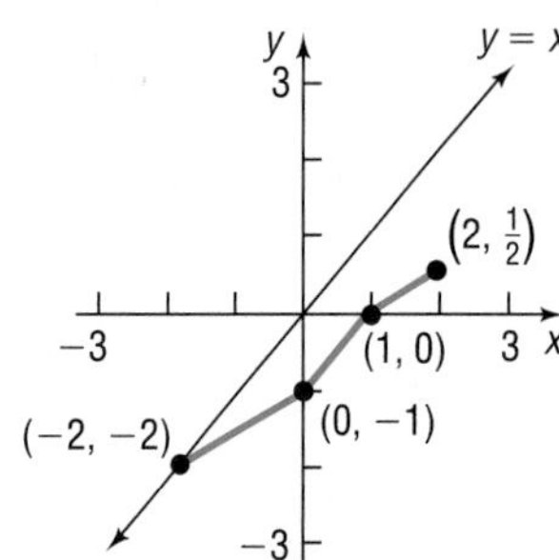

45.

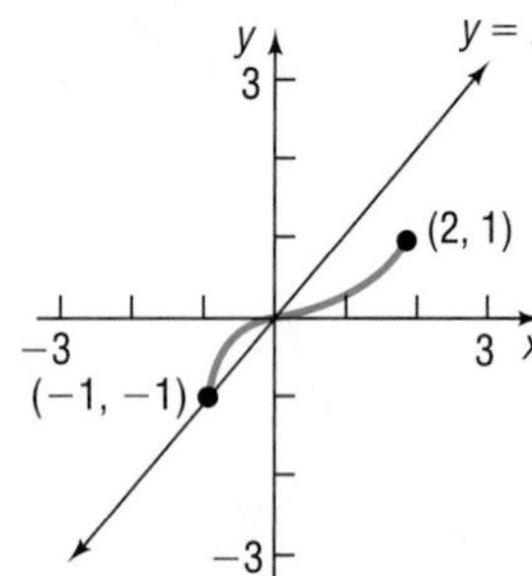

46.

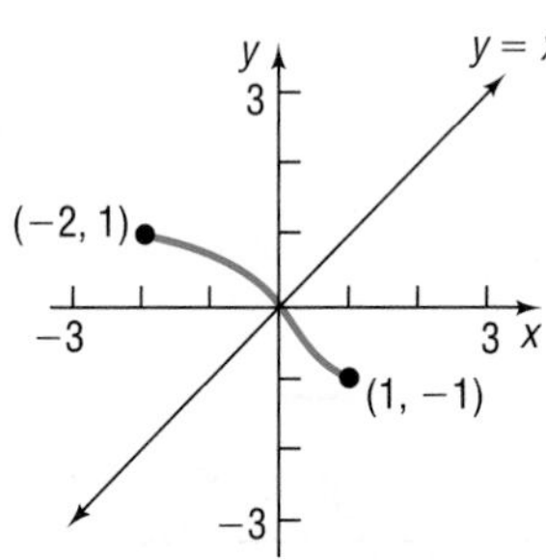

47.

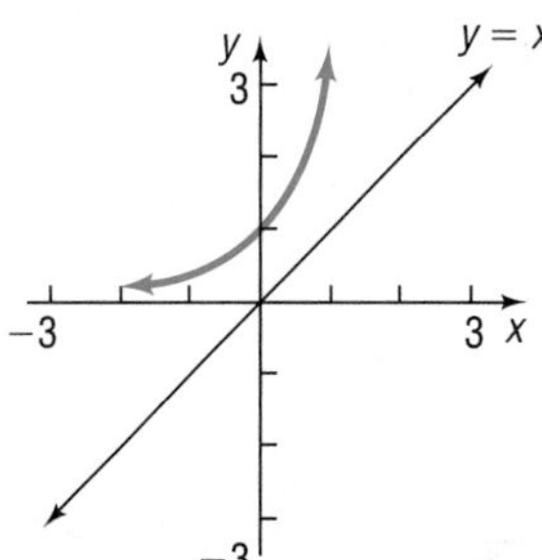

48.

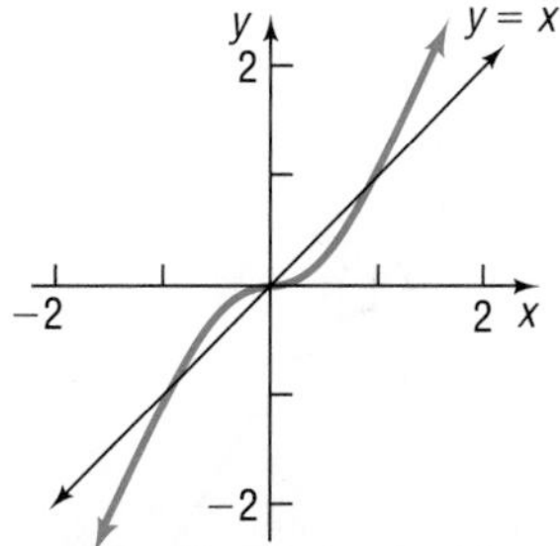

In Problems 49–60, the function f is one-to-one. Find its inverse and check your answer. Graph f, f^{-1}, and y = x on the same coordinate axes.

49. $f(x) = 3x$

50. $f(x) = -4x$

51. $f(x) = 4x + 2$

52. $f(x) = 1 - 3x$

53. $f(x) = x^3 - 1$

54. $f(x) = x^3 + 1$

55. $f(x) = x^2 + 4 \quad x \geq 0$

56. $f(x) = x^2 + 9 \quad x \geq 0$

57. $f(x) = \frac{4}{x}$

58. $f(x) = -\frac{3}{x}$

59. $f(x) = \frac{1}{x - 2}$

60. $f(x) = \frac{4}{x + 2}$

In Problems 61–72, the function f is one-to-one. Find its inverse and check your answer.

61. $f(x) = \frac{2}{3 + x}$

62. $f(x) = \frac{4}{2 - x}$

63. $f(x) = \frac{3x}{x + 2}$

64. $f(x) = -\frac{2x}{x - 1}$

65. $f(x) = \frac{2x}{3x - 1}$

66. $f(x) = -\frac{3x + 1}{x}$

67. $f(x) = \frac{3x + 4}{2x - 3}$

68. $f(x) = \frac{2x - 3}{x + 4}$

69. $f(x) = \frac{2x + 3}{x + 2}$

70. $f(x) = \frac{-3x - 4}{x - 2}$

71. $f(x) = \frac{x^2 - 4}{2x^2} \quad x > 0$

72. $f(x) = \frac{x^2 + 3}{3x^2} \quad x > 0$

Applications and Extensions

73. Use the graph of $y = f(x)$ given in Problem 43 to evaluate the following:
(a) $f(-1)$ (b) $f(1)$ (c) $f^{-1}(1)$ (d) $f^{-1}(2)$

74. Use the graph of $y = f(x)$ given in Problem 44 to evaluate the following:
(a) $f(2)$ (b) $f(1)$ (c) $f^{-1}(0)$ (d) $f^{-1}(-1)$

75. If $f(7) = 13$ and f is one-to-one, what is $f^{-1}(13)$?

76. If $g(-5) = 3$ and g is one-to-one, what is $g^{-1}(3)$?

77. The domain of a one-to-one function f is $[5, \infty)$, and its range is $[-2, \infty)$. State the domain and the range of f^{-1}.

78. The domain of a one-to-one function f is $[0, \infty)$, and its range is $[5, \infty)$. State the domain and the range of f^{-1}.

79. The domain of a one-to-one function g is $(-\infty, 0]$, and its range is $[0, \infty)$. State the domain and the range of g^{-1}.

80. The domain of a one-to-one function g is $[0, 15]$, and its range is $(0, 8)$. State the domain and the range of g^{-1}.

81. A function $y = f(x)$ is increasing on the interval $(0, 5)$. What conclusions can you draw about the graph of $y = f^{-1}(x)$?

82. A function $y = f(x)$ is decreasing on the interval $(0, 5)$. What conclusions can you draw about the graph of $y = f^{-1}(x)$?

83. Find the inverse of the linear function

$$f(x) = mx + b \quad m \neq 0$$

84. Find the inverse of the function

$$f(x) = \sqrt{r^2 - x^2} \quad 0 \le x \le r$$

85. A function f has an inverse function. If the graph of f lies in quadrant I, in which quadrant does the graph of f^{-1} lie?

86. A function f has an inverse function. If the graph of f lies in quadrant II, in which quadrant does the graph of f^{-1} lie?

87. The function $f(x) = |x|$ is not one-to-one. Find a suitable restriction on the domain of f so that the new function that results is one-to-one. Then find the inverse of f.

88. The function $f(x) = x^4$ is not one-to-one. Find a suitable restriction on the domain of f so that the new function that results is one-to-one. Then find the inverse of f.

In applications, the symbols used for the independent and dependent variables are often based on common usage. So, rather than using $y = f(x)$ to represent a function, an applied problem might use $C = C(q)$ to represent the cost C of manufacturing q units of a good since, in economics, q is used for output. Because of this, the inverse notation f^{-1} used in a pure mathematics problem is not used when finding inverses of applied problems. Rather, the inverse of a function such as $C = C(q)$ will be $q = q(C)$. So $C = C(q)$ is a function that represents the cost C as a function of the output q, while $q = q(C)$ is a function that represents the output q as a function of the cost C. Problems 89–92 illustrate this idea.

89. Vehicle Stopping Distance Taking into account reaction time, the distance d (in feet) that a car requires to come to a complete stop while traveling r miles per hour is given by the function

$$d(r) = 6.97r - 90.39$$

(a) Express the speed r at which the car is traveling as a function of the distance d required to come to a complete stop.
(b) Verify that $r = r(d)$ is the inverse of $d = d(r)$ by showing that $r(d(r)) = r$ and $d(r(d)) = d$.
(c) Predict the speed that a car was traveling if the distance required to stop was 300 feet.

90. Height and Head Circumference The head circumference C of a child is related to the height H of the child (both in inches) through the function

$$H(C) = 2.15C - 10.53$$

(a) Express the head circumference C as a function of height H.
(b) Verify that $C = C(H)$ is the inverse of $H = H(C)$ by showing that $H(C(H)) = H$ and $C(H(C)) = C$.
(c) Predict the head circumference of a child who is 26 inches tall.

91. Ideal Body Weight One model for the ideal body weight W for men (in kilograms) as a function of height h (in inches) is given by the function

$$W(h) = 50 + 2.3(h - 60)$$

(a) What is the ideal weight of a 6-foot male?
(b) Express the height h as a function of weight W.
(c) Verify that $h = h(W)$ is the inverse of $W = W(h)$ by showing that $h(W(h)) = h$ and $W(h(W)) = W$.
(d) What is the height of a male who is at his ideal weight of 80 kilograms?

[**Note:** The ideal body weight W for women (in kilograms) as a function of height h (in inches) is given by $W(h) = 45.5 + 2.3(h - 60)$.]

92. Temperature Conversion The function $F(C) = \frac{9}{5}C + 32$ converts a temperature from C degrees Celsius to F degrees Fahrenheit.

(a) Express the temperature in degrees Celsius C as a function of the temperature in degrees Fahrenheit F.
(b) Verify that $C = C(F)$ is the inverse of $F = F(C)$ by showing that $C(F(C)) = C$ and $F(C(F)) = F$.
(c) What is the temperature in degrees Celsius if it is 70 degrees Fahrenheit?

93. Income Taxes The function

$$T(g) = 4750 + 0.25(g - 34{,}500)$$

represents the 2011 federal income tax T (in dollars) due for a "single" filer whose modified adjusted gross income is g dollars, where $34{,}500 \le g \le 83{,}600$.

(a) What is the domain of the function T?
(b) Given that the tax due T is an increasing linear function of modified adjusted gross income g, find the range of the function T.
(c) Find adjusted gross income g as a function of federal income tax T. What are the domain and the range of this function?

94. Income Taxes The function

$$T(g) = 1700 + 0.15(g - 17{,}000)$$

represents the 2011 federal income tax T (in dollars) due for a "married filing jointly" filer whose modified adjusted gross income is g dollars, where $17{,}000 \le g \le 69{,}000$.

(a) What is the domain of the function T?
(b) Given that the tax due T is an increasing linear function of modified adjusted gross income g, find the range of the function T.
(c) Find adjusted gross income g as a function of federal income tax T. What are the domain and the range of this function?

95. Gravity on Earth If a rock falls from a height of 100 meters on Earth, the height H (in meters) after t seconds is approximately

$$H(t) = 100 - 4.9t^2$$

(a) In general, quadratic functions are not one-to-one. However, the function H is one-to-one. Why?

(b) Find the inverse of H and verify your result.
(c) How long will it take a rock to fall 80 meters?

96. Period of a Pendulum The period T (in seconds) of a simple pendulum as a function of its length l (in feet) is given by

$$T(l) = 2\pi\sqrt{\frac{l}{32.2}}$$

(a) Express the length l as a function of the period T.
(b) How long is a pendulum whose period is 3 seconds?

97. Given

$$f(x) = \frac{ax + b}{cx + d}$$

find $f^{-1}(x)$. If $c \neq 0$, under what conditions on a, b, c, and d is $f = f^{-1}$?

Explaining Concepts: Discussion and Writing

98. Can a one-to-one function and its inverse be equal? What must be true about the graph of f for this to happen? Give some examples to support your conclusion.

99. Draw the graph of a one-to-one function that contains the points $(-2, -3)$, $(0, 0)$, and $(1, 5)$. Now draw the graph of its inverse. Compare your graph to those of other students. Discuss any similarities. What differences do you see?

100. Give an example of a function whose domain is the set of real numbers and that is neither increasing nor decreasing on its domain, but is one-to-one.

[**Hint:** Use a piecewise-defined function.]

101. Is every odd function one-to-one? Explain.

102. Suppose that $C(g)$ represents the cost C, in dollars, of manufacturing g cars. Explain what C^{-1} (800,000) represents.

103. Explain why the horizontal-line test can be used to identify one-to-one functions from a graph.

'Are You Prepared?' Answers

1. Yes; for each input x there is one output y.
2. Increasing on $(0, \infty)$; decreasing on $(-\infty, 0)$
3. $\{x \mid x \neq -6, x \neq 3\}$
4. $\frac{x}{1 - x}$, $x \neq 0, x \neq -1$

12.3 Exponential Functions

PREPARING FOR THIS SECTION *Before getting started, review the following:*

- Graphing Techniques: Transformations (Section 9.5, pp. 605–613)
- Solving Linear and Quadratic Equations (Section 7.2, pp. 476–483)
- Average Rate of Change (Section 9.3, pp. 588–590)
- Quadratic Functions (Section 10.3, pp. 648–656)
- Linear Functions (Section 10.1, pp. 631–636)
- Horizontal Asymptotes (Section 11.4, pp. 722–725)

Now Work the **'Are You Prepared?'** problems on page 783.

OBJECTIVES
1 Evaluate Exponential Functions (p. 772)
2 Graph Exponential Functions (p. 776)
3 Define the Number e (p. 780)
4 Solve Exponential Equations (p. 781)

1 Evaluate Exponential Functions

We gave meaning to expressions of the form

$$a^r$$

where the base a is a positive real number and the exponent r is a rational number.

But what is the meaning of a^x, where the base a is a positive real number and the exponent x is an irrational number? Although a rigorous definition requires methods discussed in calculus, the basis for the definition is easy to follow: Select a rational number r that is formed by truncating (removing) all but a finite number of digits from the irrational number x. Then it is reasonable to expect that

$$a^x \approx a^r$$

For example, take the irrational number $\pi = 3.14159\ldots$. Then an approximation to a^π is

$$a^\pi \approx a^{3.14}$$

where the digits after the hundredths position have been removed from the value for π. A better approximation would be

$$a^\pi \approx a^{3.14159}$$

where the digits after the hundred-thousandths position have been removed. Continuing in this way, we can obtain approximations to a^π to any desired degree of accuracy.

Most calculators have an $\boxed{x^y}$ key or a caret key $\boxed{\wedge}$ for working with exponents. To evaluate expressions of the form a^x, enter the base a, then press the $\boxed{x^y}$ key (or the $\boxed{\wedge}$ key), enter the exponent x, and press $\boxed{=}$ (or $\boxed{\text{ENTER}}$).

EXAMPLE 1 **Using a Calculator to Evaluate Powers of 2**

Using a calculator, evaluate:

(a) $2^{1.4}$ (b) $2^{1.41}$ (c) $2^{1.414}$ (d) $2^{1.4142}$ (e) $2^{\sqrt{2}}$

Solution Figure 19 shows the solution to part (a) using a T1-84 Plus graphing calculator.

Figure 19

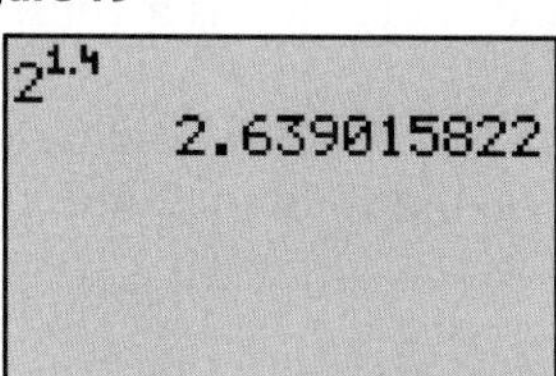

(a) $2^{1.4} \approx 2.639015822$ (b) $2^{1.41} \approx 2.657371628$
(c) $2^{1.414} \approx 2.66474965$ (d) $2^{1.4142} \approx 2.665119089$
(e) $2^{\sqrt{2}} \approx 2.665144143$ ■

Now Work PROBLEM 15

It can be shown that the familiar laws for rational exponents hold for real exponents.

THEOREM

Laws of Exponents

If s, t, a, and b are real numbers with $a > 0$ and $b > 0$, then

$$a^s \cdot a^t = a^{s+t} \qquad (a^s)^t = a^{st} \qquad (ab)^s = a^s \cdot b^s$$
$$1^s = 1 \qquad a^{-s} = \frac{1}{a^s} = \left(\frac{1}{a}\right)^s \qquad a^0 = 1 \tag{1}$$

Introduction to Exponential Growth

Suppose a function f has the following two properties:

1. The value of f doubles with every 1-unit increase in the independent variable x.
2. The value of f at $x = 0$ is 5, so $f(0) = 5$.

Table 2

x	$f(x)$
0	5
1	10
2	20
3	40
4	80

Table 2 shows values of the function f for $x = 0, 1, 2, 3$, and 4.

We seek an equation $y = f(x)$ that describes this function f. The key fact is that the value of f doubles for every 1-unit increase in x.

$f(0) = 5$
$f(1) = 2f(0) = 2 \cdot 5 = 5 \cdot 2^1$ Double the value of f at 0 to get the value at 1.
$f(2) = 2f(1) = 2(5 \cdot 2) = 5 \cdot 2^2$ Double the value of f at 1 to get the value at 2.

$$f(3) = 2f(2) = 2(5 \cdot 2^2) = 5 \cdot 2^3$$
$$f(4) = 2f(3) = 2(5 \cdot 2^3) = 5 \cdot 2^4$$

The pattern leads us to

$$f(x) = 2f(x-1) = 2(5 \cdot 2^{x-1}) = 5 \cdot 2^x$$

DEFINITION

An **exponential function** is a function of the form

$$f(x) = Ca^x$$

where a is a positive real number ($a > 0$), $a \neq 1$, and $C \neq 0$ is a real number. The domain of f is the set of all real numbers. The base a is the **growth factor,** and because $f(0) = Ca^0 = C$, we call C the **initial value.**

WARNING It is important to distinguish a power function, $g(x) = ax^n$, $n \geq 2$, an integer, from an exponential function, $f(x) = C \cdot a^x$, $a \neq 1$, $a > 0$. In a power function, the base is a variable and the exponent is a constant. In an exponential function, the base is a constant and the exponent is a variable. ■

In the definition of an exponential function, we exclude the base $a = 1$ because this function is simply the constant function $f(x) = C \cdot 1^x = C$. We also need to exclude bases that are negative; otherwise, we would have to exclude many values of x from the domain, such as $x = \frac{1}{2}$ and $x = \frac{3}{4}$. [Recall that $(-2)^{1/2} = \sqrt{-2}$, $(-3)^{3/4} = \sqrt[4]{(-3)^3} = \sqrt[4]{-27}$, and so on, are not defined in the set of real numbers.] Finally, transformations (vertical shifts, horizontal shifts, reflections, and so on) of a function of the form $f(x) = Ca^x$ also represent exponential functions.

Some examples of exponential functions are

$$f(x) = 2^x \qquad F(x) = \left(\frac{1}{3}\right)^x + 5 \qquad G(x) = 2 \cdot 3^{x-3}$$

Notice for each function that the base of the exponential expression is a constant and the exponent contains a variable.

In the function $f(x) = 5 \cdot 2^x$, notice that the ratio of consecutive outputs is constant for 1-unit increases in the input. This ratio equals the constant 2, the base of the exponential function. In other words,

$$\frac{f(1)}{f(0)} = \frac{5 \cdot 2^1}{5} = 2 \qquad \frac{f(2)}{f(1)} = \frac{5 \cdot 2^2}{5 \cdot 2^1} = 2 \qquad \frac{f(3)}{f(2)} = \frac{5 \cdot 2^3}{5 \cdot 2^2} = 2 \qquad \text{and so on}$$

This leads to the following result.

THEOREM

For an exponential function $f(x) = Ca^x$, where $a > 0$ and $a \neq 1$, if x is any real number, then

$$\frac{f(x+1)}{f(x)} = a \quad \text{or} \quad f(x+1) = af(x)$$

In Words

For 1-unit changes in the input x of an exponential function $f(x) = C \cdot a^x$, the ratio of consecutive outputs is the constant a.

Proof

$$\frac{f(x+1)}{f(x)} = \frac{Ca^{x+1}}{Ca^x} = a^{x+1-x} = a^1 = a$$ ■

EXAMPLE 2 **Identifying Linear or Exponential Functions**

Determine whether the given function is linear, exponential, or neither. For those that are linear, find a linear function that models the data. For those that are exponential, find an exponential function that models the data.

(a)

x	y
−1	5
0	2
1	−1
2	−4
3	−7

(b)

x	y
−1	32
0	16
1	8
2	4
3	2

(c)

x	y
−1	2
0	4
1	7
2	11
3	16

Solution For each function, compute the average rate of change of y with respect to x and the ratio of consecutive outputs. If the average rate of change is constant, then the function is linear. If the ratio of consecutive outputs is constant, then the function is exponential.

Table 3 (a)

x	y	Average Rate of Change	Ratio of Consecutive Outputs
−1	5		
		$\frac{\Delta y}{\Delta x} = \frac{2-5}{0-(-1)} = -3$	$\frac{2}{5}$
0	2		
		−3	$-\frac{1}{2}$
1	−1		
		−3	4
2	−4		
		−3	$\frac{7}{4}$
3	−7		

(b)

x	y	Average Rate of Change	Ratio of Consecutive Outputs
−1	32		
		$\frac{\Delta y}{\Delta x} = \frac{16-32}{0-(-1)} = -16$	$\frac{16}{32} = \frac{1}{2}$
0	16		
		−8	$\frac{8}{16} = \frac{1}{2}$
1	8		
		−4	$\frac{4}{8} = \frac{1}{2}$
2	4		
		−2	$\frac{2}{4} = \frac{1}{2}$
3	2		

(c)

x	y	Average Rate of Change	Ratio of Consecutive Outputs
−1	2		
		$\frac{\Delta y}{\Delta x} = \frac{4-2}{0-(-1)} = 2$	2
0	4		
		3	$\frac{7}{4}$
1	7		
		4	$\frac{11}{7}$
2	11		
		5	$\frac{16}{11}$
3	16		

(a) See Table 3(a). The average rate of change for every 1-unit increase in x is -3. Therefore, the function is a linear function. In a linear function the average rate of change is the slope m, so $m = -3$. The y-intercept b is the value of the function at $x = 0$, so $b = 2$. The linear function that models the data is $f(x) = mx + b = -3x + 2$.

(b) See Table 3(b). For this function, the average rate of change from -1 to 0 is -16, and the average rate of change from 0 to 1 is -8. Because the average rate of change is not constant, the function is not a linear function. The ratio of consecutive outputs for a 1-unit increase in the inputs is a constant, $\frac{1}{2}$. Because the ratio of consecutive outputs is constant, the function is an exponential function with growth factor $a = \frac{1}{2}$. The initial value of the exponential function is $C = 16$. Therefore, the exponential function that models the data is $g(x) = Ca^x = 16 \cdot \left(\frac{1}{2}\right)^x$.

(c) See Table 3(c). For this function, the average rate of change from -1 to 0 is 2, and the average rate of change from 0 to 1 is 3. Because the average rate of change is not constant, the function is not a linear function. The ratio of consecutive outputs from -1 to 0 is 2, and the ratio of consecutive outputs from 0 to 1 is $\frac{7}{4}$. Because the ratio of consecutive outputs is not a constant, the function is not an exponential function. ■

Now Work PROBLEM 25

2 Graph Exponential Functions

If we know how to graph an exponential function of the form $f(x) = a^x$, then we could use transformations (shifting, stretching, and so on) to obtain the graph of any exponential function.

First, we graph the exponential function $f(x) = 2^x$.

EXAMPLE 3 **Graphing an Exponential Function**

Graph the exponential function: $f(x) = 2^x$

Solution The domain of $f(x) = 2^x$ is the set of all real numbers. We begin by locating some points on the graph of $f(x) = 2^x$, as listed in Table 4.

Since $2^x > 0$ for all x, the range of f is $(0, \infty)$. From this, we conclude that the graph has no x-intercepts, and, in fact, the graph will lie above the x-axis for all x. As Table 4 indicates, the y-intercept is 1. Table 4 also indicates that as $x \to -\infty$ the values of $f(x) = 2^x$ get closer and closer to 0. We conclude that the x-axis ($y = 0$) is a horizontal asymptote to the graph as $x \to -\infty$. This gives us the end behavior for x large and negative.

Table 4

X	Y1
-10	9.8E-4
-3	.125
-1	.5
0	1
1	2
3	8
10	1024

Y1=2^X

To determine the end behavior for x large and positive, look again at Table 4. As $x \to \infty$, $f(x) = 2^x$ grows very quickly, causing the graph of $f(x) = 2^x$ to rise very rapidly. It is apparent that f is an increasing function and, hence, is one-to-one.

Using all this information, we plot some of the points from Table 4 and connect them with a smooth, continuous curve, as shown in Figure 20.

Figure 20

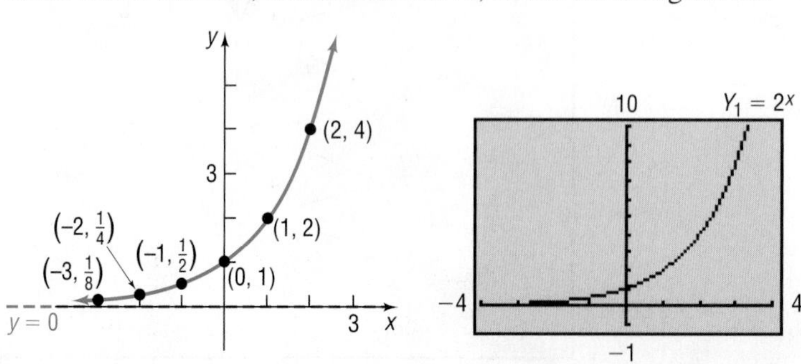

■

As we shall see, graphs that look like the one in Figure 20 occur very frequently in a variety of situations. For example, the graph in Figure 21 illustrates the number of cellular telephone subscribers at the end of each year from 1985 to 2010. We might conclude from this graph that the number of cellular telephone subscribers is growing *exponentially*.

Figure 21

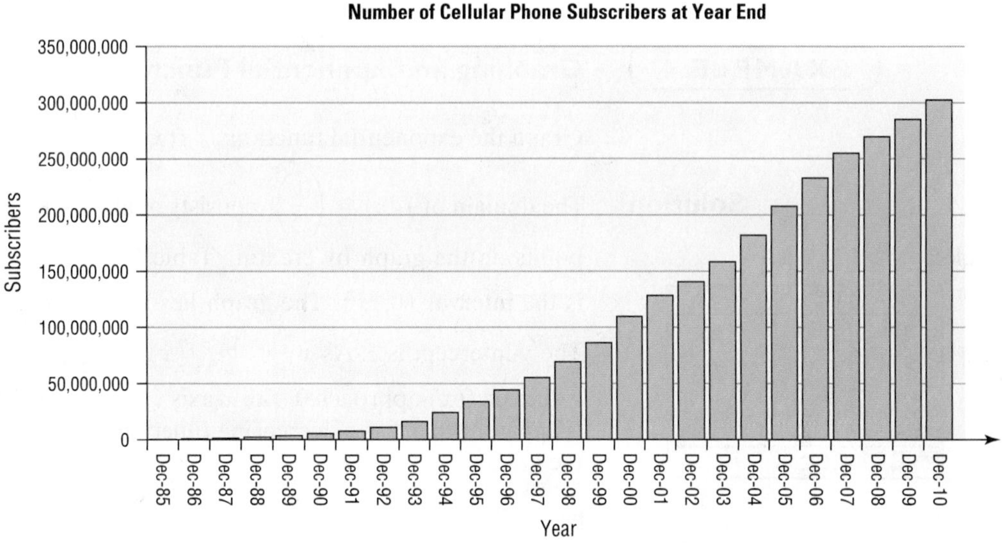

We shall have more to say about situations that lead to exponential growth later in this chapter. For now, we continue to seek properties of exponential functions.

The graph of $f(x) = 2^x$ in Figure 20 is typical of all exponential functions of the form $f(x) = a^x$ with $a > 1$. Such functions are increasing functions and, hence, are one-to-one. Their graphs lie above the x-axis, pass through the point $(0, 1)$, and thereafter rise rapidly as $x \to \infty$. As $x \to -\infty$, the x-axis $(y = 0)$ is a horizontal asymptote. There are no vertical asymptotes. Finally, the graphs are smooth and continuous with no corners or gaps.

Figure 22

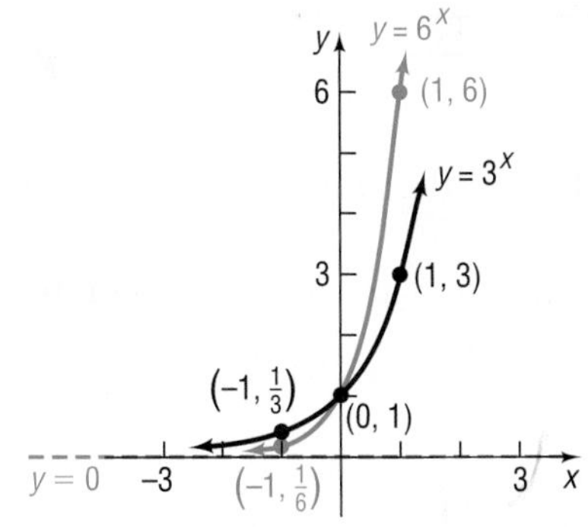

Figures 22 and 23 illustrate the graphs of two more exponential functions whose bases are larger than 1. Notice that the larger the base, the steeper the graph is when $x > 0$, and when $x < 0$, the larger the base, the closer the graph of the equation is to the x-axis.

Figure 23

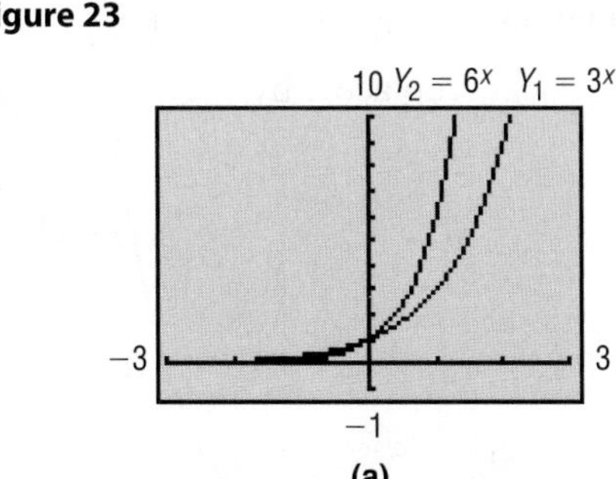

(a)

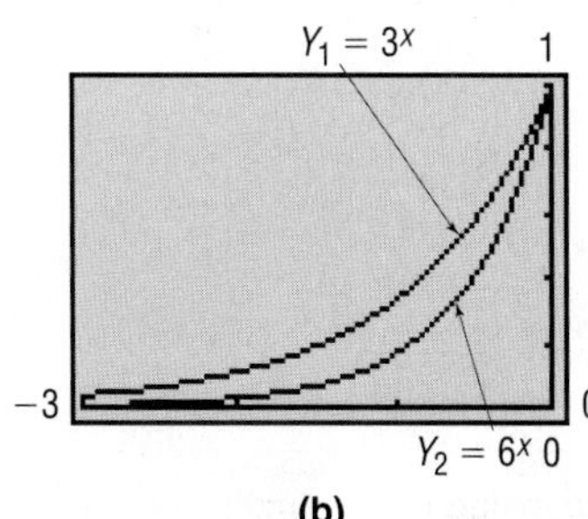

(b)

Properties of the Exponential Function $f(x) = a^x, a > 1$

1. The domain is the set of all real numbers or $(-\infty, \infty)$ using interval notation; the range is the set of positive real numbers or $(0, \infty)$ using interval notation.
2. There are no x-intercepts; the y-intercept is 1.
3. The x-axis $(y = 0)$ is a horizontal asymptote as $x \to -\infty$ $\left[\lim_{x \to -\infty} a^x = 0\right]$.
4. $f(x) = a^x$, where $a > 1$, is an increasing function and is one-to-one.

Figure 24

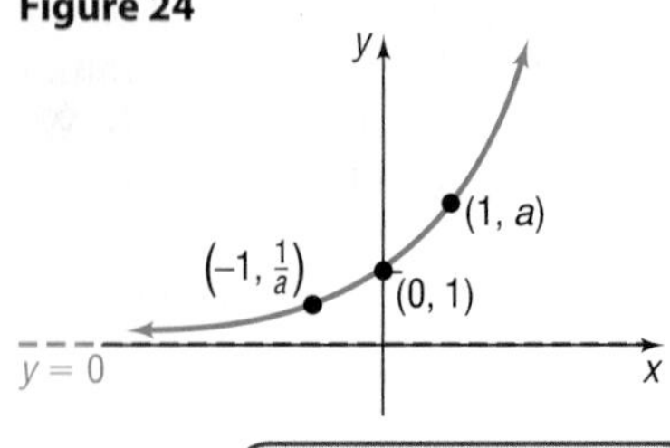

5. The graph of f contains the points $(0, 1)$, $(1, a)$, and $\left(-1, \dfrac{1}{a}\right)$.
6. The graph of f is smooth and continuous, with no corners or gaps. See Figure 24.

Now consider $f(x) = a^x$ when $0 < a < 1$.

EXAMPLE 4

Graphing an Exponential Function

Graph the exponential function: $f(x) = \left(\dfrac{1}{2}\right)^x$

Solution The domain of $f(x) = \left(\dfrac{1}{2}\right)^x$ consists of all real numbers. As before, we locate some points on the graph by creating Table 5. Since $\left(\dfrac{1}{2}\right)^x > 0$ for all x, the range of f is the interval $(0, \infty)$. The graph lies above the x-axis and so has no x-intercepts. The y-intercept is 1. As $x \to -\infty$, $f(x) = \left(\dfrac{1}{2}\right)^x$ grows very quickly. As $x \to \infty$, the values of $f(x)$ approach 0. The x-axis ($y = 0$) is a horizontal asymptote as $x \to \infty$. It is apparent that f is a decreasing function and so is one-to-one. Figure 25 illustrates the graph.

Table 5

X	Y1
-10	1024
-3	8
-1	2
0	1
1	.5
3	.125
10	9.8E-4

Y1=(1/2)^X

Figure 25

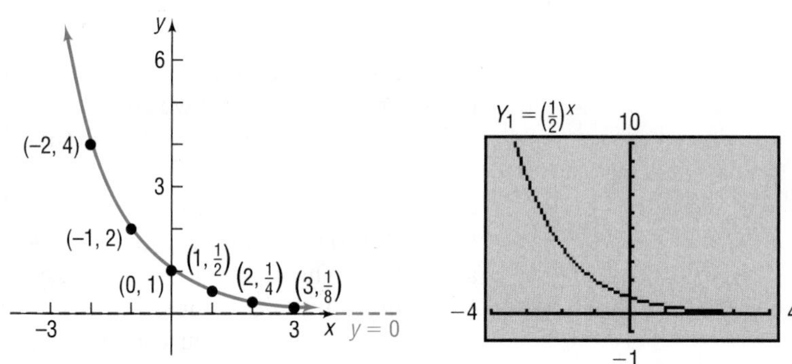

We could have obtained the graph of $y = \left(\dfrac{1}{2}\right)^x$ from the graph of $y = 2^x$ using transformations. The graph of $y = \left(\dfrac{1}{2}\right)^x = 2^{-x}$ is a reflection about the y-axis of the graph of $y = 2^x$ (replace x by $-x$). See Figures 26(a) and 26(b).

Figure 26

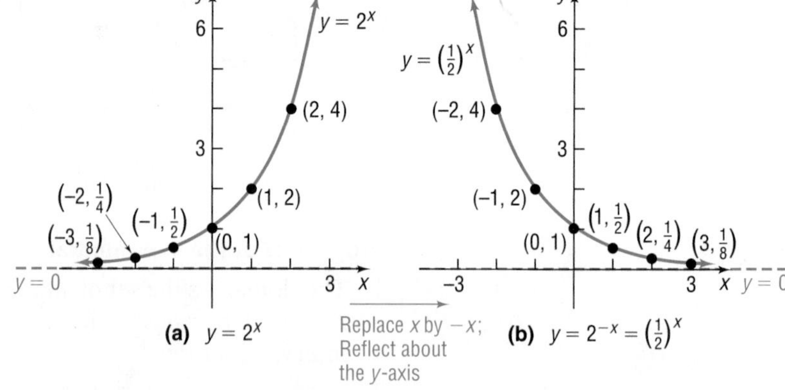

(a) $y = 2^x$ **(b)** $y = 2^{-x} = \left(\frac{1}{2}\right)^x$

Seeing the Concept

Using a graphing utility, simultaneously graph:

(a) $Y_1 = 3^x$, $Y_2 = \left(\dfrac{1}{3}\right)^x$

(b) $Y_1 = 6^x$, $Y_2 = \left(\dfrac{1}{6}\right)^x$

Conclude that the graph of $Y_2 = \left(\dfrac{1}{a}\right)^x$, for $a > 0$, is the reflection about the y-axis of the graph of $Y_1 = a^x$.

The graph of $f(x) = \left(\dfrac{1}{2}\right)^x$ in Figure 25 is typical of all exponential functions of the form $f(x) = a^x$ with $0 < a < 1$. Such functions are decreasing and one-to-one. Their graphs lie above the x-axis and pass through the point $(0, 1)$. The graphs rise rapidly as $x \to -\infty$. As $x \to \infty$, the x-axis ($y = 0$) is a horizontal asymptote. There are no vertical asymptotes. Finally, the graphs are smooth and continuous, with no corners or gaps.

Figures 27 and 28 illustrate the graphs of two more exponential functions whose bases are between 0 and 1. Notice that the smaller base results in a graph that is steeper when $x < 0$. When $x > 0$, the graph of the equation with the smaller base is closer to the x-axis.

Figure 27

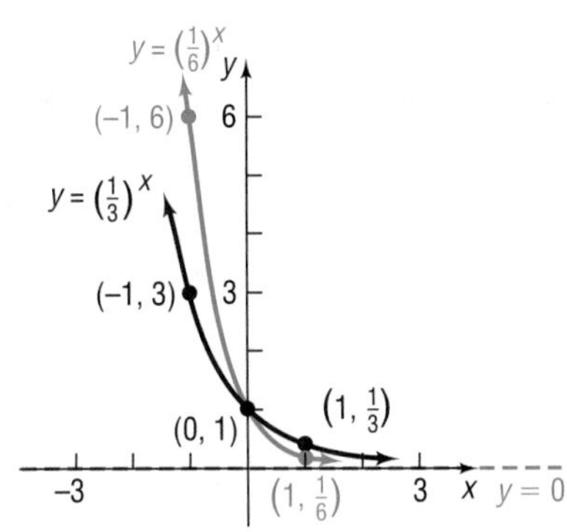

Figure 28

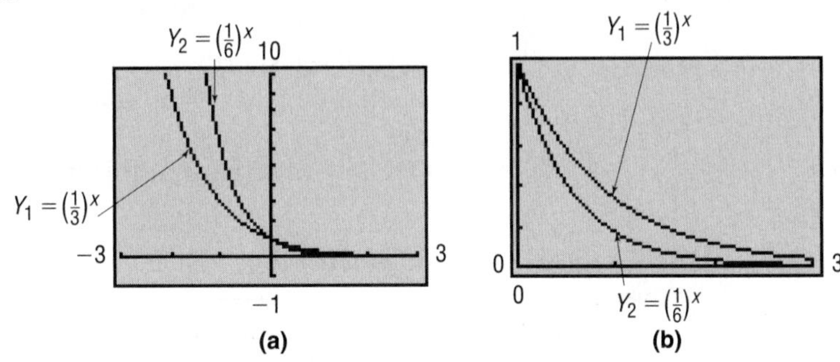

Figure 29

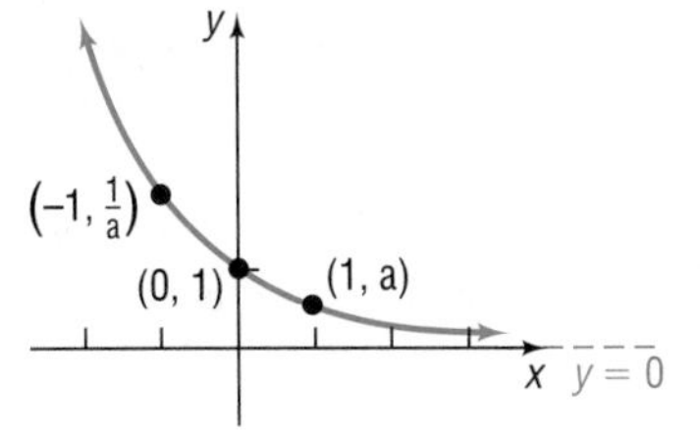

Properties of the Exponential Function $f(x) = a^x, 0 < a < 1$

1. The domain is the set of all real numbers or $(-\infty, \infty)$ using interval notation; the range is the set of positive real numbers or $(0, \infty)$ using interval notation.
2. There are no x-intercepts; the y-intercept is 1.
3. The x-axis ($y = 0$) is a horizontal asymptote as $x \to \infty$ $\left[\lim_{x\to\infty} a^x = 0\right]$.
4. $f(x) = a^x, 0 < a < 1$, is a decreasing function and is one-to-one.
5. The graph of f contains the points $\left(-1, \dfrac{1}{a}\right)$, $(0, 1)$, and $(1, a)$.
6. The graph of f is smooth and continuous, with no corners or gaps. See Figure 29.

EXAMPLE 5 Graphing Exponential Functions Using Transformations

Graph $f(x) = 2^{-x} - 3$, and determine the domain, range, and horizontal asymptote of f.

Solution Begin with the graph of $y = 2^x$. Figure 30 shows the stages.

Figure 30

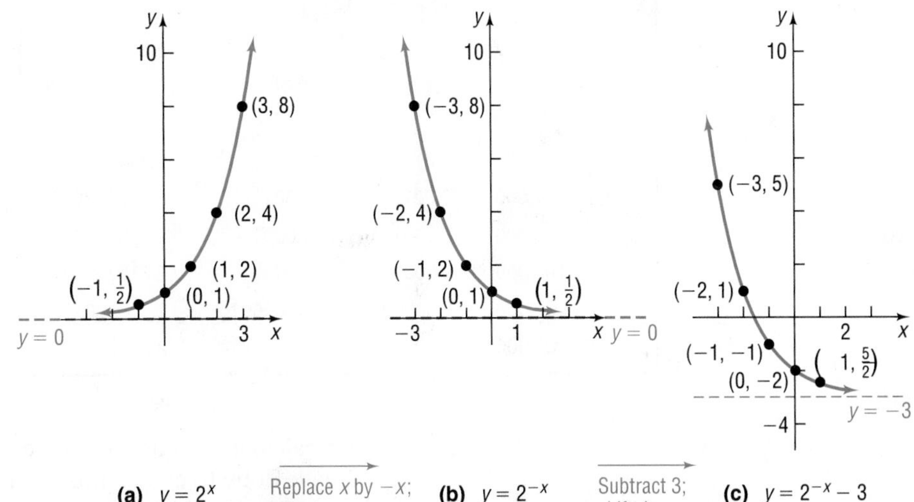

(a) $y = 2^x$ (b) $y = 2^{-x}$ (c) $y = 2^{-x} - 3$

As Figure 30(c) illustrates, the domain of $f(x) = 2^{-x} - 3$ is the interval $(-\infty, \infty)$ and the range is the interval $(-3, \infty)$. The horizontal asymptote of f is the line $y = -3$.

✓**Check:** Graph $Y_1 = 2^{-x} - 3$ to verify the graph obtained in Figure 30(c). ■

Now Work PROBLEM 41

3 Define the Number *e*

As we shall see shortly, many problems that occur in nature require the use of an exponential function whose base is a certain irrational number, symbolized by the letter *e*.

One way of arriving at this important number *e* is given next.

DEFINITION

The **number *e*** is defined as the number that the expression

$$\left(1 + \frac{1}{n}\right)^n \qquad (2)$$

approaches as $n \to \infty$. In calculus, this is expressed using limit notation as

$$e = \lim_{n\to\infty}\left(1 + \frac{1}{n}\right)^n$$

Table 6 illustrates what happens to the defining expression (2) as n takes on increasingly large values. The last number in the right column in the table is correct to nine decimal places and is the same as the entry given for e on your calculator (if expressed correctly to nine decimal places).

The exponential function $f(x) = e^x$, whose base is the number e, occurs with such frequency in applications that it is usually referred to as *the* exponential function. Indeed, most calculators have the key $\boxed{e^x}$ or $\boxed{\exp(x)}$, which may be used to evaluate the exponential function for a given value of x.

Table 6

n	$\frac{1}{n}$	$1 + \frac{1}{n}$	$\left(1 + \frac{1}{n}\right)^n$
1	1	2	2
2	0.5	1.5	2.25
5	0.2	1.2	2.48832
10	0.1	1.1	2.59374246
100	0.01	1.01	2.704813829
1,000	0.001	1.001	2.716923932
10,000	0.0001	1.0001	2.718145927
100,000	0.00001	1.00001	2.718268237
1,000,000	0.000001	1.000001	2.718280469
1,000,000,000	10^{-9}	$1 + 10^{-9}$	2.718281827

Table 7

X	Y1
-2	.13534
-1	.36788
0	1
1	2.7183
2	7.3891

Y1=e^(X)

Now use your calculator to approximate e^x for $x = -2, x = -1, x = 0, x = 1$, and $x = 2$, as we have done to create Table 7. The graph of the exponential function $f(x) = e^x$ is given in Figures 31(a) and (b) on the next page. Since $2 < e < 3$, the graph of $y = e^x$ lies between the graphs of $y = 2^x$ and $y = 3^x$. See Figure 31(c).

Figure 31

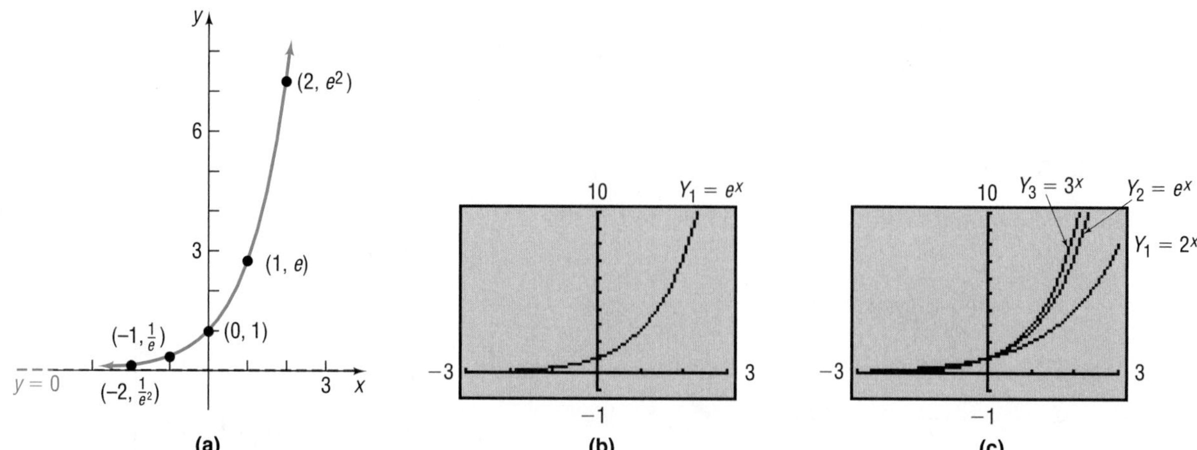

EXAMPLE 6 **Graphing Exponential Functions Using Transformations**

Graph $f(x) = -e^{x-3}$ and determine the domain, range, and horizontal asymptote of f.

Solution Begin with the graph of $y = e^x$. Figure 32 shows the stages.

Figure 32

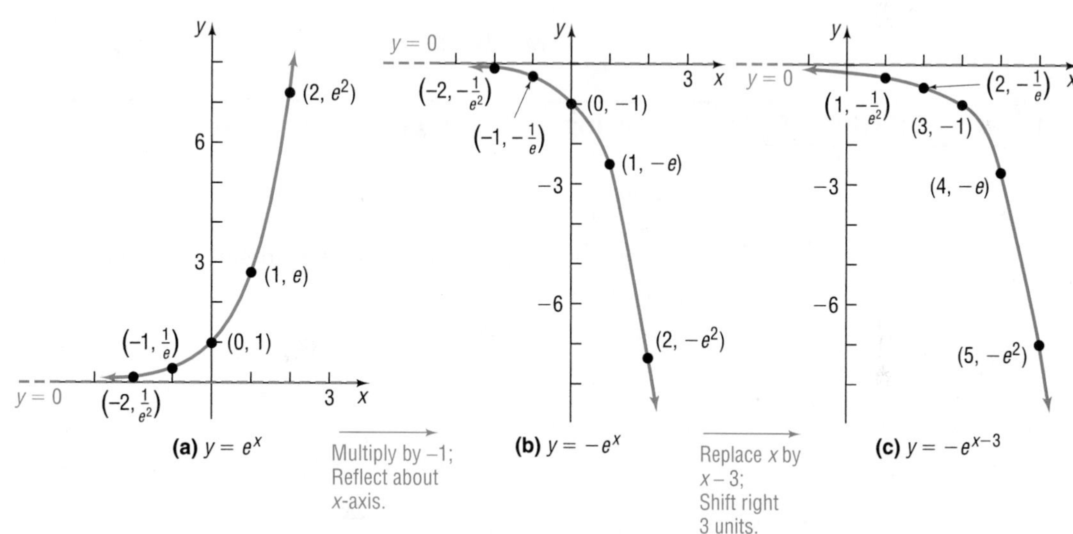

As Figure 32(c) illustrates, the domain of $f(x) = -e^{x-3}$ is the interval $(-\infty, \infty)$, and the range is the interval $(-\infty, 0)$. The horizontal asymptote is the line $y = 0$.

Check: Graph $Y_1 = -e^{x-3}$ to verify the graph obtained in Figure 32(c). ■

Now Work PROBLEM 53

4 Solve Exponential Equations

Equations that involve terms of the form a^x, where $a > 0$ and $a \neq 1$, are referred to as **exponential equations.** Such equations can sometimes be solved by appropriately applying the Laws of Exponents and property (3):

$$\text{If} \quad a^u = a^v, \quad \text{then} \quad u = v. \tag{3}$$

In Words
When two exponential expressions with the same base are equal, then their exponents are equal.

Property (3) is a consequence of the fact that exponential functions are one-to-one. To use property (3), each side of the equality must be written with the same base.

EXAMPLE 7 **Solving an Exponential Equation**

Solve: $4^{2x-1} = 8^x$

Algebraic Solution

Write each exponential expression so each has the same base.

$$4^{2x-1} = 8^x$$

$$(2^2)^{(2x-1)} = (2^3)^x \quad 4 = 2^2; 8 = 2^3$$

$$2^{2(2x-1)} = 2^{3x} \quad (a^r)^s = a^{rs}$$

$$2(2x-1) = 3x \quad \text{If } a^u = a^v, \text{ then } u = v.$$

$$4x - 2 = 3x$$

$$x = 2$$

The solution set is {2}. ■

Graphing Solution

Graph $Y_1 = 4^{2x-1}$ and $Y_2 = 8^x$. Use INTERSECT to determine the point of intersection. See Figure 33.

Figure 33

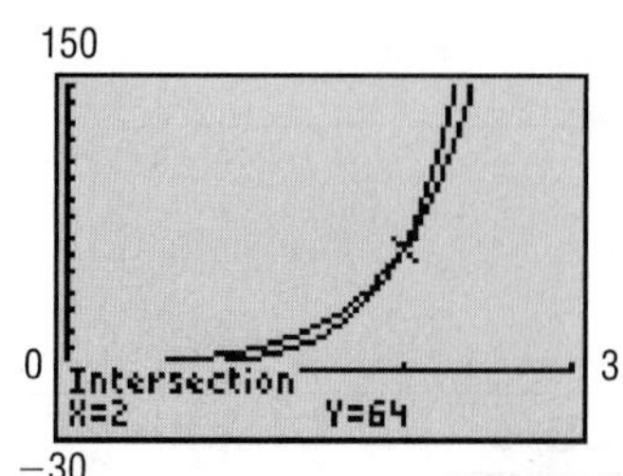

The graphs intersect at (2, 64), so the solution set is $\{2\}$. ■

Now Work PROBLEM 63

EXAMPLE 8 **Solving an Exponential Equation**

Solve: $e^{-x^2} = (e^x)^2 \cdot \dfrac{1}{e^3}$

Solution Use the Laws of Exponents first to get a single expression with the base e on the right side.

$$(e^x)^2 \cdot \frac{1}{e^3} = e^{2x} \cdot e^{-3} = e^{2x-3}$$

As a result,

$$e^{-x^2} = e^{2x-3}$$

$$-x^2 = 2x - 3 \quad \text{Apply property (3).}$$

$$x^2 + 2x - 3 = 0 \quad \text{Place the quadratic equation in standard form.}$$

$$(x+3)(x-1) = 0 \quad \text{Factor.}$$

$$x = -3 \quad \text{or} \quad x = 1 \quad \text{Use the Zero-Product Property.}$$

The solution set is $\{-3, 1\}$. ■

EXAMPLE 9 **Exponential Probability**

Between 9:00 PM and 10:00 PM cars arrive at Burger King's drive-thru at the rate of 12 cars per hour (0.2 car per minute). The following formula from statistics can be used to determine the probability that a car will arrive within t minutes of 9:00 PM.

$$F(t) = 1 - e^{-0.2t}$$

(a) Determine the probability that a car will arrive within 5 minutes of 9 PM (that is, before 9:05 PM).

(b) Determine the probability that a car will arrive within 30 minutes of 9 PM (before 9:30 PM).

(c) Graph F using your graphing utility.

(d) What value does F approach as t increases without bound in the positive direction?

Solution (a) The probability that a car will arrive within 5 minutes is found by evaluating $F(t)$ at $t = 5$.

$$F(5) = 1 - e^{-0.2(5)} \approx 0.63212$$

Use a calculator.

Figure 34

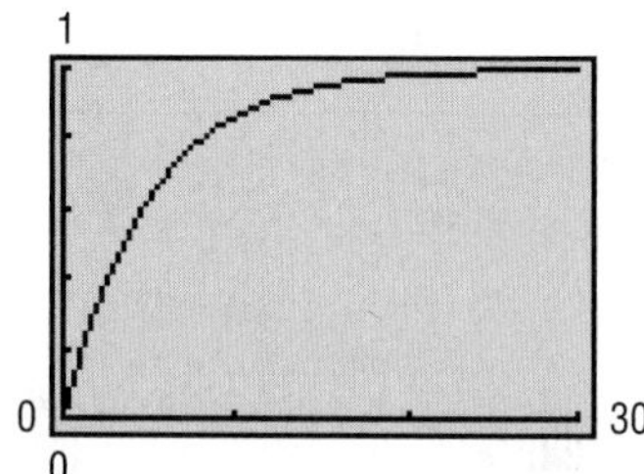

See Figure 34. We conclude that there is a 63% probability that a car will arrive within 5 minutes.

(b) The probability that a car will arrive within 30 minutes is found by evaluating $F(t)$ at $t = 30$.

$$F(30) = 1 - e^{-0.2(30)} \approx 0.9975$$

Use a calculator.

Figure 35

There is a 99.75% probability that a car will arrive within 30 minutes.

(c) See Figure 35 for the graph of F.

(d) As time passes, the probability that a car will arrive increases. The value that F approaches can be found by letting $t \to \infty$. Since $e^{-0.2t} = \dfrac{1}{e^{0.2t}}$, it follows that $e^{-0.2t} \to 0$ as $t \to \infty$. We conclude that F approaches 1 as t gets large. The algebraic analysis is confirmed by Figure 35. ■

Now Work PROBLEM 107

SUMMARY

Properties of the Exponential Function

$f(x) = a^x, \quad a > 1$	Domain: the interval $(-\infty, \infty)$; range: the interval $(0, \infty)$ x-intercepts: none; y-intercept: 1 Horizontal asymptote: x-axis ($y = 0$) as $x \to -\infty$ Increasing; one-to-one; smooth; continuous See Figure 24 for a typical graph.
$f(x) = a^x, \quad 0 < a < 1$	Domain: the interval $(-\infty, \infty)$; range: the interval $(0, \infty)$ x-intercepts: none; y-intercept: 1 Horizontal asymptote: x-axis ($y = 0$) as $x \to \infty$ Decreasing; one-to-one; smooth; continuous See Figure 29 for a typical graph.

If $a^u = a^v$, then $u = v$.

12.3 Assess Your Understanding

'Are You Prepared?' *Answers are given at the end of these exercises. If you get a wrong answer, read the pages listed in red.*

1. $4^3 =$ ____; $8^{2/3} =$ ____; $3^{-2} =$ ____.

2. Solve: $x^2 + 3x = 4$ (pp. 476–483)

3. ***True or False*** To graph $y = (x - 2)^3$, shift the graph of $y = x^3$ to the left 2 units. (pp. 605–613)

4. Find the average rate of change of $f(x) = 3x - 5$ from $x = 0$ to $x = 4$. (pp. 588–590; 631–634)

5. ***True or False*** The function $f(x) = \dfrac{2x}{x - 3}$ has $y = 2$ as a horizontal asymptote. (pp. 722–725)

Concepts and Vocabulary

6. A(n) __________ __________ is a function of the form $f(x) = Ca^x$, where $a > 0$, $a \neq 1$, and $C \neq 0$ are real numbers. The base a is the ______ ______ and C is the ______ ______.

7. For an exponential function $f(x) = Ca^x$, $\dfrac{f(x+1)}{f(x)} =$ ___.

8. ***True or False*** The domain of the exponential function $f(x) = a^x$, where $a > 0$ and $a \neq 1$, is the set of all real numbers.

9. ***True or False*** The range of the exponential function $f(x) = a^x$, where $a > 0$ and $a \neq 1$, is the set of all real numbers.

10. ***True or False*** The graph of the exponential function $f(x) = a^x$, where $a > 0$ and $a \neq 1$, has no x-intercept.

11. The graph of every exponential function $f(x) = a^x$, where $a > 0$ and $a \neq 1$, passes through three points: ________, ________, and ________.

12. If the graph of the exponential function $f(x) = a^x$, where $a > 0$ and $a \neq 1$, is decreasing, then a must be less than ______.

13. If $3^x = 3^4$, then $x =$ ______.

14. ***True or False*** The graphs of $y = 3^x$ and $y = \left(\dfrac{1}{3}\right)^x$ are identical.

Skill Building

In Problems 15–24, approximate each number using a calculator. Express your answer rounded to three decimal places.

15. (a) $3^{2.2}$ (b) $3^{2.23}$ (c) $3^{2.236}$ (d) $3^{\sqrt{5}}$
16. (a) $5^{1.7}$ (b) $5^{1.73}$ (c) $5^{1.732}$ (d) $5^{\sqrt{3}}$
17. (a) $2^{3.14}$ (b) $2^{3.141}$ (c) $2^{3.1415}$ (d) 2^{π}
18. (a) $2^{2.7}$ (b) $2^{2.71}$ (c) $2^{2.718}$ (d) 2^{e}
19. (a) $3.1^{2.7}$ (b) $3.14^{2.71}$ (c) $3.141^{2.718}$ (d) π^{e}
20. (a) $2.7^{3.1}$ (b) $2.71^{3.14}$ (c) $2.718^{3.141}$ (d) e^{π}
21. $e^{1.2}$
22. $e^{-1.3}$
23. $e^{-0.85}$
24. $e^{2.1}$

In Problems 25–32, determine whether the given function is linear, exponential, or neither. For those that are linear functions, find a linear function that models the data; for those that are exponential, find an exponential function that models the data.

25.

x	f(x)
−1	3
0	6
1	12
2	18
3	30

26.

x	g(x)
−1	2
0	5
1	8
2	11
3	14

27.

x	H(x)
−1	$\frac{1}{4}$
0	1
1	4
2	16
3	64

28.

x	F(x)
−1	$\frac{2}{3}$
0	1
1	$\frac{3}{2}$
2	$\frac{9}{4}$
3	$\frac{27}{8}$

29.

x	f(x)
−1	$\frac{3}{2}$
0	3
1	6
2	12
3	24

30.

x	g(x)
−1	6
0	1
1	0
2	3
3	10

31.

x	H(x)
−1	2
0	4
1	6
2	8
3	10

32.

x	F(x)
−1	$\frac{1}{2}$
0	$\frac{1}{4}$
1	$\frac{1}{8}$
2	$\frac{1}{16}$
3	$\frac{1}{32}$

In Problems 33–40, the graph of an exponential function is given. Match each graph to one of the following functions.

(A) $y = 3^x$ (B) $y = 3^{-x}$ (C) $y = -3^x$ (D) $y = -3^{-x}$

(E) $y = 3^x - 1$ (F) $y = 3^{x-1}$ (G) $y = 3^{1-x}$ (H) $y = 1 - 3^x$

33.

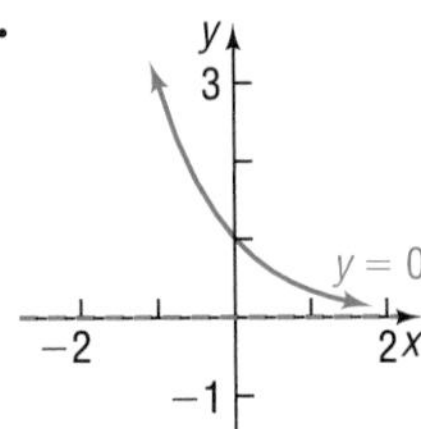

34.

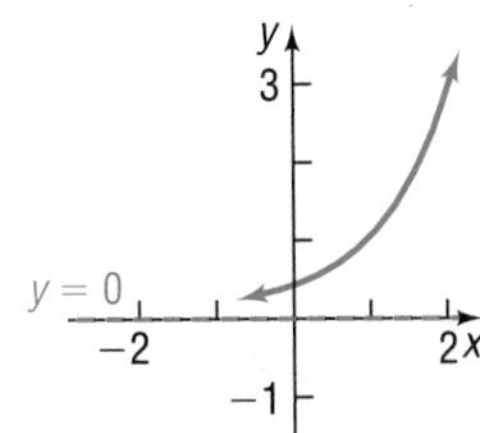

35.

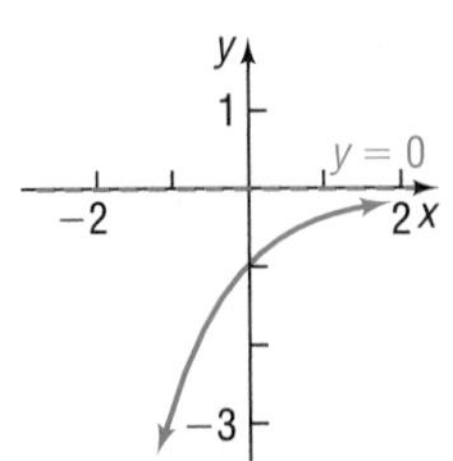

36.

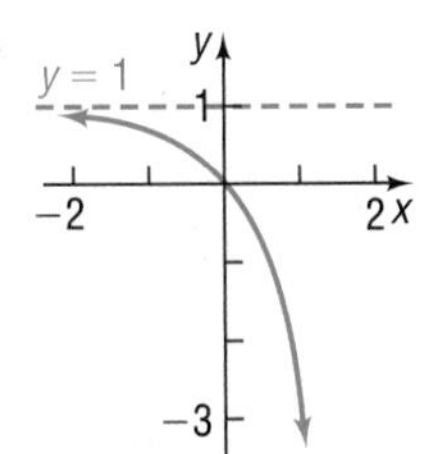

37.

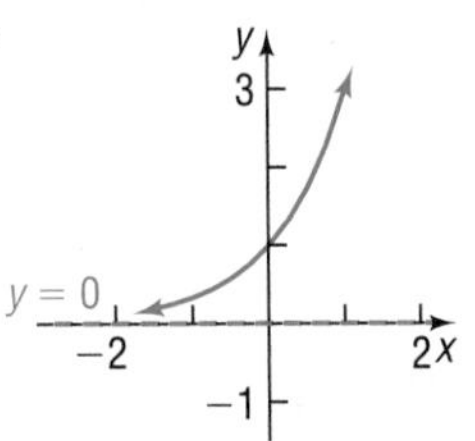

38.

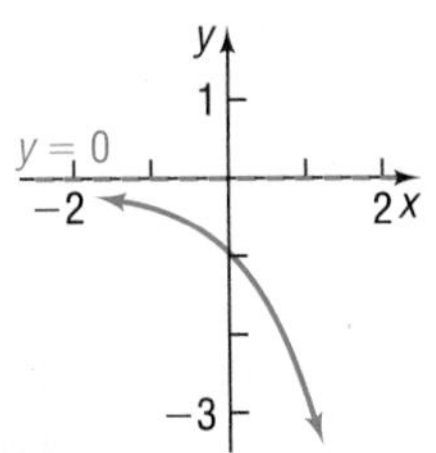

39.

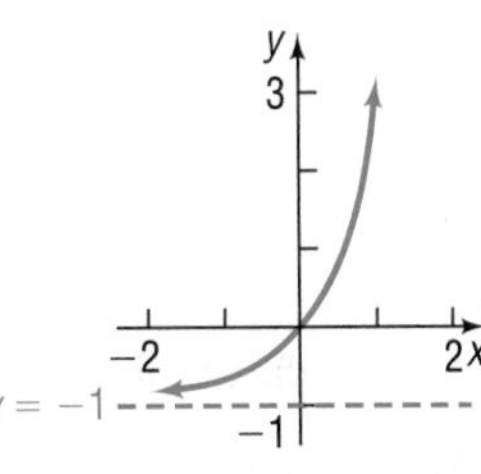

40.

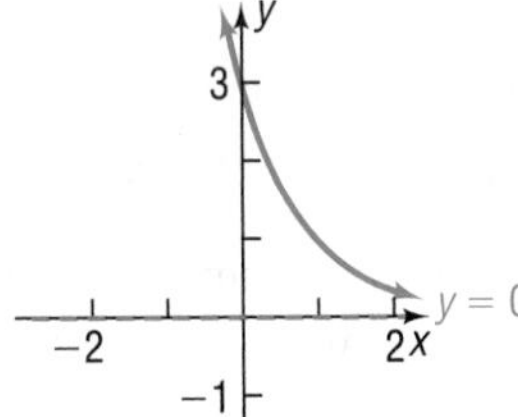

In Problems 41–52, use transformations to graph each function. Determine the domain, range, and horizontal asymptote of each function.

41. $f(x) = 2^x + 1$
42. $f(x) = 3^x - 2$
43. $f(x) = 3^{x-1}$
44. $f(x) = 2^{x+2}$
45. $f(x) = 3 \cdot \left(\frac{1}{2}\right)^x$
46. $f(x) = 4 \cdot \left(\frac{1}{3}\right)^x$
47. $f(x) = 3^{-x} - 2$
48. $f(x) = -3^x + 1$
49. $f(x) = 2 + 4^{x-1}$
50. $f(x) = 1 - 2^{x+3}$
51. $f(x) = 2 + 3^{x/2}$
52. $f(x) = 1 - 2^{-x/3}$

In Problems 53–60, begin with the graph of $y = e^x$ [Figure 31] and use transformations to graph each function. Determine the domain, range, and horizontal asymptote of each function.

53. $f(x) = e^{-x}$
54. $f(x) = -e^x$
55. $f(x) = e^{x+2}$
56. $f(x) = e^x - 1$
57. $f(x) = 5 - e^{-x}$
58. $f(x) = 9 - 3e^{-x}$
59. $f(x) = 2 - e^{-x/2}$
60. $f(x) = 7 - 3e^{2x}$

In Problems 61–80, solve each equation. Verify your results using a graphing utility.

61. $7^x = 7^3$
62. $5^x = 5^{-6}$
63. $2^{-x} = 16$
64. $3^{-x} = 81$
65. $\left(\frac{1}{5}\right)^x = \frac{1}{25}$
66. $\left(\frac{1}{4}\right)^x = \frac{1}{64}$
67. $2^{2x-1} = 4$
68. $5^{x+3} = \frac{1}{5}$
69. $3^{x^3} = 9^x$
70. $4^{x^2} = 2^x$
71. $8^{-x+14} = 16^x$
72. $9^{-x+15} = 27^x$
73. $3^{x^2-7} = 27^{2x}$
74. $5^{x^2+8} = 125^{2x}$
75. $4^x \cdot 2^{x^2} = 16^2$
76. $9^{2x} \cdot 27^{x^2} = 3^{-1}$
77. $e^x = e^{3x+8}$
78. $e^{3x} = e^{2-x}$
79. $e^{x^2} = e^{3x} \cdot \frac{1}{e^2}$
80. $(e^4)^x \cdot e^{x^2} = e^{12}$
81. If $4^x = 7$, what does 4^{-2x} equal?
82. If $2^x = 3$, what does 4^{-x} equal?
83. If $3^{-x} = 2$, what does 3^{2x} equal?
84. If $5^{-x} = 3$, what does 5^{3x} equal?

In Problems 85–88, determine the exponential function whose graph is given.

85.

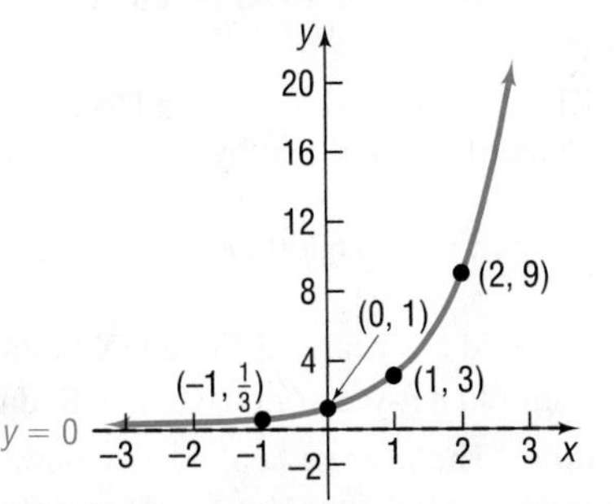

86.

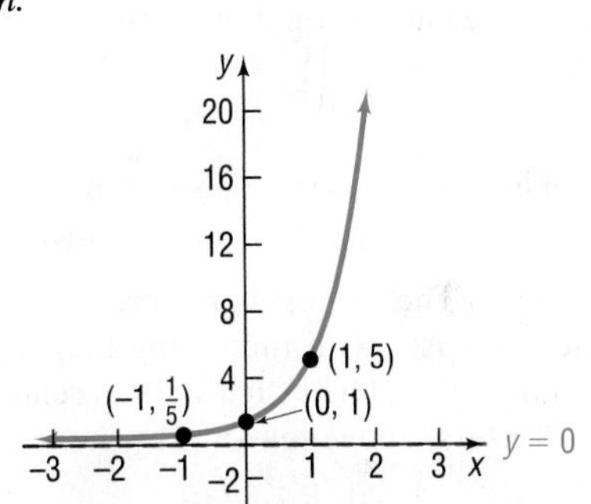

87.

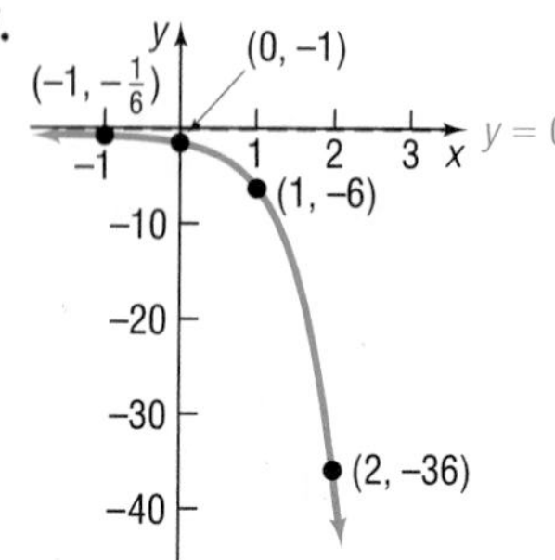

88.

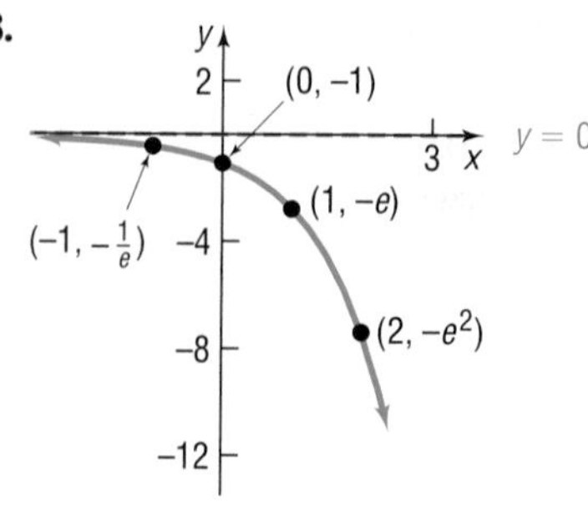

89. Find an exponential function with horizontal asymptote $y = 2$ whose graph contains the points $(0, 3)$ and $(1, 5)$.

90. Find an exponential function with horizontal asymptote $y = -3$ whose graph contains the points $(0, -2)$ and $(-2, 1)$.

Mixed Practice

91. Suppose that $f(x) = 2^x$.
   (a) What is $f(4)$? What point is on the graph of f?
   (b) If $f(x) = \frac{1}{16}$, what is x? What point is on the graph of f?

92. Suppose that $f(x) = 3^x$.
   (a) What is $f(4)$? What point is on the graph of f?
   (b) If $f(x) = \frac{1}{9}$, what is x? What point is on the graph of f?

93. Suppose that $g(x) = 4^x + 2$.
   (a) What is $g(-1)$? What point is on the graph of g?
   (b) If $g(x) = 66$, what is x? What point is on the graph of g?

94. Suppose that $g(x) = 5^x - 3$.
   (a) What is $g(-1)$? What point is on the graph of g?
   (b) If $g(x) = 122$, what is x? What point is on the graph of g?

95. Suppose that $H(x) = \left(\frac{1}{2}\right)^x - 4$.
   (a) What is $H(-6)$? What point is on the graph of H?
   (b) If $H(x) = 12$, what is x? What point is on the graph of H?
   (c) Find the zero of H.

96. Suppose that $F(x) = \left(\frac{1}{3}\right)^x - 3$.
   (a) What is $F(-5)$? What point is on the graph of F?
   (b) If $F(x) = 24$, what is x? What point is on the graph of F?
   (c) Find the zero of F.

In Problems 97–100, graph each function. Based on the graph, state the domain and the range and find any intercepts.

97. $f(x) = \begin{cases} e^{-x} & \text{if } x < 0 \\ e^x & \text{if } x \geq 0 \end{cases}$

98. $f(x) = \begin{cases} e^{x} & \text{if } x < 0 \\ e^{-x} & \text{if } x \geq 0 \end{cases}$

99. $f(x) = \begin{cases} -e^{x} & \text{if } x < 0 \\ -e^{-x} & \text{if } x \geq 0 \end{cases}$

100. $f(x) = \begin{cases} -e^{-x} & \text{if } x < 0 \\ -e^{x} & \text{if } x \geq 0 \end{cases}$

Applications and Extensions

101. **Optics** If a single pane of glass obliterates 3% of the light passing through it, the percent p of light that passes through n successive panes is given approximately by the function

$$p(n) = 100(0.97)^n$$

   (a) What percent of light will pass through 10 panes?
   (b) What percent of light will pass through 25 panes?

102. **Atmospheric Pressure** The atmospheric pressure p on a balloon or plane decreases with increasing height. This pressure, measured in millimeters of mercury, is related to the height h (in kilometers) above sea level by the function

$$p(h) = 760e^{-0.145h}$$

   (a) Find the atmospheric pressure at a height of 2 kilometers (over a mile).
   (b) What is it at a height of 10 kilometers (over 30,000 feet)?

103. **Depreciation** The price p, in dollars, of a Honda Civic DX Sedan that is x years old is modeled by

$$p(x) = 16{,}630(0.90)^x$$

   (a) How much should a 3-year-old Civic DX Sedan cost?
   (b) How much should a 9-year-old Civic DX Sedan cost?

104. **Healing of Wounds** The normal healing of wounds can be modeled by an exponential function. If A_0 represents the

original area of the wound and if A equals the area of the wound, then the function

$$A(n) = A_0 e^{-0.35n}$$

describes the area of a wound after n days following an injury when no infection is present to retard the healing. Suppose that a wound initially had an area of 100 square millimeters.

(a) If healing is taking place, how large will the area of the wound be after 3 days?

(b) How large will it be after 10 days?

105. Drug Medication The function

$$D(h) = 5e^{-0.4h}$$

can be used to find the number of milligrams D of a certain drug that is in a patient's bloodstream h hours after the drug has been administered. How many milligrams will be present after 1 hour? After 6 hours?

106. Spreading of Rumors A model for the number N of people in a college community who have heard a certain rumor is

$$N = P(1 - e^{-0.15d})$$

where P is the total population of the community and d is the number of days that have elapsed since the rumor began. In a community of 1000 students, how many students will have heard the rumor after 3 days?

107. Exponential Probability Between 12:00 PM and 1:00 PM, cars arrive at Citibank's drive-thru at the rate of 6 cars per hour (0.1 car per minute). The following formula from probability can be used to determine the probability that a car will arrive within t minutes of 12:00 PM:

$$F(t) = 1 - e^{-0.1t}$$

(a) Determine the probability that a car will arrive within 10 minutes of 12:00 PM (that is, before 12:10 PM).

(b) Determine the probability that a car will arrive within 40 minutes of 12:00 PM (before 12:40 PM).

(c) What value does F approach as t becomes unbounded in the positive direction?

(d) Graph F using a graphing utility.

(e) Using INTERSECT, determine how many minutes are needed for the probability to reach 50%.

108. Exponential Probability Between 5:00 PM and 6:00 PM, cars arrive at Jiffy Lube at the rate of 9 cars per hour (0.15 car per minute). The following formula from probability can be used to determine the probability that a car will arrive within t minutes of 5:00 PM:

$$F(t) = 1 - e^{-0.15t}$$

(a) Determine the probability that a car will arrive within 15 minutes of 5:00 PM (that is, before 5:15 PM).

(b) Determine the probability that a car will arrive within 30 minutes of 5:00 PM (before 5:30 PM).

(c) What value does F approach as t becomes unbounded in the positive direction?

(d) Graph F using a graphing utility.

(e) Using INTERSECT, determine how many minutes are needed for the probability to reach 60%.

109. Poisson Probability Between 5:00 PM and 6:00 PM, cars arrive at McDonald's drive-thru at the rate of 20 cars per hour. The following formula from probability can be used to determine the probability that x cars will arrive between 5:00 PM and 6:00 PM.

$$P(x) = \frac{20^x e^{-20}}{x!}$$

where

$$x! = x \cdot (x-1) \cdot (x-2) \cdot \cdots \cdot 3 \cdot 2 \cdot 1$$

(a) Determine the probability that $x = 15$ cars will arrive between 5:00 PM and 6:00 PM.

(b) Determine the probability that $x = 20$ cars will arrive between 5:00 PM and 6:00 PM.

110. Poisson Probability People enter a line for the *Demon Roller Coaster* at the rate of 4 per minute. The following formula from probability can be used to determine the probability that x people will arrive within the next minute.

$$P(x) = \frac{4^x e^{-4}}{x!}$$

where

$$x! = x \cdot (x-1) \cdot (x-2) \cdot \cdots \cdot 3 \cdot 2 \cdot 1$$

(a) Determine the probability that $x = 5$ people will arrive within the next minute.

(b) Determine the probability that $x = 8$ people will arrive within the next minute.

111. Relative Humidity The relative humidity is the ratio (expressed as a percent) of the amount of water vapor in the air to the maximum amount that it can hold at a specific temperature. The relative humidity, R, is found using the following formula:

$$R = 10^{\frac{4221}{T+459.4} - \frac{4221}{D+459.4} + 2}$$

where T is the air temperature (in °F) and D is the dew point temperature (in °F).

(a) Determine the relative humidity if the air temperature is 50° Fahrenheit and the dew point temperature is 41° Fahrenheit.

(b) Determine the relative humidity if the air temperature is 68° Fahrenheit and the dew point temperature is 59° Fahrenheit.

(c) What is the relative humidity if the air temperature and the dew point temperature are the same?

112. Learning Curve Suppose that a student has 500 vocabulary words to learn. If the student learns 15 words after 5 minutes, the function

$$L(t) = 500(1 - e^{-0.0061t})$$

approximates the number of words L that the student will learn after t minutes.

(a) How many words will the student learn after 30 minutes?

(b) How many words will the student learn after 60 minutes?

113. Current in a *RL* Circuit The equation governing the amount of current I (in amperes) after time t (in seconds) in a single RL circuit consisting of a resistance R (in ohms), an inductance L (in henrys), and an electromotive force E (in volts) is

$$I = \frac{E}{R}\left[1 - e^{-(R/L)t}\right]$$

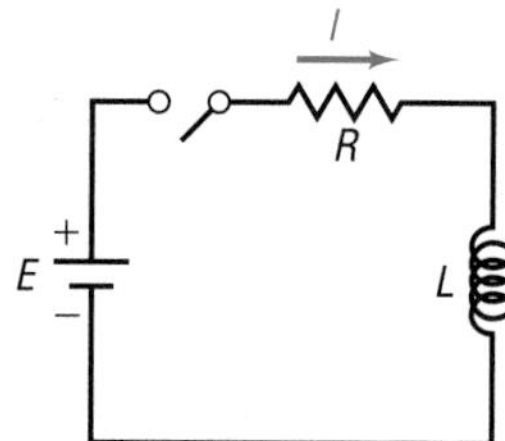

(a) If $E = 120$ volts, $R = 10$ ohms, and $L = 5$ henrys, how much current I_1 is flowing after 0.3 second? After 0.5 second? After 1 second?
(b) What is the maximum current?
(c) Graph this function $I = I_1(t)$, measuring I along the y-axis and t along the x-axis.
(d) If $E = 120$ volts, $R = 5$ ohms, and $L = 10$ henrys, how much current I_2 is flowing after 0.3 second? After 0.5 second? After 1 second?
(e) What is the maximum current?
(f) Graph the function $I = I_2(t)$ on the same coordinate axes as $I_1(t)$.

114. Current in a *RC* Circuit The equation governing the amount of current I (in amperes) after time t (in microseconds) in a single RC circuit consisting of a resistance R (in ohms), a capacitance C (in microfarads), and an electromotive force E (in volts) is

$$I = \frac{E}{R}e^{-t/(RC)}$$

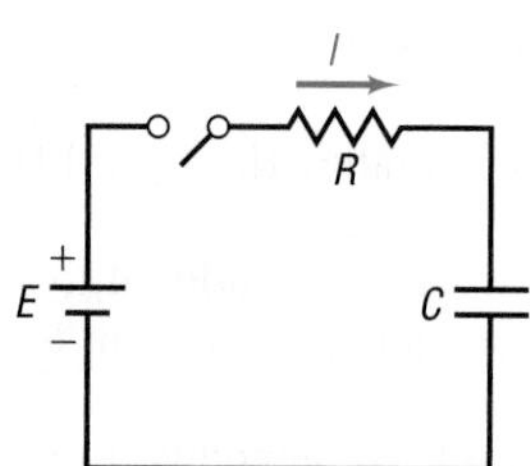

(a) If $E = 120$ volts, $R = 2000$ ohms, and $C = 1.0$ microfarad, how much current I_1 is flowing initially ($t = 0$)? After 1000 microseconds? After 3000 microseconds?
(b) What is the maximum current?
(c) Graph the function $I = I_1(t)$, measuring I along the y-axis and t along the x-axis.
(d) If $E = 120$ volts, $R = 1000$ ohms, and $C = 2.0$ microfarads, how much current I_2 is flowing initially? After 1000 microseconds? After 3000 microseconds?
(e) What is the maximum current?
(f) Graph the function $I = I_2(t)$ on the same coordinate axes as $I_1(t)$.

115. If f is an exponential function of the form $f(x) = C \cdot a^x$ with growth factor 3 and $f(6) = 12$, what is $f(7)$?

116. Another Formula for *e* Use a calculator to compute the values of

$$2 + \frac{1}{2!} + \frac{1}{3!} + \cdots + \frac{1}{n!}$$

for $n = 4, 6, 8$, and 10. Compare each result with e.

[**Hint:** $1! = 1, 2! = 2 \cdot 1, 3! = 3 \cdot 2 \cdot 1,$
$n! = n(n-1) \cdot \cdots \cdot (3)(2)(1)$.]

117. Another Formula for *e* Use a calculator to compute the various values of the expression. Compare the values to e.

$$2 + \cfrac{1}{1 + \cfrac{1}{2 + \cfrac{2}{3 + \cfrac{3}{4 + \cfrac{4}{\text{etc.}}}}}}$$

118. Difference Quotient If $f(x) = a^x$, show that

$$\frac{f(x+h) - f(x)}{h} = a^x \cdot \frac{a^h - 1}{h} \qquad h \neq 0$$

119. If $f(x) = a^x$, show that $f(A + B) = f(A) \cdot f(B)$.

120. If $f(x) = a^x$, show that $f(-x) = \dfrac{1}{f(x)}$.

121. If $f(x) = a^x$, show that $f(\alpha x) = [f(x)]^\alpha$.

Problems 122 and 123 provide definitions for two other transcendental functions.

122. The **hyperbolic sine function,** designated by $\sinh x$, is defined as

$$\sinh x = \frac{1}{2}(e^x - e^{-x})$$

(a) Show that $f(x) = \sinh x$ is an odd function.
(b) Graph $f(x) = \sinh x$ using a graphing utility.

123. The **hyperbolic cosine function,** designated by $\cosh x$, is defined as

$$\cosh x = \frac{1}{2}(e^x + e^{-x})$$

(a) Show that $f(x) = \cosh x$ is an even function.
(b) Graph $f(x) = \cosh x$ using a graphing utility.
(c) Refer to Problem 122. Show that, for every x,

$$(\cosh x)^2 - (\sinh x)^2 = 1$$

124. Historical Problem Pierre de Fermat (1601–1665) conjectured that the function

$$f(x) = 2^{(2^x)} + 1$$

for $x = 1, 2, 3, \ldots,$ would always have a value equal to a prime number. But Leonhard Euler (1707–1783) showed that this formula fails for $x = 5$. Use a calculator to determine the prime numbers produced by f for $x = 1, 2, 3, 4$. Then show that $f(5) = 641 \times 6{,}700{,}417$, which is not prime.

Explaining Concepts: Discussion and Writing

125. The bacteria in a 4-liter container double every minute. After 60 minutes the container is full. How long did it take to fill half the container?

126. Explain in your own words what the number e is. Provide at least two applications that use this number.

127. Do you think that there is a power function that increases more rapidly than an exponential function whose base is greater than 1? Explain.

128. As the base a of an exponential function $f(x) = a^x$, where $a > 1$ increases, what happens to the behavior of its graph for $x > 0$? What happens to the behavior of its graph for $x < 0$?

129. The graphs of $y = a^{-x}$ and $y = \left(\frac{1}{a}\right)^x$ are identical. Why?

'Are You Prepared?' Answers

1. 64; 4; $\frac{1}{9}$ **2.** $\{-4, 1\}$ **3.** False **4.** 3 **5.** True

12.4 Logarithmic Functions

PREPARING FOR THIS SECTION *Before getting started, review the following:*

- Solve Linear Inequalities (Section 7.5, pp. 508–509)
- Solve Quadratic Inequalities (Section 10.5, pp. 669–672)
- Polynomial and Rational Inequalities (Section 11.5, pp. 738–741)

Now Work the **'Are You Prepared?'** problems on page 798.

OBJECTIVES

1. Change Exponential Statements to Logarithmic Statements and Logarithmic Statements to Exponential Statements (p. 790)
2. Evaluate Logarithmic Expressions (p. 790)
3. Determine the Domain of a Logarithmic Function (p. 791)
4. Graph Logarithmic Functions (p. 792)
5. Solve Logarithmic Equations (p. 796)

Recall that a one-to-one function $y = f(x)$ has an inverse function that is defined (implicitly) by the equation $x = f(y)$. In particular, the exponential function $y = f(x) = a^x$, where $a > 0$ and $a \neq 1$, is one-to-one and, hence, has an inverse function that is defined implicitly by the equation

$$x = a^y, \quad a > 0, \quad a \neq 1$$

This inverse function is so important that it is given a name, the *logarithmic function*.

DEFINITION

The **logarithmic function to the base a,** where $a > 0$ and $a \neq 1$, is denoted by $y = \log_a x$ (read as "y is the logarithm to the base a of x") and is defined by

$$y = \log_a x \quad \text{if and only if} \quad x = a^y$$

The domain of the logarithmic function $y = \log_a x$ is $x > 0$.

In Words
When you read $\log_a x$, think to yourself "a raised to what power gives me x."

As this definition illustrates, **a logarithm is a name for a certain exponent.** So, $\log_a x$ represents the exponent to which a must be raised to obtain x.

EXAMPLE 1 **Relating Logarithms to Exponents**

(a) If $y = \log_3 x$, then $x = 3^y$. For example, the logarithmic statement $4 = \log_3 81$ is equivalent to the exponential statement $81 = 3^4$.

(b) If $y = \log_5 x$, then $x = 5^y$. For example, $-1 = \log_5\left(\frac{1}{5}\right)$ is equivalent to $\frac{1}{5} = 5^{-1}$. ■

1 Change Exponential Statements to Logarithmic Statements and Logarithmic Statements to Exponential Statements

We can use the definition of a logarithm to convert from exponential form to logarithmic form, and vice versa, as the following two examples illustrate.

EXAMPLE 2 **Changing Exponential Statements to Logarithmic Statements**

Change each exponential statement to an equivalent statement involving a logarithm.

(a) $1.2^3 = m$ (b) $e^b = 9$ (c) $a^4 = 24$

Solution Use the fact that $y = \log_a x$ and $x = a^y$, where $a > 0$ and $a \neq 1$, are equivalent.

(a) If $1.2^3 = m$, then $3 = \log_{1.2} m$.
(b) If $e^b = 9$, then $b = \log_e 9$.
(c) If $a^4 = 24$, then $4 = \log_a 24$. ■

Now Work PROBLEM 9

EXAMPLE 3 **Changing Logarithmic Statements to Exponential Statements**

Change each logarithmic statement to an equivalent statement involving an exponent.

(a) $\log_a 4 = 5$ (b) $\log_e b = -3$ (c) $\log_3 5 = c$

Solution (a) If $\log_a 4 = 5$, then $a^5 = 4$.
(b) If $\log_e b = -3$, then $e^{-3} = b$.
(c) If $\log_3 5 = c$, then $3^c = 5$. ■

Now Work PROBLEM 17

2 Evaluate Logarithmic Expressions

To find the exact value of a logarithm, we write the logarithm in exponential notation using the fact that $y = \log_a x$ is equivalent to $a^y = x$ and use the fact that if $a^u = a^v$, then $u = v$.

EXAMPLE 4 **Finding the Exact Value of a Logarithmic Expression**

Find the exact value of:

(a) $\log_2 16$ (b) $\log_3 \frac{1}{27}$

Solution

(a) To evaluate $\log_2 16$, think "2 raised to what power yields 16." So,

$y = \log_2 16$

$2^y = 16$ Change to exponential form.

$2^y = 2^4$ $16 = 2^4$

$y = 4$ Equate exponents.

Therefore, $\log_2 16 = 4$.

(b) To evaluate $\log_3 \frac{1}{27}$, think "3 raised to what power yields $\frac{1}{27}$." So,

$y = \log_3 \frac{1}{27}$

$3^y = \frac{1}{27}$ Change to exponential form.

$3^y = 3^{-3}$ $\frac{1}{27} = \frac{1}{3^3} = 3^{-3}$

$y = -3$ Equate exponents.

Therefore, $\log_3 \frac{1}{27} = -3$. ■

Now Work PROBLEM 25

3 Determine the Domain of a Logarithmic Function

The logarithmic function $y = \log_a x$ has been defined as the inverse of the exponential function $y = a^x$. That is, if $f(x) = a^x$, then $f^{-1}(x) = \log_a x$. Based on the discussion given in Section 12.2 on inverse functions, for a function f and its inverse f^{-1}, we have

$$\text{Domain of } f^{-1} = \text{Range of } f \quad \text{and} \quad \text{Range of } f^{-1} = \text{Domain of } f$$

Consequently, it follows that

> Domain of the logarithmic function = Range of the exponential function = $(0, \infty)$
> Range of the logarithmic function = Domain of the exponential function = $(-\infty, \infty)$

In the next box, we summarize some properties of the logarithmic function:

> $y = \log_a x$ (defining equation: $x = a^y$)
> Domain: $(0, \infty)$ Range: $(-\infty, \infty)$

The domain of a logarithmic function consists of the *positive* real numbers, so the argument of a logarithmic function must be greater than zero.

EXAMPLE 5 Finding the Domain of a Logarithmic Function

Find the domain of each logarithmic function.

(a) $F(x) = \log_2(x + 3)$ (b) $g(x) = \log_5\left(\frac{1 + x}{1 - x}\right)$ (c) $h(x) = \log_{1/2}|x|$

Solution

(a) The domain of F consists of all x for which $x + 3 > 0$, that is, $x > -3$. Using interval notation, the domain of f is $(-3, \infty)$.

(b) The domain of g is restricted to

$$\frac{1 + x}{1 - x} > 0$$

Solving this inequality, we find that the domain of g consists of all x between -1 and 1, that is, $-1 < x < 1$ or, using interval notation, $(-1, 1)$.

(c) Since $|x| > 0$, provided that $x \neq 0$, the domain of h consists of all real numbers except zero or, using interval notation, $(-\infty, 0) \cup (0, \infty)$. ■

Now Work PROBLEMS 39 AND 45

4 Graph Logarithmic Functions

Since exponential functions and logarithmic functions are inverses of each other, the graph of the logarithmic function $y = \log_a x$ is the reflection about the line $y = x$ of the graph of the exponential function $y = a^x$, as shown in Figure 36.

Figure 36

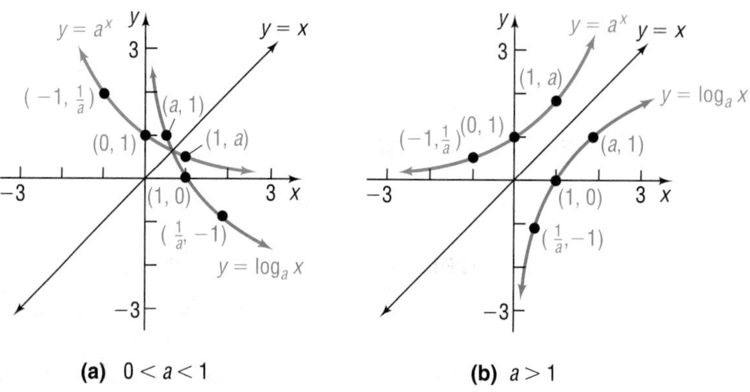

(a) $0 < a < 1$ (b) $a > 1$

For example, to graph $y = \log_2 x$, graph $y = 2^x$ and reflect it about the line $y = x$. See Figure 37. To graph $y = \log_{1/3} x$, graph $y = \left(\frac{1}{3}\right)^x$ and reflect it about the line $y = x$. See Figure 38.

Figure 37 Figure 38

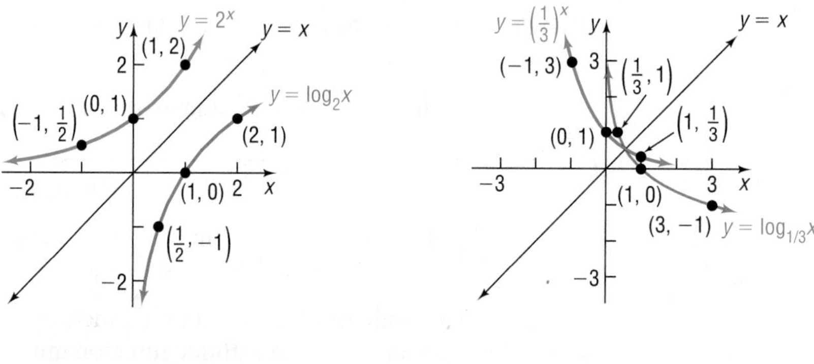

Now Work PROBLEM 59

The graphs of $y = \log_a x$ in Figures 36(a) and (b) lead to the following properties.

Properties of the Logarithmic Function $f(x) = \log_a x$

1. The domain is the set of positive real numbers or $(0, \infty)$ using interval notation; the range is the set of all real numbers or $(-\infty, \infty)$ using interval notation.
2. The x-intercept of the graph is 1. There is no y-intercept.
3. The y-axis ($x = 0$) is a vertical asymptote of the graph.
4. A logarithmic function is decreasing if $0 < a < 1$ and increasing if $a > 1$.
5. The graph of f contains the points $(1, 0)$, $(a, 1)$, and $\left(\frac{1}{a}, -1\right)$.
6. The graph is smooth and continuous, with no corners or gaps.

In Words

$y = \log_e x$ is written $y = \ln x$

If the base of a logarithmic function is the number e, then we have the **natural logarithm function.** This function occurs so frequently in applications that it is given a special symbol, **ln** (from the Latin, *logarithmus naturalis*). That is,

$$y = \ln x \quad \text{if and only if} \quad x = e^y \qquad \textbf{(1)}$$

Since $y = \ln x$ and the exponential function $y = e^x$ are inverse functions, we can obtain the graph of $y = \ln x$ by reflecting the graph of $y = e^x$ about the line $y = x$. See Figure 39.

Using a calculator with an ln key, we can obtain other points on the graph of $f(x) = \ln x$. See Table 8.

Figure 39

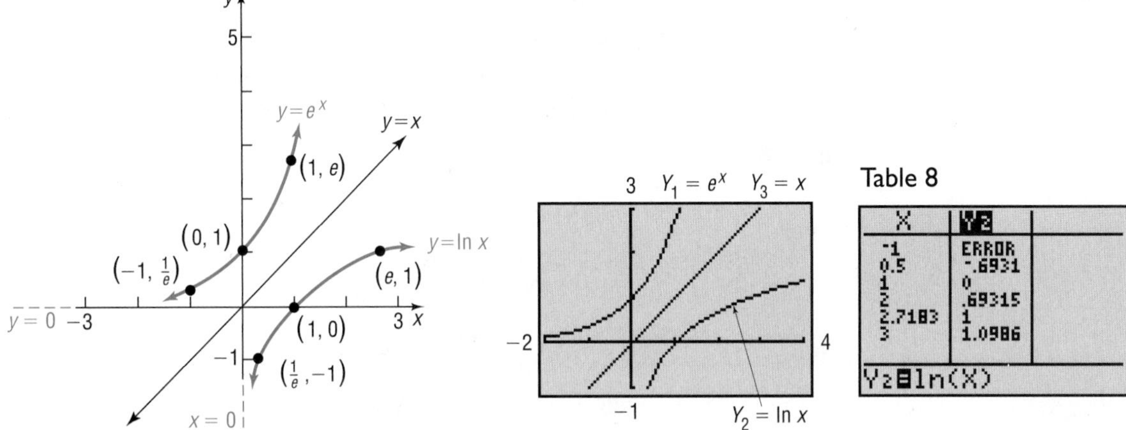

Table 8

X	Y2
-1	ERROR
0.5	-.6931
1	0
2	.69315
2.7183	1
3	1.0986

Y2=ln(X)

EXAMPLE 6 Graphing a Logarithmic Function and Its Inverse

(a) Find the domain of the logarithmic function $f(x) = -\ln(x - 2)$.
(b) Graph f.
(c) From the graph, determine the range and vertical asymptote of f.
(d) Find f^{-1}, the inverse of f.
(e) Find the domain and the range of f^{-1}.
(f) Graph f^{-1}.

Solution

(a) The domain of f consists of all x for which $x - 2 > 0$ or, equivalently, $x > 2$. The domain of f is $\{x|x > 2\}$ or $(2, \infty)$ in interval notation.

(b) To obtain the graph of $y = -\ln(x - 2)$, we begin with the graph of $y = \ln x$ and use transformations. See Figure 40.

Figure 40

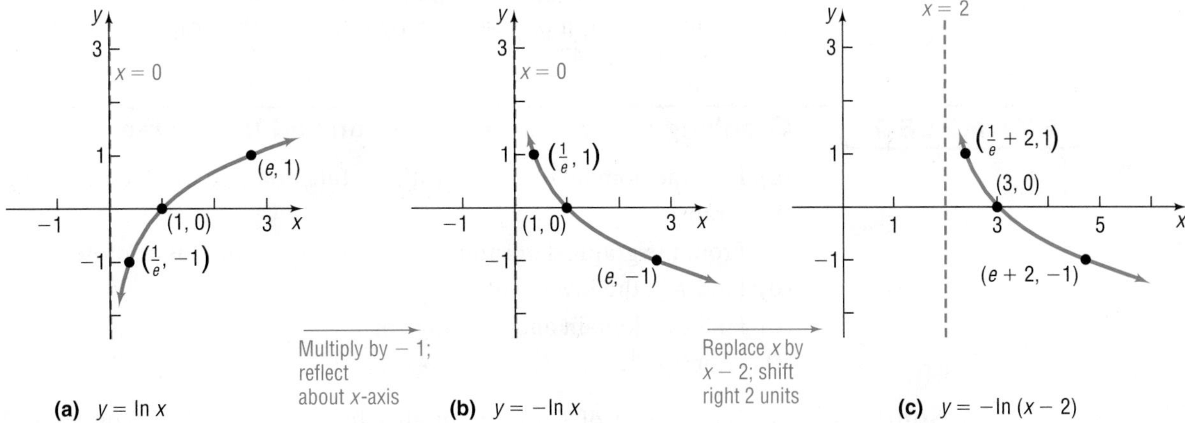

(a) $y = \ln x$ **(b)** $y = -\ln x$ **(c)** $y = -\ln(x - 2)$

(c) The range of $f(x) = -\ln(x - 2)$ is the set of all real numbers. The vertical asymptote is $x = 2$. [Do you see why? The original asymptote $(x = 0)$ is shifted to the right 2 units.]

(d) To find f^{-1}, begin with $y = -\ln(x - 2)$. The inverse function is defined (implicitly) by the equation

$$x = -\ln(y - 2)$$

Proceed to solve for y.

$$-x = \ln(y - 2) \quad \text{Isolate the logarithm.}$$
$$e^{-x} = y - 2 \quad \text{Change to an exponential statement.}$$
$$y = e^{-x} + 2 \quad \text{Solve for } y.$$

The inverse of f is $f^{-1}(x) = e^{-x} + 2$.

(e) The domain of f^{-1} equals the range of f, which is the set of all real numbers, from part (c). The range of f^{-1} is the domain of f, which is $(2, \infty)$ in interval notation.

(f) To graph f^{-1}, use the graph of f in Figure 40(c) and reflect it about the line $y = x$. See Figure 41. We could also graph $f^{-1}(x) = e^{-x} + 2$ using transformations.

Figure 41

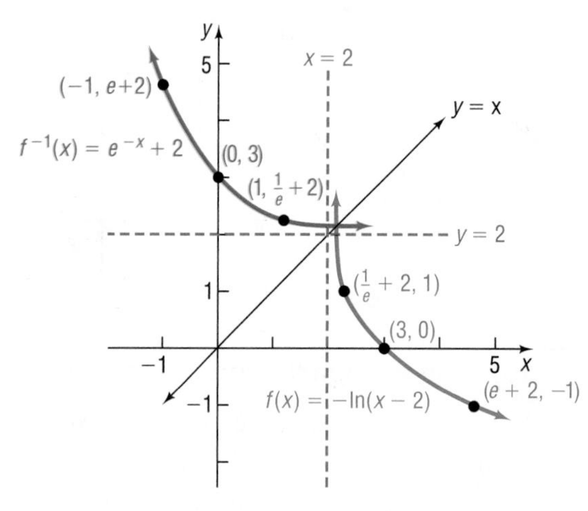

■

Now Work PROBLEM 71

If the base of a logarithmic function is the number 10, then we have the **common logarithm function.** If the base a of the logarithmic function is not indicated, it is understood to be 10. That is,

$$y = \log x \quad \text{if and only if} \quad x = 10^y$$

Since $y = \log x$ and the exponential function $y = 10^x$ are inverse functions, we can obtain the graph of $y = \log x$ by reflecting the graph of $y = 10^x$ about the line $y = x$. See Figure 42.

Figure 42

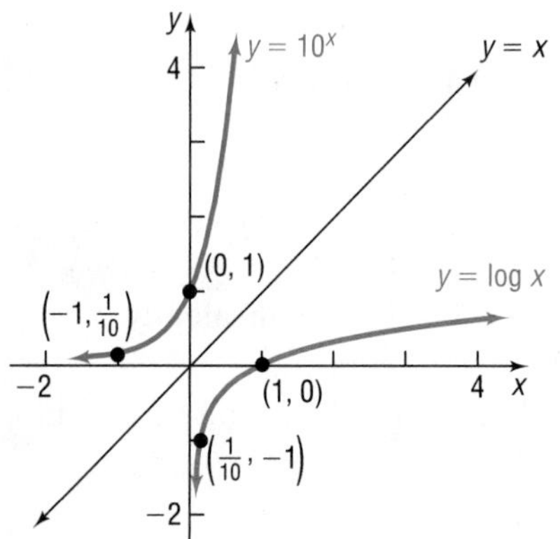

EXAMPLE 7 Graphing a Logarithmic Function and Its Inverse

(a) Find the domain of the logarithmic function $f(x) = 3\log(x - 1)$.

(b) Graph f.

(c) From the graph, determine the range and vertical asymptote of f.

(d) Find f^{-1}, the inverse of f.

(e) Find the domain and the range of f^{-1}.

(f) Graph f^{-1}.

Solution

(a) The domain of f consists of all x for which $x - 1 > 0$ or, equivalently, $x > 1$. The domain of f is $\{x \mid x > 1\}$ or $(1, \infty)$ in interval notation.

(b) To obtain the graph of $y = 3\log(x - 1)$, we begin with the graph of $y = \log x$ and use transformations. See Figure 43 on the next page.

Figure 43

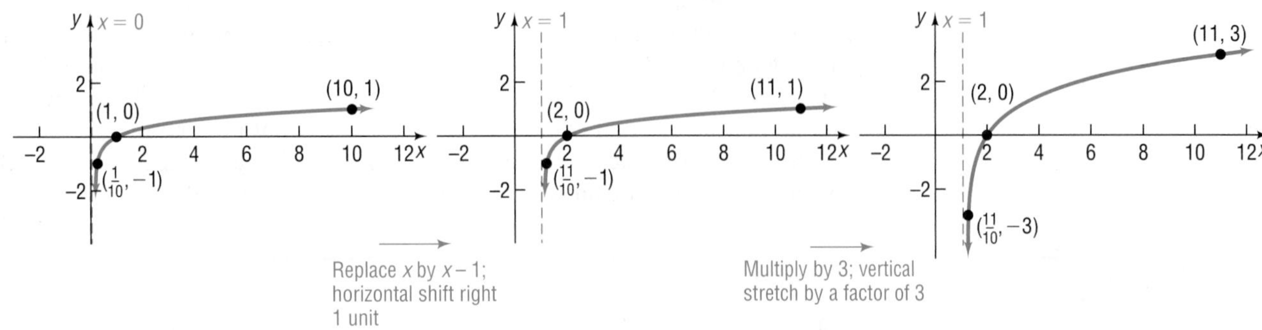

(a) $y = \log x$ **(b)** $y = \log(x - 1)$ **(c)** $y = 3\log(x - 1)$

(c) The range of $f(x) = 3\log(x - 1)$ is the set of all real numbers. The vertical asymptote is $x = 1$.

(d) Begin with $y = 3\log(x - 1)$. The inverse function is defined (implicitly) by the equation

$$x = 3\log(y - 1)$$

Proceed to solve for y.

$$\frac{x}{3} = \log(y - 1) \quad \text{Isolate the logarithm.}$$

$$10^{x/3} = y - 1 \quad \text{Change to an exponential statement.}$$

$$y = 10^{x/3} + 1 \quad \text{Solve for } y.$$

The inverse of f is $f^{-1}(x) = 10^{x/3} + 1$.

(e) The domain of f^{-1} is the range of f, which is the set of all real numbers, from part (c). The range of f^{-1} is the domain of f, which is $(1, \infty)$ in interval notation.

(f) To graph f^{-1}, we use the graph of f in Figure 43(c) and reflect it about the line $y = x$. See Figure 44. We could also graph $f^{-1}(x) = 10^{x/3} + 1$ using transformations.

Figure 44

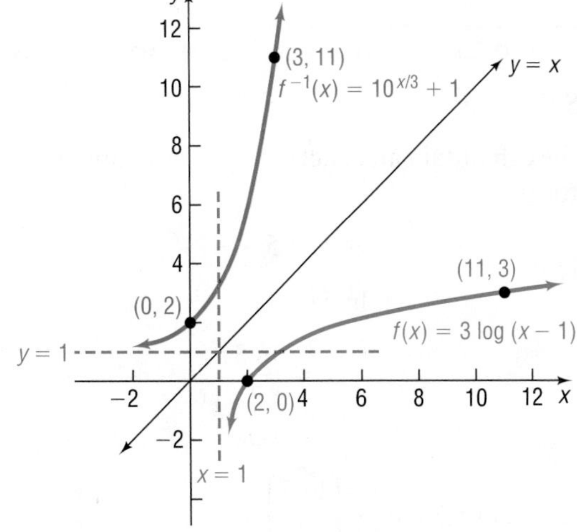

■

Now Work PROBLEM 79

5 Solve Logarithmic Equations

Equations that contain logarithms are called **logarithmic equations.** Care must be taken when solving logarithmic equations algebraically. In the expression $\log_a M$, remember that a and M are positive and $a \neq 1$. Be sure to check each apparent solution in the original equation and discard any that are extraneous.

Some logarithmic equations can be solved by changing the logarithmic equation to exponential form using the fact that $y = \log_a x$ means $a^y = x$.

EXAMPLE 8 Solving Logarithmic Equations

Solve:

(a) $\log_3(4x - 7) = 2$ (b) $\log_x 64 = 2$

Solution (a) We can obtain an exact solution by changing the logarithmic equation to exponential form.

$$\log_3(4x - 7) = 2$$

$$4x - 7 = 3^2 \quad \text{Change to exponential form using } y = \log_a x \text{ means } a^y = x.$$

$$4x - 7 = 9$$

$$4x = 16$$

$$x = 4$$

Check: $\log_3(4x - 7) = \log_3(4 \cdot 4 - 7) = \log_3 9 = 2 \quad 3^2 = 9$

The solution set is {4}.

(b) We can obtain an exact solution by changing the logarithmic equation to exponential form.

$$\log_x 64 = 2$$

$$x^2 = 64 \quad \text{Change to exponential form.}$$

$$x = \pm\sqrt{64} = \pm 8 \quad \text{Square Root Method}$$

The base of a logarithm is always positive. As a result, we discard -8. We check the solution 8.

Check: $\log_8 64 = 2 \quad 8^2 = 64$

The solution set is {8}. ■

EXAMPLE 9 Using Logarithms to Solve an Exponential Equation

Solve: $e^{2x} = 5$

Solution We can obtain an exact solution by changing the exponential equation to logarithmic form.

$$e^{2x} = 5$$

$$\ln 5 = 2x \quad \text{Change to a logarithmic equation using the fact that if } e^y = x \text{ then } y = \ln x.$$

$$x = \frac{\ln 5}{2} \quad \text{Exact solution}$$

$$\approx 0.805 \quad \text{Approximate solution}$$

The solution set is $\left\{\frac{\ln 5}{2}\right\}$. ■

Now Work PROBLEMS 87 AND 99

EXAMPLE 10 Alcohol and Driving

Blood alcohol concentration (BAC) is a measure of the amount of alcohol in a person's bloodstream. A BAC of 0.04% means that a person has 4 parts alcohol per 10,000 parts blood in the body. Relative risk is defined as the likelihood of one event occurring divided by the likelihood of a second event occurring. For example, if an individual with a BAC of 0.02% is 1.4 times as likely to have a car accident as an individual that has not been drinking, the relative risk of an accident with a BAC of 0.02% is 1.4. Recent medical research suggests that the relative risk R of having an accident while driving a car can be modeled by an equation of the form

$$R = e^{kx}$$

where x is the percent of concentration of alcohol in the bloodstream and k is a constant.

(a) Research indicates that the relative risk of a person having an accident with a BAC of 0.02% is 1.4. Find the constant k in the equation.

(b) Using this value of k, what is the relative risk if the concentration is 0.17%?

(c) Using this same value of k, what BAC corresponds to a relative risk of 100?

(d) If the law asserts that anyone with a relative risk of 4 or more should not have driving privileges, at what concentration of alcohol in the bloodstream should a driver be arrested and charged with a DUI (driving under the influence)?

Solution

(a) For a concentration of alcohol in the blood of 0.02% and a relative risk of 1.4, we let $x = 0.02$ and $R = 1.4$ in the equation and solve for k.

$$R = e^{kx}$$

$$1.4 = e^{k(0.02)} \qquad R = 1.4;\ x = 0.02$$

$$0.02k = \ln 1.4 \qquad \text{Change to a logarithmic statement.}$$

$$k = \frac{\ln 1.4}{0.02} \approx 16.82 \qquad \text{Solve for } k.$$

(b) For a concentration of 0.17%, we have $x = 0.17$. Using $k = 16.82$ in the equation, we find the relative risk R to be

$$R = e^{kx} = e^{(16.82)(0.17)} \approx 17.5$$

For a concentration of alcohol in the blood of 0.17%, the relative risk of an accident is about 17.5. That is, a person with a BAC of 0.17% is 17.5 times as likely to have a car accident as a person with no alcohol in the bloodstream.

(c) For a relative risk of 100, we have $R = 100$. Using $k = 16.82$ in the equation $R = e^{kx}$, we find the concentration x of alcohol in the blood obeys

$$100 = e^{16.82x} \qquad R = e^{kx};\ R = 100;\ k = 16.82$$

$$16.82x = \ln 100 \qquad \text{Change to a logarithmic statement.}$$

$$x = \frac{\ln 100}{16.82} \approx 0.27 \qquad \text{Solve for } x.$$

For a concentration of alcohol in the blood of 0.27%, the relative risk of an accident is 100.

NOTE A BAC of 0.30% results in a loss of consciousness in most people. ■

(d) For a relative risk of 4, we have $R = 4$. Using $k = 16.82$ in the equation $R = e^{kx}$, we find the concentration x of alcohol in the bloodstream obeys

$$4 = e^{16.82x}$$

$$16.82x = \ln 4$$

$$x = \frac{\ln 4}{16.82} \approx 0.082$$

A driver with a BAC of 0.082% or more should be arrested and charged with DUI. ■

NOTE The blood alcohol content at which a DUI citation is given is 0.08%. ■

SUMMARY

Properties of the Logarithmic Function

$f(x) = \log_a x, \quad a > 1$ $(y = \log_a x$ means $x = a^y)$	Domain: the interval $(0, \infty)$; Range: the interval $(-\infty, \infty)$ x-intercept: 1; y-intercept: none; vertical asymptote: $x = 0$ (y-axis); increasing; one-to-one See Figure 45(a) for a typical graph.
$f(x) = \log_a x, \quad 0 < a < 1$ $(y = \log_a x$ means $x = a^y)$	Domain: the interval $(0, \infty)$; Range: the interval $(-\infty, \infty)$ x-intercept: 1; y-intercept: none; vertical asymptote: $x = 0$ (y-axis); decreasing; one-to-one See Figure 45(b) for a typical graph.

Figure 45

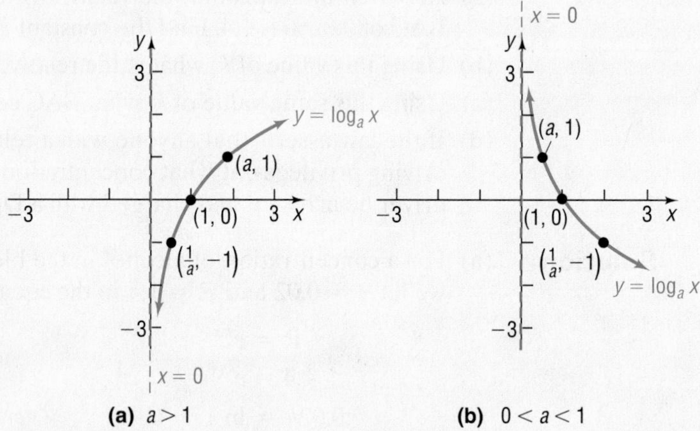

(a) $a > 1$ **(b)** $0 < a < 1$

12.4 Assess Your Understanding

'Are You Prepared?' *Answers are given at the end of these exercises. If you get a wrong answer, read the pages listed in red.*

1. Solve each inequality:
(a) $3x - 7 \le 8 - 2x$ (pp. 508–509)
(b) $x^2 - x - 6 > 0$ (pp. 669–672)

2. Solve the inequality: $\dfrac{x-1}{x+4} > 0$ (pp. 738–741)

3. Solve: $2x + 3 = 9$

Concepts and Vocabulary

4. The domain of the logarithmic function $f(x) = \log_a x$ is ______________.

5. The graph of every logarithmic function $f(x) = \log_a x$, where $a > 0$, and $a \neq 1$, passes through three points: ____, ______, and ______.

6. If the graph of a logarithmic function $f(x) = \log_a x$, where $a > 0$ and $a \neq 1$, is increasing, then its base must be larger than ______.

7. ***True or False*** If $y = \log_a x$, then $y = a^x$.

8. ***True or False*** The graph of $f(x) = \log_a x$, where $a > 0$ and $a \neq 1$, has an x-intercept equal to 1 and no y-intercept.

Skill Building

In Problems 9–16, change each exponential statement to an equivalent statement involving a logarithm.

9. $9 = 3^2$ **10.** $16 = 4^2$ **11.** $a^2 = 1.6$ **12.** $a^3 = 2.1$
13. $2^x = 7.2$ **14.** $3^x = 4.6$ **15.** $e^x = 8$ **16.** $e^{2.2} = M$

In Problems 17–24, change each logarithmic statement to an equivalent statement involving an exponent.

17. $\log_2 8 = 3$ **18.** $\log_3\left(\dfrac{1}{9}\right) = -2$ **19.** $\log_a 3 = 6$ **20.** $\log_b 4 = 2$
21. $\log_3 2 = x$ **22.** $\log_2 6 = x$ **23.** $\ln 4 = x$ **24.** $\ln x = 4$

In Problems 25–36, find the exact value of each logarithm without using a calculator.

25. $\log_2 1$ **26.** $\log_8 8$ **27.** $\log_5 25$ **28.** $\log_3\left(\frac{1}{9}\right)$

29. $\log_{1/2} 16$ **30.** $\log_{1/3} 9$ **31.** $\log_{10}\sqrt{10}$ **32.** $\log_5 \sqrt[3]{25}$

33. $\log_{\sqrt{2}} 4$ **34.** $\log_{\sqrt{3}} 9$ **35.** $\ln\sqrt{e}$ **36.** $\ln e^3$

In Problems 37–48, find the domain of each function.

37. $f(x) = \ln(x - 3)$ **38.** $g(x) = \ln(x - 1)$ **39.** $F(x) = \log_2 x^2$

40. $H(x) = \log_5 x^3$ **41.** $f(x) = 3 - 2\log_4\left[\frac{x}{2} - 5\right]$ **42.** $g(x) = 8 + 5\ln(2x + 3)$

43. $f(x) = \ln\left(\frac{1}{x + 1}\right)$ **44.** $g(x) = \ln\left(\frac{1}{x - 5}\right)$ **45.** $g(x) = \log_5\left(\frac{x + 1}{x}\right)$

46. $h(x) = \log_3\left(\frac{x}{x - 1}\right)$ **47.** $f(x) = \sqrt{\ln x}$ **48.** $g(x) = \frac{1}{\ln x}$

In Problems 49–56, use a calculator to evaluate each expression. Round your answer to three decimal places.

49. $\ln\frac{5}{3}$ **50.** $\frac{\ln 5}{3}$ **51.** $\frac{\ln\frac{10}{3}}{0.04}$ **52.** $\frac{\ln\frac{2}{3}}{-0.1}$

53. $\frac{\ln 4 + \ln 2}{\log 4 + \log 2}$ **54.** $\frac{\log 15 + \log 20}{\ln 15 + \ln 20}$ **55.** $\frac{2\ln 5 + \log 50}{\log 4 - \ln 2}$ **56.** $\frac{3\log 80 - \ln 5}{\log 5 + \ln 20}$

57. Find a so that the graph of $f(x) = \log_a x$ contains the point $(2, 2)$.

58. Find a so that the graph of $f(x) = \log_a x$ contains the point $\left(\frac{1}{2}, -4\right)$.

In Problems 59–62, graph each function and its inverse on the same Cartesian plane.

59. $f(x) = 3^x; f^{-1}(x) = \log_3 x$ **60.** $f(x) = 4^x; f^{-1}(x) = \log_4 x$

61. $f(x) = \left(\frac{1}{2}\right)^x; f^{-1}(x) = \log_{\frac{1}{2}} x$ **62.** $f(x) = \left(\frac{1}{3}\right)^x; f^{-1}(x) = \log_{\frac{1}{3}} x$

In Problems 63–70, the graph of a logarithmic function is given. Match each graph to one of the following functions.

(A) $y = \log_3 x$ (B) $y = \log_3(-x)$ (C) $y = -\log_3 x$ (D) $y = -\log_3(-x)$
(E) $y = \log_3 x - 1$ (F) $y = \log_3(x - 1)$ (G) $y = \log_3(1 - x)$ (H) $y = 1 - \log_3 x$

63.

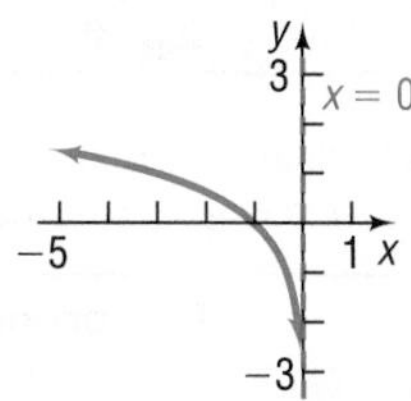

64.

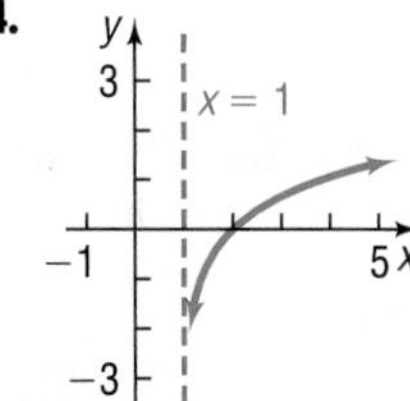

65.

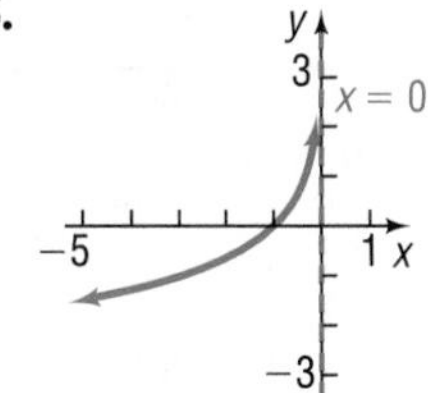

66.

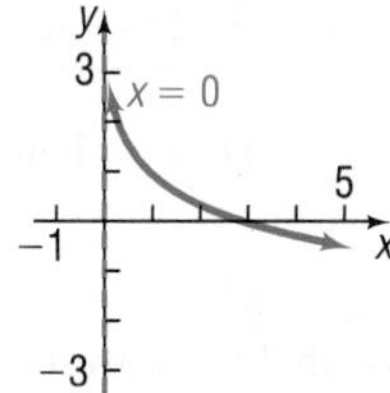

67.

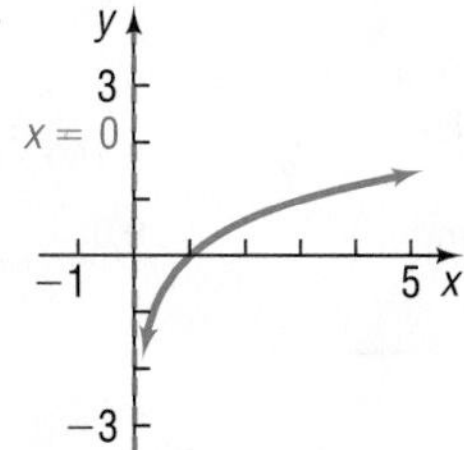

68.

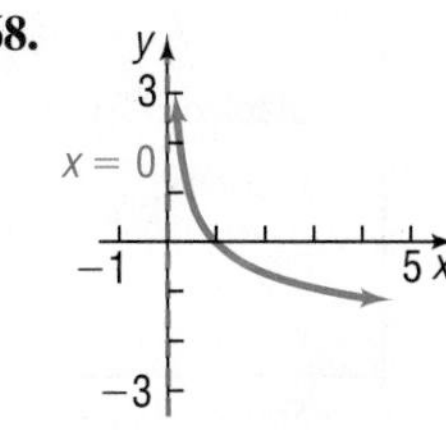

69.

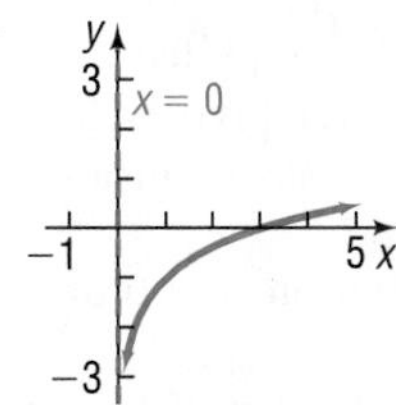

70.

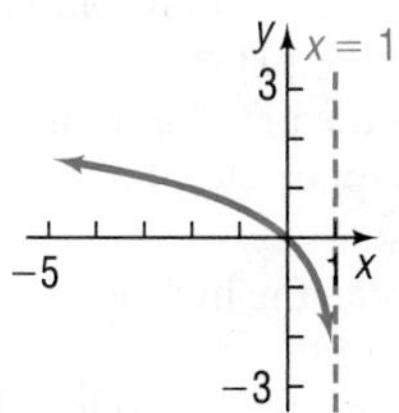

In Problems 71–86, use the given function f to:

(a) Find the domain of f. (b) Graph f. (c) From the graph, determine the range and any asymptotes of f.
(d) Find f^{-1}, the inverse of f. (e) Find the domain and the range of f^{-1}. (f) Graph f^{-1}.

71. $f(x) = \ln(x + 4)$ **72.** $f(x) = \ln(x - 3)$ **73.** $f(x) = 2 + \ln x$ **74.** $f(x) = -\ln(-x)$

75. $f(x) = \ln(2x) - 3$ **76.** $f(x) = -2\ln(x + 1)$ **77.** $f(x) = \log(x - 4) + 2$ **78.** $f(x) = \frac{1}{2}\log x - 5$

79. $f(x) = \frac{1}{2}\log(2x)$

80. $f(x) = \log(-2x)$

81. $f(x) = 3 + \log_3(x + 2)$

82. $f(x) = 2 - \log_3(x + 1)$

83. $f(x) = e^{x+2} - 3$

84. $f(x) = 3e^x + 2$

85. $f(x) = 2^{x/3} + 4$

86. $f(x) = -3^{x+1}$

In Problems 87–110, solve each equation.

87. $\log_3 x = 2$

88. $\log_5 x = 3$

89. $\log_2(2x + 1) = 3$

90. $\log_3(3x - 2) = 2$

91. $\log_x 4 = 2$

92. $\log_x\left(\frac{1}{8}\right) = 3$

93. $\ln e^x = 5$

94. $\ln e^{-2x} = 8$

95. $\log_4 64 = x$

96. $\log_5 625 = x$

97. $\log_3 243 = 2x + 1$

98. $\log_6 36 = 5x + 3$

99. $e^{3x} = 10$

100. $e^{-2x} = \frac{1}{3}$

101. $e^{2x+5} = 8$

102. $e^{-2x+1} = 13$

103. $\log_3(x^2 + 1) = 2$

104. $\log_5(x^2 + x + 4) = 2$

105. $\log_2 8^x = -3$

106. $\log_3 3^x = -1$

107. $5e^{0.2x} = 7$

108. $8 \cdot 10^{2x-7} = 3$

109. $2 \cdot 10^{2-x} = 5$

110. $4e^{x+1} = 5$

Mixed Practice

111. Suppose that $G(x) = \log_3(2x + 1) - 2$.
(a) What is the domain of G?
(b) What is $G(40)$? What point is on the graph of G?
(c) If $G(x) = 3$, what is x? What point is on the graph of G?
(d) What is the zero of G?

112. Suppose that $F(x) = \log_2(x + 1) - 3$.
(a) What is the domain of F?
(b) What is $F(7)$? What point is on the graph of F?
(c) If $F(x) = -1$, what is x? What point is on the graph of F?
(d) What is the zero of F?

In Problems 113–116, graph each function. Based on the graph, state the domain and the range and find any intercepts.

113. $f(x) = \begin{cases} \ln(-x) & \text{if } x < 0 \\ \ln x & \text{if } x > 0 \end{cases}$

114. $f(x) = \begin{cases} \ln(-x) & \text{if } x \le -1 \\ -\ln(-x) & \text{if } -1 < x < 0 \end{cases}$

115. $f(x) = \begin{cases} -\ln x & \text{if } 0 < x < 1 \\ \ln x & \text{if } x \ge 1 \end{cases}$

116. $f(x) = \begin{cases} \ln x & \text{if } 0 < x < 1 \\ -\ln x & \text{if } x \ge 1 \end{cases}$

Applications and Extensions

117. Chemistry The pH of a chemical solution is given by the formula

$$\text{pH} = -\log_{10}[\text{H}^+]$$

where $[\text{H}^+]$ is the concentration of hydrogen ions in moles per liter. Values of pH range from 0 (acidic) to 14 (alkaline).
(a) What is the pH of a solution for which $[\text{H}^+]$ is 0.1?
(b) What is the pH of a solution for which $[\text{H}^+]$ is 0.01?
(c) What is the pH of a solution for which $[\text{H}^+]$ is 0.001?
(d) What happens to pH as the hydrogen ion concentration decreases?
(e) Determine the hydrogen ion concentration of an orange (pH = 3.5).
(f) Determine the hydrogen ion concentration of human blood (pH = 7.4).

118. Diversity Index **Shannon's diversity index** is a measure of the diversity of a population. The diversity index is given by the formula

$$H = -(p_1 \log p_1 + p_2 \log p_2 + \dots + p_n \log p_n)$$

where p_1 is the proportion of the population that is species 1, p_2 is the proportion of the population that is species 2, and so on.

(a) According to the U.S. Census Bureau, the distribution of race in the United States in 2009 was as follows:

Race	Proportion
American Indian or Native Alaskan	0.008
Asian	0.045
Black or African American	0.125
Hispanic	0.159
Native Hawaiian or Pacific Islander	0.001
White	0.662

Source: U.S. Census Bureau

Compute the diversity index of the United States in 2009.
(b) The largest value of the diversity index is given by $H_{max} = \log(S)$, where S is the number of categories of race. Compute H_{max}.
(c) The **evenness ratio** is given by $E_H = \frac{H}{H_{max}}$, where $0 \le E_H \le 1$. If $E_H = 1$, there is complete evenness. Compute the evenness ratio for the United States.

(d) Obtain the distribution of race for the United States in 2010 from the Census Bureau. Compute Shannon's diversity index. Is the United States becoming more diverse? Why?

119. Atmospheric Pressure The atmospheric pressure p on an object decreases with increasing height. This pressure, measured in millimeters of mercury, is related to the height h (in kilometers) above sea level by the function

$$p(h) = 760e^{-0.145h}$$

(a) Find the height of an aircraft if the atmospheric pressure is 320 millimeters of mercury.
(b) Find the height of a mountain if the atmospheric pressure is 667 millimeters of mercury.

120. Healing of Wounds The normal healing of wounds can be modeled by an exponential function. If A_0 represents the original area of the wound and if A equals the area of the wound, then the function

$$A(n) = A_0e^{-0.35n}$$

describes the area of a wound after n days following an injury when no infection is present to retard the healing. Suppose that a wound initially had an area of 100 square millimeters.

(a) If healing is taking place, after how many days will the wound be one-half its original size?
(b) How long before the wound is 10% of its original size?

121. Exponential Probability Between 12:00 PM and 1:00 PM, cars arrive at Citibank's drive-thru at the rate of 6 cars per hour (0.1 car per minute). The following formula from statistics can be used to determine the probability that a car will arrive within t minutes of 12:00 PM.

$$F(t) = 1 - e^{-0.1t}$$

(a) Determine how many minutes are needed for the probability to reach 50%.
(b) Determine how many minutes are needed for the probability to reach 80%.
(c) Is it possible for the probability to equal 100%? Explain.

122. Exponential Probability Between 5:00 PM and 6:00 PM, cars arrive at Jiffy Lube at the rate of 9 cars per hour (0.15 car per minute). The following formula from statistics can be used to determine the probability that a car will arrive within t minutes of 5:00 PM.

$$F(t) = 1 - e^{-0.15t}$$

(a) Determine how many minutes are needed for the probability to reach 50%.
(b) Determine how many minutes are needed for the probability to reach 80%.

123. Drug Medication The formula

$$D = 5e^{-0.4h}$$

can be used to find the number of milligrams D of a certain drug that is in a patient's bloodstream h hours after the drug was administered. When the number of milligrams reaches 2, the drug is to be administered again. What is the time between injections?

124. Spreading of Rumors A model for the number N of people in a college community who have heard a certain rumor is

$$N = P(1 - e^{-0.15d})$$

where P is the total population of the community and d is the number of days that have elapsed since the rumor began. In a community of 1000 students, how many days will elapse before 450 students have heard the rumor?

125. Current in a *RL* Circuit The equation governing the amount of current I (in amperes) after time t (in seconds) in a simple RL circuit consisting of a resistance R (in ohms), an inductance L (in henrys), and an electromotive force E (in volts) is

$$I = \frac{E}{R}[1 - e^{-(R/L)t}]$$

If $E = 12$ volts, $R = 10$ ohms, and $L = 5$ henrys, how long does it take to obtain a current of 0.5 ampere? Of 1.0 ampere? Graph the equation.

126. Learning Curve Psychologists sometimes use the function

$$L(t) = A(1 - e^{-kt})$$

to measure the amount L learned at time t. The number A represents the amount to be learned, and the number k measures the rate of learning. Suppose that a student has an amount A of 200 vocabulary words to learn. A psychologist determines that the student learned 20 vocabulary words after 5 minutes.

(a) Determine the rate of learning k.
(b) Approximately how many words will the student have learned after 10 minutes?
(c) After 15 minutes?
(d) How long does it take for the student to learn 180 words?

Loudness of Sound *Problems 127–130 use the following discussion: The* ***loudness*** $L(x)$, *measured in decibels (dB), of a sound of intensity x, measured in watts per square meter, is defined as* $L(x) = 10 \log \frac{x}{I_0}$, *where* $I_0 = 10^{-12}$ *watt per square meter is the least intense sound that a human ear can detect. Determine the loudness, in decibels, of each of the following sounds.*

127. Normal conversation: intensity of $x = 10^{-7}$ watt per square meter.

128. Amplified rock music: intensity of 10^{-1} watt per square meter.

129. Heavy city traffic: intensity of $x = 10^{-3}$ watt per square meter.

130. Diesel truck traveling 40 miles per hour 50 feet away: intensity 10 times that of a passenger car traveling 50 miles per hour 50 feet away whose loudness is 70 decibels.

The Richter Scale Problems 131 and 132 use the following discussion: The ***Richter scale*** *is one way of converting seismographic readings into numbers that provide an easy reference for measuring the magnitude M of an earthquake. All earthquakes are compared to a* ***zero-level earthquake*** *whose seismographic reading measures 0.001 millimeter at a distance of 100 kilometers from the epicenter. An earthquake whose seismographic reading measures x millimeters has* ***magnitude*** *M(x), given by*

$$M(x) = \log\left(\frac{x}{x_0}\right)$$

where $x_0 = 10^{-3}$ *is the reading of a zero-level earthquake the same distance from its epicenter. In Problems 131 and 132, determine the magnitude of each earthquake.*

131. Magnitude of an Earthquake Mexico City in 1985: seismographic reading of 125,892 millimeters 100 kilometers from the center

132. Magnitude of an Earthquake San Francisco in 1906: seismographic reading of 50,119 millimeters 100 kilometers from the center

133. Alcohol and Driving The concentration of alcohol in a person's bloodstream is measurable. Suppose that the relative risk R of having an accident while driving a car can be modeled by an equation of the form

$$R = e^{kx}$$

where x is the percent of concentration of alcohol in the bloodstream and k is a constant.

(a) Suppose that a concentration of alcohol in the bloodstream of 0.03 percent results in a relative risk of an accident of 1.4. Find the constant k in the equation.

(b) Using this value of k, what is the relative risk if the concentration is 0.17 percent?

(c) Using the same value of k, what concentration of alcohol corresponds to a relative risk of 100?

(d) If the law asserts that anyone with a relative risk of having an accident of 5 or more should not have driving privileges, at what concentration of alcohol in the bloodstream should a driver be arrested and charged with a DUI?

(e) Compare this situation with that of Example 10. If you were a lawmaker, which situation would you support? Give your reasons.

Explaining Concepts: Discussion and Writing

134. Is there any function of the form $y = x^{\alpha}, 0 < \alpha < 1$, that increases more slowly than a logarithmic function whose base is greater than 1? Explain.

135. In the definition of the logarithmic function, the base a is not allowed to equal 1. Why?

136. **Critical Thinking** In buying a new car, one consideration might be how well the price of the car holds up over time. Different makes of cars have different depreciation rates. One way to compute a depreciation rate for a car is given here. Suppose that the current prices of a certain automobile are as shown in the table.

Age in Years					
New	1	2	3	4	5
\$38,000	\$36,600	\$32,400	\$28,750	\$25,400	\$21,200

Use the formula New = Old(e^{Rt}) to find R, the annual depreciation rate, for a specific time t. When might be the best time to trade in the car? Consult the NADA ("blue") book and compare two like models that you are interested in. Which has the better depreciation rate?

'Are You Prepared?' Answers

1. (a) $x \le 3$ (b) $x < -2$ or $x > 3$ **2.** $x < -4$ or $x > 1$ **3.** $\{3\}$

12.5 Properties of Logarithms

OBJECTIVES

1 Work with the Properties of Logarithms

Logarithms have some very useful properties that can be derived directly from the definition and the laws of exponents.

EXAMPLE 1 **Establishing Properties of Logarithms**

(a) Show that $\log_a 1 = 0$. (b) Show that $\log_a a = 1$.

Solution (a) This fact was established when we graphed $y = \log_a x$ (see Figure 36 on page 792). To show the result algebraically, let $y = \log_a 1$. Then

$$y = \log_a 1$$
$$a^y = 1 \quad \text{Change to an exponential statement.}$$
$$a^y = a^0 \quad a^0 = 1 \text{ since } a > 0, a \neq 1$$
$$y = 0 \quad \text{Solve for } y.$$
$$\log_a 1 = 0 \quad y = \log_a 1$$

(b) Let $y = \log_a a$. Then

$$y = \log_a a$$
$$a^y = a \quad \text{Change to an exponential statement.}$$
$$a^y = a^1 \quad a = a^1$$
$$y = 1 \quad \text{Solve for } y.$$
$$\log_a a = 1 \quad y = \log_a a$$

■

To summarize:

$$\log_a 1 = 0 \qquad \log_a a = 1$$

THEOREM

Properties of Logarithms

In the properties given next, M and a are positive real numbers, $a \neq 1$, and r is any real number.

The number $\log_a M$ is the exponent to which a must be raised to obtain M. That is,

$$a^{\log_a M} = M \qquad \textbf{(1)}$$

The logarithm to the base a of a raised to a power equals that power. That is,

$$\log_a a^r = r \qquad \textbf{(2)}$$

The proof uses the fact that $y = a^x$ and $y = \log_a x$ are inverses.

Proof of Property (1) For inverse functions,

$$f(f^{-1}(x)) = x \quad \text{for all } x \text{ in the domain of } f^{-1}$$

Using $f(x) = a^x$ and $f^{-1}(x) = \log_a x$, we find

$$f(f^{-1}(x)) = a^{\log_a x} = x \quad \text{for } x > 0$$

Now let $x = M$ to obtain $a^{\log_a M} = M$, where $M > 0$. ■

Proof of Property (2) For inverse functions,

$$f^{-1}(f(x)) = x \quad \text{for all } x \text{ in the domain of } f$$

Using $f(x) = a^x$ and $f^{-1}(x) = \log_a x$, we find

$$f^{-1}(f(x)) = \log_a a^x = x \quad \text{for all real numbers } x$$

Now let $x = r$ to obtain $\log_a a^r = r$, where r is any real number. ■

EXAMPLE 2 **Using Properties (1) and (2)**

(a) $2^{\log_2 \pi} = \pi$ (b) $\log_{0.2} 0.2^{-\sqrt{2}} = -\sqrt{2}$ (c) $\ln e^{kt} = kt$

■

Now Work PROBLEM 15

Other useful properties of logarithms are given next.

THEOREM

Properties of Logarithms

In the following properties, M, N, and a are positive real numbers, $a \neq 1$, and r is any real number.

The Log of a Product Equals the Sum of the Logs

$$\log_a(MN) = \log_a M + \log_a N \tag{3}$$

The Log of a Quotient Equals the Difference of the Logs

$$\log_a\left(\frac{M}{N}\right) = \log_a M - \log_a N \tag{4}$$

The Log of a Power Equals the Product of the Power and the Log

$$\log_a M^r = r \log_a M \tag{5}$$

$$a^x = e^{x \ln a} \tag{6}$$

We shall derive properties (3), (5), and (6) and leave the derivation of property (4) as an exercise (see Problem 109).

Proof of Property (3) Let $A = \log_a M$ and let $B = \log_a N$. These expressions are equivalent to the exponential expressions

$$a^A = M \quad \text{and} \quad a^B = N$$

Now

$$\begin{aligned} \log_a(MN) = \log_a(a^A a^B) &= \log_a a^{A+B} && \text{Law of Exponents} \\ &= A + B && \text{Property (2) of logarithms} \\ &= \log_a M + \log_a N \end{aligned}$$

■

Proof of Property (5) Let $A = \log_a M$. This expression is equivalent to

$$a^A = M$$

Now

$$\begin{aligned} \log_a M^r = \log_a(a^A)^r &= \log_a a^{rA} && \text{Law of Exponents} \\ &= rA && \text{Property (2) of logarithms} \\ &= r \log_a M \end{aligned}$$

■

Proof of Property (6) From property (1), with $a = e$, we have

$$e^{\ln M} = M$$

Now let $M = a^x$ and apply property (5).

$$e^{\ln a^x} = e^{x \ln a} = (e^{\ln a})^x = a^x$$

■

Now Work PROBLEM 19

2 Write a Logarithmic Expression as a Sum or Difference of Logarithms

Logarithms can be used to transform products into sums, quotients into differences, and powers into factors. Such transformations prove useful in certain types of calculus problems.

EXAMPLE 3 **Writing a Logarithmic Expression as a Sum of Logarithms**

Write $\log_a(x\sqrt{x^2+1})$, $x > 0$, as a sum of logarithms. Express all powers as factors.

Solution

$$\begin{aligned}\log_a(x\sqrt{x^2+1}) &= \log_a x + \log_a \sqrt{x^2+1} && \log_a(M \cdot N) = \log_a M + \log_a N\\ &= \log_a x + \log_a(x^2+1)^{1/2}\\ &= \log_a x + \frac{1}{2}\log_a(x^2+1) && \log_a M^r = r\log_a M\end{aligned}$$

■

EXAMPLE 4 **Writing a Logarithmic Expression as a Difference of Logarithms**

Write

$$\ln\frac{x^2}{(x-1)^3} \qquad x > 1$$

as a difference of logarithms. Express all powers as factors.

Solution

$$\ln\frac{x^2}{(x-1)^3} = \underset{\uparrow}{} \ln x^2 - \ln(x-1)^3 = \underset{\uparrow}{} 2\ln x - 3\ln(x-1)$$

$\log_a\left(\frac{M}{N}\right) = \log_a M - \log_a N$ $\quad \log_a M^r = r\log_a M$

■

EXAMPLE 5 **Writing a Logarithmic Expression as a Sum and Difference of Logarithms**

Write

$$\log_a\frac{\sqrt{x^2+1}}{x^3(x+1)^4} \qquad x > 0$$

as a sum and difference of logarithms. Express all powers as factors.

Solution

$$\begin{aligned}\log_a\frac{\sqrt{x^2+1}}{x^3(x+1)^4} &= \log_a\sqrt{x^2+1} - \log_a[x^3(x+1)^4] && \text{Property (4)}\\ &= \log_a\sqrt{x^2+1} - [\log_a x^3 + \log_a(x+1)^4] && \text{Property (3)}\\ &= \log_a(x^2+1)^{1/2} - \log_a x^3 - \log_a(x+1)^4\\ &= \frac{1}{2}\log_a(x^2+1) - 3\log_a x - 4\log_a(x+1) && \text{Property (5)}\end{aligned}$$

■

WARNING In using properties (3) through (5), be careful about the values that the variable may assume. For example, the domain of the variable for $\log_a x$ is $x > 0$ and for $\log_a(x-1)$ is $x > 1$. If we add these functions, the domain is $x > 1$. That is, the equality

$$\log_a x + \log_a(x-1) = \log_a[x(x-1)]$$

is true only for $x > 1$. ■

Now Work PROBLEM 51

3 Write a Logarithmic Expression as a Single Logarithm

Another use of properties (3) through (5) is to write sums and/or differences of logarithms with the same base as a single logarithm. This skill will be needed to solve certain logarithmic equations discussed in the next section.

EXAMPLE 6 **Writing Expressions as a Single Logarithm**

Write each of the following as a single logarithm.

(a) $\log_a 7 + 4\log_a 3$ (b) $\frac{2}{3}\ln 8 - \ln(5^2-1)$

(c) $\log_a x + \log_a 9 + \log_a(x^2+1) - \log_a 5$

Solution (a) $\log_a 7 + 4\log_a 3 = \log_a 7 + \log_a 3^4$ $r\log_a M = \log_a M^r$

$= \log_a 7 + \log_a 81$

$= \log_a(7\cdot 81)$ $\log_a M + \log_a N = \log_a(M\cdot N)$

$= \log_a 567$

(b) $\frac{2}{3}\ln 8 - \ln(5^2 - 1) = \ln 8^{2/3} - \ln(25 - 1)$ $r\log_a M = \log_a M^r$

$= \ln 4 - \ln 24$ $8^{2/3} = (\sqrt[3]{8})^2 = 2^2 = 4$

$= \ln\left(\frac{4}{24}\right)$ $\log_a M - \log_a N = \log_a\left(\frac{M}{N}\right)$

$= \ln\left(\frac{1}{6}\right)$

$= \ln 1 - \ln 6$

$= -\ln 6$ $\ln 1 = 0$

(c) $\log_a x + \log_a 9 + \log_a(x^2 + 1) - \log_a 5 = \log_a(9x) + \log_a(x^2 + 1) - \log_a 5$

$= \log_a[9x(x^2 + 1)] - \log_a 5$

$= \log_a\left[\frac{9x(x^2 + 1)}{5}\right]$ ■

WARNING A common error made by some students is to express the logarithm of a sum as the sum of logarithms.

$\log_a(M + N)$ is not equal to $\log_a M + \log_a N$

Correct statement $\log_a(MN) = \log_a M + \log_a N$ Property (3)

Another common error is to express the difference of logarithms as the quotient of logarithms.

$\log_a M - \log_a N$ is not equal to $\frac{\log_a M}{\log_a N}$

Correct statement $\log_a M - \log_a N = \log_a\left(\frac{M}{N}\right)$ Property (4)

A third common error is to express a logarithm raised to a power as the product of the power times the logarithm.

$(\log_a M)^r$ is not equal to $r\log_a M$

Correct statement $\log_a M^r = r\log_a M$ Property (5) ■

Now Work PROBLEM 57

Two other properties of logarithms that we need to know are consequences of the fact that the logarithmic function $y = \log_a x$ is a one-to-one function.

THEOREM

Properties of Logarithms

In the following properties, M, N, and a are positive real numbers, $a \neq 1$.

If $M = N$, then $\log_a M = \log_a N$. **(7)**

If $\log_a M = \log_a N$, then $M = N$. **(8)**

When property (7) is used, we start with the equation $M = N$ and say "take the logarithm of both sides" to obtain $\log_a M = \log_a N$.

Properties (7) and (8) are useful for solving *exponential and logarithmic equations*, a topic discussed in the next section.

4 Evaluate a Logarithm Whose Base Is Neither 10 Nor *e*

Logarithms to the base 10, common logarithms, were used to facilitate arithmetic computations before the widespread use of calculators. (See the Historical Feature at the end of this section.) Natural logarithms, that is, logarithms whose base is the number e, remain very important because they arise frequently in the study of natural phenomena.

Common logarithms are usually abbreviated by writing **log,** with the base understood to be 10, just as natural logarithms are abbreviated by **ln,** with the base understood to be e.

Most calculators have both [log] and [ln] keys to calculate the common logarithm and natural logarithm of a number. Let's look at an example to see how to approximate logarithms having a base other than 10 or e.

EXAMPLE 7 Approximating a Logarithm Whose Base Is Neither 10 Nor e

Approximate $\log_2 7$. Round the answer to four decimal places.

Solution Remember, $\log_2 7$ means "2 raised to what exponent equals 7." If we let $y = \log_2 7$, then $2^y = 7$. Because $2^2 = 4$ and $2^3 = 8$, we expect $\log_2 7$ to be between 2 and 3.

$$2^y = 7$$

$$\ln 2^y = \ln 7 \quad \text{Property (7)}$$

$$y \ln 2 = \ln 7 \quad \text{Property (5)}$$

$$y = \frac{\ln 7}{\ln 2} \quad \text{Exact value}$$

$$y \approx 2.8074 \quad \text{Approximate value rounded to four decimal places}$$

■

Example 7 shows how to approximate a logarithm whose base is 2 by changing to logarithms involving the base e. In general, we use the **Change-of-Base Formula.**

THEOREM

Change-of-Base Formula

If $a \neq 1$, $b \neq 1$, and M are positive real numbers, then

$$\log_a M = \frac{\log_b M}{\log_b a} \qquad \textbf{(9)}$$

Proof We derive this formula as follows: Let $y = \log_a M$. Then

$$a^y = M$$

$$\log_b a^y = \log_b M \quad \text{Property (7)}$$

$$y \log_b a = \log_b M \quad \text{Property (5)}$$

$$y = \frac{\log_b M}{\log_b a} \quad \text{Solve for } y.$$

$$\log_a M = \frac{\log_b M}{\log_b a} \quad y = \log_a M$$

■

Since calculators have keys only for [log] and [ln], in practice, the Change-of-Base Formula uses either $b = 10$ or $b = e$. That is,

$$\log_a M = \frac{\log M}{\log a} \quad \text{and} \quad \log_a M = \frac{\ln M}{\ln a} \qquad \textbf{(10)}$$

EXAMPLE 8 Using the Change-of-Base Formula

Approximate:

(a) $\log_5 89$ (b) $\log_{\sqrt{2}} \sqrt{5}$

Round answers to four decimal places.

Solution (a) $\log_5 89 = \dfrac{\log 89}{\log 5} \approx \dfrac{1.949390007}{0.6989700043} \approx 2.7889$

or

$\log_5 89 = \dfrac{\ln 89}{\ln 5} \approx \dfrac{4.48863637}{1.609437912} \approx 2.7889$

(b) $\log_{\sqrt{2}} \sqrt{5} = \dfrac{\log \sqrt{5}}{\log \sqrt{2}} = \dfrac{\frac{1}{2}\log 5}{\frac{1}{2}\log 2} = \dfrac{\log 5}{\log 2} \approx 2.3219$

or

$\log_{\sqrt{2}} \sqrt{5} = \dfrac{\ln \sqrt{5}}{\ln \sqrt{2}} = \dfrac{\frac{1}{2}\ln 5}{\frac{1}{2}\ln 2} = \dfrac{\ln 5}{\ln 2} \approx 2.3219$ ■

Now Work PROBLEMS 23 AND 71

5 Graph a Logarithmic Function Whose Base Is Neither 10 Nor *e*

We also use the Change-of-Base Formula to graph logarithmic functions whose base is neither 10 nor *e*.

EXAMPLE 9 **Graphing a Logarithmic Function Whose Base Is Neither 10 Nor e**

Use a graphing utility to graph $y = \log_2 x$.

Solution Since graphing utilities only have logarithms with the base 10 or the base *e*, we need to use the Change-of-Base Formula to express $y = \log_2 x$ in terms of logarithms with base 10 or base *e*. We can graph either $y = \dfrac{\ln x}{\ln 2}$ or $y = \dfrac{\log x}{\log 2}$ to obtain the graph of $y = \log_2 x$. See Figure 46.

Figure 46

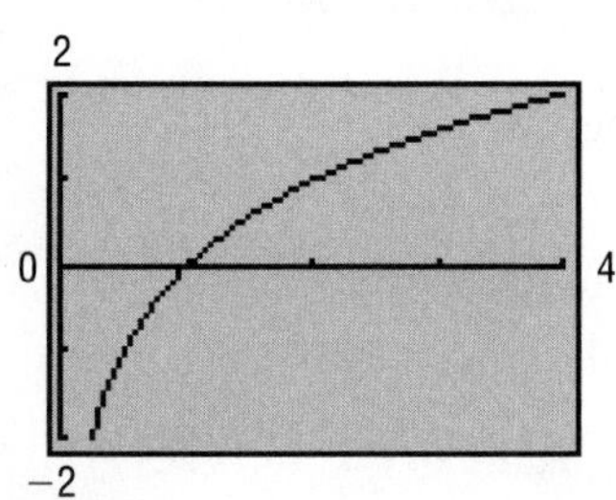

✓**Check:** Verify that $y = \dfrac{\ln x}{\ln 2}$ and $y = \dfrac{\log x}{\log 2}$ result in the same graph by graphing each on the same screen. ■

Now Work PROBLEM 79

SUMMARY

Properties of Logarithms

In the list that follows, a, b, M, N, and r are real numbers. Also, $a > 0, a \neq 1, b > 0, b \neq 1, M > 0$, and $N > 0$.

Definition $y = \log_a x$ means $x = a^y$

Properties of logarithms

$\log_a 1 = 0;\quad \log_a a = 1$ | $\log_a M^r = r\log_a M$

$a^{\log_a M} = M;\quad \log_a a^r = r$ | $a^x = e^{x \ln a}$

$\log_a(MN) = \log_a M + \log_a N$ | If $M = N$, then $\log_a M = \log_a N$.

$\log_a\left(\dfrac{M}{N}\right) = \log_a M - \log_a N$ | If $\log_a M = \log_a N$, then $M = N$.

Change-of-Base Formula $\log_a M = \dfrac{\log_b M}{\log_b a}$

Historical Feature

John Napier (1550–1617)

Logarithms were invented about 1590 by John Napier (1550–1617) and Joost Bürgi (1552–1632), working independently. Napier, whose work had the greater influence, was a Scottish lord, a secretive man whose neighbors were inclined to believe him to be in league with the devil. His approach to logarithms was very different from ours; it was based on the relationship between arithmetic and geometric sequences, discussed in a later chapter, and not on the inverse function relationship of logarithms to exponential functions (described in Section 12.4). Napier's tables, published in 1614, listed what would now be called *natural logarithms* of sines and were rather difficult to use. A London professor, Henry Briggs, became interested in the tables and visited Napier. In their conversations, they developed the idea of common logarithms, which were published in 1617. Their importance for calculation was immediately recognized, and by 1650 they were being printed as far away as China. They remained an important calculation tool until the advent of the inexpensive handheld calculator about 1972, which has decreased their calculational, but not their theoretical, importance.

A side effect of the invention of logarithms was the popularization of the decimal system of notation for real numbers.

12.5 Assess Your Understanding

Concepts and Vocabulary

1. $\log_a 1 =$ _____

2. $\log_a a =$ _____

3. $a^{\log_a M} =$ _____

4. $\log_a a^r =$ _____

5. $\log_a(MN) =$ _________ + _________

6. $\log_a\left(\dfrac{M}{N}\right) =$ _________ − _________

7. $\log_a M^r =$ _________

8. If $\log_a x = \log_a 6$, then $x =$ _____.

9. If $\log_8 M = \dfrac{\log_5 7}{\log_5 8}$, then $M =$ _____.

10. ***True or False*** $\ln(x+3) - \ln(2x) = \dfrac{\ln(x+3)}{\ln(2x)}$

11. ***True or False*** $\log_2(3x^4) = 4\log_2(3x)$

12. ***True or False*** $\dfrac{\ln 8}{\ln 4} = 2$

Skill Building

In Problems 13–28, use properties of logarithms to find the exact value of each expression. Do not use a calculator.

13. $\log_3 3^{71}$ **14.** $\log_2 2^{-13}$ **15.** $\ln e^{-4}$ **16.** $\ln e^{\sqrt{2}}$

17. $2^{\log_2 7}$ **18.** $e^{\ln 8}$ **19.** $\log_8 2 + \log_8 4$ **20.** $\log_6 9 + \log_6 4$

21. $\log_6 18 - \log_6 3$ **22.** $\log_8 16 - \log_8 2$ **23.** $\log_2 6 \cdot \log_6 8$ **24.** $\log_3 8 \cdot \log_8 9$

25. $3^{\log_3 5 - \log_3 4}$ **26.** $5^{\log_5 6 + \log_5 7}$ **27.** $e^{\log_{e^2} 16}$ **28.** $e^{\log_{e^2} 9}$

In Problems 29–36, suppose that $\ln 2 = a$ *and* $\ln 3 = b$. *Use properties of logarithms to write each logarithm in terms of a and b.*

29. $\ln 6$ **30.** $\ln \dfrac{2}{3}$ **31.** $\ln 1.5$ **32.** $\ln 0.5$

33. $\ln 8$ **34.** $\ln 27$ **35.** $\ln \sqrt[5]{6}$ **36.** $\ln \sqrt[4]{\dfrac{2}{3}}$

In Problems 37–56, write each expression as a sum and/or difference of logarithms. Express powers as factors.

37. $\log_5(25x)$ **38.** $\log_3 \dfrac{x}{9}$ **39.** $\log_2 z^3$ **40.** $\log_7 x^5$

41. $\ln(ex)$ **42.** $\ln \dfrac{e}{x}$ **43.** $\ln \dfrac{x}{e^x}$ **44.** $\ln(xe^x)$

45. $\log_a(u^2v^3) \quad u > 0, v > 0$ **46.** $\log_2\left(\dfrac{a}{b^2}\right) \quad a > 0, b > 0$ **47.** $\ln(x^2\sqrt{1-x}) \quad 0 < x < 1$

48. $\ln(x\sqrt{1+x^2}) \quad x > 0$ **49.** $\log_2\left(\dfrac{x^3}{x-3}\right) \quad x > 3$ **50.** $\log_5\left(\dfrac{\sqrt[3]{x^2+1}}{x^2-1}\right) \quad x > 1$

51. $\log\left[\dfrac{x(x+2)}{(x+3)^2}\right] \quad x > 0$ **52.** $\log\left[\dfrac{x^3\sqrt{x+1}}{(x-2)^2}\right] \quad x > 2$ **53.** $\ln\left[\dfrac{x^2-x-2}{(x+4)^2}\right]^{1/3} \quad x > 2$

54. $\ln\left[\dfrac{(x-4)^2}{x^2-1}\right]^{2/3} \quad x > 4$ **55.** $\ln \dfrac{5x\sqrt{1+3x}}{(x-4)^3} \quad x > 4$ **56.** $\ln\left[\dfrac{5x^2\sqrt[3]{1-x}}{4(x+1)^2}\right] \quad 0 < x < 1$

In Problems 57–70, write each expression as a single logarithm.

57. $3 \log_5 u + 4 \log_5 v$
58. $2 \log_3 u - \log_3 v$
59. $\log_3 \sqrt{x} - \log_3 x^3$
60. $\log_2\left(\frac{1}{x}\right) + \log_2\left(\frac{1}{x^2}\right)$
61. $\log_4(x^2 - 1) - 5 \log_4(x + 1)$
62. $\log(x^2 + 3x + 2) - 2 \log(x + 1)$
63. $\ln\left(\frac{x}{x - 1}\right) + \ln\left(\frac{x + 1}{x}\right) - \ln(x^2 - 1)$
64. $\log\left(\frac{x^2 + 2x - 3}{x^2 - 4}\right) - \log\left(\frac{x^2 + 7x + 6}{x + 2}\right)$
65. $8 \log_2 \sqrt{3x - 2} - \log_2\left(\frac{4}{x}\right) + \log_2 4$
66. $21 \log_3 \sqrt[3]{x} + \log_3(9x^2) - \log_3 9$
67. $2 \log_a(5x^3) - \frac{1}{2}\log_a(2x + 3)$
68. $\frac{1}{3}\log(x^3 + 1) + \frac{1}{2}\log(x^2 + 1)$
69. $2 \log_2(x + 1) - \log_2(x + 3) - \log_2(x - 1)$
70. $3 \log_5(3x + 1) - 2 \log_5(2x - 1) - \log_5 x$

In Problems 71–78, use the Change-of-Base Formula and a calculator to evaluate each logarithm. Round your answer to three decimal places.

71. $\log_3 21$
72. $\log_5 18$
73. $\log_{1/3} 71$
74. $\log_{1/2} 15$
75. $\log_{\sqrt{2}} 7$
76. $\log_{\sqrt{5}} 8$
77. $\log_\pi e$
78. $\log_\pi \sqrt{2}$

In Problems 79–84, graph each function using a graphing utility and the Change-of-Base Formula.

79. $y = \log_4 x$
80. $y = \log_5 x$
81. $y = \log_2(x + 2)$
82. $y = \log_4(x - 3)$
83. $y = \log_{x-1}(x + 1)$
84. $y = \log_{x+2}(x - 2)$

Mixed Practice

85. If $f(x) = \ln x$, $g(x) = e^x$, and $h(x) = x^2$, find:
  (a) $(f \circ g)(x)$. What is the domain of $f \circ g$?
  (b) $(g \circ f)(x)$. What is the domain of $g \circ f$?
  (c) $(f \circ g)(5)$
  (d) $(f \circ h)(x)$. What is the domain of $f \circ h$?
  (e) $(f \circ h)(e)$

86. If $f(x) = \log_2 x$, $g(x) = 2^x$, and $h(x) = 4x$, find:
  (a) $(f \circ g)(x)$. What is the domain of $f \circ g$?
  (b) $(g \circ f)(x)$. What is the domain of $g \circ f$?
  (c) $(f \circ g)(3)$
  (d) $(f \circ h)(x)$. What is the domain of $f \circ h$?
  (e) $(f \circ h)(8)$

Applications and Extensions

In Problems 87–96, express y as a function of x. The constant C is a positive number.

87. $\ln y = \ln x + \ln C$
88. $\ln y = \ln(x + C)$
89. $\ln y = \ln x + \ln(x + 1) + \ln C$
90. $\ln y = 2 \ln x - \ln(x + 1) + \ln C$
91. $\ln y = 3x + \ln C$
92. $\ln y = -2x + \ln C$
93. $\ln(y - 3) = -4x + \ln C$
94. $\ln(y + 4) = 5x + \ln C$
95. $3 \ln y = \frac{1}{2}\ln(2x + 1) - \frac{1}{3}\ln(x + 4) + \ln C$
96. $2 \ln y = -\frac{1}{2}\ln x + \frac{1}{3}\ln(x^2 + 1) + \ln C$
97. Find the value of $\log_2 3 \cdot \log_3 4 \cdot \log_4 5 \cdot \log_5 6 \cdot \log_6 7 \cdot \log_7 8$.
98. Find the value of $\log_2 4 \cdot \log_4 6 \cdot \log_6 8$.
99. Find the value of $\log_2 3 \cdot \log_3 4 \cdot \cdots \cdot \log_n(n + 1) \cdot \log_{n+1} 2$.
100. Find the value of $\log_2 2 \cdot \log_2 4 \cdot \cdots \cdot \log_2 2^n$.
101. Show that $\log_a(x + \sqrt{x^2 - 1}) + \log_a(x - \sqrt{x^2 - 1}) = 0$.
102. Show that $\log_a(\sqrt{x} + \sqrt{x - 1}) + \log_a(\sqrt{x} - \sqrt{x - 1}) = 0$.
103. Show that $\ln(1 + e^{2x}) = 2x + \ln(1 + e^{-2x})$.
104. **Difference Quotient** If $f(x) = \log_a x$, show that $\frac{f(x + h) - f(x)}{h} = \log_a\left(1 + \frac{h}{x}\right)^{1/h}$, $h \neq 0$.
105. If $f(x) = \log_a x$, show that $-f(x) = \log_{1/a} x$.
106. If $f(x) = \log_a x$, show that $f(AB) = f(A) + f(B)$.
107. If $f(x) = \log_a x$, show that $f\left(\frac{1}{x}\right) = -f(x)$.
108. If $f(x) = \log_a x$, show that $f(x^\alpha) = \alpha f(x)$.
109. Show that $\log_a\left(\frac{M}{N}\right) = \log_a M - \log_a N$, where a, M, and N are positive real numbers and $a \neq 1$.
110. Show that $\log_a\left(\frac{1}{N}\right) = -\log_a N$, where a and N are positive real numbers and $a \neq 1$.

Explaining Concepts: Discussion and Writing

111. Graph $Y_1 = \log(x^2)$ and $Y_2 = 2\log(x)$ using a graphing utility. Are they equivalent? What might account for any differences in the two functions?
112. Write an example that illustrates why $(\log_a x)^r \neq r\log_a x$.
113. Write an example that illustrates why $\log_2(x + y) \neq \log_2 x + \log_2 y$.
114. Does $3^{\log_3(-5)} = -5$? Why or why not?

12.6 Logarithmic and Exponential Equations

PREPARING FOR THIS SECTION *Before getting started, review the following:*

- Solve Quadratic Equations (Section 7.2, pp. 476–483)
- Solve Equations Quadratic in Form (Section 7.4, pp. 497–499)

Now Work the **'Are You Prepared?'** problems on page 816.

OBJECTIVES
1 Solve Logarithmic Equations (p. 811)
2 Solve Exponential Equations (p. 813)
3 Solve Logarithmic and Exponential Equations Using a Graphing Utility (p. 815)

1 Solve Logarithmic Equations

In Section 12.4 we solved logarithmic equations by changing a logarithmic equation to an exponential equation. That is, we used the definition of a logarithm:

$$y = \log_a x \quad \text{is equivalent to} \quad x = a^y \qquad a > 0, a \neq 1$$

For example, to solve the equation $\log_2(1 - 2x) = 3$, we use the equivalent exponential equation $1 - 2x = 2^3$ and solve for x.

$$\log_2(1 - 2x) = 3$$

$$1 - 2x = 2^3 \qquad \text{Change to an exponential expression.}$$

$$-2x = 7 \qquad \text{Simplify.}$$

$$x = -\frac{7}{2} \qquad \text{Divide both sides by } -2.$$

You should check this solution for yourself.

For most logarithmic equations, some manipulation of the equation (usually using properties of logarithms) is required to obtain a solution. Also, to avoid extraneous solutions with logarithmic equations, we determine the domain of the variable first.

Our practice will be to solve equations, whenever possible, by finding exact solutions using algebraic methods and exact or approximate solutions using a graphing utility. When algebraic methods cannot be used, approximate solutions will be obtained using a graphing utility. The reader is encouraged to pay particular attention to the form of equations for which exact solutions are possible.

We begin with an example of a logarithmic equation that requires using the fact that a logarithmic function is a one-to-one function.

$$\text{If } \log_a M = \log_a N, \text{ then } M = N \qquad M, N, \text{ and } a \text{ are positive and } a \neq 1$$

EXAMPLE 1

Solving a Logarithmic Equation

Solve: $2 \log_5 x = \log_5 9$

Algebraic Solution

Note that the domain of the variable in this equation is $x > 0$. Because each logarithm is to the same base, 5, we can obtain an exact solution as follows:

$$2 \log_5 x = \log_5 9$$

$$\log_5 x^2 = \log_5 9 \quad \log_a M^r = r \log_a M$$

$$x^2 = 9 \quad \text{If } \log_a M = \log_a N \text{, then } M = N.$$

$$x = 3 \quad \text{or} \quad \cancel{x = -3}$$ Recall that the domain of the variable is $x > 0$. Therefore, -3 is extraneous and we discard it.

✓Check:

$$2 \log_5 3 \stackrel{?}{=} \log_5 9$$

$$\log_5 3^2 \stackrel{?}{=} \log_5 9 \quad r \log_a M = \log_a M^r$$

$$\log_5 9 = \log_5 9$$

The solution set is $\{3\}$. ■

Graphing Solution

To solve the equation using a graphing utility, graph $Y_1 = 2 \log_5 x = \dfrac{2 \log x}{\log 5}$ and $Y_2 = \log_5 9 = \dfrac{\log 9}{\log 5}$, and determine the point of intersection. See Figure 47. The point of intersection is (3, 1.3652124); so $x = 3$ is the only solution. The solution set is $\{3\}$.

Figure 47

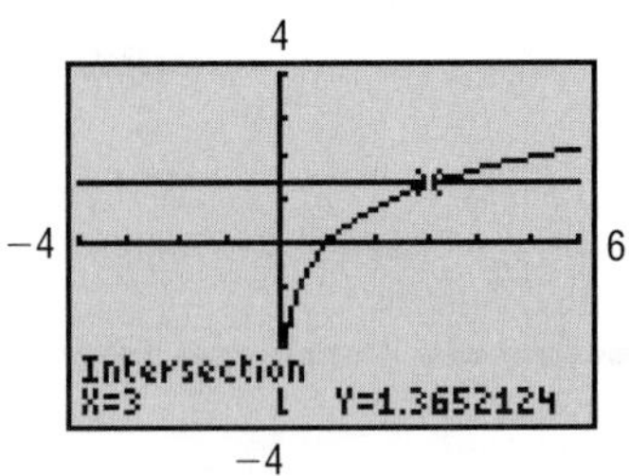

■

Now Work PROBLEM 13

EXAMPLE 2 **Solving a Logarithmic Equation**

Solve: $\log_5(x + 6) + \log_5(x + 2) = 1$

Algebraic Solution

The domain of the variable requires that $x + 6 > 0$ and $x + 2 > 0$, so $x > -6$ and $x > -2$. This means any solution must satisfy $x > -2$. To obtain an exact solution, express the left side as a single logarithm. Then change the equation to exponential form.

$$\log_5(x + 6) + \log_5(x + 2) = 1$$

$$\log_5[(x + 6)(x + 2)] = 1 \quad \log_a M + \log_a N = \log_a(MN)$$

$$(x + 6)(x + 2) = 5^1 = 5 \quad \text{Change to an exponential equation.}$$

$$x^2 + 8x + 12 = 5 \quad \text{Simplify.}$$

$$x^2 + 8x + 7 = 0 \quad \text{Place the quadratic equation in standard form.}$$

$$(x + 7)(x + 1) = 0 \quad \text{Factor.}$$

$$x = -7 \quad \text{or} \quad x = -1 \quad \text{Zero-Product Property}$$

Only $x = -1$ satisfies the restriction that $x > -2$, so $x = -7$ is extraneous. The solution set is $\{-1\}$, which you should check. ■

Graphing Solution

Graph $Y_1 = \log_5(x + 6) + \log_5(x + 2) = \dfrac{\log(x + 6)}{\log 5} + \dfrac{\log(x + 2)}{\log 5}$ and $Y_2 = 1$ and determine the point(s) of intersection. See Figure 48. The point of intersection is $(-1, 1)$, so $x = -1$ is the only solution. The solution set is $\{-1\}$.

Figure 48

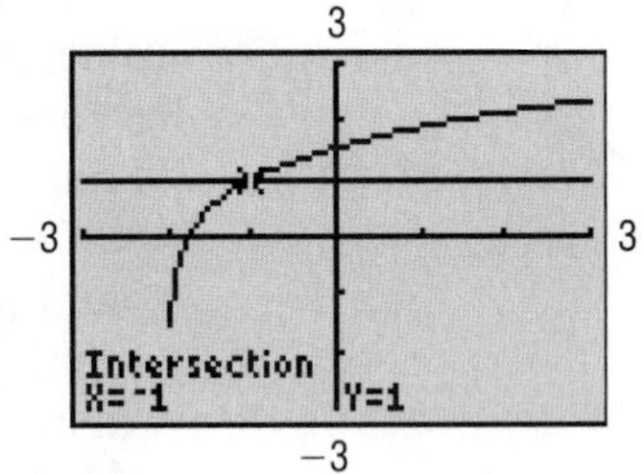

■

WARNING A negative solution is not automatically extraneous. You must determine whether the potential solution causes the argument of any logarithmic expression in the equation to be negative. ■

Now Work PROBLEM 21

EXAMPLE 3 **Solving a Logarithmic Equation**

Solve: $\ln x + \ln(x - 4) = \ln(x + 6)$

Algebraic Solution

The domain of the variable requires that $x > 0$, $x - 4 > 0$, and $x + 6 > 0$. As a result, the domain of the variable is $x > 4$. Begin the solution using the log of a product property.

$$\ln x + \ln(x - 4) = \ln(x + 6)$$

$$\ln[x(x - 4)] = \ln(x + 6) \quad \ln M + \ln N = \ln(MN)$$

$$x(x - 4) = x + 6 \quad \text{If } \ln M = \ln N, \text{ then } M = N.$$

$$x^2 - 4x = x + 6 \quad \text{Simplify.}$$

$$x^2 - 5x - 6 = 0 \quad \text{Place the quadratic equation in standard form.}$$

$$(x - 6)(x + 1) = 0 \quad \text{Factor.}$$

$$x = 6 \quad \text{or} \quad x = -1 \quad \text{Zero-Product Property}$$

Since the domain of the variable is $x > 4$, discard -1 as extraneous. The solution set is $\{6\}$, which you should check. ■

Graphing Solution

Graph $Y_1 = \ln x + \ln(x - 4)$ and $Y_2 = \ln(x + 6)$ and determine the point(s) of intersection. See Figure 49. The x-coordinate of the point of intersection is 6, so the solution set is $\{6\}$.

Figure 49

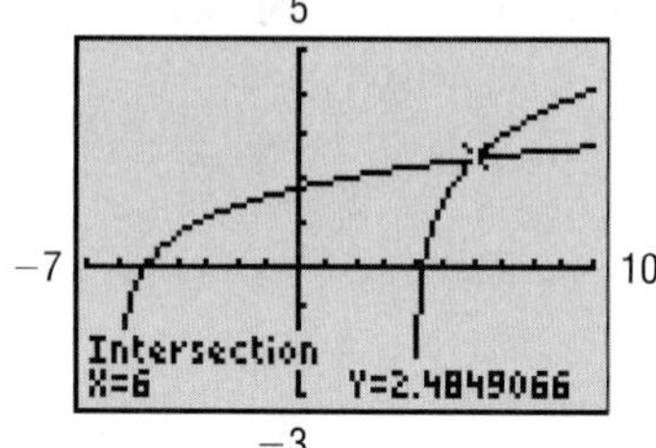

■

WARNING In using properties of logarithms to solve logarithmic equations, avoid using the property $\log_a x^r = r \log_a x$, when r is even. The reason can be seen in this example:

Solve: $\log_3 x^2 = 4$

Solution: The domain of the variable x is all real numbers except 0.

(a) $\log_3 x^2 = 4$

$x^2 = 3^4 = 81$ Change to exponential form.

$x = -9$ or $x = 9$

(b) $\log_3 x^2 = 4$ $\quad \log_a x^r = r \log_a x$

$2 \log_3 x = 4$ Domain of variable is $x > 0$.

$\log_3 x = 2$

$x = 9$

Both -9 and 9 are solutions of $\log_3 x^2 = 4$ (as you can verify). The process in part (b) does not find the solution -9 because the domain of the variable was further restricted to $x > 0$ due to the application of the property $\log_a x^r = r \log_a x$. ■

Now Work PROBLEM 31

2 Solve Exponential Equations

In Sections 12.3 and 12.4, we solved exponential equations algebraically by expressing each side of the equation using the same base. That is, we used the one-to-one property of the exponential function:

$$\text{If } a^u = a^v, \quad \text{then } u = v \qquad a > 0, a \neq 1$$

For example, to solve the exponential equation $4^{2x+1} = 16$, notice that $16 = 4^2$ and apply the property above to obtain $2x + 1 = 2$, from which we find $x = \frac{1}{2}$.

For most exponential equations, we cannot express each side of the equation using the same base. In such cases, algebraic techniques can sometimes be used to obtain exact solutions. When algebraic techniques cannot be used, we use a graphing utility to obtain approximate solutions. You should pay particular attention to the form of equations for which exact solutions are obtained.

EXAMPLE 4 **Solving an Exponential Equation**

Solve: $2^x = 5$

Algebraic Solution

Since 5 cannot be written as an integer power of 2, write the exponential equation as the equivalent logarithmic equation.

$$2^x = 5$$
$$x = \log_2 5 = \frac{\ln 5}{\ln 2}$$

Change-of-Base Formula (10), Section 6.5

Alternatively, we can solve the equation $2^x = 5$ by taking the natural logarithm (or common logarithm) of each side. Taking the natural logarithm,

$$2^x = 5$$
$$\ln 2^x = \ln 5 \quad \text{If } M = N \text{, then } \ln M = \ln N.$$
$$x \ln 2 = \ln 5 \quad \ln M^r = r \ln M$$
$$x = \frac{\ln 5}{\ln 2} \quad \text{Exact solution}$$
$$\approx 2.322 \quad \text{Approximate solution}$$

The solution set is $\left\{\frac{\ln 5}{\ln 2}\right\}$. ■

Graphing Solution

Graph $Y_1 = 2^x$ and $Y_2 = 5$ and determine the x-coordinate of the point of intersection. See Figure 50.

Figure 50

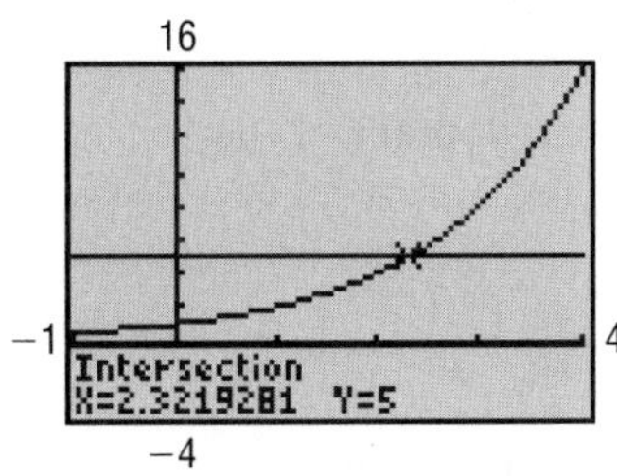

The approximate solution, rounded to three decimal places, is 2.322. ■

Now Work PROBLEM 35

EXAMPLE 5 Solving an Exponential Equation

Solve: $8 \cdot 3^x = 5$

Algebraic Solution

Isolate the exponential expression and then rewrite the statement as an equivalent logarithm.

$$8 \cdot 3^x = 5$$
$$3^x = \frac{5}{8} \quad \text{Solve for } 3^x.$$
$$x = \log_3\left(\frac{5}{8}\right) = \frac{\ln\left(\frac{5}{8}\right)}{\ln 3} \quad \text{Exact solution}$$
$$\approx -0.428 \quad \text{Approximate solution}$$

The solution set is $\left\{\log_3\left(\frac{5}{8}\right)\right\}$. ■

Graphing Solution

Graph $Y_1 = 8 \cdot 3^x$ and $Y_2 = 5$ and determine the x-coordinate of the point of intersection. See Figure 51.

Figure 51

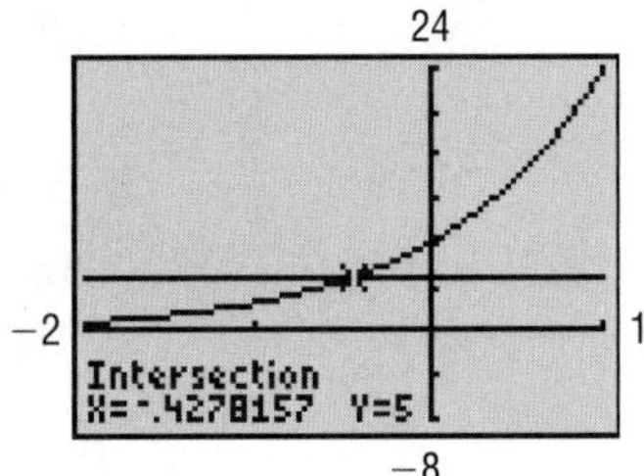

The approximate solution, rounded to three decimal places, is –0.428. ■

EXAMPLE 6 Solving an Exponential Equation

Solve: $5^{x-2} = 3^{3x+2}$

Algebraic Solution

Because the bases are different, we first apply property (7), Section 12.5 (take the natural logarithm of each side), and then use appropriate properties of logarithms. The result is a linear equation in x that we can solve.

Graphing Solution

Graph $Y_1 = 5^{x-2}$ and $Y_2 = 3^{3x+2}$ and determine the x-coordinate of the point of intersection. See Figure 52 on the next page.

$$5^{x-2} = 3^{3x+2}$$
$$\ln 5^{x-2} = \ln 3^{3x+2} \quad \text{If } M = N, \ln M = \ln N.$$
$$(x-2)\ln 5 = (3x+2)\ln 3 \quad \ln M^r = r\ln M$$
$$(\ln 5)x - 2\ln 5 = (3\ln 3)x + 2\ln 3 \quad \text{Distribute. The equation is now linear in } x.$$
$$(\ln 5)x - (3\ln 3)x = 2\ln 3 + 2\ln 5 \quad \text{Place terms involving } x \text{ on the left.}$$
$$(\ln 5 - 3\ln 3)x = 2(\ln 3 + \ln 5) \quad \text{Factor.}$$
$$x = \frac{2(\ln 3 + \ln 5)}{\ln 5 - 3\ln 3} \quad \text{Exact solution}$$
$$\approx -3.212 \quad \text{Approximate solution}$$

Figure 52

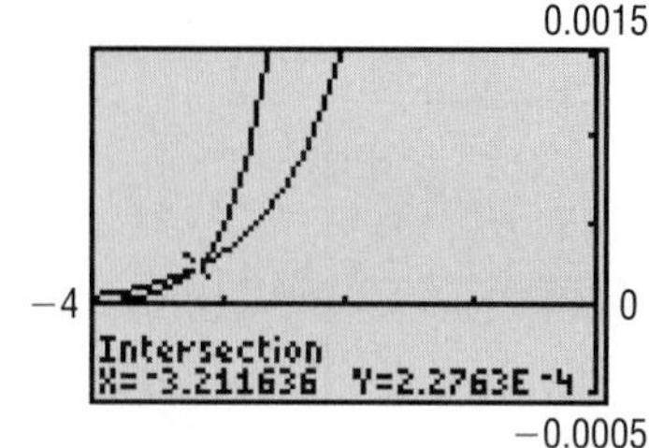

The approximate solution, rounded to three decimal places, is −3.212. Note that the y-coordinate, 2.2763E–4, is in scientific notation and means $2.2763 \times 10^{-4} = 0.0002763$.

Now Work PROBLEM 41

The next example deals with an exponential equation that is quadratic in form.

EXAMPLE 7 Solving an Exponential Equation That Is Quadratic in Form

Solve: $4^x - 2^x - 12 = 0$

Algebraic Solution

We note that $4^x = (2^2)^x = 2^{2x} = (2^x)^2$, so the equation is actually quadratic in form, and we can rewrite it as

$$(2^x)^2 - 2^x - 12 = 0 \quad \text{Let } u = 2^x\text{; then } u^2 - u - 12 = 0.$$

Now we can factor as usual.

$$(2^x - 4)(2^x + 3) = 0 \quad (u-4)(u+3) = 0$$
$$2^x - 4 = 0 \text{ or } 2^x + 3 = 0 \quad u - 4 = 0 \text{ or } u + 3 = 0$$
$$2^x = 4 \qquad 2^x = -3 \quad u = 2^x = 4 \text{ or } u = 2^x = -3$$

The equation on the left has the solution $x = 2$, since $2^x = 4 = 2^2$; the equation on the right has no solution, since $2^x > 0$ for all x. The only solution is 2. The solution set is {2}.

Graphing Solution

Graph $Y_1 = 4^x - 2^x - 12$ and determine the x-intercept. See Figure 53. The x-intercept is 2, so the solution set is {2}.

Figure 53

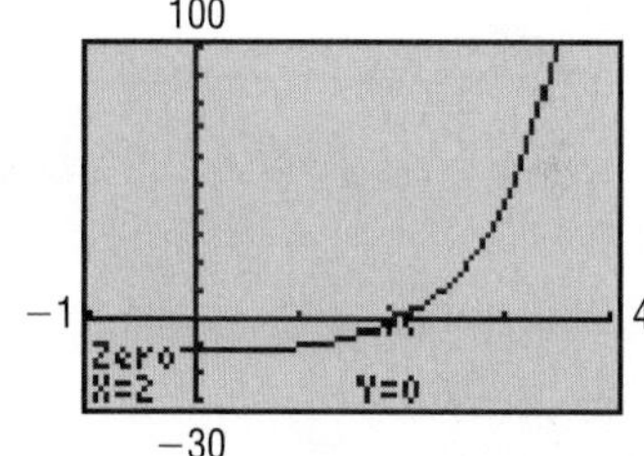

Now Work PROBLEM 53

3 Solve Logarithmic and Exponential Equations Using a Graphing Utility

The algebraic techniques introduced in this section to obtain exact solutions apply only to certain types of logarithmic and exponential equations. Solutions for other types are usually studied in calculus, using numerical methods. For such types, we can use a graphing utility to approximate the solution.

EXAMPLE 8 Solving Equations Using a Graphing Utility

Solve: $x + e^x = 2$

Express the solution(s) rounded to two decimal places.

Solution The solution is found by graphing $Y_1 = x + e^x$ and $Y_2 = 2$. Since Y_1 is an increasing function (do you know why?), there is only one point of intersection for Y_1 and Y_2.

Figure 54

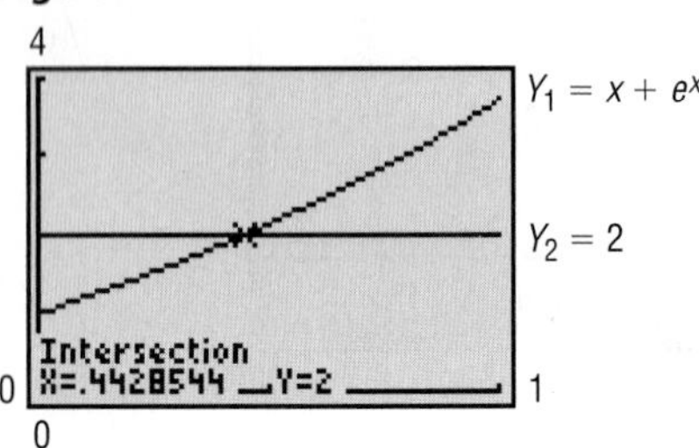

Figure 54 shows the graphs of Y_1 and Y_2. Using the INTERSECT command, the solution is 0.44 rounded to two decimal places. ■

Now Work PROBLEM 63

12.6 Assess Your Understanding

'Are You Prepared?' *Answers are given at the end of these exercises. If you get a wrong answer, read the pages listed in red.*

1. Solve $x^2 - 7x - 30 = 0$. (pp. 476–483)
2. Solve $(x + 3)^2 - 4(x + 3) + 3 = 0$. (pp. 497–498)
3. Approximate the solution(s) to $x^3 = x^2 - 5$ using a graphing utility.
4. Approximate the solution(s) to $x^3 - 2x + 2 = 0$ using a graphing utility.

Skill Building

In Problems 5–32, solve each logarithmic equation. Express irrational solutions in exact form and as a decimal rounded to three decimal places. Verify your results using a graphing utility.

5. $\log_4 x = 2$
6. $\log(x + 6) = 1$
7. $\log_2(5x) = 4$
8. $\log_3(3x - 1) = 2$
9. $\log_4(x + 2) = \log_4 8$
10. $\log_5(2x + 3) = \log_5 3$
11. $\frac{1}{2}\log_3 x = 2\log_3 2$
12. $-2\log_4 x = \log_4 9$
13. $3\log_2 x = -\log_2 27$
14. $2\log_5 x = 3\log_5 4$
15. $3\log_2(x - 1) + \log_2 4 = 5$
16. $2\log_3(x + 4) - \log_3 9 = 2$
17. $\log x + \log(x + 15) = 2$
18. $\log x + \log(x - 21) = 2$
19. $\log(2x + 1) = 1 + \log(x - 2)$
20. $\log(2x) - \log(x - 3) = 1$
21. $\log_2(x + 7) + \log_2(x + 8) = 1$
22. $\log_6(x + 4) + \log_6(x + 3) = 1$
23. $\log_8(x + 6) = 1 - \log_8(x + 4)$
24. $\log_5(x + 3) = 1 - \log_5(x - 1)$
25. $\ln x + \ln(x + 2) = 4$
26. $\ln(x + 1) - \ln x = 2$
27. $\log_3(x + 1) + \log_3(x + 4) = 2$
28. $\log_2(x + 1) + \log_2(x + 7) = 3$
29. $\log_{1/3}(x^2 + x) - \log_{1/3}(x^2 - x) = -1$
30. $\log_4(x^2 - 9) - \log_4(x + 3) = 3$
31. $\log_a(x - 1) - \log_a(x + 6) = \log_a(x - 2) - \log_a(x + 3)$
32. $\log_a x + \log_a(x - 2) = \log_a(x + 4)$

In Problems 33–60, solve each exponential equation. Express irrational solutions in exact form and as a decimal rounded to three decimal places. Verify your results using a graphing utility.

33. $2^{x-5} = 8$
34. $5^{-x} = 25$
35. $2^x = 10$
36. $3^x = 14$
37. $8^{-x} = 1.2$
38. $2^{-x} = 1.5$
39. $5(2^{3x}) = 8$
40. $0.3(4^{0.2x}) = 0.2$
41. $3^{1-2x} = 4^x$
42. $2^{x+1} = 5^{1-2x}$
43. $\left(\frac{3}{5}\right)^x = 7^{1-x}$
44. $\left(\frac{4}{3}\right)^{1-x} = 5^x$
45. $1.2^x = (0.5)^{-x}$
46. $0.3^{1+x} = 1.7^{2x-1}$
47. $\pi^{1-x} = e^x$
48. $e^{x+3} = \pi^x$
49. $2^{2x} + 2^x - 12 = 0$
50. $3^{2x} + 3^x - 2 = 0$
51. $3^{2x} + 3^{x+1} - 4 = 0$
52. $2^{2x} + 2^{x+2} - 12 = 0$
53. $16^x + 4^{x+1} - 3 = 0$
54. $9^x - 3^{x+1} + 1 = 0$
55. $25^x - 8 \cdot 5^x = -16$
56. $36^x - 6 \cdot 6^x = -9$
57. $3 \cdot 4^x + 4 \cdot 2^x + 8 = 0$
58. $2 \cdot 49^x + 11 \cdot 7^x + 5 = 0$
59. $4^x - 10 \cdot 4^{-x} = 3$
60. $3^x - 14 \cdot 3^{-x} = 5$

In Problems 61–74, use a graphing utility to solve each equation. Express your answer rounded to two decimal places.

61. $\log_5(x + 1) - \log_4(x - 2) = 1$
62. $\log_2(x - 1) - \log_6(x + 2) = 2$
63. $e^x = -x$
64. $e^{2x} = x + 2$
65. $e^x = x^2$
66. $e^x = x^3$
67. $\ln x = -x$
68. $\ln(2x) = -x + 2$
69. $\ln x = x^3 - 1$
70. $\ln x = -x^2$
71. $e^x + \ln x = 4$
72. $e^x - \ln x = 4$
73. $e^{-x} = \ln x$
74. $e^{-x} = -\ln x$

Mixed Practice

In Problems 75–86, solve each equation. Express irrational solutions in exact form and as a decimal rounded to three decimal places.

75. $\log_2(x+1) - \log_4 x = 1$
[**Hint:** Change $\log_4 x$ to base 2.]

76. $\log_2(3x+2) - \log_4 x = 3$

77. $\log_{16} x + \log_4 x + \log_2 x = 7$

78. $\log_9 x + 3\log_3 x = 14$

79. $(\sqrt[3]{2})^{2-x} = 2^{x^2}$

80. $\log_2 x^{\log_2 x} = 4$

81. $\dfrac{e^x + e^{-x}}{2} = 1$
[**Hint:** Multiply each side by e^x.]

82. $\dfrac{e^x + e^{-x}}{2} = 3$

83. $\dfrac{e^x - e^{-x}}{2} = 2$

84. $\dfrac{e^x - e^{-x}}{2} = -2$

85. $\log_5 x + \log_3 x = 1$
[**Hint:** Use the Change-of-Base Formula.]

86. $\log_2 x + \log_6 x = 3$

87. $f(x) = \log_2(x+3)$ and $g(x) = \log_2(3x+1)$.
(a) Solve $f(x) = 3$. What point is on the graph of f?
(b) Solve $g(x) = 4$. What point is on the graph of g?
(c) Solve $f(x) = g(x)$. Do the graphs of f and g intersect? If so, where?
(d) Solve $(f+g)(x) = 7$.
(e) Solve $(f-g)(x) = 2$.

88. $f(x) = \log_3(x+5)$ and $g(x) = \log_3(x-1)$.
(a) Solve $f(x) = 2$. What point is on the graph of f?
(b) Solve $g(x) = 3$. What point is on the graph of g?
(c) Solve $f(x) = g(x)$. Do the graphs of f and g intersect? If so, where?
(d) Solve $(f+g)(x) = 3$.
(e) Solve $(f-g)(x) = 2$.

89. (a) Graph $f(x) = 3^{x+1}$ and $g(x) = 2^{x+2}$, on the same Cartesian plane.
(b) Find the point(s) of intersection of the graphs of f and g by solving $f(x) = g(x)$. Round answers to three decimal places. Label any intersection points on the graph drawn in part (a).
(c) Based on the graph, solve $f(x) > g(x)$.

90. (a) Graph $f(x) = 5^{x-1}$ and $g(x) = 2^{x+1}$, on the same Cartesian plane.
(b) Find the point(s) of intersection of the graphs of f and g by solving $f(x) = g(x)$. Label any intersection points on the graph drawn in part (a).
(c) Based on the graph, solve $f(x) > g(x)$.

91. (a) Graph $f(x) = 3^x$ and $g(x) = 10$ on the same Cartesian plane.
(b) Shade the region bounded by the y-axis, $f(x) = 3^x$, and $g(x) = 10$ on the graph drawn in part (a).
(c) Solve $f(x) = g(x)$ and label the point of intersection on the graph drawn in part (a).

92. (a) Graph $f(x) = 2^x$ and $g(x) = 12$ on the same Cartesian plane.
(b) Shade the region bounded by the y-axis, $f(x) = 2^x$, and $g(x) = 12$ on the graph drawn in part (a).
(c) Solve $f(x) = g(x)$ and label the point of intersection on the graph drawn in part (a).

93. (a) Graph $f(x) = 2^{x+1}$ and $g(x) = 2^{-x+2}$ on the same Cartesian plane.
(b) Shade the region bounded by the y-axis, $f(x) = 2^{x+1}$, and $g(x) = 2^{-x+2}$ on the graph draw in part (a).
(c) Solve $f(x) = g(x)$ and label the point of intersection on the graph drawn in part (a).

94. (a) Graph $f(x) = 3^{-x+1}$ and $g(x) = 3^{x-2}$ on the same Cartesian plane.
(b) Shade the region bounded by the y-axis, $f(x) = 3^{-x+1}$, and $g(x) = 3^{x-2}$ on the graph draw in part (a).
(c) Solve $f(x) = g(x)$ and label the point of intersection on the graph drawn in part (a).

95. (a) Graph $f(x) = 2^x - 4$.
(b) Find the zero of f.
(c) Based on the graph, solve $f(x) < 0$.

96. (a) Graph $g(x) = 3^x - 9$.
(b) Find the zero of g.
(c) Based on the graph, solve $g(x) > 0$.

Applications and Extensions

97. A Population Model The resident population of the United States in 2010 was 309 million people and was growing at a rate of 0.9% per year. Assuming that this growth rate continues, the model $P(t) = 309(1.009)^{t-2010}$ represents the population P (in millions of people) in year t.
(a) According to this model, when will the population of the United States be 419 million people?
(b) According to this model, when will the population of the United States be 488 million people?

Source: U.S. Census Bureau

98. A Population Model The population of the world in 2011 was 6.91 billion people and was growing at a rate of 1.14% per year. Assuming that this growth rate continues, the model $P(t) = 6.91(1.0114)^{t-2011}$ represents the population P (in billions of people) in year t.

(a) According to this model, when will the population of the world be 9.6 billion people?

(b) According to this model, when will the population of the world be 12 billion people?

Source: U.S. Census Bureau

99. Depreciation The value V of a Chevy Cobalt that is t years old can be modeled by $V(t) = 16{,}500(0.82)^t$.

(a) According to the model, when will the car be worth \$9000?

(b) According to the model, when will the car be worth \$4000?

(c) According to the model, when will the car be worth \$2000?

Source: Kelley Blue Book

100. Depreciation The value V of a Honda Civic DX that is t years old can be modeled by $V(t) = 16{,}775(0.905)^t$.

(a) According to the model, when will the car be worth \$15,000?

(b) According to the model, when will the car be worth \$8000?

(c) According to the model, when will the car be worth \$4000?

Source: Kelley Blue Book

Explaining Concepts: Discussion and Writing

101. Fill in reasons for each step in the following two solutions.

Solve: $\log_3(x-1)^2 = 2$

Solution A	**Solution B**
$\log_3(x-1)^2 = 2$	$\log_3(x-1)^2 = 2$
$(x-1)^2 = 3^2 = 9$ ______	$2\log_3(x-1) = 2$ ______
$(x-1) = \pm 3$ ______	$\log_3(x-1) = 1$ ______
$x-1 = -3$ or $x-1 = 3$ ______	$x-1 = 3^1 = 3$ ______
$x = -2$ or $x = 4$ ______	$x = 4$ ______

Both solutions given in Solution A check. Explain what caused the solution $x = -2$ to be lost in Solution B.

'Are You Prepared?' Answers

1. $\{-3, 10\}$ **2.** $\{-2, 0\}$ **3.** $\{-1.43\}$ **4.** $\{-1.77\}$

12.7 Financial Models

OBJECTIVES

1 Determine the Future Value of a Lump Sum of Money (p. 818)

2 Calculate Effective Rates of Return (p. 822)

3 Determine the Present Value of a Lump Sum of Money (p. 823)

4 Determine the Rate of Interest or Time Required to Double a Lump Sum of Money (p. 824)

1 Determine the Future Value of a Lump Sum of Money

Interest is money paid for the use of money. The total amount borrowed (whether by an individual from a bank in the form of a loan or by a bank from an individual in the form of a savings account) is called the **principal.** The **rate of interest,** expressed as a percent, is the amount charged for the use of the principal for a given period of time, usually on a yearly (that is, per annum) basis.

THEOREM

Simple Interest Formula

If a principal of P dollars is borrowed for a period of t years at a per annum interest rate r, expressed as a decimal, the interest I charged is

$$I = Prt \tag{1}$$

Interest charged according to formula (1) is called **simple interest.**

In working with problems involving interest, we define the term **payment period** as follows:

Annually:	Once per year	**Monthly:**	12 times per year
Semiannually:	Twice per year	**Daily:**	365 times per year*
Quarterly:	Four times per year		

When the interest due at the end of a payment period is added to the principal so that the interest computed at the end of the next payment period is based on this new principal amount (old principal + interest), the interest is said to have been **compounded. Compound interest** is interest paid on the principal and previously earned interest.

EXAMPLE 1

Computing Compound Interest

A credit union pays interest of 2% per annum compounded quarterly on a certain savings plan. If \$1000 is deposited in such a plan and the interest is left to accumulate, how much is in the account after 1 year?

Solution

Use the simple interest formula, $I = Prt$. The principal P is \$1000 and the rate of interest is $2\% = 0.02$. After the first quarter of a year, the time t is $\frac{1}{4}$ year, so the interest earned is

$$I = Prt = (\$1000)(0.02)\left(\frac{1}{4}\right) = \$5$$

The new principal is $P + I = \$1000 + \$5 = \$1005$. At the end of the second quarter, the interest on this principal is

$$I = (\$1005)(0.02)\left(\frac{1}{4}\right) = \$5.03$$

At the end of the third quarter, the interest on the new principal of $\$1005 + \$5.03 = \$1010.03$ is

$$I = (\$1010.03)(0.02)\left(\frac{1}{4}\right) = \$5.05$$

Finally, after the fourth quarter, the interest is

$$I = (\$1015.08)(0.02)\left(\frac{1}{4}\right) = \$5.08$$

After 1 year the account contains $\$1015.08 + \$5.08 = \$1020.16$. ■

The pattern of the calculations performed in Example 1 leads to a general formula for compound interest. To fix our ideas, let P represent the principal to be invested at a per annum interest rate r that is compounded n times per year, so the time of each compounding period is $\frac{1}{n}$ years. (For computing purposes, r is expressed as a decimal.) The interest earned after each compounding period is given by formula (1).

$$\text{Interest} = \text{principal} \times \text{rate} \times \text{time} = P \cdot r \cdot \frac{1}{n} = P \cdot \left(\frac{r}{n}\right)$$

*Most banks use a 360-day "year." Why do you think they do?

The amount A after one compounding period is

$$A = P + P \cdot \left(\frac{r}{n}\right) = P \cdot \left(1 + \frac{r}{n}\right)$$

After two compounding periods, the amount A, based on the new principal $P \cdot \left(1 + \frac{r}{n}\right)$, is

$$A = \underbrace{P \cdot \left(1 + \frac{r}{n}\right)}_{\text{New principal}} + \underbrace{P \cdot \left(1 + \frac{r}{n}\right)\left(\frac{r}{n}\right)}_{\text{Interest on new principal}} \underset{\uparrow \text{ Factor out } P \cdot (1 + \frac{r}{n}).}{=} P \cdot \left(1 + \frac{r}{n}\right)\left(1 + \frac{r}{n}\right) = P \cdot \left(1 + \frac{r}{n}\right)^2$$

After three compounding periods, the amount A is

$$A = P \cdot \left(1 + \frac{r}{n}\right)^2 + P \cdot \left(1 + \frac{r}{n}\right)^2\left(\frac{r}{n}\right) = P \cdot \left(1 + \frac{r}{n}\right)^2 \cdot \left(1 + \frac{r}{n}\right) = P \cdot \left(1 + \frac{r}{n}\right)^3$$

Continuing this way, after n compounding periods (1 year), the amount A is

$$A = P \cdot \left(1 + \frac{r}{n}\right)^n$$

Because t years will contain $n \cdot t$ compounding periods, after t years we have

$$A = P \cdot \left(1 + \frac{r}{n}\right)^{nt}$$

THEOREM

Compound Interest Formula

The amount A after t years due to a principal P invested at an annual interest rate r compounded n times per year is

$$A = P \cdot \left(1 + \frac{r}{n}\right)^{nt} \qquad \textbf{(2)}$$

Exploration

To see the effects of compounding interest monthly on an initial deposit of \$1, graph $Y_1 = \left(1 + \frac{r}{12}\right)^{12x}$ with $r = 0.06$ and $r = 0.12$ for $0 \le x \le 30$. What is the future value of \$1 in 30 years when the interest rate per annum is $r = 0.06$ (6%)? What is the future value of \$1 in 30 years when the interest rate per annum is $r = 0.12$ (12%)? Does doubling the interest rate double the future value?

For example, to rework Example 1, use $P = \$1000$, $r = 0.08$, $n = 4$ (quarterly compounding), and $t = 1$ year to obtain

$$A = P \cdot \left(1 + \frac{r}{n}\right)^{nt} = 1000\left(1 + \frac{0.08}{4}\right)^{4 \cdot 1} = \$1082.43$$

In equation (2), the amount A is typically referred to as the **future value** of the account, while P is called the **present value.**

Now Work PROBLEM 7

EXAMPLE 2 Comparing Investments Using Different Compounding Periods

Investing \$1000 at an annual rate of 10% compounded annually, semiannually, quarterly, monthly, and daily will yield the following amounts after 1 year:

Annual compounding ($n = 1$): $A = P \cdot (1 + r)$

$$= (\$1000)(1 + 0.10) = \$1100.00$$

Semiannual compounding ($n = 2$): $A = P \cdot \left(1 + \frac{r}{2}\right)^2$

$$= (\$1000)(1 + 0.05)^2 = \$1102.50$$

Quarterly compounding ($n = 4$): $A = P \cdot \left(1 + \frac{r}{4}\right)^4$

$$= (\$1000)(1 + 0.025)^4 = \$1103.81$$

Monthly compounding $(n = 12)$:
$$A = P \cdot \left(1 + \frac{r}{12}\right)^{12}$$
$$= (\$1000)\left(1 + \frac{0.10}{12}\right)^{12} = \$1104.71$$

Daily compounding $(n = 365)$:
$$A = P \cdot \left(1 + \frac{r}{365}\right)^{365}$$
$$= (\$1000)\left(1 + \frac{0.10}{365}\right)^{365} = \$1105.16$$

■

From Example 2, we can see that the effect of compounding more frequently is that the amount after 1 year is higher: \$1000 compounded 4 times a year at 10% results in \$1103.81, \$1000 compounded 12 times a year at 10% results in \$1104.71, and \$1000 compounded 365 times a year at 10% results in \$1105.16. This leads to the following question: What would happen to the amount after 1 year if the number of times that the interest is compounded were increased without bound?

Let's find the answer. Suppose that P is the principal, r is the per annum interest rate, and n is the number of times that the interest is compounded each year. The amount after 1 year is

$$A = P \cdot \left(1 + \frac{r}{n}\right)^n$$

Rewrite this expression as follows:

$$A = P \cdot \left(1 + \frac{r}{n}\right)^n = P \cdot \left(1 + \frac{1}{\frac{n}{r}}\right)^n = P \cdot \left[\left(1 + \frac{1}{\frac{n}{r}}\right)^{n/r}\right]^r = P \cdot \left[\left(1 + \frac{1}{h}\right)^h\right]^r \quad (3)$$

$$h = \frac{n}{r}$$

Now suppose that the number n of times that the interest is compounded per year gets larger and larger; that is, suppose that $n \to \infty$. Then $h = \frac{n}{r} \to \infty$, and the expression in brackets in equation (3) equals e. That is, $A \to Pe^r$.

Table 9 compares $\left(1 + \frac{r}{n}\right)^n$, for large values of n, to e^r for $r = 0.05$, $r = 0.10$, $r = 0.15$, and $r = 1$. The larger that n gets, the closer $\left(1 + \frac{r}{n}\right)^n$ gets to e^r. No matter how frequent the compounding, the amount after 1 year has the definite ceiling Pe^r.

Table 9

	$\left(1 + \frac{r}{n}\right)^n$			
	n = 100	**n = 1000**	**n = 10,000**	e^r
$r = 0.05$	1.0512580	1.0512698	1.051271	1.0512711
$r = 0.10$	1.1051157	1.1051654	1.1051704	1.1051709
$r = 0.15$	1.1617037	1.1618212	1.1618329	1.1618342
$r = 1$	2.7048138	2.7169239	2.7181459	2.7182818

When interest is compounded so that the amount after 1 year is Pe^r, we say that the interest is **compounded continuously.**

THEOREM

Continuous Compounding

The amount A after t years due to a principal P invested at an annual interest rate r compounded continuously is

$$A = Pe^{rt} \quad (4)$$

EXAMPLE 3 **Using Continuous Compounding**

The amount A that results from investing a principal P of \$1000 at an annual rate r of 10% compounded continuously for a time t of 1 year is

$$A = \$1000e^{0.10} = (\$1000)(1.10517) = \$1105.17$$ ■

Now Work PROBLEM 13

2 Calculate Effective Rates of Return

Suppose that you have \$1000 and a bank offers to pay you 3% annual interest on a savings account with interest compounded monthly. What annual interest rate do you need to earn to have the same amount at the end of the year if the interest is compounded annually (once per year)? To answer this question, first determine the value of the \$1000 in the account that earns 3% compounded monthly.

$$A = \$1000\left(1 + \frac{0.03}{12}\right)^{12} \quad \text{Use } A = P\left(1 + \frac{r}{n}\right)^n \text{ with } P = \$1000, r = 0.03, n = 12.$$
$$= \$1030.42$$

So the interest earned is \$30.42. Using $I = Prt$ with $t = 1$, $I = \$30.42$, and $P = \$1000$, we find the annual simple interest rate is $0.03042 = 3.042\%$. This interest rate is known as the *effective rate of interest.*

The **effective rate of interest** is the equivalent annual simple interest rate that would yield the same amount as compounding n times per year, or continuously, after 1 year.

THEOREM **Effective Rate of Interest**

The effective rate of interest r_e of an investment earning an annual interest rate r is given by

$$\text{Compounding } n \text{ times per year: } r_e = \left(1 + \frac{r}{n}\right)^n - 1$$
$$\text{Continuous compounding: } r_e = e^r - 1$$

EXAMPLE 4 **Computing the Effective Rate of Interest—Which Is the Best Deal?**

Suppose you want to buy a 5-year certificate of deposit (CD). You visit three banks to determine their CD rates. American Express offers you 2.15% annual interest compounded monthly, and First Internet Bank offers you 2.20% compounded quarterly. Discover offers 2.12% compounded daily. Determine which bank is offering the best deal.

Solution The bank that offers the best deal is the one with the highest effective interest rate.

American Express	First Internet Bank	Discover
$r_e = \left(1 + \frac{0.0215}{12}\right)^{12} - 1$	$r_e = \left(1 + \frac{0.022}{4}\right)^{4} - 1$	$r_e = \left(1 + \frac{0.0212}{365}\right)^{365} - 1$
$\approx 1.02171 - 1$	$\approx 1.02218 - 1$	$\approx 1.02143 - 1$
$= 0.02171$	$= 0.02218$	$= 0.02143$
$= 2.171\%$	$= 2.218\%$	$= 2.143\%$

The effective rate of interest is highest for First Internet Bank, so First Internet Bank is offering the best deal. ■

Now Work PROBLEM 23

3 Determine the Present Value of a Lump Sum of Money

When people in finance speak of the "time value of money," they are usually referring to the *present value* of money. The **present value** of A dollars to be received at a future date is the principal that you would need to invest now so that it will grow to A dollars in the specified time period. The present value of money to be received at a future date is always less than the amount to be received, since the amount to be received will equal the present value (money invested now) *plus* the interest accrued over the time period.

We use the compound interest formula (2) to get a formula for present value. If P is the present value of A dollars to be received after t years at a per annum interest rate r compounded n times per year, then, by formula (2),

$$A = P \cdot \left(1 + \frac{r}{n}\right)^{nt}$$

To solve for P, divide both sides by $\left(1 + \frac{r}{n}\right)^{nt}$. The result is

$$\frac{A}{\left(1 + \frac{r}{n}\right)^{nt}} = P \quad \text{or} \quad P = A \cdot \left(1 + \frac{r}{n}\right)^{-nt}$$

THEOREM

Present Value Formulas

The present value P of A dollars to be received after t years, assuming a per annum interest rate r compounded n times per year, is

$$P = A \cdot \left(1 + \frac{r}{n}\right)^{-nt} \tag{5}$$

If the interest is compounded continuously,

$$P = Ae^{-rt} \tag{6}$$

To derive formula (6), solve formula (4) for P.

EXAMPLE 5

Computing the Value of a Zero-coupon Bond

A zero-coupon (noninterest-bearing) bond can be redeemed in 10 years for \$1000. How much should you be willing to pay for it now if you want a return of

(a) 8% compounded monthly? (b) 7% compounded continuously?

Solution

(a) We are seeking the present value of \$1000. Use formula (5) with $A = \$1000$, $n = 12$, $r = 0.08$, and $t = 10$.

$$P = A \cdot \left(1 + \frac{r}{n}\right)^{-nt} = \$1000\left(1 + \frac{0.08}{12}\right)^{-12(10)} = \$450.52$$

For a return of 8% compounded monthly, you should pay \$450.52 for the bond.

(b) Here use formula (6) with $A = \$1000$, $r = 0.07$, and $t = 10$.

$$P = Ae^{-rt} = \$1000e^{-(0.07)(10)} = \$496.59$$

For a return of 7% compounded continuously, you should pay \$496.59 for the bond. ■

Now Work PROBLEM 15

4 Determine the Rate of Interest or Time Required to Double a Lump Sum of Money

EXAMPLE 6 **Rate of Interest Required to Double an Investment**

What annual rate of interest compounded annually should you seek if you want to double your investment in 5 years?

Solution If P is the principal and we want P to double, the amount A will be $2P$. We use the compound interest formula with $n = 1$ and $t = 5$ to find r.

$$A = P \cdot \left(1 + \frac{r}{n}\right)^{nt}$$

$$2P = P \cdot (1 + r)^5 \qquad A = 2P, n = 1, t = 5$$

$$2 = (1 + r)^5 \qquad \text{Divide both sides by } P.$$

$$1 + r = \sqrt[5]{2} \qquad \text{Take the fifth root of each side.}$$

$$r = \sqrt[5]{2} - 1 \approx 1.148698 - 1 = 0.148698$$

The annual rate of interest needed to double the principal in 5 years is 14.87%. ■

Now Work PROBLEM 31

EXAMPLE 7 **Time Required to Double or Triple an Investment**

(a) How long will it take for an investment to double in value if it earns 5% compounded continuously?

(b) How long will it take to triple at this rate?

Solution (a) If P is the initial investment and we want P to double, the amount A will be $2P$. We use formula (4) for continuously compounded interest with $r = 0.05$. Then

$$A = Pe^{rt}$$

$$2P = Pe^{0.05t} \qquad A = 2P, r = 0.05$$

$$2 = e^{0.05t} \qquad \text{Cancel the } P\text{'s.}$$

$$0.05t = \ln 2 \qquad \text{Rewrite as a logarithm.}$$

$$t = \frac{\ln 2}{0.05} \approx 13.86 \qquad \text{Solve for } t.$$

It will take about 14 years to double the investment.

(b) To triple the investment, we set $A = 3P$ in formula (4).

$$A = Pe^{rt}$$

$$3P = Pe^{0.05t} \qquad A = 3P, r = 0.05$$

$$3 = e^{0.05t} \qquad \text{Cancel the } P\text{'s.}$$

$$0.05t = \ln 3 \qquad \text{Rewrite as a logarithm.}$$

$$t = \frac{\ln 3}{0.05} \approx 21.97 \qquad \text{Solve for } t.$$

It will take about 22 years to triple the investment. ■

Now Work PROBLEM 35

12.7 Assess Your Understanding

'Are You Prepared?' *Answers are given at the end of these exercises. If you get a wrong answer, read the page listed in red.*

1. What is the interest due if \$500 is borrowed for 6 months at a simple interest rate of 6% per annum?
2. If you borrow \$5000 and, after 9 months, pay off the loan in the amount of \$5500, what per annum rate of interest was charged?

Concepts and Vocabulary

3. The total amount borrowed (whether by an individual from a bank in the form of a loan or by a bank from an individual in the form of a savings account) is called the ________ .
4. If a principal of P dollars is borrowed for a period of t years at a per annum interest rate r, expressed as a decimal, the interest I charged is _____ = ______. Interest charged according to this formula is called ______ _______.
5. In working problems involving interest, if the payment period of the interest is quarterly, then interest is paid _____ times per year.
6. The ________ ____ __ ________ is the equivalent annual simple interest rate that would yield the same amount as compounding n times per year, or continuously, after 1 year.

Skill Building

In Problems 7–14, find the amount that results from each investment.

7. \$100 invested at 4% compounded quarterly after a period of 2 years
8. \$50 invested at 6% compounded monthly after a period of 3 years
9. \$500 invested at 8% compounded quarterly after a period of $2\frac{1}{2}$ years
10. \$300 invested at 12% compounded monthly after a period of $1\frac{1}{2}$ years
11. \$600 invested at 5% compounded daily after a period of 3 years
12. \$700 invested at 6% compounded daily after a period of 2 years
13. \$1000 invested at 11% compounded continuously after a period of 2 years
14. \$400 invested at 7% compounded continuously after a period of 3 years

In Problems 15–22, find the principal needed now to get each amount; that is, find the present value.

15. To get \$100 after 2 years at 6% compounded monthly
16. To get \$75 after 3 years at 8% compounded quarterly
17. To get \$1000 after $2\frac{1}{2}$ years at 6% compounded daily
18. To get \$800 after $3\frac{1}{2}$ years at 7% compounded monthly
19. To get \$600 after 2 years at 4% compounded quarterly
20. To get \$300 after 4 years at 3% compounded daily
21. To get \$80 after $3\frac{1}{4}$ years at 9% compounded continuously
22. To get \$800 after $2\frac{1}{2}$ years at 8% compounded continuously

In Problems 23–26, find the effective rate of interest.

23. For 5% compounded quarterly
24. For 6% compounded monthly
25. For 5% compounded continuously
26. For 6% compounded continuously

In Problems 27–30, determine the rate that represents the better deal.

27. 6% compounded quarterly or $6\frac{1}{4}$% compounded annually
28. 9% compounded quarterly or $9\frac{1}{4}$% compounded annually
29. 9% compounded monthly or 8.8% compounded daily
30. 8% compounded semiannually or 7.9% compounded daily
31. What rate of interest compounded annually is required to double an investment in 3 years?
32. What rate of interest compounded annually is required to double an investment in 6 years?
33. What rate of interest compounded annually is required to triple an investment in 5 years?
34. What rate of interest compounded annually is required to triple an investment in 10 years?
35. (a) How long does it take for an investment to double in value if it is invested at 8% compounded monthly?
    (b) How long does it take if the interest is compounded continuously?
36. (a) How long does it take for an investment to triple in value if it is invested at 6% compounded monthly?
    (b) How long does it take if the interest is compounded continuously?
37. What rate of interest compounded quarterly will yield an effective interest rate of 7%?
38. What rate of interest compounded continuously will yield an effective interest rate of 6%?

Applications and Extensions

39. **Time Required to Reach a Goal** If Tanisha has \$100 to invest at 8% per annum compounded monthly, how long will it be before she has \$150? If the compounding is continuous, how long will it be?

40. **Time Required to Reach a Goal** If Angela has \$100 to invest at 10% per annum compounded monthly, how long will it be before she has \$175? If the compounding is continuous, how long will it be?

41. **Time Required to Reach a Goal** How many years will it take for an initial investment of \$10,000 to grow to \$25,000? Assume a rate of interest of 6% compounded continuously.

42. **Time Required to Reach a Goal** How many years will it take for an initial investment of \$25,000 to grow to \$80,000? Assume a rate of interest of 7% compounded continuously.

43. **Price Appreciation of Homes** What will a \$90,000 condominium cost 5 years from now if the price appreciation for condos over that period averages 3% compounded annually?

44. **Credit Card Interest** A department store charges 1.25% per month on the unpaid balance for customers with charge accounts (interest is compounded monthly). A customer charges \$200 and does not pay her bill for 6 months. What is the bill at that time?

45. **Saving for a Car** Jerome will be buying a used car for \$15,000 in 3 years. How much money should he ask his parents for now so that, if he invests it at 5% compounded continuously, he will have enough to buy the car?

46. **Paying off a Loan** John requires \$3000 in 6 months to pay off a loan that has no prepayment privileges. If he has the \$3000 now, how much of it should he save in an account paying 3% compounded monthly so that in 6 months he will have exactly \$3000?

47. **Return on a Stock** George contemplates the purchase of 100 shares of a stock selling for \$15 per share. The stock pays no dividends. The history of the stock indicates that it should grow at an annual rate of 15% per year. How much should the 100 shares of stock be worth in 5 years?

48. **Return on an Investment** A business purchased for \$650,000 in 2005 is sold in 2008 for \$850,000. What is the annual rate of return for this investment?

49. **Comparing Savings Plans** Jim places \$1000 in a bank account that pays 5.6% compounded continuously. After 1 year, will he have enough money to buy a computer system that costs \$1060? If another bank will pay Jim 5.9% compounded monthly, is this a better deal?

50. **Savings Plans** On January 1, Kim places \$1000 in a certificate of deposit that pays 6.8% compounded continuously and matures in 3 months. Then Kim places the \$1000 and the interest in a passbook account that pays 5.25% compounded monthly. How much does Kim have in the passbook account on May 1?

51. **Comparing IRA Investments** Will invests \$2000 in his IRA in a bond trust that pays 9% interest compounded semiannually. His friend Henry invests \$2000 in his IRA in a certificate of deposit that pays $8\frac{1}{2}$% compounded continuously. Who has more money after 20 years, Will or Henry?

52. **Comparing Two Alternatives** Suppose that April has access to an investment that will pay 10% interest compounded continuously. Which is better: to be given \$1000 now so that she can take advantage of this investment opportunity or to be given \$1325 after 3 years?

53. **College Costs** The average annual cost of college at 4-year private colleges was \$25,143 in the 2008–2009 academic year. This was a 5.9% increase from the previous year.

Source: The College Board

(a) If the cost of college increases by 5.9% each year, what will be the average cost of college at a 4-year private college for the 2028–2029 academic year?

(b) College savings plans, such as a 529 plan, allow individuals to put money aside now to help pay for college later. If one such plan offers a rate of 4% compounded continuously, how much should be put in a college savings plan in 2010 to pay for 1 year of the cost of college at a 4-year private college for an incoming freshman in 2028?

54. **Analyzing Interest Rates on a Mortgage** Colleen and Bill have just purchased a house for \$650,000, with the seller holding a second mortgage of \$100,000. They promise to pay the seller \$100,000 plus all accrued interest 5 years from now. The seller offers them three interest options on the second mortgage:

(a) Simple interest at 12% per annum

(b) $11\frac{1}{2}$% interest compounded monthly

(c) $11\frac{1}{4}$% interest compounded continuously

Which option is best; that is, which results in the least interest on the loan?

55. **2009 Federal Stimulus Package** In February 2009, President Obama signed into law a \$787 billion federal stimulus package. At that time, 20-year Series EE bonds had a fixed rate of 1.3% compounded semiannually. If the federal government financed the stimulus through EE bonds, how much would it have to pay back in 2029? How much interest was paid to finance the stimulus?

Source: U.S. Treasury Department

56. **Per Capita Federal Debt** In 2011, the federal debt was about \$14 trillion. In 2011, the U.S. population was about 311 million. Assuming that the federal debt is increasing about 7.8% per year and the U.S. population is increasing about 0.9% per year, determine the per capita debt (total debt divided by population) in 2020.

Inflation *Problems 57–62 require the following discussion.* ***Inflation*** *is a term used to describe the erosion of the purchasing power of money. For example, if the annual inflation rate is 3%, then \$1000 worth of purchasing power now will have only \$970 worth of purchasing power in 1 year because 3% of the original \$1000 ($0.03 \times 1000 = 30$) has been eroded due to inflation. In general, if the rate of inflation averages r per annum over n years, the amount A that \$P will purchase after n years is*

$$A = P \cdot (1 - r)^n$$

where r is expressed as a decimal.

57. **Inflation** If the inflation rate averages 3%, how much will \$1000 purchase in 2 years?

58. **Inflation** If the inflation rate averages 2%, how much will \$1000 purchase in 3 years?

59. **Inflation** If the amount that \$1000 will purchase is only \$950 after 2 years, what was the average inflation rate?

60. **Inflation** If the amount that \$1000 will purchase is only \$930 after 2 years, what was the average inflation rate?

61. **Inflation** If the average inflation rate is 2%, how long is it until purchasing power is cut in half?

62. **Inflation** If the average inflation rate is 4%, how long is it until purchasing power is cut in half?

Problems 63–66 involve zero-coupon bonds. A ***zero-coupon bond*** *is a bond that is sold now at a discount and will pay its face value at the time when it matures; no interest payments are made.*

63. **Zero-Coupon Bonds** A zero-coupon bond can be redeemed in 20 years for \$10,000. How much should you be willing to pay for it now if you want a return of:
    (a) 10% compounded monthly?
    (b) 10% compounded continuously?

64. **Zero-Coupon Bonds** A child's grandparents are considering buying a \$40,000 face-value, zero-coupon bond at birth so that she will have money for her college education 17 years later. If they want a rate of return of 8% compounded annually, what should they pay for the bond?

65. **Zero-Coupon Bonds** How much should a \$10,000 face-value, zero-coupon bond, maturing in 10 years, be sold for now if its rate of return is to be 8% compounded annually?

66. **Zero-Coupon Bonds** If Pat pays \$12,485.52 for a \$25,000 face-value, zero-coupon bond that matures in 8 years, what is his annual rate of return?

67. **Time to Double or Triple an Investment** The formula

$$t = \frac{\ln m}{n \ln\left(1 + \frac{r}{n}\right)}$$

can be used to find the number of years t required to multiply an investment m times when r is the per annum interest rate compounded n times a year.
    (a) How many years will it take to double the value of an IRA that compounds annually at the rate of 12%?
    (b) How many years will it take to triple the value of a savings account that compounds quarterly at an annual rate of 6%?
    (c) Give a derivation of this formula.

68. **Time to Reach an Investment Goal** The formula

$$t = \frac{\ln A - \ln P}{r}$$

can be used to find the number of years t required for an investment P to grow to a value A when compounded continuously at an annual rate r.
    (a) How long will it take to increase an initial investment of \$1000 to \$8000 at an annual rate of 10%?
    (b) What annual rate is required to increase the value of a \$2000 IRA to \$30,000 in 35 years?
    (c) Give a derivation of this formula.

Problems 69–72 require the following discussion. The ***Consumer Price Index (CPI)*** *indicates the relative change in price over time for a fixed basket of goods and services. It is a cost of living index that helps measure the effect of inflation on the cost of goods and services. The CPI uses the base period 1982–1984 for comparison (the CPI for this period is 100). The CPI for January 2006 was 198.3. This means that \$100 in the period 1982–1984 had the same purchasing power as \$198.30 in January 2006. In general, if the rate of inflation averages r percent per annum over n years, then the CPI index after n years is*

$$\text{CPI} = \text{CPI}_0\left(1 + \frac{r}{100}\right)^n$$

where CPI_0 is the CPI index at the beginning of the n-year period.
Source: U.S. Bureau of Labor Statistics

69. **Consumer Price Index**
    (a) The CPI was 163.0 for 1998 and 215.3 for 2008. Assuming that annual inflation remained constant for this time period, determine the average annual inflation rate.
    (b) Using the inflation rate from part (a), in what year will the CPI reach 300?

70. **Consumer Price Index** If the current CPI is 234.2 and the average annual inflation rate is 2.8%, what will be the CPI in 5 years?

71. **Consumer Price Index** If the average annual inflation rate is 3.1%, how long will it take for the CPI index to double? (A doubling of the CPI index means purchasing power is cut in half.)

72. **Consumer Price Index** The base period for the CPI changed in 1998. Under the previous weight and item structure, the CPI for 1995 was 456.5. If the average annual inflation rate was 5.57%, what year was used as the base period for the CPI?

Explaining Concepts: Discussion and Writing

73. Explain in your own words what the term *compound interest* means. What does *continuous compounding* mean?

74. Explain in your own words the meaning of *present value*.

75. **Critical Thinking** You have just contracted to buy a house and will seek financing in the amount of \$100,000. You go to several banks. Bank 1 will lend you \$100,000 at the rate of 8.75% amortized over 30 years with a loan origination fee of 1.75%. Bank 2 will lend you \$100,000 at the rate of 8.375% amortized over 15 years with a loan origination fee of 1.5%. Bank 3 will lend you \$100,000 at the rate of 9.125% amortized over 30 years with no loan origination fee. Bank 4 will lend you \$100,000 at the rate of 8.625% amortized over 15 years with no loan origination

fee. Which loan would you take? Why? Be sure to have sound reasons for your choice. Use the information in the table to assist you. If the amount of the monthly payment does not matter to you, which loan would you take? Again, have sound reasons for your choice. Compare your final decision with others in the class. Discuss.

	Monthly Payment	Loan Origination Fee
Bank 1	\$786.70	\$1,750.00
Bank 2	\$977.42	\$1,500.00
Bank 3	\$813.63	\$0.00
Bank 4	\$992.08	\$0.00

'Are You Prepared?' Answers

1. \$15 **2.** $13\frac{1}{3}\%$

12.8 Exponential Growth and Decay Models; Newton's Law; Logistic Growth and Decay Models

OBJECTIVES

1 Find Equations of Populations That Obey the Law of Uninhibited Growth

Many natural phenomena have been found to follow the law that an amount A varies with time t according to the function

$$A(t) = A_0 e^{kt} \tag{1}$$

Here A_0 is the original amount $(t = 0)$ and $k \neq 0$ is a constant.

If $k > 0$, then equation (1) states that the amount A is increasing over time; if $k < 0$, the amount A is decreasing over time. In either case, when an amount A varies over time according to equation (1), it is said to follow the **exponential law** or the **law of uninhibited growth** $(k > 0)$ **or decay** $(k < 0)$. See Figure 55.

Figure 55

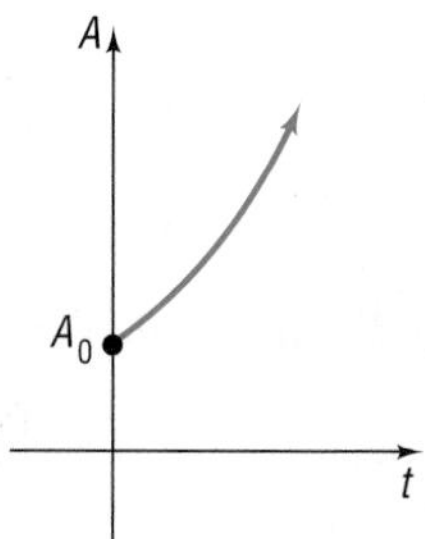

(a) $A(t) = A_0 e^{kt}, k > 0$
Exponential growth

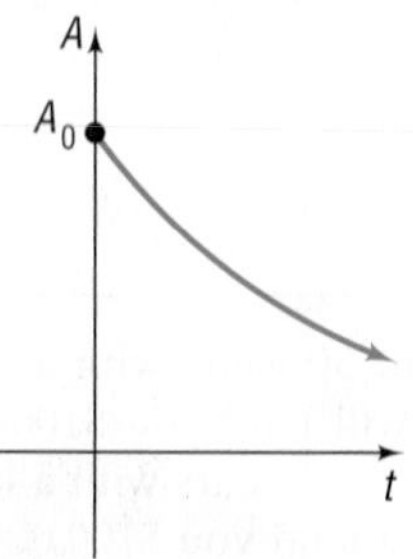

(b) $A(t) = A_0 e^{kt}, k < 0$
Exponential decay

For example, we saw in Section 12.7 that continuously compounded interest follows the law of uninhibited growth. In this section we shall look at some additional phenomena that follow the exponential law.

Cell division is the growth process of many living organisms, such as amoebas, plants, and human skin cells. Based on an ideal situation in which no cells die and no by-products are produced, the number of cells present at a given time follows the law of uninhibited growth. Actually, however, after enough time has passed, growth at an exponential rate will cease due to the influence of factors such as lack of living space and dwindling food supply. The law of uninhibited growth accurately models only the early stages of the cell division process.

The cell division process begins with a culture containing N_0 cells. Each cell in the culture grows for a certain period of time and then divides into two identical cells. We assume that the time needed for each cell to divide in two is constant and does not change as the number of cells increases. These new cells then grow, and eventually each divides in two, and so on.

Uninhibited Growth of Cells

A model that gives the number N of cells in a culture after a time t has passed (in the early stages of growth) is

$$N(t) = N_0 e^{kt} \qquad k > 0 \tag{2}$$

where N_0 is the initial number of cells and k is a positive constant that represents the growth rate of the cells.

In using formula (2) to model the growth of cells, we are using a function that yields positive real numbers, even though we are counting the number of cells, which must be an integer. This is a common practice in many applications.

EXAMPLE 1

Bacterial Growth

A colony of bacteria grows according to the law of uninhibited growth according to the function $N(t) = 100e^{0.045t}$, where N is measured in grams and t is measured in days.

(a) Determine the initial amount of bacteria.
(b) What is the growth rate of the bacteria?
(c) Graph the function using a graphing utility.
(d) What is the population after 5 days?
(e) How long will it take for the population to reach 140 grams?
(f) What is the doubling time for the population?

Solution (a) The initial amount of bacteria, N_0, is obtained when $t = 0$, so

$$N_0 = N(0) = 100e^{0.045(0)} = 100 \text{ grams}$$

(b) Compare $N(t) = 100e^{0.045t}$ to $N(t) = N_0 e^{kt}$. The value of k, 0.045, indicates a growth rate of 4.5%.

(c) Figure 56 shows the graph of $N(t) = 100e^{0.045t}$.

Figure 56

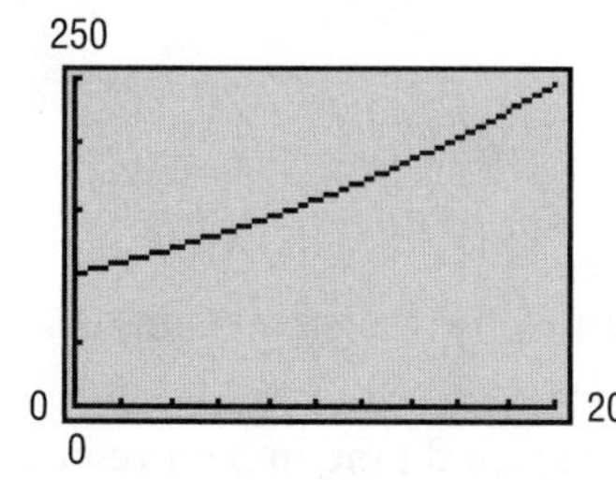

(d) The population after 5 days is $N(5) = 100e^{0.045(5)} \approx 125.2$ grams.

(e) To find how long it takes for the population to reach 140 grams, solve the equation $N(t) = 140$.

$$100e^{0.045t} = 140$$

$$e^{0.045t} = 1.4 \qquad \text{Divide both sides of the equation by 100.}$$

$$0.045t = \ln 1.4 \qquad \text{Rewrite as a logarithm.}$$

$$t = \frac{\ln 1.4}{0.045} \qquad \text{Divide both sides of the equation by 0.045.}$$

$$\approx 7.5 \text{ days}$$

(f) The population doubles when $N(t) = 200$ grams, so we find the doubling time by solving the equation $200 = 100e^{0.045t}$ for t.

$$200 = 100e^{0.045t}$$

$$2 = e^{0.045t} \qquad \text{Divide both sides of the equation by 100.}$$

$$\ln 2 = 0.045t \qquad \text{Rewrite as a logarithm.}$$

$$t = \frac{\ln 2}{0.045} \qquad \text{Divide both sides of the equation by 0.045.}$$

$$\approx 15.4 \text{ days}$$

The population doubles approximately every 15.4 days. ■

Now Work PROBLEM 1

EXAMPLE 2 **Bacterial Growth**

A colony of bacteria increases according to the law of uninhibited growth.

(a) If N is the number of cells and t is the time in hours, express N as a function of t.
(b) If the number of bacteria doubles in 3 hours, find the function that gives the number of cells in the culture.
(c) How long will it take for the size of the colony to triple?
(d) How long will it take for the population to double a second time (that is, increase four times)?

Solution (a) Using formula (2), the number N of cells at time t is

$$N(t) = N_0 e^{kt}$$

where N_0 is the initial number of bacteria present and k is a positive number.

(b) We seek the number k. The number of cells doubles in 3 hours, so we have

$$N(3) = 2N_0$$

But $N(3) = N_0 e^{k(3)}$, so

$$N_0 e^{k(3)} = 2N_0$$

$$e^{3k} = 2 \quad \text{Divide both sides by } N_0$$

$$3k = \ln 2 \quad \text{Write the exponential equation as a logarithm.}$$

$$k = \frac{1}{3}\ln 2 \approx 0.23105$$

The function that models this growth process is, therefore,

$$N(t) = N_0 e^{0.23105t}$$

(c) The time t needed for the size of the colony to triple requires that $N = 3N_0$. Substitute $3N_0$ for N to get

$$3N_0 = N_0 e^{0.23105t}$$

$$3 = e^{0.23105t} \quad \text{Divide both sides by } N_0$$

$$0.23105t = \ln 3 \quad \text{Write the exponential equation as a logarithm.}$$

$$t = \frac{\ln 3}{0.23105} \approx 4.755 \text{ hours}$$

It will take about 4.755 hours or 4 hours, 45 minutes for the size of the colony to triple.

(d) If a population doubles in 3 hours, it will double a second time in 3 more hours, for a total time of 6 hours. ■

2 Find Equations of Populations That Obey the Law of Decay

Radioactive materials follow the law of uninhibited decay.

Uninhibited Radioactive Decay

The amount A of a radioactive material present at time t is given by

$$A(t) = A_0 e^{kt} \qquad k < 0 \qquad \textbf{(3)}$$

where A_0 is the original amount of radioactive material and k is a negative number that represents the rate of decay.

All radioactive substances have a specific **half-life,** which is the time required for half of the radioactive substance to decay. In **carbon dating,** we use the fact that all living organisms contain two kinds of carbon, carbon 12 (a stable carbon) and carbon 14 (a radioactive carbon with a half-life of 5700 years). While an organism is living, the ratio of carbon 12 to carbon 14 is constant. But when an organism dies, the original amount of carbon 12 present remains unchanged, whereas the amount of carbon 14 begins to decrease. This change in the amount of carbon 14 present relative to the amount of carbon 12 present makes it possible to calculate when the organism died.

EXAMPLE 3 Estimating the Age of Ancient Tools

Traces of burned wood along with ancient stone tools in an archeological dig in Chile were found to contain approximately 1.67% of the original amount of carbon 14.

(a) If the half-life of carbon 14 is 5700 years, approximately when was the tree cut and burned?

(b) Using a graphing utility, graph the relation between the percentage of carbon 14 remaining and time.

(c) Use a graphing utility to determine the time that elapses until half of the carbon 14 remains. This answer should equal the half-life of carbon 14.

(d) Use a graphing utility to verify the answer found in part (a).

Solution (a) Using formula (3), the amount A of carbon 14 present at time t is

$$A(t) = A_0 e^{kt}$$

where A_0 is the original amount of carbon 14 present and k is a negative number. We first seek the number k. To find it, we use the fact that after 5700 years half of the original amount of carbon 14 remains, so $A(5700) = \frac{1}{2}A_0$. Then

$$\frac{1}{2}A_0 = A_0 e^{k(5700)}$$

$$\frac{1}{2} = e^{5700k} \quad \text{Divide both sides of the equation by } A_0.$$

$$5700k = \ln\frac{1}{2} \quad \text{Rewrite as a logarithm.}$$

$$k = \frac{1}{5700}\ln\frac{1}{2} \approx -0.0001216$$

Formula (3), therefore, becomes

$$A(t) = A_0 e^{-0.0001216t}$$

If the amount A of carbon 14 now present is 1.67% of the original amount, it follows that

$$0.0167A_0 = A_0 e^{-0.0001216t}$$

$$0.0167 = e^{-0.0001216t} \quad \text{Divide both sides of the equation by } A_0.$$

$$-0.0001216t = \ln 0.0167 \quad \text{Rewrite as a logarithm.}$$

$$t = \frac{\ln 0.0167}{-0.0001216} \approx 33{,}654 \text{ years}$$

The tree was cut and burned about 33,654 years ago. Some archeologists use this conclusion to argue that humans lived in the Americas over 33,000 years ago, much earlier than is generally accepted.

Figure 57

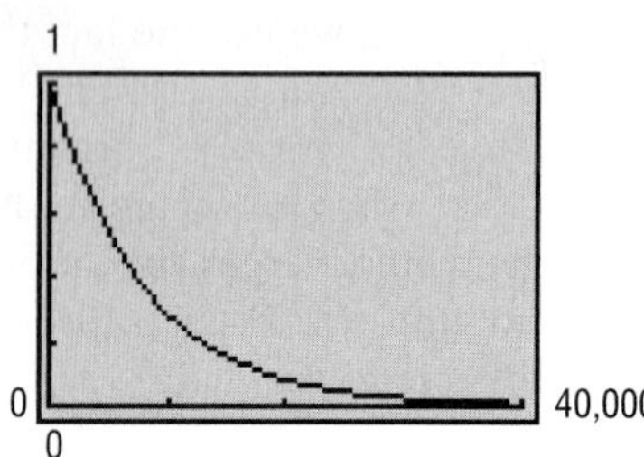

(b) Figure 57 show the graph of $y = e^{-0.0001216x}$, where y is the fraction of carbon 14 present and x is the time.

(c) By graphing $Y_1 = 0.5$ and $Y_2 = e^{-0.0001216x}$, where x is time, and using INTERSECT, we find that it takes 5700 years until half the carbon 14 remains. The half-life of carbon 14 is 5700 years.

(d) By graphing $Y_1 = 0.0167$ and $Y_2 = e^{-0.0001216x}$, where x is time, and using INTERSECT, we find that it takes 33,654 years until 1.67% of the carbon 14 remains. ■

Now Work PROBLEM 3

3 Use Newton's Law of Cooling

Newton' s Law of Cooling* states that the temperature of a heated object decreases exponentially over time toward the temperature of the surrounding medium.

Newton's Law of Cooling

The temperature u of a heated object at a given time t can be modeled by the following function:

$$u(t) = T + (u_0 - T)e^{kt} \qquad k < 0 \qquad \textbf{(4)}$$

where T is the constant temperature of the surrounding medium, u_0 is the initial temperature of the heated object, and k is a negative constant.

EXAMPLE 4 **Using Newton's Law of Cooling**

An object is heated to 100°C (degrees Celsius) and is then allowed to cool in a room whose air temperature is 30°C.

(a) If the temperature of the object is 80°C after 5 minutes, when will its temperature be 50°C?
(b) Using a graphing utility, graph the relation found between the temperature and time.
(c) Using a graphing utility, verify the results from part (a).
(d) Using a graphing utility, determine the elapsed time before the object is 35°C.
(e) What do you notice about the temperature as time passes?

Solution (a) Using formula (4) with $T = 30$ and $u_0 = 100$, the temperature (in degrees Celsius) of the object at time t (in minutes) is

$$u(t) = 30 + (100 - 30)e^{kt} = 30 + 70e^{kt}$$

where k is a negative constant. To find k, use the fact that $u = 80$ when $t = 5$ [that is, $u(5) = 80$]. Then

$$80 = 30 + 70e^{k(5)}$$
$$50 = 70e^{5k}$$
$$e^{5k} = \frac{50}{70}$$
$$5k = \ln\frac{5}{7}$$
$$k = \frac{1}{5}\ln\frac{5}{7} \approx -0.0673$$

Formula (4), therefore, becomes

$$u(t) = 30 + 70e^{-0.0673t}$$

*Named after Sir Isaac Newton (1642–1727), one of the cofounders of calculus.

We want to find t when $u = 50°C$, so

$$50 = 30 + 70e^{-0.0673t}$$

$$20 = 70e^{-0.0673t}$$

$$e^{-0.0673t} = \frac{20}{70}$$

$$-0.0673t = \ln\frac{2}{7}$$

$$t = \frac{\ln\frac{2}{7}}{-0.0673} \approx 18.6 \text{ minutes}$$

The temperature of the object will be 50°C after about 18.6 minutes or 18 minutes, 37 seconds.

Figure 58

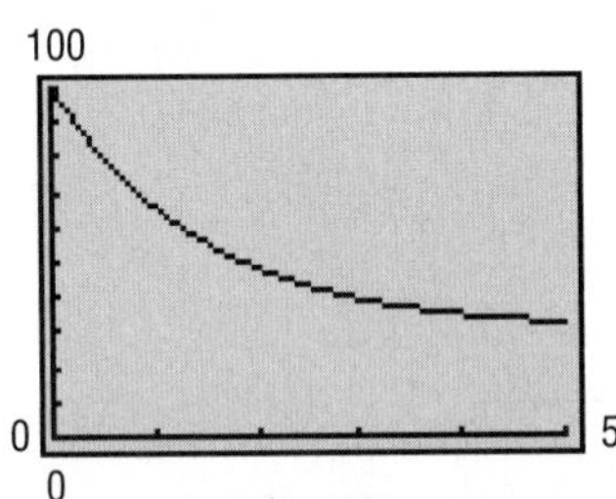

(b) Figure 58 shows the graph of $y = 30 + 70e^{-0.0673x}$, where y is the temperature and x is the time.

(c) By graphing $Y_1 = 50$ and $Y_2 = 30 + 70e^{-0.0673x}$, where x is time, and using INTERSECT, we find that it takes $x = 18.6$ minutes (18 minutes, 37 seconds) for the temperature to cool to 50°C.

(d) By graphing $Y_1 = 35$ and $Y_2 = 30 + 70e^{-0.0673x}$, where x is time, and using INTERSECT, we find that it takes $x = 39.21$ minutes (39 minutes, 13 seconds) for the temperature to cool to 35°C.

(e) As t increases, the value of $e^{-0.0673t}$ approaches zero, so the value of u, the temperature of the object, approaches 30°C, the air temperature of the room. ■

Now Work PROBLEM 13

4 Use Logistic Models

The exponential growth model $A(t) = A_0e^{kt}$, $k > 0$, assumes uninhibited growth, meaning that the value of the function grows without limit. Recall that we stated that cell division could be modeled using this function, assuming that no cells die and no by-products are produced. However, cell division eventually is limited by factors such as living space and food supply. The **logistic model,** given next, can describe situations where the growth or decay of the dependent variable is limited.

Logistic Model

In a logistic model, the population P after time t is given by the function

$$P(t) = \frac{c}{1 + ae^{-bt}} \qquad (5)$$

where a, b, and c are constants with $a > 0$ and $c > 0$. The model is a growth model if $b > 0$; the model is a decay model if $b < 0$.

The number c is called the **carrying capacity** (for growth models) because the value $P(t)$ approaches c as t approaches infinity; that is, $\lim_{t\to\infty} P(t) = c$. The number $|b|$ is the growth rate for $b > 0$ and the decay rate for $b < 0$. Figure 59(a) shows the graph of a typical logistic growth function, and Figure 59(b) shows the graph of a typical logistic decay function.

Figure 59

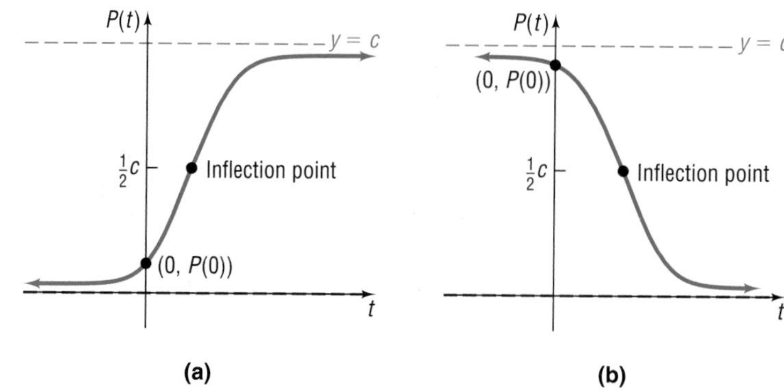

Based on the figures, we have the following properties of logistic growth functions.

Properties of the Logistic Model, Equation (5)

1. The domain is the set of all real numbers. The range is the interval $(0, c)$, where c is the carrying capacity.
2. There are no x-intercepts; the y-intercept is $P(0)$.
3. There are two horizontal asymptotes: $y = 0$ and $y = c$.
4. $P(t)$ is an increasing function if $b > 0$ and a decreasing function if $b < 0$.
5. There is an **inflection point** where $P(t)$ equals $\frac{1}{2}$ of the carrying capacity. The inflection point is the point on the graph where the graph changes from being curved upward to curved downward for growth functions and the point where the graph changes from being curved downward to curved upward for decay functions.
6. The graph is smooth and continuous, with no corners or gaps.

EXAMPLE 5 **Fruit Fly Population**

Fruit flies are placed in a half-pint milk bottle with a banana (for food) and yeast plants (for food and to provide a stimulus to lay eggs). Suppose that the fruit fly population after t days is given by

$$P(t) = \frac{230}{1 + 56.5e^{-0.37t}}$$

(a) State the carrying capacity and the growth rate.
(b) Determine the initial population.
(c) What is the population after 5 days?
(d) How long does it take for the population to reach 180?
(e) Use a graphing utility to determine how long it takes for the population to reach one-half of the carrying capacity.

Solution (a) As $t \to \infty$, $e^{-0.37t} \to 0$ and $P(t) \to \frac{230}{1}$. The carrying capacity of the half-pint bottle is 230 fruit flies. The growth rate is $|b| = |0.37| = 37\%$ per day.

(b) To find the initial number of fruit flies in the half-pint bottle, evaluate $P(0)$.

$$P(0) = \frac{230}{1 + 56.5e^{-0.37(0)}}$$

$$= \frac{230}{1 + 56.5}$$

$$= 4$$

So, initially, there were 4 fruit flies in the half-pint bottle.

(c) To find the number of fruit flies in the half-pint bottle after 5 days, evaluate $P(5)$.

$$P(5) = \frac{230}{1 + 56.5e^{-0.37(5)}} \approx 23 \text{ fruit flies}$$

After 5 days, there are approximately 23 fruit flies in the bottle.

(d) To determine when the population of fruit flies will be 180, solve the equation $P(t) = 180$.

$$\frac{230}{1 + 56.5e^{-0.37t}} = 180$$

$$230 = 180(1 + 56.5e^{-0.37t})$$

$$1.2778 = 1 + 56.5e^{-0.37t} \quad \text{Divide both sides by 180.}$$

$$0.2778 = 56.5e^{-0.37t} \quad \text{Subtract 1 from both sides.}$$

$$0.0049 = e^{-0.37t} \quad \text{Divide both sides by 56.5.}$$

$$\ln(0.0049) = -0.37t \quad \text{Rewrite as a logarithmic expression.}$$

$$t \approx 14.4 \text{ days} \quad \text{Divide both sides by } -0.37.$$

It will take approximately 14.4 days (14 days, 10 hours) for the population to reach 180 fruit flies.

(e) One-half of the carrying capacity is 115 fruit flies. We solve $P(t) = 115$ by graphing $Y_1 = \frac{230}{1 + 56.5e^{-0.37x}}$ and $Y_2 = 115$ and using INTERSECT. See Figure 60. The population will reach one-half of the carrying capacity in about 10.9 days (10 days, 22 hours). ■

Figure 60

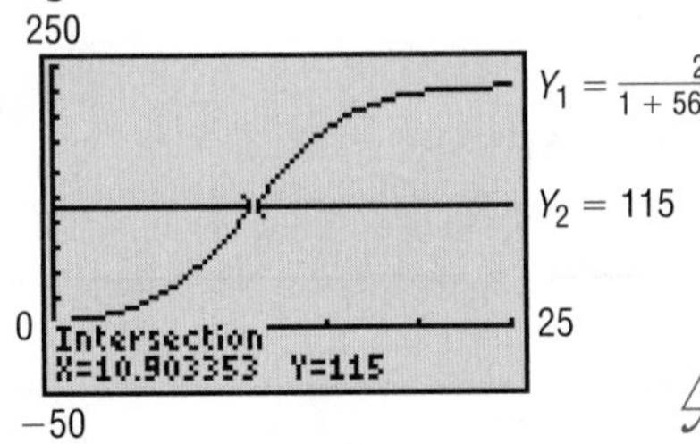

Look back at Figure 60. Notice the point where the graph reaches 115 fruit flies (one-half of the carrying capacity): the graph changes from being curved upward to being curved downward. Using the language of calculus, we say the graph changes from increasing at an increasing rate to increasing at a decreasing rate. For any logistic growth function, when the population reaches one-half the carrying capacity, the population growth starts to slow down.

Exploration

On the same viewing rectangle, graph

$Y_1 = \frac{500}{1 + 24e^{-0.03x}}$ and $Y_2 = \frac{500}{1 + 24e^{-0.08x}}$

What effect does the growth rate $|b|$ have on the logistic growth function?

Now Work PROBLEM 23

EXAMPLE 6 Wood Products

The EFISCEN wood product model classifies wood products according to their life-span. There are four classifications: short (1 year), medium short (4 years), medium long (16 years), and long (50 years). Based on data obtained from the European Forest Institute, the percentage of remaining wood products after t years for wood products with long life-spans (such as those used in the building industry) is given by

$$P(t) = \frac{100.3952}{1 + 0.0316e^{0.0581t}}$$

(a) What is the decay rate?
(b) What is the percentage of remaining wood products after 10 years?
(c) How long does it take for the percentage of remaining wood products to reach 50%?
(d) Explain why the numerator given in the model is reasonable.

Solution

(a) The decay rate is $|b| = |-0.0581| = 5.81\%$.
(b) Evaluate $P(10)$.

$$P(10) = \frac{100.3952}{1 + 0.0316e^{0.0581(10)}} \approx 95.0$$

So 95% of long-life-span wood products remain after 10 years.

(c) Solve the equation $P(t) = 50$.

$$\frac{100.3952}{1 + 0.0316e^{0.0581t}} = 50$$

$$100.3952 = 50(1 + 0.0316e^{0.0581t})$$

$$2.0079 = 1 + 0.0316e^{0.0581t} \quad \text{Divide both sides by 50.}$$

$$1.0079 = 0.0316e^{0.0581t} \quad \text{Subtract 1 from both sides.}$$

$$31.8956 = e^{0.0581t} \quad \text{Divide both sides by 0.0316.}$$

$$\ln(31.8956) = 0.0581t \quad \text{Rewrite as a logarithmic expression.}$$

$$t \approx 59.6 \text{ years} \quad \text{Divide both sides by 0.0581.}$$

It will take approximately 59.6 years for the percentage of long-life-span wood products remaining to reach 50%.

(d) The numerator of 100.3952 is reasonable because the maximum percentage of wood products remaining that is possible is 100%. ■

Now Work PROBLEM 27

12.8 Assess Your Understanding

Applications and Extensions

1. **Growth of an Insect Population** The size P of a certain insect population at time t (in days) obeys the model $P(t) = 500e^{0.02t}$.
   (a) Determine the number of insects at $t = 0$ days.
   (b) What is the growth rate of the insect population?
   (c) Graph the function using a graphing utility.
   (d) What is the population after 10 days?
   (e) When will the insect population reach 800?
   (f) When will the insect population double?

2. **Growth of Bacteria** The number N of bacteria present in a culture at time t (in hours) obeys the model $N(t) = 1000e^{0.01t}$.
   (a) Determine the number of bacteria at $t = 0$ hours.
   (b) What is the growth rate of the bacteria?
   (c) Graph the function using a graphing utility.
   (d) What is the population after 4 hours?
   (e) When will the number of bacteria reach 1700?
   (f) When will the number of bacteria double?

3. **Radioactive Decay** Strontium 90 is a radioactive material that decays according to the function $A(t) = A_0e^{-0.0244t}$, where A_0 is the initial amount present and A is the amount present at time t (in years). Assume that a scientist has a sample of 500 grams of strontium 90.
   (a) What is the decay rate of strontium 90?
   (b) Graph the function using a graphing utility.
   (c) How much strontium 90 is left after 10 years?
   (d) When will 400 grams of strontium 90 be left?
   (e) What is the half-life of strontium 90?

4. **Radioactive Decay** Iodine 131 is a radioactive material that decays according to the function $A(t) = A_0e^{-0.087t}$, where A_0 is the initial amount present and A is the amount present at time t (in days). Assume that a scientist has a sample of 100 grams of iodine 131.
   (a) What is the decay rate of iodine 131?
   (b) Graph the function using a graphing utility.
   (c) How much iodine 131 is left after 9 days?
   (d) When will 70 grams of iodine 131 be left?
   (e) What is the half-life of iodine 131?

5. **Growth of a Colony of Mosquitoes** The population of a colony of mosquitoes obeys the law of uninhibited growth.
   (a) If N is the population of the colony and t is the time in days, express N as a function of t.
   (b) If there are 1000 mosquitoes initially and there are 1800 after 1 day, what is the size of the colony after 3 days?
   (c) How long is it until there are 10,000 mosquitoes?

6. **Bacterial Growth** A culture of bacteria obeys the law of uninhibited growth.
   (a) If N is the number of bacteria in the culture and t is the time in hours, express N as a function of t.
   (b) If 500 bacteria are present initially and there are 800 after 1 hour, how many will be present in the culture after 5 hours?
   (c) How long is it until there are 20,000 bacteria?

7. **Population Growth** The population of a southern city follows the exponential law.
   (a) If N is the population of the city and t is the time in years, express N as a function of t.
   (b) If the population doubled in size over an 18-month period and the current population is 10,000, what will the population be 2 years from now?

8. **Population Decline** The population of a midwestern city follows the exponential law.
   (a) If N is the population of the city and t is the time in years, express N as a function of t.

(b) If the population decreased from 900,000 to 800,000 from 2005 to 2007, what will the population be in 2009?

9. **Radioactive Decay** The half-life of radium is 1690 years. If 10 grams is present now, how much will be present in 50 years?

10. **Radioactive Decay** The half-life of radioactive potassium is 1.3 billion years. If 10 grams is present now, how much will be present in 100 years? In 1000 years?

11. **Estimating the Age of a Tree** A piece of charcoal is found to contain 30% of the carbon 14 that it originally had.
    (a) When did the tree from which the charcoal came die? Use 5700 years as the half-life of carbon 14.
    (b) Using a graphing utility, graph the relation between the percentage of carbon 14 remaining and time.
    (c) Using INTERSECT, determine the time that elapses until half of the carbon 14 remains.
    (d) Verify the answer found in part (a).

12. **Estimating the Age of a Fossil** A fossilized leaf contains 70% of its normal amount of carbon 14.
    (a) How old is the fossil? Use 5700 years as the half-life of carbon 14.
    (b) Using a graphing utility, graph the relation between the percentage of carbon 14 remaining and time.
    (c) Using INTERSECT, determine the time that elapses until half of the carbon 14 remains.
    (d) Verify the answer found in part (a).

13. **Cooling Time of a Pizza** A pizza baked at 450°F is removed from the oven at 5:00 PM and placed in a room that is a constant 70°F. After 5 minutes, the pizza is at 300°F.
    (a) At what time can you begin eating the pizza if you want its temperature to be 135°F?
    (b) Using a graphing utility, graph the relation between temperature and time.
    (c) Using INTERSECT, determine the time that needs to elapse before the pizza is 160°F.
    (d) TRACE the function for large values of time. What do you notice about y, the temperature?

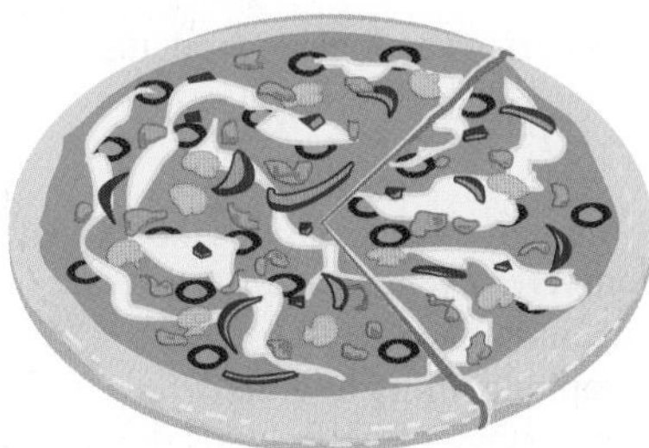

14. **Newton's Law of Cooling** A thermometer reading 72°F is placed in a refrigerator where the temperature is a constant 38°F.
    (a) If the thermometer reads 60°F after 2 minutes, what will it read after 7 minutes?
    (b) How long will it take before the thermometer reads 39°F?
    (c) Using a graphing utility, graph the relation between temperature and time.
    (d) Using INTERSECT, determine the time needed to elapse before the thermometer reads 45°F.
    (e) TRACE the function for large values of time. What do you notice about y, the temperature?

15. **Newton's Law of Heating** A thermometer reading 8°C is brought into a room with a constant temperature of 35°C.
    (a) If the thermometer reads 15°C after 3 minutes, what will it read after being in the room for 5 minutes? For 10 minutes?
    (b) Graph the relation between temperature and time. TRACE to verify that your answers are correct.
    [**Hint:** You need to construct a formula similar to equation (4).]

16. **Warming Time of a Beer Stein** A beer stein has a temperature of 28°F. It is placed in a room with a constant temperature of 70°F. After 10 minutes, the temperature of the stein has risen to 35°F. What will the temperature of the stein be after 30 minutes? How long will it take the stein to reach a temperature of 45°F? (See the hint given for Problem 15.)

17. **Decomposition of Chlorine in a Pool** Under certain water conditions, the free chlorine (hypochlorous acid, HOCl) in a swimming pool decomposes according to the law of uninhibited decay. After shocking his pool, Ben tested the water and found the amount of free chlorine to be 2.5 parts per million (ppm). Twenty-four hours later, Ben tested the water again and found the amount of free chlorine to be 2.2 ppm. What will be the reading after 3 days (that is, 72 hours)? When the chlorine level reaches 1.0 ppm, Ben must shock the pool again. How long can Ben go before he must shock the pool again?

18. **Decomposition of Dinitrogen Pentoxide** At 45°C, dinitrogen pentoxide (N_2O_5) decomposes into nitrous dioxide (NO_2) and oxygen (O_2) according to the law of uninhibited decay. An initial amount of 0.25 mole of dinitrogen pentoxide decomposes to 0.15 mole in 17 minutes. How much dinitrogen pentoxide will remain after 30 minutes? How long will it take until 0.01 mole of dinitrogen pentoxide remains?

19. **Decomposition of Sucrose** Reacting with water in an acidic solution at 35°C, sucrose ($C_{12}H_{22}O_{11}$) decomposes into glucose ($C_6H_{12}O_6$) and fructose ($C_6H_{12}O_6$)* according to the law of uninhibited decay. An initial amount of 0.40 mole of sucrose decomposes to 0.36 mole in 30 minutes. How much sucrose will remain after 2 hours? How long will it take until 0.10 mole of sucrose remains?

20. **Decomposition of Salt in Water** Salt (NaCl) decomposes in water into sodium (Na^+) and chloride (Cl^-) ions according to the law of uninhibited decay. If the initial amount of salt is 25 kilograms and, after 10 hours, 15 kilograms of salt is left, how much salt is left after 1 day? How long does it take until $\frac{1}{2}$ kilogram of salt is left?

21. **Radioactivity from Chernobyl** After the release of radioactive material into the atmosphere from a nuclear power plant at Chernobyl (Ukraine) in 1986, the hay in Austria was contaminated by iodine 131 (half-life 8 days). If it is safe to feed the hay to cows when 10% of the iodine 131 remains, how long did the farmers need to wait to use this hay?

22. **Pig Roasts** The hotel Bora-Bora is having a pig roast. At noon, the chef put the pig in a large earthen oven. The pig's original temperature was 75°F. At 2:00 PM the chef checked

*Author's Note: Surprisingly, the chemical formulas for glucose and fructose are the same: This is not a typo.

the pig's temperature and was upset because it had reached only 100°F. If the oven's temperature remains a constant 325°F, at what time may the hotel serve its guests, assuming that pork is done when it reaches 175°F?

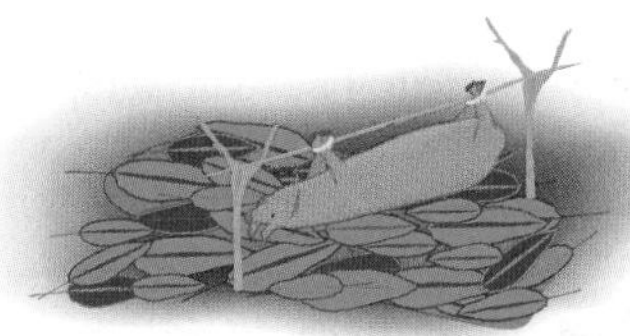

23. **Population of a Bacteria Culture** The logistic growth model

$$P(t) = \frac{1000}{1 + 32.33e^{-0.439t}}$$

represents the population (in grams) of a bacterium after t hours.
(a) Determine the carrying capacity of the environment.
(b) What is the growth rate of the bacteria?
(c) Determine the initial population size.
(d) Use a graphing utility to graph $P = P(t)$.
(e) What is the population after 9 hours?
(f) When will the population be 700 grams?
(g) How long does it take for the population to reach one-half the carrying capacity?

24. **Population of an Endangered Species** Often environmentalists capture an endangered species and transport the species to a controlled environment where the species can produce offspring and regenerate its population. Suppose that six American bald eagles are captured, transported to Montana, and set free. Based on experience, the environmentalists expect the population to grow according to the model

$$P(t) = \frac{500}{1 + 82.33e^{-0.162t}}$$

where t is measured in years.

(a) Determine the carrying capacity of the environment.
(b) What is the growth rate of the bald eagle?
(c) Use a graphing utility to graph $P = P(t)$.
(d) What is the population after 3 years?
(e) When will the population be 300 eagles?
(f) How long does it take for the population to reach one-half of the carrying capacity?

25. **The *Challenger* Disaster** After the *Challenger* disaster in 1986, a study was made of the 23 launches that preceded the fatal flight. A mathematical model was developed involving the relationship between the Fahrenheit temperature x around the O-rings and the number y of eroded or leaky primary O-rings. The model stated that

$$y = \frac{6}{1 + e^{-(5.085-0.1156x)}}$$

where the number 6 indicates the 6 primary O-rings on the spacecraft.

(a) What is the predicted number of eroded or leaky primary O-rings at a temperature of 100°F?
(b) What is the predicted number of eroded or leaky primary O-rings at a temperature of 60°F?
(c) What is the predicted number of eroded or leaky primary O-rings at a temperature of 30°F?
(d) Graph the equation. At what temperature is the predicted number of eroded or leaky O-rings 1? 3? 5?

Source: Linda Tappin, "Analyzing Data Relating to the Challenger *Disaster,"* Mathematics Teacher, *Vol. 87, No. 6, September 1994, pp. 000–000.*

26. **Word Users** According to a survey by Olsten Staffing Services, the percentage of companies reporting usage of Microsoft Word t years since 1984 is given by

$$P(t) = \frac{99.744}{1 + 3.014e^{-0.799t}}$$

(a) What is the growth rate in the percentage of Microsoft Word users?
(b) Use a graphing utility to graph $P = P(t)$.
(c) What was the percentage of Microsoft Word users in 1990?
(d) During what year did the percentage of Microsoft Word users reach 90%?
(e) Explain why the numerator given in the model is reasonable. What does it imply?

27. **Home Computers** The logistic model

$$P(t) = \frac{95.4993}{1 + 0.0405e^{0.1968t}}$$

represents the percentage of households that do not own a personal computer t years since 1984.
(a) Evaluate and interpret $P(0)$.
(b) Use a graphing utility to graph $P = P(t)$.
(c) What percentage of households did not own a personal computer in 1995?
(d) In what year did the percentage of households that do not own a personal computer reach 10%?

Source: U.S. Department of Commerce

28. **Farmers** The logistic model

$$W(t) = \frac{14{,}656{,}248}{1 + 0.059e^{0.057t}}$$

represents the number of farm workers in the United States t years after 1910.
(a) Evaluate and interpret $W(0)$.
(b) Use a graphing utility to graph $W = W(t)$.
(c) How many farm workers were there in the United States in 2010?

(d) When did the number of farm workers in the United States reach 10,000?

(e) According to this model, what happens to the number of farm workers in the United States as t approaches ∞? Based on this result, do you think that it is reasonable to use this model to predict the number of farm workers in the United States in 2060? Why?

Source: U.S. Department of Agriculture

29. Birthdays The logistic model

$$P(n) = \frac{113.3198}{1 + 0.115e^{0.0912n}}$$

models the probability that, in a room of n people, no two people share the same birthday.

(a) Use a graphing utility to graph $P = P(n)$.

(b) In a room of $n = 15$ people, what is the probability that no two share the same birthday?

(c) How many people must be in a room before the probability that no two people share the same birthday falls below 10%?

(d) What happens to the probability as n increases? Explain what this result means.

12.9 Building Exponential, Logarithmic, and Logistic Models from Data

PREPARING FOR THIS SECTION *Before getting started, review the following:*

- Building Linear Models from Data (Section 10.2, pp. 642–644)
- Building Cubic Models from Data (Section 11.1, pp. 693–694)
- Building Quadratic Models from Data (Section 10.4, pp. 664–665)

OBJECTIVES
1. Build an Exponential Model from Data (p. 840)
2. Build a Logarithmic Model from Data (p. 841)
3. Build a Logistic Model from Data (p. 842)

In Section 10.2, we discussed how to find the linear function of best fit $(y = ax + b)$, in Section 10.4, we discussed how to find the quadratic function of best fit $(y = ax^2 + bx + c)$, and in Section 11.1, we discussed how to find the cubic function of best fit $(y = ax^3 + bx^2 + cx + d)$.

In this section we discuss how to use a graphing utility to find equations of best fit that describe the relation between two variables when the relation is thought to be exponential $(y = ab^x)$, logarithmic $(y = a + b \ln x)$, or logistic $\left(y = \dfrac{c}{1 + ae^{-bx}}\right)$. As before, we draw a scatter diagram of the data to help to determine the appropriate model to use.

Figure 61 shows scatter diagrams that will typically be observed for the three models. Below each scatter diagram are any restrictions on the values of the parameters.

Figure 61

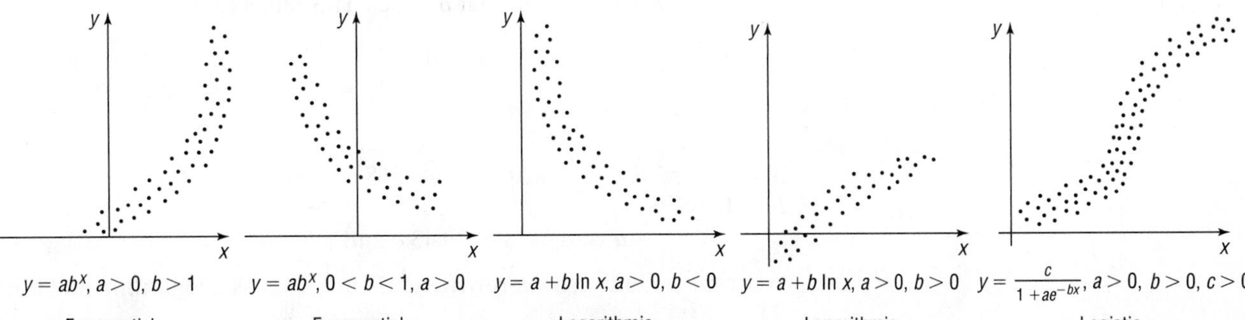

Most graphing utilities have REGression options that fit data to a specific type of curve. Once the data have been entered and a scatter diagram obtained, the type of curve that you want to fit to the data is selected. Then that REGression option is used to obtain the curve of *best fit* of the type selected.

The correlation coefficient r will appear only if the model can be written as a linear expression. As it turns out, r will appear for the linear, power, exponential, and logarithmic models, since these models can be written as a linear expression. Remember, the closer $|r|$ is to 1, the better the fit.

1 Build an Exponential Model from Data

We saw in Section 12.7 that the future value of money behaves exponentially, and we saw in Section 12.8 that growth and decay models also behave exponentially. The next example shows how data can lead to an exponential model.

EXAMPLE 1 Fitting an Exponential Function to Data

Mariah deposited \$20,000 into a well-diversified mutual fund 6 years ago. The data in Table 10 represent the value of the account each year for the last 7 years.

Table 10

Year, x	Account Value, y
0	20,000
1	21,516
2	23,355
3	24,885
4	27,484
5	30,053
6	32,622

(a) Using a graphing utility, draw a scatter diagram with year as the independent variable.

(b) Using a graphing utility, build an exponential model from the data.

(c) Express the function found in part (b) in the form $A = A_0 e^{kt}$.

(d) Graph the exponential function found in part (b) or (c) on the scatter diagram.

(e) Using the solution to part (b) or (c), predict the value of the account after 10 years.

(f) Interpret the value of k found in part (c).

Solution

(a) Enter the data into the graphing utility. We obtain the scatter diagram shown in Figure 62.

(b) A graphing utility fits the data in Table 10 to an exponential model of the form $y = ab^x$ using the EXPonential REGression option. From Figure 63 we find that $y = ab^x = 19{,}820.43(1.085568)^x$. Notice that $|r| = 0.999$, which is close to 1, indicating a good fit.

Figure 62

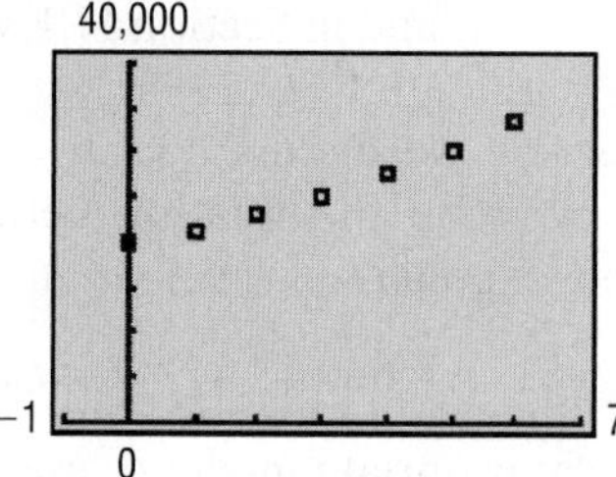

Figure 63

ExpReg
y=a*b^x
a=19820.43052
b=1.085567777
r²=.9973560202
r=.9986771351

(c) To express $y = ab^x$ in the form $A = A_0 e^{kt}$, where $x = t$ and $y = A$, proceed as follows:

$$ab^x = A_0 e^{kt} \quad x = t$$

When $x = t = 0$, we find that $a = A_0$. This leads to

$$a = A_0 \quad b^x = e^{kt}$$
$$b^x = (e^k)^t$$
$$b = e^k \quad x = t$$

Since $y = ab^x = 19{,}820.43(1.085568)^x$, we find that $a = 19{,}820.43$ and $b = 1.085568$.

$$a = A_0 = 19{,}820.43 \quad \text{and} \quad b = e^k = 1.085568$$

We want to find k, so we rewrite $e^k = 1.085568$ as a logarithm and obtain

$$k = \ln(1.085568) \approx 0.08210$$

As a result, $A = A_0 e^{kt} = 19{,}820.43e^{0.08210t}$.

(d) See Figure 64 for the graph of the exponential function of best fit.

Figure 64

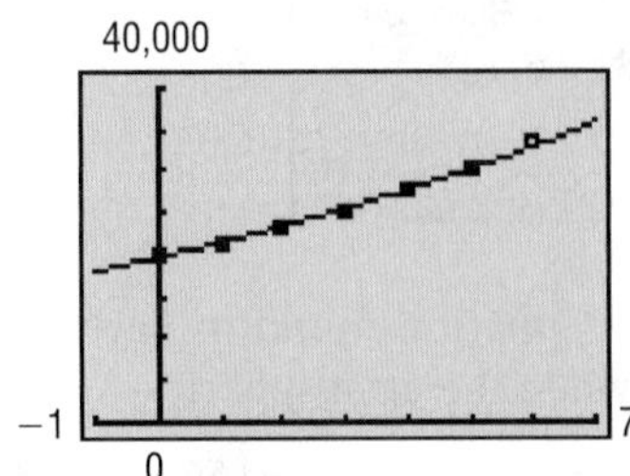

(e) Let $t = 10$ in the function found in part (c). The predicted value of the account after 10 years is

$$A = A_0 e^{kt} = 19{,}820.43e^{0.08210(10)} \approx \$45{,}047$$

(f) The value of $k = 0.08210 = 8.210\%$ represents the growth rate of the account. It represents the rate of interest earned assuming the account is growing continuously. ■

Now Work PROBLEM 1

2 Build a Logarithmic Model from Data

Many relations between variables do not follow an exponential model; instead, the independent variable is related to the dependent variable using a logarithmic model.

EXAMPLE 2 Fitting a Logarithmic Function to Data

Jodi, a meteorologist, is interested in finding a function that explains the relation between the height of a weather balloon (in kilometers) and the atmospheric pressure (measured in millimeters of mercury) on the balloon. She collects the data shown in Table 11.

Table 11

Atmospheric Pressure, p	Height, h
760	0
740	0.184
725	0.328
700	0.565
650	1.079
630	1.291
600	1.634
580	1.862
550	2.235

(a) Using a graphing utility, draw a scatter diagram of the data with atmospheric pressure as the independent variable.

(b) It is known that the relation between atmospheric pressure and height follows a logarithmic model. Using a graphing utility, build a logarithmic model from the data.

(c) Draw the logarithmic function found in part (b) on the scatter diagram.

(d) Use the function found in part (b) to predict the height of the weather balloon if the atmospheric pressure is 560 millimeters of mercury.

Solution

(a) After entering the data into the graphing utility, we obtain the scatter diagram shown in Figure 65.

Figure 65

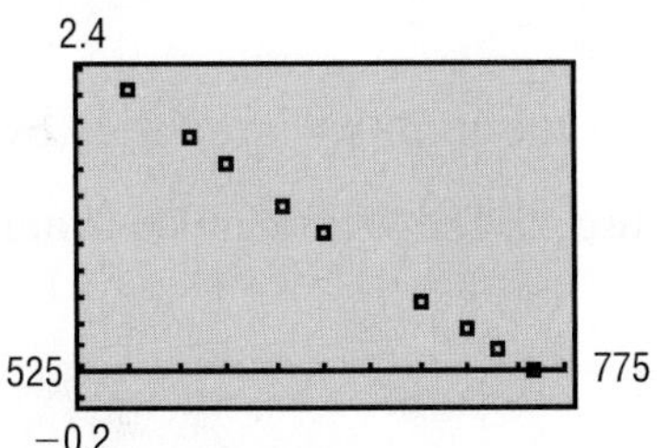

(b) A graphing utility fits the data in Table 11 to a logarithmic function of the form $y = a + b \ln x$ by using the LOGarithm REGression option. See Figure 66. The logarithmic model from the data is

$$h(p) = 45.7863 - 6.9025 \ln p$$

where h is the height of the weather balloon and p is the atmospheric pressure. Notice that $|r|$ is close to 1, indicating a good fit.

(c) Figure 67 shows the graph of $h(p) = 45.7863 - 6.9025 \ln p$ on the scatter diagram.

Figure 66

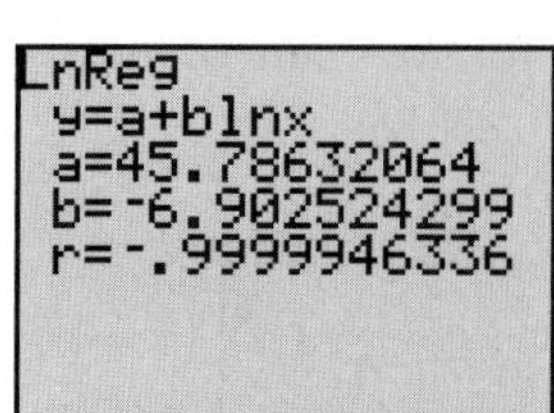

Figure 67

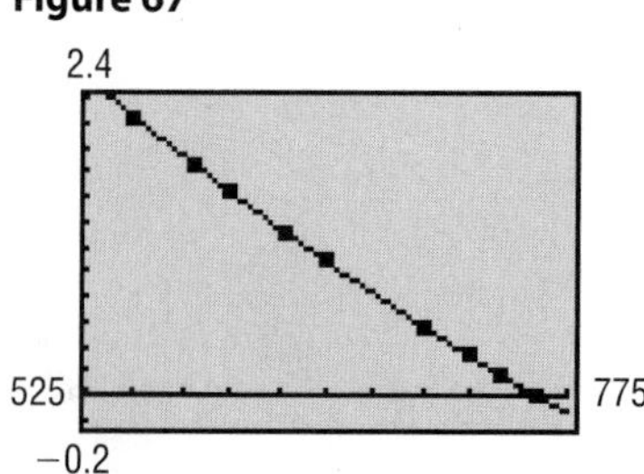

(d) Using the function found in part (b), Jodi predicts the height of the weather balloon when the atmospheric pressure is 560 to be

$$\begin{aligned} h(560) &= 45.7863 - 6.9025 \ln 560 \\ &\approx 2.108 \text{ kilometers} \end{aligned}$$

■

Now Work PROBLEM 5

3 Build a Logistic Model from Data

Logistic growth models can be used to model situations for which the value of the dependent variable is limited. Many real-world situations conform to this scenario. For example, the population of the human race is limited by the availability of natural resources such as food and shelter. When the value of the dependent variable is limited, a logistic growth model is often appropriate.

EXAMPLE 3 Fitting a Logistic Function to Data

The data in Table 12 represent the amount of yeast biomass in a culture after t hours.

Table 12

Time (in hours)	Yeast Biomass	Time (in hours)	Yeast Biomass
0	9.6	10	513.3
1	18.3	11	559.7
2	29.0	12	594.8
3	47.2	13	629.4
4	71.1	14	640.8
5	119.1	15	651.1
6	174.6	16	655.9
7	257.3	17	659.6
8	350.7	18	661.8
9	441.0		

Source: Tor Carlson (Über Geschwindigkeit und Grösse der Hefevermehrung in Würze, Biochemische Zeitschrift, Bd. 57, pp. 313–334, 1913)

Figure 68

(a) Using a graphing utility, draw a scatter diagram of the data with time as the independent variable.

(b) Using a graphing utility, build a logistic model from the data.

(c) Using a graphing utility, graph the function found in part (b) on the scatter diagram.

(d) What is the predicted carrying capacity of the culture?

(e) Use the function found in part (b) to predict the population of the culture at $t = 19$ hours.

Solution

(a) See Figure 68 for a scatter diagram of the data.

(b) A graphing utility fits a logistic growth model of the form $y = \dfrac{c}{1 + ae^{-bx}}$ by using the LOGISTIC regression option. See Figure 69. The logistic model from the data is

$$y = \frac{663.0}{1 + 71.6e^{-0.5470x}}$$

where y is the amount of yeast biomass in the culture and x is the time.

Figure 69

(c) See Figure 70 for the graph of the logistic model.

Figure 70

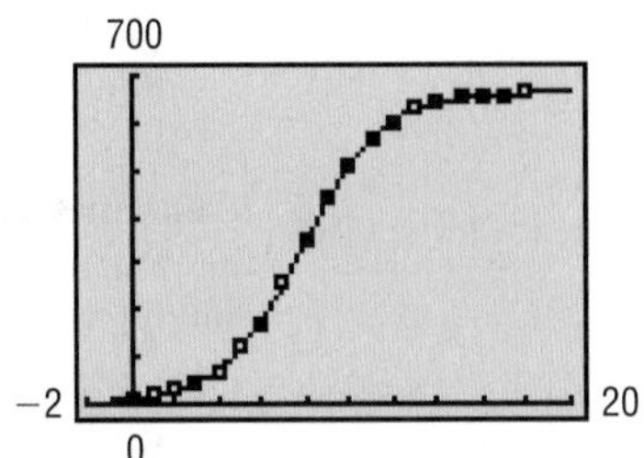

(d) Based on the logistic growth model found in part (b), the carrying capacity of the culture is 663.

(e) Using the logistic growth model found in part (b), the predicted amount of yeast biomass at $t = 19$ hours is

$$y = \frac{663.0}{1 + 71.6e^{-0.5470(19)}} \approx 661.5$$

Now Work PROBLEM 7

12.9 Assess Your Understanding

Applications and Extensions

1. **Biology** A strain of *E. coli* Beu 397-recA441 is placed into a nutrient broth at 30° Celsius and allowed to grow. The following data are collected. Theory states that the number of bacteria in the petri dish will initially grow according to the law of uninhibited growth. The population is measured using an optical device in which the amount of light that passes through the petri dish is measured.

Time (hours), x	Population, y
0	0.09
2.5	0.18
3.5	0.26
4.5	0.35
6	0.50

Source: Dr. Polly Lavery, Joliet Junior College

(a) Draw a scatter diagram treating time as the independent variable.
(b) Using a graphing utility, build an exponential model from the data.
(c) Express the function found in part (b) in the form $N(t) = N_0e^{kt}$.
(d) Graph the exponential function found in part (b) or (c) on the scatter diagram.
(e) Use the exponential function from part (b) or (c) to predict the population at $x = 7$ hours.
(f) Use the exponential function from part (b) or (c) to predict when the population will reach 0.75.

2. **Biology** A strain of *E. coli* SC18del-recA718 is placed into a nutrient broth at 30° Celsius and allowed to grow. The data below are collected. Theory states that the number of bacteria in the petri dish will initially grow according to the law of uninhibited growth. The population is measured using an optical device in which the amount of light that passes through the petri dish is measured.

Time (hours), x	Population, y
2.5	0.175
3.5	0.38
4.5	0.63
4.75	0.76
5.25	1.20

Source: Dr. Polly Lavery, Joliet Junior College

(a) Draw a scatter diagram treating time as the independent variable.
(b) Using a graphing utility, build an exponential model from the data.
(c) Express the function found in part (b) in the form $N(t) = N_0e^{kt}$.
(d) Graph the exponential function found in part (b) or (c) on the scatter diagram.
(e) Use the exponential function from part (b) or (c) to predict the population at $x = 6$ hours.
(f) Use the exponential function from part (b) or (c) to predict when the population will reach 2.1.

3. **Chemistry** A chemist has a 100-gram sample of a radioactive material. He records the amount of radioactive material every week for 7 weeks and obtains the following data:

Week	Weight (in Grams)
0	100.0
1	88.3
2	75.9
3	69.4
4	59.1
5	51.8
6	45.5

(a) Using a graphing utility, draw a scatter diagram with week as the independent variable.
(b) Using a graphing utility, build an exponential model from the data.
(c) Express the function found in part (b) in the form $A(t) = A_0e^{kt}$.
(d) Graph the exponential function found in part (b) or (c) on the scatter diagram.
(e) From the result found in part (b), determine the half-life of the radioactive material.
(f) How much radioactive material will be left after 50 weeks?
(g) When will there be 20 grams of radioactive material?

4. **Cigarette Exports** The following data represent the number of cigarettes (in billions) exported from the United States by year.

Year	Cigarette Exports (in billions of pieces)
1995	231.1
1998	201.3
1999	151.4
2000	147.9
2001	133.9
2002	127.4
2003	121.5
2004	118.7

Source: Statistical Abstract of the United States, 2006

(a) Let $t =$ the number of years since 1995. Using a graphing utility, draw a scatter diagram of the data using t as the independent variable and number of cigarettes as the dependent variable.
(b) Using a graphing utility, build an exponential model from the data.
(c) Express the function found in part (b) in the form $A(t) = A_0e^{kt}$.
(d) Graph the exponential function found in part (b) or (c) on the scatter diagram.
(e) Use the exponential function from part (b) or (c) to predict the number of cigarettes exported from the United States in 2010.
(f) Use the exponential function from part (b) or (c) to predict when the number of cigarettes exported from the United States will decrease to 50 billion.

5. **Economics and Marketing** The following data represent the price and quantity demanded in 2009 for Dell personal computers.

Price ($/Computer)	Quantity Demanded
2300	152
2000	159
1700	164
1500	171
1300	176
1200	180
1000	189

(a) Using a graphing utility, draw a scatter diagram of the data with price as the dependent variable.
(b) Using a graphing utility, build a logarithmic model from the data.
(c) Using a graphing utility, draw the logarithmic function found in part (b) on the scatter diagram.
(d) Use the function found in part (b) to predict the number of Dell personal computers that will be demanded if the price is $1650.

6. **Economics and Marketing** The following data represent the price and quantity supplied in 2009 for Dell personal computers.

Price ($/Computer)	Quantity Supplied
2300	180
2000	173
1700	160
1500	150
1300	137
1200	130
1000	113

(a) Using a graphing utility, draw a scatter diagram of the data with price as the dependent variable.
(b) Using a graphing utility, build a logarithmic model from the data.
(c) Using a graphing utility, draw the logarithmic function found in part (b) on the scatter diagram.
(d) Use the function found in part (b) to predict the number of Dell personal computers that will be supplied if the price is $1650.

7. **Population Model** The following data represent the population of the United States. An ecologist is interested in building a model that describes the population of the United States.

Year	Population
1900	76,212,168
1910	92,228,496
1920	106,021,537
1930	123,202,624
1940	132,164,569
1950	151,325,798
1960	179,323,175
1970	203,302,031
1980	226,542,203
1990	248,709,873
2000	281,421,906
2010	308,745,538

Source: U.S. Census Bureau

(a) Using a graphing utility, draw a scatter diagram of the data using years since 1900 as the independent variable and population as the dependent variable.
(b) Using a graphing utility, build a logistic model from the data.
(c) Using a graphing utility, draw the function found in part (b) on the scatter diagram.
(d) Based on the function found in part (b), what is the carrying capacity of the United States?
(e) Use the function found in part (b) to predict the population of the United States in 2012.
(f) When will the United States population be 350,000,000?
(g) Compare actual U.S. Census figures to the predictions found in parts (e) and (f). Discuss any differences.

8. Population Model The following data represent the world population. An ecologist is interested in building a model that describes the world population.

Year	Population (in Billions)
2001	6.17
2002	6.25
2003	6.32
2004	6.40
2005	6.48
2006	6.55
2007	6.63
2008	6.71
2009	6.79
2010	6.85

Source: U.S. Census Bureau

(a) Using a graphing utility, draw a scatter diagram of the data using years since 2000 as the independent variable and population as the dependent variable.
(b) Using a graphing utility, build a logistic model from the data.
(c) Using a graphing utility, draw the function found in part (b) on the scatter diagram.
(d) Based on the function found in part (b), what is the carrying capacity of the world?
(e) Use the function found in part (b) to predict the population of the world in 2015.
(f) When will world population be 10 billion?

9. Cell Phone Subscribers The following data represent the number of cell phone subscribers in the United States from 1985 through 2010.

Year, x	Number of Subscribers (in millions), y	Year, x	Number of Subscribers (in millions), y
1985 ($x = 1$)	0.34	1998 ($x = 14$)	69.21
1986 ($x = 2$)	0.68	1999 ($x = 15$)	86.05
1987 ($x = 3$)	1.23	2000 ($x = 16$)	109.48
1988 ($x = 4$)	2.07	2001 ($x = 17$)	128.37
1989 ($x = 5$)	3.51	2002 ($x = 18$)	140.77
1990 ($x = 6$)	5.28	2003 ($x = 19$)	158.72
1991 ($x = 7$)	7.56	2004 ($x = 20$)	182.14
1992 ($x = 8$)	11.03	2005 ($x = 21$)	207.90
1993 ($x = 9$)	16.01	2006 ($x = 22$)	233.00
1994 ($x = 10$)	24.13	2007 ($x = 23$)	255.40
1995 ($x = 11$)	33.76	2008 ($x = 24$)	270.33
1996 ($x = 12$)	44.04	2009 ($x = 25$)	285.60
1997 ($x = 13$)	55.31	2010 ($x = 26$)	302.90

Source: ©2010 CTIA–The Wireless Association®. All Rights Reserved.

(a) Using a graphing utility, draw a scatter diagram of the data using 1 for 1985, 2 for 1986, and so on as the independent variable and number of subscribers as the dependent variable.
(b) Using a graphing utility, build a logistic model from the data.
(c) Using a graphing utility, draw the function found in part (b) on the scatter diagram.
(d) What is the predicted carrying capacity of U.S. cell phone subscribers?
(e) Use the model to predict the number of U.S. cell phone subscribers at the end of 2015.

10. Cable Subscribers The following data represent the number of basic cable TV subscribers in the United States. A market researcher believes that external factors, such as satellite TV, have affected the growth of cable subscribers. She is interested in building a model that can be used to describe the number of cable TV subscribers in the United States.

(a) Using a graphing utility, draw a scatter diagram of the data using the number of years after 1970, t, as the independent variable and number of subscribers as the dependent variable.
(b) Using a graphing utility, build a logistic model from the data.
(c) Using a graphing utility, draw the function found in part (b) on the scatter diagram.
(d) Based on the model found in part (b), what is the maximum number of cable TV subscribers in the United States?
(e) Use the model found in part (b) to predict the number of cable TV subscribers in the United States in 2015.

Year	Subscribers (1,000)
1975 ($t = 5$)	9,800
1980 ($t = 10$)	17,500
1985 ($t = 15$)	35,440
1990 ($t = 20$)	50,520
1992 ($t = 22$)	54,300
1994 ($t = 24$)	58,373
1996 ($t = 26$)	62,300
1998 ($t = 28$)	64,650
2000 ($t = 30$)	66,054
2002 ($t = 32$)	64,556
2004 ($t = 34$)	65,263
2006 ($t = 36$)	64,908
2007 ($t = 37$)	65,913
2008 ($t = 38$)	66,218

Source: Statistical Abstract of the United States, 2011

Mixed Practice

11. Age versus Total Cholesterol The following data represent the age and average total cholesterol for adult males at various ages.

Age	Total Cholesterol
27	189
40	205
50	215
60	210
70	210
80	194

(a) Using a graphing utility, draw a scatter diagram of the data using age, x, as the independent variable and total cholesterol, y, as the dependent variable.
(b) Based on the scatter diagram drawn in part (a), decide on a model (linear, quadratic, cubic, exponential, logarithmic, or logistic) that you think best describes the relation between age and total cholesterol. Be sure to justify your choice of model.
(c) Using a graphing utility, find the model of best fit.
(d) Using a graphing utility, draw the model of best fit on the scatter diagram drawn in part (a).
(e) Use your model to predict the total cholesterol of a 35-year-old male.

12. Income versus Crime Rate The following data represent crime rate against individuals (crimes per 1000 households) and their income (in dollars) in the United States in 2007.

(a) Using a graphing utility, draw a scatter diagram of the data using income, x, as the independent variable and crime rate, y, as the dependent variable.
(b) Based on the scatter diagram drawn in part (a), decide on a model (linear, quadratic, cubic, exponential, logarithmic, or logistic) that you think best describes the relation between income and crime rate. Be sure to justify your choice of model.
(c) Using a graphing utility, find the model of best fit.
(d) Using a graphing utility, draw the model of best fit on the scatter diagram drawn in part (a).
(e) Use your model to predict the crime rate of a household whose income is $55,000.

Income	Crime Rate
5000	213.1
11,250	201.3
20,000	167.0
30,000	154.6
42,500	151.2
62,500	144.6

Source: Statistical Abstract of the United States, 2010

13. Depreciation of a Chevrolet Impala The following data represent the asking price and age of a Chevrolet Impala SS.

Age	Asking Price
1	$27,417
1	$26,750
2	$22,995
2	$23,195
3	$17,999
4	$16,995
4	$16,490

Source: cars.com

(a) Using a graphing utility, draw a scatter diagram of the data using age, x, as the independent variable and asking price, y, as the dependent variable.
(b) Based on the scatter diagram drawn in part (a), decide on a model (linear, quadratic, cubic, exponential, logarithmic, or logistic) that you think best describes the relation between age and asking price. Be sure to justify your choice of model.
(c) Using a graphing utility, find the model of best fit.
(d) Using a graphing utility, draw the model of best fit on the scatter diagram drawn in part (a).
(e) Use your model to predict the asking price of a Chevrolet Impala SS that is 5 years old.

CHAPTER REVIEW

Things to Know

Composite function (p. 752)

$(f \circ g)(x) = f(g(x))$ The domain of $f \circ g$ is the set of all numbers x in the domain of g for which $g(x)$ is in the domain of f.

One-to-one function f (p. 760)

A function for which any two different inputs in the domain correspond to two different outputs in the range

For any choice of elements x_1, x_2 in the domain of f, if $x_1 \neq x_2$, then $f(x_1) \neq f(x_2)$.

Horizontal-line test (p. 761)

If every horizontal line intersects the graph of a function f in at most one point, f is one-to-one.

Inverse function f^{-1} of f (pp. 762–763, 765)

Domain of f = range of f^{-1}; range of f = domain of f^{-1}

$f^{-1}(f(x)) = x$ for all x in the domain of f

$f(f^{-1}(x)) = x$ for all x in the domain of f^{-1}

The graphs of f and f^{-1} are symmetric with respect to the line $y = x$.

Properties of the exponential function (pp. 774, 777–778, 779)

$f(x) = Ca^x, \quad a > 1, C > 0$
Domain: the interval $(-\infty, \infty)$
Range: the interval $(0, \infty)$
x-intercepts: none; y-intercept: C
Horizontal asymptote: x-axis $(y = 0)$ as $x \to -\infty$
Increasing; one-to-one; smooth; continuous
See Figure 24 for a typical graph.

$f(x) = Ca^x, \quad 0 < a < 1, C > 0$
Domain: the interval $(-\infty, \infty)$
Range: the interval $(0, \infty)$
x-intercepts: none; y-intercept: C
Horizontal asymptote: x-axis $(y = 0)$ as $x \to \infty$
Decreasing; one-to-one; smooth; continuous
See Figure 29 for a typical graph.

Number e (p. 780)

Value approached by the expression $\left(1 + \frac{1}{n}\right)^n$ as $n \to \infty$; that is, $\lim_{n \to \infty}\left(1 + \frac{1}{n}\right)^n = e$.

Property of exponents (p. 781)

If $a^u = a^v$, then $u = v$.

Properties of the logarithmic function (pp. 789, 791, 792)

$f(x) = \log_a x, \quad a > 1$
$(y = \log_a x$ means $x = a^y)$
Domain: the interval $(0, \infty)$
Range: the interval $(-\infty, \infty)$
x-intercept: 1; y-intercept: none
Vertical asymptote: $x = 0$ (y-axis)
Increasing; one-to-one; smooth; continuous
See Figure 45(a) for a typical graph.

$f(x) = \log_a x, \quad 0 < a < 1$
$(y = \log_a x$ means $x = a^y)$
Domain: the interval $(0, \infty)$
Range: the interval $(-\infty, \infty)$
x-intercept: 1; y-intercept: none
Vertical asymptote: $x = 0$ (y-axis)
Decreasing; one-to-one; smooth; continuous
See Figure 45(b) for a typical graph.

Natural logarithm (p. 793)	$y = \ln x$ means $x = e^y$.
Properties of logarithms (pp. 803–804, 806)	$\log_a 1 = 0$ $\quad \log_a a = 1$ $\quad a^{\log_a M} = M$ $\quad \log_a a^r = r$
	$\log_a(MN) = \log_a M + \log_a N$ $\quad \log_a\left(\frac{M}{N}\right) = \log_a M - \log_a N$
	$\log_a M^r = r \log_a M$
	If $M = N$, then $\log_a M = \log_a N$. $\quad a^x = e^{x \ln a}$
	If $\log_a M = \log_a N$, then $M = N$.

Formulas

Change-of-Base Formula (p. 807)	$\log_a M = \frac{\log_b M}{\log_b a}$
Compound Interest Formula (p. 820)	$A = P \cdot \left(1 + \frac{r}{n}\right)^{nt}$
Continuous compounding (p. 821)	$A = Pe^{rt}$
Effective rate of interest (p. 822)	Compounding n times per year: $r_e = \left(1 + \frac{r}{n}\right)^n - 1$
	Continuous compounding: $r_e = e^r - 1$
Present Value Formulas (p. 823)	$P = A \cdot \left(1 + \frac{r}{n}\right)^{-nt}$ or $P = Ae^{-rt}$
Growth and decay (p. 829, 830)	$A(t) = A_0 e^{kt}$
Newton's Law of Cooling (p. 832)	$u(t) = T + (u_0 - T)e^{kt} \quad k < 0$
Logistic model (p. 833)	$P(t) = \frac{c}{1 + ae^{-bt}}$

Objectives

Section		You should be able to ...	Example(s)	Review Exercises
12.1	1	Form a composite function (p. 752)	1, 2, 4, 5	1–7
	2	Find the domain of a composite function (p. 753)	2–4	5–7
12.2	1	Determine whether a function is one-to-one (p. 760)	1, 2	8(a), 9
	2	Determine the inverse of a function defined by a map or a set of ordered pairs (p. 762)	3, 4	8(b)
	3	Obtain the graph of the inverse function from the graph of the function (p. 764)	7	9
	4	Find the inverse of a function defined by an equation (p. 765)	8, 9, 10	10–13
12.3	1	Evaluate exponential functions (p. 772)	1	14(a), (c), 47(a)
	2	Graph exponential functions (p. 776)	3–6	31–33
	3	Define the number e (p. 780)	pg. 780	33
	4	Solve exponential equations (p. 781)	7, 8	35, 36, 39, 41
12.4	1	Change exponential statements to logarithmic statements and logarithmic statements to exponential statements (p. 790)	2, 3	15, 16
	2	Evaluate logarithmic expressions (p. 790)	4	14(b), (d), 19, 46(b), 48(a), 49
	3	Determine the domain of a logarithmic function (p. 791)	5	17, 18, 34(a)
	4	Graph logarithmic functions (p. 792)	6, 7	34(b), 46(a)
	5	Solve logarithmic equations (p. 796)	8, 9	37, 40, 46(c), 48(b)
12.5	1	Work with the properties of logarithms (p. 802)	1, 2	20, 21
	2	Write a logarithmic expression as a sum or difference of logarithms (p. 805)	3–5	22–25
	3	Write a logarithmic expression as a single logarithm (p. 805)	6	26–28
	4	Evaluate a logarithm whose base is neither 10 nor e (p. 806)	7, 8	29
	5	Graph a logarithmic function whose base is neither 10 nor e (p. 808)	9	30

12.6	1	Solve logarithmic equations (p. 811)	1–3	37, 43
	2	Solve exponential equations (p. 813)	4–7	38, 42, 44, 45
	3	Solve logarithmic and exponential equations using a graphing utility (p. 815)	8	35–45
12.7	1	Determine the future value of a lump sum of money (p. 818)	1–3	50, 55
	2	Calculate effective rates of return (p. 822)	4	50
	3	Determine the present value of a lump sum of money (p. 823)	5	51
	4	Determine the rate of interest or time required to double a lump sum of money (p. 824)	6, 7	50
12.8	1	Find equations of populations that obey the law of uninhibited growth (p. 828)	1, 2	54
	2	Find equations of populations that obey the law of decay (p. 830)	3	52
	3	Use Newton's Law of Cooling (p. 832)	4	53
	4	Use logistic models (p. 833)	5, 6	56
12.9	1	Build an exponential model from data (p. 840)	1	57
	2	Build a logarithmic model from data (p. 841)	2	58
	3	Build a logistic model from data (p. 842)	3	59

Review Exercises

1. Evaluate each expression using the graphs of $y = f(x)$ and $y = g(x)$ shown in the figure.

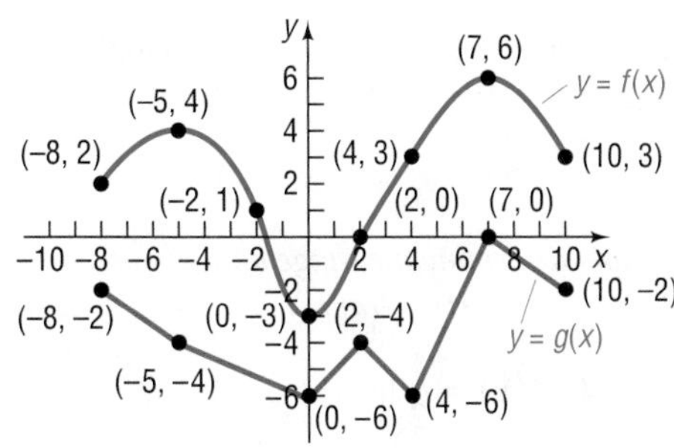

(a) $(g \circ f)(-8)$

(b) $(f \circ g)(-8)$

(c) $(g \circ g)(7)$

(d) $(g \circ f)(-5)$

In Problems 2–4, for the given functions f and g find:

(a) $(f \circ g)(2)$

(b) $(g \circ f)(-2)$

(c) $(f \circ f)(4)$

(d) $(g \circ g)(-1)$

2. $f(x) = 3x - 5;\quad g(x) = 1 - 2x^2$

3. $f(x) = \sqrt{x + 2}:\quad g(x) = 2x^2 + 1$

4. $f(x) = e^x;\quad g(x) = 3x - 2$

In Problems 5–7, find $f \circ g$, $g \circ f$, $f \circ f$, and $g \circ g$ for each pair of functions. State the domain of each composite function.

5. $f(x) = 2 - x;\quad g(x) = 3x + 1$

6. $f(x) = \sqrt{3x};\quad g(x) = 1 + x + x^2$

7. $f(x) = \dfrac{x + 1}{x - 1};\quad g(x) = \dfrac{1}{x}$

In Problem 8, (a) verify that the function is one-to-one, and (b) find the inverse of the given function.

8. $\{(1, 2), (3, 5), (5, 8), (6, 10)\}$

In Problem 9, state why the graph of the function is one-to-one. Then draw the graph of the inverse function f^{-1}. For convenience (and as a hint), the graph of $y = x$ is also given.

9.

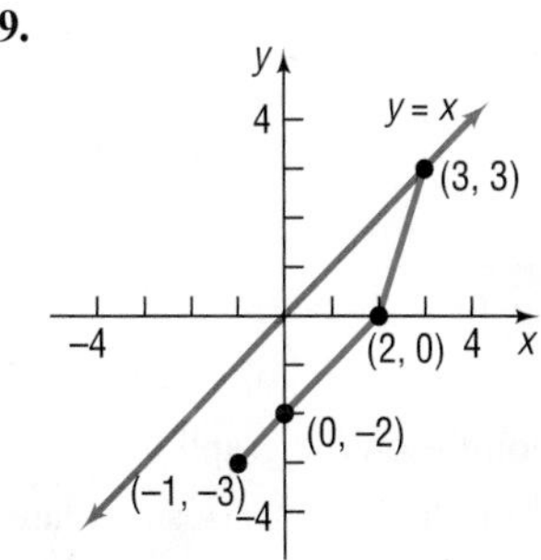

In Problems 10–13, the function f is one-to-one. Find the inverse of each function and check your answer. State the domain and the range of f and f^{-1}

10. $f(x) = \dfrac{2x + 3}{5x - 2}$

11. $f(x) = \dfrac{1}{x - 1}$

12. $f(x) = \sqrt{x - 2}$

13. $f(x) = x^{1/3} + 1$

In Problem 14, $f(x) = 3^x$ and $g(x) = \log_3 x$.

14. Evaluate: (a) $f(4)$ (b) $g(9)$ (c) $f(-2)$ (d) $g\left(\frac{1}{27}\right)$

15. Convert $5^2 = z$ to an equivalent statement involving a logarithm.

16. Convert $\log_5 u = 13$ to an equivalent statement involving an exponent.

In Problems 17 and 18, find the domain of each logarithmic function.

17. $f(x) = \log(3x - 2)$

18. $H(x) = \log_2(x^2 - 3x + 2)$

In Problems 19–21, evaluate each expression. Do not use a calculator.

19. $\log_2\left(\frac{1}{8}\right)$

20. $\ln e^{\sqrt{2}}$

21. $2^{\log_2 0.4}$

In Problems 22–25, write each expression as the sum and/or difference of logarithms. Express powers as factors.

22. $\log_3\left(\frac{uv^2}{w}\right)$, $u > 0, v > 0, w > 0$

23. $\log_2(a^2\sqrt{b})^4$, $a > 0, b > 0$

24. $\log(x^2\sqrt{x^3 + 1})$, $x > 0$

25. $\ln\left(\frac{2x + 3}{x^2 - 3x + 2}\right)^2$, $x > 2$

In Problems 26–28, write each expression as a single logarithm.

26. $3\log_4 x^2 + \frac{1}{2}\log_4\sqrt{x}$

27. $\ln\left(\frac{x - 1}{x}\right) + \ln\left(\frac{x}{x + 1}\right) - \ln(x^2 - 1)$

28. $\frac{1}{2}\ln(x^2 + 1) - 4\ln\frac{1}{2} - \frac{1}{2}[\ln(x - 4) + \ln x]$

29. Use the Change-of-Base Formula and a calculator to evaluate $\log_4 19$. Round your answer to three decimal places.

30. Graph $y = \log_3 x$ using a graphing utility and the Change-of-Base Formula.

In Problems 31–34, use the given function f to:

(a) Find the domain of f. *(b) Graph f.* *(c) From the graph, determine the range and any asymptotes of f.*
(d) Find f^{-1}, the inverse of f. *(e) Find the domain and the range of f^{-1}.* *(f) Graph f^{-1}.*

31. $f(x) = 2^{x-3}$

32. $f(x) = 1 + 3^{-x}$

33. $f(x) = 3e^{x-2}$

34. $f(x) = \frac{1}{2}\ln(x + 3)$

In Problems 35–45, solve each equation. Express irrational solutions in exact form and as a decimal rounded to 3 decimal places. Verify your results using a graphing utility.

35. $8^{6+3x} = 4$

36. $3^{x^2+x} = \sqrt{3}$

37. $\log_x 64 = -3$

38. $5^x = 3^{x+2}$

39. $25^{2x} = 5^{x^2-12}$

40. $\log_3\sqrt{x - 2} = 2$

41. $8 = 4^{x^2} \cdot 2^{5x}$

42. $2^x \cdot 5 = 10^x$

43. $\log_6(x + 3) + \log_6(x + 4) = 1$

44. $e^{1-x} = 5$

45. $9^x + 4 \cdot 3^x - 3 = 0$

46. Suppose that $f(x) = \log_2(x - 2) + 1$.

(a) Graph f.

(b) What is $f(6)$? What point is on the graph of f?

(c) Solve $f(x) = 4$. What point is on the graph of f?

(d) Based on the graph drawn in part (a), solve $f(x) > 0$.

(e) Find $f^{-1}(x)$. Graph f^{-1} on the same Cartesian plane as f.

47. Amplifying Sound An amplifier's power output P (in watts) is related to its decibel voltage gain d by the formula

$$P = 25e^{0.1d}$$

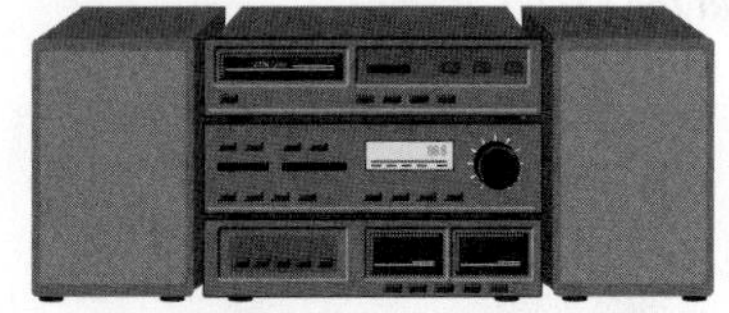

(a) Find the power output for a decibel voltage gain of 4 decibels.

(b) For a power output of 50 watts, what is the decibel voltage gain?

48. Limiting Magnitude of a Telescope A telescope is limited in its usefulness by the brightness of the star that it is aimed at and by the diameter of its lens. One measure of a star's brightness is its *magnitude;* the dimmer the star, the larger its magnitude. A formula for the limiting magnitude L of a telescope, that is, the magnitude of the dimmest star that it can be used to view, is given by

$$L = 9 + 5.1 \log d$$

where d is the diameter (in inches) of the lens.

(a) What is the limiting magnitude of a 3.5-inch telescope?
(b) What diameter is required to view a star of magnitude 14?

49. Salvage Value The number of years n for a piece of machinery to depreciate to a known salvage value can be found using the formula

$$n = \frac{\log s - \log i}{\log(1 - d)}$$

where s is the salvage value of the machinery, i is its initial value, and d is the annual rate of depreciation.

(a) How many years will it take for a piece of machinery to decline in value from \$90,000 to \$10,000 if the annual rate of depreciation is 0.20 (20%)?
(b) How many years will it take for a piece of machinery to lose half of its value if the annual rate of depreciation is 15%?

50. Funding a College Education A child's grandparents purchase a \$10,000 bond fund that matures in 18 years to be used for her college education. The bond fund pays 4% interest compounded semiannually. How much will the bond fund be worth at maturity? What is the effective rate of interest? How long will it take the bond to double in value under these terms?

51. Funding a College Education A child's grandparents wish to purchase a bond that matures in 18 years to be used for her college education. The bond pays 4% interest compounded semiannually. How much should they pay so that the bond will be worth \$85,000 at maturity?

52. Estimating the Date That a Prehistoric Man Died The bones of a prehistoric man found in the desert of New Mexico contain approximately 5% of the original amount of carbon 14. If the half-life of carbon 14 is 5700 years, approximately how long ago did the man die?

53. Temperature of a Skillet A skillet is removed from an oven whose temperature is 450°F and placed in a room whose temperature is 70°F. After 5 minutes, the temperature of the skillet is 400°F. How long will it be until its temperature is 150°F?

54. World Population The annual growth rate of the world's population in 2010 was $k = 1.15\% = 0.0115$. The population of the world in 2010 was 6,852,472,823. Letting $t = 0$ represent 2010, use the uninhibited growth model to predict the world's population in the year 2015.

Source: U.S. Census Bureau

55. Federal Deficit In fiscal year 2010, the federal deficit was \$1.3 trillion. At that time, 10-year treasury notes were paying 3.35% interest per annum. If the federal government financed this deficit through 10-year notes, how much would it have to pay back in 2020? How much was the interest?

Source: U.S. Treasury Department

56. Logistic Growth The logistic growth model

$$P(t) = \frac{0.8}{1 + 1.67e^{-0.16t}}$$

represents the proportion of new cars with a global positioning system (GPS). Let $t = 0$ represent 2006, $t = 1$ represent 2007, and so on.

(a) What proportion of new cars in 2006 had a GPS?
(b) Determine the maximum proportion of new cars that have a GPS.
(c) Using a graphing utility, graph $P = P(t)$.
(d) When will 75% of new cars have a GPS?

57. CBL Experiment The following data were collected by placing a temperature probe in a portable heater, removing the probe, and then recording temperature over time.

Time (sec.)	Temperature (°F)
0	165.07
1	164.77
2	163.99
3	163.22
4	162.82
5	161.96
6	161.20
7	160.45
8	159.35
9	158.61
10	157.89
11	156.83
12	156.11
13	155.08
14	154.40
15	153.72

According to Newton's Law of Cooling, these data should follow an exponential model.

(a) Using a graphing utility, draw a scatter diagram for the data.
(b) Using a graphing utility, build an exponential model from the data.
(c) Graph the exponential function found in part (b) on the scatter diagram.
(d) Predict how long it will take for the probe to reach a temperature of 110°F.

58. Wind Chill Factor The data on the next page represent the wind speed (mph) and wind chill factor at an air temperature of 15°F.

(a) Using a graphing utility, draw a scatter diagram with wind speed as the independent variable.
(b) Using a graphing utility, build a logarithmic model from the data.
(c) Using a graphing utility, draw the logarithmic function found in part (b) on the scatter diagram.
(d) Use the function found in part (b) to predict the wind chill factor if the air temperature is 15°F and the wind speed is 23 mph.

Wind Speed (mph)	Wind Chill Factor (°F)
5	7
10	3
15	0
20	−2
25	−4
30	−5
35	−7

Source: U.S. National Weather Service

59. Spreading of a Disease Jack and Diane live in a small town of 50 people. Unfortunately, both Jack and Diane have a cold. Those who come in contact with someone who has this cold will themselves catch the cold. The following data represent the number of people in the small town who have caught the cold after t days.

(a) Using a graphing utility, draw a scatter diagram of the data. Comment on the type of relation that appears to exist between the days and number of people with a cold.
(b) Using a graphing utility, build a logistic model from the data.
(c) Graph the function found in part (b) on the scatter diagram.
(d) According to the function found in part (b), what is the maximum number of people who will catch the cold? In reality, what is the maximum number of people who could catch the cold?
(e) Sometime between the second and third day, 10 people in the town had a cold. According to the model found in part (b), when did 10 people have a cold?
(f) How long will it take for 46 people to catch the cold?

Days, t	Number of People with Cold, C
0	2
1	4
2	8
3	14
4	22
5	30
6	37
7	42
8	44

CHAPTER TEST

The Chapter Test Prep Videos are step-by-step test solutions available in the Video Resources DVD, in MyMathLab, or on this text's YouTube Channel. Flip back to the Student Resources page to see the exact web address for this text's YouTube channel.

1. Given $f(x) = \dfrac{x+2}{x-2}$ and $g(x) = 2x + 5$, find:
(a) $f \circ g$ and state its domain (b) $(g \circ f)(-2)$
(c) $(f \circ g)(-2)$

2. Determine whether the function is one-to-one.
(a) $y = 4x^2 + 3$
(b) $y = \sqrt{x+3} - 5$

3. Find the inverse of $f(x) = \dfrac{2}{3x-5}$ and check your answer. State the domain and the range of f and f^{-1}.

4. If the point $(3, -5)$ is on the graph of a one-to-one function f, what point must be on the graph of f^{-1}?

In Problems 5–7, solve each equation.

5. $3^x = 243$ **6.** $\log_b 16 = 2$

7. $\log_5 x = 4$

In Problems 8–11, use a calculator to evaluate each expression. Round your answer to three decimal places.

8. $e^3 + 2$ **9.** $\log 20$

10. $\log_3 21$ **11.** $\ln 133$

In Problems 12 and 13, use the given function f to:
(a) Find the domain of f.
(b) Graph f.
(c) From the graph, determine the range and any asymptotes of f.
(d) Find f^{-1}, the inverse of f.
(e) Find the domain and the range of f^{-1}.
(f) Graph f^{-1}.

12. $f(x) = 4^{x+1} - 2$

13. $f(x) = 1 - \log_5(x - 2)$

In Problems 14–19, solve each equation.

14. $5^{x+2} = 125$ **15.** $\log(x + 9) = 2$

16. $8 - 2e^{-x} = 4$ **17.** $\log(x^2 + 3) = \log(x + 6)$

18. $7^{x+3} = e^x$ **19.** $\log_2(x - 4) + \log_2(x + 4) = 3$

20. Write $\log_2\left(\dfrac{4x^3}{x^2 - 3x - 18}\right)$ as the sum and/or difference of logarithms. Express powers as factors.

21. A 50-mg sample of a radioactive substance decays to 34 mg after 30 days. How long will it take for there to be 2 mg remaining?

22. (a) If \$1000 is invested at 5% compounded monthly, how much is there after 8 months?
(b) If you want to have \$1000 in 9 months, how much do you need to place in a savings account now that pays 5% compounded quarterly?
(c) How long does it take to double your money if you can invest it at 6% compounded annually?

23. The decibel level, D, of sound is given by the equation $D = 10 \log\left(\dfrac{I}{I_0}\right)$, where I is the intensity of the sound and $I_0 = 10^{-12}$ watt per square meter.

(a) If the shout of a single person measures 80 decibels, how loud will the sound be if two people shout at the same time? That is, how loud would the sound be if the intensity doubled?
(b) The pain threshold for sound is 125 decibels. If the Athens Olympic Stadium 2004 (Olympiako Stadio Athinas

'Spyros Louis') can seat 74,400 people, how many people in the crowd need to shout at the same time for the resulting sound level to meet or exceed the pain threshold? (Ignore any possible sound dampening.)

CUMULATIVE REVIEW

1. (a) Is the following graph the graph of a function? If it is, is the function one-to-one?

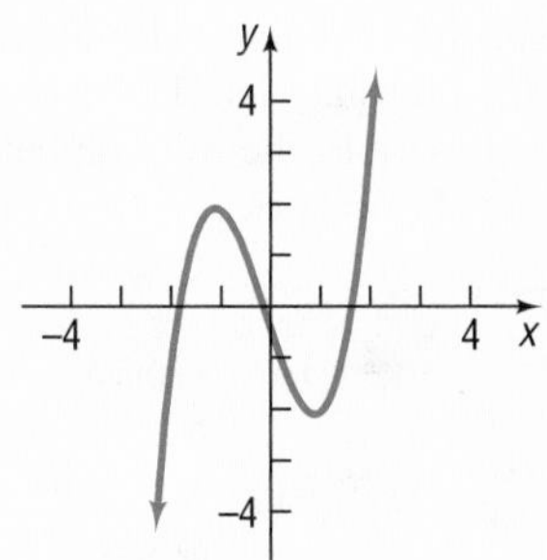

(b) Assuming the graph is a function, what type of function might it be (polynomial, exponential, and so on)? Why?

2. For the function $f(x) = 2x^2 - 3x + 1$, find the following:
(a) $f(3)$ (b) $f(-x)$ (c) $f(x + h)$

3. Determine which of the following points are on the graph of $x^2 + y^2 = 1$.
(a) $\left(\frac{1}{2}, \frac{1}{2}\right)$ (b) $\left(\frac{1}{2}, \frac{\sqrt{3}}{2}\right)$

4. Solve the equation $3(x - 2) = 4(x + 5)$.

5. Graph the line $2x - 4y = 16$.

6. (a) Graph the quadratic function $f(x) = -x^2 + 2x - 3$ by determining whether its graph opens up or down and by finding its vertex, axis of symmetry, y-intercept, and x-intercept(s), if any.
(b) Solve $f(x) \leq 0$.

7. Determine the quadratic function whose graph is given in the figure.

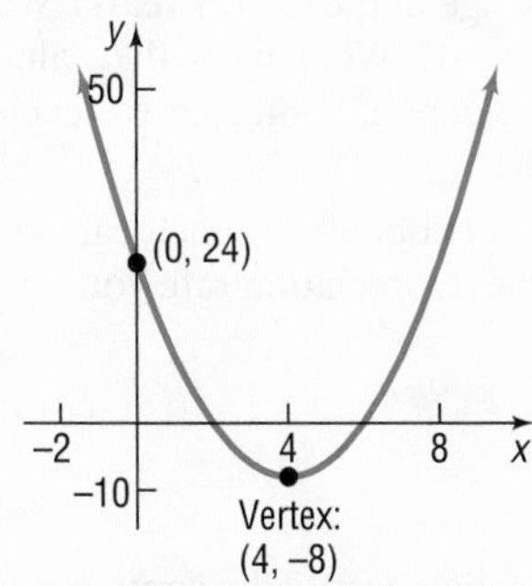

8. Is the graph of the following function a polynomial, exponential, or logarithmic function? Determine the function whose graph is given.

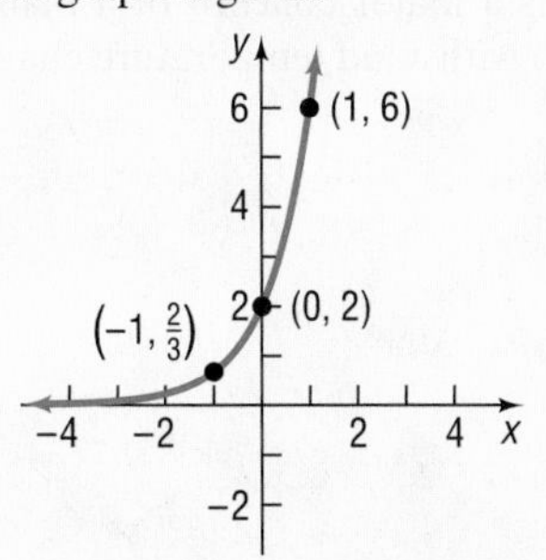

9. Graph $f(x) = 3(x + 1)^3 - 2$ using transformations.

10. (a) Given that $f(x) = x^2 + 2$ and $g(x) = \dfrac{2}{x - 3}$, find $f(g(x))$ and state its domain. What is $f(g(5))$?
(b) If $f(x) = x + 2$ and $g(x) = \log_2 x$, find $(f(g(x))$ and state its domain. What is $f(g(14))$?

11. For the polynomial function $f(x) = 4x^3 + 9x^2 - 30x - 8$:
(a) Find the real zeros of f.
(b) Determine the intercepts of the graph of f.
(c) Use a graphing utility to approximate the local maxima and local minima.
(d) Draw a complete graph of f. Be sure to label the intercepts and turning points.

12. For the function $g(x) = 3^x + 2$:
(a) Graph g using transformations. State the domain, range, and horizontal asymptote of g.
(b) Determine the inverse of g. State the domain, range, and vertical asymptote of g^{-1}.
(c) On the same graph as g, graph g^{-1}.

13. Solve the equation $4^{x-3} = 8^{2x}$.

14. Solve the equation: $\log_3(x + 1) + \log_3(2x - 3) = \log_9 9$

15. Suppose that $f(x) = \log_3(x + 2)$. Solve:
(a) $f(x) = 0$ (b) $f(x) > 0$
(c) $f(x) = 3$

16. **Data Analysis** The following data represent the percent of all drivers by age that have been stopped by the police for any reason within the past year. The median age represents the midpoint of the upper and lower limit for the age range.

Age Range	Median Age, x	Percentage Stopped, y
16–19	17.5	18.2
20–29	24.5	16.8
30–39	34.5	11.3
40–49	44.5	9.4
50–59	54.5	7.7
≥60	69.5	3.8

(a) Using your graphing utility, draw a scatter diagram of the data treating median age, x, as the independent variable.
(b) Determine a model that you feel best describes the relation between median age and percentage stopped. You may choose from among linear, quadratic, cubic, exponential, logarithmic, or logistic models.
(c) Provide a justification for the model that you selected in part (b).

CHAPTER PROJECTS

Internet-based Project

I. Depreciation of Cars Kelley Blue Book is an official guide that provides the current retail price of cars. You can access the Kelley Blue Book at your library or online at *www.kbb.com*.

1. Identify three cars that you are considering purchasing, and find the Kelley Blue Book value of the cars for 0 (brand new), 1, 2, 3, 4, and 5 years of age. Online, the value of the car can be found by selecting Used Cars, then Used Car Values. Enter the year, make, and model of the car you are selecting. To be consistent, we will assume the cars will be driven 12,000 miles per year, so a 1-year-old car will have 12,000 miles, a 2-year-old car will have 24,000 miles, and so on. Choose the same options for each year, and finally determine the suggested retail price for cars that are in Excellent, Good, and Fair shape. So, you should have a total of 16 observations (one for a brand new car, 3 for a 1-year-old car, 3 for a 2-year-old car, and so on).
2. Draw a scatter diagram of the data with age as the independent variable and value as the dependent variable using Excel, a TI-graphing calculator, or some other spreadsheet. The Chapter 10 project describes how to draw a scatter diagram in Excel.
3. Determine the exponential function of best fit. Graph the exponential function of best fit on the scatter diagram. To do this in Excel, click on any data point in the scatter diagram. Now click the Layout menu, select Trendline within the Analysis region, select More Trendline Options. Select the Exponential radio button and select Display Equation on Chart. See Figure 71. Move the Trendline Options window off to the side and you will see the exponential function of best fit displayed on the scatter diagram. Do you think the function accurately describes the relation between age of the car and suggested retail price?

Figure 71

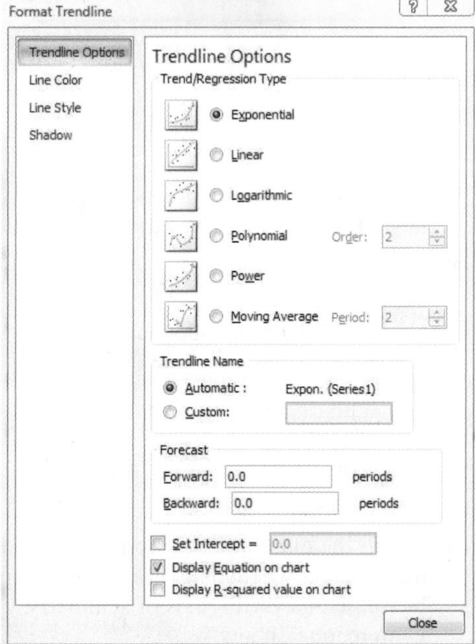

4. The exponential function of best fit is of the form $y = Ce^{rx}$ where y is the suggested retail value of the car and x is the age of the car (in years). What does the value of C represent? What does the value of r represent? What is the depreciation rate for each car that you are considering?
5. Write a report detailing which car you would purchase based on the depreciation rate you found for each car.

The following projects are available on the Instructor's Resource Center (IRC):

II. Hot Coffee A fast-food restaurant wants a special container to hold coffee. The restaurant wishes the container to quickly cool the coffee from 200° to 130°F and keep the liquid between 110° and 130°F as long as possible. The restaurant has three containers to select from. Which one should be purchased?

III. Project at Motorola *Thermal Fatigue of Solder Connections* Product reliability is a major concern of a manufacturer. Here a logarithmic transformation is used to simplify the analysis of a cell phone's ability to withstand temperature change.

Systems of Equations and Inequalities

13

Outline

Economic Outcomes

Annual Earnings of Young Adults

For both males and females, earnings increase with education: full-time workers with at least a bachelor's degree have higher median earnings than those with less education. For example, in 2003, male college graduates earned 93 percent more than male high school completers. Females with a bachelor's or higher degree earned 91 percent more than female high school completers. Males and females who dropped out of high school earned 37 and 39 percent less, respectively, than male and female high school completers.

The median earnings of young adults who have at least a bachelor's degree declined in the 1970s relative to their counterparts who were high school completers, before increasing between 1980 and 2003. Males with a bachelor's degree or higher had earnings 19 percent higher than male high school completers in 1980 and had earnings 93 percent higher in 2003. Among females, those with at least a bachelor's degree had earnings 34 percent higher than female high school completers in 1980, compared with earnings 91 percent higher in 2003.

—See Chapter Project I—

◐ **A LOOK BACK** In Chapters 7, 10, 11 and 12, we solved various kinds of equations and inequalities involving a single variable.

◑ **A LOOK AHEAD** In this chapter we take up the problem of solving equations and inequalities containing two or more variables. There are various ways to solve such problems.

The *method of substitution* for solving equations in several unknowns goes back to ancient times.

The *method of elimination*, although it had existed for centuries, was put into systematic order by Karl Friedrich Gauss (1777–1855) and by Camille Jordan (1838–1922).

The theory of *matrices* was developed in 1857 by Arthur Cayley (1821–1895), although only later were matrices used as we use them in this chapter. Matrices have become a very flexible instrument, useful in almost all areas of mathematics.

The method of *determinants* was invented by Takakazu Seki Kôwa (1642–1708) in 1683 in Japan and by Gottfried Wilhelm von Leibniz (1646–1716) in 1693 in Germany. *Cramer's Rule* is named after Gabriel Cramer (1704–1752) of Switzerland, who popularized the use of determinants for solving linear systems.

13.1 Systems of Linear Equations: Substitution and Elimination

PREPARING FOR THIS SECTION *Before getting started, review the following:*

- Lines (Section 8.2, pp. 532–541)

Now Work the **'Are You Prepared?'** problems on page 866.

OBJECTIVES

1. Solve Systems of Equations by Substitution (p. 858)
2. Solve Systems of Equations by Elimination (p. 859)
3. Identify Inconsistent Systems of Equations Containing Two Variables (p. 861)
4. Express the Solution of a System of Dependent Equations Containing Two Variables (p. 861)
5. Solve Systems of Three Equations Containing Three Variables (p. 862)
6. Identify Inconsistent Systems of Equations Containing Three Variables (p. 864)
7. Express the Solution of a System of Dependent Equations Containing Three Variables (p. 865)

EXAMPLE 1 **Movie Theater Ticket Sales**

A movie theater sells tickets for \$8.00 each, with seniors receiving a discount of \$2.00. One evening the theater took in \$3580 in revenue. If x represents the number of tickets sold at \$8.00 and y the number of tickets sold at the discounted price of \$6.00, write an equation that relates these variables.

Solution Each nondiscounted ticket brings in \$8.00, so x tickets will bring in $8x$ dollars. Similarly, y discounted tickets bring in $6y$ dollars. Since the total brought in is \$3580, we must have

$$8x + 6y = 3580$$ ■

In Example 1, suppose that we also know that 525 tickets were sold that evening. Then we have another equation relating the variables x and y:

$$x + y = 525$$

The two equations

$$\begin{aligned} 8x + 6y &= 3580 \\ x + y &= 525 \end{aligned}$$

form a *system* of equations.

In general, a **system of equations** is a collection of two or more equations, each containing one or more variables. Example 2 gives some illustrations of systems of equations.

EXAMPLE 2 **Examples of Systems of Equations**

(a) $\begin{cases} 2x + y = 5 & (1) \\ -4x + 6y = -2 & (2) \end{cases}$ Two equations containing two variables, x and y

(b) $\begin{cases} x + y^2 = 5 & (1) \\ 2x + y = 4 & (2) \end{cases}$ Two equations containing two variables, x and y

(c) $\begin{cases} x + y + z = 6 & (1) \\ 3x - 2y + 4z = 9 & (2) \\ x - y - z = 0 & (3) \end{cases}$ Three equations containing three variables, x, y, and z

(d) $\begin{cases} x + y + z = 5 & (1) \\ x - y = 2 & (2) \end{cases}$ Two equations containing three variables, x, y, and z

(e) $\begin{cases} x + y + z = 6 & (1) \\ 2x + 2z = 4 & (2) \\ y + z = 2 & (3) \\ x = 4 & (4) \end{cases}$ Four equations containing three variables, x, y, and z

■

We use a brace to remind us that we are dealing with a system of equations and we number each equation in the system.

A **solution** of a system of equations consists of values for the variables that are solutions of each equation of the system. To **solve** a system of equations means to find all solutions of the system.

For example, $x = 2, y = 1$ is a solution of the system in Example 2(a), because

$$\begin{cases} 2x + y = 5 & (1) \\ -4x + 6y = -2 & (2) \end{cases} \qquad \begin{cases} 2(2) + 1 = 4 + 1 = 5 \\ -4(2) + 6(1) = -8 + 6 = -2 \end{cases}$$

We may also write this solution as the ordered pair (2, 1).

A solution of the system in Example 2(b) is $x = 1, y = 2$, because

$$\begin{cases} x + y^2 = 5 & (1) \\ 2x + y = 4 & (2) \end{cases} \qquad \begin{cases} 1 + 2^2 = 1 + 4 = 5 \\ 2(1) + 2 = 2 + 2 = 4 \end{cases}$$

Another solution of the system in Example 2(b) is $x = \frac{11}{4}, y = -\frac{3}{2}$, which you can check for yourself.

A solution of the system in Example 2(c) is $x = 3, y = 2, z = 1$, because

$$\begin{cases} x + y + z = 6 & (1) \\ 3x - 2y + 4z = 9 & (2) \\ x - y - z = 0 & (3) \end{cases} \qquad \begin{cases} 3 + 2 + 1 = 6 \\ 3(3) - 2(2) + 4(1) = 9 - 4 + 4 = 9 \\ 3 - 2 - 1 = 0 \end{cases}$$

We may also write this solution as the ordered triplet (3, 2, 1).

Note that $x = 3, y = 3, z = 0$ is not a solution of the system in Example 2(c).

$$\begin{cases} x + y + z = 6 & (1) \\ 3x - 2y + 4z = 9 & (2) \\ x - y - z = 0 & (3) \end{cases} \qquad \begin{cases} 3 + 3 + 0 = 6 \\ 3(3) - 2(3) + 4(0) = 3 \neq 9 \\ 3 - 3 - 0 = 0 \end{cases}$$

Although $x = 3, y = 3$, and $z = 0$ satisfy equations (1) and (3), they do not satisfy equation (2). Any solution of the system must satisfy *each* equation of the system.

Now Work PROBLEM 9

When a system of equations has at least one solution, it is said to be **consistent.** If a system of equations has no solution, it is called **inconsistent.**

An equation in n variables is said to be **linear** if it is equivalent to an equation of the form

$$a_1x_1 + a_2x_2 + \cdots + a_nx_n = b$$

where $x_1, x_2, \ldots, x_n$ are n distinct variables, $a_1, a_2, \ldots, a_n, b$ are constants, and at least one of the a's is not 0.

Some examples of linear equations are

$$2x + 3y = 2 \qquad 5x - 2y + 3z = 10 \qquad 8x + 8y - 2z + 5w = 0$$

If each equation in a system of equations is linear, we have a **system of linear equations.** The systems in Examples 2(a), (c), (d), and (e) are linear, whereas the system in Example 2(b) is nonlinear. In this chapter we shall solve linear systems in Sections 13.1 to 13.3.

We begin by discussing a system of two linear equations containing two variables. We can view the problem of solving such a system as a geometry problem. The graph of each equation in such a system is a line. So a system of two linear equations containing two variables represents a pair of lines. The lines either (1) intersect or (2) are parallel or (3) are **coincident** (that is, identical).

1. If the lines intersect, the system of equations has one solution, given by the point of intersection. The system is **consistent** and the equations are **independent.** See Figure 1(a).
2. If the lines are parallel, the system of equations has no solution, because the lines never intersect. The system is **inconsistent.** See Figure 1(b).
3. If the lines are coincident (the lines lie on top of each other), the system of equations has infinitely many solutions, represented by the totality of points on the line. The system is **consistent** and the equations are **dependent.** See Figure 1(c).

Figure 1

Consistent and Independent

Solution

(a) Intersecting lines; system has one solution

Inconsistent

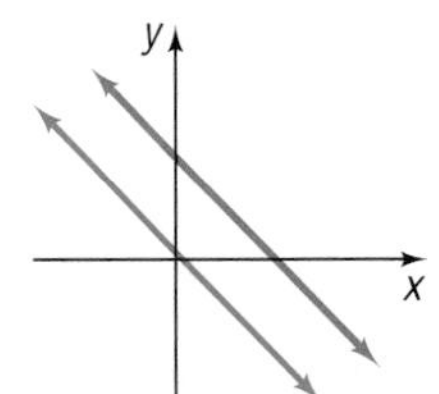

(b) Parallel lines; system has no solution

Consistent and Dependent

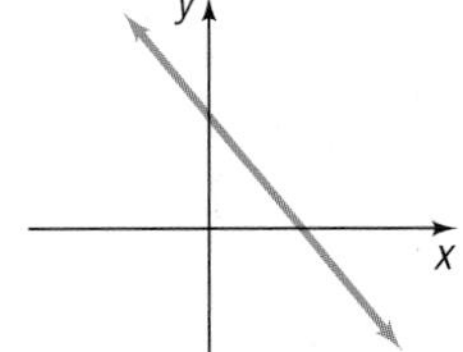

(c) Coincident lines; system has infinitely many solutions

EXAMPLE 3 **Solving a System of Linear Equations Using a Graphing Utility**

Solve: $\begin{cases} 2x + y = -1 & (1) \\ -4x + 6y = 42 & (2) \end{cases}$

Solution First, we solve each equation for y. This is equivalent to writing each equation in slope–intercept form. Equation (1) in slope–intercept form is $Y_1 = -2x - 1$. Equation (2) in slope–intercept form is $Y_2 = \frac{2}{3}x + 7$. Figure 2 shows the graphs using a graphing utility. From the graph in Figure 2, we see that the lines intersect, so the system is consistent and the equations are independent. Using INTERSECT, we obtain the solution $(-3, 5)$. ■

Figure 2

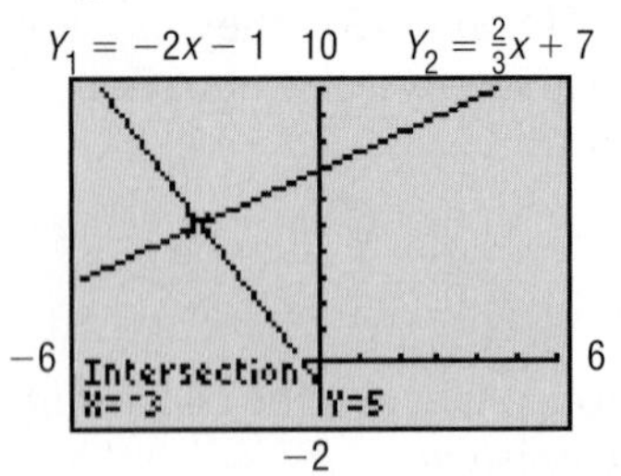

1 Solve Systems of Equations by Substitution

Most of the time we must use algebraic methods to obtain exact solutions. A number of methods are available to us for solving systems of linear equations algebraically. In this section, we introduce two methods: *substitution* and *elimination*. We illustrate the **method of substitution** by solving the system given in Example 3.

EXAMPLE 4 **How to Solve a System of Linear Equations by Substitution**

Solve: $\begin{cases} 2x + y = -1 & (1) \\ -4x + 6y = 42 & (2) \end{cases}$

Step-by-Step Solution

Step 1 Pick one of the equations and solve for one of the variables in terms of the remaining variable(s).

Solve equation (1) for y.

$$2x + y = -1 \qquad \text{Equation (1)}$$
$$y = -2x - 1 \qquad \text{Subtract } 2x \text{ from each side of (1).}$$

Step 2 Substitute the result into the remaining equation(s).

Substitute $-2x - 1$ for y in equation (2). The result is an equation containing just the variable x, which we can solve.

$$-4x + 6y = 42 \qquad \text{Equation (2)}$$
$$-4x + 6(-2x - 1) = 42 \qquad \text{Substitute } -2x - 1 \text{ for } y \text{ in (2).}$$

Step 3 If one equation in one variable results, solve this equation. Otherwise, repeat Steps 1 and 2 until a single equation with one variable remains.

$$-4x - 12x - 6 = 42 \qquad \text{Distribute.}$$
$$-16x - 6 = 42 \qquad \text{Combine like terms.}$$
$$-16x = 48 \qquad \text{Add 6 to both sides.}$$
$$x = \frac{48}{-16} \qquad \text{Divide both sides by } -16.$$
$$x = -3 \qquad \text{Simplify.}$$

Step 4 Find the values of the remaining variables by back-substitution.

Because we know that $x = -3$, we can find the value of y by **back-substitution,** that is, by substituting -3 for x in one of the original equations. Equation (1) seems easier to work with, so we will back-substitute into equation (1).

$$2x + y = -1 \qquad \text{Equation (1)}$$
$$2(-3) + y = -1 \qquad \text{Substitute } x = -3 \text{ into equation (1).}$$
$$-6 + y = -1 \qquad \text{Simplify.}$$
$$y = -1 + 6 \qquad \text{Add 6 to both sides.}$$
$$y = 5$$

Step 5 Check the solution found.

We have $x = -3$ and $y = 5$. We verify that both equations are satisfied (true) for these values.

$$\begin{cases} 2x + y = -1;\ 2(-3) + 5 = -6 + 5 = -1 \\ -4x + 6y = 42;\ -4(-3) + 6(5) = 12 + 30 = 42 \end{cases}$$

The solution of the system is $x = -3$ and $y = 5$. We can also write the solution as the ordered pair $(-3, 5)$. ■

Now Use Substitution to Work PROBLEM 19

2 Solve Systems of Equations by Elimination

A second method for solving a system of linear equations is the *method of elimination*. This method is usually preferred over substitution if substitution leads to fractions or if the system contains more than two variables. Elimination also provides the necessary motivation for solving systems using matrices (the subject of Section 13.2).

In Words

When using elimination, we want to get the coefficients of one of the variables to be negatives of one another.

The idea behind the **method of elimination** is to replace the original system of equations by an equivalent system so that adding two of the equations eliminates a variable. The rules for obtaining equivalent equations are the same as those studied earlier. However, we may also interchange any two equations of the system and/or replace any equation in the system by the sum (or difference) of that equation and a nonzero multiple of any other equation in the system.

Rules for Obtaining an Equivalent System of Equations

1. Interchange any two equations of the system.
2. Multiply (or divide) each side of an equation by the same nonzero constant.
3. Replace any equation in the system by the sum (or difference) of that equation and a nonzero multiple of any other equation in the system.

An example will give you the idea. As you work through the example, pay particular attention to the pattern being followed.

EXAMPLE 5 **How to Solve a System of Linear Equations by Elimination**

Solve: $\begin{cases} 2x + 3y = 1 & (1) \\ -x + y = -3 & (2) \end{cases}$

Step-by-Step Solution

Step 1 Multiply both sides of one or both equations by a nonzero constant so that the coefficients of one of the variables are additive inverses.

Multiply both sides of equation (2) by 2 so that the coefficients of x in the two equations are additive inverses.

$$\begin{cases} 2x + 3y = 1 & (1) \\ -x + y = -3 & (2) \end{cases}$$

$$\begin{cases} 2x + 3y = 1 & (1) \\ 2(-x + y) = 2(-3) & (2) \quad \text{Multiply by 2.} \end{cases}$$

$$\begin{cases} 2x + 3y = 1 & (1) \\ -2x + 2y = -6 & (2) \end{cases}$$

Step 2 Add the equations to eliminate the variable. Solve the resulting equation for the remaining unknown.

$$\begin{cases} 2x + 3y = 1 & (1) \\ -2x + 2y = -6 & (2) \end{cases}$$

$$5y = -5 \quad \text{Add equations (1) and (2).}$$

$$y = -1 \quad \text{Divide both sides by 5.}$$

Step 3 Back-substitute the value of the variable found in Step 2 into one of the *original* equations to find the value of the remaining variable.

Back-substitute $y = -1$ into equation (1) and solve for x.

$$\begin{aligned} 2x + 3y &= 1 && \text{Equation (1)} \\ 2x + 3(-1) &= 1 && \text{Substitute } y = -1 \text{ into equation (1).} \\ 2x - 3 &= 1 && \text{Simplify.} \\ 2x &= 4 && \text{Add 3 to both sides.} \\ x &= 2 && \text{Divide both sides by 2.} \end{aligned}$$

Step 4 Check the solution found.

We leave the check to you.

The solution of the system is $x = 2$ and $y = -1$. We can also write the solution as the ordered pair $(2, -1)$. ■

Now Use Elimination to Work PROBLEM 19

EXAMPLE 6 **Movie Theater Ticket Sales**

A movie theater sells tickets for \$8.00 each, with seniors receiving a discount of \$2.00. One evening the theater sold 525 tickets and took in \$3580 in revenue. How many of each type of ticket were sold?

Solution If x represents the number of tickets sold at \$8.00 and y the number of tickets sold at the discounted price of \$6.00, then the given information results in the system of equations

$$\begin{cases} 8x + 6y = 3580 & (1) \\ x + y = 525 & (2) \end{cases}$$

We use the method of elimination. First, multiply the second equation by -6, and then add the equations.

$$\begin{cases} 8x + 6y = 3580 \\ -6x - 6y = -3150 \end{cases}$$
$$2x = 430 \quad \text{Add the equations.}$$
$$x = 215$$

Since $x + y = 525$, then $y = 525 - x = 525 - 215 = 310$. So 215 nondiscounted tickets and 310 senior discount tickets were sold. ■

3 Identify Inconsistent Systems of Equations Containing Two Variables

The previous examples dealt with consistent systems of equations that had a single solution. The next two examples deal with two other possibilities that may occur, the first being a system that has no solution.

EXAMPLE 7 An Inconsistent System of Linear Equations

Solve: $\begin{cases} 2x + y = 5 & (1) \\ 4x + 2y = 8 & (2) \end{cases}$

Solution We choose to use the method of substitution and solve equation (1) for y.

$$2x + y = 5 \quad (1)$$
$$y = -2x + 5 \quad \text{Subtract } 2x \text{ from each side.}$$

Now substitute $-2x + 5$ for y in equation (2) and solve for x.

$$4x + 2y = 8 \quad (2)$$
$$4x + 2(-2x + 5) = 8 \quad \text{Substitute } y = -2x + 5 \text{ in (2).}$$
$$4x - 4x + 10 = 8 \quad \text{Remove parentheses.}$$
$$0 = -2 \quad \text{Subtract 10 from both sides.}$$

This statement is false. We conclude that the system has no solution and is therefore inconsistent. ■

Figure 3

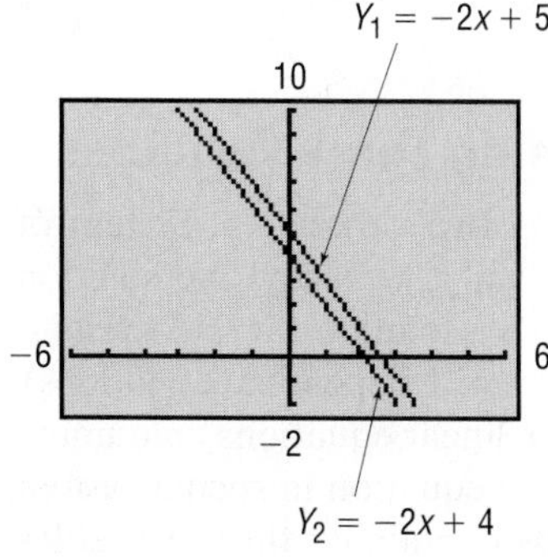

Figure 3 illustrates the pair of lines whose equations form the system in Example 7. Notice that the graphs of the two equations are lines, each with slope -2; one has a y-intercept of 5, the other a y-intercept of 4. The lines are parallel and have no point of intersection. This geometric statement is equivalent to the algebraic statement that the system has no solution.

4 Express the Solution of a System of Dependent Equations Containing Two Variables

EXAMPLE 8 Solving a System of Dependent Equations

Solve: $\begin{cases} 2x + y = 4 & (1) \\ -6x - 3y = -12 & (2) \end{cases}$

Solution We choose to use the method of elimination.

$$\begin{cases} 2x + y = 4 & (1) \\ -6x - 3y = -12 & (2) \end{cases}$$

$$\begin{cases} 6x + 3y = 12 & (1) \quad \text{Multiply each side of equation (1) by 3.} \\ -6x - 3y = -12 & (2) \end{cases}$$

$$0 = 0 \quad \text{Add equations (1) and (2).}$$

The statement $0 = 0$ is true. This means the equation $6x + 3y = 12$ is equivalent to $-6x - 3y = -12$. Therefore, the original system is equivalent to a system containing one equation, so the equations are dependent. This means that any values of x and y that satisfy $6x + 3y = 12$ or, equivalently, $2x + y = 4$ are solutions. For example, $x = 2$, $y = 0$; $x = 0$, $y = 4$; $x = -2$, $y = 8$; $x = 4$, $y = -4$; and so on, are solutions. There are, in fact, infinitely many values of x and y for which $2x + y = 4$, so the original system has infinitely many solutions. We will write the solution of the original system either as

$$y = -2x + 4 \quad \text{where } x \text{ can be any real number}$$

or as

$$x = -\frac{1}{2}y + 2 \quad \text{where } y \text{ can be any real number.}$$

We can also express the solution as $\{(x, y) \mid y = -2x + 4, x \text{ is any real number}\}$ or as $\left\{(x, y) \middle| x = -\frac{1}{2}y + 2, y \text{ is any real number}\right\}$. ■

Figure 4

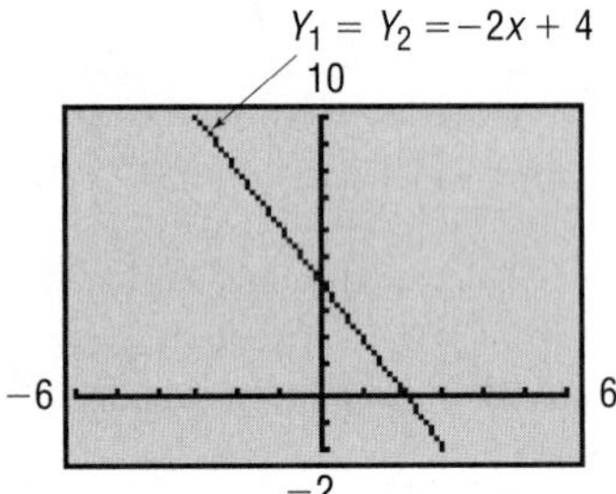

Figure 4 illustrates the situation presented in Example 8. Notice that the graphs of the two equations are lines, each with slope -2 and each with y-intercept 4. The lines are coincident. Notice also that equation (2) in the original system is -3 times equation (1), indicating that the two equations are dependent.

For the system in Example 8, we can write down some of the infinite number of solutions by assigning values to x and then finding $y = -2x + 4$.

If $x = -1$, then $y = -2(-1) + 4 = 6$.
If $x = 0$, then $y = 4$.
If $x = 2$, then $y = 0$.

The ordered pairs $(-1, 6)$, $(0, 4)$, and $(2, 0)$ are three of the points on the line in Figure 4.

Now Work PROBLEMS 25 AND 29

5 Solve Systems of Three Equations Containing Three Variables

Just as with a system of two linear equations containing two variables, a system of three linear equations containing three variables has either (1) exactly one solution (a consistent system with independent equations), or (2) no solution (an inconsistent system), or (3) infinitely many solutions (a consistent system with dependent equations).

We can view the problem of solving a system of three linear equations containing three variables as a geometry problem. The graph of each equation in such a system is a plane in space. A system of three linear equations containing three variables represents three planes in space. Figure 5 illustrates some of the possibilities.

Figure 5

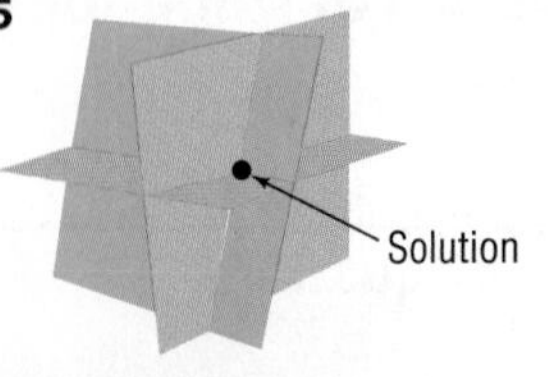

(a) Consistent system; one solution

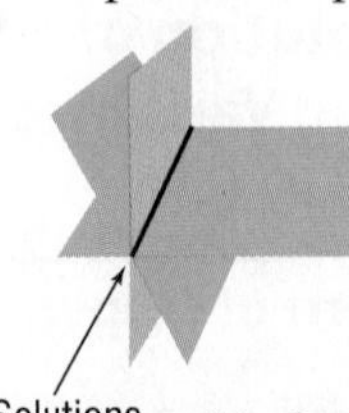

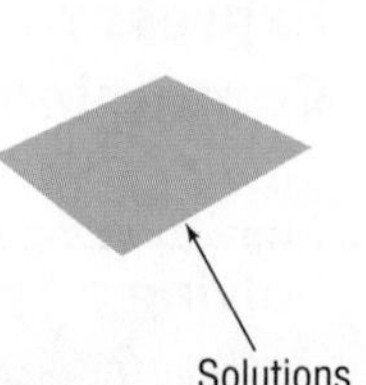

(b) Consistent system; infinite number of solutions

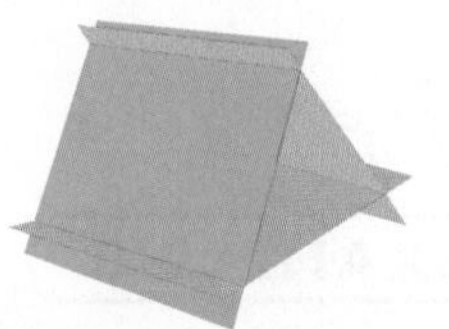

(c) Inconsistent system; no solution

Recall that a **solution** to a system of equations consists of values for the variables that are solutions of each equation of the system. For example, $x = 3$, $y = -1$, $z = -5$ or, using an ordered triplet, $(3, -1, -5)$ is a solution to the system of equations

$$\begin{cases} x + y + z = -3 & (1) \\ 2x - 3y + 6z = -21 & (2) \\ -3x + 5y = -14 & (3) \end{cases} \qquad \begin{aligned} &3 + (-1) + (-5) = -3 \\ &2(3) - 3(-1) + 6(-5) = 6 + 3 - 30 = -21 \\ &-3(3) + 5(-1) = -9 - 5 = -14 \end{aligned}$$

because these values of the variables are solutions of each equation.

Typically, when solving a system of three linear equations containing three variables, we use the method of elimination. Recall that the idea behind the method of elimination is to form equivalent equations so that adding two of the equations eliminates a variable.

EXAMPLE 9 Solving a System of Three Linear Equations with Three Variables

Use the method of elimination to solve the system of equations.

$$\begin{cases} x + y - z = -1 & (1) \\ 4x - 3y + 2z = 16 & (2) \\ 2x - 2y - 3z = 5 & (3) \end{cases}$$

Solution For a system of three equations, we attempt to eliminate one variable at a time, using pairs of equations until an equation with a single variable remains. Our strategy for solving this system is to use equation (1) to eliminate the variable x from equations (2) and (3). We can then treat the new equations (2) and (3) as a system with two unknowns. Alternatively, we could use equation (1) to eliminate either y or z from equations (2) and (3). Try one of these approaches for yourself.

Begin by multiplying each side of equation (1) by -4 and adding the result to equation (2). (Do you see why? The coefficients of x are now negatives of one another.) We also multiply equation (1) by -2 and add the result to equation (3). Notice that these two procedures result in the elimination of the variable x from equations (2) and (3).

$$\begin{aligned} x + y - z &= -1 \; (1) \\ 4x - 3y + 2z &= 16 \; (2) \end{aligned} \quad \text{Multiply by } -4. \quad \begin{aligned} -4x - 4y + 4z &= 4 \; (1) \\ 4x - 3y + 2z &= 16 \; (2) \\ \hline -7y + 6z &= 20 \quad \text{Add.} \end{aligned}$$

$$\begin{aligned} x + y - z &= -1 \; (1) \\ 2x - 2y - 3z &= 5 \; (3) \end{aligned} \quad \text{Multiply by } -2. \quad \begin{aligned} -2x - 2y + 2z &= 2 \; (1) \\ 2x - 2y - 3z &= 5 \; (3) \\ \hline -4y - z &= 7 \quad \text{Add.} \end{aligned}$$

$$\begin{cases} x + y - z = -1 & (1) \\ -7y + 6z = 20 & (2) \\ -4y - z = 7 & (3) \end{cases}$$

Now concentrate on the new equations (2) and (3), treating them as a system of two equations containing two variables. It is easier to eliminate z. Multiply each side of equation (3) by 6 and add equations (2) and (3). The result is the new equation (3).

$$\begin{aligned} -7y + 6z &= 20 \; (2) \\ -4y - z &= 7 \; (3) \end{aligned} \quad \text{Multiply by 6.} \quad \begin{aligned} -7y + 6z &= 20 \; (2) \\ -24y - 6z &= 42 \; (3) \\ \hline -31y &= 62 \quad \text{Add.} \end{aligned} \longrightarrow \begin{cases} x + y - z = -1 & (1) \\ -7y + 6z = 20 & (2) \\ -31y = 62 & (3) \end{cases}$$

Now solve equation (3) for y by dividing both sides of the equation by -31.

$$\begin{cases} x + y - z = -1 & (1) \\ -7y + 6z = 20 & (2) \\ y = -2 & (3) \end{cases}$$

Back-substitute $y = -2$ in equation (2) and solve for z.

$$\begin{aligned} -7y + 6z &= 20 && \text{(2)} \\ -7(-2) + 6z &= 20 && \text{Substitute } y = -2 \text{ in (2).} \\ 6z &= 6 && \text{Subtract 14 from both sides of the equation.} \\ z &= 1 && \text{Divide both sides of the equation by 6.} \end{aligned}$$

Finally, back-substitute $y = -2$ and $z = 1$ in equation (1) and solve for x.

$$\begin{aligned} x + y - z &= -1 && \text{(1)} \\ x + (-2) - 1 &= -1 && \text{Substitute } y = -2 \text{ and } z = 1 \text{ in (1).} \\ x - 3 &= -1 && \text{Simplify.} \\ x &= 2 && \text{Add 3 to both sides.} \end{aligned}$$

The solution of the original system is $x = 2, y = -2, z = 1$ or, using an ordered triplet, $(2, -2, 1)$. You should check this solution. ■

Look back over the solution given in Example 9. Note the pattern of removing one of the variables from two of the equations, followed by solving this system of two equations and two unknowns. Although which variables to remove is your choice, the methodology remains the same for all systems.

Now Work PROBLEM 43

6 Identify Inconsistent Systems of Equations Containing Three Variables

EXAMPLE 10 **Identify an Inconsistent System of Linear Equations**

Solve: $\begin{cases} 2x + y - z = -2 & \text{(1)} \\ x + 2y - z = -9 & \text{(2)} \\ x - 4y + z = 1 & \text{(3)} \end{cases}$

Solution Our strategy is the same as in Example 9. However, in this system, it seems easiest to eliminate the variable z first. Do you see why?

Multiply each side of equation (1) by -1 and add the result to equation (2). Also, add equations (2) and (3).

$$\begin{aligned} 2x + y - z &= -2 \ \text{(1)} \ \text{Multiply by } -1. & -2x - y + z &= 2 \ \text{(1)} \\ x + 2y - z &= -9 \ \text{(2)} & x + 2y - z &= -9 \ \text{(2)} \\ & & \hline -x + y &= -7 \ \text{Add.} \end{aligned}$$

$$\begin{aligned} x + 2y - z &= -9 \ \text{(2)} \\ x - 4y + z &= 1 \ \text{(3)} \\ \hline 2x - 2y &= -8 \ \text{Add.} \end{aligned}$$

$$\begin{cases} 2x + y - z = -2 & \text{(1)} \\ -x + y = -7 & \text{(2)} \\ 2x - 2y = -8 & \text{(3)} \end{cases}$$

Now concentrate on the new equations (2) and (3), treating them as a system of two equations containing two variables. Multiply each side of equation (2) by 2 and add the result to equation (3).

$$\begin{aligned} -x + y &= -7 \ \text{(2)} \ \text{Multiply by 2.} & -2x + 2y &= -14 \ \text{(2)} \\ 2x - 2y &= -8 \ \text{(3)} & 2x - 2y &= -8 \ \text{(3)} \\ & & \hline 0 &= -22 \ \text{Add.} \end{aligned} \longrightarrow \begin{cases} 2x + y - z = -2 & \text{(1)} \\ -x + y = -7 & \text{(2)} \\ 0 = -22 & \text{(3)} \end{cases}$$

Equation (3) has no solution, so the system is inconsistent. ■

7 Express the Solution of a System of Dependent Equations Containing Three Variables

EXAMPLE 11 **Solving a System of Dependent Equations**

$$\text{Solve: } \begin{cases} x - 2y - z = 8 & (1) \\ 2x - 3y + z = 23 & (2) \\ 4x - 5y + 5z = 53 & (3) \end{cases}$$

Solution Our plan is to eliminate x from equations (2) and (3). Multiply each side of equation (1) by -2 and add the result to equation (2). Also, multiply each side of equation (1) by -4 and add the result to equation (3).

$$\begin{array}{ll} x - 2y - z = 8 \ (1) & \text{Multiply by } -2. \quad -2x + 4y + 2z = -16 \ (1) \\ 2x - 3y + z = 23 \ (2) & \qquad 2x - 3y + z = 23 \ (2) \\ & \qquad y + 3z = 7 \ \text{Add.} \end{array}$$

$$\begin{array}{ll} x - 2y - z = 8 \ (1) & \text{Multiply by } -4. \quad -4x + 8y + 4z = -32 \ (1) \\ 4x - 5y + 5z = 53 \ (3) & \qquad 4x - 5y + 5z = 53 \ (3) \\ & \qquad 3y + 9z = 21 \ \text{Add.} \end{array}$$

$$\begin{cases} x - 2y - z = 8 & (1) \\ y + 3z = 7 & (2) \\ 3y + 9z = 21 & (3) \end{cases}$$

Treat equations (2) and (3) as a system of two equations containing two variables, and eliminate the variable y by multiplying both sides of equation (2) by -3 and adding the result to equation (3).

$$\begin{array}{ll} y + 3z = 7 \ (2) & \text{Multiply by } -3. \quad -3y - 9z = -21 \\ 3y + 9z = 21 \ (3) & \qquad 3y + 9z = 21 \ \text{Add.} \\ & \qquad 0 = 0 \end{array} \qquad \begin{cases} x - 2y - z = 8 & (1) \\ y + 3z = 7 & (2) \\ 0 = 0 & (3) \end{cases}$$

The original system is equivalent to a system containing two equations, so the equations are dependent and the system has infinitely many solutions. If we solve equation (2) for y, we can express y in terms of z as $y = -3z + 7$. Substitute this expression into equation (1) to determine x in terms of z.

$$\begin{aligned} x - 2y - z &= 8 && (1) \\ x - 2(-3z + 7) - z &= 8 && \text{Substitute } y = -3z + 7 \text{ in (1).} \\ x + 6z - 14 - z &= 8 && \text{Remove parentheses.} \\ x + 5z &= 22 && \text{Combine like terms.} \\ x &= -5z + 22 && \text{Solve for } x. \end{aligned}$$

We write the solution to the system as

$$\begin{cases} x = -5z + 22 \\ y = -3z + 7 \end{cases} \quad \text{where } z \text{ can be any real number.}$$

This way of writing the solution makes it easier to find specific solutions of the system. To find specific solutions, choose any value of z and use the equations $x = -5z + 22$ and $y = -3z + 7$ to determine x and y. For example, if $z = 0$, then $x = 22$ and $y = 7$, and if $z = 1$, then $x = 17$ and $y = 4$.

Using ordered triplets, the solution is

$$\{(x, y, z) \mid x = -5z + 22, y = -3z + 7, z \text{ is any real number}\}$$

■

Now Work PROBLEM 45

Two distinct points in the Cartesian plane determine a unique line. Given three noncollinear points, we can find the (unique) quadratic function whose graph contains these three points.

EXAMPLE 12 **Curve Fitting**

Find real numbers a, b, and c so that the graph of the quadratic function $y = ax^2 + bx + c$ contains the points $(-1, -4)$, $(1, 6)$, and $(3, 0)$.

Solution We require that the three points satisfy the equation $y = ax^2 + bx + c$.

For the point $(-1, -4)$ we have: $-4 = a(-1)^2 + b(-1) + c \quad -4 = a - b + c$

For the point $(1, 6)$ we have: $6 = a(1)^2 + b(1) + c \quad 6 = a + b + c$

For the point $(3, 0)$ we have: $0 = a(3)^2 + b(3) + c \quad 0 = 9a + 3b + c$

Figure 6

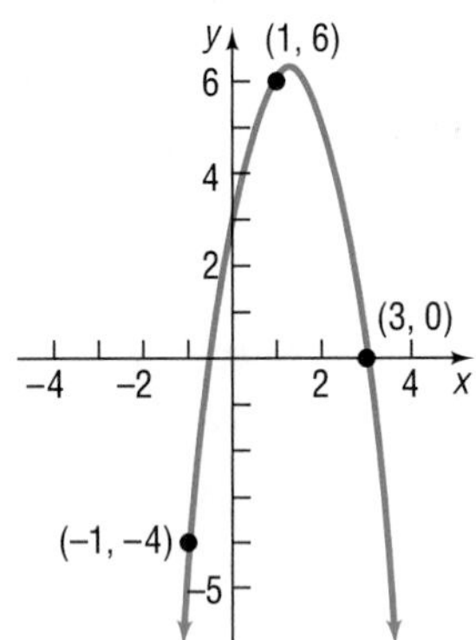

We wish to determine a, b, and c so that each equation is satisfied. That is, we want to solve the following system of three equations containing three variables:

$$\begin{cases} a - b + c = -4 & (1) \\ a + b + c = 6 & (2) \\ 9a + 3b + c = 0 & (3) \end{cases}$$

Solving this system of equations, we obtain $a = -2$, $b = 5$, and $c = 3$. So the quadratic function whose graph contains the points $(-1, -4)$, $(1, 6)$, and $(3, 0)$ is

$$y = -2x^2 + 5x + 3 \quad y = ax^2 + bx + c,\ a = -2, b = 5, c = 3$$

Figure 6 shows the graph of the function along with the three points. ■

Now Work PROBLEM 69

13.1 Assess Your Understanding

'Are You Prepared?' *Answers are given at the end of these exercises. If you get a wrong answer, read the pages listed in red.*

1. Solve the equation: $3x + 4 = 8 - x$.

2. (a) Graph the line: $3x + 4y = 12$.

(b) What is the slope of a line parallel to this line? (pp. 537–539)

Concepts and Vocabulary

3. If a system of equations has no solution, it is said to be ________.

4. If a system of equations has one solution, the system is ________ and the equations are ________.

5. If the solution to a system of two linear equations containing two unknowns is $x = 3, y = -2$, then the lines intersect at the point ______.

6. If the lines that make up a system of two linear equations are coincident, then the system is ________ and the equations are ________.

Skill Building

In Problems 7–16, verify that the values of the variables listed are solutions of the system of equations.

7. $\begin{cases} 2x - y = 5 \\ 5x + 2y = 8 \end{cases}$ $x = 2, y = -1;\ (2, -1)$

8. $\begin{cases} 3x + 2y = 2 \\ x - 7y = -30 \end{cases}$ $x = -2, y = 4;\ (-2, 4)$

9. $\begin{cases} 3x - 4y = 4 \\ \frac{1}{2}x - 3y = -\frac{1}{2} \end{cases}$ $x = 2, y = \frac{1}{2};\ \left(2, \frac{1}{2}\right)$

10. $\begin{cases} 2x + \frac{1}{2}y = 0 \\ 3x - 4y = -\frac{19}{2} \end{cases}$ $x = -\frac{1}{2}, y = 2;\ \left(-\frac{1}{2}, 2\right)$

11. $\begin{cases} x - y = 3 \\ \frac{1}{2}x + y = 3 \end{cases}$ $x = 4, y = 1;\ (4, 1)$

12. $\begin{cases} x - y = 3 \\ -3x + y = 1 \end{cases}$ $x = -2, y = -5;\ (-2, -5)$

13. $\begin{cases} 3x + 3y + 2z = 4 \\ x - y - z = 0 \\ 2y - 3z = -8 \end{cases}$ $x = 1, y = -1, z = 2;\ (1, -1, 2)$

14. $\begin{cases} 4x - z = 7 \\ 8x + 5y - z = 0 \\ -x - y + 5z = 6 \end{cases}$ $x = 2, y = -3, z = 1;\ (2, -3, 1)$

15. $\begin{cases} 3x + 3y + 2z = 4 \\ x - 3y + z = 10 \\ 5x - 2y - 3z = 8 \end{cases}$
$x = 2, y = -2, z = 2; (2, -2, 2)$

16. $\begin{cases} 4x - 5z = 6 \\ 5y - z = -17 \\ -x - 6y + 5z = 24 \end{cases}$
$x = 4, y = -3, z = 2; (4, -3, 2)$

In Problems 17–54, solve each system of equations. If the system has no solution, say that it is inconsistent.

17. $\begin{cases} x + y = 8 \\ x - y = 4 \end{cases}$

18. $\begin{cases} x + 2y = -7 \\ x + y = -3 \end{cases}$

19. $\begin{cases} 5x - y = 21 \\ 2x + 3y = -12 \end{cases}$

20. $\begin{cases} x + 3y = 5 \\ 2x - 3y = -8 \end{cases}$

21. $\begin{cases} 3x = 24 \\ x + 2y = 0 \end{cases}$

22. $\begin{cases} 4x + 5y = -3 \\ -2y = -8 \end{cases}$

23. $\begin{cases} 3x - 6y = 2 \\ 5x + 4y = 1 \end{cases}$

24. $\begin{cases} 2x + 4y = \frac{2}{3} \\ 3x - 5y = -10 \end{cases}$

25. $\begin{cases} 2x + y = 1 \\ 4x + 2y = 3 \end{cases}$

26. $\begin{cases} x - y = 5 \\ -3x + 3y = 2 \end{cases}$

27. $\begin{cases} 2x - y = 0 \\ 4x + 2y = 12 \end{cases}$

28. $\begin{cases} 3x + 3y = -1 \\ 4x + y = \frac{8}{3} \end{cases}$

29. $\begin{cases} x + 2y = 4 \\ 2x + 4y = 8 \end{cases}$

30. $\begin{cases} 3x - y = 7 \\ 9x - 3y = 21 \end{cases}$

31. $\begin{cases} 2x - 3y = -1 \\ 10x + y = 11 \end{cases}$

32. $\begin{cases} 3x - 2y = 0 \\ 5x + 10y = 4 \end{cases}$

33. $\begin{cases} 2x + 3y = 6 \\ x - y = \frac{1}{2} \end{cases}$

34. $\begin{cases} \frac{1}{2}x + y = -2 \\ x - 2y = 8 \end{cases}$

35. $\begin{cases} \frac{1}{2}x + \frac{1}{3}y = 3 \\ \frac{1}{4}x - \frac{2}{3}y = -1 \end{cases}$

36. $\begin{cases} \frac{1}{3}x - \frac{3}{2}y = -5 \\ \frac{3}{4}x + \frac{1}{3}y = 11 \end{cases}$

37. $\begin{cases} 3x - 5y = 3 \\ 15x + 5y = 21 \end{cases}$

38. $\begin{cases} 2x - y = -1 \\ x + \frac{1}{2}y = \frac{3}{2} \end{cases}$

39. $\begin{cases} \frac{1}{x} + \frac{1}{y} = 8 \\ \frac{3}{x} - \frac{5}{y} = 0 \end{cases}$

40. $\begin{cases} \frac{4}{x} - \frac{3}{y} = 0 \\ \frac{6}{x} + \frac{3}{2y} = 2 \end{cases}$

[**Hint**: Let $u = \frac{1}{x}$ and $v = \frac{1}{y}$, and solve for u and v. Then $x = \frac{1}{u}$ and $y = \frac{1}{v}$.]

41. $\begin{cases} x - y = 6 \\ 2x - 3z = 16 \\ 2y + z = 4 \end{cases}$

42. $\begin{cases} 2x + y = -4 \\ -2y + 4z = 0 \\ 3x - 2z = -11 \end{cases}$

43. $\begin{cases} x - 2y + 3z = 7 \\ 2x + y + z = 4 \\ -3x + 2y - 2z = -10 \end{cases}$

44. $\begin{cases} 2x + y - 3z = 0 \\ -2x + 2y + z = -7 \\ 3x - 4y - 3z = 7 \end{cases}$

45. $\begin{cases} x - y - z = 1 \\ 2x + 3y + z = 2 \\ 3x + 2y = 0 \end{cases}$

46. $\begin{cases} 2x - 3y - z = 0 \\ -x + 2y + z = 5 \\ 3x - 4y - z = 1 \end{cases}$

47. $\begin{cases} x - y - z = 1 \\ -x + 2y - 3z = -4 \\ 3x - 2y - 7z = 0 \end{cases}$

48. $\begin{cases} 2x - 3y - z = 0 \\ 3x + 2y + 2z = 2 \\ x + 5y + 3z = 2 \end{cases}$

49. $\begin{cases} 2x - 2y + 3z = 6 \\ 4x - 3y + 2z = 0 \\ -2x + 3y - 7z = 1 \end{cases}$

50. $\begin{cases} 3x - 2y + 2z = 6 \\ 7x - 3y + 2z = -1 \\ 2x - 3y + 4z = 0 \end{cases}$

51. $\begin{cases} x + y - z = 6 \\ 3x - 2y + z = -5 \\ x + 3y - 2z = 14 \end{cases}$

52. $\begin{cases} x - y + z = -4 \\ 2x - 3y + 4z = -15 \\ 5x + y - 2z = 12 \end{cases}$

53. $\begin{cases} x + 2y - z = -3 \\ 2x - 4y + z = -7 \\ -2x + 2y - 3z = 4 \end{cases}$

54. $\begin{cases} x + 4y - 3z = -8 \\ 3x - y + 3z = 12 \\ x + y + 6z = 1 \end{cases}$

Applications and Extensions

55. The perimeter of a rectangular floor is 90 feet. Find the dimensions of the floor if the length is twice the width.

56. The length of fence required to enclose a rectangular field is 3000 meters. What are the dimensions of the field if it is known that the difference between its length and width is 50 meters?

57. Orbital Launches In 2005 there was a total of 55 commercial and noncommercial orbital launches worldwide. In addition, the number of noncommercial orbital launches was one more than twice the number of commercial orbital launches. Determine the number of commercial and noncommercial orbital launches in 2005.

Source: Federal Aviation Administration

58. Movie Theater Tickets A movie theater charges \$9.00 for adults and \$7.00 for senior citizens. On a day when 325 people paid an admission, the total receipts were \$2495. How many who paid were adults? How many were seniors?

59. Mixing Nuts A store sells cashews for \$5.00 per pound and peanuts for \$1.50 per pound. The manager decides to mix 30 pounds of peanuts with some cashews and sell the mixture for \$3.00 per pound. How many pounds of cashews should be mixed with the peanuts so that the mixture will produce the same revenue as would selling the nuts separately?

60. Financial Planning A recently retired couple needs \$12,000 per year to supplement their Social Security. They have \$150,000 to invest to obtain this income. They have decided on two investment options: AA bonds yielding 10% per annum and a Bank Certificate yielding 5%.

(a) How much should be invested in each to realize exactly \$12,000?

(b) If, after 2 years, the couple requires \$14,000 per year in income, how should they reallocate their investment to achieve the new amount?

61. Computing Wind Speed With a tail wind, a small Piper aircraft can fly 600 miles in 3 hours. Against this same wind, the Piper can fly the same distance in 4 hours. Find the average wind speed and the average airspeed of the Piper.

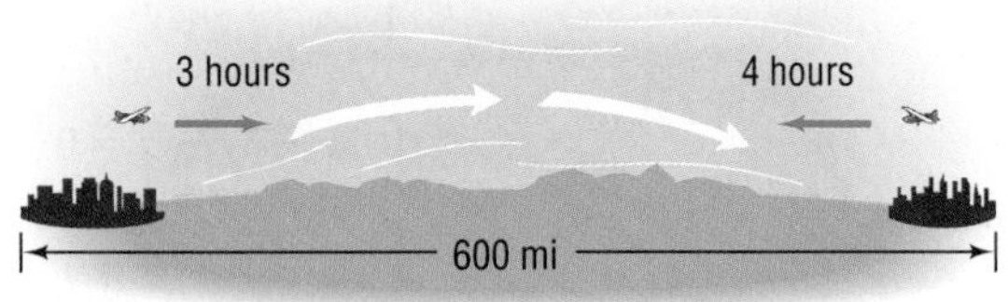

62. Computing Wind Speed The average airspeed of a single-engine aircraft is 150 miles per hour. If the aircraft flew the same distance in 2 hours with the wind as it flew in 3 hours against the wind, what was the wind speed?

63. Restaurant Management A restaurant manager wants to purchase 200 sets of dishes. One design costs \$25 per set, while another costs \$45 per set. If she only has \$7400 to spend, how many of each design should be ordered?

64. Cost of Fast Food One group of people purchased 10 hot dogs and 5 soft drinks at a cost of \$35.00. A second bought 7 hot dogs and 4 soft drinks at a cost of \$25.25. What is the cost of a single hot dog? A single soft drink?

65. Computing a Refund The grocery store we use does not mark prices on its goods. My wife went to this store, bought three 1-pound packages of bacon and two cartons of eggs, and paid a total of \$13.45. Not knowing that she went to the store, I also went to the same store, purchased two 1-pound packages of bacon and three cartons of eggs, and paid a total of \$11.45. Now we want to return two 1-pound packages of bacon and two cartons of eggs. How much will be refunded?

66. Finding the Current of a Stream Pamela requires 3 hours to swim 15 miles downstream on the Illinois River. The return trip upstream takes 5 hours. Find Pamela's average speed in still water. How fast is the current? (Assume that Pamela's speed is the same in each direction.)

67. Pharmacy A doctor's prescription calls for a daily intake containing 40 milligrams (mg) of vitamin C and 30 mg of vitamin D. Your pharmacy stocks two liquids that can be used: one contains 20% vitamin C and 30% vitamin D, the other 40% vitamin C and 20% vitamin D. How many milligrams of each compound should be mixed to fill the prescription?

68. Pharmacy A doctor's prescription calls for the creation of pills that contain 12 units of vitamin B_{12} and 12 units of vitamin E. Your pharmacy stocks two powders that can be used to make these pills: one contains 20% vitamin B_{12} and 30% vitamin E, the other 40% vitamin B_{12} and 20% vitamin E. How many units of each powder should be mixed in each pill?

69. Curve Fitting Find real numbers a, b, and c so that the graph of the function $y = ax^2 + bx + c$ contains the points $(-1, 4)$, $(2, 3)$, and $(0, 1)$.

70. Curve Fitting Find real numbers a, b, and c so that the graph of the function $y = ax^2 + bx + c$ contains the points $(-1, -2)$, $(1, -4)$, and $(2, 4)$.

71. IS–LM Model in Economics In economics, the IS curve is a linear equation that represents all combinations of income Y and interest rates r that maintain an equilibrium in the market for goods in the economy. The LM curve is a linear equation that represents all combinations of income Y and interest rates r that maintain an equilibrium in the market for money in the economy. In an economy, suppose that the equilibrium level of income (in millions of dollars) and interest rates satisfy the system of equations

$$\begin{cases} 0.06Y - 5000r = 240 \\ 0.06Y + 6000r = 900 \end{cases}$$

Find the equilibrium level of income and interest rates.

72. **IS–LM Model in Economics** In economics, the IS curve is a linear equation that represents all combinations of income Y and interest rates r that maintain an equilibrium in the market for goods in the economy. The LM curve is a linear equation that represents all combinations of income Y and interest rates r that maintain an equilibrium in the market for money in the economy. In an economy, suppose that the equilibrium level of income (in millions of dollars) and interest rates satisfy the system of equations

$$\begin{cases} 0.05Y - 1000r = 10 \\ 0.05Y + 800r = 100 \end{cases}$$

Find the equilibrium level of income and interest rates.

73. **Electricity: Kirchhoff's Rules** An application of Kirchhoff's Rules to the circuit shown below results in the following system of equations:

$$\begin{cases} I_2 = I_1 + I_3 \\ 5 - 3I_1 - 5I_2 = 0 \\ 10 - 5I_2 - 7I_3 = 0 \end{cases}$$

Find the currents I_1, I_2, and I_3.

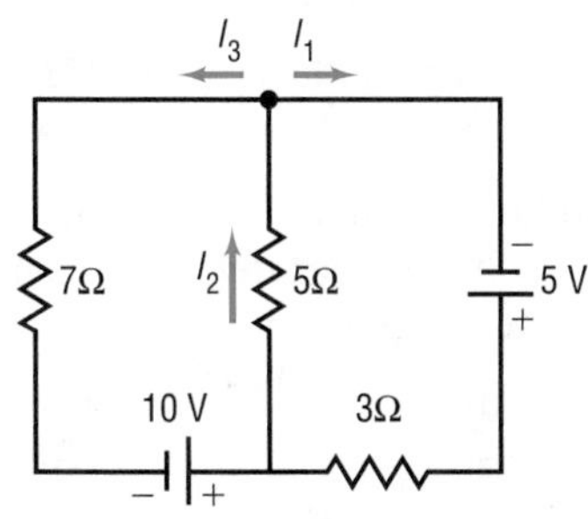

Source: Physics for Scientists & Engineers, 3rd ed., by Serway. © 1990 Brooks/Cole, a division of Thomson Learning.

74. **Electricity: Kirchhoff's Rules** An application of Kirchhoff's Rules to the circuit shown results in the following system of equations:

$$\begin{cases} I_3 = I_1 + I_2 \\ 8 = 4I_3 + 6I_2 \\ 8I_1 = 4 + 6I_2 \end{cases}$$

Find the currents I_1, I_2, and I_3.

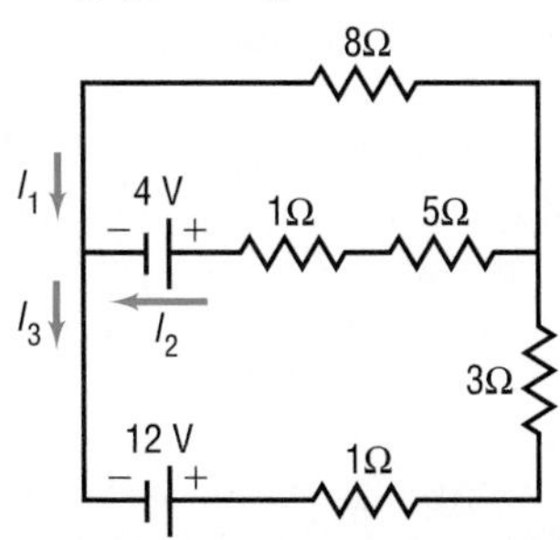

Source: Physics for Scientists & Engineers, 3rd ed., by Serway. © 1990 Brooks/Cole, a division of Thomson Learning.

75. **Theater Revenues** A Broadway theater has 500 seats, divided into orchestra, main, and balcony seating. Orchestra seats sell for \$50, main seats for \$35, and balcony seats for \$25. If all the seats are sold, the gross revenue to the theater is \$17,100. If all the main and balcony seats are sold, but only half the orchestra seats are sold, the gross revenue is \$14,600. How many are there of each kind of seat?

76. **Theater Revenues** A movie theater charges \$8.00 for adults, \$4.50 for children, and \$6.00 for senior citizens. One day the theater sold 405 tickets and collected \$2320 in receipts. Twice as many children's tickets were sold as adult tickets. How many adults, children, and senior citizens went to the theater that day?

77. **Nutrition** A dietitian wishes a patient to have a meal that has 66 grams (g) of protein, 94.5 g of carbohydrates, and 910 milligrams (mg) of calcium. The hospital food service tells the dietitian that the dinner for today is chicken, corn, and 2% milk. Each serving of chicken has 30 g of protein, 35 g of carbohydrates, and 200 mg of calcium. Each serving of corn has 3 g of protein, 16 g of carbohydrates, and 10 mg of calcium. Each glass of 2% milk has 9 g of protein, 13 g of carbohydrates, and 300 mg of calcium. How many servings of each food should the dietitian provide for the patient?

78. **Investments** Kelly has \$20,000 to invest. As her financial planner, you recommend that she diversify into three investments: Treasury bills that yield 5% simple interest, Treasury bonds that yield 7% simple interest, and corporate bonds that yield 10% simple interest. Kelly wishes to earn \$1390 per year in income. Also, Kelly wants her investment in Treasury bills to be \$3000 more than her investment in corporate bonds. How much money should Kelly place in each investment?

79. **Prices of Fast Food** One group of customers bought 8 deluxe hamburgers, 6 orders of large fries, and 6 large colas for \$26.10. A second group ordered 10 deluxe hamburgers, 6 large fries, and 8 large colas and paid \$31.60. Is there sufficient information to determine the price of each food item? If not, construct a table showing the various possibilities. Assume that the hamburgers cost between \$1.75 and \$2.25, the fries between \$0.75 and \$1.00, and the colas between \$0.60 and \$0.90.

80. **Prices of Fast Food** Use the information given in Problem 79. Suppose that a third group purchased 3 deluxe hamburgers, 2 large fries, and 4 large colas for \$10.95. Now is there sufficient information to determine the price of each food item? If so, determine each price.

81. **Painting a House** Three painters, Beth, Bill, and Edie, working together, can paint the exterior of a home in 10 hours (hr). Bill and Edie together have painted a similar house in 15 hr. One day, all three worked on this same kind of house for 4 hr, after which Edie left. Beth and Bill required 8 more hr to finish. Assuming no gain or loss in efficiency, how long should it take each person to complete such a job alone?

Explaining Concepts: Discussion and Writing

82. Make up a system of three linear equations containing three variables that has:
(a) No solution
(b) Exactly one solution
(c) Infinitely many solutions
Give the three systems to a friend to solve and critique.

83. Write a brief paragraph outlining your strategy for solving a system of two linear equations containing two variables.

84. Do you prefer the method of substitution or the method of elimination for solving a system of two linear equations containing two variables? Give reasons.

'Are You Prepared?' Answers

1. $\{1\}$ 2. (a)

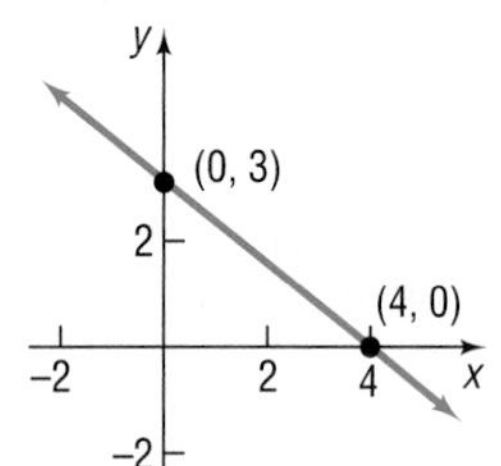

(b) $-\frac{3}{4}$

13.2 Systems of Linear Equations: Matrices

OBJECTIVES
1 Write the Augmented Matrix of a System of Linear Equations (p. 871)
2 Write the System of Equations from the Augmented Matrix (p. 872)
3 Perform Row Operations on a Matrix (p. 872)
4 Solve a System of Linear Equations Using Matrices (p. 873)

The systematic approach of the method of elimination for solving a system of linear equations provides another method of solution that involves a simplified notation.

Consider the following system of linear equations:

$$\begin{cases} x + 4y = 14 \\ 3x - 2y = 0 \end{cases}$$

If we choose not to write the symbols used for the variables, we can represent this system as

$$\left[\begin{array}{cc|c} 1 & 4 & 14 \\ 3 & -2 & 0 \end{array}\right]$$

where it is understood that the first column represents the coefficients of the variable x, the second column the coefficients of y, and the third column the constants on the right side of the equal signs. The vertical line serves as a reminder of the equal signs. The large square brackets are used to denote a *matrix* in algebra.

DEFINITION

A **matrix** is defined as a rectangular array of numbers,

$$\begin{array}{c} \\ \text{Row } 1 \\ \text{Row } 2 \\ \vdots \\ \text{Row } i \\ \vdots \\ \text{Row } m \end{array} \begin{array}{c} \begin{array}{ccccccc} \text{Column } 1 & \text{Column } 2 & & \text{Column } j & & \text{Column } n \end{array} \\ \begin{bmatrix} a_{11} & a_{12} & \cdots & a_{1j} & \cdots & a_{1n} \\ a_{21} & a_{22} & \cdots & a_{2j} & \cdots & a_{2n} \\ \vdots & \vdots & & \vdots & & \vdots \\ a_{i1} & a_{i2} & \cdots & a_{ij} & \cdots & a_{in} \\ \vdots & \vdots & & \vdots & & \vdots \\ a_{m1} & a_{m2} & \cdots & a_{mj} & \cdots & a_{mn} \end{bmatrix} \end{array} \quad (1)$$

Each number a_{ij} of the matrix has two indexes: the **row index** i and the **column index** j. The matrix shown in display (1) has m rows and n columns. The numbers a_{ij} are usually referred to as the **entries** of the matrix. For example, a_{23} refers to the entry in the second row, third column.

1 Write the Augmented Matrix of a System of Linear Equations

Now we will use matrix notation to represent a system of linear equations. The matrix used to represent a system of linear equations is called an **augmented matrix.** In writing the augmented matrix of a system, the variables of each equation must be on the left side of the equal sign and the constants on the right side. A variable that does not appear in an equation has a coefficient of 0.

EXAMPLE 1 Writing the Augmented Matrix of a System of Linear Equations

Write the augmented matrix of each system of equations.

(a) $\begin{cases} 3x - 4y = -6 & (1) \\ 2x - 3y = -5 & (2) \end{cases}$ (b) $\begin{cases} 2x - y + z = 0 & (1) \\ x + z - 1 = 0 & (2) \\ x + 2y - 8 = 0 & (3) \end{cases}$

Solution (a) The augmented matrix is

$$\left[\begin{array}{cc|c} 3 & -4 & -6 \\ 2 & -3 & -5 \end{array}\right]$$

(b) Care must be taken that the system be written so that the coefficients of all variables are present (if any variable is missing, its coefficient is 0). Also, all constants must be to the right of the equal sign. We need to rearrange the given system as follows:

$$\begin{cases} 2x - y + z = 0 & (1) \\ x + z - 1 = 0 & (2) \\ x + 2y - 8 = 0 & (3) \end{cases}$$

$$\begin{cases} 2x - y + z = 0 & (1) \\ x + 0 \cdot y + z = 1 & (2) \\ x + 2y + 0 \cdot z = 8 & (3) \end{cases}$$

The augmented matrix is

$$\left[\begin{array}{ccc|c} 2 & -1 & 1 & 0 \\ 1 & 0 & 1 & 1 \\ 1 & 2 & 0 & 8 \end{array}\right]$$

■

If we do not include the constants to the right of the equal sign, that is, to the right of the vertical bar in the augmented matrix of a system of equations, the resulting matrix is called the **coefficient matrix** of the system. For the systems discussed in Example 1, the coefficient matrices are

$$\begin{bmatrix} 3 & -4 \\ 2 & -3 \end{bmatrix} \text{ and } \begin{bmatrix} 2 & -1 & 1 \\ 1 & 0 & 1 \\ 1 & 2 & 0 \end{bmatrix}$$

Now Work PROBLEM 7

2 Write the System of Equations from the Augmented Matrix

EXAMPLE 2 **Writing the System of Linear Equations from the Augmented Matrix**

Write the system of linear equations corresponding to each augmented matrix.

(a) $\left[\begin{array}{cc|c} 5 & 2 & 13 \\ -3 & 1 & -10 \end{array}\right]$ (b) $\left[\begin{array}{ccc|c} 3 & -1 & -1 & 7 \\ 2 & 0 & 2 & 8 \\ 0 & 1 & 1 & 0 \end{array}\right]$

Solution (a) The matrix has two rows and so represents a system of two equations. The two columns to the left of the vertical bar indicate that the system has two variables. If x and y are used to denote these variables, the system of equations is

$$\begin{cases} 5x + 2y = 13 & (1) \\ -3x + y = -10 & (2) \end{cases}$$

(b) Since the augmented matrix has three rows, it represents a system of three equations. Since there are three columns to the left of the vertical bar, the system contains three variables. If x, y, and z are the three variables, the system of equations is

$$\begin{cases} 3x - y - z = 7 & (1) \\ 2x + 2z = 8 & (2) \\ y + z = 0 & (3) \end{cases}$$

■

3 Perform Row Operations on a Matrix

Row operations on a matrix are used to solve systems of equations when the system is written as an augmented matrix. There are three basic row operations.

Row Operations

1. Interchange any two rows.
2. Replace a row by a nonzero multiple of that row.
3. Replace a row by the sum of that row and a constant nonzero multiple of some other row.

These three row operations correspond to the three rules given earlier for obtaining an equivalent system of equations. When a row operation is performed on a matrix, the resulting matrix represents a system of equations equivalent to the system represented by the original matrix.

For example, consider the augmented matrix

$$\left[\begin{array}{cc|c} 1 & 2 & 3 \\ 4 & -1 & 2 \end{array}\right]$$

Suppose that we want to apply a row operation to this matrix that results in a matrix whose entry in row 2, column 1 is a 0. The row operation to use is

Multiply each entry in row 1 by -4 and add the result to the corresponding entries in row 2. **(2)**

If we use R_2 to represent the new entries in row 2 and r_1 and r_2 to represent the original entries in rows 1 and 2, respectively, we can represent the row operation in statement (2) by

$$R_2 = -4r_1 + r_2$$

Then

$$\left[\begin{array}{cc|c} 1 & 2 & 3 \\ 4 & -1 & 2 \end{array}\right] \underset{\substack{\uparrow \\ R_2 = -4r_1 + r_2}}{\rightarrow} \left[\begin{array}{cc|c} 1 & 2 & 3 \\ -4(1)+4 & -4(2)+(-1) & -4(3)+2 \end{array}\right] = \left[\begin{array}{cc|c} 1 & 2 & 3 \\ 0 & -9 & -10 \end{array}\right]$$

As desired, we now have the entry 0 in row 2, column 1.

EXAMPLE 3 Applying a Row Operation to an Augmented Matrix

Apply the row operation $R_2 = -3r_1 + r_2$ to the augmented matrix

$$\left[\begin{array}{cc|c} 1 & -2 & 2 \\ 3 & -5 & 9 \end{array}\right]$$

Solution The row operation $R_2 = -3r_1 + r_2$ tells us that the entries in row 2 are to be replaced by the entries obtained after multiplying each entry in row 1 by -3 and adding the result to the corresponding entries in row 2.

$$\left[\begin{array}{cc|c} 1 & -2 & 2 \\ 3 & -5 & 9 \end{array}\right] \underset{\substack{\uparrow \\ R_2 = -3r_1 + r_2}}{\rightarrow} \left[\begin{array}{cc|c} 1 & -2 & 2 \\ -3(1)+3 & (-3)(-2)+(-5) & -3(2)+9 \end{array}\right] = \left[\begin{array}{cc|c} 1 & -2 & 2 \\ 0 & 1 & 3 \end{array}\right]$$

■

Now Work PROBLEM 17

EXAMPLE 4 Finding a Particular Row Operation

Find a row operation that results in the augmented matrix

$$\left[\begin{array}{cc|c} 1 & -2 & 2 \\ 0 & 1 & 3 \end{array}\right]$$

having a 0 in row 1, column 2.

Solution We want a 0 in row 1, column 2. Because there is a 1 in row 2, column 2, this result can be accomplished by multiplying row 2 by 2 and adding the result to row 1. That is, we apply the row operation $R_1 = 2r_2 + r_1$.

$$\left[\begin{array}{cc|c} 1 & -2 & 2 \\ 0 & 1 & 3 \end{array}\right] \underset{\substack{\uparrow \\ R_1 = 2r_2 + r_1}}{\rightarrow} \left[\begin{array}{cc|c} 2(0)+1 & 2(1)+(-2) & 2(3)+2 \\ 0 & 1 & 3 \end{array}\right] = \left[\begin{array}{cc|c} 1 & 0 & 8 \\ 0 & 1 & 3 \end{array}\right]$$

■

A word about the notation introduced here. A row operation such as $R_1 = 2r_2 + r_1$ changes the entries in row 1. Note also that for this type of row operation we change the entries in a given row by multiplying the entries in some other row by an appropriate nonzero number and adding the results to the original entries of the row to be changed.

4 Solve a System of Linear Equations Using Matrices

To solve a system of linear equations using matrices, we use row operations on the augmented matrix of the system to obtain a matrix that is in *row echelon form*.

DEFINITION

A matrix is in **row echelon form** when the following conditions are met:

1. The entry in row 1, column 1 is a 1, and only 0's appear below it.
2. The first nonzero entry in each row after the first row is a 1, only 0's appear below it, and the 1 appears to the right of the first nonzero entry in any row above.
3. Any rows that contain all 0's to the left of the vertical bar appear at the bottom.

For example, for a system of three equations containing three variables, x, y, and z, with a unique solution, the augmented matrix is in row echelon form if it is of the form

$$\left[\begin{array}{ccc|c} 1 & a & b & d \\ 0 & 1 & c & e \\ 0 & 0 & 1 & f \end{array}\right]$$

where a, b, c, d, e, and f are real numbers. The last row of this augmented matrix states that $z = f$. We can then determine the value of y using back-substitution with $z = f$, since row 2 represents the equation $y + cz = e$. Finally, x is determined using back-substitution again.

Two advantages of solving a system of equations by writing the augmented matrix in row echelon form are the following:

1. The process is algorithmic; that is, it consists of repetitive steps that can be programmed on a computer.
2. The process works on any system of linear equations, no matter how many equations or variables are present.

The next example shows how to write a matrix in row echelon form.

EXAMPLE 5 **How to Solve a System of Linear Equations Using Matrices**

Solve: $\begin{cases} 2x + 2y = 6 & (1) \\ x + y + z = 1 & (2) \\ 3x + 4y - z = 13 & (3) \end{cases}$

Step-by-Step Solution

Step 1 Write the augmented matrix that represents the system.

Write the augmented matrix of the system.

$$\left[\begin{array}{ccc|c} 2 & 2 & 0 & 6 \\ 1 & 1 & 1 & 1 \\ 3 & 4 & -1 & 13 \end{array}\right]$$

Step 2 Perform row operations that result in the entry in row 1, column 1 becoming 1.

To get a 1 in row 1, column 1, interchange rows 1 and 2. [Note that this is equivalent to interchanging equations (1) and (2) of the system.]

$$\left[\begin{array}{ccc|c} 1 & 1 & 1 & 1 \\ 2 & 2 & 0 & 6 \\ 3 & 4 & -1 & 13 \end{array}\right]$$

Step 3 Perform row operations that leave the entry in row 1, column 1 a 1, while causing the entries in column 1 below row 1 to become 0's.

Next, we want a 0 in row 2, column 1 and a 0 in row 3, column 1. Use the row operations $R_2 = -2r_1 + r_2$ and $R_3 = -3r_1 + r_3$ to accomplish this. Notice that row 1 is unchanged using these row operations. Also, do you see that performing these row operations simultaneously is the same as doing one followed by the other?

$$\left[\begin{array}{ccc|c} 1 & 1 & 1 & 1 \\ 2 & 2 & 0 & 6 \\ 3 & 4 & -1 & 13 \end{array}\right] \rightarrow \left[\begin{array}{ccc|c} 1 & 1 & 1 & 1 \\ 0 & 0 & -2 & 4 \\ 0 & 1 & -4 & 10 \end{array}\right]$$

$R_2 = -2r_1 + r_2$
$R_3 = -3r_1 + r_3$

Step 4 Perform row operations that result in the entry in row 2, column 2 becoming 1 with 0's below it.

We want the entry in row 2, column 2 to be 1. We also want to have a 0 below the 1 in row 2, column 2. Interchanging rows 2 and 3 accomplishes both goals.

$$\left[\begin{array}{ccc|c} 1 & 1 & 1 & 1 \\ 0 & 0 & -2 & 4 \\ 0 & 1 & -4 & 10 \end{array}\right] \rightarrow \left[\begin{array}{ccc|c} 1 & 1 & 1 & 1 \\ 0 & 1 & -4 & 10 \\ 0 & 0 & -2 & 4 \end{array}\right]$$

Step 5 Repeat Step 4, placing a 1 in row 3, column 3.

To obtain a 1 in row 3, column 3, we use the row operation $R_3 = -\frac{1}{2}r_3$. The result is

$$\left[\begin{array}{ccc|c} 1 & 1 & 1 & 1 \\ 0 & 1 & -4 & 10 \\ 0 & 0 & -2 & 4 \end{array}\right] \underset{R_3 = -\frac{1}{2}r_3}{\rightarrow} \left[\begin{array}{ccc|c} 1 & 1 & 1 & 1 \\ 0 & 1 & -4 & 10 \\ 0 & 0 & 1 & -2 \end{array}\right]$$

Step 6 The matrix on the right in Step 5 is the row echelon form of the augmented matrix. Use back-substitution to solve the original system.

The third row of the augmented matrix represents the equation $z = -2$. Using $z = -2$, back-substitute into the equation $y - 4z = 10$ (from the second row) and obtain

$$\begin{aligned} y - 4z &= 10 \\ y - 4(-2) &= 10 \quad z = -2 \\ y &= 2 \quad \text{Solve for } y. \end{aligned}$$

Finally, back-substitute $y = 2$ and $z = -2$ into the equation $x + y + z = 1$ (from the first row) and obtain

$$\begin{aligned} x + y + z &= 1 \\ x + 2 + (-2) &= 1 \quad y = 2, z = -2 \\ x &= 1 \quad \text{Solve for } x. \end{aligned}$$

The solution of the system is $x = 1, y = 2, z = -2$ or, using an ordered triplet, $(1, 2, -2)$. ■

In Words

To obtain an augmented matrix in row echelon form:

- Add rows, exchange rows, or multiply a row by a nonzero constant.
- Work from top to bottom and left to right.
- Get 1's in the main diagonal with 0's below the 1's.
- Once the entry in row 1, column 1 is 1 with 0's below it, we do not use row 1 in our row operations. Once the entries in row 1, column 1 and row 2, column 2 are 1 with 0's below, we do not use rows 1 or 2 in our row operations (and so on).

Matrix Method for Solving a System of Linear Equations (Row Echelon Form)

STEP 1: Write the augmented matrix that represents the system.

STEP 2: Perform row operations that place the entry 1 in row 1, column 1.

STEP 3: Perform row operations that leave the entry 1 in row 1, column 1 unchanged, while causing 0's to appear below it in column 1.

STEP 4: Perform row operations that place the entry 1 in row 2, column 2, but leave the entries in columns to the left unchanged. If it is impossible to place a 1 in row 2, column 2, proceed to place a 1 in row 2, column 3. Once a 1 is in place, perform row operations to place 0's below it. (Place any rows that contain only 0's on the left side of the vertical bar, at the bottom of the matrix.)

STEP 5: Now repeat Step 4, placing a 1 in the next row, but one column to the right. Continue until the bottom row or the vertical bar is reached.

STEP 6: The matrix that results is the row echelon form of the augmented matrix. Analyze the system of equations corresponding to it to solve the original system.

EXAMPLE 6 **Solving a System of Linear Equations Using Matrices (Row Echelon Form)**

Solve: $\begin{cases} x - y + z = 8 & (1) \\ 2x + 3y - z = -2 & (2) \\ 3x - 2y - 9z = 9 & (3) \end{cases}$

Algebraic Solution

STEP 1: The augmented matrix of the system is

$$\left[\begin{array}{ccc|c} 1 & -1 & 1 & 8 \\ 2 & 3 & -1 & -2 \\ 3 & -2 & -9 & 9 \end{array}\right]$$

STEP 2: Because the entry 1 is already present in row 1, column 1, we can go to step 3.

STEP 3: Perform the row operations $R_2 = -2r_1 + r_2$ and $R_3 = -3r_1 + r_3$. Each of these leaves the entry 1 in row 1, column 1 unchanged, while causing 0's to appear under it.

$$\left[\begin{array}{ccc|c} 1 & -1 & 1 & 8 \\ 2 & 3 & -1 & -2 \\ 3 & -2 & -9 & 9 \end{array}\right] \rightarrow \left[\begin{array}{ccc|c} 1 & -1 & 1 & 8 \\ 0 & 5 & -3 & -18 \\ 0 & 1 & -12 & -15 \end{array}\right]$$

$R_2 = -2r_1 + r_2$
$R_3 = -3r_1 + r_3$

STEP 4: The easiest way to obtain the entry 1 in row 2, column 2 without altering column 1 is to interchange rows 2 and 3 (another way would be to multiply row 2 by $\frac{1}{5}$, but this introduces fractions).

$$\left[\begin{array}{ccc|c} 1 & -1 & 1 & 8 \\ 0 & 1 & -12 & -15 \\ 0 & 5 & -3 & -18 \end{array}\right]$$

To get a 0 under the 1 in row 2, column 2, perform the row operation $R_3 = -5r_2 + r_3$.

$$\left[\begin{array}{ccc|c} 1 & -1 & 1 & 8 \\ 0 & 1 & -12 & -15 \\ 0 & 5 & -3 & -18 \end{array}\right] \rightarrow \left[\begin{array}{ccc|c} 1 & -1 & 1 & 8 \\ 0 & 1 & -12 & -15 \\ 0 & 0 & 57 & 57 \end{array}\right]$$

$R_3 = -5r_2 + r_3$

STEP 5: Continuing, we obtain a 1 in row 3, column 3 by using $R_3 = \frac{1}{57}r_3$.

$$\left[\begin{array}{ccc|c} 1 & -1 & 1 & 8 \\ 0 & 1 & -12 & -15 \\ 0 & 0 & 57 & 57 \end{array}\right] \rightarrow \left[\begin{array}{ccc|c} 1 & -1 & 1 & 8 \\ 0 & 1 & -12 & -15 \\ 0 & 0 & 1 & 1 \end{array}\right]$$

$R_3 = \frac{1}{57}r_3$

STEP 6: The matrix on the right is the row echelon form of the augmented matrix. The system of equations represented by the matrix in row echelon form is

$$\begin{cases} x - y + \quad z = 8 & (1) \\ y - 12z = -15 & (2) \\ z = 1 & (3) \end{cases}$$

Using $z = 1$, we back-substitute to get

$$\begin{cases} x - y + \quad 1 = 8 & (1) \\ y - 12(1) = -15 & (2) \end{cases} \xrightarrow{\text{Simplify.}} \begin{cases} x - y = 7 & (1) \\ y = -3 & (2) \end{cases}$$

Graphing Solution

The augmented matrix of the system is

$$\left[\begin{array}{ccc|c} 1 & -1 & 1 & 8 \\ 2 & 3 & -1 & -2 \\ 3 & -2 & -9 & 9 \end{array}\right]$$

We enter this matrix into our graphing utility and name it A. See Figure 7(a). Using the REF (Row Echelon Form) command on matrix A, we obtain the results shown in Figure 7(b).

Figure 7

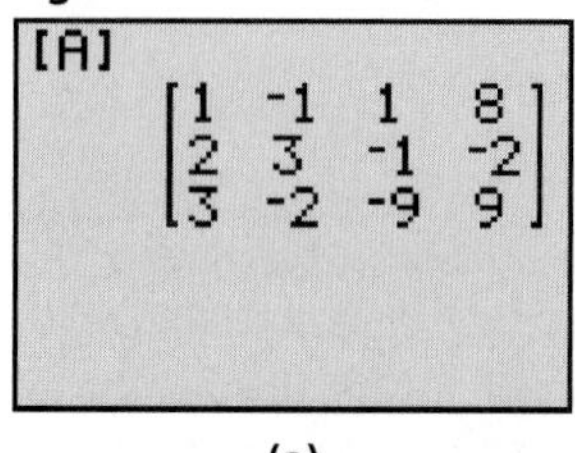

(a)

ref([A])▸Frac

$$\begin{bmatrix} 1 & -\frac{2}{3} & -3 & 3 \\ 0 & 1 & \frac{15}{13} & -\frac{24}{13} \\ 0 & 0 & 1 & 1 \end{bmatrix}$$

(b)

The system of equations represented by the matrix in row echelon form is

$$\begin{cases} x - \frac{2}{3}y - \quad 3z = 3 & (1) \\ y + \frac{15}{13}z = -\frac{24}{13} & (2) \\ z = 1 & (3) \end{cases}$$

Using $z = 1$, we back-substitute to get

$$\begin{cases} x - \frac{2}{3}y - 3(1) = 3 & (1) \\ y + \frac{15}{13}(1) = -\frac{24}{13} & (2) \end{cases}$$

$$\begin{cases} x - \frac{2}{3}y = 6 & (1) \\ y = -\frac{39}{13} = -3 & (2) \end{cases}$$

From the second equation we find that $y = -3$. Back-substituting $y = -3$ into $x - \frac{2}{3}y = 6$, we find that $x = 4$. The solution of the system is $x = 4$, $y = -3$, $z = 1$ or, using ordered triplets, $(4, -3, 1)$. ■

We get $y = -3$, and back-substituting into $x - y = 7$, we find that $x = 4$. The solution of the system is $x = 4, y = -3, z = 1$ or, using ordered triplets, $(4, -3, 1)$. ■

Notice that the row echelon form of the augmented matrix in the graphing solution differs from the row echelon form in the algebraic solution, yet both matrices provide the same solution! This is because the two solutions used different row operations to obtain the row echelon form. In all likelihood, the two solutions parted ways in Step 4 of the algebraic solution, where we avoided introducing fractions by interchanging rows 2 and 3.

Sometimes it is advantageous to write a matrix in **reduced row echelon form.** In this form, row operations are used to obtain entries that are 0 above (as well as below) the leading 1 in a row. For example, the row echelon form obtained in the algebraic solution to Example 6 is

$$\left[\begin{array}{ccc|c} 1 & -1 & 1 & 8 \\ 0 & 1 & -12 & -15 \\ 0 & 0 & 1 & 1 \end{array}\right]$$

To write this matrix in reduced row echelon form, we proceed as follows:

$$\left[\begin{array}{ccc|c} 1 & -1 & 1 & 8 \\ 0 & 1 & -12 & -15 \\ 0 & 0 & 1 & 1 \end{array}\right] \underset{R_1 = r_2 + r_1}{\rightarrow} \left[\begin{array}{ccc|c} 1 & 0 & -11 & -7 \\ 0 & 1 & -12 & -15 \\ 0 & 0 & 1 & 1 \end{array}\right] \underset{\substack{R_1 = 11r_3 + r_1 \\ R_2 = 12r_3 + r_2}}{\rightarrow} \left[\begin{array}{ccc|c} 1 & 0 & 0 & 4 \\ 0 & 1 & 0 & -3 \\ 0 & 0 & 1 & 1 \end{array}\right]$$

Figure 8

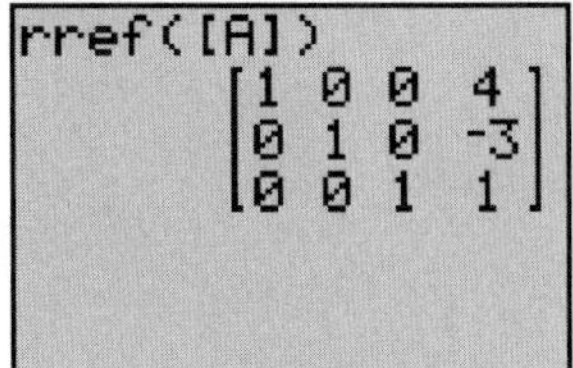

The matrix is now written in reduced row echelon form. The advantage of writing the matrix in this form is that the solution to the system, $x = 4$, $y = -3$, $z = 1$, is readily found, without the need to back-substitute. The methodology used to write a matrix in reduced row echelon form is called **Gauss–Jordan elimination.**

Most graphing utilities also have the ability to put a matrix in reduced row echelon form. Figure 8 shows the reduced row echelon form of the augmented matrix from Example 6 using the RREF command on a TI-84 Plus graphing calculator.

Now Work PROBLEMS 37 AND 47

The matrix method for solving a system of linear equations also identifies systems that have infinitely many solutions and systems that are inconsistent.

EXAMPLE 7 Solving a Dependent System of Linear Equations Using Matrices

Solve: $\begin{cases} 6x - y - z = 4 & (1) \\ -12x + 2y + 2z = -8 & (2) \\ 5x + y - z = 3 & (3) \end{cases}$

Solution Start with the augmented matrix of the system and proceed to obtain a 1 in row 1, column 1 with 0's below.

$$\left[\begin{array}{ccc|c} 6 & -1 & -1 & 4 \\ -12 & 2 & 2 & -8 \\ 5 & 1 & -1 & 3 \end{array}\right] \underset{R_1 = -1r_3 + r_1}{\rightarrow} \left[\begin{array}{ccc|c} 1 & -2 & 0 & 1 \\ -12 & 2 & 2 & -8 \\ 5 & 1 & -1 & 3 \end{array}\right] \underset{\substack{R_2 = 12r_1 + r_2 \\ R_3 = -5r_1 + r_3}}{\rightarrow} \left[\begin{array}{ccc|c} 1 & -2 & 0 & 1 \\ 0 & -22 & 2 & 4 \\ 0 & 11 & -1 & -2 \end{array}\right]$$

Obtaining a 1 in row 2, column 2 without altering column 1 can be accomplished by $R_2 = -\frac{1}{22}r_2$ or by $R_3 = \frac{1}{11}r_3$ and interchanging rows 2 and 3 or by $R_2 = \frac{23}{11}r_3 + r_2$. We shall use the first of these.

$$\left[\begin{array}{rrr|r} 1 & -2 & 0 & 1 \\ 0 & -22 & 2 & 4 \\ 0 & 11 & -1 & -2 \end{array}\right] \underset{R_2 = -\frac{1}{22}r_2}{\rightarrow} \left[\begin{array}{rrr|r} 1 & -2 & 0 & 1 \\ 0 & 1 & -\frac{1}{11} & -\frac{2}{11} \\ 0 & 11 & -1 & -2 \end{array}\right] \underset{R_3 = -11r_2 + r_3}{\rightarrow} \left[\begin{array}{rrr|r} 1 & -2 & 0 & 1 \\ 0 & 1 & -\frac{1}{11} & -\frac{2}{11} \\ 0 & 0 & 0 & 0 \end{array}\right]$$

This matrix is in row echelon form. Because the bottom row consists entirely of 0's, the system actually consists of only two equations.

$$\begin{cases} x - 2y = 1 & (1) \\ y - \frac{1}{11}z = -\frac{2}{11} & (2) \end{cases}$$

To make it easier to write down some of the solutions, we express both x and y in terms of z.

From the second equation, $y = \frac{1}{11}z - \frac{2}{11}$. Now back-substitute this solution for y into the first equation to get

$$x = 2y + 1 = 2\left(\frac{1}{11}z - \frac{2}{11}\right) + 1 = \frac{2}{11}z + \frac{7}{11}$$

The original system is equivalent to the system

$$\begin{cases} x = \frac{2}{11}z + \frac{7}{11} & (1) \\ y = \frac{1}{11}z - \frac{2}{11} & (2) \end{cases} \quad \text{where } z \text{ can be any real number.}$$

Let's look at the situation. The original system of three equations is equivalent to a system containing two equations. This means that any values of x, y, z that satisfy both

$$x = \frac{2}{11}z + \frac{7}{11} \quad \text{and} \quad y = \frac{1}{11}z - \frac{2}{11}$$

are solutions. For example, $z = 0, x = \frac{7}{11}, y = -\frac{2}{11}$; $z = 1, x = \frac{9}{11}, y = -\frac{1}{11}$; and $z = -1, x = \frac{5}{11}, y = -\frac{3}{11}$ are some of the solutions of the original system. There are, in fact, infinitely many values of x, y, and z for which the two equations are satisfied. That is, the original system has infinitely many solutions. We write the solution of the original system as

$$\begin{cases} x = \frac{2}{11}z + \frac{7}{11} \\ y = \frac{1}{11}z - \frac{2}{11} \end{cases} \quad \text{where } z \text{ can be any real number}$$

or, using ordered triplets, as

$$\left\{(x, y, z) \,\middle|\, x = \frac{2}{11}z + \frac{7}{11}, y = \frac{1}{11}z - \frac{2}{11}, z \text{ any real number}\right\}.$$

■

We can also find the solution by writing the augmented matrix in reduced row echelon form. Starting with the row echelon form, we have

$$\left[\begin{array}{ccc|c} 1 & -2 & 0 & 1 \\ 0 & 1 & -\frac{1}{11} & -\frac{2}{11} \\ 0 & 0 & 0 & 0 \end{array}\right] \rightarrow \left[\begin{array}{ccc|c} 1 & 0 & -\frac{2}{11} & \frac{7}{11} \\ 0 & 1 & -\frac{1}{11} & -\frac{2}{11} \\ 0 & 0 & 0 & 0 \end{array}\right]$$

$R_1 = 2r_2 + r_1$

The matrix on the right is in reduced row echelon form. The corresponding system of equations is

$$\begin{cases} x - \dfrac{2}{11}z = \dfrac{7}{11} & (1) \\ y - \dfrac{1}{11}z = -\dfrac{2}{11} & (2) \end{cases} \quad \text{where } z \text{ can be any real number}$$

or, equivalently,

$$\begin{cases} x = \dfrac{2}{11}z + \dfrac{7}{11} \\ y = \dfrac{1}{11}z - \dfrac{2}{11} \end{cases} \quad \text{where } z \text{ can be any real number}$$

Now Work PROBLEM 53

EXAMPLE 8 Solving an Inconsistent System of Linear Equations Using Matrices

Solve: $\begin{cases} x + y + z = 6 \\ 2x - y - z = 3 \\ x + 2y + 2z = 0 \end{cases}$

Solution Begin with the augmented matrix.

$$\left[\begin{array}{ccc|c} 1 & 1 & 1 & 6 \\ 2 & -1 & -1 & 3 \\ 1 & 2 & 2 & 0 \end{array}\right] \rightarrow \left[\begin{array}{ccc|c} 1 & 1 & 1 & 6 \\ 0 & -3 & -3 & -9 \\ 0 & 1 & 1 & -6 \end{array}\right] \rightarrow \left[\begin{array}{ccc|c} 1 & 1 & 1 & 6 \\ 0 & 1 & 1 & -6 \\ 0 & -3 & -3 & -9 \end{array}\right] \rightarrow \left[\begin{array}{ccc|c} 1 & 1 & 1 & 6 \\ 0 & 1 & 1 & -6 \\ 0 & 0 & 0 & -27 \end{array}\right]$$

$R_2 = -2r_1 + r_2$, $R_3 = -1r_1 + r_3$; Interchange rows 2 and 3.; $R_3 = 3r_2 + r_3$

This matrix is in row echelon form. The bottom row is equivalent to the equation

$$0x + 0y + 0z = -27$$

which has no solution. The original system is inconsistent. ■

Now Work PROBLEM 27

The matrix method is especially effective for systems of equations for which the number of equations and the number of variables are unequal. Here, too, such a system is either inconsistent or consistent. If it is consistent, it has either exactly one solution or infinitely many solutions.

EXAMPLE 9 Solving a System of Linear Equations Using Matrices

$$\text{Solve: } \begin{cases} x - 2y + z = 0 & (1) \\ 2x + 2y - 3z = -3 & (2) \\ y - z = -1 & (3) \\ -x + 4y + 2z = 13 & (4) \end{cases}$$

Solution Begin with the augmented matrix.

$$\left[\begin{array}{rrr|r} 1 & -2 & 1 & 0 \\ 2 & 2 & -3 & -3 \\ 0 & 1 & -1 & -1 \\ -1 & 4 & 2 & 13 \end{array}\right] \underset{\substack{R_2 = -2r_1 + r_2 \\ R_4 = r_1 + r_4}}{\rightarrow} \left[\begin{array}{rrr|r} 1 & -2 & 1 & 0 \\ 0 & 6 & -5 & -3 \\ 0 & 1 & -1 & -1 \\ 0 & 2 & 3 & 13 \end{array}\right] \underset{\text{Interchange rows 2 and 3.}}{\rightarrow} \left[\begin{array}{rrr|r} 1 & -2 & 1 & 0 \\ 0 & 1 & -1 & -1 \\ 0 & 6 & -5 & -3 \\ 0 & 2 & 3 & 13 \end{array}\right]$$

$$\underset{\substack{R_3 = -6r_2 + r_3 \\ R_4 = -2r_2 + r_4}}{\rightarrow} \left[\begin{array}{rrr|r} 1 & -2 & 1 & 0 \\ 0 & 1 & -1 & -1 \\ 0 & 0 & 1 & 3 \\ 0 & 0 & 5 & 15 \end{array}\right] \underset{R_4 = -5r_3 + r_4}{\rightarrow} \left[\begin{array}{rrr|r} 1 & -2 & 1 & 0 \\ 0 & 1 & -1 & -1 \\ 0 & 0 & 1 & 3 \\ 0 & 0 & 0 & 0 \end{array}\right]$$

We could stop here, since the matrix is in row echelon form, and back-substitute $z = 3$ to find x and y. Or we can continue and obtain the reduced row echelon form.

$$\left[\begin{array}{rrr|r} 1 & -2 & 1 & 0 \\ 0 & 1 & -1 & -1 \\ 0 & 0 & 1 & 3 \\ 0 & 0 & 0 & 0 \end{array}\right] \underset{R_1 = 2r_2 + r_1}{\rightarrow} \left[\begin{array}{rrr|r} 1 & 0 & -1 & -2 \\ 0 & 1 & -1 & -1 \\ 0 & 0 & 1 & 3 \\ 0 & 0 & 0 & 0 \end{array}\right] \underset{\substack{R_1 = r_3 + r_1 \\ R_2 = r_3 + r_2}}{\rightarrow} \left[\begin{array}{rrr|r} 1 & 0 & 0 & 1 \\ 0 & 1 & 0 & 2 \\ 0 & 0 & 1 & 3 \\ 0 & 0 & 0 & 0 \end{array}\right]$$

The matrix is now in reduced row echelon form, and we can see that the solution is $x = 1, y = 2, z = 3$ or, using an ordered triplet, $(1, 2, 3)$. ■

Now Work PROBLEM 69

EXAMPLE 10 Financial Planning

Adam and Michelle require an additional \$25,000 in annual income (beyond their pension benefits). They are rather risk averse and have narrowed their investment choices down to Treasury notes that yield 3%, Treasury bonds that yield 5%, or corporate bonds that yield 6%. If they have \$600,000 to invest and want the amount invested in Treasury notes to equal the total amount invested in Treasury bonds and corporate bonds, how much should be placed in each investment?

Solution Let n, b, and c represent the amounts invested in Treasury notes, Treasury bonds, and corporate bonds, respectively. There is a total of \$600,000 to invest, which means that the sum of the amounts invested in Treasury notes, Treasury bonds, and corporate bonds should equal \$600,000. The first equation is

$$n + b + c = 600{,}000 \quad (1)$$

If \$100,000 were invested in Treasury notes, the income would be $0.03(\$100{,}000) = \$3000$. In general, if n dollars were invested in Treasury notes, the income would be $0.03n$. Since the total income is to be \$25,000, the second equation is

$$0.03n + 0.05b + 0.06c = 25{,}000 \quad (2)$$

The amount invested in Treasury notes should equal the amount invested in Treasury bonds and corporate bonds, so the third equation is

$$n = b + c \quad \text{or} \quad n - b - c = 0 \quad (3)$$

We have the following system of equations:

$$\begin{cases} n + b + c = 600{,}000 & (1) \\ 0.03n + 0.05b + 0.06c = 25{,}000 & (2) \\ n - b - c = 0 & (3) \end{cases}$$

Begin with the augmented matrix and proceed as follows:

$$\left[\begin{array}{ccc|c} 1 & 1 & 1 & 600{,}000 \\ 0.03 & 0.05 & 0.06 & 25{,}000 \\ 1 & -1 & -1 & 0 \end{array}\right] \rightarrow \left[\begin{array}{ccc|c} 1 & 1 & 1 & 600{,}000 \\ 0 & 0.02 & 0.03 & 7000 \\ 0 & -2 & -2 & -600{,}000 \end{array}\right]$$

$R_2 = -0.03r_1 + r_2$
$R_3 = -r_1 + r_2$

$$\rightarrow \left[\begin{array}{ccc|c} 1 & 1 & 1 & 600{,}000 \\ 0 & 1 & 1.5 & 350{,}000 \\ 0 & -2 & -2 & -600{,}000 \end{array}\right] \rightarrow \left[\begin{array}{ccc|c} 1 & 1 & 1 & 600{,}000 \\ 0 & 1 & 1.5 & 350{,}000 \\ 0 & 0 & 1 & 100{,}000 \end{array}\right]$$

$R_2 = \dfrac{1}{0.02}r_2$ $\qquad$ $R_3 = 2r_2 + r_3$

The matrix is now in row echelon form. The final matrix represents the system

$$\begin{cases} n + b + c = 600{,}000 & (1) \\ b + 1.5c = 350{,}000 & (2) \\ c = 100{,}000 & (3) \end{cases}$$

From equation (3), we determine that Adam and Michelle should invest \$100,000 in corporate bonds. Back-substitute \$100,000 into equation (2) to find that $b = 200{,}000$, so Adam and Michelle should invest \$200,000 in Treasury bonds. Back-substitute these values into equation (1) and find that $n = 300{,}000$, so \$300,000 should be invested in Treasury notes. ■

13.2 Assess Your Understanding

Concepts and Vocabulary

1. An m by n rectangular array of numbers is called a(n) ______.

2. The matrix used to represent a system of linear equations is called a(n) ______ matrix.

3. The notation a_{35} refers to the entry in the ______ row and ______ column of a matrix.

4. ***True or False*** The matrix $\left[\begin{array}{cc|c} 1 & 3 & -2 \\ 0 & 1 & 5 \\ 0 & 0 & 0 \end{array}\right]$ is in row echelon form.

Skill Building

In Problems 5–16, write the augmented matrix of the given system of equations.

5. $\begin{cases} x - 5y = 5 \\ 4x + 3y = 6 \end{cases}$

6. $\begin{cases} 3x + 4y = 7 \\ 4x - 2y = 5 \end{cases}$

7. $\begin{cases} 2x + 3y - 6 = 0 \\ 4x - 6y + 2 = 0 \end{cases}$

8. $\begin{cases} 9x - y = 0 \\ 3x - y - 4 = 0 \end{cases}$

9. $\begin{cases} 0.01x - 0.03y = 0.06 \\ 0.13x + 0.10y = 0.20 \end{cases}$

10. $\begin{cases} \frac{4}{3}x - \frac{3}{2}y = \frac{3}{4} \\ -\frac{1}{4}x + \frac{1}{3}y = \frac{2}{3} \end{cases}$

11. $\begin{cases} x - y + z = 10 \\ 3x + 3y = 5 \\ x + y + 2z = 2 \end{cases}$

12. $\begin{cases} 5x - y - z = 0 \\ x + y = 5 \\ 2x - 3z = 2 \end{cases}$

13. $\begin{cases} x + y - z = 2 \\ 3x - 2y = 2 \\ 5x + 3y - z = 1 \end{cases}$

14. $\begin{cases} 2x + 3y - 4z = 0 \\ x - 5z + 2 = 0 \\ x + 2y - 3z = -2 \end{cases}$

15. $\begin{cases} x - y - z = 10 \\ 2x + y + 2z = -1 \\ -3x + 4y = 5 \\ 4x - 5y + z = 0 \end{cases}$

16. $\begin{cases} x - y + 2z - w = 5 \\ x + 3y - 4z + 2w = 2 \\ 3x - y - 5z - w = -1 \end{cases}$

In Problems 17–24, write the system of equations corresponding to each augmented matrix. Then perform the indicated row operation(s) on the given augmented matrix.

17. $\left[\begin{array}{cc|c} 1 & -3 & -2 \\ 2 & -5 & 5 \end{array}\right]$ $R_2 = -2r_1 + r_2$

18. $\left[\begin{array}{cc|c} 1 & -3 & -3 \\ 2 & -5 & -4 \end{array}\right]$ $R_2 = -2r_1 + r_2$

19. $\left[\begin{array}{ccc|c} 1 & -3 & 4 & 3 \\ 3 & -5 & 6 & 6 \\ -5 & 3 & 4 & 6 \end{array}\right]$ $R_2 = -3r_1 + r_2$, $R_3 = 5r_1 + r_3$

20. $\left[\begin{array}{ccc|c} 1 & -3 & 3 & -5 \\ -4 & -5 & -3 & -5 \\ -3 & -2 & 4 & 6 \end{array}\right]$ $R_2 = 4r_1 + r_2$, $R_3 = 3r_1 + r_3$

21. $\left[\begin{array}{ccc|c} 1 & -3 & 2 & -6 \\ 2 & -5 & 3 & -4 \\ -3 & -6 & 4 & 6 \end{array}\right]$ $R_2 = -2r_1 + r_2$, $R_3 = 3r_1 + r_3$

22. $\left[\begin{array}{ccc|c} 1 & -3 & -4 & -6 \\ 6 & -5 & 6 & -6 \\ -1 & 1 & 4 & 6 \end{array}\right]$ $R_2 = -6r_1 + r_2$, $R_3 = r_1 + r_3$

23. $\left[\begin{array}{ccc|c} 5 & -3 & 1 & -2 \\ 2 & -5 & 6 & -2 \\ -4 & 1 & 4 & 6 \end{array}\right]$ $R_1 = -2r_2 + r_1$, $R_3 = 2r_2 + r_3$

24. $\left[\begin{array}{ccc|c} 4 & -3 & -1 & 2 \\ 3 & -5 & 2 & 6 \\ -3 & -6 & 4 & 6 \end{array}\right]$ $R_1 = -r_2 + r_1$, $R_3 = r_2 + r_3$

In Problems 25–36, the reduced row echelon form of a system of linear equations is given. Write the system of equations corresponding to the given matrix. Use x, y; or x, y, z; or x_1, x_2, x_3, x_4 as variables. Determine whether the system is consistent or inconsistent. If it is consistent, give the solution.

25. $\left[\begin{array}{cc|c} 1 & 0 & 5 \\ 0 & 1 & -1 \end{array}\right]$

26. $\left[\begin{array}{cc|c} 1 & 0 & -4 \\ 0 & 1 & 0 \end{array}\right]$

27. $\left[\begin{array}{ccc|c} 1 & 0 & 0 & 1 \\ 0 & 1 & 0 & 2 \\ 0 & 0 & 0 & 3 \end{array}\right]$

28. $\left[\begin{array}{ccc|c} 1 & 0 & 0 & 0 \\ 0 & 1 & 0 & 0 \\ 0 & 0 & 0 & 2 \end{array}\right]$

29. $\left[\begin{array}{ccc|c} 1 & 0 & 2 & -1 \\ 0 & 1 & -4 & -2 \\ 0 & 0 & 0 & 0 \end{array}\right]$

30. $\left[\begin{array}{ccc|c} 1 & 0 & 4 & 4 \\ 0 & 1 & 3 & 2 \\ 0 & 0 & 0 & 0 \end{array}\right]$

31. $\left[\begin{array}{cccc|c} 1 & 0 & 0 & 0 & 1 \\ 0 & 1 & 0 & 1 & 2 \\ 0 & 0 & 1 & 2 & 3 \end{array}\right]$

32. $\left[\begin{array}{cccc|c} 1 & 0 & 0 & 0 & 1 \\ 0 & 1 & 0 & 2 & 2 \\ 0 & 0 & 1 & 3 & 0 \end{array}\right]$

33. $\left[\begin{array}{cccc|c} 1 & 0 & 0 & 4 & 2 \\ 0 & 1 & 1 & 3 & 3 \\ 0 & 0 & 0 & 0 & 0 \end{array}\right]$

34. $\left[\begin{array}{cccc|c} 1 & 0 & 0 & 0 & 1 \\ 0 & 1 & 0 & 0 & 2 \\ 0 & 0 & 1 & 2 & 3 \end{array}\right]$

35. $\left[\begin{array}{cccc|c} 1 & 0 & 0 & 1 & -2 \\ 0 & 1 & 0 & 2 & 2 \\ 0 & 0 & 1 & -1 & 0 \\ 0 & 0 & 0 & 0 & 0 \end{array}\right]$

36. $\left[\begin{array}{cccc|c} 1 & 0 & 0 & 0 & 1 \\ 0 & 1 & 0 & 0 & 2 \\ 0 & 0 & 1 & 0 & 3 \\ 0 & 0 & 0 & 1 & 0 \end{array}\right]$

In Problems 37–72, solve each system of equations using matrices (row operations). If the system has no solution, say that it is inconsistent.

37. $\begin{cases} x + y = 8 \\ x - y = 4 \end{cases}$

38. $\begin{cases} x + 2y = 5 \\ x + y = 3 \end{cases}$

39. $\begin{cases} 2x - 4y = -2 \\ 3x + 2y = 3 \end{cases}$

40. $\begin{cases} 3x + 3y = 3 \\ 4x + 2y = \frac{8}{3} \end{cases}$

41. $\begin{cases} x + 2y = 4 \\ 2x + 4y = 8 \end{cases}$

42. $\begin{cases} 3x - y = 7 \\ 9x - 3y = 21 \end{cases}$

43. $\begin{cases} 2x + 3y = 6 \\ x - y = \frac{1}{2} \end{cases}$

44. $\begin{cases} \frac{1}{2}x + y = -2 \\ x - 2y = 8 \end{cases}$

45. $\begin{cases} 3x - 5y = 3 \\ 15x + 5y = 21 \end{cases}$

46. $\begin{cases} 2x - y = -1 \\ x + \frac{1}{2}y = \frac{3}{2} \end{cases}$

47. $\begin{cases} x - y = 6 \\ 2x - 3z = 16 \\ 2y + z = 4 \end{cases}$

48. $\begin{cases} 2x + y = -4 \\ -2y + 4z = 0 \\ 3x - 2z = -11 \end{cases}$

49. $\begin{cases} x - 2y + 3z = 7 \\ 2x + y + z = 4 \\ -3x + 2y - 2z = -10 \end{cases}$

50. $\begin{cases} 2x + y - 3z = 0 \\ -2x + 2y + z = -7 \\ 3x - 4y - 3z = 7 \end{cases}$

51. $\begin{cases} 2x - 2y - 2z = 2 \\ 2x + 3y + z = 2 \\ 3x + 2y = 0 \end{cases}$

52. $\begin{cases} 2x - 3y - z = 0 \\ -x + 2y + z = 5 \\ 3x - 4y - z = 1 \end{cases}$

53. $\begin{cases} -x + y + z = -1 \\ -x + 2y - 3z = -4 \\ 3x - 2y - 7z = 0 \end{cases}$

54. $\begin{cases} 2x - 3y - z = 0 \\ 3x + 2y + 2z = 2 \\ x + 5y + 3z = 2 \end{cases}$

55. $\begin{cases} 2x - 2y + 3z = 6 \\ 4x - 3y + 2z = 0 \\ -2x + 3y - 7z = 1 \end{cases}$

56. $\begin{cases} 3x - 2y + 2z = 6 \\ 7x - 3y + 2z = -1 \\ 2x - 3y + 4z = 0 \end{cases}$

57. $\begin{cases} x + y - z = 6 \\ 3x - 2y + z = -5 \\ x + 3y - 2z = 14 \end{cases}$

58. $\begin{cases} x - y + z = -4 \\ 2x - 3y + 4z = -15 \\ 5x + y - 2z = 12 \end{cases}$

59. $\begin{cases} x + 2y - z = -3 \\ 2x - 4y + z = -7 \\ -2x + 2y - 3z = 4 \end{cases}$

60. $\begin{cases} x + 4y - 3z = -8 \\ 3x - y + 3z = 12 \\ x + y + 6z = 1 \end{cases}$

61. $\begin{cases} 3x + y - z = \frac{2}{3} \\ 2x - y + z = 1 \\ 4x + 2y = \frac{8}{3} \end{cases}$

62. $\begin{cases} x + y = 1 \\ 2x - y + z = 1 \\ x + 2y + z = \frac{8}{3} \end{cases}$

63. $\begin{cases} x + y + z + w = 4 \\ 2x - y + z = 0 \\ 3x + 2y + z - w = 6 \\ x - 2y - 2z + 2w = -1 \end{cases}$

64. $\begin{cases} x + y + z + w = 4 \\ -x + 2y + z = 0 \\ 2x + 3y + z - w = 6 \\ -2x + y - 2z + 2w = -1 \end{cases}$

65. $\begin{cases} x + 2y + z = 1 \\ 2x - y + 2z = 2 \\ 3x + y + 3z = 3 \end{cases}$

66. $\begin{cases} x + 2y - z = 3 \\ 2x - y + 2z = 6 \\ x - 3y + 3z = 4 \end{cases}$

67. $\begin{cases} x - y + z = 5 \\ 3x + 2y - 2z = 0 \end{cases}$

68. $\begin{cases} 2x + y - z = 4 \\ -x + y + 3z = 1 \end{cases}$

69. $\begin{cases} 2x + 3y - z = 3 \\ x - y - z = 0 \\ -x + y + z = 0 \\ x + y + 3z = 5 \end{cases}$

70. $\begin{cases} x - 3y + z = 1 \\ 2x - y - 4z = 0 \\ x - 3y + 2z = 1 \\ x - 2y = 5 \end{cases}$

71. $\begin{cases} 4x + y + z - w = 4 \\ x - y + 2z + 3w = 3 \end{cases}$

72. $\begin{cases} -4x + y = 5 \\ 2x - y + z - w = 5 \\ z + w = 4 \end{cases}$

Applications and Extensions

73. **Curve Fitting** Find the function $y = ax^2 + bx + c$ whose graph contains the points $(1, 2)$, $(-2, -7)$, and $(2, -3)$.

74. **Curve Fitting** Find the function $y = ax^2 + bx + c$ whose graph contains the points $(1, -1)$, $(3, -1)$, and $(-2, 14)$.

75. **Curve Fitting** Find the function $f(x) = ax^3 + bx^2 + cx + d$ for which $f(-3) = -112, f(-1) = -2, f(1) = 4$, and $f(2) = 13$.

76. **Curve Fitting** Find the function $f(x) = ax^3 + bx^2 + cx + d$ for which $f(-2) = -10, f(-1) = 3, f(1) = 5$, and $f(3) = 15$.

77. **Nutrition** A dietitian at Palos Community Hospital wants a patient to have a meal that has 78 grams (g) of protein, 59 g of carbohydrates, and 75 milligrams (mg) of vitamin A. The hospital food service tells the dietitian that the dinner for today is salmon steak, baked eggs, and acorn squash. Each serving of salmon steak has 30 g of protein, 20 g of carbohydrates, and 2 mg of vitamin A. Each serving of baked eggs contains 15 g of protein, 2 g of carbohydrates, and 20 mg of vitamin A. Each serving of acorn squash contains 3 g of protein, 25 g of carbohydrates, and 32 mg of vitamin A. How many servings of each food should the dietitian provide for the patient?

78. **Nutrition** A dietitian at General Hospital wants a patient to have a meal that has 47 grams (g) of protein, 58 g of carbohydrates, and 630 milligrams (mg) of calcium. The hospital food service tells the dietitian that the dinner for today is pork chops, corn on the cob, and 2% milk. Each serving of pork chops has 23 g of protein, 0 g of carbohydrates, and 10 mg of calcium. Each serving of corn on the cob contains 3 g of protein, 16 g of carbohydrates, and 10 mg of calcium. Each glass of 2% milk contains 9 g of protein, 13 g of carbohydrates, and 300 mg of calcium. How many servings of each food should the dietitian provide for the patient?

79. **Financial Planning** Carletta has \$10,000 to invest. As her financial consultant, you recommend that she invest in Treasury bills that yield 6%, Treasury bonds that yield 7%, and corporate bonds that yield 8%. Carletta wants to have an annual income of \$680, and the amount invested in corporate bonds must be half that invested in Treasury bills. Find the amount in each investment.

80. **Landscaping** A landscape company is hired to plant trees in three new subdivisions. The company charges the developer for each tree planted, an hourly rate to plant the trees, and a fixed delivery charge. In one subdivision it took 166 labor hours to plant 250 trees for a cost of \$7520. In a second subdivision it took 124 labor hours to plant 200 trees for a cost of \$5945. In the final subdivision it took 200 labor hours to plant 300 trees for a cost of \$8985. Determine the cost for each tree, the hourly labor charge, and the fixed delivery charge.
Sources: www.bx.org

81. **Production** To manufacture an automobile requires painting, drying, and polishing. Epsilon Motor Company produces three types of cars: the Delta, the Beta, and the Sigma. Each Delta requires 10 hours (hr) for painting, 3 hr for drying, and 2 hr for polishing. A Beta requires 16 hr for painting, 5 hr for drying, and 3 hr for polishing, and a Sigma requires 8 hr for painting, 2 hr for drying, and 1 hr for polishing. If the company has 240 hr for painting, 69 hr for drying, and 41 hr for polishing per month, how many of each type of car are produced?

82. **Production** A Florida juice company completes the preparation of its products by sterilizing, filling, and labeling bottles. Each case of orange juice requires 9 minutes (min) for sterilizing, 6 min for filling, and 1 min for labeling. Each case of grapefruit juice requires 10 min for sterilizing, 4 min for filling, and 2 min for labeling. Each case of tomato juice requires 12 min for sterilizing, 4 min for filling, and 1 min for labeling. If the company runs the sterilizing machine for 398 min, the filling machine for 164 min, and the labeling machine for 58 min, how many cases of each type of juice are prepared?

83. **Electricity: Kirchhoff's Rules** An application of Kirchhoff's Rules to the circuit shown results in the following system of equations:

$$\begin{cases} -4 + 8 - 2I_2 = 0 \\ 8 = 5I_4 + I_1 \\ 4 = 3I_3 + I_1 \\ I_3 + I_4 = I_1 \end{cases}$$

Find the currents I_1, I_2, I_3, and I_4.

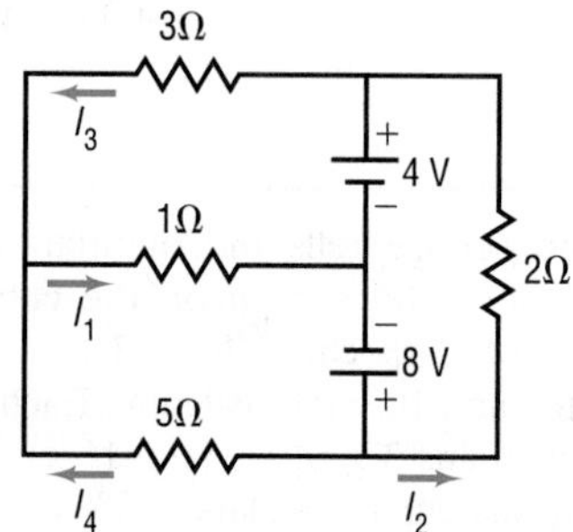

Source: Based on Raymond Serway. Physics, *3rd ed. (Philadelphia: Saunders, 1990), Prob. 34. p. 790.*

84. **Electricity: Kirchhoff's Rules** An application of Kirchhoff's Rules to the circuit shown results in the following system of equations:

$$\begin{cases} I_1 = I_3 + I_2 \\ 24 - 6I_1 - 3I_3 = 0 \\ 12 + 24 - 6I_1 - 6I_2 = 0 \end{cases}$$

Find the currents I_1, I_2, and I_3.

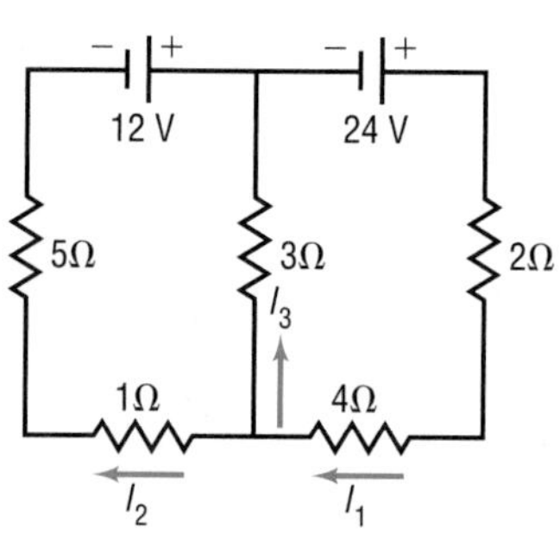

Source: Ibid., Prob. 38, p. 791.

85. **Financial Planning** Three retired couples each require an additional annual income of $2000 per year. As their financial consultant, you recommend that they invest some money in Treasury bills that yield 7%, some money in corporate bonds that yield 9%, and some money in junk bonds that yield 11%. Prepare a table for each couple showing the various ways that their goals can be achieved:
(a) If the first couple has $20,000 to invest.
(b) If the second couple has $25,000 to invest.
(c) If the third couple has $30,000 to invest.
(d) What advice would you give each couple regarding the amount to invest and the choices available?

[**Hint:** Higher yields generally carry more risk.]

86. **Financial Planning** A young couple has $25,000 to invest. As their financial consultant, you recommend that they invest some money in Treasury bills that yield 7%, some money in corporate bonds that yield 9%, and some money in junk bonds that yield 11%. Prepare a table showing the various ways that this couple can achieve the following goals:
(a) $1500 per year in income
(b) $2000 per year in income
(c) $2500 per year in income
(d) What advice would you give this couple regarding the income that they require and the choices available?

[**Hint:** Higher yields generally carry more risk.]

87. **Pharmacy** A doctor's prescription calls for a daily intake of a supplement containing 40 milligrams (mg) of vitamin C and 30 mg of vitamin D. Your pharmacy stocks three supplements that can be used: one contains 20% vitamin C and 30% vitamin D; a second, 40% vitamin C and 20% vitamin D; and a third, 30% vitamin C and 50% vitamin D. Create a table showing the possible combinations that could be used to fill the prescription.

88. **Pharmacy** A doctor's prescription calls for the creation of pills that contain 12 units of vitamin B_{12} and 12 units of vitamin E. Your pharmacy stocks three powders that can be used to make these pills: one contains 20% vitamin B_{12} and 30% vitamin E; a second, 40% vitamin B_{12} and 20% vitamin E; and a third, 30% vitamin B_{12} and 40% vitamin E. Create a table showing the possible combinations of each powder that could be mixed in each pill.

Explaining Concepts: Discussion and Writing

89. Write a brief paragraph or two that outlines your strategy for solving a system of linear equations using matrices.

90. When solving a system of linear equations using matrices, do you prefer to place the augmented matrix in row echelon form or in reduced row echelon form? Give reasons for your choice.

91. Make up a system of three linear equations containing three variables that has:
(a) No solution
(b) Exactly one solution
(c) Infinitely many solutions
Give the three systems to a friend to solve and critique.

13.3 Systems of Linear Equations: Determinants

OBJECTIVES
1 Evaluate 2 by 2 Determinants (p. 885)
2 Use Cramer's Rule to Solve a System of Two Equations Containing Two Variables (p. 886)
3 Evaluate 3 by 3 Determinants (p. 888)
4 Use Cramer's Rule to Solve a System of Three Equations Containing Three Variables (p. 890)
5 Know Properties of Determinants (p. 891)

In the preceding section, we described a method of using matrices to solve a system of linear equations. This section deals with yet another method for solving systems of linear equations; however, it can be used only when the number of equations equals the number of variables. Although the method works for any system (provided that the number of equations equals the number of variables), it is most often used for systems of two equations containing two variables or three equations containing three variables. This method, called *Cramer's Rule,* is based on the concept of a *determinant.*

1 Evaluate 2 by 2 Determinants

DEFINITION

If a, b, c, and d are four real numbers, the symbol

$$D = \begin{vmatrix} a & b \\ c & d \end{vmatrix}$$

is called a **2 by 2 determinant.** Its value is the number $ad - bc$; that is,

$$D = \begin{vmatrix} a & b \\ c & d \end{vmatrix} = ad - bc \quad \textbf{(1)}$$

The following device may be helpful for remembering the value of a 2 by 2 determinant:

$$\begin{vmatrix} a & b \\ c & d \end{vmatrix} = ad - bc$$

Minus

EXAMPLE 1 **Evaluating a 2 × 2 Determinant**

Evaluate: $\begin{vmatrix} 3 & -2 \\ 6 & 1 \end{vmatrix}$

Algebraic Solution

$$\begin{vmatrix} 3 & -2 \\ 6 & 1 \end{vmatrix} = (3)(1) - (-2)(6) = 3 - (-12) = 15$$

Graphing Solution

First, we enter the matrix whose entries are those of the determinant into the graphing utility and name it A. Using the determinant command, we obtain the result shown in Figure 9.

Figure 9

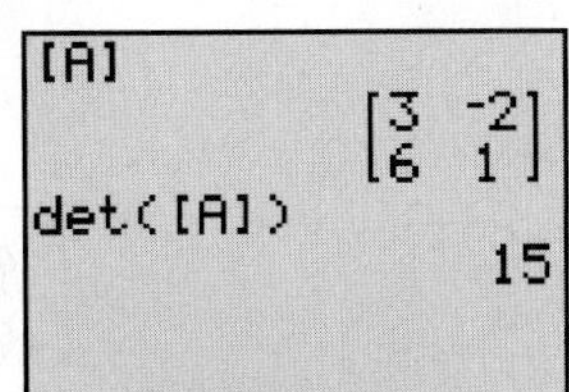

Now Work PROBLEM 7

2 Use Cramer's Rule to Solve a System of Two Equations Containing Two Variables

Let's see the role that a 2 by 2 determinant plays in the solution of a system of two equations containing two variables. Consider the system

$$\begin{cases} ax + by = s & (1) \\ cx + dy = t & (2) \end{cases} \qquad \textbf{(2)}$$

We use the method of elimination to solve this system.

Provided $d \neq 0$ and $b \neq 0$, this system is equivalent to the system

$$\begin{cases} adx + bdy = sd & (1) \quad \text{Multiply by } d. \\ bcx + bdy = tb & (2) \quad \text{Multiply by } b. \end{cases}$$

Subtract the second equation from the first equation and obtain

$$\begin{cases} (ad - bc)x + 0 \cdot y = sd - tb & (1) \\ bcx + bdy = tb & (2) \end{cases}$$

Now the first equation can be rewritten using determinant notation.

$$\begin{vmatrix} a & b \\ c & d \end{vmatrix} x = \begin{vmatrix} s & b \\ t & d \end{vmatrix}$$

If $D = \begin{vmatrix} a & b \\ c & d \end{vmatrix} = ad - bc \neq 0$, we can solve for x to get

$$x = \frac{\begin{vmatrix} s & b \\ t & d \end{vmatrix}}{\begin{vmatrix} a & b \\ c & d \end{vmatrix}} = \frac{\begin{vmatrix} s & b \\ t & d \end{vmatrix}}{D} \qquad \textbf{(3)}$$

Return now to the original system (2). Provided that $a \neq 0$ and $c \neq 0$, the system is equivalent to

$$\begin{cases} acx + bcy = cs & (1) \quad \text{Multiply by } c. \\ acx + ady = at & (2) \quad \text{Multiply by } a. \end{cases}$$

Subtract the first equation from the second equation and obtain

$$\begin{cases} acx + bcy = cs & (1) \\ 0 \cdot x + (ad - bc)y = at - cs & (2) \end{cases}$$

The second equation can now be rewritten using determinant notation.

$$\begin{vmatrix} a & b \\ c & d \end{vmatrix} y = \begin{vmatrix} a & s \\ c & t \end{vmatrix}$$

If $D = \begin{vmatrix} a & b \\ c & d \end{vmatrix} = ad - bc \neq 0$, we can solve for y to get

$$y = \frac{\begin{vmatrix} a & s \\ c & t \end{vmatrix}}{\begin{vmatrix} a & b \\ c & d \end{vmatrix}} = \frac{\begin{vmatrix} a & s \\ c & t \end{vmatrix}}{D} \qquad \textbf{(4)}$$

Equations (3) and (4) lead us to the following result, called **Cramer's Rule.**

THEOREM

Cramer's Rule for Two Equations Containing Two Variables

The solution to the system of equations

$$\begin{cases} ax + by = s & (1) \\ cx + dy = t & (2) \end{cases} \qquad (5)$$

is given by

$$x = \frac{\begin{vmatrix} s & b \\ t & d \end{vmatrix}}{\begin{vmatrix} a & b \\ c & d \end{vmatrix}} \qquad y = \frac{\begin{vmatrix} a & s \\ c & t \end{vmatrix}}{\begin{vmatrix} a & b \\ c & d \end{vmatrix}} \qquad (6)$$

provided that

$$D = \begin{vmatrix} a & b \\ c & d \end{vmatrix} = ad - bc \neq 0$$

In the derivation given for Cramer's Rule, we assumed that none of the numbers $a, b, c,$ and d was 0. In Problem 61 you will be asked to complete the proof under the less stringent condition that $D = ad - bc \neq 0$.

Now look carefully at the pattern in Cramer's Rule. The denominator in the solution (6) is the determinant of the coefficients of the variables.

$$\begin{cases} ax + by = s \\ cx + dy = t \end{cases} \qquad D = \begin{vmatrix} a & b \\ c & d \end{vmatrix}$$

In the solution for x, the numerator is the determinant, denoted by D_x, formed by replacing the entries in the first column (the coefficients of x) of D by the constants on the right side of the equal sign.

$$D_x = \begin{vmatrix} s & b \\ t & d \end{vmatrix}$$

In the solution for y, the numerator is the determinant, denoted by D_y, formed by replacing the entries in the second column (the coefficients of y) of D by the constants on the right side of the equal sign.

$$D_y = \begin{vmatrix} a & s \\ c & t \end{vmatrix}$$

Cramer's Rule then states that, if $D \neq 0$,

$$x = \frac{D_x}{D} \qquad y = \frac{D_y}{D} \qquad (7)$$

EXAMPLE 2 **Solving a System of Linear Equations Using Determinants**

Use Cramer's Rule, if applicable, to solve the system

$$\begin{cases} 3x - 2y = 4 & (1) \\ 6x + y = 13 & (2) \end{cases}$$

Algebraic Solution

The determinant D of the coefficients of the variables is

$$D = \begin{vmatrix} 3 & -2 \\ 6 & 1 \end{vmatrix} = (3)(1) - (-2)(6) = 15$$

Graphing Solution

We enter the coefficient matrix into our graphing utility. Call it A and evaluate $\det[A]$. Since $\det[A] \neq 0$, we can use Cramer's Rule. We enter the matrices D_x and D_y into our

Because $D \neq 0$, Cramer's Rule (7) can be used.

$$x = \frac{D_x}{D} = \frac{\begin{vmatrix} 4 & -2 \\ 13 & 1 \end{vmatrix}}{15} = \frac{(4)(1) - (-2)(13)}{15} = \frac{30}{15} = 2$$

$$y = \frac{D_y}{D} = \frac{\begin{vmatrix} 3 & 4 \\ 6 & 13 \end{vmatrix}}{15} = \frac{(3)(13) - (4)(6)}{15} = \frac{15}{15} = 1$$

graphing utility and call them B and C, respectively. Finally, we find x by calculating $\frac{\det[B]}{\det[A]}$ and y by calculating $\frac{\det[C]}{\det[A]}$. The results are shown in Figure 10.

Figure 10

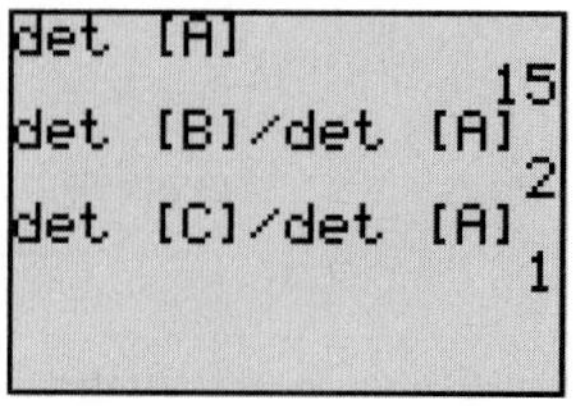

```
det [A]
                  15
det [B]/det [A]
                   2
det [C]/det [A]
                   1
```

The solution is $x = 2$, $y = 1$ or, using ordered pairs, $(2, 1)$. ■

In attempting to use Cramer's Rule, if the determinant D of the coefficients of the variables is found to equal 0 (so that Cramer's Rule is not applicable), then the system is either inconsistent or has infinitely many solutions.

Now Work PROBLEM 15

3 Evaluate 3 by 3 Determinants

To use Cramer's Rule to solve a system of three equations containing three variables, we need to define a 3 by 3 determinant.

A **3 by 3 determinant** is symbolized by

$$\begin{vmatrix} a_{11} & a_{12} & a_{13} \\ a_{21} & a_{22} & a_{23} \\ a_{31} & a_{32} & a_{33} \end{vmatrix} \tag{8}$$

in which $a_{11}, a_{12}, \ldots,$ are real numbers.

As with matrices, we use a double subscript to identify an entry by indicating its row and column numbers. For example, the entry a_{23} is in row 2, column 3.

The value of a 3 by 3 determinant may be defined in terms of 2 by 2 determinants by the following formula:

$$\begin{vmatrix} a_{11} & a_{12} & a_{13} \\ a_{21} & a_{22} & a_{23} \\ a_{31} & a_{32} & a_{33} \end{vmatrix} = a_{11}\begin{vmatrix} a_{22} & a_{23} \\ a_{32} & a_{33} \end{vmatrix} - a_{12}\begin{vmatrix} a_{21} & a_{23} \\ a_{31} & a_{33} \end{vmatrix} + a_{13}\begin{vmatrix} a_{21} & a_{22} \\ a_{31} & a_{32} \end{vmatrix} \tag{9}$$

Minus (pointing to the − sign); Plus (pointing to the + sign)

2 by 2 determinant left after removing the row and column containing a_{11}

2 by 2 determinant left after removing the row and column containing a_{12}

2 by 2 determinant left after removing the row and column containing a_{13}

In Words

The graphic below should help to visualize the minor of a_{11} in a 3 by 3 determinant:

$$\begin{vmatrix} a_{11} & a_{12} & a_{13} \\ a_{21} & a_{22} & a_{23} \\ a_{31} & a_{32} & a_{33} \end{vmatrix}$$

The 2 by 2 determinants shown in formula (9) are called **minors** of the 3 by 3 determinant. For an n by n determinant, the **minor** M_{ij} of entry a_{ij} is the determinant resulting from removing the ith row and jth column.

EXAMPLE 3 **Finding Minors of a 3 by 3 Determinant**

For the determinant $A = \begin{vmatrix} 2 & -1 & 3 \\ -2 & 5 & 1 \\ 0 & 6 & -9 \end{vmatrix}$, find: (a) M_{12} (b) M_{23}

Solution (a) M_{12} is the determinant that results from removing the first row and second column from A.

$$A = \begin{vmatrix} 2 & -1 & 3 \\ -2 & 5 & 1 \\ 0 & 6 & -9 \end{vmatrix} \qquad M_{12} = \begin{vmatrix} -2 & 1 \\ 0 & -9 \end{vmatrix} = (-2)(-9) - (1)(0) = 18$$

(b) M_{23} is the determinant that results from removing the second row and third column from A.

$$A = \begin{vmatrix} 2 & -1 & 3 \\ -2 & 5 & 1 \\ 0 & 6 & -9 \end{vmatrix} \qquad M_{23} = \begin{vmatrix} 2 & -1 \\ 0 & 6 \end{vmatrix} = (2)(6) - (-1)(0) = 12$$

■

Referring back to formula (9), we see that each element a_{ij} in the first row of the determinant is multiplied by its minor, but sometimes this term is added and other times subtracted. To determine whether to add or subtract a term, we must consider the *cofactor*.

DEFINITION

For an n by n determinant A, the **cofactor** of entry a_{ij}, denoted by A_{ij}, is given by

$$A_{ij} = (-1)^{i+j} M_{ij}$$

where M_{ij} is the minor of entry a_{ij}.

The exponent of $(-1)^{i+j}$ is the sum of the row and column of the entry a_{ij}, so if $i + j$ is even, $(-1)^{i+j}$ equals 1, and if $i + j$ is odd, $(-1)^{i+j}$ equals -1.

To find the value of a determinant, multiply each entry in any row or column by its cofactor and sum the results. This process is referred to as **expanding across a row or column.** For example, the value of the 3 by 3 determinant in formula (9) was found by expanding across row 1.

If we choose to expand down column 2, we obtain

$$\begin{vmatrix} a_{11} & a_{12} & a_{13} \\ a_{21} & a_{22} & a_{23} \\ a_{31} & a_{32} & a_{33} \end{vmatrix} = (-1)^{1+2} a_{12} \begin{vmatrix} a_{21} & a_{23} \\ a_{31} & a_{33} \end{vmatrix} + (-1)^{2+2} a_{22} \begin{vmatrix} a_{11} & a_{13} \\ a_{31} & a_{33} \end{vmatrix} + (-1)^{3+2} a_{32} \begin{vmatrix} a_{11} & a_{13} \\ a_{21} & a_{23} \end{vmatrix}$$

Expand down column 2.

If we choose to expand across row 3, we obtain

$$\begin{vmatrix} a_{11} & a_{12} & a_{13} \\ a_{21} & a_{22} & a_{23} \\ a_{31} & a_{32} & a_{33} \end{vmatrix} = (-1)^{3+1} a_{31} \begin{vmatrix} a_{12} & a_{13} \\ a_{22} & a_{23} \end{vmatrix} + (-1)^{3+2} a_{32} \begin{vmatrix} a_{11} & a_{13} \\ a_{21} & a_{23} \end{vmatrix} + (-1)^{3+3} a_{33} \begin{vmatrix} a_{11} & a_{12} \\ a_{21} & a_{22} \end{vmatrix}$$

Expand across row 3.

It can be shown that the value of a determinant does not depend on the choice of the row or column used in the expansion. However, expanding across a row or column that has an entry equal to 0 reduces the amount of work needed to compute the value of the determinant.

EXAMPLE 4 Evaluating a 3 × 3 Determinant

Find the value of the 3 by 3 determinant: $\begin{vmatrix} 3 & 0 & -1 \\ 4 & 6 & 2 \\ 8 & -2 & 3 \end{vmatrix}$

Solution Because of the 0 in row 1, column 2, it is easiest to expand across row 1 or down column 2. We choose to expand across row 1.

$$\begin{vmatrix} 3 & 0 & -1 \\ 4 & 6 & 2 \\ 8 & -2 & 3 \end{vmatrix} = (-1)^{1+1} \cdot 3 \cdot \begin{vmatrix} 6 & 2 \\ -2 & 3 \end{vmatrix} + (-1)^{1+2} \cdot 0 \cdot \begin{vmatrix} 4 & 2 \\ 8 & 3 \end{vmatrix} + (-1)^{1+3} \cdot (-1) \cdot \begin{vmatrix} 4 & 6 \\ 8 & -2 \end{vmatrix}$$

$$= 3(18 - (-4)) - 0 + (-1)(-8 - 48)$$
$$= 3(22) + (-1)(-56)$$
$$= 66 + 56 = 122$$

■

Now Work PROBLEM 11

4 Use Cramer's Rule to Solve a System of Three Equations Containing Three Variables

Consider the following system of three equations containing three variables.

$$\begin{cases} a_{11}x + a_{12}y + a_{13}z = c_1 \\ a_{21}x + a_{22}y + a_{23}z = c_2 \\ a_{31}x + a_{32}y + a_{33}z = c_3 \end{cases} \qquad \textbf{(10)}$$

It can be shown that if the determinant D of the coefficients of the variables is not 0, that is, if

$$D = \begin{vmatrix} a_{11} & a_{12} & a_{13} \\ a_{21} & a_{22} & a_{23} \\ a_{31} & a_{32} & a_{33} \end{vmatrix} \neq 0$$

the unique solution of system (10) is given by

THEOREM

Cramer's Rule for Three Equations Containing Three Variables

$$x = \frac{D_x}{D} \qquad y = \frac{D_y}{D} \qquad z = \frac{D_z}{D}$$

where

$$D_x = \begin{vmatrix} c_1 & a_{12} & a_{13} \\ c_2 & a_{22} & a_{23} \\ c_3 & a_{32} & a_{33} \end{vmatrix} \qquad D_y = \begin{vmatrix} a_{11} & c_1 & a_{13} \\ a_{21} & c_2 & a_{23} \\ a_{31} & c_3 & a_{33} \end{vmatrix} \qquad D_z = \begin{vmatrix} a_{11} & a_{12} & c_1 \\ a_{21} & a_{22} & c_2 \\ a_{31} & a_{32} & c_3 \end{vmatrix}$$

Do you see the similarity of this pattern and the pattern observed earlier for a system of two equations containing two variables?

EXAMPLE 5 **Using Cramer's Rule**

Use Cramer's Rule, if applicable, to solve the following system:

$$\begin{cases} 2x + y - z = 3 & (1) \\ -x + 2y + 4z = -3 & (2) \\ x - 2y - 3z = 4 & (3) \end{cases}$$

Solution The value of the determinant D of the coefficients of the variables is

$$D = \begin{vmatrix} 2 & 1 & -1 \\ -1 & 2 & 4 \\ 1 & -2 & -3 \end{vmatrix} = (-1)^{1+1} \cdot 2 \cdot \begin{vmatrix} 2 & 4 \\ -2 & -3 \end{vmatrix} + (-1)^{1+2} \cdot 1 \cdot \begin{vmatrix} -1 & 4 \\ 1 & -3 \end{vmatrix} + (-1)^{1+3}(-1)\begin{vmatrix} -1 & 2 \\ 1 & -2 \end{vmatrix}$$

$$= 2(2) - 1(-1) + (-1)(0)$$
$$= 4 + 1 = 5$$

Because $D \neq 0$ we proceed to find the values of D_x, D_y, and D_z. To find D_x, we replace the coefficients of x in D with the constants and then evaluate the determinant.

$$D_x = \begin{vmatrix} 3 & 1 & -1 \\ -3 & 2 & 4 \\ 4 & -2 & -3 \end{vmatrix} = (-1)^{1+1} \cdot 3 \cdot \begin{vmatrix} 2 & 4 \\ -2 & -3 \end{vmatrix} + (-1)^{1+2} \cdot 1 \cdot \begin{vmatrix} -3 & 4 \\ 4 & -3 \end{vmatrix} + (-1)^{1+3}(-1) \begin{vmatrix} -3 & 2 \\ 4 & -2 \end{vmatrix}$$

$$= 3(2) - 1(-7) + (-1)(-2) = 15$$

$$D_y = \begin{vmatrix} 2 & 3 & -1 \\ -1 & -3 & 4 \\ 1 & 4 & -3 \end{vmatrix} = (-1)^{1+1} \cdot 2 \cdot \begin{vmatrix} -3 & 4 \\ 4 & -3 \end{vmatrix} + (-1)^{1+2} \cdot 3 \cdot \begin{vmatrix} -1 & 4 \\ 1 & -3 \end{vmatrix} + (-1)^{1+3}(-1) \begin{vmatrix} -1 & -3 \\ 1 & 4 \end{vmatrix}$$

$$= 2(-7) - 3(-1) + (-1)(-1) = -10$$

$$D_z = \begin{vmatrix} 2 & 1 & 3 \\ -1 & 2 & -3 \\ 1 & -2 & 4 \end{vmatrix} = (-1)^{1+1} \cdot 2 \cdot \begin{vmatrix} 2 & -3 \\ -2 & 4 \end{vmatrix} + (-1)^{1+2} \cdot 1 \cdot \begin{vmatrix} -1 & -3 \\ 1 & 4 \end{vmatrix} + (-1)^{1+3} \cdot 3 \cdot \begin{vmatrix} -1 & 2 \\ 1 & -2 \end{vmatrix}$$

$$= 2(2) - 1(-1) + 3(0) = 5$$

As a result,

$$x = \frac{D_x}{D} = \frac{15}{5} = 3 \qquad y = \frac{D_y}{D} = \frac{-10}{5} = -2 \qquad z = \frac{D_z}{D} = \frac{5}{5} = 1$$

The solution is $x = 3$, $y = -2$, $z = 1$ or, using an ordered triplet, $(3, -2, 1)$. ■

We already know that Cramer's Rule does not apply when the determinant of the coefficients on the variables, D, is 0. But can we learn anything about the system other than it is not a consistent and independent system if $D = 0$? The answer is yes!

Cramer's Rule with Inconsistent or Dependent Systems

- If $D = 0$ and at least one of the determinants D_x, D_y, or D_z is different from 0, then the system is inconsistent and the solution set is $\varnothing$ or $\{\ \}$.
- If $D = 0$ and all the determinants D_x, D_y, and D_z equal 0, then the system is consistent and dependent so that there are infinitely many solutions. The system must be solved using row reduction techniques.

Now Work PROBLEM 33

5 Know Properties of Determinants

Determinants have several properties that are sometimes helpful for obtaining their value. We list some of them here.

THEOREM

The value of a determinant changes sign if any two rows (or any two columns) are interchanged. **(11)**

Proof for 2 by 2 Determinants

$$\begin{vmatrix} a & b \\ c & d \end{vmatrix} = ad - bc \quad \text{and} \quad \begin{vmatrix} c & d \\ a & b \end{vmatrix} = bc - ad = -(ad - bc)$$ ■

EXAMPLE 6 **Demonstrating Theorem (11)**

$$\begin{vmatrix} 3 & 4 \\ 1 & 2 \end{vmatrix} = 6 - 4 = 2 \qquad \begin{vmatrix} 1 & 2 \\ 3 & 4 \end{vmatrix} = 4 - 6 = -2$$

■

THEOREM If all the entries in any row (or any column) equal 0, the value of the determinant is 0. **(12)**

Proof Expand across the row (or down the column) containing the 0's. ■

THEOREM If any two rows (or any two columns) of a determinant have corresponding entries that are equal, the value of the determinant is 0. **(13)**

You are asked to prove this result for a 3 by 3 determinant in which the entries in column 1 equal the entries in column 3 in Problem 64.

EXAMPLE 7 **Demonstrating Theorem (13)**

$$\begin{vmatrix} 1 & 2 & 3 \\ 1 & 2 & 3 \\ 4 & 5 & 6 \end{vmatrix} = (-1)^{1+1} \cdot 1 \cdot \begin{vmatrix} 2 & 3 \\ 5 & 6 \end{vmatrix} + (-1)^{1+2} \cdot 2 \cdot \begin{vmatrix} 1 & 3 \\ 4 & 6 \end{vmatrix} + (-1)^{1+3} \cdot 3 \cdot \begin{vmatrix} 1 & 2 \\ 4 & 5 \end{vmatrix}$$

$$= 1(-3) - 2(-6) + 3(-3) = -3 + 12 - 9 = 0$$

■

THEOREM If any row (or any column) of a determinant is multiplied by a nonzero number k, the value of the determinant is also changed by a factor of k. **(14)**

You are asked to prove this result for a 3 by 3 determinant using row 2 in Problem 63.

EXAMPLE 8 **Demonstrating Theorem (14)**

$$\begin{vmatrix} 1 & 2 \\ 4 & 6 \end{vmatrix} = 6 - 8 = -2$$

$$\begin{vmatrix} k & 2k \\ 4 & 6 \end{vmatrix} = 6k - 8k = -2k = k(-2) = k\begin{vmatrix} 1 & 2 \\ 4 & 6 \end{vmatrix}$$

■

THEOREM If the entries of any row (or any column) of a determinant are multiplied by a nonzero number k and the result is added to the corresponding entries of another row (or column), the value of the determinant remains unchanged. **(15)**

In Problem 65, you are asked to prove this result for a 3 by 3 determinant using rows 1 and 2.

EXAMPLE 9 **Demonstrating Theorem (15)**

$$\begin{vmatrix} 3 & 4 \\ 5 & 2 \end{vmatrix} = -14 \qquad \begin{vmatrix} 3 & 4 \\ 5 & 2 \end{vmatrix} \rightarrow \begin{vmatrix} -7 & 0 \\ 5 & 2 \end{vmatrix} = -14$$

Multiply row 2 by −2 and add to row 1.

■

13.3 Assess Your Understanding

Concepts and Vocabulary

1. $D = \begin{vmatrix} a & b \\ c & d \end{vmatrix} =$ ______.

2. Using Cramer's Rule, the value of x that satisfies the system of equations $\begin{cases} 2x + 3y = 5 \\ x - 4y = -3 \end{cases}$ is $x = \dfrac{\quad}{\begin{vmatrix} 2 & 3 \\ 1 & -4 \end{vmatrix}}$.

3. ***True or False*** A determinant can never equal 0.

4. ***True or False*** When using Cramer's Rule, if $D = 0$, then the system of linear equations is inconsistent.

5. ***True or False*** The value of a determinant remains unchanged if any two rows or any two columns are interchanged.

6. ***True or False*** If any row (or any column) of a determinant is multiplied by a nonzero number k, the value of the determinant remains unchanged.

Skill Building

In Problems 7–14, find the value of each determinant.

7. $\begin{vmatrix} 6 & 4 \\ -1 & 3 \end{vmatrix}$

8. $\begin{vmatrix} 8 & -3 \\ 4 & 2 \end{vmatrix}$

9. $\begin{vmatrix} -3 & -1 \\ 4 & 2 \end{vmatrix}$

10. $\begin{vmatrix} -4 & 2 \\ -5 & 3 \end{vmatrix}$

11. $\begin{vmatrix} 3 & 4 & 2 \\ 1 & -1 & 5 \\ 1 & 2 & -2 \end{vmatrix}$

12. $\begin{vmatrix} 1 & 3 & -2 \\ 6 & 1 & -5 \\ 8 & 2 & 3 \end{vmatrix}$

13. $\begin{vmatrix} 4 & -1 & 2 \\ 6 & -1 & 0 \\ 1 & -3 & 4 \end{vmatrix}$

14. $\begin{vmatrix} 3 & -9 & 4 \\ 1 & 4 & 0 \\ 8 & -3 & 1 \end{vmatrix}$

In Problems 15–42, solve each system of equations using Cramer's Rule if it is applicable. If Cramer's Rule is not applicable, say so.

15. $\begin{cases} x + y = 8 \\ x - y = 4 \end{cases}$

16. $\begin{cases} x + 2y = 5 \\ x - y = 3 \end{cases}$

17. $\begin{cases} 5x - y = 13 \\ 2x + 3y = 12 \end{cases}$

18. $\begin{cases} x + 3y = 5 \\ 2x - 3y = -8 \end{cases}$

19. $\begin{cases} 3x = 24 \\ x + 2y = 0 \end{cases}$

20. $\begin{cases} 4x + 5y = -3 \\ -2y = -4 \end{cases}$

21. $\begin{cases} 3x - 6y = 24 \\ 5x + 4y = 12 \end{cases}$

22. $\begin{cases} 2x + 4y = 16 \\ 3x - 5y = -9 \end{cases}$

23. $\begin{cases} 3x - 2y = 4 \\ 6x - 4y = 0 \end{cases}$

24. $\begin{cases} -x + 2y = 5 \\ 4x - 8y = 6 \end{cases}$

25. $\begin{cases} 2x - 4y = -2 \\ 3x + 2y = 3 \end{cases}$

26. $\begin{cases} 3x + 3y = 3 \\ 4x + 2y = \dfrac{8}{3} \end{cases}$

27. $\begin{cases} 2x - 3y = -1 \\ 10x + 10y = 5 \end{cases}$

28. $\begin{cases} 3x - 2y = 0 \\ 5x + 10y = 4 \end{cases}$

29. $\begin{cases} 2x + 3y = 6 \\ x - y = \dfrac{1}{2} \end{cases}$

30. $\begin{cases} \dfrac{1}{2}x + y = -2 \\ x - 2y = 8 \end{cases}$

31. $\begin{cases} 3x - 5y = 3 \\ 15x + 5y = 21 \end{cases}$

32. $\begin{cases} 2x - y = -1 \\ x + \dfrac{1}{2}y = \dfrac{3}{2} \end{cases}$

33. $\begin{cases} x + y - z = 6 \\ 3x - 2y + z = -5 \\ x + 3y - 2z = 14 \end{cases}$

34. $\begin{cases} x - y + z = -4 \\ 2x - 3y + 4z = -15 \\ 5x + y - 2z = 12 \end{cases}$

35. $\begin{cases} x + 2y - z = -3 \\ 2x - 4y + z = -7 \\ -2x + 2y - 3z = 4 \end{cases}$

36. $\begin{cases} x + 4y - 3z = -8 \\ 3x - y + 3z = 12 \\ x + y + 6z = 1 \end{cases}$

37. $\begin{cases} x - 2y + 3z = 1 \\ 3x + y - 2z = 0 \\ 2x - 4y + 6z = 2 \end{cases}$

38. $\begin{cases} x - y + 2z = 5 \\ 3x + 2y = 4 \\ -2x + 2y - 4z = -10 \end{cases}$

39. $\begin{cases} x + 2y - z = 0 \\ 2x - 4y + z = 0 \\ -2x + 2y - 3z = 0 \end{cases}$

40. $\begin{cases} x + 4y - 3z = 0 \\ 3x - y + 3z = 0 \\ x + y + 6z = 0 \end{cases}$

41. $\begin{cases} x - 2y + 3z = 0 \\ 3x + y - 2z = 0 \\ 2x - 4y + 6z = 0 \end{cases}$

42. $\begin{cases} x - y + 2z = 0 \\ 3x + 2y = 0 \\ -2x + 2y - 4z = 0 \end{cases}$

In Problems 43–50, use properties of determinants to find the value of each determinant if it is known that

$$\begin{vmatrix} x & y & z \\ u & v & w \\ 1 & 2 & 3 \end{vmatrix} = 4.$$

43. $\begin{vmatrix} 1 & 2 & 3 \\ u & v & w \\ x & y & z \end{vmatrix}$

44. $\begin{vmatrix} x & y & z \\ u & v & w \\ 2 & 4 & 6 \end{vmatrix}$

45. $\begin{vmatrix} x & y & z \\ -3 & -6 & -9 \\ u & v & w \end{vmatrix}$

46. $\begin{vmatrix} 1 & 2 & 3 \\ x-u & y-v & z-w \\ u & v & w \end{vmatrix}$

47. $\begin{vmatrix} 1 & 2 & 3 \\ x-3 & y-6 & z-9 \\ 2u & 2v & 2w \end{vmatrix}$

48. $\begin{vmatrix} x & y & z-x \\ u & v & w-u \\ 1 & 2 & 2 \end{vmatrix}$

49. $\begin{vmatrix} 1 & 2 & 3 \\ 2x & 2y & 2z \\ u-1 & v-2 & w-3 \end{vmatrix}$

50. $\begin{vmatrix} x+3 & y+6 & z+9 \\ 3u-1 & 3v-2 & 3w-3 \\ 1 & 2 & 3 \end{vmatrix}$

Mixed Practice

In Problems 51–56, solve for x.

51. $\begin{vmatrix} x & x \\ 4 & 3 \end{vmatrix} = 5$

52. $\begin{vmatrix} x & 1 \\ 3 & x \end{vmatrix} = -2$

53. $\begin{vmatrix} x & 1 & 1 \\ 4 & 3 & 2 \\ -1 & 2 & 5 \end{vmatrix} = 2$

54. $\begin{vmatrix} 3 & 2 & 4 \\ 1 & x & 5 \\ 0 & 1 & -2 \end{vmatrix} = 0$

55. $\begin{vmatrix} x & 2 & 3 \\ 1 & x & 0 \\ 6 & 1 & -2 \end{vmatrix} = 7$

56. $\begin{vmatrix} x & 1 & 2 \\ 1 & x & 3 \\ 0 & 1 & 2 \end{vmatrix} = -4x$

Applications and Extensions

57. Geometry: Equation of a Line An equation of the line containing the two points (x_1, y_1) and (x_2, y_2) may be expressed as the determinant

$$\begin{vmatrix} x & y & 1 \\ x_1 & y_1 & 1 \\ x_2 & y_2 & 1 \end{vmatrix} = 0$$

Prove this result by expanding the determinant and comparing the result to the two-point form of the equation of a line.

58. Geometry: Collinear Points Using the result obtained in Problem 57, show that three distinct points (x_1, y_1), (x_2, y_2), and (x_3, y_3) are collinear (lie on the same line) if and only if

$$\begin{vmatrix} x_1 & y_1 & 1 \\ x_2 & y_2 & 1 \\ x_3 & y_3 & 1 \end{vmatrix} = 0$$

59. Geometry: Area of a Triangle A triangle has vertices $(x_1, y_1), (x_2, y_2)$, and (x_3, y_3). The area of the triangle is given by the absolute value of D, where $D = \frac{1}{2}\begin{vmatrix} x_1 & x_2 & x_3 \\ y_1 & y_2 & y_3 \\ 1 & 1 & 1 \end{vmatrix}$. Use this formula to find the area of a triangle with vertices $(2, 3)$, $(5, 2)$, and $(6, 5)$.

60. Show that $\begin{vmatrix} x^2 & x & 1 \\ y^2 & y & 1 \\ z^2 & z & 1 \end{vmatrix} = (y-z)(x-y)(x-z)$.

61. Complete the proof of Cramer's Rule for two equations containing two variables.

[**Hint:** In system (5), page 887, if $a = 0$, then $b \neq 0$ and $c \neq 0$, since $D = -bc \neq 0$. Now show that equation (6) provides a solution of the system when $a = 0$. Then three cases remain: $b = 0$, $c = 0$, and $d = 0$.]

62. Interchange columns 1 and 3 of a 3 by 3 determinant. Show that the value of the new determinant is -1 times the value of the original determinant.

63. Multiply each entry in row 2 of a 3 by 3 determinant by the number k, $k \neq 0$. Show that the value of the new determinant is k times the value of the original determinant.

64. Prove that a 3 by 3 determinant in which the entries in column 1 equal those in column 3 has the value 0.

65. Prove that, if row 2 of a 3 by 3 determinant is multiplied by k, $k \neq 0$, and the result is added to the entries in row 1, there is no change in the value of the determinant.

CHAPTER REVIEW

Things to Know

Systems of equations (pp. 857–858)

Systems with no solutions are inconsistent. Systems with a solution are consistent.

Consistent systems of linear equations have either a unique solution (independent) or an infinite number of solutions (dependent).

Matrix (p. 870) Rectangular array of numbers, called entries

Augmented matrix (p. 871)

Row operations (p. 872)

Row echelon form (p. 874)

Objectives

Section		You should be able to ...	Example(s)	Review Exercises
13.1	1	Solve systems of equations by substitution (p. 858)	4	1–7, 56, 59, 60
	2	Solve systems of equations by elimination (p. 859)	5, 6	1–7, 56, 59, 60
	3	Identify inconsistent systems of equations containing two variables (p. 861)	7	5, 54
	4	Express the solution of a system of dependent equations containing two variables (p. 861)	8	7, 53
	5	Solve systems of three equations containing three variables (p. 862)	9	8–10, 55, 57
	6	Identify inconsistent systems of equations containing three variables (p. 864)	10	10
	7	Express the solution of a system of dependent equations containing three variables (p. 865)	11	9
13.2	1	Write the augmented matrix of a system of linear equations (p. 871)	1	20–25
	2	Write the system of equations from the augmented matrix (p. 872)	2	11, 12
	3	Perform row operations on a matrix (p. 872)	3, 4	20–25
	4	Solve a system of linear equations using matrices (p. 873)	5–10	20–25
13.3	1	Evaluate 2 by 2 determinants (p. 885)	1	26
	2	Use Cramer's Rule to solve a system of two equations containing two variables (p. 886)	2	29, 30
	3	Evaluate 3 by 3 determinants (p. 888)	4	27, 28
	4	Use Cramer's Rule to solve a system of three equations containing three variables (p. 890)	5	31
	5	Know properties of determinants (p. 891)	6–9	32, 33

Review Exercises

In Problems 1–10, solve each system of equations using the method of substitution or the method of elimination. If the system has no solution, say that it is inconsistent.

1. $\begin{cases} 2x - y = 5 \\ 5x + 2y = 8 \end{cases}$

2. $\begin{cases} 3x - 4y = 4 \\ x - 3y = \frac{1}{2} \end{cases}$

3. $\begin{cases} x - 2y - 4 = 0 \\ 3x + 2y - 4 = 0 \end{cases}$

4. $\begin{cases} y = 2x - 5 \\ x = 3y + 4 \end{cases}$

5. $\begin{cases} x - 3y + 4 = 0 \\ \frac{1}{2}x - \frac{3}{2}y + \frac{4}{3} = 0 \end{cases}$

6. $\begin{cases} 2x + 3y - 13 = 0 \\ 3x - 2y = 0 \end{cases}$

7. $\begin{cases} 2x + 5y = 10 \\ 4x + 10y = 20 \end{cases}$

8. $\begin{cases} x + 2y - z = 6 \\ 2x - y + 3z = -13 \\ 3x - 2y + 3z = -16 \end{cases}$

9. $\begin{cases} 2x - 4y + z = -15 \\ x + 2y - 4z = 27 \\ 5x - 6y - 2z = -3 \end{cases}$

10. $\begin{cases} x - 4y + 3z = 15 \\ -3x + y - 5z = -5 \\ -7x - 5y - 9z = 10 \end{cases}$

In Problems 11 and 12, write the system of equations corresponding to the given augmented matrix.

11. $\left[\begin{array}{cc|c} 3 & 2 & 8 \\ 1 & 4 & -1 \end{array}\right]$

12. $\left[\begin{array}{ccc|c} 1 & 2 & 5 & -2 \\ 5 & 0 & -3 & 8 \\ 2 & -1 & 0 & 0 \end{array}\right]$

In Problems 13–16, use the following matrices to compute each expression.

$$A = \begin{bmatrix} 1 & 0 \\ 2 & 4 \\ -1 & 2 \end{bmatrix} \quad B = \begin{bmatrix} 4 & -3 & 0 \\ 1 & 1 & -2 \end{bmatrix} \quad C = \begin{bmatrix} 3 & -4 \\ 1 & 5 \\ 5 & 2 \end{bmatrix}$$

13. $A + C$

14. $6A$

15. AB

16. BC

In Problems 17–19, find the inverse, if there is one, of each matrix. If there is not an inverse, say that the matrix is singular.

17. $\begin{bmatrix} 4 & 6 \\ 1 & 3 \end{bmatrix}$ **18.** $\begin{bmatrix} 1 & 3 & 3 \\ 1 & 2 & 1 \\ 1 & -1 & 2 \end{bmatrix}$ **19.** $\begin{bmatrix} 4 & -8 \\ -1 & 2 \end{bmatrix}$

In Problems 20–25, solve each system of equations using matrices. If the system has no solution, say that it is inconsistent.

20. $\begin{cases} 3x - 2y = 1 \\ 10x + 10y = 5 \end{cases}$ **21.** $\begin{cases} 5x - 6y - 3z = 6 \\ 4x - 7y - 2z = -3 \\ 3x + y - 7z = 1 \end{cases}$ **22.** $\begin{cases} 2x + y + z = 5 \\ 4x - y - 3z = 1 \\ 8x + y - z = 5 \end{cases}$

23. $\begin{cases} x - 2z = 1 \\ 2x + 3y = -3 \\ 4x - 3y - 4z = 3 \end{cases}$ **24.** $\begin{cases} x - y + z = 0 \\ x - y - 5z - 6 = 0 \\ 2x - 2y + z - 1 = 0 \end{cases}$ **25.** $\begin{cases} x - y - z - t = 1 \\ 2x + y - z + 2t = 3 \\ x - 2y - 2z - 3t = 0 \\ 3x - 4y + z + 5t = -3 \end{cases}$

In Problems 26–28, find the value of each determinant.

26. $\begin{vmatrix} 3 & 4 \\ 1 & 3 \end{vmatrix}$ **27.** $\begin{vmatrix} 1 & 4 & 0 \\ -1 & 2 & 6 \\ 4 & 1 & 3 \end{vmatrix}$ **28.** $\begin{vmatrix} 2 & 1 & -3 \\ 5 & 0 & 1 \\ 2 & 6 & 0 \end{vmatrix}$

In Problems 29–31, use Cramer's Rule, if applicable, to solve each system.

29. $\begin{cases} x - 2y = 4 \\ 3x + 2y = 4 \end{cases}$ **30.** $\begin{cases} 2x + 3y - 13 = 0 \\ 3x - 2y = 0 \end{cases}$ **31.** $\begin{cases} x + 2y - z = 6 \\ 2x - y + 3z = -13 \\ 3x - 2y + 3z = -16 \end{cases}$

In Problems 32 and 33, use properties of determinants to find the value of each determinant if it is known that $\begin{vmatrix} x & y \\ a & b \end{vmatrix} = 8$.

32. $\begin{vmatrix} 2x & y \\ 2a & b \end{vmatrix}$ **33.** $\begin{vmatrix} y & x \\ b & a \end{vmatrix}$

In Problems 34–38, write the partial fraction decomposition of each rational expression.

34. $\dfrac{6}{x(x-4)}$ **35.** $\dfrac{x-4}{x^2(x-1)}$ **36.** $\dfrac{x}{(x^2+9)(x+1)}$ **37.** $\dfrac{x^3}{(x^2+4)^2}$ **38.** $\dfrac{x^2}{(x^2+1)(x^2-1)}$

In Problems 39–43, solve each system of equations.

39. $\begin{cases} 2x + y + 3 = 0 \\ x^2 + y^2 = 5 \end{cases}$ **40.** $\begin{cases} 2xy + y^2 = 10 \\ 3y^2 - xy = 2 \end{cases}$ **41.** $\begin{cases} x^2 + y^2 = 6y \\ x^2 = 3y \end{cases}$ **42.** $\begin{cases} 3x^2 + 4xy + 5y^2 = 8 \\ x^2 + 3xy + 2y^2 = 0 \end{cases}$

43. $\begin{cases} x^2 - 3x + y^2 + y = -2 \\ \dfrac{x^2 - x}{y} + y + 1 = 0 \end{cases}$

In Problems 44 and 45, graph each inequality by hand. Verify your results using a graphing utility.

44. $3x + 4y \le 12$ **45.** $y \le x^2$

In Problems 46–48, graph each system of inequalities by hand. Tell whether the graph is bounded or unbounded, and label the corner points.

46. $\begin{cases} -2x + y \le 2 \\ x + y \ge 2 \end{cases}$ **47.** $\begin{cases} x \ge 0 \\ y \ge 0 \\ x + y \le 4 \\ 2x + 3y \le 6 \end{cases}$ **48.** $\begin{cases} x \ge 0 \\ y \ge 0 \\ 2x + y \le 8 \\ x + 2y \ge 2 \end{cases}$

In Problems 49 and 50, graph each system of inequalities by hand.

49. $\begin{cases} x^2 + y^2 \le 16 \\ x + y \ge 2 \end{cases}$ **50.** $\begin{cases} x^2 + y^2 \le 25 \\ xy \le 4 \end{cases}$

In Problems 51 and 52, solve each linear programming problem.

51. Maximize $z = 3x + 4y$ subject to $x \ge 0, y \ge 0, 3x + 2y \ge 6, x + y \le 8$

52. Minimize $z = 3x + 5y$ subject to $x \ge 0, y \ge 0, x + y \ge 1, 3x + 2y \le 12, x + 3y \le 12$

53. Find A so that the system of equations has infinitely many solutions.

$$\begin{cases} 2x + 5y = 5 \\ 4x + 10y = A \end{cases}$$

54. Find A so that the system in Problem 53 is inconsistent.

55. **Curve Fitting** Find the quadratic function $y = ax^2 + bx + c$ that passes through the three points $(0, 1)$, $(1, 0)$, and $(-2, 1)$.

56. **Blending Coffee** A coffee distributor is blending a new coffee that will cost \$6.90 per pound. It will consist of a blend of \$6.00 per pound coffee and \$9.00 per pound coffee. What amounts of each type of coffee should be mixed to achieve the desired blend?

[**Hint:** Assume that the weight of the blended coffee is 100 pounds.]

57. **Cookie Orders** A cookie company makes three kinds of cookies, oatmeal raisin, chocolate chip, and shortbread, packaged in small, medium, and large boxes. The small box contains 1 dozen oatmeal raisin and 1 dozen chocolate chip; the medium box has 2 dozen oatmeal raisin, 1 dozen chocolate chip, and 1 dozen shortbread; the large box contains 2 dozen oatmeal raisin, 2 dozen chocolate chip, and 3 dozen shortbread. If you require exactly 15 dozen oatmeal raisin, 10 dozen chocolate chip, and 11 dozen shortbread, how many of each size box should you buy?

58. **Mixed Nuts** A store that specializes in selling nuts has available 72 pounds (lb) of cashews and 120 lb of peanuts. These are to be mixed in 12-ounce (oz) packages as follows: a lower-priced package containing 8 oz of peanuts and 4 oz of cashews and a quality package containing 6 oz of peanuts and 6 oz of cashews.
    (a) Use x to denote the number of lower-priced packages, and use y to denote the number of quality packages. Write a system of linear inequalities that describes the possible number of each kind of package.
    (b) Graph the system and label the corner points.

59. **Determining the Speed of the Current of the Aguarico River** On a recent trip to the Cuyabeno Wildlife Reserve in the Amazon region of Ecuador, Mike took a 100-kilometer trip by speedboat down the Aguarico River from Chiritza to the Flotel Orellana. As Mike watched the Amazon unfold, he wondered how fast the speedboat was going and how fast the current of the white-water Aguarico River was. Mike timed the trip downstream at 2.5 hours and the return trip at 3 hours. What were the two speeds?

60. **Constant Rate Jobs** If Bruce and Bryce work together for 1 hour and 20 minutes, they will finish a certain job. If Bryce and Marty work together for 1 hour and 36 minutes, the same job can be finished. If Marty and Bruce work together, they can complete this job in 2 hours and 40 minutes. How long will it take each of them working alone to finish the job?

61. **Minimizing Production Cost** A factory produces gasoline engines and diesel engines. Each week the factory is obligated to deliver at least 20 gasoline engines and at least 15 diesel engines. Due to physical limitations, however, the factory cannot make more than 60 gasoline engines nor more than 40 diesel engines in any given week. Finally, to prevent layoffs, a total of at least 50 engines must be produced. If gasoline engines cost \$450 each to produce and diesel engines cost \$550 each to produce, how many of each should be produced per week to minimize the cost? What is the excess capacity of the factory; that is, how many of each kind of engine is being produced in excess of the number that the factory is obligated to deliver?

62. Describe four ways of solving a system of three linear equations containing three variables. Which method do you prefer? Why?

CHAPTER TEST

The Chapter Test Prep Videos are step-by-step test solutions available in the Video Resources DVD, in, MyMathLab, or on this text's YouTube Channel. Flip back to the Student Resources page to see the exact web address for this text's YouTube channel.

In Problems 1–4, solve each system of equations using the method of substitution or the method of elimination. If the system has no solution, say that it is inconsistent.

1. $\begin{cases} -2x + y = -7 \\ 4x + 3y = 9 \end{cases}$

2. $\begin{cases} \frac{1}{3}x - 2y = 1 \\ 5x - 30y = 18 \end{cases}$

3. $\begin{cases} x - y + 2z = 5 \\ 3x + 4y - z = -2 \\ 5x + 2y + 3z = 8 \end{cases}$

4. $\begin{cases} 3x + 2y - 8z = -3 \\ -x - \frac{2}{3}y + z = 1 \\ 6x - 3y + 15z = 8 \end{cases}$

5. Write the augmented matrix corresponding to the system of equations: $\begin{cases} 4x - 5y + z = 0 \\ -2x - y + 6 = -19 \\ x + 5y - 5z = 10 \end{cases}$

6. Write the system of equations corresponding to the augmented matrix: $\left[\begin{array}{ccc|c} 3 & 2 & 4 & -6 \\ 1 & 0 & 8 & 2 \\ -2 & 1 & 3 & -11 \end{array}\right]$

In Problems 7–10, use the given matrices to compute each expression.

$$A = \begin{bmatrix} 1 & -1 \\ 0 & -4 \\ 3 & 2 \end{bmatrix} \quad B = \begin{bmatrix} 1 & -2 & 5 \\ 0 & 3 & 1 \end{bmatrix} \quad C = \begin{bmatrix} 4 & 6 \\ 1 & -3 \\ -1 & 8 \end{bmatrix}$$

7. $2A + C$ **8.** $A - 3C$

9. CB **10.** BA

In Problems 11 and 12, find the inverse of each nonsingular matrix.

11. $A = \begin{bmatrix} 3 & 2 \\ 5 & 4 \end{bmatrix}$ **12.** $B = \begin{bmatrix} 1 & -1 & 1 \\ 2 & 5 & -1 \\ 2 & 3 & 0 \end{bmatrix}$

In Problems 13–16, solve each system of equations us1ing matrices. If the system has no solution, say that it is inconsistent.

13. $\begin{cases} 6x + 3y = 12 \\ 2x - y = -2 \end{cases}$

14. $\begin{cases} x + \frac{1}{4}y = 7 \\ 8x + 2y = 56 \end{cases}$

15. $\begin{cases} x + 2y + 4z = -3 \\ 2x + 7y + 15z = -12 \\ 4x + 7y + 13z = -10 \end{cases}$

16. $\begin{cases} 2x + 2y - 3z = 5 \\ x - y + 2z = 8 \\ 3x + 5y - 8z = -2 \end{cases}$

In Problems 17 and 18, find the value of each determinant.

17. $\begin{vmatrix} -2 & 5 \\ 3 & 7 \end{vmatrix}$ **18.** $\begin{vmatrix} 2 & -4 & 6 \\ 1 & 4 & 0 \\ -1 & 2 & -4 \end{vmatrix}$

In Problems 19 and 20, use Cramer's Rule, if possible, to solve each system.

19. $\begin{cases} 4x + 3y = -23 \\ 3x - 5y = 19 \end{cases}$

20. $\begin{cases} 4x - 3y + 2z = 15 \\ -2x + y - 3z = -15 \\ 5x - 5y + 2z = 18 \end{cases}$

In Problems 21 and 22, solve each system of equations.

21. $\begin{cases} 3x^2 + y^2 = 12 \\ y^2 = 9x \end{cases}$

22. $\begin{cases} 2y^2 - 3x^2 = 5 \\ y - x = 1 \end{cases}$

23. Graph the system of inequalities: $\begin{cases} x^2 + y^2 \le 100 \\ 4x - 3y \ge 0 \end{cases}$

In Problems 24 and 25, write the partial fraction decomposition of each rational expression.

24. $\dfrac{3x + 7}{(x + 3)^2}$ **25.** $\dfrac{4x^2 - 3}{x(x^2 + 3)^2}$

26. Graph the system of inequalities. Tell whether the graph is bounded or unbounded, and label all corner points.

$$\begin{cases} x \ge 0 \\ y \ge 0 \\ x + 2y \ge 8 \\ 2x - 3y \ge 2 \end{cases}$$

27. Maximize $z = 5x + 8y$ subject to $x \ge 0, 2x + y \le 8$, and $x - 3y \le -3$.

28. Megan went clothes shopping and bought 2 pairs of flare jeans, 2 camisoles, and 4 T-shirts for \$90.00. At the same store, Paige bought one pair of flare jeans and 3 T-shirts for \$42.50, while Kara bought 1 pair of flare jeans, 3 camisoles, and 2 T-shirts for \$62.00. Determine the price of each clothing item.

CUMULATIVE REVIEW

In Problems 1–6, solve each equation.

1. $2x^2 - x = 0$ **2.** $\sqrt{3x + 1} = 4$ **3.** $2x^3 - 3x^2 - 8x - 3 = 0$

4. $3^x = 9^{x+1}$ **5.** $\log_3(x - 1) + \log_3(2x + 1) = 2$ **6.** $3^x = e$

7. Determine whether the function $g(x) = \dfrac{2x^3}{x^4 + 1}$ is even, odd, or neither. Is the graph of g symmetric with respect to the x-axis, y-axis, or origin?

8. Find the center and radius of the circle $x^2 + y^2 - 2x + 4y - 11 = 0$. Graph the circle.

9. Graph $f(x) = 3^{x-2} + 1$ using transformations. What is the domain, range, and horizontal asymptote of f?

10. The function $f(x) = \dfrac{5}{x + 2}$ is one-to-one. Find f^{-1}. Find the domain and the range of f and the domain and the range of f^{-1}.

11. Graph each equation.

(a) $y = 3x + 6$ (b) $x^2 + y^2 = 4$

(c) $y = x^3$ (d) $y = \dfrac{1}{x}$

(e) $y = \sqrt{x}$ (f) $y = e^x$

(g) $y = \ln x$ (h) $2x^2 + 5y^2 = 1$

(i) $x^2 - 3y^2 = 1$ (j) $x^2 - 2x - 4y + 1 = 0$

12. $f(x) = x^3 - 3x + 5$

(a) Using a graphing utility, graph f and approximate the zero(s) of f.

(b) Using a graphing utility, approximate the local maxima and local minima.

(c) Determine the intervals on which f is increasing.

CHAPTER PROJECTS

I. Markov Chains A **Markov chain** (or process) is one in which future outcomes are determined by a current state. Future outcomes are based on probabilities. The probability of moving to a certain state depends only on the state previously occupied and does not vary with time. An example of a Markov chain is the maximum education achieved by children based on the highest education attained by their parents, where the states are (1) earned college degree, (2) high school diploma only, (3) elementary school only. If p_{ij} is the probability of moving from state i to state j, the **transition matrix** is the $m \times m$ matrix

$$P = \begin{bmatrix} p_{11} & p_{12} & \cdots & p_{1m} \\ \vdots & \vdots & & \vdots \\ p_{m1} & p_{m2} & \cdots & p_{mm} \end{bmatrix}$$

The table represents the probabilities of the highest educational level of children based on the highest educational level of their parents. For example, the table shows that the probability p_{21} is 40% that parents with a high-school education (row 2) will have children with a college education (column 1).

Highest Educational Level of Parents	Maximum Education That Children Achieve		
	College	High School	Elementary
College	80%	18%	2%
High school	40%	50%	10%
Elementary	20%	60%	20%

1. Convert the percentages to decimals.
2. What is the transition matrix?
3. Sum across the rows. What do you notice? Why do you think that you obtained this result?
4. If P is the transition matrix of a Markov chain, the (i, j)th entry of P^n (nth power of P) gives the probability of passing from state i to state j in n stages. What is the probability that a grandchild of a college graduate is a college graduate?
5. What is the probability that the grandchild of a high school graduate finishes college?
6. The row vector $v^{(0)} = [0.288 \quad 0.569 \quad 0.143]$ represents the proportion of the U.S. population 25 years or older that has college, high school, and elementary school, respectively, as the highest educational level in 2007.* In a Markov chain the probability distribution $v^{(k)}$ after k stages is $v^{(k)} = v^{(0)}P^k$, where P^k is the kth power of the transition matrix. What will be the distribution of highest educational attainment of the grandchildren of the current population?
7. Calculate $P^3, P^4, P^5, \ldots$. Continue until the matrix does not change. This is called the long-run distribution. What is the long-run distribution of highest educational attainment of the population?

**Source:* U.S. Census Bureau.

The following projects are available at the Instructor's Resource Center (IRC):

II. Project at Motorola: *Error Control Coding* The high-powered engineering needed to assure that wireless communications are transmitted correctly is analyzed using matrices to control coding errors.

III. Using Matrices to Find the Line of Best Fit Have you wondered how our calculators get a line of best fit? See how to find the line by solving a matrix equation.

IV. CBL Experiment Simulate two people walking toward each other at a constant rate. Then solve the resulting system of equations to determine when and where they will meet.

Appendix A

Operations on Decimals/Table of Percent, Decimal, and Fraction Equivalents

A.1 Operations on Decimals

To **add** or **subtract** decimals, write the numbers vertically with decimal points lined up. Add or subtract as with whole numbers and place the decimal point in the answer directly below the decimal points in the problem.

EXAMPLE 1 Add 5.87 + 23.279 + 0.003.

Solution

$$\begin{array}{r} 5.87 \\ 23.279 \\ +0.003 \\ \hline 29.152 \end{array}$$

□

EXAMPLE 2 Subtract 32.15 − 11.237.

Solution

$$\begin{array}{rcccccc} & 3 & \overset{1}{\not{2}} & . & \overset{11}{\not{1}} & \overset{4}{\not{5}} & \overset{10}{\not{0}} \\ - & 1 & 1 & . & 2 & 3 & 7 \\ \hline & 2 & 0 & . & 9 & 1 & 3 \end{array}$$

□

To **multiply** decimals, multiply the numbers as if they were whole numbers. The decimal point in the product is placed so that the number of decimal places in the product is the same as the sum of the number of decimal places in the factors.

EXAMPLE 3 Multiply 0.072 × 3.5.

Solution

$$\begin{array}{rl} 0.072 & \text{3 decimal places} \\ \times \quad 3.5 & \text{1 decimal place} \\ \hline 360 & \\ 216 & \\ \hline 0.2520 & \text{4 decimal places} \end{array}$$

□

To **divide** decimals, move the decimal point in the divisor to the right of the last digit. Move the decimal point in the dividend the same number of places that the decimal point in the divisor was moved. The decimal point in the quotient lies directly above the decimal point in the dividend.

EXAMPLE 4 Divide 9.46 ÷ 0.04.

Solution

$$\begin{array}{r} 236.5 \\ 04.\overline{)946.0} \\ -8 \\ \hline 14 \\ -12 \\ \hline 26 \\ -24 \\ \hline 20 \\ -20 \\ \hline \end{array}$$

□

A Exercise Set

MyMathLab®

Perform the indicated operations.

1. $9.076 + 8.004$

2. $\begin{array}{r} 6.3 \\ \times\ 0.05 \\ \hline \end{array}$

3. $\begin{array}{r} 27.004 \\ -14.2 \\ \hline \end{array}$

4. $\begin{array}{r} 0.0036 \\ 7.12 \\ 32.502 \\ +0.05 \\ \hline \end{array}$

5. $\begin{array}{r} 107.92 \\ +3.04 \\ \hline \end{array}$

6. $7.2 \div 4$

7. $10 - 7.6$

8. $40 \div 0.25$

9. $126.32 - 97.89$

10. $\begin{array}{r} 3.62 \\ 7.11 \\ 12.36 \\ 4.15 \\ +2.29 \\ \hline \end{array}$

11. $\begin{array}{r} 3.25 \\ \times\ 70 \\ \hline \end{array}$

12. $\begin{array}{r} 26.014 \\ -\ 7.8 \\ \hline \end{array}$

13. $8.1 \div 3$

14. $\begin{array}{r} 1.2366 \\ 0.005 \\ 15.17 \\ +\ 0.97 \\ \hline \end{array}$

15. $55.405 - 6.1711$

16. $8.09 + 0.22$

17. $60 \div 0.75$

18. $20 - 12.29$

19. $7.612 \div 100$

20. $\begin{array}{r} 8.72 \\ 1.12 \\ 14.86 \\ 3.98 \\ +\ 1.99 \\ \hline \end{array}$

21. $12.312 \div 2.7$

22. $0.443 \div 100$

23. $\begin{array}{r} 569.2 \\ 71.25 \\ +\ 8.01 \\ \hline \end{array}$

24. $3.706 - 2.91$

25. $768 - 0.17$

26. $63 \div 0.28$

27. $12 + 0.062$

28. $0.42 + 18$

29. $76 - 14.52$

30. $1.1092 \div 0.47$

31. $3.311 \div 0.43$

32. $7.61 + 0.0004$

33. $\begin{array}{r} 762.12 \\ 89.7 \\ +\ 11.55 \\ \hline \end{array}$

34. $444 \div 0.6$

35. $23.4 - 0.821$

36. $3.7 + 5.6$

37. $476.12 - 112.97$

38. $19.872 \div 0.54$

39. $0.007 + 7$

40. $\begin{array}{r} 51.77 \\ +\ 3.6 \\ \hline \end{array}$

A.2 Table of Percent, Decimal, and Fraction Equivalents

Percent, Decimal, and Fraction Equivalents		
Percent	***Decimal***	***Fraction***
1%	0.01	$\frac{1}{100}$
5%	0.05	$\frac{1}{20}$
10%	0.1	$\frac{1}{10}$
12.5% or $12\frac{1}{2}\%$	0.125	$\frac{1}{8}$
$16.\overline{6}\%$ or $16\frac{2}{3}\%$	$0.1\overline{6}$	$\frac{1}{6}$
20%	0.2	$\frac{1}{5}$
25%	0.25	$\frac{1}{4}$
30%	0.3	$\frac{3}{10}$
$33.\overline{3}\%$ or $33\frac{1}{3}\%$	$0.\overline{3}$	$\frac{1}{3}$
37.5% or $37\frac{1}{2}\%$	0.375	$\frac{3}{8}$
40%	0.4	$\frac{2}{5}$
50%	0.5	$\frac{1}{2}$
60%	0.6	$\frac{3}{5}$
62.5% or $62\frac{1}{2}\%$	0.625	$\frac{5}{8}$
$66.\overline{6}\%$ or $66\frac{2}{3}\%$	$0.\overline{6}$	$\frac{2}{3}$
70%	0.7	$\frac{7}{10}$
75%	0.75	$\frac{3}{4}$
80%	0.8	$\frac{4}{5}$
$83.\overline{3}\%$ or $83\frac{1}{3}\%$	$08.\overline{3}$	$\frac{5}{6}$
87.5% or $87\frac{1}{2}\%$	0.875	$\frac{7}{8}$
90%	0.9	$\frac{9}{10}$
100%	1.0	1
110%	1.1	$1\frac{1}{10}$
125%	1.25	$1\frac{1}{4}$
$133.\overline{3}\%$ or $133\frac{1}{3}\%$	$1.\overline{3}$	$1\frac{1}{3}$
150%	1.5	$1\frac{1}{2}$
$166.\overline{6}\%$ or $166\frac{2}{3}\%$	$1.\overline{6}$	$1\frac{2}{3}$
175%	1.75	$1\frac{3}{4}$
200%	2.0	2

Appendix B

Review of Algebra Topics

Recall that equations model many real-life problems. For example, we can use a linear equation to calculate the increase in the number (in millions) of Wi-Fi-enabled cell phones.

Wi-Fi-enabled cell phones let you carry your Internet access with you. There are already several of these smart phones available, and this technology will continue to expand. Predicted numbers of Wi-Fi-enabled cell phones in the United States for various years are shown below.

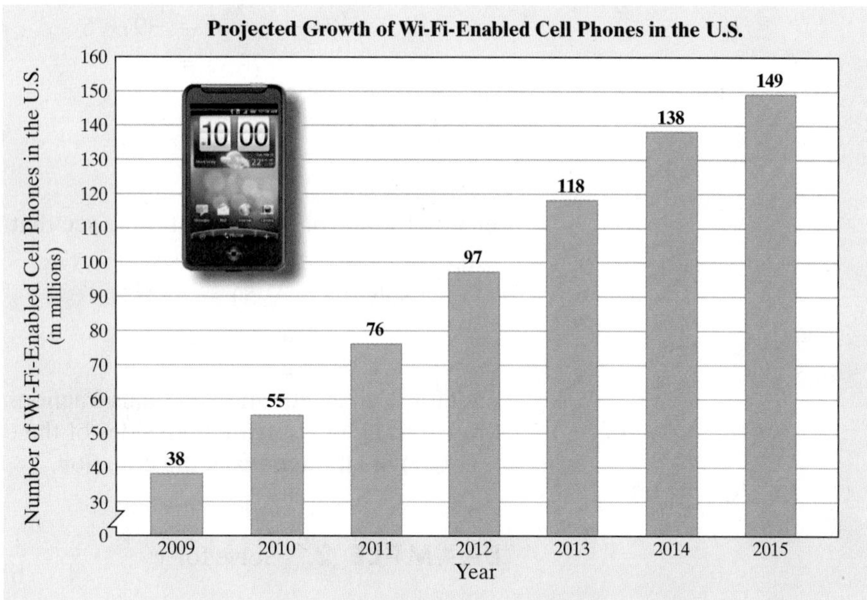

To find the projected increase in the number of Wi-Fi-enabled cell phones in the United States from 2014 to 2015, for example, we can use the equation below.

In words:	Increase in cell phones	is	cell phones in 2015	minus	cell phones in 2014
Translate:	x	$=$	149	$-$	138

Since our variable x (increase in Wi-Fi-enabled cell phones) is by itself on one side of the equation, we can find the value of x by simplifying the right side.

$$x = 11$$

The projected increase in the number of Wi-Fi-enabled cell phones from 2014 to 2015 is 11 million.

The **equation** $x = 149 - 138$ is a linear equation in one variable. In this section, we review solving linear equations and quadratic equations that can be solved by factoring. We will learn other methods for solving quadratic equations in Chapter 6.

B.1 Equations (Linear and Quadratic Solved by Factoring) 

OBJECTIVE

1 Solve linear and quadratic equations.

OBJECTIVE

1 Solving Linear and Quadratic Equations 

EXAMPLE 1 Solve: $2(x - 3) = 5x - 9$.

Solution First, use the distributive property.

$$2(x - 3) = 5x - 9$$

$$2x - 6 = 5x - 9 \quad \text{Use the distributive property.}$$

Next, get variable terms on the same side of the equation by subtracting $5x$ from both sides.

$$2x - 6 - 5x = 5x - 9 - 5x \quad \text{Subtract } 5x \text{ from both sides.}$$

$$-3x - 6 = -9 \quad \text{Simplify.}$$

$$-3x - 6 + 6 = -9 + 6 \quad \text{Add 6 to both sides.}$$

$$-3x = -3 \quad \text{Simplify.}$$

$$\frac{-3x}{-3} = \frac{-3}{-3} \quad \text{Divide both sides by } -3.$$

$$x = 1$$

Let $x = 1$ in the original equation to see that 1 is the solution. □

PRACTICE

1 Solve: $3(x - 5) = 6x - 3$.

Don't forget, if an equation contains fractions, you may want to first clear the equation of fractions by multiplying both sides of the equation by the *least common denominator* (LCD) of all fractions in the equation.

EXAMPLE 2 Solve for y: $\frac{y}{3} - \frac{y}{4} = \frac{1}{6}$.

Solution First, clear the equation of fractions by multiplying both sides of the equation by 12, the LCD of denominators 3, 4, and 6.

$$\frac{y}{3} - \frac{y}{4} = \frac{1}{6}$$

$$12\left(\frac{y}{3} - \frac{y}{4}\right) = 12\left(\frac{1}{6}\right) \quad \text{Multiply both sides by the LCD 12.}$$

$$12\left(\frac{y}{3}\right) - 12\left(\frac{y}{4}\right) = 2 \quad \text{Apply the distributive property.}$$

$$4y - 3y = 2 \quad \text{Simplify.}$$

$$y = 2 \quad \text{Simplify.}$$

Check: To check, let $y = 2$ in the original equation.

$$\frac{y}{3} - \frac{y}{4} = \frac{1}{6} \quad \text{Original equation.}$$

$$\frac{2}{3} - \frac{2}{4} \stackrel{?}{=} \frac{1}{6} \quad \text{Let } y = 2.$$

$$\frac{8}{12} - \frac{6}{12} \stackrel{?}{=} \frac{1}{6} \quad \text{Write fractions with the LCD.}$$

$$\frac{2}{12} \stackrel{?}{=} \frac{1}{6} \quad \text{Subtract.}$$

$$\frac{1}{6} = \frac{1}{6} \quad \text{Simplify.}$$

This is a true statement, so the solution is 2. □

PRACTICE 2 Solve for y: $\frac{y}{2} - \frac{y}{5} = \frac{1}{4}$.

EXAMPLE 3 Solve: $3(x^2 + 4) + 5 = -6(x^2 + 2x) + 13$.

Solution Rewrite the equation so that one side is 0.

$$3(x^2 + 4) + 5 = -6(x^2 + 2x) + 13$$

$$3x^2 + 12 + 5 = -6x^2 - 12x + 13 \quad \text{Apply the distributive property.}$$

$$9x^2 + 12x + 4 = 0 \quad \text{Rewrite the equation so that one side is 0.}$$

$$(3x + 2)(3x + 2) = 0 \quad \text{Factor.}$$

$$3x + 2 = 0 \quad \text{or} \quad 3x + 2 = 0 \quad \text{Set each factor equal to 0.}$$

$$3x = -2 \quad \text{or} \quad 3x = -2$$

$$x = -\frac{2}{3} \quad \text{or} \quad x = -\frac{2}{3} \quad \text{Solve each equation.}$$

The solution is $-\frac{2}{3}$. Check by substituting $-\frac{2}{3}$ into the original equation. □

PRACTICE 3 Solve: $8(x^2 + 3) + 4 = -8x(x + 3) + 19$.

EXAMPLE 4 Solve for x: $\frac{x + 5}{2} + \frac{1}{2} = 2x - \frac{x - 3}{8}$.

Solution Multiply both sides of the equation by 8, the LCD of 2 and 8.

$$8\left(\frac{x + 5}{2} + \frac{1}{2}\right) = 8\left(2x - \frac{x - 3}{8}\right) \quad \text{Multiply both sides by 8.}$$

$$8\left(\frac{x + 5}{2}\right) + 8 \cdot \frac{1}{2} = 8 \cdot 2x - 8\left(\frac{x - 3}{8}\right) \quad \text{Apply the distributive property.}$$

$$4(x + 5) + 4 = 16x - (x - 3) \quad \text{Simplify.}$$

$$4x + 20 + 4 = 16x - x + 3 \quad \text{Use the distributive property to remove parentheses.}$$

$$4x + 24 = 15x + 3 \quad \text{Combine like terms.}$$

$$-11x + 24 = 3 \quad \text{Subtract } 15x \text{ from both sides.}$$

$$-11x = -21 \quad \text{Subtract 24 from both sides.}$$

$$\frac{-11x}{-11} = \frac{-21}{-11} \quad \text{Divide both sides by } -11.$$

$$x = \frac{21}{11} \quad \text{Simplify.}$$

Helpful Hint
When we multiply both sides of an equation by a number, the distributive property tells us that each term of the equation is multiplied by the number.

Check: To check, verify that replacing x with $\frac{21}{11}$ makes the original equation true. The solution is $\frac{21}{11}$. □

PRACTICE 4 Solve for x: $x - \frac{x - 2}{12} = \frac{x + 3}{4} + \frac{1}{4}$.

EXAMPLE 5 Solve: $2x^2 = \frac{17}{3}x + 1$.

Solution

$$2x^2 = \frac{17}{3}x + 1$$

$$3(2x^2) = 3\left(\frac{17}{3}x + 1\right) \quad \text{Clear the equation of fractions.}$$

$$6x^2 = 17x + 3 \quad \text{Apply the distributive property.}$$

$$6x^2 - 17x - 3 = 0 \quad \text{Rewrite the equation in standard form.}$$

$$(6x + 1)(x - 3) = 0 \quad \text{Factor.}$$

$$6x + 1 = 0 \quad \text{or} \quad x - 3 = 0 \quad \text{Set each factor equal to zero.}$$

$$6x = -1$$

$$x = -\frac{1}{6} \quad \text{or} \quad x = 3 \quad \text{Solve each equation.}$$

The solutions are $-\frac{1}{6}$ and 3. □

PRACTICE 5 Solve: $4x^2 = \frac{15}{2}x + 1$.

B.1 Exercise Set

MyMathLab®

MIXED PRACTICE

Solve each equation. See Examples 1 through 5.

1. $x^2 + 11x + 24 = 0$

2. $y^2 - 10y + 24 = 0$

3. $3x - 4 - 5x = x + 4 + x$

4. $13x - 15x + 8 = 4x + 2 - 24$

5. $12x^2 + 5x - 2 = 0$

6. $3y^2 - y - 14 = 0$

7. $z^2 + 9 = 10z$

8. $n^2 + n = 72$

9. $5(y + 4) = 4(y + 5)$

10. $6(y - 4) = 3(y - 8)$

11. $0.6x - 10 = 1.4x - 14$

12. $0.3x + 2.4 = 0.1x + 4$

13. $x(5x + 2) = 3$

14. $n(2n - 3) = 2$

15. $6x - 2(x - 3) = 4(x + 1) + 4$

16. $10x - 2(x + 4) = 8(x - 2) + 6$

17. $\frac{3}{8} + \frac{b}{3} = \frac{5}{12}$

18. $\frac{a}{2} + \frac{7}{4} = 5$

19. $x^2 - 6x = x(8 + x)$

20. $n(3 + n) = n^2 + 4n$

21. $\frac{z^2}{6} - \frac{z}{2} - 3 = 0$

22. $\frac{c^2}{20} - \frac{c}{4} + \frac{1}{5} = 0$

23. $-z + 3(2 + 4z) = 6(z + 1) + 5z$

24. $4(m - 6) - m = 8(m - 3) - 5m$

25. $\frac{x^2}{2} + \frac{x}{20} = \frac{1}{10}$

26. $\frac{y^2}{30} = \frac{y}{15} + \frac{1}{2}$

27. $\frac{4t^2}{5} = \frac{t}{5} + \frac{3}{10}$

28. $\frac{5x^2}{6} - \frac{7x}{2} + \frac{2}{3} = 0$

29. $\frac{3t + 1}{8} = \frac{5 + 2t}{7} + 2$

30. $4 - \frac{2z + 7}{9} = \frac{7 - z}{12}$

31. $\frac{m - 4}{3} - \frac{3m - 1}{5} = 1$

32. $\frac{n + 1}{8} - \frac{2 - n}{3} = \frac{5}{6}$

33. $3x^2 = -x$

34. $y^2 = -5y$

35. $x(x - 3) = x^2 + 5x + 7$

36. $z^2 - 4z + 10 = z(z - 5)$

37. $3(t - 8) + 2t = 7 + t$

38. $7c - 2(3c + 1) = 5(4 - 2c)$

39. $-3(x - 4) + x = 5(3 - x)$

40. $-4(a + 1) - 3a = -7(2a - 3)$

41. $(x - 1)(x + 4) = 24$

42. $(2x - 1)(x + 2) = -3$

43. $\frac{x^2}{4} - \frac{5}{2}x + 6 = 0$

44. $\frac{x^2}{18} + \frac{x}{2} + 1 = 0$

45. $y^2 + \frac{1}{4} = -y$

46. $\frac{x^2}{10} + \frac{5}{2} = x$

47. Which solution strategies are incorrect? Why?

a. Solve $(y - 2)(y + 2) = 4$ by setting each factor equal to 4.

b. Solve $(x + 1)(x + 3) = 0$ by setting each factor equal to 0.

c. Solve $z^2 + 5z + 6 = 0$ by factoring $z^2 + 5z + 6$ and setting each factor equal to 0.

d. Solve $x^2 + 6x + 8 = 10$ by factoring $x^2 + 6x + 8$ and setting each factor equal to 0.

48. Describe two ways a linear equation differs from a quadratic equation.

Find the value of K such that the equations are equivalent.

49. $3.2x + 4 = 5.4x - 7$
$3.2x = 5.4x + K$

50. $-7.6y - 10 = -1.1y + 12$
$-7.6y = -1.1y + K$

51. $\frac{x}{6} + 4 = \frac{x}{3}$
$x + K = 2x$

52. $\frac{5x}{4} + \frac{1}{2} = \frac{x}{2}$
$5x + K = 2x$

Solve and check.

53. $2.569x = -12.48534$

54. $-9.112y = -47.537304$

55. $2.86z - 8.1258 = -3.75$

56. $1.25x - 20.175 = -8.15$

B.2 Problem Solving 

OBJECTIVES

1 Write Algebraic Expressions That Can Be Simplified.

2 Apply the Steps for Problem Solving.

OBJECTIVE

1 Writing and Simplifying Algebraic Expressions 

In order to prepare for problem solving, we practice writing algebraic expressions that can be simplified.

Our first example involves consecutive integers and perimeter. Recall that *consecutive integers* are integers that follow one another in order. Study the examples of consecutive, even, and odd integers and their representations.

Consecutive Integers:

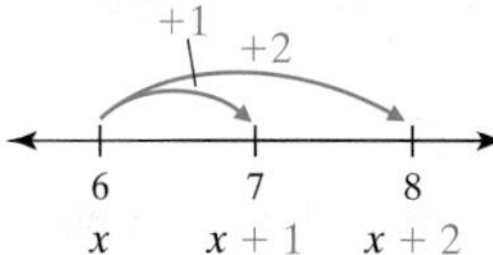

Consecutive Even Integers:

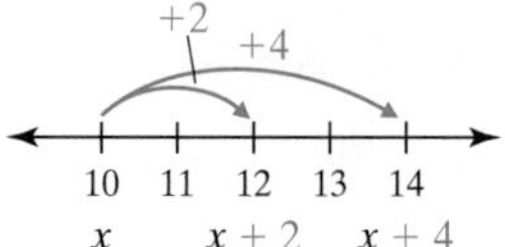

Consecutive Odd Integers:

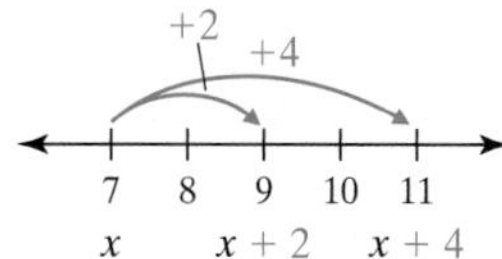

EXAMPLE 1 Write the following as algebraic expressions. Then simplify.

a. The sum of three consecutive integers, if x is the first consecutive integer.

△ **b.** The perimeter of the triangle with sides of length x, $5x$, and $6x - 3$.

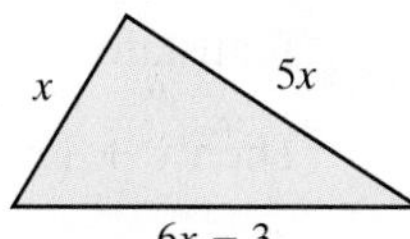

(Continued on next page)

Solution

a. Recall that if x is the first integer, then the next consecutive integer is 1 more, or $x + 1$, and the next consecutive integer is 1 more than $x + 1$, or $x + 2$.

In words:	first integer	plus	next consecutive integer	plus	next consecutive integer
	↓	↓	↓	↓	↓
Translate:	x	$+$	$(x + 1)$	$+$	$(x + 2)$

Then $x + (x + 1) + (x + 2) = x + x + 1 + x + 2$

$= 3x + 3$ Simplify by combining like terms.

b. The perimeter of a triangle is the sum of the lengths of the sides.

In words:	side	+	side	+	side
	↓		↓		↓
Translate:	x	$+$	$5x$	$+$	$(6x - 3)$

Then $x + 5x + (6x - 3) = x + 5x + 6x - 3$

$= 12x - 3$ Simplify. □

PRACTICE

1 Write the following algebraic expressions. Then simplify.

a. The sum of three consecutive odd integers if x is the first consecutive odd integer

b. The perimeter of a trapezoid with bases x and $2x$ and sides of $x + 2$ and $2x - 3$

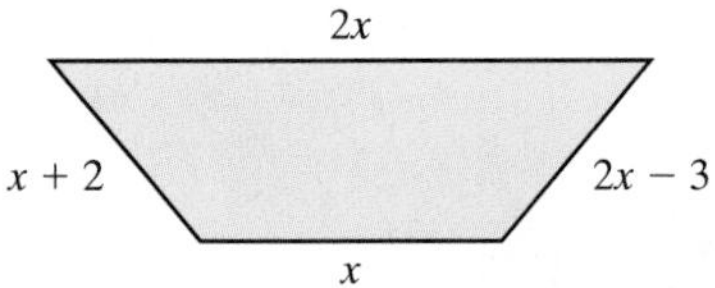

EXAMPLE 2 Writing Algebraic Expressions Representing Metropolitan Regions

The most populous metropolitan region in the United States is New York City, although it is only the sixth most populous metropolis in the world. Tokyo is the most populous metropolitan region. Mexico City is the fifth most populous metropolis in the world. Mexico City's population is 0.03 million more than New York's, and Tokyo's is twice that of New York, decreased by 2.19 million. Write the sum of the populations of these three metropolitan regions as an algebraic expression. Let x be the population of New York (in millions). (*Source:* United Nations, Department of Economic and Social Affairs)

Solution:

If $x =$ the population of New York (in millions), then

$x + 0.03 =$ the population of Mexico City (in millions) and

$2x - 2.19 =$ the population of Tokyo (in millions)

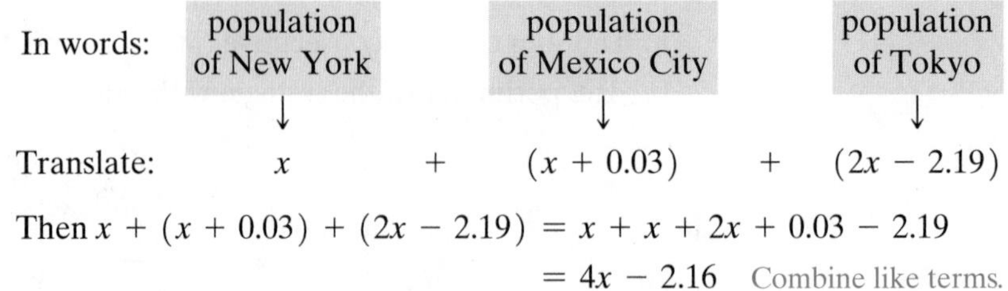

In words:	population of New York		population of Mexico City		population of Tokyo
	↓		↓		↓
Translate:	x	$+$	$(x + 0.03)$	$+$	$(2x - 2.19)$

Then $x + (x + 0.03) + (2x - 2.19) = x + x + 2x + 0.03 - 2.19$

$= 4x - 2.16$ Combine like terms.

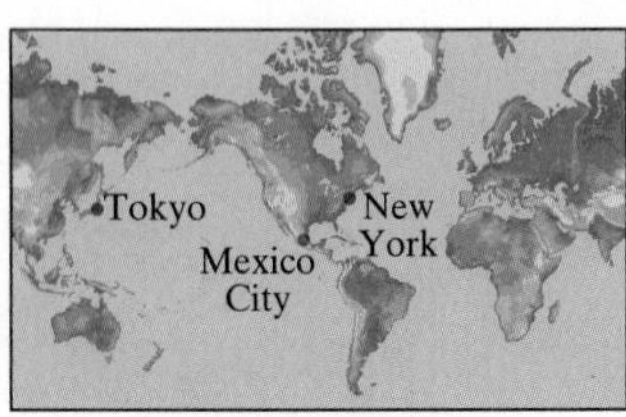

In Exercise 57, we will find the actual populations of these cities. □

PRACTICE

2 The three busiest airports in Europe are in London, England; Paris, France; and Frankfurt, Germany. The airport in London has 12.9 million more arrivals and departures than the Frankfurt airport. The Paris airport has 5.2 million more arrivals and departures than the Frankfurt airport. Write the sum of the arrivals and departures from these three cities as a simplified algebraic expression. Let x be the number of arrivals and departures at the Frankfurt airport. (*Source:* Association of European Airlines)

OBJECTIVE

2 Applying Steps for Problem Solving 

Our main purpose for studying algebra is to solve problems. The following problem-solving strategy will be used throughout this text and may also be used to solve real-life problems that occur outside the mathematics classroom.

General Strategy for Problem Solving

1. UNDERSTAND the problem. During this step, become comfortable with the problem. Some ways of doing this are to:

   Read and reread the problem.

   Propose a solution and check. Pay careful attention to how you check your proposed solution. This will help when writing an equation to model the problem.

   Construct a drawing.

   Choose a variable to represent the unknown. (Very important part)

2. TRANSLATE the problem into an equation.
3. SOLVE the equation.
4. INTERPRET the results: *Check* the proposed solution in the stated problem and *state* your conclusion.

Let's review this strategy by solving a problem involving unknown numbers.

EXAMPLE 3 **Finding Unknown Numbers**

Find three numbers such that the second number is 3 more than twice the first number, and the third number is four times the first number. The sum of the three numbers is 164.

Solution

> **Helpful Hint**
> The purpose of guessing a solution is not to guess correctly but to gain confidence and to help understand the problem and how to model it.

1. UNDERSTAND the problem. First let's read and reread the problem and then propose a solution. For example, if the first number is 25, then the second number is 3 more than twice 25, or 53. The third number is four times 25, or 100. The sum of 25, 53, and 100 is 178, not the required sum, but we have gained some valuable information about the problem. First, we know that the first number is less than 25 since our guess led to a sum greater than the required sum. Also, we have gained some information as to how to model the problem.

   Next let's assign a variable and use this variable to represent any other unknown quantities. If we let

$$x = \text{the first number, then}$$

$$2x + 3 = \text{the second number}$$

($2x$: twice the first number; $+ 3$: 3 more than)

$$4x = \text{the third number}$$

(Continued on next page)

2. TRANSLATE the problem into an equation. To do so, we use the fact that the sum of the numbers is 164. First let's write this relationship in words and then translate to an equation.

In words:	first number	added to	second number	added to	third number	is	164
	↓	↓	↓	↓	↓	↓	↓
Translate:	x	$+$	$(2x + 3)$	$+$	$4x$	$=$	164

3. SOLVE the equation.

$$x + (2x + 3) + 4x = 164$$
$$x + 2x + 4x + 3 = 164 \quad \text{Remove parentheses.}$$
$$7x + 3 = 164 \quad \text{Combine like terms.}$$
$$7x = 161 \quad \text{Subtract 3 from both sides.}$$
$$x = 23 \quad \text{Divide both sides by 7.}$$

4. INTERPRET. Here, we *check* our work and *state* the solution. Recall that if the first number $x = 23$, then the second number $2x + 3 = 2 \cdot 23 + 3 = 49$ and the third number $4x = 4 \cdot 23 = 92$.

Check: Is the second number 3 more than twice the first number? Yes, since 3 more than twice 23 is $46 + 3$, or 49. Also, their sum, $23 + 49 + 92 = 164$, is the required sum.

State: The three numbers are 23, 49, and 92. □

PRACTICE

3 Find three numbers such that the second number is 8 less than triple the first number, the third number is five times the first number, and the sum of the three numbers is 118.

Many of today's rates and statistics are given as percents. Interest rates, tax rates, nutrition labeling, and percent of households in a given category are just a few examples. Before we practice solving problems containing percents, let's briefly review the meaning of percent and how to find a percent of a number.

The word *percent* means "per hundred," and the symbol % denotes percent.

This means that 23% is 23 per hundred, or $\frac{23}{100}$. Also,

$$41\% = \frac{41}{100} = 0.41$$

To find a percent of a number, we multiply.

$$16\% \text{ of } 25 = 16\% \cdot 25 = 0.16 \cdot 25 = 4$$

Thus, 16% of 25 is 4.

Study the table below. It will help you become more familiar with finding percents.

Percent	*Meaning/Shortcut*	*Example*
50%	$\frac{1}{2}$ or half of a number	50% of 60 is 30.
25%	$\frac{1}{4}$ or a quarter of a number	25% of 60 is 15.
10%	0.1 or $\frac{1}{10}$ of a number (move the decimal point 1 place to the left)	10% of 60 is 6.0 or 6.
1%	0.01 or $\frac{1}{100}$ of a number (move the decimal point 2 places to the left)	1% of 60 is 0.60 or 0.6.
100%	1 or all of a number	100% of 60 is 60.
200%	2 or double a number	200% of 60 is 120.

✓CONCEPT CHECK

Suppose you are finding 112% of a number x. Which of the following is a correct description of the result? Explain.

a. The result is less than x. **b.** The result is equal to x. **c.** The result is greater than x.

Next, we solve a problem containing a percent.

EXAMPLE 4 **Finding the Original Price of a Computer**

Suppose that a computer store just announced an 8% decrease in the price of a particular computer model. If this computer sells for $2162 after the decrease, find the original price of this computer.

Solution

1. UNDERSTAND. Read and reread the problem. Recall that a percent decrease means a percent of the original price. Let's guess that the original price of the computer is $2500. The amount of decrease is then 8% of $2500, or $(0.08)(\$2500) = \$200$. This means that the new price of the computer is the original price minus the decrease, or $\$2500 - \$200 = \$2300$. Our guess is incorrect, but we now have an idea of how to model this problem. In our model, we will let $x =$ the original price of the computer.

2. TRANSLATE.

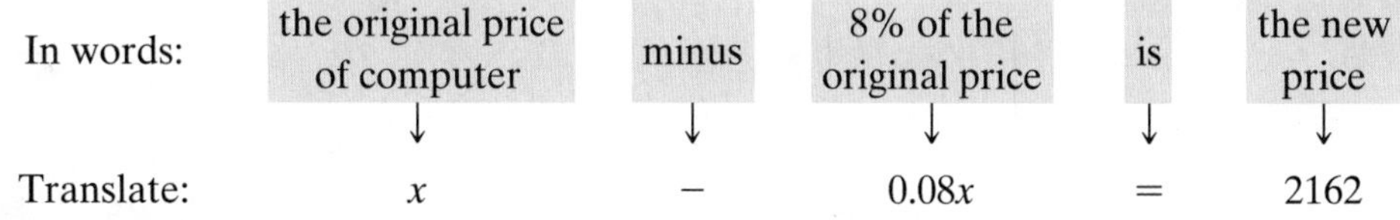

In words:	the original price of computer	minus	8% of the original price	is	the new price
	↓	↓	↓	↓	↓
Translate:	x	$-$	$0.08x$	$=$	2162

3. SOLVE the equation.

$$x - 0.08x = 2162$$

$$0.92x = 2162 \quad \text{Combine like terms.}$$

$$x = \frac{2162}{0.92} = 2350 \quad \text{Divide both sides by 0.92.}$$

4. INTERPRET.

Check: If the original price of the computer was $2350, the new price is

$$\$2350 - (0.08)(\$2350) = \$2350 - \$188$$

$$= \$2162 \quad \text{The given new price}$$

State: The original price of the computer was $2350. □

Answer to Concept Check:
c; answers may vary

PRACTICE

4 At the end of the season, the cost of a snowboard was reduced by 40%. If the snowboard sells for $270 after the decrease, find the original price of the board.

Vocabulary & Readiness Check

Fill in each blank with <, >, *or* =. *(Assume that the unknown number is a positive number.)*

1. 130% of a number ___ the number.

2. 70% of a number ___ the number.

3. 100% of a number ___ the number.

4. 200% of a number ___ the number.

Complete the table. The first row has been completed for you.

	First Integer	*All Described Integers*
Three consecutive integers	18	18, 19, 20
5. Four consecutive integers	31	
6. Three consecutive odd integers	31	
7. Three consecutive even integers	18	
8. Four consecutive even integers	92	
9. Three consecutive integers	y	
10. Three consecutive even integers	z (z is even)	
11. Four consecutive integers	p	
12. Three consecutive odd integers	s (s is odd)	

B.2 Exercise Set

MyMathLab®

Write the following as algebraic expressions. Then simplify. See Examples 1 and 2.

△ **1.** The perimeter of a square with side length y.

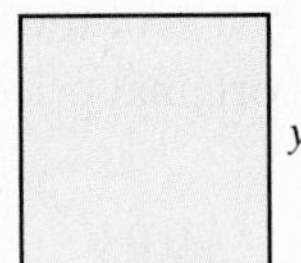

△ **2.** The perimeter of a rectangle with length x and width $x - 5$.

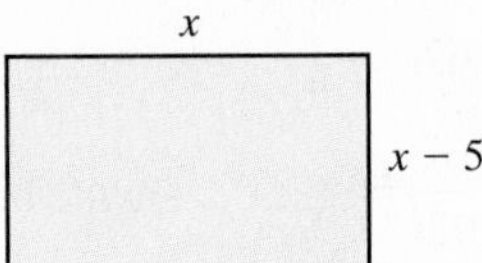

3. The sum of three consecutive integers if the first is z.

4. The sum of three consecutive odd integers if the first integer is z.

5. The total amount of money (in cents) in x nickels, $(x + 3)$ dimes, and $2x$ quarters. (*Hint:* The value of a nickel is 5 cents, the value of a dime is 10 cents, and the value of a quarter is 25 cents.)

6. The total amount of money (in cents) in y quarters, $7y$ dimes, and $(2y - 1)$ nickels. (Use the hint for Exercise 5.)

△ **7.** A piece of land along Bayou Liberty is to be fenced and subdivided as shown so that each rectangle has the same dimensions. Express the total amount of fencing needed as an algebraic expression in x.

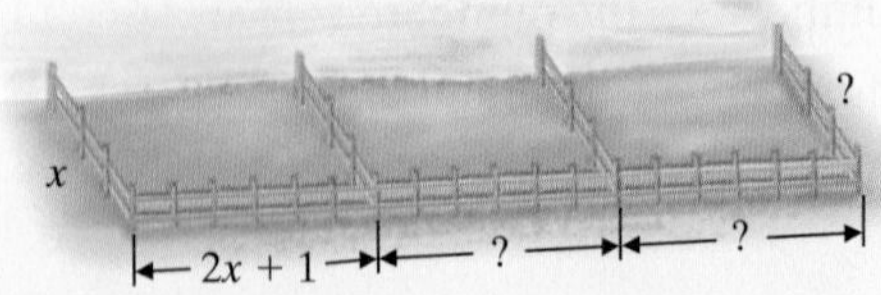

8. A flooded piece of land near the Mississippi River in New Orleans is to be surveyed and divided into 4 rectangles of equal dimension. Express the total amount of fencing needed as an algebraic expression in x.

△ **9.** Write the perimeter of the floor plan shown as an algebraic expression in x.

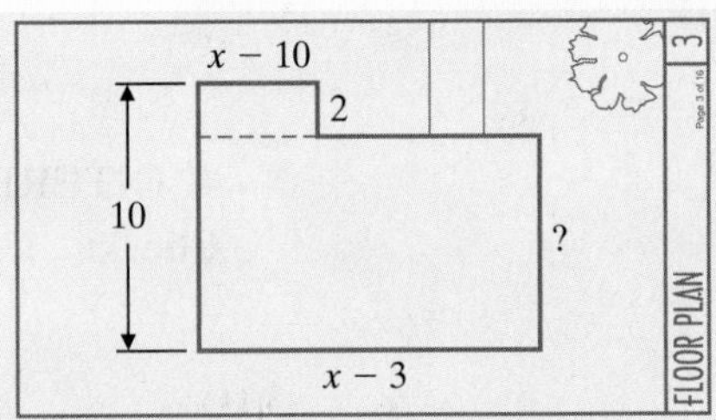

10. Write the perimeter of the floor plan shown as an algebraic expression in x.

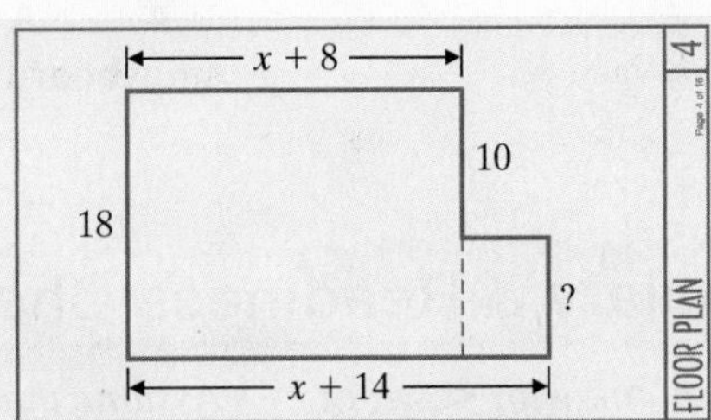

Solve. For Exercises 11 and 12, the solutions have been started for you. See Example 3.

11. Four times the difference of a number and 2 is the same as 2, increased by four times the number, plus twice the number. Find the number.

Start the solution:

1. UNDERSTAND the problem. Reread it as many times as needed.
2. TRANSLATE into an equation. (Fill in the blanks below.)

Four times	the difference of a number and 2	is the same as	2	increased by	four times the number	plus	twice the number
↓	↓	↓	↓	↓	↓	↓	↓
4 ·	$(x - 2)$	=	2	___	___	___	___

Finish with:

3. SOLVE and 4. INTERPRET

12. Twice the sum of a number and 3 is the same as five times the number, minus 1, minus four times the number. Find the number.

Start the solution:

1. UNDERSTAND the problem. Reread it as many times as needed.
2. TRANSLATE into an equation. (Fill in the blanks below.)

Twice	the sum of a number and 3	is the same as	five times the number	minus	1	minus	four times the number
↓	↓	↓	↓	↓	↓	↓	↓
2	$(x + 3)$	=	___	___	1	___	___

Finish with:

3. SOLVE and 4. INTERPRET

13. A second number is five times a first number. A third number is 100 more than the first number. If the sum of the three numbers is 415, find the numbers.

14. A second number is 6 less than a first number. A third number is twice the first number. If the sum of the three numbers is 306, find the numbers.

Solve. See Example 4.

15. The United States consists of 2271 million acres of land. Approximately 29% of this land is federally owned. Find the number of acres that are not federally owned. (*Source:* U.S. General Services Administration)

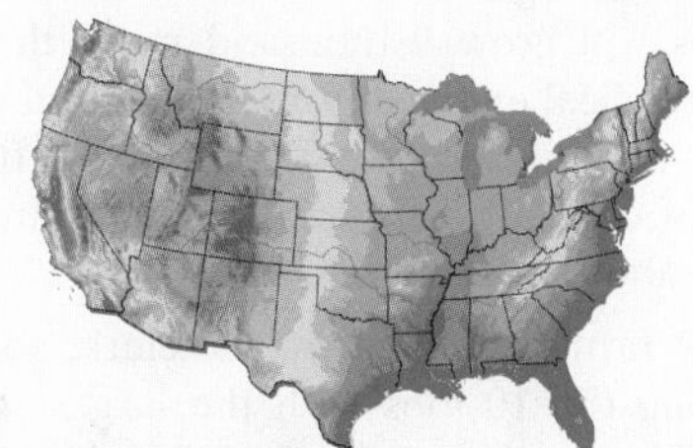

16. The state of Nevada contains the most federally owned acres of land in the United States. If 90% of the state's 70 million acres of land is federally owned, find the number of acres that are not federally owned. (*Source:* U.S. General Services Administration)

17. In 2010, 8476 earthquakes occurred in the United States. Of these, 91.4% were minor tremors with magnitudes of 3.9 or less on the Richter scale. How many minor earthquakes occurred in the United States in 2010? Round to the nearest whole. (*Source:* U.S. Geological Survey National Earthquake Information Center)

18. Of the 1543 tornadoes that occurred in the United States during 2010, 27.7% occurred during the month of June. How many tornadoes occurred in the United States during June 2010? Round to the nearest whole. (*Source:* Storm Prediction Center)

19. In a recent survey, 15% of online shoppers in the United States say that they prefer to do business only with large, well-known retailers. In a group of 1500 online shoppers, how many are willing to do business with any size retailers? (*Source:* Inc.com)

20. In 2010, the restaurant industry employed 9% of the U.S. workforce. If there are estimated to be 141 million Americans in the workforce, how many people are employed by the restaurant industry? Round to the nearest tenth. (*Source:* National Restaurant Association, U.S. Bureau of Labor Statistics)

The following graph is called a circle graph or a pie chart. The circle represents a whole, or in this case, 100%. This particular graph shows the number of minutes per day that people use email at work. Use this graph to answer Exercises 21 through 24.

Time Spent on Email at Work

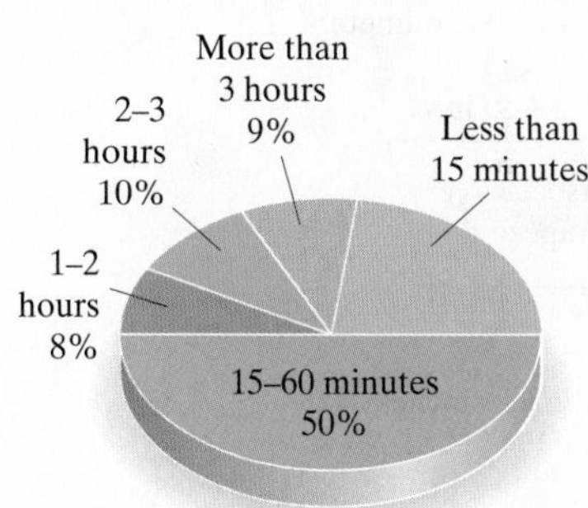

Source: Pew Internet & American Life Project

21. What percent of email users at work spend less than 15 minutes on email per day?

22. Among email users at work, what is the most common time spent on email per day?

23. If it were estimated that a large company has 4633 employees, how many of these would you expect to be using email more than 3 hours per day?

24. If it were estimated that a medium-size company has 250 employees, how many of these would you expect to be using email between 2 and 3 hours per day?

MIXED PRACTICE

Use the diagrams to find the unknown measures of angles or lengths of sides. Recall that the sum of the angle measures of a triangle is 180°.

25.

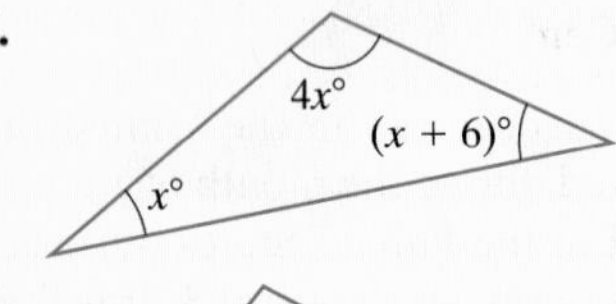

26.

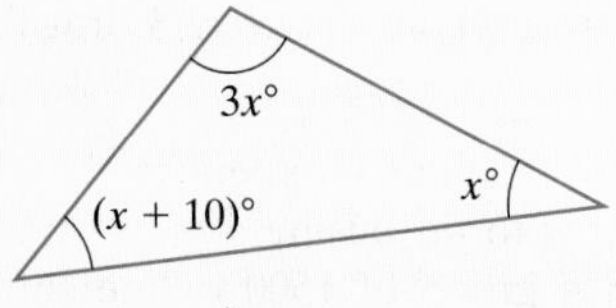

27.

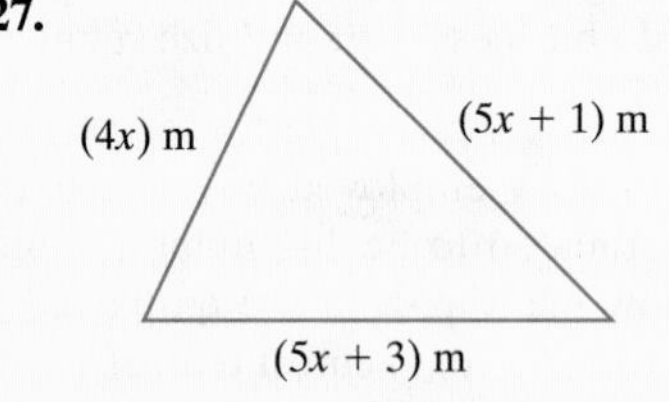

Perimeter is 102 meters.

28.

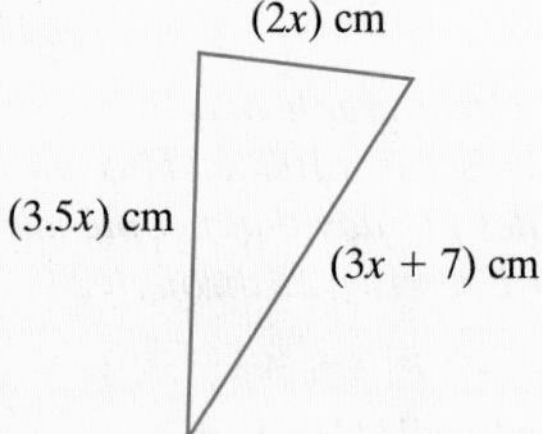

Perimeter is 75 centimeters.

29.

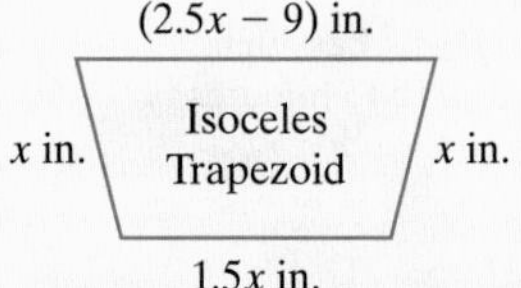

Perimeter is 99 inches.

30.

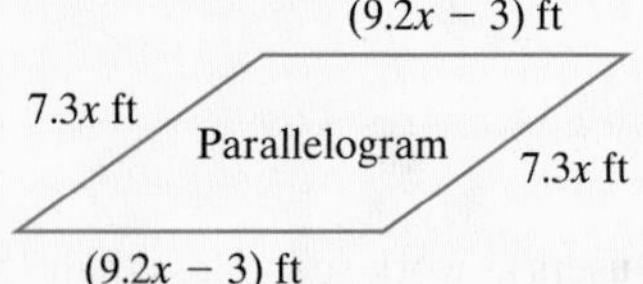

Perimeter is 324 feet.

Solve.

31. The sum of three consecutive integers is 228. Find the integers.

32. The sum of three consecutive odd integers is 327. Find the integers.

33. The ZIP codes of three Nevada locations—Fallon, Fernley, and Gardnerville Ranchos—are three consecutive even integers. If twice the first integer added to the third is 268,222, find each ZIP code.

34. During a recent year, the average SAT scores in math for the states of Alabama, Louisiana, and Michigan were 3 consecutive integers. If the sum of the first integer, second integer, and three times the third integer is 2637, find each score.

Many companies predict the growth or decline of various technologies. The following data is based on information from Techcrunchies, a technological information site. Notice that the first table is the predicted increase in the number of Wi-Fi-enabled cell phones (in millions), and the second is the predicted percent increase in the number of Wi-Fi-enabled cell phones in the United States.

35. Use the middle column in the table to find the predicted number of Wi-Fi-enabled cell phones for each year.

Year	***Increase in Wi-Fi-Enabled Cell Phones***	***Predicted Number***
2010	$2x - 21$	
2012	$\frac{5}{2}x + 2$	
2014	$3x + 24$	
Total	290 million	

36. Use the middle column in the table to find the predicted percent increase in the number of Wi-Fi-enabled cell phones for each year.

Year	***Percent Increase in Wi-Fi-Enabled Cell Phones since 2009***	***Predicted Percent Increase***
2010	x	
2011	$2x + 10$	
2012	$4x - 25$	
	300%	

Solve.

37. The occupations of biomedical engineers, skin care specialists, and physician assistants are among the 10 with the largest growth from 2008 to 2018. The number of physician assistant jobs will grow 7 thousand less than three times the number of biomedical engineer jobs. The number of skin care specialist jobs will grow 9 thousand more than half the number of biomedical engineer jobs. If the total growth of these three jobs is predicted to be 56 thousand, find the predicted growth of each job. (*Source:* U.S. Department of Labor, Bureau of Labor Statistics)

38. The occupations of farmer or rancher, file clerk, and telemarketer are among the 10 jobs with the largest decline from 2008 to 2018. The number of file clerk jobs is predicted to decline 11 thousand more than the number of telemarketer jobs. The number of farmer or rancher jobs is predicted to decline 3 thousand more than twice the number of telemarketer jobs. If the total decline of these three jobs is predicted to be 166 thousand, find the predicted decline of each job. (*Source:* U.S. Department of Labor, Bureau of Labor Statistics)

39. The B767-300ER aircraft has 88 more seats than the B737-200 aircraft. The F-100 has 32 fewer seats than the B737-200 aircraft. If their total number of seats is 413, find the number of seats for each aircraft. (*Source:* Air Transport Association of America)

40. Cowboy Stadium, home of the Dallas Cowboys of the NFL, seats approximately 9800 more fans than does Candlestick Park, home of the San Francisco 49ers. Soldier Field, home of the Chicago Bears, seats 8700 fewer fans than Candlestick Park. If the total seats in these three stadiums is 211,700, how many seats are in each of the three stadiums?

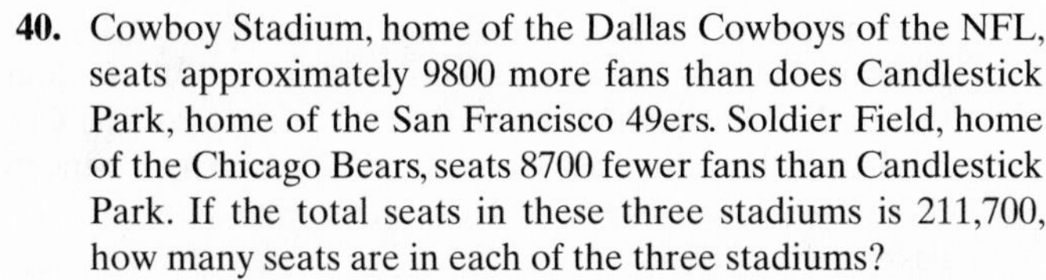

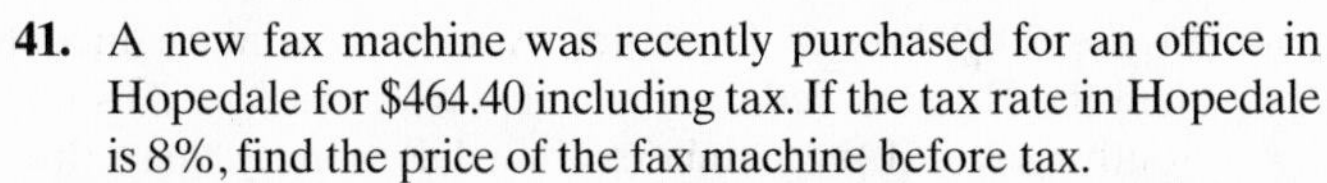

41. A new fax machine was recently purchased for an office in Hopedale for \$464.40 including tax. If the tax rate in Hopedale is 8%, find the price of the fax machine before tax.

42. A premedical student at a local university was complaining that she had just paid \$158.60 for her human anatomy book, including tax. Find the price of the book before taxes if the tax rate at this university is 9%.

43. The median compensation for a U.S. university president was \$436,000 for the 2008–2009 academic year. Calculate the salary of a university president who received a 2.3% raise.

44. In 2009, the population of Brazil was 191.5 million. This represented a decrease in population of 3.7% from 2000. What was the population of Brazil in 2000? Round to the nearest tenth of a million. (*Source:* Population Reference Bureau)

45. In 2010, the population of Swaziland was 1,200,000 people. From 2010 to 2050, Swaziland's population is expected to increase by 50%. Find the expected population of Swaziland in 2050. (*Source:* Population Reference Bureau)

46. Dana, an auto parts supplier headquartered in Toledo, Ohio, recently announced it would be cutting 11,000 jobs worldwide. This is equivalent to 15% of Dana's workforce. Find the size of Dana's workforce prior to this round of job layoffs. Round to the nearest whole. (*Source:* Dana Corporation)

Recall that two angles are complements of each other if their sum is 90°. Two angles are supplements of each other if their sum is 180°. Find the measure of each angle.

47. One angle is three times its supplement increased by 20°. Find the measures of the two supplementary angles.

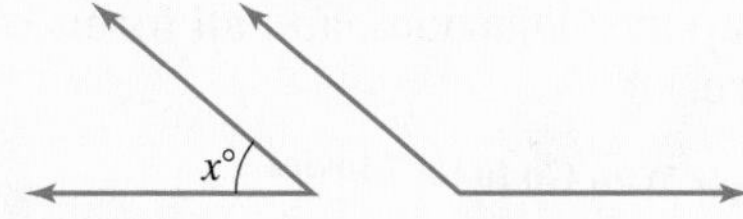

48. One angle is twice its complement increased by 30°. Find the measure of the two complementary angles.

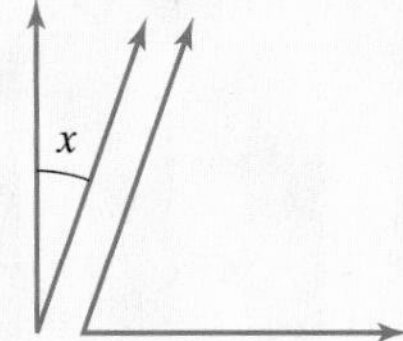

Recall that the sum of the angle measures of a triangle is 180°.

△ **49.** Find the measures of the angles of a triangle if the measure of one angle is twice the measure of a second angle and the third angle measures 3 times the second angle decreased by 12.

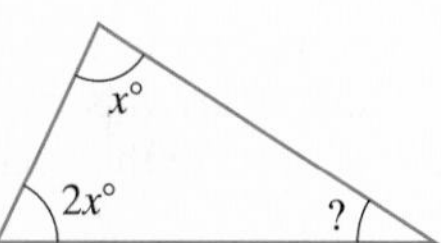

△ **50.** Find the angles of an isoceles triangle whose two base angles are equal and whose third angle is 10° less than three times a base angle.

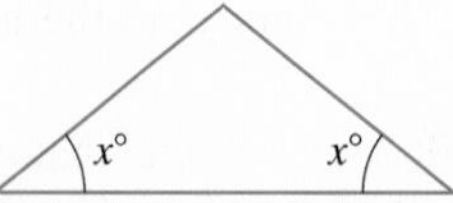

△ **51.** Two frames are needed with the same perimeter: one frame in the shape of a square and one in the shape of an equilateral triangle. Each side of the triangle is 6 centimeters longer than each side of the square. Find the dimensions of each frame. (An equilateral triangle has sides that are the same length.)

52. Two frames are needed with the same perimeter: one frame in the shape of a square and one in the shape of a regular pentagon. Each side of the square is 7 inches longer than each side of the pentagon. Find the dimensions of each frame. (A regular polygon has sides that are the same length.)

53. The sum of the first and third of three consecutive even integers is 156. Find the three even integers.

54. The sum of the second and fourth of four consecutive integers is 110. Find the four integers.

55. Daytona International Speedway in Florida has 37,000 more grandstand seats than twice the number of grandstand seats at Darlington Motor Raceway in South Carolina. Together, these two race tracks seat 220,000 NASCAR fans. How many seats does each race track have? (*Source:* NASCAR)

56. For the 2010–2011 National Hockey League season, the payroll for the San Jose Sharks was \$5,986,667 more than that for the Montreal Canadiens. The total payroll for these two teams was \$113,103,333. What were the payrolls for these two teams for the 2010–2011 NHL season?

57. The sum of the populations of the metropolitan regions of New York, Tokyo, and Mexico City is 75.56 million. Use this information and Example 2 in this section to find the population of each metropolitan region. (*Source:* United Nations Department of Economic and Social Affairs)

58. The airports in London, Paris, and Frankfurt have a total of 177.1 million annual arrivals and departures. Use this information and Practice 2 in this section to find the number from each airport.

59. Suppose the perimeter of the triangle in Example 1b in this section is 483 feet. Find the length of each side.

60. Suppose the perimeter of the trapezoid in Practice 1b in this section is 110 meters. Find the lengths of its sides and bases.

61. Incandescent, fluorescent, and halogen bulbs are lasting longer today than ever before. On average, the number of bulb hours for a fluorescent bulb is 25 times the number of bulb hours for a halogen bulb. The number of bulb hours for an incandescent bulb is 2500 less than the halogen bulb. If the total number of bulb hours for the three types of bulbs is 105,500, find the number of bulb hours for each type. (*Source: Popular Science* magazine)

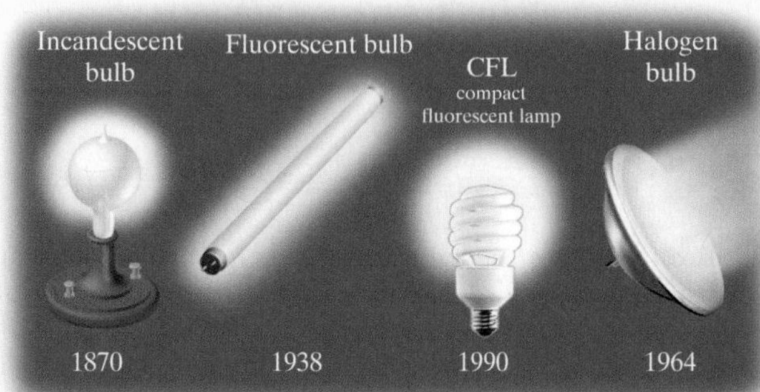

62. Falkland Islands, Iceland, and Norway are the top three countries that have the greatest Internet penetration rate (percent of population) in the world. Falkland Islands has a 6.8 percent greater penetration rate than Iceland. Norway has a 2.3 percent less penetration rate than Iceland. If the sum of the penetration rates is 284.1, find the Internet penetration rate in each of these countries. (*Source*: Internet World Stats)

63. During the 2010 Major League Baseball season, the number of wins for the Milwaukee Brewers, Houston Astros, and Chicago Cubs was three consecutive integers. Of these three teams, the Milwaukee Brewers had the most wins. The Chicago Cubs had the least wins. The total number of wins by these three teams was 228. How many wins did each team have in the 2010 season?

64. In the 2010 Winter Olympics, Austria won more medals than the Russian Federation, which won more medals than South Korea. If the numbers of medals won by these three countries is three consecutive integers whose sum is 45, find the number of medals won by each. (*Source*: Vancouver 2010)

65. The three tallest hospitals in the world are Guy's Tower in London, Queen Mary Hospital in Hong Kong, and Galter Pavilion in Chicago. These buildings have a total height of 1320 feet. Guy's Tower is 67 feet taller than Galter Pavilion, and the Queen Mary Hospital is 47 feet taller than Galter Pavilion. Find the heights of the three hospitals.

△ **66.** The official manual for traffic signs is the *Manual on Uniform Traffic Control Devices* published by the Government Printing Office. The rectangular sign below has a length 12 inches more than twice its height. If the perimeter of the sign is 312 inches, find its dimensions.

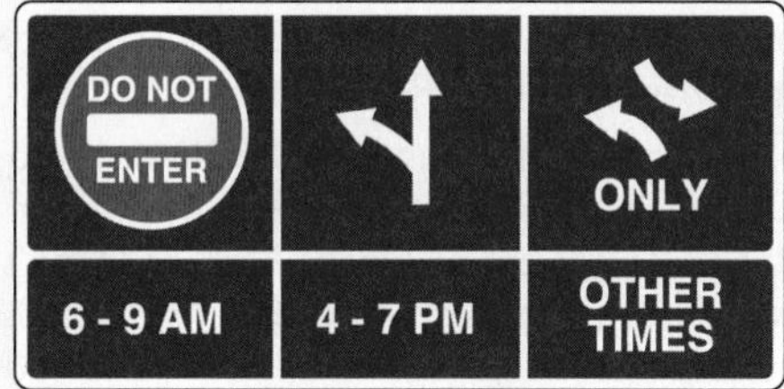

B.3 Graphing

OBJECTIVES

1 Plot Ordered Pairs.

2 Graph Linear Equations.

OBJECTIVE

1 Plotting Ordered Pairs 

Graphs are widely used today in newspapers, magazines, and all forms of newsletters. A few examples of graphs are shown here.

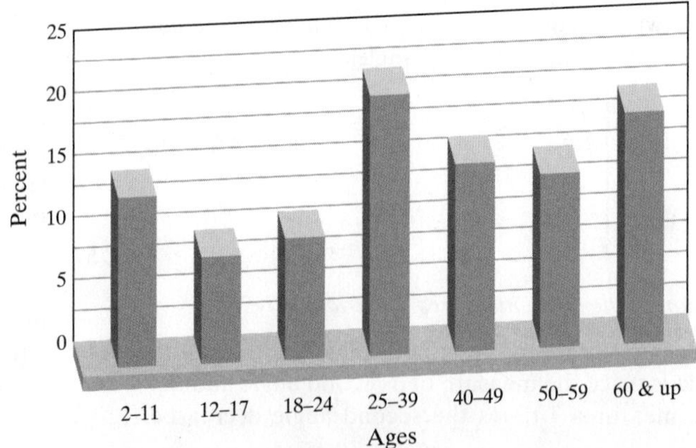

Source: Motion Picture Association of America

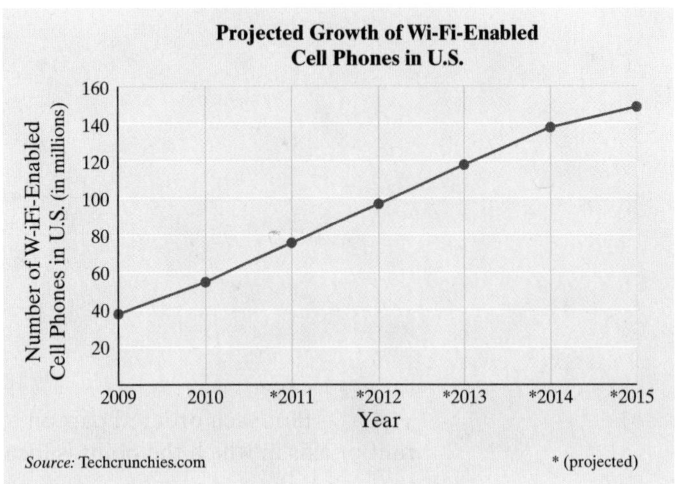

To review how to read these graphs, we review their origin—the rectangular coordinate system. One way to locate points on a plane is by using a **rectangular coordinate system,** which is also called a **Cartesian coordinate system** after its inventor, René Descartes (1596–1650). The next diagram to the left shows the rectangular coordinate system. For further review of this system, see Section 1.1.

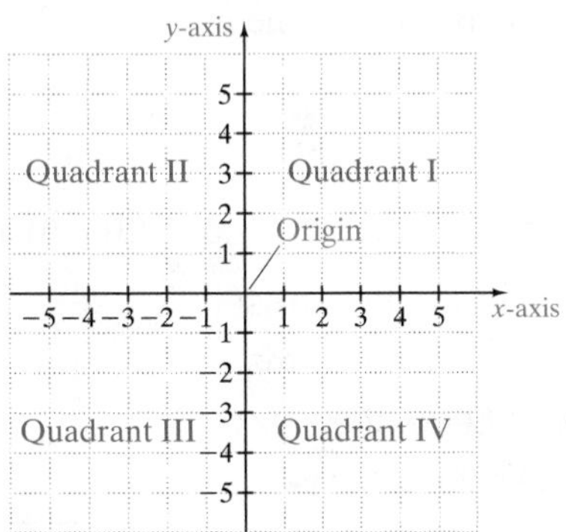

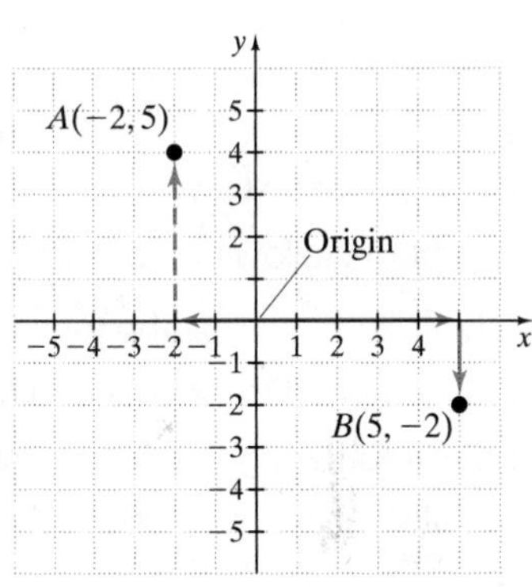

Recall that the location of point A in the figure above is described as 2 units to the left of the origin along the x-axis and 5 units upward parallel to the y-axis. Thus, we identify point A with the ordered pair $(-2, 5)$. Notice that the order of these numbers is *critical.* The x-value -2 is called the ***x*-coordinate** and is associated with the x-axis. The y-value 5 is called the ***y*-coordinate** and is associated with the y-axis. Compare the location of point A with the location of point B, which corresponds to the ordered pair $(5, -2)$.

Keep in mind that **each ordered pair corresponds to exactly one point in the real plane and that each point in the plane corresponds to exactly one ordered pair.** Thus, we may refer to the ordered pair (x, y) as the point (x, y).

EXAMPLE 1 Plot each ordered pair on a Cartesian coordinate system and name the quadrant or axis in which the point is located.

a. $(2, -1)$ **b.** $(0, 5)$ **c.** $(-3, 5)$

d. $(-2, 0)$ **e.** $\left(-\frac{1}{2}, -4\right)$ **f.** $(1.5, 1.5)$

Solution The six points are graphed as shown on the next page.

a. $(2, -1)$ is in quadrant IV. **b.** $(0, 5)$ is on the y-axis.

c. $(-3, 5)$ is in quadrant II. **d.** $(-2, 0)$ is on the x-axis.

e. $\left(-\frac{1}{2}, -4\right)$ is in quadrant III. **f.** $(1.5, 1.5)$ is in quadrant I.

(Continued on next page)

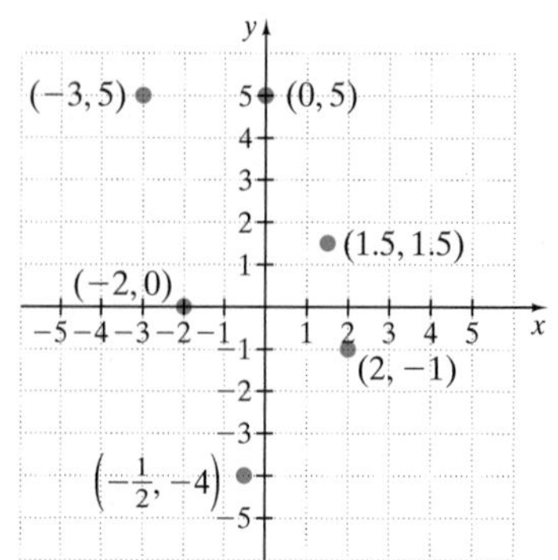

PRACTICE

1 Plot each ordered pair on a Cartesian coordinate system and name the quadrant or axis in which the point is located.

a. $(3, -4)$ **b.** $(0, -2)$ **c.** $(-2, 4)$ **d.** $(4, 0)$ **e.** $\left(-1\frac{1}{2}, -2\right)$ **f.** $(2.5, 3.5)$

Notice that the y-coordinate of any point on the x-axis is 0. For example, the point with coordinates $(-2, 0)$ lies on the x-axis. Also, the x-coordinate of any point on the y-axis is 0. For example, the point with coordinates $(0, 5)$ lies on the y-axis. These points that lie on the axes do not lie in any quadrants.

✓CONCEPT CHECK

Which of the following correctly describes the location of the point $(3, -6)$ in a rectangular coordinate system?

a. 3 units to the left of the y-axis and 6 units above the x-axis
b. 3 units above the x-axis and 6 units to the left of the y-axis
c. 3 units to the right of the y-axis and 6 units below the x-axis
d. 3 units below the x-axis and 6 units to the right of the y-axis

OBJECTIVE

2 Graphing Linear Equations 

Recall that an equation such as $3x - y = 12$ is called a linear equation in two variables, and **the graph of every linear equation in two variables is a line.**

Linear Equation in Two Variables

A linear equation in two variables is an equation that can be written in the form

$$Ax + By = C$$

where A and B are not both 0. This form is called **standard form.**

Some examples of equations in standard form:

$$3x - y = 12$$
$$-2.1x + 5.6y = 0$$

Helpful Hint

Remember: A linear equation is written in standard form when all of the variable terms are on one side of the equation and the constant is on the other side.

Answer to Concept Check:
c

EXAMPLE 2 Graph the equation $y = -2x + 3$.

Solution This is a linear equation. (In standard form it is $2x + y = 3$.) Find three ordered pair solutions, and plot the ordered pairs. The line through the plotted points is the graph. Since the equation is solved for y, let's choose three x-values. We'll choose 0, 2, and then -1 for x to find our three ordered pair solutions.

Let $x = 0$	Let $x = 2$	Let $x = -1$
$y = -2x + 3$	$y = -2x + 3$	$y = -2x + 3$
$y = -2 \cdot 0 + 3$	$y = -2 \cdot 2 + 3$	$y = -2(-1) + 3$
$y = 3$ Simplify.	$y = -1$ Simplify.	$y = 5$ Simplify.

The three ordered pairs (0, 3), (2, −1), and (−1, 5) are listed in the table and the graph is shown.

x	y
0	3
2	−1
−1	5

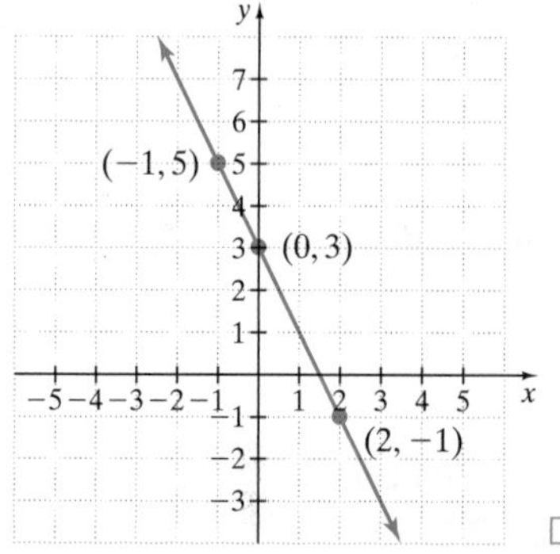

PRACTICE 2 Graph the equation $y = -3x - 2$.

Notice that the graph crosses the y-axis at the point (0, 3). This point is called the **y-intercept.** (You may sometimes see just the number 3 called the y-intercept.) This graph also crosses the x-axis at the point $\left(\frac{3}{2}, 0\right)$. This point is called the **x-intercept.** (You may also see just the number $\frac{3}{2}$ called the x-intercept.)

Since every point on the y-axis has an x-value of 0, we can find the y-intercept of a graph by letting $x = 0$ and solving for y. Also, every point on the x-axis has a y-value of 0. To find the x-intercept, we let $y = 0$ and solve for x.

Finding x- and y-Intercepts

To find an x-intercept, let $y = 0$ and solve for x.
To find a y-intercept, let $x = 0$ and solve for y.

EXAMPLE 3 Graph the linear equation $y = \frac{1}{3}x$.

Solution To graph, we find ordered pair solutions, plot the ordered pairs, and draw a line through the plotted points. We will choose x-values and substitute in the equation. To avoid fractions, we choose x-values that are multiples of 3. To find the y-intercept, we let $x = 0$.

$$y = \frac{1}{3}x$$

If $x = 0$, then $y = \frac{1}{3}(0)$, or 0.

If $x = 6$, then $y = \frac{1}{3}(6)$, or 2.

If $x = -3$, then $y = \frac{1}{3}(-3)$, or -1.

x	y
0	0
6	2
−3	−1

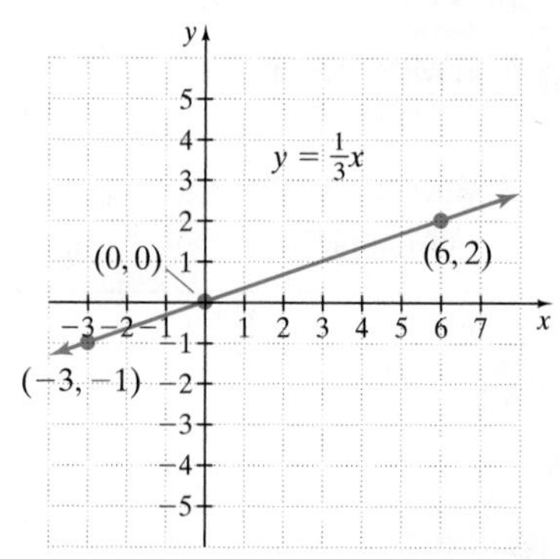

(Continued on next page)

Helpful Hint
Notice that by using multiples of 3 for x, we avoid fractions.

Helpful Hint
Since the equation $y = \frac{1}{3}x$ is solved for y, we choose x-values for finding points. This way, we simply need to evaluate an expression to find the y-value, as shown.

This graph crosses the x-axis at (0, 0) and the y-axis at (0, 0). This means that the x-intercept is (0, 0) and that the y-intercept is (0, 0). □

PRACTICE 3 Graph the linear equation $y = -\frac{1}{2}x$.

B.3 Exercise Set

MyMathLab®

Determine the coordinates of each point on the graph.

1. Point A
2. Point B
3. Point C
4. Point D
5. Point E
6. Point F
7. Point G
8. Point H

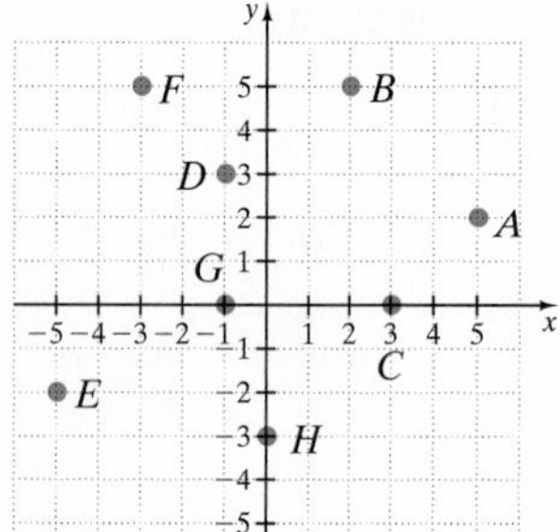

Without graphing, visualize the location of each point. Then give its location by quadrant or x- or y-axis. See Example 1.

9. (2, 3)
10. (0, 5)
11. (−2, 7)
12. (−3, 0)
13. (−1, −4)
14. (4, −2)
15. (0, −100)
16. (10, 30)
17. (−10, −30)
18. (0, 0)
19. (−87, 0)
20. (−42, 17)

Given that x is a positive number and that y is a positive number, determine the quadrant or axis in which each point lies.

21. $(x, -y)$
22. $(-x, y)$
23. $(x, 0)$
24. $(0, -y)$
25. $(-x, -y)$
26. (0, 0)

Graph each linear equation. See Examples 2 and 3.

27. $y = -x - 2$
28. $y = -2x + 1$
29. $3x - 4y = 8$
30. $x - 9y = 3$
31. $y = \frac{1}{3}x$
32. $y = \frac{3}{2}x$
33. $y + 4 = 0$
34. $x = -1.5$

Recall that if f(2) = 7, for example, this corresponds to the ordered pair (2, 7) on the graph of f. Use this information and the graphs of f and g below to answer Exercises 35 through 42.

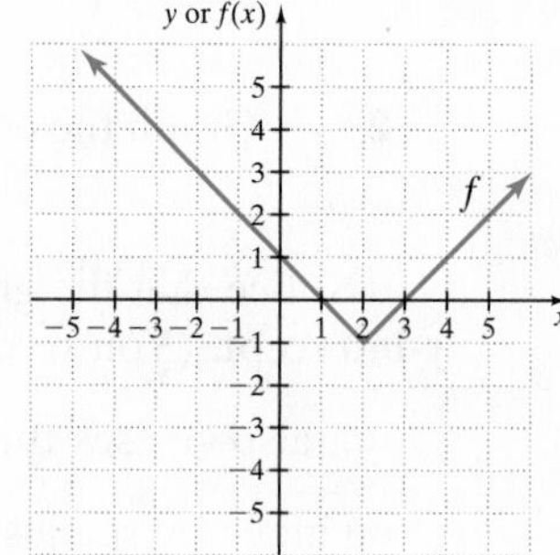

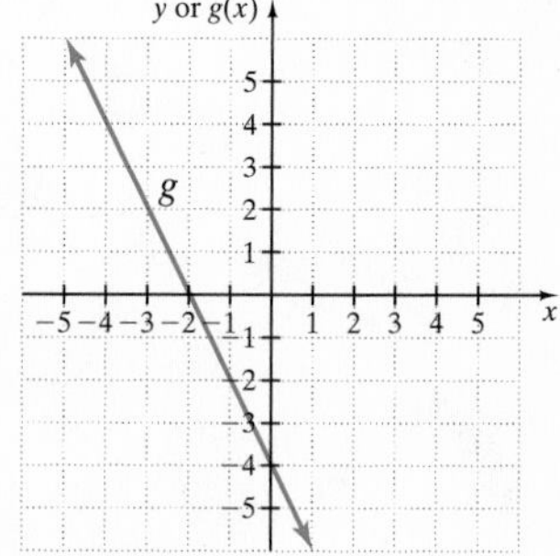

35. $f(4) =$
36. $f(0) =$
37. $g(0) =$
38. $g(-1) =$
39. Find all values for x such that $f(x) = 0$.
40. Find all values for x such that $g(x) = 0$.
41. If (−1, −2) is a point on the graph of g, write this using function notation.
42. If (−1, 2) is a point on the graph of f, write this using function notation.

B.4 Polynomials and Factoring

OBJECTIVES

1 Review Operations on Polynomials.

2 Review Factoring Polynomials.

OBJECTIVE 1 **Operations on Polynomials**

B.4 Exercise Set, Part 1

MyMathLab®

Perform each indicated operation.

1. $(-y^2 + 6y - 1) + (3y^2 - 4y - 10)$
2. $(5z^4 - 6z^2 + z + 1) - (7z^4 - 2z + 1)$
3. Subtract $(x - 5)$ from $(x^2 - 6x + 2)$.
4. $(2x^2 + 6x - 5) + (5x^2 - 10x)$
5. $(5x - 3)^2$
6. $(5x^2 - 14x - 3) \div (5x + 1)$

7. $(2x^4 - 3x^2 + 5x - 2) \div (x + 2)$

8. $(4x - 1)(x^2 - 3x - 2)$

OBJECTIVE

2 Factoring Strategies

The key to proficiency in factoring polynomials is to practice until you are comfortable with each technique. A strategy for factoring polynomials completely is given next.

Factoring a Polynomial

Step 1. Are there any common factors? If so, factor out the greatest common factor.

Step 2. How many terms are in the polynomial?

a. If there are *two* terms, decide if one of the following formulas may be applied:

i. Difference of two squares: $a^2 - b^2 = (a - b)(a + b)$

ii. Difference of two cubes: $a^3 - b^3 = (a - b)(a^2 + ab + b^2)$

iii. Sum of two cubes: $a^3 + b^3 = (a + b)(a^2 - ab + b^2)$

b. If there are *three* terms, try one of the following:

i. Perfect square trinomial: $a^2 + 2ab + b^2 = (a + b)^2$
$a^2 - 2ab + b^2 = (a - b)^2$

ii. If not a perfect square trinomial, factor by using the methods presented in Sections 3.2 through 3.4.

c. If there are *four* or more terms, try factoring by grouping.

Step 3. See whether any factors in the factored polynomial can be factored further.

A few examples are worked for you below.

EXAMPLE 1 Factor each polynomial completely.

a. $8a^2b - 4ab$ **b.** $36x^2 - 9$ **c.** $2x^2 - 5x - 7$

d. $5p^2 + 5 + qp^2 + q$ **e.** $9x^2 + 24x + 16$ **f.** $y^2 + 25$

Solution

a. Step 1. The terms have a common factor of $4ab$, which we factor out.

$$8a^2b - 4ab = 4ab(2a - 1)$$

Step 2. There are two terms, but the binomial $2a - 1$ is not the difference of two squares or the sum or difference of two cubes.

Step 3. The factor $2a - 1$ cannot be factored further.

b. Step 1. Factor out a common factor of 9.

$$36x^2 - 9 = 9(4x^2 - 1)$$

Step 2. The factor $4x^2 - 1$ has two terms, and it is the difference of two squares.

$$9(4x^2 - 1) = 9(2x + 1)(2x - 1)$$

Step 3. No factor with more than one term can be factored further.

c. Step 1. The terms of $2x^2 - 5x - 7$ contain no common factor other than 1 or -1.

Step 2. There are three terms. The trinomial is not a perfect square, so we factor by methods from Section 3.3 or 3.4.

$$2x^2 - 5x - 7 = (2x - 7)(x + 1)$$

Step 3. No factor with more than one term can be factored further.

(Continued on next page)

d. Step 1. There is no common factor of all terms of $5p^2 + 5 + qp^2 + q$.

Step 2. The polynomial has four terms, so try factoring by grouping.

$$\begin{aligned} 5p^2 + 5 + qp^2 + q &= (5p^2 + 5) + (qp^2 + q) && \text{Group the terms.} \\ &= 5(p^2 + 1) + q(p^2 + 1) \\ &= (p^2 + 1)(5 + q) \end{aligned}$$

Step 3. No factor can be factored further.

e. Step 1. The terms of $9x^2 + 24x + 16$ contain no common factor other than 1 or -1.

Step 2. The trinomial $9x^2 + 24x + 16$ is a perfect square trinomial, and $9x^2 + 24x + 16 = (3x + 4)^2$.

Step 3. No factor can be factored further.

f. Step 1. There is no common factor of $y^2 + 25$ other than 1.

Step 2. This binomial is the sum of two squares and is prime.

Step 3. The binomial $y^2 + 25$ cannot be factored further. □

PRACTICE

1 Factor each polynomial completely.

a. $12x^2y - 3xy$ **b.** $49x^2 - 4$

c. $5x^2 + 2x - 3$ **d.** $3x^2 + 6 + x^3 + 2x$

e. $4x^2 + 20x + 25$ **f.** $b^2 + 100$

EXAMPLE 2 Factor each polynomial completely.

a. $27a^3 - b^3$ **b.** $3n^2m^4 - 48m^6$ **c.** $2x^2 - 12x + 18 - 2z^2$

d. $8x^4y^2 + 125xy^2$ **e.** $(x - 5)^2 - 49y^2$

Solution

a. This binomial is the difference of two cubes.

$$\begin{aligned} 27a^3 - b^3 &= (3a)^3 - b^3 \\ &= (3a - b)[(3a)^2 + (3a)(b) + b^2] \\ &= (3a - b)(9a^2 + 3ab + b^2) \end{aligned}$$

b.
$$\begin{aligned} 3n^2m^4 - 48m^6 &= 3m^4(n^2 - 16m^2) && \text{Factor out the GCF } 3m^4. \\ &= 3m^4(n + 4m)(n - 4m) && \text{Factor the difference of squares.} \end{aligned}$$

c.
$$\begin{aligned} 2x^2 - 12x + 18 - 2z^2 &= 2(x^2 - 6x + 9 - z^2) && \text{The GCF is 2.} \\ &= 2[(x^2 - 6x + 9) - z^2] && \text{Group the first three terms together.} \\ &= 2[(x - 3)^2 - z^2] && \text{Factor the perfect square trinomial.} \\ &= 2[(x - 3) + z][(x - 3) - z] && \text{Factor the difference of squares.} \\ &= 2(x - 3 + z)(x - 3 - z) \end{aligned}$$

d.
$$\begin{aligned} 8x^4y^2 + 125xy^2 &= xy^2(8x^3 + 125) && \text{The GCF is } xy^2. \\ &= xy^2[(2x)^3 + 5^3] \\ &= xy^2(2x + 5)[(2x)^2 - (2x)(5) + 5^2] && \text{Factor the sum of cubes.} \\ &= xy^2(2x + 5)(4x^2 - 10x + 25) \end{aligned}$$

e. This binomial is the difference of squares.

$$\begin{aligned} (x - 5)^2 - 49y^2 &= (x - 5)^2 - (7y)^2 \\ &= [(x - 5) + 7y][(x - 5) - 7y] \\ &= (x - 5 + 7y)(x - 5 - 7y) \end{aligned}$$ □

PRACTICE 2 Factor each polynomial completely.

a. $64x^3 + y^3$
b. $7x^2y^2 - 63y^4$
c. $3x^2 + 12x + 12 - 3b^2$
d. $x^5y^4 + 27x^2y$
e. $(x + 7)^2 - 81y^2$

B.4 Exercise Set, Part 2

MyMathLab®

Factor completely.

9. $x^2 - 8x + 16 - y^2$
10. $12x^2 - 22x - 20$
11. $x^4 - x$
12. $(2x + 1)^2 - 3(2x + 1) + 2$
13. $14x^2y - 2xy$
14. $24ab^2 - 6ab$
15. $4x^2 - 16$
16. $9x^2 - 81$
17. $3x^2 - 8x - 11$
18. $5x^2 - 2x - 3$
19. $4x^2 + 8x - 12$
20. $6x^2 - 6x - 12$
21. $4x^2 + 36x + 81$
22. $25x^2 + 40x + 16$
23. $8x^3 + 125y^3$
24. $27x^3 - 64y^3$
25. $64x^2y^3 - 8x^2$
26. $27x^5y^4 - 216x^2y$
27. $(x + 5)^3 + y^3$
28. $(y - 1)^3 + 27x^3$
29. $(5a - 3)^2 - 6(5a - 3) + 9$
30. $(4r + 1)^2 + 8(4r + 1) + 16$
31. $7x^2 - 63x$
32. $20x^2 + 23x + 6$

△ **57.** Express the area of the shaded region as a polynomial. Factor the polynomial completely.

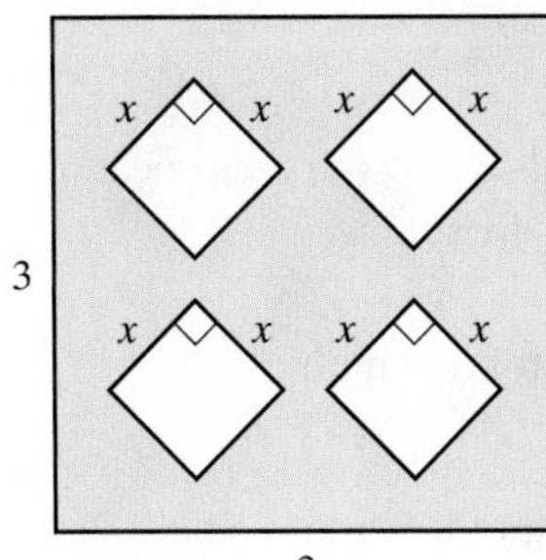

33. $ab - 6a + 7b - 42$
34. $20x^2 - 220x + 600$
35. $x^4 - 1$
36. $15x^2 - 20x$
37. $10x^2 - 7x - 33$
38. $45m^3n^3 - 27m^2n^2$
39. $5a^3b^3 - 50a^3b$
40. $x^4 + x$
41. $16x^2 + 25$
42. $20x^3 + 20y^3$
43. $10x^3 - 210x^2 + 1100x$
44. $9y^2 - 42y + 49$
45. $64a^3b^4 - 27a^3b$
46. $y^4 - 16$
47. $2x^3 - 54$
48. $2sr + 10s - r - 5$
49. $3y^5 - 5y^4 + 6y - 10$
50. $64a^2 + b^2$
51. $100z^3 + 100$
52. $250x^4 - 16x$
53. $4b^2 - 36b + 81$
54. $2a^5 - a^4 + 6a - 3$
55. $(y - 6)^2 + 3(y - 6) + 2$
56. $(c + 2)^2 - 6(c + 2) + 5$

B.5 Rational Expressions 

OBJECTIVE

1 Perform Operations on Rational Expressions and Solve Equations Containing Rational Expressions.

OBJECTIVE

1 Performing Operations on Rational Expressions and Solving Equations Containing Rational Expressions

It is very important that you understand the difference between an expression and an equation containing rational expressions. An equation contains an equal sign; an expression does not.

Expression to be Simplified

$$\frac{x}{2}+\frac{x}{6}$$

Write both rational expressions with the LCD, 6, as the denominator.

$$\frac{x}{2}+\frac{x}{6}=\frac{x\cdot 3}{2\cdot 3}+\frac{x}{6}=\frac{3x}{6}+\frac{x}{6}=\frac{4x}{6}=\frac{2x}{3}$$

Equation to be Solved

$$\frac{x}{2}+\frac{x}{6}=\frac{2}{3}$$

Multiply both sides by the LCD, 6.

$$6\left(\frac{x}{2}+\frac{x}{6}\right)=6\left(\frac{2}{3}\right)$$

$$3x+x=4$$

$$4x=4$$

$$x=1$$

Check to see that the solution is 1.

Helpful Hint

Remember: Equations can be cleared of fractions; expressions cannot.

EXAMPLE 1 Multiply. $\frac{x^3-1}{-3x+3}\cdot\frac{15x^2}{x^2+x+1}$

Solution

$$\frac{x^3-1}{-3x+3}\cdot\frac{15x^2}{x^2+x+1}=\frac{(x-1)(x^2+x+1)}{-3(x-1)}\cdot\frac{15x^2}{x^2+x+1}\quad\text{Factor.}$$

$$=\frac{(x-1)(x^2+x+1)\cdot 3\cdot 5x^2}{-1\cdot 3(x-1)(x^2+x+1)}\quad\text{Factor.}$$

$$=\frac{5x^2}{-1}=-5x^2\quad\text{Simplest form}$$

□

PRACTICE

1 Multiply.

a. $\frac{2+5n}{3n}\cdot\frac{6n+3}{5n^2-3n-2}$

b. $\frac{x^3-8}{-6x+12}\cdot\frac{6x^2}{x^2+2x+4}$

EXAMPLE 2 Divide. $\frac{8m^2}{3m^2-12}\div\frac{40}{2-m}$

Solution

$$\frac{8m^2}{3m^2-12}\div\frac{40}{2-m}=\frac{8m^2}{3m^2-12}\cdot\frac{2-m}{40}\quad\text{Multiply by the reciprocal of the divisor.}$$

$$=\frac{8m^2(2-m)}{3(m+2)(m-2)\cdot 40}\quad\text{Factor and multiply.}$$

$$=\frac{8\,m^2\cdot -1\,(m-2)}{3(m+2)\,(m-2)\cdot 8\cdot 5}\quad\text{Write }(2-m)\text{ as }-1(m-2).$$

$$=-\frac{m^2}{15(m+2)}\quad\text{Simplify.}$$

□

PRACTICE

2 Divide.

a. $\dfrac{6y^3}{3y^2 - 27} \div \dfrac{42}{3 - y}$ **b.** $\dfrac{10x^2 + 23x - 5}{5x^2 - 51x + 10} \div \dfrac{2x^2 + 9x + 10}{7x^2 - 68x - 20}$

EXAMPLE 3 Perform the indicated operation.

$$\frac{3}{x + 2} + \frac{2x}{x - 2}$$

Solution The LCD is the product of the two denominators: $(x + 2)(x - 2)$.

$$\frac{3}{x+2} + \frac{2x}{x-2} = \frac{3 \cdot (x-2)}{(x+2) \cdot (x-2)} + \frac{2x \cdot (x+2)}{(x-2) \cdot (x+2)} \quad \text{Write equivalent rational expressions.}$$

$$= \frac{3x - 6}{(x + 2)(x - 2)} + \frac{2x^2 + 4x}{(x + 2)(x - 2)} \quad \text{Multiply in the numerators.}$$

$$= \frac{3x - 6 + 2x^2 + 4x}{(x + 2)(x - 2)} \quad \text{Add the numerators.}$$

$$= \frac{2x^2 + 7x - 6}{(x + 2)(x - 2)} \quad \text{Simplify the numerator.}$$

□

PRACTICE

3 Perform the indicated operation.

a. $\dfrac{4}{p^3q} + \dfrac{3}{5p^4q}$ **b.** $\dfrac{4}{y + 3} + \dfrac{5y}{y - 3}$ **c.** $\dfrac{3z - 18}{z - 5} - \dfrac{3}{5 - z}$

EXAMPLE 4 Solve: $\dfrac{2x}{x - 3} + \dfrac{6 - 2x}{x^2 - 9} = \dfrac{x}{x + 3}$.

Solution We factor the second denominator to find that the LCD is $(x + 3)(x - 3)$. We multiply both sides of the equation by $(x + 3)(x - 3)$. By the distributive property, this is the same as multiplying each term by $(x + 3)(x - 3)$.

$$\frac{2x}{x - 3} + \frac{6 - 2x}{x^2 - 9} = \frac{x}{x + 3}$$

$$(x + 3)(x - 3) \cdot \frac{2x}{x - 3} + (x + 3)(x - 3) \cdot \frac{6 - 2x}{(x + 3)(x - 3)} = (x + 3)(x - 3)\left(\frac{x}{x + 3}\right)$$

$$2x(x + 3) + (6 - 2x) = x(x - 3) \quad \text{Simplify.}$$

$$2x^2 + 6x + 6 - 2x = x^2 - 3x \quad \text{Use the distributive property.}$$

Next we solve this quadratic equation by the factoring method. To do so, we first write the equation so that one side is 0.

$$x^2 + 7x + 6 = 0$$

$$(x + 6)(x + 1) = 0 \quad \text{Factor.}$$

$$x = -6 \quad \text{or} \quad x = -1 \quad \text{Set each factor equal to 0.}$$

Neither -6 nor -1 makes any denominator 0, so they are both solutions. The solutions are -6 and -1. □

PRACTICE

4 Solve: $\dfrac{2}{x - 2} - \dfrac{5 + 2x}{x^2 - 4} = \dfrac{x}{x + 2}$.

B.5 Exercise Set

MyMathLab®

Perform each indicated operation and simplify, or solve the equation for the variable.

1. $\frac{x}{2} = \frac{1}{8} + \frac{x}{4}$

2. $\frac{x}{4} = \frac{3}{2} + \frac{x}{10}$

3. $\frac{1}{8} + \frac{x}{4}$

4. $\frac{3}{2} + \frac{x}{10}$

5. $\frac{4}{x+2} - \frac{2}{x-1}$

6. $\frac{5}{x-2} - \frac{10}{x+4}$

7. $\frac{4}{x+2} = \frac{2}{x-1}$

8. $\frac{5}{x-2} = \frac{10}{x+4}$

9. $\frac{2}{x^2-4} = \frac{1}{x+2} - \frac{3}{x-2}$

10. $\frac{3}{x^2-25} = \frac{1}{x+5} + \frac{2}{x-5}$

11. $\frac{5}{x^2-3x} + \frac{4}{2x-6}$

12. $\frac{5}{x^2-3x} \div \frac{4}{2x-6}$

13. $\frac{x-1}{x+1} + \frac{x+7}{x-1} = \frac{4}{x^2-1}$

14. $\left(1 - \frac{y}{x}\right) \div \left(1 - \frac{x}{y}\right)$

15. $\frac{a^2-9}{a-6} \cdot \frac{a^2-5a-6}{a^2-a-6}$

16. $\frac{2}{a-6} + \frac{3a}{a^2-5a-6} - \frac{a}{5a+5}$

17. $\frac{2x+3}{3x-2} = \frac{4x+1}{6x+1}$

18. $\frac{5x-3}{2x} = \frac{10x+3}{4x+1}$

19. $\frac{a}{9a^2-1} + \frac{2}{6a-2}$

20. $\frac{3}{4a-8} - \frac{a+2}{a^2-2a}$

21. $-\frac{3}{x^2} - \frac{1}{x} + 2 = 0$

22. $\frac{x}{2x+6} + \frac{5}{x^2-9}$

23. $\frac{x-8}{x^2-x-2} + \frac{2}{x-2}$

24. $\frac{x-8}{x^2-x-2} + \frac{2}{x-2} = \frac{3}{x+1}$

25. $\frac{3}{a} - 5 = \frac{7}{a} - 1$

26. $\frac{7}{3z-9} + \frac{5}{z}$

Use $\frac{x}{5} - \frac{x}{4} = \frac{1}{10}$ *and* $\frac{x}{5} - \frac{x}{4} + \frac{1}{10}$ *for Exercises 27 and 28.*

27. a. Which one above is an expression?
    b. Describe the first step to simplify this expression.
    c. Simplify the expression.

28. a. Which one above is an equation?
    b. Describe the first step to solve this equation.
    c. Solve the equation.

For each exercise, choose the correct statement. Each figure represents a real number, and no denominators are 0.*

29. a. $\frac{\triangle + \square}{\triangle} = \square$ b. $\frac{\triangle + \square}{\triangle} = 1 + \frac{\square}{\triangle}$
    c. $\frac{\triangle + \square}{\triangle} = \frac{\square}{\triangle}$ d. $\frac{\triangle + \square}{\triangle} = 1 + \square$
    e. $\frac{\triangle + \square}{\triangle - \square} = -1$

*My thanks to Kelly Champagne for permission to use her Exercises for 29 through 33.

Helpful Hint
Remember: Equations can be cleared of fractions; expressions cannot.

30. **a.** $\frac{\triangle}{\square} + \frac{\square}{\triangle} = \frac{\triangle + \square}{\square + \triangle} = 1$

b. $\frac{\triangle}{\square} + \frac{\square}{\triangle} = \frac{\triangle + \square}{\triangle\square}$

c. $\frac{\triangle}{\square} + \frac{\square}{\triangle} = \triangle\triangle + \square\square$

d. $\frac{\triangle}{\square} + \frac{\square}{\triangle} = \frac{\triangle\triangle + \square\square}{\square\triangle}$

e. $\frac{\triangle}{\square} + \frac{\square}{\triangle} = \frac{\triangle\square}{\square\triangle} = 1$

31. **a.** $\frac{\triangle}{\square} \cdot \frac{\bigcirc}{\square} = \frac{\triangle\bigcirc}{\square}$ **b.** $\frac{\triangle}{\square} \cdot \frac{\bigcirc}{\square} = \triangle\bigcirc$

c. $\frac{\triangle}{\square} \cdot \frac{\bigcirc}{\square} = \frac{\triangle + \bigcirc}{\square + \square}$ **d.** $\frac{\triangle}{\square} \cdot \frac{\bigcirc}{\square} = \frac{\triangle\bigcirc}{\square\square}$

32. **a.** $\frac{\triangle}{\square} \div \frac{\bigcirc}{\triangle} = \frac{\triangle\triangle}{\square\bigcirc}$ **b.** $\frac{\triangle}{\square} \div \frac{\bigcirc}{\triangle} = \frac{\bigcirc\square}{\triangle\triangle}$

c. $\frac{\triangle}{\square} \div \frac{\bigcirc}{\triangle} = \frac{\bigcirc}{\square}$ **d.** $\frac{\triangle}{\square} \div \frac{\bigcirc}{\triangle} = \frac{\triangle + \triangle}{\square + \bigcirc}$

33. **a.** $\frac{\frac{\triangle + \square}{\bigcirc}}{\frac{\triangle}{\bigcirc}} = \square$ **b.** $\frac{\frac{\triangle + \square}{\bigcirc}}{\frac{\triangle}{\bigcirc}} = \frac{\triangle\triangle + \triangle\square}{\bigcirc\bigcirc}$

c. $\frac{\frac{\triangle + \square}{\bigcirc}}{\frac{\triangle}{\bigcirc}} = 1 + \square$ **d.** $\frac{\frac{\triangle + \square}{\bigcirc}}{\frac{\triangle}{\bigcirc}} = \frac{\triangle + \square}{\triangle}$

Appendix C

An Introduction to Using a Graphing Utility

The Viewing Window and Interpreting Window Settings

In this appendix, we will use the term **graphing utility** to mean a graphing calculator or a computer software graphing package. All graphing utilities graph equations by plotting points on a screen. While plotting several points can be slow and sometimes tedious for us, a graphing utility can quickly and accurately plot hundreds of points. How does a graphing utility show plotted points? A computer or calculator screen is made up of a grid of small rectangular areas called **pixels.** If a pixel contains a point to be plotted, the pixel is turned "on"; otherwise, the pixel remains "off." The graph of an equation is then a collection of pixels turned "on." The graph of $y = 3x + 1$ from a graphing calculator is shown in Figure A-1. Notice the irregular shape of the line caused by the rectangular pixels.

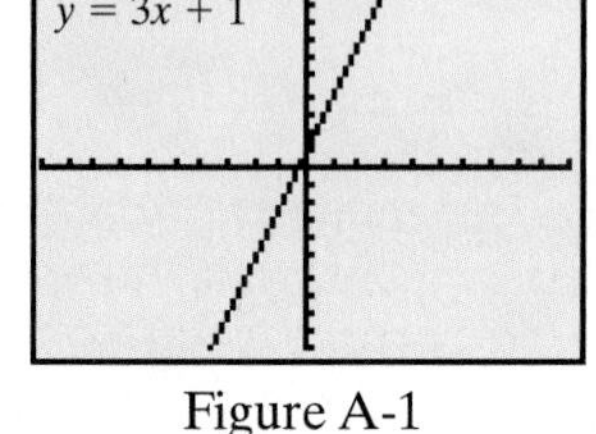

Figure A-1

The portion of the coordinate plane shown on the screen in Figure A-1 is called the **viewing window** or the **viewing rectangle.** Notice the x-axis and the y-axis on the graph. While tick marks are shown on the axes, they are not labeled. This means that from this screen alone, we do not know how many units each tick mark represents. To see what each tick mark represents and the minimum and maximum values on the axes, check the window setting of the graphing utility. It defines the viewing window. The window of the graph of $y = 3x + 1$ shown in Figure A-1 has the following settings (Figure A-2):

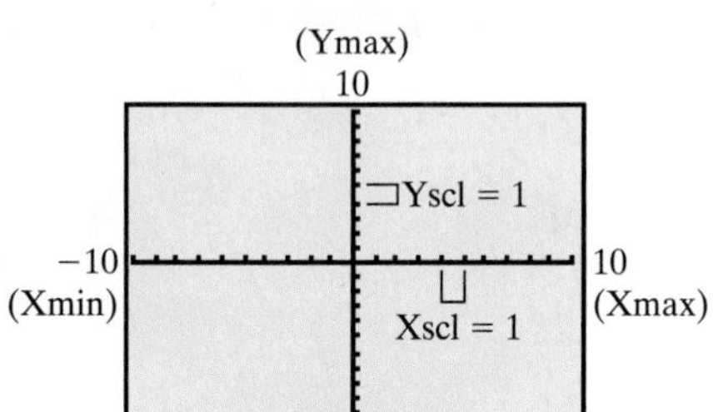

Figure A-2

Xmin = −10	The minimum x-value is −10.
Xmax = 10	The maximum x-value is 10.
Xscl = 1	The x-axis scale is 1 unit per tick mark.
Ymin = −10	The minimum y-value is −10.
Ymax = 10	The maximum y-value is 10.
Yscl = 1	The y-axis scale is 1 unit per tick mark.

By knowing the scale, we can find the minimum and the maximum values on the axes simply by counting tick marks. For example, if both the Xscl (x-axis scale) and the Yscl (y-axis scale) are 1 unit per tick mark on the graph in Figure A-3, we can count the tick marks and find that the minimum x-value is −10 and the maximum x-value is 10. Also, the minimum y-value is −10 and the maximum y-value is 10. If the Xscl changes to 2 units per tick mark (shown in Figure A-4), by counting tick marks, we see that the minimum x-value is now −20 and the maximum x-value is now 20.

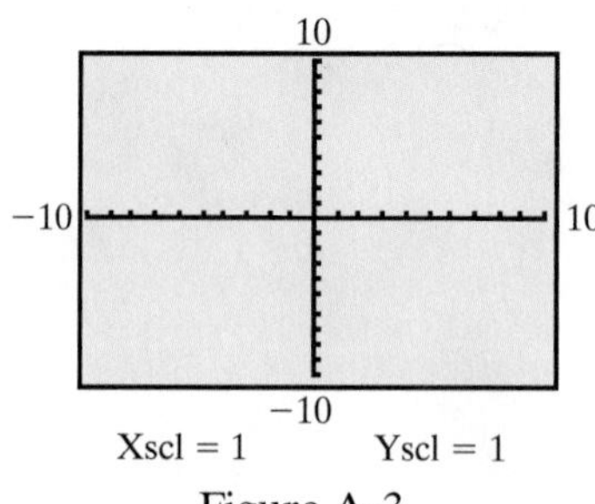

Figure A-3

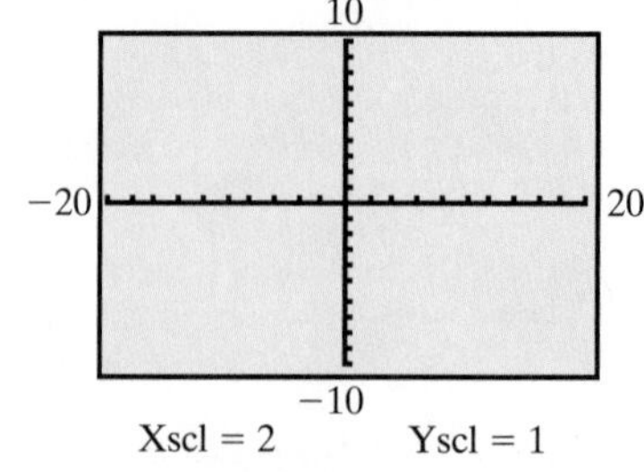

Figure A-4

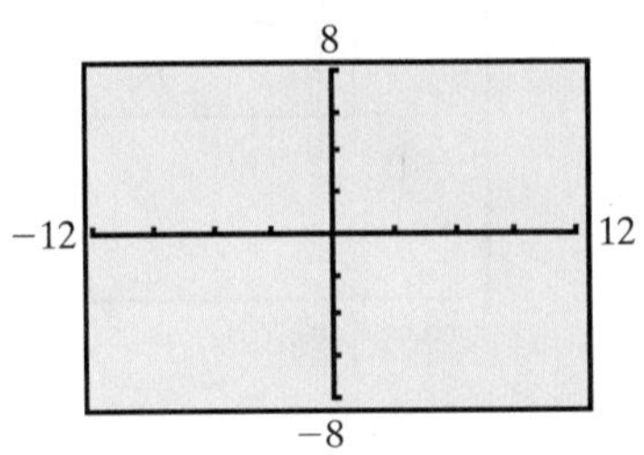

Figure A-5

It is also true that if we know the Xmin and the Xmax values, we can calculate the Xscl by the displayed axes. For example, the Xscl of the graph in Figure A-5 must be 3 units per tick mark for the maximum and minimum x-values to be as shown. Also, the Yscl of that graph must be 2 units per tick mark for the maximum and minimum y-values to be as shown.

We will call the viewing window in Figure A-3 a *standard* viewing window or rectangle. Although a standard viewing window is sufficient for much of this text, special care must be taken to ensure that all key features of a graph are shown. Figures A-6, A-7, and A-8 show the graph of $y = x^2 + 11x - 1$ on three different viewing windows. Note that certain viewing windows for this equation are misleading.

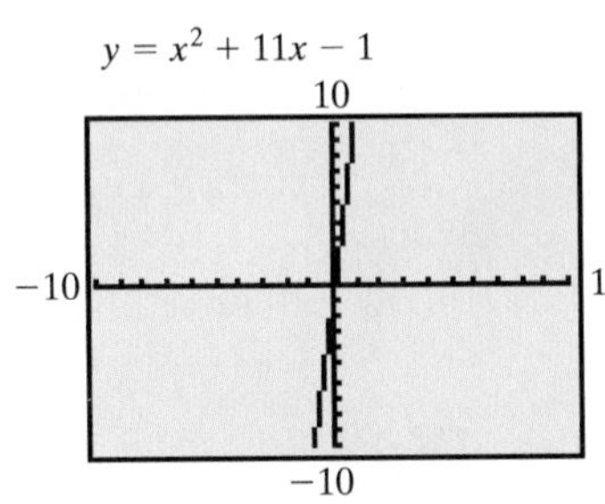

Figure A-6

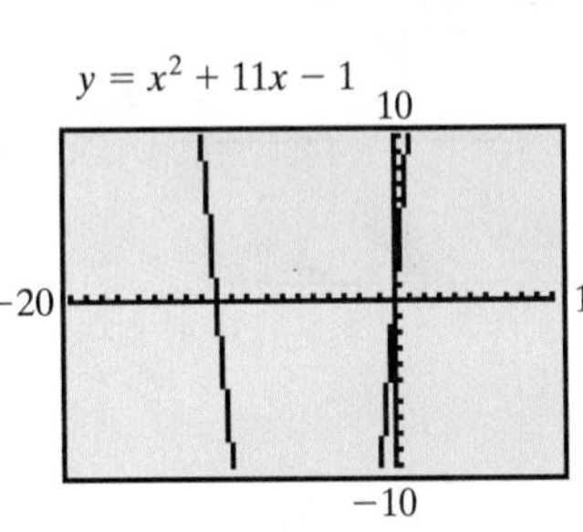

Figure A-7

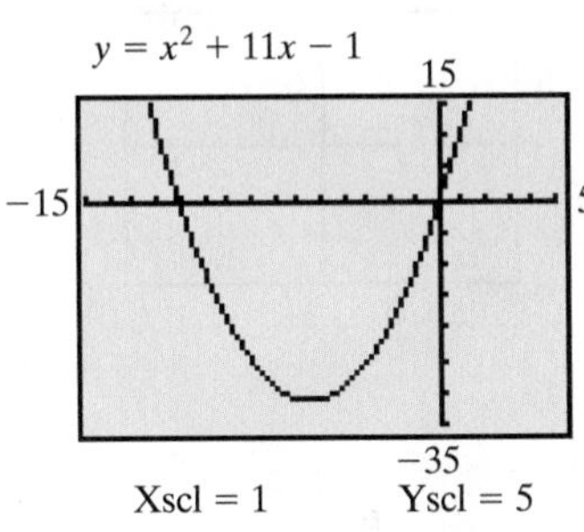

Figure A-8

How do we ensure that all distinguishing features of the graph of an equation are shown? It helps to know about the equation that is being graphed. For example, the equation $y = x^2 + 11x - 1$ is not a linear equation and its graph is not a line. This equation is a quadratic equation and, therefore, its graph is a parabola. By knowing this information, we know that the graph shown in Figure A-6, although correct, is misleading. Of the three viewing rectangles shown, the graph in Figure A-8 is best because it shows more of the distinguishing features of the parabola. Properties of equations needed for graphing will be studied in this text.

The Viewing Window and Interpreting Window Settings Exercise Set

In Exercises 1–4, determine whether all ordered pairs listed will lie within a standard viewing rectangle.

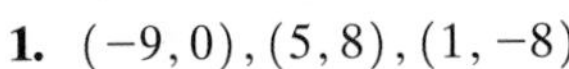

1. $(-9, 0), (5, 8), (1, -8)$
2. $(4, 7), (0, 0), (-8, 9)$
3. $(-11, 0), (2, 2), (7, -5)$
4. $(3, 5), (-3, -5), (15, 0)$

In Exercises 5–10, choose an Xmin, Xmax, Ymin, and Ymax so that all ordered pairs listed will lie within the viewing rectangle.

5. $(-90, 0), (55, 80), (0, -80)$
6. $(4, 70), (20, 20), (-18, 90)$
7. $(-11, 0), (2, 2), (7, -5)$
8. $(3, 5), (-3, -5), (15, 0)$
9. $(200, 200), (50, -50), (70, -50)$
10. $(40, 800), (-30, 500), (15, 0)$

Write the window setting for each viewing window shown. Use the following format:

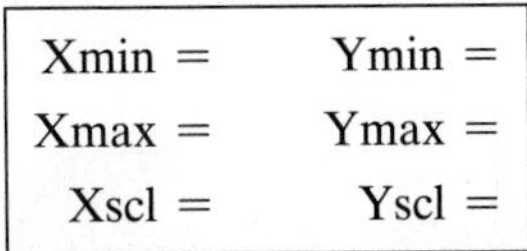

Xmin =	Ymin =
Xmax =	Ymax =
Xscl =	Yscl =

11.

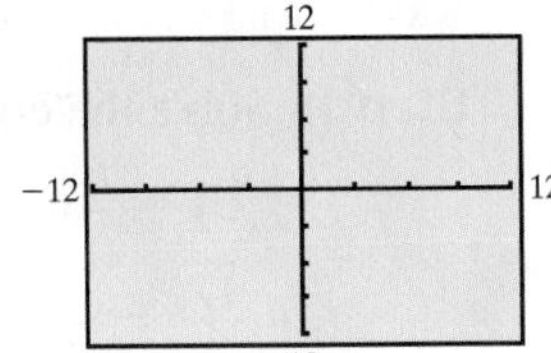

12.

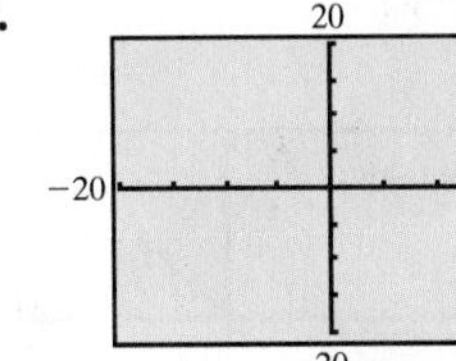

13.

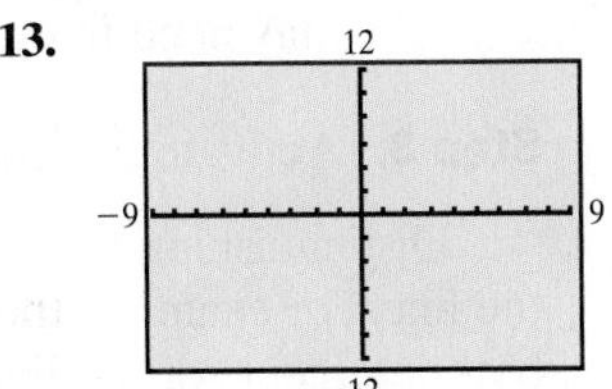

14.

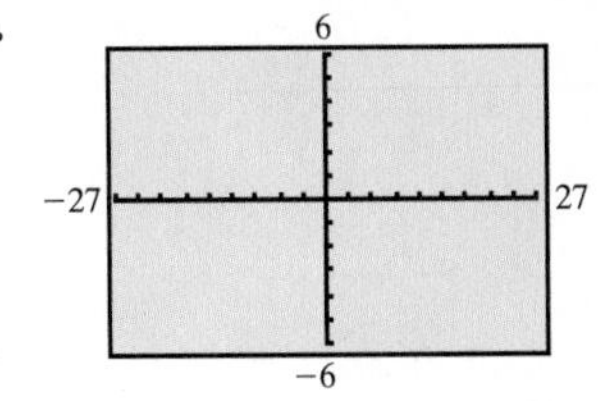

15.

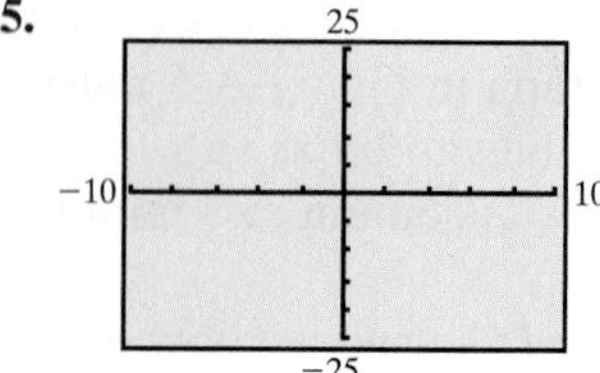

16.

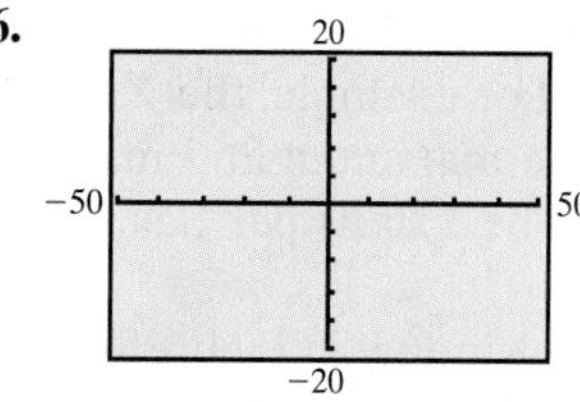

19.

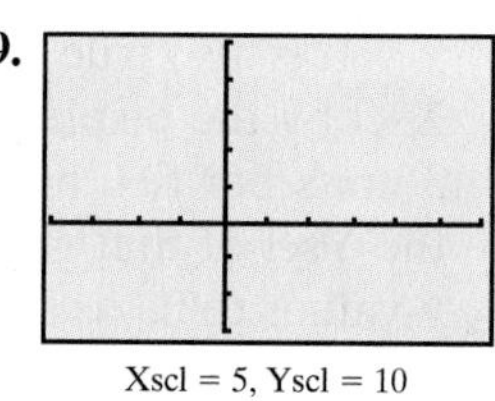

Xscl = 5, Yscl = 10

20.

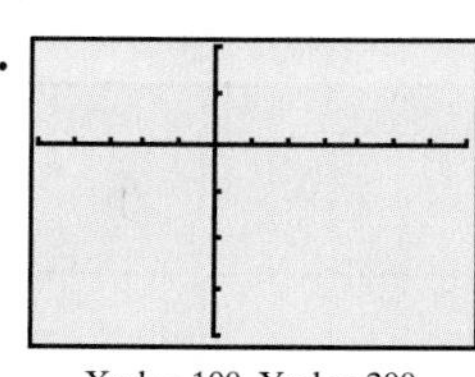

Xscl = 100, Yscl = 200

17.

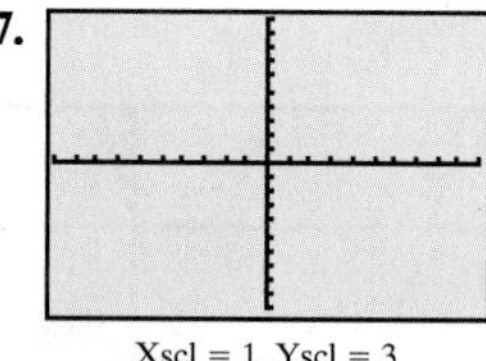

Xscl = 1, Yscl = 3

18.

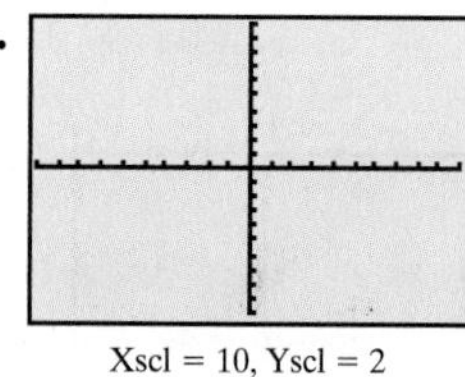

Xscl = 10, Yscl = 2

Graphing Equations and Square Viewing Window

In general, the following steps may be used to graph an equation on a standard viewing window.

> **Graphing an Equation in *X* and *Y* with a Graphing Utility on a Standard Viewing Window**
>
> **Step 1:** Solve the equation for y.
>
> **Step 2:** Using your graphing utility, enter the equation in the form Y = *expression involving x*.
>
> **Step 3:** Activate the graphing utility.

Special care must be taken when entering the *expression involving x* in Step 2. You must be sure that the graphing utility you are using interprets the expression as you want it to. For example, let's graph $3y = 4x$. To do so,

Step 1: Solve the equation for y.

$$3y = 4x$$

$$\frac{3y}{3} = \frac{4x}{3}$$

$$y = \frac{4}{3}x$$

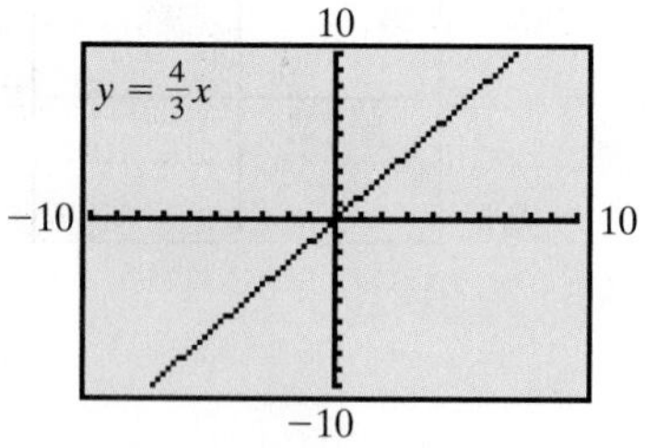

Figure A-9

Step 2: Using your graphing utility, enter the expression $\frac{4}{3}x$ after the $\text{Y} =$ prompt. In order for your graphing utility to correctly interpret the expression, you may need to enter (4/3)x or $(4 \div 3)x$.

Step 3: Activate the graphing utility. The graph should appear as in Figure A-9.

Distinguishing features of the graph of a line include showing all the intercepts of the line. For example, the window of the graph of the line in Figure A-10 does not show both intercepts of the line, but the window of the graph of the same line in Figure A-11 does show both intercepts. Notice the notation below each graph. This is a shorthand notation of the range setting of the graph. This notation means [Xmin, Xmax] by [Ymin, Ymax].

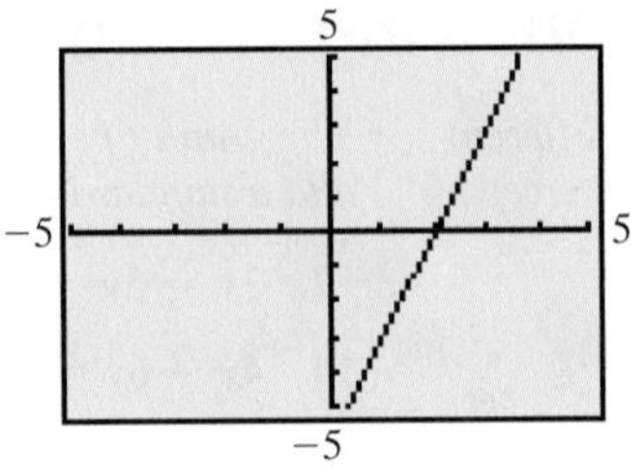

[−5, 5] by [−5, 5]

Figure A-10

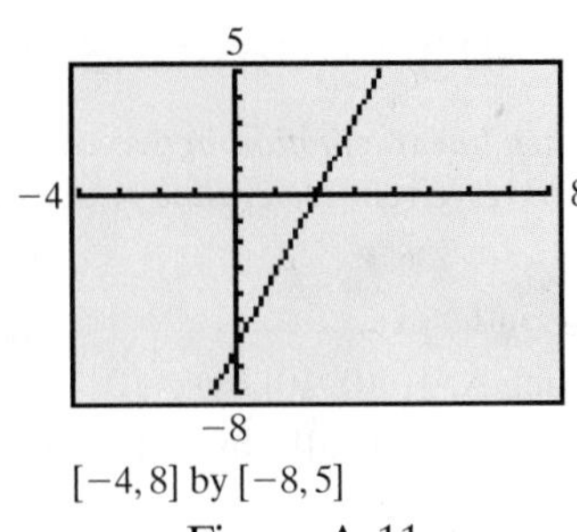

[−4, 8] by [−8, 5]

Figure A-11

On a standard viewing window, the tick marks on the y-axis are closer together than the tick marks on the x-axis. This happens because the viewing window is a rectangle, and so 10 equally spaced tick marks on the positive y-axis will be closer together than 10 equally spaced tick marks on the positive x-axis. This causes the appearance of graphs to be distorted.

For example, notice the different appearances of the same line graphed using different viewing windows. The line in Figure A-12 is distorted because the tick marks along the x-axis are farther apart than the tick marks along the y-axis. The graph of the same line in Figure A-13 is not distorted because the viewing rectangle has been selected so that there is equal spacing between tick marks on both axes.

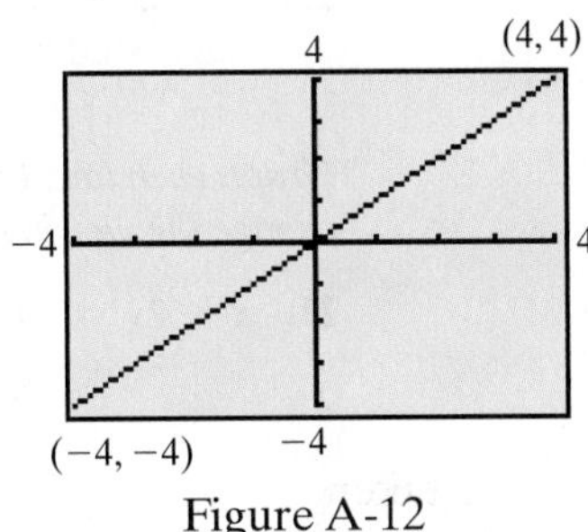

Figure A-12

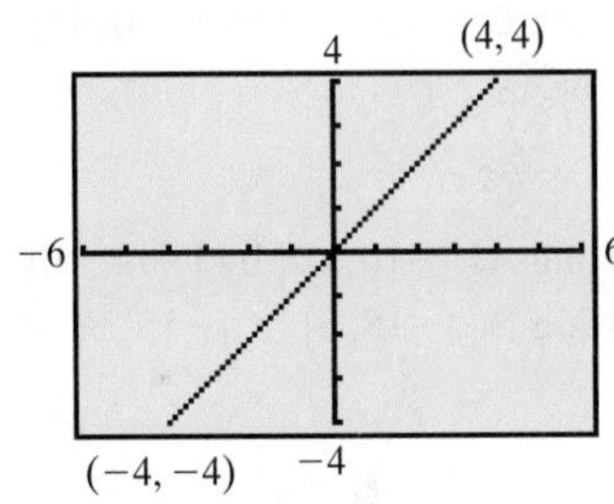

Figure A-13

We say that the line in Figure A-13 is graphed on a *square* setting. Some graphing utilities have a built-in program that, if activated, will automatically provide a square setting. A square setting is especially helpful when we are graphing perpendicular lines, circles, or when a true geometric perspective is desired. Some examples of square screens are shown in Figures A-14 and A-15.

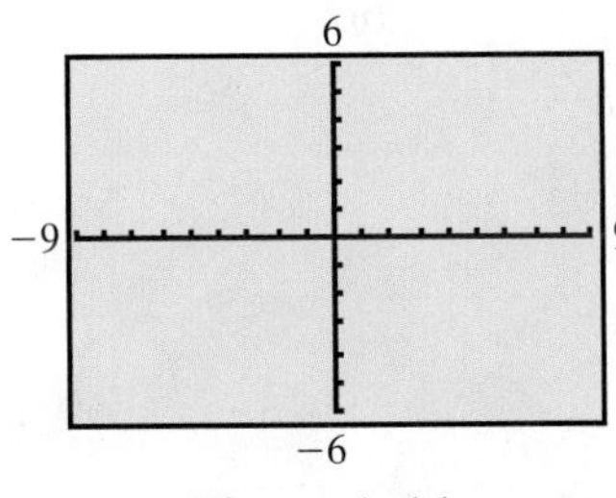

Figure A-14

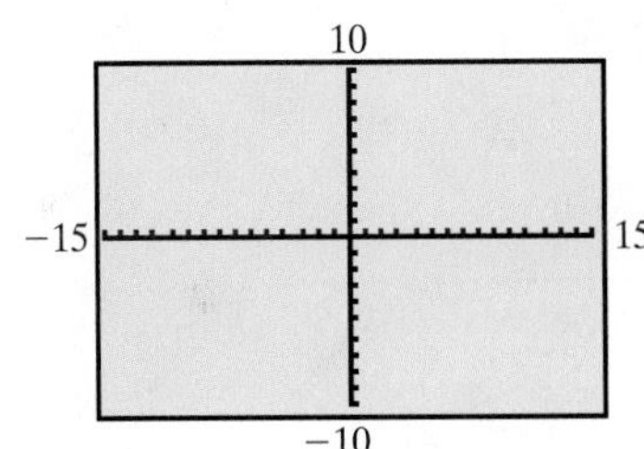

Figure A-15

Other features of a graphing utility such as Trace, Zoom, Intersect, and Table are discussed in appropriate Graphing Calculator Explorations in this text.

Graphing Equations and Square Viewing Window Exercise Set

Graph each linear equation in two variables using the two different range settings given. Determine which setting shows all intercepts of a line.

1. $y = 2x + 12$
Setting A: $[-10, 10]$ by $[-10, 10]$
Setting B: $[-10, 10]$ by $[-10, 15]$

2. $y = -3x + 25$
Setting A: $[-5, 5]$ by $[-30, 10]$
Setting B: $[-10, 10]$ by $[-10, 30]$

3. $y = -x - 41$
Setting A: $[-50, 10]$ by $[-10, 10]$
Setting B: $[-50, 10]$ by $[-50, 15]$

4. $y = 6x - 18$
Setting A: $[-10, 10]$ by $[-20, 10]$
Setting B: $[-10, 10]$ by $[-10, 10]$

5. $y = \frac{1}{2}x - 15$
Setting B: $[-10, 10]$ by $[-20, 10]$
Setting B: $[-10, 35]$ by $[-20, 15]$

6. $y = -\frac{2}{3}x - \frac{29}{3}$
Setting A: $[-10, 10]$ by $[-10, 10]$
Setting B: $[-15, 5]$ by $[-15, 5]$

The graph of each equation is a line. Use a graphing utility and a standard viewing window to graph each equation.

7. $3x = 5y$ **8.** $7y = -3x$ **9.** $9x - 5y = 30$

10. $4x + 6y = 20$ **11.** $y = -7$ **12.** $y = 2$

13. $x + 10y = -5$ **14.** $x - 5y = 9$

Graph the following equations using the square setting given. Some keystrokes that may be helpful are given.

15. $y = \sqrt{x}$ $[-12, 12]$ by $[-8, 8]$
Suggested keystrokes: $\sqrt{\ }\,x$

16. $y = \sqrt{2x}$ $[-12, 12]$ by $[-8, 8]$
Suggested keystrokes: $\sqrt{\ }\,(2x)$

17. $y = x^2 + 2x + 1$ $[-15, 15]$ by $[-10, 10]$
Suggested keystrokes: x^$2 + 2x + 1$

18. $y = x^2 - 5$ $[-15, 15]$ by $[-10, 10]$
Suggested keystrokes: x^$2 - 5$

19. $y = |x|$ $[-9, 9]$ by $[-6, 6]$
Suggested keystrokes: $ABS\ (x)$

20. $y = |x - 2|$ $[-9, 9]$ by $[-6, 6]$
Suggested keystrokes: $ABS\ (x - 2)$

Graph each line. Use a standard viewing window; then, if necessary, change the viewing window so that all intercepts of each line show.

21. $x + 2y = 30$ **22.** $1.5x - 3.7y = 40.3$

Answers to Selected Exercises

CHAPTER R REVIEW OF REAL NUMBERS

Section R.2

Practice Exercises

1. a. $<$ **b.** $>$ **c.** $<$ **2. a.** True **b.** False **c.** True **d.** True **3. a.** $3 < 8$ **b.** $15 \geq 9$ **c.** $6 \neq 7$ **4.** -10 **5. a.** 25 **b.** 25 **c.** $25, -15, -99$ **d.** $25, \frac{7}{3}, -15, -\frac{3}{4}, -3.7, 8.8, -99$ **e.** $\sqrt{5}$ **f.** $25, \frac{7}{3}, -15, -\frac{3}{4}, \sqrt{5}, -3.7, 8.8, -99$ **6. a.** $<$ **b.** $>$ **c.** $=$ **7. a.** 8 **b.** 9 **c.** 2.5 **d.** $\frac{5}{11}$ **e.** $\sqrt{3}$ **8. a.** $=$ **b.** $>$ **c.** $<$ **d.** $>$ **e.** $<$

Vocabulary, Readiness & Video Check R.2

1. whole **3.** inequality **5.** real **7.** irrational **9.** To form a true statement: $0 < 7$. **11.** 0 belongs to the whole numbers, the integers, the rational numbers, and the real numbers; because 0 is a rational number, it cannot also be an irrational number

Exercise Set R.2

1. $>$ **3.** $=$ **5.** $<$ **7.** $<$ **9.** $32 < 212$ **11.** $30 \leq 45$ **13.** true **15.** false **17.** false **19.** true **21.** false **23.** $8 < 12$ **25.** $5 \geq 4$ **27.** $15 \neq -2$ **29.** 14,494; -282 **31.** $-28{,}000$ **33.** 350; -126 **35.** whole, integers, rational, real **37.** integers, rational, real **39.** natural, whole, integers, rational, real **41.** rational, real **43.** irrational, real **45.** false **47.** true **49.** true **51.** true **53.** false **55.** $>$ **57.** $>$ **59.** $<$ **61.** $<$ **63.** $>$ **65.** $=$ **67.** $<$ **69.** $<$ **71.** 2009 **73.** 2009, 2010 **75.** 280 million < 281 million **77.** 49 million > 16 million **79.** 38 million pounds less, or -38 million **81.** $-0.04 > -26.7$ **83.** sun **85.** sun **87.** $20 \leq 25$ **89.** $6 > 0$ **91.** $-12 < -10$ **93.** answers may vary

Section R.3

Practice Exercises

1. a. $2 \cdot 2 \cdot 3 \cdot 3$ **b.** $2 \cdot 2 \cdot 2 \cdot 5 \cdot 5$ **2. a.** $\frac{7}{8}$ **b.** $\frac{16}{3}$ **c.** $\frac{7}{25}$ **3.** $\frac{7}{24}$ **4. a.** $\frac{27}{16}$ **b.** $\frac{1}{36}$ **c.** $\frac{5}{2}$ **5. a.** 1 **b.** $\frac{6}{5}$ **c.** $\frac{4}{5}$ **d.** $\frac{1}{2}$ **6.** $\frac{14}{21}$ **7. a.** $\frac{46}{77}$ **b.** $\frac{1}{14}$ **c.** $\frac{1}{2}$ **8.** $22\frac{11}{15}$ **9.** $40\frac{5}{6}$

Vocabulary, Readiness & Video Check R.3

1. fraction **3.** product **5.** factors, product **7.** equivalent **9.** The division operation changes to multiplication and the second fraction $\frac{1}{20}$ changes to its reciprocal $\frac{20}{1}$. **11.** The number $4\frac{7}{6}$ is not in proper mixed number form as the fraction part, $\frac{7}{6}$, should not be an improper fraction.

Exercise Set R.3

1. $\frac{3}{8}$ **3.** $\frac{5}{7}$ **5.** $3 \cdot 11$ **7.** $2 \cdot 7 \cdot 7$ **9.** $2 \cdot 2 \cdot 5$ **11.** $3 \cdot 5 \cdot 5$ **13.** $3 \cdot 3 \cdot 5$ **15.** $\frac{1}{2}$ **17.** $\frac{2}{3}$ **19.** $\frac{3}{7}$ **21.** $\frac{3}{5}$ **23.** $\frac{30}{61}$ **25.** $\frac{3}{8}$ **27.** $\frac{1}{2}$ **29.** $\frac{6}{7}$ **31.** 15 **33.** $\frac{1}{6}$ **35.** $\frac{25}{27}$ **37.** $\frac{11}{20}$ sq mi **39.** $\frac{7}{36}$ sq ft **41.** $\frac{3}{5}$ **43.** 1 **45.** $\frac{1}{3}$ **47.** $\frac{9}{35}$ **49.** $\frac{21}{30}$ **51.** $\frac{4}{18}$ **53.** $\frac{16}{20}$ **55.** $\frac{23}{21}$ **57.** $\frac{11}{60}$ **59.** $\frac{5}{66}$ **61.** $\frac{7}{5}$ **63.** $\frac{1}{5}$ **65.** $\frac{3}{8}$ **67.** $\frac{1}{9}$ **69.** $18\frac{20}{27}$ **71.** $2\frac{28}{29}$ **73.** $48\frac{1}{15}$ **75.** $7\frac{1}{12}$ **77.** $\frac{5}{7}$ **79.** $\frac{65}{21}$ **81.** $\frac{2}{5}$ **83.** $\frac{10}{9}$ **85.** $\frac{17}{3}$ **87.** 37 **89.** $\frac{5}{66}$ **91.** $\frac{1}{5}$ **93.** $5\frac{1}{6}$ **95.** $\frac{17}{18}$ **97.** $55\frac{1}{4}$ ft **99.** answers may vary **101.** $3\frac{3}{8}$ mi **103.** $\frac{21}{100}$ **105.** multiplexes **107.** incorrect; $\frac{12}{24} = \frac{2 \cdot 2 \cdot 3}{2 \cdot 2 \cdot 2 \cdot 3} = \frac{1}{2}$ **109.** incorrect; $\frac{2}{7} + \frac{9}{7} = \frac{11}{7}$

Section R.4

Practice Exercises

1. a. 1 **b.** 25 **c.** $\frac{1}{100}$ **d.** 9 **e.** $\frac{8}{125}$ **2. a.** 33 **b.** 11 **c.** $\frac{32}{9}$ or $3\frac{5}{9}$ **d.** 36 **e.** $\frac{3}{16}$ **3.** $\frac{31}{11}$ **4.** 4 **5.** $\frac{9}{22}$ **6. a.** 9 **b.** $\frac{8}{15}$ **c.** $\frac{19}{10}$ **d.** 33 **7.** No **8. a.** $6x$ **b.** $x - 8$ **c.** $x \cdot 9$ or $9x$ **d.** $2x + 3$ **e.** $7 + x$ **9. a.** $x + 7 = 13$ **b.** $x - 2 = 11$ **c.** $2x + 9 \neq 25$ **d.** $5(11) \geq x$

Graphing Calculator Explorations R.4

1. 625 **3.** 59,049 **5.** 30 **7.** 9857 **9.** 2376

Vocabulary, Readiness & Video Check R.4

1. base; exponent **3.** variable **5.** equation **7.** solving **9.** The replacement value for z is not used because it's not needed–there is no variable z in the given algebraic expression. **11.** We translate phrases to mathematical expressions and sentences to mathematical equations.

Exercise Set R.4

1. 243 **3.** 27 **5.** 1 **7.** 5 **9.** 49 **11.** $\frac{16}{81}$ **13.** $\frac{1}{125}$ **15.** 1.44 **17.** 0.000064 **19.** 17 **21.** 20 **23.** 10 **25.** 21 **27.** 45 **29.** 0 **31.** 30 **33.** 2 **35.** $\frac{7}{18}$ **37.** $\frac{27}{10}$ **39.** $\frac{7}{5}$ **41.** 32 **43.** $\frac{23}{27}$ **45. a.** 64 **b.** 43 **c.** 19 **d.** 22 **47.** 9 **49.** 1 **51.** 1 **53.** 11 **55.** 8 **57.** 45 **59.** 27 **61.** 132 **63.** $\frac{37}{18}$ **65.** 16; 64; 144; 256 **67.** yes **69.** no **71.** no **73.** yes **75.** no **77.** $x + 15$ **79.** $x - 5$ **81.** $\frac{x}{4}$ **83.** $3x + 22$ **85.** $1 + 2 = 9 \div 3$ **87.** $3 \neq 4 \div 2$ **89.** $5 + x = 20$ **91.** $7.6x = 17$ **93.** $13 - 3x = 13$ **95.** multiply **97.** subtract **99.** no; answers may vary **101.** 14 in., 12 sq in. **103.** 14 in., 9.01 sq in. **105.** Rectangles with the same perimeter can have different areas. **107.** $(20 - 4) \cdot 4 \div 2$ **109. a.** expression **b.** equation **c.** equation **d.** expression **e.** expression **111.** answers may vary **113.** answers may vary, for example, $-2(5) - 1$ **115.** 12,000 sq ft **117.** 51 mph

Section R.5

Practice Exercises

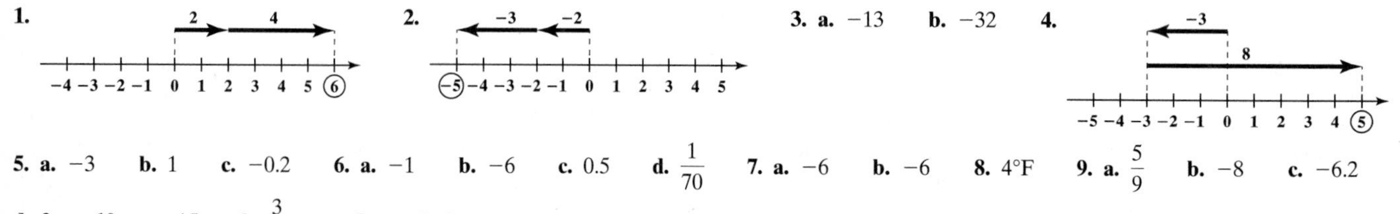

3. a. −13 **b.** −32

5. a. −3 **b.** 1 **c.** −0.2 **6. a.** −1 **b.** −6 **c.** 0.5 **d.** $\frac{1}{70}$ **7. a.** −6 **b.** −6 **8.** 4°F **9. a.** $\frac{5}{9}$ **b.** −8 **c.** −6.2 **d.** 3 **10. a.** −15 **b.** $\frac{3}{5}$ **c.** $5y$ **d.** 8

Vocabulary, Readiness & Video Check R.5

1. opposites **3.** n **5.** absolute values **7.** Negative temperatures; the high temperature for the day was −6°F

Exercise Set R.5

1. 9 **3.** −14 **5.** 1 **7.** −12 **9.** −5 **11.** −12 **13.** −4 **15.** 7 **17.** −2 **19.** 0 **21.** −19 **23.** 31 **25.** −47 **27.** −2.1 **29.** −8 **31.** 38 **33.** −13.1 **35.** $\frac{2}{8} = \frac{1}{4}$ **37.** $-\frac{3}{16}$ **39.** $-\frac{13}{10}$ **41.** −8 **43.** −59 **45.** −9 **47.** 5 **49.** 11 **51.** −18 **53.** 19 **55.** −0.7 **57.** −6° **59.** 146 ft **61.** −$6.9 million **63.** −16 **65.** −6 **67.** 2 **69.** 0 **71.** −6 **73.** −2 **75.** 0 **77.** $-\frac{2}{3}$ **79.** yes **81.** no **83.** July **85.** October **87.** 4.7°F **89.** −3 **91.** −22 **93.** negative **95.** positive **97.** true **99.** false **101.** answers may vary **103.** answers may vary

Section R.6

Practice Exercises

1. a. −13 **b.** −7 **c.** 12 **d.** −2 **2. a.** 10.9 **b.** $-\frac{1}{2}$ **c.** $-\frac{19}{20}$ **3.** −7 **4. a.** −6 **b.** 6.1 **5. a.** −20 **b.** 13 **6. a.** 2 **b.** 13 **7.** $357 **8. a.** 28° **b.** 137°

Vocabulary, Readiness & Video Check R.6

1. $7 - x$ **3.** $x - 7$ **5.** $7 - x$ **7.** $-10 - (-14)$; d **9.** addition; opposite **11.** There's a minus sign in the numerator and the replacement value is negative (notice parentheses are used around the replacement value), and it's always good to be careful when working with negative signs. **13.** In Example 9, you have two supplementary angles and know the measure of one of them. From the definition, you know that two supplementary angles must sum to 180°. Therefore you can subtract the known angle measure from 180° to get the measure of the other angle.

Exercise Set R.6

1. −10 **3.** −5 **5.** 19 **7.** $\frac{1}{6}$ **9.** 2 **11.** −11 **13.** 11 **15.** 5 **17.** 37 **19.** −6.4 **21.** −71 **23.** 0 **25.** 4.1 **27.** $\frac{2}{11}$ **29.** $-\frac{11}{12}$ **31.** 8.92 **33.** 13 **35.** −5 **37.** −1 **39.** −23 **41.** −26 **43.** −24 **45.** 3 **47.** −45 **49.** −4 **51.** 13 **53.** 6 **55.** 9 **57.** −9 **59.** −7 **61.** $\frac{7}{5}$ **63.** 21 **65.** $\frac{1}{4}$ **67.** 100°F **69.** 265°F **71.** 35,653 ft **73.** −308 ft **75.** 19,852 ft **77.** 130° **79.** 30° **81.** no **83.** no **85.** yes **87.** $-5 + x$ **89.** $-20 - x$ **91.** −4.4°; 2.6°; 12°; 23.5°; 15.3° **93.** May **95.** answers may vary **97.** 16 **99.** −20 **101.** true; answers may vary **103.** false; answers may vary **105.** negative, −30,387

Integrated Review

1. negative **2.** negative **3.** positive **4.** 0 **5.** positive **6.** 0 **7.** positive **8.** positive **9.** $-\frac{1}{7}; \frac{1}{7}$ **10.** $\frac{12}{5}; \frac{12}{5}$ **11.** 3; 3 **12.** $-\frac{9}{11}; \frac{9}{11}$ **13.** −42 **14.** 10 **15.** 2 **16.** −18 **17.** −7 **18.** −39 **19.** −2 **20.** −9 **21.** −3.4 **22.** −9.8 **23.** $-\frac{25}{28}$

24. $-\frac{5}{24}$ **25.** -4 **26.** -24 **27.** 6 **28.** 20 **29.** 6 **30.** 61 **31.** -6 **32.** -16 **33.** -19 **34.** -13 **35.** -4 **36.** -1 **37.** $\frac{13}{20}$ **38.** $-\frac{29}{40}$ **39.** 4 **40.** 9 **41.** -1 **42.** -3 **43.** 8 **44.** 10 **45.** 47 **46.** $\frac{2}{3}$

Section R.7

Practice Exercises

1. a. -40 **b.** 12 **c.** -54 **2. a.** -30 **b.** 24 **c.** 0 **d.** 26 **3. a.** -0.046 **b.** $-\frac{4}{15}$ **c.** 14 **4. a.** 36 **b.** -36 **c.** -64 **d.** -64 **5. a.** $\frac{3}{8}$ **b.** $\frac{1}{15}$ **c.** $-\frac{7}{2}$ **d.** $-\frac{1}{5}$ **6. a.** -8 **b.** -4 **c.** 5 **7. a.** 3 **b.** -16 **c.** $-\frac{6}{5}$ **d.** $-\frac{1}{18}$ **8. a.** 0 **b.** undefined **c.** undefined **9. a.** $-\frac{84}{5}$ **b.** 11 **10. a.** -9 **b.** 33 **c.** $\frac{5}{3}$ **11.** -52

Graphing Calculator Explorations R.7

1. 38 **3.** -441 **5.** $163.\overline{3}$ **7.** 54,499 **9.** 15,625

Vocabulary, Readiness & Video Check R.7

1. 0; 0 **3.** positive **5.** negative **7.** positive **9.** The parentheses, or lack of them, determine the base of the expression. In Example 6, $(-2)^4$, the base is -2 and all of -2 is raised to 4. In Example 7, -2^4, the base is 2 and only 2 is raised to 4. **11.** Yes; because division of real numbers is defined in terms of multiplication. **13.** The football team lost 4 yards on each play and a loss of yardage is represented by a negative number.

Exercise Set R.7

1. -24 **3.** -2 **5.** 50 **7.** -12 **9.** 0 **11.** -18 **13.** $\frac{3}{10}$ **15.** $\frac{2}{3}$ **17.** -7 **19.** 0.14 **21.** -800 **23.** -28 **25.** 25 **27.** $-\frac{8}{27}$ **29.** -121 **31.** $-\frac{1}{4}$ **33.** -30 **35.** 23 **37.** -7 **39.** true **41.** false **43.** 16 **45.** -1 **47.** 25 **49.** -49 **51.** $\frac{1}{9}$ **53.** $\frac{3}{2}$ **55.** $-\frac{1}{14}$ **57.** $-\frac{11}{3}$ **59.** $\frac{1}{0.2}$ **61.** -6.3 **63.** -9 **65.** 4 **67.** -4 **69.** 0 **71.** -5 **73.** undefined **75.** 3 **77.** -15 **79.** $-\frac{18}{7}$ **81.** $\frac{20}{27}$ **83.** -1 **85.** $-\frac{9}{2}$ **87.** -4 **89.** 16 **91.** -3 **93.** $-\frac{16}{7}$ **95.** 2 **97.** $\frac{6}{5}$ **99.** -5 **101.** $\frac{3}{2}$ **103.** -21 **105.** 41 **107.** -134 **109.** 3 **111.** 0 **113.** $-71 \cdot x$ or $-71x$ **115.** $-16 - x$ **117.** $-29 + x$ **119.** $\frac{x}{-33}$ or $x \div (-33)$ **121.** $3 \cdot (-4) = -12$; a loss of 12 yd **123.** $5(-20) = -100$; a depth of 100 ft **125.** yes **127.** no **129.** yes **131.** -162°F **133.** answers may vary **135.** 1, -1 **137.** positive **139.** not possible **141.** negative **143.** $-2 + \frac{-15}{3}$; -7 **145.** $2[-5 + (-3)]$; -16

Section R.8

Practice Exercises

1. a. $8 \cdot x$ **b.** $17 + x$ **2. a.** $2 + (9 + 7)$ **b.** $(-4 \cdot 2) \cdot 7$ **3. a.** $x + 14$ **b.** $-30x$ **4. a.** $5x - 5y$ **b.** $-24 - 12t$ **c.** $6x - 8y - 2z$ **d.** $-3 + y$ **e.** $-x + 7 - 2s$ **f.** $x + 11$ **5. a.** $5(w + 3)$ **b.** $9(w + z)$ **6. a.** commutative property of multiplication **b.** associative property of addition **c.** identity element for addition **d.** multiplicative inverse property **e.** commutative property of addition **f.** additive inverse property **g.** commutative and associative properties of multiplication

Vocabulary, Readiness & Video Check R.8

1. commutative property of addition **3.** distributive property **5.** associative property of addition **7.** opposites or additive inverses **9.** 2 is outside the parentheses, so the point is made that you should only distribute the -9 to the terms within the parentheses and not also to the 2.

Exercise Set R.8

1. $16 + x$ **3.** $y \cdot (-4)$ **5.** yx **7.** $13 + 2x$ **9.** $x \cdot (yz)$ **11.** $(2 + a) + b$ **13.** $(4a) \cdot b$ **15.** $a + (b + c)$ **17.** $17 + b$ **19.** $24y$ **21.** y **23.** $26 + a$ **25.** $-72x$ **27.** s **29.** $2 + x$ **31.** $4x + 4y$ **33.** $9x - 54$ **35.** $6x + 10$ **37.** $28x - 21$ **39.** $18 + 3x$ **41.** $-2y + 2z$ **43.** $-21y - 35$ **45.** $5x + 20m + 10$ **47.** $-4 + 8m - 4n$ **49.** $-5x - 2$ **51.** $-r + 3 + 7p$ **53.** $3x + 4$ **55.** $-x + 3y$ **57.** $6r + 8$ **59.** $-36x - 70$ **61.** $-16x - 25$ **63.** $4(1 + y)$ **65.** $11(x + y)$ **67.** $-1(5 + x)$ **69.** $30(a + b)$ **71.** commutative property of multiplication **73.** associative property of addition **75.** distributive property **77.** associative property of multiplication **79.** identity element of addition **81.** distributive property **83.** commutative and associative properties of multiplication **85.** -8; $\frac{1}{8}$ **87.** $-x$; $\frac{1}{x}$ **89.** $2x$; $-2x$ **91.** false **93.** no **95.** yes **97.** yes **99.** no **101. a.** commutative property of addition **b.** commutative property of addition **c.** associative property of addition **103.** answers may vary **105.** answers may vary

Chapter R Vocabulary Check

1. inequality symbols **2.** equation **3.** absolute value **4.** variable **5.** opposites **6.** numerator **7.** solution **8.** reciprocals **9.** base; exponent **10.** denominator **11.** grouping symbols **12.** set

Chapter R Review

1. $<$ **3.** $>$ **5.** $<$ **7.** $=$ **9.** $>$ **11.** $4 \geq -3$ **13.** $0.03 < 0.3$ **15. a.** 1, 3 **b.** 0, 1, 3 **c.** $-6, 0, 1, 3$ **d.** $-6, 0, 1, 1\frac{1}{2}, 3, 9.62$ **e.** π **f.** $-6, 0, 1, 1\frac{1}{2}, 3, \pi, 9.62$ **17.** Friday **19.** $2 \cdot 2 \cdot 3 \cdot 3$ **21.** $\frac{12}{25}$ **23.** $\frac{13}{10}$ **25.** $9\frac{3}{8}$ **27.** 15

29. $\frac{7}{12}$ **31.** $A = 1\frac{1}{6}$ sq m; $P = 4\frac{5}{12}$ m **33.** $14\frac{1}{8}$ lb **35.** $18\frac{7}{16}$ lb **37.** Baby E **39.** c **41.** $\frac{4}{49}$ **43.** 37 **45.** $\frac{18}{7}$
47. $20 - 12 = 2 \cdot 4$ **49.** 18 **51.** 5 **53.** 63° **55.** yes **57.** 9 **59.** −2 **61.** −11 **63.** $-\frac{3}{16}$ **65.** −13.9 **67.** −14
69. 5 **71.** −19 **73.** a **75.** \$51 **77.** $-\frac{1}{6}$ **79.** −48 **81.** 3 **83.** undefined **85.** undefined **87.** −12 **89.** 9
91. $-7 \cdot x$ or $-7x$ **93.** $-20 - x$ **95.** commutative property of addition **97.** distributive property **99.** associative property of addition
101. distributive property **103.** multiplicative inverse property **105.** $5y - 10$ **107.** $-7 + x - 4z$ **109.** $-12z - 27$ **111.** <
113. −15.3 **115.** −80 **117.** $-\frac{1}{4}$ **119.** 16 **121.** −5 **123.** $-\frac{5}{6}$ **125.** $1\frac{3}{8}$ ft

Chapter R Test

1. $|-7| > 5$ **2.** $9 + 5 \geq 4$ **3.** −5 **4.** −11 **5.** −3 **6.** −39 **7.** 12 **8.** −2 **9.** undefined **10.** −8 **11.** $-\frac{1}{3}$ **12.** $4\frac{5}{8}$
13. 1.275 **14.** −32 **15.** −48 **16.** 3 **17.** 0 **18.** > **19.** > **20.** < **21.** = **22.** 2221 < 10,993 **23. a.** 1, 7 **b.** 0, 1, 7
c. −5, −1, 0, 1, 7 **d.** $-5, -1, 0, \frac{1}{4}, 1, 7, 11.6$ **e.** $\sqrt{7}, 3\pi$ **f.** $-5, -1, 0, \frac{1}{4}, 1, 7, 11.6, \sqrt{7}, 3\pi$ **24.** 40 **25.** 12 **26.** 22 **27.** −1
28. associative property of addition **29.** commutative property of multiplication **30.** distributive property **31.** multiplicative inverse property
32. 9 **33.** −3 **34.** second down **35.** yes **36.** 17° **37.** \$650 million **38.** \$420

CHAPTER 1 GRAPHING

Section 1.1

Practice Exercises

1. a. Africa/Middle East region, 145 million Internet users **b.** 640 million more Internet users **2. a.** 70 beats per minute **b.** 60 beats per minute **c.** 5 minutes after lighting **3.**

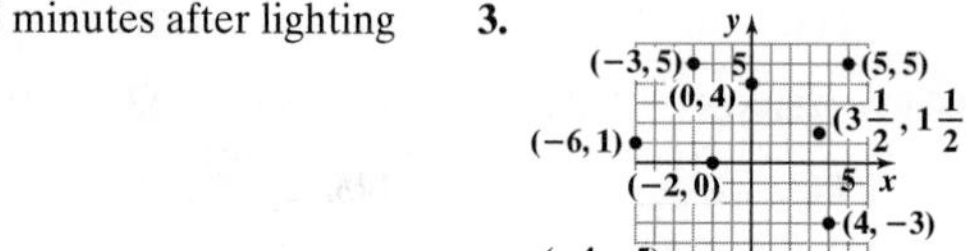
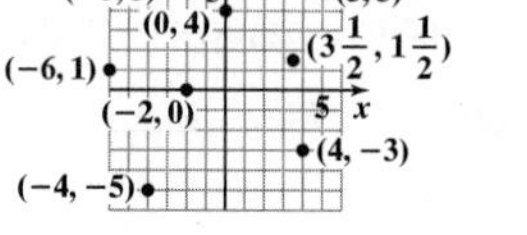

4. a. (2004, 65), (2005, 67), (2006, 96), (2007, 86), (2008, 79), (2009, 79), (2010, 72)

b.

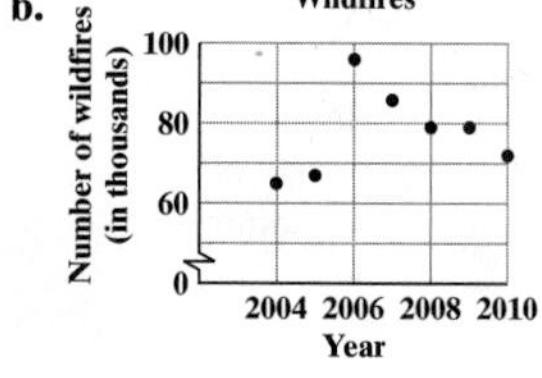

5. a. yes **b.** yes **c.** no **6. a.** (0, −8) **b.** (6, 4) **c.** (−3, −14)

7.

	x	y
a.	−2	8
b.	3	−12
c.	0	0

8.

	x	y
a.	−10	−4
b.	0	−2
c.	10	0

9.

x	0	1	2	3	4
y	12,000	10,200	8400	6600	4800

Vocabulary, Readiness & Video Check 1.1

1. x-axis; y-axis **3.** quadrants; four **5.** one **7.** horizontal: top tourist countries; vertical: number of arrivals (in millions) to these countries **9.** Data occurring in pairs of numbers can be written as ordered pairs, called paired data, and then graphed on a coordinate system. **11.** a linear equation in one variable

Exercise Set 1.1

1. France **3.** France, U.S., Spain, Italy, and China **5.** 43 million **7.** 71,000 **9.** 2011; 103,000 **11.** 15.9 **13.** from 1998 to 2000
15. 2014 **17.** (1, 5) and (3.7, 2.2) are in quadrant I, $\left(-1, 4\frac{1}{2}\right)$ is in quadrant II, (−5, −2) is in quadrant III, (2, −4) and $\left(\frac{1}{2}, -3\right)$ are in quadrant IV, (−3, 0) lies on the x-axis, (0, −1) lies on the y-axis **19.** (0, 0) **21.** (3, 2) **23.** (−2, −2) **25.** (2, −1) **27.** (0, −3) **29.** (1, 3) **31.** (−3, −1)

33. a. (2006, 25.5), (2007, 26.3), (2008, 27.7), (2009, 29.4), (2010, 31.8) **b.** In the year 2010, the worldwide box office was \$31.8 billion. **c.** **d.** The worldwide box office increased every year. **35. a.** (0.50, 10), (0.75, 12), (1.00, 15), (1.25, 16), (1.50, 18), (1.50, 19), (1.75, 19), (2.00, 20) **b.** When Minh studied 1.25 hours, her quiz score was 16. **c.**

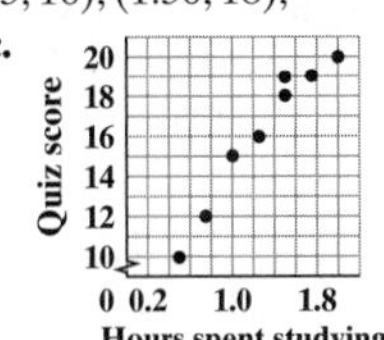

d. answers may very

37. a. (2313, 2), (2085, 1), (2711, 21), (2869, 39), (2920, 42), (4038, 99), (1783, 0), (2493, 9) **b.** **c.** The farther from the equator, the more snowfall. **39.** yes; no; yes **41.** yes; yes **43.** no; yes; yes

45. $(-4, -2), (4, 0)$ **47.** $(-8, -5), (16, 1)$ **49.** $0; 7; -\frac{2}{7}$ **51.** 2; 2; 5

53. 0; −3; 2 **55.** 2; 6; 3 **57.** −12; 5; −6 **59.** $\frac{5}{7}; \frac{5}{2}; -1$ **61.** 0; −5; −2

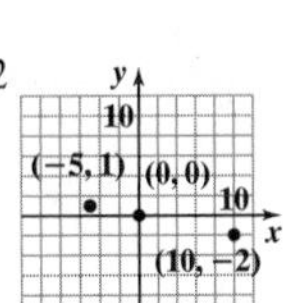

63. 2; 1; −6 **65. a.** 13,000; 21,000; 29,000 **b.** 45 desks **67. a.** 5.52; 6.00; 6.48 **b.** year 9; 2009 **c.** 2016 **d.** In 2005, the average cinema admission price was \$6.48. **69.** In 2010, there were 3755 Walmart stores in the U.S. **71.** year 8: 100 stores; year 9: 105 stores; year 10: 100 stores **73.** The y-values are all 0. **75.** $y = 5 - x$ **77.** $y = -\frac{1}{2}x + \frac{5}{4}$ **79.** $y = -2x$ **81.** $y = \frac{1}{3}x - 2$ **83.** false **85.** true **87.** negative; negative

89. positive; negative **91.** 0; 0 **93.** y **95.** no; answers may vary **97.** answers may vary **99.** (4, −7) **101.** 26 units **103. a.** (−2, 6) **b.** 28 units **c.** 45 sq units

Section 1.2

Practice Exercises

1. a. yes **b.** no **c.** yes **d.** yes **2.** **3.** **4.**

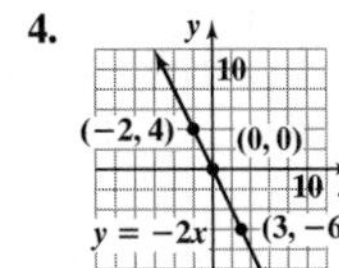

5.

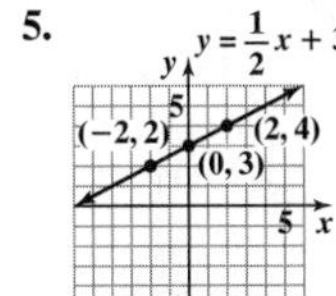

6.

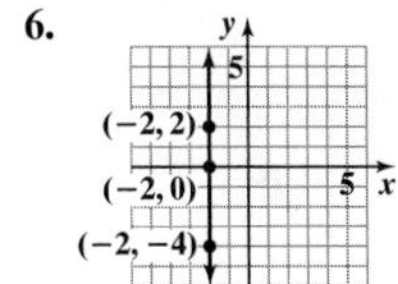

7. The graph of $y = -2x + 3$ is the same as the graph of $y = -2x$ except that the graph of $y = -2x + 3$ is moved 3 units upward.

8. a.

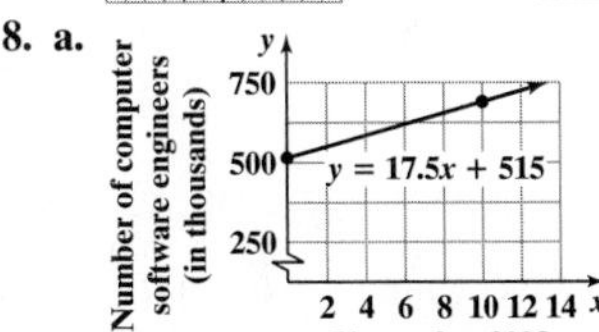
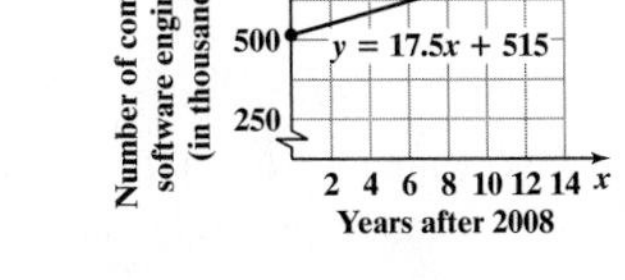

b. We predict 725 thousand computer software application engineers in the year 2020.

Graphing Calculator Explorations 1.2

1.

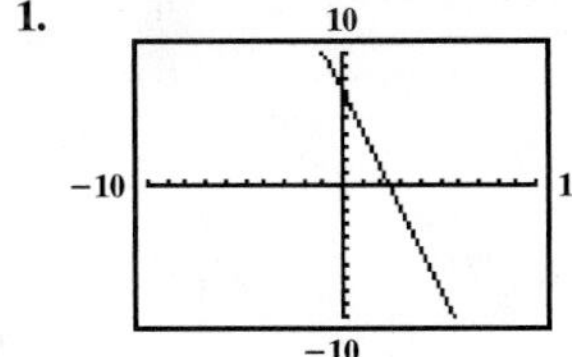

3.

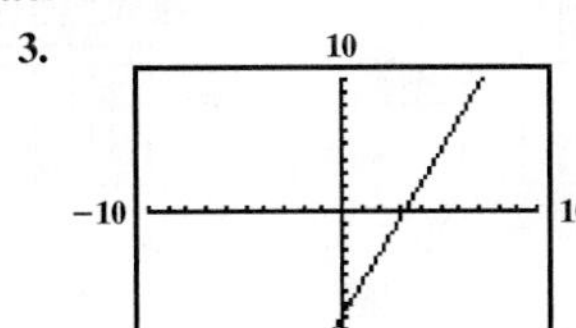

5.

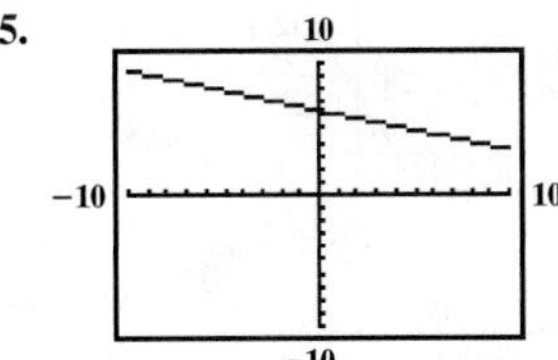

Vocabulary, Readiness & Video Check 1.2

1. In the definition, x and y both have an understood power of 1. Example 3 shows an equation where y has a power of 2, so it is not a linear equation in two variables. **3.** An infinite number of points make up the line and each point corresponds to an ordered pair that is a solution of the linear equation in two variables.

Exercise Set 1.2

1. yes **3.** yes **5.** no **7.** yes **9.**

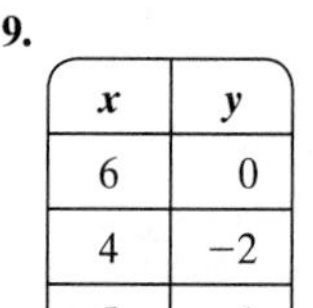

x	y
6	0
4	−2
5	−1

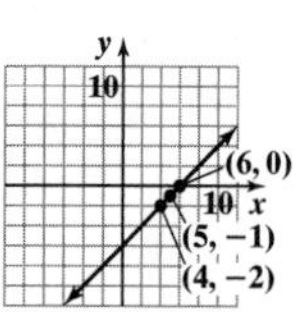

11.

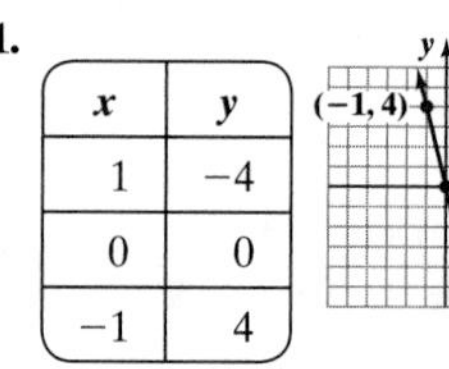

x	y
1	−4
0	0
−1	4

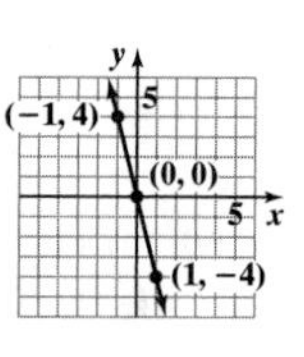

13.

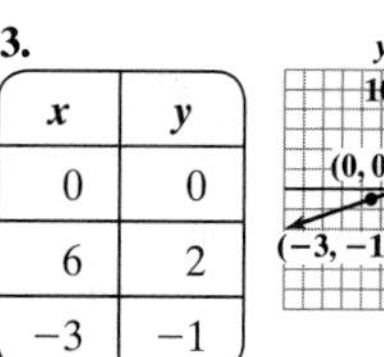

x	y
0	0
6	2
−3	−1

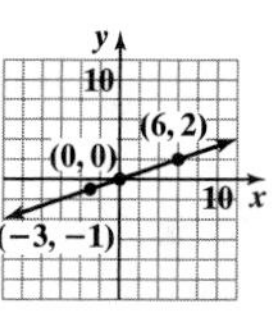

15.

x	y
0	3
1	−1
2	−5

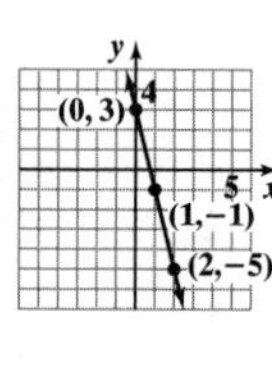

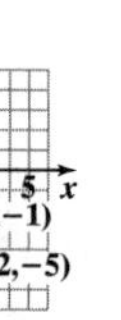

17.

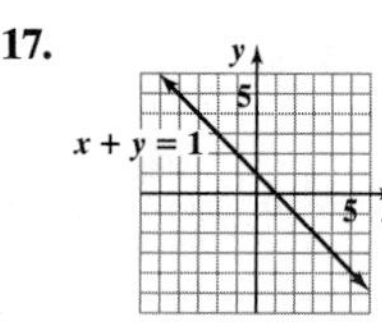

19.

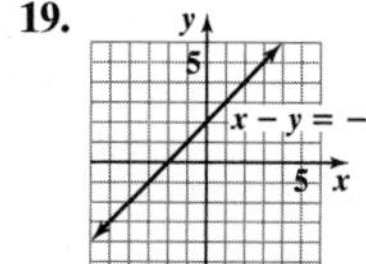

21.

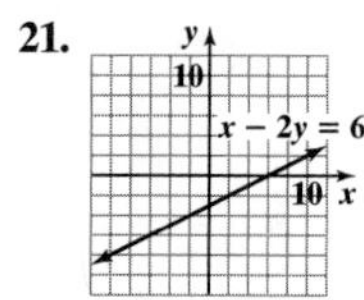

23.

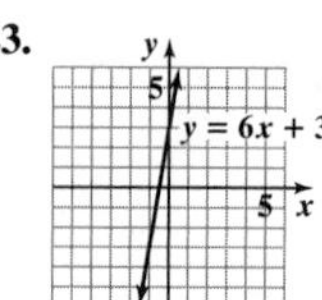

25.

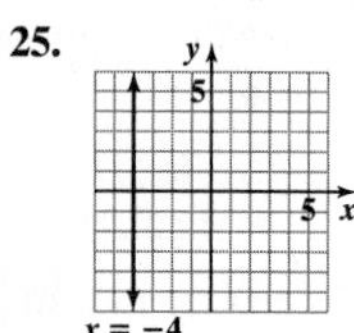

27.

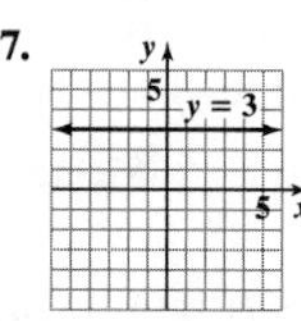

29.

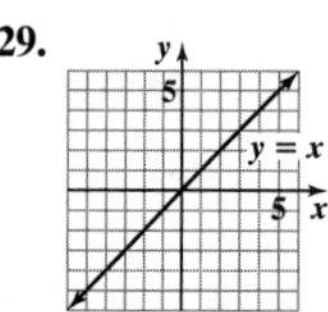

31.

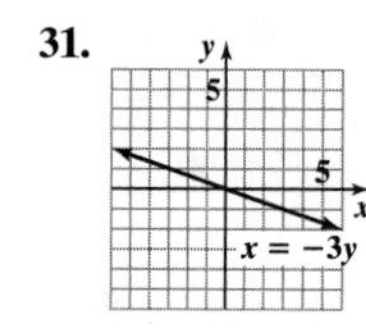

33.

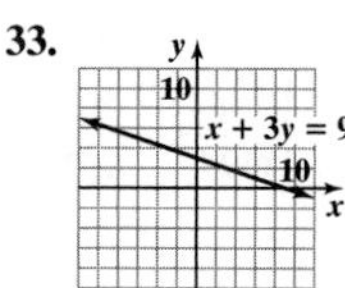

35.

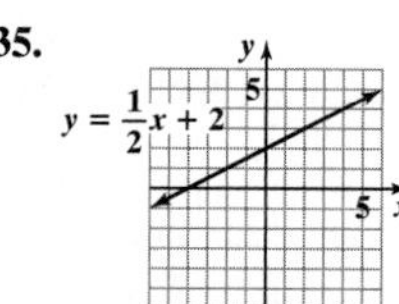

37.

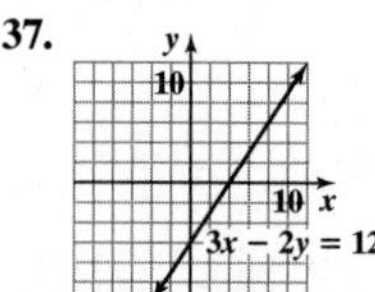

39.

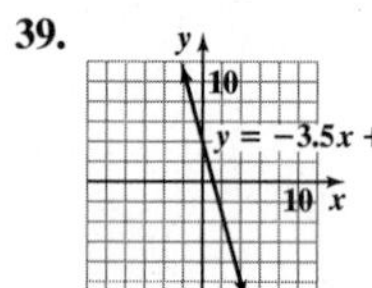

41.

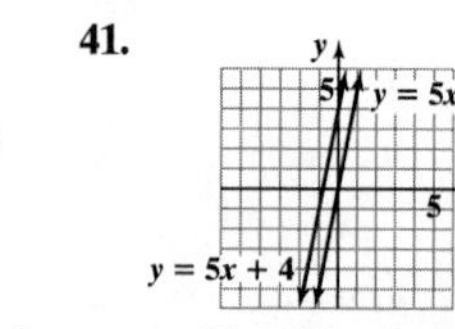

43.

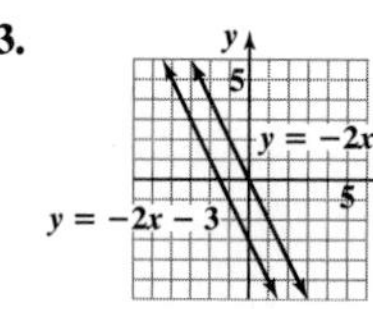

45.

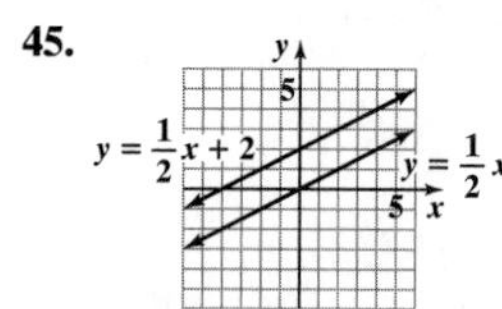

47. c **49.** d **51. a.** (8, 31) **b.** In 2008, there were 31 million joggers. **c.** 40 million joggers **53. a.** (8, 207.6) **b.** In 2008, there were 207.6 million people with driver's licenses. **c.** 225.2 million **55.** (4, −1) **57.** 3; −3 **59.** 0; 0 **61.** $y = x + 5$

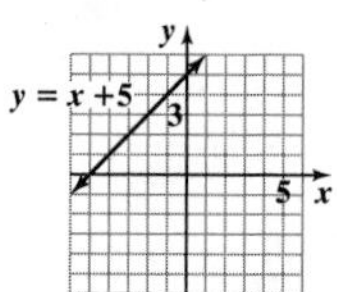

63. $2x + 3y = 6$

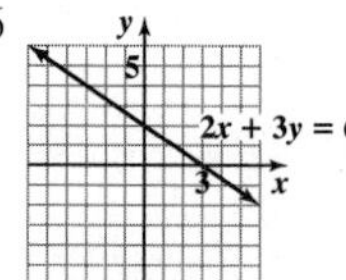

65. $x + y = 12$; $y = 9$ cm **67.** answers may vary **69.** 0; 1; 1; 4; 4

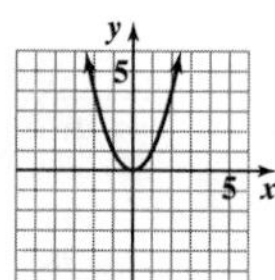

Section 1.3

Practice Exercises

1. x-intercept: $(-4, 0)$ y-intercept: $(0, -6)$ **2.** x-intercepts: $(-2, 0)$, $(2, 0)$ y-intercept: $(0, -3)$ **3.** x-intercept: $(0, 0)$ y-intercept: $(0, 0)$ **4.** x-intercept: none y-intercept: $(0, 3)$ **5.** x-intercepts: $(-1, 0)$, $(5, 0)$ y-intercepts: $(0, 2)$, $(0, -2)$

6. **7.**

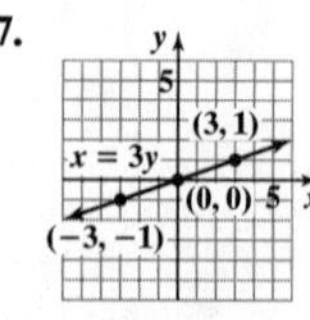

8.

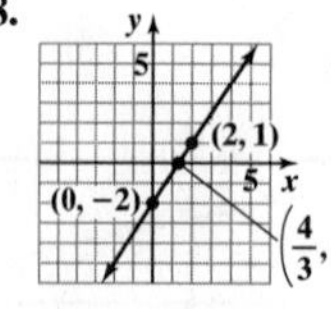

9.

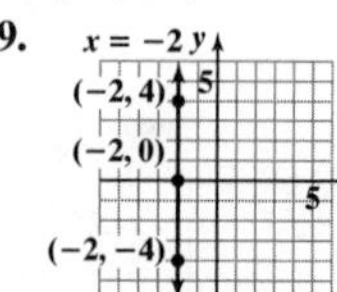

10.

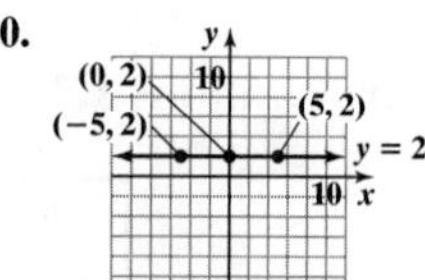

Graphing Calculator Explorations 1.3

1. **3.**

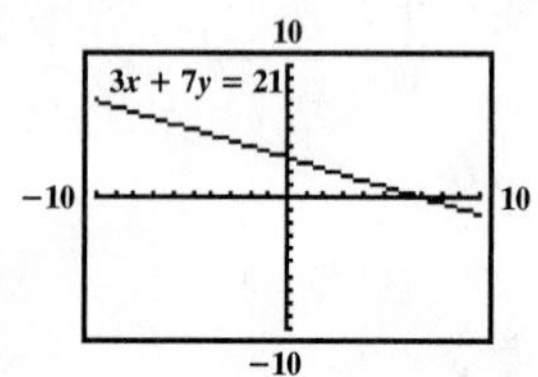

5.

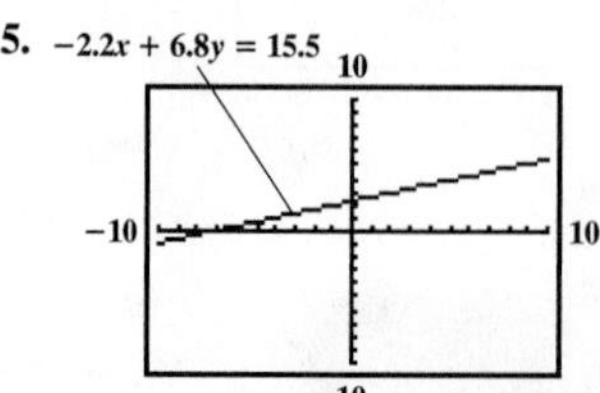

Vocabulary, Readiness & Video Check 1.3

1. linear **3.** horizontal **5.** y-intercept **7.** $y; x$ **9.** Because x-intercepts lie on the x-axis; because y-intercepts lie on the y-axis. **11.** For a horizontal line, the coefficient of x will be 0 and the coefficient of y will be 1; for a vertical line, the coefficient of y will be 0 and the coefficient of x will be 1.

Exercise Set 1.3

1. $(-1, 0); (0, 1)$ **3.** $(-2, 0); (2, 0); (0, -2)$ **5.** $(-2, 0); (1, 0); (3, 0); (0, 3)$ **7.** $(-1, 0); (1, 0); (0, 1); (0, -2)$ **9.** infinite **11.** 0

13.

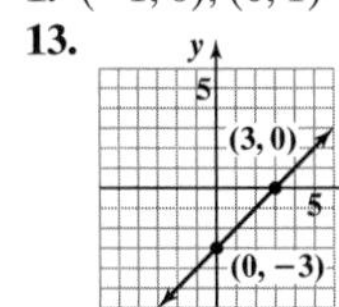

15.

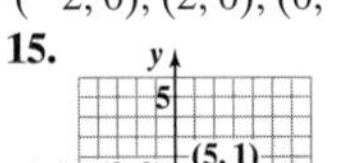
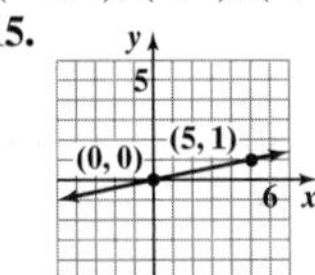

17.

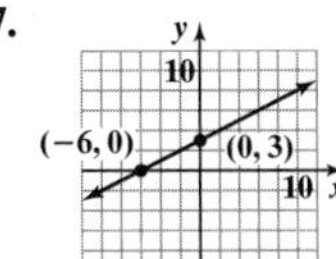

19. **21.**

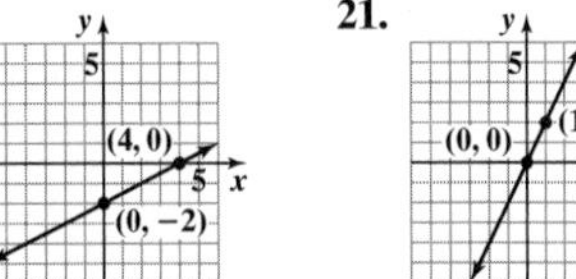

23.

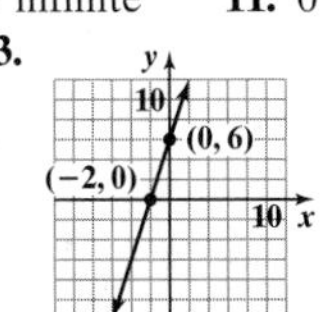

25.

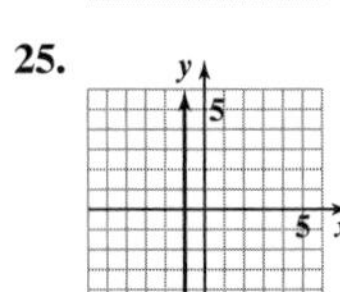

27.

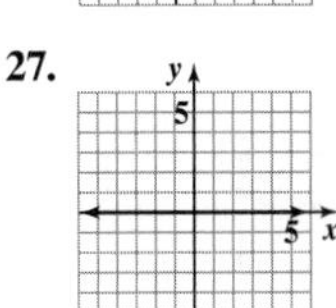

29.

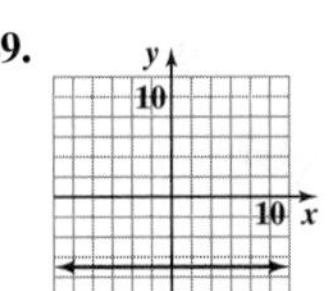

31.

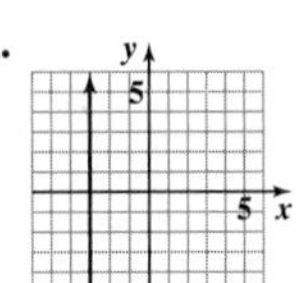

33.

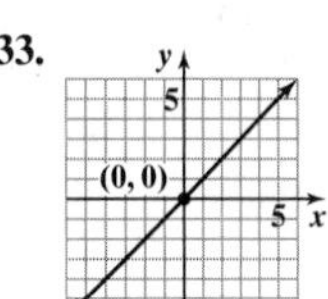

35.

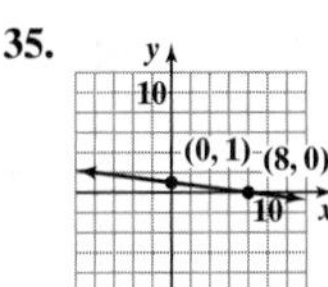

37.

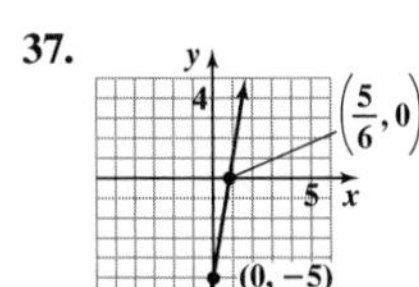

39.

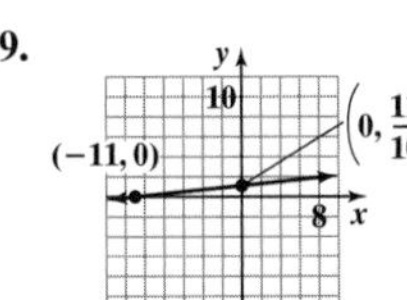

41.

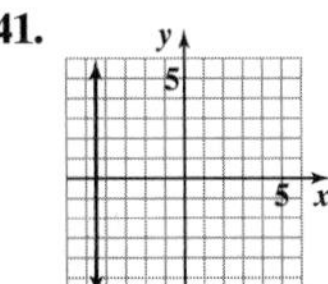

43.

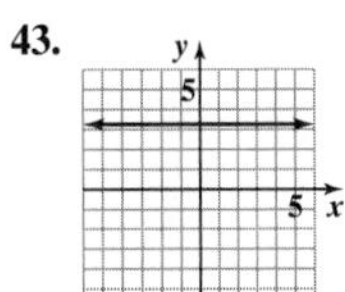

45.

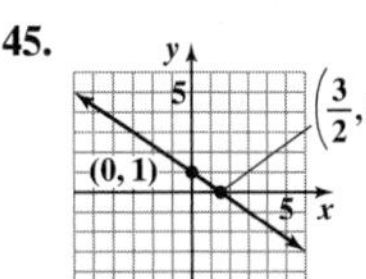

47.

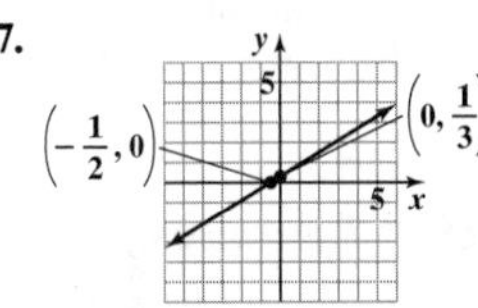

49. C **51.** E **53.** B **55.** $\frac{3}{2}$ **57.** 6 **59.** $-\frac{6}{5}$ **61.** false **63.** true **65.** $(0, 200)$; no chairs and 200 desks are manufactured, **67.** 300 chairs **69. a.** $(62, 0)$ **b.** 62 years after 2002, 0 people will attend the movies at the theater. **c.** answers may very **71.** $x = 1$ **73.** answers may vary **75.** answers may vary

Section 1.4

Practice Exercises

1. -1 **2.** $\frac{1}{3}$ **3.** $m = \frac{2}{3}$; y-intercept: $(0, -2)$ **4.** $m = 6$; y-intercept: $(0, -5)$ **5.** $m = -\frac{5}{2}$; y-intercept: $(0, 4)$ **6.** $m = 0$ **7.** slope is undefined **8. a.** perpendicular **b.** neither **c.** parallel **9.** 25% **10.** $m = \frac{0.75 \text{ dollar}}{1 \text{ pound}}$; The Wash-n-Fold charges \$0.75 per pound of laundry.

Graphing Calculator Explorations 1.4

1.

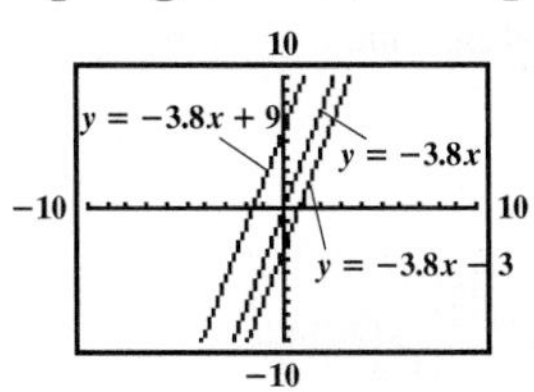

3.

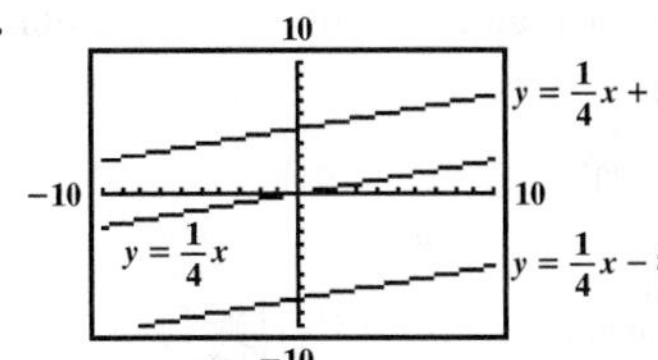

Vocabulary, Readiness & Video Check 1.4

1. slope **3.** 0 **5.** positive **7.** $y; x$ **9.** solve the equation for y; the slope is the coefficient of x. **11.** slope-intercept form; this form makes the slope easy to see, and you need to compare slopes to determine if two lines are parallel or perpendicular.

Exercise Set 1.4

1. -1 **3.** undefined **5.** $-\frac{2}{3}$ **7.** 0 **9.** $m = -\frac{4}{3}$ **11.** undefined slope **13.** $m = \frac{5}{2}$ **15.** negative **17.** undefined **19.** upward **21.** horizontal **23.** line 1 **25.** line 2 **27.** D **29.** B **31.** E **33.** undefined slope **35.** $m = 0$ **37.** undefined slope **39.** $m = 0$ **41.** $m = 5$ **43.** $m = -0.3$ **45.** $m = -2$ **47.** $m = \frac{2}{3}$ **49.** undefined slope **51.** $m = \frac{1}{2}$ **53.** $m = 0$ **55.** $m = -\frac{3}{4}$ **57.** $m = 4$ **59. a.** 1 **b.** -1 **61. a.** $\frac{9}{11}$ **b.** $-\frac{11}{9}$ **63.** neither **65.** neither **67.** parallel **69.** perpendicular **71.** $\frac{3}{5}$ **73.** 12.5% **75.** 40% **77.** 37%; 35% **79.** $m = \frac{1}{1}$ or 1; Every 1 year, there are 1 million more U.S. households with televisions. **81.** $m = 0.47$; It costs \$0.47 per 1 mile to own and operate a compact car. **83.** $y = 2x - 14$ **85.** $y = -6x - 11$ **87.** $m = \frac{1}{2}$ **89.** answers may vary **91.** 2005 to 2006 **93.** 2000; 28.5 mi per gallon **95.** from 2008 to 2009 **97.** $x = 6$ **99. a.** $(2007, 2207); (2010, 2333)$ **b.** 42 **c.** For the years 2007 through 2010, the number of heart transplants increased at a rate of 42 per year. **101.** The slope through $(-3, 0)$ and $(1, 1)$ is $\frac{1}{4}$. The slope through $(-3, 0)$ and $(-4, 4)$ is -4. The product of the slopes is -1, so the sides are perpendicular. **103.** -0.25 **105.** 0.875 **107.** The line becomes steeper.

Integrated Review

1. $m = 2$ **2.** $m = 0$ **3.** $m = -\frac{2}{3}$ **4.** undefined slope **5.** **6.** 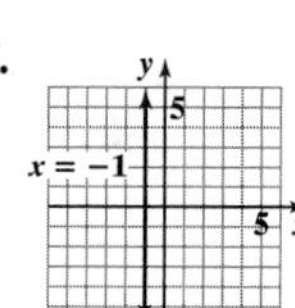

7. **8.** **9.** **10.** **11.** **12.**

13. parallel **14.** neither **15. a.** $(0, 587)$ **b.** In 2000, there were 587 thousand bridges on public roads. **c.** 1.7 **d.** For the years 2000 through 2009, the number of bridges on public roads increased at a rate of 1.7 thousand per year. **16. a.** $(9, 26.6)$ **b.** In 2009, the revenue for online advertising was \$26.6 billion.

Section 1.5

Practice Exercises

1. **2.** **3.** $y = \frac{1}{2}x + 7$ **4.** $4x - y = 5$ **5.** $5x + 4y = 19$ **6.** $x = 3$ **7.** $y = 3$ **8. a.** $y = -1500x + 195{,}000$ **b.** \$105,000

Graphing Calculator Explorations 1.5

1. 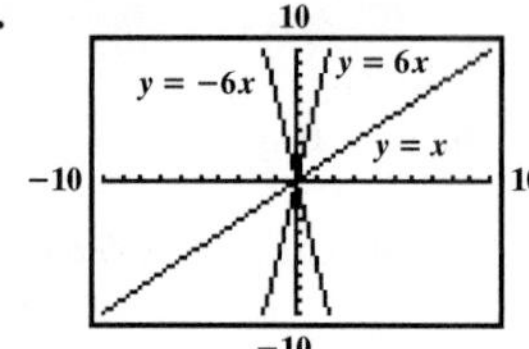

3. 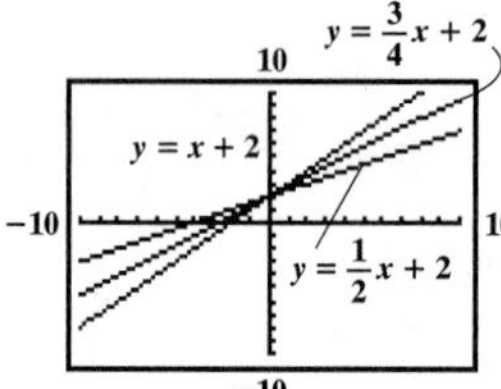

5. 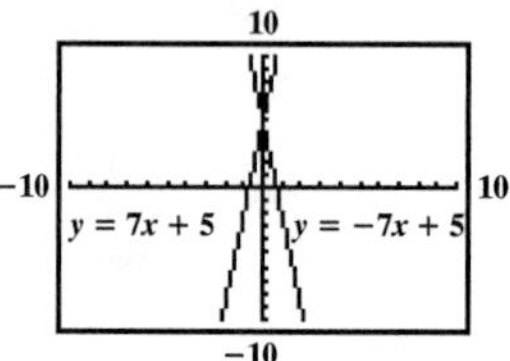

Vocabulary, Readiness & Video Check 1.5

1. slope-intercept; m; b **3.** y-intercept; fraction **5.** Write the equation with x- and y- terms on one side of the equal sign and a constant on the other side. **7.** Example 6: $y = -3$; Example 7: $x = -2$

Exercise Set 1.5

1. 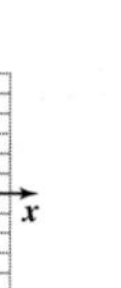
3. **5.** **7.** **9.** **11.** 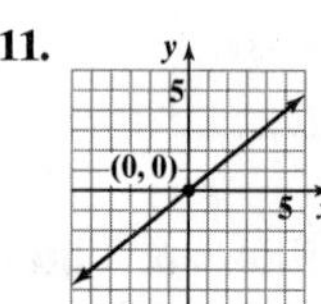

13. $y = 5x + 3$ **15.** $y = -4x - \frac{1}{6}$ **17.** $y = \frac{2}{3}x$ **19.** $y = -8$ **21.** $y = -\frac{1}{5}x + \frac{1}{9}$ **23.** $-6x + y = -10$ **25.** $8x + y = -13$ **27.** $3x - 2y = 27$ **29.** $x + 2y = -3$ **31.** $2x - y = 4$ **33.** $8x - y = -11$ **35.** $4x - 3y = -1$ **37.** $8x + 13y = 0$ **39.** $x = 0$ **41.** $y = 3$ **43.** $x = -\frac{7}{3}$ **45.** $y = 2$ **47.** $y = 5$ **49.** $x = 6$ **51.** $y = -\frac{1}{2}x + \frac{5}{3}$ **53.** $y = -x + 17$ **55.** $x = -\frac{3}{4}$ **57.** $y = x + 16$ **59.** $y = -5x + 7$ **61.** $y = 7$ **63.** $y = \frac{3}{2}x$ **65.** $y = -3$ **67.** $y = -\frac{4}{7}x - \frac{18}{7}$ **69. a.** $s = 32t$ **b.** 128 ft/sec **71. a.** $y = -33x + 356$ **b.** 92 thousand gasoline-electric hybrids **73. a.** $y = 0.6x + 85$ **b.** 93.4 persons per sq mi **75. a.** $y = -1.75x + 60$ **b.** 32 million **77. a.** $S = -1000p + 13{,}000$ **b.** 9500 Fun Noodles **79.** -1 **81.** 5 **83.** no **85.** yes **87.** point-slope **89.** slope-intercept **91.** horizontal **93.** answers may vary **95. a.** $3x - y = -5$ **b.** $x + 3y = 5$ **97. a.** $3x + 2y = -1$ **b.** $2x - 3y = 21$

Chapter 1 Vocabulary Check

1. solution **2.** y-axis **3.** linear **4.** x-intercept **5.** standard **6.** y-intercept **7.** slope-intercept **8.** point-slope **9.** y **10.** x-axis **11.** x **12.** slope **13.** function **14.** domain **15.** range **16.** relation

Chapter 1 Review

1. **3.** **5.** **7. a.** (5.00, 50), (8.50, 100), (20.00, 250), (27.00, 500) **b.**

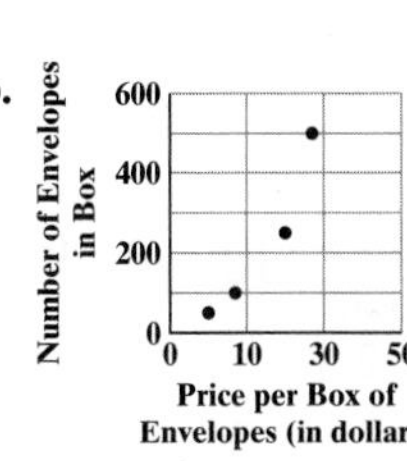

9. no; yes **11.** yes; yes **13.** (7, 44) **15.** (−3, 0); (1, 3); (9, 9)

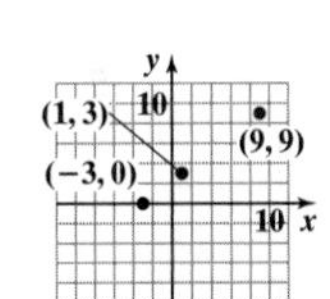

17. 2005; 2500; 7000 **19.**

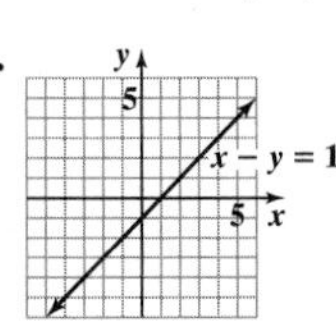

21.

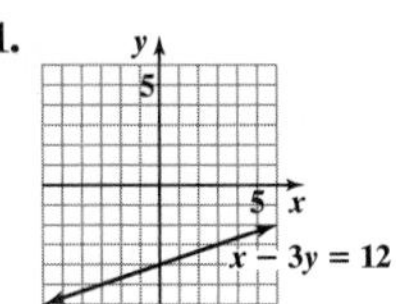

23.

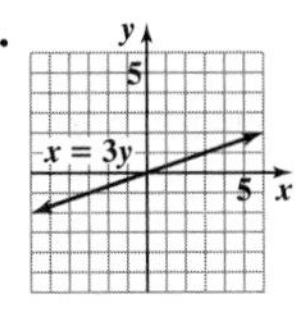

25.

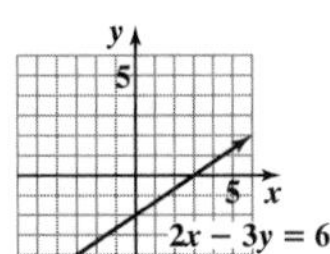

27. (4, 0), (0, −2) **29.** (−2, 0), (2, 0), (0, 2), (0, −2)

31.

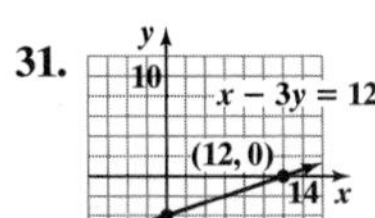
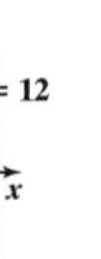

33.

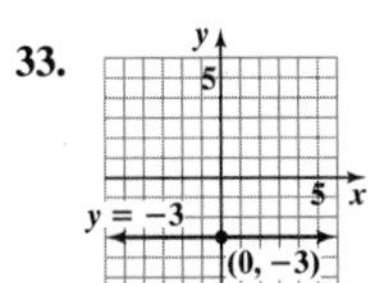

35. **37.** **39.** $m = -\frac{3}{4}$ **41.** d **43.** c **45.** $\frac{3}{4}$ **47.** 4

49. 3 **51.** 0 **53.** perpendicular **55.** neither **57.** $m = 44$; Every 1 year, 44 thousand (44,000) more students graduate with an associate's degree. **59.** $m = -3$; (0, 7) **61.** $m = 0$; (0, 2) **63.** **65.**

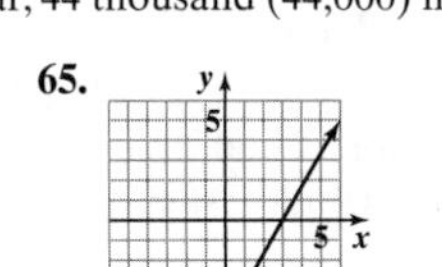

67. $y = -5x + \frac{1}{2}$ **69.** c

71. b **73.** (0, 1859) **75.** $3x + y = -5$ **77.** $y = -3$ **79.** $6x + y = 11$ **81.** $x + y = 6$ **83.** $x = 5$ **85.** $x = 6$

Chapter 1 Test

1.

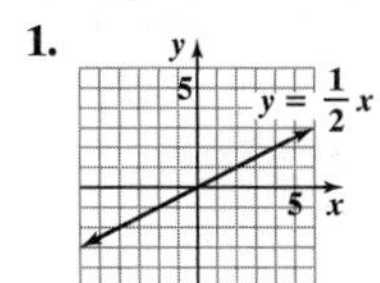

2.

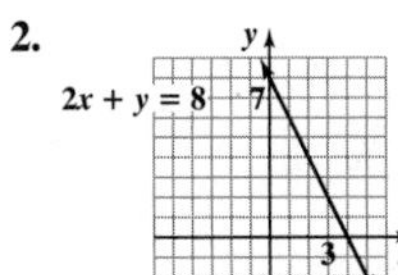

3. **4.** **5.**

6. $\frac{2}{5}$ **7.** 0 **8.** −1 **9.** 3 **10.** undefined **11.** $m = \frac{7}{3}; \left(0, -\frac{2}{3}\right)$ **12.** neither **13.** $x + 4y = 10$ **14.** $7x + 6y = 0$ **15.** $8x + y = 11$ **16.** $x = -5$ **17.** $x - 8y = -96$ **18.** yes **19.** no **20. a.** 0 **b.** 0 **c.** 60 **21.** all real numbers except −1 or $(-\infty, -1) \cup (-1, \infty)$ **22. a.** x-intercepts: (0, 0), (4, 0); y-intercept: (0, 0) **b.** domain: $(-\infty, \infty)$; range: $(-\infty, 4]$ **23. a.** x-intercept: (2, 0); y-intercept; (0, −2) **b.** domain: $(-\infty, \infty)$; range: $(-\infty, \infty)$ **24.** (7, 20) **25.** 210 liters **26.** 490 liters **27.** July **28.** 63°F **29.** January, February, March, November, December **30. a.** (2003, 66.0); (2004, 65.4); (2005, 65.4); (2006, 65.6); (2007, 64.9); (2008, 63.7); (2009, 62.1) **b.** **31. a.** $m = -8$; Every 1 year, 8 million fewer movie tickets are sold. **b.** (0, 1380), (5, 1340) **c.** $y = -8x + 1380$ **d.** In 2015, we predict that 1300 million movie tickets will be sold in the U.S. and Canada.

Chapter 1 Cumulative Review

1. a. < **b.** > **c.** >; Sec. 1.2, Ex. 1 **3.** $\frac{2}{39}$; Sec. 1.3, Ex. 3 **5.** $\frac{8}{3}$; Sec. 1.4, Ex. 3 **7. a.** −19 **b.** 30 **c.** −0.5 **d.** $-\frac{4}{5}$ **e.** 6.7 **f.** $\frac{1}{40}$; Sec. 1.5, Ex. 6 **9. a.** −6; **b.** 6.3; Sec. 1.6, Ex. 4 **11. a.** −6 **b.** 0 **c.** $\frac{3}{4}$; Sec. 1.7, Ex. 10 **13. a.** $22 + x$ **b.** $-21x$; Sec. 1.8, Ex. 3 **15. a.** −3 **b.** 22 **c.** 1 **d.** −1 **e.** $\frac{1}{7}$; Sec. 2.1, Ex. 1 **17.** 17; Sec. 2.2, Ex. 1 **19.** 6; Sec. 2.2, Ex. 5 **21.** $3x + 3$; Sec. 2.2, Ex. 10 **23.** 0; Sec. 2.3, Ex. 4 **25.** 242 Republicans, 193 Democrats; Sec. 2.4, Ex. 4 **27.** 40 ft; Sec. 2.5, Ex. 2 **29.** $\frac{y - b}{m} = x$; Sec. 2.5, Ex. 6 **31.** 40% solution: 8 liters; 70% solution: 4 liters; Sec. 2.6, Ex. 7 **33.** $[-1, \infty)$; Sec. 2.8, Ex. 1 **35.** $[1, 4)$; Sec. 2.8, Ex. 10

37. a. solution **b.** not a solution **c.** solution; Sec. 3.1, Ex. 5 **39. a.** yes **b.** yes **c.** no **d.** yes; Sec. 3.2, Ex. 1 **41.** 0; Sec. 3.4, Ex. 6 **43.** $y = \frac{1}{4}x - 3$; Sec. 3.5, Ex. 3

CHAPTER 2 SOLVING SYSTEMS OF LINEAR EQUATIONS

Section 2.1

Practice Exercises

1. no **2.** yes

3. $(8, 5)$

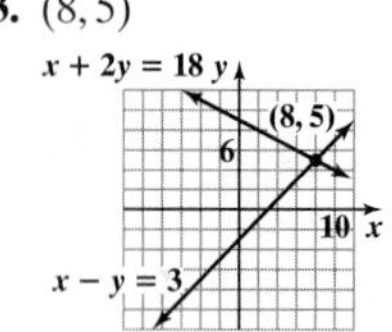

4. $(-3, -5)$

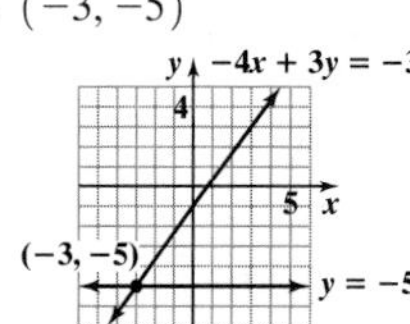

5. no solution; inconsistent system; { } or ∅

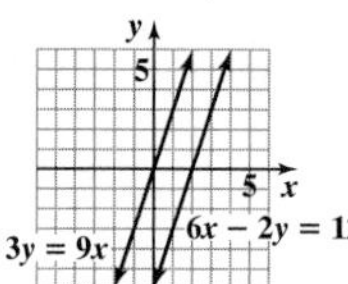

6. infinite number of solutions; consistent system, $\{(x, y) \mid 3x + 4y = 12\}$ or $\{(x, y) \mid 9x + 12y = 36\}$ **7.** one solution **8.** no solution

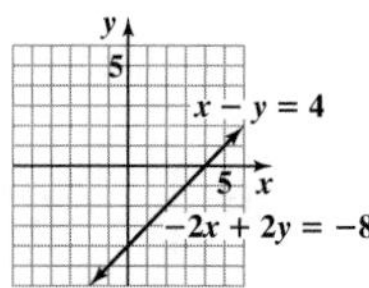

Graphing Calculator Explorations 2.1

1. $(0.37, 0.23)$ **3.** $(0.03, -1.89)$

Vocabulary, Readiness & Video Check 2.1

1. dependent **3.** consistent **5.** inconsistent **7.** The ordered pair must satisfy all equations of the system in order to be a solution of the system, so we must check that the ordered pair is a solution of both equations. **9.** Writing the equations of a system in slope-intercept form lets you see their slope and y-intercept. Different slopes mean one solution; same slope with different y-intercepts means no solution; same slope with same y-intercept means infinite number of solutions.

Exercise Set 2.1

1. one solution, $(-1, 3)$ **3.** infinite number of solutions **5. a.** no **b.** yes **7. a.** yes **b.** no **9. a.** yes **b.** yes **11. a.** no **b.** no

13. (3, 1)

15.

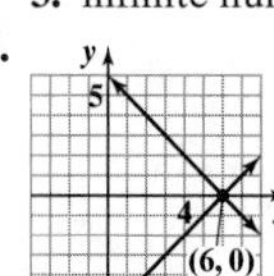

17.

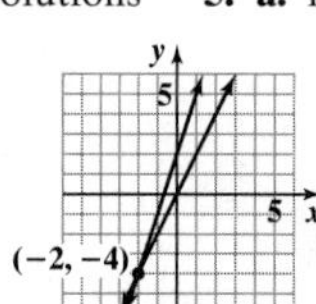

19.

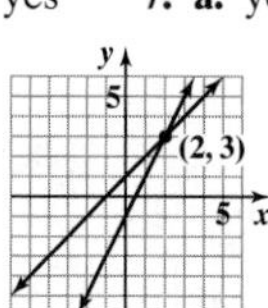

21.

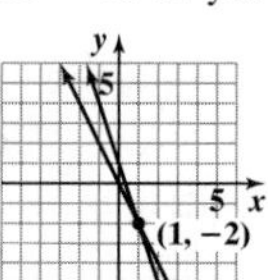

25. no solution

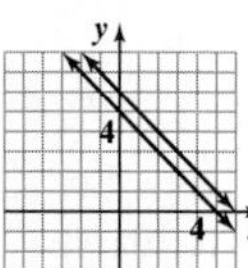

27.

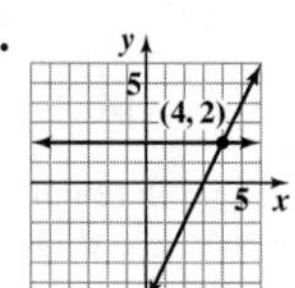

29.

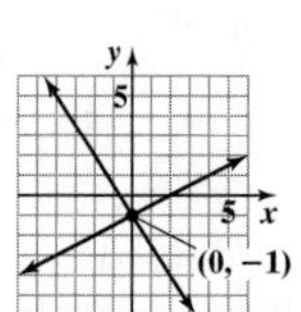

31. no solution; { } or ∅

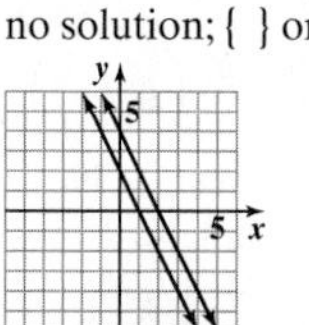

33. infinite number of solutions; $\{(x, y) \mid y - 3x = -2\}$ or $\{(x, y) \mid 6x - 2y = 4\}$

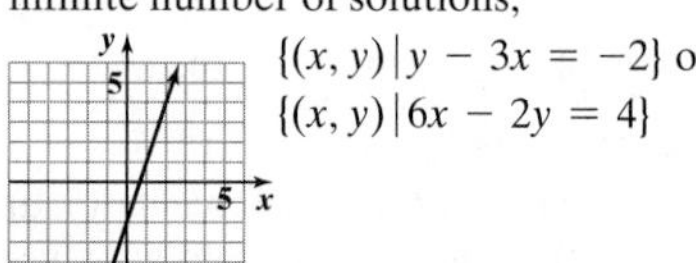

35. (3, −1)

37.

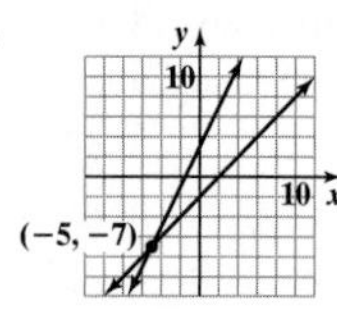

39.

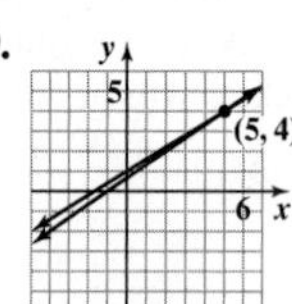

41. infinite number of solutions; $\{(x, y) \mid 6x - y = 4\}$ or $\left\{(x, y) \middle| \frac{1}{2}y = -2 + 3x\right\}$

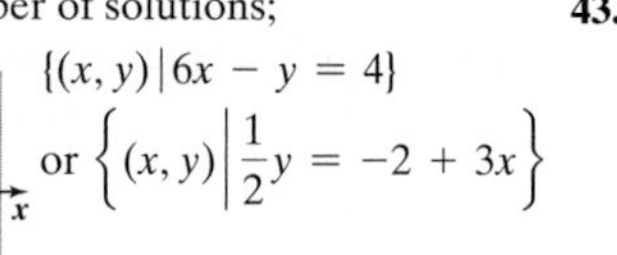

43. intersecting, one solution

45. parallel; no solution **47.** identical lines; infinite number of solutions **49.** intersecting; one solution **51.** intersecting; one solution **53.** identical lines; infinite number of solutions **55.** parallel; no solution **57.** 2 **59.** $-\frac{2}{5}$ **61.** 2

63. answers may vary; possible answer

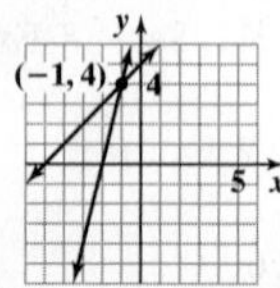

65. answers may vary; possible answer

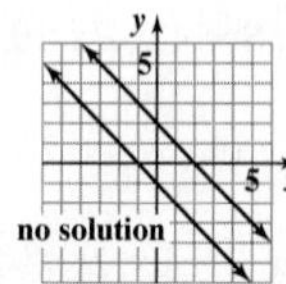

67. answers may vary **69.** 1988–1989; 2001–2002

71. 2003, 2004, 2005, 2006, 2007 **73.** answers may vary **75. a.** (4, 9) **b.**

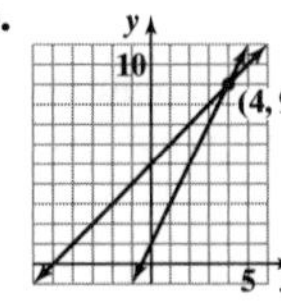

c. yes **77.** answers may vary

Section 2.2
Practice Exercises

1. (8, 7) **2.** (−3, −6) **3.** $\left(4, \frac{2}{3}\right)$ **4.** (−3, 2) **5.** infinite number of solutions; $\left\{(x, y) \middle| \frac{1}{4}x - y = 2\right\}$ or $\{(x, y) | x = 4y + 8\}$
6. no solution; { } or ∅

Vocabulary, Readiness & Video Check 2.2
1. (1, 4) **3.** infinite number of solutions **5.** (0, 0) **7.** You solved one equation for a variable. Now be sure to substitute this expression for the variable into the *other* equation.

Exercise Set 2.2
1. (2, 1) **3.** (−3, 9) **5.** (2, 7) **7.** $\left(-\frac{1}{5}, \frac{43}{5}\right)$ **9.** (2, −1) **11.** (−2, 4) **13.** (4, 2) **15.** (−2, −1) **17.** no solution; { } or ∅
19. (3, −1) **21.** (3, 5) **23.** $\left(\frac{2}{3}, -\frac{1}{3}\right)$ **25.** (−1, −4) **27.** (−6, 2) **29.** (2, 1) **31.** no solution; { } or ∅ **33.** infinite number of solutions; $\left\{(x, y) \middle| \frac{1}{3}x - y = 2\right\}$ or $\{(x, y) | x - 3y = 6\}$ **35.** $\left(\frac{1}{2}, 2\right)$ **37.** (1, −3) **39.** $-6x - 4y = -12$ **41.** $-12x + 3y = 9$ **43.** $5n$
45. $-15b$ **47.** answers may vary **49.** no; answers may vary **51. c;** answers may vary **53. a.** (13, 492) **b.** In 1970 + 13 = 1983, the number of men and women receiving bachelor's degrees was the same. **c.** answers may vary

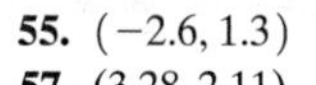

55. (−2.6, 1.3)
57. (3.28, 2.11)

Section 2.3
Practice Exercises
1. (5, 3) **2.** (3, −4) **3.** no solution; { } or ∅ **4.** infinite number of solutions; $\{(x, y) | 4x - 3y = 5\}$ or $\{(x, y) | -8x + 6y = -10\}$
5. (2, 2) **6.** $\left(-\frac{8}{5}, \frac{6}{5}\right)$

Vocabulary, Readiness & Video Check 2.3
1. false **3.** true **5.** The multiplication property of equality; be sure to multiply *both* sides of the equation by the number chosen.

Exercise Set 2.3
1. (1, 2) **3.** (2, −3) **5.** (−2, −5) **7.** (5, −2) **9.** (−7, 5) **11.** (6, 0) **13.** no solution; { } or ∅ **15.** infinite number of solutions; $\{(x, y) | -x + 5y = -1\}$ or $\{(x, y) | 3x - 15y = 3\}$ **17.** $\left(2, -\frac{1}{2}\right)$ **19.** (−2, 0) **21.** (1, −1) **23.** no solution; { } or ∅ **25.** $\left(\frac{12}{11}, -\frac{4}{11}\right)$
27. $\left(\frac{3}{2}, 3\right)$ **29.** infinite number of solutions; $\left\{(x, y) \middle| \frac{10}{3}x + 4y = -4\right\}$ or $\{(x, y) | 5x + 6y = -6\}$ **31.** (1, 6) **33.** $\left(-\frac{1}{2}, -2\right)$ **35.** infinite number of solutions; $\left\{(x, y) \middle| \frac{x}{3} - y = 2\right\}$ or $\left\{(x, y) \middle| -\frac{x}{2} + \frac{3y}{2} = -3\right\}$ **37.** $\left(-\frac{2}{3}, \frac{2}{5}\right)$ **39.** (2, 4) **41.** (−0.5, 2.5) **43.** (2, 5)
45. (−3, 2) **47.** (0, 3) **49.** (5, 7) **51.** $\left(\frac{1}{3}, 1\right)$ **53.** infinite number of solutions; $\left\{(x, y) \middle| \frac{x + 2}{2} = \frac{y + 11}{3}\right\}$ or $\left\{(x, y) \middle| \frac{x}{2} = \left(\frac{2y + 16}{6}\right)\right\}$
55. (−8.9, 10.6) **57.** $2x + 6 = x - 3$ **59.** $20 - 3x = 2$ **61.** $4(n + 6) = 2n$ **63.** 2; $6x - 2y = -24$ **65. b;** answers may vary
67. answers may vary **69. a.** $b = 15$ **b.** any real number except 15 **71.** (−4.2, 9.6) **73. a.** (7, 22) **b.** In 2015 (2008 + 7), the percent of workers age 25–34 and the percent of workers age 55 and older will be the same. **c.** 22% of the workforce for each of these age groups.

Integrated Review
1. (2, 5) **2.** (4, 2) **3.** (5, −2) **4.** (6, −14) **5.** (−3, 2) **6.** (−4, 3) **7.** (0, 3) **8.** (−2, 4) **9.** (5, 7) **10.** (−3, −23)
11. $\left(\frac{1}{3}, 1\right)$ **12.** $\left(-\frac{1}{4}, 2\right)$ **13.** no solution; { } or ∅ **14.** infinite number of solutions; $\{(x, y) | -x + 2y = 3\}$ or $\{(x, y) | 3x - 6y = -9\}$
15. (0.5, 3.5) **16.** (−0.75, 1.25) **17.** infinite number of solutions; $\{(x, y) | x = 3y - 7\}$ or $\{(x, y) | 2x - 6y = -14\}$ **18.** no solution; { } or ∅
19. (7, −3) **20.** (−1, −3) **21.** answers may vary **22.** answers may vary

Section 2.4
Practice Exercises

1. (−1, 2, 1) **2.** { } or ∅ **3.** $\left(\frac{2}{3}, -\frac{1}{2}, 0\right)$ **4.** $\{(x, y, z) | 2x + y - 3z = 6\}$ **5.** (6, 15, −5)

Vocabulary, Readiness & Video Check 2.4

1. a, b, d **3.** yes; answers may vary **5.** Once we have one equation in two variables, we need to get another equation in the *same* two variables, giving us a system of two equations in two variables. We solve this new system to find the value of two variables. We then substitute these values into an original equation to find the value of the third.

Exercise Set 2.4

1. $(-1, 5, 2)$ **3.** $(-2, 5, 1)$ **5.** $(-2, 3, -1)$ **7.** $\{(x, y, z) \mid x - 2y + z = -5\}$ **9.** $\varnothing$ **11.** $(0, 0, 0)$ **13.** $(-3, -35, -7)$ **15.** $(6, 22, -20)$ **17.** $\varnothing$ **19.** $(3, 2, 2)$ **21.** $\{(x, y, z) \mid x + 2y - 3z = 4\}$ **23.** $(-3, -4, -5)$ **25.** $\left(0, \frac{1}{2}, -4\right)$ **27.** $(12, 6, 4)$ **29.** 15 and 30 **31.** 5 **33.** $-\frac{5}{3}$ **35.** answers may vary **37.** answers may vary **39.** $(1, 1, -1)$ **41.** $(1, 1, 0, 2)$ **43.** $(1, -1, 2, 3)$ **45.** answers may vary

Section 2.5

Practice Exercises

1. a. 2208 **b.** yes; answers may vary **2.** 18, 12 **3.** 17 and 12 **4. a.** Adult: \$19 **b.** Child: \$6 **c.** No, the regular rates are less than the group rate **5.** Atlantique: 500 kph; V150: 575 kph **6.** 0.95 liter of water; 0.05 liter of 99% HCL **7.** 1500 packages **8.** 40°, 60°, 80°

Vocabulary, Readiness & Video Check 2.5

1. Up to now we've been choosing one variable/unknown and translating to one equation. To solve by a system of equations, we'll choose two variables to represent two unknowns and translate to two equations. **3.** The ordered triple still needs to be interpreted in the context of the application. Each value actually represents the angle measure of a triangle, in degrees.

Exercise Set 2.5

1. c **3.** b **5.** a **7.** $\begin{cases} x + y = 15 \\ x - y = 7 \end{cases}$ **9.** $\begin{cases} x + y = 6500 \\ x = y + 800 \end{cases}$ **11.** 33 and 50 **13.** 10 and 8 **15.** 14 and -3 **17.** Cabrera: 126; Rodriguez: 125 **19.** child's ticket: \$18; adult's ticket: \$29 **21.** quarters: 53; nickels: 27 **23.** McDonald's: \$73.50; The Ohio Art Company: \$3.50 **25.** daily fee: \$32; mileage charge: \$0.25 per mi **27.** distance downstream = distance upstream = 18 mi; time downstream: 2 hr; time upstream: $4\frac{1}{2}$ hr; still water: 6.5 mph; current: 2.5 mph **29.** still air: 455 mph; wind: 65 mph **31.** $4\frac{1}{2}$ hr **33.** 12% solution: $7\frac{1}{2}$ liters; 4% solution: $4\frac{1}{2}$ liters **35.** \$4.95 beans: 113 lb; \$2.65 beans: 87 lb **37.** 60°, 30° **39.** 20°, 70° **41.** number sold at \$9.50: 23; number sold at \$7.50: 67 **43.** $2\frac{1}{4}$ mph and $2\frac{3}{4}$ mph **45.** 30%: 50 gal; 60%: 100 gal **47.** length: 42 in.; width: 30 in. **49. a.** 2010 **b.** answers may vary **51. a.** answers may vary **b.** 2003 **53.** $x = 75; y = 105$ **55.** 625 units **57.** 3000 units **59.** 1280 units **61. a.** $R(x) = 450x$ **b.** $C(x) = 200x + 6000$ **c.** 24 desks **63.** 2 units of Mix A; 3 units of Mix B; 1 unit of Mix C **65.** 5 in.; 7 in.; 7 in.; 10 in. **67.** 18, 13, and 9 **69.** free throws: 594; 2-pt field goals: 566; 3-pt fields goals: 145 **71.** $x = 60; y = 55; z = 65$ **73.** $(3, \infty)$ **75.** $\left[\frac{1}{2}, \infty\right)$ **77.** a **79.** width: 9 ft; length: 15 ft **81.** $a = 3, b = 4, c = -1$ **83.** $a = 0.5, b = 24.5, c = 849$; 2015: 1774 thousand students **85.** $(7, 215)$

Chapter 2 Vocabulary Check

1. dependent **2.** system of linear equations **3.** consistent **4.** solution **5.** addition; substitution **6.** inconsistent **7.** independent

Chapter 2 Review

1. a. no **b.** yes **c.** no **3. a.** no **b.** no **c.** yes **5.** (3, 2) **7.** (5, −1) **9.** (3, −1) **11.** no solution; { } or 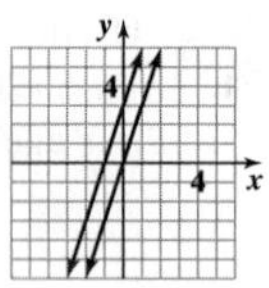 $\varnothing$ **13.** $(-1, 4)$ **15.** $(3, -2)$ **17.** infinite number of solutions; $\{(x, y) \mid 4y = 2x + 6\}$ or $\{(x, y) \mid x - 2y = -3\}$ **19.** no solution; { } or $\varnothing$ **21.** $(-6, 2)$ **23.** $(3, 7)$ **25.** infinite number of solutions; $\{(x, y) \mid 2x - 6y = -1\}$ or $\left\{(x, y) \middle| -x + 3y = \frac{1}{2}\right\}$ **27.** $(8, -6)$ **29.** $(2, 0, 2)$ **31.** $\left(-\frac{1}{2}, \frac{3}{4}, 1\right)$ **33.** $\varnothing$ **35.** $(1, 1, -2)$ **37.** -6 and 22 **39.** current of river: 3.2 mph; speed in still water: 21.1 mph **41.** egg: \$0.40; strip of bacon: \$0.65 **43.** 17 pennies; 20 nickels; 16 dimes **45.** two sides: 22 cm each; third side: 29 cm

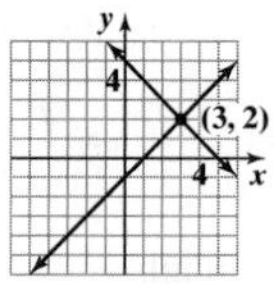

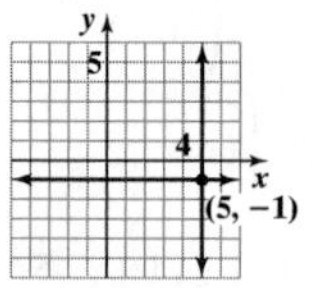

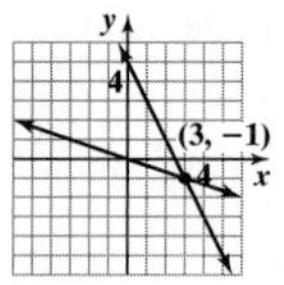

Section 2.6

Exercise Set 2.6

47. f

49. 
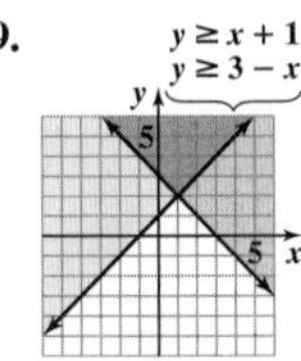

51. 
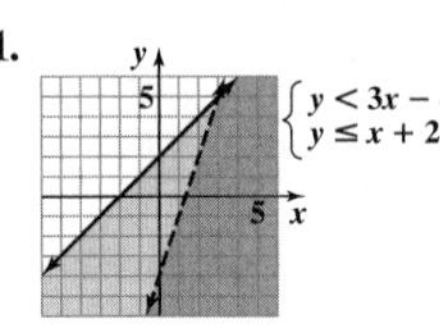

53. 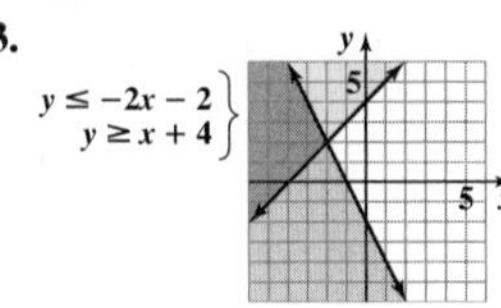

55. 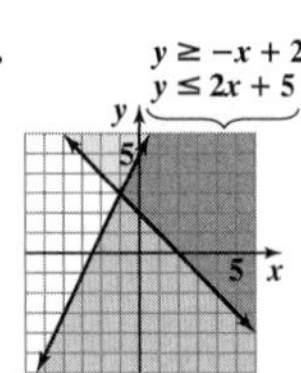

57. 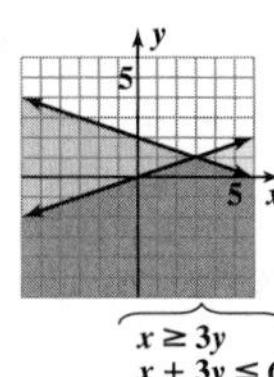

59. 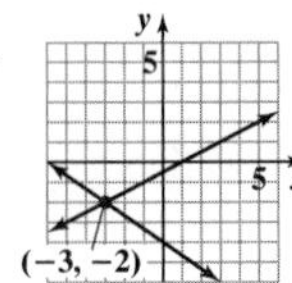

61. $(3, 2)$ **63.** $\left(1\frac{1}{2}, -3\right)$ **65.** infinite number of solutions; $\{(x, y) | 3x - y = 4\}$ or $\{(x, y) | 4y = 12x - 16\}$ **67.** $(-5, 2)$ **69.** $(-1, 3, 5)$ **71.** 4 and 8 **73.** 24 nickels and 41 dimes **75.** 28 units, 42 units, 56 units

Chapter 2 Test

1. false **2.** false **3.** true **4.** false **5.** no **6.** yes

7. $(-4, 2)$ **8.** $(-4, 1)$ **9.** $\left(\frac{1}{2}, -2\right)$ **10.** $(4, -2)$ **11.** no solution; { } or ∅ **12.** $(4, -5)$ **13.** $(7, 2)$ **14.** $(5, -2)$ **15.** 78, 46 **16.** 120 cc **17.** Texas: 248 thousand; Missouri: 108 thousand **18.** 3 mph; 6 mph **19.** $(-1, -2, 4)$ **20.** ∅ **21.** 23°, 45°, 112°

Chapter 2 Cumulative Review

1. a. $<$ **b.** $=$ **c.** $>$; Sec. 1.2, Ex. 6 **3. a.** commutative property of multiplication **b.** associative property of addition **c.** identity element for addition **d.** commutative property of multiplication **e.** multiplicative inverse property **f.** additive inverse property **g.** commutative and associative properties of multiplication; Sec. 1.8, Ex. 6 **5.** $-2x - 1$; Sec. 2.1, Ex. 7 **7.** 8; Sec. 2.2, Ex. 4 **9.** 6; Sec. 2.2, Ex. 5 **11.** 12; Sec. 2.3, Ex. 3 **13.** 10; Sec. 2.4, Ex. 2 **15.** $x = \frac{y - b}{m}$; Sec. 2.5, Ex. 6 **17.** $[2, \infty)$; Sec. 2.8, Ex. 3

19. 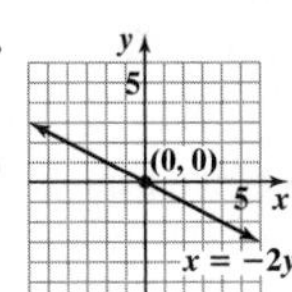

; Sec. 3.3, Ex. 7 **21.** $-\frac{8}{3}$; Sec. 3.4, Ex. 1 **23.** slope: $\frac{3}{4}$; y-intercept: $(0, 6)$; Sec. 3.4, Ex. 3 **25.** slope: $\frac{3}{4}$; y-intercept: $(0, -1)$; Sec. 3.4, Ex. 5 **27.** $y = -2x + 3$; $2x + y = 3$; Sec. 3.5, Ex. 4 **29.** $x = -1$; Sec. 3.5, Ex. 6 **31.** domain: $\{-1, 0, 3\}$; range: $\{-2, 0, 2, 3\}$; Sec. 3.6, Ex. 1 **33. a.** function **b.** not a function; Sec. 3.6, Ex. 2 **35.** one solution; Sec. 4.1, Ex. 8 **37.** $\left(6, \frac{1}{2}\right)$; Sec. 4.2, Ex. 3 **39.** $(6, 1)$; Sec. 4.3, Ex. 1 **41.** $(-4, 2, -1)$; Sec. 4.4, Ex. 1 **43.** 7 and 11; Sec. 4.5, Ex. 3

CHAPTER 3 FACTORING POLYNOMIALS

Section 3.1

Practice Exercises

1. a. 6 **b.** 1 **c.** 4 **2. a.** y^4 **b.** x **3. a.** $5y^2$ **b.** x^2 **c.** a^2b^2 **4. a.** $4(t + 3)$ **b.** $y^4(y^4 + 1)$ **5.** $8b^2(-b^4 + 2b^2 - 1)$ or $-8b^2(b^4 - 2b^2 + 1)$ **6.** $5x(x^3 - 4)$ **7.** $\frac{1}{9}z^3(5z^2 + z - 2)$ **8.** $4ab^3(2ab - 5a^2 + 3)$ **9.** $(y - 2)(8 + x)$ **10.** $(p + q)(7xy^3 - 1)$ **11.** $(x + 3)(y + 4)$ **12.** $(5x - 3)(8x^2 + 3)$ **13.** $(2x + 3y)(y - 1)$ **14.** $(7a + 5)(a^2 + 1)$ **15.** $(y - 3)(4x - 5)$ **16.** cannot be factored by grouping **17.** $3(x - a)(y - 2a)$

Vocabulary, Readiness & Video Check 3.1

1. factors **3.** least **5.** false **7.** The GCF of a list of numbers is the largest number that is a factor of all numbers in the list. **9.** When factoring out a GCF, the number of terms in the other factor should have the same number of terms as your original polynomial.

Exercise Set 3.1

1. 4 **3.** 6 **5.** 1 **7.** y^2 **9.** z^7 **11.** xy^2 **13.** 7 **15.** $4y^3$ **17.** $5x^2$ **19.** $3x^3$ **21.** $9x^2y$ **23.** $10a^6b$ **25.** $3(a + 2)$ **27.** $15(2x - 1)$ **29.** $x^2(x + 5)$ **31.** $2y^3(3y + 1)$ **33.** $4(x - 2y + 1)$ **35.** $3x(2x^2 - 3x + 4)$ **37.** $a^2b^2(a^5b^4 - a + b^3 - 1)$ **39.** $4(2x^5 + 4x^4 - 5x^3 + 3)$ **41.** $\frac{1}{3}x(x^3 + 2x^2 - 4x^4 + 1)$ **43.** $(x^2 + 2)(y + 3)$ **45.** $(y + 4)(z - 3)$ **47.** $(z^2 - 6)(r + 1)$

49. $-2(x + 7)$ **51.** $-x^5(2 - x^2)$ **53.** $-3a^2(2a^2 - 3a + 1)$ **55.** $(x + 2)(x^2 + 5)$ **57.** $(x + 3)(5 + y)$ **59.** $(3x - 2)(2x^2 + 5)$ **61.** $(5m^2 + 6n)(m + 1)$ **63.** $(y - 4)(2 + x)$ **65.** $(2x - 1)(x^2 + 4)$ **67.** not factorable by grouping **69.** $(x - 2y)(4x - 3)$ **71.** $(5q - 4p)(q - 1)$ **73.** $x(x^2 + 1)(2x + 5)$ **75.** $2(2y - 7)(3x^2 - 1)$ **77.** $2x(16y - 9x)$ **79.** $(x + 2)(y - 3)$ **81.** $7xy(2x^2 + x - 1)$ **83.** $(4x - 1)(7x^2 + 3)$ **85.** $-8x^8y^5(5y + 2x)$ **87.** $3(2a + 3b^2)(a + b)$ **89.** $x^2 + 7x + 10$ **91.** $b^2 - 3b - 4$ **93.** 2, 6 **95.** $-1, -8$ **97.** $-2, 5$ **99.** b **101.** factored **103.** not factored **105.** answers may vary **107.** answers may vary **109. a.** 1200 million **b.** 1120 million **c.** $-20(x^2 - 15x - 6)$ **111.** $12x^3 - 2x; 2x(6x^2 - 1)$ **113.** $(n^3 - 6)$units **115.** $(x^n + 2)(x^n + 3)$ **117.** $(3x^n - 5)(x^n + 7)$

Section 3.2

Practice Exercises

1. $(x + 2)(x + 3)$ **2.** $(x - 10)(x - 7)$ **3.** $(x + 7)(x - 2)$ **4.** $(p - 9)(p + 7)$ **5.** prime polynomial **6.** $(x + 3y)(x + 4y)$ **7.** $(x^2 + 12)(x^2 + 1)$ **8.** $(x - 6)(x - 8)$ **9.** $4(x - 3)(x - 3)$ **10.** $3y^2(y - 7)(y + 1)$

Vocabulary, Readiness & Video Check 3.2

1. true **3.** false **5.** $+5$ **7.** -3 **9.** $+2$ **11.** 15 is positive, so its factors would have to either be both positive or both negative. Since the factors need to sum to -8, both factors must be negative.

Exercise Set 3.2

1. $(x + 6)(x + 1)$ **3.** $(y - 9)(y - 1)$ **5.** $(x - 3)(x - 3)$ or $(x - 3)^2$ **7.** $(x - 6)(x + 3)$ **9.** $(x + 10)(x - 7)$ **11.** prime **13.** $(x + 5y)(x + 3y)$ **15.** $(a^2 - 5)(a^2 + 3)$ **17.** $(m + 13)(m + 1)$ **19.** $(t - 2)(t + 12)$ **21.** $(a - 2b)(a - 8b)$ **23.** $2(z + 8)(z + 2)$ **25.** $2x(x - 5)(x - 4)$ **27.** $(x - 4y)(x + y)$ **29.** $(x + 12)(x + 3)$ **31.** $(x - 2)(x + 1)$ **33.** $(r - 12)(r - 4)$ **35.** $(x + 2y)(x - y)$ **37.** $3(x + 5)(x - 2)$ **39.** $3(x - 18)(x - 2)$ **41.** $(x - 24)(x + 6)$ **43.** prime **45.** $(x - 5)(x - 3)$ **47.** $6x(x + 4)(x + 5)$ **49.** $4y(x^2 + x - 3)$ **51.** $(x - 7)(x + 3)$ **53.** $(x + 5y)(x + 2y)$ **55.** $2(t + 8)(t + 4)$ **57.** $x(x - 6)(x + 4)$ **59.** $2t^3(t - 4)(t - 3)$ **61.** $5xy(x - 8y)(x + 3y)$ **63.** $3(m - 9)(m - 6)$ **65.** $-1(x - 11)(x - 1)$ **67.** $\frac{1}{2}(y - 11)(y + 2)$ **69.** $x(xy - 4)(xy + 5)$ **71.** $2x^2 + 11x + 5$ **73.** $15y^2 - 17y + 4$ **75.** $9a^2 + 23ab - 12b^2$ **77.** $x^2 + 5x - 24$ **79.** answers may vary **81.** $2x^2 + 28x + 66; 2(x + 3)(x + 11)$ **83.** $-16(t - 5)(t + 1)$ **85.** $\left(x + \frac{1}{4}\right)\left(x + \frac{1}{4}\right)$ or $\left(x + \frac{1}{4}\right)^2$ **87.** $(x + 1)(z - 10)(z + 7)$ **89.** $(x^n + 10)(x^n - 2)$ **91.** 5; 8; 9 **93.** 3; 4 **95.** 8; 16 **97.** 6; 26

Section 3.3

Practice Exercises

1. $(2x + 5)(x + 3)$ **2.** $(5x - 4)(3x - 2)$ **3.** $(4x - 1)(x + 3)$ **4.** $(7x - y)(3x + 2y)$ **5.** $(2x^2 - 7)(x^2 + 1)$ **6.** $x(3x + 2)(x + 5)$ **7.** $-1(4x - 3)(2x + 1)$ **8.** $(x + 7)^2$ **9.** $(2x + 9y)(2x + y)$ **10.** $(6n^2 - 1)^2$ **11.** $3x(2x - 7)^2$

Vocabulary, Readiness & Video Check 3.3

1. perfect square trinomial **3.** perfect square trinomial **5.** d **7.** Consider the factors of the first and last terms and the signs of the trinomial. Continue to check by multiplying until you get the middle term of the trinomial. **9.** The first and last terms are squares, a^2 and b^2, and the middle term is $2 \cdot a \cdot b$ or $-2 \cdot a \cdot b$.

Exercise Set 3.3

1. $x + 4$ **3.** $10x - 1$ **5.** $5x - 2$ **7.** $(2x + 3)(x + 5)$ **9.** $(y - 1)(8y - 9)$ **11.** $(2x + 1)(x - 5)$ **13.** $(4r - 1)(5r + 8)$ **15.** $(10x + 1)(x + 3)$ **17.** prime **19.** $(3x - 5y)(2x - y)$ **21.** $(3m - 5)(5m + 3)$ **23.** $x(3x + 2)(4x + 1)$ **25.** $3(7b + 5)(b - 3)$ **27.** $(3z + 4)(4z - 3)$ **29.** $2y^2(3x - 10)(x + 3)$ **31.** $(2x - 7)(2x + 3)$ **33.** $-1(x - 6)(x + 4)$ **35.** $x(4x + 3)(x - 3)$ **37.** $(4x - 9)(6x - 1)$ **39.** $(x + 11)^2$ **41.** $(x - 8)^2$ **43.** $(4a - 3)^2$ **45.** $(x^2 + 2)^2$ **47.** $2(n - 7)^2$ **49.** $(4y + 5)^2$ **51.** $(2x + 11)(x - 9)$ **53.** $(8x + 3)(3x + 4)$ **55.** $(3a + b)(a + 3b)$ **57.** $(x - 4)(x - 5)$ **59.** $(p + 6q)^2$ **61.** $(xy - 5)^2$ **63.** $b(8a - 3)(5a + 3)$ **65.** $2x(3x + 2)(5x + 3)$ **67.** $2y(3y + 5)(y - 3)$ **69.** $5x^2(2x - y)(x + 3y)$ **71.** $-1(2x - 5)(7x - 2)$ **73.** $p^2(4p - 5)^2$ **75.** $(3x - 2)(x + 1)$ **77.** $(4x + 9y)(2x - 3y)$ **79.** prime **81.** $(3x - 4y)^2$ **83.** $(6x - 7)(3x + 2)$ **85.** $(7t + 1)(t - 4)$ **87.** $(7p + 1)(7p - 2)$ **89.** $m(m + 9)^2$ **91.** prime **93.** $a(6a^2 + b^2)(a^2 + 6b^2)$ **95.** $x^2 - 4$ **97.** $a^3 + 27$ **99.** 25–34 **101.** answers may vary **103.** no **105.** answers may vary **107.** $4x^2 + 21x + 5; (4x + 1)(x + 5)$ **109.** $\left(2x + \frac{1}{2}\right)^2$ **111.** $(y - 1)^2(4x^2 + 10x + 25)$ **113.** 8 **115.** $a^2 + 2ab + b^2$ **117.** 2; 14 **119.** 2 **121.** $-3xy^2(4x - 5)(x + 1)$ **123.** $(y - 1)^2(2x + 5)^2$ **125.** $(3x^n + 2)(x^n + 5)$ **127.** answers may vary

Section 3.4

Practice Exercises

1. $(5x + 1)(x + 12)$ **2.** $(4x - 5)(3x - 1)$ **3.** $2(5x + 1)(3x - 2)$ **4.** $5m^2(8m - 7)(m + 1)$ **5.** $(4x + 3)^2$

Vocabulary, Readiness & Video Check 3.4

1. a **3.** b **5.** This gives us a four-term polynomial, which may be factored by grouping.

Exercise Set 3.4

1. $(x + 3)(x + 2)$ **3.** $(y + 8)(y - 2)$ **5.** $(8x - 5)(x - 3)$ **7.** $(5x^2 - 3)(x^2 + 5)$ **9. a.** 9, 2 **b.** $9x + 2x$ **c.** $(3x + 1)(2x + 3)$ **11. a.** $-20, -3$ **b.** $-20x - 3x$ **c.** $(3x - 4)(5x - 1)$ **13.** $(3y + 2)(7y + 1)$ **15.** $(7x - 11)(x + 1)$ **17.** $(5x - 2)(2x - 1)$

19. $(2x - 5)(x - 1)$ **21.** $(2x + 3)^2$ **23.** $(2x + 3)(2x - 7)$ **25.** $(5x - 4)(2x - 3)$ **27.** $x(2x + 3)(x + 5)$
29. $2(8y - 9)(y - 1)$ **31.** $(2x - 3)(3x - 2)$ **33.** $3(3a + 2)(6a - 5)$ **35.** $a(4a + 1)(5a + 8)$ **37.** $3x(4x + 3)(x - 3)$
39. $y(3x + y)(x + y)$ **41.** prime **43.** $5(x + 5y)^2$ **45.** $6(a + b)(4a - 5b)$ **47.** $p^2(15p + q)(p + 2q)$ **49.** $2(9a^2 - 2)^2$
51. $(7 + x)(5 + x)$ or $(x + 7)(x + 5)$ **53.** $(6 - 5x)(1 - x)$ or $(5x - 6)(x - 1)$ **55.** $x^2 - 4$ **57.** $y^2 + 8y + 16$ **59.** $81z^2 - 25$
61. $x^3 - 27$ **63.** $10x^2 + 45x + 45; 5(2x + 3)(x + 3)$ **65.** $(x^n + 2)(x^n + 3)$ **67.** $(3x^n - 5)(x^n + 7)$ **69.** answers may vary

Section 3.5
Practice Exercises

1. $(x + 9)(x - 9)$ **2. a.** $(3x - 1)(3x + 1)$ **b.** $(6a - 7b)(6a + 7b)$ **c.** $\left(p + \frac{5}{6}\right)\left(p - \frac{5}{6}\right)$ **3.** $(p^2 - q^5)(p^2 + q^5)$
4. a. $(z^2 + 9)(z + 3)(z - 3)$ **b.** prime polynomial **5.** $y(6y + 5)(6y - 5)$ **6.** $5(4y^2 + 1)(2y + 1)(2y - 1)$
7. $-1(3x + 10)(3x - 10)$ or $(10 + 3x)(10 - 3x)$ **8.** $(x + 4)(x^2 - 4x + 16)$ **9.** $(x - 5)(x^2 + 5x + 25)$ **10.** $(3y + 1)(9y^2 - 3y + 1)$
11. $4(2x - 5y)(4x^2 + 10xy + 25y^2)$

Graphing Calculator Explorations 3.5

	$x^2 - 2x + 1$	$x^2 - 2x - 1$	$(x - 1)^2$
$x = 5$	16	14	16
$x = -3$	16	14	16
$x = 2.7$	2.89	0.89	2.89
$x = -12.1$	171.61	169.61	171.61
$x = 0$	1	−1	1

Vocabulary, Readiness & Video Check 3.5

1. difference of two cubes **3.** sum of two cubes **5.** $(7x)^2$ **7.** $(2y)^3$ **9.** In order to recognize the binomial as a difference of squares and also to identify the terms to use in the special factoring formula. **11.** First rewrite the original binomial with terms writtten as cubes. Answers will then vary depending on your interpretation.

Exercise Set 3.5

1. $(x + 2)(x - 2)$ **3.** $(9p + 1)(9p - 1)$ **5.** $(5y - 3)(5y + 3)$ **7.** $(11m + 10n)(11m - 10n)$ **9.** $(xy - 1)(xy + 1)$
11. $\left(x - \frac{1}{2}\right)\left(x + \frac{1}{2}\right)$ **13.** $-1(2r + 1)(2r - 1)$ **15.** prime **17.** $(-6 + x)(6 + x)$ or $-1(6 + x)(6 - x)$
19. $(m^2 + 1)(m + 1)(m - 1)$ **21.** $(m^2 + n^9)(m^2 - n^9)$ **23.** $(x + 5)(x^2 - 5x + 25)$ **25.** $(2a - 1)(4a^2 + 2a + 1)$
27. $(m + 3n)(m^2 - 3mn + 9n^2)$ **29.** $5(k + 2)(k^2 - 2k + 4)$ **31.** $(xy - 4)(x^2y^2 + 4xy + 16)$ **33.** $2(5r - 4t)(25r^2 + 20rt + 16t^2)$
35. $(r + 8)(r - 8)$ **37.** $(x + 13y)(x - 13y)$ **39.** $(3 - t)(9 + 3t + t^2)$ **41.** $2(3r + 2)(3r - 2)$ **43.** $x(3y + 2)(3y - 2)$
45. $8(m + 2)(m^2 - 2m + 4)$ **47.** $xy(y - 3z)(y + 3z)$ **49.** $4(3x - 4y)(3x + 4y)$ **51.** $9(4 - 3x)(4 + 3x)$
53. $(xy - z^2)(x^2y^2 + xyz^2 + z^4)$ **55.** $\left(7 - \frac{3}{5}m\right)\left(7 + \frac{3}{5}m\right)$ **57.** $(t + 7)(t^2 - 7t + 49)$ **59.** $n(n^2 + 49)$
61. $x^2(x^2 + 9)(x + 3)(x - 3)$ **63.** $pq(8p + 9q)(8p - 9q)$ **65.** $xy^2(27xy + 1)$ **67.** $a(5a - 4b)(25a^2 + 20ab + 16b^2)$
69. $16x^2(x + 2)(x - 2)$ **71.** 6 **73.** −2 **75.** $\frac{1}{5}$ **77.** $(x + 2 + y)(x + 2 - y)$ **79.** $(a + 4)(a - 4)(b - 4)$
81. $(x + 3 + 2y)(x + 3 - 2y)$ **83.** $(x^n + 10)(x^n - 10)$ **85.** $(x + 6)$ **87.** answers may vary
89. a. 2560 ft **b.** 1920 ft **c.** 13 sec **d.** $16(13 - t)(13 + t)$ **91. a.** 1456 ft **b.** 816 ft **c.** 10 sec **d.** $16(10 + t)(10 - t)$

Integrated Review
Practice Exercises

1. $(3x - 1)(2x - 3)$ **2.** $(3x + 1)(x - 2)(x + 2)$ **3.** $3(3x - y)(3x + y)$ **4.** $(2a + b)(4a^2 - 2ab + b^2)$ **5.** $6xy^2(5x + 2)(2x - 3)$

Exercise Set

1. $(x + y)^2$ **2.** $(x - y)^2$ **3.** $(a + 12)(a - 1)$ **4.** $(a - 10)(a - 1)$ **5.** $(a + 2)(a - 3)$ **6.** $(a - 1)^2$ **7.** $(x + 1)^2$
8. $(x + 2)(x - 1)$ **9.** $(x + 1)(x + 3)$ **10.** $(x + 3)(x - 2)$ **11.** $(x + 3)(x + 4)$ **12.** $(x + 4)(x - 3)$ **13.** $(x + 4)(x - 1)$
14. $(x - 5)(x - 2)$ **15.** $(x + 5)(x - 3)$ **16.** $(x + 6)(x + 5)$ **17.** $(x - 6)(x + 5)$ **18.** $(x + 8)(x + 3)$ **19.** $2(x + 7)(x - 7)$
20. $3(x + 5)(x - 5)$ **21.** $(x + 3)(x + y)$ **22.** $(y - 7)(3 + x)$ **23.** $(x + 8)(x - 2)$ **24.** $(x - 7)(x + 4)$ **25.** $4x(x + 7)(x - 2)$
26. $6x(x - 5)(x + 4)$ **27.** $2(3x + 4)(2x + 3)$ **28.** $(2a - b)(4a + 5b)$ **29.** $(2a + b)(2a - b)$ **30.** $(4 - 3x)(7 + 2x)$
31. $(5 - 2x)(4 + x)$ **32.** prime **33.** prime **34.** $(3y + 5)(2y - 3)$ **35.** $(4x - 5)(x + 1)$ **36.** $y(x + y)(x - y)$ **37.** $4(t^2 + 9)$
38. $(x + 1)(x + y)$ **39.** $(x + 1)(a + 2)$ **40.** $9x(2x^2 - 7x + 1)$ **41.** $4a(3a^2 - 6a + 1)$ **42.** $(x + 16)(x - 2)$ **43.** prime
44. $(4a - 7b)^2$ **45.** $(5p - 7q)^2$ **46.** $(7x + 3y)(x + 3y)$ **47.** $(5 - 2y)(25 + 10y + 4y^2)$ **48.** $(4x + 3)(16x^2 - 12x + 9)$
49. $-(x - 5)(x + 6)$ **50.** $-(x - 2)(x - 4)$ **51.** $(7 - x)(2 + x)$ **52.** $(3 + x)(1 - x)$ **53.** $3x^2y(x + 6)(x - 4)$ **54.** $2xy(x + 5y)(x - y)$
55. $5xy^2(x - 7y)(x - y)$ **56.** $4x^2y(x - 5)(x + 3)$ **57.** $3xy(4x^2 + 81)$ **58.** $2xy^2(3x^2 + 4)$ **59.** $(2 + x)(2 - x)$ **60.** $(3 + y)(3 - y)$
61. $(s + 4)(3r - 1)$ **62.** $(x - 2)(x^2 + 3)$ **63.** $(4x - 3)(x - 2y)$ **64.** $(2x - y)(2x + 7z)$ **65.** $6(x + 2y)(x + y)$
66. $2(x + 4y)(6x - y)$ **67.** $(x + 3)(y + 2)(y - 2)$ **68.** $(y + 3)(y - 3)(x^2 + 3)$ **69.** $(5 + x)(x + y)$ **70.** $(x - y)(7 + y)$

71. $(7t-1)(2t-1)$ **72.** prime **73.** $(3x+5)(x-1)$ **74.** $(7x-2)(x+3)$ **75.** $(x+12y)(x-3y)$ **76.** $(3x-2y)(x+4y)$ **77.** $(1-10ab)(1+2ab)$ **78.** $(1+5ab)(1-12ab)$ **79.** $(3+x)(3-x)(1+x)(1-x)$ **80.** $(3+x)(3-x)(2+x)(2-x)$ **81.** $(x+4)(x-4)(x^2+2)$ **82.** $(x+5)(x-5)(x^2+3)$ **83.** $(x-15)(x-8)$ **84.** $(y+16)(y+6)$ **85.** $2x(3x-2)(x-4)$ **86.** $2y(3y+5)(y-3)$ **87.** $(3x-5y)(9x^2+15xy+25y^2)$ **88.** $(6y-z)(36y^2+6yz+z^2)$ **89.** $(xy+2z)(x^2y^2-2xyz+4z^2)$ **90.** $(3ab+2)(9a^2b^2-6ab+4)$ **91.** $2xy(1+6x)(1-6x)$ **92.** $2x(x+3)(x-3)$ **93.** $(x+2)(x-2)(x+6)$ **94.** $(x-2)(x+6)(x-6)$ **95.** $2a^2(3a+5)$ **96.** $2n(2n-3)$ **97.** $(a^2+2)(a+2)$ **98.** $(a-b)(1+x)$ **99.** $(x+2)(x-2)(x+7)$ **100.** $(a+3)(a-3)(a+5)$ **101.** $(x-y+z)(x-y-z)$ **102.** $(x+2y+3)(x+2y-3)$ **103.** $(9+5x+1)(9-5x-1)$ **104.** $(b+4a+c)(b-4a-c)$ **105.** answers may vary **106.** yes; $9(x^2+9y^2)$ **107.** a, c **108.** b, c

Section 3.6

Practice Exercises

1. $-4, 5$ **2.** $-\frac{3}{4}, 12$ **3.** $0, \frac{6}{7}$ **4.** $-4, 12$ **5.** $\frac{4}{3}$ **6.** $-3, \frac{2}{3}$ **7.** $-6, 4$ **8.** $-3, 0, 3$ **9.** $\frac{2}{3}, \frac{3}{2}, 5$ **10.** $-3, 0, 2$ **11.** The x-intercepts are $(2, 0)$ and $(4, 0)$.

Graphing Calculator Explorations 3.6

1. $-0.9, 2.2$ **3.** no real solution **5.** $-1.8, 2.8$

Vocabulary, Readiness & Video Check 3.6

1. quadratic **3.** $3, -5$ **5.** One side of the equation must be a factored polynomial and the other side must be zero. **7.** To find the x-intercepts of any graph in two variables, we let $y = 0$. Doing this with our quadratic equation gives us an equation = 0, which we can solve by factoring.

Exercise Set 3.6

1. $6, 7$ **3.** $2, -1$ **5.** $-9, -17$ **7.** $0, -6$ **9.** $0, 8$ **11.** $-\frac{3}{2}, \frac{5}{4}$ **13.** $\frac{7}{2}, -\frac{2}{7}$ **15.** $\frac{1}{2}, -\frac{1}{3}$ **17.** $-0.2, -1.5$ **19.** $9, 4$ **21.** $-4, 2$ **23.** $0, 7$ **25.** $8, -4$ **27.** $4, -4$ **29.** $-3, 12$ **31.** $\frac{7}{3}, -2$ **33.** $-5, 5$ **35.** $-2, \frac{1}{6}$ **37.** $0, 4, 8$ **39.** $\frac{3}{4}$ **41.** $-\frac{1}{2}, 0, \frac{1}{2}$ **43.** $-\frac{3}{8}, 0, \frac{1}{2}$ **45.** $-3, 2$ **47.** $-20, 0$ **49.** $\frac{17}{2}$ **51.** $-\frac{1}{2}, \frac{1}{2}$ **53.** $-\frac{3}{2}, -\frac{1}{2}, 3$ **55.** $-5, 3$ **57.** $-\frac{5}{6}, \frac{6}{5}$ **59.** $2, -\frac{4}{5}$ **61.** $-\frac{4}{3}, 5$ **63.** $-4, 3$ **65.** $\frac{8}{3}, -9, 0$ **67.** -7 **69.** $0, \frac{3}{2}$ **71.** $0, 1, -1$ **73.** $-6, \frac{4}{3}$ **75.** $\frac{6}{7}, 1$ **77.** $\left(-\frac{4}{3}, 0\right), (1, 0)$ **79.** $(-2, 0), (5, 0)$ **81.** $(-6, 0), \left(\frac{1}{2}, 0\right)$ **83.** e **85.** b **87.** c **89.** $\frac{47}{45}$ **91.** $\frac{17}{60}$ **93.** $\frac{15}{8}$ **95.** $\frac{7}{10}$ **97.** didn't write equation in standard form; should be $x = 4$ or $x = -2$ **99.** answers may vary; for example $(x-6)(x+1) = 0$ **101.** answers may vary; for example, $x^2 - 12x + 35 = 0$ **103. a.** 300; 304; 276; 216; 124; 0; -156 **b.** 5 sec **c.** 304 ft **d.**

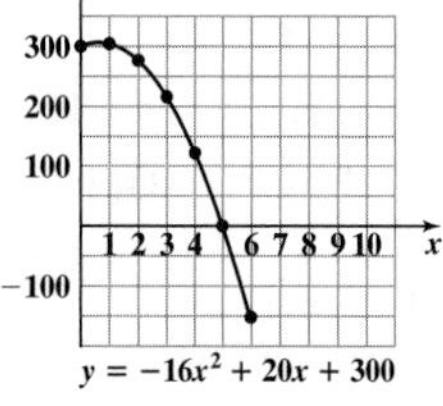

105. $0, \frac{1}{2}$ **107.** $0, -15$

Section 3.7

Practice Exercises

1. 2 sec **2.** There are two numbers. They are -4 and 12. **3.** base: 35 ft; height: 12 ft **4.** 7 and 8 or -6 and -5 **5.** leg: 8 units; leg: 15 units; hypotenuse: 17 units

Vocabulary, Readiness & Video Check 3.7

1. In applications, the context of the problem needs to be considered. Each exercise resulted in both a positive and a negative solution, and a negative solution is not appropriate for any of the problems.

Exercise Set 3.7

1. width $= x$; length $= x + 4$ **3.** x and $x + 2$ if x is an odd integer **5.** base $= x$; height $= 4x + 1$ **7.** 11 units **9.** 15 cm, 13 cm, 70 cm, 22 cm **11.** base = 16 mi; height = 6 mi **13.** 5 sec **15.** width = 5 cm; length = 6 cm **17.** 54 diagonals **19.** 10 sides **21.** -12 or 11 **23.** 14, 15 **25.** 13 feet **27.** 5 in. **29.** 12 mm, 16 mm, 20 mm **31.** 10 km **33.** 36 ft **35.** 9.5 sec **37.** 20% **39.** length: 15 mi; width: 8 mi **41.** 105 units **43.** 2 million **45.** 1.9 million **47.** 2003 **49.** answers may vary **51.** $\frac{4}{7}$ **53.** $\frac{3}{2}$ **55.** $\frac{1}{3}$ **57.** slow boat: 8 mph; fast boat: 15 mph **59.** 13 and 7 **61.** width: 29 m; length: 35 m **63.** answers may vary

Chapter 3 Vocabulary Check

1. quadratic equation **2.** factoring **3.** greatest common factor **4.** perfect square trinomial **5.** difference of two squares **6.** difference of two cubes **7.** sum of two cubes **8.** 0 **9.** hypotenuse **10.** leg **11.** hypotenuse

Chapter 3 Review

1. $2x - 5$ **3.** $4x(5x + 3)$ **5.** $(2x + 3)(3x - 5)$ **7.** $(x - 1)(3x + 2)$ **9.** $(2a + b)(5a + 7b)$ **11.** $(x + 4)(x + 2)$ **13.** prime **15.** $(x + 6y)(x - 2y)$ **17.** $2(3 - x)(12 + x)$ **19.** $10a(a - 1)(a - 10)$ **21.** $-48, 2$ **23.** $(2x + 1)(x + 6)$ **25.** $(3x + 4y)(2x - y)$ **27.** $5y(2y - 3)(y + 4)$ **29.** $2(3x - 5)^2$ **31.** $(2x + 3)(2x - 3)$ **33.** prime **35.** $(2x + 3)(4x^2 - 6x + 9)$ **37.** $2(3 - xy)(9 + 3xy + x^2y^2)$ **39.** $(4x^2 + 1)(2x + 1)(2x - 1)$ **41.** $-6, 2$ **43.** $-\frac{1}{5}, -3$ **45.** $-4, 6$ **47.** $2, 8$ **49.** $-\frac{2}{7}, \frac{3}{8}$ **51.** $-\frac{2}{5}$ **53.** 3 **55.** $0, -\frac{7}{4}, 3$ **57.** c **59.** 9 units **61.** width: 20 in.; length: 25 in. **63.** 19 and 20 **65. a.** 17.5 sec and 10 sec; The rocket reaches a height of 2800 ft on its way up and on its way back down. **b.** 27.5 sec **67.** $7(x - 9)$ **69.** $\left(m + \frac{2}{5}\right)\left(m - \frac{2}{5}\right)$ **71.** $(y + 2)(x - 1)$ **73.** $3x(x - 9)(x - 1)$ **75.** $2(x + 3)(x - 3)$ **77.** $5(x + 2)^2$ **79.** $2xy(2x - 3y)$ **81.** $3(8x^2 - x - 6)$ **83.** $(x + 3)(x + 2)(x - 2)$ **85.** $5x^2 - 9x - 2; (5x + 1)(x - 2)$ **87.** $-\frac{7}{2}, 4$ **89.** $0, -7, -4$ **91.** $0, 16$ **93.** length: 6 in.; width: 2 in. **95.** $28x^2 - \pi x^2; x^2(28 - \pi)$

Chapter 3 Test

1. $(x + 7)(x + 4)$ **2.** $(7 - m)(7 + m)$ **3.** $(y + 11)^2$ **4.** $(a + 3)(4 - y)$ **5.** prime **6.** $(y - 12)(y + 4)$ **7.** prime **8.** $3x(3x + 1)(x + 4)$ **9.** $(3a - 7)(a + b)$ **10.** $(3x - 2)(x - 1)$ **11.** $(x + 12y)(x + 2y)$ **12.** $5(6 + x)(6 - x)$ **13.** $(6t + 5)(t - 1)$ **14.** $(y + 2)(y - 2)(x - 7)$ **15.** $x(1 + x^2)(1 + x)(1 - x)$ **16.** $-xy(y^2 + x^2)$ **17.** $(4x - 1)(16x^2 + 4x + 1)$ **18.** $8(y - 2)(y^2 + 2y + 4)$ **19.** $-9, 3$ **20.** $-7, 2$ **21.** $-7, 1$ **22.** $0, \frac{3}{2}, -\frac{4}{3}$ **23.** $0, 3, -3$ **24.** $-3, 5$ **25.** $0, \frac{5}{2}$ **26.** 17 ft **27.** 8 and 9 **28.** 7 sec **29.** hypotenuse: 25 cm; legs: 15 cm, 20 cm

Chapter 3 Cumulative Review

1. a. $9 \le 11$ **b.** $8 > 1$ **c.** $3 \neq 4$; Sec. 1.2, Ex. 3 **3. a.** $\frac{6}{7}$ **b.** $\frac{11}{27}$ **c.** $\frac{22}{5}$; Sec. 1.3, Ex. 2 **5.** $\frac{14}{3}$; Sec. 1.4, Ex. 5 **7. a.** -12 **b.** -1; Sec. 1.5, Ex. 7 **9. a.** -32 **b.** -14 **c.** 90; Sec. 1.7, Ex. 1 **11. a.** $4x$ **b.** $11y^2$ **c.** $8x^2 - x$ **d.** $5n^2$; Sec. 2.1, Ex. 3 **13.** 140; Sec. 2.2, Ex. 7 **15.** -11; Sec. 2.2, Ex. 6 **17.** $\frac{16}{3}$; Sec. 2.3, Ex. 2 **19.** shorter: 12 in.; longer: 36 in.; Sec. 2.4, Ex. 3 **21.** ; Sec. 3.2, Ex. 5 **23.** $m = \frac{3}{4}$; y-intercept: $(0, -1)$; Sec. 3.4, Ex. 5 **25. a.** 250 **b.** 1; Sec. 5.1, Ex. 2 **27. a.** 2 **b.** 5 **c.** 1 **d.** 6 **e.** 0; Sec. 5.2, Ex. 1 **29.** $9x^2 - 6x - 1$; Sec. 5.2, Ex. 11 **31.** $6x^2 - 11x - 10$; Sec. 5.3, Ex. 5 **33.** $9y^2 + 6y + 1$; Sec. 5.4, Ex. 4 **35. a.** $\frac{1}{9}$ **b.** $\frac{2}{x^3}$ **c.** $\frac{3}{4}$ **d.** $\frac{1}{16}$ **e.** $\frac{1}{y^4}$ (Sec. 5.5, Ex. 1) **37. a.** 3.67×10^8 **b.** 3.0×10^{-6} **c.** 2.052×10^{10} **d.** 8.5×10^{-4}; Sec. 5.5, Ex. 5 **39.** $x + 4$; Sec. 5.6, Ex. 4 **41. a.** x^3 **b.** y; Sec. 6.1, Ex. 2 **43.** $(x + 3)(x + 4)$; Sec. 6.2, Ex. 1 **45.** $(4x - 1)(2x - 5)$; Sec. 6.3, Ex. 2 **47.** $(5a + 3b)(5a - 3b)$; Sec. 6.5, Ex. 2b **49.** $3, -1$; Sec. 6.6, Ex. 1

CHAPTER 4 RATIONAL EXPRESSIONS

Section 4.1

Practice Exercises

1. a. $\{x \mid x \text{ is a real number}\}$ **b.** $\{x \mid x \text{ is a real number and } x \neq -3\}$ **c.** $\{x \mid x \text{ is a real number and } x \neq 2, x \neq 3\}$ **2. a.** $\frac{1}{2z - 1}$ **b.** $\frac{5x + 3}{6x - 5}$ **3. a.** 1 **b.** -1 **4.** $-\frac{5(2 + x)}{x + 3}$ **5. a.** $x^2 - 4x + 16$ **b.** $\frac{5}{z - 3}$ **6.** $\frac{-(x + 3)}{6x - 11}; \frac{-x - 3}{6x - 11}; \frac{x + 3}{-(6x - 11)}; \frac{x + 3}{-6x + 11}; \frac{x + 3}{11 - 6x}$ **7. a.** \$7.20 **b.** \$3.60

Graphing Calculator Explorations 4.1

1. $\{x \mid x \text{ is a real number and } x \neq -2, x \neq 2\}$

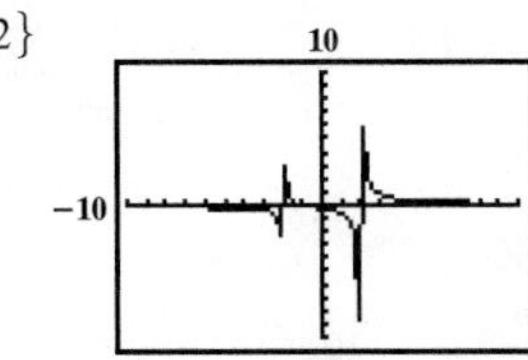

3. $\left\{x \,\middle|\, x \text{ is a real number and } x \neq -4, x \neq \frac{1}{2}\right\}$

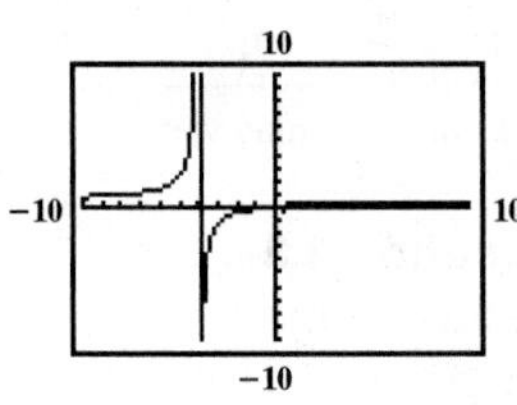

Vocabulary, Readiness & Video Check 4.1

1. rational **3.** domain **5.** 1 **7.** $\frac{-a}{b}; \frac{a}{-b}$ **9.** Rational expressions are fractions and are therefore undefined if the denominator is zero; the domain of a rational function is all real numbers except those that make the denominator of the related rational expression equal to 0. **11.** You would need to write parentheses around the numerator or denominator if it had more than one term because the negative sign needs to apply to the entire numerator or denominator.

Vocabulary, Readiness & Video Check 4.1

1. rational **3.** domain **5.** 1 **7.** $\frac{-a}{b}; \frac{a}{-b}$ **9.** Rational expressions are fractions and are therefore undefined if the denominator is zero; the domain of a rational function is all real numbers except those that make the denominator of the related rational expression equal to 0. **11.** You would need to write parentheses around the numerator or denominator if it had more than one term because the negative sign needs to apply to the entire numerator or denominator.

Exercise Set 4.1

1. $\{x|x \text{ is a real number}\}$ **3.** $\{t|t \text{ is a real number and } t \neq 0\}$ **5.** $\{x|x \text{ is a real number and } x \neq 7\}$ **7.** $\left\{x\middle|x \text{ is a real number and } x \neq \frac{1}{3}\right\}$ **9.** $\{x|x \text{ is a real number and } x \neq -2, x \neq 0, x \neq 1\}$ **11.** $\{x|x \text{ is a real number and } x \neq 2, x \neq -2\}$ **13.** $\frac{-(x-10)}{x+8}; \frac{-x+10}{x+8}; \frac{x-10}{-(x+8)}; \frac{x-10}{-x-8}$ **15.** $\frac{-(5y-3)}{y-12}; \frac{-5y+3}{y-12}; \frac{5y-3}{-(y-12)}; \frac{5y-3}{-y+12}$ **17.** 1 **19.** -1 **21.** $\frac{1}{4(x+2)}$ **23.** -5 **25.** $\frac{7}{x}$ **27.** $\frac{1}{x-9}$ **29.** $5x+1$ **31.** $\frac{x^2}{x-2}$ **33.** $\frac{x+2}{2}$ **35.** $-(x+2)$ or $-x-2$ **37.** $\frac{11x}{6}$ **39.** $x+y$ **41.** x^2-2x+4 **43.** $-x^2-x-1$ **45.** $\frac{2y+5}{3y+4}$ **47.** $\frac{x-2}{2x^2+1}$ **49.** $\frac{1}{3x+5}$ **51.** correct **53.** correct **55.** $\frac{10}{3}, -8, -\frac{7}{3}$ **57.** $-\frac{17}{48}, \frac{2}{7}, -\frac{3}{8}$ **59. a.** \$200 million **b.** \$500 million **c.** \$300 million **d.** $\{x|x \text{ is a real number}\}$ **61.** 400 mg **63.** $C = 78.125$; medium **65.** 59.6% **67.** $\frac{3}{11}$ **69.** $\frac{4}{3}$ **71.** $\frac{117}{40}$ **73.** correct **75.** incorrect; $\frac{1+2}{1+3} = \frac{3}{4}$ **77.** no **79.** yes; 1 **81.** yes; -1 **83.** no; answers may vary **85.** answers may vary **87.** $0, \frac{20}{9}, \frac{60}{7}, 20, \frac{140}{3}$, 180, 380, 1980;

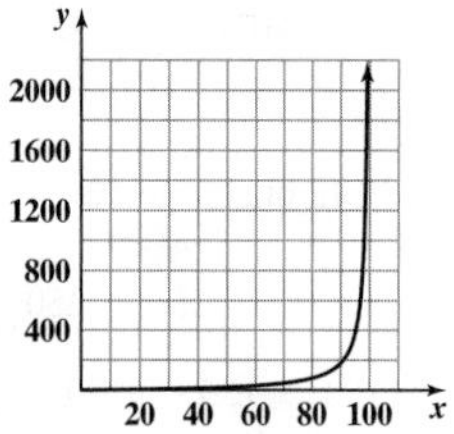

89.

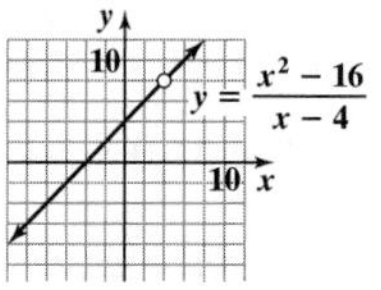

91.

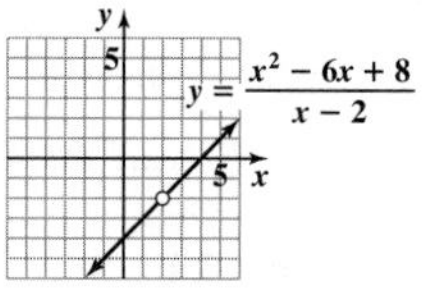

Section 4.2
Practice Exercises

1. a. $\frac{12a}{5b^2}$ **b.** $-\frac{2q}{3}$ **2.** $\frac{3}{x+1}$ **3.** $-\frac{3x-5}{2x(x+2)}$ **4.** $\frac{b^2}{8a^2}$ **5.** $\frac{3(x-5)}{4}$ **6.** $\frac{2}{x(x-3)}$ **7.** 1 **8. a.** $\frac{(y+9)^2}{16x^2}$ **b.** $\frac{1}{4x}$ **c.** $-\frac{7(x-2)}{x+4}$ **9.** 2 sq ft **10.** 504 sq in. **11.** 549,000 sq ft **12.** 70.0 miles per hour

Vocabulary, Readiness & Video Check 4.2

1. reciprocals **3.** $\frac{a \cdot d}{b \cdot c}$ or $\frac{ad}{bc}$ **5.** $\frac{6}{7}$ **7.** fractions; reciprocal **9.** The units in the unit fraction consist of $\frac{\text{units converting to}}{\text{original units}}$.

Exercise Set 4.2

1. $\frac{21}{4y}$ **3.** x^4 **5.** $-\frac{b^2}{6}$ **7.** $\frac{x^2}{10}$ **9.** $\frac{1}{3}$ **11.** $\frac{m+n}{m-n}$ **13.** $\frac{x+5}{x}$ **15.** $\frac{(x+2)(x-3)}{(x-4)(x+4)}$ **17.** $\frac{2x^4}{3}$ **19.** $\frac{12}{y^6}$ **21.** $x(x+4)$ **23.** $\frac{3(x+1)}{x^3(x-1)}$ **25.** m^2-n^2 **27.** $-\frac{x+2}{x-3}$ **29.** $\frac{x+2}{x-3}$ **31.** $\frac{5}{6}$ **33.** $\frac{3x}{8}$ **35.** $\frac{3}{2}$ **37.** $\frac{3x+4y}{2(x+2y)}$ **39.** $\frac{2(x+2)}{x-2}$ **41.** $-\frac{y(x+2)}{4}$ **43.** $\frac{(a+5)(a+3)}{(a+2)(a+1)}$ **45.** $\frac{5}{x}$ **47.** $\frac{2(n-8)}{3n-1}$ **49.** $4x^3(x-3)$ **51.** $\frac{(a+b)^2}{a-b}$ **53.** $\frac{3x+5}{x^2+4}$ **55.** $\frac{4}{x-2}$ **57.** $\frac{a-b}{6(a^2+ab+b^2)}$ **59.** 1440 **61.** 5 **63.** 81 **65.** 73 **67.** 56.7 **69.** 1,201,500 sq ft **71.** 244.9 miles/hour **73.** 1 **75.** $-\frac{10}{9}$ **77.** $-\frac{1}{5}$ **79.**

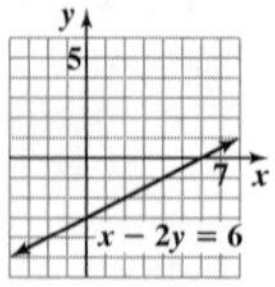

81. true **83.** false; $\frac{x^2+3x}{20}$ **85.** $\frac{2}{9(x-5)}$ sq ft **87.** $\frac{x}{2}$ **89.** $\frac{5a(2a+b)(3a-2b)}{b^2(a-b)(a+2b)}$ **91.** answers may vary

Section 4.3
Practice Exercises

1. $2t+1$ **2.** $4x^4+5x-\frac{3}{x}$ **3.** $3x^3y^3-2+\frac{1}{5x}$ **4.** $x+3$ **5.** $2x+3+\frac{-10}{2x+1}$ or $2x+3-\frac{10}{2x+1}$ **6.** $3x^2-2x+5+\frac{-13}{3x+2}$ or $3x^2-2x+5-\frac{13}{3x-2}$ **7.** $3x^2-2x-9+\frac{5x+22}{x^2+2}$ **8.** x^2-3x+9

Vocabulary, Readiness & Video Check 4.3

1. dividend, quotient, divisor **3.** a^2 **5.** y **7.** the common denominator

Exercise Set 4.3

1. $12x^3 + 3x$ **3.** $4x^3 - 6x^2 + x + 1$ **5.** $5p^2 + 6p$ **7.** $-\frac{3}{2x} + 3$ **9.** $-3x^2 + x - \frac{4}{x^3}$ **11.** $-1 + \frac{3}{2x} - \frac{7}{4x^4}$ **13.** $x + 1$ **15.** $2x + 3$ **17.** $2x + 1 + \frac{7}{x - 4}$ **19.** $3a^2 - 3a + 1 + \frac{2}{3a + 2}$ **21.** $4x + 3 - \frac{2}{2x + 1}$ **23.** $2x^2 + 6x - 5 - \frac{2}{x - 2}$ **25.** $x + 6$ **27.** $x^2 + 3x + 9$ **29.** $-3x + 6 - \frac{11}{x + 2}$ **31.** $2b - 1 - \frac{6}{2b - 1}$ **33.** $ab - b^2$ **35.** $4x + 9$ **37.** $x + 4xy - \frac{y}{2}$ **39.** $2b^2 + b + 2 - \frac{12}{b + 4}$ **41.** $5x - 2 + \frac{2}{x + 6}$ **43.** $x^2 - \frac{12x}{5} - 1$ **45.** $6x - 1 - \frac{1}{x + 3}$ **47.** $6x - 1$ **49.** $-x^3 + 3x^2 - \frac{4}{x}$ **51.** $x^2 + 3x + 9$ **53.** $y^2 + 5y + 10 + \frac{24}{y - 2}$ **55.** $-6x - 12 - \frac{19}{x - 2}$ **57.** $x^3 - x^2 + x$ **59.** $2a^3 + 2a$ **61.** $2x^3 + 14x^2 - 10x$ **63.** $-3x^2y^3 - 21x^3y^2 - 24xy$ **65.** $9a^2b^3c + 36ab^2c - 72ab$ **67.** $(3x^3 + x - 4)$ ft **69.** c **71.** answers may vary **73.** $(2x + 5)$ m **75.** $9x^{7a} - 6x^{5a} + 7x^{2a} - 1$

Section 4.4

Practice Exercises

1. $\frac{2a}{b}$ **2.** 1 **3.** $4x - 5$ **4. a.** 42 **b.** $45y^3$ **5. a.** $(y - 5)(y - 4)$ **b.** $a(a + 2)$ **6.** $3(2x - 1)^2$ **7.** $(x + 4)(x - 4)(x + 1)$ **8.** $3 - x$ or $x - 3$ **9. a.** $\frac{21x^2y}{35xy^2}$ **b.** $\frac{18x}{8x + 14}$ **10.** $\frac{3x - 6}{(x - 2)(x + 3)(x - 5)}$

Vocabulary, Readiness & Video Check 4.4

1. $\frac{9}{11}$ **3.** $\frac{a + c}{b}$ **5.** $\frac{5 - (6 + x)}{x}$ **7.** We factor denominators into the smallest factors—including coefficients—so we can determine the most number of times each unique factor occurs in any one denominator for the LCD.

Exercise Set 4.4

1. $\frac{a + 9}{13}$ **3.** $\frac{3m}{n}$ **5.** 4 **7.** $\frac{y + 10}{3 + y}$ **9.** $5x + 3$ **11.** $\frac{4}{a + 5}$ **13.** $\frac{1}{x - 6}$ **15.** $\frac{5x + 7}{x - 3}$ **17.** $x + 5$ **19.** 3 **21.** $4x^3$ **23.** $8x(x + 2)$ **25.** $(x + 3)(x - 2)$ **27.** $3(x + 6)$ **29.** $5(x - 6)^2$ **31.** $6(x + 1)^2$ **33.** $x - 8$ or $8 - x$ **35.** $(x - 1)(x + 4)(x + 3)$ **37.** $(3x + 1)(x + 1)(x - 1)(2x + 1)$ **39.** $2x^2(x + 4)(x - 4)$ **41.** $\frac{6x}{4x^2}$ **43.** $\frac{24b^2}{12ab^2}$ **45.** $\frac{9y}{2y(x + 3)}$ **47.** $\frac{9ab + 2b}{5b(a + 2)}$ **49.** $\frac{x^2 + x}{x(x + 4)(x + 2)(x + 1)}$ **51.** $\frac{18y - 2}{30x^2 - 60}$ **53.** $2x$ **55.** $\frac{x + 3}{2x - 1}$ **57.** $x + 1$ **59.** $\frac{1}{x^2 - 8}$ **61.** $\frac{6(4x + 1)}{x(2x + 1)}$ **63.** $\frac{29}{21}$ **65.** $-\frac{7}{12}$ **67.** $\frac{7}{30}$ **69.** d **71.** answers may vary **73.** c **75.** b **77.** $-\frac{5}{x - 2}$ **79.** $\frac{7 + x}{x - 2}$ **81.** $\frac{20}{x - 2}$ m **83.** answers may vary **85.** 95,304 Earth days **87.** answers may vary **89.** answers may vary

Section 4.5

Practice Exercises

1. a. 0 **b.** $\frac{21a + 10}{24a^2}$ **2.** $\frac{6}{x - 5}$ **3.** $\frac{13y + 3}{5y(y + 1)}$ **4.** $\frac{13}{x - 5}$ **5.** $\frac{3b + 6}{b + 3}$ or $\frac{3(b + 2)}{b + 3}$ **6.** $\frac{10 - 3x^2}{2x(2x + 3)}$ **7.** $\frac{x(5x + 6)}{(x + 4)(x + 3)(x - 3)}$

Vocabulary, Readiness & Video Check 4.5

1. d **3.** a **5.** The problem adds two rational expressions with denominators that are opposites of each other. Recognizing this special case can save you time and effort. If you recognize that one denominator is -1 times the other denominator, you may save time.

Exercise Set 4.5

1. $\frac{5}{x}$ **3.** $\frac{75a - 6b^2}{5b}$ **5.** $\frac{6x + 5}{2x^2}$ **7.** $\frac{11}{x + 1}$ **9.** $\frac{x - 6}{(x - 2)(x + 2)}$ **11.** $\frac{35x - 6}{4x(x - 2)}$ **13.** $-\frac{2}{x - 3}$ **15.** 0 **17.** $-\frac{1}{x^2 - 1}$ **19.** $\frac{5 + 2x}{x}$ **21.** $\frac{6x - 7}{x - 2}$ **23.** $-\frac{y + 4}{y + 3}$ **25.** $\frac{-5x + 14}{4x}$ or $-\frac{5x - 14}{4x}$ **27.** 2 **29.** $\frac{9x^4 - 4x^2}{21}$ **31.** $\frac{x + 2}{(x + 3)^2}$ **33.** $\frac{9b - 4}{5b(b - 1)}$ **35.** $\frac{2 + m}{m}$ **37.** $\frac{x^2 + 3x}{(x - 7)(x - 2)}$ or $\frac{x(x + 3)}{(x - 7)(x - 2)}$ **39.** $\frac{10}{1 - 2x}$ **41.** $\frac{15x - 1}{(x + 1)^2(x - 1)}$ **43.** $\frac{x^2 - 3x - 2}{(x - 1)^2(x + 1)}$ **45.** $\frac{a + 2}{2(a + 3)}$ **47.** $\frac{y(2y + 1)}{(2y + 3)^2}$ **49.** $\frac{x - 10}{2(x - 2)}$ **51.** $\frac{2x + 21}{(x + 3)^2}$ **53.** $\frac{-5x + 23}{(x - 2)(x - 3)}$ **55.** $\frac{7}{2(m - 10)}$ **57.** $\frac{2x^2 - 2x - 46}{(x + 1)(x - 6)(x - 5)}$ or $\frac{2(x^2 - x - 23)}{(x + 1)(x - 6)(x - 5)}$ **59.** $\frac{n + 4}{4n(n - 1)(n - 2)}$ **61.** 10 **63.** 2 **65.** $\frac{25a}{9(a - 2)}$ **67.** $\frac{x + 4}{(x - 2)(x - 1)}$ **69.** $x = \frac{2}{3}$ **71.** $x = -\frac{1}{2}, x = 1$ **73.** $x = -\frac{15}{2}$ **75.** $\frac{6x^2 - 5x - 3}{x(x + 1)(x - 1)}$ **77.** $\frac{4x^2 - 15x + 6}{(x - 2)^2(x + 2)(x - 3)}$ **79.** $\frac{-2x^2 + 14x + 55}{(x + 2)(x + 7)(x + 3)}$ **81.** $\frac{2x - 16}{(x + 4)(x - 4)}$ in. **83.** $\frac{P - G}{P}$ **85.** answers may vary **87.** $\left(\frac{90x - 40}{x}\right)^\circ$ **89.** answers may vary

Section 4.6

Practice Exercises

1. -2 **2.** 13 **3.** $-1, 7$ **4.** $-\frac{19}{2}$ **5.** 3 **6.** -8 **7.** $b = \frac{ax}{a - x}$

Graphing Calculator Explorations 4.6

1. **3.**

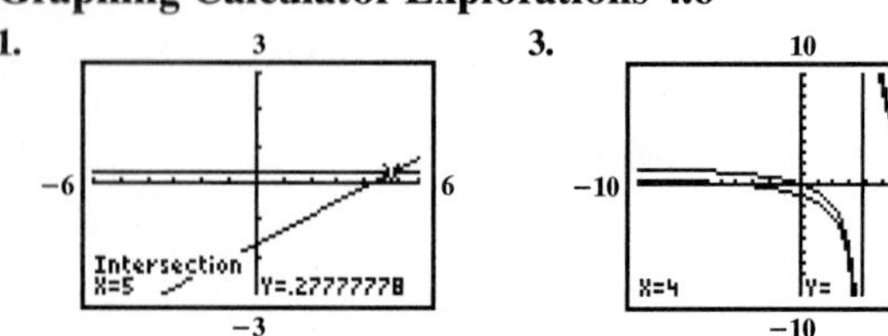

Vocabulary, Readiness & Video Check 4.6

1. c **3.** b **5.** a **7.** These equations are solved in very different ways, so you need to determine the next correct move to make. For a linear equation, you first "move" variable terms on one side and numbers on the other; for a quadratic equation, you first set the equation equal to 0. **9.** the steps for solving an equation containing rational expressions; as if it's the only variable in the equation

Exercise Set 4.6

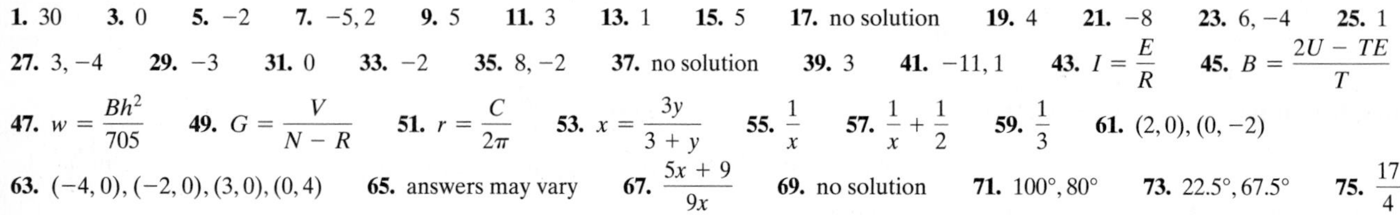

1. 30 **3.** 0 **5.** -2 **7.** $-5, 2$ **9.** 5 **11.** 3 **13.** 1 **15.** 5 **17.** no solution **19.** 4 **21.** -8 **23.** $6, -4$ **25.** 1 **27.** $3, -4$ **29.** -3 **31.** 0 **33.** -2 **35.** $8, -2$ **37.** no solution **39.** 3 **41.** $-11, 1$ **43.** $I = \frac{E}{R}$ **45.** $B = \frac{2U - TE}{T}$ **47.** $w = \frac{Bh^2}{705}$ **49.** $G = \frac{V}{N - R}$ **51.** $r = \frac{C}{2\pi}$ **53.** $x = \frac{3y}{3 + y}$ **55.** $\frac{1}{x}$ **57.** $\frac{1}{x} + \frac{1}{2}$ **59.** $\frac{1}{3}$ **61.** $(2, 0), (0, -2)$ **63.** $(-4, 0), (-2, 0), (3, 0), (0, 4)$ **65.** answers may vary **67.** $\frac{5x + 9}{9x}$ **69.** no solution **71.** $100°, 80°$ **73.** $22.5°, 67.5°$ **75.** $\frac{17}{4}$

Integrated Review

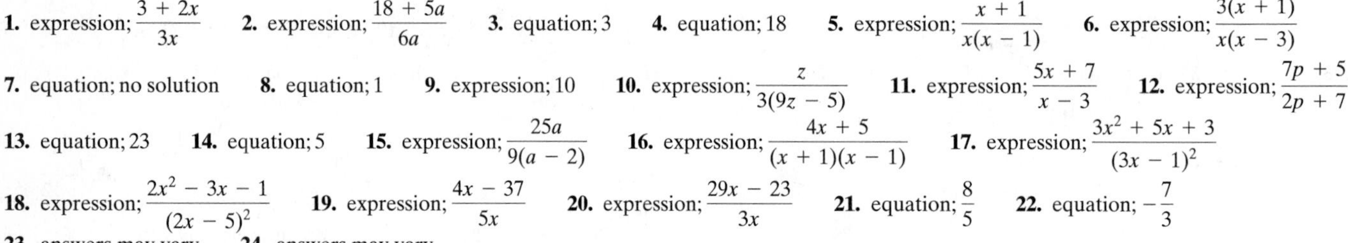

1. expression; $\frac{3 + 2x}{3x}$ **2.** expression; $\frac{18 + 5a}{6a}$ **3.** equation; 3 **4.** equation; 18 **5.** expression; $\frac{x + 1}{x(x - 1)}$ **6.** expression; $\frac{3(x + 1)}{x(x - 3)}$ **7.** equation; no solution **8.** equation; 1 **9.** expression; 10 **10.** expression; $\frac{z}{3(9z - 5)}$ **11.** expression; $\frac{5x + 7}{x - 3}$ **12.** expression; $\frac{7p + 5}{2p + 7}$ **13.** equation; 23 **14.** equation; 5 **15.** expression; $\frac{25a}{9(a - 2)}$ **16.** expression; $\frac{4x + 5}{(x + 1)(x - 1)}$ **17.** expression; $\frac{3x^2 + 5x + 3}{(3x - 1)^2}$ **18.** expression; $\frac{2x^2 - 3x - 1}{(2x - 5)^2}$ **19.** expression; $\frac{4x - 37}{5x}$ **20.** expression; $\frac{29x - 23}{3x}$ **21.** equation; $\frac{8}{5}$ **22.** equation; $-\frac{7}{3}$ **23.** answers may vary **24.** answers may vary

Section 4.7

Practice Exercises

1. a. $\frac{1}{12m}$ **b.** $\frac{8x(x + 4)}{3(x - 4)}$ **c.** $\frac{b^2}{a^2}$ **2. a.** $\frac{8x(x + 4)}{3(x - 4)}$ **b.** $\frac{b^2}{a^2}$ **3.** $\frac{y(3xy + 1)}{x^2(1 + xy)}$ **4.** $\frac{1 - 6x}{15 + 6x}$

Vocabulary, Readiness & Video Check 4.7

1. $\frac{7}{1 + z}$ **3.** $\frac{1}{x^2}$ **5.** $\frac{2}{x}$ **7.** $\frac{1}{9y}$ **9.** a single fraction in the numerator and in the denominator **11.** Since a negative exponent moves its base from a numerator to a denominator of the expression only, a rational expression containing negative exponents can become a complex fraction when rewritten with positive exponents.

Exercise Set 4.7

1. 4 **3.** $\frac{7}{13}$ **5.** $\frac{4}{x}$ **7.** $\frac{9(x - 2)}{9x^2 + 4}$ **9.** $2x + y$ **11.** $\frac{2(x + 1)}{2x - 1}$ **13.** $\frac{2x + 3}{4 - 9x}$ **15.** $\frac{1}{x^2 - 2x + 4}$ **17.** $\frac{x}{5(x - 2)}$ **19.** $\frac{x - 2}{2x - 1}$ **21.** $\frac{x}{2 - 3x}$ **23.** $-\frac{y}{x + y}$ **25.** $-\frac{2x^3}{y(x - y)}$ **27.** $\frac{2x + 1}{y}$ **29.** $\frac{x - 3}{9}$ **31.** $\frac{1}{x + 2}$ **33.** 2 **35.** $\frac{xy^2}{x^2 + y^2}$ **37.** $\frac{2b^2 + 3a}{b(b - a)}$ **39.** $\frac{x}{(x + 1)(x - 1)}$ **41.** $\frac{1 + a}{1 - a}$ **43.** $\frac{x(x + 6y)}{2y}$ **45.** $\frac{5a}{2(a + 2)}$ **47.** $xy(5y + 2x)$ **49.** $\frac{xy}{2x + 5y}$ **51.** $\frac{x^2y^2}{4}$ **53.** $-9x^3y^4$ **55.** -9 **57.** a and c **59.** $\frac{770a}{770 - s}$ **61.** a, b **63.** answers may vary **65.** $\frac{1 + x}{2 + x}$ **67.** $x(x + 1)$ **69.** $\frac{x - 3y}{x + 3y}$ **71.** $3a^2 + 4a + 4$ **73. a.** $\frac{1}{a + h}$ **b.** $\frac{1}{a}$ **c.** $\frac{\frac{1}{a + h} - \frac{1}{a}}{h}$ **d.** $-\frac{1}{a(a + h)}$ **75. a.** $\frac{3}{a + h + 1}$ **b.** $\frac{3}{a + 1}$ **c.** $\frac{\frac{3}{a + h + 1} - \frac{3}{a + 1}}{h}$ **d.** $-\frac{3}{(a + h + 1)(a + 1)}$

Section 4.8

Practice Exercises

1. 99 **2.** $\frac{13}{3}$ **3.** \$9.03 **4.** 6 **5.** 15 **6.** $1\frac{5}{7}$ hr **7.** bus: 45 mph; car: 60 mph

Vocabulary, Readiness & Video Check 4.8

1. c **3.** $\frac{1}{x}; \frac{1}{x} - 3$ **5.** $z + 5; \frac{1}{z + 5}$ **7.** $2y; \frac{11}{2y}$ **9.** No. Proportions are actually equations containing rational expressions, so they can also be solved by using the steps to solve those equations. **11.** divided by, quotient **13.** $\frac{325}{x + 7} = \frac{290}{x}$

Exercise Set 4.8

1. 4 **3.** $\frac{50}{9}$ **5.** -3 **7.** $\frac{14}{9}$ **9.** 123 lb **11.** 165 cal **13.** $y = 21.25$ **15.** $y = 5\frac{5}{7}$ ft **17.** 2 **19.** -3 **21.** $2\frac{2}{9}$ hr **23.** $1\frac{1}{2}$ min **25.** trip to park rate: r; to park time: $\frac{12}{r}$; return trip rate: r; return time: $\frac{18}{r} = \frac{12}{r} + 1$; $r = 6$ mph **27.** 1st portion: 10 mph; cooldown: 8 mph **29.** 360 sq ft **31.** 2 **33.** \$108.00 **35.** 20 mph **37.** $y = 37\frac{1}{2}$ ft **39.** 41 mph; 51 mph **41.** 5 **43.** 217 mph **45.** 9 gal **47.** 8 mph **49.** 2.2 mph; 3.3 mph **51.** 3 hr **53.** $26\frac{2}{3}$ ft **55.** 216 nuts **57.** $666\frac{2}{3}$ mi **59.** 20 hr **61.** car: 70 mph; motorcycle: 60 mph **63.** $5\frac{1}{4}$ hr **65.** 8 **67.** first car: 64 mph; second car: 50 mph **69.** 510 mph **71.** $x = 5$ **73.** $x = 13.5$ **75.** $-\frac{4}{3}$; downward **77.** $\frac{11}{4}$; upward **79.** undefined slope; vertical **81.** 40,200 megawatts **83.** 22,510,000 people **85.** yes **87.** first pump: 28 min; second pump: 84 min **89.** none; answers may vary **91.** answers may vary **93.** $R = \frac{D}{T}$

Section 4.9

Practice Exercises

1. $k = \frac{4}{3}; y = \frac{4}{3}x$ **2.** $18\frac{3}{4}$ in. **3.** $k = 45; b = \frac{45}{a}$ **4.** $653\frac{1}{3}$ kilopascals **5.** $A = kpa$ **6.** $k = 4; y = \frac{4}{x^3}$ **7.** $k = 81; y = \frac{81z}{x^3}$

Vocabulary, Readiness & Video Check 4.9

1. direct **3.** joint **5.** inverse **7.** direct **9.** linear; slope **11.** $y = ka^2b^5$

Exercise Set 4.9

1. $k = \frac{1}{5}; y = \frac{1}{5}x$ **3.** $k = \frac{3}{2}; y = \frac{3}{2}x$ **5.** $k = 14; y = 14x$ **7.** $k = 0.25; y = 0.25x$ **9.** 4.05 lb **11.** 187,239 tons **13.** $k = 30; y = \frac{30}{x}$ **15.** $k = 700; y = \frac{700}{x}$ **17.** $k = 2; y = \frac{2}{x}$ **19.** $k = 0.14; y = \frac{0.14}{x}$ **21.** 54 mph **23.** 72 amps **25.** divided by 4 **27.** $x = kyz$ **29.** $r = kst^3$ **31.** $k = \frac{1}{3}; y = \frac{1}{3}x^3$ **33.** $k = 0.2; y = 0.2\sqrt{x}$ **35.** $k = 1.3; y = \frac{1.3}{x^2}$ **37.** $k = 3; y = 3xz^3$ **39.** 22.5 tons **41.** 15π cu in. **43.** 8 ft **45.** $y = kx$ **47.** $a = \frac{k}{b}$ **49.** $y = kxz$ **51.** $y = \frac{k}{x^3}$ **53.** $y = \frac{kx}{p^2}$ **55.** $C = 8\pi$ in.; $A = 16\pi$ sq in. **57.** $C = 18\pi$ cm; $A = 81\pi$ sq cm **59.** 1.2 **61.** -7 **63.** $-\frac{1}{2}$ **65.** $\frac{8}{27}$ **67.** a **69.** c **71.** multiplied by 8 **73.** multiplied by 2

75.

77.

Chapter 4 Vocabulary Check

1. rational expression **2.** complex fraction **3.** $\frac{-a}{b}; \frac{a}{-b}$ **4.** denominator **5.** simplifying **6.** reciprocals **7.** least common denominator **8.** ratio **9.** proportion **10.** cross products **11.** domain

Chapter 4 Review

1. $\{x \mid x \text{ is a real number}\}$ **3.** $\{x \mid x \text{ is a real number and } x \neq 5\}$ **5.** $\{x \mid x \text{ is a real number and } x \neq 0, x \neq -8\}$ **7.** -1 **9.** $\frac{1}{x - 7}$ **11.** $\frac{x + a}{x - c}$ **13.** $-\frac{1}{x^2 + 4x + 16}$ **15.** \$119 **17.** $\frac{3x^2}{y}$ **19.** $\frac{x - 3}{x + 2}$ **21.** $\frac{x + 3}{x - 4}$ **23.** $(x - 6)(x - 3)$ **25.** $\frac{1}{2}$

27. $-\frac{2(2x+3)}{y-2}$ **29.** $\frac{1}{7}+\frac{3}{x}+\frac{7}{x^2}$ **31.** $a+1+\frac{6}{a-2}$ **33.** $a^2+3a+8+\frac{22}{a-2}$ **35.** $2x^3-x^2+2-\frac{1}{2x-1}$ **37.** $\left(5x-1+\frac{20}{x^2}\right)$ ft **39.** $\frac{1}{x+2}$ **41.** $\frac{2x-10}{3x^2}$ **43.** $14x$ **45.** $\frac{10x^2y}{14x^3y}$ **47.** $\frac{x^2-3x-10}{(x+2)(x-5)(x+9)}$ **49.** $\frac{4y-30x^2}{5x^2y}$ **51.** $\frac{-2x-2}{x+3}$ **53.** $\frac{x-4}{3x}$ **54.** $\frac{x^2+2x+4}{4x}$; $\frac{x+2}{32}$ **57.** 30 **59.** no solution **61.** $\frac{9}{7}$ **63.** $b=\frac{4A}{5x^2}$ **65.** $-\frac{7}{18y}$ **67.** $\frac{3y-1}{2y-1}$ **69.** $-\frac{x^2+9}{6x}$ **71.** $\frac{xy+1}{x}$ **73.** $x=6$ **75.** $x=9$ **77.** 675 parts **79.** 3 **81.** fast car speed: 30 mph; slow car speed: 20 mph **83.** $17\frac{1}{2}$ hr **85.** $x=15$ **87.** 9 **89.** 3.125 cu ft **91.** $\frac{1}{2x}$ **93.** $\frac{x-4}{x+4}$ **95.** $\frac{1}{x-6}$ **97.** $\frac{2}{(x+3)(x-2)}$ **99.** $\frac{1}{2}$ **101.** 1 **103.** $x=6$ **105.** $\frac{3}{10}$ **107.** $\frac{1}{y^2-1}$

Chapter 4 Test

1. $\{x \mid x \text{ is a real number}, x \neq -1, x \neq -3\}$ **2. a.** \$115 **b.** \$103 **3.** $\frac{3}{5}$ **4.** $\frac{1}{x+6}$ **5.** $\frac{1}{x^2-3x+9}$ **6.** $\frac{2m(m+2)}{m-2}$ **7.** $\frac{a+2}{a+5}$ **8.** $-\frac{1}{x+y}$ **9.** 15 **10.** $\frac{y-2}{4}$ **11.** $\frac{19x-6}{2x+5}$ **12.** $\frac{3a-4}{(a-3)(a+2)}$ **13.** $\frac{3}{x-1}$ **14.** $\frac{2(x+5)}{x(y+5)}$ **15.** $\frac{x^2+2x+35}{(x+9)(x+2)(x-5)}$ **16.** $\frac{30}{11}$ **17.** -6 **18.** no solution **19.** $-2, 5$ **20.** no solution **21.** $\frac{xz}{2y}$ **22.** $\frac{5y^2-1}{y+2}$ **23.** $b-a$ **24.** 18 bulbs **25.** 5 or 1 **26.** 30 mph **27.** $6\frac{2}{3}$ hr **28.** $x=12$

Chapter 4 Cumulative Review

1. a. $\frac{15}{x}=4$ **b.** $12-3=x$ **c.** $4x+17\neq 21$ **d.** $3x<48$; Sec. 1.4, Ex. 9 **3.** amount at 7%: \$12,500; amount at 9%: \$7500; Sec. 2.7, Ex. 4 **5.**

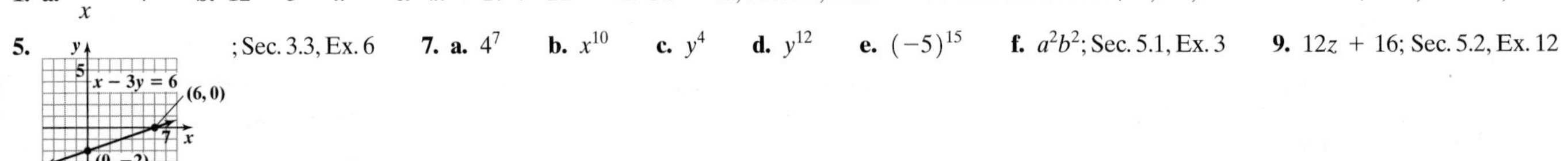

; Sec. 3.3, Ex. 6 **7. a.** 4^7 **b.** x^{10} **c.** y^4 **d.** y^{12} **e.** $(-5)^{15}$ **f.** a^2b^2; Sec. 5.1, Ex. 3 **9.** $12z+16$; Sec. 5.2, Ex. 12 **11.** $27a^3+27a^2b+9ab^2+b^3$; Sec. 5.3, Ex. 8 **13. a.** t^2+4t+4 **b.** $p^2-2pq+q^2$ **c.** $4x^2+20x+25$ **d.** $x^4-14x^2y+49y^2$; Sec. 5.4, Ex. 5 **15. a.** x^3 **b.** 81 **c.** $\frac{q^9}{p^4}$ **d.** $\frac{32}{125}$; Sec. 5.5, Ex. 2 **17.** $4x^2-4x+6+\frac{-11}{2x+3}$; Sec. 5.6, Ex. 6 **19. a.** 4 **b.** 1 **c.** 3; Sec. 6.1, Ex. 1 **21.** $-3a(3a^4-6a+1)$; Sec. 6.1, Ex. 5 **23.** $3(m+2)(m-10)$; Sec. 6.2, Ex. 9 **25.** $(3x+2)(x+3)$; Sec. 6.3, Ex. 1 **27.** $(x+6)^2$; Sec. 6.3, Ex. 8 **29.** prime polynomial; Sec. 6.5, Ex. 4b **31.** $(x+2)(x^2-2x+4)$; Sec. 6.5, Ex. 8 **33.** $(2x+3)(x+1)(x-1)$; Ch. 6 Int. Rev., Ex. 2 **35.** $3(2m+n)(2m-n)$; Ch. 6 Int. Rev., Ex. 3 **37.** $-\frac{1}{2}, 4$; Sec. 6.6, Ex. 6 **39.** $(1,0), (4,0)$; Sec. 6.6, Ex. 11 **41.** base: 6 m; height: 10 m; Sec. 6.7, Ex. 3 **43.** $-\frac{2(3+x)}{x+1}$; Sec. 7.1, Ex. 4 **45.** $\frac{2}{x(x+1)}$; Sec. 7.2, Ex. 6 **47.** $\frac{1+2x}{2(2-x)}$; Sec. 7.7, Ex. 4

CHAPTER 5 RATIONAL EXPONENTS, RADICALS, AND COMPLEX NUMBERS

Section 5.1

Practice Exercises

1. a. 7 **b.** 0 **c.** $\frac{4}{9}$ **d.** 0.8 **e.** z^4 **f.** $4b^2$ **g.** -6 **h.** not a real number **2.** 6.708 **3. a.** -1 **b.** 3 **c.** $\frac{3}{4}$ **d.** x^4 **e.** $-2x$ **4. a.** 10 **b.** -1 **c.** -9 **d.** not a real number **e.** $3x^3$ **5. a.** 4 **b.** $|x^7|$ **c.** $|x+7|$ **d.** -7 **e.** $3x-5$ **f.** $7|x|$ **g.** $|x+8|$ **6. a.** 4 **b.** 2 **c.** 2 **d.** $\sqrt[3]{-9}$ **7.** **8.**

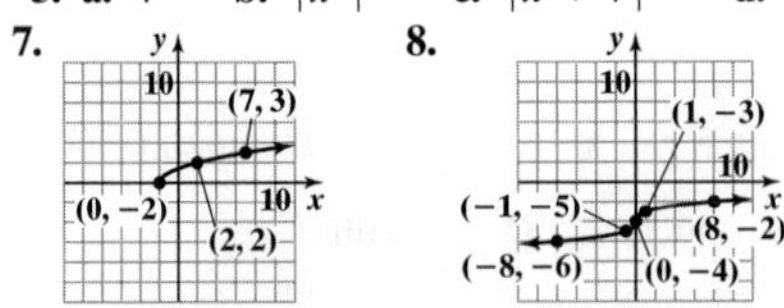

Vocabulary, Readiness & Video Check 5.1

1. index; radical sign; radicand **3.** is not **5.** $[0, \infty)$ **7.** $(16, 4)$ **9.** Divide the index into each exponent in the radicand. **11.** The square root of a negative number is not a real number, but the cube root of a negative number is a real number. **13.** For odd roots, there's only one root/answer whether the radicand is positive or negative, so absolute value bars aren't needed.

Exercise Set 5.1

1. 10 **3.** $\frac{1}{2}$ **5.** 0.01 **7.** -6 **9.** x^5 **11.** $4y^3$ **13.** 2.646 **15.** 6.164 **17.** 14.142 **19.** 4 **21.** $\frac{1}{2}$ **23.** -1 **25.** x^4 **27.** $-3x^3$ **29.** -2 **31.** not a real number **33.** -2 **35.** x^4 **37.** $2x^2$ **39.** $9x^2$ **41.** $4x^2$ **43.** 8 **45.** -8 **47.** $2|x|$ **49.** x **51.** $|x-5|$ **53.** $|x+2|$ **55.** -11 **57.** $2x$ **59.** y^6 **61.** $5ab^{10}$ **63.** $-3x^4y^3$ **65.** a^4b **67.** $-2x^2y$ **69.** $\frac{5}{7}$ **71.** $\frac{x^{10}}{2y}$ **73.** $-\frac{z^7}{3x}$ **75.** $\frac{x}{2}$ **77.** $\sqrt{3}$ **79.** -1 **81.** -3 **83.** $\sqrt{7}$

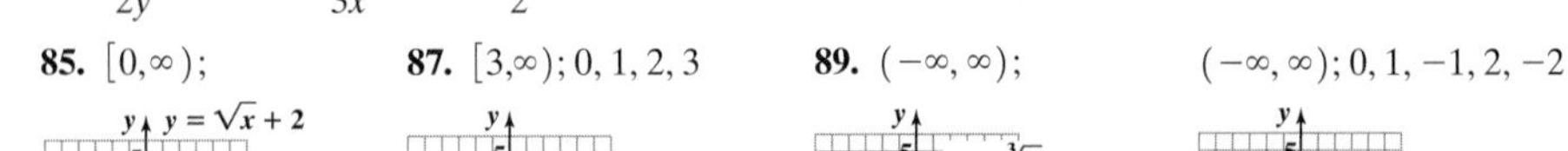

85. $[0,\infty)$; **87.** $[3,\infty)$; 0, 1, 2, 3 **89.** $(-\infty,\infty)$; **91.** $(-\infty,\infty)$; 0, 1, -1, 2, -2

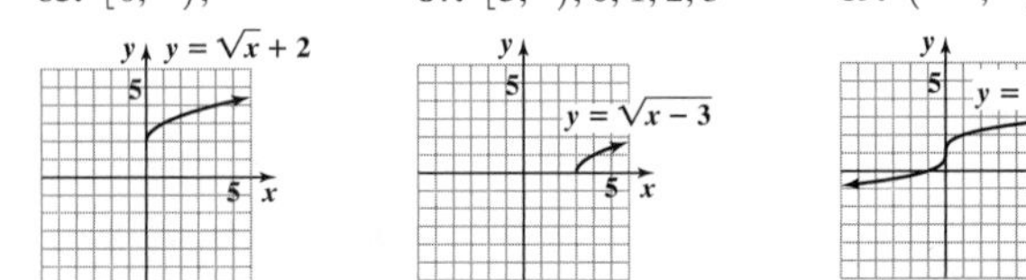

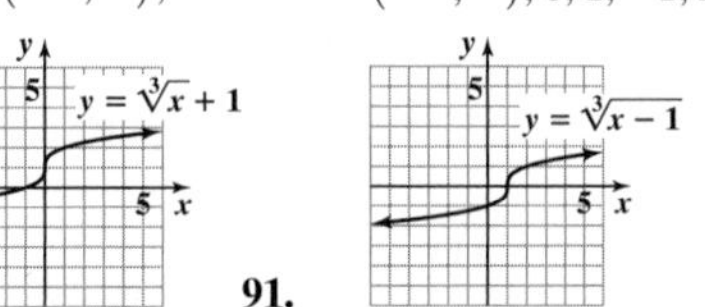

$y = \sqrt[3]{x-1}$

93. $-32x^{15}y^{10}$ **95.** $-60x^7y^{10}z^5$ **97.** $\frac{x^9y^5}{2}$ **99.** not a real number **101.** not a real number **103.** d **105.** d **107.** b **109.** b **111.** answers may vary **113.** 1.69 sq m **115.** 11,181 m per sec **117.** answers may vary **119.**

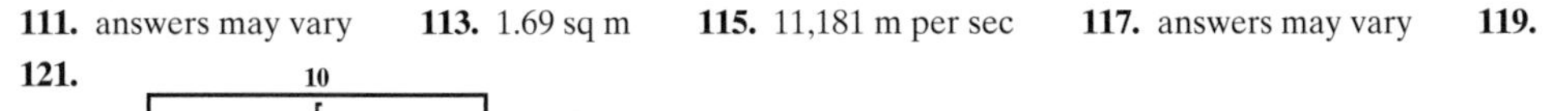

121.

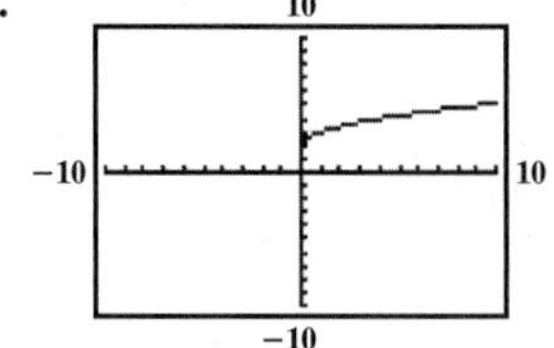

Section 5.2

Practice Exercises

1. a. 6 **b.** 10 **c.** $\sqrt[3]{x}$ **d.** 1 **e.** -8 **f.** $5x^3$ **g.** $3\sqrt[4]{x}$ **2. a.** 64 **b.** -1 **c.** -27 **d.** $\frac{1}{125}$ **e.** $\sqrt[9]{(3x+2)^5}$ **3. a.** $\frac{1}{27}$ **b.** $\frac{1}{16}$ **4. a.** $y^{10/3}$ **b.** $x^{17/20}$ **c.** $\frac{1}{9}$ **d.** $b^{2/9}$ **e.** $\frac{81}{x^3y^{11/3}}$ **5. a.** $x^{14/15} - x^{13/5}$ **b.** $x + 4x^{1/2} - 12$ **6.** $x^{-1/5}(2-7x)$ **7. a.** $\sqrt[3]{x}$ **b.** $\sqrt{6}$ **c.** $\sqrt[4]{a^2b}$ **8. a.** $\sqrt[12]{x^7}$ **b.** $\sqrt[15]{y^2}$ **c.** $\sqrt[6]{675}$

Vocabulary, Readiness & Video Check 5.2

1. true **3.** true **5.** multiply, c **7.** $-\sqrt[5]{3x}$ **9.** denominator; positive **11.** Write the radical using an equivalent fractional exponent form, simplify the fraction, then write as a radical again.

Exercise Set 5.2

1. 7 **3.** 3 **5.** $\frac{1}{2}$ **7.** 13 **9.** $2\sqrt[3]{m}$ **11.** $3x^2$ **13.** -3 **15.** -2 **17.** 8 **19.** 16 **21.** not a real number **23.** $\sqrt[5]{(2x)^3}$ **25.** $\sqrt[3]{(7x+2)^2}$ **27.** $\frac{64}{27}$ **29.** $\frac{1}{16}$ **31.** $\frac{1}{16}$ **33.** not a real number **35.** $\frac{1}{x^{1/4}}$ **37.** $a^{2/3}$ **39.** $\frac{5x^{3/4}}{7}$ **41.** $a^{7/3}$ **43.** x **45.** $3^{5/8}$ **47.** $y^{1/6}$ **49.** $8u^3$ **51.** $-b$ **53.** $\frac{1}{x^2}$ **55.** $27x^{2/3}$ **57.** $\frac{y}{z^{1/6}}$ **59.** $\frac{1}{x^{7/4}}$ **61.** $y - y^{7/6}$ **63.** $x^{5/3} - 2x^{2/3}$ **65.** $4x^{2/3} - 9$ **67.** $x^{8/3}(1 + x^{2/3})$ **69.** $x^{1/5}(x^{1/5} - 3)$ **71.** $x^{-1/3}(5 + x)$ **73.** $\sqrt{x}$ **75.** $\sqrt[3]{2}$ **77.** $2\sqrt{x}$ **79.** $\sqrt{xy}$ **81.** $\sqrt[3]{a^2b}$ **83.** $\sqrt{x+3}$ **85.** $\sqrt[15]{y^{11}}$ **87.** $\sqrt[12]{b^5}$ **89.** $\sqrt[24]{x^{23}}$ **91.** $\sqrt{a}$ **93.** $\sqrt[6]{432}$ **95.** $\sqrt[15]{343y^5}$ **97.** $\sqrt[6]{125r^3s^2}$ **99.** $25 \cdot 3$ **101.** $16 \cdot 3$ or $4 \cdot 12$ **103.** $8 \cdot 2$ **105.** $27 \cdot 2$ **107.** A **109.** C **111.** B **113.** 1509 calories **115.** 302.0 million **117.** answers may vary **119.** $a^{1/3}$ **121.** $x^{1/5}$ **123.** 1.6818 **125.** 5.6645 **127.** $\frac{t^{1/2}}{u^{1/2}}$

Section 5.3

Practice Exercises

1. a. $\sqrt{35}$ **b.** $\sqrt{13z}$ **c.** 5 **d.** $\sqrt[3]{15x^2y}$ **e.** $\sqrt{\frac{5t}{2m}}$ **2. a.** $\frac{6}{7}$ **b.** $\frac{\sqrt{z}}{4}$ **c.** $\frac{5}{2}$ **d.** $\frac{\sqrt[4]{5}}{3x^2}$ **3. a.** $7\sqrt{2}$ **b.** $3\sqrt[3]{2}$ **c.** $\sqrt{35}$ **d.** $3\sqrt[4]{3}$ **4. a.** $6z^3\sqrt{z}$ **b.** $2pq^2\sqrt[3]{4pq}$ **c.** $2x^3\sqrt[4]{x^3}$ **5. a.** 4 **b.** $\frac{7}{3}\sqrt{z}$ **c.** $10xy^2\sqrt[3]{x^2}$ **d.** $6x^2y\sqrt[5]{2y}$ **6.** $\sqrt{17}$ units $\approx$ 4.123 units **7.** $\left(\frac{13}{2}, -4\right)$

Vocabulary, Readiness & Video Check 5.3

1. midpoint; point **3.** distance **5.** the indexes must be the same **7.** The power must be 1. Any even power is a perfect square and will leave no factor in the radicand; any higher odd power can have an even power factored from it, leaving one factor remaining in the radicand. **9.** average; average

Exercise Set 5.3

1. $\sqrt{14}$ **3.** 2 **5.** $\sqrt[3]{36}$ **7.** $\sqrt{6x}$ **9.** $\sqrt{\frac{14}{xy}}$ **11.** $\sqrt[4]{20x^3}$ **13.** $\frac{\sqrt{6}}{7}$ **15.** $\frac{\sqrt{2}}{7}$ **17.** $\frac{\sqrt[4]{x^3}}{2}$ **19.** $\frac{\sqrt[3]{4}}{3}$ **21.** $\frac{\sqrt[4]{8}}{x^2}$ **23.** $\frac{\sqrt[3]{2x}}{3y^4\sqrt[3]{3}}$ **25.** $\frac{x\sqrt{y}}{10}$ **27.** $\frac{x\sqrt{5}}{2y}$ **29.** $-\frac{z^2\sqrt[3]{z}}{3x}$ **31.** $4\sqrt{2}$ **33.** $4\sqrt[3]{3}$ **35.** $25\sqrt{3}$ **37.** $2\sqrt{6}$ **39.** $10x^2\sqrt{x}$ **41.** $2y^2\sqrt[3]{2y}$ **43.** $a^2b\sqrt[4]{b^3}$ **45.** $y^2\sqrt{y}$ **47.** $5ab\sqrt{b}$ **49.** $-2x^2\sqrt[5]{y}$ **51.** $x^4\sqrt[3]{50x^2}$ **53.** $-4a^4b^3\sqrt{2b}$ **55.** $3x^3y^4\sqrt{xy}$ **57.** $5r^3s^4$ **59.** $2x^3y\sqrt[4]{2y}$ **61.** $\sqrt{2}$ **63.** 2 **65.** 10 **67.** x^2y **69.** $24m^2$ **71.** $\frac{15x\sqrt{2x}}{2}$ or $\frac{15x}{2}\sqrt{2x}$ **73.** $2a^2\sqrt[4]{2}$ **75.** $2xy^2\sqrt[5]{x^2}$ **77.** 5 units **79.** $\sqrt{41}$ units $\approx$ 6.403 units **81.** $\sqrt{10}$ units $\approx$ 3.162 units **83.** $\sqrt{5}$ units $\approx$ 2.236 units **85.** $\sqrt{192.58}$ units $\approx$ 13.877 units **87.** $(4,-2)$ **89.** $\left(-5,\frac{5}{2}\right)$ **91.** $(3,0)$ **93.** $\left(-\frac{1}{2},\frac{1}{2}\right)$ **95.** $\left(\sqrt{2},\frac{\sqrt{5}}{2}\right)$ **97.** $(6.2,-6.65)$ **99.** $14x$ **101.** $2x^2-7x-15$ **103.** y^2 **105.** $-3x-15$ **107.** $x^2-8x+16$ **109.** true **111.** false **113.** true **115.** $\frac{\sqrt[3]{64}}{\sqrt{64}}=\frac{4}{8}=\frac{1}{2}$ **117.** x^7 **119.** a^3bc^5 **121.** $z^{10}\sqrt[3]{z^2}$ **123.** $q^2r^5s\sqrt[7]{q^3r^5}$ **125.** 1.6 m **127. a.** 20π sq cm **b.** 211.57 sq ft

Section 5.4

Practice Exercises

1. a. $8\sqrt{17}$ **b.** $-5\sqrt[3]{5z}$ **c.** $3\sqrt{2}+5\sqrt[3]{2}$ **2. a.** $11\sqrt{6}$ **b.** $-9\sqrt[3]{3}$ **c.** $-2\sqrt{3x}$ **d.** $2\sqrt{10}+2\sqrt[3]{5}$ **e.** $4x\sqrt[3]{3x}$ **3. a.** $\frac{5\sqrt{7}}{12}$ **b.** $\frac{13\sqrt[3]{6y}}{4}$ **4. a.** $2\sqrt{5}+5\sqrt{3}$ **b.** $2\sqrt{3}+2\sqrt{2}-\sqrt{30}-2\sqrt{5}$ **c.** $6z+\sqrt{z}-12$ **d.** $-6\sqrt{6}+15$ **e.** $5x-9$ **f.** $6\sqrt{x+2}+x+11$

Vocabulary, Readiness & Video Check 5.4

1. Unlike **3.** Like **5.** $6\sqrt{3}$ **7.** $7\sqrt{x}$ **9.** $8\sqrt[3]{x}$ **11.** Sometimes you can't see that there are like radicals until you simplify, so you may incorrectly think you cannot add or subtract if you don't simplify first.

Exercise Set 5.4

1. $-2\sqrt{2}$ **3.** $10x\sqrt{2x}$ **5.** $17\sqrt{2}-15\sqrt{5}$ **7.** $-\sqrt[3]{2x}$ **9.** $5b\sqrt{b}$ **11.** $\frac{31\sqrt{2}}{15}$ **13.** $\frac{\sqrt[3]{11}}{3}$ **15.** $\frac{5\sqrt{5x}}{9}$ **17.** $14+\sqrt{3}$ **19.** $7-3y$ **21.** $6\sqrt{3}-6\sqrt{2}$ **23.** $-23\sqrt[3]{5}$ **25.** $2a^3b\sqrt{ab}$ **27.** $20y\sqrt{2y}$ **29.** $2y\sqrt[3]{2x}$ **31.** $6\sqrt[3]{11}-4\sqrt{11}$ **33.** $3x\sqrt[4]{x^3}$ **35.** $\frac{2\sqrt{3}}{3}$ **37.** $\frac{5x\sqrt[3]{x}}{7}$ **39.** $\frac{5\sqrt{7}}{2x}$ **41.** $\frac{\sqrt[3]{2}}{6}$ **43.** $\frac{14x\sqrt[3]{2x}}{9}$ **45.** $15\sqrt{3}$ in. **47.** $\sqrt{35}+\sqrt{21}$ **49.** $7-2\sqrt{10}$ **51.** $3\sqrt{x}-x\sqrt{3}$ **53.** $6x-13\sqrt{x}-5$ **55.** $\sqrt[3]{a^2}+\sqrt[3]{a}-20$ **57.** $6\sqrt{2}-12$ **59.** $2+2x\sqrt{3}$ **61.** $-16-\sqrt{35}$ **63.** $x-y^2$ **65.** $3+2x\sqrt{3}+x^2$ **67.** $23x-5x\sqrt{15}$ **69.** $2\sqrt[3]{2}-\sqrt[3]{4}$ **71.** $x+1$ **73.** $x+24+10\sqrt{x-1}$ **75.** $2x+6-2\sqrt{2x+5}$ **77.** $x-7$ **79.** $\frac{7}{x+y}$ **81.** $2a-3$ **83.** $\frac{-2+\sqrt{3}}{3}$ **85.** $22\sqrt{5}$ ft; 150 sq ft **87. a.** $2\sqrt{3}$ **b.** 3 **c.** answers may vary **89.** $2\sqrt{6}-2\sqrt{2}-2\sqrt{3}+6$ **91.** answers may vary

Section 5.5

Practice Exercises

1. a. $\frac{5\sqrt{3}}{3}$ **b.** $\frac{15\sqrt{x}}{2x}$ **c.** $\frac{\sqrt[3]{6}}{3}$ **2.** $\frac{\sqrt{15yz}}{5y}$ **3.** $\frac{\sqrt[3]{z^2x^2}}{3x^2}$ **4. a.** $\frac{5(3\sqrt{5}-2)}{41}$ **b.** $\frac{\sqrt{6}+5\sqrt{3}+\sqrt{10}+5\sqrt{5}}{-2}$ **c.** $\frac{6x-3\sqrt{xy}}{4x-y}$ **5.** $\frac{2}{\sqrt{10}}$ **6.** $\frac{5b}{\sqrt[3]{50ab^2}}$ **7.** $\frac{x-9}{4(\sqrt{x}+3)}$

Vocabulary, Readiness & Video Check 5.5

1. conjugate **3.** rationalizing the numerator **5.** To write an equivalent expression without a radical in the denominator. **7.** No, except for the fact you're working with numerators, the process is the same.

Exercise Set 5.5

1. $\frac{\sqrt{14}}{7}$ **3.** $\frac{\sqrt{5}}{5}$ **5.** $\frac{2\sqrt{x}}{x}$ **7.** $\frac{4\sqrt[3]{9}}{3}$ **9.** $\frac{3\sqrt{2x}}{4x}$ **11.** $\frac{3\sqrt[3]{2x}}{2x}$ **13.** $\frac{3\sqrt{3a}}{a}$ **15.** $\frac{3\sqrt[3]{4}}{2}$ **17.** $\frac{2\sqrt{21}}{7}$ **19.** $\frac{\sqrt{10xy}}{5y}$ **21.** $\frac{\sqrt[3]{75}}{5}$ **23.** $\frac{\sqrt{6x}}{10}$ **25.** $\frac{\sqrt{3z}}{6z}$ **27.** $\frac{\sqrt[3]{6xy^2}}{3x}$ **29.** $\frac{3\sqrt[4]{2}}{2}$ **31.** $\frac{2\sqrt[4]{9x}}{3x^2}$ **33.** $\frac{5\sqrt[5]{4ab^4}}{2ab^3}$ **35.** $\sqrt{2}-x$ **37.** $5+\sqrt{a}$ **39.** $-7\sqrt{5}-8\sqrt{x}$ **41.** $-2(2+\sqrt{7})$ **43.** $\frac{7(3+\sqrt{x})}{9-x}$ **45.** $-5+2\sqrt{6}$ **47.** $\frac{2a+2\sqrt{a}+\sqrt{ab}+\sqrt{b}}{4a-b}$ **49.** $-\frac{8(1-\sqrt{10})}{9}$ **51.** $\frac{x-\sqrt{xy}}{x-y}$ **53.** $\frac{5+3\sqrt{2}}{7}$ **55.** $\frac{5}{\sqrt{15}}$ **57.** $\frac{6}{\sqrt{10}}$ **59.** $\frac{2x}{7\sqrt{x}}$ **61.** $\frac{5y}{\sqrt[3]{100xy}}$ **63.** $\frac{2}{\sqrt{10}}$ **65.** $\frac{2x}{11\sqrt{2x}}$ **67.** $\frac{7}{2\sqrt[3]{49}}$ **69.** $\frac{3x^2}{10\sqrt[3]{9x}}$ **71.** $\frac{6x^2y^3}{\sqrt{6z}}$

73. $\frac{-7}{12+6\sqrt{11}}$ **75.** $\frac{3}{10+5\sqrt{7}}$ **77.** $\frac{x-9}{x-3\sqrt{x}}$ **79.** $\frac{1}{3+2\sqrt{2}}$ **81.** $\frac{x-1}{x-2\sqrt{x}+1}$ **83.** 5 **85.** $-\frac{1}{2}, 6$ **87.** 2, 6 **89.** $r=\frac{\sqrt{A\pi}}{2\pi}$ **91. a.** $\frac{y\sqrt{15xy}}{6x^2}$ **b.** $\frac{y\sqrt{15xy}}{6x^2}$ **c.** answers may vary **93.** $\sqrt[3]{25}$ **95.** answers may vary **97.** answers may vary

Integrated Review

1. 9 **2.** −2 **3.** $\frac{1}{2}$ **4.** x^3 **5.** y^3 **6.** $2y^5$ **7.** $-2y$ **8.** $3b^3$ **9.** 6 **10.** $\sqrt[4]{3y}$ **11.** $\frac{1}{16}$ **12.** $\sqrt[5]{(x+1)^3}$ **13.** y **14.** $16x^{1/2}$ **15.** $x^{5/4}$ **16.** $4^{11/15}$ **17.** $2x^2$ **18.** $\sqrt[4]{a^3b^2}$ **19.** $\sqrt[4]{x^3}$ **20.** $\sqrt[6]{500}$ **21.** $2\sqrt{10}$ **22.** $2xy^2\sqrt[4]{x^3y^2}$ **23.** $3x\sqrt[3]{2x}$ **24.** $-2b^2\sqrt[5]{2}$ **25.** $\sqrt{5x}$ **26.** $4x$ **27.** $7y^2\sqrt{y}$ **28.** $2a^2\sqrt[4]{3}$ **29.** $2\sqrt{5}-5\sqrt{3}+5\sqrt{7}$ **30.** $y\sqrt[3]{2y}$ **31.** $\sqrt{15}-\sqrt{6}$ **32.** $10+2\sqrt{21}$ **33.** $4x^2-5$ **34.** $x+2-2\sqrt{x+1}$ **35.** $\frac{\sqrt{21}}{3}$ **36.** $\frac{5\sqrt[3]{4x}}{2x}$ **37.** $\frac{13-3\sqrt{21}}{5}$ **38.** $\frac{7}{\sqrt{21}}$ **39.** $\frac{3y}{\sqrt[3]{33y^2}}$ **40.** $\frac{x-4}{x+2\sqrt{x}}$

Section 5.6

Practice Exercises

1. 18 **2.** $\frac{1}{4}, \frac{3}{4}$ **3.** 10 **4.** 9 **5.** $\frac{3}{25}$ **6.** $6\sqrt{3}$ meters **7.** $\sqrt{193}$ in. ≈ 13.89 in.

Graphing Calculator Explorations 5.6

1. 3.19 **3.** ∅ **5.** 3.23

Vocabulary, Readiness & Video Check 5.6

1. extraneous solution **3.** $x^2-10x+25$ **5.** Applying the power rule can result in an equation with more solutions than the original equation, so you need to check all proposed solutions in the original equation. **7.** Our answer is either a positive square root of a value or a negative square root of a value. We're looking for a length, which must be positive, so our answer must be the positive square root.

Exercise Set 5.6

1. 8 **3.** 7 **5.** ∅ **7.** 7 **9.** 6 **11.** $-\frac{9}{2}$ **13.** 29 **15.** 4 **17.** −4 **19.** ∅ **21.** 7 **23.** 9 **25.** 50 **27.** ∅ **29.** $\frac{15}{4}$ **31.** 13 **33.** 5 **35.** −12 **37.** 9 **39.** −3 **41.** 1 **43.** 1 **45.** $\frac{1}{2}$ **47.** 0, 4 **49.** $\frac{37}{4}$ **51.** $3\sqrt{5}$ ft **53.** $2\sqrt{10}$ m **55.** $2\sqrt{131}$ m ≈ 22.9 m **57.** $\sqrt{100.84}$ mm ≈ 10.0 mm **59.** 17 ft **61.** 13 ft **63.** 14,657,415 sq mi **65.** 100 ft **67.** 100 **69.** $\frac{\pi}{2}$ sec ≈ 1.57 sec **71.** 12.97 ft **73.** answers may vary **75.** $15\sqrt{3}$ sq mi ≈ 25.98 sq mi **77.** answers may vary **79.** 0.51 km **81.** function **83.** function **85.** not a function **87.** $\frac{x}{4x+3}$ **89.** $-\frac{4z+2}{3z}$

91.
$$\begin{aligned}\sqrt{5x-1}+4&=7\\ \sqrt{5x-1}&=3\\ (\sqrt{5x-1})^2&=3^2\\ 5x-1&=9\\ 5x&=10\\ x&=2\end{aligned}$$

93. 1 **95. a.–b.** answers may vary **97.** −1, 0, 8, 9 **99.** −1, 4

Section 5.7

Practice Exercises

1. a. $2i$ **b.** $i\sqrt{7}$ **c.** $-3i\sqrt{2}$ **2. a.** $-\sqrt{30}$ **b.** −3 **c.** $25i$ **d.** $3i$ **3. a.** $-1-4i$ **b.** $-3+5i$ **c.** $3-2i$ **4. a.** $20+0i$ **b.** $-5+10i$ **c.** $15+16i$ **d.** $8-6i$ **e.** $85+0i$ **5. a.** $\frac{11}{10}-\frac{7i}{10}$ **b.** $0-\frac{5i}{2}$ **6. a.** i **b.** 1 **c.** −1 **d.** 1

Vocabulary, Readiness & Video Check 5.7

1. complex **3.** −1 **5.** real **7.** The product rule for radicals; you need to first simplify each separate radical and have nonnegative radicands before applying the product rule. **9.** the fact that $i^2=-1$ **11.** $i, i^2=-1, i^3=-i, i^4=1$

Exercise Set 5.7

1. $9i$ **3.** $i\sqrt{7}$ **5.** −4 **7.** $8i$ **9.** $2i\sqrt{6}$ **11.** $-6i$ **13.** $24i\sqrt{7}$ **15.** $-3\sqrt{6}+0i$ **17.** $-\sqrt{14}$ **19.** $-5\sqrt{2}$ **21.** $4i$ **23.** $i\sqrt{3}$ **25.** $2\sqrt{2}$ **27.** $6-4i$ **29.** $-2+6i$ **31.** $-2-4i$ **33.** $-40+0i$ **35.** $18+12i$ **37.** $7+0i$ **39.** $12-16i$ **41.** $0-4i$ **43.** $\frac{28}{25}-\frac{21}{25}i$ **45.** $4+i$ **47.** $\frac{17}{13}+\frac{7}{13}i$ **49.** $63+0i$ **51.** $2-i$ **53.** $27+3i$ **55.** $-\frac{5}{2}-2i$ **57.** $18+13i$ **59.** $20+0i$ **61.** $10+0i$ **63.** $2+0i$ **65.** $-5+\frac{16}{3}i$ **67.** $17+144i$ **69.** $\frac{3}{5}-\frac{1}{5}i$ **71.** $5-10i$ **73.** $\frac{1}{5}-\frac{8}{5}i$ **75.** $8-i$ **77.** $7+0i$

79. $12 - 16i$ **81.** 1 **83.** i **85.** $-i$ **87.** -1 **89.** -64 **91.** $-243i$ **93.** 40° **95.** $x^2 - 5x - 2 - \frac{6}{x-1}$ **97.** 5 people **99.** 14 people **101.** 16.7% **103.** $-1 - i$ **105.** $0 + 0i$ **107.** $2 + 3i$ **109.** $2 + i\sqrt{2}$ **111.** $\frac{1}{2} - \frac{\sqrt{3}}{2}i$ **113.** answers may vary **115.** $6 - 3i\sqrt{3}$ **117.** yes

Chapter 5 Vocabulary Check

1. conjugate **2.** principal square root **3.** rationalizing **4.** imaginary unit **5.** cube root **6.** index; radicand **7.** like radicals **8.** complex number **9.** distance **10.** midpoint

Chapter 5 Review

1. 9 **3.** -2 **5.** $-\frac{1}{7}$ **7.** -6 **9.** $-a^2b^3$ **11.** $2ab^2$ **13.** $\frac{x^6}{6y}$ **15.** $|-x|$ **17.** -27 **19.** $-x$ **21.** $2|2y + z|$ **23.** y **25. a.** 3, 6 **b.** $[0, \infty)$ **c.**

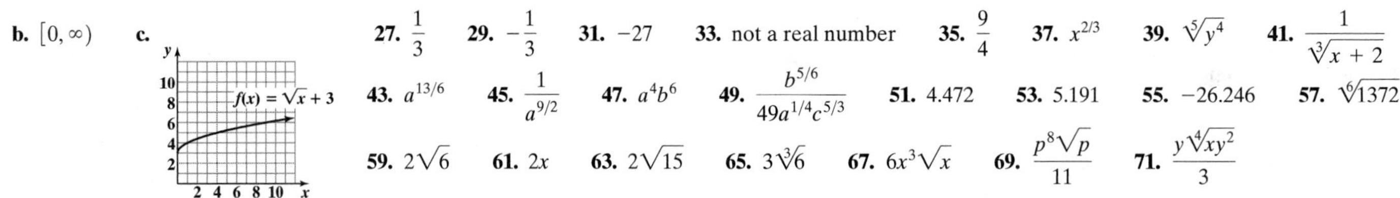

27. $\frac{1}{3}$ **29.** $-\frac{1}{3}$ **31.** -27 **33.** not a real number **35.** $\frac{9}{4}$ **37.** $x^{2/3}$ **39.** $\sqrt[5]{y^4}$ **41.** $\frac{1}{\sqrt[3]{x+2}}$ **43.** $a^{13/6}$ **45.** $\frac{1}{a^{9/2}}$ **47.** a^4b^6 **49.** $\frac{b^{5/6}}{49a^{1/4}c^{5/3}}$ **51.** 4.472 **53.** 5.191 **55.** -26.246 **57.** $\sqrt[6]{1372}$ **59.** $2\sqrt{6}$ **61.** $2x$ **63.** $2\sqrt{15}$ **65.** $3\sqrt[3]{6}$ **67.** $6x^3\sqrt{x}$ **69.** $\frac{p^8\sqrt{p}}{11}$ **71.** $\frac{y\sqrt[4]{xy^2}}{3}$

73. $\frac{5}{\sqrt{\pi}}$ m or $\frac{5\sqrt{\pi}}{\pi}$ m **75.** $\sqrt{197}$ units $\approx$ 14.036 units **77.** $\sqrt{73}$ units $\approx$ 8.544 units **79.** $2\sqrt{11}$ units $\approx$ 6.633 units **81.** $(-5, 5)$ **83.** $\left(-\frac{11}{2}, -2\right)$ **85.** $\left(\frac{1}{4}, -\frac{2}{7}\right)$ **87.** $-2\sqrt{5}$ **89.** $9\sqrt[3]{2}$ **91.** $\frac{15 + 2\sqrt{3}}{6}$ **93.** $17\sqrt{2} - 15\sqrt{5}$ **95.** 6 **97.** $-8\sqrt{5}$ **99.** $a - 9$ **101.** $\sqrt[3]{25x^2} - 81$ **103.** $\frac{3\sqrt{7}}{7}$ **105.** $\frac{5\sqrt[3]{2}}{2}$ **107.** $\frac{x^2y^2\sqrt[3]{15yz}}{z}$ **109.** $\frac{3\sqrt{y} + 6}{y - 4}$ **111.** $\frac{11}{3\sqrt{11}}$ **113.** $\frac{3}{7\sqrt[3]{3}}$ **115.** $\frac{xy}{\sqrt[3]{10x^2yz}}$ **117.** 32 **119.** 35 **121.** 9 **123.** $3\sqrt{2}$ cm **125.** 51.2 ft **127.** $0 + 2i\sqrt{2}$ **129.** $0 + 6i$ **131.** $15 - 4i$ **133.** -64 **135.** $-12 - 18i$ **137.** $-5 - 12i$ **139.** $\frac{3}{2} - i$ **141.** x **143.** -10 **145.** $\frac{y^5}{2x^3}$ **147.** $\frac{1}{8}$ **149.** $\frac{1}{x^{13/2}}$ **151.** $\frac{n\sqrt{3n}}{11m^5}$ **153.** $4x - 20\sqrt{x} + 25$ **155.** $(4, 16)$ **157.** $\frac{2\sqrt{x} - 6}{x - 9}$ **159.** 5

Chapter 5 Test

1. $6\sqrt{6}$ **2.** $-x^{16}$ **3.** $\frac{1}{5}$ **4.** 5 **5.** $\frac{4x^2}{9}$ **6.** $-a^6b^3$ **7.** $\frac{8a^{1/3}c^{2/3}}{b^{5/12}}$ **8.** $a^{7/12} - a^{7/3}$ **9.** $|4xy|$ or $4|xy|$ **10.** -27 **11.** $\frac{3\sqrt{y}}{y}$ **12.** $\frac{8 - 6\sqrt{x} + x}{8 - 2x}$ **13.** $\frac{\sqrt[3]{b^2}}{b}$ **14.** $\frac{6 - x^2}{8(\sqrt{6} - x)}$ **15.** $-x\sqrt{5x}$ **16.** $4\sqrt{3} - \sqrt{6}$ **17.** $x + 2\sqrt{x} + 1$ **18.** $\sqrt{6} - 4\sqrt{3} + \sqrt{2} - 4$ **19.** -20 **20.** 23.685 **21.** 0.019 **22.** 2, 3 **23.** $\varnothing$ **24.** 6 **25.** $0 + i\sqrt{2}$ **26.** $0 - 2i\sqrt{2}$ **27.** $0 - 3i$ **28.** $40 + 0i$ **29.** $7 + 24i$ **30.** $-\frac{3}{2} + \frac{5}{2}i$ **31.** $\frac{5\sqrt{2}}{2}$ **32.** $[-2, \infty)$; 0, 1, 2, 3;

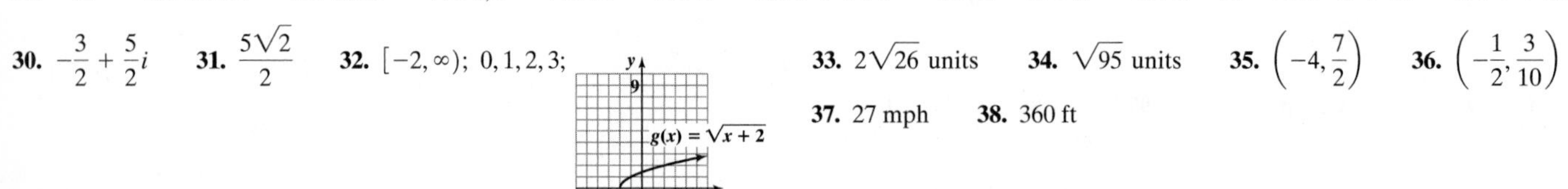

33. $2\sqrt{26}$ units **34.** $\sqrt{95}$ units **35.** $\left(-4, \frac{7}{2}\right)$ **36.** $\left(-\frac{1}{2}, \frac{3}{10}\right)$ **37.** 27 mph **38.** 360 ft

Chapter 5 Cumulative Review

1. a. -12 **b.** -3; Sec. 1.6, Ex. 5 **3.** 12; Sec. 2.3, Ex. 3 **5.** 12 in., 36 in.; Sec. 2.4, Ex. 3 **7.** one; Sec. 4.1, Ex. 8 **9.** $\left(6, \frac{1}{2}\right)$; Sec. 4.2, Ex. 3 **11.** no solution; { } or $\varnothing$; Sec. 4.3, Ex. 3 **13.** 30% solution: 42 L; 80% solution: 28 L; Sec. 4.5, Ex. 6 **15. a.** -4 **b.** 11; Sec. 5.2, Ex. 4 **17.** $3m + 1$; Sec. 5.6, Ex. 1 **19.** $2x^2 + 5x + 2 + \frac{7}{x - 3}$; Sec. 5.7, Ex. 1 **21.** $(t - 8)(t - 5)$; Sec. 6.2, Ex. 8 **23. a.** $x^2 - 2x + 4$ **b.** $\frac{2}{y - 5}$; Sec. 7.1, Ex. 5 **25.** 4; Sec. 9.2, Ex. 9 **27.** $3x - 5$; Sec. 7.3, Ex. 3 **29.** $\frac{2m + 1}{m + 1}$; Sec. 7.4, Ex. 5 **31. a.** $\frac{x(x - 2)}{2(x + 2)}$ **b.** $\frac{x^2}{y^2}$; Sec. 7.7, Ex. 2 **33.** $\left[-2, \frac{8}{5}\right]$; Sec. 9.3, Ex. 3 **35.** 15 yd; Sec. 7.6, Ex. 4 **37. a.** 1 **b.** -4 **c.** $\frac{2}{5}$ **d.** x^2 **e.** $-3x^3$; Sec. 10.1, Ex. 3 **39. a.** $\frac{1}{8}$ **b.** $\frac{1}{9}$; Sec. 10.2, Ex. 3 **41.** $\frac{x - 4}{5(\sqrt{x} - 2)}$; Sec. 10.5, Ex. 7 **43.** constant of variation: 15, $u = \frac{15}{w}$; Sec. 8.4, Ex. 3

CHAPTER 6 QUADRATIC EQUATIONS AND FUNCTIONS

Section 6.1

Practice Exercises

1. $-4\sqrt{2}, 4\sqrt{2}$ **2.** $-\sqrt{10}, \sqrt{10}$ **3.** $-3 - 2\sqrt{5}, -3 + 2\sqrt{5}$ **4.** $\frac{2+3i}{5}, \frac{2-3i}{5}$ or $\frac{2}{5} \pm \frac{3}{5}i$ **5.** $-2 - \sqrt{7}, -2 + \sqrt{7}$ **6.** $\frac{3-\sqrt{5}}{2}, \frac{3+\sqrt{5}}{2}$ **7.** $\frac{6-\sqrt{33}}{3}, \frac{6+\sqrt{33}}{3}$ **8.** $\frac{5-i\sqrt{31}}{4}, \frac{5+i\sqrt{31}}{4}$ or $\frac{5}{4} \pm \frac{\sqrt{31}}{4}i$ **9.** 6%

Graphing Calculator Explorations 6.1

1. $-1.27, 6.27$

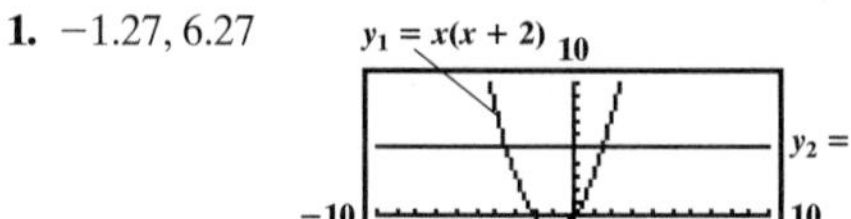

3. $-1.10, 0.90$

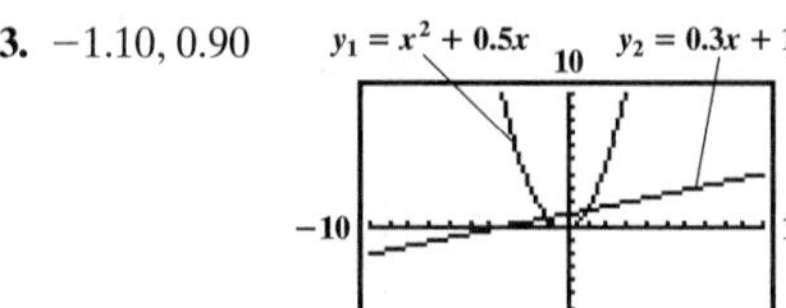

5. no real solutions

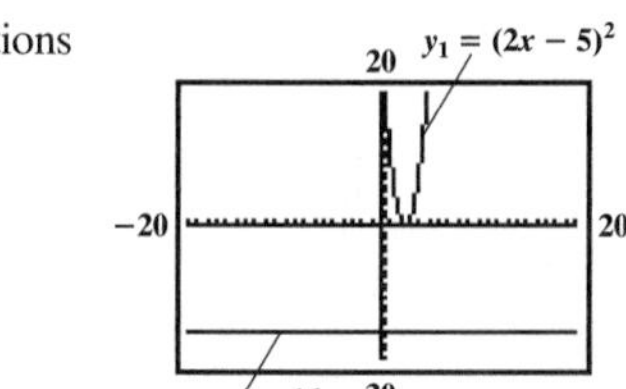

Vocabulary, Readiness & Video Check 6.1

1. $\pm\sqrt{b}$ **3.** completing the square **5.** 9 **7.** We need a quantity squared by itself on one side of the equation. The only quantity squared is x, so we need to divide both sides by 2 before applying the square root property. **9.** We're looking for an interest rate so a negative value does not make sense.

Exercise Set 6.1

1. $-4, 4$ **3.** $-\sqrt{7}, \sqrt{7}$ **5.** $-3\sqrt{2}, 3\sqrt{2}$ **7.** $-\sqrt{10}, \sqrt{10}$ **9.** $-8, -2$ **11.** $6 - 3\sqrt{2}, 6 + 3\sqrt{2}$ **13.** $\frac{3-2\sqrt{2}}{2}, \frac{3+2\sqrt{2}}{2}$ **15.** $-3i, 3i$ **17.** $-\sqrt{6}, \sqrt{6}$ **19.** $-2i\sqrt{2}, 2i\sqrt{2}$ **21.** $\frac{1-4i}{3}, \frac{1+4i}{3}$ or $\frac{1}{3} \pm \frac{4}{3}i$ **23.** $-7 - \sqrt{5}, -7 + \sqrt{5}$ **25.** $-3 - 2i\sqrt{2}, -3 + 2i\sqrt{2}$ **27.** $x^2 + 16x + 64 = (x+8)^2$ **29.** $z^2 - 12z + 36 = (z-6)^2$ **31.** $p^2 + 9p + \frac{81}{4} = \left(p + \frac{9}{2}\right)^2$ **33.** $x^2 + x + \frac{1}{4} = \left(x + \frac{1}{2}\right)^2$ **35.** $-5, -3$ **37.** $-3 - \sqrt{7}, -3 + \sqrt{7}$ **39.** $\frac{-1-\sqrt{5}}{2}, \frac{-1+\sqrt{5}}{2}$ **41.** $-1 - \sqrt{6}, -1 + \sqrt{6}$ **43.** $\frac{-1-\sqrt{29}}{2}, \frac{-1+\sqrt{29}}{2}$ **45.** $\frac{6-\sqrt{30}}{3}, \frac{6+\sqrt{30}}{3}$ **47.** $\frac{3-\sqrt{11}}{2}, \frac{3+\sqrt{11}}{2}$ **49.** $-4, \frac{1}{2}$ **51.** $-4 - \sqrt{15}, -4 + \sqrt{15}$ **53.** $\frac{-3-\sqrt{21}}{3}, \frac{-3+\sqrt{21}}{3}$ **55.** $-1, \frac{5}{2}$ **57.** $-1 - i, -1 + i$ **59.** $3 - \sqrt{17}, 3 + \sqrt{17}$ **61.** $-2 - i\sqrt{2}, -2 + i\sqrt{2}$ **63.** $\frac{-15-7\sqrt{5}}{10}, \frac{-15+7\sqrt{5}}{10}$ **65.** $\frac{1-i\sqrt{47}}{4}, \frac{1+i\sqrt{47}}{4}$ or $\frac{1}{4} \pm \frac{\sqrt{47}}{4}i$ **67.** $-5 - i\sqrt{3}, -5 + i\sqrt{3}$ **69.** $-4, 1$ **71.** $\frac{2-i\sqrt{2}}{2}, \frac{2+i\sqrt{2}}{2}$ or $1 \pm \frac{\sqrt{2}}{2}i$ **73.** $\frac{-3-\sqrt{69}}{6}, \frac{-3+\sqrt{69}}{6}$ **75.** 20% **77.** 4% **79.** 9.63 sec **81.** 8.29 sec **83.** 15 ft by 15 ft **85.** $10\sqrt{2}$ cm **87.** -1 **89.** $3 + 2\sqrt{5}$ **91.** $\frac{1-3\sqrt{2}}{2}$ **93.** $2\sqrt{6}$ **95.** 5 **97.** complex, but not real numbers **99.** real numbers **101.** complex, but not real numbers **103.** $-8x, 8x$ **105.** $-5z, 5z$ **107.** answers may vary **109.** compound; answers may vary **111.** 6 thousand scissors

Section 6.2

Practice Exercises

1. $2, -\frac{1}{3}$ **2.** $\frac{4-\sqrt{22}}{3}, \frac{4+\sqrt{22}}{3}$ **3.** $1 - \sqrt{17}, 1 + \sqrt{17}$ **4.** $\frac{-1-i\sqrt{15}}{4}, \frac{-1+i\sqrt{15}}{4}$ or $-\frac{1}{4} \pm \frac{\sqrt{15}}{4}i$ **5. a.** one real solution **b.** two real solutions **c.** two complex, but not real solutions **6.** 6 ft **7.** 2.4 sec

Vocabulary, Readiness & Video Check 6.2

1. $x = \frac{-b \pm \sqrt{b^2 - 4ac}}{2a}$ **3.** $-5; -7$ **5.** $1; 0$ **7. a.** Yes, in order to make sure we have correct values for a, b, and c. **b.** No; clearing fractions makes the work less tedious, but it's not a necessary step. **9.** With applications, we need to make sure we answer the question(s) asked. Here we're asked how much distance is saved, so once the dimensions of the triangle are known, further calculations are needed to answer this question and solve the problem.

Exercise Set 6.2

1. $-6, 1$ **3.** $-\frac{3}{5}, 1$ **5.** 3 **7.** $\frac{-7-\sqrt{33}}{2}, \frac{-7+\sqrt{33}}{2}$ **9.** $\frac{1-\sqrt{57}}{8}, \frac{1+\sqrt{57}}{8}$ **11.** $\frac{7-\sqrt{85}}{6}, \frac{7+\sqrt{85}}{6}$ **13.** $1 - \sqrt{3}, 1 + \sqrt{3}$ **15.** $-\frac{3}{2}, 1$ **17.** $\frac{3-\sqrt{11}}{2}, \frac{3+\sqrt{11}}{2}$ **19.** $\frac{-5-\sqrt{17}}{2}, \frac{-5+\sqrt{17}}{2}$ **21.** $\frac{5}{2}, 1$ **23.** $-3 - 2i, -3 + 2i$ **25.** $-2 - \sqrt{11}, -2 + \sqrt{11}$ **27.** $\frac{3-i\sqrt{87}}{8}, \frac{3+i\sqrt{87}}{8}$ or $\frac{3}{8} \pm \frac{\sqrt{87}}{8}i$ **29.** $\frac{3-\sqrt{29}}{2}, \frac{3+\sqrt{29}}{2}$ **31.** $\frac{-5-i\sqrt{5}}{10}, \frac{-5+i\sqrt{5}}{10}$ or $-\frac{1}{2} \pm \frac{\sqrt{5}}{10}i$ **33.** $\frac{-1-\sqrt{19}}{6}, \frac{-1+\sqrt{19}}{6}$

35. $\frac{-1 - i\sqrt{23}}{4}, \frac{-1 + i\sqrt{23}}{4}$ or $-\frac{1}{4} \pm \frac{\sqrt{23}}{4}i$ **37.** 1 **39.** $3 - \sqrt{5}, 3 + \sqrt{5}$ **41.** two real solutions **43.** one real solution **45.** two real solutions **47.** two complex but not real solutions **49.** two real solutions **51.** 14 ft **53.** $(2 + 2\sqrt{2})$ cm, $(2 + 2\sqrt{2})$ cm, $(4 + 2\sqrt{2})$ cm **55.** width: $(-5 + 5\sqrt{17})$ ft; length: $(5 + 5\sqrt{17})$ ft **57. a.** $50\sqrt{2}$ m **b.** 5000 sq m **59.** 37.4 ft by 38.5 ft **61.** base, $(2 + 2\sqrt{43})$ cm; height, $(-1 + \sqrt{43})$ cm **63.** 8.9 sec **65.** 2.8 sec **67.** $\frac{11}{5}$ **69.** 15 **71.** $(x^2 + 5)(x + 2)(x - 2)$ **73.** $(z + 3)(z - 3)(z + 2)(z - 2)$ **75.** b **77.** answers may vary **79.** 0.6, 2.4 **81.** Sunday to Monday **83.** Wednesday **85.** 32; yes **87. a.** 20,568 students **b.** 2015 **89. a.** 9076 thousand barrels per day **b.** 2007 **c.** 2012 **91.** answers may vary **93.** $\frac{\sqrt{3}}{3}$ **95.** $\frac{-\sqrt{2} - i\sqrt{2}}{2}, \frac{-\sqrt{2} + i\sqrt{2}}{2}$ or $-\frac{\sqrt{2}}{2} \pm \frac{\sqrt{2}}{2}i$ **97.** $\frac{\sqrt{3} - \sqrt{11}}{4}, \frac{\sqrt{3} + \sqrt{11}}{4}$

99. 8.9 sec:

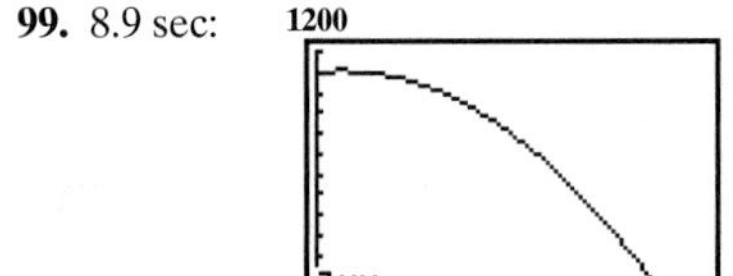

2.8 sec:

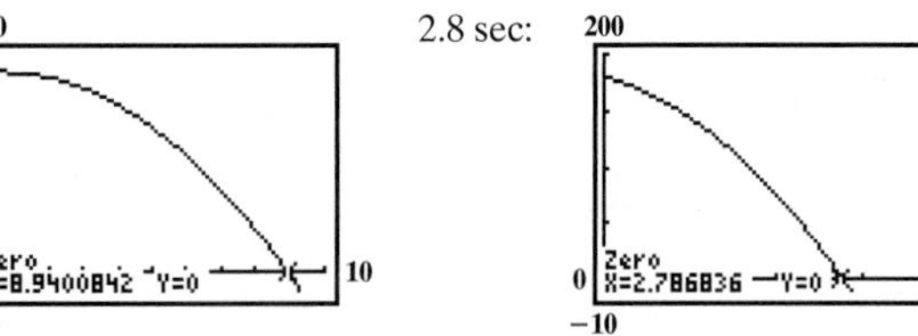

101. two real solutions

Chapter 6 Vocabulary Check

1. discriminant **2.** $\pm\sqrt{b}$ **3.** $\frac{-b}{2a}$ **4.** quadratic inequality **5.** completing the square **6.** $(0, k)$ **7.** $(h, 0)$ **8.** (h, k) **9.** quadratic formula **10.** quadratic

Chapter 6 Review

1. 14, 1 **3.** −7, 7 **5.** $\frac{-3 - \sqrt{5}}{2}, \frac{-3 + \sqrt{5}}{2}$ **7.** 4.25% **9.** two complex but not real solutions **11.** two real solutions **13.** 8 **15.** $-\frac{5}{2}, 1$ **17.** $\frac{5 - i\sqrt{143}}{12}, \frac{5 + i\sqrt{143}}{12}$ or $\frac{5}{12} \pm \frac{\sqrt{143}}{12}i$ **19. a.** 20 ft **b.** $\frac{15 + \sqrt{321}}{16}$ sec; 2.1 sec

Chapter 6 Test

1. $\frac{7}{5}, -1$ **2.** $-1 - \sqrt{10}, -1 + \sqrt{10}$ **3.** $\frac{1 - i\sqrt{31}}{2}, \frac{1 + i\sqrt{31}}{2}$ or $\frac{1}{2} \pm \frac{\sqrt{31}}{2}i$ **4.** $3 - \sqrt{7}, 3 + \sqrt{7}$ **5.** $-\frac{1}{7}, -1$ **6.** $\frac{3 - \sqrt{29}}{2}, \frac{3 + \sqrt{29}}{2}$ **7.** $-2 - \sqrt{11}, -2 + \sqrt{11}$ **8.** $-1, 1, -i, i, -3$ **9.** $-1, 1, -i, i$ **10.** 6, 7 **11.** $3 - \sqrt{7}, 3 + \sqrt{7}$ **12.** $\frac{2 - i\sqrt{6}}{2}, \frac{2 + i\sqrt{6}}{2}$ or $1 \pm \frac{\sqrt{6}}{2}i$ **13.** $\left(-\infty, -\frac{3}{2}\right) \cup (5, \infty)$ **14.** $(-\infty, -5] \cup [-4, 4] \cup [5, \infty)$ **15.** $(-\infty, -3) \cup (2, \infty)$ **16.** $(-\infty, -3) \cup [2, 3)$

17. **18.** **19.** **20.**

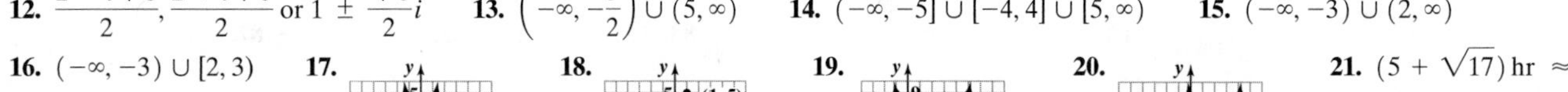
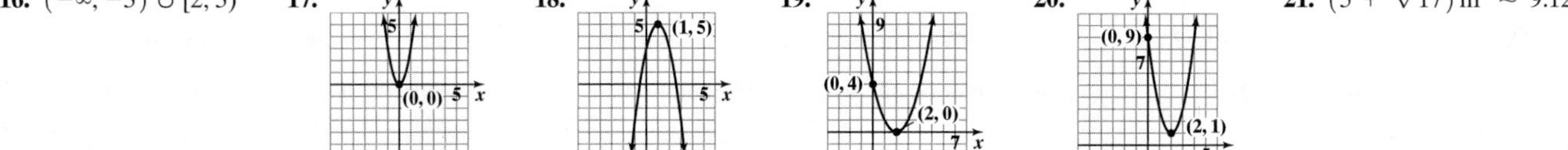

21. $(5 + \sqrt{17})$ hr $\approx$ 9.12 hr **22. a.** 272 ft **b.** 5.12 sec **23.** 7.2 ft

Chapter 6 Cumulative Review

1. a. $\frac{1}{2}$ **b.** 19; Sec. 1.6, Ex. 6 **3. a.** $5x + 7$ **b.** $-4a - 1$ **c.** $4y - 3y^2$ **d.** $7.3x - 6$ **e.** $\frac{1}{2}b$; Sec. 2.1, Ex. 4 **5.** no solution; Sec. 4.1, Ex. 5 **7.** $(-2, 0)$; Sec. 4.2, Ex. 4 **9. a.** x^3 **b.** 256 **c.** −27 **d.** cannot be simplified **e.** $2x^4y$; Sec. 5.1, Ex. 9 **11. a.** 5 **b.** 5; Sec. 5.7, Ex. 3 **13.** $-6, -\frac{3}{2}, \frac{1}{5}$; Sec. 6.6, Ex. 9 **15.** $\frac{1}{5x - 1}$; Sec. 7.1, Ex. 2a **17.** $\frac{xy + 2x^3}{y - 1}$; Sec. 7.7, Ex. 3 **19.** $(2m^2 - 1)^2$; Sec. 6.3, Ex. 10 **21.** −10 and 7; Sec. 6.7, Ex. 2 **23. a.** $5x\sqrt{x}$ **b.** $3x^2y^2\sqrt[3]{2y^2}$ **c.** $3z^2\sqrt[4]{z^3}$; Sec. 10.3, Ex. 4 **25. a.** $\frac{2\sqrt{5}}{5}$ **b.** $\frac{8\sqrt{x}}{3x}$ **c.** $\frac{\sqrt[3]{4}}{2}$; Sec. 10.5, Ex. 1 **27.** $\frac{2}{9}$; Sec. 10.6, Ex. 5 **29.** −5; Sec. 7.5, Ex. 1 **31.** −5; Sec. 7.6, Ex. 5 **33.** $k = \frac{1}{6}$; $y = \frac{1}{6}x$; Sec. 8.4, Ex. 1 **35. a.** 3 **b.** $|x|$ **c.** $|x - 2|$ **d.** −5 **e.** $2x - 7$ **f.** $5|x|$ **g.** $|x + 1|$; Sec. 10.1, Ex. 5 **37. a.** $\sqrt{x}$ **b.** $\sqrt[3]{5}$ **c.** $\sqrt{rs^3}$; Sec. 10.2, Ex. 7 **39. a.** $\frac{1}{2} + \frac{3}{2}i$ **b.** $0 - \frac{7}{3}i$; Sec. 10.7, Ex. 5 **41.** $-1 + 2\sqrt{3}, -1 - 2\sqrt{3}$; Sec. 11.1, Ex. 3 **43.** 9; Sec. 11.3, Ex. 1

Answers

CHAPTER 7 Graphs, Equations, and Inequalities

7.1 Assess Your Understanding *(page 471)*

7. x-coordinate or abscissa; y-coordinate or ordinate **8.** quadrants **9.** midpoint **10.** F **11.** F **12.** T

13. **(a)** Quadrant II **(b)** x-axis **(c)** Quadrant III **(d)** Quadrant I
(e) y-axis **(f)** Quadrant IV

15. The points will be on a vertical line that is 2 units to the right of the y-axis.

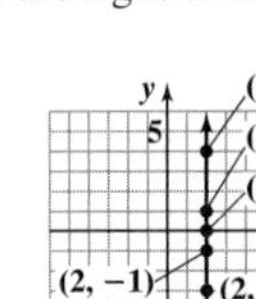

17. $(-1, 4)$; Quadrant II
19. $(3, 1)$; Quadrant I
21. $Xmin = -11, Xmax = 5, Xscl = 1,$
$Ymin = -3, Ymax = 6, Yscl = 1$
23. $Xmin = -30, Xmax = 50, Xscl = 10,$
$Ymin = -90, Ymax = 50, Yscl = 10$
25. $Xmin = -10, Xmax = 110, Xscl = 10,$
$Ymin = -10, Ymax = 160, Yscl = 10$
27. $Xmin = -6, Xmax = 6, Xscl = 2,$
$Ymin = -4, Ymax = 4, Yscl = 2$

29. $Xmin = -6,\ Xmax = 6, Xscl = 2,\ Ymin = -1,\ Ymax = 3, Yscl = 1$ **31.** $Xmin = 3, Xmax = 9, Xscl = 1, Ymin = 2, Ymax = 10, Yscl = 2$

33. $\sqrt{5}$ **35.** $\sqrt{10}$ **37.** $2\sqrt{17}$ **39.** 20 **41.** $\sqrt{53}$ **43.** $\sqrt{a^2 + b^2}$ **45.** $4\sqrt{10}$ **47.** $2\sqrt{65}$

49. $d(A, B) = \sqrt{13}$
$d(B, C) = \sqrt{13}$
$d(A, C) = \sqrt{26}$
$(\sqrt{13})^2 + (\sqrt{13})^2 = (\sqrt{26})^2$
Area $= \dfrac{13}{2}$ square units

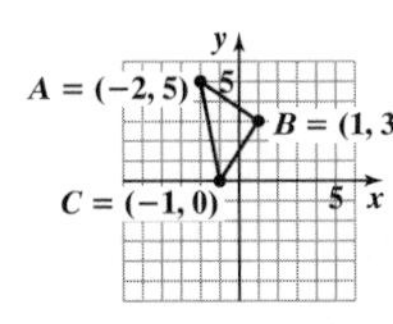

51. $d(A, B) = \sqrt{130}$
$d(B, C) = \sqrt{26}$
$d(A, C) = 2\sqrt{26}$
$(\sqrt{26})^2 + (2\sqrt{26})^2 = (\sqrt{130})^2$
Area $= 26$ square units

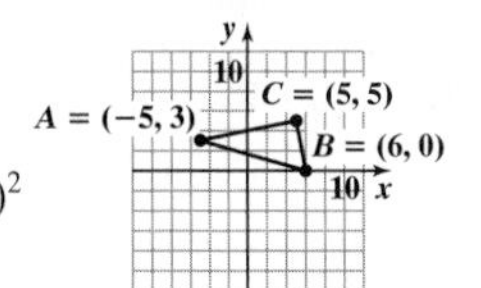

53. $d(A, B) = 4$
$d(B, C) = \sqrt{41}$
$d(A, C) = 5$
$4^2 + 5^2 = (\sqrt{41})^2$
Area $= 10$ square units

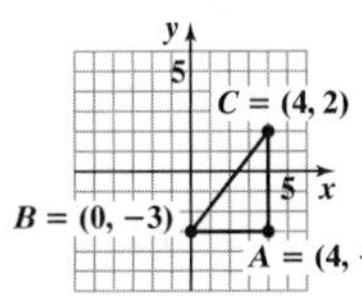

55. $(4, 0)$ **57.** $(3, 3)$ **59.** $(5, -1)$ **61.** $\left(\dfrac{a}{2}, \dfrac{b}{2}\right)$

63. $(0, 0)$ is on the graph. **65.** $(0, 3)$ is on the graph.

67. $(0, 2)$ and $(\sqrt{2}, \sqrt{2})$ are on the graph. **69.** $(-1, 0), (1, 0)$ **71.** $\left(-\dfrac{\pi}{2}, 0\right), (0, 1), \left(\dfrac{\pi}{2}, 0\right)$

73. $(0, 2), (1, 0), (0, -2)$ **75.** $(-4, 0), (-1, 0), (0, -3), (4, 0)$

77.

79.

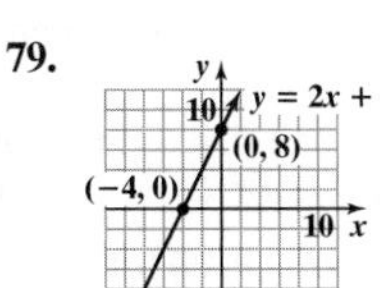

81.

83.

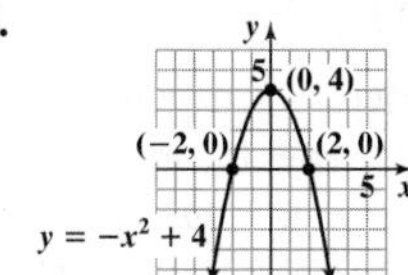

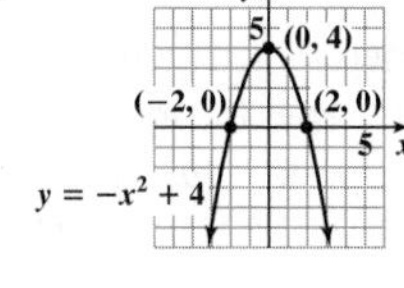

85.

87.

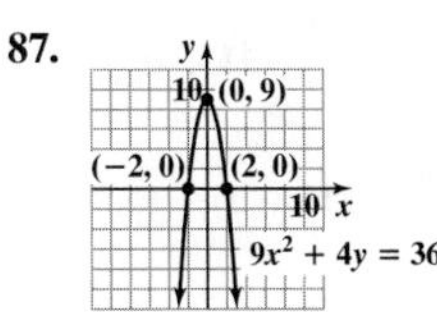

89. x-intercept: 6.5 y-intercept: -13

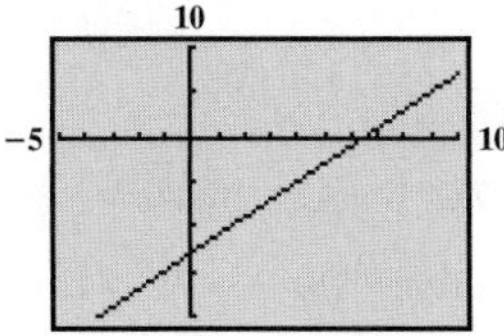

91. x-intercepts: -2.74, 2.74
y-intercept: -15

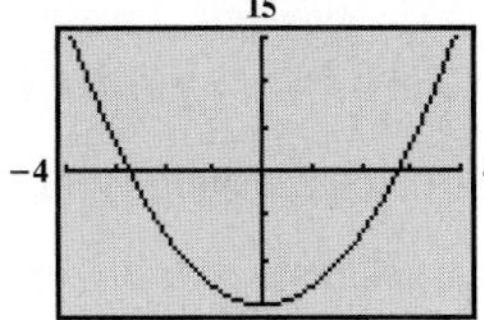

93. x-intercept: 14.33
y-intercept: -21.5

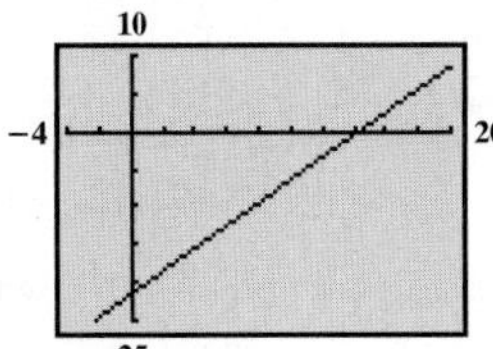

95. x-intercepts: -2.72, 2.72
y-intercept: 12.33

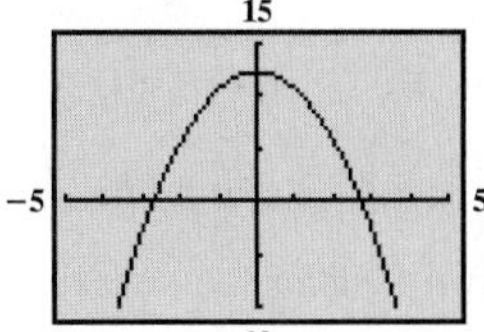

97. $(5, 3)$ **99.** $\sqrt{17}; 2\sqrt{5}; \sqrt{29}$ **101.** $d(P_1, P_2) = 6; d(P_2, P_3) = 4; d(P_1, P_3) = 2\sqrt{13}$; right triangle

103. $d(P_1, P_2) = 2\sqrt{17}; d(P_2, P_3) = \sqrt{34}; d(P_1, P_3) = \sqrt{34}$; isosceles right triangle **105.** $90\sqrt{2} \approx 127.28$ ft

107. **(a)** (90, 0), (90, 90), (0, 90) **(b)** $5\sqrt{2161} \approx 232.43$ ft **(c)** $30\sqrt{149} \approx 366.20$ ft **109.** $d = 50t$ **111.** **(a)** (2.65, 1.6) **(b)** ≈ 1.285 units **113.** \$20,155

Historical Problems *(page 483)*

1. The area of each shaded square is 9, so the larger square will have area $85 + 4(9) = 121$. The area of the larger square is also given by the expression $(x + 6)^2$, so $(x + 6)^2 = 121$. Taking the positive square root of each side, $x + 6 = 11$ or $x = 5$.
2. Let $z = -6$, so $z^2 + 12z - 85 = -121$. We get the equation $u^2 - 121 = 0$ or $u^2 = 121$. Thus $u = \pm 11$, so $x = \pm 11 - 6$. $x = -17$ or $x = 5$.

3.

$$\left(x + \frac{b}{2a}\right)^2 = \left(\frac{\sqrt{b^2 - 4ac}}{2a}\right)^2$$

$$\left(x + \frac{b}{2a}\right)^2 - \left(\frac{\sqrt{b^2 - 4ac}}{2a}\right)^2 = 0$$

$$\left(x + \frac{b}{2a} - \frac{\sqrt{b^2 - 4ac}}{2a}\right)\left(x + \frac{b}{2a} + \frac{\sqrt{b^2 - 4ac}}{2a}\right) = 0$$

$$\left(x + \frac{b - \sqrt{b^2 - 4ac}}{2a}\right)\left(x + \frac{b + \sqrt{b^2 - 4ac}}{2a}\right) = 0$$

$$x = \frac{-b + \sqrt{b^2 - 4ac}}{2a} \text{ or } x = \frac{-b - \sqrt{b^2 - 4ac}}{2a}$$

7.2 Assess Your Understanding *(page 483)*

6. repeated; multiplicity two **7.** discriminant; negative **8.** second **9.** F **10.** T **11.** $\{0, 9\}$ **13.** $\{-5, 5\}$ **15.** $\{-3, 2\}$ **17.** $\left\{-\frac{1}{2}, 3\right\}$ **19.** $\{-4, 4\}$ **21.** $\{2, 6\}$ **23.** $\left\{\frac{3}{2}\right\}$ **25.** $\left\{-\frac{2}{3}, \frac{3}{2}\right\}$ **27.** $\left\{-\frac{2}{3}, \frac{3}{2}\right\}$ **29.** $\left\{-\frac{3}{4}, 2\right\}$ **31.** $\{-5, 5\}$ **33.** $\{-1, 3\}$ **35.** $\{-3, 0\}$ **37.** $\{-7, 3\}$ **39.** $\left\{-\frac{1}{4}, \frac{3}{4}\right\}$ **41.** $\left\{\frac{-1 - \sqrt{7}}{6}, \frac{-1 + \sqrt{7}}{6}\right\}$ **43.** $\{2 - \sqrt{2}, 2 + \sqrt{2}\}$ **45.** $\{2 - \sqrt{5}, 2 + \sqrt{5}\}$ **47.** $\left\{1, \frac{3}{2}\right\}$ **49.** No real solution **51.** $\left\{\frac{-1 - \sqrt{5}}{4}, \frac{-1 + \sqrt{5}}{4}\right\}$ **53.** $\left\{0, \frac{9}{4}\right\}$ **55.** $\left\{\frac{1}{3}\right\}$ **57.** $\left\{-\frac{2}{3}, 1\right\}$ **59.** $\left\{\frac{3 - \sqrt{29}}{10}, \frac{3 + \sqrt{29}}{10}\right\}$ **61.** $\left\{\frac{-2 - \sqrt{10}}{2}, \frac{-2 + \sqrt{10}}{2}\right\}$ **63.** $\left\{\frac{1 - \sqrt{33}}{8}, \frac{1 + \sqrt{33}}{8}\right\}$ **65.** $\left\{\frac{9 - \sqrt{73}}{2}, \frac{9 + \sqrt{73}}{2}\right\}$ **67.** No real solution **69.** Repeated real solution **71.** Two unequal real solutions **73.** $\{-\sqrt{5}, \sqrt{5}\}$ **75.** $\left\{\frac{1}{4}\right\}$ **77.** $\left\{-\frac{3}{5}, \frac{5}{2}\right\}$ **79.** $\left\{-\frac{1}{2}, \frac{2}{3}\right\}$ **81.** $\left\{\frac{7}{3}\right\}$ **83.** $\left\{\frac{-1 - \sqrt{17}}{2}, \frac{-1 + \sqrt{17}}{2}\right\}$ **85.** $\left\{-\frac{1}{4}, \frac{2}{3}\right\}$ **87.** $\{5\}$ **89.** 2; 5 meters, 12 meters, 13 meters; 20 meters, 21 meters; 29 meters **91.** The dimensions are 11 ft by 13 ft.

93. The dimensions are 5 m by 8 m. **95.** The dimensions should be 4 ft by 4 ft. **97.** **(a)** The ball strikes the ground after 6 sec. **(b)** The ball passes the top of the building on its way down after 5 sec. **99.** The dimensions should be 11.55 cm by 6.55 cm by 3 cm. **101.** The border will be 2.71 ft wide. **103.** The border will be 2.56 ft wide. **105.** The screen of a 37-inch TV in 4:3 format has an area of 657.12 square inches; the screen of a 37-inch TV in 16 : 9 format has an area of 584.97 square inches. The traditional TV has a larger screen. **107.** 36 consecutive integers must be added. **109.** $\frac{-b + \sqrt{b^2 - 4ac}}{2a} + \frac{-b - \sqrt{b^2 - 4ac}}{2a} = \frac{-2b}{2a} = -\frac{b}{a}$ **111.** $k = \frac{1}{2}$ or $k = -\frac{1}{2}$ **113.** $ax^2 + bx + c = 0, x = \frac{-b \pm \sqrt{b^2 - 4ac}}{2a}$; $ax^2 - bx + c = 0, x = \frac{b \pm \sqrt{(-b)^2 - 4ac}}{2a} = \frac{b \pm \sqrt{b^2 - 4ac}}{2a} = -\frac{-b \pm \sqrt{b^2 - 4ac}}{2a}$ **115.** (b)

7.3 Assess Your Understanding *(page 494)*

4. real; imaginary; imaginary unit **5.** $\{-2i, 2i\}$ **6.** F **7.** T **8.** F **9.** $8 + 5i$ **11.** $-7 + 6i$ **13.** $-6 - 11i$ **15.** $6 - 18i$ **17.** $6 + 4i$ **19.** $10 - 5i$ **21.** 37 **23.** $\frac{6}{5} + \frac{8}{5}i$ **25.** $1 - 2i$ **27.** $\frac{5}{2} - \frac{7}{2}i$ **29.** $-\frac{1}{2} + \frac{\sqrt{3}}{2}i$ **31.** $2i$ **33.** $-i$ **35.** i **37.** -6 **39.** $-10i$ **41.** $-2 + 2i$ **43.** 0 **45.** 0 **47.** $2i$ **49.** $5i$ **51.** $5i$ **53.** $\{-2i, 2i\}$ **55.** $\{-4, 4\}$ **57.** $\{3 - 2i, 3 + 2i\}$ **59.** $\{3 - i, 3 + i\}$ **61.** $\left\{\frac{1}{4} - \frac{1}{4}i, \frac{1}{4} + \frac{1}{4}i\right\}$ **63.** $\left\{\frac{1}{5} - \frac{2}{5}i, \frac{1}{5} + \frac{2}{5}i\right\}$ **65.** $\left\{-\frac{1}{2} - \frac{\sqrt{3}}{2}i, -\frac{1}{2} + \frac{\sqrt{3}}{2}i\right\}$ **67.** $\{2, -1 - \sqrt{3}i, -1 + \sqrt{3}i\}$ **69.** $\{-2, 2, -2i, 2i\}$ **71.** $\{-3i, -2i, 2i, 3i\}$ **73.** Two complex solutions that are conjugates of each other **75.** Two unequal real solutions **77.** A repeated real solution **79.** $2 - 3i$ **81.** 6 **83.** 25 **85.** $2 + 3i$ ohms **87.** $z + \bar{z} = (a + bi) + (a - bi) = 2a$; $z - \bar{z} = (a + bi) - (a - bi) = 2bi$ **89.** $\overline{z + w} = \overline{(a + bi) + (c + di)} = \overline{(a + c) + (b + d)i} = (a + c) - (b + d)i = (a - bi) + (c - di) = \bar{z} + \bar{w}$

7.4 Assess Your Understanding *(page 501)*

6. extraneous **7.** quadratic in form **8.** T **9.** $\{22\}$ **11.** $\{1\}$ **13.** No real solution **15.** $\{-13\}$ **17.** $\{4\}$ **19.** $\{-1\}$ **21.** $\{0, 64\}$ **23.** $\{3\}$

25. $\left\{-\frac{8}{5}\right\}$ **27.** {8} **29.** $\{-1, 3\}$ **31.** {1, 5} **33.** {1} **35.** {5} **37.** {2} **39.** $\{-4, 4\}$ **41.** $\{-2, 2\}$ **43.** $\{-2, -1, 1, 2\}$ **45.** $\{-1, 1\}$

47. {−2, 1} **49.** $\{-6, -5\}$ **51.** $\left\{-\frac{3}{2}, 2\right\}$ **53.** {0, 16} **55.** {16} **57.** {1} **59.** $\left\{\left(\frac{9-\sqrt{17}}{8}\right)^4, \left(\frac{9+\sqrt{17}}{8}\right)^4\right\}$ **61.** $\left\{-2, -\frac{1}{2}\right\}$ **63.** $\left\{-\frac{3}{2}, \frac{1}{3}\right\}$

65. $\left\{-\frac{1}{8}, 27\right\}$ **67.** {−4, 1} **69.** $\left\{-1, \frac{3}{2}\right\}$ **71.** {−4, 4} **73.** $\left\{-\frac{1}{2}, \frac{1}{2}\right\}$ **75.** $\left\{-\frac{27}{2}, \frac{27}{2}\right\}$ **77.** $\left\{-\frac{36}{5}, \frac{24}{5}\right\}$ **79.** No real solution **81.** $\{-3, 3\}$

83. $\{-1, 3\}$ **85.** $\{-3, 0, 3\}$ **87.** $\{-5, 0, 4\}$ **89.** $\{-1, 1\}$ **91.** $\{-2, 2, 3\}$ **93.** $\left\{-2, \frac{1}{2}, 2\right\}$ **95.** {0.34, 11.66} **97.** $\{-1.03, 1.03\}$

99. $\left\{-4, \frac{5}{3}\right\}$ **101.** $\left\{-3, -\frac{2}{5}, 3\right\}$ **103.** $\left\{-\frac{1}{5}, 1\right\}$ **105.** {5} **107.** $\left\{-2, -\frac{4}{5}\right\}$ **109.** $\{-2, 6\}$ **111.** {2} **113.** $\left\{\frac{-3-\sqrt{6}}{3}, \frac{-3+\sqrt{6}}{3}\right\}$

115. $\{-2, -1, 0, 1\}$ **117.** $\{\sqrt{2}, \sqrt{3}\}$ **119.** $\{-2, 2, -2i, 2i\}$ **121.** $\left\{1, 2, -1-\sqrt{3}i, -1+\sqrt{3}i, -\frac{1}{2}-\frac{\sqrt{3}}{2}i, -\frac{1}{2}+\frac{\sqrt{3}}{2}i\right\}$ **123.** $\left\{\frac{3}{2}, 5\right\}$

125. $(2, 2)$; $(2, -4)$ **127.** $(0, 0)$; $(8, 0)$ **129.** The distance is approximately 229.94 ft. **131.** approx. 221 feet

7.5 Assess Your Understanding *(page 511)*

4. negative **5.** closed interval **6.** $-a \le u \le a$ **7.** $(-\infty, a]$ **8.** T **9.** T **10.** F **11.** $[0, 2]; 0 \le x \le 2$ **13.** $[2, \infty); x \ge 2$
15. $[0, 3); 0 \le x < 3$ **17. (a)** $6 < 8$ **(b)** $-2 < 0$ **(c)** $9 < 15$ **(d)** $-6 > -10$ **19. (a)** $2x + 4 < 5$ **(b)** $2x - 4 < -3$ **(c)** $6x + 3 < 6$
(d) $-4x - 2 > -4$ **21.** $[0, 4]$ **23.** $[4, 6)$ **25.** $[4, \infty)$

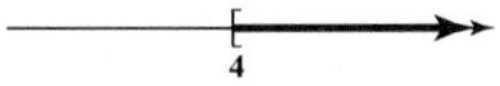

27. $(-\infty, -4)$ 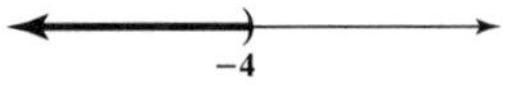 **29.** $2 \le x \le 5$ **31.** $-3 < x < -2$ **33.** $x \ge 4$

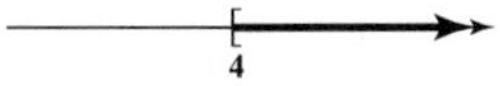

35. $x < -3$ **37.** $<$ **39.** $>$ **41.** $\ge$ **43.** $<$ **45.** $<$ **47.** $\ge$ **49.** $\{x \mid x > 3\}$ or $(3, \infty)$

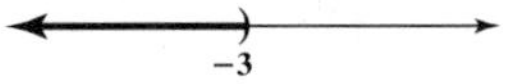

51. $\{x \mid x \ge -1\}$ or $[-1, \infty)$ **53.** $\{x \mid x \ge 2\}$ or $[2, \infty)$ **55.** $\{x \mid x > -7\}$ or $(-7, \infty)$ **57.** $\left\{x \,\middle|\, x \le \frac{2}{3}\right\}$ or $\left(-\infty, \frac{2}{3}\right]$

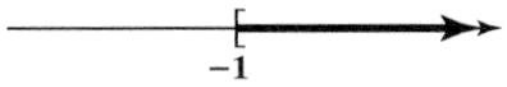

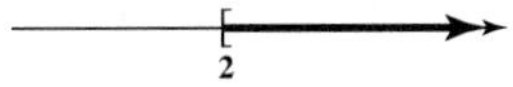

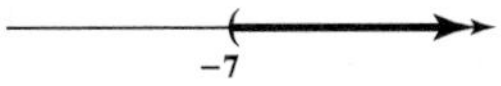

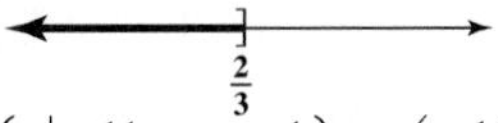

59. $\{x \mid x < -20\}$ or $(-\infty, -20)$ **61.** $\{x \mid 3 \le x \le 5\}$ or $[3, 5]$ **63.** $\left\{x \,\middle|\, \frac{2}{3} \le x \le 3\right\}$ or $\left[\frac{2}{3}, 3\right]$ **65.** $\left\{x \,\middle|\, -\frac{11}{2} < x < \frac{1}{2}\right\}$ or $\left(-\frac{11}{2}, \frac{1}{2}\right)$

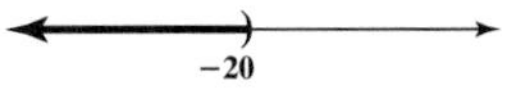

67. $\{x \mid -6 < x < 0\}$ or $(-6, 0)$ **69.** $\{x \mid x < -5\}$ or $(-\infty, -5)$ **71.** $\{x \mid -4 < x < 4\}$; $(-4, 4)$

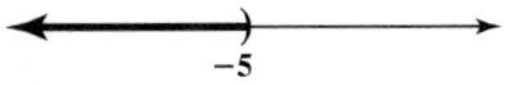

73. $\{x \mid x < -4 \text{ or } x > 4\}$; $(-\infty, -4) \cup (4, \infty)$ **75.** $\left\{t \,\middle|\, -\frac{2}{3} \le t \le 2\right\}$; $\left[-\frac{2}{3}, 2\right]$ **77.** $\{x \mid 1 < x < 3\}$; $(1, 3)$

79. $\{x \mid x \le 1 \text{ or } x \ge 5\}$; $(-\infty, 1] \cup [5, \infty)$ **81.** $\{x \mid x < -1 \text{ or } x > 2\}$; $(-\infty, -1)$ or $(2, \infty)$ **83.** $\left\{x \,\middle|\, -1 < x < \frac{3}{2}\right\}$; $\left(-1, \frac{3}{2}\right)$

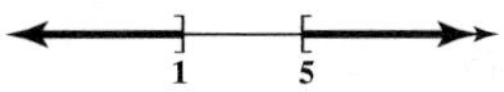

85. No solution  **87.** $\{x \mid x > -2\}$; $(-2, \infty)$ 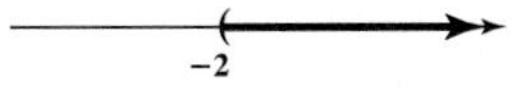 **89.** $\left\{x \,\middle|\, x \le -\frac{5}{2} \text{ or } x \ge \frac{3}{2}\right\}$; $\left(-\infty, -\frac{5}{2}\right] \cup \left[\frac{3}{2}, \infty\right)$

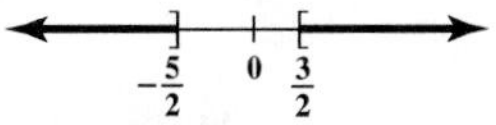

91. $\left\{x \,\middle|\, x \ge \frac{4}{3}\right\}$; $\left[\frac{4}{3}, \infty\right)$ **93.** $\{x \mid -3 \le x < 7\}$; $[-3, 7)$ **95.** $\{x \mid x \ge -1\}$; $[-1, \infty)$;

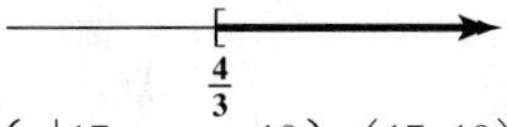

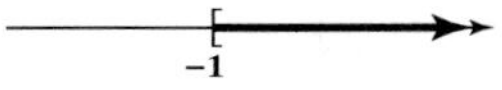

97. $\left\{x \,\middle|\, \frac{17}{6} < x < \frac{19}{6}\right\}$; $\left(\frac{17}{6}, \frac{19}{6}\right)$ **99.** $\{x \mid -3 \le x < 4\}$; $[-3, 4)$ **101.** $\{x \mid -2 < x < 4\}$; $(-2, 4)$

103. $\{x \mid x > 5\}$; $(5, \infty)$ 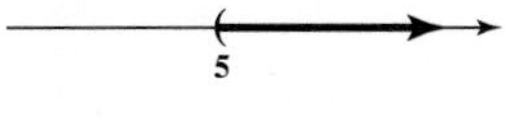 **105.** $\{x \mid x > 3\}$; $(3, \infty)$ 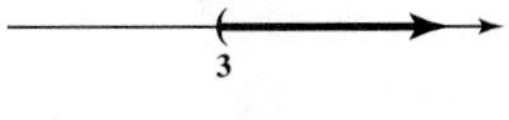 **107.** $|x - 2| < \frac{1}{2}$; $\left\{x \,\middle|\, \frac{3}{2} < x < \frac{5}{2}\right\}$

109. $|x + 3| > 2$; $\{x \mid x < -5 \text{ or } x > -1\}$ **111.** $21 < \text{age} < 30$ **113.** $|x - 98.6| \geq 1.5$; $\{x \mid x \leq 97.1 \text{ or } x \geq 100.1\}$ **115. (a)** Male ≥ 77.1 **(b)** Female ≥ 81.5 **(c)** A female can expect to live at least 4.4 years longer. **117.** The agent's commission ranges from \$45,000 to \$95,000, inclusive. As a percent of selling price, the commission ranges from 5% to approximately 8.6%, inclusive. **119.** The amount withheld varies from \$106.40 to \$156.40, inclusive. **121.** The usage varies from approximately 710 to 1530 kilowatt-hours, inclusive. **123.** The dealer's cost varies from \$7457.63 to \$7857.14, inclusive. **125. (a)** You need at least a 74 on the last test. **(b)** You need at least a 77 on the last test.

127. $|x - 13.4| < 1.35$; between 12.05 and 14.75 books per year are read, on average.

129. $\dfrac{a+b}{2} - a = \dfrac{a+b-2a}{2} = \dfrac{b-a}{2} > 0$; therefore, $a < \dfrac{a+b}{2}$

$b - \dfrac{a+b}{2} = \dfrac{2b-a-b}{2} = \dfrac{b-a}{2} > 0$; therefore, $b > \dfrac{a+b}{2}$.

131. $(\sqrt{ab})^2 - a^2 = ab - a^2 = a(b-a) > 0$; thus,

$b^2 - (\sqrt{ab})^2 = b^2 - ab = b(b-a) > 0$; thus, $b^2 > (\sqrt{ab})^2$ and $b > \sqrt{ab}$.

133. $\dfrac{1}{h} = \dfrac{1}{2}\left(\dfrac{1}{a} + \dfrac{1}{b}\right) = \dfrac{1}{2}\left(\dfrac{b+a}{ab}\right); h = \dfrac{2ab}{b+a}$

$h - a = \dfrac{2ab}{b+a} - a = \dfrac{2ab - a(b+a)}{b+a} = \dfrac{2ab - ab - a^2}{b+a} = \dfrac{ab - a^2}{b+a} = \dfrac{a(b-a)}{b+a} > 0$, since $0 < a < b$.

$b - h = b - \dfrac{2ab}{b+a} = \dfrac{b(b+a) - 2ab}{b+a} = \dfrac{b^2 + ab - 2ab}{b+a} = \dfrac{b^2 - ab}{b+a} = \dfrac{b(b-a)}{b+a} > 0$, since $0 < a < b$.

Review Exercises *(page 516)*

1. $\{-18\}$ **2.** $\{6\}$ **3.** $\left\{\dfrac{1}{5}\right\}$ **4.** $\{6\}$ **5.** No real solution **6.** $\left\{-\dfrac{27}{13}\right\}$ **7.** $\left\{-2, \dfrac{3}{2}\right\}$ **8.** $\left\{\dfrac{1-\sqrt{13}}{4}, \dfrac{1+\sqrt{13}}{4}\right\}$ **9.** $\{-3, 3\}$

10. No real solution **11.** No real solution **12.** $\{-2, -1, 1, 2\}$ **13.** $\{2\}$ **14.** $\left\{\dfrac{13}{2}\right\}$ **15.** $\left\{\dfrac{\sqrt{5}}{2}\right\}$ **16.** $\left\{\dfrac{9}{4}\right\}$ **17.** $\left\{-1, \dfrac{1}{2}\right\}$

18. $\left\{\dfrac{m}{1-n}, \dfrac{m}{1+n}\right\}$ **19.** $\left\{-\dfrac{9b}{5a}, \dfrac{2b}{a}\right\}$ **20.** $\left\{-\dfrac{9}{5}\right\}$ **21.** $\{-5, 2\}$ **22.** $\left\{-\dfrac{5}{3}, 3\right\}$ **23.** $\left\{0, \dfrac{3}{2}\right\}$ **24.** $\left\{-\dfrac{5}{2}, -2, 2\right\}$ **25.** $\{3\}$ **26.** $\{-1, 5\}$

27. $\{-2.49, 0.66, 1.83\}$ **28.** $\{-1.14, 1.64\}$ **29.** $\{x \mid x \geq 14\}$; $[14, \infty)$

14

30. $\left\{x \,\middle|\, -\dfrac{31}{2} \leq x \leq \dfrac{33}{2}\right\}$; $\left[-\dfrac{31}{2}, \dfrac{33}{2}\right]$

$-\frac{31}{2}$ $\frac{33}{2}$

31. $\{x \mid -23 < x < -7\}$; $(-23, -7)$

−23 −7

32. $\left\{x \,\middle|\, -\dfrac{3}{2} < x < -\dfrac{7}{6}\right\}$; $\left(-\dfrac{3}{2}, -\dfrac{7}{6}\right)$

$-\frac{3}{2}$ $-\frac{7}{6}$

33. $\{x \mid x \leq -2 \text{ or } x \geq 7\}$; $(-\infty, -2] \cup [7, \infty)$

−2 7

34. $\left\{x \,\middle|\, 0 \leq x \leq \dfrac{4}{3}\right\}$; $\left[0, \dfrac{4}{3}\right]$

0 $\frac{4}{3}$

35. $\left\{x \,\middle|\, x < -1 \text{ or } x > \dfrac{7}{3}\right\}$; $(-\infty, -1) \cup \left(\dfrac{7}{3}, \infty\right)$

−1 $\frac{7}{3}$

36. $4 + 7i$ **37.** $-3 + 2i$ **38.** $\dfrac{9}{10} - \dfrac{3}{10}i$ **39.** -1 **40.** $-46 + 9i$ **41.** $\left\{-\dfrac{1}{2} - \dfrac{\sqrt{3}}{2}i, -\dfrac{1}{2} + \dfrac{\sqrt{3}}{2}i\right\}$ **42.** $\left\{\dfrac{-1-\sqrt{17}}{4}, \dfrac{-1+\sqrt{17}}{4}\right\}$

43. $\left\{\dfrac{1}{2} - \dfrac{\sqrt{11}}{2}i, \dfrac{1}{2} + \dfrac{\sqrt{11}}{2}i\right\}$ **44.** $\{-2, 1\}$ **45. (a)** $2\sqrt{5}$ **(b)** $(2, 1)$ **46. (a)** 5 **(b)** $\left(-\dfrac{1}{2}, 1\right)$ **47. (a)** 12 **(b)** $(4, 2)$

48.

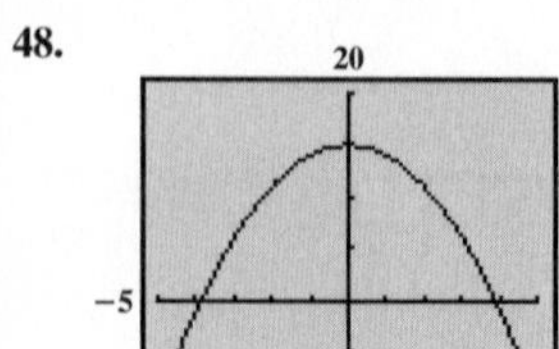

49. $(-4, 0), (0, 2), (0, 0), (0, -2), (2, 0)$

50.

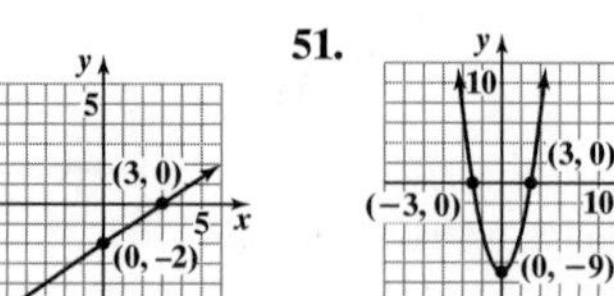

51.

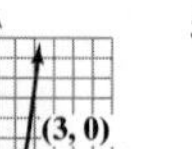

52.

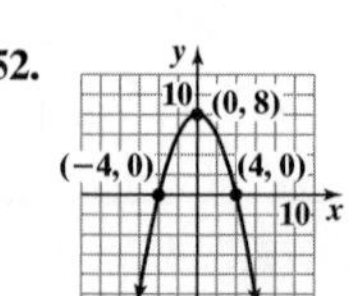

53. $d(A, B) = \sqrt{13}; d(B, C) = \sqrt{13}$ **54.** -4 and 8 **55.** $p = 2l + 2w$ **56.** The interest is \$630. **57.** He should invest \$50,000 in A-rated bonds and \$20,000 in the CD. **58.** The storm is 3300 ft away. **59.** The range of distances is from 0.5 to 0.75 m, $0.5 \le x \le 0.75$. **60.** The search plane can go as far as 616 mi. **61.** The helicopter will reach the life raft in a little less than 1 hr 35 min. **62.** The bees meet for the first time in 18.75 seconds. The bees meet for the second time 37.5 seconds later. **63. (a)** The object will strike the ground in 8 seconds. **(b)** The height is 896 ft. **64.** It takes Clarissa 10 days by herself. **65.** Add $6\frac{2}{3}$ lb of \$8/lb coffee to get $26\frac{2}{3}$ lb of \$5/lb coffee. **66.** Evaporate 51.2 oz of water. **67.** 5 cm and 12 cm **68.** The freight train is 190.67 ft long. **69. (a)** 6.5 in. by 6.5 in.; 12.5 in. by 12.5 in. **(b)** $8\frac{2}{3}$ in. by $4\frac{1}{3}$ in.; $14\frac{2}{3}$ in. by $10\frac{1}{3}$ in. **70.** It will take the smaller pump 2 hr. **71.** The length should be approximately 6.47 ft. **72.** 36 seniors went on the trip; each paid \$13.40. **73. (a)** No **(b)** Todd wins again. **(c)** Todd wins by $\frac{1}{4}$ m. **(d)** Todd should line up 5.26 m behind the start line. **(e)** Yes

Chapter Test *(page 519)*

1. (a) $d = 10$ **(b)** $M = (1, 1)$ **2.** $\left\{-\frac{3}{2}, -1\right\}$ **3.** $\{2\}$ **4.** $\left\{-\frac{3}{2}, 2\right\}$ **5.** $\{2\}$ **6.** $\{0, 3\}$ **7.** $\{-2, 2\}$ **8.** $\{2 - \sqrt{2}, 2 + \sqrt{2}\}$

9. $\{3 - 2\sqrt{3}, 3 + 2\sqrt{3}\}$ **10.**

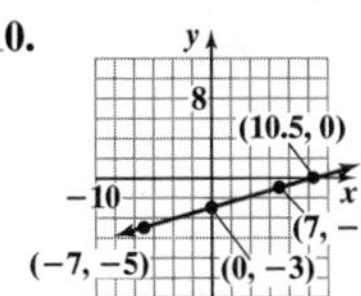

11.

(−2.24, 0) (2.24, 0) (−2, −1) (2, −1) (1, −4) (−1, −4) (0, −5)

12. $-1, 0.5$, and 1

13. -2.50 and 2.50

14. $-2.46, -0.24$, and 1.70

15. $\left\{x \middle| x < -\frac{11}{2}\right\}; \left(-\infty, -\frac{11}{2}\right)$

16. $\{x \mid x \le -5 \text{ or } x \ge 2\}; (\infty, -5] \cup [2, \infty)$ **17.** $\{x \mid -1 \le x < 2\}; [-1, 2)$ **18.** $\left\{x \middle| -4 < x < \frac{4}{3}\right\}; \left(-4, \frac{4}{3}\right)$

19. $2 - 25i$ **20.** $14 + 83i$ **21.** $\frac{7}{34} + \frac{11}{34}i$ **22.** $\left\{\frac{1}{2} - i, \frac{1}{2} + i\right\}$ **23.** About 204.63 min (3.41 hr) **24.** 23.75 lb of banana chips **25.** The sale price is \$159.50. **26.** Glenn will make \$100 in interest after 3 months.

CHAPTER 8 Graphs

8.1 Assess Your Understanding *(page 527)*

3. intercepts **4.** $y = 0$ **5.** y-axis **6.** 4 **7.** $(-3, 4)$ **8.** T **9.** F **10.** F

11. $(-2, 0), (0, 2)$

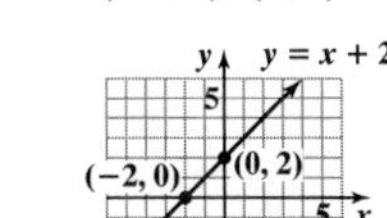

13. $(-4, 0), (0, 8)$

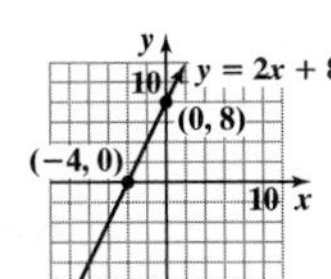

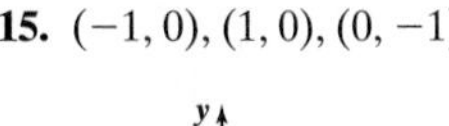

15. $(-1, 0), (1, 0), (0, -1)$

17. $(-2, 0), (2, 0), (0, 4)$

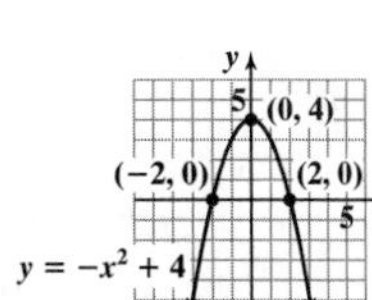

19. $(3, 0), (0, 2)$

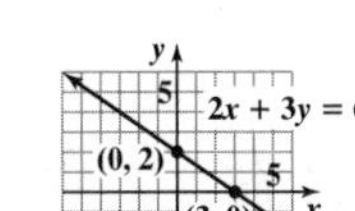

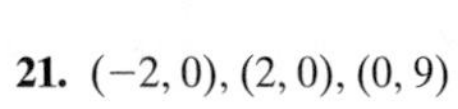

21. $(-2, 0), (2, 0), (0, 9)$

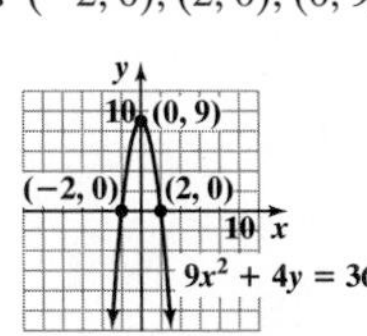

23.

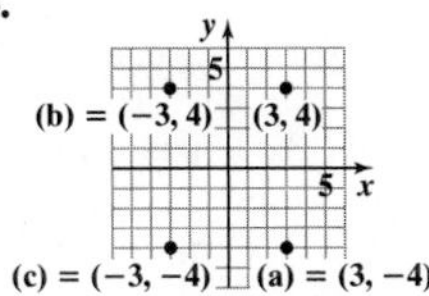

25.

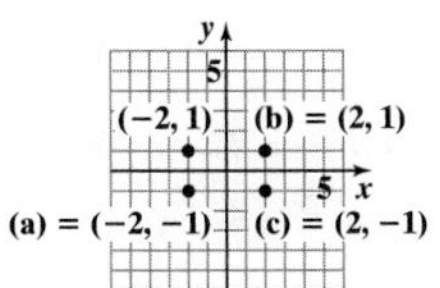

27.

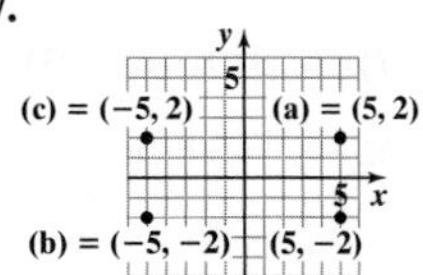

29.

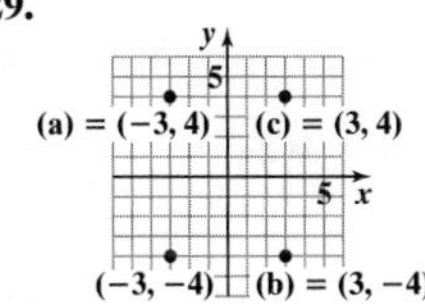

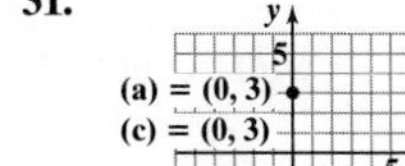

31.

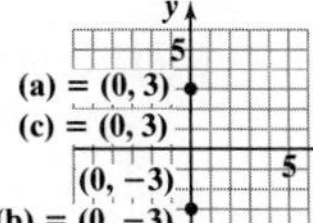

33. (a) $(-1, 0), (1, 0)$
(b) Symmetric with respect to the x-axis, the y-axis, and the origin

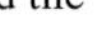

39. (a) $(-2, 0), (0, 0), (2, 0)$
(b) Symmetric with respect to the origin

35. (a) $\left(-\frac{\pi}{2}, 0\right), (0, 1), \left(\frac{\pi}{2}, 0\right)$
(b) Symmetric with respect to the y-axis

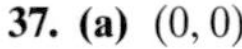

37. (a) $(0, 0)$
(b) Symmetric with respect to the x-axis

41.

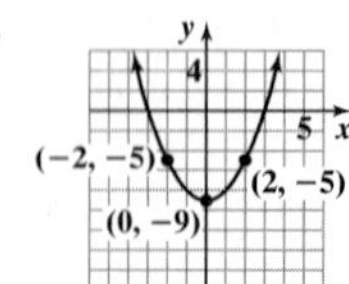

43.

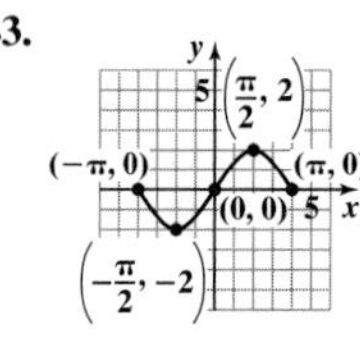

45. $(-4, 0), (0, -2), (0, 2)$; symmetric with respect to the x-axis **47.** $(0, 0)$; symmetric with respect to the origin **49.** $(0, -9), (3, 0), (-3, 0)$; symmetric with respect to the y-axis **51.** $(-2, 0), (2, 0), (0, -3), (0, 3)$; symmetric with respect to the x-axis, y-axis, and origin **53.** $(0, -27), (3, 0)$; no symmetry **55.** $(0, -4), (4, 0), (-1, 0)$; no symmetry **57.** $(0, 0)$; symmetric with respect to the origin **59.** $(0, 0)$; symmetric with respect to the origin

61.

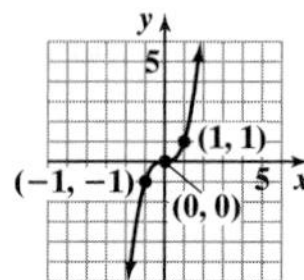

63.

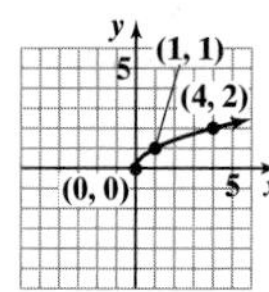

65. $b = 13$ **67.** $a = -4$ or $a = 1$

69. **(a)** $(0, -5), (-\sqrt{5}, 0), (\sqrt{5}, 0)$ **(b)** symmetric with respect to the y-axis **(c)**

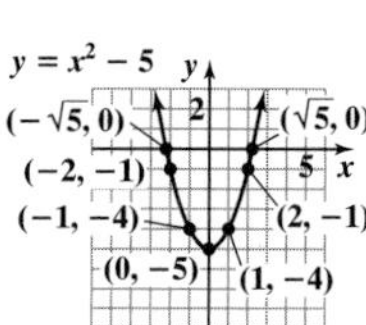

71. **(a)** $(-9, 0), (0, -3), (0, 3)$ **(b)** symmetric with respect to the x-axis **(c)**

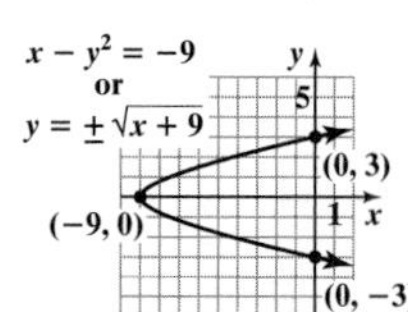

73. **(a)** $(0, 3), (0, -3), (-3, 0), (3, 0)$ **(b)** symmetric with respect to the x-axis, y-axis, and origin **(c)**

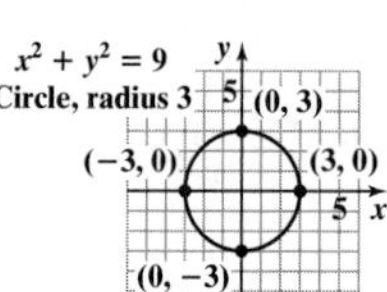

75. **(a)** $(0, 0), (-2, 0), (2, 0)$ **(b)** symmetric with respect to the origin **(c)**

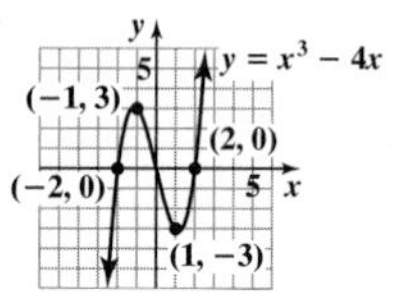

77. $(-1, -2)$ **79.** 4 **81.** **(a)** $(0, 0), (2, 0), (0, 1), (0, -1)$ **(b)** x-axis symmetry **83.** **(a)** $y = \sqrt{x^2}$ and $y = |x|$ have the same graph. **(b)** $\sqrt{x^2} = |x|$ **(c)** $x \geq 0$ for $y = (\sqrt{x})^2$, while x can be any real number for $y = x$. **(d)** $y \geq 0$ for $y = \sqrt{x^2}$

8.2 Assess Your Understanding *(page 541)*

1. undefined; 0 **2.** 3; 2 **3.** $y = b$; y-intercept **4.** T **5.** F **6.** T **7.** $m_1 = m_2$; y-intercepts; $m_1 m_2 = -1$ **8.** 2 **9.** $-\frac{1}{2}$ **10.** F **11.** **(a)** Slope $= \frac{1}{2}$ **(b)** If x increases by 2 units, y will increase by 1 unit. **13.** **(a)** Slope $= -\frac{1}{3}$ **(b)** If x increases by 3 units, y will decrease by 1 unit.

15. Slope $= -\frac{3}{2}$

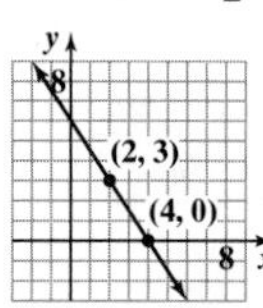

17. Slope $= -\frac{1}{2}$

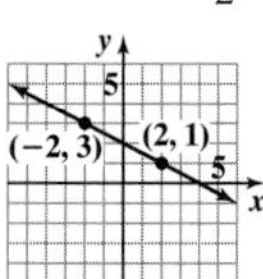

19. Slope = 0

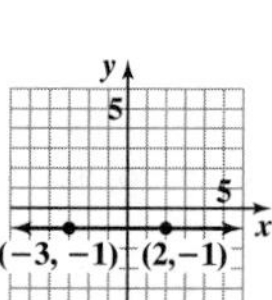

21. Slope undefined

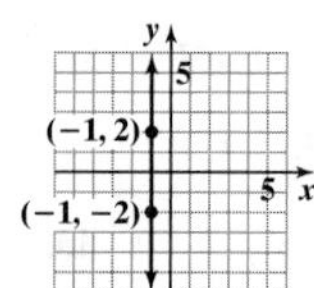

23.

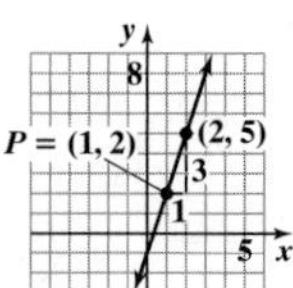

25.

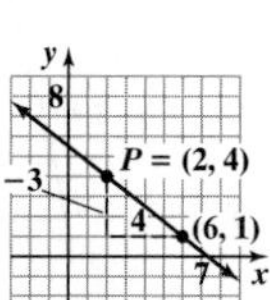

27.

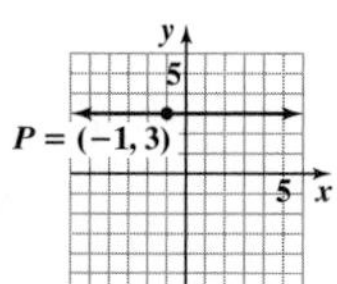

29.

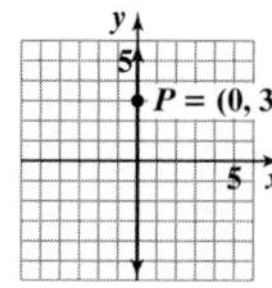

31. (2, 6); (3, 10); (4, 14) **33.** (4, −7); (6, −10); (8, −13) **35.** (−1, −5); (0, −7); (1, −9) **37.** $x - 2y = 0$ or $y = \frac{1}{2}x$ **39.** $x + y = 2$ or $y = -x + 2$ **41.** $2x - y = 3$ or $y = 2x - 3$ **43.** $x + 2y = 5$ or $y = -\frac{1}{2}x + \frac{5}{2}$ **45.** $3x - y = -9$ or $y = 3x + 9$ **47.** $2x + 3y = -1$ or $y = -\frac{2}{3}x - \frac{1}{3}$ **49.** $x - 2y = -5$ or $y = \frac{1}{2}x + \frac{5}{2}$ **51.** $3x + y = 3$ or $y = -3x + 3$ **53.** $x - 2y = 2$ or $y = \frac{1}{2}x - 1$ **55.** $x = 2$; no slope–intercept form **57.** $y = 2$ **59.** $2x - y = -4$ or $y = 2x + 4$ **61.** $2x - y = 0$ or $y = 2x$ **63.** $x = 4$; no slope–intercept form **65.** $2x + y = 0$ or $y = -2x$ **67.** $x - 2y = -3$ or $y = \frac{1}{2}x + \frac{3}{2}$ **69.** $y = 4$

71. Slope = 2; y-intercept = 3

73. Slope = 2; y-intercept = −2

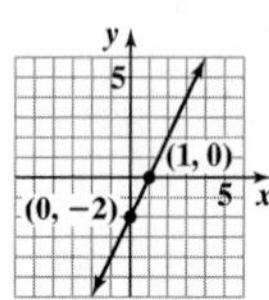

75. Slope $= \frac{1}{2}$; y-intercept = 2

77. Slope $= -\frac{1}{2}$; y-intercept = 2

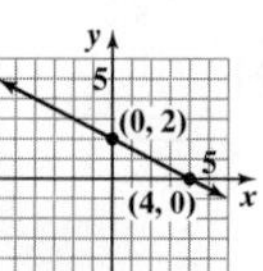

79. Slope $= \frac{2}{3}$; y-intercept $= -2$

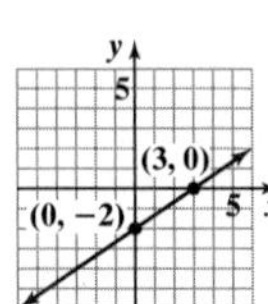

81. Slope $= -1$; y-intercept $= 1$

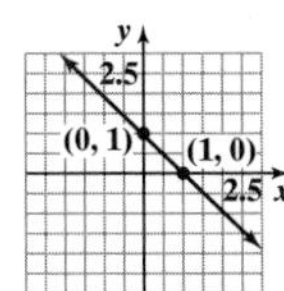

83. Slope undefined; no y-intercept

85. Slope $= 0$; y-intercept $= 5$

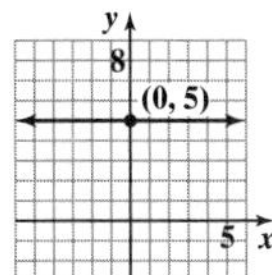

87. Slope $= 1$; y-intercept $= 0$

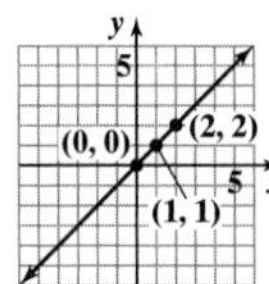

89. Slope $= \frac{3}{2}$; y-intercept $= 0$

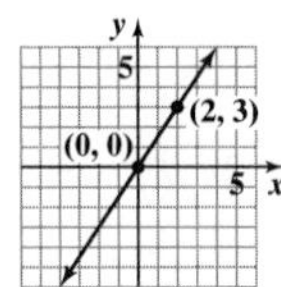

91. (a) x-intercept: 3; y-intercept: 2 **(b)**

93. (a) 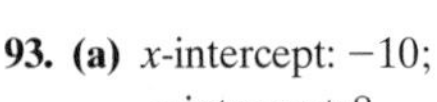
x-intercept: -10; y-intercept: 8 **(b)**

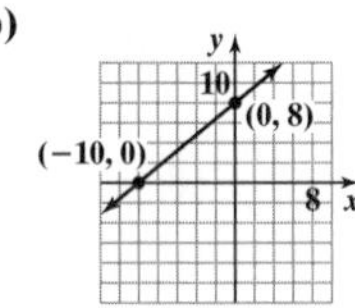

95. (a) x-intercept: 3;
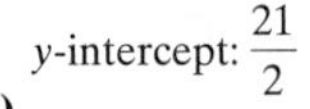
y-intercept: $\frac{21}{2}$
(b)

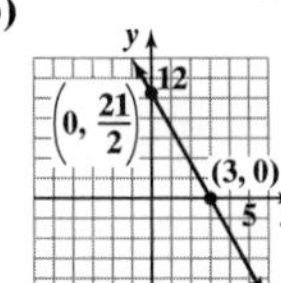

97. (a) x-intercept: 2; y-intercept: 3 **(b)**

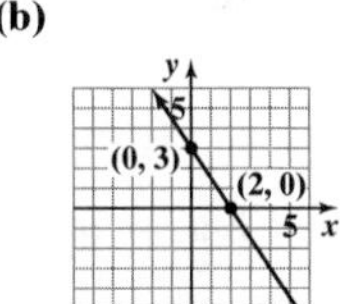

99. (a) x-intercept: 5; y-intercept: -2 **(b)**

101. $y = 0$
103. Parallel
105. Neither
107. $x - y = -2$ or $y = x + 2$
109. $x + 3y = 3$ or $y = -\frac{1}{3}x + 1$

111. $P_1 = (-2, 5)$, $P_2 = (1, 3)$, $m_1 = -\frac{2}{3}$; $P_2 = (1, 3)$, $P_3 = (-1, 0)$, $m_2 = \frac{3}{2}$; because $m_1 m_2 = -1$, the lines are perpendicular and the points $(-2, 5)$, $(1, 3)$, and $(-1, 0)$ are the vertices of a right triangle.
113. $P_1 = (-1, 0)$, $P_2 = (2, 3)$, $m = 1$; $P_3 = (1, -2)$, $P_4 = (4, 1)$, $m = 1$; $P_1 = (-1, 0)$, $P_3 = (1, -2)$, $m = -1$; $P_2 = (2, 3)$, $P_4 = (4, 1)$, $m = -1$; opposite sides are parallel, and adjacent sides are perpendicular; the points are the vertices of a rectangle.
115. $C = 0.20x + 29$; \$51.00; \$75.00 **117.** $C = 0.15x + 1289$
119. (a) $C = 0.11x + 11.47, 0 \le x \le 600$ **(b)** **(c)** \$33.47 **(d)** \$66.47 **(e)** Each additional kW-hr used adds \$0.11 to the bill.

121. $°C = \frac{5}{9}(°F - 32)$; approximately 21.1°C **123. (a)** $y = -\frac{2}{25}x + 30$ **(b)** x-intercept: 375; The ramp meets the floor 375 in. (31.25 ft) from the base of the platform. **(c)** The ramp does not meet design requirements. It has a run of 31.25 ft long. **(d)** The only slope possible for the ramp to comply with the requirement is for it to drop 1 in. for every 12-in. run. **125. (a)** $A = \frac{1}{5}x + 20{,}000$ **(b)** \$80,000 **(c)** Each additional box sold requires an additional \$0.20 in advertising. **127.** All have the same slope, 2; the lines are parallel.

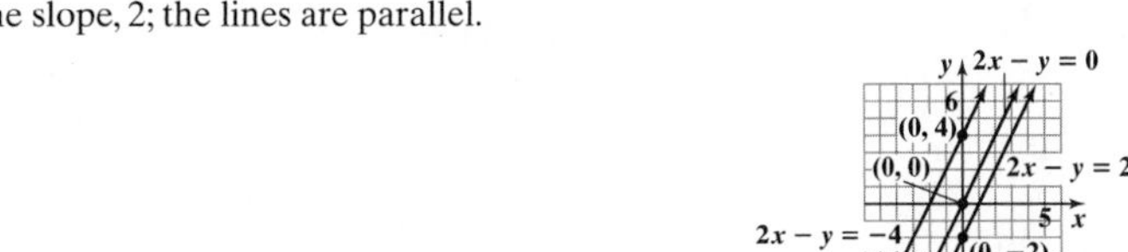

129. (b), (c), (e), (g) **131.** (c) **137.** No; no
139. They are the same line. **141.** Yes, if the y-intercept is 0.

8.3 Assess Your Understanding *(page 550)*

3. F **4.** radius **5.** T **6.** F **7.** Center (2, 1); radius $= 2$; $(x - 2)^2 + (y - 1)^2 = 4$ **9.** Center $\left(\frac{5}{2}, 2\right)$; radius $= \frac{3}{2}$; $\left(x - \frac{5}{2}\right)^2 + (y - 2)^2 = \frac{9}{4}$

11. 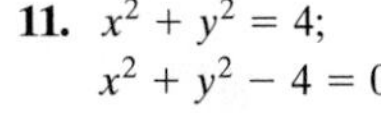
$x^2 + y^2 = 4$; $x^2 + y^2 - 4 = 0$

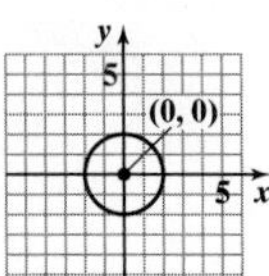

13. $x^2 + (y - 2)^2 = 4$; $x^2 + y^2 - 4y = 0$

15. 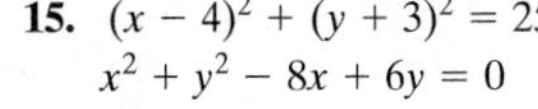
$(x - 4)^2 + (y + 3)^2 = 25$; $x^2 + y^2 - 8x + 6y = 0$

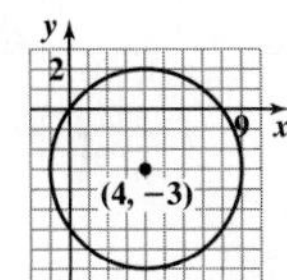

17. 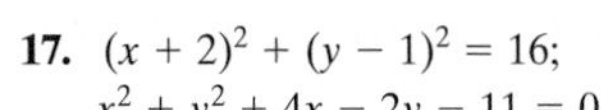
$(x + 2)^2 + (y - 1)^2 = 16$; $x^2 + y^2 + 4x - 2y - 11 = 0$

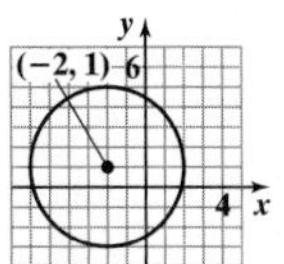

19. $\left(x - \frac{1}{2}\right)^2 + y^2 = \frac{1}{4}$; $x^2 + y^2 - x = 0$

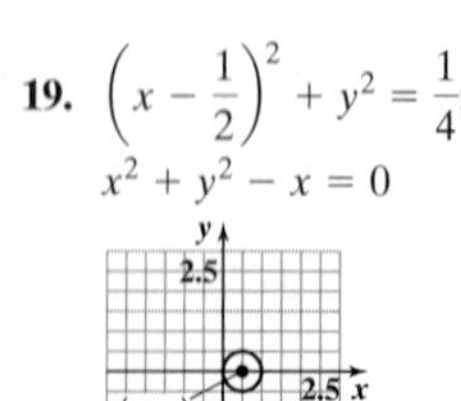

21. (a) $(h, k) = (0, 0)$; $r = 2$
(b)

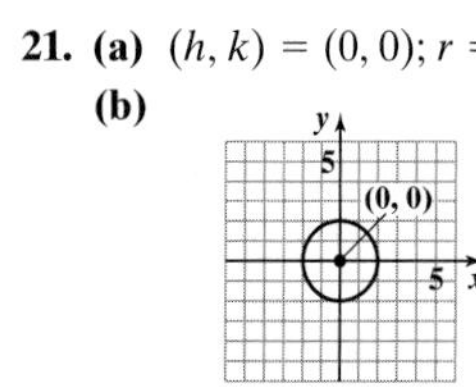
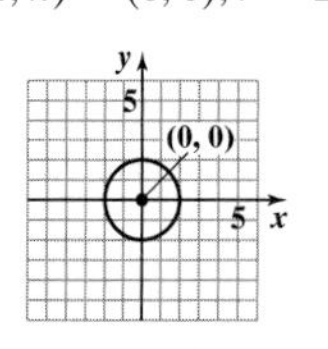

(c) $(\pm 2, 0)$; $(0, \pm 2)$

23. (a) $(h, k) = (3, 0)$; $r = 2$
(b)

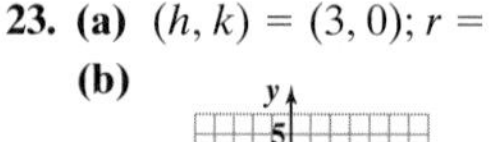
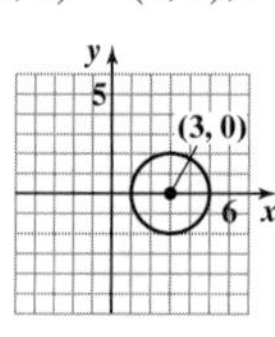

(c) $(1, 0)$; $(5, 0)$

25. (a) $(h, k) = (1, 2)$; $r = 3$
(b)

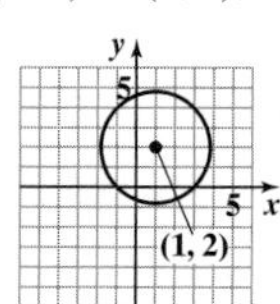

(c) $(1 \pm \sqrt{5}, 0)$; $(0, 2 \pm 2\sqrt{2})$

27. (a) $(h, k) = (-2, 2)$; $r = 3$
(b)

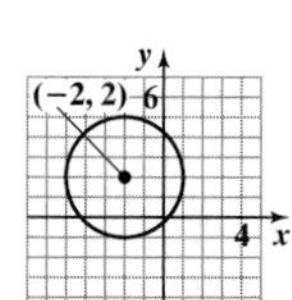

(c) $(-2 \pm \sqrt{5}, 0)$; $(0, 2 \pm \sqrt{5})$

29. (a) $(h, k) = \left(\frac{1}{2}, -1\right)$; $r = \frac{1}{2}$
(b)

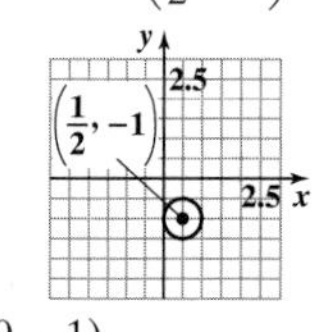

(c) $(0, -1)$

31. (a) $(h, k) = (3, -2)$; $r = 5$
(b)

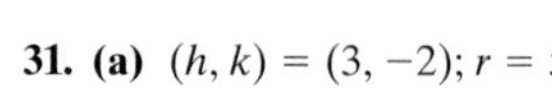

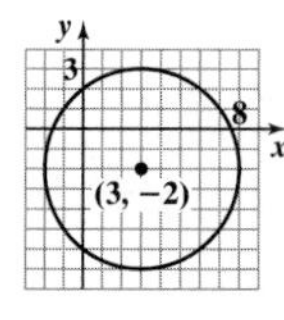

(c) $(3 \pm \sqrt{21}, 0)$; $(0, -6)$, $(0, 2)$

33. (a) $(h, k) = (-2, 0)$; $r = 2$
(b)

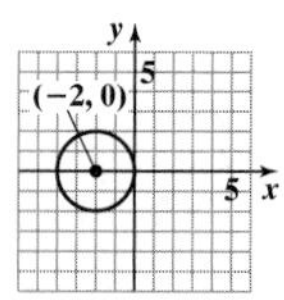

(c) $(0, 0)$, $(-4, 0)$

35. $x^2 + y^2 = 13$ **37.** $(x - 2)^2 + (y - 3)^2 = 9$ **39.** $(x + 1)^2 + (y - 3)^2 = 5$ **41.** $(x + 1)^2 + (y - 3)^2 = 1$ **43.** (c) **45.** (b) **47.** 18 units^2 **49.** $x^2 + (y - 139)^2 = 15{,}625$ **51.** $x^2 + y^2 + 2x + 4y - 4168.16 = 0$ **53.** $\sqrt{2}x + 4y - 9\sqrt{2} = 0$ **55.** $(1, 0)$ **57.** $y = 2$ **59.** (b), (c), (e), (g)

Review Exercises *(page 554)*

1. (a) $\frac{1}{2}$ **(b)** For each run of 2, there is a rise of 1. **2. (a)** $-\frac{4}{3}$ **(b)** For each run of 3, there is a rise of -4. **3. (a)** undefined **(b)** no change in x **4. (a)** 0 **(b)** no change in y **5.** $(0, 0)$; symmetric with respect to the x-axis **6.** $(\pm 4, 0)$, $(0, \pm 2)$; symmetric with respect to the x-axis, y-axis, and origin **7.** $(\pm 2, 0)$, $(0, -4)$; symmetric with respect to the y-axis **8.** $(0, 0)$, $(\pm 1, 0)$; symmetric with respect to the origin **9.** $(0, 0)$, $(-1, 0)$, $(0, -2)$; no symmetry **10.** $(x + 2)^2 + (y - 3)^2 = 16$ **11.** $(x + 1)^2 + (y + 2)^2 = 1$

12. Center $(0, 1)$; radius $= 2$

Intercepts: $(-\sqrt{3}, 0)$, $(\sqrt{3}, 0)$, $(0, -1)$, $(0, 3)$

13. Center $(1, -2)$; radius $= 3$

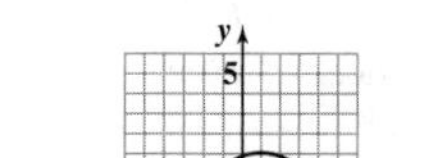
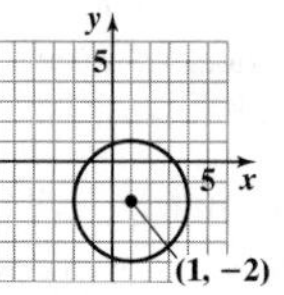

Intercepts: $(1 - \sqrt{5}, 0)$, $(1 + \sqrt{5}, 0)$, $(0, -2 - 2\sqrt{2})$, $(0, -2 + 2\sqrt{2})$

14. Center $(1, -2)$; radius $= \sqrt{5}$

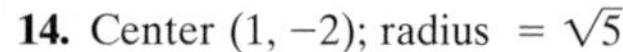
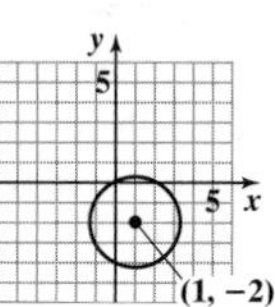

Intercepts: $(0, 0)$, $(2, 0)$, $(0, -4)$

15. $2x + y = 5$ or $y = -2x + 5$ **16.** $y = 4$ **17.** $x = -3$; no slope–intercept form **18.** $5x + 2y = 10$ or $y = -\frac{5}{2}x + 5$ **19.** $x + 5y = -10$ or $y = -\frac{1}{5}x - 2$ **20.** $5x + y = 11$ or $y = -5x + 11$ **21.** $2x - 3y = -19$ or $y = \frac{2}{3}x + \frac{19}{3}$ **22.** $x + 3y = 10$ or $y = -\frac{1}{3}x + \frac{10}{3}$

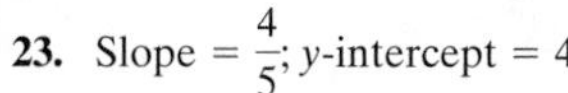

23. Slope $= \frac{4}{5}$; y-intercept $= 4$

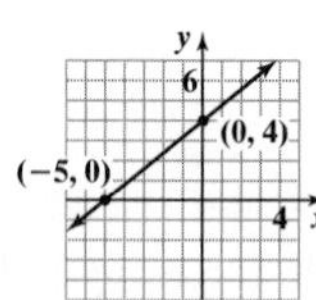

24. Slope $= \frac{3}{2}$; y-intercept $= \frac{1}{2}$

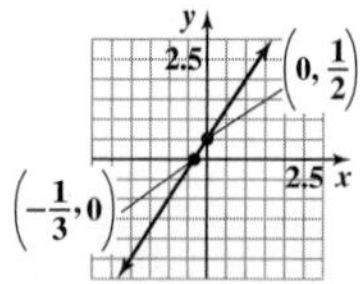

25. Intercepts: $(6, 0)$, $(0, -4)$

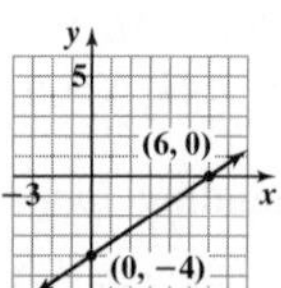

26. Intercepts: $(4, 0)$, $(0, 6)$

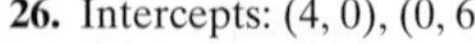
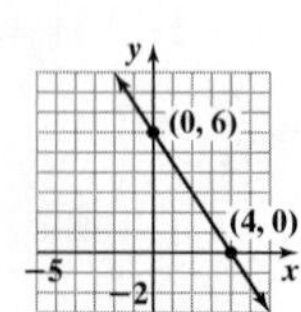

27.

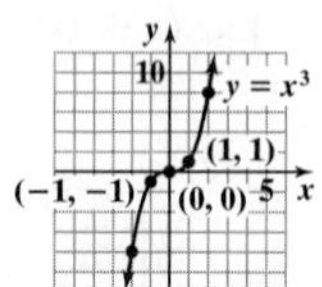

28.

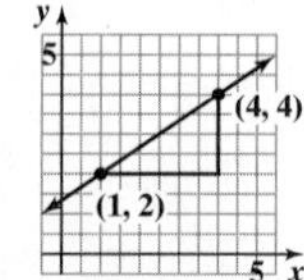

29. Slope from A to B is -2; slope from A to C is $\frac{1}{2}$. Since $(-2)\left(\frac{1}{2}\right) = -1$, the lines are perpendicular. **30.** Center: $(1, -2)$; radius: $4\sqrt{2}$; $(x - 1)^2 + (y + 2)^2 = 32$ **31.** Slope from A to B is -1; slope from A to C is -1. **32.** $p = \frac{854}{130{,}000}B$; \$1083.92 **33.** 199.9 lb **34.** $a \approx 36$ million miles

Chapter Test *(page 556)*

1. (a) $m = -\frac{2}{3}$ **(b)** For every 3-unit change in x, y will change by -2 units.

2.

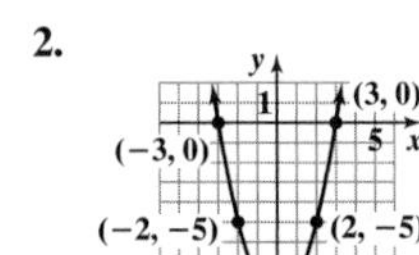

3.

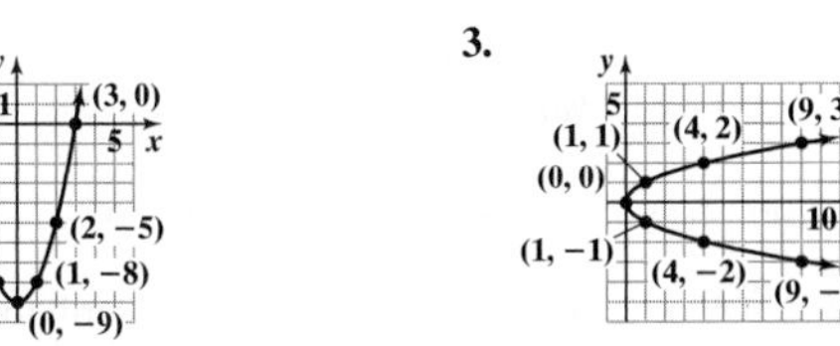

4. Intercepts: $(-3, 0)$, $(3, 0)$, $(0, 9)$; symmetric with respect to the y-axis

5. $y = -2x + 2$

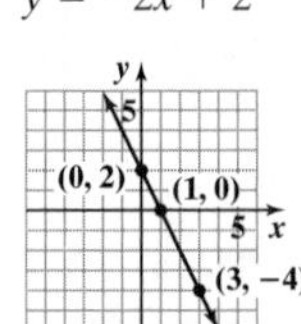

6. Slope $= -\frac{2}{3}$; y-intercept $= 3$

7.

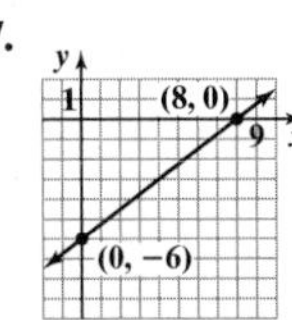

8. $x^2 + y^2 - 8x + 6y = 0$

9. Center: $(-2, 1)$; radius: 3

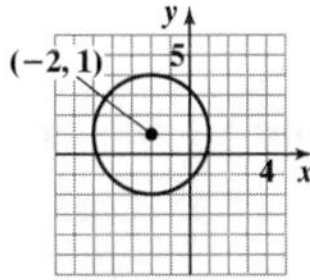

10. Parallel line: $y = -\frac{2}{3}x - \frac{1}{3}$; perpendicular line: $y = \frac{3}{2}x + 3$ **11.** 14.69 ohms

Cumulative Review *(page 556)*

1. $\left\{\frac{5}{3}\right\}$ **2.** $\{-3, 4\}$ **3.** $\left\{-\frac{1}{2}, 3\right\}$ **4.** $\{1 - \sqrt{3}, 1 + \sqrt{3}\}$ **5.** No real solution

6. $\{4\}$ **7.** $\{1, 3\}$ **8.** $\{-2 - 2\sqrt{2}, -2 + 2\sqrt{2}\}$ **9.** $\{-3i, 3i\}$ **10.** $\{1 - 2i, 1 + 2i\}$ **11.** $\{x \mid x \le 5\}$ or $(\infty, 5]$;

12. $\{x \mid -5 < x < 1\}$ or $(-5, 1)$;

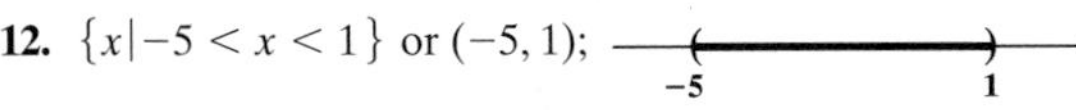

13. $\{x \mid 1 \le x \le 3\}$ or $[1, 3]$;

14. $\{x \mid x < -5$ or $x > 1\}$ or $(\infty, -5) \cup (1, \infty)$;

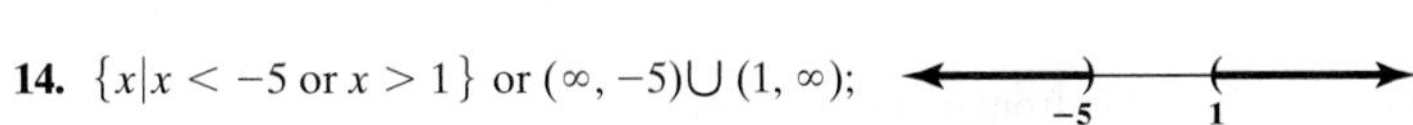

15. $5\sqrt{2}$; $\left(\frac{3}{2}, \frac{1}{2}\right)$ **16.** (a), (b)

17.

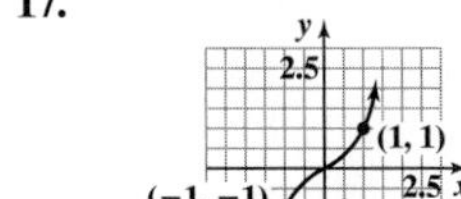

18. $y = -2x + 2$ **19.** $y = -\frac{1}{2}x + \frac{13}{2}$;

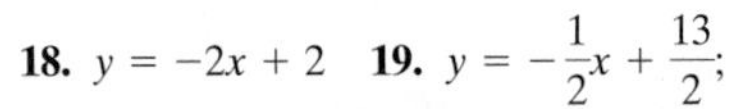

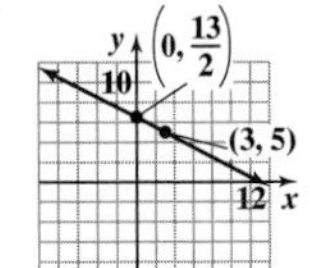

20.

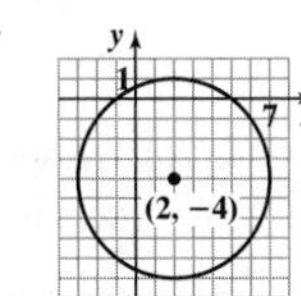

CHAPTER 9 Functions and Their Graphs

9.1 Assess Your Understanding *(page 569)*

5. independent; dependent **6.** range **7.** $[0, 5]$ **8.** $\neq$; f; g **9.** $(g - f)(x)$ **10.** F **11.** T **12.** T **13.** F **14.** F **15.** Function; Domain: {Elvis, Colleen, Kaleigh, Marissa}; Range: {January 8, March 15, September 17} **17.** Not a function **19.** Not a function **21.** Function; Domain: $\{1, 2, 3, 4\}$; Range: $\{3\}$ **23.** Not a function **25.** Function; Domain: $\{-2, -1, 0, 1\}$; Range: $\{0, 1, 4\}$ **27.** Function **29.** Function **31.** Not a function **33.** Not a function **35.** Function **37.** Not a function **39. (a)** -4 **(b)** 1 **(c)** -3 **(d)** $3x^2 - 2x - 4$ **(e)** $-3x^2 - 2x + 4$ **(f)** $3x^2 + 8x + 1$ **(g)** $12x^2 + 4x - 4$ **(h)** $3x^2 + 6xh + 3h^2 + 2x + 2h - 4$ **41. (a)** 0 **(b)** $\frac{1}{2}$ **(c)** $-\frac{1}{2}$ **(d)** $\frac{-x}{x^2 + 1}$ **(e)** $\frac{-x}{x^2 + 1}$ **(f)** $\frac{x + 1}{x^2 + 2x + 2}$ **(g)** $\frac{2x}{4x^2 + 1}$ **(h)** $\frac{x + h}{x^2 + 2xh + h^2 + 1}$ **43. (a)** 4 **(b)** 5 **(c)** 5 **(d)** $|x| + 4$ **(e)** $-|x| - 4$ **(f)** $|x + 1| + 4$ **(g)** $2|x| + 4$ **(h)** $|x + h| + 4$ **45. (a)** $-\frac{1}{5}$ **(b)** $-\frac{3}{2}$ **(c)** $\frac{1}{8}$ **(d)** $\frac{2x - 1}{3x + 5}$ **(e)** $\frac{-2x - 1}{3x - 5}$ **(f)** $\frac{2x + 3}{3x - 2}$ **(g)** $\frac{4x + 1}{6x - 5}$ **(h)** $\frac{2x + 2h + 1}{3x + 3h - 5}$ **47.** All real numbers **49.** All real numbers **51.** $\{x \mid x \neq -4, x \neq 4\}$ **53.** $\{x \mid x \neq 0\}$ **55.** $\{x \mid x \ge 4\}$ **57.** $\{x \mid x > 9\}$ **59.** $\{x \mid x > 1\}$ **61.** $\{t \mid t \ge 4, t \neq 7\}$ **63. (a)** $(f + g)(x) = 5x + 1$; All real numbers **(b)** $(f - g)(x) = x + 7$; All real numbers **(c)** $(f \cdot g)(x) = 6x^2 - x - 12$;

All real numbers **(d)** $\left(\frac{f}{g}\right)(x) = \frac{3x+4}{2x-3}$; $\left\{x \middle| x \neq \frac{3}{2}\right\}$ **(e)** 16 **(f)** 11 **(g)** 10 **(h)** −7 **65. (a)** $(f+g)(x) = 2x^2 + x - 1$; All real numbers **(b)** $(f-g)(x) = -2x^2 + x - 1$; All real numbers **(c)** $(f \cdot g)(x) = 2x^3 - 2x^2$; All real numbers **(d)** $\left(\frac{f}{g}\right)(x) = \frac{x-1}{2x^2}$; $\{x \mid x \neq 0\}$ **(e)** 20 **(f)** −29 **(g)** 8 **(h)** 0 **67. (a)** $(f+g)(x) = \sqrt{x} + 3x - 5$; $\{x \mid x \geq 0\}$ **(b)** $(f-g)(x) = \sqrt{x} - 3x + 5$; $\{x \mid x \geq 0\}$ **(c)** $(f \cdot g)(x) = 3x\sqrt{x} - 5\sqrt{x}$; $\{x \mid x \geq 0\}$ **(d)** $\left(\frac{f}{g}\right)(x) = \frac{\sqrt{x}}{3x-5}$; $\left\{x \middle| x \geq 0, x \neq \frac{5}{3}\right\}$ **(e)** $\sqrt{3} + 4$ **(f)** −5 **(g)** $\sqrt{2}$ **(h)** $-\frac{1}{2}$ **69. (a)** $(f+g)(x) = 1 + \frac{2}{x}$; $\{x \mid x \neq 0\}$ **(b)** $(f-g)(x) = 1$; $\{x \mid x \neq 0\}$ **(c)** $(f \cdot g)(x) = \frac{1}{x} + \frac{1}{x^2}$; $\{x \mid x \neq 0\}$ **(d)** $\left(\frac{f}{g}\right)(x) = x + 1$; $\{x \mid x \neq 0\}$ **(e)** $\frac{5}{3}$ **(f)** 1 **(g)** $\frac{3}{4}$ **(h)** 2 **71. (a)** $(f+g)(x) = \frac{6x+3}{3x-2}$; $\left\{x \middle| x \neq \frac{2}{3}\right\}$ **(b)** $(f-g)(x) = \frac{-2x+3}{3x-2}$; $\left\{x \middle| x \neq \frac{2}{3}\right\}$ **(c)** $(f \cdot g)(x) = \frac{8x^2+12x}{(3x-2)^2}$; $\left\{x \middle| x \neq \frac{2}{3}\right\}$ **(d)** $\left(\frac{f}{g}\right)(x) = \frac{2x+3}{4x}$; $\left\{x \middle| x \neq 0, x \neq \frac{2}{3}\right\}$ **(e)** 3 **(f)** $-\frac{1}{2}$ **(g)** $\frac{7}{2}$ **(h)** $\frac{5}{4}$ **73.** $g(x) = 5 - \frac{7}{2}x$ **75.** 4 **77.** $2x + h - 1$ **79.** $\frac{-(2x+h)}{x^2(x+h)^2}$ **81.** $\frac{1}{\sqrt{x+h} + \sqrt{x}}$ **83.** $A = -\frac{7}{2}$ **85.** $A = -4$ **87.** $A = 8$; undefined at $x = 3$ **89.** $A(x) = \frac{1}{2}x^2$ **91.** $G(x) = 10x$ **93. (a)** P is the dependent variable; a is the independent variable. **(b)** $P(20) = 197.34$ million; There are 197.34 million Americans 20 years of age or older. **(c)** $P(0) = 290.580$ million; There are 290.580 million Americans. **95. (a)** 15.1 m, 14.071 m, 12.944 m, 11.719 m **(b)** 1.01 sec, 1.43 sec, 1.75 sec **(c)** 2.02 sec **97. (a)** \$222 **(b)** \$225 **(c)** \$220 **(d)** \$230 **99.** $R(x) = \frac{L(x)}{P(x)}$ **101.** $H(x) = P(x) \cdot I(x)$ **103. (a)** $P(x) = -0.05x^3 + 0.8x^2 + 155x - 500$ **(b)** $P(15) = \$1836.25$ **(c)** When 15 hundred cellphones are sold, the profit is \$1836.25. **105.** Only $h(x) = 2x$

9.2 Assess Your Understanding *(page 577)*

3. vertical **4.** 5; −3 **5.** $a = -2$ **6.** F **7.** F **8.** T **9. (a)** $f(0) = 3$; $f(-6) = -3$ **(b)** $f(6) = 0$; $f(11) = 1$ **(c)** Positive **(d)** Negative **(e)** −3, 6, and 10 **(f)** $-3 < x < 6$; $10 < x \leq 11$ **(g)** $\{x \mid -6 \leq x \leq 11\}$ **(h)** $\{y \mid -3 \leq y \leq 4\}$ **(i)** −3, 6, 10 **(j)** 3 **(k)** 3 times **(l)** Once **(m)** 0, 4 **(n)** −5, 8 **11.** Not a function **13.** Function **(a)** Domain: $\{x \mid -\pi \leq x \leq \pi\}$; Range: $\{y \mid -1 \leq y \leq 1\}$ **(b)** $\left(-\frac{\pi}{2}, 0\right), \left(\frac{\pi}{2}, 0\right), (0, 1)$ **(c)** y-axis **15.** Not a function **17.** Function **(a)** Domain: $\{x \mid 0 < x < 3\}$; Range: $\{y \mid y < 2\}$ **(b)** (1, 0) **(c)** None **19.** Function **(a)** Domain: all real numbers; Range: $\{y \mid y \leq 2\}$ **(b)** (−3, 0), (3, 0), (0, 2) **(c)** y-axis **21.** Function **(a)** Domain: all real numbers; Range: $\{y \mid y \geq -3\}$ **(b)** (1, 0), (3, 0), (0, 9) **(c)** None **23. (a)** Yes **(b)** $f(-2) = 9$; $(-2, 9)$ **(c)** $0, \frac{1}{2}$; $(0, -1), \left(\frac{1}{2}, -1\right)$ **(d)** All real numbers **(e)** $-\frac{1}{2}, 1$ **(f)** −1 **25. (a)** No **(b)** $f(4) = -3$; $(4, -3)$ **(c)** 14; (14, 2) **(d)** $\{x \mid x \neq 6\}$ **(e)** −2 **(f)** $-\frac{1}{3}$ **27. (a)** Yes **(b)** $f(2) = \frac{8}{17}$; $\left(2, \frac{8}{17}\right)$ **(c)** −1, 1; (−1, 1), (1, 1) **(d)** All real numbers **(e)** 0 **(f)** 0

29. (a) Approximately 10.4 ft high
(b) $h(12) \approx 9.9$ represents the height of the ball, in feet, after it has traveled 12 feet in front of the foul line.

(c)

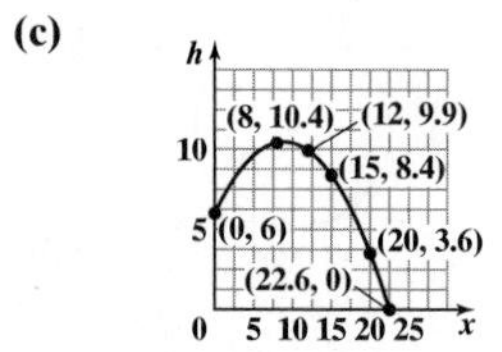

(d) The ball will not go through the hoop; $h(15) \approx 8.4$ ft. If $v = 30$ ft/sec, $h(15) = 10$ ft.

31. (a) About 81.07 ft **(b)** About 129.59 ft
(c) $h(500) \approx 26.63$ represents the height of the golf ball, in feet, after it has traveled a horizontal distance of 500 feet. **(d)** About 528.13 ft
(e)

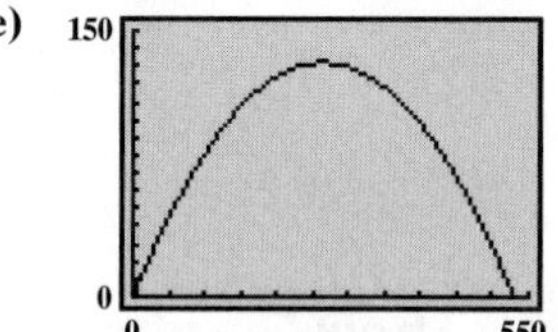

(f) About 115.07 ft and 413.05 ft
(g) 275 ft; maximum height shown in the table is 131.8 ft
(h) 264 ft

33. (a)

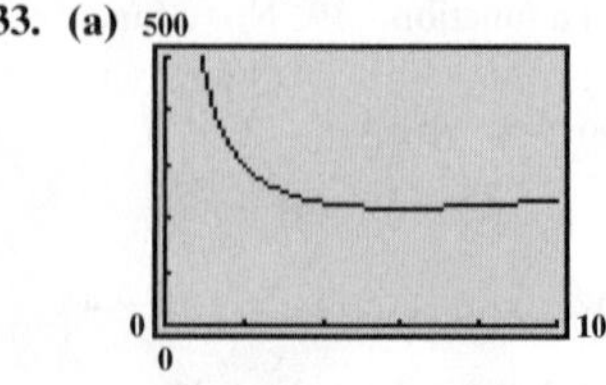

(b)

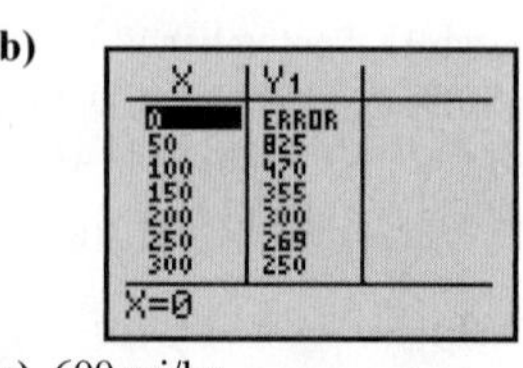

(c) 600 mi/hr

35. (a) 3 **(b)** −2 **(c)** −1 **(d)** 1 **(e)** 2 **(f)** $-\frac{1}{3}$
37. (a) \$80; it costs \$80 if you use 0 minutes. **(b)** \$80; it costs \$80 if you use 1000 minutes. **(c)** \$210; it costs \$210 if you use 2000 minutes. **(d)** $\{m \mid 0 \leq m \leq 14{,}400\}$. There are at most 14,400 anytime minutes in a month. **39.** The x-intercepts can number anywhere from 0 to infinitely many. There is at most one y-intercept. **41. (a)** III **(b)** IV **(c)** I **(d)** V **(e)** II

43. (a)

Distance (in blocks)
(22, 5)
(5, 2)
(7, 0)
(29, 0)
(6, 0)
Time (in minutes)

45. (a) 2 hr elapsed during which Kevin was between 0 and 3 mi from home **(b)** 0.5 hr elapsed during which Kevin was 3 mi from home **(c)** 0.3 hr elapsed during which Kevin was between 0 and 3 mi from home **(d)** 0.2 hr elapsed during which Kevin was 0 mi from home **(e)** 0.9 hr elapsed during which Kevin was between 0 and 2.8 mi from home **(f)** 0.3 hr elapsed during which Kevin was 2.8 mi from home **(g)** 1.1 hr elapsed during which Kevin was between 0 and 2.8 mi from home **(h)** 3 mi **(i)** 2 times **47.** No points whose x-coordinate is 5 or whose y-coordinate is 0 can be on the graph.

9.3 Assess Your Understanding *(page 590)*

6. increasing **7.** even; odd **8.** T **9.** T **10.** F **11.** Yes **13.** No **15.** $(-8, -2)$; $(0, 2)$; $(5, \infty)$ **17.** Yes; 10 **19.** $-2, 2$; $6, 10$ **21. (a)** $(-2, 0), (0, 3), (2, 0)$ **(b)** Domain: $\{x \mid -4 \le x \le 4\}$ or $[-4, 4]$; Range: $\{y \mid 0 \le y \le 3\}$ or $[0, 3]$ **(c)** Increasing on $(-2, 0)$ and $(2, 4)$; Decreasing on $(-4, -2)$ and $(0, 2)$ **(d)** Even **23. (a)** $(0, 1)$ **(b)** Domain: all real numbers; Range: $\{y \mid y > 0\}$ or $(0, \infty)$ **(c)** Increasing on $(-\infty, \infty)$ **(d)** Neither **25. (a)** $(-\pi, 0), (0, 0), (\pi, 0)$ **(b)** Domain: $\{x \mid -\pi \le x \le \pi\}$ or $[-\pi, \pi]$; Range: $\{y \mid -1 \le y \le 1\}$ or $[-1, 1]$ **(c)** Increasing on $\left(-\frac{\pi}{2}, \frac{\pi}{2}\right)$; Decreasing on $\left(-\pi, -\frac{\pi}{2}\right)$ and $\left(\frac{\pi}{2}, \pi\right)$ **(d)** Odd **27. (a)** $\left(0, \frac{1}{2}\right), \left(\frac{1}{3}, 0\right), \left(\frac{5}{2}, 0\right)$ **(b)** Domain: $\{x \mid -3 \le x \le 3\}$ or $[-3, 3]$; Range: $\{y \mid -1 \le y \le 2\}$ or $[-1, 2]$ **(c)** Increasing on $(2, 3)$; Decreasing on $(-1, 1)$; Constant on $(-3, -1)$ and $(1, 2)$ **(d)** Neither **29. (a)** 0; 3 **(b)** $-2, 2$; $0, 0$ **31. (a)** $\frac{\pi}{2}$; 1 **(b)** $-\frac{\pi}{2}$; -1 **33.** Odd **35.** Even **37.** Odd **39.** Neither **41.** Even **43.** Odd **45.** Absolute maximum: $f(1) = 4$; absolute minimum: $f(5) = 1$ **47.** Absolute maximum: $f(3) = 4$; absolute minimum: $f(1) = 1$ **49.** Absolute maximum: none; absolute minimum: $f(0) = 0$ **51.** Absolute maximum: none; absolute minimum: none

53.

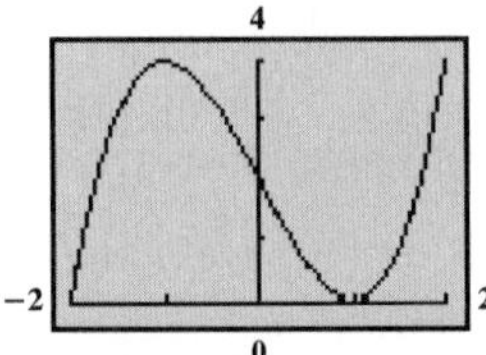

Increasing: $(-2, -1), (1, 2)$
Decreasing: $(-1, 1)$
Local maximum: $(-1, 4)$
Local minimum: $(1, 0)$

55.

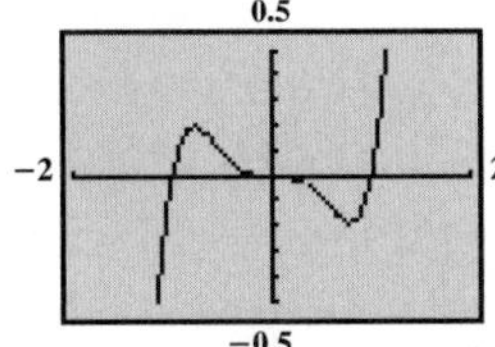

Increasing: $(-2, -0.77), (0.77, 2)$
Decreasing: $(-0.77, 0.77)$
Local maximum: $(-0.77, 0.19)$
Local minimum: $(0.77, -0.19)$

57.

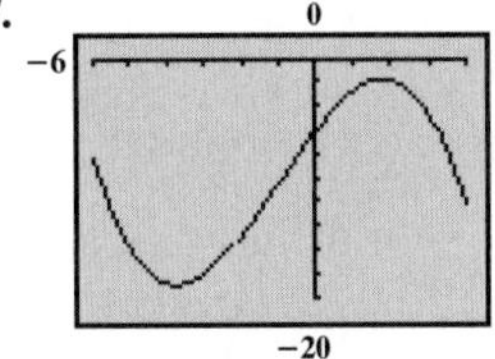

Increasing: $(-3.77, 1.77)$
Decreasing: $(-6, -3.77), (1.77, 4)$
Local maximum: $(-1.77, -1.91)$
Local minimum: $(-3.77, -18.89)$

59.

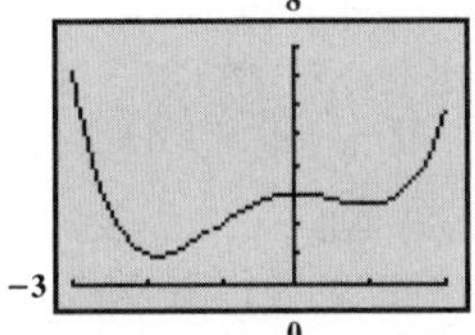

Increasing: $(-1.87, 0), (0.97, 2)$
Decreasing: $(-3, -1.87), (0, 0.97)$
Local maximum: $(0, 3)$
Local minima: $(-1.87, 0.95)$, $(0.97, 2.65)$

61. (a) -4 **(b)** -8 **(c)** -10 **63. (a)** 17 **(b)** -1 **(c)** 11 **65. (a)** 5 **(b)** $y = 5x - 2$ **67. (a)** -1 **(b)** $y = -x$ **69. (a)** 4 **(b)** $y = 4x - 8$ **71. (a)** Odd **(b)** Local maximum value: 54 at $x = -3$ **73. (a)** Even **(b)** Local maximum value: 24 at $x = -2$ **(c)** 47.4 sq. units

75. (a)

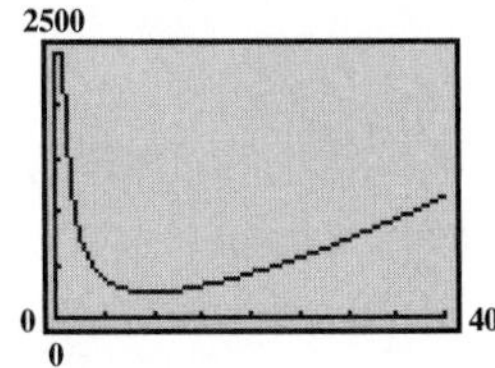

(b) 10 riding lawn mowers/hr
(c) \$239/mower

77. (a), (b)

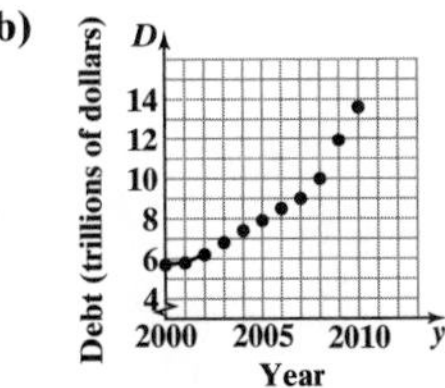

The slope represents the average rate of change of the debt from 2000 to 2002.

(c) \$277 billion
(d) \$564 billion
(e) \$1768.5 billion
(f) The average rate of change is increasing over time.

79. (a) 1 **(b)** 0.5 **(c)** 0.1 **(d)** 0.01 **(e)** 0.001 **(f)**

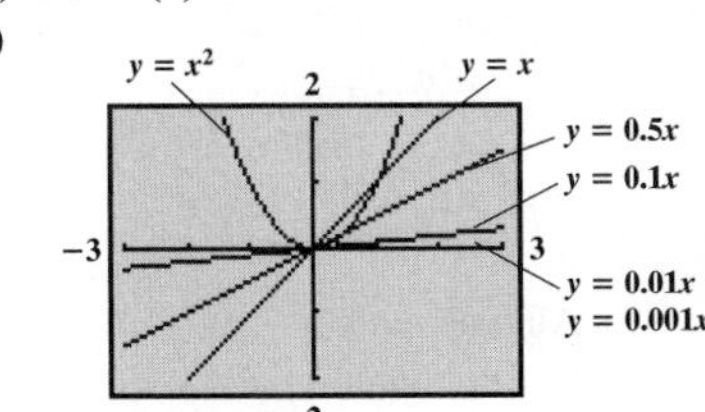

(g) They are getting closer to the tangent line at $(0, 0)$.
(h) They are getting closer to 0.

81. **(a)** 2
(b) 2; 2; 2; 2
(c) $y = 2x + 5$
(d)

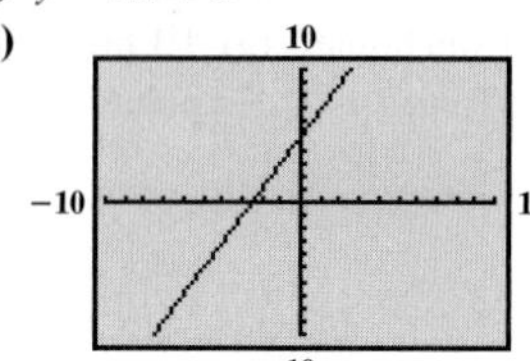

83. **(a)** $2x + h + 2$
(b) 4.5; 4.1; 4.01; 4
(c) $y = 4.01x - 1.01$
(d)

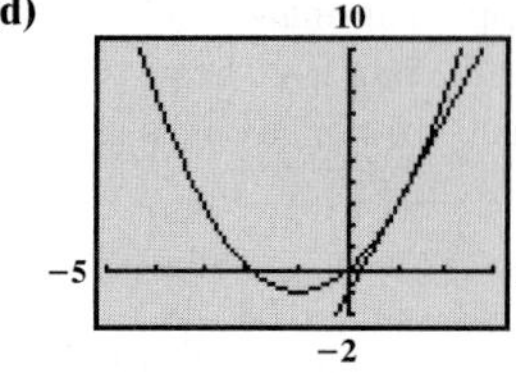

85. **(a)** $4x + 2h - 3$
(b) 2; 1.2; 1.02; 1
(c) $y = 1.02x - 1.02$
(d)

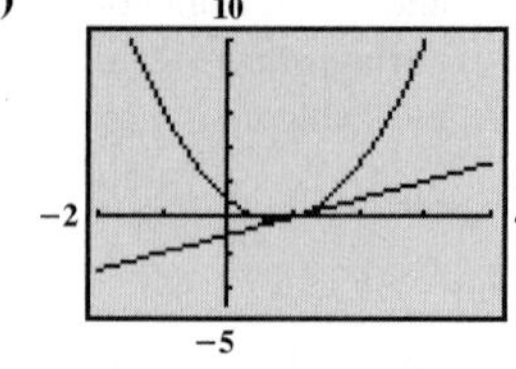

87. **(a)** $-\dfrac{1}{(x+h)x}$
(b) $-\dfrac{2}{3}; -\dfrac{10}{11}; -\dfrac{100}{101}; -1$
(c) $y = -\dfrac{100}{101}x + \dfrac{201}{101}$
(d)

91. At most one **93.** Yes; the function $f(x) = 0$ is both even and odd. **95.** Not necessarily. It just means $f(5) > f(2)$.

9.4 Assess Your Understanding *(page 601)*

4. $(-\infty, 0)$ **5.** piecewise-defined **6.** T **7.** F **8.** F **9.** C **11.** E **13.** B **15.** F

17.

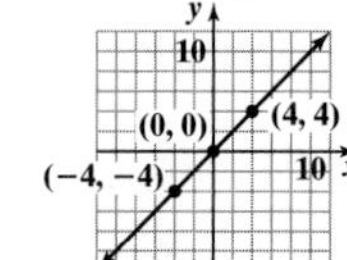

19.

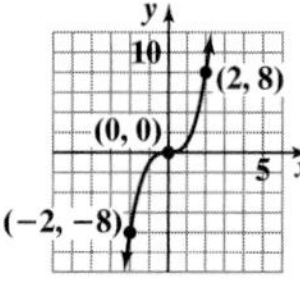

21.

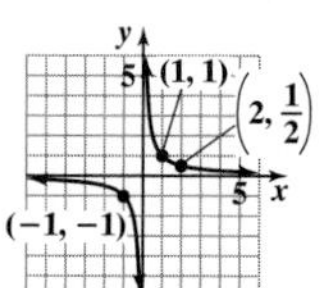

23.

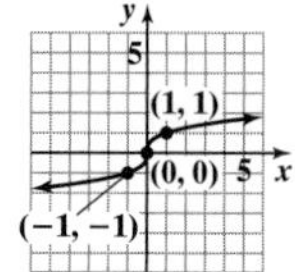

25. **(a)** 4 **(b)** 2 **(c)** 5 **27.** **(a)** −4 **(b)** −2 **(c)** 0 **(d)** 25

29. **(a)** All real numbers
(b) (0, 1)
(c)

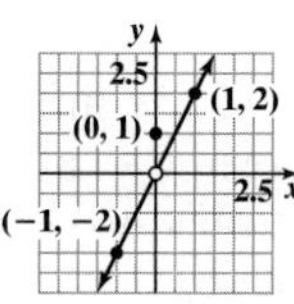

(d) $\{y \mid y \neq 0\}; (-\infty, 0) \cup (0, \infty)$
(e) Discontinuous at $x = 0$

31. **(a)** All real numbers
(b) (0, 3)
(c)

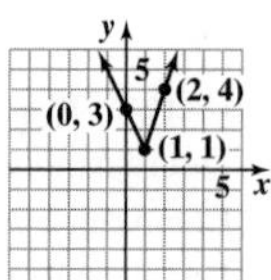

(d) $\{y \mid y \geq 1\}; [1, \infty)$
(e) Continuous

33. **(a)** $\{x \mid x \geq -2\}; [-2, \infty)$
(b) (0, 3), (2, 0)
(c)

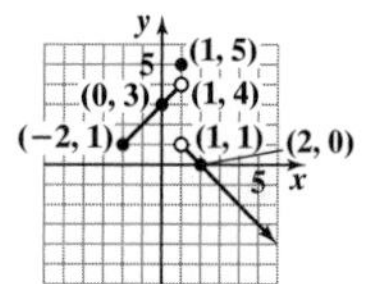

(d) $\{y \mid y < 4 \text{ or } y = 5\}; (-\infty, 4) \cup \{5\}$
(e) Discontinuous at $x = 1$

35. **(a)** All real numbers
(b) (−1, 0), (0, 0)
(c)

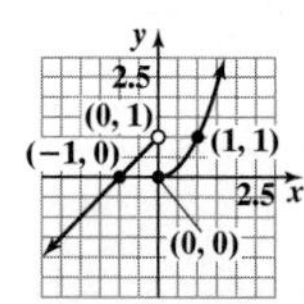

(d) All real numbers
(e) Discontinuous at $x = 0$

37. **(a)** $\{x \mid x \geq -2, x \neq 0\}; [-2, 0) \cup (0, \infty)$
(b) No intercepts
(c)

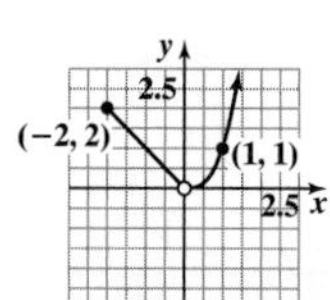

(d) $\{y \mid y > 0\}; (0, \infty)$
(e) Discontinuous at $x = 0$

39. **(a)** All real numbers
(b) $(x, 0)$ for $0 \leq x < 1$
(c)

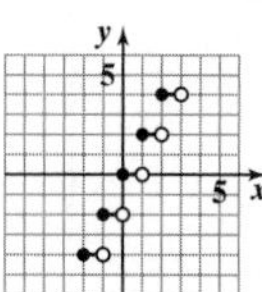

(d) Set of even integers
(e) Discontinuous at $\{x \mid x \text{ is an integer}\}$

41. $f(x) = \begin{cases} -x & \text{if } -1 \leq x \leq 0 \\ \frac{1}{2}x & \text{if } 0 < x \leq 2 \end{cases}$ (Other answers are possible.) **43.** $f(x) = \begin{cases} -x & \text{if } x \leq 0 \\ -x + 2 & \text{if } 0 < x \leq 2 \end{cases}$ (Other answers are possible.)

45. **(a)** 2 **(b)** 3 **(c)** −4 **47.** **(a)** \$39.99 **(b)** \$46.74 **(c)** \$40.44

49. **(a)** \$60.83 **(b)** \$343.16 **(c)** $C(x) = \begin{cases} 0.83752x + 18.95 & \text{if } 0 \leq x \leq 50 \\ 0.6274x + 29.456 & \text{if } x > 50 \end{cases}$ **(d)**

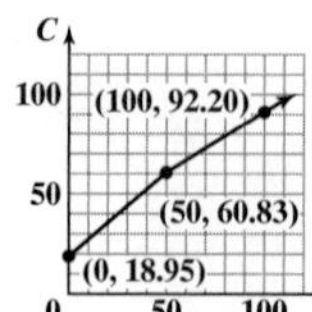

51. For schedule X:

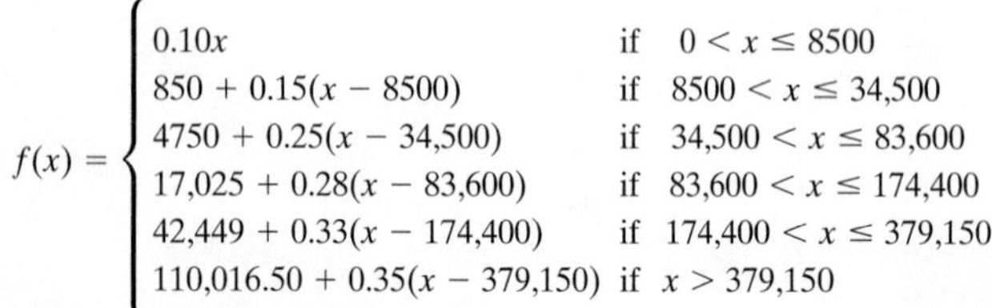

$$f(x) = \begin{cases} 0.10x & \text{if } 0 < x \leq 8500 \\ 850 + 0.15(x - 8500) & \text{if } 8500 < x \leq 34{,}500 \\ 4750 + 0.25(x - 34{,}500) & \text{if } 34{,}500 < x \leq 83{,}600 \\ 17{,}025 + 0.28(x - 83{,}600) & \text{if } 83{,}600 < x \leq 174{,}400 \\ 42{,}449 + 0.33(x - 174{,}400) & \text{if } 174{,}400 < x \leq 379{,}150 \\ 110{,}016.50 + 0.35(x - 379{,}150) & \text{if } x > 379{,}150 \end{cases}$$

53. **(a)**

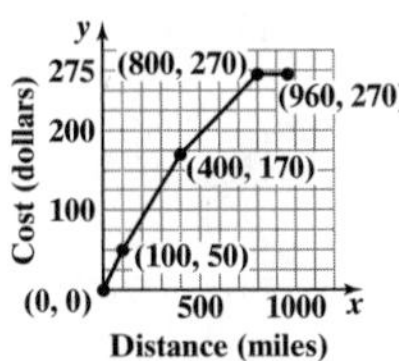

(b) $C(x) = 10 + 0.4x$ **(c)** $C(x) = 70 + 0.25x$

55. **(a)** $C(s) = \begin{cases} 9750 & \text{if } s \le 659 \\ 8250 & \text{if } 660 \le s \le 679 \\ 4500 & \text{if } 680 \le s \le 699 \\ 3000 & \text{if } 700 \le s \le 719 \\ 1500 & \text{if } 720 \le s \le 739 \\ 750 & \text{if } s \ge 740 \end{cases}$ **(b)** \$1500 **(c)** \$8250

57. **(a)** 10°C **(b)** 4°C **(c)** −3°C **(d)** −4°C
(e) The wind chill is equal to the air temperature.
(f) At wind speed greater than 20 m/s, the wind chill factor depends only on the air temperature.

59. $C(x) = \begin{cases} 0.88 & 0 < x \le 1 \\ 1.05 & 1 < x \le 2 \\ 1.22 & 2 < x \le 3 \\ 1.39 & 3 < x \le 4 \\ 1.56 & 4 < x \le 5 \\ 1.73 & 5 < x \le 6 \\ 1.90 & 6 < x \le 7 \\ 2.07 & 7 < x \le 8 \\ 2.24 & 8 < x \le 9 \\ 2.41 & 9 < x \le 10 \\ 2.58 & 10 < x \le 11 \\ 2.75 & 11 < x \le 12 \\ 2.92 & 12 < x \le 13 \end{cases}$

61. Each graph is that of $y = x^2$, but shifted horizontally. If $y = (x - k)^2, k > 0$, the shift is right k units; if $y = (x + k)^2, k > 0$, the shift is left k units.
63. The graph of $y = -f(x)$ is the reflection about the x-axis of the graph of $y = f(x)$.
65. Yes. The graph of $y = (x - 1)^3 + 2$ is the graph of $y = x^3$ shifted right 1 unit and up 2 units. **67.** They all have the same general shape. All three go through the points $(-1, -1)$, $(0, 0)$, and $(1, 1)$. As the exponent increases, the steepness of the curve increases (except near $x = 0$).

9.5 Assess Your Understanding *(page 613)*

1. horizontal; right **2.** y **3.** vertical; up **4.** T **5.** F **6.** T **7.** B **9.** H **11.** I **13.** L **15.** F **17.** G **19.** $y = (x - 4)^3$ **21.** $y = x^3 + 4$ **23.** $y = -x^3$ **25.** $y = 4x^3$ **27.** $y = -(\sqrt{-x} + 2)$ **29.** $y = -\sqrt{x + 3} + 2$ **31.** (c) **33.** (c) **35.** **(a)** −7 and 1 **(b)** −3 and 5 **(c)** −5 and 3 **(d)** −3 and 5 **37.** **(a)** $(-3, 3)$ **(b)** $(4, 10)$ **(c)** Decreasing on $(-1, 5)$ **(d)** Decreasing on $(-5, 1)$

39.

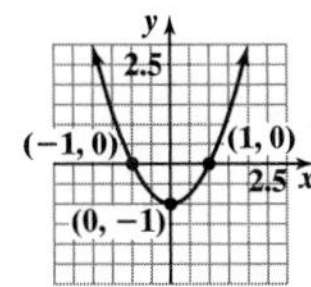

Domain: $(-\infty, \infty)$; Range: $[-1, \infty)$

41.

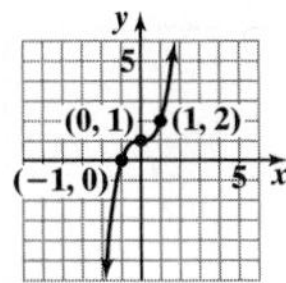

Domain: $(-\infty, \infty)$; Range: $(-\infty, \infty)$

43.

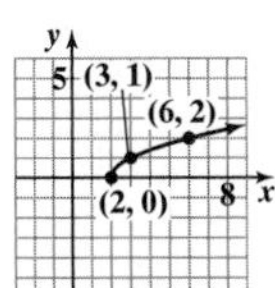

Domain: $[2, \infty)$; Range: $[0, \infty)$

45.

Domain: $(-\infty, \infty)$; Range: $(-\infty, \infty)$

47.

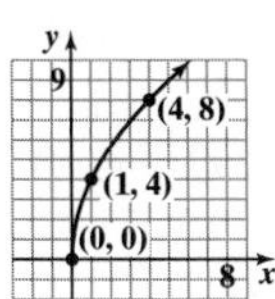

Domain: $[0, \infty)$; Range: $[0, \infty)$

49.

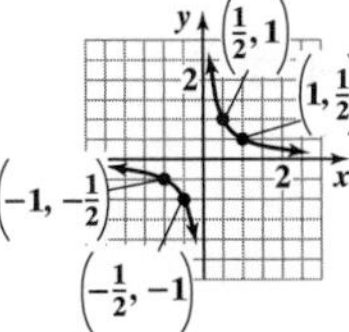

Domain: $(-\infty, 0) \cup (0, \infty)$; Range: $(-\infty, 0) \cup (0, \infty)$

51.

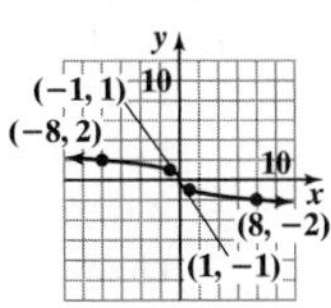

Domain: $(-\infty, \infty)$; Range: $(-\infty, \infty)$

53.

Domain: $(-\infty, \infty)$; Range: $(-\infty, \infty)$

55.

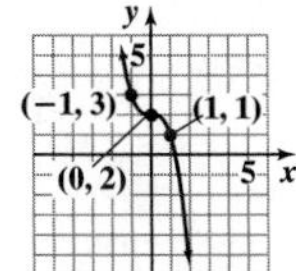

Domain: $(-\infty, \infty)$; Range: $(-\infty, \infty)$;

57.

Domain: $(-\infty, \infty)$; Range: $[-3, \infty)$

59.

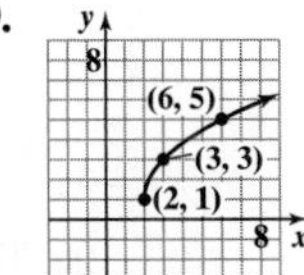

Domain: $[2, \infty)$; Range: $[1, \infty)$

61.

Domain: $(-\infty, 0]$; Range: $[-2, \infty)$

63.

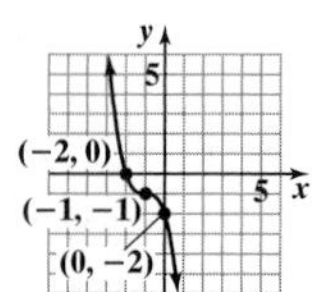

Domain: $(-\infty, \infty)$;
Range: $(-\infty, \infty)$

65.

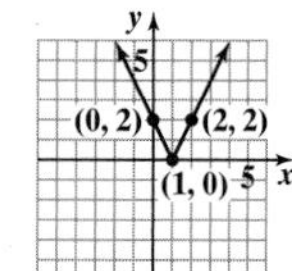

Domain: $(-\infty, \infty)$;
Range: $[0, \infty)$

67.

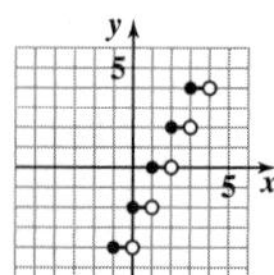

Domain: $(-\infty, \infty)$;
Range: $\{y \mid y \text{ is an even integer}\}$

69. (a) $F(x) = f(x) + 3$

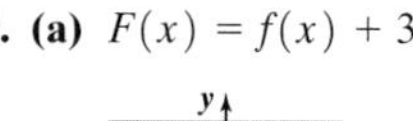
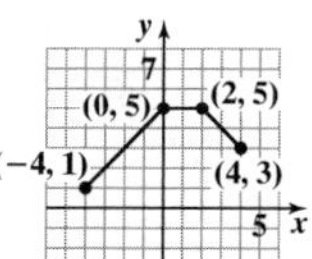

(b) $G(x) = f(x + 2)$

(c) $P(x) = -f(x)$

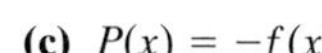
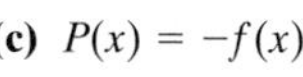

(d) $H(x) = f(x + 1) - 2$

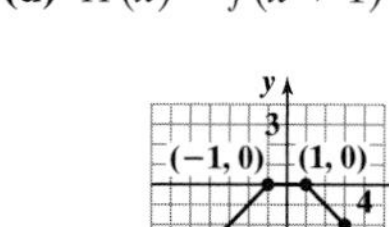
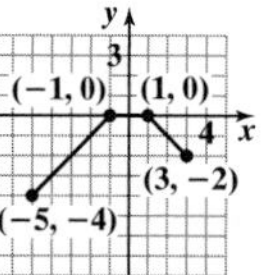

(e) $Q(x) = \frac{1}{2}f(x)$

(f) $g(x) = f(-x)$

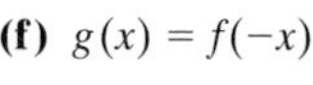
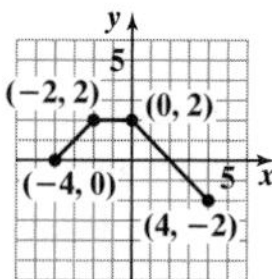

(g) $h(x) = f(2x)$

71. (a) $F(x) = f(x) + 3$

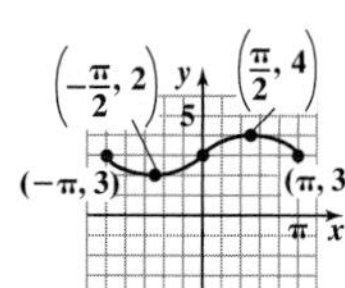

(b) $G(x) = f(x + 2)$

(c) $P(x) = -f(x)$

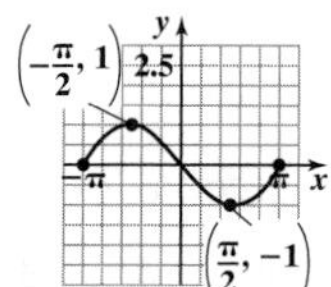

(d) $H(x) = f(x + 1) - 2$

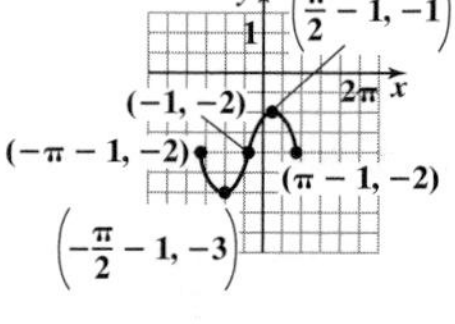

(e) $Q(x) = \frac{1}{2}f(x)$

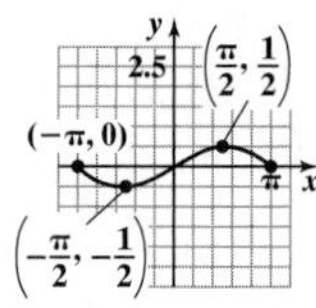

(f) $g(x) = f(-x)$

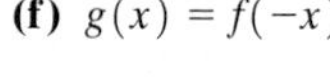

(g) $h(x) = f(2x)$

73. (a)

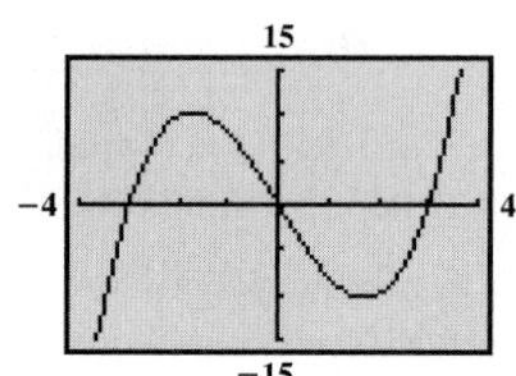

(b) $-3, 0, 3$

(c) Local maximum: 10.39 at $x = -1.73$
Local minimum: -10.39 at $x = 1.73$

(d) Increasing: $(-4, -1.73)$, $(1.73, 4)$
Decreasing: $(-1.73, 1.73)$

(e) Intercepts: $-5, -2, 1$;
Local maximum: 10.39 at $x = -3.73$;
Local minimum: -10.39 at $x = -0.27$
Increasing: $(-6, -3.73)$, $(-0.27, 2)$;
Decreasing: $(-3.73, -0.27)$

(f) Intercepts: $-3, 0, 3$;
Local maximum: 20.78 at $x = 1.73$;
Local minimum: -20.78 at $x = 1.73$;
Increasing: $(-4, -1.73)$, $(1.73, 4)$;
Decreasing: $(-1.73, 1.73)$;

(g) Intercepts: $-3, 0, 3$;
Local maximum: 10.39 at $x = 1.73$;
Local minimum: -10.39 at $x = -1.73$;
Decreasing: $(-4, -1.73)$, $(1.73, 4)$
Increasing: $(-1.73, 1.73)$;

75. $f(x) = (x + 1)^2 - 1$

77. $f(x) = (x - 4)^2 - 15$

79. $f(x) = 2(x - 3)^2 + 1$

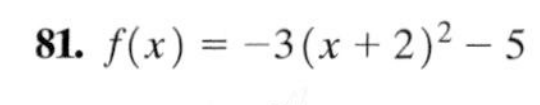

81. $f(x) = -3(x + 2)^2 - 5$

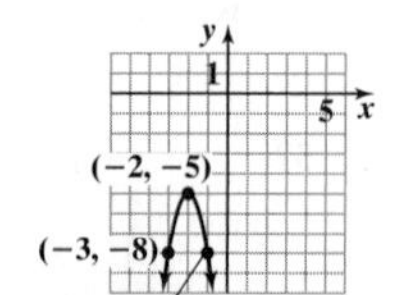

83.

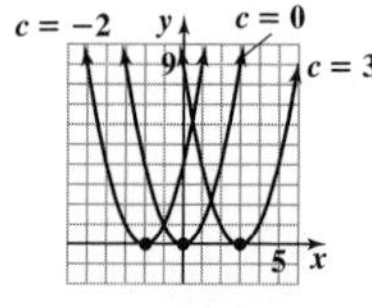

85. (a) 72°F; 65°F
(b) The temperature decreases by 2° to 70°F during the day and 63°F overnight.

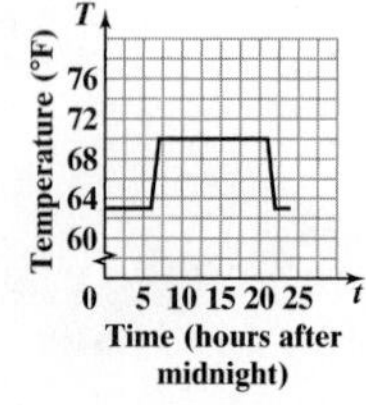

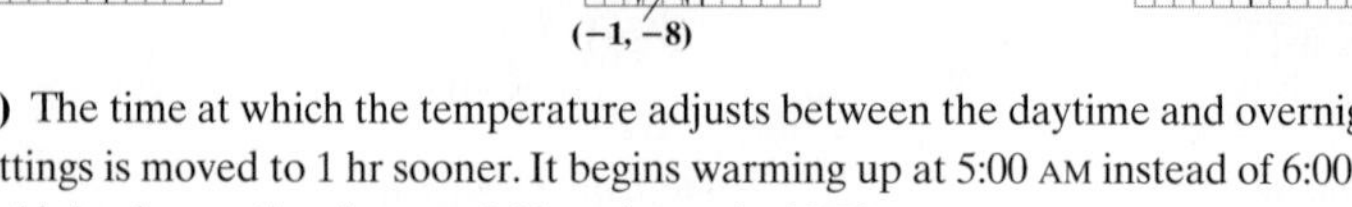

(c) The time at which the temperature adjusts between the daytime and overnight settings is moved to 1 hr sooner. It begins warming up at 5:00 AM instead of 6:00 AM, and it begins cooling down at 8:00 PM instead of 9:00 PM.

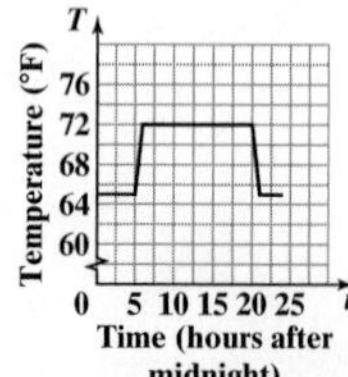

87. 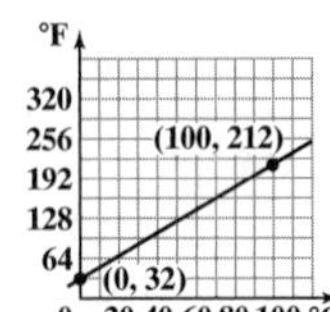

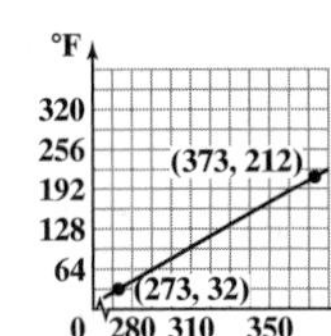

89. (a) 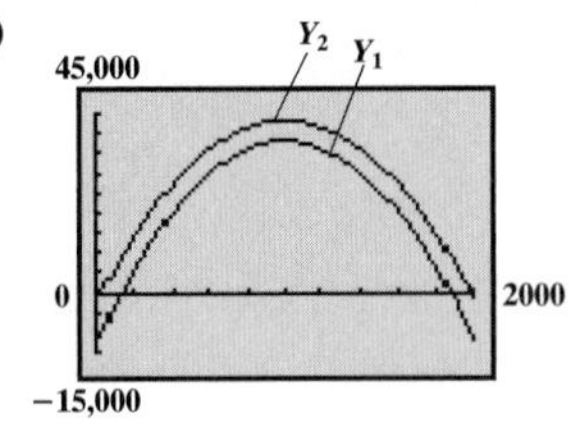

(b) 10% tax
(c) Y_1 is the graph of $p(x)$ shifted down vertically 10,000 units. Y_2 is the graph of $p(x)$ vertically compressed by a factor of 0.9.
(d) 10% tax

91. (a) 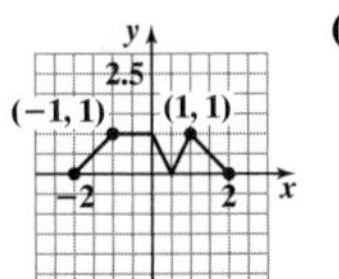

(b) 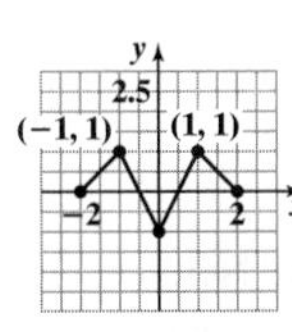

93. (a) $(-4, 2)$ **(b)** $(1, -12)$ **(c)** $(-4, 5)$
95. The graph of $y = f(x) - 2$ is the graph of $y = f(x)$ shifted down 2 units. The graph of $y = f(x - 2)$ is the graph of $y = f(x)$ shifted right 2 units.
97. The range of $y = f(x) = x^2$ is $[0, \infty)$. Since the graph of $y = g(x) = f(x) + k$ is the graph of f shifted up k units if $k > 0$ and down $|k|$ units if $k < 0$, the range of g is $[k, \infty)$.

9.6 Assess Your Understanding *(page 620)*

1. (a) $d(x) = \sqrt{x^4 - 15x^2 + 64}$
(b) $d(0) = 8$
(c) $d(1) = \sqrt{50} \approx 7.07$
(d)
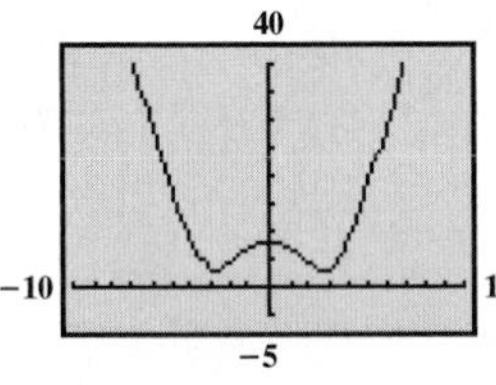

(e) d is smallest when $x \approx -2.74$ or $x \approx 2.74$

3. (a) $d(x) = \sqrt{x^2 - x + 1}$
(b)
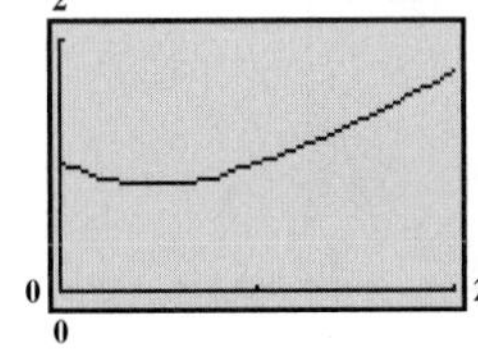

(c) d is smallest when $x = 0.5$.

5. $A(x) = \frac{1}{2}x^4$
7. (a) $A(x) = x(16 - x^2)$
(b) Domain: $\{x|0 < x < 4\}$
(c) The area is largest when $x \approx 2.31$.
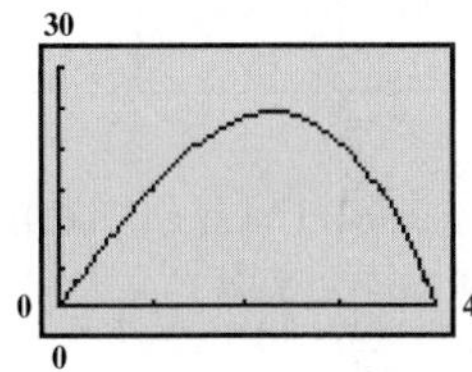

9. (a) $A(x) = 4x\sqrt{4 - x^2}$
(b) $p(x) = 4x + 4\sqrt{4 - x^2}$
(c) A is largest when $x \approx 1.41$.
(d) p is largest when $x \approx 1.41$.

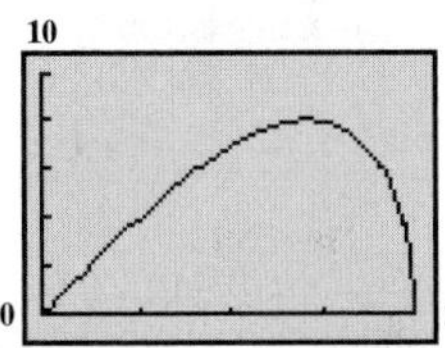

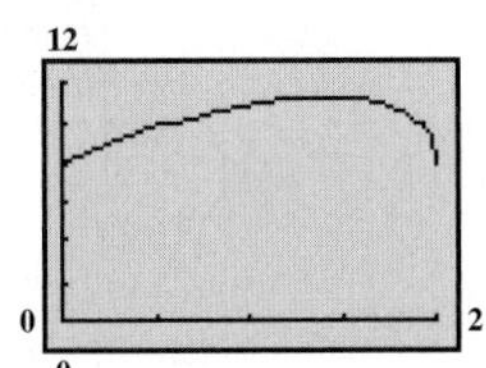

11. (a) $A(x) = x^2 + \dfrac{25 - 20x + 4x^2}{\pi}$
(b) Domain: $\{x|0 < x < 2.5\}$
(c) A is smallest when $x \approx 1.40$ m.
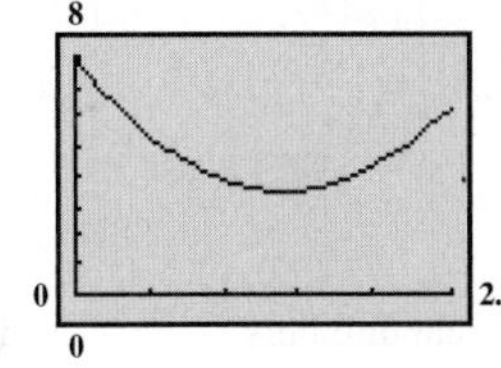

13. (a) $C(x) = x$ **(b)** $A(x) = \dfrac{x^2}{4\pi}$ **15. (a)** $A(r) = 2r^2$ **(b)** $p(r) = 6r$ **17.** $A(x) = \left(\dfrac{\pi}{3} - \dfrac{\sqrt{3}}{4}\right)x^2$

19. (a) $d(t) = \sqrt{2500t^2 - 360t + 13}$
(b) d is smallest when $t \approx 0.07$ hr.
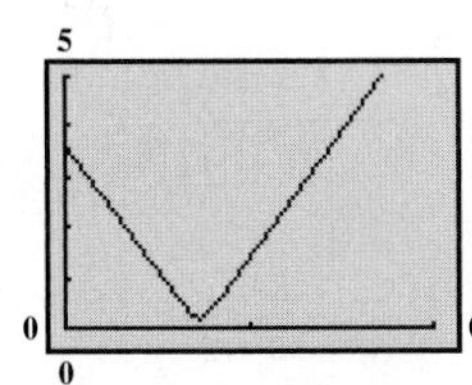

21. $V(r) = \dfrac{\pi H(R - r)r^2}{R}$

23. (a) $T(x) = \dfrac{12 - x}{5} + \dfrac{\sqrt{x^2 + 4}}{3}$
(b) $\{x|0 \le x \le 12\}$
(c) 3.09 hr
(d) 3.55 hr

25. (a) $V(x) = x(24 - 2x)^2$
(b) 972 in.^{3}
(c) 160 in.^{3}
(d) V is largest when $x = 4$.
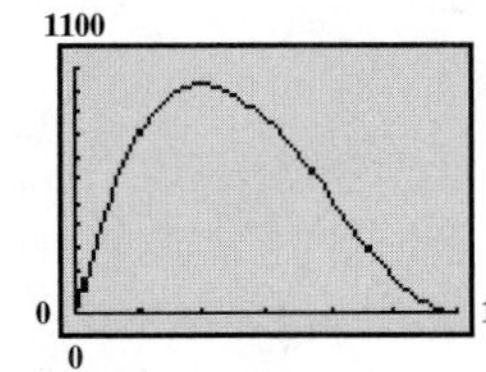

Review Exercises *(page 625)*

1. Function; domain $\{-1, 2, 4\}$, range $\{0, 3\}$ **2.** Not a function **3. (a)** 2 **(b)** -2 **(c)** $-\dfrac{3x}{x^2 - 1}$ **(d)** $-\dfrac{3x}{x^2 - 1}$ **(e)** $\dfrac{3(x - 2)}{x^2 - 4x + 3}$ **(f)** $\dfrac{6x}{4x^2 - 1}$

4. (a) 0 **(b)** 0 **(c)** $\sqrt{x^2 - 4}$ **(d)** $-\sqrt{x^2 - 4}$ **(e)** $\sqrt{x^2 - 4x}$ **(f)** $2\sqrt{x^2 - 1}$ **5. (a)** 0 **(b)** 0 **(c)** $\dfrac{x^2 - 4}{x^2}$ **(d)** $-\dfrac{x^2 - 4}{x^2}$ **(e)** $\dfrac{x(x - 4)}{(x - 2)^2}$ **(f)** $\dfrac{x^2 - 1}{x^2}$ **6.** $\{x|x \ne -3, x \ne 3\}$ **7.** $\{x|x \le 2\}$ **8.** $\{x|x \ne 0\}$ **9.** $\{x|x \ne -3, x \ne 1\}$ **10.** $\{x|x \ge -1, x \ne 2\}$ **11.** $\{x|x > -8\}$

12. $(f + g)(x) = 2x + 3$; Domain: all real numbers
$(f - g)(x) = -4x + 1$; Domain: all real numbers
$(f \cdot g)(x) = -3x^2 + 5x + 2$; Domain: all real numbers
$\left(\dfrac{f}{g}\right)(x) = \dfrac{2 - x}{3x + 1}$; Domain: $\left\{x \middle| x \ne -\dfrac{1}{3}\right\}$

13. $(f + g)(x) = 3x^2 + 4x + 1$; Domain: all real numbers
$(f - g)(x) = 3x^2 - 2x + 1$; Domain: all real numbers
$(f \cdot g)(x) = 9x^3 + 3x^2 + 3x$; Domain: all real numbers
$\left(\dfrac{f}{g}\right)(x) = \dfrac{3x^2 + x + 1}{3x}$; Domain: $\{x|x \ne 0\}$

14. $(f+g)(x) = \dfrac{x^2+2x-1}{x(x-1)}$; Domain: $\{x \mid x \neq 0, x \neq 1\}$

$(f-g)(x) = \dfrac{x^2+1}{x(x-1)}$; Domain: $\{x \mid x \neq 0, x \neq 1\}$

$(f \cdot g)(x) = \dfrac{x+1}{x(x-1)}$; Domain: $\{x \mid x \neq 0, x \neq 1\}$

$\left(\dfrac{f}{g}\right)(x) = \dfrac{x(x+1)}{x-1}$; Domain: $\{x \mid x \neq 0, x \neq 1\}$

15. $-4x + 1 - 2h$ **16. (a)** Domain: $\{x \mid -4 \le x \le 3\}$; Range: $\{y \mid -3 \le y \le 3\}$ **(b)** $(0, 0)$ **(c)** -1 **(d)** -4 **(e)** $\{x \mid 0 < x \le 3\}$

(f)

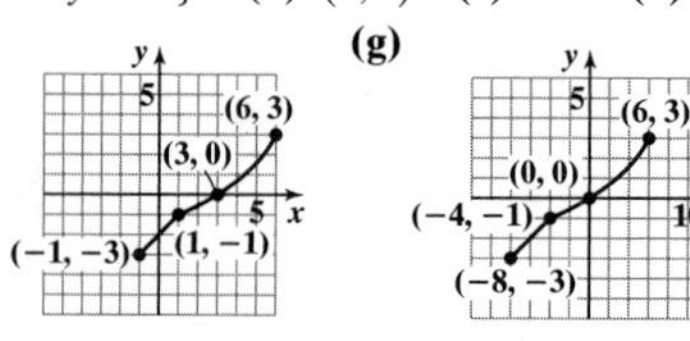

(g)

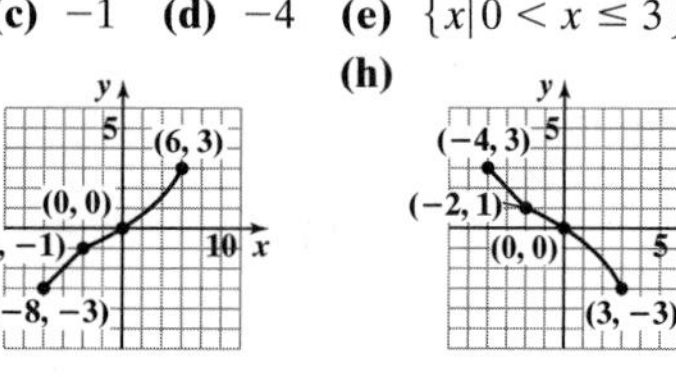

(h)

17. (a) Domain: $\{x \mid x \le 4\}$ or $(-\infty, 4]$;
Range: $\{y \mid y \le 3\}$ or $(-\infty, 3]$
(b) Increasing on $(-\infty, -2)$ and $(2, 4)$; Decreasing on $(-2, 2)$
(c) Local maximum value is 1 and occurs at $x = -2$.
Local minimum value is -1 and occurs at $x = 2$.
(d) Absolute maximum: $f(4) = 3$
Absolute minimum: none
(e) No symmetry **(f)** Neither
(g) x-intercepts: $-3, 0, 3$; y-intercept: 0

18. Odd **19.** Even **20.** Neither **21.** Odd

22.

Local maximum value: 4.04 at $x = -0.91$
Local minimum value: -2.04 at $x = 0.91$
Increasing: $(-3, -0.91)$; $(0.91, 3)$
Decreasing: $(-0.91, 0.91)$

23.

Local maximum value: 1.53 at $x = 0.41$
Local minima values: -0.54 at $x = -0.34$ and -3.56 at $x = 1.80$
Increasing: $(-0.34, 0.41)$; $(1.80, 3)$
Decreasing: $(-2, -0.34)$; $(0.41, 1.80)$

24. (a) 23 **(b)** 7 **(c)** 47 **25.** -5 **26.** -17 **27.** No **28.** Yes **29.** **30.**

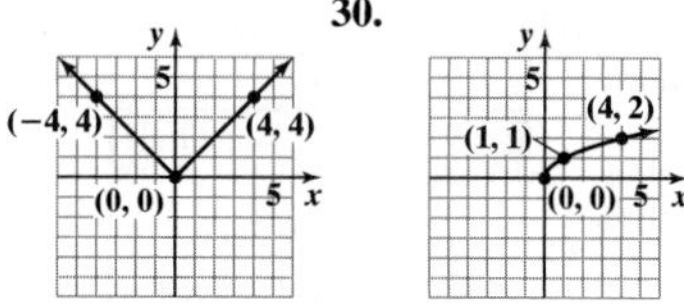

31.

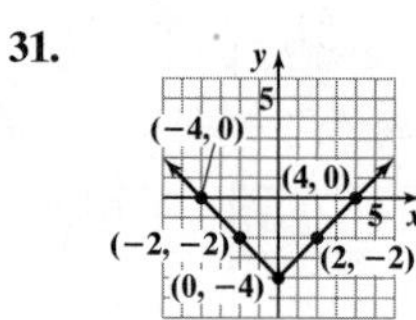

Intercepts: $(-4, 0), (4, 0), (0, -4)$
Domain: all real numbers
Range: $\{y \mid y \ge -4\}$ or $[-4, \infty)$

32.

Intercept: $(0, 0)$
Domain: all real numbers
Range: $\{y \mid y \le 0\}$ or $(-\infty, 0]$

33.

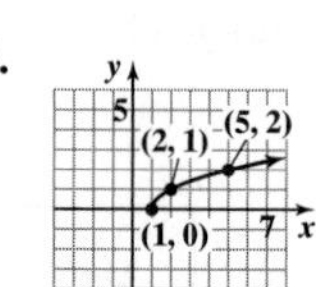

Intercept: $(1, 0)$
Domain: $\{x \mid x \ge 1\}$ or $[1, \infty)$
Range: $\{y \mid y \ge 0\}$ or $[0, \infty)$

34.

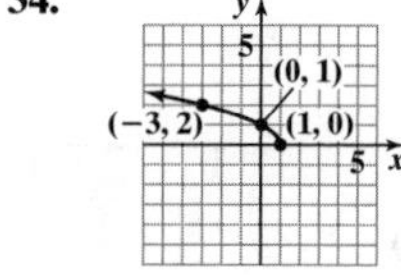

Intercepts: $(0, 1), (1, 0)$
Domain: $\{x \mid x \le 1\}$ or $(-\infty, 1]$
Range: $\{y \mid y \ge 0\}$ or $[0, \infty)$

35.

Intercept: $(0, 3)$
Domain: all real numbers
Range: $\{y \mid y \ge 2\}$ or $[2, \infty)$

36.

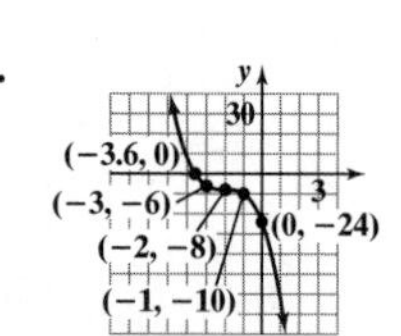

Intercepts: $(0, -24)$, $(-2-\sqrt[3]{4}, 0)$ or about $(-3.6, 0)$
Domain: all real numbers
Range: all real numbers

37. (a) $\{x \mid x > -2\}$ or $(-2, \infty)$
(b) $(0, 0)$
(c)

(d) $\{y \mid y > -6\}$ or $(-6, \infty)$
(e) Discontinuous at $x = 1$

38. (a) $\{x \mid x \ge -4\}$ or $[-4, \infty)$
(b) $(0, 1)$
(c)

(d) $\{y \mid -4 \le y < 0 \text{ or } y > 0\}$ or $[-4, 0) \cup (0, \infty)$
(e) Discontinuous at $x = 0$

39. $A = 11$

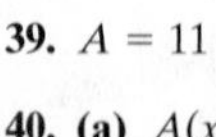

40. (a) $A(x) = 2x^2 + \dfrac{40}{x}$ **(b)** 42 ft^2 **(c)** 28 ft^2

(d)

A is smallest when $x \approx 2.15$ ft.

41. (a) $A(x) = 10x - x^3$
(b) The largest area that can be enclosed by the rectangle is approximately 12.17 square units.

Chapter Test *(page 626)*

1. (a) Function; domain: $\{2, 4, 6, 8\}$; range: $\{5, 6, 7, 8\}$ **(b)** Not a function **(c)** Not a function **(d)** Function; domain: all real numbers; range: $\{y \mid y \geq 2\}$ **2.** Domain: $\left\{x \middle| x \leq \frac{4}{5}\right\}$; $f(-1) = 3$ **3.** Domain: $\{x \mid x \neq -2\}$; $g(-1) = 1$ **4.** Domain: $\{x \mid x \neq -9, x \neq 4\}$; $h(-1) = \frac{1}{8}$ **5. (a)** Domain: $\{x \mid -5 \leq x \leq 5\}$; range: $\{y \mid -3 \leq y \leq 3\}$ **(b)** $(0, 2), (-2, 0)$, and $(2, 0)$ **(c)** $f(1) = 3$ **(d)** $x = -5$ and $x = 3$ **(e)** $\{x \mid -5 \leq x < -2 \text{ or } 2 < x \leq 5\}$ or $[-5, -2) \cup (2, 5]$ **6.** Local maximum values: $f(-0.85) \approx -0.86$; $f(2.35) \approx 15.55$; local minimum value: $f(0) = -2$; the function is increasing on the intervals $(-5, -0.85)$ and $(0, 2.35)$ and decreasing on the intervals $(-0.85, 0)$ and $(2.35, 5)$.

7. (a)

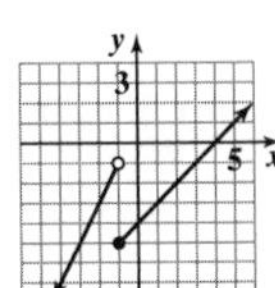

(b) $(0, -4), (4, 0)$ **(c)** $g(-5) = -9$ **(d)** $g(2) = -2$ **8.** 19 **9. (a)** $(f - g)(x) = 2x^2 - 3x + 3$ **(b)** $(f \cdot g)(x) = 6x^3 - 4x^2 + 3x - 2$ **(c)** $f(x + h) - f(x) = 4xh + 2h^2$

10. (a)

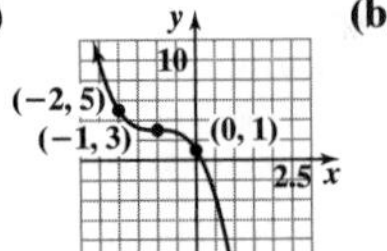

(b)

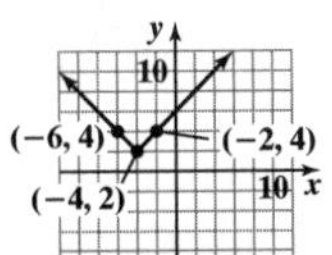

11. (a) 8.67% occurring in 1997 ($x \approx 5$) **(b)** The model predicts that the interest rate will be -10.343%. This is not reasonable.
12. (a) $V(x) = \frac{x^2}{8} - \frac{5x}{4} + \frac{\pi x^2}{64}$ **(b)** 1297.61 ft^3

Cumulative Review *(page 627)*

1. {6} **2.** $\left\{0, \frac{1}{3}\right\}$ **3.** $\{-1, 9\}$ **4.** $\left\{\frac{1}{3}, \frac{1}{2}\right\}$ **5.** $\left\{-\frac{7}{2}, \frac{1}{2}\right\}$ **6.** $\left\{\frac{1}{2}\right\}$
7. $\left\{x \middle| x < -\frac{4}{3}\right\}$; $\left(-\infty, -\frac{4}{3}\right)$ **8.** $\{x \mid 1 < x < 4\}$; $(1, 4)$ **9.** $\left\{x \middle| x \leq -2 \text{ or } x \geq \frac{3}{2}\right\}$; $(-\infty, -2] \cup \left[\frac{3}{2}, \infty\right)$

$-\frac{4}{3}$ | 1 4 | −2 $\frac{3}{2}$

10. (a) distance: $\sqrt{29}$ **(b)** midpoint: $\left(\frac{1}{2}, -4\right)$ **(c)** slope: $-\frac{2}{5}$

11.

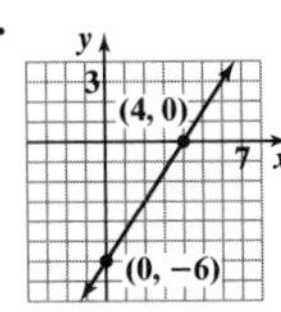

12.

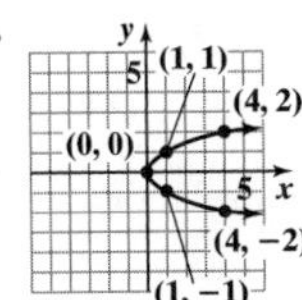

13.

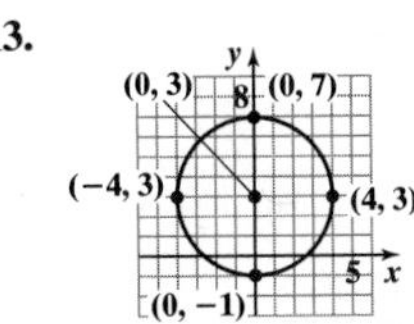

14.

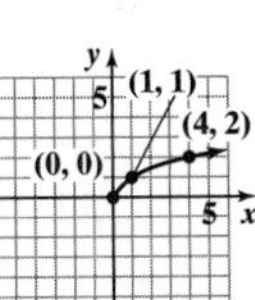

15. Intercepts: $(0, -3), (-2, 0), (2, 0)$; symmetry with respect to the y-axis
16. $y = \frac{1}{2}x + 5$

17.

18.

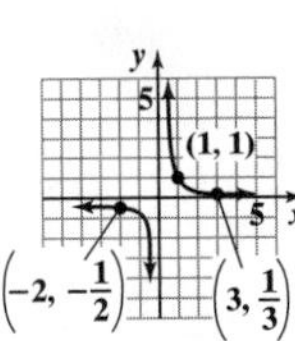

19.

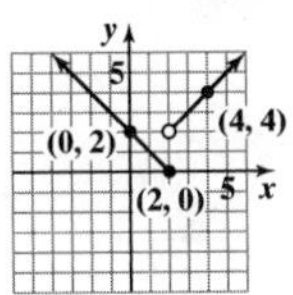

CHAPTER 10 Linear and Quadratic Functions

10.1 Assess Your Understanding *(page 637)*

7. slope; y-intercept **8.** −4; 3 **9.** positive **10.** T **11.** F **12.** F

13. (a) $m = 2$; $b = 3$ **(b)**

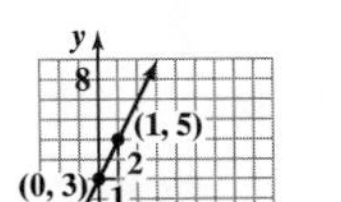

(c) 2 **(d)** Increasing

15. (a) $m = -3$; $b = 4$ **(b)**

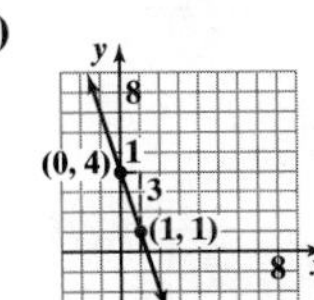

(c) −3 **(d)** Decreasing

17. (a) $m = \frac{1}{4}$; $b = -3$ **(b)**

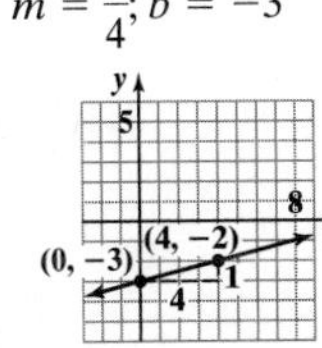

(c) $\frac{1}{4}$ **(d)** Increasing

19. (a) $m = 0$; $b = 4$ **(b)**

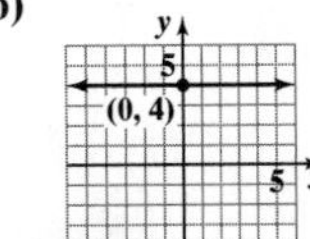

(c) 0 **(d)** Constant

21. Linear; $f(x) = -3x - 2$
23. Nonlinear
25. Nonlinear
27. Linear; $f(x) = 8$

29. (a) $\frac{1}{4}$ **(b)** $\left\{x \middle| x > \frac{1}{4}\right\}$ or $\left(\frac{1}{4}, \infty\right)$ **(c)** 1 **(d)** $\{x \mid x \leq 1\}$ or $(-\infty, 1]$ **(e)**

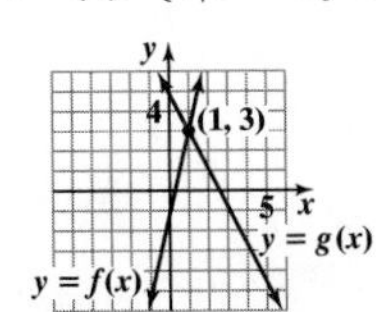

31. (a) 40 **(b)** 88 **(c)** −40 **(d)** $\{x \mid x > 40\}$ or $(40, \infty)$ **(e)** $\{x \mid x \leq 88\}$ or $(-\infty, 88]$ **(f)** $\{x \mid -40 < x < 88\}$ or $(-40, 88)$ **33. (a)** −4 **(b)** $\{x \mid x < -4\}$ or $(-\infty, -4)$ **35. (a)** −6 **(b)** $\{x \mid -6 \leq x < 5\}$ or $[-6, 5)$ **37. (a)** \$45 **(b)** 180 mi **(c)** 260 mi **(d)** $\{x \mid x \geq 0\}$ or $[0, \infty)$ **(e)** The cost of renting the moving truck for a day increases \$0.25 for each mile driven, or there is a charge of \$0.25 per mile to rent the truck in addition to a fixed charge of \$35. **(f)** It costs \$35 to rent the moving truck if 0 miles are driven, or there is a fixed charge of \$35 to rent the truck in addition to a charge that depends on mileage. **39. (a)** \$16; 600 T-shirts **(b)** $\$0 \leq p < \$16$ **(c)** The price will increase.

41. (a) $\{x \mid 8350 \le x \le 33{,}950\}$ or $[8350, 33{,}950]$ **(b)** \$2582.50 **(c)** The independent variable is adjusted gross income, x. The dependent variable is the tax bill, T. **(d)**

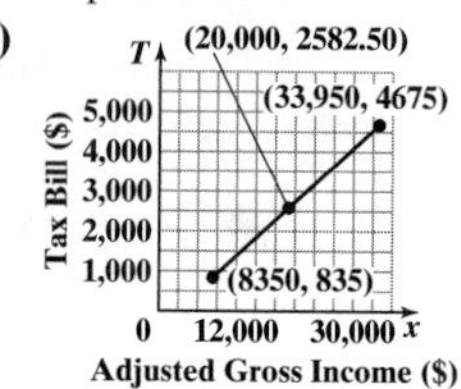

(e) \$27,500 **(f)** For each additional dollar of taxable income between \$8350 and \$33,950, the tax bill of a single person in 2009 increased by \$0.15.

43. (a) $x = 5000$ **(b)** $x > 5000$

45. (a) $V(x) = -1000x + 3000$ **(b)** $\{x \mid 0 \le x \le 3\}$ or $[0, 3]$ **(c)**

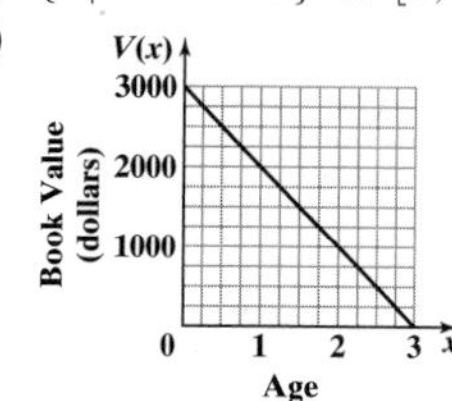

(d) \$1000 **(e)** After 1 year

47. (a) $C(x) = 90x + 1800$ **(b)**

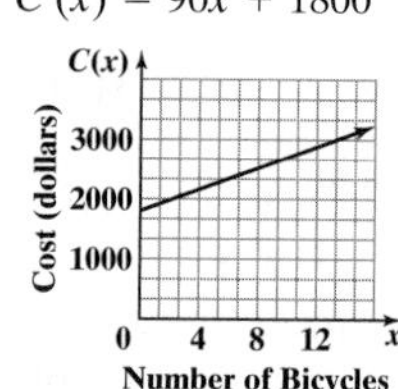

(c) \$3060 **(d)** 22 bicycles

49. (a) $C(x) = 0.07x + 29$ **(b)** \$36.70; \$45.10

51. (a)

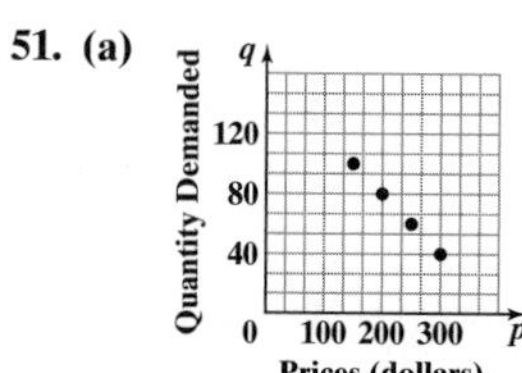

(b) Since each input (price) corresponds to a single output (quantity demanded), we know that quantity demanded is a function of price. Also, because the average rate of change is a constant −0.4 24″ LCD monitor per dollar, the function is linear. **(c)** $q(p) = -0.4p + 160$ **(d)** $\{p \mid 0 \le p \le 400\}$ or $[0, 400]$ **(e)**

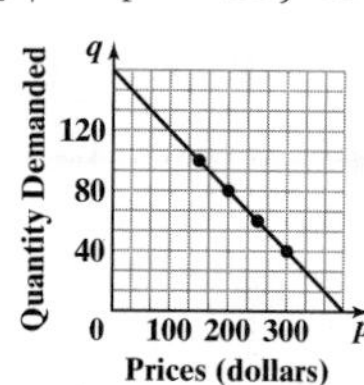

(f) If price increases by \$1, quantity demanded of 24″ LCD monitors decreases by 0.4 monitor. **(g)** q-intercept: When the price is \$0, 160 24″ LCD monitors will be demanded p-intercept: There will be 0 24″ LCD monitors demanded when the price is \$400.

53. (d), (e) **55.** $b = 0$; yes, $f(x) = b$

10.2 Assess Your Understanding *(page 644)*

3. scatter diagram **4.** decrease; 0.008 **5.** Linear relation, $m > 0$ **7.** Linear relation, $m < 0$ **9.** Nonlinear relation

11. (a)

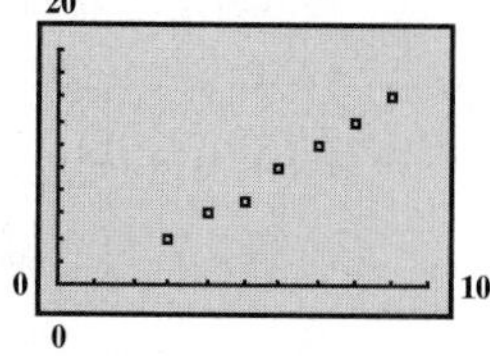

(b) Answers will vary. Using (4, 6) and (8, 14), $y = 2x - 2$. **(c)**

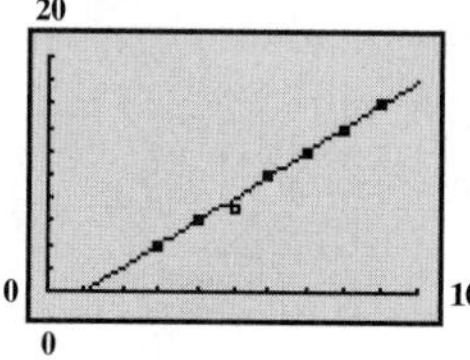

(d) $y = 2.0357x - 2.3571$ **(e)**

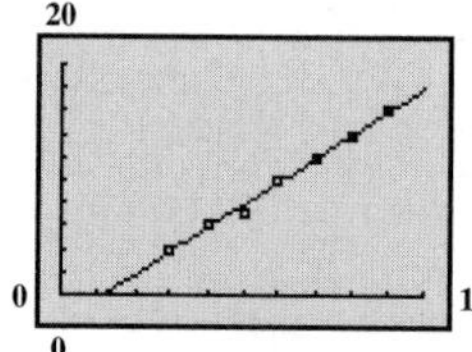

13. (a)

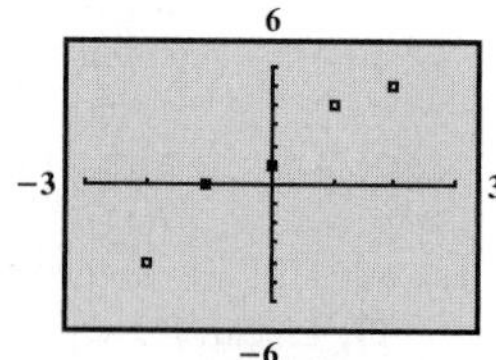

(b) Answers will vary. Using (−2, −4) and (2, 5), $y = \frac{9}{4}x + \frac{1}{2}$. **(c)**

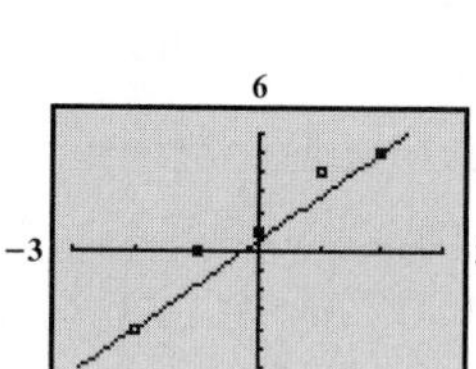

(d) $y = 2.2x + 1.2$ **(e)**

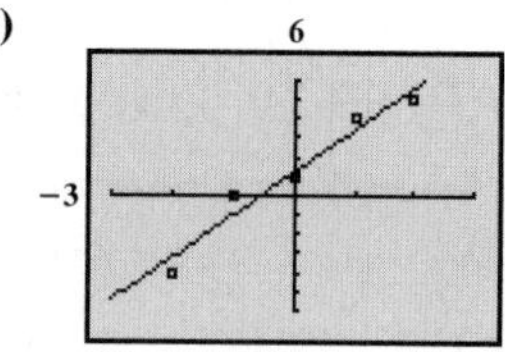

15. (a)

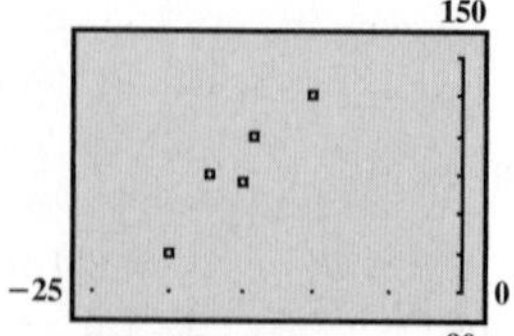

(b) Answers will vary. Using (−20, 100) and (−10, 140), $y = 4x + 180$. **(c)**

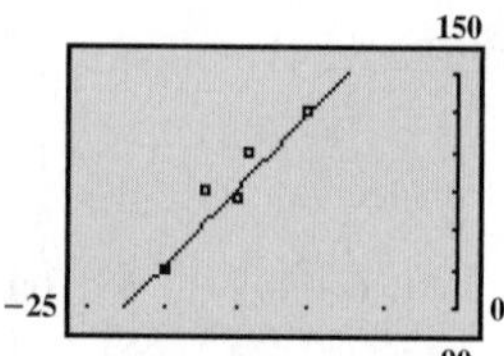

(d) $y = 3.8613x + 180.2920$ **(e)**

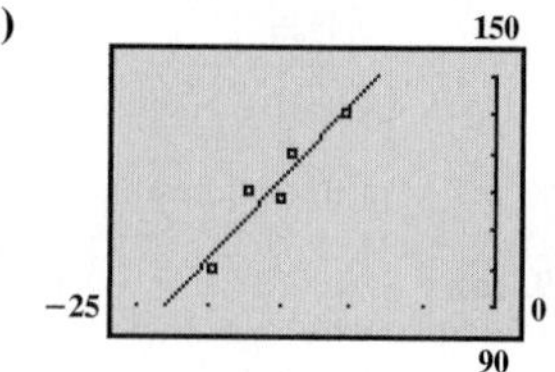

17. (a)

(b) Linear with positive slope

(c) Answers will vary. Using the points (39.52, 210) and (66.45, 280), $y = 2.599x + 107.288$.

(d)

(e) 269 calories

(f) If the weight of a candy bar is increased by 1 gram, the number of calories will increase by 2.599, on average.

19. (a) The independent variable is the number of hours spent playing video games and cumulative grade-point average is the dependent variable because we are using number of hours playing video games to predict (or explain) cumulative grade-point average.

(b)

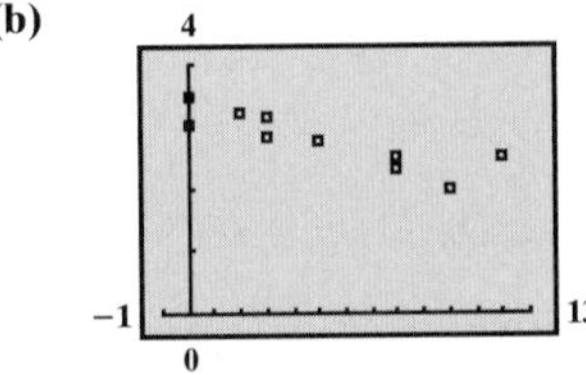

(c) $G(h) = -0.0942h + 3.2763$

(d) If the number of hours playing video games in a week increases by 1 hour, the cumulative grade-point average decreases 0.09, on average.

(e) 2.52

(f) Approximately 9.3 hours

21. (a) No

(b)

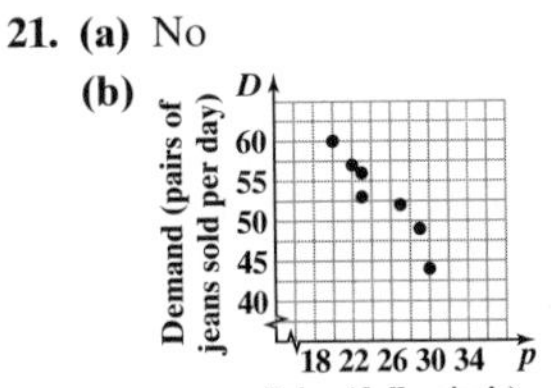

(c) $D = -1.3355p + 86.1974$

(d) If the price increases \$1, the quantity sold per day decreases by about 1.34 pairs of jeans, on average.

(e) $D(p) = -1.3355p + 86.1974$

(f) $\{p \mid 0 < p \le 64\}$

(g) About 49 pairs

23.

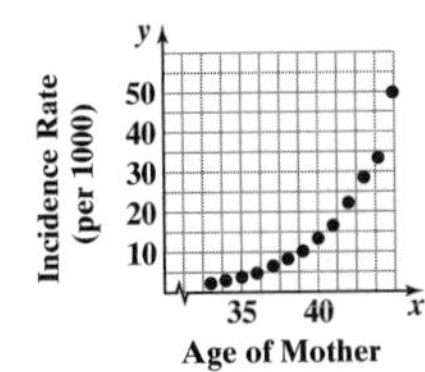

No, the data do not follow a linear pattern.

25. 34.8 hours; A student whose GPA is 0 spends 34.8 hours each week playing video games.; $G(0) = 3.28$; The average GPA of a student who does not play video games is 3.28.

10.3 Assess Your Understanding *(page 656)*

5. parabola **6.** axis or axis of symmetry **7.** $-\dfrac{b}{2a}$ **8.** T **9.** T **10.** T **11.** *C* **13.** *F* **15.** *G* **17.** *H*

19.

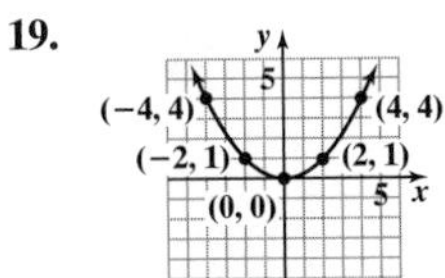

21.

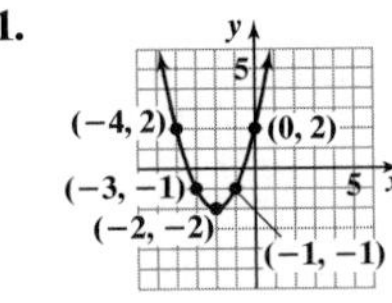

23. $f(x) = (x + 2)^2 - 2$

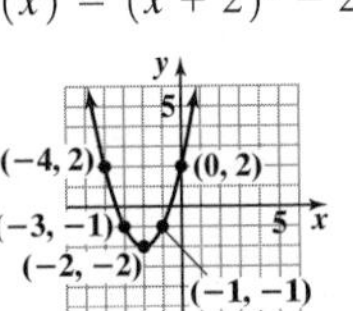

25. $f(x) = 2(x - 1)^2 - 1$

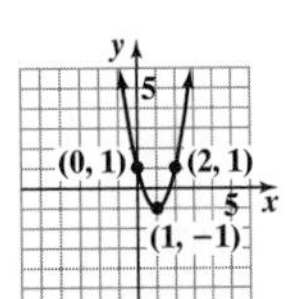

27. $f(x) = -(x + 1)^2 + 1$

29. $f(x) = \dfrac{1}{2}(x + 1)^2 - \dfrac{3}{2}$

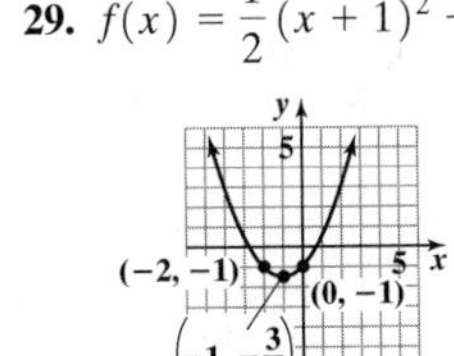

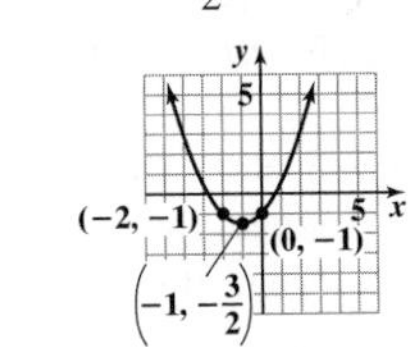

31. (a)

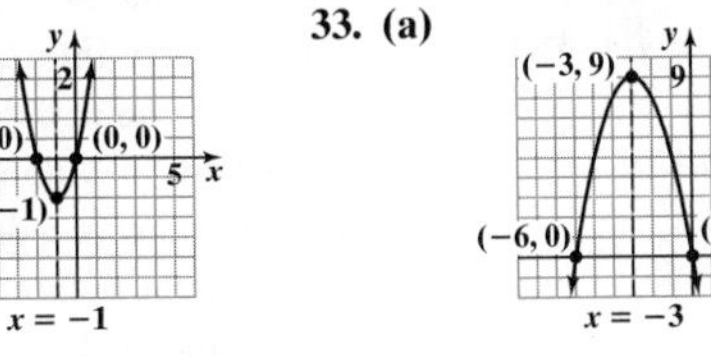

(b) Domain: $(-\infty, \infty)$
Range: $[-1, \infty)$

(c) Decreasing: $(-\infty, -1)$
Increasing: $(-1, \infty)$

33. (a)

(b) Domain: $(-\infty, \infty)$
Range: $(-\infty, 9]$

(c) Increasing: $(-\infty, -3)$
Decreasing: $(-3, \infty)$

35. (a)

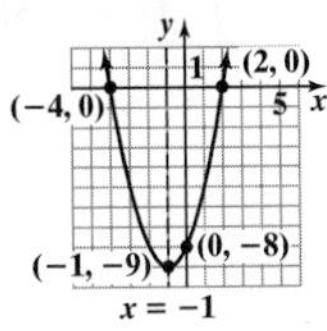

(b) Domain: $(-\infty, \infty)$
Range: $[-9, \infty)$

(c) Decreasing: $(-\infty, -1)$
Increasing: $(-1, \infty)$

37. (a)

(b) Domain: $(-\infty, \infty)$
Range: $[0, \infty)$

(c) Decreasing: $(-\infty, -1)$
Increasing: $(-1, \infty)$

39. (a)

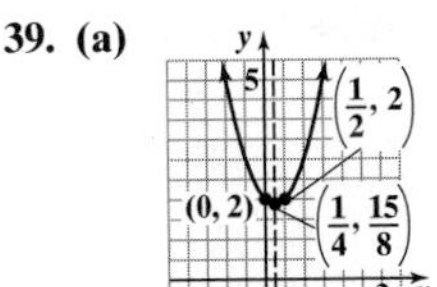

(b) Domain: $(-\infty, \infty)$

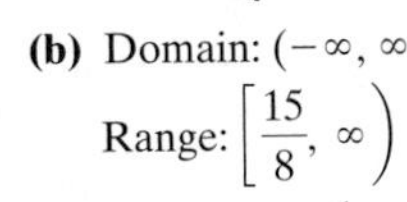

Range: $\left[\dfrac{15}{8}, \infty\right)$

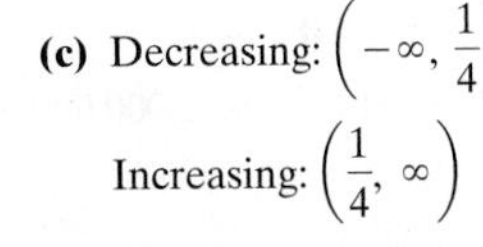

(c) Decreasing: $\left(-\infty, \dfrac{1}{4}\right)$

Increasing: $\left(\dfrac{1}{4}, \infty\right)$

41. (a)

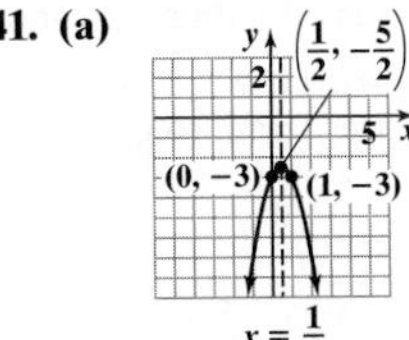

(b) Domain: $(-\infty, \infty)$

Range: $\left(-\infty, -\dfrac{5}{2}\right]$

(c) Increasing: $\left(-\infty, \dfrac{1}{2}\right)$

Decreasing: $\left(\dfrac{1}{2}, \infty\right)$

43. (a)

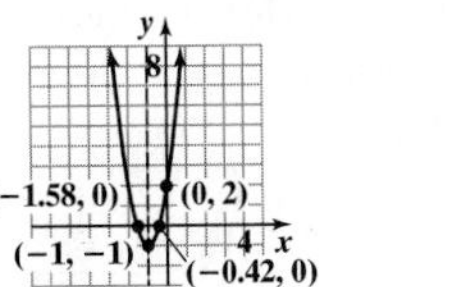

(b) Domain: $(-\infty, \infty)$
Range: $[-1, \infty)$

(c) Decreasing: $(-\infty, -1)$
Increasing: $(-1, \infty)$

45. (a)

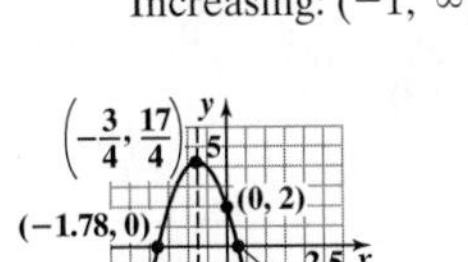

(b) Domain: $(-\infty, \infty)$

Range: $\left(-\infty, \dfrac{17}{4}\right]$

(c) Increasing: $\left(-\infty, -\dfrac{3}{4}\right)$

Decreasing: $\left(-\dfrac{3}{4}, \infty\right)$

47. $f(x) = (x+1)^2 - 2 = x^2 + 2x - 1$ **49.** $f(x) = -(x+3)^2 + 5 = -x^2 - 6x - 4$ **51.** $f(x) = 2(x-1)^2 - 3 = 2x^2 - 4x - 1$
53. Minimum value; -18 **55.** Minimum value; -21 **57.** Maximum value; 21 **59.** Maximum value; 13

61. (a)

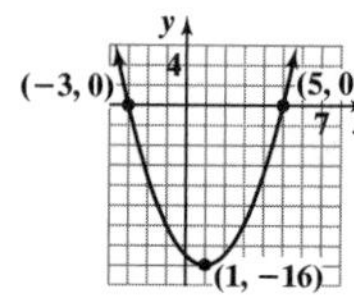

(b) Domain: $(-\infty, \infty)$
Range: $[-16, \infty)$
(c) Decreasing: $(-\infty, 1)$
Increasing: $(1, \infty)$

63. (a)

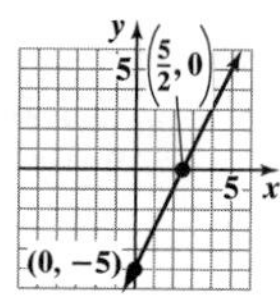

(b) Domain: $(-\infty, \infty)$
Range: $(-\infty, \infty)$
(c) Increasing: $(-\infty, \infty)$

65. (a)

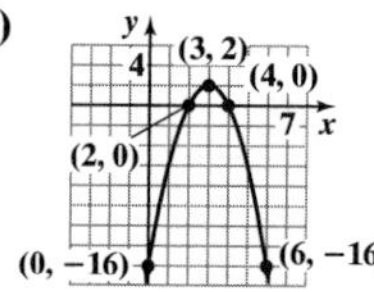

(b) Domain: $(-\infty, \infty)$
Range: $(-\infty, 2]$
(c) Increasing: $(-\infty, 3)$
Decreasing: $(3, \infty)$

67. (a)

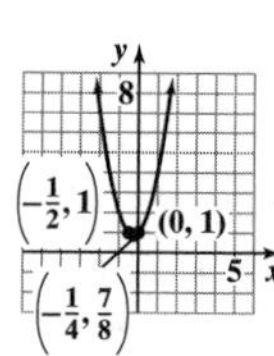

(b) Domain: $(-\infty, \infty)$
Range: $\left[\frac{7}{8}, \infty\right)$
(c) Decreasing: $\left(-\infty, -\frac{1}{4}\right)$
Increasing: $\left(-\frac{1}{4}, \infty\right)$

69. (a)

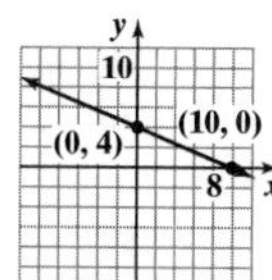

(b) Domain: $(-\infty, \infty)$
Range: $(-\infty, \infty)$
(c) Decreasing: $(-\infty, \infty)$

71. (a)

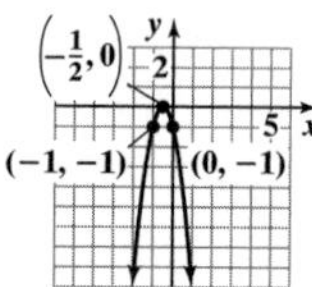

(b) Domain: $(-\infty, \infty)$
Range: $(-\infty, 0]$
(c) Increasing: $\left(-\infty, -\frac{1}{2}\right)$
Decreasing: $\left(-\frac{1}{2}, \infty\right)$

73. $a = 6, b = 0, c = 2$

75. (a), (c), (d)

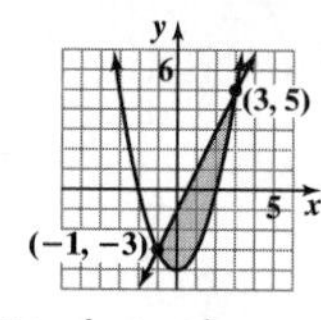

(b) $\{-1, 3\}$

77. (a), (c), (d)

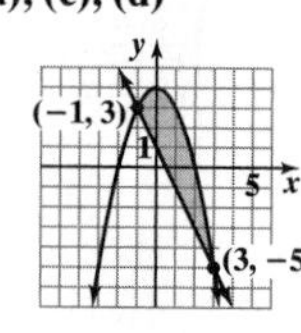

(b) $\{-1, 3\}$

79. (a), (c), (d)

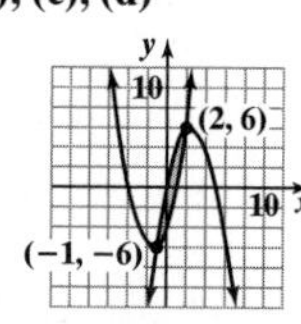

(b) $\{-1, 2\}$

81. (a) $a = 1: f(x) = (x+3)(x-1) = x^2 + 2x - 3$
$a = 2: f(x) = 2(x+3)(x-1) = 2x^2 + 4x - 6$
$a = -2: f(x) = -2(x+3)(x-1) = -2x^2 - 4x + 6$
$a = 5: f(x) = 5(x+3)(x-1) = 5x^2 + 10x - 15$
(b) The value of a does not affect the x-intercepts, but it changes the y-intercept by a factor of a.
(c) The value of a does not affect the axis of symmetry. It is $x = -1$ for all values of a.
(d) The value of a does not affect the x-coordinate of the vertex. However, the y-coordinate of the vertex is multiplied by a.
(e) The mean of the x-intercepts is the x-coordinate of the vertex.

83. (a) $(-2, -25)$
(b) $-7, 3$
(c) $-4, 0; (-4, -21), (0, -21)$
(d)

85. $(2, 2)$ **87.** \$500; \$1,000,000 **89. (a)** 70,000 mp3 players **(b)** \$2500 **91. (a)** 187 or 188 watches; \$7031.20 **(b)** $P(x) = -0.2x^2 + 43x - 1750$ **(c)** 107 or 108 watches; \$561.20 **93. (a)** 171 ft **(b)** 49 mph **(c)** Reaction time **95.** $f(x) = 2(x+4)(x-2)$ **97.** If x is even, then ax^2 and bx are even and $ax^2 + bx$ is even, which means that $ax^2 + bx + c$ is odd. If x is odd, then ax^2 and bx are odd and $ax^2 + bx$ is even, which means that $ax^2 + bx + c$ is odd. In either case, $f(x)$ is odd.

99.

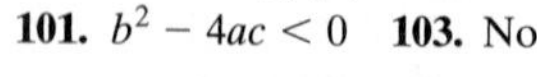

101. $b^2 - 4ac < 0$ **103.** No

10.4 Assess Your Understanding *(page 665)*

3. (a) $R(x) = -\frac{1}{6}x^2 + 100x$ **(b)** $\{x \mid 0 \le x \le 600\}$ **(c)** \$13,333.33 **(d)** 300; \$15,000 **(e)** \$50 **5. (a)** $R(x) = -\frac{1}{5}x^2 + 20x$ **(b)** \$255 **(c)** 50; \$500 **(d)** \$10 **(e)** Between \$8 and \$12 **7. (a)** $A(w) = -w^2 + 200w$ **(b)** A is largest when $w = 100$ yd. **(c)** 10,000 yd^2 **9.** 2,000,000 m^2
11. (a) $\frac{625}{16} \approx 39$ ft **(b)** $\frac{7025}{32} \approx 219.5$ ft **(c)** About 170 ft

(d) 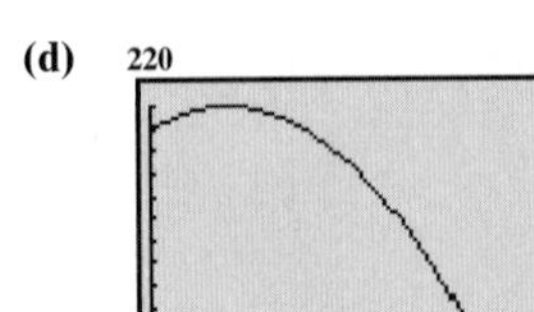

(f) When the height is 100 ft, the projectile is about 135.7 ft from the cliff.

13. 18.75 m **15. (a)** 3 in. **(b)** Between 2 in. and 4 in. **17.** $\frac{750}{\pi} \approx 238.73$ m by 375 m **19.** $x = \frac{a}{2}$ **21.** $\frac{38}{3}$ **23.** $\frac{248}{3}$

25. (a) 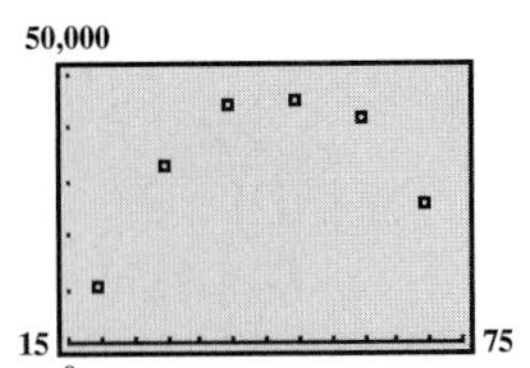

The data appear to follow a quadratic relation with $a < 0$.

(b) $I(x) = -45.122x^2 + 4301.575x - 55{,}376.404$ **(c)** About 47.7 years of age **(d)** Approximately \$47,143

(e) 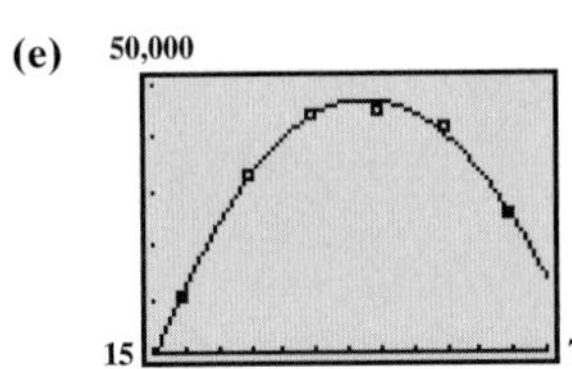

27. (a) 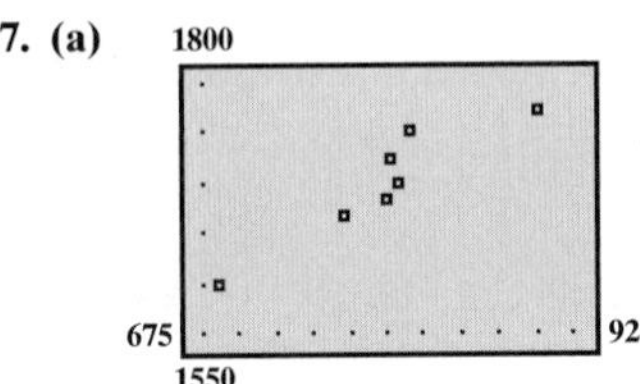

The data appear to be linearly related with positive slope.

(b) $R(x) = 0.836x + 1032.273$ **(c)** \$1743

29. (a) 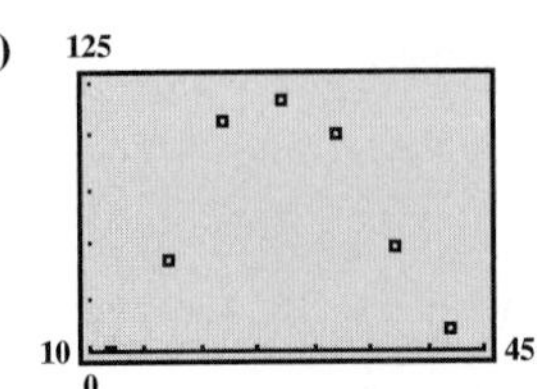

The data appear to follow a quadratic relation with $a < 0$.

(b) $B(a) = -0.495a^2 + 26.928a - 256.398$
(c) 79.7 births per 1000 population

10.5 Assess Your Understanding *(page 672)*

3. (a) $\{x|x < -2 \text{ or } x > 2\}; (-\infty, -2) \text{ or } (2, \infty)$ **(b)** $\{x|-2 \le x \le 2\}; [-2, 2]$ **5. (a)** $\{x|-2 \le x \le 1\}; [-2, 1]$ **(b)** $\{x|x < -2 \text{ or } x > 1\}; (-\infty, -2) \text{ or } (1, \infty)$ **7.** $\{x|-2 < x < 5\}; (-2, 5)$ **9.** $\{x|x < 0 \text{ or } x > 4\}; (-\infty, 0) \text{ or } (4, \infty)$ **11.** $\{x|-3 < x < 3\}; (-3, 3)$ **13.** $\{x|x < -4 \text{ or } x > 3\}; (-\infty, -4) \text{ or } (3, \infty)$ **15.** $\left\{x\middle|-\frac{1}{2} < x < 3\right\}; \left(-\frac{1}{2}, 3\right)$ **17.** No real solution **19.** No real solution **21.** $\left\{x\middle| x < -\frac{2}{3} \text{ or } x > \frac{3}{2}\right\}; \left(-\infty, -\frac{2}{3}\right) \text{ or } \left(\frac{3}{2}, \infty\right)$ **23.** $\{x|x \le -4 \text{ or } x \ge 4\}; (-\infty, -4] \text{ or } [4, \infty)$ **25. (a)** $\{-1, 1\}$ **(b)** $\{-1\}$ **(c)** $\{-1, 4\}$ **(d)** $\{x|x < -1 \text{ or } x > 1\}; (-\infty, -1) \text{ or } (1, \infty)$ **(e)** $\{x|x \le -1\}$ or $(-\infty, -1]$ **(f)** $\{x|x < -1 \text{ or } x > 4\}; (-\infty, -1) \text{ or } (4, \infty)$ **(g)** $\{x|x \le -\sqrt{2} \text{ or } x \ge \sqrt{2}\}; (-\infty, -\sqrt{2}] \text{ or } [\sqrt{2}, \infty)$ **27. (a)** $\{-1, 1\}$ **(b)** $\left\{-\frac{1}{4}\right\}$ **(c)** $\{-4, 0\}$ **(d)** $\{x|-1 < x < 1\}; (-1, 1)$ **(e)** $\left\{x\middle|x \le -\frac{1}{4}\right\}$ or $\left(-\infty, -\frac{1}{4}\right]$ **(f)** $\{x|-4 < x < 0\}; (-4, 0)$ **(g)** $\{0\}$ **29. (a)** $\{-2, 2\}$ **(b)** $\{-2, 2\}$ **(c)** $\{-2, 2\}$ **(d)** $\{x|x < -2 \text{ or } x > 2\}; (-\infty, -2) \text{ or } (2, \infty)$ **(e)** $\{x|x \le -2 \text{ or } x \ge 2\}; (-\infty, -2] \text{ or } [2, \infty)$ **(f)** $\{x|x < -2 \text{ or } x > 2\}; (-\infty, -2) \text{ or } (2, \infty)$ **(g)** $\{x|x \le -\sqrt{5} \text{ or } x \ge \sqrt{5}\}; (-\infty, -\sqrt{5}] \text{ or } [\sqrt{5}, \infty)$ **31. (a)** $\{-1, 2\}$ **(b)** $\{-2, 1\}$ **(c)** $\{0\}$ **(d)** $\{x|x < -1 \text{ or } x > 2\}; (-\infty, -1) \text{ or } (2, \infty)$ **(e)** $\{x|-2 \le x \le 1\}; [-2, 1]$ **(f)** $\{x|x < 0\}; (-\infty, 0)$ **(g)** $\left\{x\middle|x \le \frac{1-\sqrt{13}}{2} \text{ or } x \ge \frac{1+\sqrt{13}}{2}\right\}; \left(-\infty, \frac{1-\sqrt{13}}{2}\right] \text{ or } \left[\frac{1+\sqrt{13}}{2}, \infty\right)$

33. (a) 5 sec **(b)** The ball is more than 96 ft above the ground for time t between 2 and 3 sec, $2 < t < 3$. **35. (a)** \$0, \$1000 **(b)** The revenue is more than \$800,000 for prices between \$276.39 and \$723.61, $\$276.39 < p < \$723.61$. **37. (a)** $\{c \mid 0.112 < c < 81.907\}$; $(0.112, 81.907)$ **(b)** It is possible to hit a target 75 km away if $c = 0.651$ or $c = 1.536$.

Review Exercises *(page 674)*

1. (a) $m = 2; b = -5$ **(b)** 2
(c) 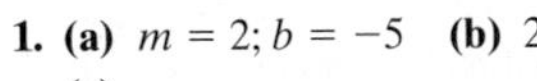
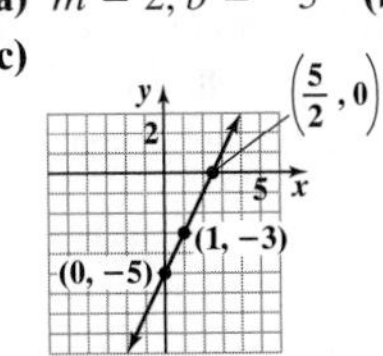

(d) Increasing

2. (a) $m = -\frac{1}{3}; b = 1$ **(b)** $-\frac{1}{3}$
(c) 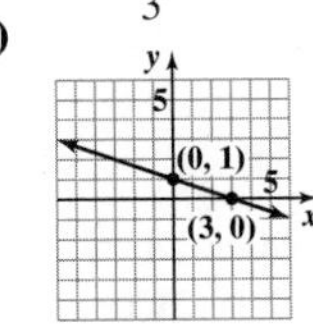

(d) Decreasing

3. (a) $m = 0; b = 4$ **(b)** 0
(c) 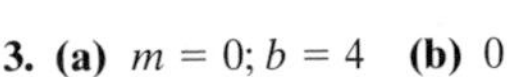
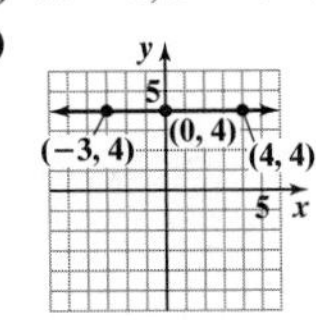
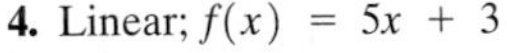

(d) Constant

4. Linear; $f(x) = 5x + 3$
5. Nonlinear

6.

7. 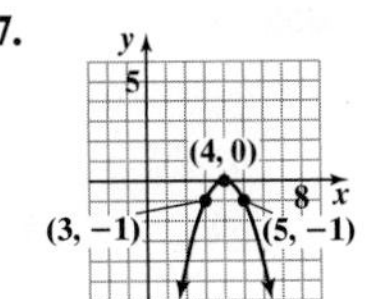

8. 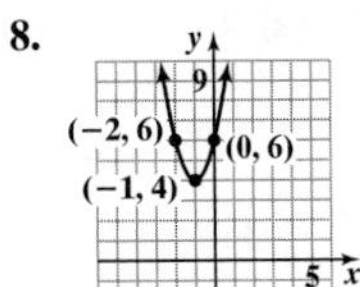

9. (a) 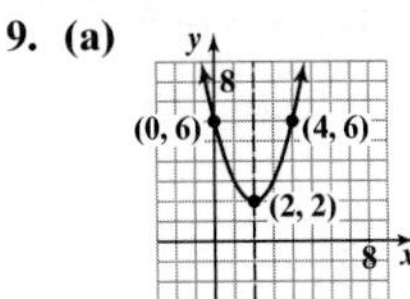
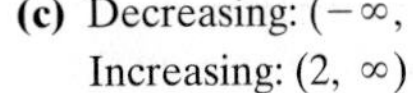

(b) Domain: $(-\infty, \infty)$
Range: $[2, \infty)$
(c) Decreasing: $(-\infty, 2)$
Increasing: $(2, \infty)$

10. (a) 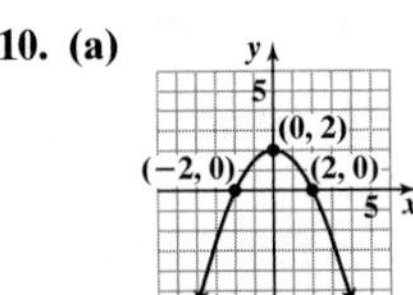

(b) Domain: $(-\infty, \infty)$
Range: $(-\infty, 2]$
(c) Increasing: $(-\infty, 0)$
Decreasing: $(0, \infty)$

11. (a)

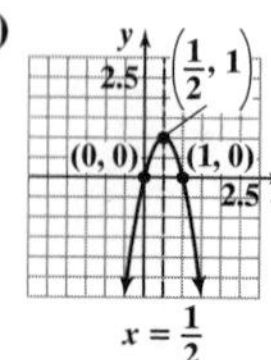

(b) Domain: $(-\infty, \infty)$
Range: $(-\infty, 1]$
(c) Increasing: $\left(-\infty, \frac{1}{2}\right)$
Decreasing: $\left(\frac{1}{2}, \infty\right)$

12. (a)

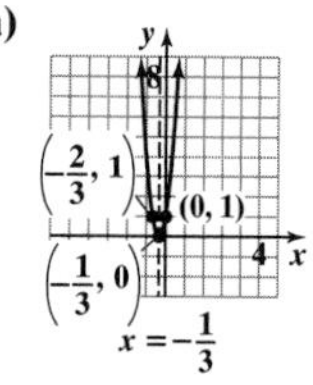

(b) Domain: $(-\infty, \infty)$
Range: $[0, \infty)$
(c) Decreasing: $\left(-\infty, -\frac{1}{3}\right)$
Increasing: $\left(-\frac{1}{3}, \infty\right)$

13. (a)

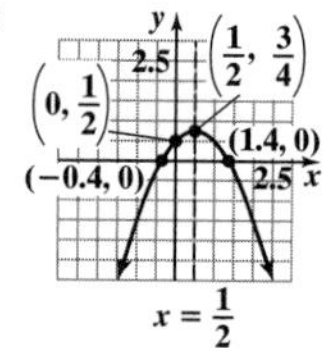

(b) Domain: $(-\infty, \infty)$
Range: $\left(-\infty, \frac{3}{4}\right]$
(c) Increasing: $\left(-\infty, \frac{1}{2}\right)$
Decreasing: $\left(\frac{1}{2}, \infty\right)$

14. (a)

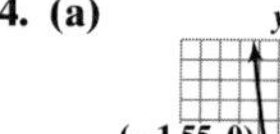

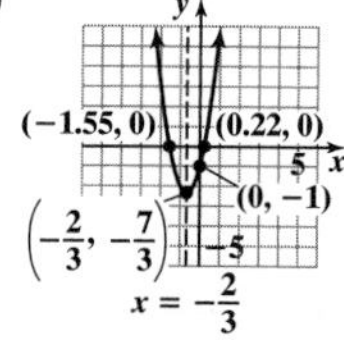

(b) Domain: $(-\infty, \infty)$
Range: $\left[-\frac{7}{3}, \infty\right)$
(c) Decreasing: $\left(-\infty, -\frac{2}{3}\right)$
Increasing: $\left(-\frac{2}{3}, \infty\right)$

15. Minimum value; 1 **16.** Maximum value; 12 **17.** Maximum value; 4 **18.** $\{x \mid -8 < x < 2\}$; $(-8, -2)$

19. $\left\{x \,\middle|\, x \le -\frac{1}{3} \text{ or } x \ge 5\right\}$; $\left(-\infty, -\frac{1}{3}\right]$ or $[5, \infty)$ **20.** $y = x^2 + 2x + 3$ **21.** $y = x^2 - 4x + 5$ **22. (a)** Company A: $C(x) = 0.06x + 7$; Company B: $C(x) = 0.08x$ **(b)** 350 min **(c)** $0 \le x < 350$ **23. (a)** $R(x) = -\frac{1}{10}x^2 + 150x$ **(b)** \$14,000 **(c)** 750; \$56,250 **(d)** \$75 **24.** 4,166,666.7 m^2

25. (a) 63 clubs **(b)** \$151.90 **26. (a)** $A(x) = -x^2 + 10x$; 25 units^2 **27.** 3.6 ft

28. (a)

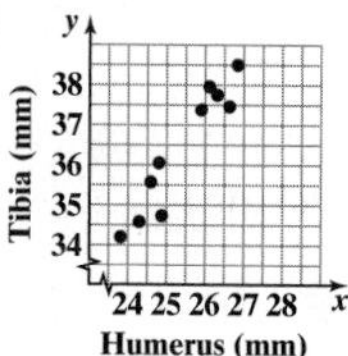

(b) Yes **(c)** $y = 1.3092x + 1.1140$
(d) 37.95 mm

29. (a) Quadratic, $a < 0$

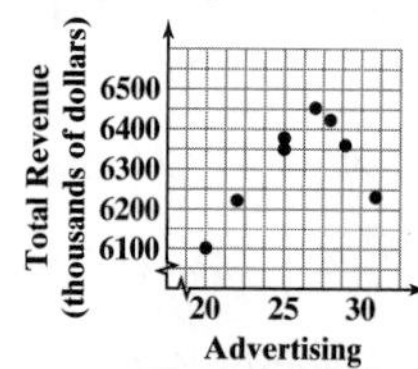

(b) About \$26.5 thousand
(c) \$6408 thousand

(e)

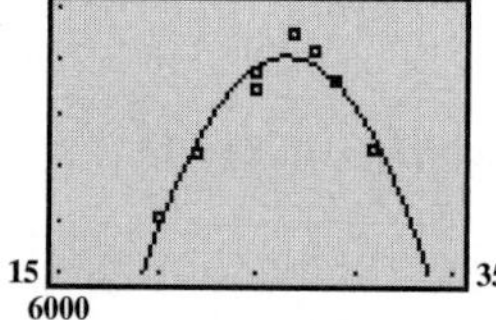

Chapter Test *(page 676)*

1. (a) Slope: −4; y-intercept: 3
(b) Decreasing
(c)

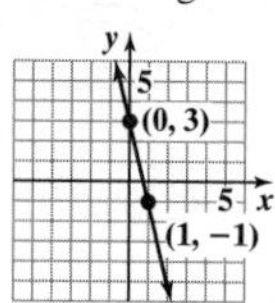

2. Linear; $y = -5x + 2$

3.

(0, 7) (6, 7) (2, −1) (4, −1) (3, −2)

4. (a) Opens up **(b)** $(2, -8)$ **(c)** $x = 2$
(d) x-intercepts: $\frac{6 - 2\sqrt{6}}{3}$, $\frac{6 + 2\sqrt{6}}{3}$; y-intercept: 4
(e)

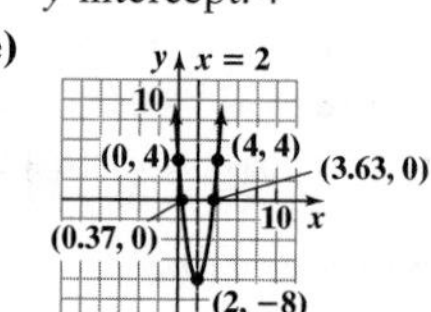

(f) Domain: All real numbers; $(-\infty, \infty)$
Range: $\{y \mid y \ge -8\}$; $[-8, \infty)$
(g) Decreasing: $(-\infty, 2)$; Increasing: $(2, \infty)$

5. (a) Opens down
(b) $(1, -3)$ **(c)** $x = 1$
(d) *No* x-intercepts: y-intercept: −5

(e) $x = 1$; (1, −3); (0, −5); (2, −5)

(f) Domain: All real numbers; $(-\infty, \infty)$
Range: $\{y \mid y \le -3\}$; $(-\infty, -3]$
(g) Increasing: $(-\infty, 1)$; Decreasing: $(1, \infty)$

6. $f(x) = 2x^2 - 4x - 30$ **7.** Maximum value; 21 **8.** $\{x \mid x \le 4 \text{ or } x \ge 6\}$; $(-\infty, 4] \cup [6, \infty)$ **9. (a)** $C(m) = 0.15m + 129.50$ **(b)** \$258.50 **(c)** 562 miles **10. (a)** $R(x) = -\frac{1}{10}x^2 + 1000x$ **(b)** \$384,000 **(c)** 5000 units; \$2,500,000 **(d)** \$500

11. (a)

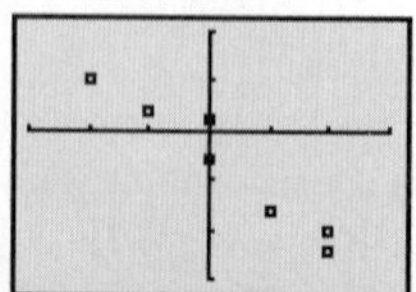

Linear with negative slope

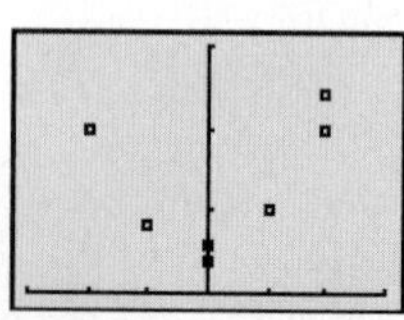

Quadratic that opens up

(b) $y = -4.234x - 2.362$

(c) $y = 1.993x^2 + 0.289x + 2.503$

Cumulative Review *(page 677)*

1. $5\sqrt{2}$; $\left(\frac{3}{2}, \frac{1}{2}\right)$ **2.** $(-2, -1)$ and $(2, 3)$ are on the graph.

3. $\left\{x \middle| x \geq -\frac{3}{5}\right\}$ or $\left[-\frac{3}{5}, \infty\right)$

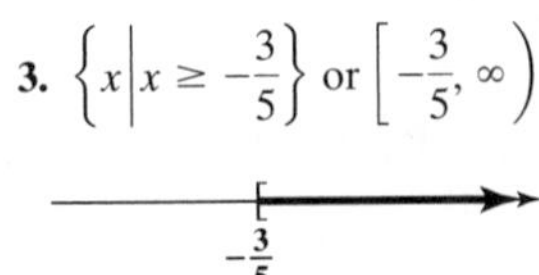

4. $y = -2x + 2$

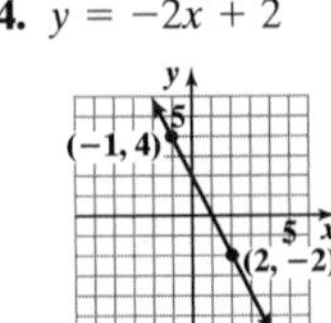

5. $y = -\frac{1}{2}x + \frac{13}{2}$

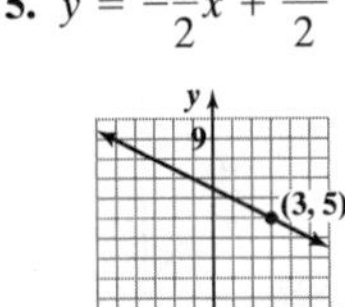

6. $(x - 2)^2 + (y + 4)^2 = 25$

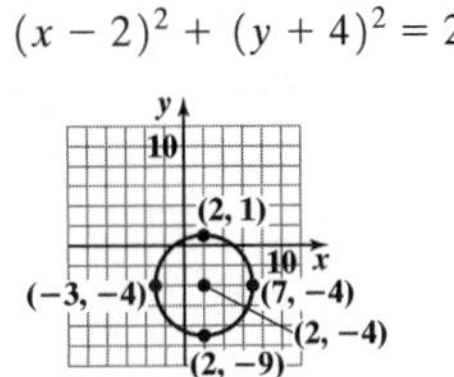

7. Yes **8. (a)** -3 **(b)** $x^2 - 4x - 2$ **(c)** $x^2 + 4x + 1$ **(d)** $-x^2 + 4x - 1$ **(e)** $x^2 - 3$ **(f)** $2x + h - 4$ **9.** $\left\{z \middle| z \neq \frac{7}{6}\right\}$ **10.** Yes **11. (a)** No **(b)** -1; $(-2, -1)$ is on the graph. **(c)** -8; $(-8, 2)$ is on the graph. **12.** Neither **13.** Local maximum value is 5.30 and occurs at $x = -1.29$. Local minimum value is -3.30 and occurs at $x = 1.29$. Increasing: $(-4, -1.29)$ and $(1.29, 4)$; Decreasing: $(-1.29, 1.29)$ **14. (a)** -4 **(b)** $\{x|x > -4\}$ or $(-4, \infty)$ **15. (a)** Domain: $\{x|-4 \leq x \leq 4\}$; Range: $\{y|-1 \leq y \leq 3\}$ **(b)** $(-1, 0), (0, -1), (1, 0)$ **(c)** y-axis **(d)** 1 **(e)** -4 and 4 **(f)** $\{x|-1 < x < 1\}$

(g)

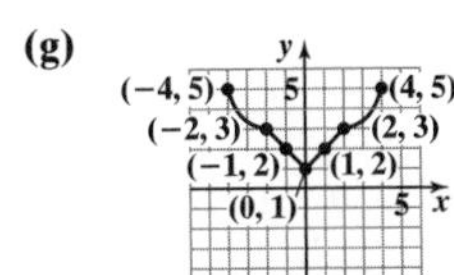

(h)

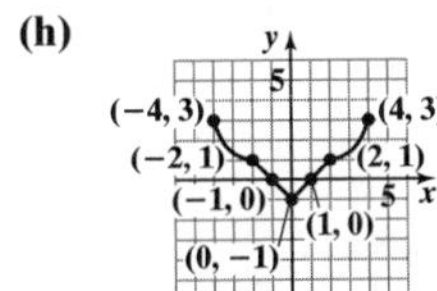

(i)

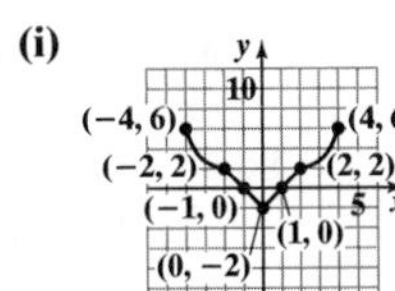

(j) Even **(k)** $(0, 4)$

CHAPTER 11 Polynomial and Rational Functions

11.1 Assess Your Understanding *(page 694)*

7. smooth; continuous **8.** touches **9.** $(-1, 1)$; $(0, 0)$; $(1, 1)$ **10.** r is a real zero of f; r is an x-intercept of the graph of f; $x - r$ is a factor of f. **11.** turning points **12.** $y = 3x^4$ **13.** ∞; $-\infty$ **14.** As x increases in the positive direction, $f(x)$ decreases without bound. **15.** Yes; degree 3 **17.** Yes; degree 2 **19.** No; x is raised to the -1 power. **21.** No; x is raised to the $\frac{3}{2}$ power. **23.** Yes; degree 4 **25.** Yes; degree 4

27.

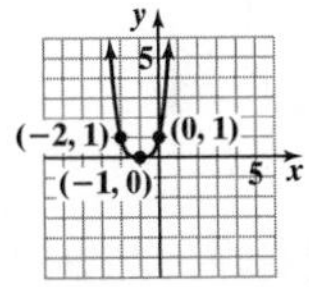

29.

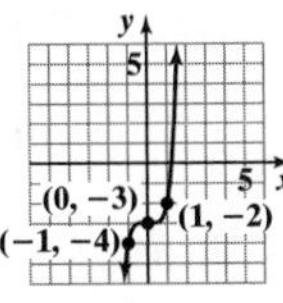

31.

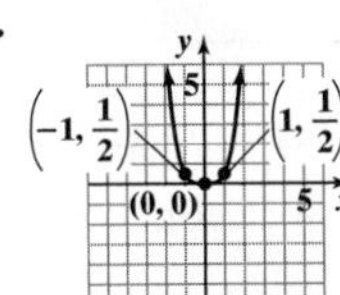

33.

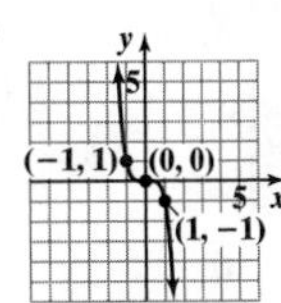

35.

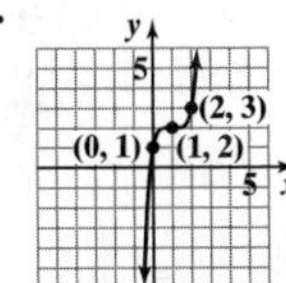

37.

39.

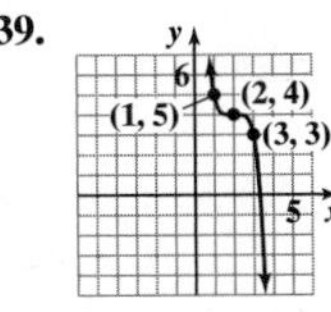

41. $f(x) = x^3 - 3x^2 - x + 3$ for $a = 1$ **43.** $f(x) = x^3 - x^2 - 12x$ for $a = 1$ **45.** $f(x) = x^4 - 15x^2 + 10x + 24$ for $a = 1$ **47.** $f(x) = x^3 - 5x^2 + 3x + 9$ for $a = 1$ **49. (a)** 7, multiplicity 1; -3, multiplicity 2 **(b)** Graph touches the x-axis at -3 and crosses it at 7. **(c)** 2 **(d)** $y = 3x^3$ **51. (a)** 2, multiplicity 3 **(b)** Graph crosses the x-axis at 2. **(c)** 4 **(d)** $y = 4x^5$ **53. (a)** $-\frac{1}{2}$, multiplicity 2; -4, multiplicity 3 **(b)** Graph touches the x-axis at $-\frac{1}{2}$ and crosses at -4. **(c)** 4 **(d)** $y = -2x^5$ **55. (a)** 5, multiplicity 3; -4, multiplicity 2 **(b)** Graph touches the x-axis at -4 and crosses it at 5. **(c)** 4 **(d)** $y = x^5$ **57. (a)** No real zeros **(b)** Graph neither crosses nor touches the x-axis. **(c)** 5 **(d)** $y = 3x^6$ **59. (a)** 0, multiplicity 2; $-\sqrt{2}, \sqrt{2}$, multiplicity 1 **(b)** Graph touches the x-axis at 0 and crosses at $-\sqrt{2}$ and $\sqrt{2}$. **(c)** 3 **(d)** $y = -2x^4$ **61.** Could be; zeros: $-1, 1, 2$; Least degree is 3. **63.** Cannot be the graph of a polynomial; gap at $x = -1$ **65.** $f(x) = x(x - 1)(x - 2)$ **67.** $f(x) = -\frac{1}{2}(x + 1)(x - 1)^2(x - 2)$

69. Step 1: $y = x^3$
Step 2: x-intercepts: 0, 3; y-intercept: 0
Step 3: 0: multiplicity 2; touches; 3: multiplicity 1; crosses

Step 4:

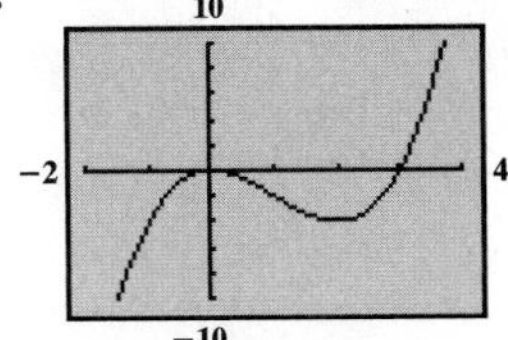

Step 5: $(2, -4)$; $(0, 0)$

Step 6:

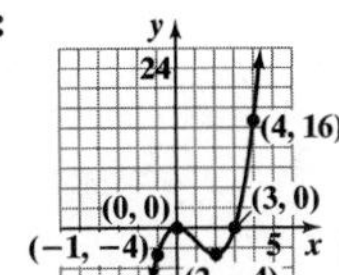

Step 7: Domain: $(-\infty, \infty)$; Range: $(-\infty, \infty)$
Step 8: Increasing on $(-\infty, 0)$ and $(2, \infty)$
Decreasing on $(0, 2)$

71. Step 1: $y = x^3$
Step 2: x-intercepts: $-4, 2$
y-intercept: 16
Step 3: -4: multiplicity 1, crosses;
2: multiplicity 2, touches
Step 4:

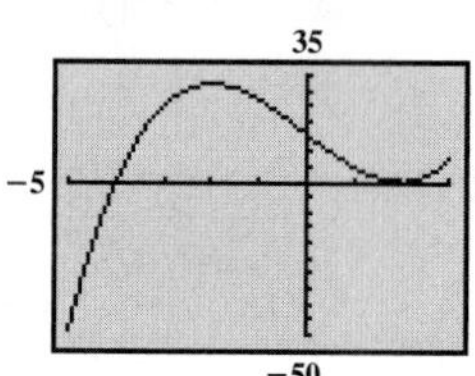

Step 5: $(-2, 32)$; $(2, 0)$
Step 6:

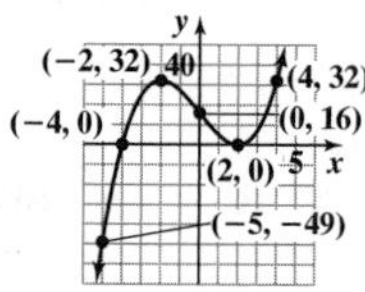

Step 7: Domain: $(-\infty, \infty)$;
Range: $(-\infty, \infty)$
Step 8: Increasing on
$(-\infty, -2)$ and $(2, \infty)$
Decreasing on $(-2, 2)$

73. Step 1: $y = -2x^4$
Step 2: x-intercepts: $-2, 2$
y-intercept: 32
Step 3: -2: multiplicity 1, crosses;
2: multiplicity 3, crosses
Step 4:

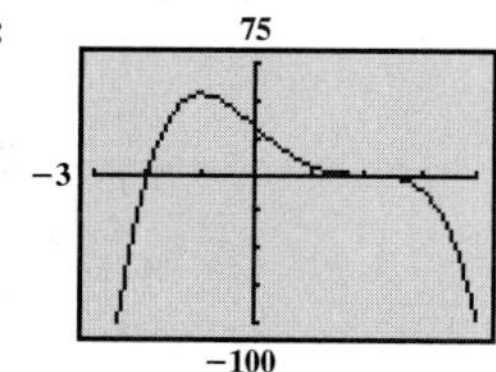

Step 5: $(-1, 54)$
Step 6:

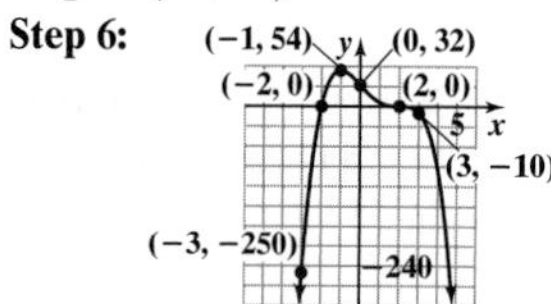

Step 7: Domain: $(-\infty, \infty)$;
Range: $(-\infty, 54]$
Step 8: Increasing on $(-\infty, -1)$
Decreasing on $(-1, \infty)$

75. Step 1: $y = x^3$
Step 2: x-intercepts: $-4, -1, 2$; y-intercept: -8
Step 3: $-4, -1, 2$: multiplicity 1, crosses
Step 4:

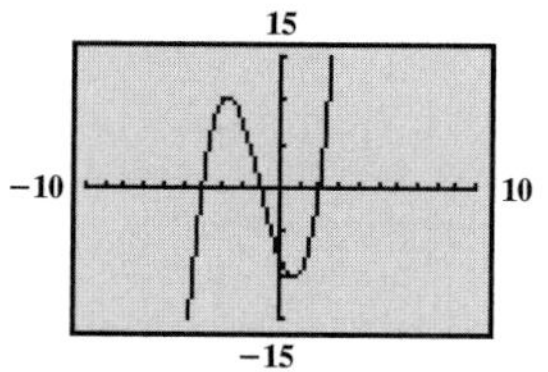

Step 5: $(-2.73, 10.39)$; $(0.73, -10.39)$
Step 6:

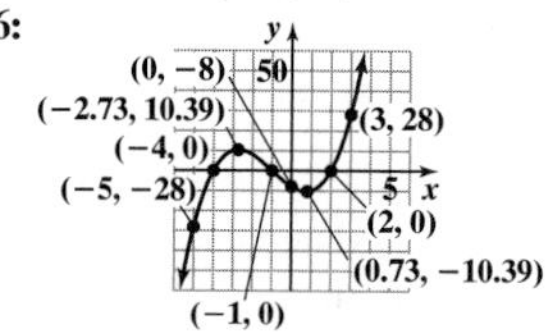

Step 7: Domain: $(-\infty, \infty)$;
Range: $(-\infty, \infty)$
Step 8: Increasing on $(-\infty, -2.73)$
and $(0.73, \infty)$
Decreasing on $(-2.73, 0.73)$

77. Step 1: $y = x^4$
Step 2: x-intercepts: $-2, 0, 2$; y-intercept: 0
Step 3: $-2, 2$: multiplicity 1, crosses;
0: multiplicity 2, touches
Step 4:

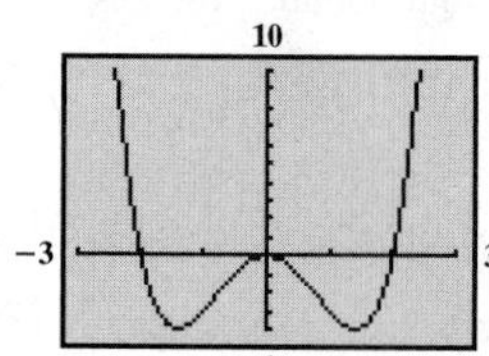

Step 5: $(-1.41, -4)$; $(1.41, -4)$; $(0, 0)$
Step 6:

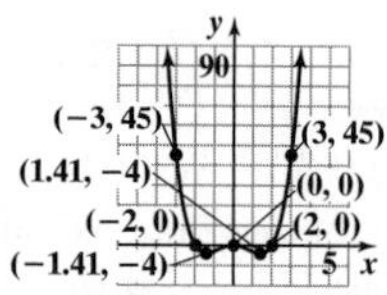

Step 7: Domain: $(-\infty, \infty)$;
Range: $[-4, \infty)$
Step 8: Increasing on $(-1.41, 0)$ and
$(1.41, \infty)$
Decreasing on $(-\infty, -1.41)$
and $(0, 1.41)$

79. Step 1: $y = x^4$
Step 2: x-intercepts: $-1, 2$; y-intercept: 4
Step 3: $-1, 2$; multiplicity 2, touches
Step 4:

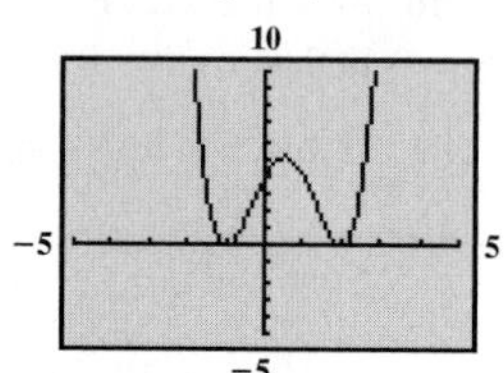

Step 5: $(-1, 0)$; $(2, 0)$; $(0.5, 5.06)$
Step 6:

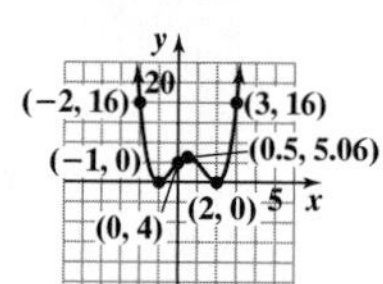

Step 7: Domain: $(-\infty, \infty)$; Range: $[0, \infty)$
Step 8: Increasing on $(-1, 0.5)$ and $(2, \infty)$
Decreasing on $(-\infty, -1)$ and $(0.5, 2)$

81. Step 1: $y = x^4$
Step 2: x-intercepts: $-1, 0, 3$; y-intercept: 0
Step 3: $-1, 3$; multiplicity 1, crosses;
0: multiplicity 2, touches
Step 4:

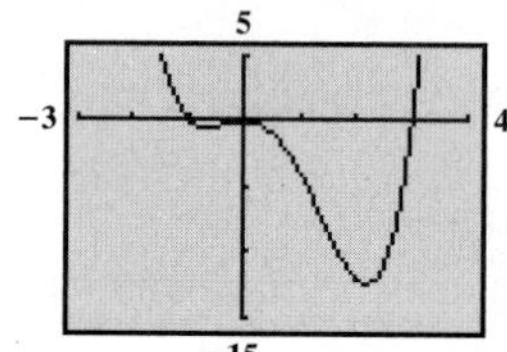

Step 5: $(-0.69, -0.54)$; $(2.19, -12.39)$; $(0, 0)$
Step 6:

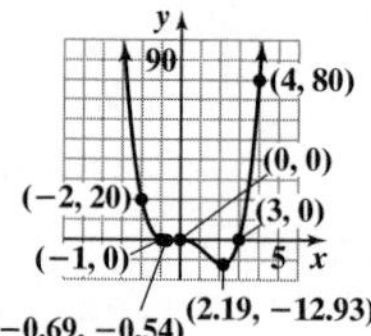

Step 7: Domain: $(-\infty, \infty)$; Range: $[-12.39, \infty)$
Step 8: Increasing on $(-0.69, 0)$ and $(2.19, \infty)$
Decreasing on $(-\infty, -0.69)$ and $(0, 2.19)$

83. Step 1: $y = x^4$
Step 2: x-intercepts: $-2, 4$; y-intercept: 64
Step 3: $-2, 4$; multiplicity 2, touches
Step 4:

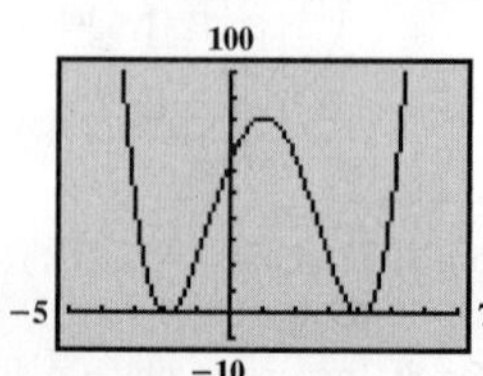

Step 5: $(-2, 0)$; $(4, 0)$; $(1, 81)$
Step 6:

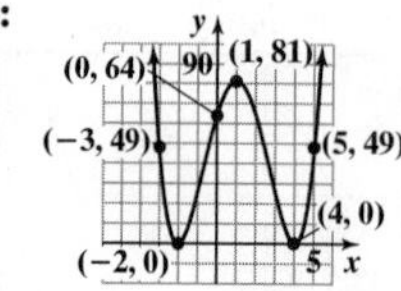

Step 7: Domain: $(-\infty, \infty)$; Range: $[0, \infty)$
Step 8: Increasing on $(-2, 1)$ and $(4, \infty)$
Decreasing on $(-\infty, -2)$ and
$(1, 4)$

85. Step 1: $y = x^5$

Step 2: x-intercepts: 0, 2; y-intercept: 0

Step 3: 0: multiplicity 2, touches; 2: multiplicity 1, crosses

Step 4:

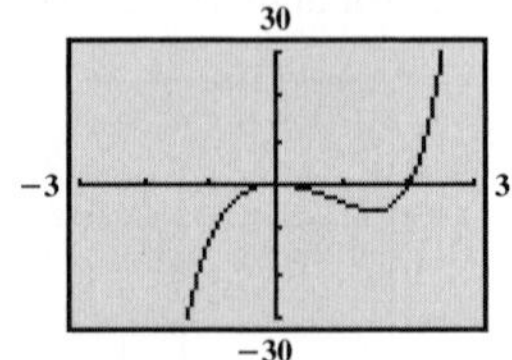

Step 5: $(0, 0)$; $(1.48, -5.91)$

Step 6:

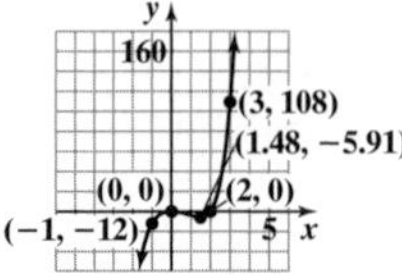

Step 7: Domain: $(-\infty, \infty)$; Range: $(-\infty, \infty)$

Step 8: Increasing on $(-\infty, 0)$ and $(1.48, \infty)$
Decreasing on $(0, 1.48)$

87. Step 1: $y = x^3$

Step 2:

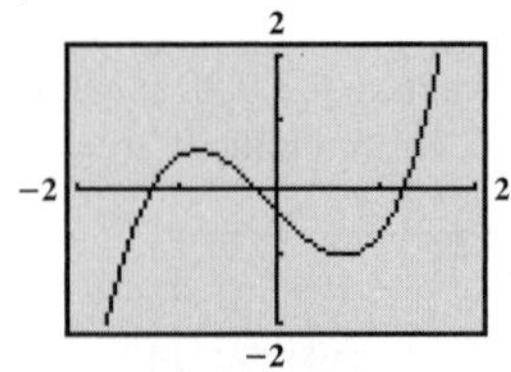

Step 3: x-intercepts: $-1.26, -0.20, 1.26$
y-intercept: -0.31752

Step 4:

X	Y1
-1.5	-.8611
-.5	.40128
0	-.3175
1.5	1.1261

Y1=X^3+0.2X^2-1.5...

Step 5: $(-0.80, 0.57)$; $(0.66, -0.99)$

Step 6:

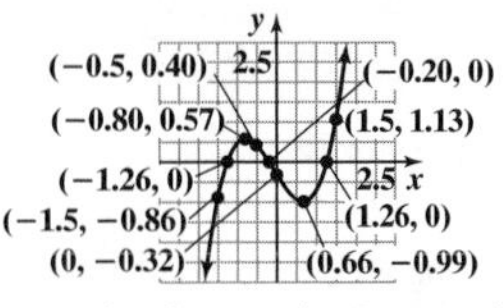

Step 7: Domain: $(-\infty, \infty)$: Range: $(-\infty, \infty)$

Step 8: Increasing on $(-\infty, -0.80)$ and $(0.66, \infty)$
Decreasing on $(-0.80, 0.66)$

89. Step 1: $y = x^3$

Step 2:

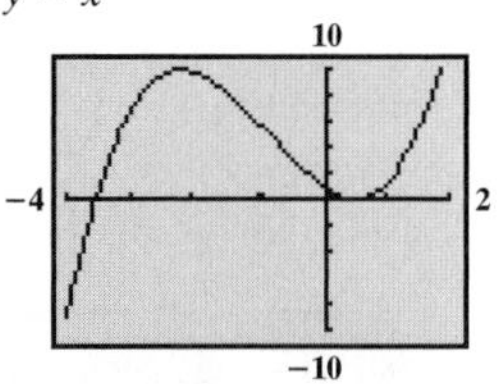

Step 3: x-intercepts: $-3.56, 0.50$; y-intercept: 0.89

Step 4:

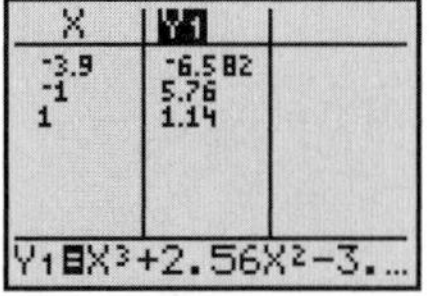

X	Y1
-3.9	-6.582
-1	5.76
1	1.14

Y1=X^3+2.56X^2-3....

Step 5: $(-2.21, 9.91)$; $(0.50, 0)$

Step 6:

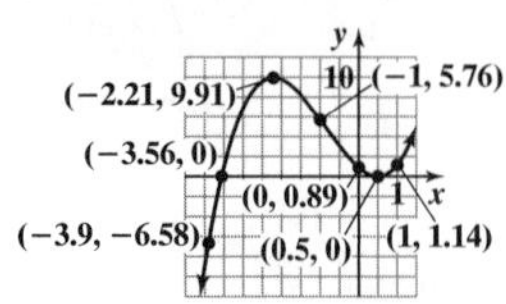

Step 7: Domain: $(-\infty, \infty)$; Range: $(-\infty, \infty)$

Step 8: Increasing on $(-\infty, -2.21)$ and $(0.50, \infty)$
Decreasing on $(-2.21, 0.50)$

91. Step 1: $y = x^4$

Step 2:

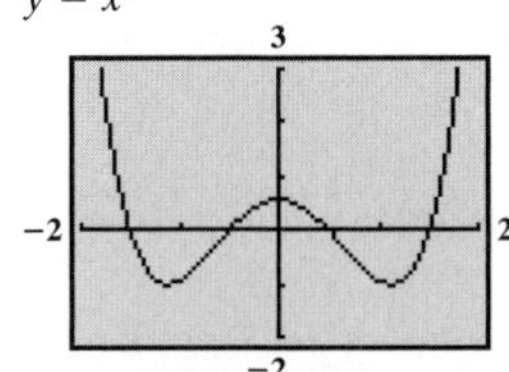

Step 3: x-intercepts: $-1.5, -0.5, 0.5, 1.5$
y-intercept: 0.5625

Step 4:

X	Y1
-1.75	2.2852
-1	-.9375
0	.5625
1	-.9375
1.75	2.2852

Y1=X^4-2.5X^2+0....

Step 5: $(-1.12, -1)$; $(1.12, -1)$; $(0, 0.56)$

Step 6:

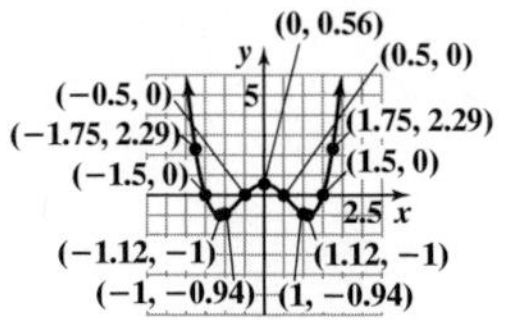

Step 7: Domain: $(-\infty, \infty)$: Range: $[-1, \infty)$

Step 8: Increasing on $(-1.12, 0)$ and $(1.12, \infty)$
Decreasing on $(-\infty, -1.12)$ and $(0, 1.12)$

93. Step 1: $y = 2x^4$

Step 2:

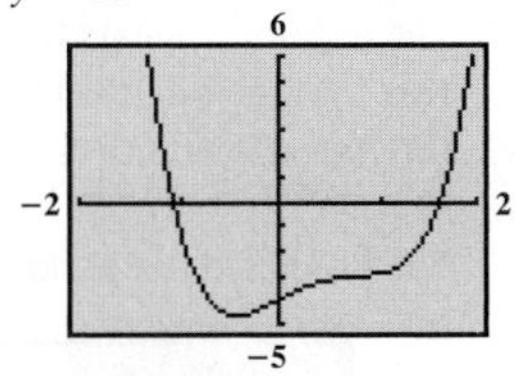

Step 3: x-intercepts: $-1.07, 1.62$
y-intercept: -4

Step 4:

X	Y1
-1.25	4.2237
0	-4
1.75	1.834

Y1=2X^4-πX^3+√(5...

Step 5: $(-0.42, -4.64)$

Step 6:

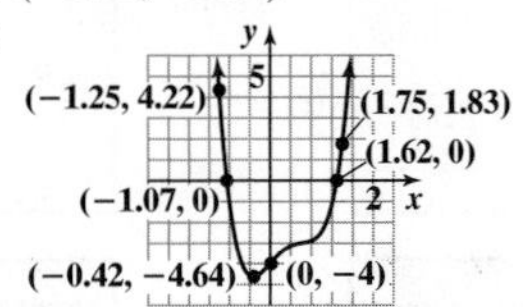

Step 7: Domain: $(-\infty, \infty)$; Range: $[-4.64, \infty)$

Step 8: Increasing on $(-0.42, \infty)$
Decreasing on $(-\infty, -0.42)$

95. $f(x) = -x(x + 2)(x - 2)$

Step 1: $y = -x^3$

Step 2: x-intercepts: $-2, 0, 2$; y-intercept: 0

Step 3: $-2, 0, 2$: multiplicity 1, crosses

Step 4:

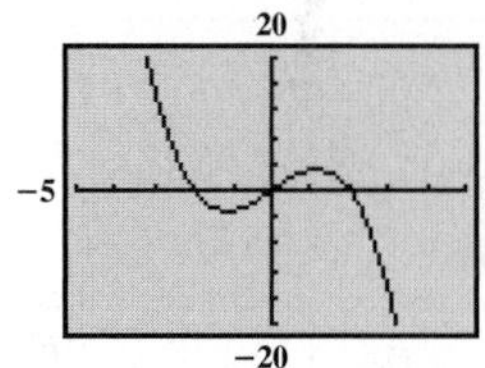

Step 5: $(-1.15, -3.08)$; $(1.15, 3.08)$

Step 6:

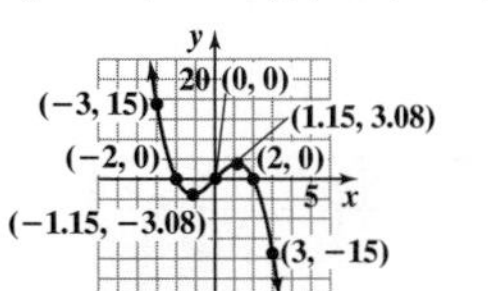

Step 7: Domain: $(-\infty, \infty)$; Range: $(-\infty, \infty)$

Step 8: Increasing on $(-1.15, 1.15)$
Decreasing on $(-\infty, -1.15)$ and $(1.15, \infty)$

97. $f(x) = x(x + 4)(x - 3)$
Step 1: $y = x^3$
Step 2: x-intercepts: $-4, 0, 3$; y-intercept: 0
Step 3: $-4, 0, 3$: multiplicity 1, crosses
Step 4:

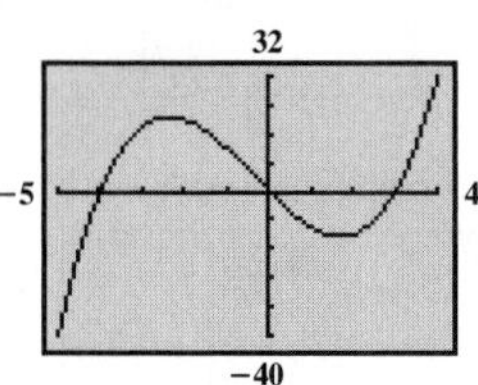

Step 5: $(-2.36, 20.75)$; $(1.69, -12.60)$
Step 6:

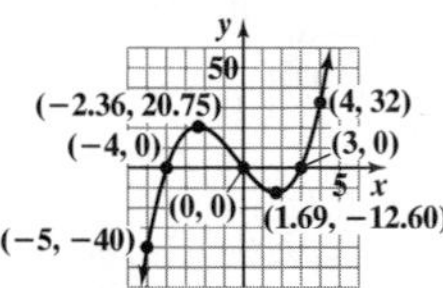

Step 7: Domain: $(-\infty, \infty)$; Range: $(-\infty, \infty)$
Step 8: Increasing on $(-\infty, -2.36)$ and $(1.69, \infty)$
Decreasing on $(-2.36, 1.69)$

99. $f(x) = 2x(x + 6)(x - 2)(x + 2)$
Step 1: $y = 2x^4$
Step 2: x-intercepts: $-6, -2, 0, 2$; y-intercept: 0
Step 3: $-6, -2, 0, 2$: multiplicity 1, crosses
Step 4:

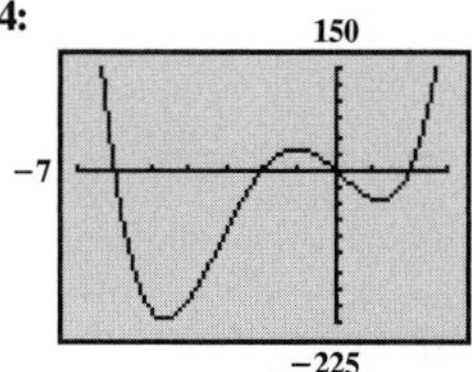

Step 5: $(-4.65, -221.25)$; $(-1.06, 30.12)$; $(1.21, -44.25)$
Step 6:

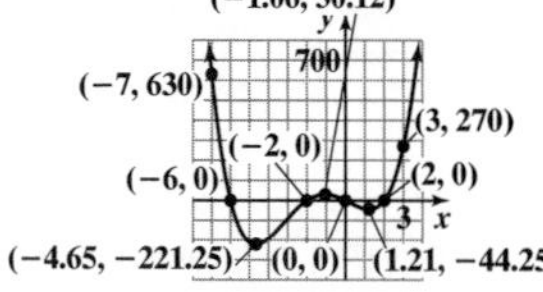

Step 7: Domain: $(-\infty, \infty)$; Range: $[-221.25, \infty)$
Step 8: Decreasing on $(-\infty, -4.65)$ and $(-1.06, 1.21)$
Increasing on $(-4.65, -1.06)$ and $(1.21, \infty)$

101. $f(x) = -x^2(x + 1)^2(x - 1)$
Step 1: $y = -x^5$
Step 2: x-intercepts: $-1, 0, 1$; y-intercept: 0
Step 3: 1: multiplicity 1, crosses; $-1, 0$: multiplicity 2, touches
Step 4:

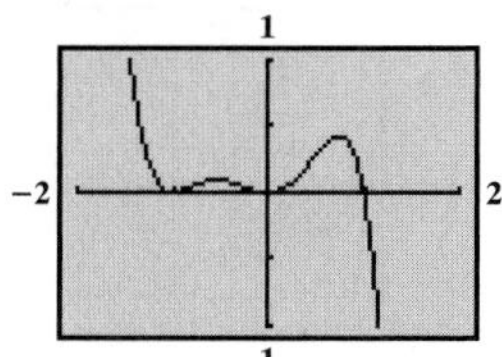

Step 5: $(-1, 0)$; $(-0.54, 0.10)$; $(0, 0)$; $(0.74, 0.43)$
Step 6:

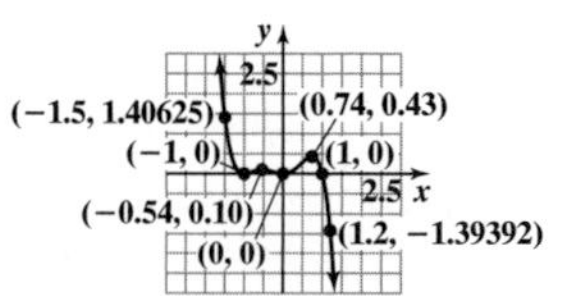

Step 7: Domain: $(-\infty, \infty)$; Range: $(-\infty, \infty)$
Step 8: Increasing on $(-1, -0.54)$ and $(0, 0.74)$
Decreasing on $(-\infty, -1)$, $(-0.54, 0)$, and $(0.74, \infty)$

103. $f(x) = 3(x + 3)(x - 1)(x - 4)$ **105.** $f(x) = -2(x + 5)^2(x - 2)(x - 4)$ **107.** **(a)** $-3, 2$ **(b)** $-6, -1$

109. **(a)**

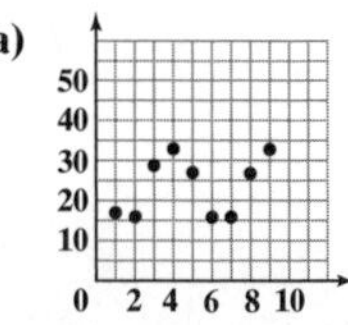

The relation appears to be cubic.
(b) $H(x) = 0.3948x^3 - 5.9563x^2 + 26.1965x - 7.4127$
(c) About 24 major hurricanes
(d)

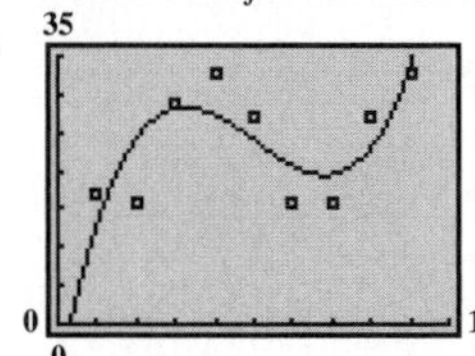

(e) Approximately 54 major hurricanes; no

111. **(a)**

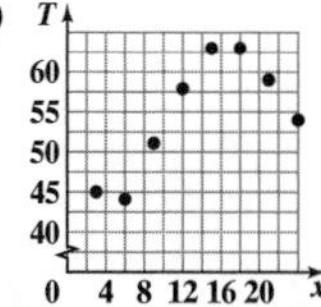

The relation appears to be cubic.
(b) Average rate of change: 2.27°F/h
(c) Average rate of change: 0°F/h
(d) $T(x) = -0.0103x^3 + 0.3174x^2 - 1.3742x + 45.3929$;
The predicted temperature at 5 PM is 63.2°F.
(e)

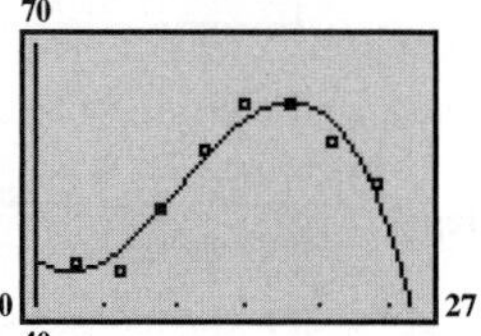

(f) The y-intercept, 45.4°, is the predicted temperature at midnight.

113. **(a)**

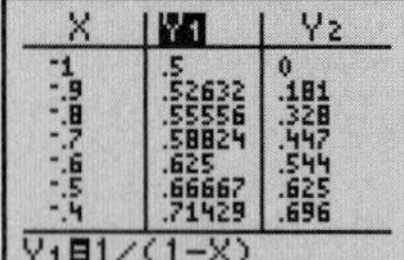

X	Y1	Y2
-1	.5	0
-.9	.52632	.181
-.8	.55556	.328
-.7	.58824	.447
-.6	.625	.544
-.5	.66667	.625
-.4	.71429	.696

Y1 = 1/(1−X)

X	Y1	Y2
-.3	.76923	.763
-.2	.83333	.832
-.1	.90909	.909
0	1	1
.1	1.1111	1.111
.2	1.25	1.248
.3	1.4286	1.417

X = −.3

X	Y1	Y2
.4	1.6667	1.624
.5	2	1.875
.6	2.5	2.176
.7	3.3333	2.533
.8	5	2.952
.9	10	3.439
1	ERROR	4

Y1 = 1/(1−X)

(b)

X	Y1	Y2
-1	.5	1
-.9	.52632	.8371
-.8	.55556	.7376
-.7	.58824	.6871
-.6	.625	.6736
-.5	.66667	.6875
-.4	.71429	.7216

Y1 = 1/(1−X)

X	Y1	Y2
-.3	.76923	.7711
-.2	.83333	.8336
-.1	.90909	.9091
0	1	1
.1	1.1111	1.1111
.2	1.25	1.2496
.3	1.4286	1.4251

Y1 = 1/(1−X)

X	Y1	Y2
.4	1.6667	1.6496
.5	2	1.9375
.6	2.5	2.3056
.7	3.3333	2.7731
.8	5	3.3616
.9	10	4.0951
1	ERROR	5

Y1 = 1/(1−X)

(c)

X	Y1	Y2
-1	.5	0
-.9	.52632	.24661
-.8	.55556	.40992
-.7	.58824	.51903
-.6	.625	.59584
-.5	.66667	.65625
-.4	.71429	.71136

Y1 = 1/(1−X)

X	Y1	Y2
-.3	.76923	.76867
-.2	.83333	.83328
-.1	.90909	.90909
0	1	1
.1	1.1111	1.1111
.2	1.25	1.2499
.3	1.4286	1.4275

Y1 = 1/(1−X)

X	Y1	Y2
.4	1.6667	1.6598
.5	2	1.9688
.6	2.5	2.3834
.7	3.3333	2.9412
.8	5	3.6893
.9	10	4.6856
1	ERROR	6

Y1 = 1/(1−X)

(d) As more terms are added, the values of the polynomial function get closer to the values of f. The approximations near 0 are better than those near -1 or 1. **119.** (a)−(d)

Historical Problems *(page 709)*

1.
$$\left(x-\frac{b}{3}\right)^3+b\left(x-\frac{b}{3}\right)^2+c\left(x-\frac{b}{3}\right)+d=0$$
$$x^3-bx^2+\frac{b^2x}{3}-\frac{b^3}{27}+bx^2-\frac{2b^2x}{3}+\frac{b^3}{9}+cx-\frac{bc}{3}+d=0$$
$$x^3+\left(c-\frac{b^2}{3}\right)x+\left(\frac{2b^3}{27}-\frac{bc}{3}+d\right)=0$$
Let $p=c-\frac{b^2}{3}$ and $q=\frac{2b^3}{27}-\frac{bc}{3}+d$. Then $x^3+px+q=0$.

2. $(H+K)^3+p(H+K)+q=0$
$H^3+3H^2K+3HK^2+K^3+pH+pK+q=0$
Let $3HK=-p$.
$H^3-pH-pK+K^3+pH+pK+q=0,$
$H^3+K^3=-q$

3.
$$3HK=-p$$
$$K=-\frac{p}{3H}$$
$$H^3+\left(-\frac{p}{3H}\right)^3=-q$$
$$H^3-\frac{p^3}{27H^3}=-q$$
$$27H^6-p^3=-27qH^3$$
$$27H^6+27qH^3-p^3=0$$
$$H^3=\frac{-27q\pm\sqrt{(27q)^2-4(27)(-p^3)}}{2\cdot 27}$$
$$H^3=\frac{-q}{2}\pm\sqrt{\frac{27^2q^2}{2^2(27^2)}+\frac{4(27)p^3}{2^2(27^2)}}$$
$$H^3=\frac{-q}{2}\pm\sqrt{\frac{q^2}{4}+\frac{p^3}{27}}$$
$$H=\sqrt[3]{\frac{-q}{2}+\sqrt{\frac{q^2}{4}+\frac{p^3}{27}}}$$
Choose the positive root for now.

4. $H^3+K^3=-q$
$$K^3=-q-H^3$$
$$K^3=-q-\left[\frac{-q}{2}+\sqrt{\frac{q^2}{4}+\frac{p^3}{27}}\right]$$
$$K^3=\frac{-q}{2}-\sqrt{\frac{q^2}{4}+\frac{p^3}{27}}$$
$$K=\sqrt[3]{\frac{-q}{2}-\sqrt{\frac{q^2}{4}+\frac{p^3}{27}}}$$

5. $x=H+K$
$$x=\sqrt[3]{\frac{-q}{2}+\sqrt{\frac{q^2}{4}+\frac{p^3}{27}}}+\sqrt[3]{\frac{-q}{2}-\sqrt{\frac{q^2}{4}+\frac{p^3}{27}}}$$
(Note that had we used the negative root in 3 the result would be the same.)

6. $x=3$ **7.** $x=2$ **8.** $x=2$

11.2 Assess Your Understanding *(page 710)*

5. Remainder; dividend **6.** $f(c)$ **7.** -4 **8.** F **9.** 0 **10.** T **11.** $R=f(2)=8$; no **13.** $R=f(2)=0$; yes **15.** $R=f(-3)=0$; yes **17.** $R=f(-4)=1$; no **19.** $R=f\left(\frac{1}{2}\right)=0$; yes **21.** 4; $\pm1, \pm\frac{1}{3}$ **23.** 5; $\pm1, \pm3$ **25.** 3; $\pm1, \pm2, \pm\frac{1}{4}, \pm\frac{1}{2}$ **27.** 4; $\pm1, \pm3, \pm9, \pm\frac{1}{2}, \pm\frac{1}{3}, \pm\frac{1}{6}, \pm\frac{3}{2}, \pm\frac{9}{2}$ **29.** 5; $\pm1, \pm2, \pm3, \pm4, \pm6, \pm12, \pm\frac{1}{2}, \pm\frac{3}{2}$
31. 4; $\pm1, \pm2, \pm4, \pm5, \pm10, \pm20, \pm\frac{1}{2}, \pm\frac{5}{2}, \pm\frac{1}{3}, \pm\frac{2}{3}, \pm\frac{4}{3}, \pm\frac{5}{3}, \pm\frac{10}{3}, \pm\frac{20}{3}, \pm\frac{1}{6}, \pm\frac{5}{6}$

33. –1 and 1

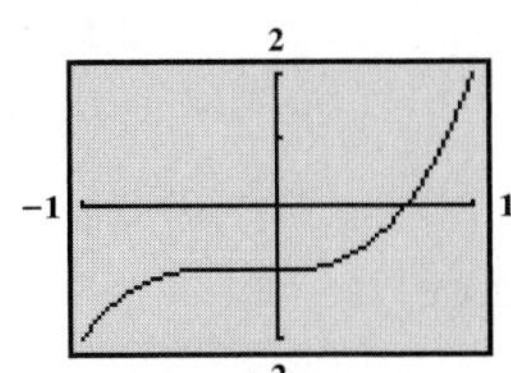

35. –12 and 12

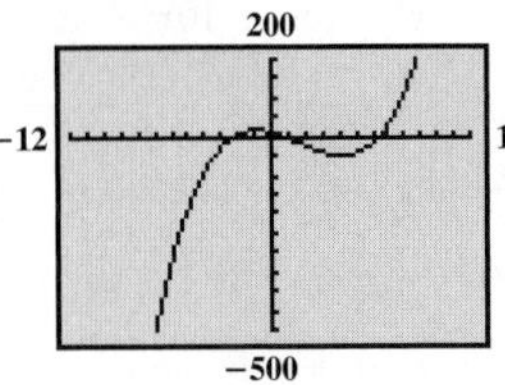

37. –10 and 10

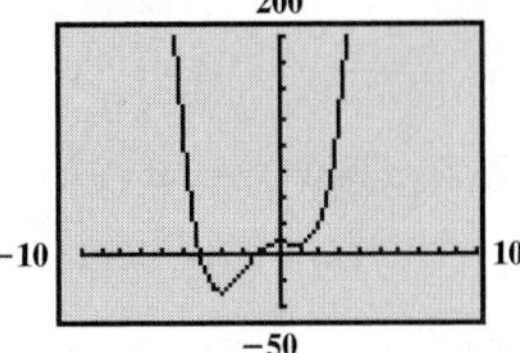

39. $-3, -1, 2; f(x)=(x+3)(x+1)(x-2)$ **41.** $\frac{1}{2}, 3, 3; f(x)=(2x-1)(x-3)^2$ **43.** $-\frac{1}{3}; f(x)=(3x+1)(x^2+x+1)$
45. $3, \frac{5+\sqrt{17}}{2}, \frac{5-\sqrt{17}}{2}; f(x)=(x-3)\left(x-\frac{5+\sqrt{17}}{2}\right)\left(x-\frac{5-\sqrt{17}}{2}\right)$ **47.** $-2, -1, 1, 1; f(x)=(x+2)(x+1)(x-1)^2$
49. $-5, -3, -\frac{3}{2}, 1; f(x)=(x+5)(x+3)(2x+3)(x-1)$ **51.** $-2, -\frac{3}{2}, 1, 4; f(x)=(x+2)(2x+3)(x-1)(x-4)$
53. $-\frac{1}{2}, \frac{1}{2}; f(x)=(2x+1)(2x-1)(x^2+2)$ **55.** $\frac{\sqrt{2}}{2}, -\frac{\sqrt{2}}{2}, 2; f(x)=(x-2)(\sqrt{2}x-1)(\sqrt{2}x+1)(2x^2+1)$ **57.** $-5.9, -0.3, 3$ **59.** $-3.8, 4.5$
61. $-43.5, 1, 23$ **63.** $\{-1, 2\}$ **65.** $\left\{\frac{2}{3}, -1+\sqrt{2}, -1-\sqrt{2}\right\}$ **67.** $\left\{\frac{1}{3}, \sqrt{5}, -\sqrt{5}\right\}$ **69.** $\{-3, -2\}$ **71.** $\left\{-\frac{1}{3}\right\}$ **73.** $f(0)=-1; f(1)=10$; Zero: 0.22 **75.** $f(-5)=-58; f(-4)=2$; Zero: -4.05 **77.** $f(1.4)=-0.17536; f(1.5)=1.40625$; Zero: 1.41

79. Step 1: $y=x^3$
Step 2: x-intercepts: $-3, -1, 2$;
y-intercept: -6
Step 3: $-3, -1, 2$: multiplicity 1, crosses

Step 4:

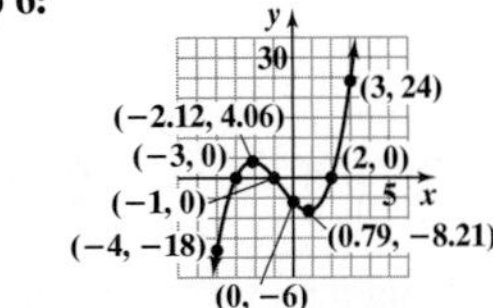

Step 5: $(-2.12, 4.06)$; $(0.79, -8.21)$

Step 6:

Step 7: Domain and range: $(-\infty, \infty)$
Step 8: Increasing: $(-\infty, -2.12), (0.79, \infty)$
Decreasing: $(-2.12, 0.79)$

81. Step 1: $y = x^4$
Step 2: x-intercepts: $-2, -1, 1$; y-intercept: 2
Step 3: $-2, -1$: multiplicity 1, crosses; 1: multiplicity 2, touches

Step 4:

Step 5: $(-1.59, -1.62), (-0.16, 2.08), (1, 0)$

Step 6:

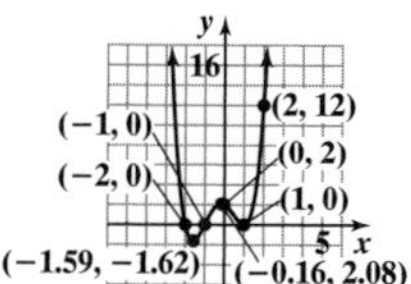

Step 7: Domain: $(-\infty, \infty)$; Range: $[-1.62, \infty)$
Step 8: Increasing: $(-1.59, -0.16), (1, \infty)$
Decreasing: $(-\infty, -1.59), (-0.16, 1)$

83. Step 1: $y = 4x^5$
Step 2: x-intercepts: $-\frac{\sqrt{2}}{2}, \frac{\sqrt{2}}{2}, 2$; y-intercept: 2
Step 3: $-\frac{\sqrt{2}}{2}, \frac{\sqrt{2}}{2}, 2$: multiplicity 1, crosses

Step 4:

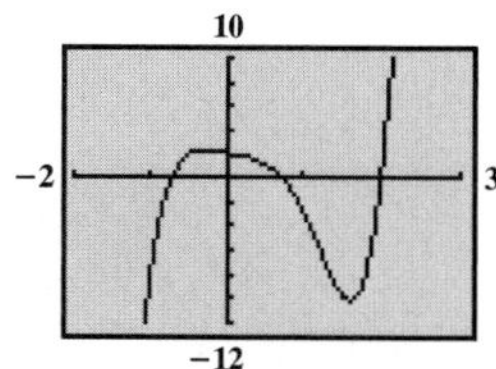

Step 5: $(-0.30, 2.23); (1.61, -10.09)$

Step 6:

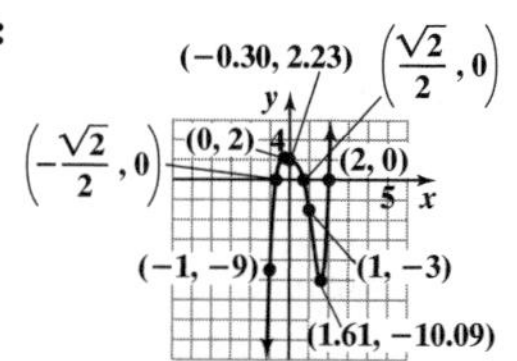

Step 7: Domain and range: $(-\infty, \infty)$
Step 8: Increasing: $(-\infty, -0.30), (1.61, \infty)$
Decreasing: $(-0.30, 1.61)$

85. Step 1: $y = 6x^4$
Step 2: x-intercepts: $-\frac{1}{2}, \frac{2}{3}, 3$;
y-intercept: -18
Step 3: $-\frac{1}{2}, \frac{2}{3}$: multiplicity 1, crosses;
3: multiplicity 2, touches
Step 4:

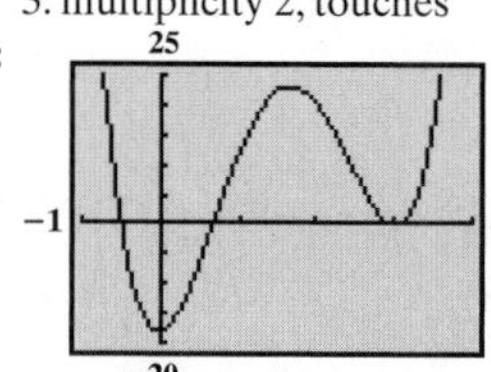

Step 5: $(-0.03, -18.04), (1.65, 23.12), (3, 0)$
Step 6:

Step 7: Domain: $(-\infty, \infty)$;
Range: $[-18.04, \infty)$
Step 8: Increasing: $(-0.03, 1.65), (3, \infty)$;
Decreasing: $(-\infty, -0.03), (1.65, 3)$

87. $k = 5$ **89.** -7
91. If $f(x) = x^n - c^n$, then $f(c) = c^n - c^n = 0$; so $x - c$ is a factor of f.
93. 5 **95.** 7 in.
97. All the potential rational zeros are integers, so r is either an integer or is not a rational zero (and is, therefore, irrational).
99. 0.215

101. No; by the Rational Zeros Theorem, $\frac{1}{3}$ is not a potential rational zero. **103.** No; by the Rational Zeros Theorem, $\frac{2}{3}$ is not a potential rational zero.

11.3 Assess Your Understanding *(page 716)*

3. one **4.** $3 - 4i$ **5.** T **6.** F **7.** $4 + i$ **9.** $-i, 1 - i$ **11.** $-i, -2i$ **13.** $-i$ **15.** $2 - i, -3 + i$ **17.** $f(x) = x^4 - 14x^3 + 77x^2 - 200x + 208; a = 1$
19. $f(x) = x^5 - 4x^4 + 7x^3 - 8x^2 + 6x - 4; a = 1$ **21.** $f(x) = x^4 - 6x^3 + 10x^2 - 6x + 9; a = 1$ **23.** $-2i, 4$ **25.** $2i, -3, \frac{1}{2}$ **27.** $3 + 2i, -2, 5$
29. $4i, -\sqrt{11}, \sqrt{11}, -\frac{2}{3}$ **31.** $1, -\frac{1}{2} - \frac{\sqrt{3}}{2}i, -\frac{1}{2} + \frac{\sqrt{3}}{2}i; f(x) = (x - 1)\left(x + \frac{1}{2} + \frac{\sqrt{3}}{2}i\right)\left(x + \frac{1}{2} - \frac{\sqrt{3}}{2}i\right)$
33. $2, 3 - 2i, 3 + 2i; f(x) = (x - 2)(x - 3 + 2i)(x - 3 - 2i)$ **35.** $-i, i, -2i, 2i; f(x) = (x + i)(x - i)(x + 2i)(x - 2i)$
37. $-5i, 5i, -3, 1; f(x) = (x + 5i)(x - 5i)(x + 3)(x - 1)$ **39.** $-4, \frac{1}{3}, 2 - 3i, 2 + 3i; f(x) = 3(x + 4)\left(x - \frac{1}{3}\right)(x - 2 + 3i)(x - 2 - 3i)$
41. Zeros that are complex numbers must occur in conjugate pairs; or a polynomial with real coefficients of odd degree must have at least one real zero.
43. If the remaining zero were a complex number, its conjugate would also be a zero, creating a polynomial of degree 5.

11.4 Assess Your Understanding *(page 725)*

5. F **6.** horizontal asymptote **7.** vertical asymptote **8.** proper **9.** T **10.** F **11.** $y = 0$ **12.** T **13.** All real numbers except 3; $\{x|x \neq 3\}$
15. All real numbers except 2 and -4; $\{x|x \neq 2, x \neq -4\}$ **17.** All real numbers except $-\frac{1}{2}$ and 3; $\left\{x\middle|x \neq -\frac{1}{2}, x \neq 3\right\}$
19. All real numbers except 2; $\{x|x \neq 2\}$ **21.** All real numbers **23.** All real numbers except -3 and 3; $\{x|x \neq -3, x \neq 3\}$
25. **(a)** Domain: $\{x|x \neq 2\}$; Range: $\{y|y \neq 1\}$ **(b)** $(0, 0)$ **(c)** $y = 1$ **(d)** $x = 2$ **(e)** None
27. **(a)** Domain: $\{x|x \neq 0\}$; Range: all real numbers **(b)** $(-1, 0), (1, 0)$ **(c)** None **(d)** $x = 0$ **(e)** $y = 2x$
29. **(a)** Domain: $\{x|x \neq -2, x \neq 2\}$; Range: $\{y|y \leq 0, y > 1\}$ **(b)** $(0, 0)$ **(c)** $y = 1$ **(d)** $x = -2, x = 2$ **(e)** None

31.

33.

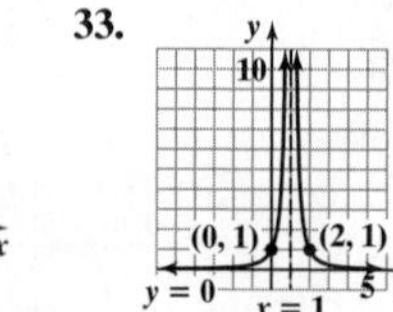

35.

37.

39.

41.

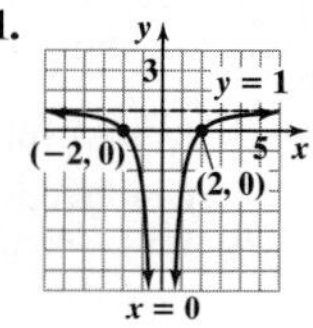

43. Vertical asymptote: $x = -4$; horizontal asymptote: $y = 3$ **45.** Vertical asymptote: $x = 3$; oblique asymptote: $y = x + 5$
47. Vertical asymptotes: $x = 1, x = -1$; horizontal asymptote: $y = 0$ **49.** Vertical asymptote: $x = -\frac{1}{3}$; horizontal asymptote: $y = \frac{2}{3}$
51. Vertical asymptote: none; oblique asymptote: $y = 2x - 1$ **53.** Vertical asymptote: $x = 0$; no horizontal or oblique asymptote
55. **(a)** 9.8208 m/sec^2 **(b)** 9.8195 m/sec^2 **(c)** 9.7936 m/sec^2 **(d)** h-axis **(e)** $\varnothing$

57. (a)

(b) Horizontal: $R_{tot} = 10$; as the resistance of R_2 increases without bound, the total resistance approaches 10 ohms, the resistance R_1. **(c)** $R_1 \approx 103.5$ ohms

11.5 Assess Your Understanding *(page 735)*

2. in lowest terms **3.** vertical **4.** True **5.** True **6. (a)** $\{x | x \neq 2\}$ **(b)** 0

7. Step 1: Domain: $\{x | x \neq 0, x \neq -4\}$
Step 2: R is in lowest terms
Step 3: no y-intercept; x-intercept: -1
Step 4: R is in lowest terms; vertical asymptotes: $x = 0$, $x = -4$
Step 5: Horizontal asymptote: $y = 0$, intersected at $(-1, 0)$
Step 6:

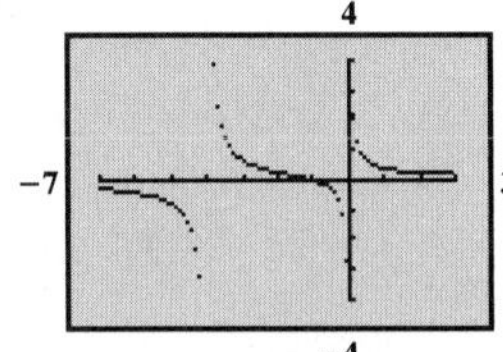

Step 7:

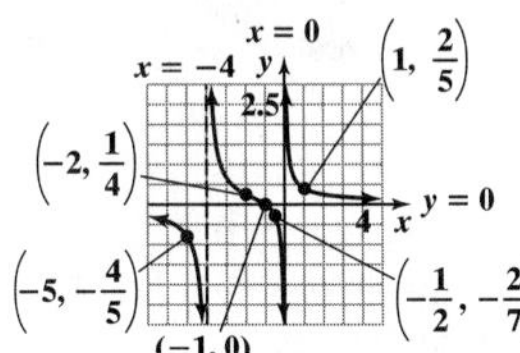

9. Step 1: $R(x) = \dfrac{3(x+1)}{2(x+2)}$; domain: $\{x | x \neq -2\}$
Step 2: R is in lowest terms
Step 3: y-intercept: $\frac{3}{4}$; x-intercept: -1
Step 4: R is in lowest terms; vertical asymptote: $x = -2$
Step 5: Horizontal asymptote: $y = \frac{3}{2}$, not intersected
Step 6:

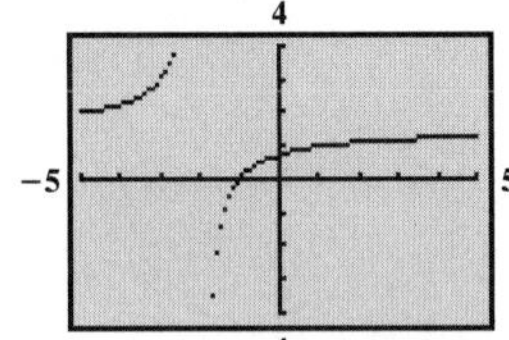

Step 7:

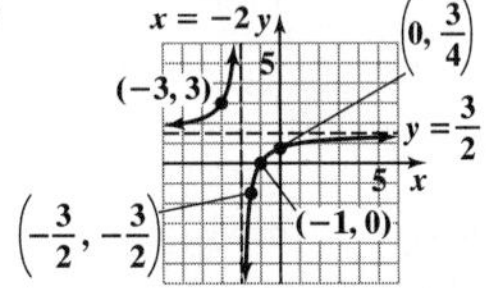

11. Step 1: $R(x) = \dfrac{3}{(x+2)(x-2)}$; domain: $\{x | x \neq -2, x \neq 2\}$
Step 2: R is in lowest terms
Step 3: y-intercept: $-\frac{3}{4}$; no x-intercept
Step 4: R is in lowest terms; vertical asymptotes: $x = 2$, $x = -2$
Step 5: Horizontal asymptote: $y = 0$, not intersected
Step 6:

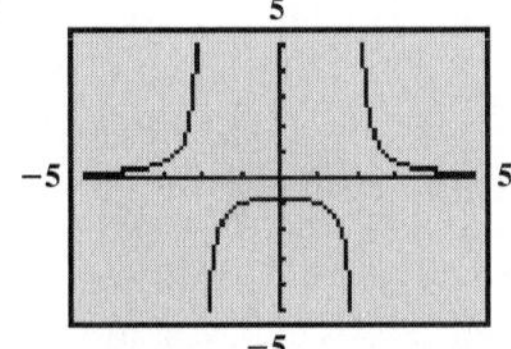

Step 7:

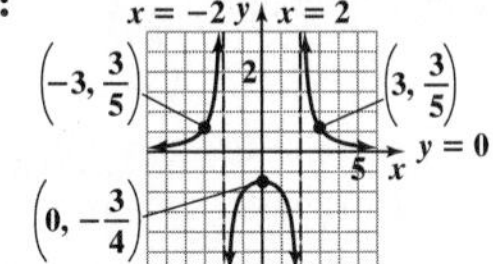

13. Step 1: $P(x) = \dfrac{(x^2+x+1)(x^2-x+1)}{(x+1)(x-1)}$; domain: $\{x | x \neq -1, x \neq 1\}$
Step 2: P is in lowest terms
Step 3: y-intercept: -1; no x-intercept
Step 4: P is in lowest terms; vertical asymptotes: $x = -1$, $x = 1$
Step 5: No horizontal or oblique asymptote
Step 6:

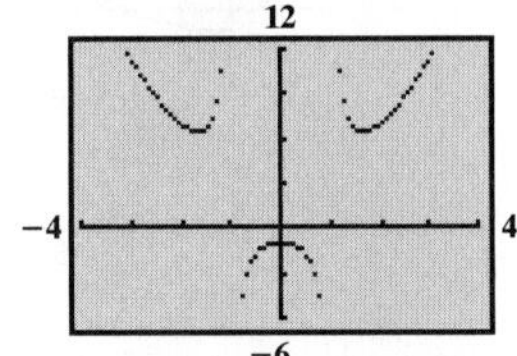

Step 7:

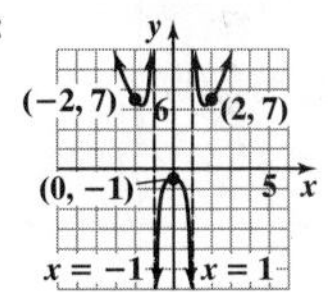

15. Step 1: $H(x) = \dfrac{(x-1)(x^2+x+1)}{(x+3)(x-3)}$; domain: $\{x | x \neq -3, x \neq 3\}$
Step 2: H is in lowest terms
Step 3: y-intercept: $\frac{1}{9}$; x-intercept: 1
Step 4: H is in lowest terms; vertical asymptotes: $x = 3$, $x = -3$
Step 5: Oblique asymptote: $y = x$, intersected at $\left(\frac{1}{9}, \frac{1}{9}\right)$
Step 6:

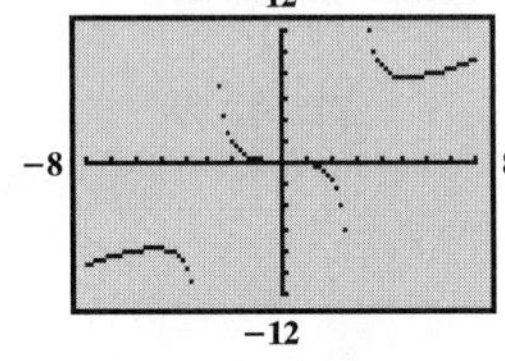

Step 7:

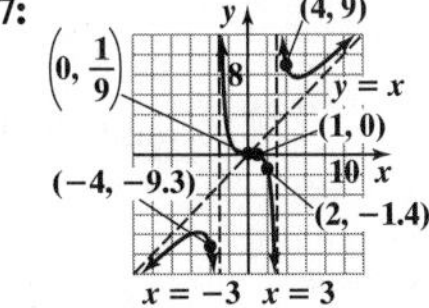

17. Step 1: $R(x) = \dfrac{x^2}{(x+3)(x-2)}$; domain: $\{x \neq -3, x \neq 2\}$
Step 2: R is in lowest terms
Step 3: y-intercept: 0; x-intercept: 0
Step 4: R is in lowest terms; vertical asymptotes: $x = 2$, $x = -3$
Step 5: Horizontal asymptote: $y = 1$, intersected at $(6, 1)$
Step 6:

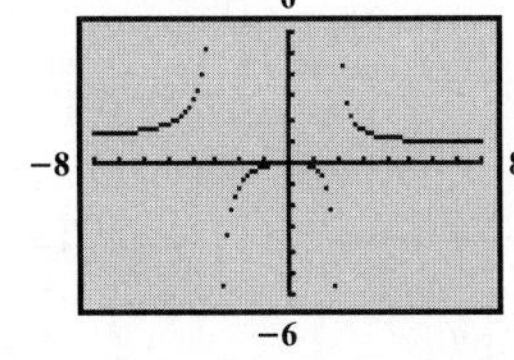

Step 7:

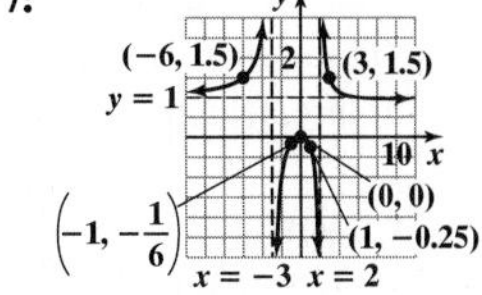

19. Step 1: $G(x) = \dfrac{x}{(x+2)(x-2)}$; domain: $\{x \mid x \neq -2, x \neq 2\}$

Step 2: G is in lowest terms

Step 3: y-intercept: 0; x-intercept: 0

Step 4: G is in lowest terms; vertical asymptotes: $x = -2, x = 2$

Step 5: Horizontal asymptote: $y = 0$, intersected at $(0, 0)$

Step 6:

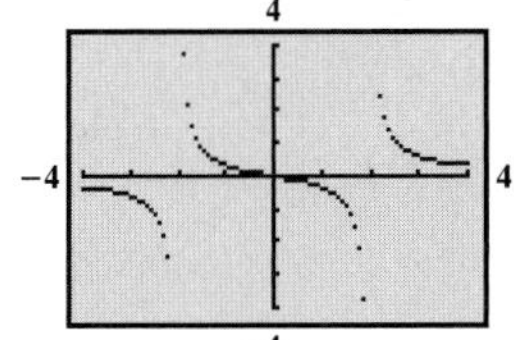

Step 7:

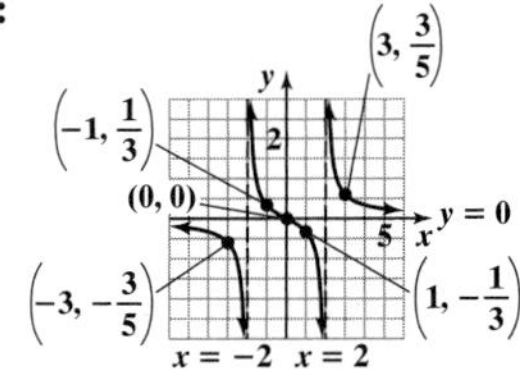

21. Step 1: $R(x) = \dfrac{3}{(x-1)(x+2)(x-2)}$; domain: $\{x \mid x \neq 1, x \neq -2, x \neq 2\}$

Step 2: R is in lowest terms

Step 3: y-intercept: $\dfrac{3}{4}$; no x-intercept

Step 4: R is in lowest terms; vertical asymptotes: $x = -2, x = 1, x = 2$

Step 5: Horizontal asymptote: $y = 0$, not intersected

Step 6:

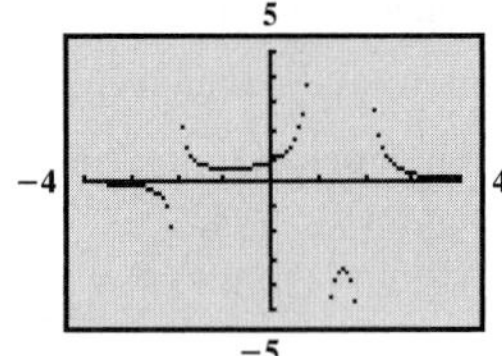

Step 7:

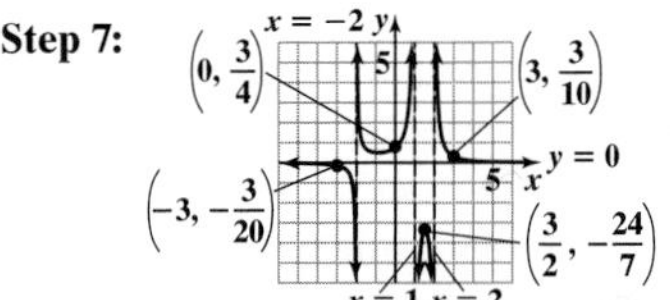

23. Step 1: $H(x) = \dfrac{(x+1)(x-1)}{(x^2+4)(x+2)(x-2)}$; domain: $\{x \mid x \neq -2, x \neq 2\}$

Step 2: H is in lowest terms

Step 3: y-intercept: $\dfrac{1}{16}$; x-intercepts: $-1, 1$

Step 4: H is in lowest terms; vertical asymptotes: $x = -2, x = 2$

Step 5: Horizontal asymptote: $y = 0$, intersected at $(-1, 0)$ and $(1, 0)$

Step 6:

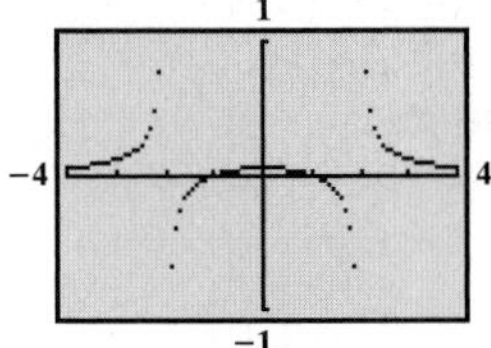

Step 7:

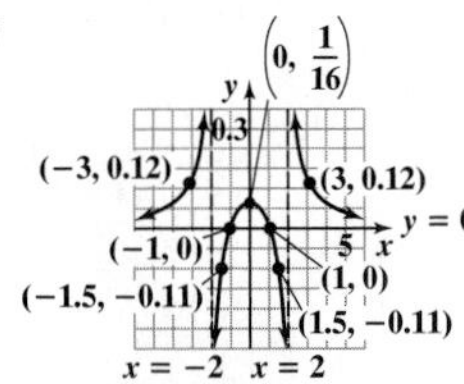

25. Step 1: $F(x) = \dfrac{(x+1)(x-4)}{x+2}$; domain: $\{x \mid x \neq -2\}$

Step 2: F is in lowest terms

Step 3: y-intercept: -2; x-intercepts: $-1, 4$

Step 4: F is in lowest terms; vertical asymptote: $x = -2$

Step 5: Oblique asymptote: $y = x - 5$, not intersected

Step 6:

Step 7:

27. Step 1: $R(x) = \dfrac{(x+4)(x-3)}{x-4}$; domain: $\{x \mid x \neq 4\}$

Step 2: R is in lowest terms

Step 3: y-intercept: 3; x-intercepts: $-4, 3$

Step 4: R is in lowest terms; vertical asymptote: $x = 4$

Step 5: Oblique asymptote: $y = x + 5$, not intersected

Step 6:

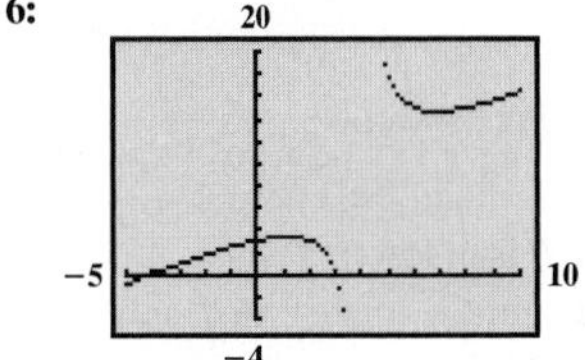

Step 7:

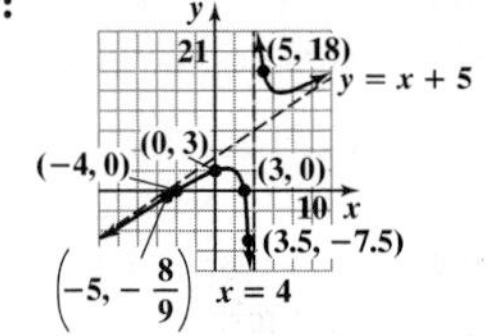

29. Step 1: $F(x) = \dfrac{(x+4)(x-3)}{x+2}$; domain: $\{x \mid x \neq -2\}$

Step 2: F is in lowest terms

Step 3: y-intercept: -6; x-intercepts: $-4, 3$

Step 4: F is in lowest terms; vertical asymptote: $x = -2$

Step 5: Oblique asymptote: $y = x - 1$, not intersected

Step 6:

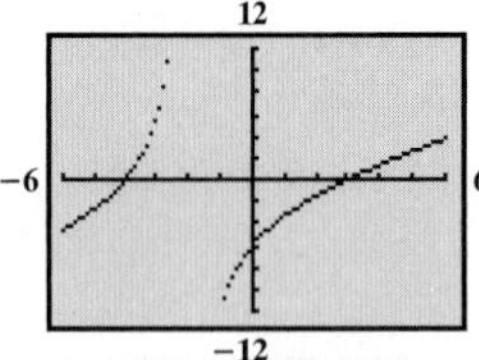

Step 7:

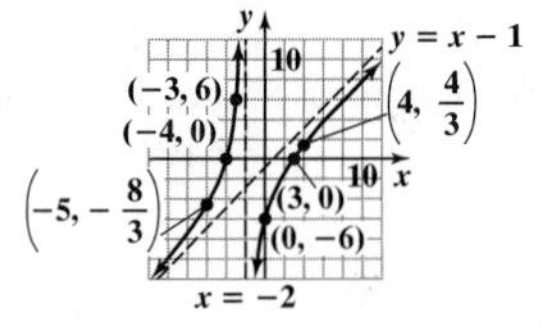

31. Step 1: Domain: $\{x \mid x \neq -3\}$

Step 2: R is in lowest terms

Step 3: y-intercept: 0; x-intercepts: 0, 1

Step 4: Vertical asymptote: $x = -3$

Step 5: Horizontal asymptote: $y = 1$, not intersected

Step 6:

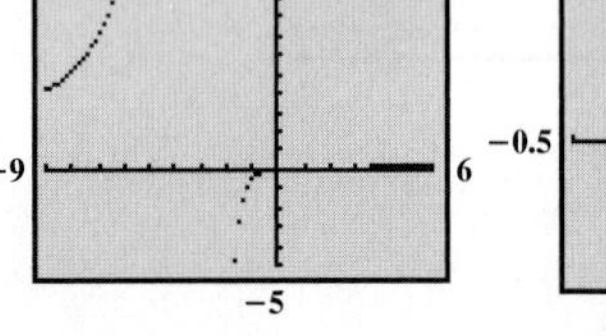

Step 7:

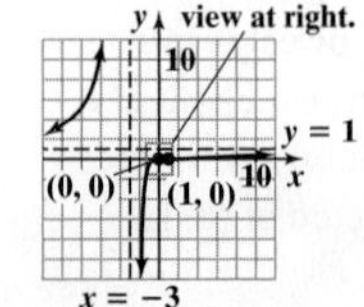

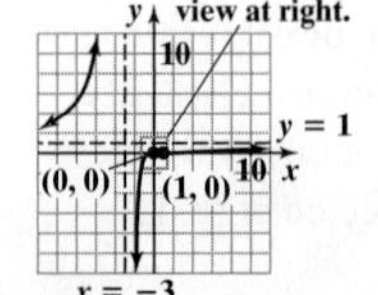

Enlarged view

33. Step 1: $R(x) = \dfrac{(x+4)(x-3)}{(x+2)(x-3)}$; domain: $\{x \mid x \neq -2, x \neq 3\}$

Step 2: In lowest terms, $R(x) = \dfrac{x+4}{x+2}$

Step 3: y-intercept: 2; x-intercept: -4

Step 4: Vertical asymptote: $x = -2$; hole at $\left(3, \dfrac{7}{5}\right)$

Step 5: Horizontal asymptote: $y = 1$, not intersected

Step 6:

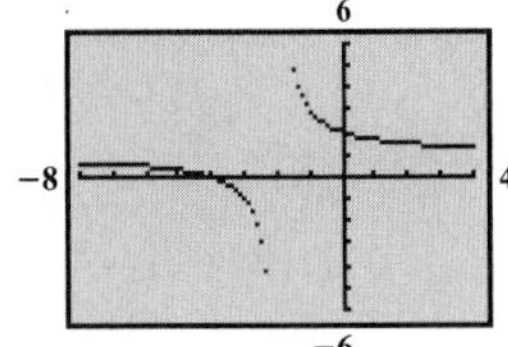

Step 7:

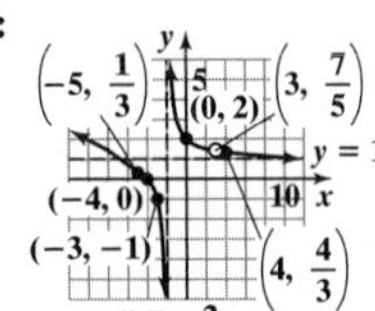

35. Step 1: $R(x) = \dfrac{(3x+1)(2x-3)}{(x-2)(2x-3)}$; domain: $\left\{x \,\middle|\, x \neq \dfrac{3}{2}, x \neq 2\right\}$

Step 2: In lowest terms, $R(x) = \dfrac{3x+1}{x-2}$

Step 3: y-intercept: $-\dfrac{1}{2}$; x-intercept: $-\dfrac{1}{3}$

Step 4: Vertical asymptote: $x = 2$; hole at $\left(\dfrac{3}{2}, -11\right)$

Step 5: Horizontal asymptote: $y = 3$, not intersected

Step 6:

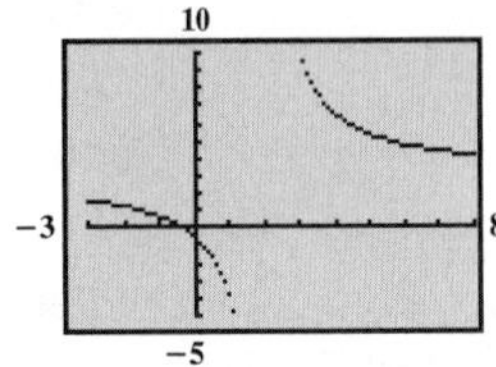

Step 7:

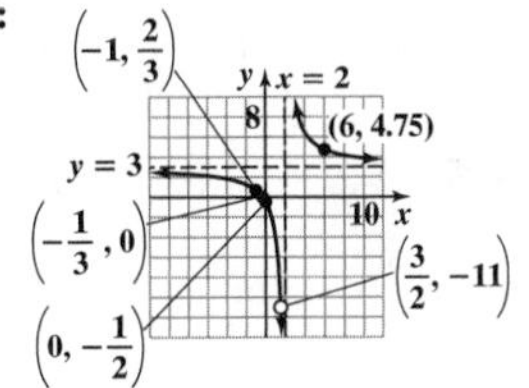

37. Step 1: $R(x) = \dfrac{(x+3)(x+2)}{x+3}$; domain: $\{x \mid x \neq -3\}$

Step 2: In lowest terms, $R(x) = x + 2$

Step 3: y-intercept: 2; x-intercept: -2

Step 4: Vertical asymptote: none; hole at $(-3, -1)$

Step 5: Oblique asymptote: $y = x + 2$ intersected at all points except $x = -3$

Step 6:

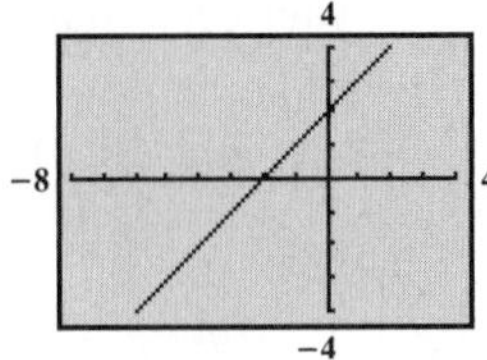

Step 7:

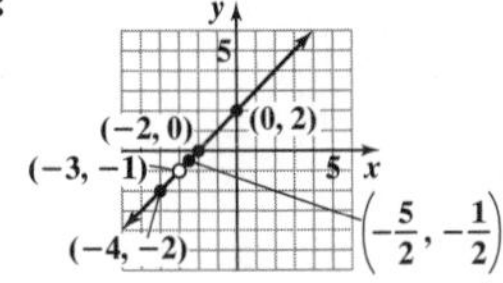

39. Step 1: $f(x) = \dfrac{x^2+1}{x}$; domain: $\{x \mid x \neq 0\}$

Step 2: f is in lowest terms

Step 3: no y-intercept; no x-intercepts

Step 4: f is in lowest terms; vertical asymptote: $x = 0$

Step 5: Oblique asymptote: $y = x$, not intersected

Step 6:

Step 7:

41. Step 1: $f(x) = \dfrac{x^3+1}{x} = \dfrac{(x+1)(x^2-x+1)}{x}$; domain: $\{x \mid x \neq 0\}$

Step 2: f is in lowest terms

Step 3: no y-intercept; x-intercept: -1

Step 4: f is in lowest terms; vertical asymptote: $x = 0$

Step 5: No horizontal or oblique asymptote

Step 6:

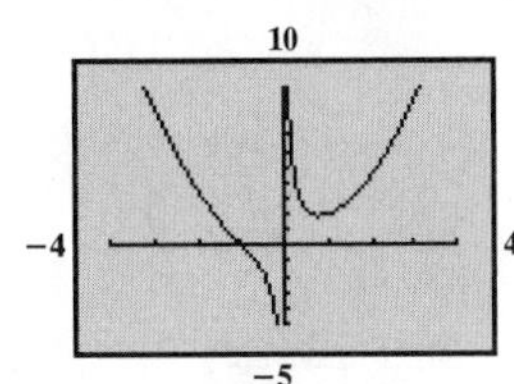

Step 7:

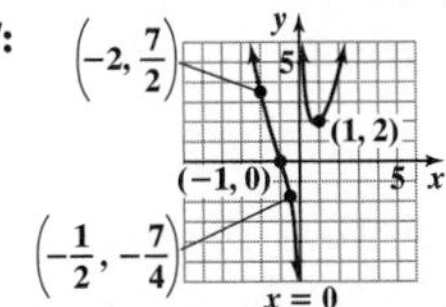

43. Step 1: $f(x) = \dfrac{x^4+1}{x^3}$; domain: $\{x \mid x \neq 0\}$

Step 2: f is in lowest terms

Step 3: no y-intercept; no x-intercepts

Step 4: f is in lowest terms; vertical asymptote: $x = 0$

Step 5: Oblique asymptote: $y = x$, not intersected

Step 6:

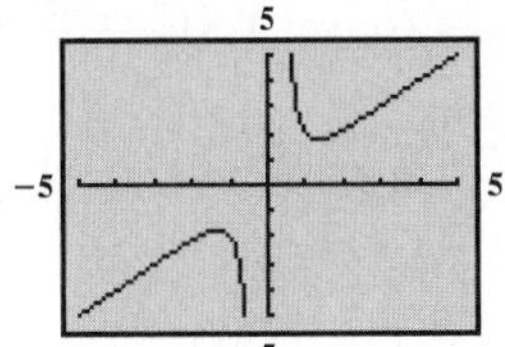

Step 7:

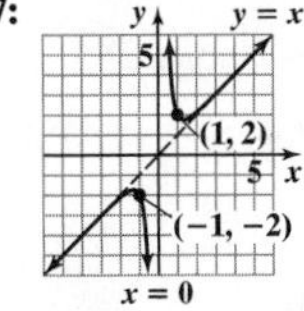

45. One possibility: $R(x) = \dfrac{x^2}{x^2-4}$

47. One possibility: $R(x) = \dfrac{(x-1)(x-3)\left(x^2 + \dfrac{4}{3}\right)}{(x+1)^2(x-2)^2}$

49. (a) t-axis; $C(t) \to 0$

(b)

(c) 0.71 h after injection

51. (a) $C(x) = 16x + \dfrac{5000}{x} + 100$

(b) $x > 0$

(c)

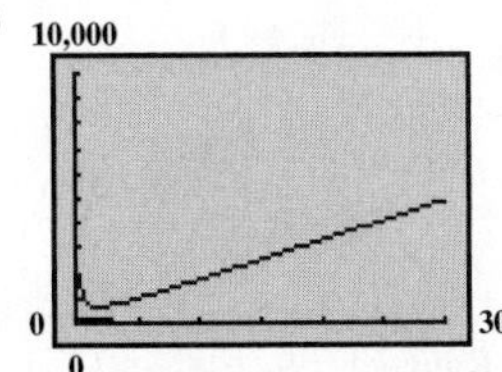

(d) Approximately 17.7 ft by 56.6 ft (longer side parallel to river)

53. (a) $S(x) = 2x^2 + \dfrac{40{,}000}{x}$

(b)

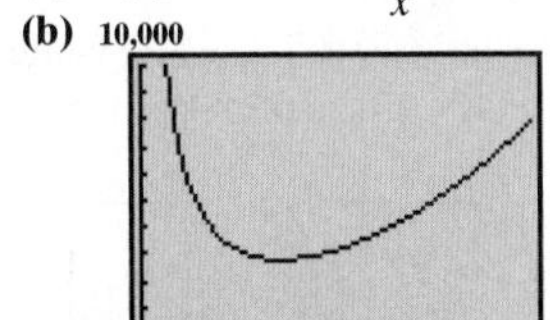

(c) 2784.95 in.^{2}

(d) 21.54 in. × 21.54 in. × 21.54 in.

(e) To minimize the cost of materials needed for construction

55. (a) $C(r) = 0.12\pi r^2 + \frac{40}{r}$

(b)

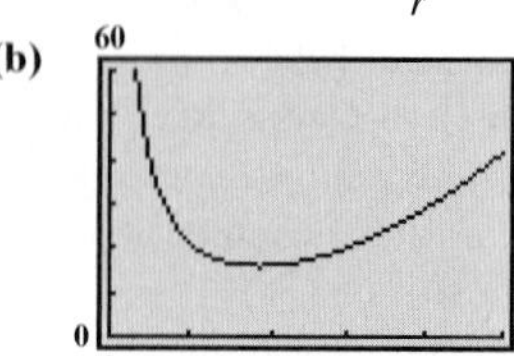

The cost is smallest when $r = 3.76$ cm.

57. No. Each function is a quotient of polynomials, but it is not written in lowest terms. Each function is undefined for $x = 1$; each graph has a hole at $x = 1$. **63.** If there is a common factor between the numerator and the denominator, and the factor yields a real zero, then the graph will have a hole.

11.6 Assess Your Understanding *(page 742)*

3. T **4.** F **5. (a)** $\{x|0 < x < 1 \text{ or } x > 2\}; (0, 1) \cup (2, \infty)$ **(b)** $\{x|x \le 0 \text{ or } 1 \le x \le 2\}; (-\infty, 0] \cup [1, 2]$
7. (a) $\{x|-1 < x < 0 \text{ or } x > 1\}; (-1, 0) \cup (1, \infty)$ **(b)** $\{x|x < -1 \text{ or } 0 \le x < 1\}; (-\infty, -1) \cup [0, 1)$
9. $\{x|x < 0 \text{ or } 0 < x < 3\}; (-\infty, 0) \cup (0, 3)$ **11.** $\{x|x \ge -4\}; [-4, \infty)$ **13.** $\{x|x \le -2 \text{ or } x \ge 2\}; (-\infty, -2] \cup [2, \infty)$
15. $\{x|-4 < x < -1 \text{ or } x > 0\}; (-4, 1) \cup (0, \infty)$ **17.** $\{x|-2 < x \le -1\}; (-2, -1]$ **19.** $\{x|x < -2\}; (-\infty, -2)$ **21.** $\{x|x > 4\}; (4, \infty)$
23. $\{x|-4 < x < 0 \text{ or } x > 0\}; (-4, 0) \cup (0, \infty)$ **25.** $\{x|x \le 1 \text{ or } 2 \le x \le 3\}; (-\infty, 1] \cup [2, 3]$ **27.** $\{x|-1 < x < 0 \text{ or } x > 3\}; (-1, 0) \cup (3, \infty)$
29. $\{x|x < -1 \text{ or } x > 1\}; (-\infty, -1) \cup (1, \infty)$ **31.** $\{x|x < -1 \text{ or } x > 1\}; (-\infty, -1) \cup (1, \infty)$ **33.** $\{x|x < -1 \text{ or } x > 1\}; (-\infty, -1) \cup (1, \infty)$
35. $\{x|x \le -1 \text{ or } 0 < x \le 1\}; (-\infty, -1] \cup (0, 1]$ **37.** $\{x|x < -1 \text{ or } x > 1\}; (-\infty, -1) \cup (1, \infty)$ **39.** $\{x|x < 2\}; (-\infty, 2)$
41. $\{x|-2 < x \le 9\}; (-2, 9]$ **43.** $\{x|x < 2 \text{ or } 3 < x < 5\}; (-\infty, 2) \cup (3, 5)$ **45.** $\{x|x < -5 \text{ or } -4 \le x \le -3 \text{ or } x = 0 \text{ or } x > 1\};$
$(-\infty, -5) \cup [-4, -3] \cup \{0\} \cup (1, \infty)$ **47.** $\left\{x \middle| -\frac{1}{2} < x < 1 \text{ or } x > 3\right\}; \left(-\frac{1}{2}, 1\right) \cup (3, \infty)$ **49.** $\{x|-1 < x < 3 \text{ or } x > 5\}; (-1, 3) \cup (5, \infty)$
51. $\left\{x \middle| x \le -4 \text{ or } x \ge \frac{1}{2}\right\}; (-\infty, -4] \cup \left[\frac{1}{2}, \infty\right)$ **53.** $\{x|x < 3 \text{ or } x \ge 7\}; (-\infty, 3) \cup [7, \infty)$ **55.** $\{x|x < 2\}; (-\infty, 2)$
57. $\left\{x \middle| x < -\frac{2}{3} \text{ or } 0 < x < \frac{3}{2}\right\}; \left(-\infty, -\frac{2}{3}\right) \cup \left(0, \frac{3}{2}\right)$ **59.** $\{x|x \le -3 \text{ or } 0 \le x \le 3\}; (-\infty, -3] \cup [0, 3]$

61. (a) $-4, -\frac{1}{2}, 3$
(b) $f(x) = (x + 4)^2(2x + 1)(x - 3)$
(c)
(d) $\left(-\frac{1}{2}, 3\right)$

63. (a)

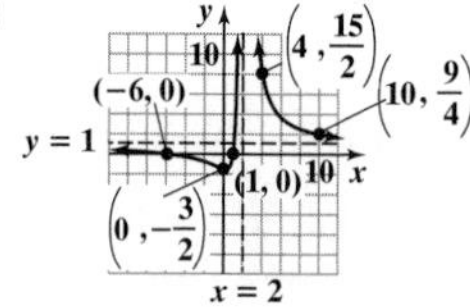

(b) $[1, 2) \cup (2, \infty)$

65. (a)

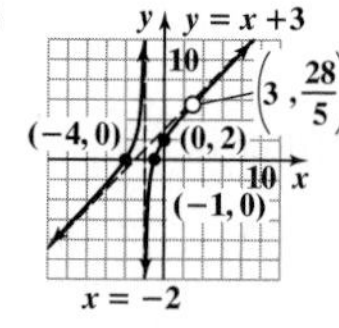

(b) $[-4, -2) \cup [-1, 3) \cup (3, \infty)$

67. $\{x|x > 4\}; (4, \infty)$
69. $\{x|x \le -2 \text{ or } x \ge 2\}; (-\infty, -2] \cup [2, \infty)$
71. $\{x|x < -4 \text{ or } x \ge 2\}; (-\infty, -4) \cup [2, \infty)$

73. $f(x) \le g(x)$ if $-1 \le x \le 1$

75. $f(x) \le g(x)$ if $-2 \le x \le 2$

77. Produce at least 250 bicycles
79. (a) The stretch is less than 39 ft.
(b) The ledge should be at least 84 ft above the ground for a 150-lb jumper.
81. At least 50 students must attend.

Review Exercises *(page 745)*

1. Polynomial of degree 5 **2.** Rational **3.** Neither **4.** Polynomial of degree 0

5.

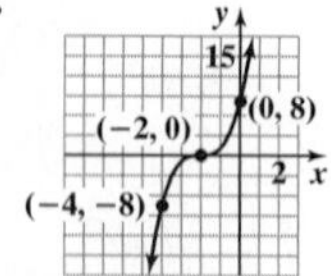

6.

7.

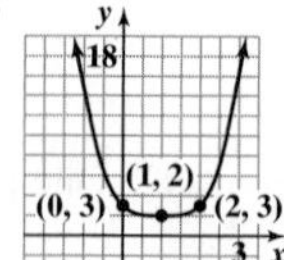

8. Step 1: $y = x^3$
Step 2: x-intercepts: $-4, -2, 0$; y-intercept: 0
Step 3: $-4, -2, 0$: multiplicity 1; crosses
Step 4:

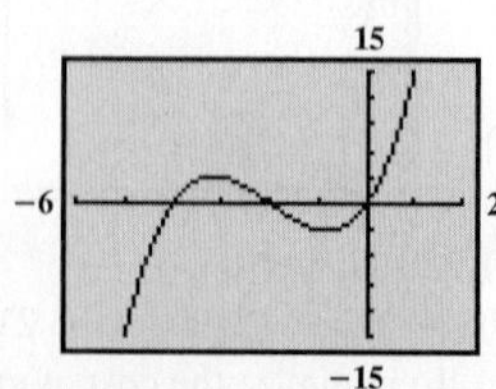

Step 5: $(-3.15, 3.08), (-0.85, -3.08)$
Step 6:

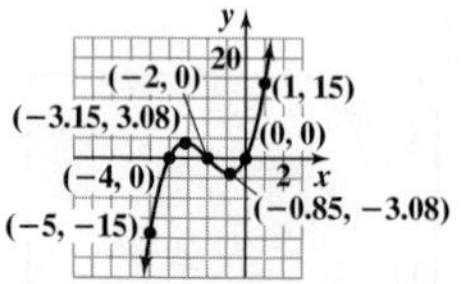

Step 7: Domain: $(-\infty, \infty)$; Range: $(-\infty, \infty)$

Step 8: Increasing on $(-\infty, -3.15)$ and $(-0.85, \infty)$
Decreasing on $(-3.15, -0.85)$

9. Step 1: $y = x^3$
Step 2: x-intercepts: $-4, 2$; y-intercept: 16
Step 3: -4: multiplicity 1; crosses; 2: multiplicity 2; touches
Step 4:

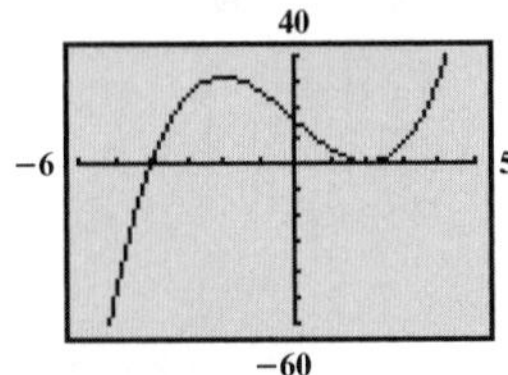

Step 5: $(-2, 32), (2, 0)$
Step 6:

Step 7: Domain: $(-\infty, \infty)$; Range: $(-\infty, \infty)$
Step 8: Increasing on $(-\infty, -2)$ and $(2, \infty)$
Decreasing on $(-2, 2)$

10. Step 1: $y = -2x^3$
Step 2: x-intercepts: 0, 2; y-intercept: 0
Step 3: 0: multiplicity 2; touches; 2: multiplicity 1; crosses
Step 4:

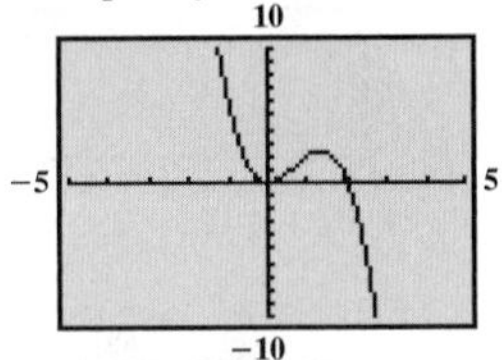

Step 5: $(0, 0), (1.33, 2.37)$
Step 6:

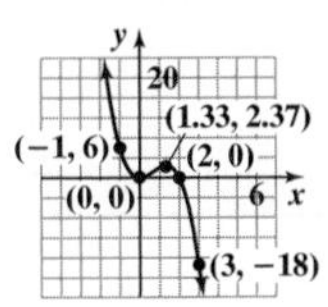

Step 7: Domain: $(-\infty, \infty)$ Range: $(-\infty, \infty)$
Step 8: Increasing on $(0, 1.33)$
Decreasing on $(-\infty, 0)$ and $(1.33, \infty)$

11. Step 1: $y = x^4$
Step 2: x-intercepts: $-3, -1, 1$; y-intercept: 3
Step 3: $-3, -1$: multiplicity 1; crosses; 1: multiplicity 2; touches
Step 4:

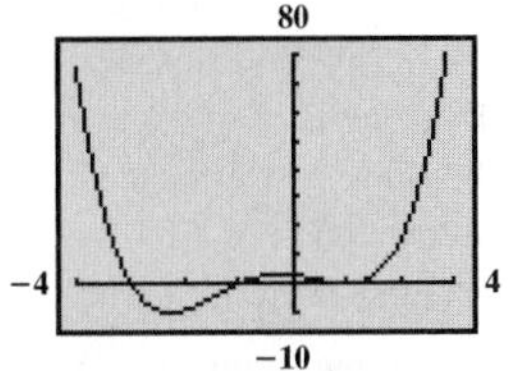

Step 5: $(-2.28, -9.91), (-0.22, 3.23), (1, 0)$
Step 6:

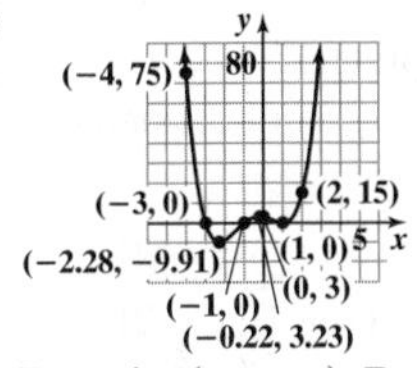

Step 7: Domain: $(-\infty, \infty)$; Range: $[-9.91, \infty)$
Step 8: Increasing on $(-2.28, -0.22)$ and $(1, \infty)$
Decreasing on $(-\infty, -2.28)$ and $(-0.22, 1)$

12. $R = 10$; g is not a factor of f. **13.** $R = 0$; g is a factor of f. **14.** $f(4) = 47{,}105$ **15.** $\pm 1, \pm 3, \pm\frac{1}{2}, \pm\frac{3}{2}, \pm\frac{1}{3}, \pm\frac{1}{4}, \pm\frac{3}{4}, \pm\frac{1}{6}, \pm\frac{1}{12}$

16. $-2, 1, 4; f(x) = (x + 2)(x - 1)(x - 4)$ **17.** $\frac{1}{2}$, multiplicity 2; $-2; f(x) = 4\left(x - \frac{1}{2}\right)^2(x + 2)$ **18.** 2, multiplicity 2; $f(x) = (x - 2)^2(x^2 + 5)$

19. $\{-3, 2\}$ **20.** $\left\{-3, -1, -\frac{1}{2}, 1\right\}$

21. -5 and 5

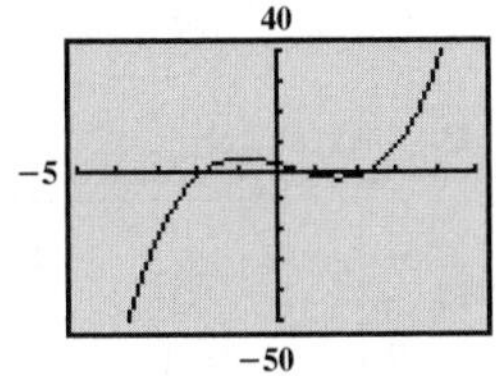

22. $-\frac{37}{2}$ and $\frac{37}{2}$

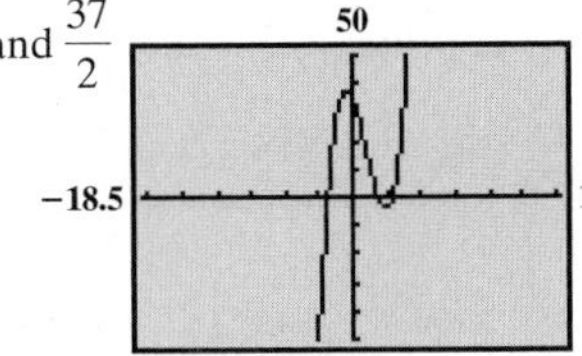

23. $f(0) = -1; f(1) = 1$ **24.** $f(0) = -1; f(1) = 1$
25. $4 - i; f(x) = x^3 - 14x^2 + 65x - 102$
26. $-i, 1 - i; f(x) = x^4 - 2x^3 + 3x^2 - 2x + 2$
27. $-2, 1, 4; f(x) = (x + 2)(x - 1)(x - 4)$
28. $-2, \frac{1}{2}$ (multiplicity 2); $f(x) = 4(x + 2)\left(x - \frac{1}{2}\right)^2$

29. 2 (multiplicity 2), $-\sqrt{5}i, \sqrt{5}i; f(x) = (x + \sqrt{5}i)(x - \sqrt{5}i)(x - 2)^2$ **30.** $-3, 2, -\frac{\sqrt{2}}{2}i, \frac{\sqrt{2}}{2}i; f(x) = 2(x + 3)(x - 2)\left(x + \frac{\sqrt{2}}{2}i\right)\left(x - \frac{\sqrt{2}}{2}i\right)$

31. Domain: $\{x \mid x \neq -3, x \neq 3\}$: horizontal asymptote: $y = 0$; vertical asymptotes: $x = -3, x = 3$ **32.** Domain: $\{x \mid x \neq -2\}$; horizontal asymptote: $y = 1$; vertical asymptote: $x = -2$

33. Step 1: $R(x) = \frac{2(x - 3)}{x}$; domain: $\{x \mid x \neq 0\}$
Step 2: R is in lowest terms
Step 3: no y-intercept; x-intercept: 3
Step 4: R is in lowest terms; vertical asymptote: $x = 0$
Step 5: Horizontal asymptote: $y = 2$; not intersected
Step 6:

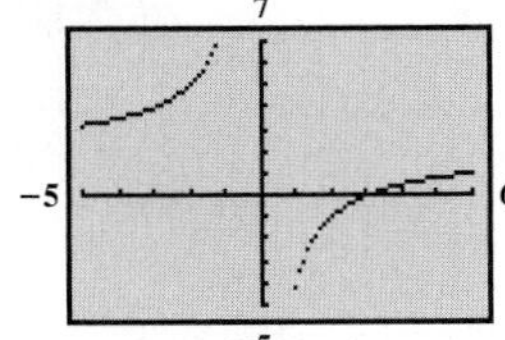

Step 7:

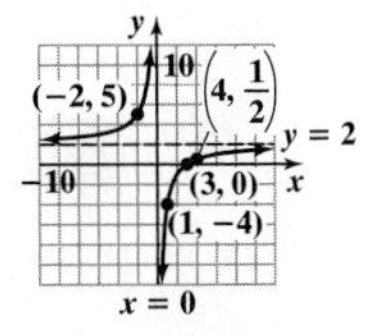

34. Step 1: Domain: $\{x \mid x \neq 0, x \neq 2\}$
Step 2: H is in lowest terms
Step 3: no y-intercept; x-intercept: -2
Step 4: H is in lowest terms; vertical asymptote: $x = 0, x = 2$
Step 5: Horizontal asymptote: $y = 0$; intersected at $(-2, 0)$
Step 6:

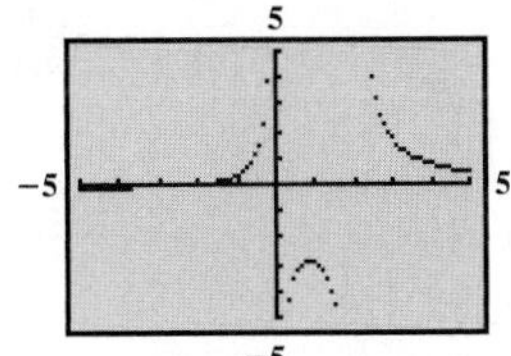

Step 7:

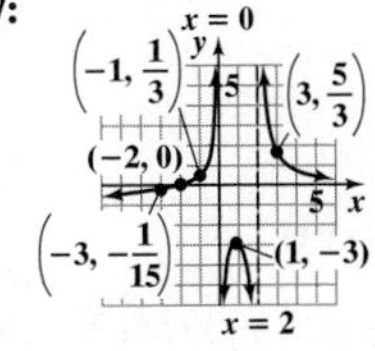

35. Step 1: $R(x) = \frac{(x + 3)(x - 2)}{(x - 3)(x + 2)}$; domain: $\{x \mid x \neq -2, x \neq 3\}$
Step 2: R is in lowest terms
Step 3: y-intercept: 1; x-intercepts: $-3, 2$
Step 4: R is in lowest terms; vertical asymptotes: $x = -2, x = 3$
Step 5: Horizontal asymptote: $y = 1$; intersected at $(0, 1)$
Step 6:

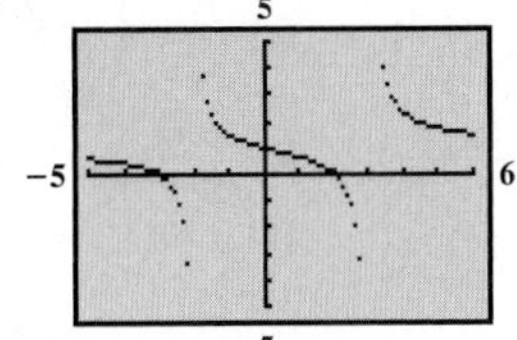

Step 7:

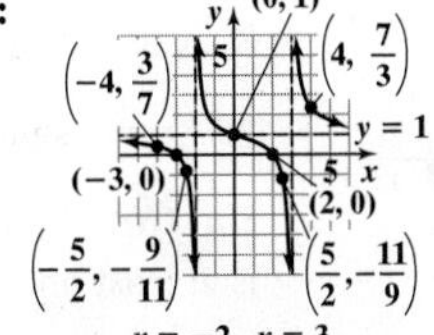

36. Step 1: $F(x) = \dfrac{x^3}{(x+2)(x-2)}$; domain: $\{x \mid x \neq -2, x \neq 2\}$
Step 2: F is in lowest terms
Step 3: y-intercept: 0; x-intercept: 0
Step 4: F is in lowest terms; vertical asymptotes: $x = -2, x = 2$
Step 5: Oblique asymptote: $y = x$; intersected at $(0, 0)$

Step 6:

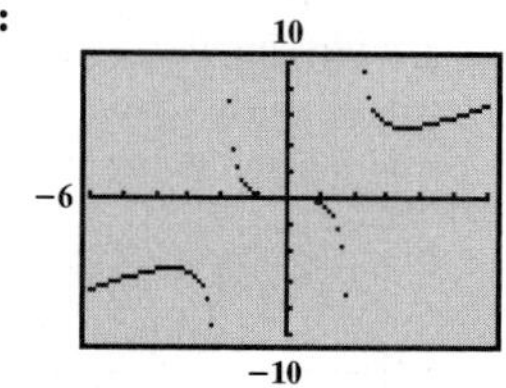

Step 7:

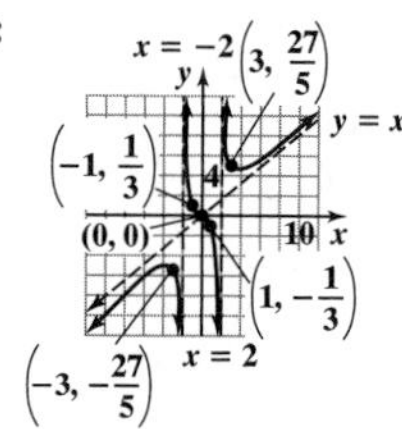

37. Step 1: Domain: $\{x \mid x \neq 1\}$
Step 2: R is in lowest terms
Step 3: y-intercept: 0; x-intercept: 0
Step 4: R is in lowest terms; vertical asymptote: $x = 1$
Step 5: No oblique or horizontal asymptote:

Step 6:

Step 7:

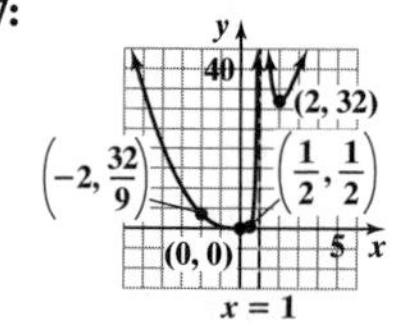

38. Step 1: $G(x) = \dfrac{(x+2)(x-2)}{(x+1)(x-2)}$; domain: $\{x \mid x \neq -1, x \neq 2\}$
Step 2: In lowest terms, $G(x) = \dfrac{x+2}{x+1}$
Step 3: y-intercept: 2; x-intercept: -2
Step 4: Vertical asymptote: $x = -1$; hole at $\left(2, \dfrac{4}{3}\right)$
Step 5: Horizontal asymptote: $y = 1$, not intersected

Step 6:

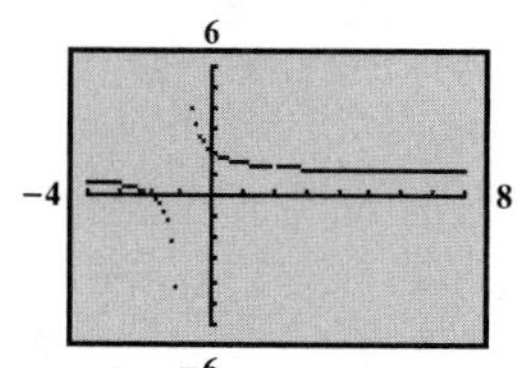

Step 7:

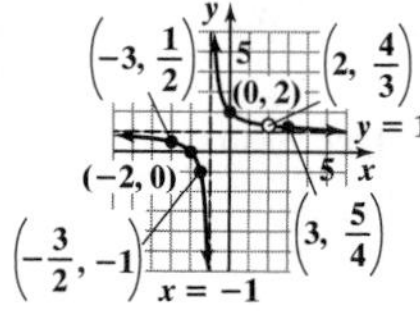

39. (a) $\{-3, 2\}$ **(b)** $(-3, 2) \cup (2, \infty)$ **(c)** $(-\infty, -3] \cup \{2\}$ **(d)** $f(x) = (x-2)^2(x+3)$ **40. (a)** $y = 0.25$ **(b)** $x = -2, x = 2$ **(c)** $(-3, -2) \cup (-1, 2)$ **(d)** $(-\infty, -3] \cup (-2, -1] \cup (2, \infty)$ **(e)** $R(x) = \dfrac{x^2 + 4x + 3}{4x^2 - 16}$

41. $\{x \mid x < -2 \text{ or } -1 < x < 2\}$; $(-\infty, -2) \cup (-1, 2)$

42. $\{x \mid -3 < x \leq 3\}$; $(-3, 3]$

43. $\{x \mid x < 1 \text{ or } x > 2\}$; $(-\infty, 1) \cup (2, \infty)$

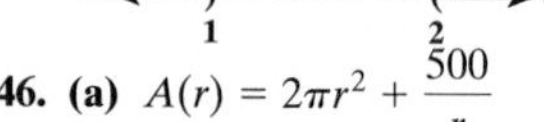

44. $\{x \mid 1 \leq x \leq 2 \text{ or } x > 3\}$; $[1, 2] \cup (3, \infty)$

45. $\{x \mid x < -4 \text{ or } 2 < x < 4 \text{ or } x > 6\}$; $(-\infty, -4) \cup (2, 4) \cup (6, \infty)$

46. (a) $A(r) = 2\pi r^2 + \dfrac{500}{r}$
(b) 223.22 cm²
(c) 257.08 cm²
(d)

A is smallest when $r \approx 3.41$ cm.

47. (a)

Data appear to follow a cubic relation.

(b) $P(t) = 0.0033t^3 - 0.0856t^2 + 0.4013t + 13.8330$; 15.5%
(c)

50. (a) Even **(b)** Positive **(c)** Even **(d)** The graph touches the x-axis at $x = 0$, but does not cross it there. **(e)** 8

Chapter Test *(page 747)*

1.

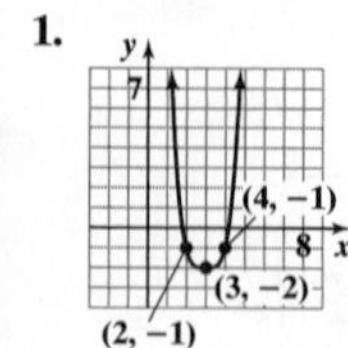

2. (a) 3 **(b)** Every zero of g lies between -15 and 15.
(c) $\dfrac{p}{q}$: $\pm\dfrac{1}{2}, \pm 1, \pm\dfrac{3}{2}, \pm\dfrac{5}{2}, \pm 3, \pm 5, \pm\dfrac{15}{2}, \pm 15$
(d) $-5, -\dfrac{1}{2}, 3$; $g(x) = (x+5)(2x+1)(x-3)$
(e) y-intercept: -15; x-intercepts: $-5, -\dfrac{1}{2}, 3$
(f) Crosses at $-5, -\dfrac{1}{2}, 3$ **(g)** $y = 2x^3$
(h) $(-3.15, 60.30), (1.48, -39.00)$
(i)

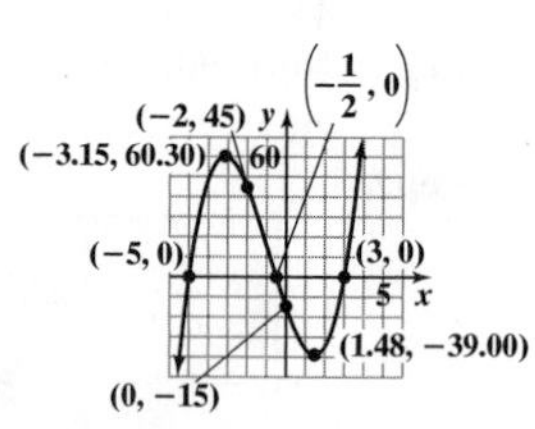

3. $4, -5i, 5i$ **4.** $\left\{1, \dfrac{5 - \sqrt{61}}{6}, \dfrac{5 + \sqrt{61}}{6}\right\}$ **5.** Domain: $\{x \mid x \neq -10, x \neq 4\}$; asymptotes: $x = -10, y = 2$ **6.** Domain: $\{x \mid x \neq -1\}$; asymptotes: $x = -1, y = x + 1$

7.

8. Answers may vary. One possibility is $f(x) = x^4 - 4x^3 - 2x^2 + 20x$.

9. Answers may vary. One possibility is $r(x) = \dfrac{2(x-9)(x-1)}{(x-4)(x-9)}$.

10. $f(0) = 8$; $f(4) = -36$; Since $f(0) = 8 > 0$ and $f(4) = -36 < 0$, the Intermediate Value Theorem guarantees that there is at least one real zero between 0 and 4. **11.** $\{x \mid x < 3 \text{ or } x > 8\}$; $(-\infty, 3) \cup (8, \infty)$

Cumulative Review *(page 748)*

1. $\sqrt{26}$ **2.** $\{x|x \le 0 \text{ or } x \ge 1\}$; $(-\infty, 0]$ or $[1, \infty)$ **3.** $\{x|-1 < x < 4\}$; $(-1, 4)$ **4.** $f(x) = -3x + 1$ **5.** $y = 2x - 1$

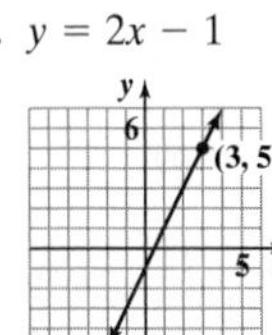

6.

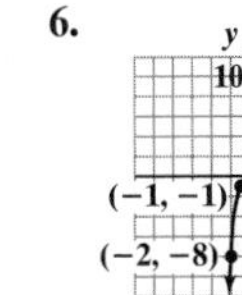

7. Not a functions; 3 has two images. **8.** $\{0, 2, 4\}$ **9.** $\left\{x \middle| x \ge \frac{3}{2}\right\}$; $\left[\frac{3}{2}, \infty\right)$

10. Center: $(-2, 1)$; radius: 3 **11.** x-intercepts: $-3, 0, 3$; y-intercept: 0; symmetric with respect to the origin **12.** $y = -\frac{2}{3}x + \frac{17}{3}$

13. Not a function; it fails the Vertical Line Test. **14. (a)** 22 **(b)** $x^2 - 5x - 2$ **(c)** $-x^2 - 5x + 2$ **(d)** $9x^2 + 15x - 2$ **(e)** $2x + h + 5$ **15. (a)** $\{x|x \ne 1\}$ **(b)** No; (2,7) is on the graph. **(c)** 4; (3, 4) is on the graph. **(d)** $\frac{7}{4}$; $\left(\frac{7}{4}, 9\right)$ is on the graph. **(e)** Rational

16.

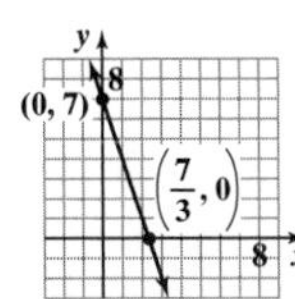

17.

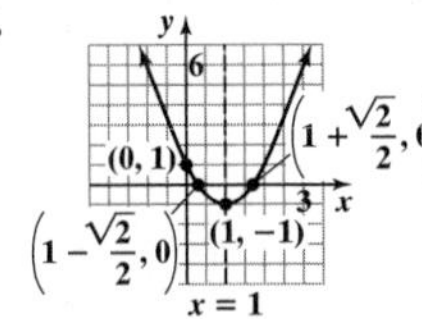

18. 6; $y = 6x - 1$ **19. (a)** x-intercepts: $-5, -1, 5$; y-intercept: -3 **(b)** No symmetry **(c)** Neither **(d)** Increasing: $(-\infty, -3)$ and $(2, \infty)$; decreasing: $(-3, 2)$ **(e)** Local maximum value is 5 and occurs at $x = -3$. **(f)** Local minimum value is -6 and occurs at $x = 2$. **20.** Odd

21. (a) Domain: $\{x|x > -3\}$ or $(-3, \infty)$ **(b)** x-intercept: $-\frac{1}{2}$; y-intercept: 1 **(c)**

(d) Range:

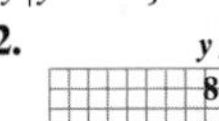

$\{y|y < 5\}$ or $(-\infty, 5)$

22.

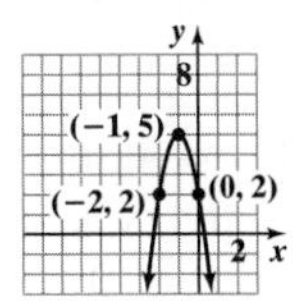

23. (a) $(f + g)(x) = x^2 - 9x - 6$; domain: all real numbers **(b)** $\left(\frac{f}{g}\right)(x) = \frac{x^2 - 5x + 1}{-4x - 7}$; domain: $\left\{x \middle| x \ne -\frac{7}{4}\right\}$

24. (a) $R(x) = -\frac{1}{10}x^2 + 150x$ **(b)** \$14,000 **(c)** 750; \$56,250 **(d)** \$75

CHAPTER 12 Exponential and Logarithmic Functions

12.1 Assess Your Understanding *(page 757)*

4. composite function; $f(g(x))$ **5.** F **6.** F **7. (a)** -1 **(b)** -1 **(c)** 8 **(d)** 0 **(e)** 8 **(f)** -7 **9. (a)** 4 **(b)** 5 **(c)** -1 **(d)** -2 **11. (a)** 98 **(b)** 49 **(c)** 4 **(d)** 4 **13. (a)** 97 **(b)** $-\frac{163}{2}$ **(c)** 1 **(d)** $-\frac{3}{2}$ **15. (a)** $2\sqrt{2}$ **(b)** $2\sqrt{2}$ **(c)** 1 **(d)** 0 **17. (a)** $\frac{1}{17}$ **(b)** $\frac{1}{5}$ **(c)** 1 **(d)** $\frac{1}{2}$ **19. (a)** $\frac{3}{\sqrt[3]{4} + 1}$ **(b)** 1 **(c)** $\frac{6}{5}$ **(d)** 0 **21.** $\{x|x \ne 0, x \ne 2\}$ **23.** $\{x|x \ne -4, x \ne 0\}$ **25.** $\left\{x \middle| x \ge -\frac{3}{2}\right\}$ **27.** $\{x|x \ge 1\}$

29. (a) $(f \circ g)(x) = 6x + 3$; all real numbers **(b)** $(g \circ f)(x) = 6x + 9$; all real numbers **(c)** $(f \circ f)(x) = 4x + 9$; all real numbers **(d)** $(g \circ g)(x) = 9x$; all real numbers

31. (a) $(f \circ g)(x) = 3x^2 + 1$; all real numbers **(b)** $(g \circ f)(x) = 9x^2 + 6x + 1$; all real numbers **(c)** $(f \circ f)(x) = 9x + 4$; all real numbers **(d)** $(g \circ g)(x) = x^4$; all real numbers

33. (a) $(f \circ g)(x) = x^4 + 8x^2 + 16$; all real numbers **(b)** $(g \circ f)(x) = x^4 + 4$; all real numbers **(c)** $(f \circ f)(x) = x^4$; all real numbers **(d)** $(g \circ g)(x) = x^4 + 8x^2 + 20$; all real numbers

35. (a) $(f \circ g)(x) = \frac{3x}{2 - x}$; $\{x|x \ne 0, x \ne 2\}$ **(b)** $(g \circ f)(x) = \frac{2(x - 1)}{3}$; $\{x|x \ne 1\}$ **(c)** $(f \circ f)(x) = \frac{3(x - 1)}{4 - x}$; $\{x|x \ne 1, x \ne 4\}$ **(d)** $(g \circ g)(x) = x$; $\{x|x \ne 0\}$ **37. (a)** $(f \circ g)(x) = \frac{4}{4 + x}$; $\{x|x \ne -4, x \ne 0\}$ **(b)** $(g \circ f)(x) = \frac{-4(x - 1)}{x}$; $\{x|x \ne 0, x \ne 1\}$ **(c)** $(f \circ f)(x) = x$; $\{x|x \ne 1\}$ **(d)** $(g \circ g)(x) = x$; $\{x|x \ne 0\}$ **39. (a)** $(f \circ g)(x) = \sqrt{2x + 3}$; $\left\{x \middle| x \ge -\frac{3}{2}\right\}$ **(b)** $(g \circ f)(x) = 2\sqrt{x} + 3$; $\{x|x \ge 0\}$ **(c)** $(f \circ f)(x) = \sqrt[4]{x}$; $\{x|x \ge 0\}$ **(d)** $(g \circ g)(x) = 4x + 9$; all real numbers **41. (a)** $(f \circ g)(x) = x$; $\{x|x \ge 1\}$ **(b)** $(g \circ f)(x) = |x|$; all real numbers **(c)** $(f \circ f)(x) = x^4 + 2x^2 + 2$; all real numbers **(d)** $(g \circ g)(x) = \sqrt{\sqrt{x - 1} - 1}$; $\{x|x \ge 2\}$ **43. (a)** $(f \circ g)(x) = -\frac{4x - 17}{2x - 1}$; $\left\{x \middle| x \ne 3; x \ne \frac{1}{2}\right\}$ **(b)** $(g \circ f)(x) = -\frac{3x - 3}{2x + 8}$; $\{x|x \ne -4; x \ne -1\}$ **(c)** $(f \circ f)(x) = -\frac{2x + 5}{x - 2}$; $\{x|x \ne -1; x \ne 2\}$ **(d)** $(g \circ g)(x) = -\frac{3x - 4}{2x - 11}$; $\left\{x \middle| x \ne \frac{11}{2}; x \ne 3\right\}$

45. $(f \circ g)(x) = f(g(x)) = f\left(\frac{1}{2}x\right) = 2\left(\frac{1}{2}x\right) = x;\ (g \circ f)(x) = g(f(x)) = g(2x) = \frac{1}{2}(2x) = x$
47. $(f \circ g)(x) = f(g(x)) = f(\sqrt[3]{x}) = (\sqrt[3]{x})^3 = x;\ (g \circ f)(x) = g(f(x)) = g(x^3) = \sqrt[3]{x^3} = x$
49. $(f \circ g)(x) = f(g(x)) = f\left(\frac{1}{2}(x+6)\right) = 2\left[\frac{1}{2}(x+6)\right] - 6 = x + 6 - 6 = x;$

$(g \circ f)(x) = g(f(x)) = g(2x - 6) = \frac{1}{2}(2x - 6 + 6) = \frac{1}{2}(2x) = x$

51. $(f \circ g)(x) = f(g(x)) = f\left(\frac{1}{a}(x - b)\right) = a\left[\frac{1}{a}(x - b)\right] + b = x;\ (g \circ f)(x) = g(f(x)) = g(ax + b) = \frac{1}{a}(ax + b - b) = x$
53. $f(x) = x^4;\ g(x) = 2x + 3$ (Other answers are possible.) **55.** $f(x) = \sqrt{x};\ g(x) = x^2 + 1$ (Other answers are possible.)
57. $f(x) = |x|;\ g(x) = 2x + 1$ (Other answers are possible.) **59.** $(f \circ g)(x) = 11;\ (g \circ f)(x) = 2$ **61.** $-3, 3$
63. **(a)** $(f \circ g)(x) = acx + ad + b$ **(b)** $(g \circ f)(x) = acx + bc + d$ **(c)** The domains of both $f \circ g$ and $g \circ f$ are all real numbers.
(d) $f \circ g = g \circ f$ when $ad + b = bc + d$ **65.** $S(t) = \frac{16}{9}\pi t^6$ **67.** $C(t) = 15{,}000 + 800{,}000t - 40{,}000t^2$
69. $C(p) = \frac{2\sqrt{100 - p}}{25} + 600, 0 \le p \le 100$ **71.** $V(r) = 2\pi r^3$ **73.** **(a)** $f(x) = 0.7045x$ **(b)** $g(x) = 114.9278x$
(c) $g(f(x)) = g(0.7045x) = 80.9666351x$ **(d)** $g(f(1000)) = 80{,}966.6351$; On March 22, 2011, one thousand dollars could purchase 80,966.6351 yen.
75. **(a)** $f(p) = p - 200$ **(b)** $g(p) = 0.8p$ **(c)** $(f \circ g)(p) = 0.8p - 200;\ (g \circ f)(p) = 0.8p - 160$; The 20% discount followed by the \$200 rebate is the better deal. **77.** f is an odd function, so $f(-x) = -f(x)$. g is an even function, so $g(-x) = g(x)$. Then $(f \circ g)(-x) = f(g(-x)) = f(g(x)) = (f \circ g)(x)$. So $f \circ g$ is even. Also, $(g \circ f)(-x) = g(f(-x)) = g(-f(x)) = g(f(x)) = (g \circ f)(x)$, so $g \circ f$ is even.

12.2 Assess Your Understanding *(Page 768)*

5. $f(x_1) \ne f(x_2)$ **6.** one-to-one **7.** 3 **8.** $y = x$ **9.** $[4, \infty)$ **10.** T **11.** one-to-one **13.** not one-to-one **15.** not one-to-one **17.** one-to-one **19.** one-to-one **21.** not one-to-one **23.** one-to-one

25.

Annual Rainfall (inches)		Location
460.00	→	Mt Waialeale, Hawaii
202.01	→	Monrovia, Liberia
196.46	→	Pago Pago, American Samoa
191.02	→	Moulmein, Burma
182.87	→	Lae, Papua New Guinea

Domain: {460.00, 202.01, 196.46, 191.02, 182.87}
Range: {Mt Waialeale, Monrovia, Pago Pago, Moulmein, Lae}

27.

Monthly Cost of Life Insurance		Age
\$7.09	→	30
\$8.40	→	40
\$11.29	→	45

Domain: {\$7.09, \$8.40, \$11.29}
Range: {30, 40, 45}

29. $\{(5, -3), (9, -2), (2, -1), (11, 0), (-5, 1)\}$
Domain: $\{5, 9, 2, 11, -5\}$
Range: $\{-3, -2, -1, 0, 1\}$

31. $\{(1, -2), (2, -3), (0, -10), (9, 1), (4, 2)\}$
Domain: $\{1, 2, 0, 9, 4\}$
Range: $\{-2, -3, -10, 1, 2\}$

33. $f(g(x)) = f\left(\frac{1}{3}(x - 4)\right) = 3\left[\frac{1}{3}(x - 4)\right] + 4 = (x - 4) + 4 = x$
$g(f(x)) = g(3x + 4) = \frac{1}{3}[(3x + 4) - 4] = \frac{1}{3}(3x) = x$

35. $f(g(x)) = f\left(\frac{x}{4} + 2\right) = 4\left[\frac{x}{4} + 2\right] - 8 = (x + 8) - 8 = x$
$g(f(x)) = g(4x - 8) = \frac{4x - 8}{4} + 2 = (x - 2) + 2 = x$

37. $f(g(x)) = f(\sqrt[3]{x + 8}) = (\sqrt[3]{x + 8})^3 - 8 = (x + 8) - 8 = x$
$g(f(x)) = g(x^3 - 8) = \sqrt[3]{(x^3 - 8) + 8} = \sqrt[3]{x^3} = x$

39. $f(g(x)) = f\left(\frac{1}{x}\right) = \frac{1}{\left(\frac{1}{x}\right)} = x;\ x \ne 0,\ g(f(x)) = g\left(\frac{1}{x}\right) = \frac{1}{\left(\frac{1}{x}\right)} = x, x \ne 0$

41. $f(g(x)) = f\left(\frac{4x - 3}{2 - x}\right) = \frac{2\left(\frac{4x - 3}{2 - x}\right) + 3}{\frac{4x - 3}{2 - x} + 4}$
$= \frac{2(4x - 3) + 3(2 - x)}{4x - 3 + 4(2 - x)} = \frac{5x}{5} = x, x \ne 2$

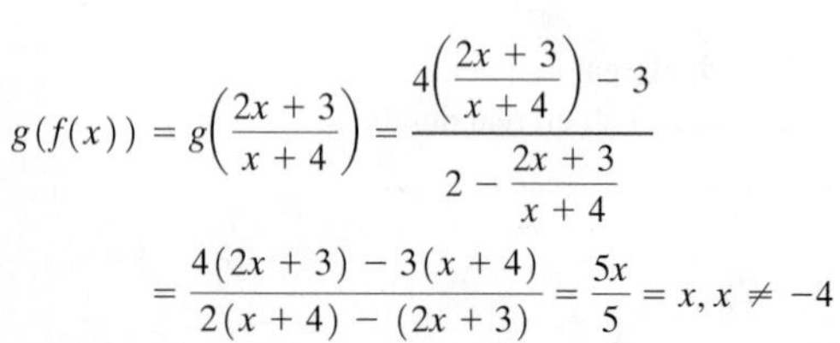

$g(f(x)) = g\left(\frac{2x + 3}{x + 4}\right) = \frac{4\left(\frac{2x + 3}{x + 4}\right) - 3}{2 - \frac{2x + 3}{x + 4}}$
$= \frac{4(2x + 3) - 3(x + 4)}{2(x + 4) - (2x + 3)} = \frac{5x}{5} = x, x \ne -4$

43.

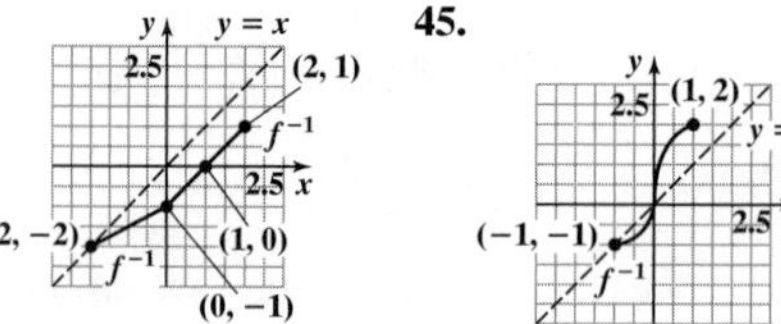

45.

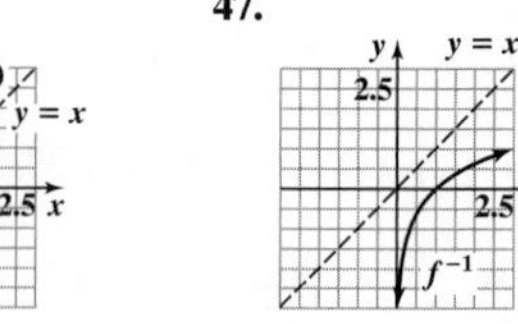

47.

y = x, 2.5, 2.5 x, f^{-1}

49. $f^{-1}(x) = \frac{1}{3}x$

$$f(f^{-1}(x)) = f\left(\frac{1}{3}x\right) = 3\left(\frac{1}{3}x\right) = x$$

$$f^{-1}(f(x)) = f^{-1}(3x) = \frac{1}{3}(3x) = x$$

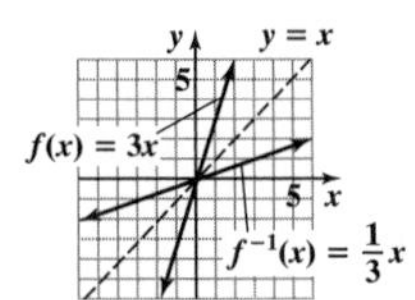

51. $f^{-1}(x) = \frac{x}{4} - \frac{1}{2}$

$$f(f^{-1}(x)) = f\left(\frac{x}{4} - \frac{1}{2}\right) = 4\left(\frac{x}{4} - \frac{1}{2}\right) + 2$$
$$= (x - 2) + 2 = x$$

$$f^{-1}(f(x)) = f^{-1}(4x + 2) = \frac{4x + 2}{4} - \frac{1}{2}$$
$$= \left(x + \frac{1}{2}\right) - \frac{1}{2} = x$$

53. $f^{-1}(x) = \sqrt[3]{x + 1}$

$$f(f^{-1}(x)) = f(\sqrt[3]{x + 1})$$
$$= (\sqrt[3]{x + 1})^3 - 1 = x$$

$$f^{-1}(f(x)) = f^{-1}(x^3 - 1)$$
$$= \sqrt[3]{(x^3 - 1) + 1} = x$$

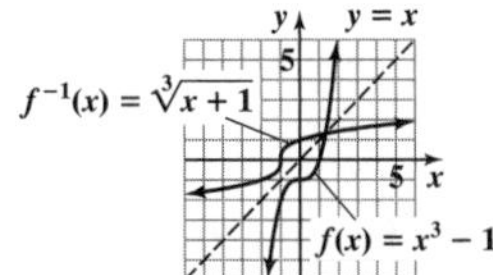

55. $f^{-1}(x) = \sqrt{x - 4},\ x \geq 4$

$$f(f^{-1}(x)) = f(\sqrt{x - 4}) = (\sqrt{x - 4})^2 + 4 = x$$

$$f^{-1}(f(x)) = f^{-1}(x^2 + 4) = \sqrt{(x^2 + 4) - 4} = \sqrt{x^2} = x,\ x \geq 0$$

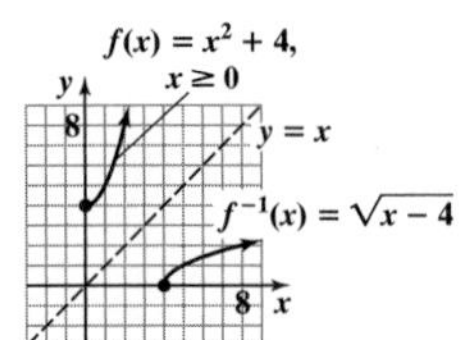

57. $f^{-1}(x) = \frac{4}{x}$

$$f(f^{-1}(x)) = f\left(\frac{4}{x}\right) = \frac{4}{\left(\frac{4}{x}\right)} = x$$

$$f^{-1}(f(x)) = f^{-1}\left(\frac{4}{x}\right) = \frac{4}{\left(\frac{4}{x}\right)} = x$$

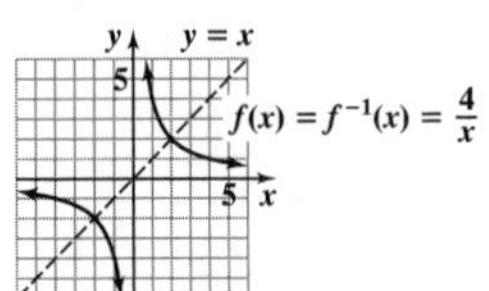

59. $f^{-1}(x) = \frac{2x + 1}{x}$

$$f(f^{-1}(x)) = f\left(\frac{2x + 1}{x}\right) = \frac{1}{\frac{2x + 1}{x} - 2} = \frac{x}{(2x + 1) - 2x} = x$$

$$f^{-1}(f(x)) = f^{-1}\left(\frac{1}{x - 2}\right) = \frac{2\left(\frac{1}{x - 2}\right) + 1}{\frac{1}{x - 2}} = \frac{2 + (x - 2)}{1} = x$$

61. $f^{-1}(x) = \frac{2 - 3x}{x}$

$$f(f^{-1}(x)) = f\left(\frac{2 - 3x}{x}\right) = \frac{2}{3 + \frac{2 - 3x}{x}} = \frac{2x}{3x + 2 - 3x} = \frac{2x}{2} = x$$

$$f^{-1}(f(x)) = f^{-1}\left(\frac{2}{3 + x}\right) = \frac{2 - 3\left(\frac{2}{3 + x}\right)}{\frac{2}{3 + x}} = \frac{2(3 + x) - 3 \cdot 2}{2} = \frac{2x}{2} = x$$

63. $f^{-1}(x) = \frac{-2x}{x - 3}$

$$f(f^{-1}(x)) = f\left(\frac{-2x}{x - 3}\right) = \frac{3\left(\frac{-2x}{x - 3}\right)}{\frac{-2x}{x - 3} + 2}$$
$$= \frac{3(-2x)}{-2x + 2(x - 3)} = \frac{-6x}{-6} = x$$

$$f^{-1}(f(x)) = f^{-1}\left(\frac{3x}{x + 2}\right) = \frac{-2\left(\frac{3x}{x + 2}\right)}{\frac{3x}{x + 2} - 3}$$
$$= \frac{-2(3x)}{3x - 3(x + 2)} = \frac{-6x}{-6} = x$$

65. $f^{-1}(x) = \frac{x}{3x - 2}$

$$f(f^{-1}(x)) = f\left(\frac{x}{3x - 2}\right) = \frac{2\left(\frac{x}{3x - 2}\right)}{3\left(\frac{x}{3x - 2}\right) - 1}$$
$$= \frac{2x}{3x - (3x - 2)} = \frac{2x}{2} = x$$

$$f^{-1}(f(x)) = f^{-1}\left(\frac{2x}{3x - 1}\right) = \frac{\frac{2x}{3x - 1}}{3\left(\frac{2x}{3x - 1}\right) - 2}$$
$$= \frac{2x}{6x - 2(3x - 1)} = \frac{2x}{2} = x$$

67. $f^{-1}(x) = \dfrac{3x+4}{2x-3}$

$$f(f^{-1}(x)) = f\left(\frac{3x+4}{2x-3}\right) = \frac{3\left(\frac{3x+4}{2x-3}\right)+4}{2\left(\frac{3x+4}{2x-3}\right)-3} = \frac{3(3x+4)+4(2x-3)}{2(3x+4)-3(2x-3)} = \frac{17x}{17} = x$$

$$f^{-1}(f(x)) = f^{-1}\left(\frac{3x+4}{2x-3}\right) = \frac{3\left(\frac{3x+4}{2x-3}\right)+4}{2\left(\frac{3x+4}{2x-3}\right)-3} = \frac{3(3x+4)+4(2x-3)}{2(3x+4)-3(2x-3)} = \frac{17x}{17} = x$$

69. $f^{-1}(x) = \dfrac{-2x+3}{x-2}$

$$f(f^{-1}(x)) = f\left(\frac{-2x+3}{x-2}\right) = \frac{2\left(\frac{-2x+3}{x-2}\right)+3}{\frac{-2x+3}{x-2}+2} = \frac{2(-2x+3)+3(x-2)}{-2x+3+2(x-2)} = \frac{-x}{-1} = x$$

$$f^{-1}(f(x)) = f^{-1}\left(\frac{2x+3}{x+2}\right) = \frac{-2\left(\frac{2x+3}{x+2}\right)+3}{\frac{2x+3}{x+2}-2} = \frac{-2(2x+3)+3(x+2)}{2x+3-2(x+2)} = \frac{-x}{-1} = x$$

71. $f^{-1}(x) = \dfrac{2}{\sqrt{1-2x}}$

$$f(f^{-1}(x)) = f\left(\frac{2}{\sqrt{1-2x}}\right) = \frac{\frac{4}{1-2x}-4}{2\cdot\frac{4}{1-2x}} = \frac{4-4(1-2x)}{2\cdot 4} = \frac{8x}{8} = x$$

$$f^{-1}(f(x)) = f^{-1}\left(\frac{x^2-4}{2x^2}\right) = \frac{2}{\sqrt{1-2\left(\frac{x^2-4}{2x^2}\right)}} = \frac{2}{\sqrt{\frac{4}{x^2}}} = \sqrt{x^2} = x, \text{ since } x > 0$$

73. **(a)** 0 **(b)** 2 **(c)** 0 **(d)** 1 **75.** 7

77. Domain of f^{-1}: $[-2, \infty)$; range of f^{-1}: $[5, \infty)$

79. Domain of g^{-1}: $[0, \infty)$; range of g^{-1}: $(-\infty, 0]$

81. Increasing on the interval $(f(0), f(5))$

83. $f^{-1}(x) = \dfrac{1}{m}(x-b), m \neq 0$ **85.** Quadrant I

87. Possible answer: $f(x) = |x|, x \geq 0$, is one-to-one; $f^{-1}(x) = x, x \geq 0$

89. **(a)** $r(d) = \dfrac{d+90.39}{6.97}$

(b) $r(d(r)) = \dfrac{6.97r - 90.39 + 90.39}{6.97} = \dfrac{6.97r}{6.97} = r$

$d(r(d)) = 6.97\left(\dfrac{d+90.39}{6.97}\right) - 90.39 = d + 90.39 - 90.39 = d$

(c) 56 miles per hour

91. **(a)** 77.6 kg

(b) $h(W) = \dfrac{W-50}{2.3} + 60 = \dfrac{W+88}{2.3}$

(c) $h(W(h)) = \dfrac{50 + 2.3(h-60) + 88}{2.3} = \dfrac{2.3h}{2.3} = h$

$W(h(W)) = 50 + 2.3\left(\dfrac{W+88}{2.3} - 60\right)$

$= 50 + W + 88 - 138 = W$

(d) 73 inches

93. **(a)** $\{g \mid 34{,}500 \leq g \leq 83{,}600\}$ **(b)** $\{T \mid 4750 \leq T \leq 17{,}025\}$

(c) $g(T) = \dfrac{T-4750}{0.25} + 34{,}500$;

Domain: $\{T \mid 4750 \leq T \leq 17{,}025\}$;

Range: $\{g \mid 34{,}500 \leq g \leq 83{,}600\}$

95. **(a)** t represents time, so $t \geq 0$.

(b) $t(H) = \sqrt{\dfrac{H-100}{-4.9}} = \sqrt{\dfrac{100-H}{4.9}}$ **(c)** 2.02 seconds

97. $f^{-1}(x) = \dfrac{-dx+b}{cx-a}$; $f = f^{-1}$ if $a = -d$ **101.** No

12.3 Assess Your Understanding *(page 798)*

6. exponential function; growth factor; initial value **7.** a **8.** T **9.** F **10.** T **11.** $\left(-1, \dfrac{1}{a}\right)$; $(0, 1)$; $(1, a)$ **12.** 1 **13.** 4 **14.** F

15. **(a)** 11.212 **(b)** 11.587 **(c)** 11.664 **(d)** 11.665 **17.** **(a)** 8.815 **(b)** 8.821 **(c)** 8.824 **(d)** 8.825 **19.** **(a)** 21.217 **(b)** 22.217 **(c)** 22.440 **(d)** 22.459 **21.** 3.320 **23.** 0.427 **25.** Neither **27.** Exponential; $H(x) = 4^x$ **29.** Exponential; $f(x) = 3(2^x)$ **31.** Linear; $H(x) = 2x + 4$ **33.** B **35.** D **37.** A **39.** E

41. Domain: All real numbers
Range: $\{y \mid y > 1\}$ or $(1, \infty)$
Horizontal asymptote: $y = 1$

43. Domain: All real numbers
Range: $\{y \mid y > 0\}$ or $(0, \infty)$
Horizontal asymptote: $y = 0$

45. Domain: All real numbers
Range: $\{y \mid y > 0\}$ or $(0, \infty)$
Horizontal asymptote: $y = 0$

47.

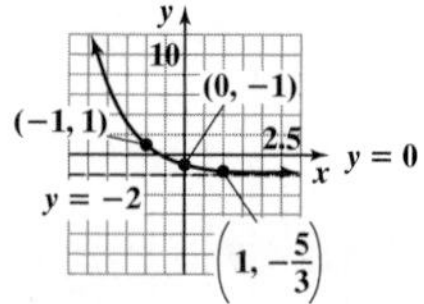

Domain: All real numbers
Range: $\{y \mid y > -2\}$ or $(-2, \infty)$
Horizontal asymptote: $y = -2$

49.

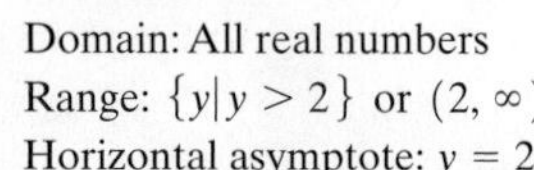

Domain: All real numbers
Range: $\{y \mid y > 2\}$ or $(2, \infty)$
Horizontal asymptote: $y = 2$

51.

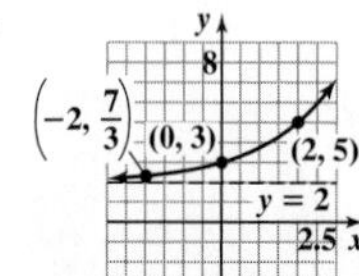

Domain: All real numbers
Range: $\{y \mid y > 2\}$ or $(2, \infty)$
Horizontal asymptote: $y = 2$

53.

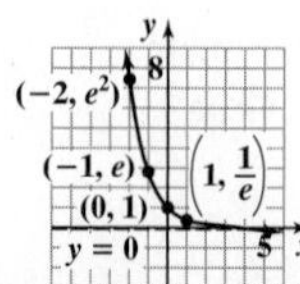

Domain: All real numbers
Range: $\{y \mid y > 0\}$ or $(0, \infty)$
Horizontal asymptote: $y = 0$

55.

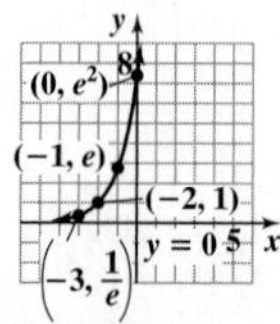

Domain: All real numbers
Range: $\{y \mid y > 0\}$ or $(0, \infty)$
Horizontal asymptote: $y = 0$

57.

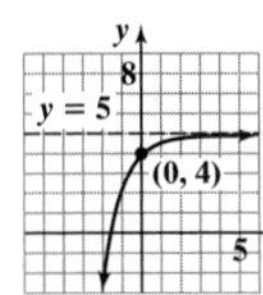

Domain: All real numbers
Range: $\{y | y < 5\}$ or $(-\infty, 5)$
Horizontal asymptote: $y = 5$

59.

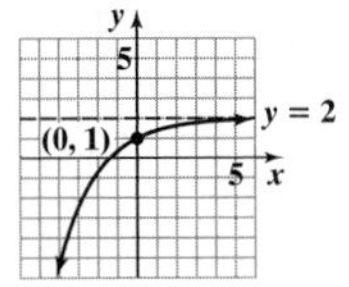

Domain: All real numbers
Range: $\{y | y < 2\}$ or $(-\infty, 2)$
Horizontal asymptote: $y = 2$

61. $\{3\}$ **63.** $\{-4\}$ **65.** $\{2\}$ **67.** $\left\{\frac{3}{2}\right\}$ **69.** $\{-\sqrt{2}, 0, \sqrt{2}\}$
71. $\{6\}$ **73.** $\{-1, 7\}$ **75.** $\{-4, 2\}$ **77.** $\{-4\}$ **79.** $\{1, 2\}$
81. $\frac{1}{49}$ **83.** $\frac{1}{4}$ **85.** $f(x) = 3^x$ **87.** $f(x) = -6^x$ **89.** $f(x) = 3^x + 2$
91. **(a)** 16; (4, 16) **(b)** -4; $\left(-4, \frac{1}{16}\right)$ **93.** **(a)** $\frac{9}{4}$; $\left(-1, \frac{9}{4}\right)$
(b) 3; (3, 66) **95.** **(a)** 60; $(-6, 60)$ **(b)** -4; $(-4, 12)$ **(c)** -2

97.

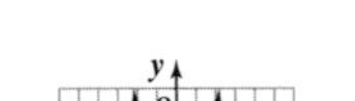

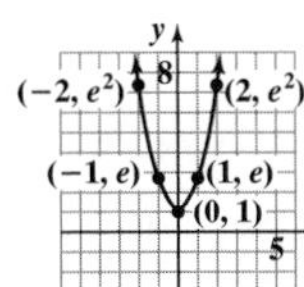

Domain: $(-\infty, \infty)$
Range: $[1, \infty)$
Intercept: $(0, 1)$

99.

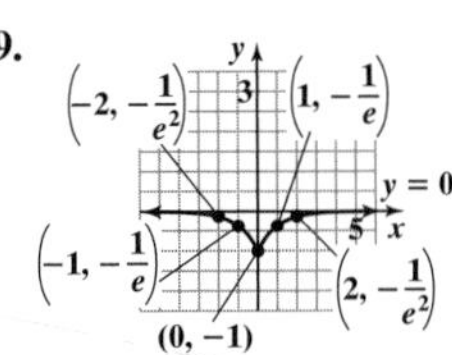

Domain: $(-\infty, \infty)$
Range: $[-1, 0)$
Intercept: $(0, -1)$

101. **(a)** 74% **(b)** 47%
103. **(a)** \$12,123 **(b)** \$6443
105. 3.35 mg; 0.45 mg

107. **(a)** 0.632 **(b)** 0.982 **(c)** 1
(d)

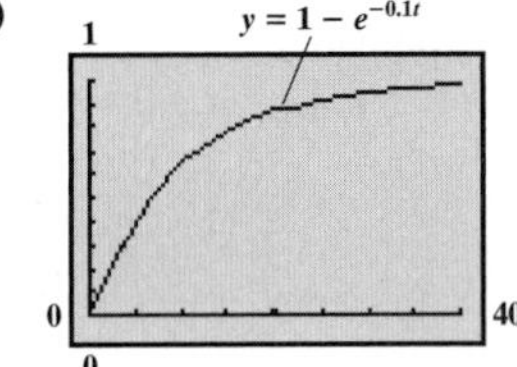

(e) About 7 min

109. **(a)** 0.0516 **(b)** 0.0888 **111.** **(a)** 70.95% **(b)** 72.62% **(c)** 100%
113. **(a)** 5.41 amp, 7.59 amp, 10.38 amp **(b)** 12 amp
(d) 3.34 amp, 5.31 amp, 9.44 amp **(e)** 24 amp
(c), (f)

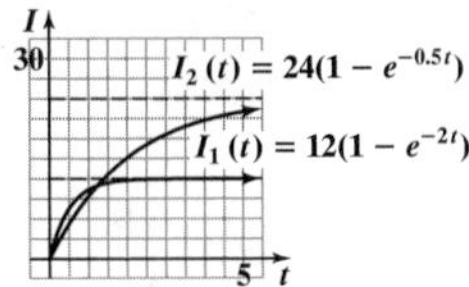

115. 36

117.

Final Denominator	Value of Expression	Compare Value to $e \approx 2.718281828$
1 + 1	2.5	$2.5 < e$
2 + 2	2.8	$2.8 > e$
3 + 3	2.7	$2.7 < e$
4 + 4	2.721649485	$2.721649485 > e$
5 + 5	2.717770035	$2.717770035 < e$
6 + 6	2.718348855	$2.718348855 > e$

119. $f(A + B) = a^{A+B} = a^A \cdot a^B = f(A) \cdot f(B)$ **121.** $f(\alpha x) = a^{\alpha x} = (a^x)^\alpha = [f(x)]^\alpha$

123. **(a)**
$$f(-x) = \frac{1}{2}(e^{-x} + e^{-(-x)}) = \frac{1}{2}(e^{-x} + e^{x}) = \frac{1}{2}(e^{x} + e^{-x}) = f(x)$$

(b) $y = \frac{1}{2}(e^x + e^{-x})$; window -6 to 6, -1 to 6

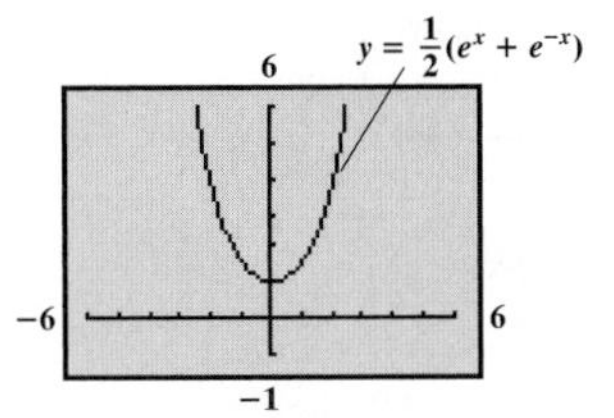

(c)
$$(\cosh x)^2 - (\sinh x)^2 = \left[\frac{1}{2}(e^x + e^{-x})\right]^2 - \left[\frac{1}{2}(e^x - e^{-x})\right]^2 = \frac{1}{4}[e^{2x} + 2 + e^{-2x} - e^{2x} + 2 - e^{-2x}] = \frac{1}{4}(4) = 1$$

125. 59 minutes

12.4 Assess Your Understanding *(page 802)*

4. $\{x | x > 0\}$ or $(0, \infty)$ **5.** $\left(\frac{1}{a}, -1\right)$, $(1, 0)$, $(a, 1)$ **6.** 1 **7.** F **8.** T **9.** $2 = \log_3 9$ **11.** $2 = \log_a 1.6$ **13.** $x = \log_2 7.2$ **15.** $x = \ln 8$
17. $2^3 = 8$ **19.** $a^6 = 3$ **21.** $3^x = 2$ **23.** $e^x = 4$ **25.** 0 **27.** 2 **29.** -4 **31.** $\frac{1}{2}$ **33.** 4 **35.** $\frac{1}{2}$ **37.** $\{x | x > 3\}$; $(3, \infty)$
39. All real numbers except 0; $\{x | x \neq 0\}$ **41.** $\{x | x > 10\}$; $(10, \infty)$ **43.** $\{x | x > -1\}$; $(-1, \infty)$ **45.** $\{x | x < -1 \text{ or } x > 0\}$; $(-\infty, -1) \cup (0, \infty)$
47. $\{x | x \geq 1\}$; $[1, \infty)$ **49.** 0.511 **51.** 30.099 **53.** 2.303 **55.** -53.991 **57.** $\sqrt{2}$

59.

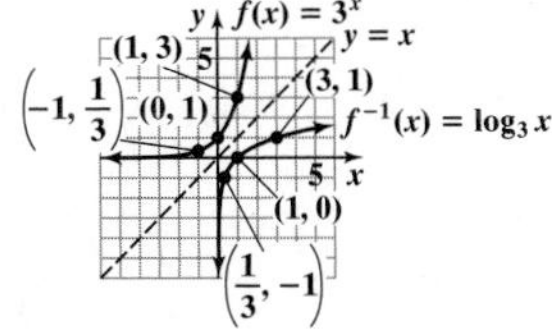

61.

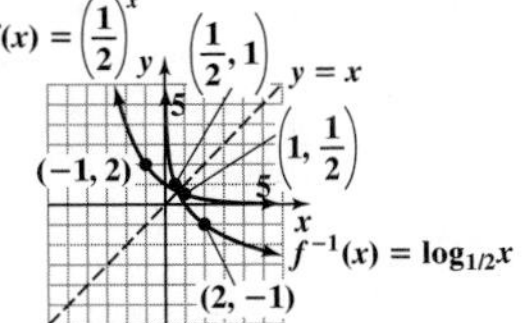

63. B **65.** D **67.** A **69.** E

71. **(a)** Domain: $(-4, \infty)$
(b)

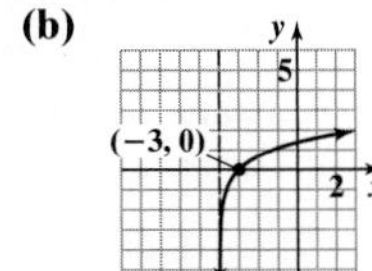

(c) Range: $(-\infty, \infty)$
Vertical asymptote: $x = -4$

(d) $f^{-1}(x) = e^x - 4$
(e) Domain of f^{-1}: $(-\infty, \infty)$
Range of f^{-1}: $(-4, \infty)$

(f)

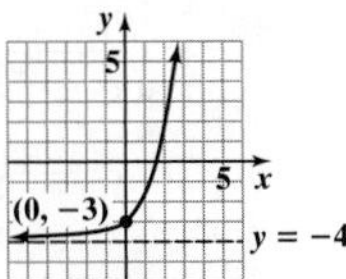

73. **(a)** Domain: $(0, \infty)$
(b)

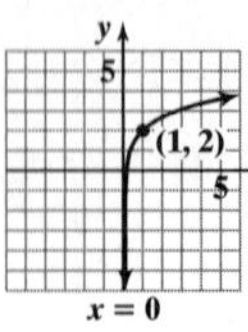

(c) Range: $(-\infty, \infty)$
Vertical asymptote: $x = 0$
(d) $f^{-1}(x) = e^{x-2}$
(e) Domain of f^{-1}: $(-\infty, \infty)$
Range of f^{-1}: $(0, \infty)$
(f)

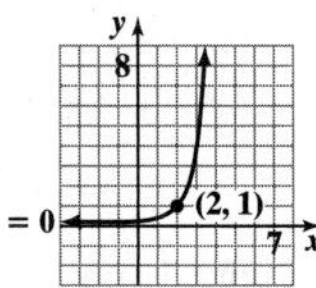

75. **(a)** Domain: $(0, \infty)$
(b)

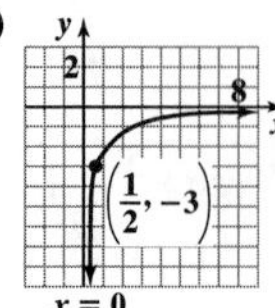

(c) Range: $(-\infty, \infty)$
Vertical asymptote: $x = 0$
(d) $f^{-1}(x) = \dfrac{1}{2}e^{x+3}$
(e) Domain of f^{-1}: $(-\infty, \infty)$
Range of f^{-1}: $(0, \infty)$
(f)

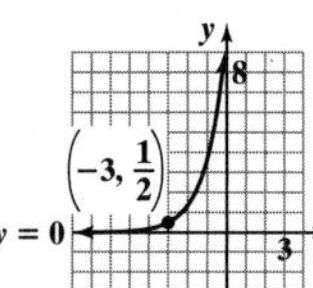

77. **(a)** Domain: $(4, \infty)$
(b)

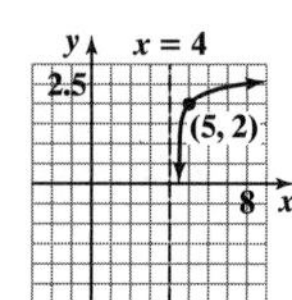

(c) Range: $(-\infty, \infty)$
Vertical asymptote: $x = 4$
(d) $f^{-1}(x) = 10^{x-2} + 4$
(e) Domain of f^{-1}: $(-\infty, \infty)$
Range of f^{-1}: $(4, \infty)$

(f)

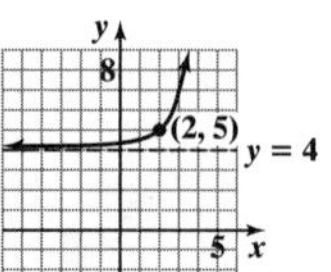

79. **(a)** Domain: $(0, \infty)$
(b)

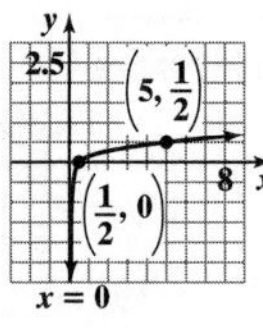

(c) Range: $(-\infty, \infty)$
Vertical asymptote: $x = 0$
(d) $f^{-1}(x) = \dfrac{1}{2} \cdot 10^{2x}$
(e) Domain of f^{-1}: $(-\infty, \infty)$
Range of f^{-1}: $(0, \infty)$
(f)

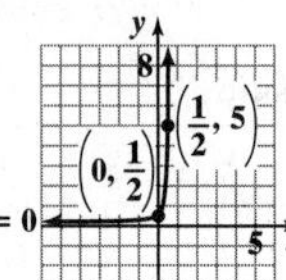

81. **(a)** Domain: $(-2, \infty)$
(b)

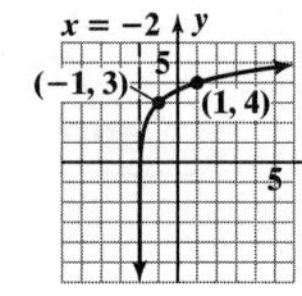

(c) Range: $(-\infty, \infty)$
Vertical asymptote: $x = -2$
(d) $f^{-1}(x) = 3^{x-3} - 2$
(e) Domain of f^{-1}: $(-\infty, \infty)$
Range of f^{-1}: $(-2, \infty)$
(f)

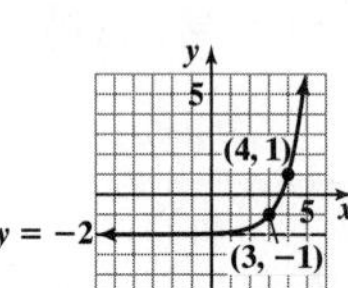

83. **(a)** Domain: $(-\infty, \infty)$
(b)

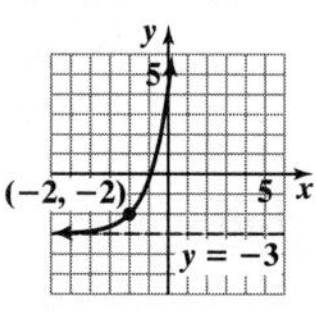

(c) Range: $(-3, \infty)$
Horizontal asymptote: $y = -3$
(d) $f^{-1}(x) = \ln(x + 3) - 2$
(e) Domain of f^{-1}: $(-3, \infty)$
Range of f^{-1}: $(-\infty, \infty)$
(f)

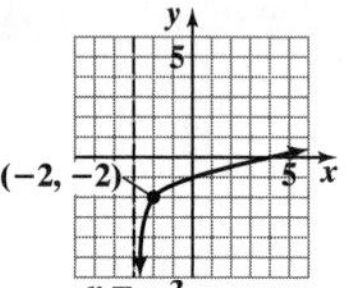

85. **(a)** Domain: $(-\infty, \infty)$
(b)

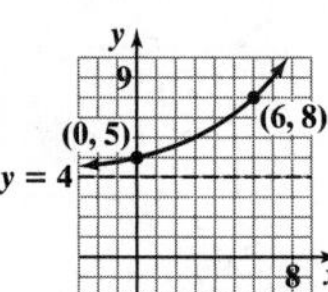

(c) Range: $(4, \infty)$
Horizontal asymptote: $y = 4$
(d) $f^{-1}(x) = 3\log_2(x - 4)$
(e) Domain of f^{-1}: $(4, \infty)$
Range of f^{-1}: $(-\infty, \infty)$
(f)

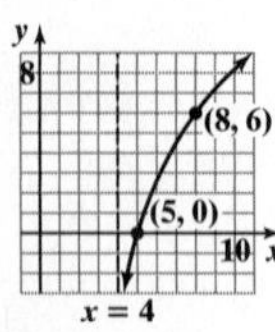

87. $\{9\}$ **89.** $\left\{\dfrac{7}{2}\right\}$ **91.** $\{2\}$ **93.** $\{5\}$
95. $\{3\}$ **97.** $\{2\}$ **99.** $\left\{\dfrac{\ln 10}{3}\right\}$
101. $\left\{\dfrac{\ln 8 - 5}{2}\right\}$ **103.** $\{-2\sqrt{2}, 2\sqrt{2}\}$
105. $\{-1\}$ **107.** $\left\{5 \ln \dfrac{7}{5}\right\}$
109. $\left\{2 - \log \dfrac{5}{2}\right\}$
111. **(a)** $\left\{x \middle| x > -\dfrac{1}{2}\right\}; \left(-\dfrac{1}{2}, \infty\right)$
(b) 2; (40, 2) **(c)** 121; (121, 3) **(d)** 4

113.

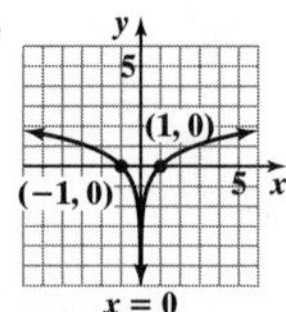

Domain: $\{x | x \neq 0\}$
Range: $(-\infty, \infty)$
Intercepts: $(-1, 0), (1, 0)$

115.

Domain: $\{x | x > 0\}$
Range: $\{y | y \geq 0\}$
Intercept: $(1, 0)$

117. **(a)** 1 **(b)** 2 **(c)** 3
(d) It increases. **(e)** 0.000316
(f) 3.981×10^{-8}
119. **(a)** 5.97 km **(b)** 0.90 km
121. **(a)** 6.93 min **(b)** 16.09 min
123. $h \approx 2.29$, so the time between injections is about 2 h, 17 min.

125. 0.2695 s
0.8959 s

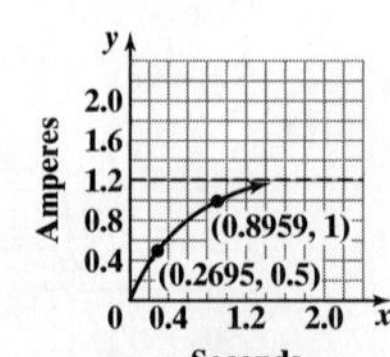

127. 50 decibels (dB) **129.** 90 dB
131. 8.1 **133.** **(a)** $k \approx 11.216$ **(b)** 6.73
(c) 0.41% **(d)** 0.14%
135. Because $y = \log_1 x$ means $1^y = 1 = x$, which cannot be true for $x \neq 1$

12.5 Assess Your Understanding *(page 809)*

1. 0 **2.** 1 **3.** M **4.** r **5.** $\log_a M$; $\log_a N$ **6.** $\log_a M$; $\log_a N$ **7.** $r\log_a M$ **8.** 6 **9.** 7 **10.** F **11.** F **12.** F **13.** 71 **15.** −4 **17.** 7 **19.** 1 **21.** 1 **23.** 3 **25.** $\frac{5}{4}$ **27.** 4 **29.** $a + b$ **31.** $b - a$ **33.** 3a **35.** $\frac{1}{5}(a + b)$ **37.** $2 + \log_5 x$ **39.** $3 \log_2 z$ **41.** $1 + \ln x$ **43.** $\ln x - x$ **45.** $2 \log_a u + 3 \log_a v$ **47.** $2 \ln x + \frac{1}{2}\ln(1 - x)$ **49.** $3 \log_2 x - \log_2(x - 3)$ **51.** $\log x + \log(x + 2) - 2 \log(x + 3)$ **53.** $\frac{1}{3}\ln(x - 2) + \frac{1}{3}\ln(x + 1) - \frac{2}{3}\ln(x + 4)$ **55.** $\ln 5 + \ln x + \frac{1}{2}\ln(1 + 3x) - 3 \ln(x - 4)$ **57.** $\log_5 u^3v^4$ **59.** $\log_3\left(\frac{1}{x^{5/2}}\right)$ **61.** $\log_4\left[\frac{x - 1}{(x + 1)^4}\right]$ **63.** $-2 \ln(x - 1)$ **65.** $\log_2[x(3x - 2)^4]$ **67.** $\log_a\left(\frac{25x^6}{\sqrt{2x + 3}}\right)$ **69.** $\log_2\left[\frac{(x + 1)^2}{(x + 3)(x - 1)}\right]$ **71.** 2.771 **73.** −3.880 **75.** 5.615 **77.** 0.874

79. $y = \frac{\log x}{\log 4}$

81. $y = \frac{\log(x + 2)}{\log 2}$

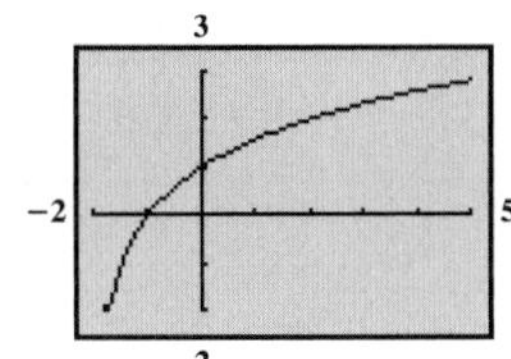

83. $y = \frac{\log(x + 1)}{\log(x - 1)}$

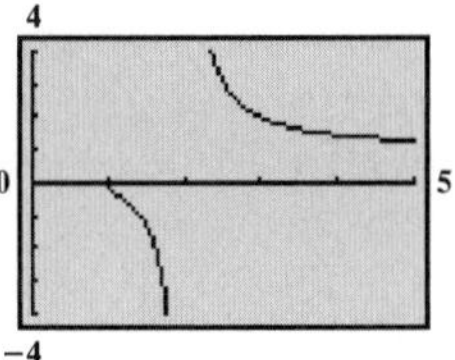

85. (a) $(f \circ g)(x) = x$; $\{x|x \text{ is any real number}\}$ or $(-\infty, \infty)$ **(b)** $(g \circ f)(x) = x$; $\{x|x > 0\}$ or $(0, \infty)$ **(c)** 5 **(d)** $(f \circ h)(x) = \ln x^2$; $\{x|\, x \neq 0\}$ or $(-\infty, 0) \cup (0, \infty)$ **(e)** 2

87. $y = Cx$ **89.** $y = Cx(x + 1)$ **91.** $y = Ce^{3x}$ **93.** $y = Ce^{-4x} + 3$ **95.** $y = \frac{\sqrt[3]{C}(2x + 1)^{1/6}}{(x + 4)^{1/9}}$ **97.** 3 **99.** 1

101. $\log_a(x + \sqrt{x^2 - 1}) + \log_a(x - \sqrt{x^2 - 1}) = \log_a[(x + \sqrt{x^2 - 1})(x - \sqrt{x^2 - 1})] = \log_a[x^2 - (x^2 - 1)] = \log_a 1 = 0$

103. $\ln(1 + e^{2x}) = \ln[e^{2x}(e^{-2x} + 1)] = \ln e^{2x} + \ln(e^{-2x} + 1) = 2x + \ln(1 + e^{-2x})$

105. $y = f(x) = \log_a x$; $a^y = x$ implies $a^y = \left(\frac{1}{a}\right)^{-y} = x$, so $-y = \log_{1/a} x = -f(x)$.

107. $f(x) = \log_a x$; $f\left(\frac{1}{x}\right) = \log_a \frac{1}{x} = \log_a 1 - \log_a x = -f(x)$

109. $\log_a \frac{M}{N} = \log_a(M \cdot N^{-1}) = \log_a M + \log_a N^{-1} = \log_a M - \log_a N$, since $a^{\log_a N^{-1}} = N^{-1}$ implies $a^{-\log_a N^{-1}} = N$; i.e., $\log_a N = -\log_a N^{-1}$.

12.6 Assess Your Understanding *(page 816)*

5. $\{16\}$ **7.** $\left\{\frac{16}{5}\right\}$ **9.** $\{6\}$ **11.** $\{16\}$ **13.** $\left\{\frac{1}{3}\right\}$ **15.** $\{3\}$ **17.** $\{5\}$ **19.** $\left\{\frac{21}{8}\right\}$ **21.** $\{-6\}$ **23.** $\{-2\}$ **25.** $\{-1 + \sqrt{1 + e^4}\} \approx \{6.456\}$ **27.** $\left\{\frac{-5 + 3\sqrt{5}}{2}\right\} \approx \{0.854\}$ **29.** $\{2\}$ **31.** $\left\{\frac{9}{2}\right\}$ **33.** $\{8\}$ **35.** $\{\log_2 10\} = \left\{\frac{\ln 10}{\ln 2}\right\} \approx \{3.322\}$ **37.** $\{-\log_8 1.2\} = \left\{-\frac{\ln 1.2}{\ln 8}\right\} \approx \{-0.088\}$ **39.** $\left\{\frac{1}{3}\log_2 \frac{8}{5}\right\} = \left\{\frac{\ln\frac{8}{5}}{3 \ln 2}\right\} \approx \{0.226\}$ **41.** $\left\{\frac{\ln 3}{2 \ln 3 + \ln 4}\right\} \approx \{0.307\}$ **43.** $\left\{\frac{\ln 7}{\ln 0.6 + \ln 7}\right\} \approx \{1.356\}$ **45.** $\{0\}$ **47.** $\left\{\frac{\ln \pi}{1 + \ln \pi}\right\} \approx \{0.534\}$ **49.** $\left\{\frac{\ln 3}{\ln 2}\right\} \approx \{1.585\}$ **51.** $\{0\}$ **53.** $\left\{\log_4\left(-2 + \sqrt{7}\right)\right\} \approx \{-0.315\}$ **55.** $\{\log_5 4\} \approx \{0.861\}$ **57.** No real solution **59.** $\{\log_4 5\} \approx \{1.161\}$ **61.** $\{2.79\}$ **63.** $\{-0.57\}$ **65.** $\{-0.70\}$ **67.** $\{0.57\}$ **69.** $\{0.39, 1.00\}$ **71.** $\{1.32\}$ **73.** $\{1.31\}$ **75.** $\{1\}$ **77.** $\{16\}$ **79.** $\left\{-1, \frac{2}{3}\right\}$ **81.** $\{0\}$ **83.** $\{\ln(2 + \sqrt{5})\} \approx \{1.444\}$ **85.** $\left\{e^{\frac{\ln 5 \cdot \ln 3}{\ln 15}}\right\} \approx \{1.921\}$ **87. (a)** $\{5\}$; $(5, 3)$ **(b)** $\{5\}$; $(5, 4)$ **(c)** $\{1\}$; yes, at $(1, 2)$ **(d)** $\{5\}$ **(e)** $\left\{-\frac{1}{11}\right\}$

89. (a), (b)

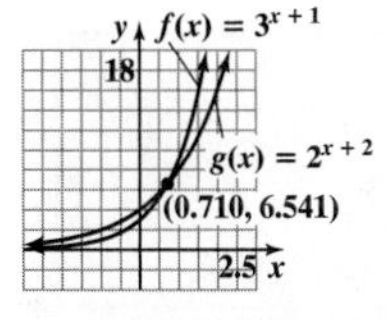

(c) $\{x|x > 0.710\}$ or $(0.710, \infty)$

91. (a), (b), (c)

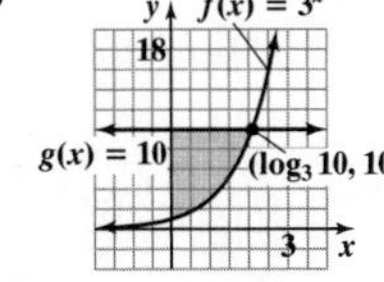

93. (a), (b), (c)

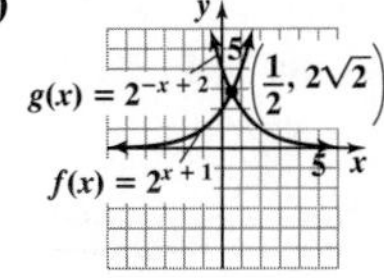

95. (a)

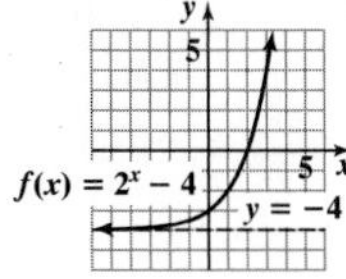

(b) 2
(c) $\{x|x < 2\}$ or $(-\infty, 2)$

97. (a) 2044
(b) 2061

99. (a) After 3.1 yr
(b) After 7.1 yr
(c) After 10.6 yr

12.7 Assess Your Understanding *(page 825)*

3. principal **4.** I; Prt; simple interest **5.** 4 **6.** effective rate of interest **7.** \$108.29 **9.** \$609.50 **11.** \$697.09 **13.** \$1246.08 **15.** \$88.72 **17.** \$860.72 **19.** \$554.09 **21.** \$59.71 **23.** 5.095% **25.** 5.127% **27.** $6\frac{1}{4}$% compounded annually **29.** 9% compounded monthly **31.** 25.992% **33.** 24.573% **35. (a)** About 8.69 yr **(b)** About 8.66 yr **37.** 6.823% **39.** 5.09 yr; 5.07 yr **41.** 15.27 yr or 15 yr, 3 mo **43.** \$104,335 **45.** \$12,910.62 **47.** About \$30.17 per share or \$3017 **49.** Not quite. Jim will have \$1057.60. The second bank gives a better deal, since Jim will have \$1060.62 after 1 yr. **51.** Will has \$11,632.73; Henry has \$10,947.89. **53. (a)** \$79,129 **(b)** \$38,516 **55.** About \$1020 billion; about \$233 billion **57.** \$940.90 **59.** 2.53% **61.** 34.31 yr **63. (a)** \$1364.62 **(b)** \$1353.35 **65.** \$4631.93

67. (a) 6.12 yr
(b) 18.45 yr
(c)
$$mP = P\left(1+\frac{r}{n}\right)^{nt}$$
$$m = \left(1+\frac{r}{n}\right)^{nt}$$
$$\ln m = \ln\left(1+\frac{r}{n}\right)^{nt} = nt\ln\left(1+\frac{r}{n}\right)$$
$$t = \frac{\ln m}{n\ln\left(1+\frac{r}{n}\right)}$$

69. (a) 2.82% **(b)** In 2020
71. 22.7 yr

12.8 Assess Your Understanding *(page 836)*

1. (a) 500 insects
(b) 0.02 = 2%
(c)

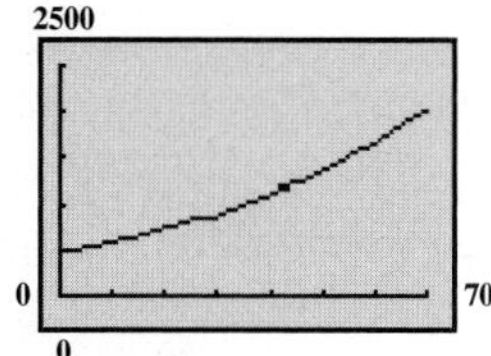

(d) About 611 insects
(e) After about 23.5 days
(f) After about 34.7 days

3. (a) −0.0244 = −2.44%
(b)

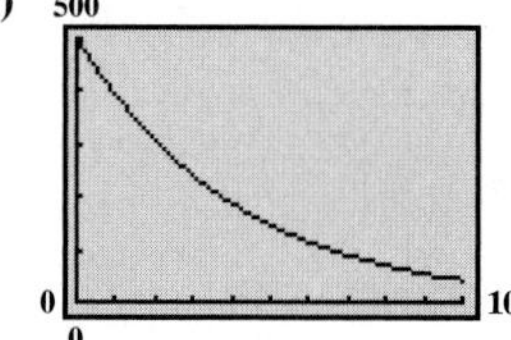

(c) About 391.7 g
(d) After about 9.1 yr
(e) 28.4 yr

5. (a) $N(t) = N_0 e^{kt}$
(b) 5832
(c) 3.9 days
7. (a) $N(t) = N_0 e^{kt}$
(b) 25,198
9. 9.797 g

11. (a) 9901 yr ago
(b)

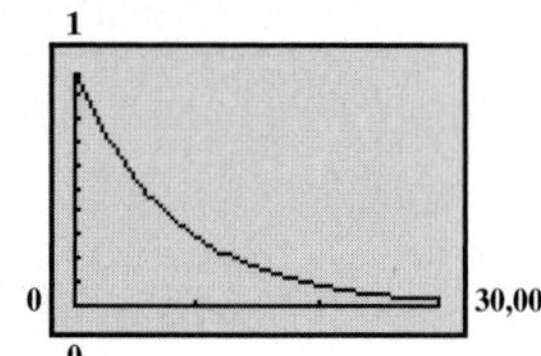

(c) 5700 yr

13. (a) About 5:18 PM
(b)

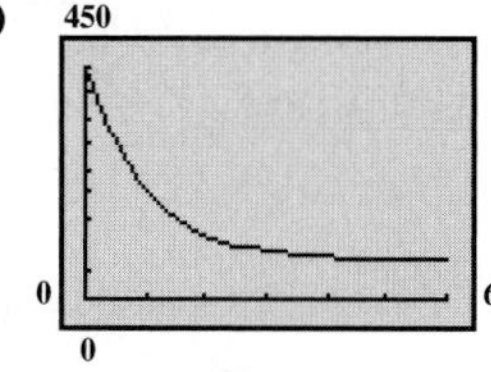

(c) About 14.3 min
(d) The temperature of the pizza approaches 70°F.

15. (a) 18.63°C; 25.07°C
(b) 35, 0, 50, 0

17. 1.7 ppm; 7.17 days or 172 h **19.** 0.26 mol; 6.58 h or 395 min **21.** 26.6 days

23. (a) 1000 g **(b)** 43.9% **(c)** 30 g
(d)

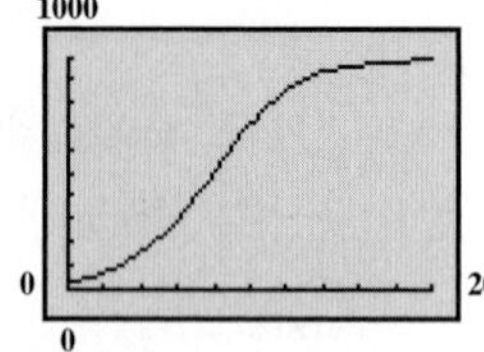

(e) 616.6 g **(f)** After 9.85 h
(g) About 7.9 h

25. (a) 9.23×10^{-3}, or about 0
(b) 0.81, or about 1
(c) 5.01, or about 5
(d) 57.91°, 43.99°, 30.07°

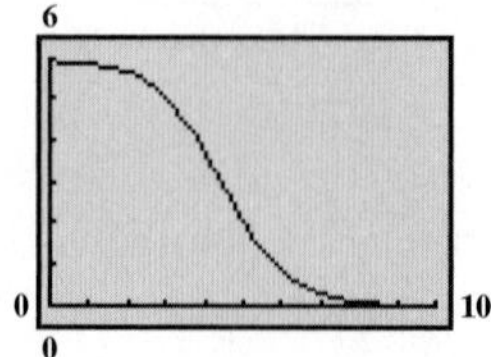

27. (a) In 1984, 91.8% of households did not own a personal computer.
(b)

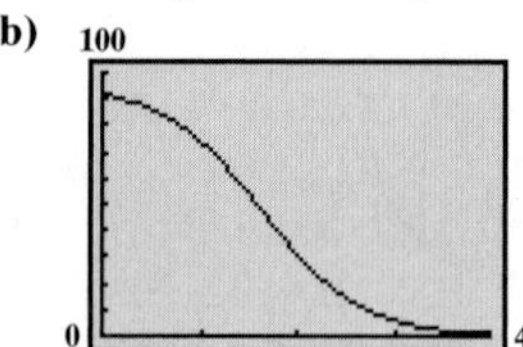

(c) 70.6% **(d)** During 2011

29. (a) 120, 0, 100, 0

(b) 0.78 or 78% **(c)** 50 people
(d) As n increases, the probability decreases.

12.9 Assess Your Understanding *(page 843)*

1. (a)

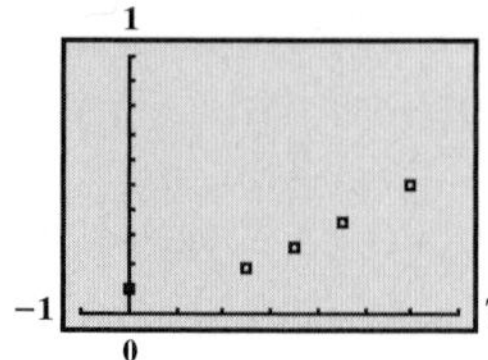

(b) $y = 0.0903(1.3384)^x$
(c) $N(t) = 0.0903e^{0.2915t}$

(d)

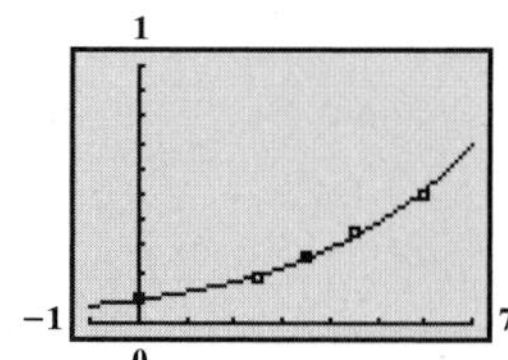

(e) 0.69
(f) After about 7.26 hr

3. (a)

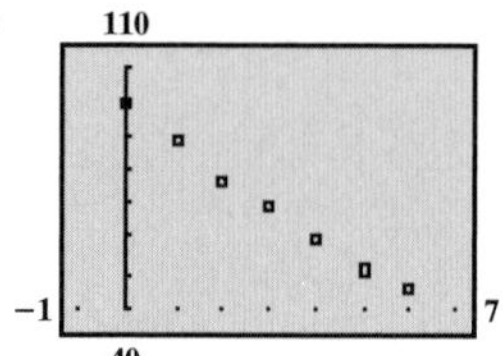

(b) $y = 100.326(0.8769)^x$
(c) $A(t) = 100.326e^{-0.1314t}$

(d)

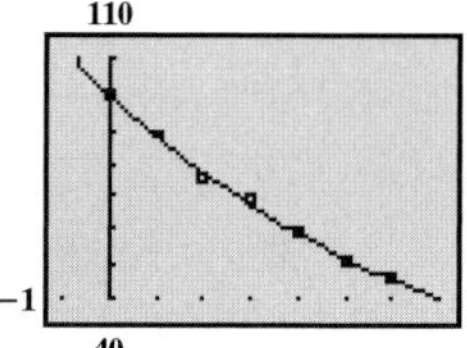

(e) 5.3 weeks **(f)** 0.14 g
(g) After about 12.3 weeks

5. (a)

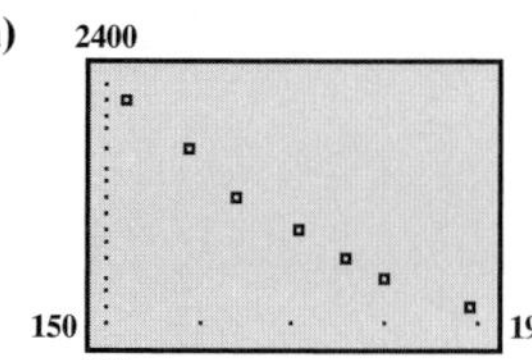

(b) $y = 32{,}741.02 - 6070.96 \ln x$

(c)

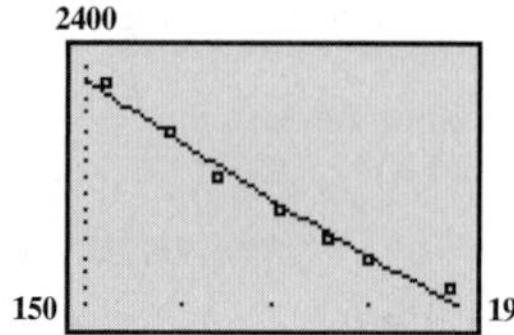

(d) Approximately 168 computers

7. (a)

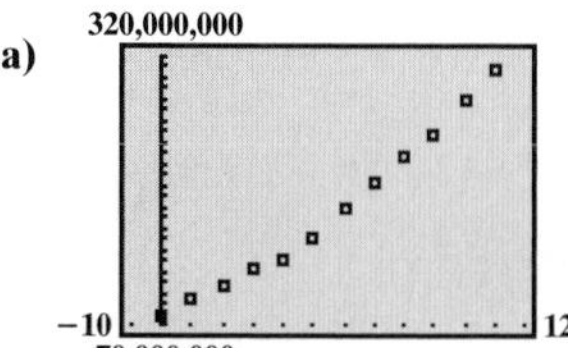

(b) $y = \dfrac{762{,}176{,}844.4}{1 + 8.7428e^{-0.0162x}}$

(c)

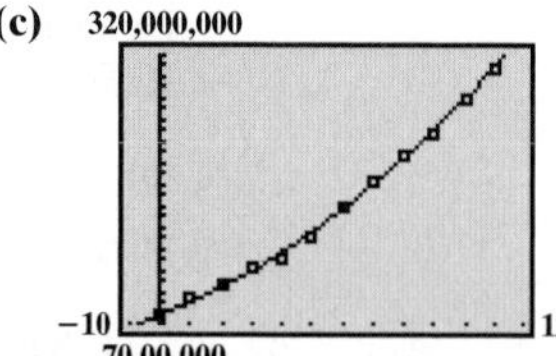

(d) 762,176,844
(e) Approximately 315,203,288
(f) 2023

9. (a)

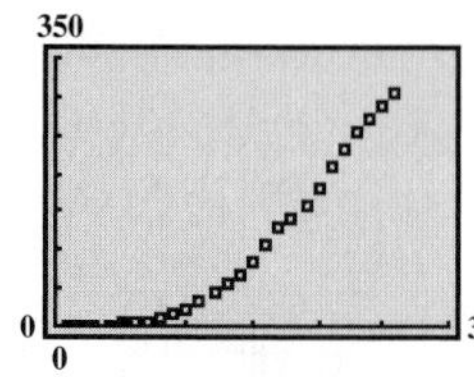

(b) $y = \dfrac{353.7175}{1 + 171.1548e^{-0.2636x}}$

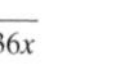

(c)

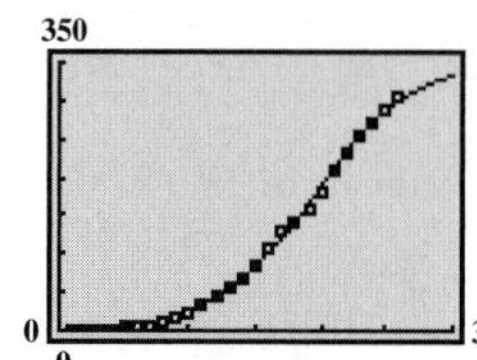

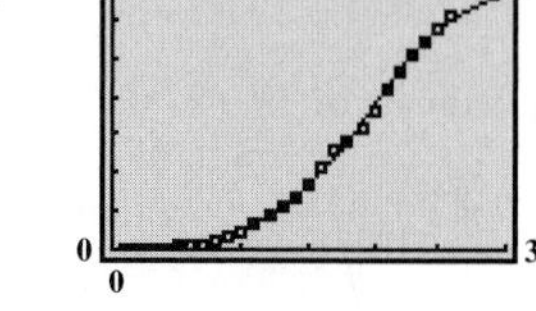

(d) About 353.72 million subscribers
(e) About 337.42 million subscribers

11. (a)

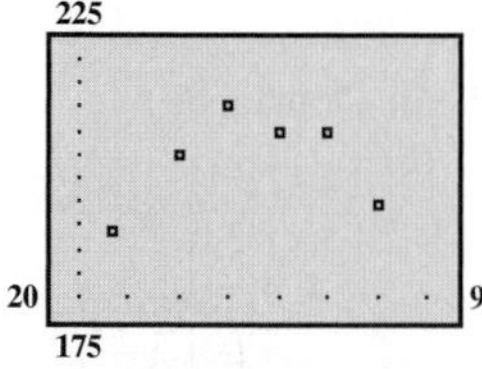

(b) Quadratic with $a < 0$ because of the "upside down U-shape" of the data
(c) $y = -0.0311x^2 + 3.4444x + 118.2493$

(d)

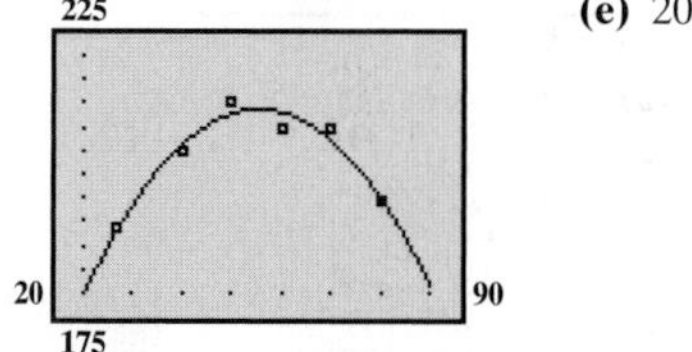

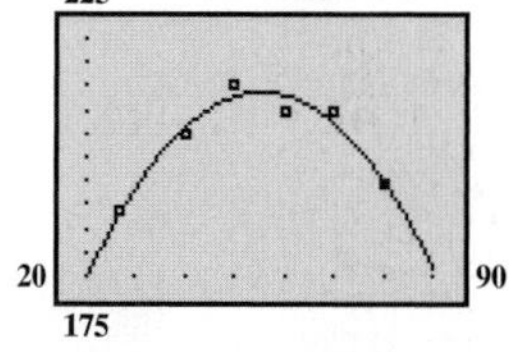

(e) 201

13. (a)

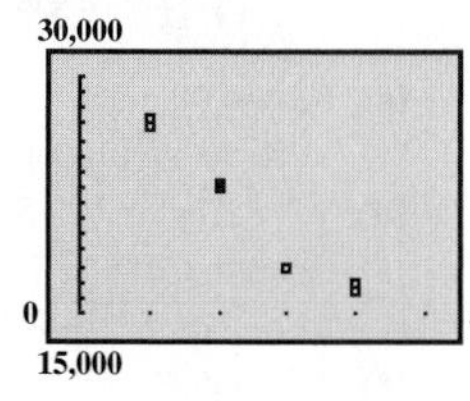

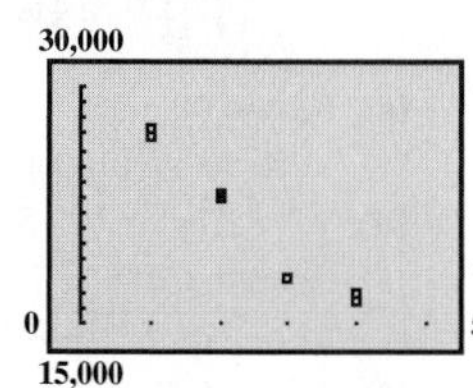

(b) Exponential because depreciation of a car is described by exponential models in the theory of finance.
(c) $y = 31{,}808.51(0.8474)^x$

(d)

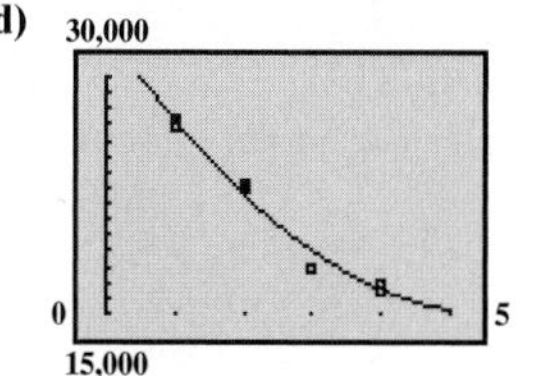

(e) \$13,899

Review Exercises *(page 849)*

1. (a) -4 **(b)** 1 **(c)** -6 **(d)** -6 **2. (a)** -26 **(b)** -241 **(c)** 16 **(d)** -1 **3. (a)** $\sqrt{11}$ **(b)** 1 **(c)** $\sqrt{\sqrt{6}+2}$ **(d)** 19 **4. (a)** e^4 **(b)** $3e^{-2} - 2$ **(c)** e^{e^4} **(d)** -17

5. $(f \circ g)(x) = 1 - 3x$, all real numbers; $(g \circ f)(x) = 7 - 3x$, all real numbers; $(f \circ f)(x) = x$, all real numbers; $(g \circ g)(x) = 9x + 4$, all real numbers

6. $(f \circ g)(x) = \sqrt{3 + 3x + 3x^2}$, all real numbers; $(g \circ f)(x) = 1 + \sqrt{3x} + 3x, \{x|x \geq 0\}$; $(f \circ f)(x) = \sqrt{3\sqrt{3x}}, \{x|x \geq 0\}$; $(g \circ g)(x) = 3 + 3x + 4x^2 + 2x^3 + x^4$, all real numbers

7. $(f \circ g)(x) = \dfrac{1+x}{1-x}, \{x|x \neq 0, x \neq 1\}$; $(g \circ f)(x) = \dfrac{x-1}{x+1}, \{x|x \neq -1, x \neq 1\}$; $(f \circ f)(x) = x, \{x|x \neq 1\}$; $(g \circ g)(x) = x, \{x|x \neq 0\}$

8. (a) one-to-one **(b)** $\{(2,1), (5,3), (8,5), (10,6)\}$

9. The graph passes the horizontal line test.

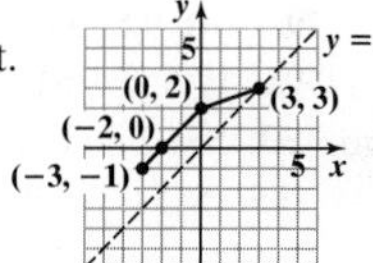

10. $f^{-1}(x) = \dfrac{2x+3}{5x-2}$

$$f(f^{-1}(x)) = \frac{2\left(\frac{2x+3}{5x-2}\right)+3}{5\left(\frac{2x+3}{5x-2}\right)-2} = \frac{2(2x+3)+3(5x-2)}{5(2x+3)-2(5x-2)} = \frac{19x}{19} = x$$

$$f^{-1}(f(x)) = \frac{2\left(\frac{2x+3}{5x-2}\right)+3}{5\left(\frac{2x+3}{5x-2}\right)-2} = \frac{2(2x+3)+3(5x-2)}{5(2x+3)-2(5x-2)} = \frac{19x}{19} = x$$

Domain of f = range of f^{-1} = all real numbers except $\frac{2}{5}$

Range of f = domain of f^{-1} = all real numbers except $\frac{2}{5}$

11. $f^{-1}(x) = \dfrac{x+1}{x}$

$$f^{-1}(f(x)) = \frac{\frac{1}{x-1}+1}{\frac{1}{x-1}} = \frac{1+x-1}{1} = x$$

$$f(f^{-1}(x)) = \frac{\frac{x+1}{x}}{\frac{x+1}{x}-1} = \frac{x}{x+1-x} = x$$

Domain of f = range of f^{-1} = all real numbers except 1

Range of f = domain of f^{-1} = all real numbers except 0

12. $f^{-1}(x) = x^2 + 2, x \geq 2$
$f(f^{-1}(x)) = \sqrt{x^2+2-2} = |x| = x, x \geq 0$
$f^{-1}(f(x)) = \left(\sqrt{x-2}\right)^2 + 2 = x$
Domain of f = range of f^{-1} = $[2, \infty)$
Range of f = domain of f^{-1} = $[0, \infty)$

13. $f^{-1}(x) = (x-1)^3$
$f(f^{-1}(x)) = ((x-1)^3)^{1/3} + 1 = x$
$f^{-1}(f(x)) = (x^{1/3}+1-1)^3 = x$
Domain of f = range of f^{-1} = $(-\infty, \infty)$
Range of f = domain of f^{-1} = $(-\infty, \infty)$

14. (a) 81 **(b)** 2 **(c)** $\frac{1}{9}$ **(d)** -3 **15.** $\log_5 z = 2$ **16.** $5^{13} = u$ **17.** $\left\{x \middle| x > \frac{2}{3}\right\}; \left(\frac{2}{3}, \infty\right)$
18. $\{x | x < 1 \text{ or } x > 2\}; (-\infty, 1) \cup (2, \infty)$

19. -3 **20.** $\sqrt{2}$ **21.** 0.4 **22.** $\log_3 u + 2\log_3 v - \log_3 w$ **23.** $8\log_2 a + 2\log_2 b$ **24.** $2\log x + \frac{1}{2}\log(x^3+1)$

25. $2\ln(2x+3) - 2\ln(x-1) - 2\ln(x-2)$ **26.** $\frac{25}{4}\log_4 x$ **27.** $-2\ln(x+1)$ **28.** $\ln\left[\frac{16\sqrt{x^2+1}}{\sqrt{x(x-4)}}\right]$ **29.** 2.124

30.

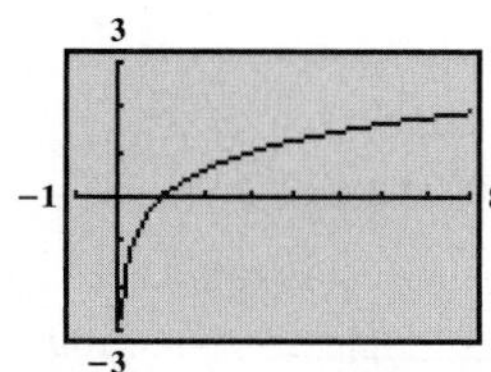

31. (a) Domain of f: $(-\infty, \infty)$
(b)

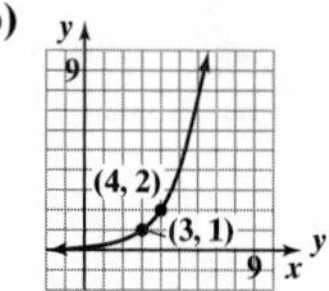

(c) Range of f: $(0, \infty)$
Horizontal asymptote: $y = 0$
(d) $f^{-1}(x) = 3 + \log_2 x$
(e) Domain of f^{-1}: $(0, \infty)$
Range of f^{-1}: $(-\infty, \infty)$
(f)

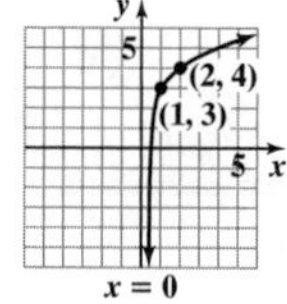

32. (a) Domain of f: $(-\infty, \infty)$
(b)
(c) Range of f: $(1, \infty)$
Horizontal asymptote:
$y = 1$
(d) $f^{-1}(x) = -\log_3(x-1)$
(e) Domain of f^{-1}: $(1, \infty)$
Range of f^{-1}: $(-\infty, \infty)$
(f)

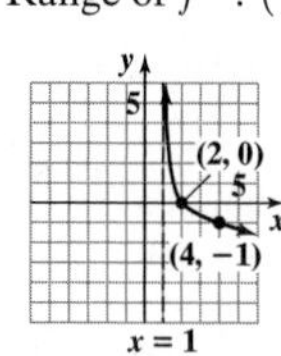

33. (a) Domain of f: $(-\infty, \infty)$
(b)

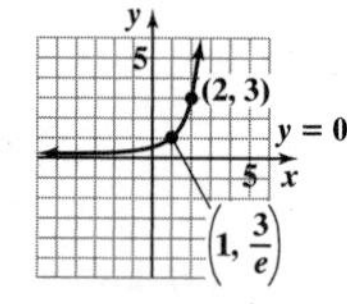

(c) Range of f: $(0, \infty)$
Horizontal asymptote: $y = 0$

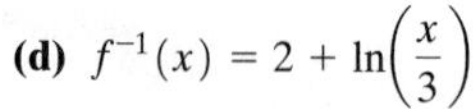

(d) $f^{-1}(x) = 2 + \ln\left(\frac{x}{3}\right)$
(e) Domain of f^{-1}: $(0, \infty)$
Range of f^{-1}: $(-\infty, \infty)$
(f)

34. (a) Domain of f: $(-3, \infty)$
(b)

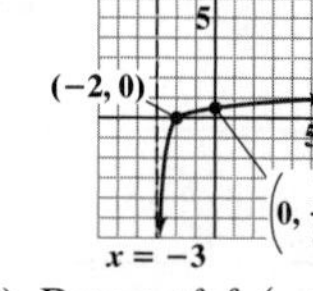

(c) Range of f: $(-\infty, \infty)$
Vertical asymptote: $x = -3$
(d) $f^{-1}(x) = e^{2x} - 3$
(e) Domain of f^{-1}: $(-\infty, \infty)$
Range of f^{-1}: $(-3, \infty)$
(f)

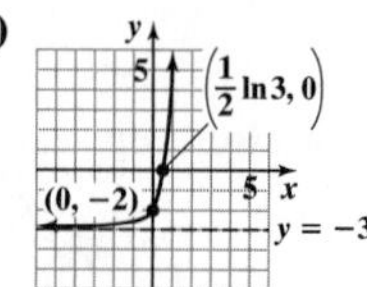

35. $\left\{-\frac{16}{9}\right\}$ **36.** $\left\{\frac{-1-\sqrt{3}}{2}, \frac{-1+\sqrt{3}}{2}\right\} \approx \{-1.366, 0.366\}$ **37.** $\left\{\frac{1}{4}\right\}$ **38.** $\left\{\frac{2\ln 3}{\ln 5 - \ln 3}\right\} \approx \{4.301\}$ **39.** $\{-2, 6\}$ **40.** $\{83\}$

41. $\left\{\frac{1}{2}, -3\right\}$ **42.** $\{1\}$ **43.** $\{-1\}$ **44.** $\{1 - \ln 5\} \approx \{-0.609\}$ **45.** $\left\{\log_3(-2+\sqrt{7})\right\} = \left\{\frac{\ln(-2+\sqrt{7})}{\ln 3}\right\} \approx \{-0.398\}$

46. (a), (e)

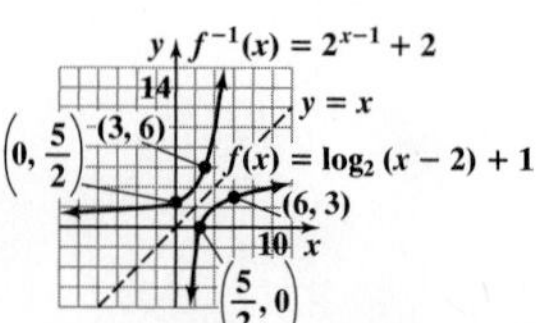

(b) 3; (6, 3)
(c) 10; (10, 4)
(d) $\left\{x \middle| x > \frac{5}{2}\right\}$ or $\left(\frac{5}{2}, \infty\right)$
(e) $f^{-1}(x) = 2^{x-1} + 2$

47. (a) 37.3 W **(b)** 6.9 dB **48. (a)** 11.77 **(b)** 9.56 in. **49. (a)** 9.85 yr **(b)** 4.27 yr
50. \$20,398.87; 4.04%; 17.5 yr **51.** \$41,668.97
52. 24,636 yr ago **53.** 55.22 min or 55 min, 13 sec
54. 7,255,657,224 **55.** \$1.807 trillion; ≈ \$507 billion

56. (a) 0.3 **(b)** 0.8
(c)

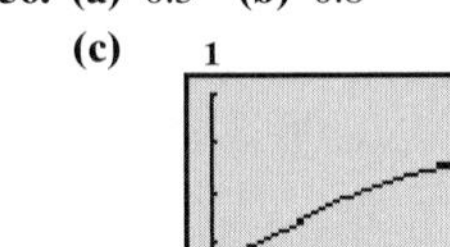

(d) In 2026

57. (a)

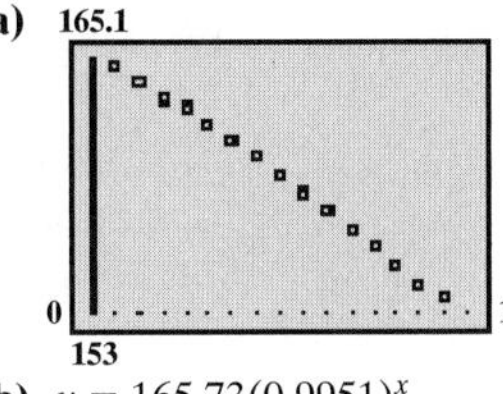

(b) $y = 165.73(0.9951)^x$

(c)

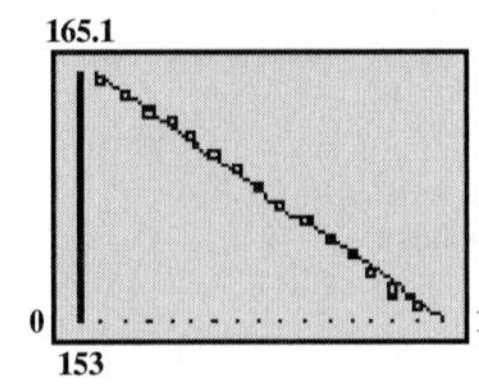

(d) Approximately 83 s

58. (a)

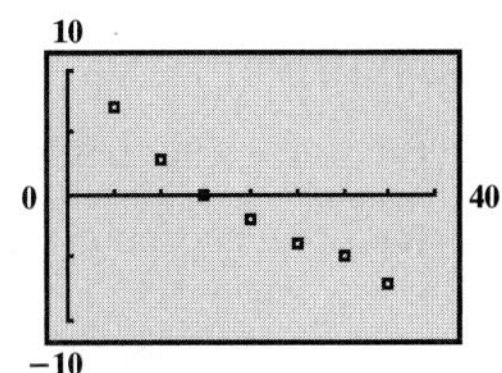

(b) $y = 18.921 - 7.096 \ln x$

(c)

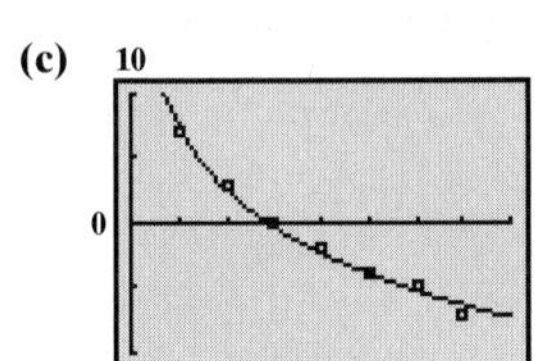

(d) $\approx -3^\circ$F

(e) 2.4 days; during the tenth hour of day 3
(f) 9.5 days

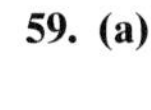

59. (a)

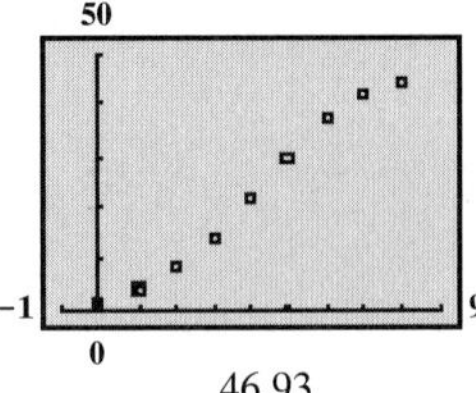

(b) $C = \dfrac{46.93}{1 + 21.273e^{-0.7306t}}$

(c)

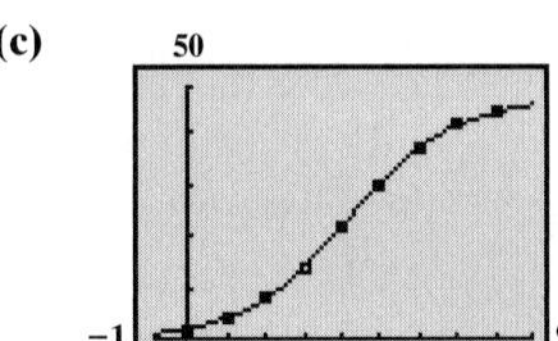

(d) About 47 people; 50 people

Chapter Test *(page 852)*

1. (a) $f \circ g = \dfrac{2x+7}{2x+3}$; domain: $\left\{x \middle| x \neq -\dfrac{3}{2}\right\}$ **(b)** $(g \circ f)(-2) = 5$ **(c)** $(f \circ g)(-2) = -3$
2. (a) The function is not one-to-one. **(b)** The function is one-to-one.
3. $f^{-1}(x) = \dfrac{2+5x}{3x}$; domain of $f = \left\{x \middle| x \neq \dfrac{5}{3}\right\}$, range of $f = \{y | y \neq 0\}$; domain of $f^{-1} = \{x | x \neq 0\}$; range of $f^{-1} = \left\{y \middle| y \neq \dfrac{5}{3}\right\}$
4. The point $(-5, 3)$ must be on the graph of f^{-1}. **5.** $x = 5$ **6.** $b = 4$ **7.** $x = 625$ **8.** $e^3 + 2 \approx 22.086$ **9.** $\log 20 \approx 1.301$
10. $\log_3 21 = \dfrac{\ln 21}{\ln 3} \approx 2.771$ **11.** $\ln 133 \approx 4.890$

12. (a) Domain of f: $\{x| -\infty < x < \infty\}$ or $(-\infty, \infty)$
(b)

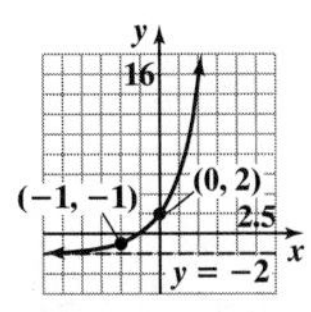

(c) Range of f: $\{y | y > -2\}$ or $(-2, \infty)$; Horizontal asymptote: $y = -2$
(d) $f^{-1}(x) = \log_4(x+2) - 1$
(e) Domain of f^{-1}: $\{x | x > -2\}$ or $(-2, \infty)$
Range of f^{-1}: $\{y | -\infty < y < \infty\}$ or $(-\infty, \infty)$
(f)

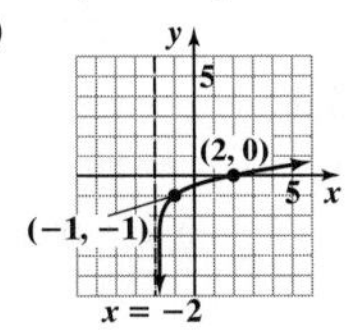

13. (a) Domain of f: $\{x | x > 2\}$ or $(2, \infty)$
(b)

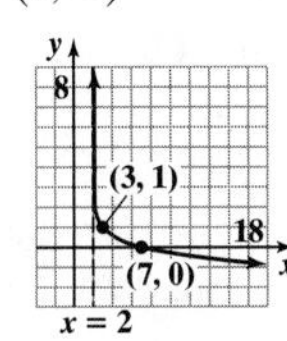

(c) Range of f: $\{y| -\infty < y < \infty\}$ or $(-\infty, \infty)$; vertical asymptote: $x = 2$
(d) $f^{-1}(x) = 5^{1-x} + 2$
(e) Domain of f^{-1}: $\{x| -\infty < x < \infty\}$ or $(-\infty, \infty)$
Range of f^{-1}: $\{y | y > 2\}$ or $(2, \infty)$
(f)

14. $\{1\}$ **15.** $\{91\}$ **16.** $\{-\ln 2\} \approx \{-0.693\}$ **17.** $\left\{\dfrac{1-\sqrt{13}}{2}, \dfrac{1+\sqrt{13}}{2}\right\} \approx \{-1.303, 2.303\}$ **18.** $\left\{\dfrac{3\ln 7}{1 - \ln 7}\right\} \approx \{-6.172\}$
19. $\{2\sqrt{6}\} \approx \{4.899\}$ **20.** $2 + 3\log_2 x - \log_2(x-6) - \log_2(x+3)$ **21.** About 250.39 days **22. (a)** \$1033.82 **(b)** \$963.42 **(c)** 11.9 yr
23. (a) About 83 dB **(b)** The pain threshold will be exceeded if 31,623 people shout at the same time.

Cumulative Review *(page 853)*

1. (a) Yes; no **(b)** Polynomial; The graph is smooth and continuous. **2. (a)** 10 **(b)** $2x^2 + 3x + 1$ **(c)** $2x^2 + 4xh + 2h^2 - 3x - 3h + 1$

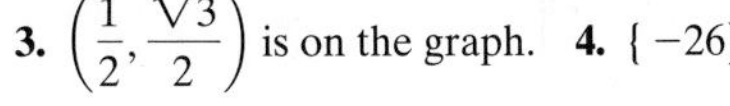

3. $\left(\dfrac{1}{2}, \dfrac{\sqrt{3}}{2}\right)$ is on the graph. **4.** $\{-26\}$

5.

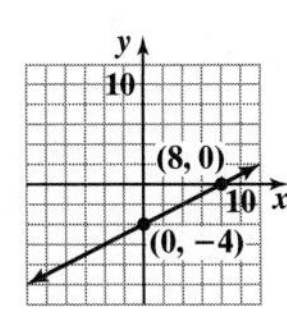

6. (a)

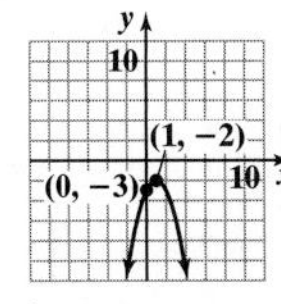

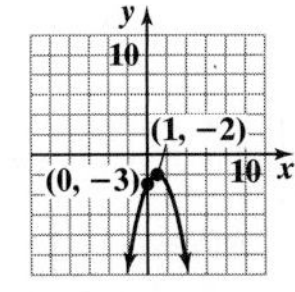

(b) $\{x| -\infty < x < \infty\}$

7. $f(x) = 2(x-4)^2 - 8 = 2x^2 - 16x + 24$
8. Exponential; $f(x) = 2 \cdot 3^x$
9.

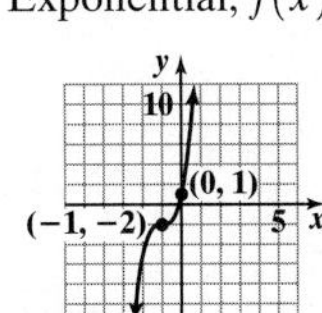

10. (a) $f(g(x)) = \dfrac{4}{(x-3)^2} + 2$; domain: $\{x | x \neq 3\}$; 3
(b) $f(g(x)) = \log_2 x + 2$; domain: $\{x | x > 0\}$; $2 + \log_2 14$

11. (a) Zeros: $-4, -\frac{1}{4}, 2$

(b) x-intercepts: $-4, -\frac{1}{4}, 2$; y-intercept: -8

(c) Local maximum value of 60.75 occurs at $x = -2.5$.
Local minimum value of -25 occurs at $x = 1$.

(d)

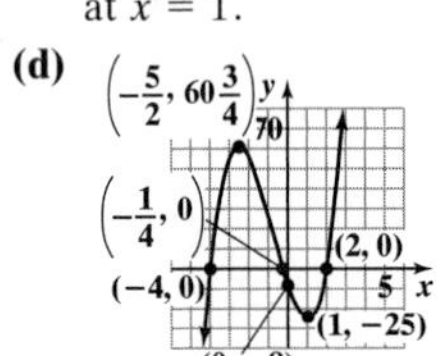

12. (a),(c)

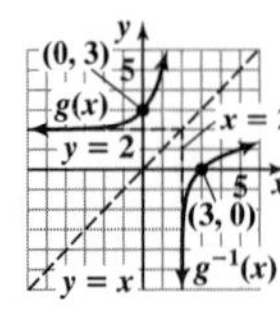

Domain g = range $g^{-1} = (-\infty, \infty)$
Range g = domain $g^{-1} = (2, \infty)$

(b) $g^{-1}(x) = \log_3(x - 2)$

13. $\left\{-\frac{3}{2}\right\}$

14. $\{2\}$ **15. (a)** $\{-1\}$ **(b)** $\{x \mid x > -1\}$ or $(-1, \infty)$ **(c)** $\{25\}$

16. (a)

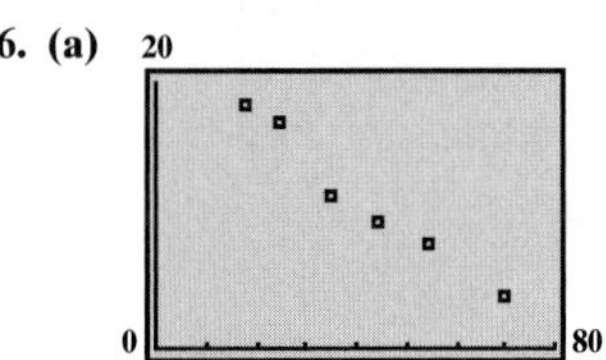

(b) Logarithmic; $y = 49.293 - 10.563 \ln x$
(c) Highest value of $|r|$

CHAPTER 13 Systems of Equations and Inequalities

13.1 Assess Your Understanding *(page 866)*

3. inconsistent **4.** consistent; independent **5.** $(3, -2)$ **6.** consistent; dependent

7. $\begin{cases} 2(2) - (-1) = 5 \\ 5(2) + 2(-1) = 8 \end{cases}$ **9.** $\begin{cases} 3(2) - 4\left(\frac{1}{2}\right) = 4 \\ \frac{1}{2}(2) - 3\left(\frac{1}{2}\right) = -\frac{1}{2} \end{cases}$ **11.** $\begin{cases} 4 - 1 = 3 \\ \frac{1}{2}(4) + 1 = 3 \end{cases}$ **13.** $\begin{cases} 3(1) + 3(-1) + 2(2) = 4 \\ 1 - (-1) - 2 = 0 \\ 2(-1) - 3(2) = -8 \end{cases}$ **15.** $\begin{cases} 3(2) + 3(-2) + 2(2) = 4 \\ 2 - 3(-2) + 2 = 10 \\ 5(2) - 2(-2) - 3(2) = 8 \end{cases}$

17. $x = 6, y = 2$; $(6, 2)$ **19.** $x = 3, y = -6$; $(3, -6)$ **21.** $x = 8, y = -4$; $(8, -4)$ **23.** $x = \frac{1}{3}, y = -\frac{1}{6}$; $\left(\frac{1}{3}, -\frac{1}{6}\right)$ **25.** Inconsistent

27. $x = \frac{3}{2}, y = 3$; $\left(\frac{3}{2}, 3\right)$ **29.** $\{(x, y) \mid x = 4 - 2y, y \text{ is any real number}\}$ or $\left\{(x, y) \,\middle|\, y = \frac{4 - x}{2}, x \text{ is any real number}\right\}$ **31.** $x = 1, y = 1$; $(1, 1)$

33. $x = \frac{3}{2}, y = 1$; $\left(\frac{3}{2}, 1\right)$ **35.** $x = 4, y = 3$; $(4, 3)$ **37.** $x = \frac{4}{3}, y = \frac{1}{5}$; $\left(\frac{4}{3}, \frac{1}{5}\right)$ **39.** $x = \frac{1}{5}, y = \frac{1}{3}$; $\left(\frac{1}{5}, \frac{1}{3}\right)$ **41.** $x = 8, y = 2, z = 0$; $(8, 2, 0)$

43. $x = 2, y = -1, z = 1$; $(2, -1, 1)$ **45.** Inconsistent **47.** $\{(x, y, z) \mid x = 5z - 2, y = 4z - 3; z \text{ is any real number}\}$ **49.** Inconsistent

51. $x = 1, y = 3, z = -2$; $(1, 3, -2)$ **53.** $x = -3, y = \frac{1}{2}, z = 1$; $\left(-3, \frac{1}{2}, 1\right)$ **55.** Length 30 ft; width 15 ft

57. There were 18 commercial launches and 37 noncommercial launches in 2005. **59.** 22.5 lb

61. Average wind speed 25 mph; average airspeed 175 mph **63.** 80 \$25 sets and 120 \$45 sets **65.** \$9.96

67. Mix 50 mg of first compound with 75 mg of second. **69.** $a = \frac{4}{3}, b = -\frac{5}{3}, c = 1$ **71.** $Y = 9000, r = 0.06$ **73.** $I_1 = \frac{10}{71}, I_2 = \frac{65}{71}, I_3 = \frac{55}{71}$

75. 100 orchestra, 210 main, and 190 balcony seats **77.** 1.5 chicken, 1 corn, 2 milk

79. If x = price of hamburgers, y = price of fries, and z = price of colas, then $x = 2.75 - z$, $y = \frac{41}{60} + \frac{1}{3}z$, $\$0.60 \le z \le \$0.90$.
There is not sufficient information:

x	\$2.13	\$2.01	\$1.86
y	\$0.89	\$0.93	\$0.98
z	\$0.62	\$0.74	\$0.89

81. It will take Beth 30 hr, Bill 24 hr, and Edie 40 hr.

13.2 Assess Your Understanding *(page 881)*

1. matrix **2.** augmented **3.** third; fifth **4.** T

5. $\left[\begin{array}{rr|r} 1 & -5 & 5 \\ 4 & 3 & 6 \end{array}\right]$ **7.** $\left[\begin{array}{rr|r} 2 & 3 & 6 \\ 4 & -6 & -2 \end{array}\right]$ **9.** $\left[\begin{array}{rr|r} 0.01 & -0.03 & 0.06 \\ 0.13 & 0.10 & 0.20 \end{array}\right]$ **11.** $\left[\begin{array}{rrr|r} 1 & -1 & 1 & 10 \\ 3 & 3 & 0 & 5 \\ 1 & 1 & 2 & 2 \end{array}\right]$ **13.** $\left[\begin{array}{rrr|r} 1 & 1 & -1 & 2 \\ 3 & -2 & 0 & 2 \\ 5 & 3 & -1 & 1 \end{array}\right]$ **15.** $\left[\begin{array}{rrr|r} 1 & -1 & -1 & 10 \\ 2 & 1 & 2 & -1 \\ -3 & 4 & 0 & 5 \\ 4 & -5 & 1 & 0 \end{array}\right]$

17. $\begin{cases} x - 3y = -2 & (1) \\ 2x - 5y = 5 & (2) \end{cases}$ $\left[\begin{array}{rr|r} 1 & -3 & -2 \\ 0 & 1 & 9 \end{array}\right]$ **19.** $\begin{cases} x - 3y + 4z = 3 & (1) \\ 3x - 5y + 6z = 6 & (2); \\ -5x + 3y + 4z = 6 & (3) \end{cases}$ $\left[\begin{array}{rrr|r} 1 & -3 & 4 & 3 \\ 0 & 4 & -6 & -3 \\ 0 & -12 & 24 & 21 \end{array}\right]$

21. $\begin{cases} x - 3y + 2z = -6 & (1) \\ 2x - 5y + 3z = -4 & (2); \\ -3x - 6y + 4z = 6 & (3) \end{cases}$ $\left[\begin{array}{rrr|r} 1 & -3 & 2 & -6 \\ 0 & 1 & -1 & 8 \\ 0 & -15 & 10 & -12 \end{array}\right]$ **23.** $\begin{cases} 5x - 3y + z = -2 & (1) \\ 2x - 5y + 6z = -2 & (2); \\ -4x + y + 4z = 6 & (3) \end{cases}$ $\left[\begin{array}{rrr|r} 1 & 7 & -11 & 2 \\ 2 & -5 & 6 & -2 \\ 0 & -9 & 16 & 2 \end{array}\right]$

25. $\begin{cases} x = 5 \\ y = -1 \end{cases}$
Consistent; $x = 5, y = -1$ or $(5, -1)$

27. $\begin{cases} x = 1 \\ y = 2 \\ 0 = 3 \end{cases}$
Inconsistent

29. $\begin{cases} x + 2z = -1 \\ y - 4z = -2 \\ 0 = 0 \end{cases}$
Consistent:
$\begin{cases} x = -1 - 2z \\ y = -2 + 4z \\ z \text{ is any real number or} \end{cases}$
$\{(x, y, z) \mid x = -1 - 2z, y = -2 + 4z, z \text{ is any real number}\}$

31. $\begin{cases} x_1 = 1 \\ x_2 + x_4 = 2 \\ x_3 + 2x_4 = 3 \end{cases}$
Consistent:
$\begin{cases} x_1 = 1, x_2 = 2 - x_4 \\ x_3 = 3 - 2x_4 \\ x_4 \text{ is any real number or} \end{cases}$
$\{(x_1, x_2, x_3, x_4) \mid x_1 = 1, x_2 = 2 - x_4, x_3 = 3 - 2x_4, x_4 \text{ is any real number}\}$

33. $\begin{cases} x_1 + 4x_4 = 2 \\ x_2 + x_3 + 3x_4 = 3 \\ 0 = 0 \end{cases}$
Consistent:
$\begin{cases} x_1 = 2 - 4x_4 \\ x_2 = 3 - x_3 - 3x_4 \\ x_3, x_4 \text{ are any real numbers or} \end{cases}$
$\{(x_1, x_2, x_3, x_4) \mid x_1 = 2 - 4x_4, x_2 = 3 - x_3 - 3x_4, x_3, x_4 \text{ are any real numbers}\}$

35. $\begin{cases} x_1 + x_4 = -2 \\ x_2 + 2x_4 = 2 \\ x_3 - x_4 = 0 \\ 0 = 0 \end{cases}$
Consistent:
$\begin{cases} x_1 = -2 - x_4 \\ x_2 = 2 - 2x_4 \\ x_3 = x_4 \\ x_4 \text{ is any real number or} \end{cases}$
$\{(x_1, x_2, x_3, x_4) \mid x_1 = -2 - x_4, x_2 = 2 - 2x_4, x_3 = x_4, x_4 \text{ is any real number}\}$

37. $x = 6, y = 2; (6, 2)$ **39.** $x = \frac{1}{2}, y = \frac{3}{4}; \left(\frac{1}{2}, \frac{3}{4}\right)$ **41.** $x = 4 - 2y$, y is any real number; $\{(x, y) \mid x = 4 - 2y, y \text{ is any real number}\}$
43. $x = \frac{3}{2}, y = 1; \left(\frac{3}{2}, 1\right)$ **45.** $x = \frac{4}{3}, y = \frac{1}{5}; \left(\frac{4}{3}, \frac{1}{5}\right)$ **47.** $x = 8, y = 2, z = 0; (8, 2, 0)$ **49.** $x = 2, y = -1, z = 1; (2, -1, 1)$ **51.** Inconsistent
53. $x = 5z - 2, y = 4z - 3$, where z is any real number; $\{(x, y, z) \mid x = 5z - 2, y = 4z - 3, z \text{ is any real number}\}$ **55.** Inconsistent
57. $x = 1, y = 3, z = -2; (1, 3, -2)$ **59.** $x = -3, y = \frac{1}{2}, z = 1; \left(-3, \frac{1}{2}, 1\right)$ **61.** $x = \frac{1}{3}, y = \frac{2}{3}, z = 1; \left(\frac{1}{3}, \frac{2}{3}, 1\right)$
63. $x = 1, y = 2, z = 0, w = 1; (1, 2, 0, 1)$ **65.** $y = 0, z = 1 - x$, x is any real number; $\{(x, y, z) \mid y = 0, z = 1 - x, x \text{ is any real number}\}$
67. $x = 2, y = z - 3$, z is any real number; $\{(x, y, z) \mid x = 2, y = z - 3, z \text{ is any real number}\}$ **69.** $x = \frac{13}{9}, y = \frac{7}{18}, z = \frac{19}{18}; \left(\frac{13}{9}, \frac{7}{18}, \frac{19}{18}\right)$
71. $x = \frac{7}{5} - \frac{3}{5}z - \frac{2}{5}w, y = -\frac{8}{5} + \frac{7}{5}z + \frac{13}{5}w$, where z and w are any real numbers; $\left\{(x, y, z, w) \middle| x = \frac{7}{5} - \frac{3}{5}z - \frac{2}{5}w, y = -\frac{8}{5} + \frac{7}{5}z + \frac{13}{5}w, z \text{ and } w \text{ are any real numbers}\right\}$ **73.** $y = -2x^2 + x + 3$ **75.** $f(x) = 3x^3 - 4x^2 + 5$ **77.** 1.5 salmon steak, 2 baked eggs, 1 acorn squash
79. \$4000 in Treasury bills, \$4000 in Treasury bonds, \$2000 in corporate bonds **81.** 8 Deltas, 5 Betas, 10 Sigmas **83.** $I_1 = \frac{44}{23}, I_2 = 2, I_3 = \frac{16}{23}, I_4 = \frac{28}{23}$

85. (a)

Amount Invested At		
7%	**9%**	**11%**
0	10,000	10,000
1000	8000	11,000
2000	6000	12,000
3000	4000	13,000
4000	2000	14,000
5000	0	15,000

(b)

Amount Invested At		
7%	**9%**	**11%**
12,500	12,500	0
14,500	8500	2000
16,500	4500	4000
18,750	0	6250

(c) All the money invested at 7% provides \$2100, more than what is required.

87.

First Supplement	Second Supplement	Third Supplement
50 mg	75 mg	0 mg
36 mg	76 mg	8 mg
22 mg	77 mg	16 mg
8 mg	78 mg	24 mg

13.3 Assess Your Understanding *(page 893)*

1. $ad - bc$ **2.** $\begin{vmatrix} 5 & 3 \\ -3 & -4 \end{vmatrix}$ **3.** F **4.** F **5.** F **6.** F **7.** 22 **9.** -2 **11.** 10 **13.** -26 **15.** $x = 6, y = 2; (6, 2)$ **17.** $x = 3, y = 2; (3, 2)$
19. $x = 8, y = -4; (8, -4)$ **21.** $x = 4, y = -2; (4, -2)$ **23.** Not applicable **25.** $x = \frac{1}{2}, y = \frac{3}{4}; \left(\frac{1}{2}, \frac{3}{4}\right)$ **27.** $x = \frac{1}{10}, y = \frac{2}{5}; \left(\frac{1}{10}, \frac{2}{5}\right)$
29. $x = \frac{3}{2}, y = 1; \left(\frac{3}{2}, 1\right)$ **31.** $x = \frac{4}{3}, y = \frac{1}{5}; \left(\frac{4}{3}, \frac{1}{5}\right)$ **33.** $x = 1, y = 3, z = -2; (1, 3, -2)$ **35.** $x = -3, y = \frac{1}{2}, z = 1; \left(-3, \frac{1}{2}, 1\right)$
37. Not applicable **39.** $x = 0, y = 0, z = 0; (0, 0, 0)$ **41.** Not applicable **43.** -4 **45.** 12 **47.** 8 **49.** 8 **51.** -5 **53.** $\frac{13}{11}$ **55.** 0 or -9

57.
$$\begin{aligned}(y_1 - y_2)x - (x_1 - x_2)y + (x_1y_2 - x_2y_1) &= 0\\ (y_1 - y_2)x + (x_2 - x_1)y &= x_2y_1 - x_1y_2\\ (x_2 - x_1)y - (x_2 - x_1)y_1 &= (y_2 - y_1)x + x_2y_1 - x_1y_2 - (x_2 - x_1)y_1\\ (x_2 - x_1)(y - y_1) &= (y_2 - y_1)x - (y_2 - y_1)x_1\\ y - y_1 &= \frac{y_2 - y_1}{x_2 - x_1}(x - x_1)\end{aligned}$$

59. The triangle has an area of 5 square units.

61. If $a = 0$, we have
$$by = s$$
$$cx + dy = t$$
Thus, $y = \dfrac{s}{b}$ and
$$x = \frac{t - dy}{c} = \frac{tb - ds}{bc}$$
Using Cramer's Rule, we get
$$x = \frac{sd - tb}{-bc} = \frac{tb - sd}{bc}$$
$$y = \frac{-sc}{-bc} = \frac{s}{b}$$

If $b = 0$, we have
$$ax = s$$
$$cx + dy = t$$
Since $D = ad \neq 0$, then $a \neq 0$ and $d \neq 0$.
Thus, $x = \dfrac{s}{a}$ and
$$y = \frac{t - cx}{d} = \frac{ta - cs}{ad}$$
Using Cramer's Rule, we get
$$x = \frac{sd}{ad} = \frac{s}{a}$$
$$y = \frac{ta - cs}{ad}$$

If $c = 0$, we have
$$ax + by = s$$
$$dy = t$$
Since $D = ad \neq 0$, then $a \neq 0$ and $d \neq 0$.
Thus, $y = \dfrac{t}{d}$ and
$$x = \frac{s - by}{a} = \frac{sd - bt}{ad}$$
Using Cramer's Rule, we get
$$x = \frac{sd - bt}{ad}$$
$$y = \frac{at}{ad} = \frac{t}{d}$$

If $d = 0$, we have
$$ax + by = s$$
$$cx = t$$
Since $D = -bc \neq 0$, then $b \neq 0$ and $c \neq 0$.
Thus, $x = \dfrac{t}{c}$ and
$$y = \frac{s - ax}{b} = \frac{sc - at}{bc}$$
Using Cramer's Rule, we get
$$x = \frac{-tb}{-bc} = \frac{t}{c}$$
$$y = \frac{at - sc}{-bc} = \frac{sc - at}{bc}$$

63.
$$\begin{vmatrix} a_{11} & a_{12} & a_{13}\\ ka_{21} & ka_{22} & ka_{23}\\ a_{31} & a_{32} & a_{33}\end{vmatrix} = -ka_{21}(a_{12}a_{33} - a_{32}a_{13}) + ka_{22}(a_{11}a_{33} - a_{31}a_{13}) - ka_{23}(a_{11}a_{32} - a_{31}a_{12})$$
$$= k[-a_{21}(a_{12}a_{33} - a_{32}a_{13}) + a_{22}(a_{11}a_{33} - a_{31}a_{13}) - a_{23}(a_{11}a_{32} - a_{31}a_{12})] = k\begin{vmatrix} a_{11} & a_{12} & a_{13}\\ a_{21} & a_{22} & a_{23}\\ a_{31} & a_{32} & a_{33}\end{vmatrix}$$

65.
$$\begin{vmatrix} a_{11} + ka_{21} & a_{12} + ka_{22} & a_{13} + ka_{23}\\ a_{21} & a_{22} & a_{23}\\ a_{31} & a_{32} & a_{33}\end{vmatrix} = (a_{11} + ka_{21})(a_{22}a_{33} - a_{32}a_{23}) - (a_{12} + ka_{22})(a_{21}a_{33} - a_{31}a_{23}) + (a_{13} + ka_{23})(a_{21}a_{32} - a_{31}a_{22})$$
$$\begin{aligned}&= a_{11}a_{22}a_{33} - a_{11}a_{32}a_{23} + \cancel{ka_{21}a_{22}a_{33}} - \cancel{ka_{21}a_{32}a_{23}} - a_{12}a_{21}a_{33} + a_{12}a_{31}a_{23}\\ &\quad - \cancel{ka_{22}a_{21}a_{33}} + \cancel{ka_{22}a_{31}a_{23}} + a_{13}a_{21}a_{32} - a_{13}a_{31}a_{22} + \cancel{ka_{23}a_{21}a_{32}} - \cancel{ka_{23}a_{31}a_{22}}\\ &= a_{11}a_{22}a_{33} - a_{11}a_{32}a_{23} - a_{12}a_{21}a_{33} + a_{12}a_{31}a_{23} + a_{13}a_{21}a_{32} - a_{13}a_{31}a_{22}\\ &= a_{11}(a_{22}a_{33} - a_{32}a_{23}) - a_{12}(a_{21}a_{33} - a_{31}a_{23}) + a_{13}(a_{21}a_{32} - a_{31}a_{22})\\ &= \begin{vmatrix} a_{11} & a_{12} & a_{13}\\ a_{21} & a_{22} & a_{23}\\ a_{31} & a_{32} & a_{33}\end{vmatrix}\end{aligned}$$

Review Exercises *(page 895)*

1. $x = 2, y = -1$ or $(2, -1)$ **2.** $x = 2, y = \frac{1}{2}$ or $\left(2, \frac{1}{2}\right)$ **3.** $x = 2, y = -1$ or $(2, -1)$ **4.** $x = \frac{11}{5}, y = -\frac{3}{5}$ or $\left(\frac{11}{5}, -\frac{3}{5}\right)$ **5.** Inconsistent **6.** $x = 2, y = 3$ or $(2, 3)$ **7.** $y = -\frac{2}{5}x + 2$, where x is any real number or $\left\{(x, y) \mid y = -\frac{2}{5}x + 2, x \text{ is any real number}\right\}$ **8.** $x = -1, y = 2, z = -3$ or $(-1, 2, -3)$

9. $x = \frac{7}{4}z + \frac{39}{4}, y = \frac{9}{8}z + \frac{69}{8}$, where z is any real number or $\left\{(x, y, z)\,\middle|\, x = \frac{7}{4}z + \frac{39}{4}, y = \frac{9}{8}z + \frac{69}{8}, z \text{ is any real number}\right\}$

10. Inconsistent **11.** $\begin{cases} 3x + 2y = 8\\ x + 4y = -1\end{cases}$ **12.** $\begin{cases} x + 2y + 5z = -2\\ 5x \qquad - 3z = 8\\ 2x - y \qquad = 0\end{cases}$ **13.** $\begin{bmatrix} 4 & -4\\ 3 & 9\\ 4 & 4\end{bmatrix}$ **14.** $\begin{bmatrix} 6 & 0\\ 12 & 24\\ -6 & 12\end{bmatrix}$ **15.** $\begin{bmatrix} 4 & -3 & 0\\ 12 & -2 & -8\\ -2 & 5 & -4\end{bmatrix}$ **16.** $\begin{bmatrix} 9 & -31\\ -6 & -3\end{bmatrix}$

17. $\begin{bmatrix} \frac{1}{2} & -1\\ -\frac{1}{6} & \frac{2}{3}\end{bmatrix}$ **18.** $\begin{bmatrix} -\frac{5}{7} & \frac{9}{7} & \frac{3}{7}\\ \frac{1}{7} & \frac{1}{7} & -\frac{2}{7}\\ \frac{3}{7} & -\frac{4}{7} & \frac{1}{7}\end{bmatrix}$ **19.** Singular **20.** $x = \frac{2}{5}, y = \frac{1}{10}$ or $\left(\frac{2}{5}, \frac{1}{10}\right)$ **21.** $x = 9, y = \frac{13}{3}, z = \frac{13}{3}$ or $\left(9, \frac{13}{3}, \frac{13}{3}\right)$ **22.** Inconsistent **23.** $x = -\frac{1}{2}, y = -\frac{2}{3}, z = -\frac{3}{4}$, or $\left(-\frac{1}{2}, -\frac{2}{3}, -\frac{3}{4}\right)$

24. $z = -1, x = y + 1$, where y is any real number or $\{(x, y, z) \mid x = y + 1, z = -1, y \text{ is any real number}\}$

25. $x = 4, y = 2, z = 3, t = -2$ or $(4, 2, 3, -2)$ **26.** 5 **27.** 108 **28.** -100 **29.** $x = 2, y = -1$ or $(2, -1)$ **30.** $x = 2, y = 3$ or $(2, 3)$

31. $x = -1, y = 2, z = -3$ or $(-1, 2, -3)$ **32.** 16 **33.** -8 **34.** $\dfrac{-\frac{3}{2}}{x} + \dfrac{\frac{3}{2}}{x-4}$ **35.** $\dfrac{-3}{x-1} + \dfrac{3}{x} + \dfrac{4}{x^2}$ **36.** $\dfrac{-\frac{1}{10}}{x+1} + \dfrac{\frac{1}{10}x + \frac{9}{10}}{x^2+9}$

37. $\dfrac{x}{x^2+4} + \dfrac{-4x}{(x^2+4)^2}$ **38.** $\dfrac{\frac{1}{2}}{x^2+1} + \dfrac{\frac{1}{4}}{x-1} + \dfrac{-\frac{1}{4}}{x+1}$ **39.** $x = -\frac{2}{5}, y = -\frac{11}{5}; x = -2, y = 1$ or $\left(-\frac{2}{5}, -\frac{11}{5}\right), (-2, 1)$

40. $x = 2\sqrt{2}, y = \sqrt{2}; x = -2\sqrt{2}, y = -\sqrt{2}$ or $(2\sqrt{2}, \sqrt{2}), (-2\sqrt{2}, -\sqrt{2})$ **41.** $x = 0, y = 0; x = -3, y = 3; x = 3, y = 3$ or $(0, 0), (-3, 3), (3, 3)$ **42.** $x = \sqrt{2}, y = -\sqrt{2}; x = -\sqrt{2}, y = \sqrt{2}; x = \frac{4}{3}\sqrt{2}, y = -\frac{2}{3}\sqrt{2}; x = -\frac{4}{3}\sqrt{2}, y = \frac{2}{3}\sqrt{2}$ or $(\sqrt{2}, -\sqrt{2}), (-\sqrt{2}, \sqrt{2}), \left(\frac{4}{3}\sqrt{2}, -\frac{2}{3}\sqrt{2}\right), \left(-\frac{4}{3}\sqrt{2}, \frac{2}{3}\sqrt{2}\right)$ **43.** $x = 1, y = -1$ or $(1, -1)$

44.

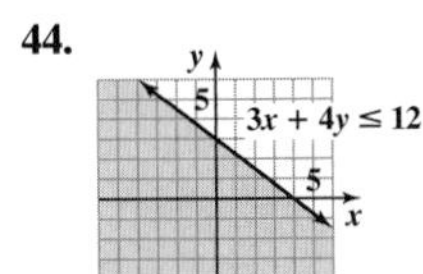

45.

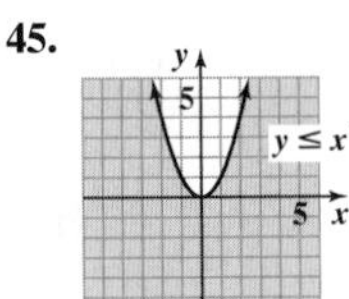

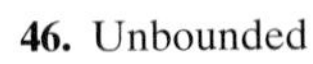

46. Unbounded

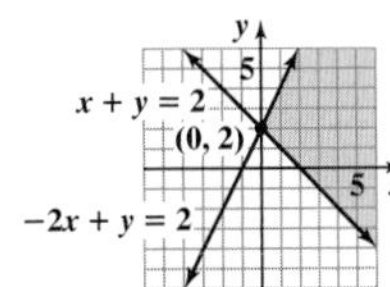

47. Bounded

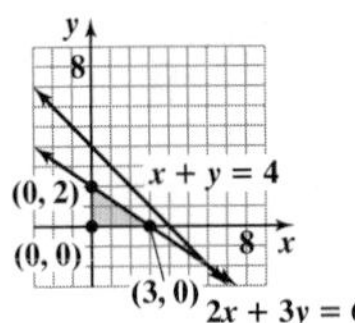

48. Bounded

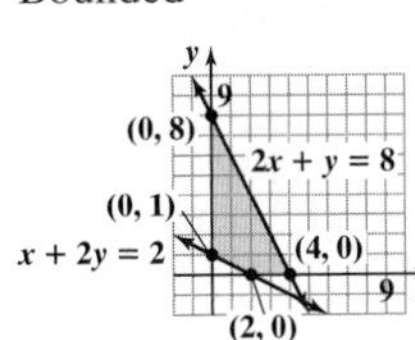

49.

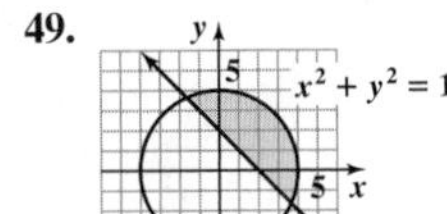

50.

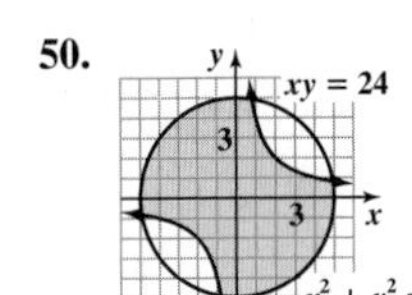

51. The maximum value is 32 when $x = 0$ and $y = 8$. **52.** The minimum value is 3 when $x = 1$ and $y = 0$. **53.** 10 **54.** A is any real number, $A \neq 10$.

55. $y = -\frac{1}{3}x^2 - \frac{2}{3}x + 1$ **56.** Mix 70 lb of \$6.00 coffee and 30 lb of \$9.00 coffee. **57.** Buy 1 small, 5 medium, and 2 large.

58. (a)

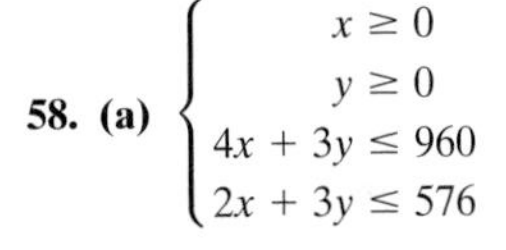

$$\begin{cases} x \geq 0 \\ y \geq 0 \\ 4x + 3y \leq 960 \\ 2x + 3y \leq 576 \end{cases}$$

(b)

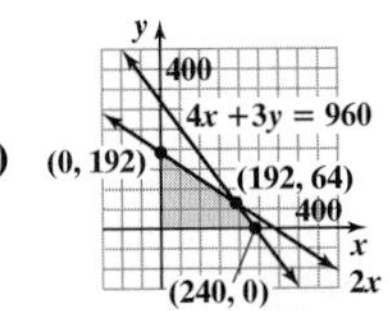

59. Speedboat: 36.67 km/hr; Aguarico River: 3.33 km/hr **60.** Bruce: 4 hr; Bryce: 2 hr; Marty: 8 hr

61. Produce 35 gasoline engines and 15 diesel engines; the factory is producing an excess of 15 gasoline engines and 0 diesel engines.

Chapter Test *(page 897)*

1. $x = 3, y = -1$ or $(3, -1)$ **2.** Inconsistent **3.** $x = -z + \frac{18}{7}, y = z - \frac{17}{7}$, where z is any real number or $\left\{(x, y, z) \,\middle|\, x = -z + \frac{18}{7}, y = z - \frac{17}{7}, z \text{ is any real number}\right\}$ **4.** $x = \frac{1}{3}, y = -2, z = 0$ or $\left(\frac{1}{3}, -2, 0\right)$ **5.** $\left[\begin{array}{ccc|c} 4 & -5 & 1 & 0 \\ -2 & -1 & 0 & -25 \\ 1 & 5 & -5 & 10 \end{array}\right]$

6. $\begin{cases} 3x + 2y + 4z = -6 \\ 1x + 0y + 8z = 2 \\ -2x + 1y + 3z = -11 \end{cases}$ or $\begin{cases} 3x + 2y + 4z = -6 \\ x + 8z = 2 \\ -2x + y + 3z = -11 \end{cases}$ **7.** $\begin{bmatrix} 6 & 4 \\ 1 & -11 \\ 5 & 12 \end{bmatrix}$ **8.** $\begin{bmatrix} -11 & -19 \\ -3 & 5 \\ 6 & -22 \end{bmatrix}$ **9.** $\begin{bmatrix} 4 & 10 & 26 \\ 1 & -11 & 2 \\ -1 & 26 & 3 \end{bmatrix}$ **10.** $\begin{bmatrix} 16 & 17 \\ 3 & -10 \end{bmatrix}$ **11.** $\begin{bmatrix} 2 & -1 \\ -\frac{5}{2} & \frac{3}{2} \end{bmatrix}$

12. $\begin{bmatrix} 3 & 3 & -4 \\ -2 & -2 & 3 \\ -4 & -5 & 7 \end{bmatrix}$ **13.** $x = \frac{1}{2}, y = 3$ or $\left(\frac{1}{2}, 3\right)$ **14.** $x = -\frac{1}{4}y + 7$, where y is any real number or $\left\{(x, y) \,\middle|\, x = -\frac{1}{4}y + 7, y \text{ is any real number}\right\}$

15. $x = 1, y = -2, z = 0$ or $(1, -2, 0)$ **16.** Inconsistent **17.** -29 **18.** -12 **19.** $x = -2, y = -5$ or $(-2, -5)$

20. $x = 1, y = -1, z = 4$ or $(1, -1, 4)$ **21.** $(1, -3)$ and $(1, 3)$ **22.** $(3, 4)$ and $(1, 2)$

23. y 15 $x^2 + y^2 = 100$ 15 x $4x - 3y = 0$

24. $\dfrac{3}{x+3} + \dfrac{-2}{(x+3)^2}$

25. $\dfrac{-\frac{1}{3}}{x} + \dfrac{\frac{1}{3}x}{(x^2+3)} + \dfrac{5x}{(x^2+3)^2}$

26. Unbounded

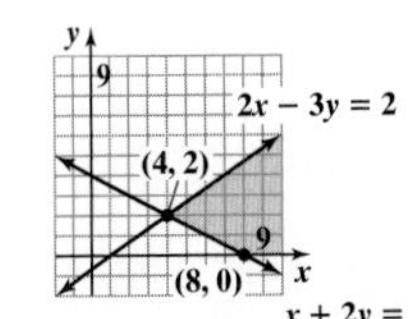

27. The maximum value of z is 64, and it occurs at the point $(0, 8)$. **28.** Flare jeans cost $24.50, camisoles cost $8.50, and T-shirts cost $6.00.

Cumulative Review *(page 898)*

1. $\left\{0, \frac{1}{2}\right\}$ **2.** $\{5\}$ **3.** $\left\{-1, -\frac{1}{2}, 3\right\}$ **4.** $\{-2\}$ **5.** $\left\{\frac{5}{2}\right\}$ **6.** $\left\{\frac{1}{\ln 3}\right\}$ **7.** Odd; symmetric with respect to the origin

8. Center: $(1, -2)$; radius $= 4$

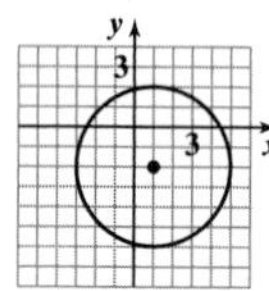

9. Domain: all real numbers
Range: $\{y|y > 1\}$
Horizontal asymptote: $y = 1$

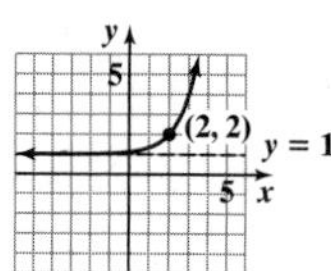

10. $f^{-1}(x) = \frac{5}{x} - 2$
Domain of f: $\{x|x \neq -2\}$
Range of f: $\{y|y \neq 0\}$
Domain of f^{-1}: $\{x|x \neq 0\}$
Range of f^{-1}: $\{y|y \neq -2\}$

11. (a)

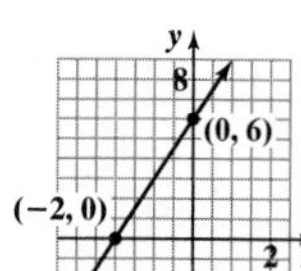

(b)

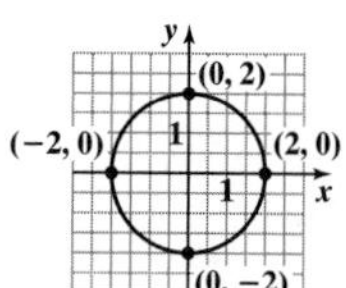

(c)

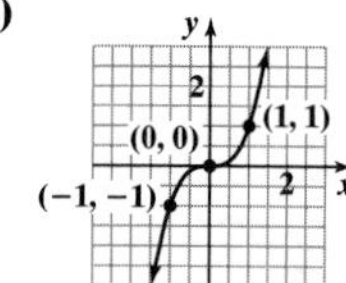

(d)

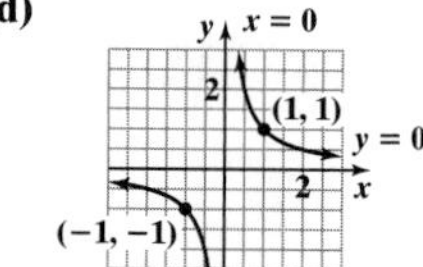

(e)

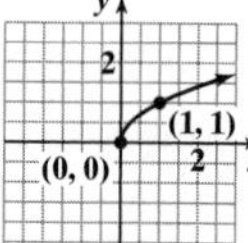

(f)

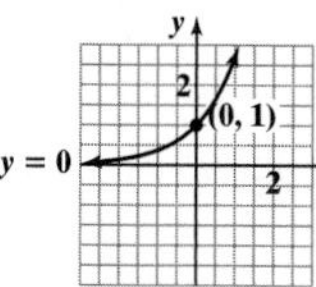

(g)

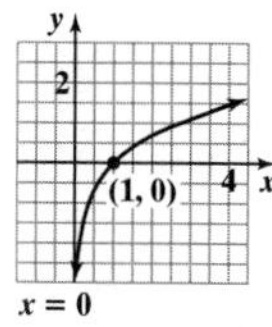

(h)

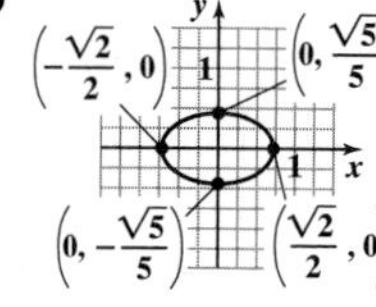

(i)

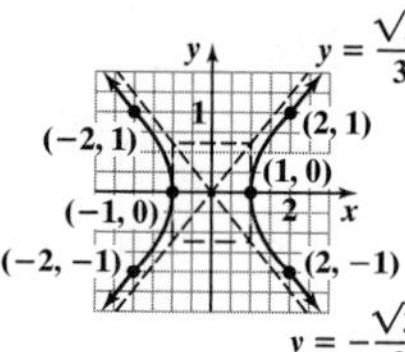

(j)

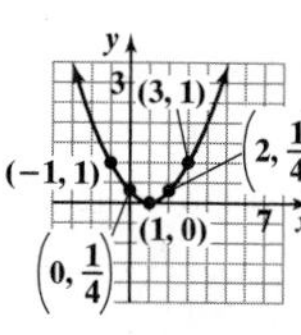

12. (a)

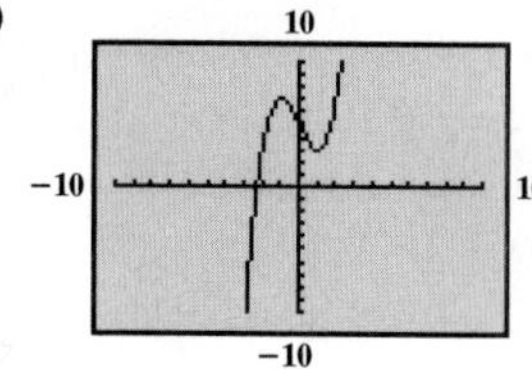

;−2.28

(b) Local maximum of 7 at $x = -1$; local minimum of 3 at $x = 1$

(c) $(-\infty, -1), (1, \infty)$

Index

A

B

C

G

T

U

V

W

X

Y

Photo Credits

Chapter R Page 5 Stylephotographs/Dreamstime; Page 9 Martin Fischer/Shutterstock; Page 15 Thinkstock; Page 28 Digital Vision/Thinkstock; Page 39 Dorling Kindersley, Inc.; Page 41 **(top)** Endless Traveller/Shutterstock; Page 41 **(bottom)** ALCE/Fotolia; Page 49 **(top)** Peter Zaharov/Shutterstock; Page 49 **(bottom)** Rjlerich/Dreamstime; Page 57 Lunamarina/Fotolia

Chapter 1 Page 76 Interlight/Shutterstock; Page 77 Stephen Coburn/Shutterstock; Page 85 Pcruciatti/Dreamstime; Page 88 **(top right)** Franckgrondin/Dreamstime; Page 88 **(bottom right)** Einstein/Shutterstock; Page 97 Alexander Raths/Shutterstock; Page 100 **(top)** Kenneystudios/Dreamstime; Page 100 **(bottom left)** Stockbyte/Thinkstock; Page 100 **(bottom right)** Petdcat/Dreamstime; Page 109 Corbis/Fotolia; Page 118 Georgeburba/Dreamstime; Page 124 **(top)** Still Representation/Fotolia; Page 124 **(bottom)** Uzi Tzur/Fotolia; Page 125 Ralukatudor/Dreamstime; Page 129 GoodMood Photo/Fotolia; Page 133 **(left)** Fabinus08/Dreamstime; Page 133 **(right)** Fotovampir/Dreamstime; Page 138 Cpbackpacker/Shutterstock

Chapter 2 Page 145 Wavebreakmedia/Shutterstock; Page 161 Comstock/Thinkstock; Page 167 Wavebreakmedia/Shutterstock; Page 168 Kzenon/Fotolia; Page 180 Paha_l/Dreamstime; Page 189 **(top)** Smontgom65/Dreamstime; Page 189 **(bottom)** Olaf Loose/iStockphoto; Page 190 Ekaterinasemenova/Dreamstime; Page 192 Jupiterimages/Thinkstock; Page 193 **(top)** Oleksiy Naumov/Shutterstock; Page 193 **(bottom)** Fstockfoto/Shutterstock; Page 210 DCW Creations/Shutterstock.

Chapter 3 Page 213 CandyBoxPhoto/Shutterstock; Page 248 Tondafoto/Dreamstime; Page 249 **(left)** Chin-Cheng Liu/Shutterstock; Page 249 **(right)** Paha_l/Dreamstime; Page 262 Zensu/Dreamstime

Chapter 4 Page 279 **(left)** Jerry Sharp/Shutterstock; Page 279 **(right)** Aspenphoto/Dreamstime; Page 289 Wavebreakmedia, Ltd./Shutterstock; Page 296 Christopher Parypa/Shutterstock; Page 297 Testing/Shutterstock; Page 335 **(top)** SVLuma/Shutterstock; Page 335 **(bottom)** Ffooter/Shutterstock; Page 340 Digital Vision/Thinkstock; Page 351 Neil Roy Johnson/Shutterstock; Page 355 Johanna Goodyear/Shutterstock; Page 365 James Steidl/Shutterstock.

Chapter 5 Page 368 Zinaida/Shutterstock; Page 384 Jerryb8/Dreamstime; Page 393 Jorg Hackemann/Shutterstock; Page 413 Tramper2/Dreamstime

Chapter 6 Page 433 Typhoonski/Dreamstime; Page 440 Stockbyte/Thinkstock; Page 443 Andy Z./Shutterstock; Page 452 **(left)** Copyright © National Institute for Fusion Science, Japan; Page 452 **(right)** Tim Hester Photography/Shutterstock; Page 456 Keith10999/Dreamstime

Chapter 7 Pages 459 and 519, Andy Dean Photography/Shutterstock; Page 485, The Crimson Monkey/iStockphoto; Page 513, Nancy R. Cohen/Photodisc/Getty Images; Page 517, Hemera Technologies/ Thinkstock.

Chapter 8 Pages 521 and 556, Andy Dean Photography/Shutterstock; Page 523, Barrett & MacKay/Glow Images; Page 529, Department of Energy (DOE) Digital Photo Archive; Page 544, Tetra Images/Alamy; Page 552, Jasonleehl/Shutterstock.

Chapter 9 Pages 558 and 628, Stephen Coburn/Shutterstock; Page 571, JPL/NASA; Page 579, Exactostock/SuperStock; Page 616, Kenzee/Dreamstime.

Chapter 10 Pages 630 and 678, Peter Morgan/AP Images; Page 667, Sajko/Shutterstock.

Chapter 11 Pages 679 and 749, Formiktopus/Shutterstock; Page 737, Oonal/Shutterstock.

Chapter 12 Pages 751 and 854, Don Hammond/Design Pics, Inc./Alamy; Page 809, Hulton Archive/Getty Images; Page 817, Stockbyte/Thinkstock; Page 818, Transtock/SuperStock; Page 823, iStockphoto/Thinkstock; Page 838, Jupiterimages/Photos.com/Thinkstock.

Chapter 13 Pages 855 and 899, Stock Connection Blue/Alamy.

Appendix B Page 911 Pcruciatti/Dreamstime; Page 915 ■.

CONICS

Parabola

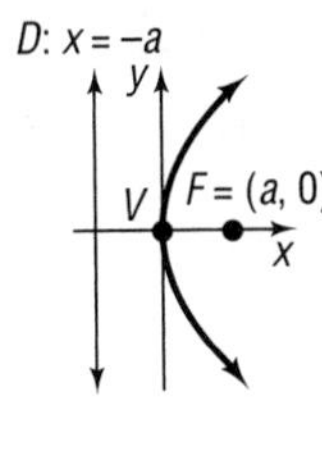

$$y^2 = 4ax$$

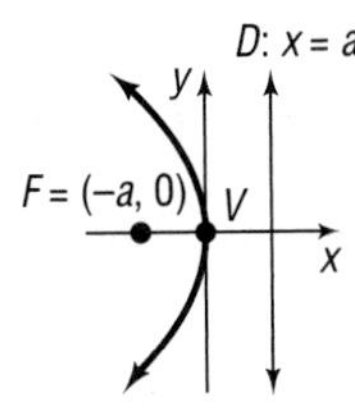

$$y^2 = -4ax$$

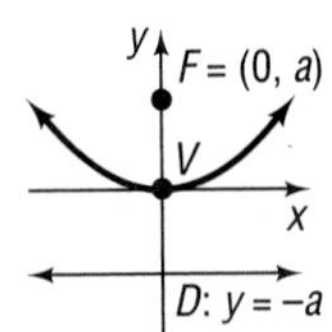

$$x^2 = 4ay$$

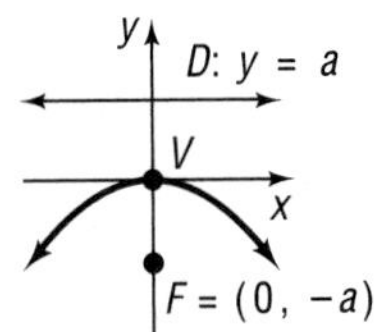

$$x^2 = -4ay$$

Ellipse

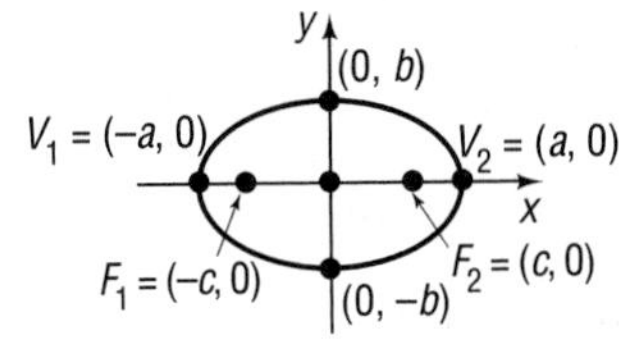

$$\frac{x^2}{a^2} + \frac{y^2}{b^2} = 1, \quad a > b, \quad c^2 = a^2 - b^2$$

y
$V_2 = (0, a)$
$F_2 = (0, c)$
$(b, 0)$
$(-b, 0)$
x
$F_1 = (0, -c)$
$V_1 = (0, -a)$

$$\frac{x^2}{b^2} + \frac{y^2}{a^2} = 1, \quad a > b, \quad c^2 = a^2 - b^2$$

Hyperbola

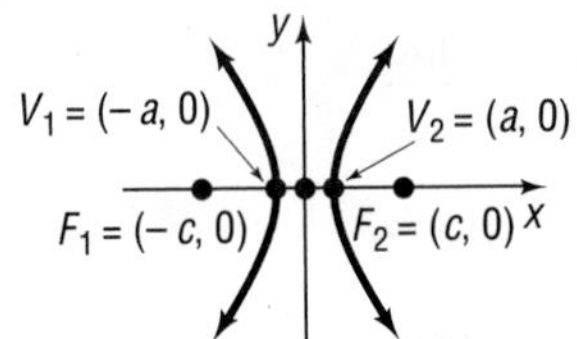

$$\frac{x^2}{a^2} - \frac{y^2}{b^2} = 1, \quad c^2 = a^2 + b^2$$

Asymptotes: $y = \frac{b}{a}x, \quad y = -\frac{b}{a}x$

y
$F_2 = (0, c)$
$V_2 = (0, a)$
x
$V_1 = (0, -a)$
$F_1 = (0, -c)$

$$\frac{y^2}{a^2} - \frac{x^2}{b^2} = 1, \quad c^2 = a^2 + b^2$$

Asymptotes: $y = \frac{a}{b}x, \quad y = -\frac{a}{b}x$

PROPERTIES OF LOGARITHMS

$$\log_a(MN) = \log_a M + \log_a N$$

$$\log_a\left(\frac{M}{N}\right) = \log_a M - \log_a N$$

$$\log_a M^r = r\log_a M$$

$$\log_a M = \frac{\log M}{\log a} = \frac{\ln M}{\ln a}$$

$$a^x = e^{x \ln a}$$

PERMUTATIONS/COMBINATIONS

$$0! = 1 \qquad 1! = 1$$

$$n! = n(n-1)\cdot \ldots \cdot(3)(2)(1)$$

$$P(n, r) = \frac{n!}{(n-r)!}$$

$$C(n, r) = \binom{n}{r} = \frac{n!}{(n-r)!\,r!}$$

BINOMIAL THEOREM

$$(a+b)^n = a^n + \binom{n}{1}ba^{n-1} + \binom{n}{2}b^2a^{n-2} + \cdots + \binom{n}{n-1}b^{n-1}a + b^n$$

ARITHMETIC SEQUENCE

$$a_1 + (a_1 + d) + (a_1 + 2d) + \cdots + [a_1 + (n-1)d] = \frac{n}{2}[2a_1 + (n-1)d] = \frac{n}{2}[a_1 + a_n]$$

GEOMETRIC SEQUENCE

$$a_1 + a_1r + a_1r^2 + \cdots + a_1r^{n-1} = a_1 \cdot \frac{1 - r^n}{1 - r}$$

GEOMETRIC SERIES

If $|r| < 1, a_1 + a_1r + a_1r^2 + \cdots = \sum_{k=1}^{\infty} a_1r^{k-1} = \frac{a_1}{1-r}$

FORMULAS/EQUATIONS

Distance Formula

If $P_1 = (x_1, y_1)$ and $P_2 = (x_2, y_2)$, the distance from P_1 to P_2 is

$$d(P_1, P_2) = \sqrt{(x_2 - x_1)^2 + (y_2 - y_1)^2}$$

Standard Equation of a Circle

The standard equation of a circle of radius r with center at (h, k) is

$$(x - h)^2 + (y - k)^2 = r^2$$

Slope Formula

The slope m of the line containing the points $P_1 = (x_1, y_1)$ and $P_2 = (x_2, y_2)$ is

$$m = \frac{y_2 - y_1}{x_2 - x_1} \qquad \text{if } x_1 \neq x_2$$

$$m \text{ is undefined} \qquad \text{if } x_1 = x_2$$

Point–Slope Equation of a Line

The equation of a line with slope m containing the point (x_1, y_1) is

$$y - y_1 = m(x - x_1)$$

Slope–Intercept Equation of a Line

The equation of a line with slope m and y-intercept b is

$$y = mx + b$$

Quadratic Formula

The solutions of the equation $ax^2 + bx + c = 0$, $a \neq 0$, are

$$x = \frac{-b \pm \sqrt{b^2 - 4ac}}{2a}$$

If $b^2 - 4ac > 0$, there are two unequal real solutions.
If $b^2 - 4ac = 0$, there is a repeated real solution.
If $b^2 - 4ac < 0$, there are two complex solutions that are not real.

GEOMETRY FORMULAS

Circle

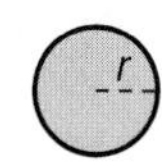

r = Radius, A = Area, C = Circumference

$$A = \pi r^2 \qquad C = 2\pi r$$

Triangle

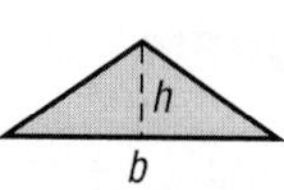

b = Base, h = Altitude (Height), A = area

$$A = \tfrac{1}{2}bh$$

Rectangle

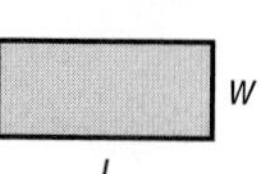
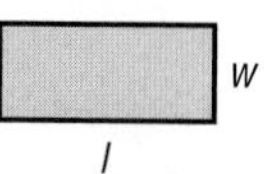

l = Length, w = Width, A = area, P = perimeter

$$A = lw \qquad P = 2l + 2w$$

Rectangular Box

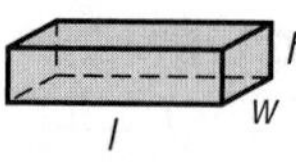

l = Length, w = Width, h = Height, V = Volume, S = Surface area

$$V = lwh \qquad S = 2lw + 2lh + 2wh$$

Sphere

r = Radius, V = Volume, S = Surface area

$$V = \tfrac{4}{3}\pi r^3 \qquad S = 4\pi r^2$$

Right Circular Cylinder

r = Radius, h = Height, V = Volume, S = Surface area

$$V = \pi r^2 h \qquad S = 2\pi r^2 + 2\pi rh$$

TRIGONOMETRIC FUNCTIONS

Of an Acute Angle

$$\sin\theta = \frac{b}{c} = \frac{\text{Opposite}}{\text{Hypotenuse}} \qquad \cos\theta = \frac{a}{c} = \frac{\text{Adjacent}}{\text{Hypotenuse}} \qquad \tan\theta = \frac{b}{a} = \frac{\text{Opposite}}{\text{Adjacent}}$$

$$\csc\theta = \frac{c}{b} = \frac{\text{Hypotenuse}}{\text{Opposite}} \qquad \sec\theta = \frac{c}{a} = \frac{\text{Hypotenuse}}{\text{Adjacent}} \qquad \cot\theta = \frac{a}{b} = \frac{\text{Adjacent}}{\text{Opposite}}$$

Hypotenuse c

Opposite θ b

θ

a Adjacent to θ

Of a General Angle

$$\sin\theta = \frac{b}{r} \qquad \cos\theta = \frac{a}{r} \qquad \tan\theta = \frac{b}{a},\quad a \neq 0$$

$$\csc\theta = \frac{r}{b},\quad b \neq 0 \qquad \sec\theta = \frac{r}{a},\quad a \neq 0 \qquad \cot\theta = \frac{a}{b},\quad b \neq 0$$

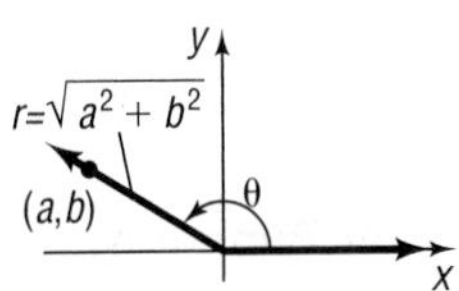

TRIGONOMETRIC IDENTITIES

Fundamental Identities

$$\tan\theta = \frac{\sin\theta}{\cos\theta} \qquad \cot\theta = \frac{\cos\theta}{\sin\theta}$$

$$\csc\theta = \frac{1}{\sin\theta} \qquad \sec\theta = \frac{1}{\cos\theta} \qquad \cot\theta = \frac{1}{\tan\theta}$$

$$\sin^2\theta + \cos^2\theta = 1$$

$$\tan^2\theta + 1 = \sec^2\theta$$

$$\cot^2\theta + 1 = \csc^2\theta$$

Half-Angle Formulas

$$\sin\frac{\theta}{2} = \pm\sqrt{\frac{1-\cos\theta}{2}}$$

$$\cos\frac{\theta}{2} = \pm\sqrt{\frac{1+\cos\theta}{2}}$$

$$\tan\frac{\theta}{2} = \frac{1-\cos\theta}{\sin\theta}$$

Double-Angle Formulas

$$\sin(2\theta) = 2\sin\theta\cos\theta$$

$$\cos(2\theta) = \cos^2\theta - \sin^2\theta$$

$$\cos(2\theta) = 2\cos^2\theta - 1$$

$$\cos(2\theta) = 1 - 2\sin^2\theta$$

$$\tan(2\theta) = \frac{2\tan\theta}{1-\tan^2\theta}$$

Even-Odd Identities

$$\sin(-\theta) = -\sin\theta \qquad \csc(-\theta) = -\csc\theta$$

$$\cos(-\theta) = \cos\theta \qquad \sec(-\theta) = \sec\theta$$

$$\tan(-\theta) = -\tan\theta \qquad \cot(-\theta) = -\cot\theta$$

Product-to-Sum Formulas

$$\sin\alpha\sin\beta = \tfrac{1}{2}[\cos(\alpha-\beta) - \cos(\alpha+\beta)]$$

$$\cos\alpha\cos\beta = \tfrac{1}{2}[\cos(\alpha-\beta) + \cos(\alpha+\beta)]$$

$$\sin\alpha\cos\beta = \tfrac{1}{2}[\sin(\alpha+\beta) + \sin(\alpha-\beta)]$$

Sum and Difference Formulas

$$\sin(\alpha+\beta) = \sin\alpha\cos\beta + \cos\alpha\sin\beta$$

$$\sin(\alpha-\beta) = \sin\alpha\cos\beta - \cos\alpha\sin\beta$$

$$\cos(\alpha+\beta) = \cos\alpha\cos\beta - \sin\alpha\sin\beta$$

$$\cos(\alpha-\beta) = \cos\alpha\cos\beta + \sin\alpha\sin\beta$$

$$\tan(\alpha+\beta) = \frac{\tan\alpha+\tan\beta}{1-\tan\alpha\tan\beta}$$

$$\tan(\alpha-\beta) = \frac{\tan\alpha-\tan\beta}{1+\tan\alpha\tan\beta}$$

Sum-to-Product Formulas

$$\sin\alpha + \sin\beta = 2\sin\frac{\alpha+\beta}{2}\cos\frac{\alpha-\beta}{2}$$

$$\sin\alpha - \sin\beta = 2\sin\frac{\alpha-\beta}{2}\cos\frac{\alpha+\beta}{2}$$

$$\cos\alpha + \cos\beta = 2\cos\frac{\alpha+\beta}{2}\cos\frac{\alpha-\beta}{2}$$

$$\cos\alpha - \cos\beta = -2\sin\frac{\alpha+\beta}{2}\sin\frac{\alpha-\beta}{2}$$

SOLVING TRIANGLES

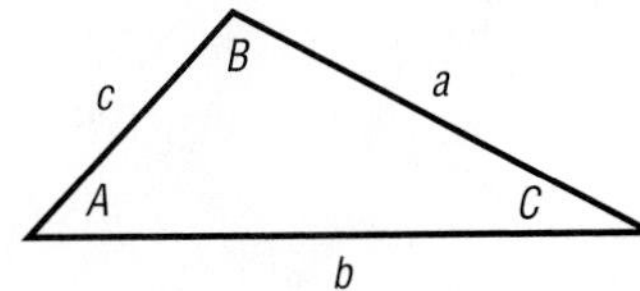

Law of Sines

$$\frac{\sin A}{a} = \frac{\sin B}{b} = \frac{\sin C}{c}$$

Law of Cosines

$$a^2 = b^2 + c^2 - 2bc\cos A$$

$$b^2 = a^2 + c^2 - 2ac\cos B$$

$$c^2 = a^2 + b^2 - 2ab\cos C$$

LIBRARY OF FUNCTIONS

Identity Function

$f(x) = x$

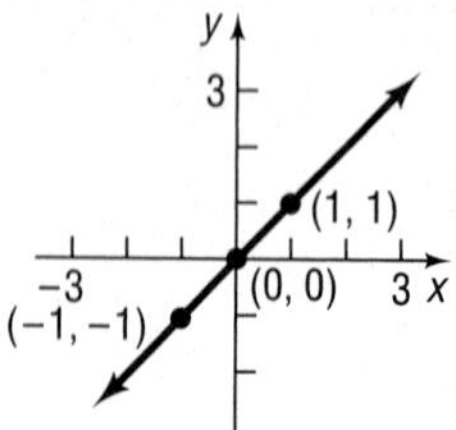

Square Function

$f(x) = x^2$

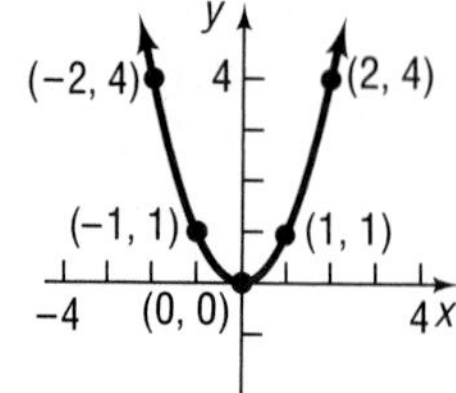

Cube Function

$f(x) = x^3$

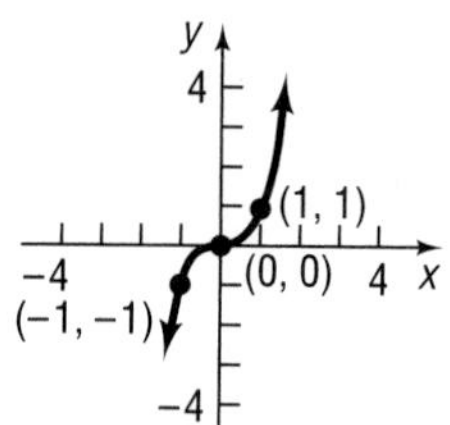

Square Root Function

$f(x) = \sqrt{x}$

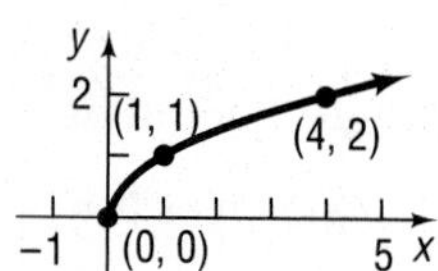

Reciprocal Function

$f(x) = \dfrac{1}{x}$

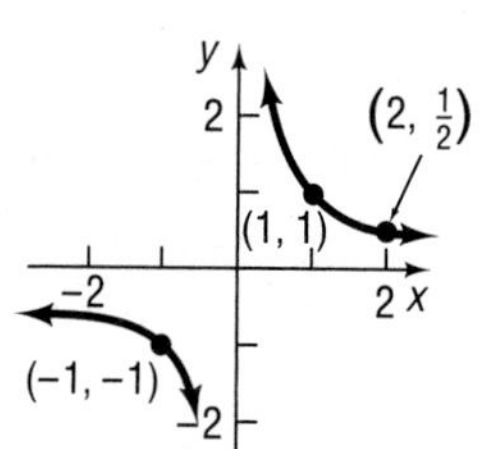

Cube Root Function

$f(x) = \sqrt[3]{x}$

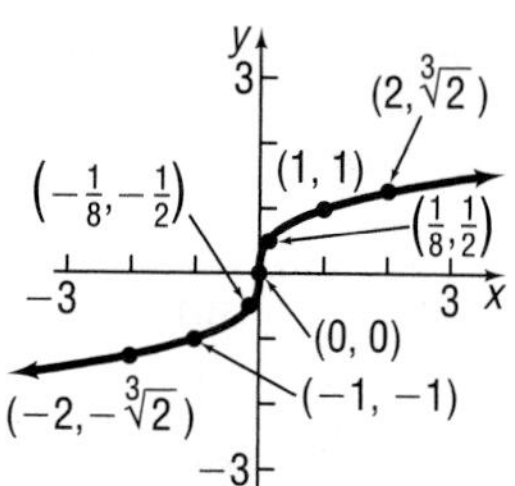

Absolute Value Function

$f(x) = |x|$

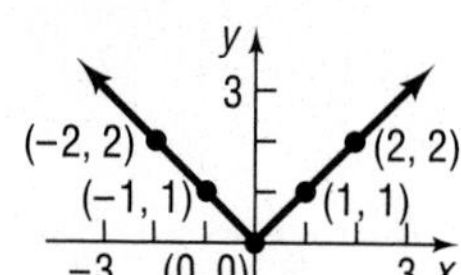

Exponential Function

$f(x) = e^x$

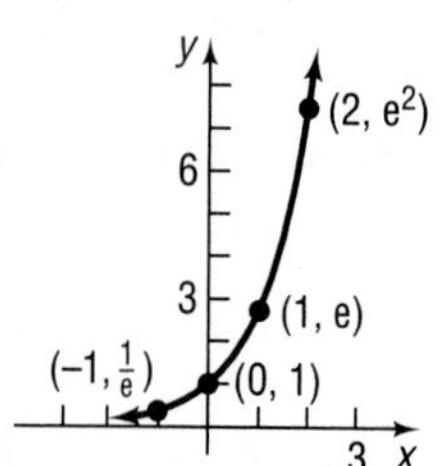

Natural Logarithm Function

$f(x) = \ln x$

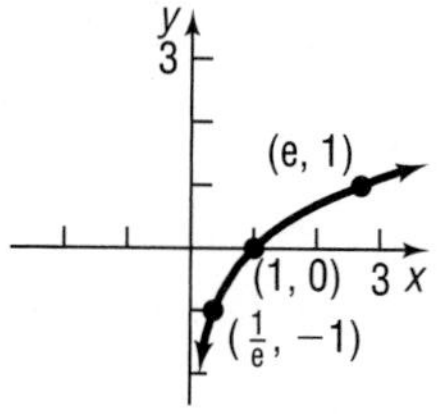

Sine Function

$f(x) = \sin x$

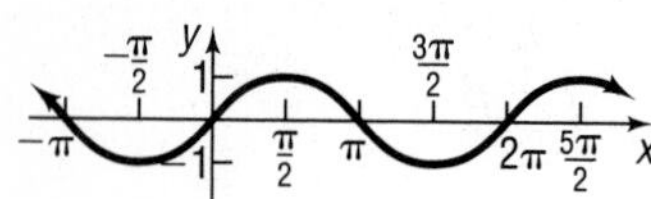

Cosine Function

$f(x) = \cos x$

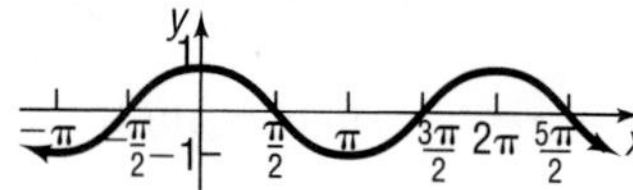

Tangent Function

$f(x) = \tan x$

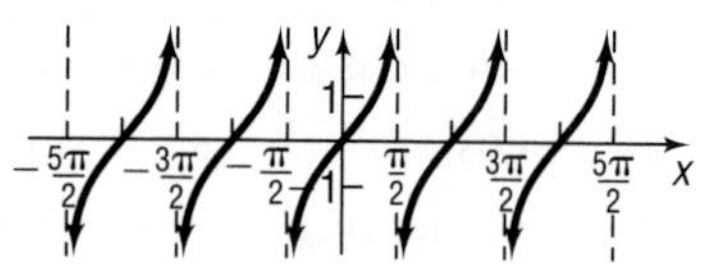

Cosecant Function

$f(x) = \csc x$

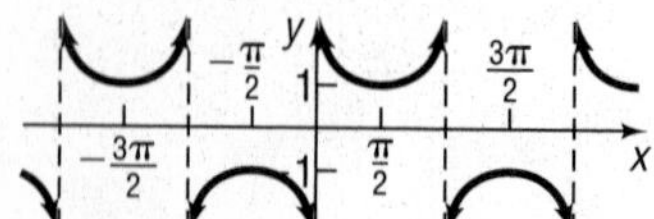

Secant Function

$f(x) = \sec x$

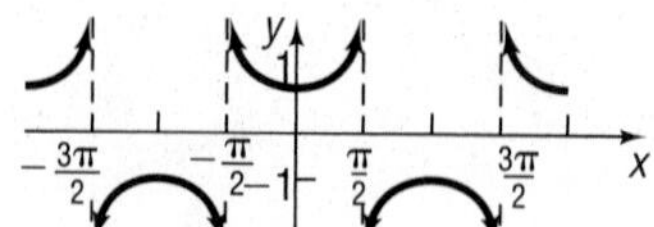

Cotangent Function

$f(x) = \cot x$

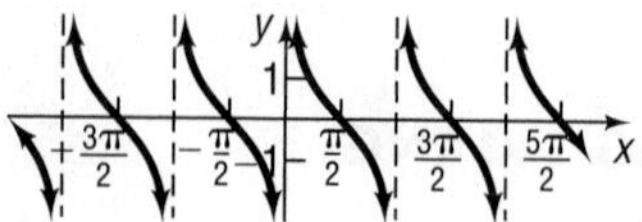